HOLT SCIENCE & TECHNOLOGY

Integrated Science level RED

Teacher's Edition WALK-THROUGH

Student Edition CONTENTS IN BRIEF

HOLT, RINEHART AND WINSTON

A Harcourt Education Company

Orlando • **Austin** • New York • San Diego • Toronto • London

A program that gets EVERYONE pointed in the right direction.

HOLT SCIENCE & TECHNOLOGY Integrated Science *level RED*

Live Ink® Online Reading Help

Interactive Online Edition

National Science Teachers Association

Every student, every class, every teacher is unique. Holt is here to help pave the way to success for each and every one.

MEETS THE INDIVIDUAL NEEDS OF YOUR STUDENTS

- **Strategies** that address inclusion classrooms and different learning styles adapt instruction for students with identified special needs.
- **Differentiated activities** and **datasheets** make inquiry accessible to all students.
- **Directed Reading worksheets** and **Chapter Tests** are available that address different ability levels.
- **Interactive Textbook** makes science content accessible to struggling readers and ELL students.
- English Language Learner support includes **Strategies for English Language Learners**, a **Multilingual Glossary for Science**, and **Spanish Resources**.

FOSTERS READING FOR UNDERSTANDING

- The *Student Edition* is accessible with a clean, easy-to-follow design and highlighted vocabulary words that are defined in the margin at point of reference.
- Reading strategies are built into both the *Student Edition* and the *Teacher's Edition.*
- **Reading Comprehension Guide** and **Guided Reading Audio** help students better understand the content.
- **Live Ink**—exclusive to Holt—is a scientifically-researched tool that improves reading comprehension and raises test scores.
- **Student One Stop** provides students with the *Student Edition,* and **Interactive Textbook** student workbooks on a CD-ROM so that they have less to carry home.

ONGOING ASSESSMENT TARGETS YOUR INSTRUCTION

- **Comprehensive Section** and **Chapter Reviews** and **Standardized Test Preparation** allow students to practice their test-taking skills.

- Customize your assessment with the **One-Stop Planner CD-ROM with Test Generator and State-Specific Resources.**

- **Science Tutor CD-ROM** serves as a personal tutor to help students practice what they learn.

- **Brain Food Video Quizzes** (on DVD) are game show-style quizzes that assess students' progress and help them prepare for tests.

BUILDS SCIENCE SKILLS THROUGH ACTIVITIES

- The laboratory program includes Startup Activities, Quick Labs, Chapter Labs, labs in the **LabBook** at the end of the *Student Edition,* six different lab books, and **Video Labs.**

- All of the program labs are provided on the **Holt Lab Generator CD-ROM.**

- Differentiated datasheets for additional labs available for each chapter can be found online.

- **Virtual Investigations CD-ROM** allow students to perform lab activities in a safe simulated environment.

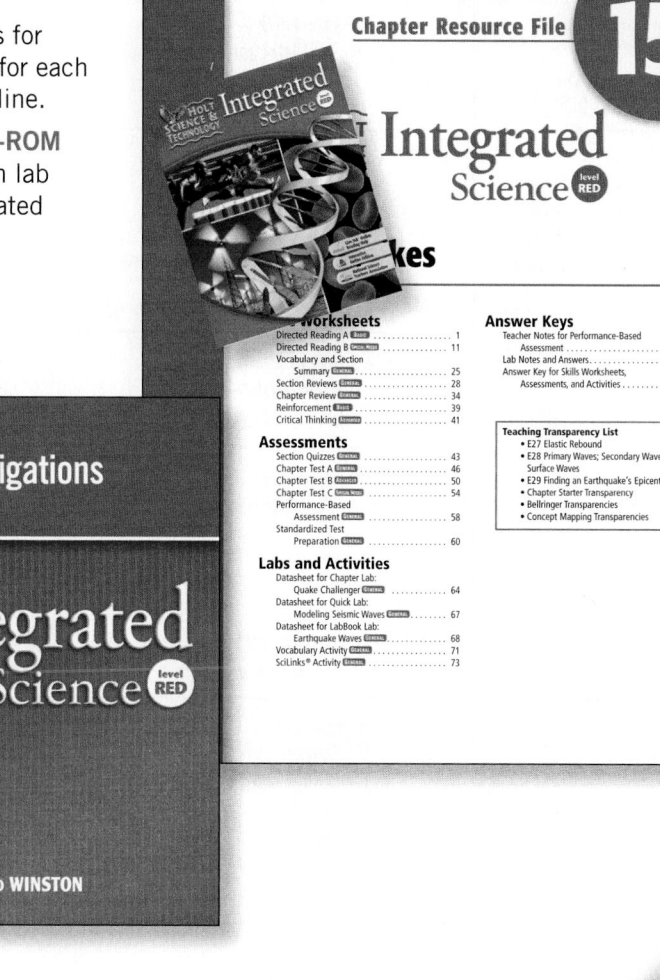

T3

Meeting Individual Needs

Students have a wide range of abilities and learning exceptionalities. These pages show you how *Holt Science & Technology* provides resources and strategies to help you tailor your instruction to engage every student in your classroom. Furthermore, activities in the *Teacher's Edition* are labeled with one or more learning styles designed to engage a variety of skills and strengths in every student.

LS Visual activities emphasize learning through pictures, colors, and shapes.

LS Verbal activities emphasize learning through words.

LS Logical activities emphasize learning through patterns, reason, or numbers.

LS Kinesthetic activities emphasize learning through physical activity and touch.

LS Auditory activities emphasize learning through sound.

LS Interpersonal activities emphasize learning through interactions with others.

LS Intrapersonal activities emphasize learning through independent work and reflection.

Learning exceptionality	Inclusion Strategies and Activities	
Learning Disabilities and Slow Learners Students who have dyslexia or dysgraphia, students reading below grade level, students having difficulty understanding abstract or complex concepts, and slow learners	• Inclusion Strategies labeled *Learning Disabled* • Activities and Alternative Assessments labeled *Basic* • *Reteaching* activities	• Activities labeled *Visual, Kinesthetic,* or *Auditory* • Hands-on activities or projects • Oral presentations instead of written tests or assignments
Developmental Delays Students who are functioning far below grade level because of mental retardation, autism, or brain injury; goals are to learn or retain basic concepts	• Inclusion Strategies labeled *Developmentally Delayed* • Activities and Alternative Assessments labeled *Basic*	• *Reteaching* activities • Project-based activities
Attention Deficit Disorders Students experiencing difficulty completing a task that has multiple steps, difficulty handling long assignments, or difficulty concentrating without sensory input from physical activity	• Inclusion Strategies labeled *Attention Deficit Disorder* • Activities and Alternative Assessments labeled *Basic* • *Reteaching* activities • Activities labeled *Co-op Learning*	• Activities labeled *Visual, Kinesthetic,* or *Auditory* • Concepts broken into small chunks • Oral presentations instead of written tests or assignments
English as a Second Language Students learning English	• Activities labeled *English-Language Learners* • Activities labeled *Basic*	• *Reteaching* activities • Activities labeled *Visual*
Gifted and Talented Students who are performing above grade level and demonstrate aptitude in crosscurricular assignments	• Inclusion Strategies labeled *Gifted and Talented* • Activities and Alternative Assessments labeled *Advanced*	• *Connection* activities • Activities that involve multiple tasks, a strong degree of independence, and student initiative
Hearing Impairments Students who are deaf or who have difficulty hearing	• Inclusion Strategies labeled *Hearing Impaired* • Activities labeled *Visual*	• Activities labeled *Co-op Learning* • Assessments that use written presentations
Visual Impairments Students who are blind or who have difficulty seeing	• Inclusion strategies labeled *Visually Impaired* • Activities labeled *Auditory*	• Activities labeled *Co-op Learning* • Assessments that use oral presentations
Behavior Control Issues Students learning to manage their behavior	• Inclusion Strategies labeled *Behavior Control Issues* • Activities labeled *Basic*	• Assignments that actively involve students and help students develop confidence and improved behaviors

GENERAL INCLUSION STRATEGIES

The following strategies can help you modify instruction to help students who struggle with common classroom difficulties.

A student experiencing difficulty with...	May benefit if you...	
Beginning assignments	• Assign work in small amounts • Have the student use cooperative or paired learning • Provide varied and interesting activities	• Allow choice in assignments or projects • Reinforce participation • Seat the student closer to you
Following directions	• Gain the student's attention before giving directions • Break up the task into small steps • Give written directions rather than oral directions • Use short, simple phrases	• Stand near the student when you are giving directions • Have the student repeat directions to you • Prepare the student for changes in activity • Give visual cues by posting general routines • Reinforce improvement in or approximation of following directions
Keeping track of assignments	• Have the student use folders for assignments • Have the student use assignment notebooks	• Have the student keep a checklist of assignments and highlight assignments when they are turned in
Reading the textbook	• Provide outlines of the textbook content • Reduce the length of required reading • Allow extra time for reading • Have the students read aloud in small groups	• Have the student use peer or mentor readers • Have the student use books on tape or CD • Discuss the content of the textbook in class after reading
Staying on task	• Reduce distracting elements in the classroom • Provide a task-completion checklist • Seat the student near you	• Provide alternative ways to complete assignments, such as oral projects taped with a buddy
Behavioral or social skills	• Model the appropriate behaviors • Establish class rules, and reiterate them often • Reinforce positive behavior • Assign a mentor as a positive role model to the student • Contract with the student for expected behaviors • Reinforce the desired behaviors or any steps toward improvement	• Separate the student from any peer who stimulates the inappropriate behavior • Provide a "cooling off" period before talking with the student • Address academic/instructional problems that may contribute to disruptive behaviors • Include parents in the problem-solving process through conferences, home visits, and frequent communication
Attendance	• Recognize and reinforce attendance by giving incentives or verbal praise • Emphasize the importance of attendance by letting the student know that he or she was missed when he or she was absent	• Encourage the student's desire to be in school by planning activities that are likely to be enjoyable, giving the student a preferred responsibility to be performed in class, and involving the student in extracurricular activities • Schedule problem-solving meeting with parents, faculty, or both
Test-taking skills	• Prepare the student for testing by teaching ways to study in pairs, such as using flashcards, practice tests, and study guides, and by promoting adequate sleep, nourishment, and exercise • Decrease visual distraction by improving the visual design of the test through use of larger type, spacing, consistent layout, and shorter sentences	• During testing, allow the student to respond orally on tape or to respond using a computer; to use notes; to take breaks; to take the test in another location; to work without time constraints; or to take the test in several short sessions

Meets the individual needs of your students

ACTIVITIES AND DEMONSTRATIONS FOR EVERY LEARNING LEVEL

Activities in the teacher's wrap are labeled by ability level—**Basic, General,** and **Advanced**—helping you choose appropriate activities for each student.

- **Basic** activities are designed to be accessible to all students.
- **General** activities are appropriate for most students and require more critical-thinking skills than Basic activities.
- **Advanced** activities are more challenging than General activities and can be used to extend learning.

Learning styles—**Interpersonal, Intrapersonal, Auditory, Kinesthetic, Logical, Visual,** and **Verbal**—are addressed throughout so you can adapt material to different ways of learning. In addition, some labels identify the activities that help with **Co-op Learning** and **English Language Learners.**

Bellringer activities begin each section with an activity designed to get students thinking. **Bellringers** are also available on transparency.

🎯 Bellringer

Have students describe their position in the classroom using a reference point and a set of reference directions. For example, a student might say, "I sit three desks behind Ahmed's desk," or "I sit 2 m east of the vent hood and 10 m north of the emergency shower."

Activity, Group Activity, Connection Activity, Demonstrations, and **Homework** provide more quick activities that you can integrate into your lesson.

ACTIVITY ──────── GENERAL

Bridge Building Have students work in groups to build a bridge using toothpicks and glue. The bridge should span a 15 cm gap and be wide enough to hold a toy car. Students should identify the forces acting on their bridge. (An alternate and less time consuming activity would be to have students build a house of cards that can support a 500 g mass.) LS **Kinesthetic**

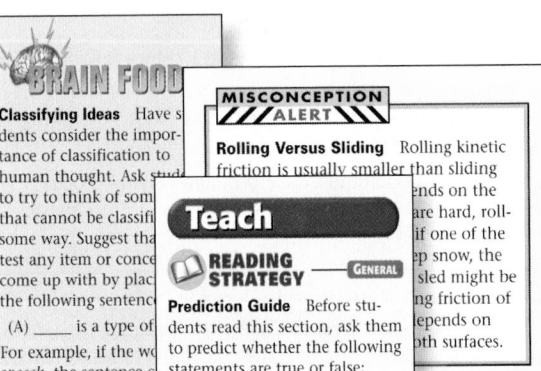

BRAIN FOOD

Classifying Ideas Have s[tu]dents consider the importance of classification to human thought. Ask stud[ents] to try to think of som[e] that cannot be classifi[ed] some way. Suggest tha[t] test any item or conce[pt] come up with by plac[ing] the following sentenc[e]

(A) _____ is a type of

For example, if the wo[rd] *speech,* the sentence c[ould be] filled in as follows:

Speech is a type of communication.

You may wish to hol[d a] test or have students [share] their examples in clas[s]. LS **Logical/Verbal**

MISCONCEPTION ALERT

Rolling Versus Sliding Rolling kinetic friction is usually smaller than sliding friction [........] [.....]ends on the [......] are hard, roll[....] if one of the [....]p snow, the [....] sled might be [....]ng friction of [....]epends on [....]th surfaces.

Teach

📖 READING STRATEGY ──── GENERAL

Prediction Guide Before students read this section, ask them to predict whether the following statements are true or false:

- Objects of any size exert a gravitational force. (true)
- The moon is held in its orbit by unbalanced forces. (true)
- If you traveled to Jupiter and you neither gained nor lost mass, your weight on Jupiter would be much greater than your weight on Earth. (true)

LS **Verbal**

TEACHING TIPS AND ENGAGING FEATURES KEEP STUDENTS INTERESTED AND INVOLVED.

- Reading and Teaching Strategies
- Misconception Alert
- Cultural Awareness
- Scientists at Odds
- Weird Science
- Brain Food
- Connections to other disciplines and sciences
- Science Humor
- Is That a Fact!

🔵 INCLUSION Strategies

- *Gifted and Talented*
- *Behavior Control Issues*

Students may benefit from expanding on a topic. Ask these students to make a list of 30 items in the classroom, 15 of which would work as thermal conductors and 15 that would work as thermal insulators. LS **Logical**

INCLUSION STRATEGIES MAKE MATERIAL ACCESSIBLE TO ALL.

Written by professionals in the field of special needs education, **Inclusion Strategies** address many different learning exceptionalities in the classroom.

- Hearing Impaired
- Visually Impaired
- Developmentally Delayed
- Attention Deficit Disorder
- Behavior Control Issues
- Gifted and Talented

LEVELED WORKSHEETS AND WORKBOOKS PROVIDE ADDITIONAL SUPPORT.

- **Chapter Resource Files** contain leveled Directed Reading, Reinforcement, and Critical Thinking worksheets as well as Chapter Tests.

- **Special Needs Workbook** includes **Special Needs Directed Reading Worksheets** and the **Special Needs Chapter Tests.**

- **Interactive Textbook** provides a full adapted read of the *Student Edition,* complete with reading skills development, review, and National Science Education Standards checks.

- Go online to select additional leveled labs correlated to chapter content.

RESOURCES FOR ENGLISH-LANGUAGE LEARNERS

These resources and translations open the door to students who are frequently locked out.

- **ELL Strategies** written by a professional in the field are included in each section of every chapter.

- **Interactive Textbook** makes content from the *Student Edition* accessible to ELL students.

- **Multilingual Glossary** provides simple definitions of key science terms in multiple languages.

- *Student Edition* in Spanish

- Spanish glossary in both the English and Spanish *Student Edition*

- **Study Guide** in Spanish

- **Reading Comprehension Guide** in Spanish

- **Assessments** in Spanish

- **Guided Reading Audio Program** in Spanish

- **Strategies for English Language Learners** provides effective strategies for teaching English Language Learners and shows you how to implement these strategies using resources from *Holt Science & Technology.*

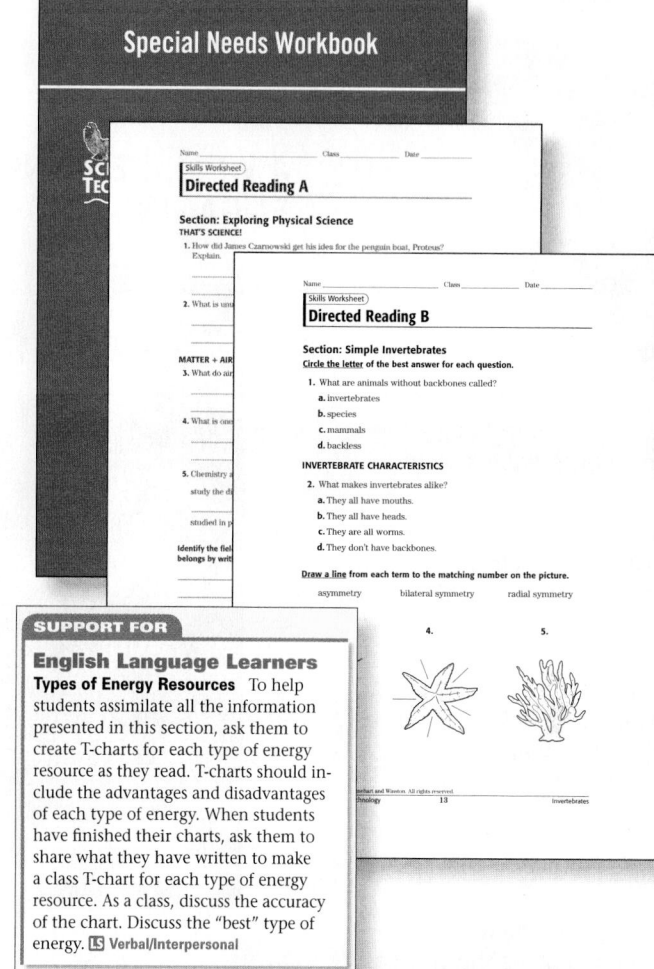

Reading support that fosters understanding

A WELL-DESIGNED TEXT MAKES SCIENCE ENGAGING AND ACCESSIBLE.

The **Big Idea** prepares students for learning by introducing the key concept in each chapter.

A preview of the upcoming content guides students' reading.

FoldNote and **Graphic Organizer** are provided to help students organize their ideas and improve their comprehension and retention.

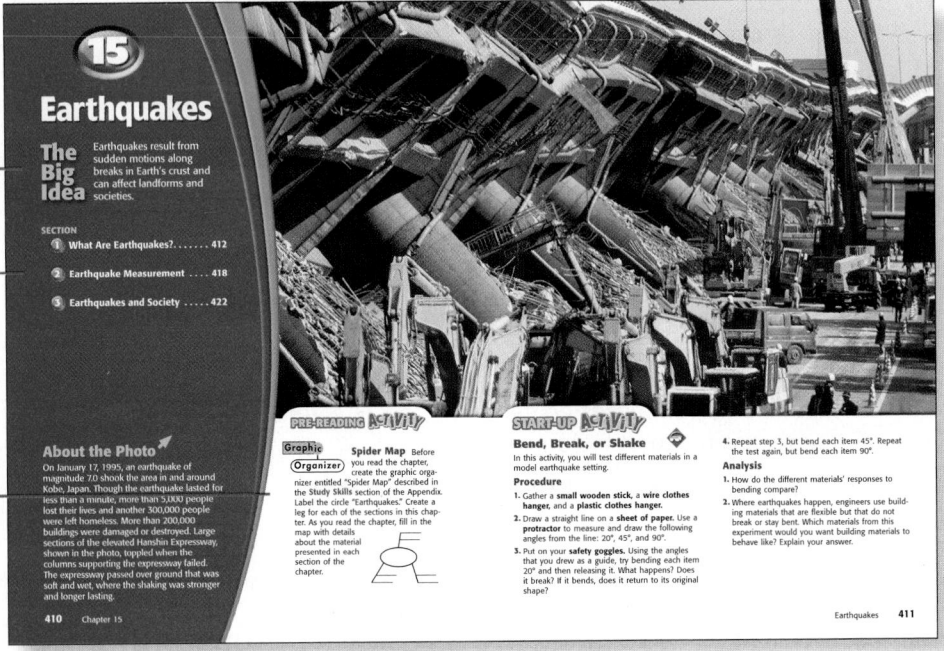

Every page begins with a new head which makes the text easy to navigate and more accessible.

Each section begins with **What You Will Learn** that lists what the students will learn and the **Vocabulary** covered in the section. This feature helps students focus on the content being presented and understand what they read.

Reading Strategy helps students better understand what they read.

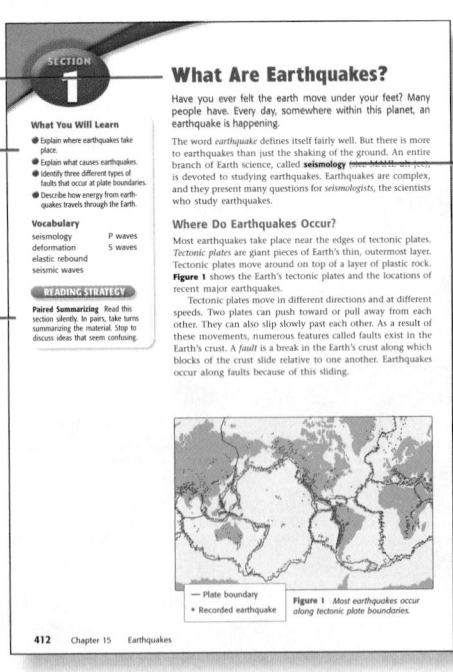

Vocabulary are highlighted in yellow and defined in the margin to develop students' vocabulary skills.

Reading Checks allow students to check their understanding at least once every two-page spread. Answers are found in the **Appendix**.

LIVE INK® READING HELP IS PROVEN TO RAISE STUDENT TEST SCORES.

Live Ink Reading Help, a scientifically researched tool for improving students' reading comprehension, is proven to raise students' test scores. Live Ink is available on the Premier Online Edition of Holt Science & Technology.

ADDITIONAL RESOURCES HELP STUDENTS DEVELOP READING COMPREHENSION SKILLS.

Interactive Textbook is a full adapted read of each chapter's key concepts and makes the content from the *Student Edition* accessible to both English Language Learners and struggling readers. Reading strategies, directed reading questions, and interactive illustrations are provided to help develop students' reading skills.

Reading Comprehension Guide includes Directed Reading Worksheets and Vocabulary and Section Summary Worksheets that make reading an active process.

- **Directed Reading Worksheets** guide students through each section and focus their attention on key elements. These worksheets are available in two levels: Basic and Special Needs.

- **Vocabulary and Section Summary Worksheets** help students review vocabulary words and provide a bulleted list of main topics from each section.

Reinforcement Worksheets, found in each Chapter Resource File, make reviewing and reinforcing chapter content easy.

Guided Reading Audio Program, a direct reading of the student text, is helpful to students who benefit from different teaching styles. This program is available in English and Spanish.

Student One Stop on CD-ROM includes the entire *Student Edition,* the *Interactive Textbook, Study Guide, Directed Reading Worksheets A* and *B, Vocabulary and Section Summary Worksheets, Math Skills for Science Worksheets, Science Skills Worksheets,* and the *Multilingual Glossary.*

Holt Science Skills Workshop: Reading in the Content Area targets the reading skills specific to the comprehension of science texts. Using these activities and exercises, students learn to analyze text structures, recognize patterns, and organize information in ways that help them construct meaning.

Ongoing Assessment
targets your instruction

Holt Science & Technology provides many ways to accurately measure students' mastery of content.

THE EXAMVIEW® VERSION 5 ASSESSMENT SUITE GIVES YOU THE POWER TO CUSTOMIZE YOUR OWN ASSESSMENTS.

With the **Examview® Version 5 Assessment Suite** on the *One-Stop Planner®* you can also do the following:

- Customize assessments by selecting from a bank of questions that are organized by chapter and correlated to the National Science Education Standards.

- Post tests to **Holt Online Assessment.** The system automatically grades tests so that you can diagnose student proficiency and track student progress.

  - Develop multiple reports that track students' progress and mastery of science objectives.

SECTION ASSESSMENT

Reading Check is found at least once on each two-page spread. Students are encouraged to check their understanding of content by answering these questions found throughout the chapter and comparing their answers to the answer key in the **Appendix.**

Section Review provides a summary of the section and a comprehensive assessment of students' understanding of Section objectives. **Math, Interpreting Graphics, and Critical Thinking** questions are included.

Section Quiz in the *Teacher's Edition* and the *Chapter Resource Files* provides additional questions to check students' understanding.

Alternative Assessment gives you different evaluation options, such as expository writing and concept mapping, to ensure a thorough assessment.

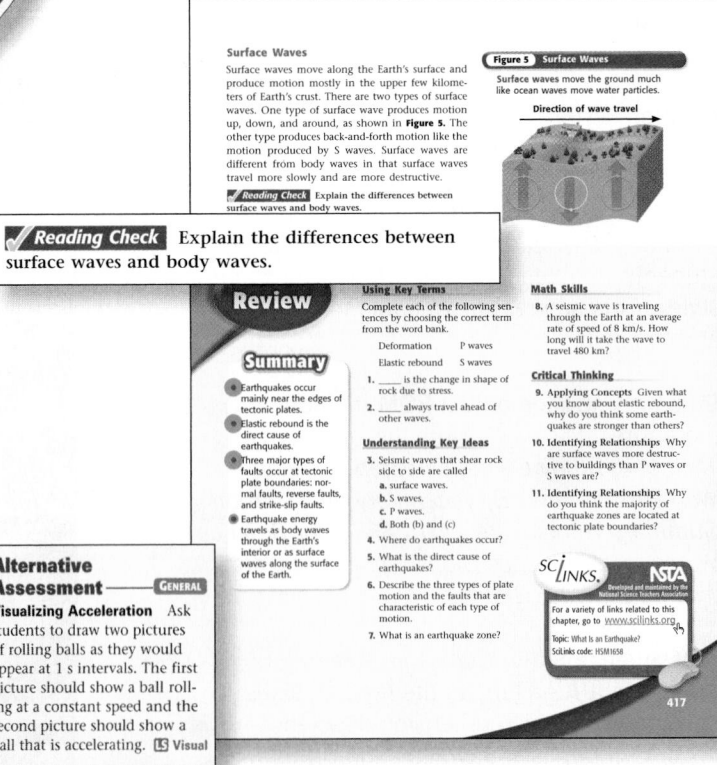

CHAPTER ASSESSMENT

Chapter Review checks students' understanding of all of the Section objectives covered in the chapter. This review includes a variety of question types and a range of thinking levels. Question types are similar to those found on Chapter Tests, making this an excellent resource for pretest practice.

- **Assignment Guide** in the Teacher's Edition lets you see which review questions correlate with a specific section's content.

- **Study Guide** provides blackline masters of the **Section** and **Chapter Reviews** to help students prepare for testing.

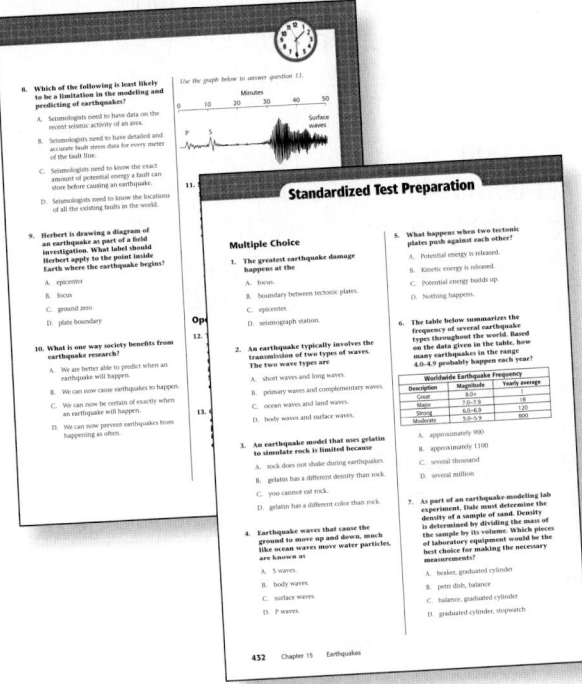

Standardized Test Preparation helps students prepare for testing with two full pages of test preparation in the *Student Edition.* Blackline masters of these pages appear in the *Chapter Resource Files.*

Test Doctor in the *Teacher's Edition* helps you diagnose why a student answered a **Standardized Test Preparation** question incorrectly.

Chapter Resource Files include a **Performance-Based Assessment** plus three levels of **Chapter Tests** to meet the needs of your classroom—Special Needs, General, and Advanced.

Assessment Checklists & Rubrics provide guidelines for evaluating your students' progress. You can create a customized checklist for each class to help you gather daily scores and determine grades.

Brain Food Video Quizzes (on DVD) are game show-style quizzes that assess students' progress and help them prepare for tests.

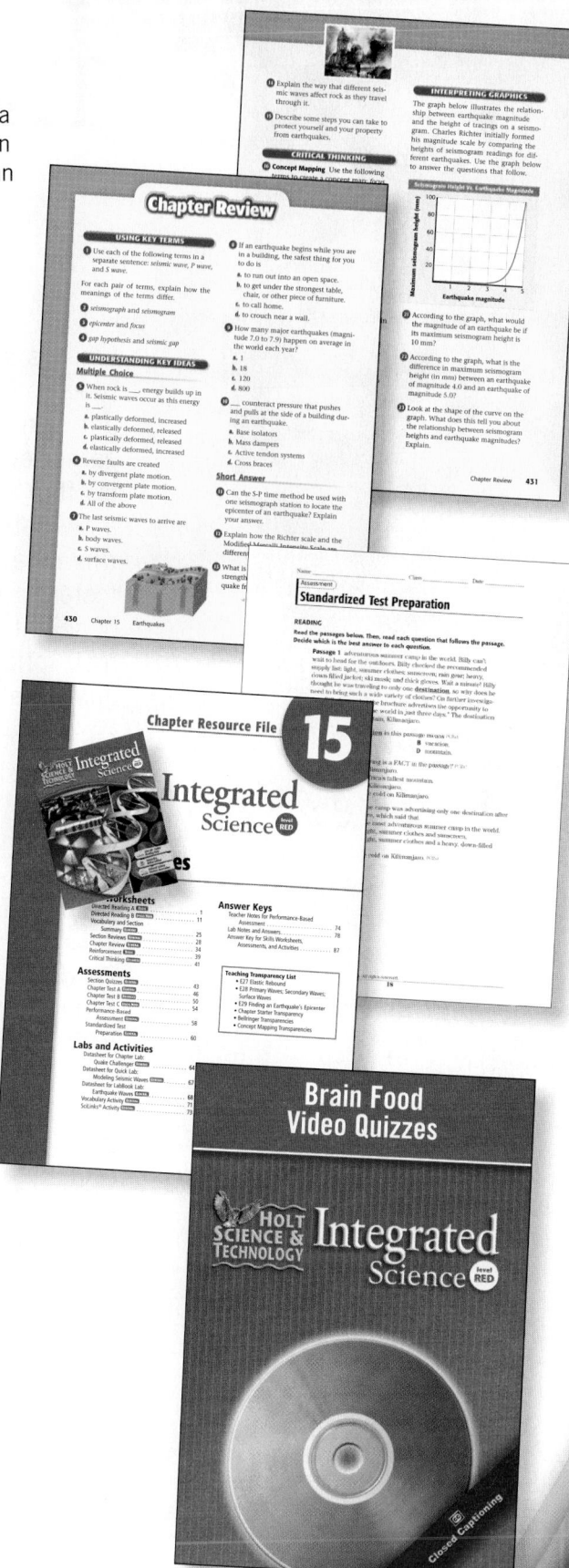

Teaching Science Inquiry

What is ***scientific inquiry?*** Scientific inquiry is the process by which scientists ask questions, develop and carry out investigations, make predictions, gather evidence, and propose explanations. Inquiry is often associated with "hands-on" learning or activity-based instruction. Research shows that this type of instruction has been effective in fostering scientific literacy and the understanding of scientific processes. Furthermore, inquiry-based instruction has been reported to improve students' analytical skills.

As students practice inquiry, they develop process skills and behaviors used by scientists and thus begin thinking like a scientist. The development of these process skills involves the student being in a situation in which he or she has to think like a scientist. Process skills can be developed through simple activities but students need to be continually exposed to these activities. Listed below are process skills that students develop while doing inquiry.

- Observation
- Experimentation
- Data Collection
- Measuring
- Sorting, Classifying, and Comparing
- Analysis
- Communication

INQUIRY IN HOLT SCIENCE & TECHNOLOGY

Listed below are three different approaches to teaching scientific inquiry. **Holt Science & Technology** provides a variety of activities and labs throughout their program that introduce the student to each of these approaches and thus to a different learning situation. The different types of labs and activities provide flexibility to accommodate any classroom and any teaching situation. By using **Holt Science & Technology** students actively learn by incorporating key science concepts through hands-on activity. This reinforces science concepts, improving science literacy and developing science skills.

- **Structured Inquiry** Students follow teacher's instructions to perform an activity but are not provided with the expected outcome.

- **Guided Inquiry** Students develop a procedure to investigate a problem selected by the teacher.

- **Open Inquiry** Students develop a problem to investigate and design their own investigation.

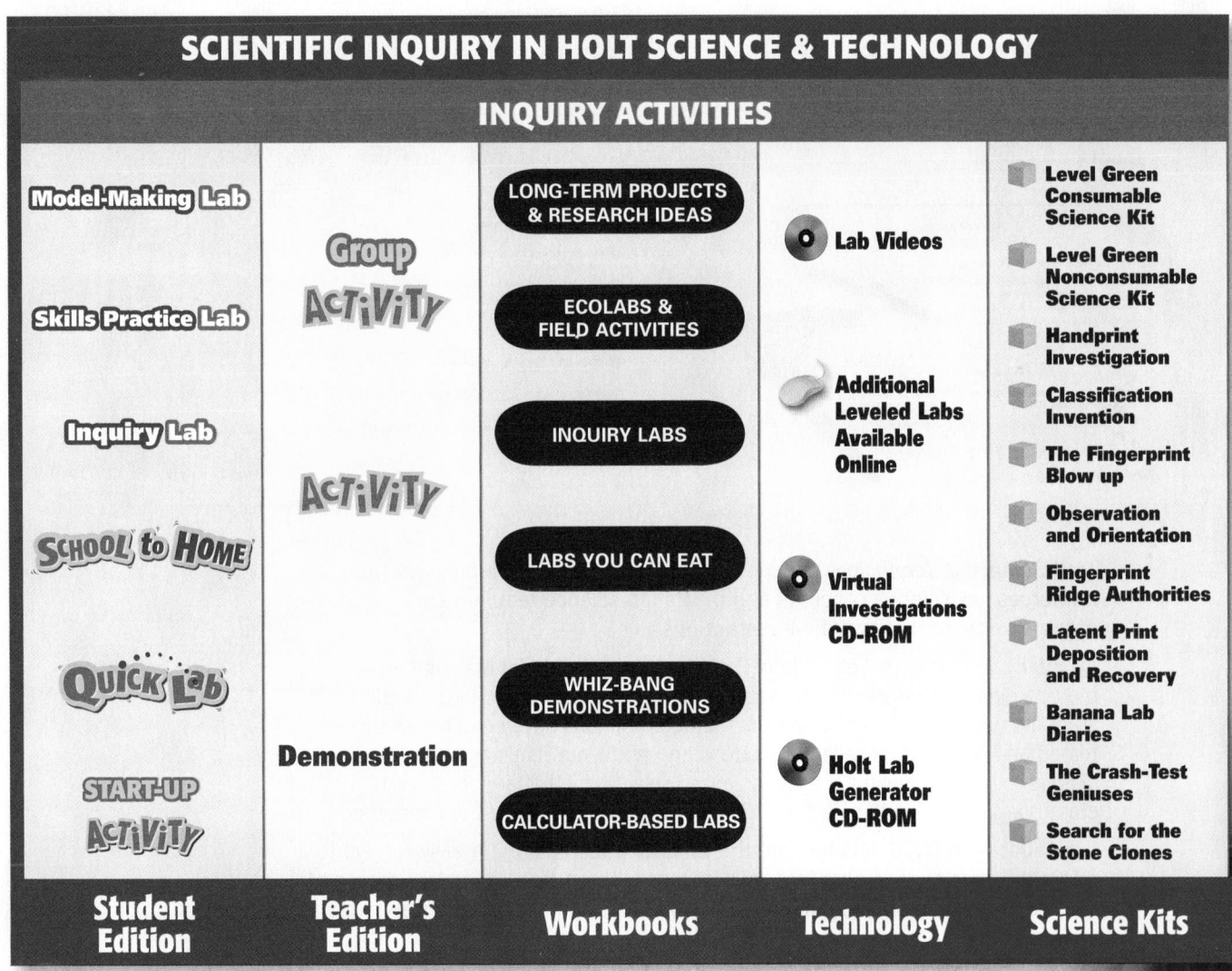

SCIENTIFIC INQUIRY IN HOLT SCIENCE & TECHNOLOGY

INQUIRY ACTIVITIES

Student Edition	Teacher's Edition	Workbooks	Technology	Science Kits
Model-Making Lab	Group ACTIVITY	LONG-TERM PROJECTS & RESEARCH IDEAS	Lab Videos	Level Green Consumable Science Kit
Skills Practice Lab		ECOLABS & FIELD ACTIVITIES	Additional Leveled Labs Available Online	Level Green Nonconsumable Science Kit
Inquiry Lab	ACTIVITY	INQUIRY LABS		Handprint Investigation
SCHOOL to HOME		LABS YOU CAN EAT	Virtual Investigations CD-ROM	Classification Invention
Quick Lab		WHIZ-BANG DEMONSTRATIONS		The Fingerprint Blow up
START-UP ACTIVITY	Demonstration	CALCULATOR-BASED LABS	Holt Lab Generator CD-ROM	Observation and Orientation
				Fingerprint Ridge Authorities
				Latent Print Deposition and Recovery
				Banana Lab Diaries
				The Crash-Test Geniuses
				Search for the Stone Clones

Activities reinforce students' understanding of key concepts

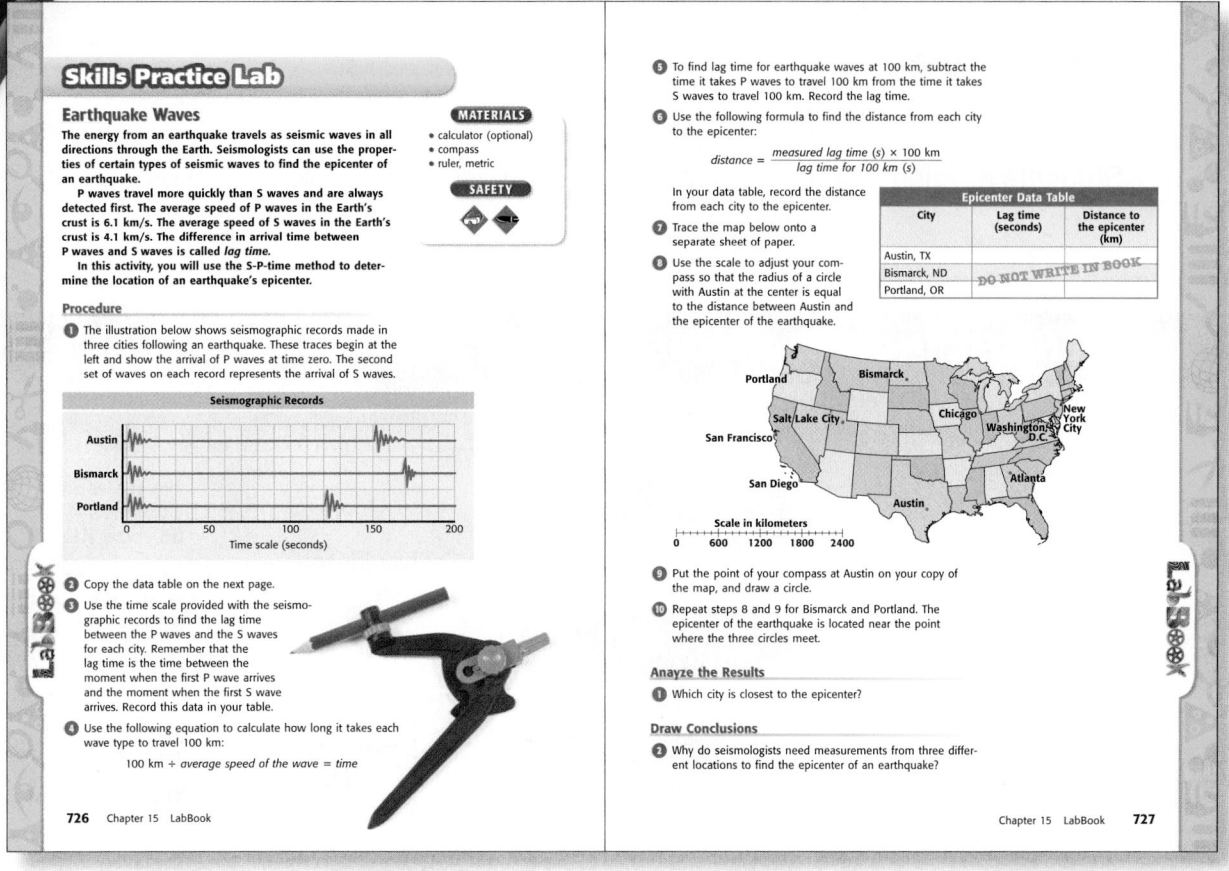

Skills Practice Lab

Earthquake Waves

The energy from an earthquake travels as seismic waves in all directions through the Earth. Seismologists can use the properties of certain types of seismic waves to find the epicenter of an earthquake.

P waves travel more quickly than S waves and are always detected first. The average speed of P waves in the Earth's crust is 6.1 km/s. The average speed of S waves in the Earth's crust is 4.1 km/s. The difference in arrival time between P waves and S waves is called *lag time*.

In this activity, you will use the S-P-time method to determine the location of an earthquake's epicenter.

MATERIALS
- calculator (optional)
- compass
- ruler, metric

SAFETY

Procedure

1. The illustration below shows seismographic records made in three cities following an earthquake. These traces begin at the left and show the arrival of P waves at time zero. The second set of waves on each record represents the arrival of S waves.

Seismographic Records

Austin

Bismarck

Portland

Time scale (seconds): 0, 50, 100, 150, 200

2. Copy the data table on the next page.

3. Use the time scale provided with the seismographic records to find the lag time between the P waves and the S waves for each city. Remember that the lag time is the time between the moment when the first P wave arrives and the moment when the first S wave arrives. Record this data in your table.

4. Use the following equation to calculate how long it takes each wave type to travel 100 km:

$$100 \text{ km} \div average \ speed \ of \ the \ wave = time$$

5. To find lag time for earthquake waves at 100 km, subtract the time it takes P waves to travel 100 km from the time it takes S waves to travel 100 km. Record the lag time.

6. Use the following formula to find the distance from each city to the epicenter:

$$distance = \frac{measured \ lag \ time \ (s) \times 100 \text{ km}}{lag \ time \ for \ 100 \text{ km} \ (s)}$$

In your data table, record the distance from each city to the epicenter.

7. Trace the map below onto a separate sheet of paper.

8. Use the scale to adjust your compass so that the radius of a circle with Austin at the center is equal to the distance between Austin and the epicenter of the earthquake.

Epicenter Data Table

City	Lag time (seconds)	Distance to the epicenter (km)
Austin, TX		
Bismarck, ND	DO NOT WRITE IN BOOK	
Portland, OR		

Scale in kilometers: 0, 600, 1200, 1800, 2400

9. Put the point of your compass at Austin on your copy of the map, and draw a circle.

10. Repeat steps 8 and 9 for Bismarck and Portland. The epicenter of the earthquake is located near the point where the three circles meet.

Analyze the Results

1. Which city is closest to the epicenter?

Draw Conclusions

2. Why do seismologists need measurements from three different locations to find the epicenter of an earthquake?

726   Chapter 15   LabBook

Chapter 15   LabBook   727

Holt Science & Technology provides a strong and flexible lab program that reinforces key science concepts and meets lab science requirements, regardless of lab equipment limits or time restrictions.

Chapter Labs—Inquiry Labs, Skills Practice Labs, and **Model Making Labs—** include clear procedures, demonstrate scientific concepts, and help develop students' understanding of scientific methods. All labs have been classroom-tested and reviewed for reliability, safety, and efficiency. Labs are rated in the *Teacher's Edition,* making it easy for you to select labs that are appropriate for your classroom. Go online to select additional leveled labs correlated to chapter content.

Lab Videos (on DVD) demonstrate the **Chapter Labs,** making it easy for you to integrate more experiments into your lessons without the preparation time and costs of a traditional laboratory setup. **Lab Videos** can also provide reinforcement and reteaching opportunities for students.

LabBook provides additional experiments at the end of the *Student Edition,* giving you even more full-length labs to choose from.

Datasheets for all **Quick Labs, Chapter Labs,** and **LabBook Labs** are available in the *Chapter Resource Files.*

START-UP ACTIVITY

Making Rain

Do you have the power to make rain? Yes!—on a small scale. In this activity, you will cause water to change state in the same way that rain is formed. This process is one way that water is reused on Earth.

Start-Up Activity is a short, but engaging activity at the beginning of the chapter that motivates students to learn.

Quick Lab

Heat Exchange

1. Fill a **film canister** with **hot water.** Insert the

Quick Lab is easy to execute and requires minimal time and materials—great for an in-class activity, teacher demonstration, or group presentation.

SCHOOL to HOME

How You Measure Matters

Measure the length and width of a desk or table, but do not use a ruler. Pick

School-to-Home Activity provides an opportunity for parents or guardians to get involved with student learning. These activities require little or no equipment and do not require safety precautions.

INTERNET ACTIVITY

For another activity related to this chapter, go to **go.hrw.com** and type in the keyword **HP5WPSW.**

Internet Activity sends students online for a variety of projects, such as creating scientist biographies and writing science articles.

Language Arts ACTIVITY

WRITING SKILL Write your own short story about a
mysterious
to the reade
but do not r

Social Studies ACTIVITY

WRITING SKILL Research a location where there
forest fires.
forests or pa
about the iss

Math ACTIVITY

In space flight, astronauts experience changes in gravity that affect their bodies in several ways. Because of gravity, a person who has a mass of 50 kg weighs 110 pounds on Earth. But on the

Cross-Disciplinary Activity gives students the opportunity to see how science relates to social studies, language arts, or mathematics.

Motivate

Demonstration —— GENERAL

Ball-and-Ring Heat Expansion
Obtain a metal ball-and-ring set. Heat the ball for a minute or

You can also integrate additional activities from the *Teacher's Edition* into your lessons— **Activity, Group Activity, Connection Activity, Demonstration,** and **Homework.**

Lab options for every need

Holt Science & Technology provides a variety of additional meaningful activities that are cost effective and fun. A variety of ancillary materials complement and complete your presentations.

Calculator-Based Labs integrate calculator use into science labs, providing a link to help students develop mathematics skills. **20 labs in all!**

Whiz-Bang Demonstrations include compelling demonstrations that students will enjoy—proving that learning science can be fun, as well as meaningful. **65 labs in all!**

Labs You Can Eat spark student interest, while explaining important scientific concepts. **25 labs in all!**

Inquiry Labs introduce students to the world of science inquiry and foster the skills necessary to develop hands-on science literacy. **23 labs in all!**

EcoLabs & Field Activities provide students with ideas for exploring the world of science outside the classroom. **23 labs in all!**

Long-Term Projects and Research Ideas help students think about science as a long-term process. Students are encouraged to study topics they find intriguing and to construct their own types of investigation. **2 for every chapter!**

Holt Lab Generator CD-ROM features all labs from *Holt Science & Technology* plus additional labs from the lab bank.

- Search for labs by topic, difficulty level, lab duration, National Science Education Standard, or state standard.

- Edit labs to fit classroom needs.

- Develop new labs from our easy-to-use formatted template.

- Customize your own science kits and save time ordering materials using the **Lab Materials QuickList Software.**

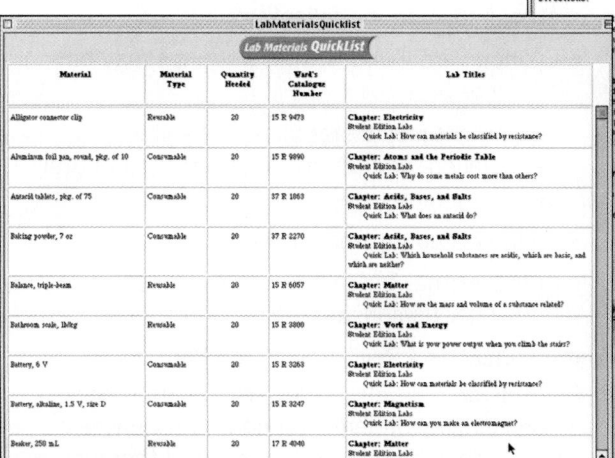

Lab Videos make it easier to integrate more experiments into your lessons without the preparation time and costs of a traditional laboratory set-up. These videos demonstrate the end-of-chapter labs.

Virtual Investigations CD-ROM makes it easy for students to practice science skills without the expense. Students perform lab activities in a safe, simulated environment.

Safety in your laboratory

RISK ASSESSMENT

MAKING YOUR LABORATORY A SAFE PLACE TO WORK AND LEARN

Concern for safety must begin before any activity in the classroom and before students enter the lab. A careful review of the facilities should be a basic part of preparation for each school term. You should investigate the physical environment, identify any safety risks, and inspect your work areas for compliance with safety regulations.

The review of the lab should be thorough, and all safety issues must be addressed immediately. Keep a file of your review, and add to the list each year. This will allow you to continue to raise the standard of safety in your lab and classroom.

Many classroom experiments, demonstrations, and other activities are classics that have been used for years. This familiarity may lead to a comfort that can obscure inherent safety concerns. Review all experiments, demonstrations, and activities for safety concerns before presenting them to the class. Identify and eliminate potential safety hazards.

1. Identify the Risks

Before introducing any activity, demonstration, or experiment to the class, analyze it and consider what could possibly go wrong. Carefully review the list of materials to make sure they are safe. Inspect the equipment in your lab or classroom to make sure it is in good working order. Read the procedures to make sure they are safe. Record any hazards or concerns you identify.

2. Evaluate the Risks

Minimize the risks you identified in the last step without sacrificing learning. Remember that no activity you perform in the lab or classroom is worth risking injury. Thus, extremely hazardous activities, or those that violate your school's policies, must be eliminated. For activities that present smaller risks, analyze each risk carefully to determine its likelihood. If the pedagogical value of the activity does not outweigh the risks, the activity must be eliminated.

3. Select Controls to Address Risks

Even low-risk activities require controls to eliminate or minimize the risks. Make sure that in devising controls you do not substitute an equally or more hazardous alternative. Some control methods include the following:

- Explicit verbal and written warnings may be added or posted.

- Equipment may be rebuilt or relocated, parts may be replaced, or equipment be replaced entirely by safer alternatives.

- Risky procedures may be eliminated.

- Activities may be changed from student activities to teacher demonstrations.

4. Implement and Review Selected Controls

Controls do not help if they are forgotten or not enforced. The implementation and review of controls should be as systematic and thorough as the initial analysis of safety concerns in the lab and laboratory activities.

SOME SAFETY RISKS AND PREVENTATIVE CONTROLS

The following list describes several possible safety hazards and controls that can be implemented to resolve them. This list is not complete, but it can be used as a starting point to identify hazards in your laboratory.

Identified risk	Preventative control
Facilities and Equipment	
Lab tables are in disrepair, room is poorly lighted and ventilated, faucets and electrical outlets do not work or are difficult to use because of their location.	Work surfaces should be level and stable. There should be adequate lighting and ventilation. Water supplies, drains, and electrical outlets should be in good working order. Any equipment in a dangerous location should not be used; it should be relocated or rendered inoperable.
Wiring, plumbing, and air circulation systems do not work or do not meet current specifications.	Specifications should be kept on file. Conduct a periodic review of all equipment, and document compliance. Damaged fixtures must be labeled as such and must be repaired as soon as possible.
Eyewash fountains and safety showers are present, but no one knows anything about their specifications.	Ensure that eyewash fountains and safety showers meet the requirements of the ANSI standard (Z358.1).
Eyewash fountains are checked and cleaned once at the beginning of each school year. No records are kept of routine checks and maintenance on the safety showers and eyewash fountains.	Flush eyewash fountains for 5 min. every month to remove any bacteria or other organisms from pipes. Test safety showers (measure flow in gallons per min.) and eyewash fountains every 6 months and keep records of the test results.
Labs are conducted in multipurpose rooms, and equipment from other courses remains accessible.	Only the items necessary for a given activity should be available to students. All equipment should be locked away when not in use.
Students are permitted to enter or work in the lab without teacher supervision.	Lock all laboratory rooms whenever a teacher is not present. Supervising teachers must be trained in lab safety and emergency procedures.
Safety equipment and emergency procedures	
Fire and other emergency drills are infrequent, and no records or measurements are made of the results of the drills.	Always carry out critical reviews of fire or other emergency drills. Be sure that plans include alternate routes. Don't wait until an emergency to find the flaws in your plans.
Emergency evacuation plans do not include instructions for securing the lab in the event of an evacuation during a lab activity.	Plan actions in case of emergency: establish what devices should be turned off, which escape route to use, and where to meet outside the building.
Fire extinguishers are in out-of-the-way locations, not on the escape route.	Place fire extinguishers near escape routes so that they will be of use during an emergency.
Fire extinguishers are not maintained. Teachers are not trained to use them.	Document regular maintenance of fire extinguishers. Train supervisory personnel in the proper use of extinguishers. Instruct students not to use an extinguisher but to call for a teacher.

Identified risk	Preventative control
Safety equipment and emergency procedures, *continued*	
Teachers in labs and neighboring classrooms are not trained in CPR or first aid.	Teachers should receive training. The American Red Cross and other groups offer training. Certifications should be kept current with frequent refresher courses.
Teachers are not aware of their legal responsibilities in case of an injury or accident.	Review your faculty handbook for your responsibilities regarding safety in the classroom and laboratory. Contact the legal counsel for your school district to find out the extent of their support and any rules, regulations, or procedures you must follow.
Emergency procedures are not posted. Emergency numbers are kept only at the switchboard or main office. Instructions are given verbally only at the beginning of the year.	Emergency procedures should be posted at all exits and near all safety equipment. Emergency numbers should be posted at all phones, and a script should be provided for the caller to use. Emergency procedures must be reviewed periodically, and students should be reminded of them at the beginning of each activity.
Spills are handled on a case-by-case basis and are cleaned up with whatever materials happen to be on hand.	Have the appropriate equipment and materials available for cleaning up; replace them before expiration dates. Make sure students know to alert you to spilled chemicals, blood, and broken glass.
Work habits and environment	
Safety wear is only used for activities involving chemicals or hot plates.	Aprons and goggles should be worn in the lab at all times. Long hair, loose clothing, and loose jewelry should be secured.
There is no dress code established for the laboratory; students are allowed to wear sandals or open-toed shoes.	Open-toed shoes should never be worn in the laboratory. Do not allow any footwear in the lab that does not cover feet completely.
Students are required to wear safety gear, but teachers and visitors are not.	Always wear safety gear in the lab. Keep extra equipment on hand for visitors.
Safety is emphasized at the beginning of the term but is not mentioned later in the year.	Safety must be the first priority in all lab work. Students should be warned of risks and instructed in emergency procedures for each activity.
There is no assessment of students' knowledge and attitudes regarding safety.	Conduct frequent safety quizzes. Only students with perfect scores should be allowed to work in the lab.
You work alone during your preparation period to organize the day's labs.	Never work alone in a science laboratory or a storage area.
Safety inspections are conducted irregularly and are not documented. Teachers and administrators are unaware of what documentation will be necessary in case of a lawsuit.	Safety reviews should be frequent and regular. All reviews should be documented, and improvements must be implemented immediately. Contact legal counsel for your district to make sure your procedures will protect you in case of a lawsuit.

Identified risk	Preventative control
Purchasing, storing, and using chemicals	
The storeroom is too crowded, so you decide to keep some equipment on the lab benches.	Do not store reagents or equipment on lab benches and keep shelves organized. Never place reactive chemicals (in bottles, beakers, flasks, wash bottles, etc.) near the edges of a lab bench.
You prepare solutions from concentrated stock to save money.	Reduce risks by ordering diluted instead of concentrated substances.
You purchase plenty of chemicals to be sure that you won't run out or to save money.	Purchase chemicals in class-size quantities. Do not purchase or have on hand more than one year's supply of each chemical.
You don't generally read labels on chemicals when preparing solutions for a lab because you already know about a chemical.	Read each label to be sure it states the hazards and describes the precautions and first aid procedures (when appropriate) that apply to the contents in case someone else has to deal with that chemical in an emergency.
You never read the Material Safety Data Sheets (MSDSs) that come with your chemicals.	Always read the Material Safety Data Sheet (MSDS) for a chemical before using it and follow the precautions described. File and organize MSDSs for all chemicals where they can be found easily in case of an emergency.
The main stockroom contains chemicals that haven't been used for years.	Do not leave bottles of chemicals unused on the shelves of the lab for more than one week or unused in the main stockroom for more than one year. Dispose of or use up any leftover chemicals.
No extra precautions are taken when flammable liquids are dispensed from their containers.	When transferring flammable liquids from bulk containers, ground the container, and before transferring to a smaller metal container, ground both containers.
Students are told to put their broken glass and solid chemical wastes in the trash can.	Have separate containers for trash, for broken glass, and for different categories of hazardous chemical wastes.
You store chemicals alphabetically instead of by hazard class. Chemicals are stored without consideration of possible emergencies (fire, earthquake, flood, etc.), which could compound the hazard.	Use MSDSs to determine which chemicals are incompatible. Store chemicals by the hazard class indicated on the MSDS. Store chemicals that are incompatible with common fire-fighting media like water (such as alkali metals) or carbon dioxide (such as alkali and alkaline-earth metals) under conditions that eliminate the possibility of a reaction with water or carbon dioxide if it is necessary to fight a fire in the storage area.
Corrosives are kept above eye level, out of reach from anyone who is not authorized to be in the storeroom.	Always store corrosive chemicals on shelves below eye level. Remember, fumes from many corrosives can destroy metal cabinets and shelving.
Chemicals are kept on the stockroom floor on the days that they will be used so that they are easy to find.	Never store chemicals or other materials on floors or in the aisles of the laboratory or storeroom, even for a few minutes.

Safety symbols and safety guidelines for students

EYE PROTECTION

- Wear safety goggles, and know where the eyewash station is located and how to use it.
- Avoid swinging objects, which can cause serious injury.
- Avoid directly looking at a light source, as this may cause permanent eye damage.

HAND SAFETY

- Wear latex or nitrile gloves to protect yourself from chemicals in the lab.
- Use a hot mitt to handle resistors, light sources, and other equipment that may be hot. Allow equipment to cool before handling it and storing it.

CLOTHING PROTECTION

- Wear a laboratory apron to protect your clothing.
- Tie back long hair, secure loose clothing, and remove loose jewelry to prevent their getting caught in moving parts or coming in contact with chemicals.

HEATING SAFETY

- When using a Bunsen burner or a hot plate, always wear safety goggles and a laboratory apron to protect your eyes and clothing. Tie back long hair, secure loose clothing, and remove loose jewelry.
- Never leave a hot plate unattended while it is turned on.
- If your clothing catches on fire, walk to the emergency lab shower, and use the shower to put out the fire.
- Wire coils may heat up rapidly during experiments. If heating occurs, open the switch immediately, and handle the equipment with a hot mitt.
- Allow all equipment to cool before storing it.

 ## CHEMICAL SAFETY

- Do not eat or drink anything in the lab. Never taste chemicals.
- If a chemical gets on your skin or clothing or in your eyes, rinse it immediately with lukewarm water, and alert your teacher.
- If a chemical is spilled, tell your teacher, but do not clean it up yourself unless your teacher says it is OK to do so.

 ## ELECTRICAL SAFETY

- Never close a circuit until it has been approved by your teacher. Never rewire or adjust any element of a closed circuit.
- Never work with electricity near water; be sure the floor and all work surfaces are dry.
- If the pointer of any kind of meter moves off the scale, open the circuit immediately by opening the switch.
- Light bulbs or wires that are conducting electricity can become very hot.
- Do not work with any batteries, electrical devices, or magnets other than those provided by your teacher.

 ## ANIMAL SAFETY

- Handle animals only as directed by your teacher.
- Always treat animals carefully and with respect.
- Wash your hands thoroughly after handling any animal.

 ## PLANT SAFETY

- Wash your hands thoroughly after handling any part of a plant.

 ## SHARP/POINTED OBJECTS

- Use knives and other sharp instruments with extreme care.
- Do not cut an object while holding it in your hands. Instead, place it on a suitable work surface for cutting.

Linking science to other disciplines

Science does not occur in a vacuum. It is an integral part of the human quest to understand the world. Connection features help students become more aware of the interconnectedness of their school studies and prepare them for standardized testing.

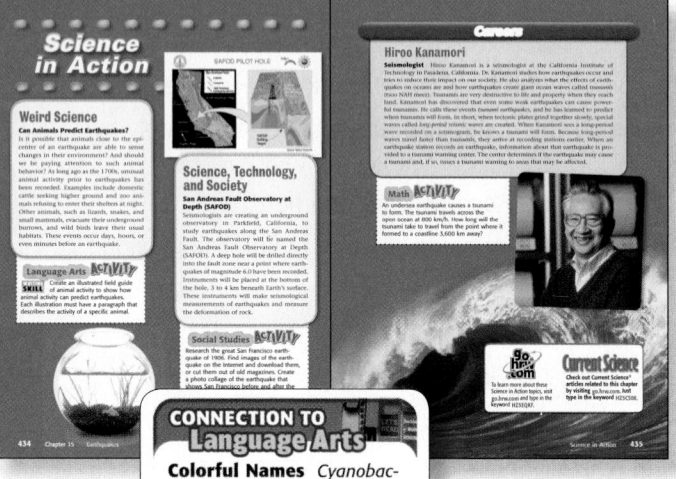

Science in Action features provide short articles designed to spark students' interest in science topics. Cross-Disciplinary activities including social studies, language arts, and math activities are also included for each article. Students can extend their learning by visiting **go.hrw.com.**

Connection to Language Arts links science with various language arts skills.

Holt Anthology of Science Fiction connects science to literature with interesting and relevant stories.

Writing Skills icon occurs in any activity that requires students to practice their writing skills.

Connection to Social Studies links science to social studies, presenting students with opportunities to see how science relates to history, geography, and wider society concerns.

Connection to Science links various sciences to explain phenomena in the natural world. This feature provides students with opportunities to recognize and explore important links to sciences such as environmental science, geology, physics, and oceanography.

CONNECTION TO Language Arts

Colorful Names *Cyanobacteria* means "blue bacteria." Many other names also refer to colors. You might not recognize these colors because the words for the colors are in another language. Look at the list of Greek color words below. Write down two English words that have one of the color roots in them. (Hint: Many words have the color as the first part of the word.)

melano = black

chloro = green

erythro = red

leuko = white

CONNECTION TO Chemistry

Round and Wrinkled Round seeds may look better, but wrinkled seeds taste sweeter. The dominant a__ causes sugar to be changed into starch (__ ecule for sugar). This change makes the s__ the genotype *rr* do not make or store this __ sugar has not been changed into starch, t__ you had a pea plant with round seeds (*R__* it with to get some offspring with wrinkle__ square showing your cross.

CONNECTION TO Social Studies

Disease and History Many diseases have shaped history. For example, yellow fe__ which is caused by a __ is spread by mosquito__ one of the obstacles i__ ing the Panama Canal__ after people learned h__ prevent the spread of__ low fever virus could __ be completed.

Use information fro__ net and library resear__ create a poster descri__ one infectious disease__ history.

CONNECTION ACTIVITY Earth Science — GENERAL

Ancient Mountains Provide a large wall map of the world, and provide map pins o__ tacks in three colors. Have students locate the following mountain ranges on a map. Have students place pins on the map for each range to match the eras when each range was formed. Use the following list for reference:

CONNECTION to Math — GENERAL

Energy Loss There are 12,000 units of the sun's energy available to grass, which occupies the base of an energy pyramid. Grass stores this 10% of available energy in its tissues. This energy becomes available to the next consumer, a prairie dog. In turn, the prairie dog, a consumer of grass, stores 10% of the energy that was stored in the grass. A coyote, a consumer of prairie dogs, stores 10% of the energy that was stored in the prairie dog. Calculate the units of food energy stored in the grass, the prairie dog, and the

dian (New__
__rth

(western

urope),

ADDITIONAL MATH CONNECTIONS

Math Practice provides practice in simple mathematical computations. Students can hone math skills by using the exercises provided in this feature.

Averages

Finding the average, or mean, of a group of numbers is a common way to analyze data.

For example, three seeds were kept at 25°C and sprouted in 8, 8, and 5 days. To find the average number of days that it took the seeds to sprout, add 8, 8, and 5

MATH FOCUS

Probability If you roll a pair of dice, what is the probability that you will roll 2 threes?

Step 1: Count the number of faces on a single die. Put this number in the denominator: 6.

Step 2: Count how many ways you can roll a three with one die. Put this number in the numerator: 1/6.

Step 3: To find the probability that you will throw 2 threes, multiply the probability of throwing the first three by the probability of throwing the second three: $1/6 \times 1/6 = 1/36$.

Now It's Your Turn

If you roll a single die, what is the probability that you will roll an even number?

Math Focus feature links mathematics directly to the science being presented. Problems are solved to show students the natural links between these two disciplines. Following the solved problem, students are presented with an application that checks their understanding.

Math Activity

Suppose that each dolphin in the Navy's program is trained for 5 years and each trained dolphin works for 25 years. If 10 dolphins began training each year for 10 years, how many would be working at the end of those 10 years? How many would still be in training?

Math Activity in **Science in Action** provides additional integrated exposure to mathematics problems.

Math Skills

9. A certain toad species spends 2 months of its life as a tadpole and 3 years of its life as an adult. What percentage of its life is spent in the water? What percentage is spent on land?

Math Skills problem is presented in most Section Reviews, providing additional math practice.

Math Refresher, found in the **Appendix,** reviews basic math skills such as averages, ratios, percentages, and more.

Math Skills for Science helps students develop and apply basic math skills to scientific problems.

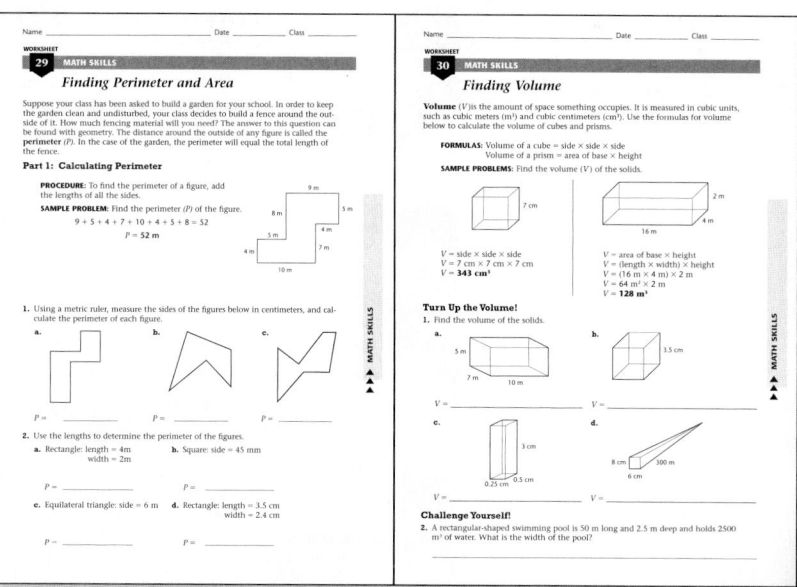

Pacing and Compression Guide

Pacing and Compression Guide

Pacing Each **Chapter Planning Guide** breaks down the chapter into instructional blocks. Each instructional block consists of sections and labs that you can cover in 45 or 90 minutes. The **Chapter Planning Guide** also lists activities, demonstrations, and resources that are available to accompany each section.

15 Earthquakes
Chapter Planning Guide

Compression guide:
To shorten instruction because of time limitations, omit the Chapter Lab.

OBJECTIVES	LABS, DEMONSTRATIONS, AND ACTIVITIES	TECHNOLOGY RESOURCES
PACING • 90 min pp. 410–417 **Chapter Opener**	SE **Start-up Activity,** p. 411 ◆ GENERAL	OSP **Parent Letter** ■ CD **Student Edition on CD-ROM** CD **Guided Reading Audio CD** ■ TR **Chapter Starter Transparency*** VID **Brain Food Video Quiz**
Section 1 What Are Earthquakes? • Explain where earthquakes take place. • Explain what causes earthquakes. • Identify three different types of faults that occur at plate boundaries. • Describe how energy from earthquakes travels through the Earth.	TE **Demonstration** Faults and Earthquakes, p. 413 ◆ BASIC SE **Quick Lab** Modeling Seismic Waves, p. 416 GENERAL CRF **Datasheet for Quick Lab*** SE **Science in Action** Math, Social Studies, and Language Arts Activities, pp. 434–435 GENERAL	OSP **Lesson Plans** (also in print) TR **Bellringer Transparency*** TR **E27 Elastic Rebound*** TR **LINK TO PHYSICAL SCIENCE** P82 Comparing Longitudinal and Transverse Waves* TR **E28 Primary Waves; Secondary Waves; Surface Waves*** CRF **SciLinks Activity*** GENERAL
PACING • 45 min pp. 418–421 **Section 2 Earthquake Measurement** • Explain how earthquakes are detected. • Describe how to locate an earthquake's epicenter. • Explain how the strength of an earthquake is measured. • Explain how the intensity of an earthquake is measured.	TE **Activity** Exploring a Seismic Network, p. 418 GENERAL SE **Skills Practice Lab** Earthquake Waves, p. 726 GENERAL CRF **Datasheet for LabBook*** LB **Long-Term Projects & Research Ideas** A Whole Lotta Shakin'* ADVANCED	OSP **Lesson Plans** (also in print) TR **Bellringer Transparency*** TR **E29 Finding an Earthquake's Epicenter***
PACING • 90 min pp. 422–427 **Section 3 Earthquakes and Society** • Explain how earthquake-hazard level is determined. • Compare methods of earthquake forecasting. • Describe five ways to safeguard buildings against earthquakes. • Outline earthquake safety procedures.	TE **Connection Activity** Art, p. 422 GENERAL TE **Connection Activity** Math, p. 423 GENERAL TE **Activity** Tools of the Trade, p. 424 ADVANCED TE **Demonstration** Flexible Buildings, p. 425 BASIC TE **Connection Activity** Real Life, p. 425 GENERAL SE **Connection to Physics** Earthquake Proof Buildings, p. 426 GENERAL SE **School-to-Home Activity** Disaster Planning, p. 427 GENERAL SE **Inquiry Lab** Quake Challenge, p. 428 ◆ GENERAL CRF **Datasheet for Chapter Lab*** LB **Whiz-Bang Demonstrations** When Buildings Boogie* ◆ GENERAL	OSP **Lesson Plans** (also in print) TR **Bellringer Transparency*** SE **Internet Activity,** p. 423 GENERAL VID **Lab Videos for Earth Science**

PACING • 90 min

CHAPTER REVIEW, ASSESSMENT, AND STANDARDIZED TEST PREPARATION

CRF **Vocabulary Activity*** GENERAL
SE **Chapter Review,** pp. 430–431 GENERAL
CRF **Chapter Review** ■ GENERAL
CRF **Chapter Tests A*** ■ GENERAL, **B*** ADVANCED, **C*** SPECIAL NEEDS
SE **Standardized Test Preparation,** pp. 432–433 GENERAL
CRF **Standardized Test Preparation*** GENERAL
CRF **Performance-Based Assessment*** GENERAL
OSP **Test Generator, Test Item Listing**

Online and Technology Resources

Visit **go.hrw.com** for access to Holt Online Learning, or enter the keyword **HZ7 Home** for a variety of free online resources.

This CD-ROM package includes:
• Lab Materials QuickList Software
• Holt Calendar Planner
• Customizable Lesson Plans
• Printable Worksheets
• ExamView® Test Generator
• Interactive Teacher's Edition
• Holt PuzzlePro®
• Holt PowerPoint® Resources

Assessment
Each chapter includes enough chapter assessment material to fill two 45-minute periods.

409A Chapter 15 • Earthquakes

Compression In many cases, a chapter contains more material than you will have time to teach. The Compression Guide in each **Chapter Planning Guide** suggests sections or labs you can omit if you are short on time. The sections or labs that can be omitted often contain advanced material. You may wish to also consider using the material suggested for omission as extension material for advanced students.

KEY				
	CRF Chapter Resource File	SS Science Skills Worksheets	WB Workbook	
	OSP One-Stop Planner	MS Math Skills for Science Worksheets	* Also on One-Stop Planner	
SE Student Edition	LB Lab Bank	CD CD or CD-ROM	◆ Requires advance prep	
TE Teacher Edition	TR Transparencies	VID Classroom Video/DVD	■ Also available in Spanish	

SKILLS DEVELOPMENT RESOURCES	SECTION REVIEW AND ASSESSMENT	CORRELATIONS
SE **Pre-Reading Activity**, p. 410 GENERAL OSP **Science Puzzlers, Twisters & Teasers** GENERAL		**National Science Education Standards** SAI 1, 2
CRF **Directed Reading A*** ■ BASIC, **B*** SPECIAL NEEDS WB **Workbook*** Struggling Readers CRF **Vocabulary and Section Summary*** ■ GENERAL SE **Reading Strategy** Paired Summarizing, p. 412 GENERAL TE **Support for English Language Learners**, p. 413 TE **Inclusion Strategies**, p. 416	SE **Reading Checks**, pp. 413, 415, 417 GENERAL TE **Homework**, p. 413 ADVANCED TE **Homework**, p. 414 GENERAL TE **Reteaching**, p. 416 BASIC TE **Quiz**, p. 416 GENERAL TE **Alternative Assessment**, p. 416 GENERAL SE **Section Review,*** p. 417 ■ GENERAL CRF **Section Quiz*** ■ GENERAL	UCP 2; SAI 1, 2; SPSP 3, 4; ES 1b
CRF **Directed Reading A*** ■ BASIC, **B*** SPECIAL NEEDS WB **Workbook*** Struggling Readers CRF **Vocabulary and Section Summary*** ■ GENERAL SE **Reading Strategy** Reading Organizer, p. 418 GENERAL TE **Support for English Language Learners**, p. 419 SE **Connection to Social Studies** New Madrid Earthquakes, p. 420 GENERAL CRF **Reinforcement Worksheet** Complete a Seismic Story* BASIC MS **Math Skills for Science** Earthquake Power!* GENERAL	SE **Reading Checks**, pp. 418, 420 GENERAL TE **Reteaching**, p. 420 BASIC TE **Quiz**, p. 420 GENERAL TE **Alternative Assessment**, p. 420 GENERAL SE **Section Review,*** p. 421 ■ GENERAL CRF **Section Quiz*** ■ GENERAL	UCP 3; SAI 1, 2; ST 2; SPSP 3, 4; HNS 1, 3; *LabBook:* SAI 1, 2
CRF **Directed Reading A*** ■ BASIC, **B*** SPECIAL NEEDS WB **Workbook*** Struggling Readers CRF **Vocabulary and Section Summary*** ■ GENERAL SE **Reading Strategy** Discussion, p. 422 GENERAL TE **Reading Strategy** Prediction Guide, p. 423 GENERAL TE **Support for English Language Learners**, p. 423 TE **Inclusion Strategies**, p. 426 ◆ MS **Math Skills for Science** Dividing Whole Numbers with Long Division* GENERAL CRF **Critical Thinking** Nearthlings Unite!* ADVANCED	SE **Reading Checks**, pp. 423, 424, 426 GENERAL TE **Homework**, p. 424 GENERAL TE **Reteaching**, p. 426 BASIC TE **Quiz**, p. 426 GENERAL TE **Alternative Assessment**, p. 426 GENERAL SE **Section Review,*** p. 427 ■ GENERAL CRF **Section Quiz*** ■ GENERAL	UCP 2, 3; SAI 1; ST 2; SPSP 1, 3, 4, 5; ES 1b; HNS 2 *Chapter Lab:* SAI 1, 2

sciLINKS. NSTA
www.scilinks.org
Maintained by the **National Science Teachers Association.** See Chapter Enrichment pages that follow for a complete list of topics.

Current Science®
Check out *Current Science* articles and activities by visiting the HRW Web site at go.hrw.com. Just type in the keyword **HZ5CS08T.**

 **Classroom Videos**
• **Lab Videos** demonstrate the chapter lab.
• **Brain Food Video Quizzes** help students review the chapter material.

 **Classroom CD-ROMs**
• **Guided Reading Audio CD** (Also in Spanish)
• **Interactive Explorations**
• **Virtual Investigations**
• **Visual Concepts**
• **Science Tutor**

Holt Lab Generator CD-ROM
Search for any lab by topic, standard, difficulty level, or time. Edit any lab to fit your needs, or create your own labs. Use the Lab Materials QuickList software to customize your lab materials list.

Resources to make teaching easier

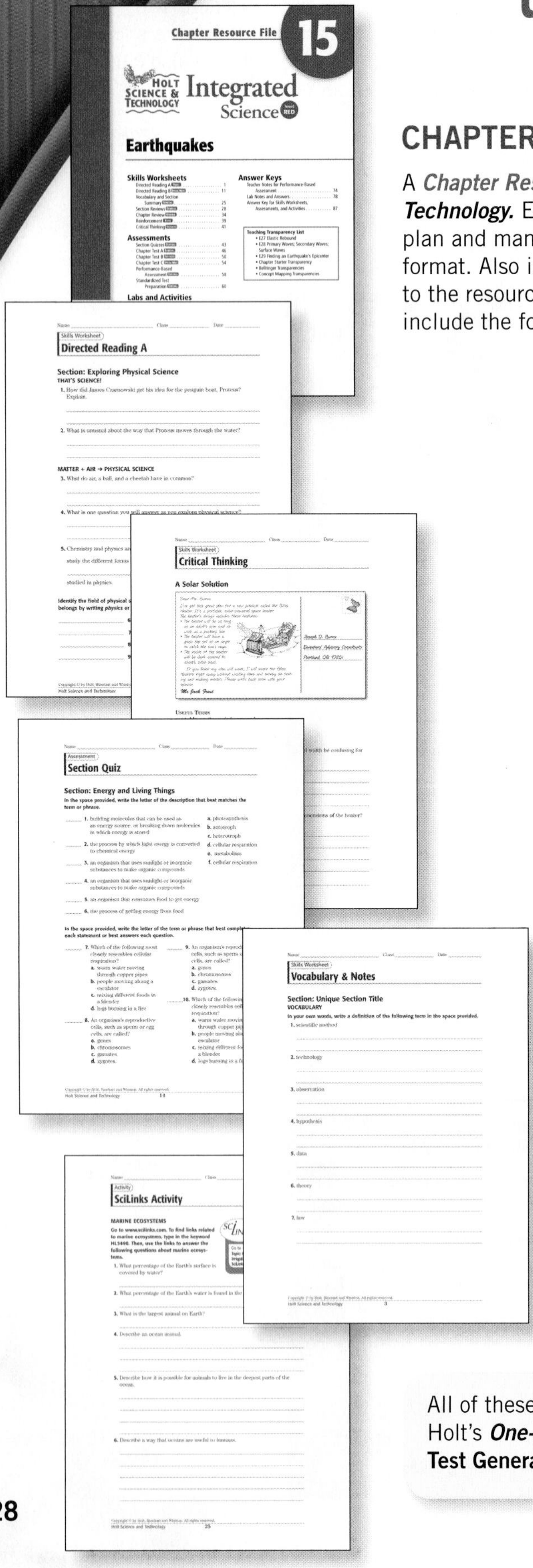

CHAPTER RESOURCE FILES

A *Chapter Resource File* is provided for each chapter of **Holt Science & Technology.** Each *Chapter Resource File* provides everything you need to plan and manage your lessons for the chapter in a convenient, time-saving format. Also included is a **Program Resource Introduction File,** your guide to the resources in each *Chapter Resource File. Chapter Resource Files* include the following:

Skills Worksheets
- Directed Reading A: Basic
- Directed Reading B: Special Needs
- Vocabulary and Section Summary
- Section Reviews
- Chapter Review
- Reinforcement
- Critical Thinking

Assessments
- Section Quizzes
- Chapter Test A: General
- Chapter Test B: Advanced
- Chapter Test C: Special Needs
- Performance-Based Assessment
- Standardized Test Preparation

Labs and Activities
- Datasheet for Chapter Lab
- Datasheets for Quick Labs
- Datasheets for LabBook Labs
- Vocabulary Activity
- SciLinks Activity

Teacher Resources
- Teacher Notes for Performance-Based Assessment
- Lab Notes and Answers
- Answer Keys

All of these additional resources can also be found in one place on Holt's *One-Stop Planner CD-ROM.* Also included on this *CD-ROM* is a **Test Generator** that allows you to customize your quizzes and tests.

Study Guide contains **Section** and **Chapter Review Worksheets.** Answers are contained in the corresponding *Chapter Resource File.*

Interactive Textbook makes content in the *Student Edition* accessible to struggling readers.

Reading Comprehension Guide includes **Directed Reading Worksheets** and **Vocabulary and Section Summary** worksheets to improve students' understanding of the text.

Special Needs Workbook includes **Special Needs Directed Reading Worksheets** and the **Special Needs Chapter Tests.**

Program Teaching Resources includes a variety of resources for additional skill development—Science Puzzlers, Twisters & Teasers; Science Skills Worksheets; Math Skills for Science; Science Fair Guide; Assessment Checklists & Rubrics.

Professional Reference for Teachers provides current information about issues in science education today. In professional articles, you can learn more about the National Science Education Standards, block scheduling, classroom management, and more.

Holt Science Posters includes seven colorful posters.

Holt Anthology of Science Fiction sparks your students' imaginations.

Holt Science Skills Workshop: Reading in the Content Area contains exercises that target key reading skills using excerpts from Holt's science textbooks.

Transparencies visually reinforce important science concepts with 300 *Teaching Transparencies* plus *Bellringer, Chapter Starter,* and *Concept Mapping Transparencies.*

RESOURCES BRING HOLT SCIENCE & TECHNOLOGY TO ENGLISH-LANGUAGE LEARNERS.

These translations open the door to students who are frequently locked out.

- **Multilingual Glossary**
- **Strategies for English Language Learners**
- *Student Edition* in Spanish
- Spanish glossary in both the English and Spanish *Student Edition*

- **Study Guide** in Spanish
- **Reading Comprehension Guide** in Spanish
- **Assessments** in Spanish
- **Guided Reading Audio Program** in Spanish

Technology that expands your teaching options

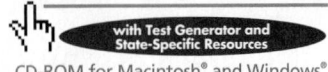

One-Stop Planner®

with Test Generator and State-Specific Resources

CD-ROM for Macintosh® and Windows®

Holt Science & Technology provides the correct combination of integrated technology resources—including CD-ROMs, videotapes, and DVD products—to make teaching more effective, efficient, and creative.

With the One-Stop Planner, planning and managing lessons has never been easier. This convenient, all-in-one CD-ROM includes the following time-saving features:

Printable

- Teaching Resources
- Transparency Masters
- Special Needs Resources

Customizable

- **Lesson Plans**—traditional and block-scheduling lesson plans correlated to the National Science Education Standards in several word processing formats
- **Holt Calendar Planner**—a tool that allows you to manage your time and resources by the day, week, month, or year
- **PowerPoint® Resources**—graphic organizers and key concepts that you can use to develop your own customized lectures for each section

Powerful

- **ExamView® 5 Assessment Suite**—a tool containing test items organized by chapter, plus thousands of editable questions correlated to the National Science Education Standards, so that you can put together your own tests and quizzes
- **Lab Materials QuickList Software**—a tool to easily create a customizable list of the lab materials you need
- **Holt PuzzlePro**—an easy way to create crossword puzzles and word searches that make learning vocabulary fun
- **Interactive Teacher's Edition**—the entire teacher text, with links to related Teaching Resources

CD-ROM RESOURCES

Guided Reading Audio Program is a direct read of the *Student Edition* providing extra support for English Language Learners, auditory learners and reluctant readers.

Holt Lab Generator CD-ROM features all labs from the *Holt Science & Technology* program and lab bank. Labs can be edited to fit classroom needs.

Virtual Investigations CD-ROM contains interactive activities for every chapter making it easy for students to practice science skills without the expense of costly materials.

***Science* One Stop** on CD-ROM includes the entire *Student Edition,* the *Interactive Textbook, Study Guide, Directed Reading Worksheets A* and *B, Vocabulary and Section Summary Worksheets, Math Skills for Science Worksheets, Science Skills Worksheets,* and the *Multilingual Glossary.*

Visual Concepts CD-ROM provides you with graphics, animations, and movie clips that demonstrate key chapter concepts. Visual Concepts work well as a student tutor or as a teacher-presentation tool.

VIDEO RESOURCES

Lab Videos (on DVD) allow you to integrate more experiments into your lessons without the preparation time and costs of a traditional laboratory setup.

Brain Food Video Quizzes (on DVD) are game show-style quizzes that assess students' progress and help them prepare for tests.

Online resources available anytime, anywhere!

ENHANCED ONLINE EDITIONS ARE PORTABLE, EXPANDABLE, AND INTERACTIVE, AND YET WEIGH NOTHING AT ALL.

Enhanced Online Editions of **Holt Science & Technology** engage students in ways that were never before possible. You'll find the following resources:

- Entire Student Edition online
- Web links
- **Visual Concepts** for student study or teacher presentation
- Interactive activities, such as Concept Maps and Self-Check Quizzes
- Helpful tools, such as a glossary, periodic table, and Grapher
- The **Classroom Manager** and **One-Stop Planner** to create a lesson and manage resources
- The **Holt Online Assessment,** which saves you time by automatically grading tests so that you can focus on improving student proficiency

This Web service, developed and maintained by the National Science Teachers Association, contains a large collection of prescreened links that include current information and activities directly related to chapter topics.

- Prescreening saves you valuable time searching for relevant and up-to-date Web sites.
- Sites are reviewed by science-content experts and educators.
- **Internet Connect** boxes within each chapter offer opportunities to enrich, enhance, and extend learning.
- Each topic leads to many links.

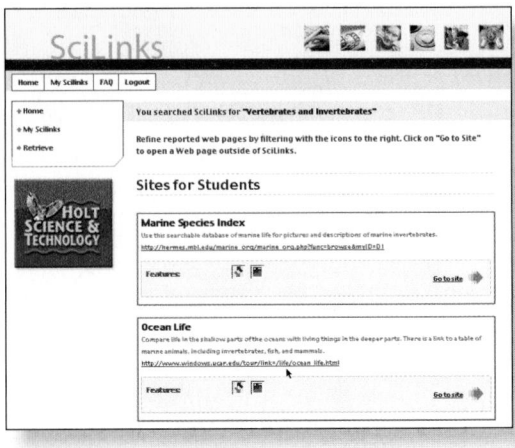

Current Science

Current Science is a science magazine containing articles that speak directly to middle school students and relate to students' lives. A collection of articles and activities have been placed online and are correlated to the text.

live ink
a new way to read

Live Ink® Reading Help is a scientifically-researched tool to improve students' reading comprehension and is proven to raise students' test scores.

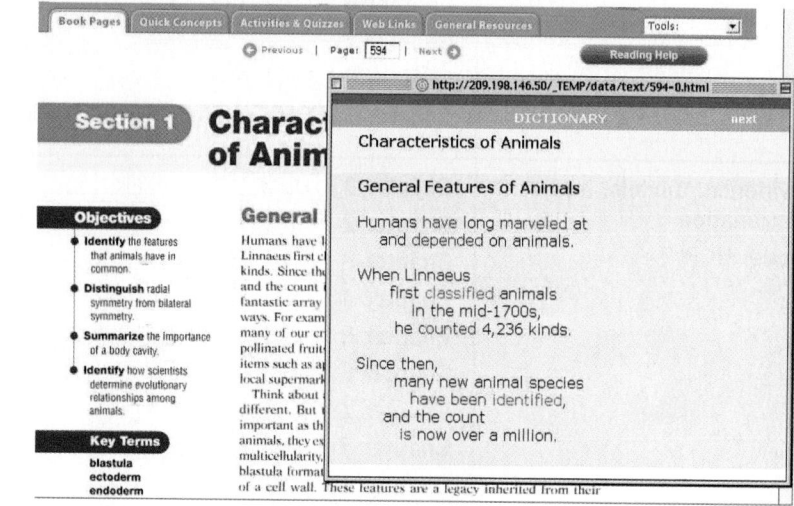

go.hrw.com

go.hrw.com enriches student learning with activities and resources keyed to the chapters in the textbook.

National Science Education Standards

The following lists show the chapter correlation of *Holt Science & Technology: Integrated Science Level Red* with the *National Science Education Standards* (grades 6–8).

The chapter correlations for the Science Content Standards begin on page 34.

Unifying Concepts and Processes

Standard	Chapter Correlation			
Systems, order, and organization Code: UCP 1	Chapter 2	2.1, 2.2	Chapter 11	11.2, 11.3, 11.4, 11.5
	Chapter 3	3.1, 3.3	Chapter 13	13.1, 13.2
	Chapter 4	4.1	Chapter 18	18.1, 18.2
	Chapter 5	5.2	Chapter 19	19.1, 19.2, 19.3
	Chapter 6	6.2, 6.3	Chapter 21	21.1
	Chapter 7	7.1, 7.2	Chapter 22	22.1, 22.2, 22.3
	Chapter 9	9.1, 9.2	Chapter 24	24.1, 24.2, 24.3, 24.4
	Chapter 10	10.1, 10.2, 10.3, 10.4	Chapter 25	25.1
Evidence, models, and explanation Code: UCP 2	Chapter 1	1.3	Chapter 12	12.1, 12.2, 12.3
	Chapter 2	2.1	Chapter 13	13.1
	Chapter 3	3.1, 3.2, 3.3	Chapter 14	14.1, 14.2, 14.3, 14.4
	Chapter 4	4.1, 4.2	Chapter 15	15.1, 15.3
	Chapter 5	5.1	Chapter 18	18.1, 18.2
	Chapter 6	6.1, 6.2	Chapter 19	19.1, 19.2, 19.3
	Chapter 7	7.1, 7.2, 7.3	Chapter 20	20.1
	Chapter 8	8.1, 8.2, 8.3	Chapter 22	22.1, 22.2, 22.3
	Chapter 10	10.2, 10.3, 10.4	Chapter 24	24.3
	Chapter 11	11.1, 11.2, 11.4	Chapter 25	25.1, 25.2
Change, constancy, and measurement Code: UCP 3	Chapter 1	1.4	Chapter 12	12.2, 12.3
	Chapter 2	2.1, 2.2	Chapter 15	15.2, 15.3
	Chapter 3	3.1, 3.2, 3.3	Chapter 16	16.3
	Chapter 4	4.2	Chapter 18	18.2, 18.3
	Chapter 6	6.3	Chapter 22	22.2, 22.3
	Chapter 7	7.2	Chapter 23	23.1, 23.2, 23.3, 23.4
	Chapter 8	8.1, 8.2, 8.3	Chapter 25	25.1, 25.2
	Chapter 11	11.3, 11.4, 11.5		
Evolution and equilibrium Code: UCP 4	Chapter 2	2.1, 2.2	Chapter 7	7.1, 7.2, 7.3
	Chapter 3	3.1, 3.2	Chapter 11	11.1, 11.4
	Chapter 4	4.3	Chapter 12	12.1, 12.3
	Chapter 5	5.2	Chapter 24	24.3
	Chapter 6	6.1, 6.2, 6.3		

Unifying Concepts and Processes (continued)

Standard	Chapter Correlation			
Form and function Code: UCP 5	Chapter 2	2.2	Chapter 7	7.3
	Chapter 3	3.1, 3.2	Chapter 8	8.1, 8.2, 8.3
	Chapter 4	4.3	Chapter 9	9.1, 9.2, 9.3
	Chapter 5	5.1, 5.2	Chapter 12	12.1
	Chapter 6	6.1, 6.2	Chapter 13	13.1

Science as Inquiry

Standard	Chapter Correlation			
Abilities necessary to do scientific inquiry Code: SAI 1	Chapter 1	1.1, 1.2, 1.3	Chapter 11	11.1, 11.3, 11.4, 11.5
	Chapter 2	2.2, 2.3	Chapter 12	12.1, 12.2, 12.3
	Chapter 3	3.1, 3.2, 3.3	Chapter 14	14.1, 14.2, 14.3, 14.4
	Chapter 4	4.1, 4.3	Chapter 15	15.1, 15.2, 15.3
	Chapter 5	5.1, 5.2	Chapter 16	16.1, 16.3
	Chapter 6	6.2	Chapter 18	18.3
	Chapter 7	7.1, 7.2, 7.3	Chapter 19	19.1, 19.3
	Chapter 8	8.1, 8.2, 8.3	Chapter 23	23.2, 23.4
	Chapter 9	9.2, 9.3	Chapter 24	24.2, 24.3, 24.4
	Chapter 10	10.1, 10.2, 10.3, 10.4		
Understandings about scientific inquiry Code: SAI 2	Chapter 1	1.2	Chapter 12	12.2, 12.3
	Chapter 3	3.1, 3.2, 3.3	Chapter 14	14.1, 14.2, 14.3, 14.4
	Chapter 4	4.1	Chapter 15	15.1, 15.2
	Chapter 5	5.1, 5.2	Chapter 19	19.2, 19.3
	Chapter 6	6.1, 6.2	Chapter 20	20.1
	Chapter 7	7.1, 7.3	Chapter 21	21.1
	Chapter 10	10.1, 10.2, 10.3, 10.4	Chapter 24	24.1
	Chapter 11	11.1, 11.3, 11.4, 11.5	Chapter 25	25.1

Science and Technology

Standard	Chapter Correlation			
Abilities of technological design Code: ST 1	Chapter 5	5.1	Chapter 12	12.1
	Chapter 7	7.3	Chapter 17	17.1
	Chapter 8	8.1	Chapter 25	25.2
Understandings about science and technology Code: ST 2	Chapter 1	1.1	Chapter 14	14.1, 14.2
	Chapter 2	2.2	Chapter 15	15.2, 15.3
	Chapter 4	4.1	Chapter 16	16.2, 16.3
	Chapter 5	5.1, 5.2	Chapter 17	17.1
	Chapter 7	7.3	Chapter 21	21.2
	Chapter 8	8.1, 8.2, 8.3	Chapter 24	24.3, 24.4
	Chapter 10	10.1	Chapter 25	25.1, 25.2
	Chapter 11	11.3, 11.4		

Science in Personal and Social Perspectives

Standard	Chapter Correlation			
Personal health Code: SPSP 1	Chapter 1 Chapter 15 Chapter 17	1.4 15.3 17.1	Chapter 24 Chapter 25	24.2, 24.3, 24.4 25.1
Populations, resources, and environments Code: SPSP 2	Chapter 3 Chapter 6 Chapter 8	3.3 6.2 8.3	Chapter 9 Chapter 12	9.3 12.1, 12.2, 12.3
Natural hazards Code: SPSP 3	Chapter 1 Chapter 3 Chapter 12 Chapter 14 Chapter 15	1.1, 1.3 3.1, 3.3 12.1 14.3 15.1, 15.2, 15.3	Chapter 16 Chapter 19 Chapter 24 Chapter 25	16.2 19.3 24.3 25.2
Risks and benefits Code: SPSP 4	Chapter 1 Chapter 2 Chapter 3 Chapter 5 Chapter 6 Chapter 9	1.1, 1.3 2.2 3.2 5.2 6.3 9.3	Chapter 14 Chapter 15 Chapter 16 Chapter 24 Chapter 25	14.3 15.1, 15.2, 15.3 16.2 24.2 25.1, 25.2
Science and technology in society Code: SPSP 5	Chapter 3 Chapter 4 Chapter 5 Chapter 6 Chapter 8 Chapter 10 Chapter 11	3.3 4.1, 4.3 5.1, 5.2 6.2, 6.3 8.1, 8.2, 8.3 10.1 11.1, 11.3, 11.4	Chapter 14 Chapter 15 Chapter 17 Chapter 19 Chapter 21 Chapter 25	14.2, 14.3 15.3 17.1 19.2 21.1 25.1, 25.2

History and Nature of Science

Standard	Chapter Correlation			
Science as a human endeavor Code: HNS 1	Chapter 1 Chapter 3 Chapter 4 Chapter 5 Chapter 6 Chapter 7 Chapter 8	1.1 3.1, 3.2 4.1 5.1 6.2 7.1 8.1, 8.3	Chapter 10 Chapter 11 Chapter 14 Chapter 15 Chapter 20 Chapter 21 Chapter 25	10.1 11.1, 11.3 14.2 15.2 20.1 21.1 25.1
Nature of science Code: HNS 2	Chapter 1 Chapter 3 Chapter 4 Chapter 5 Chapter 6 Chapter 7 Chapter 11	1.2, 1.3 3.1, 3.3 4.1, 4.3 5.1 6.1, 6.2 7.1, 7.3 11.1, 11.2, 11.3, 11.5	Chapter 14 Chapter 15 Chapter 16 Chapter 20 Chapter 21 Chapter 25	14.2, 14.3 15.3 16.1 20.1 21.1 25.1

History and Nature of Science (continued)

Standard	Chapter Correlation			
History of science Code: HNS 3	Chapter 1	1.4	Chapter 11	11.1, 11.3
	Chapter 4	4.1, 4.3	Chapter 14	14.2
	Chapter 5	5.1	Chapter 15	15.2
	Chapter 6	6.2	Chapter 20	20.1
	Chapter 7	7.1, 7.3	Chapter 21	21.1
	Chapter 8	8.1, 8.2	Chapter 25	25.1

Physical Science Content Standards

Properties and Changes of Properties in Matter

Standard	Chapter Correlation	
A substance has characteristic properties, such as density, a boiling point, and solubility, all of which are independent of the amount of the sample. A mixture of substances often can be separated into the original substances using one or more of the characteristic properties. Code: PS 1a	Chapter 17 Chapter 18 Chapter 19 Chapter 24	17.1, 17.2, 17.3 18.1, 18.2, 18.3 19.1, 19.2 24.1, 24.2, 24.4
Substances react chemically in characteristic ways with other substances to form new substances (compounds) with different characteristic properties. In chemical reactions, the total mass in conserved. Substances often are placed in categories or groups if they react in similar ways; metals is an example of such a group. Code: PS 1b	Chapter 17 Chapter 21 Chapter 22 Chapter 23 Chapter 24	17.2 21.1, 21.2 22.1, 22.2, 22.3 23.1, 23.2, 23.3, 23.4 24.1, 24.2, 24.3, 24.4
Chemical elements do not break down during normal laboratory reactions involving such treatments as heating, exposure to electric current, or reaction with acids. There are more than 100 known elements that combine in a multitude of ways to produce compounds, which account for the living and nonliving substances that we encounter. Code: PS 1c	Chapter 17 Chapter 19 Chapter 20 Chapter 22 Chapter 24	17.1 19.1, 19.2 20.2 22.1 24.4

Transfer of energy

Standard	Chapter Correlation	
Energy is a property of many substances and is associated with heat, light, electricity, mechanical motion, sound, nuclei, and the nature of a chemical. Energy is transferred in many ways. Code: PS 3a	Chapter 18 Chapter 22 Chapter 23 Chapter 25	18.3 22.2 23.1, 23.4 25.1, 25.2
In most chemical and nuclear reactions, energy is transferred into or out of a system. Heat, light, mechanical motion, or electricity might all be involved in such transfers. Code: PS 3e	Chapter 21 Chapter 22 Chapter 23 Chapter 25	21.2 22.2 23.1, 23.4 25.1, 25.2

Life Science Content Standards

Structure and Function in Living Systems

Standard	Chapter Correlation	
Living systems at all levels of organization demonstrate the complementary nature of structure and function. Important levels of organization for structure and function include cells, organs, tissues, organ systems, whole organisms, and ecosystems. Code: LS 1a	**Chapter 3** **Chapter 5** **Chapter 7** **Chapter 12**	3.1, 3.2 5.1 7.1, 7.2, 7.3 12.1, 12.2, 12.3
All organisms are composed of cells—the fundamental unit of life. Most organisms are single cells; other organisms, including humans, are multicellular. Code: LS 1b	**Chapter 7**	7.2
Cells carry on the many functions needed to sustain life. They grow and divide, thereby producing more cells. This requires that they take in nutrients, which they use to provide energy for the work that cells do and to make the materials that a cell or an organism needs. Code: LS 1c	**Chapter 2** **Chapter 3** **Chapter 4** **Chapter 5**	2.1, 2.2, 2.3 3.1 4.3 5.2
Specialized cells perform specialized functions in multicellular organisms. Groups of specialized cells cooperate to form a tissue, such as a muscle. Different tissues are in turn grouped together to form larger functional units, called organs. Each type of cell, tissue, and organ has a distinct structure and set of functions that serve the organism as a whole. Code: LS 1d	**Chapter 4**	4.3
The human organism has systems for digestion, respiration, reproduction, circulation, excretion, movement, control and coordination, and protection from disease. These systems interact with one another. Code: LS 1e	**Chapter 5**	5.2
Disease is the breakdown in structures or functions of an organism. Some diseases are the result of intrinsic failures of the system. Others are the result of damage by infection by other organisms. Code: LS 1f	**Chapter 5**	5.2

Reproduction and Heredity

Standard	Chapter Correlation	
Reproduction is a characteristic of all living systems; because no individual organism lives forever, reproduction is essential to the continuation of every species. Some organisms reproduce asexually. Others reproduce sexually. Code: LS 2a	**Chapter 3** **Chapter 4** **Chapter 6**	3.2 4.2, 4.3 6.2, 6.3
In many species, including humans, females produce eggs and males produce sperm. Plants also reproduce sexually— the egg and sperm are produced in the flowers of flowering plants. An egg and sperm unite to begin development of a new individual. That new individual receives genetic information from its mother (via the egg) and its father (via the sperm). Sexually produced offspring never are identical to either of their parents. Code: LS 2b	**Chapter 3** **Chapter 4** **Chapter 5** **Chapter 6**	3.2, 3.3 4.1, 4.2, 4.3 5.2 6.2
Every organism requires a set of instructions for specifying its traits. Heredity is the passage of these instructions from one generation to another. Code: LS 2c	**Chapter 3** **Chapter 4** **Chapter 5**	3.3 4.2, 4.3 5.2
Hereditary information is contained in genes, located in the chromosomes of each cell. Each gene carries a single unit of information. An inherited trait of an individual can be determined by one or by many genes, and a single gene can influence more than one trait. A human cell contains many thousands of different genes. Code: LS 2d	**Chapter 2** **Chapter 3** **Chapter 4** **Chapter 5** **Chapter 6**	2.3 3.2 4.2, 4.3 5.1, 5.2 6.2
The characteristics of an organism can be described in terms of a combination of traits. Some traits are inherited and others result from interactions with the environment. Code: LS 2e	**Chapter 4** **Chapter 5** **Chapter 6**	4.1, 4.2 5.2 6.1, 6.2, 6.3

Regulation and Behavior

Standard	Chapter Correlation	
All organisms must be able to obtain and use resources, grow, reproduce, and maintain stable internal conditions while living in a constantly changing external environment. Code: LS 3a	**Chapter 3** **Chapter 6** **Chapter 12**	3.3 6.1 12.1
Behavior is one kind of response an organism can make to an internal or environmental stimulus. A behavioral response requires coordination and communication at many levels, including cells, organ systems, and whole organisms. Behavioral response is a set of actions determined in part by heredity and in part from experience. Code: LS 3c	**Chapter 3** **Chapter 12**	3.1, 3.3 12.1
An organism's behavior evolves through adaptation to its environment. How a species moves, obtains food, reproduces, and responds to danger are based in the species' evolutionary history. Code: LS 3d	**Chapter 3** **Chapter 6** **Chapter 7** **Chapter 12**	3.3 6.1, 6.2, 6.3 7.1, 7.2, 7.3 12.1, 12.2, 12.3

Populations and Ecosystems

Standard	Chapter Correlation	
A population consists of all individuals of a species that occur together at a given place and time. All populations living together and the physical factors with which they interact compose an ecosystem. Code: LS 4a	**Chapter 6** **Chapter 12**	6.1 12.2, 12.3
Populations of organisms can be categorized by the function they serve in an ecosystem. Plants and some micro-organisms are producers—they make their own food. All animals, including humans, are consumers, which obtain food by eating other organisms. Decomposers, primarily bacteria and fungi, are consumers that use waste materials and dead organisms for food. Food webs identify the relationship among producers, consumers, and decomposers in an ecosystem. Code: LS 4b	**Chapter 12**	12.1, 12.2, 12.3

Populations and Ecosystems (continued)

Standard	Chapter Correlation	
For ecosystems, the major source of energy is sunlight. Energy entering ecosystems as sunlight is transferred by producers into chemical energy through photosynthesis. That energy then passes from organism to organism in food webs. Code: LS 4c	**Chapter 2** **Chapter 3** **Chapter 12**	2.2 3.1 12.1, 12.2, 12.3
The number of organisms an ecosystem can support depends on the resources available and abiotic factors, such as the quantity of light and water, range of temperatures, and soil composition. Given adequate biotic and abiotic resources and no disease or predators, populations (including humans) increase at rapid rates. Lack of resources and other factors, such as predation and climate, limit the growth of populations in specific niches in the ecosystem. Code: LS 4d	**Chapter 6** **Chapter 12**	6.3 12.1, 12.2, 12.3

Diversity and Adaptation of Organisms

Standard	Chapter Correlation	
Millions of species of animals, plants, and microorganisms are alive today. Although different species might look dissimilar, the unity among organisms becomes apparent from an analysis of internal structures, the similarity of their chemical processes, and the evidence of common ancestry. Code: LS 5a	**Chapter 5** **Chapter 6** **Chapter 7** **Chapter 12**	5.1 6.1, 6.2 7.2, 7.3 12.1
Biological evolution accounts for the diversity of species developed through gradual processes over many generations. Species acquire many of their unique characteristics through biological adaptation, which involves the selection of naturally occurring variations in populations. Biological adaptations include changes in structures, behaviors, or physiology that enhance survival and reproductive success in a particular environment. Code: LS 5b	**Chapter 3** **Chapter 5** **Chapter 6** **Chapter 7** **Chapter 12**	3.2, 3.3 5.2 6.1, 6.2, 6.3 7.1, 7.2, 7.3 12.1
Extinction of a species occurs when the environment changes and the adaptive characteristics of a species are insufficient to allow its survival. Fossils indicate that many organisms that lived long ago are extinct. Extinction of species is common; most of the species that have lived on Earth no longer exist. Code: LS 5c	**Chapter 6** **Chapter 7**	6.1 7.1, 7.2, 7.3

Earth Science Content Standards

Structure of the earth system

Standard	Chapter Correlation		
The solid earth is layered with a lithosphere; hot, convecting mantle; and dense, metallic core. Code: ES 1a	**Chapter 13** 13.1 **Chapter 14** 14.1		
Lithospheric plates on the scales of continents and oceans constantly move at rates of centimeters per year in response to movements in the mantle. Major geological events, such as earthquakes, volcanic eruptions, and mountain building result from these plate motions. Code: ES 1b	**Chapter 13** 13.1 **Chapter 14** 14.2, 14.3, 14.4 **Chapter 15** 15.1, 15.3 **Chapter 16** 16.3		
Land forms are the result of a combination of constructive and destructive forces. Constructive forces include crustal deformation, volcanic eruption, and deposition of sediment, while destructive forces include weathering and erosion. Code: ES 1c	**Chapter 10** 10.1, 10.2, 10.3, 10.4 **Chapter 13** 13.1 **Chapter 16** 16.1, 16.2, 16.3		
Some changes in the solid earth can be described as the "rock cycle." Old rocks at the earth's surface weather, forming sediments that are buried, then compacted, heated, and often recrystallized in to new rock. Eventually, those new rocks may be brought to the surface by the forces that drive plate motions, and the rock cycle continues. Code: ES 1d	**Chapter 10** 10.1, 10.2, 10.3 **Chapter 13** 13.1, 13.4		
Water, which covers the majority of the earth's surface, circulates through the crust, oceans, and atmosphere in what is known as the "water cycle." Water evaporates from the earth's surface, rises and cools as it moves to higher elevations, condenses as rain or snow, and falls to the surface where it collects in lakes, oceans, soil, and in rocks underground. Code: ES 1f	**Chapter 13** 13.2, 13.3		
Water is a solvent. As it passes through the water cycle it dissolves minerals and gases and carries them to the oceans. Code: ES 1g	**Chapter 13** 13.4		
The atmosphere is a mixture of nitrogen, oxygen, and trace gases that include water vapor. The atmosphere has different properties at different elevations. Code: ES 1h	**Chapter 13** 13.2, 13.3		

Structure of the earth system (continued)

Standard	Chapter Correlation	
Clouds, formed by the condensation of water vapor, affect weather and climate. Code: ES 1i	**Chapter 13**	13.2, 13.3
Global patterns of atmospheric movement influence local weather. Oceans have a major effect on climate, because water in the oceans holds a large amount of heat. Code: ES 1j	**Chapter 13**	13.2, 13.3
Living organisms have played many roles in the earth system, including affecting the composition of the atmosphere, producing some types of rocks, and contributing to the weathering of rocks. Code: ES 1k	**Chapter 10** **Chapter 11** **Chapter 13**	10.3 11.4 13.4

Earth's history

Standard	Chapter Correlation	
The earth processes we see today, including erosion, movement of lithospheric plates, and changes in atmospheric composition, are similar to those that occurred in the past, earth history is also influenced by occasional catastrophes, such as the impact of an asteroid or comet. Code: ES 2a	**Chapter 11** **Chapter 14**	11.1 14.2, 14.3, 14.4
Fossils provide important evidence of how life and environmental conditions have changed. Code: ES 2b	**Chapter 10** **Chapter 11**	10.3 11.2, 11.3, 11.4, 11.5

Science and Math Skills Worksheets

The **Holt Science & Technology** program helps you meet the needs of a wide variety of students, regardless of their skill level. The following pages provide examples of the worksheets available to improve your students' science and math skills whether they already have a strong science and math background or are weak in these areas. Samples of assessment checklists and rubrics are also provided.

In addition to the skills worksheets represented here, **Holt Science & Technology** provides a variety of worksheets that are correlated directly with each chapter of the program. Representations of these worksheets are found at the beginning of each chapter in this *Teacher Edition*.

Many worksheets are also available on the Holt Web site. The address is **go.hrw.com**.

Science Skills Worksheets: Thinking Skills

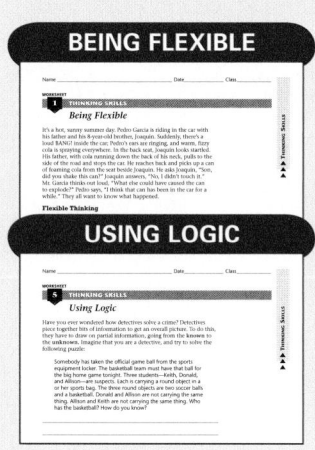

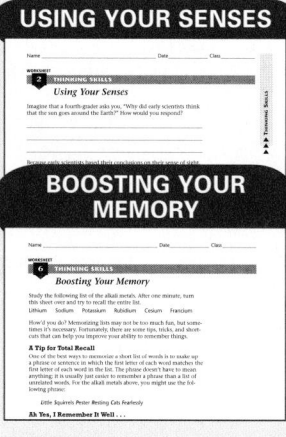

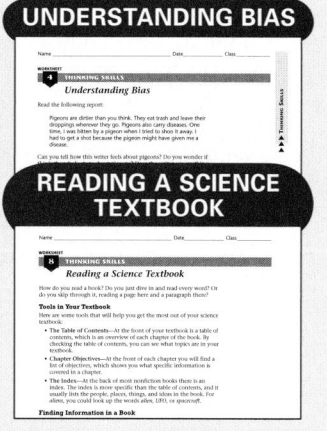

Science Skills Worksheets: Experimenting Skills

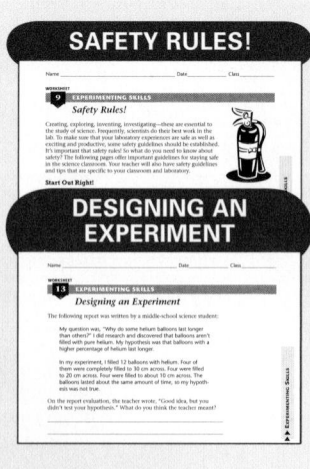

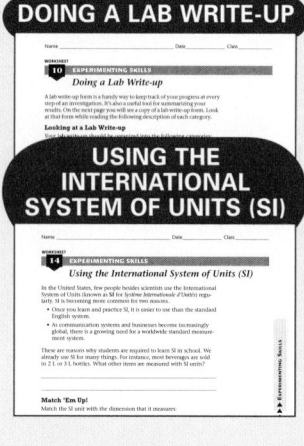

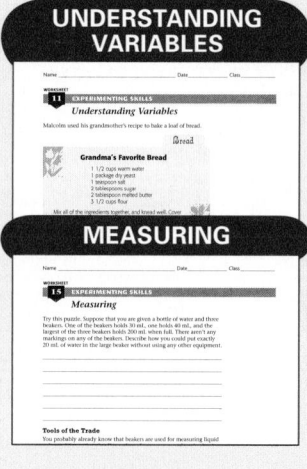

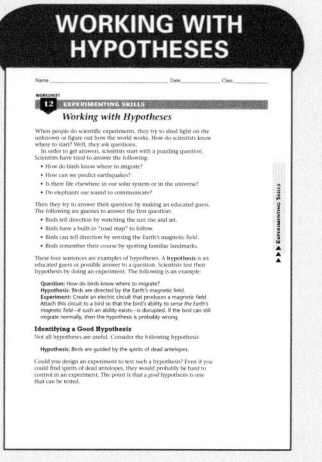

Science Skills Worksheets: Researching Skills

CHOOSING YOUR TOPIC
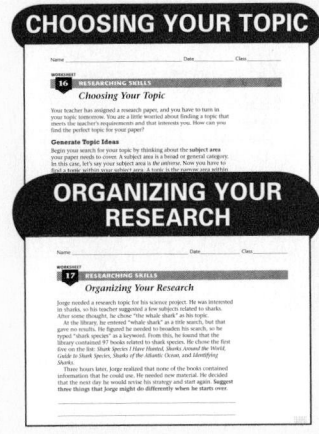

FINDING USEFUL SOURCES
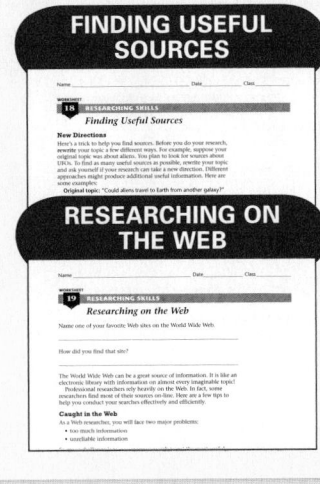

IDENTIFYING BIAS
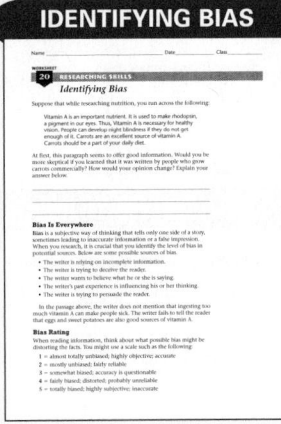

TAKING NOTES
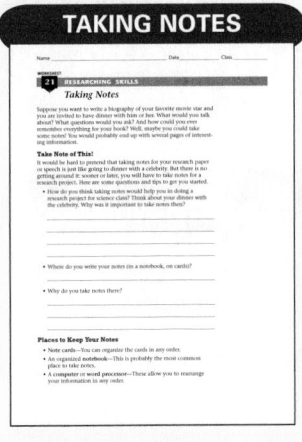

ORGANIZING YOUR RESEARCH

RESEARCHING ON THE WEB

Science Skills Worksheets: Communicating Skills

SCIENCE WRITING
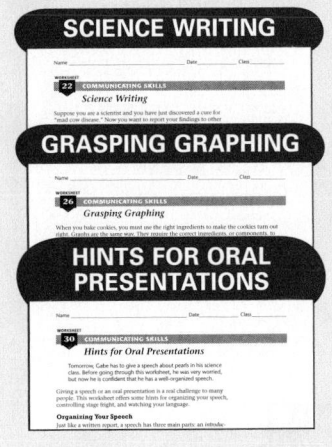

SCIENCE DRAWING
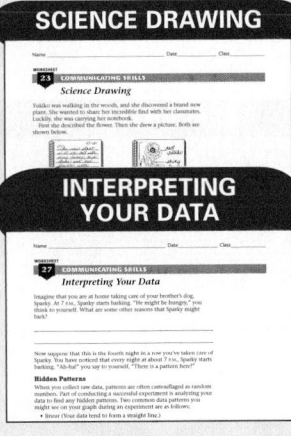

USING MODELS TO COMMUNICATE
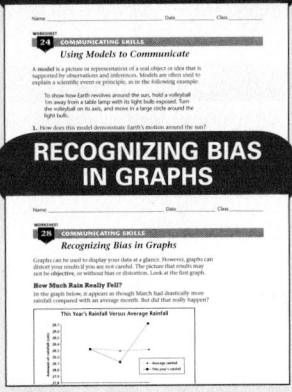

INTRODUCTION TO GRAPHS
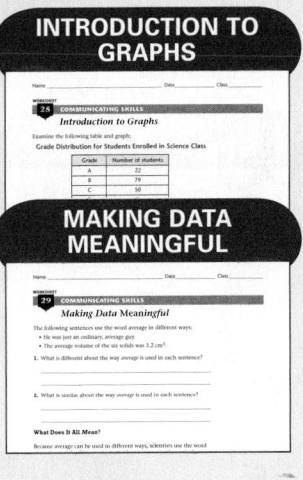

GRASPING GRAPHING

INTERPRETING YOUR DATA

RECOGNIZING BIAS IN GRAPHS

MAKING DATA MEANINGFUL

HINTS FOR ORAL PRESENTATIONS

Math Skills for Science

ADDITION
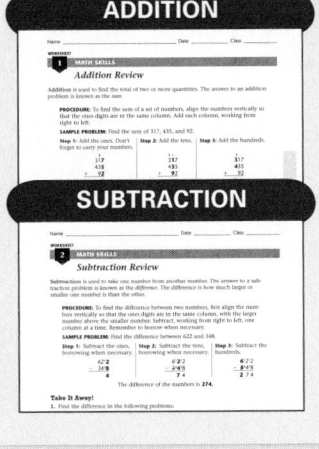

MULTIPLICATION
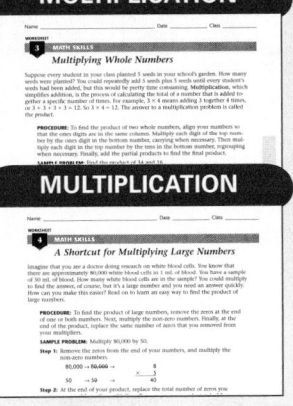

DIVISION
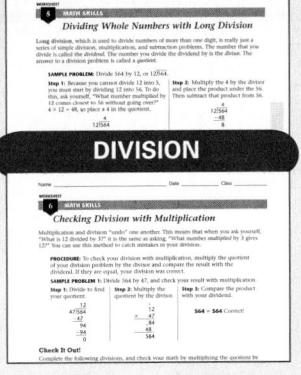

AVERAGES
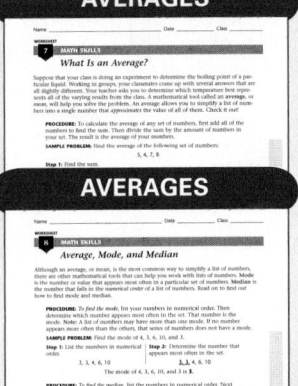

SUBTRACTION

MULTIPLICATION

DIVISION

AVERAGES

Math Skills for Science (continued)

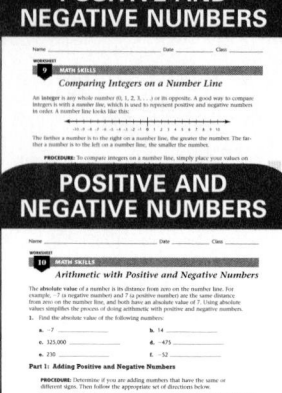

POSITIVE AND NEGATIVE NUMBERS

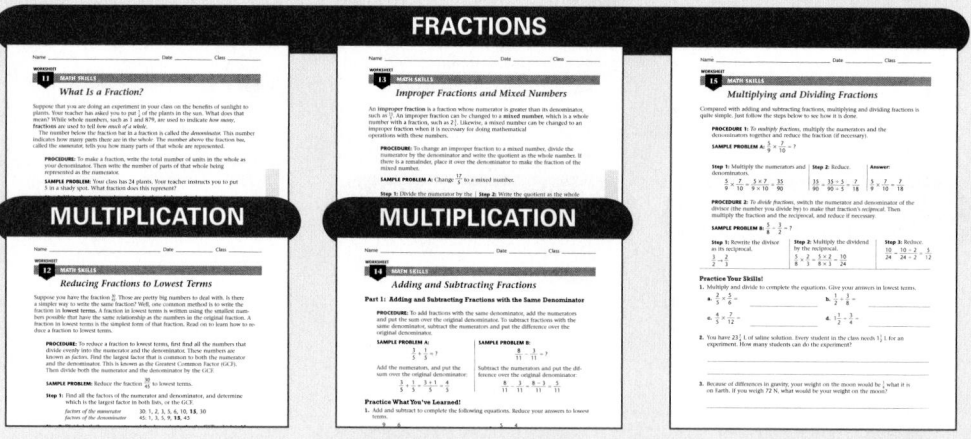

FRACTIONS

MULTIPLICATION

MULTIPLICATION

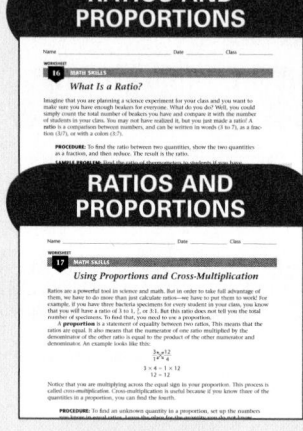

RATIOS AND PROPORTIONS

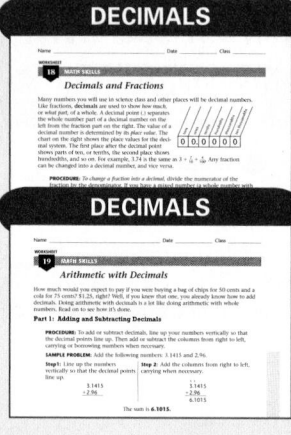

DECIMALS

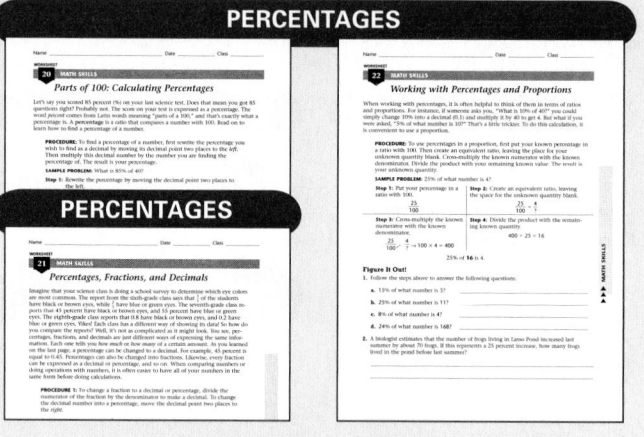

PERCENTAGES

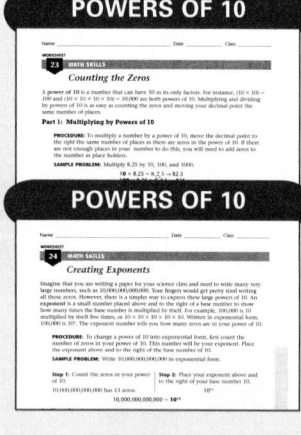

POWERS OF 10

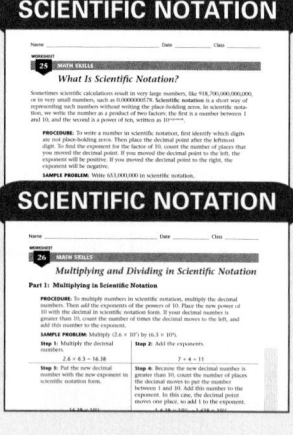

SCIENTIFIC NOTATION

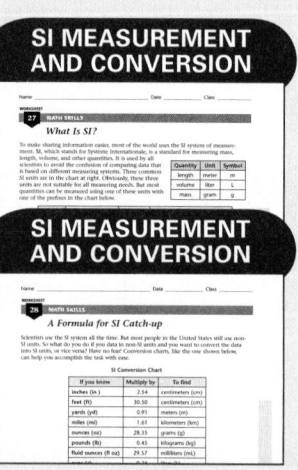

SI MEASUREMENT AND CONVERSION

Math Skills for Science (continued)

GEOMETRY

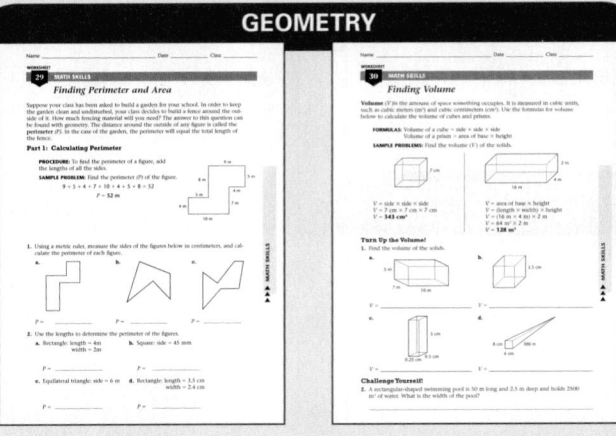

THE UNIT FACTOR AND DIMENSIONAL ANALYSIS

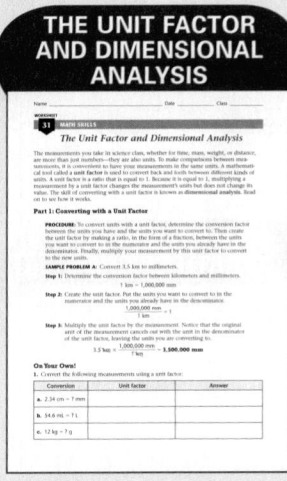

MATH IN SCIENCE: INTEGRATED SCIENCE

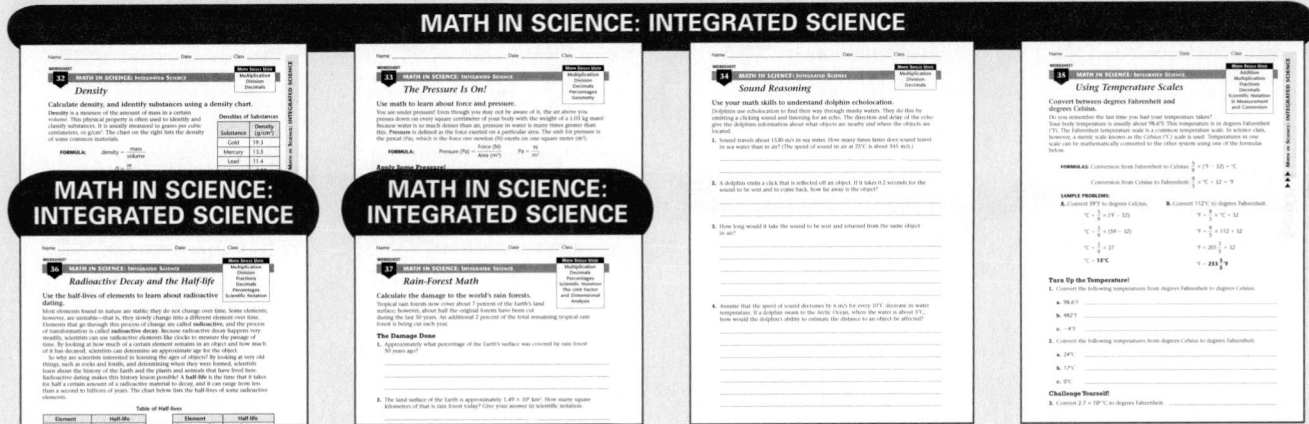

MATH IN SCIENCE: LIFE SCIENCE

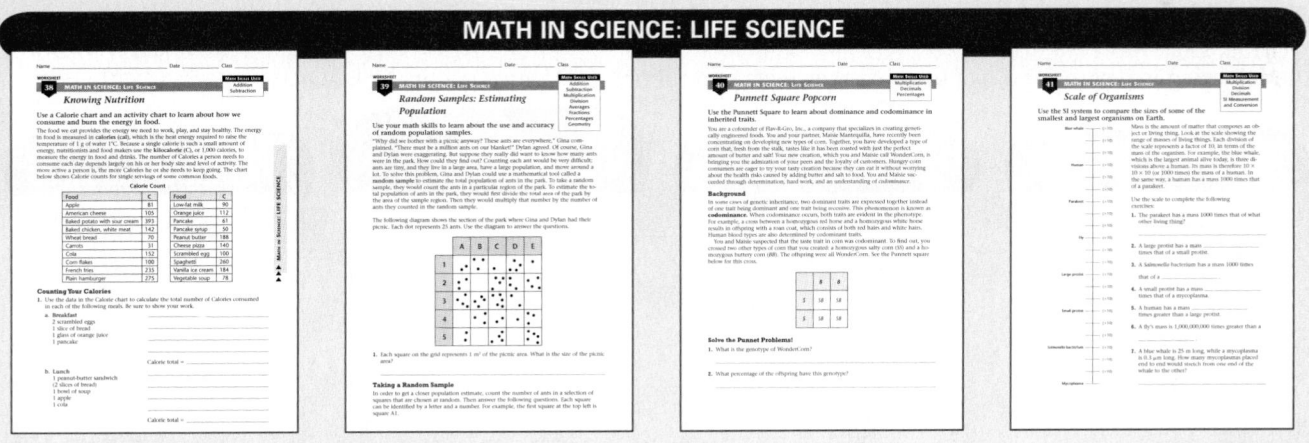

Math Skills for Science (continued)

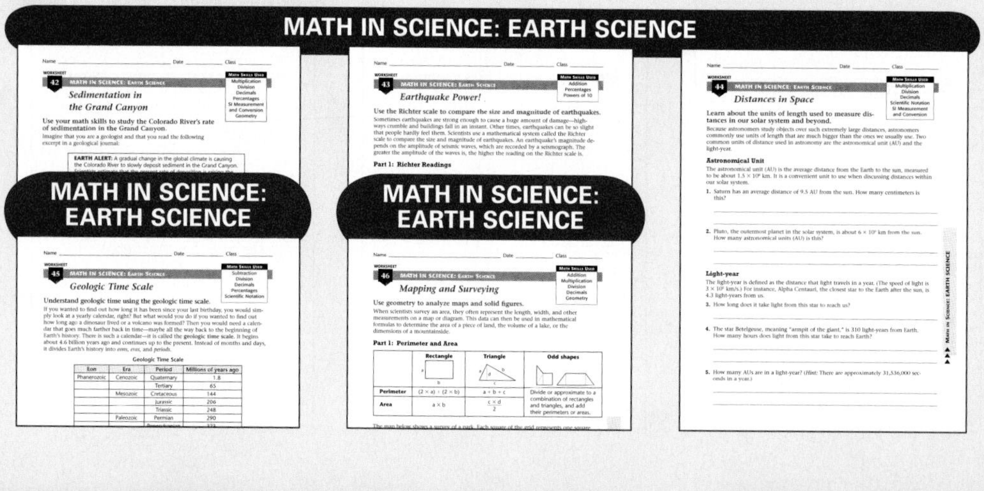

MATH IN SCIENCE: EARTH SCIENCE

WORKSHEET 42 — MATH IN SCIENCE: EARTH SCIENCE
Sedimentation in the Grand Canyon

Main Skills Used: Subtraction, Division, Multiplication, Percentages, SI Measurement and Conversion, Geometry

Use your math skills to study the Colorado River's rate of sedimentation in the Grand Canyon.
Imagine that you are a geologist and that you read the following excerpt in a geological journal.

EARTH ALERT: A gradual change in the global climate is causing the Colorado River to slowly deposit sediment in the Grand Canyon.

WORKSHEET 43 — MATH IN SCIENCE: EARTH SCIENCE
Earthquake Power!

Main Skills Used: Addition, Division, Percentages, Powers of 10

Use the Richter scale to compare the size and magnitude of earthquakes.
Sometimes earthquakes are strong enough to cause a huge amount of damage—high-ways crumble and buildings fall in an instant. Other times, earthquakes can be so slight that people barely feel them. Scientists use a mathematical system called the Richter scale to compare the size and magnitude of earthquakes. An earthquake's magnitude depends on the amplitude of seismic waves, which are recorded by a seismograph. The greater the amplitude of the waves is, the higher the reading on the Richter scale is.

Part 1: Richter Readings

WORKSHEET 44 — MATH IN SCIENCE: EARTH SCIENCE
Distances in Space

Main Skills Used: Addition, Multiplication, Division, Decimals, Scientific Notation, SI Measurement and Conversion

Learn about the units of length used to measure distances in our solar system and beyond.
Because astronomers study objects over such extremely large distances, astronomers commonly use units of length that are much bigger than the ones we usually use. Two common units of distance used in astronomy are the astronomical unit (AU) and the light-year.

Astronomical Unit
The astronomical unit (AU) is the average distance from the Earth to the sun, measured to be about 1.5×10^8 km. It is a convenient unit to use when discussing distances within our solar system.

1. Saturn has an average distance of 9.5 AU from the sun. How many kilometers is this?

2. Pluto, the outermost planet in the solar system, is about 6×10^9 km from the sun. How many astronomical units (AU) is this?

Light-year
The light-year is defined as the distance that light travels in a year. (The speed of light is 3×10^5 km/s.) For instance, Alpha Centauri, the closest star to the Earth after the sun, is 4.3 light-years from us.

3. How long does it take light from this star to reach us?

4. The star Betelgeuse, meaning "armpit of the giant," is 310 light-years from Earth. How many hours does light from this star take to reach Earth?

5. How many AUs are in a light-year? (Hint: There are approximately 31,536,000 seconds in a year.)

WORKSHEET 45 — MATH IN SCIENCE: EARTH SCIENCE
Geologic Time Scale

Main Skills Used: Subtraction, Division, Multiplication, Percentages, Decimals

Understand geologic time using the geologic time scale.
If you wanted to find out how long it has been since your last birthday, you would simply look at a yearly calendar. But what would you do if you wanted to find out how long ago a dinosaur lived or a volcano was formed? Then you would need a calendar that goes much farther back in time—maybe all the way back to the beginning of Earth's history. There is such a calendar—it is called the geologic time scale. It begins about 4.6 billion years ago and continues up to the present. Instead of months and days, it divides Earth's history into eons, eras, and periods.

Geologic Time Scale

Eon	Era	Period	Millions of years ago
Phanerozoic	Cenozoic	Quaternary	1.8
		Tertiary	65
	Mesozoic	Cretaceous	144
		Jurassic	206
		Triassic	248
	Paleozoic	Permian	290

WORKSHEET 46 — MATH IN SCIENCE: EARTH SCIENCE
Mapping and Surveying

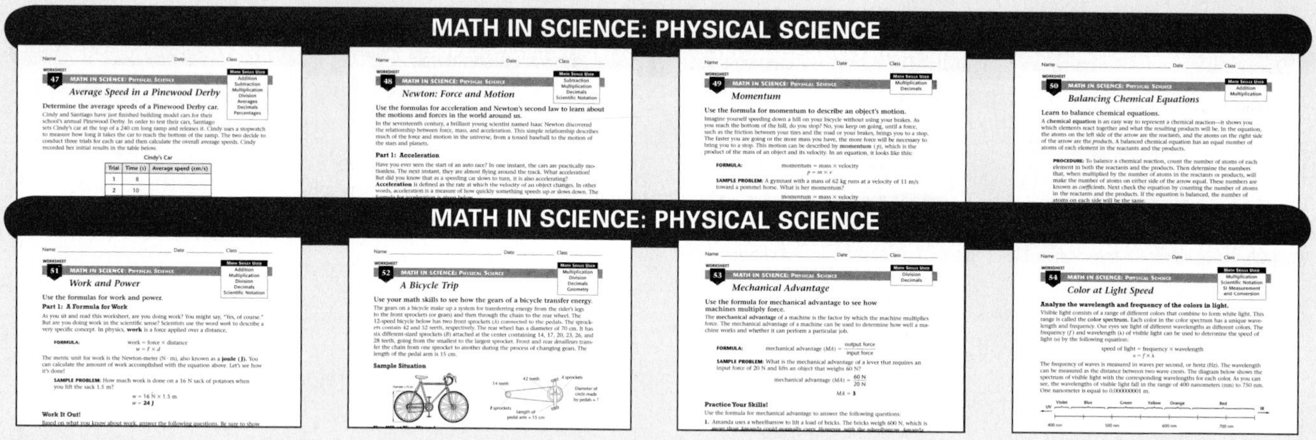

Main Skills Used: Addition, Multiplication, Division, Decimals, Geometry

Use geometry to analyze maps and solid figures.
When scientists survey an area, they often represent the length, width, and other measurements on a map or diagram. This also can then be used in mathematical formulas to determine the area of a piece of land, the volume of a lake, or the dimensions of a mountainside.

Part 1: Perimeter and Area

	Rectangle	Triangle	Odd shapes
Perimeter	$(2 \times a) + (2 \times b)$	$a + b + c$	Divide or approximate to a combination of rectangles and triangles, and add their perimeters or areas.
Area	$a \times b$	$\dfrac{c \times d}{2}$	

MATH IN SCIENCE: PHYSICAL SCIENCE

WORKSHEET 47 — MATH IN SCIENCE: PHYSICAL SCIENCE
Average Speed in a Pinewood Derby

Main Skills Used: Addition, Subtraction, Multiplication, Division, Averages, Percentages

Determine the average speed in a Pinewood Derby car.
Cindy and Santiago have just finished building model cars for their school's annual Pinewood Derby. In order to test their cars, Santiago sets Cindy's car at the top of a 240 cm long ramp and releases it. Cindy uses a stopwatch to measure how long it takes the car to reach the bottom of the ramp. The two decide to conduct three trials for each car and then calculate the overall average speed. Cindy recorded her initial results in the table below.

Cindy's Car

Trial	Time (s)	Average speed (cm/s)
1	8	
2	10	

WORKSHEET 48 — MATH IN SCIENCE: PHYSICAL SCIENCE
Newton: Force and Motion

Main Skills Used: Multiplication, Decimals, Scientific Notation

Use the formula for acceleration and Newton's second law to learn about the motions and forces in the world around us.
In the seventeenth century, a brilliant young scientist named Isaac Newton discovered the relationship between force, mass, and acceleration. This simple relationship describes much of the force and motion in the universe, from a tossed baseball to the motion of the stars and planets.

Part 1: Acceleration
Have you ever seen the start of an auto race? In one instant, the cars are practically motionless. The next instant, they are almost flying around the track. The cars are accelerating. But did you know that as a speeding car slows to turn, it is also accelerating? **Acceleration** is defined as the rate at which the velocity of an object changes. In other words, acceleration is a measure of how quickly something speeds up or slows down. The formula for acceleration is shown below.

WORKSHEET 49 — MATH IN SCIENCE: PHYSICAL SCIENCE
Momentum

Main Skills Used: Multiplication, Decimals

Use the formula for momentum to describe an object's motion.
Imagine yourself speeding down a hill on your bicycle without using your brakes. As you reach the bottom of the hill, do you stop? No, you keep on going, until a force, such as the friction between your tires and the road or your brakes, brings you to a stop. The faster you are going or the more mass you have, the more force will be necessary to bring you to a stop. This motion can be described by momentum (p), which is the product of the mass of an object and its velocity. In an equation, it looks like this:

FORMULA: momentum = mass × velocity

SAMPLE PROBLEM: A gymnast with a mass of 42 kg runs at a velocity of 11 m/s toward a pommel horse. What is her momentum?

momentum = mass × velocity

WORKSHEET 50 — MATH IN SCIENCE: PHYSICAL SCIENCE
Balancing Chemical Equations

Main Skills Used: Multiplication, Addition, Multiplication

Learn to balance chemical equations.
A **chemical equation** is an easy way to represent a chemical reaction—it shows you which elements react together and what the resulting products will be. In the equation, the atoms on the left side of the arrow are the reactants, and the atoms on the right side of the arrow are the products. A balanced chemical equation has an equal number of atoms of each element in the reactants and the products.

PROCEDURE: To balance a chemical reaction, count the number of atoms of each element in both the reactants and the products. Then determine the numbers that, when multiplied by the number of atoms in the reactants or products, will make the number of atoms on either side of the arrow equal. These numbers are known as coefficients. Next check the equation by counting the number of atoms in the reactants and the products. If the equation is balanced, the number of atoms on each side will be equal.

WORKSHEET 51 — MATH IN SCIENCE: PHYSICAL SCIENCE
Work and Power

Main Skills Used: Addition, Multiplication, Division, Decimals, Scientific Notation

Use the formulas for work and power.

Part 1: A Formula for Work
As you sit and read this worksheet, are you doing work? You might say, "Yes, of course." But are you doing work in the scientific sense? Scientists use the word *work* to describe a very specific concept. In physics, **work** is a force applied over a distance.

FORMULA: work = force × distance

$$w = F \times d$$

The metric unit for work is the Newton-meter (N · m), also known as a **joule (J)**. You can calculate the amount of work accomplished with the equation above. Let's see how it's done!

SAMPLE PROBLEM: How much work is done or a 16 N sack of potatoes when you lift the sack 1.5 m?

$w = 16 \text{ N} \times 1.5 \text{ m}$
$w = 24 \text{ J}$

Work It Out!
Based on what you know about work, answer the following questions. Be sure to show

WORKSHEET 52 — MATH IN SCIENCE: PHYSICAL SCIENCE
A Bicycle Trip

Main Skills Used: Division, Decimals

Use your math skills to see how the gears of a bicycle transfer energy.
The gears on a bicycle make up a system for transferring energy from the rider's legs to the front sprockets (or gears) and then through the chain to the rear wheel. The 12-speed bicycle below has two front sprockets (A) connected to the pedals. The sprockets contain 42 and 52 teeth, respectively. The rear wheel has a diameter of 70 cm. It has six different-sized sprockets (B) attached at the center containing 14, 17, 20, 23, 26, and 28 teeth, going from the smallest to the largest. Front and rear derailleurs transfer the chain from one sprocket to another during the process of changing gears. The length of the pedal arm is 15 cm.

Sample Situation

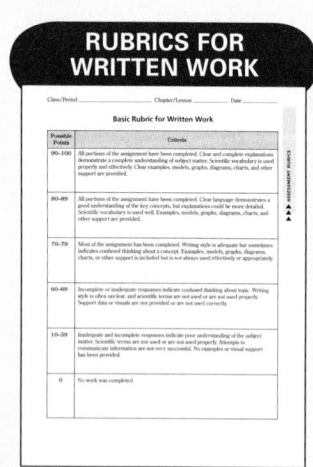

WORKSHEET 53 — MATH IN SCIENCE: PHYSICAL SCIENCE
Mechanical Advantage

Main Skills Used: Division, Decimals

Use the formula for mechanical advantage to see how machines multiply force.
The **mechanical advantage** of a machine is the factor by which the machine multiplies force. The mechanical advantage of a machine can be used to determine how much a machine works and whether it can perform a particular job.

FORMULA: mechanical advantage (MA) = $\dfrac{\text{output force}}{\text{input force}}$

SAMPLE PROBLEM: What is the mechanical advantage of a lever that requires an input force of 20 N and lifts an object that weighs 60 N?

mechanical advantage (MA) = $\dfrac{60 \text{ N}}{20 \text{ N}}$

MA = 3

Practice Your Skills!
Use the formula for mechanical advantage to answer the following questions.
1. Amanda uses a wheelbarrow to lift a load of bricks. The bricks weigh 600 N, which is

WORKSHEET — MATH IN SCIENCE: PHYSICAL SCIENCE
Color at Light Speed

Main Skills Used: Multiplication, Scientific Notation and Conversion

Analyze the wavelength and frequency of the colors in light.
Visible light consists of a range of different colors that combine to form white light. This range is called the **color spectrum**. Each color in the color spectrum has a unique wavelength and frequency. Our eyes see light of different wavelengths as different colors. The frequency (f) and wavelength (λ) of visible light can be used to determine the speed of light (c) by the following equation.

speed of light = frequency × wavelength

$$c = f \times \lambda$$

The frequency of waves is measured in waves per second, or hertz (Hz). The wavelength can be measured in the distance between two wave crests. The diagram below shows the spectrum of visible light with the corresponding wavelengths for each color. As you can see, the wavelengths of visible light fall in the range of 400 nanometers (nm) to 750 nm. One nanometer is equal to 0.000000001 m.

| Violet | Blue | Cyan | Yellow | Orange | | Red | |

Assessment Checklist & Rubrics

The following is just a sample of over 50 checklists and rubrics contained in this booklet.

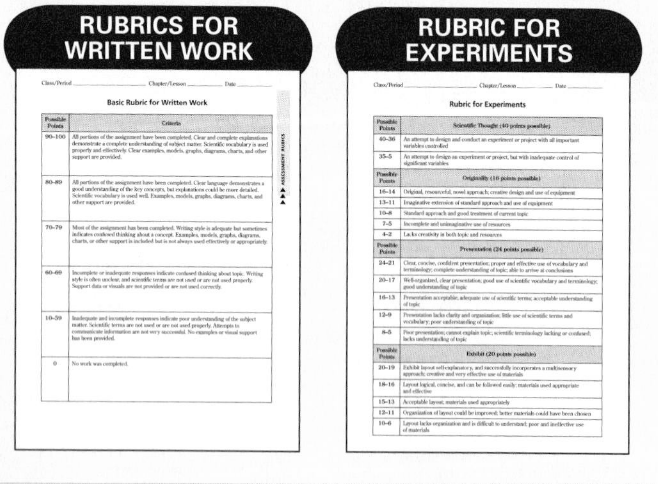

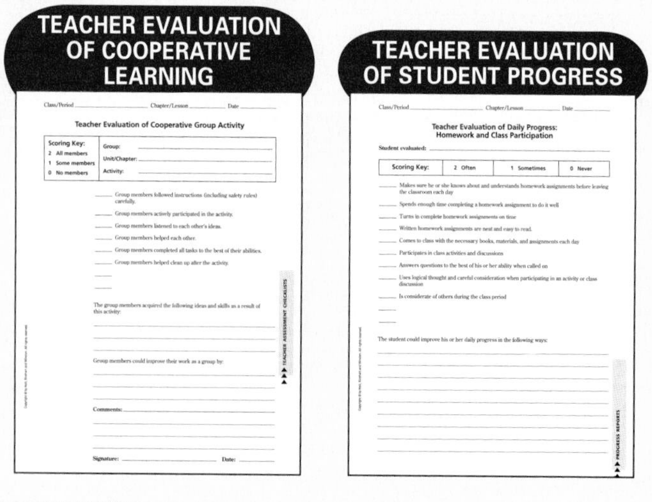

RUBRICS FOR WRITTEN WORK

Class/Period _____ Chapter/Lesson _____ Date _____

Basic Rubric for Written Work

Possible Points	Criteria
90–100	All portions of the assignment have been completed. Clear and complete explanations demonstrate a complete understanding of subject matter. Scientific vocabulary is used properly and effectively. Clear examples, models, graphs, diagrams, charts, and other support are provided.
80–89	All portions of the assignment have been completed. Clear language demonstrates a good understanding of the key concepts, but explanations could be more detailed. Scientific vocabulary is used well. Examples, models, graphs, diagrams, charts, and other support are provided.
70–79	Most of the assignment has been completed. Writing style is adequate but sometimes indicates confused thinking about a concept. Examples, models, graphs, diagrams, charts, or other support is included but is not always used effectively or appropriately.
60–69	Incomplete or inadequate responses indicate confused thinking about topic. Writing style is often unclear, and scientific terms are not used or are used improperly. Support data or visuals are not provided or are not used correctly.
10–59	Inadequate and incomplete responses indicate poor understanding of the subject matter. Scientific terms are not used or are not used properly. Attempts to communicate information are not very successful. No examples or visual support has been provided.
0	No work completed.

RUBRIC FOR EXPERIMENTS

Class/Period _____ Chapter/Lesson _____ Date _____

Rubric for Experiments

Possible Points	Scientific Thought (40 points possible)
40–36	An attempt to design and conduct an experiment or project with all important variables controlled
35–5	An attempt to design an experiment or project, but with inadequate control of significant variables

Possible Points	Originality (18 points possible)
16–14	Original, resourceful, novel approach; creative design and use of equipment
13–11	Imaginative extension of standard approach and use of equipment
10–8	Standard approach and good treatment of current topic
7–5	Incomplete and unimaginative use of resources
4–2	Lacks creativity in both topic and resources

Possible Points	Presentation (24 points possible)
24–21	Clear, concise, confident presentation; proper and effective use of vocabulary and terminology; complete understanding of topic; able to arrive at conclusions
20–17	Well-organized, clear presentation; good use of scientific vocabulary and terminology; good understanding of topic
16–13	Presentation acceptable; adequate use of scientific terms; acceptable understanding of topic
12–9	Presentation acceptable; logical organization; little use of scientific terms and vocabulary; poor understanding of topic
8–5	Poor presentation; cannot explain topic; scientific terminology lacking or confused; lacks understanding of topic

Possible Points	Exhibit (20 points possible)
20–19	Exhibit layout self-explanatory, and successfully incorporates a multisensory approach; creative and very effective use of materials
18–16	Layout logical, concise, and can be followed easily; materials used appropriate
15–13	Acceptable layout; materials used appropriately
12–11	Organization of layout could be improved; better materials could have been chosen
10–6	Exhibit layout; organization and is difficult to understand; poor and ineffective use of materials

TEACHER EVALUATION OF COOPERATIVE LEARNING

Class/Period _____ Chapter/Lesson _____ Date _____

Teacher Evaluation of Cooperative Group Activity

Scoring Key:
2 All members
1 Some members
0 No members

Group: _____
Unit/Chapter: _____
Activity: _____

_____ Group members followed instructions (including safety rules) carefully.
_____ Group members actively participated in the activity.
_____ Group members listened to each other's ideas.
_____ Group members helped each other.
_____ Group members completed all tasks to the best of their abilities.
_____ Group members helped clean up after the activity.

The group members acquired the following ideas and skills as a result of this activity:

Group members could improve their work as a group by:

Comments:

Signature: _____ Date: _____

TEACHER EVALUATION OF STUDENT PROGRESS

Class/Period _____ Chapter/Lesson _____ Date _____

Teacher Evaluation of Daily Progress: Homework and Class Participation

Student evaluated: _____

Scoring Key: 2 Often 1 Sometimes 0 Never

_____ Makes sure he or she knows about and understands homework assignments before leaving the classroom each day
_____ Spends enough time completing a homework assignment to do it well
_____ Turns in complete homework assignments on time
_____ Written homework assignments are neat and easy to read
_____ Comes to class with the necessary books, materials, and assignments each day
_____ Participates in class activities and discussions
_____ Answers questions to the best of his or her ability when called on
_____ Uses logical thought and careful consideration when participating in an activity or class discussion
_____ Is considerate of others during the class period

The student could improve his or her daily progress in the following ways:

HOLT SCIENCE & TECHNOLOGY

Integrated Science

Science level RED

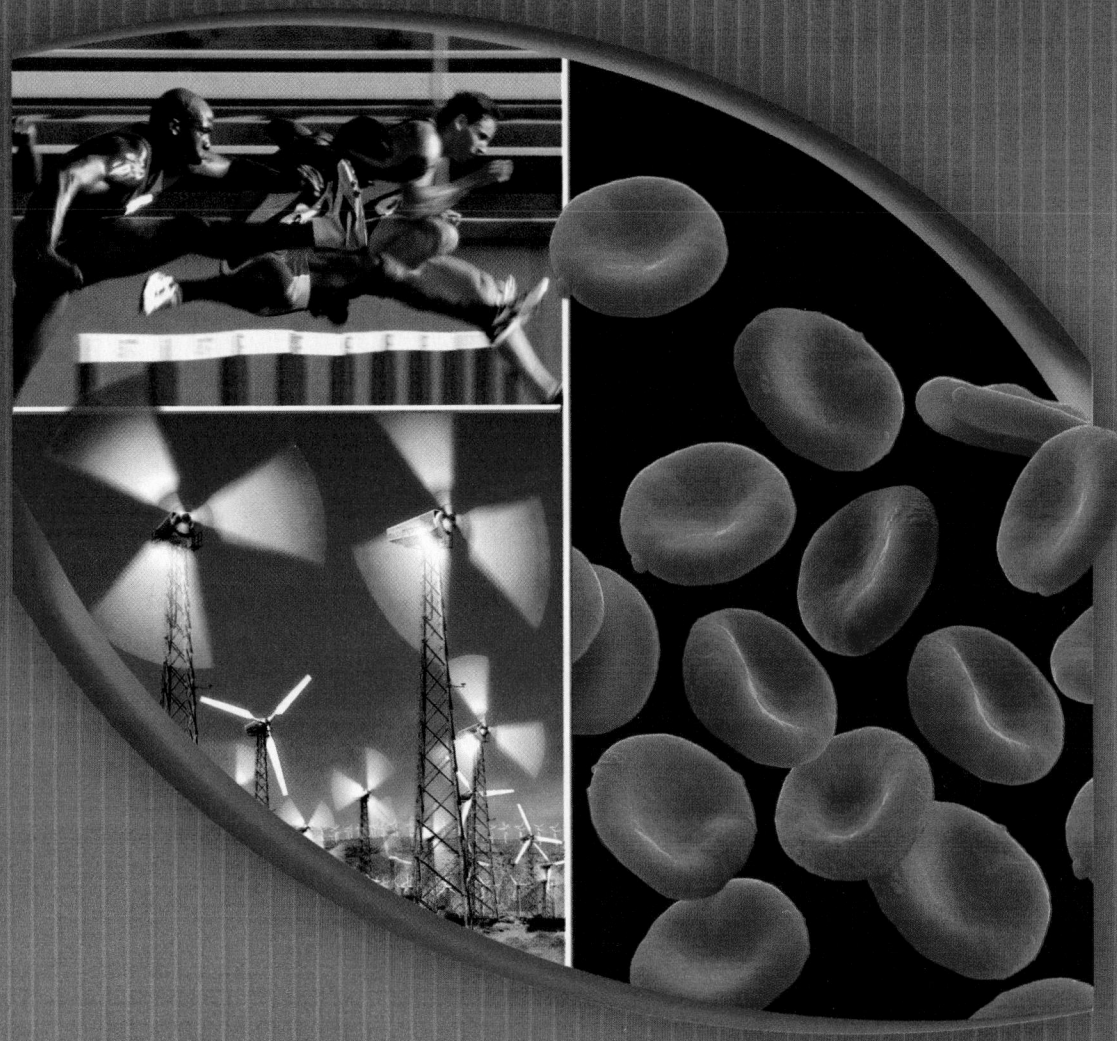

HOLT, RINEHART AND WINSTON

A Harcourt Education Company

Orlando • **Austin** • New York • San Diego • Toronto • London

Acknowledgments

Contributing Authors

Katy Z. Allen
Science Writer
Wayland, Massachusetts

Linda Ruth Berg, Ph.D.
Adjunct Professor of Natural Sciences
St. Petersburg College
St. Petersburg, Florida

Kathleen Meehan Berry
Science Chairman
Canon-McMillan School District
Canonsburg, Pennsylvania

Christie Borgford, Ph.D.
Assistant Professor of Chemistry
Department of Chemistry
The University of Alabama
Birmingham, Alabama

Barbara Christopher
Science Writer and Editor
Austin, Texas

Mapi Cuevas, Ph.D.
Professor of Chemistry
Department of Natural Sciences
Santa Fe Community College
Gainesville, Florida

Robert H. Fronk, Ph.D.
Chair of Science and Mathematics Education
Florida Institute of Technology
West Melbourne, Florida

Joel S. Leventhal, Ph.D.
Emeritus Scientist, Geochemistry
U.S. Geological Survey
Denver, Colorado

Peter E. Malin, Ph.D.
Professor of Geology
Division of Earth and Ocean Sciences
Duke University
Durham, North Carolina

Mark F. Taylor, Ph.D.
Associate Professor of Biology
Biology Department
Baylor University
Waco, Texas

Sally Ann Vonderbrink, Ph.D.
Chemistry Teacher (retired)
Cincinnati, Ohio

Safety Reviewer

Jack Gerlovich, Ph.D.
Associate Professor
School of Education
Drake University
Des Moines, Iowa

Inclusion Specialist

Karen Clay
Inclusion Consultant
Boston, Massachusetts

Ellen McPeek Glisan
Special Needs Consultant
San Antonio, Texas

Academic Reviewers

Glenn Adelson, Ph.D.
Instructor
Department of Organismic and Evolutionary Biology
Harvard University
Cambridge, Massachusetts

Mead Allison, Ph.D.
Associate Professor
Department of Earth and Environmental Sciences
Tulane University
New Orleans, Louisiana

Katy Z. Allen
Science Writer
Wayland, Massachusetts

Linda Ruth Berg, Ph.D.
Adjunct Professor of Natural Sciences
St. Petersburg College
St. Petersburg, Florida

Acknowledgments
continued on page 813

ISBN-13: 978-0-03-095884-7
ISBN-10: 0-03-095884-9

1 2 3 4 5 6 7 048 10 09 08 07 06

Contents in Brief

Contents

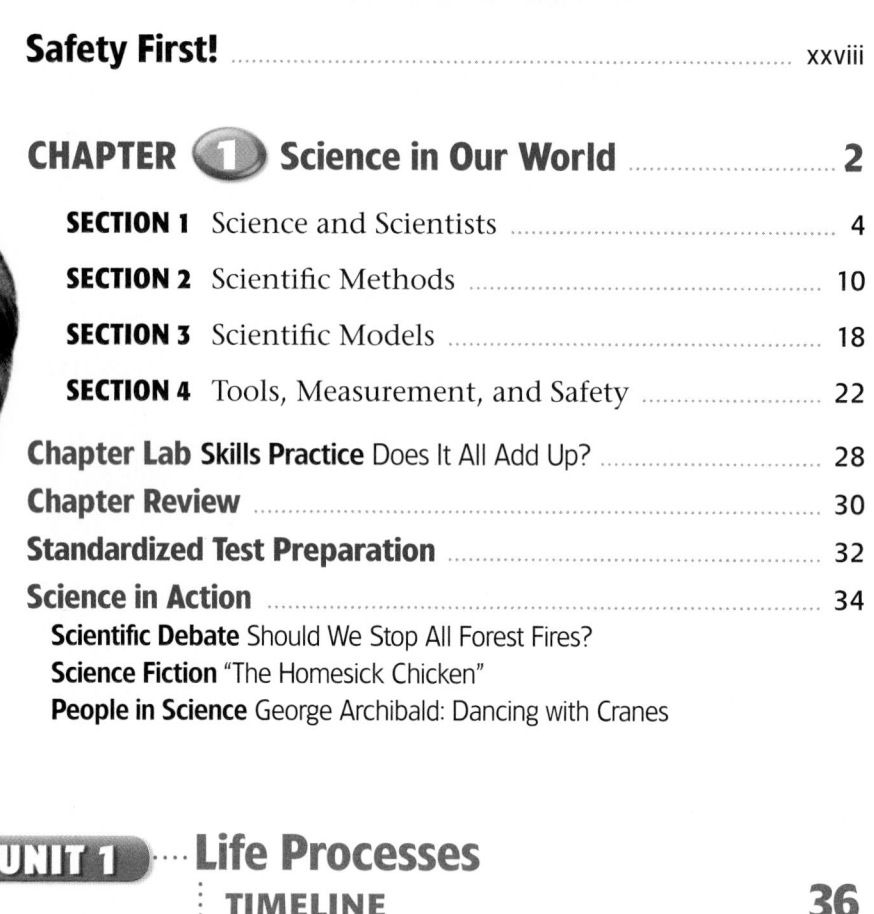

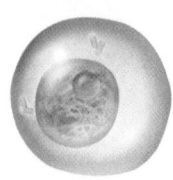
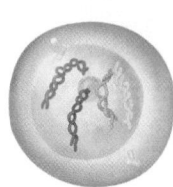

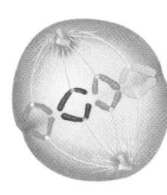
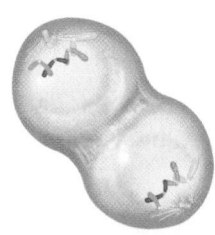

UNIT 2 ···· Heredity and Evolution

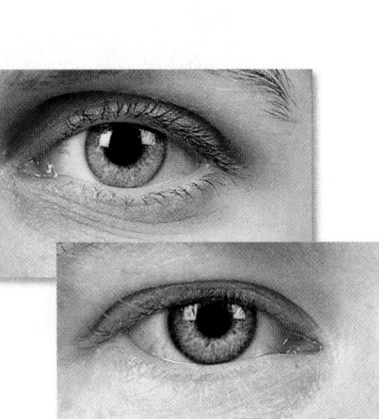

UNIT 3 ····Earth's Resources

Contents   **vii**

UNIT 4 ····The Restless Earth

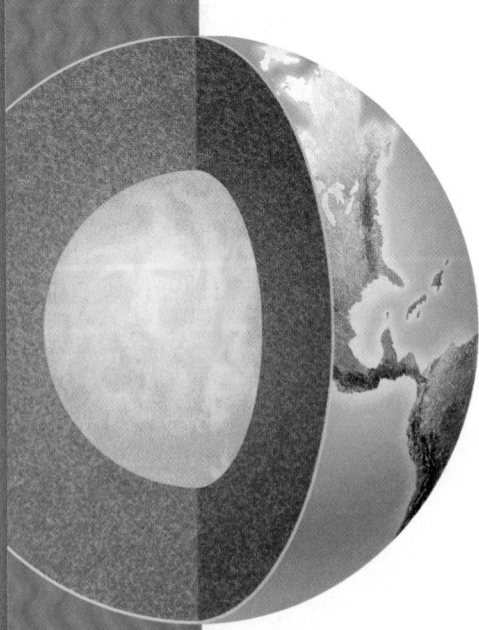

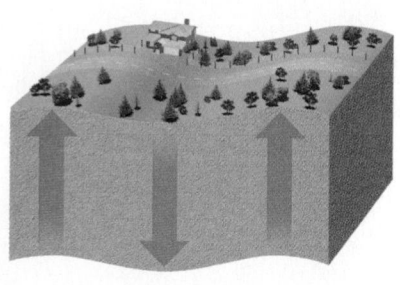

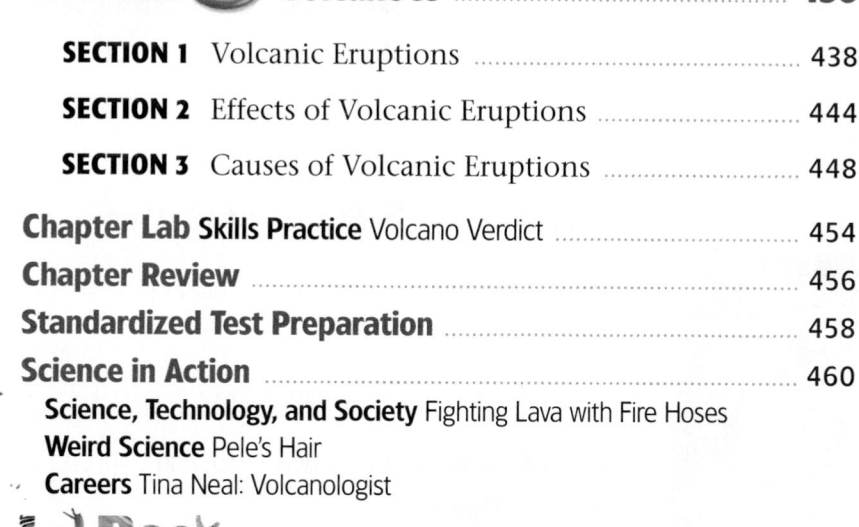

Contents   **xi**

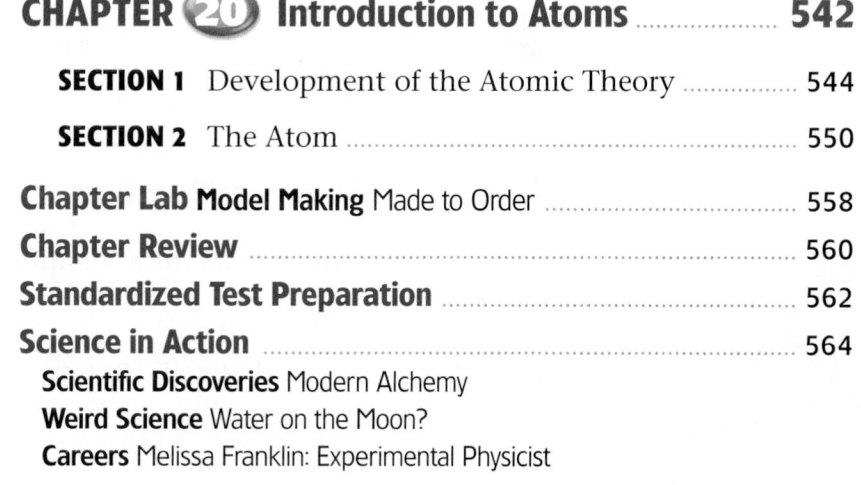

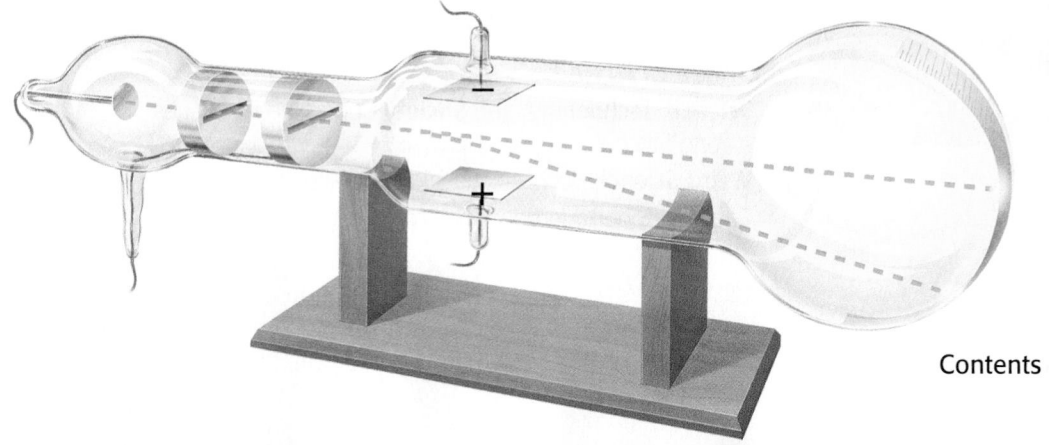

UNIT 6 ···· Interactions of Matter

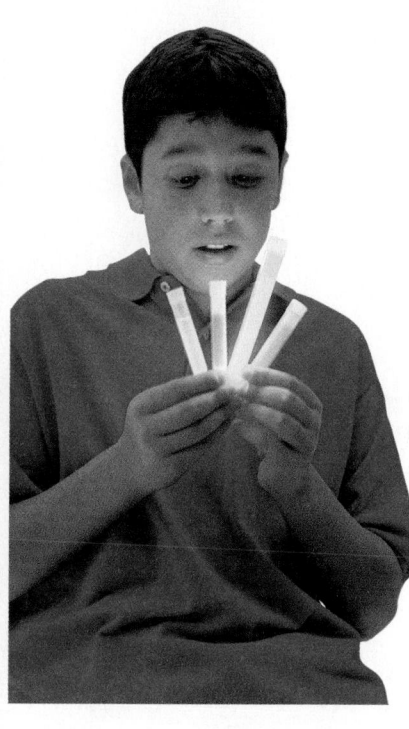

Chapter Labs

Labs

Make science a "hands-on" experience.

Each chapter ends with a chapter lab designed to help you experience science firsthand. But please don't forget to be safe. Read the **Safety First!** section before starting any of the labs.

Contents   **xvii**

LabBook Labs

The more labs, the better!

Additional labs appear within a special **LabBook** in the back of the textbook. Use these labs to help you extend your lab skills. Don't forget to read the **Safety First!** section before starting any of the labs.

Quick Labs

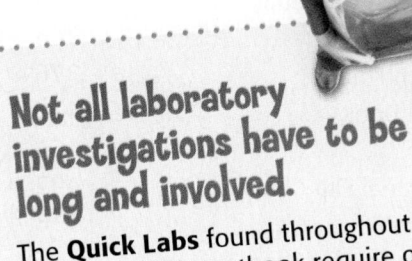

Not all laboratory investigations have to be long and involved.

The **Quick Labs** found throughout the chapters of this textbook require only a small amount of time and limited equipment. But just because they are quick, don't skimp on safety.

Labs

Pre-Reading Activities

Start your engines with an activity!

Get motivated to learn by doing the two activities at the beginning of each chapter. The **Pre-Reading Activity** helps you organize information as you read the chapter. The **Start-Up Activity** helps you gain scientific understanding of the topic through hands-on experience.

Graphic Organizer

Start-Up Activities

Activities

Reading Strategies

Remembering what you read doesn't have to be hard!

A **Reading Strategy** at the beginning of every section provides tips to help you remember and/or organize the information covered in the section.

Internet Activities

Get caught in the Web!

Go to **go.hrw.com** for **Internet Activities** related to each chapter. To find the Internet Activity for a particular chapter, just type in the keyword listed below.

School to Home

Science brings you closer together!

Bring science into your home by doing **School-to-Home Activities** with a family member or another adult in your household.

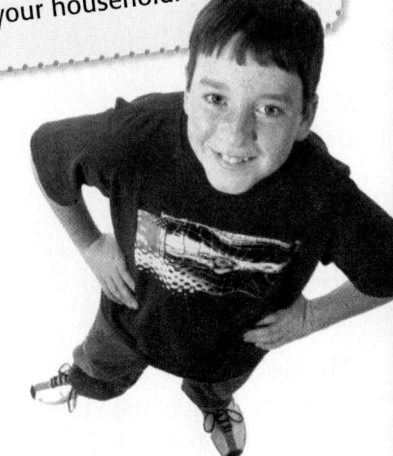

Science and math go hand in hand.

Each **Math Practice** activity contains a word problem related to the topic at hand. **Math Focus** activities provide step-by-step instructions and practice questions designed to help you apply math directly to science.

Math Practice

Math Focus

Connection to...

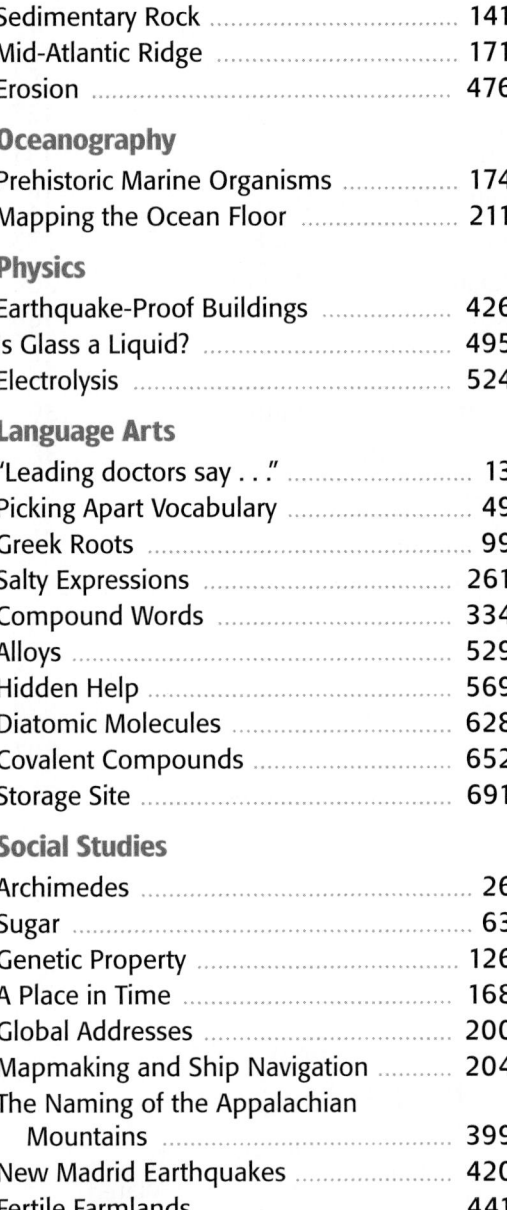

One subject leads to another.

You may not realize it at first, but different subjects are related to each other in many ways. Each **Connection** explores a topic from the viewpoint of another discipline. In this way, all of the subjects you learn about in school merge to improve your understanding of the world around you.

Science In Action

How to Use Your Textbook

Your Roadmap for Success with Holt Science and Technology

What You Will Learn

At the beginning of every section you will find the section's objectives and vocabulary terms. The objectives tell you what you'll need to know after you finish reading the section.

Vocabulary terms are listed for each section. Learn the definitions of these terms because you will most likely be tested on them. Each term is highlighted in the text and is defined at point of use and in the margin. You can also use the glossary to locate definitions quickly.

STUDY TIP Reread the objectives and the definitions to the terms when studying for a test to be sure you know the material.

Get Organized

A Reading Strategy at the beginning of every section provides tips to help you organize and remember the information covered in the section. Keep a science notebook so that you are ready to take notes when your teacher reviews the material in class. Keep your assignments in this notebook so that you can review them when studying for the chapter test.

SECTION 1

The Rock Cycle

You know that paper, plastic, and aluminum can be recycled. But did you know that the Earth also recycles? And one of the things that Earth recycles is rock.

What You Will Learn
- Describe two ways rocks have been used by humans.
- Describe four processes that shape Earth's features.
- Describe how each type of rock changes into another type as it moves through the rock cycle.
- List two characteristics of rock that are used to help classify it.

Vocabulary
rock cycle   deposition
rock   composition
erosion   texture

READING STRATEGY

Reading Organizer As you read this section, make a flowchart of the steps of the rock cycle.

Scientists define **rock** as a naturally occurring solid mixture of one or more minerals and organic matter. It may be hard to believe, but rocks are always changing. The continual process by which new rock forms from old rock material is called the **rock cycle.**

The Value of Rock

Rock has been an important natural resource as long as humans have existed. Early humans used rocks as hammers to make other tools. They discovered that they could make arrowheads, spear points, knives, and scrapers by carefully shaping rocks such as chert and obsidian.

Rock has also been used for centuries to make buildings, monuments, and roads. **Figure 1** shows how rock has been used as a construction material by both ancient and modern civilizations. Buildings have been made out of granite, limestone, marble, sandstone, slate, and other rocks. Modern buildings also contain concrete and plaster, in which rock is an important ingredient.

Reading Check Name some types of rock that have been used to construct buildings. (*See the Appendix for answers to Reading Checks.*)

Figure 1 *The ancient Egyptians used a sedimentary rock called limestone to construct the pyramids at Giza (left). Granite, an igneous rock, was used to construct the Texas state capitol building in Austin (right).*

248 Chapter 10 Rocks: Mineral Mixtures

↗ Be Resourceful—Use the Web

SciLinks boxes in your textbook take you to resources that you can use for science projects, reports, and research papers. Go to **scilinks.org** and type in the **SciLinks code** to find information on a topic.

Visit go.hrw.com
Check out the **Current Science**® magazine articles and other materials that go with your textbook at **go.hrw.com.** Click on the textbook icon and the table of contents to see all of the resources for each chapter.

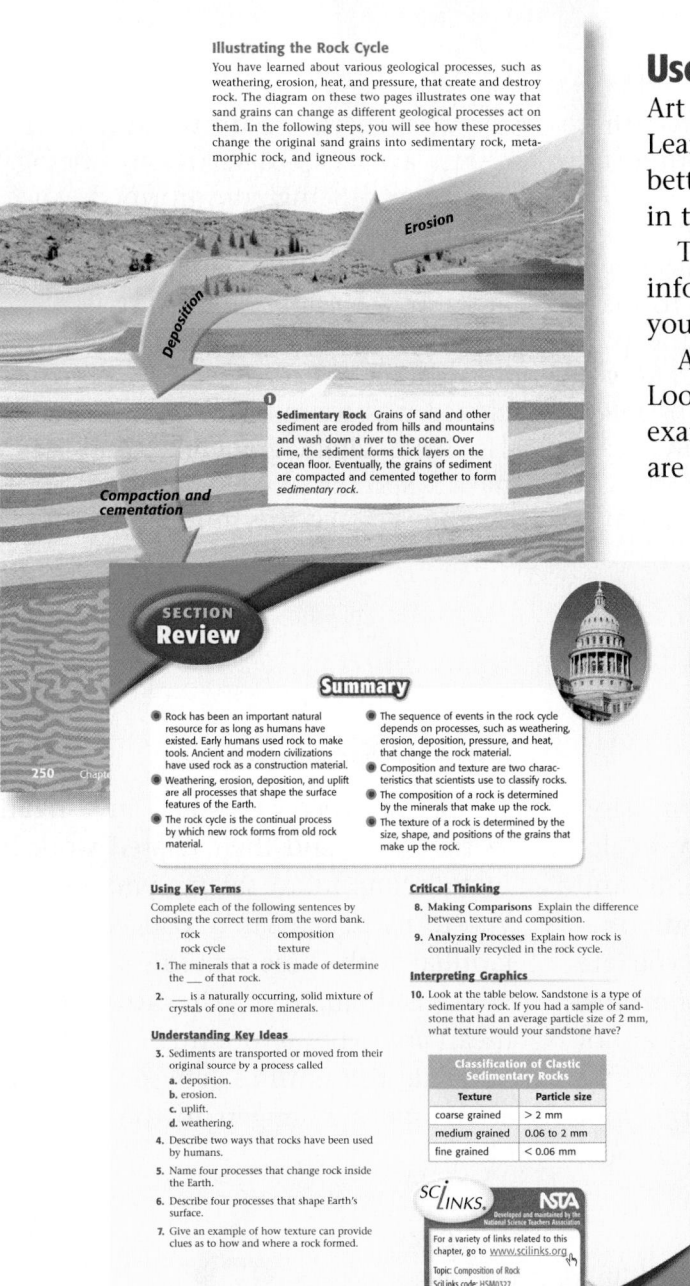

Illustrating the Rock Cycle

You have learned about various geological processes, such as weathering, erosion, heat, and pressure, that create and destroy rock. The diagram on these two pages illustrates one way that sand grains can change as different geological processes act on them. In the following steps, you will see how these processes change the original sand grains into sedimentary rock, metamorphic rock, and igneous rock.

Erosion

Deposition

Sedimentary Rock Grains of sand and other sediment are eroded from hills and mountains and wash down a river to the ocean. Over time, the sediment forms thick layers on the ocean floor. Eventually, the grains of sediment are compacted and cemented together to form *sedimentary rock.*

Compaction and cementation

250 Chapter

SECTION Review

Summary

- Rock has been an important natural resource for as long as humans have existed. Early humans used rock to make tools. Ancient and modern civilizations have used rock as a construction material.
- Weathering, erosion, deposition, and uplift are all processes that shape the surface features of the Earth.
- The rock cycle is the continual process by which new rock forms from old rock material.

- The sequence of events in the rock cycle depends on processes, such as weathering, erosion, deposition, pressure, and heat, that change the rock material.
- Composition and texture are two characteristics that scientists use to classify rocks.
- The composition of a rock is determined by the minerals that make up the rock.
- The texture of a rock is determined by the size, shape, and positions of the grains that make up the rock.

Using Key Terms

Complete each of the following sentences by choosing the correct term from the word bank.

| rock | composition |
| rock cycle | texture |

1. The minerals that a rock is made of determine the ___ of that rock.

2. ___ is a naturally occurring, solid mixture of crystals of one or more minerals.

Understanding Key Ideas

3. Sediments are transported or moved from their original source by a process called
   a. deposition.
   b. erosion.
   c. uplift.
   d. weathering.

4. Describe two ways that rocks have been used by humans.

5. Name four processes that change rock inside the Earth.

6. Describe four processes that shape Earth's surface.

7. Give an example of how texture can provide clues as to how and where a rock formed.

Critical Thinking

8. **Making Comparisons** Explain the difference between texture and composition.

9. **Analyzing Processes** Explain how rock is continually recycled in the rock cycle.

Interpreting Graphics

10. Look at the table below. Sandstone is a type of sedimentary rock. If you had a sample of sandstone that had an average particle size of 2 mm, what texture would your sandstone have?

Classification of Clastic Sedimentary Rocks

Texture	Particle size
coarse grained	> 2 mm
medium grained	0.06 to 2 mm
fine grained	< 0.06 mm

SciLINKS. NSTA

Developed and maintained by the National Science Teachers Association

For a variety of links related to this chapter, go to www.scilinks.org

Topic: Composition of Rock
SciLinks code: HSM0327

255

Use the Illustrations and Photos

Art shows complex ideas and processes. Learn to analyze the art so that you better understand the material you read in the text.

Tables and graphs display important information in an organized way to help you see relationships.

A picture is worth a thousand words. Look at the photographs to see relevant examples of science concepts that you are reading about.

Answer the Section Reviews

Section Reviews test your knowledge of the main points of the section. Critical Thinking items challenge you to think about the material in greater depth and to find connections that you infer from the text.

STUDY TIP When you can't answer a question, reread the section. The answer is usually there.

Do Your Homework

Your teacher may assign worksheets to help you understand and remember the material in the chapter.

STUDY TIP Don't try to answer the questions without reading the text and reviewing your class notes. A little preparation up front will make your homework assignments a lot easier. Answering the items in the Chapter Review will help prepare you for the chapter test.

Holt Online Learning

Visit Holt Online Learning

If your teacher gives you a special password to log onto the **Holt Online Learning** site, you'll find your complete textbook on the Web. In addition, you'll find some great learning tools and practice quizzes. You'll be able to see how well you know the material from your textbook.

SAFETY FIRST!

Exploring, inventing, and investigating are essential to the study of science. However, these activities can also be dangerous. To make sure that your experiments and explorations are safe, you must be aware of a variety of safety guidelines. You have probably heard of the saying, "It is better to be safe than sorry." This is particularly true in a science classroom where experiments and explorations are being performed. Being uninformed and careless can result in serious injuries. Don't take chances with your own safety or with anyone else's.

The following pages describe important guidelines for staying safe in the science classroom. Your teacher may also have safety guidelines and tips that are specific to your classroom and laboratory. Take the time to be safe.

Safety Rules!

Start Out Right

Always get your teacher's permission before attempting any laboratory exploration. Read the procedures carefully, and pay particular attention to safety information and caution statements. If you are unsure about what a safety symbol means, look it up or ask your teacher. You cannot be too careful when it comes to safety. If an accident does occur, inform your teacher immediately regardless of how minor you think the accident is.

If you are instructed to note the odor of a substance, wave the fumes toward your nose with your hand. Never put your nose close to the source.

Safety Symbols

All of the experiments and investigations in this book and their related worksheets include important safety symbols to alert you to particular safety concerns. Become familiar with these symbols so that when you see them, you will know what they mean and what to do. It is important that you read this entire safety section to learn about specific dangers in the laboratory.

Eye protection

Clothing protection

Hand safety

Heating safety

Electric safety

Chemical safety

Animal safety

Sharp object

Plant safety

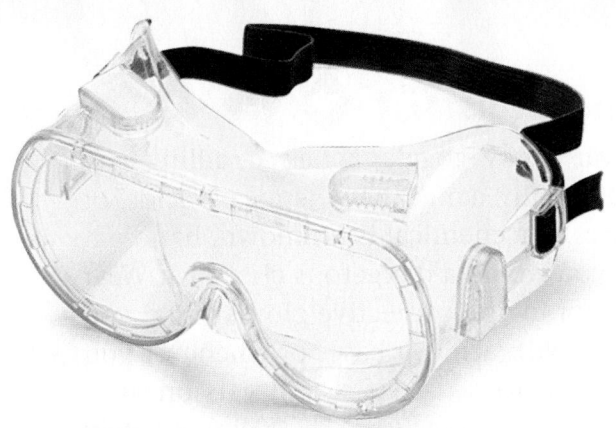

Eye Safety

Wear safety goggles when working around chemicals, acids, bases, or any type of flame or heating device. Wear safety goggles any time there is even the slightest chance that harm could come to your eyes. If any substance gets into your eyes, notify your teacher immediately and flush your eyes with running water for at least 15 minutes. Treat any unknown chemical as if it were a dangerous chemical. Never look directly into the sun. Doing so could cause permanent blindness.

Avoid wearing contact lenses in a laboratory situation. Even if you are wearing safety goggles, chemicals can get between the contact lenses and your eyes. If your doctor requires that you wear contact lenses instead of glasses, wear eye-cup safety goggles in the lab.

Safety Equipment

Know the locations of the nearest fire alarms and any other safety equipment, such as fire blankets and eyewash fountains, as identified by your teacher, and know the procedures for using the equipment.

Neatness

Keep your work area free of all unnecessary books and papers. Tie back long hair, and secure loose sleeves or other loose articles of clothing, such as ties and bows. Remove dangling jewelry. Don't wear open-toed shoes or sandals in the laboratory. Never eat, drink, or apply cosmetics in a laboratory setting. Food, drink, and cosmetics can easily become contaminated with dangerous materials.

Certain hair products (such as aerosol hair spray) are flammable and should not be worn while working near an open flame. Avoid wearing hair spray or hair gel on lab days.

Sharp/Pointed Objects

Use knives and other sharp instruments with extreme care. Never cut objects while holding them in your hands. Place objects on a suitable work surface for cutting.

Be extra careful when using any glassware. When adding a heavy object to a graduated cylinder, tilt the cylinder so that the object slides slowly to the bottom.

Heat

Wear safety goggles when using a heating device or a flame. Whenever possible, use an electric hot plate as a heat source instead of using an open flame. When heating materials in a test tube, always angle the test tube away from yourself and others. To avoid burns, wear heat-resistant gloves whenever instructed to do so.

Electricity

Be careful with electrical cords. When using a microscope with a lamp, do not place the cord where it could trip someone. Do not let cords hang over a table edge in a way that could cause equipment to fall if the cord is accidentally pulled. Do not use equipment with damaged cords. Be sure that your hands are dry and that the electrical equipment is in the "off" position before plugging it in. Turn off and unplug electrical equipment when you are finished.

Chemicals

Wear safety goggles when handling any potentially dangerous chemicals, acids, or bases. If a chemical is unknown, handle it as you would a dangerous chemical. Wear an apron and protective gloves when you work with acids or bases or whenever you are told to do so. If a spill gets on your skin or clothing, rinse it off immediately with water for at least 5 minutes while calling to your teacher.

Never mix chemicals unless your teacher tells you to do so. Never taste, touch, or smell chemicals unless you are specifically directed to do so. Before working with a flammable liquid or gas, check for the presence of any source of flame, spark, or heat.

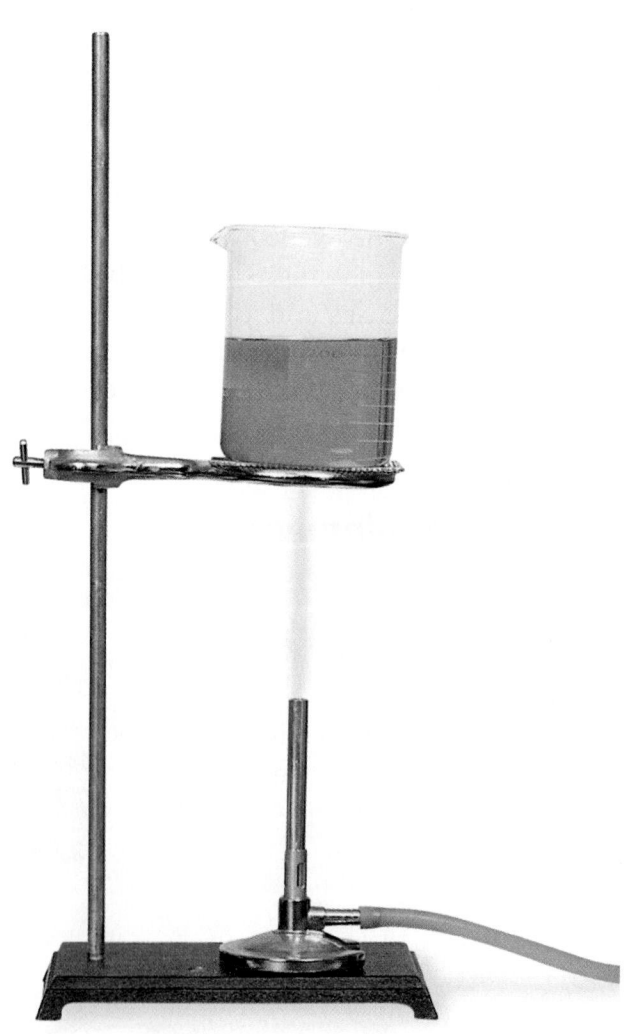

Animal Safety

Always obtain your teacher's permission before bringing any animal into the school building. Handle animals only as your teacher directs. Always treat animals carefully and respectfully. Wash your hands thoroughly after handling any animal.

Plant Safety

Do not eat any part of a plant or plant seed used in the laboratory. Wash your hands thoroughly after handling any part of a plant. When in nature, do not pick any wild plants unless your teacher instructs you to do so.

Glassware

Examine all glassware before use. Be sure that glassware is clean and free of chips and cracks. Report damaged glassware to your teacher. Glass containers used for heating should be made of heat-resistant glass.

Science in Our World
Chapter Planning Guide

1

Compression guide:
To shorten instruction because of time limitations, omit Section 1.

OBJECTIVES	LABS, DEMONSTRATIONS, AND ACTIVITIES	TECHNOLOGY RESOURCES
PACING • 90 min pp. 2–9 **Chapter Opener**	SE **Start-up Activity**, p. 3 ◆ GENERAL	OSP **Parent Letter** GENERAL CD **Student Edition on CD-ROM** CD **Guided Reading Audio CD** TR **Chapter Starter Transparency*** VID **Brain Food Video Quiz**
Section 1 Asking About Life • Describe three methods of investigation. • Identify benefits of science in the world around you. • Describe five jobs that use science.	TE **Group Activity** Scientists in Your Town, p. 4 ◆ GENERAL TE **Group Activity** Wildlife Safari, p. 7 ◆ GENERAL TE **Demonstration** Spreading Disease, p. 6 TE **Connection Activity** Environmental Science, p. 8 ◆ BASIC LB **Long-Term Projects & Research Ideas** The Length of a Fethel* ADVANCED	CRF **Lesson Plans*** TR **Bellringer Transparency*** TE **Internet Activity** p. 5 GENERAL
PACING • 90 min pp. 10–17 **Section 2 Scientific Methods** • Explain why scientists use scientific methods. • Determine the appropriate design of a controlled experiment. • Use information in tables and graphs to analyze experimental results. • Explain how scientific knowledge can change.	TE **Activity** Now You See It, p. 10 ◆ GENERAL TE **Connection Activity** Social Studies, p. 11 GENERAL TE **Demonstration** Frog Call, p. 12 ◆ GENERAL TE **Activity** Test a Hypothesis, p. 12 ADVANCED TE **Activity** Roots of Words, p. 13 BASIC TE **Activity** Writing Predictions, p. 13 GENERAL TE **Connection Activity** Math, p. 16 BASIC SE **Skills Practice Lab** Does It All Add Up?, p. 28 ◆ GENERAL LB **Whiz-Bang Demonstrations** Air Ball* ◆ GENERAL LB **Whiz-Bang Demonstrations** Getting to the Point* ◆ GENERAL	CRF **Lesson Plans*** TR **Bellringer Transparency*** TR **Scientific Methods*** VID **Lab Videos for Life Science**
PACING • 45 min pp. 18–21 **Section 3 Scientific Models** • Give examples of three types of models. • Identify the benefits and limitations of models. • Compare the ways that scientists use hypotheses, theories, and laws.	TE **Group Activity** Classifying, p. 19 ◆ GENERAL CRF **Datasheet for LabBook*** LB **Inquiry Lab** One Side or Two?* ◆ GENERAL SE **Science in Action** Math, Social Studies, and Language Arts Activities, pp. 34–35 GENERAL	CRF **Lesson Plans*** TR **Bellringer Transparency***
PACING • 45 min pp. 22–27 **Section 4 Tools, Measurement, and Safety** • Collect, record, and analyze information by using various tools. • Explain the importance of the International System of Units. • Calculate area and density. • Identify lab safety symbols, and demonstrate safe practices during lab investigations.	TE **Demonstration** Tools of the Trade, p. 22 ◆ GENERAL SE **Quick Lab** No Rules Allowed, p. 23 TE **Connection Activity** International System of Units, p. 23 ◆ GENERAL TE **Group Activity** X Rays, p. 23 GENERAL SE **Math Focus** Significant Figures, p. 24 GENERAL TE **Demonstration** Displacement, p. 25 ◆ BASIC SE **Connection to Social Studies** Archimedes, p. 26 ◆ GENERAL	CRF **Lesson Plans*** TR **Bellringer Transparency*** TR **Compound Light Microscope*** TR **Common SI Units and Conversions*** TR **LINK TO PHYSICAL SCIENCE** Three Temperature Scales* CRF **SciLinks Activity*** GENERAL CD **Interactive Explorations CD-ROM** Something's Fishy! GENERAL

PACING • 90 min

CHAPTER REVIEW, ASSESSMENT, AND STANDARDIZED TEST PREPARATION

CRF **Vocabulary Activity*** GENERAL
SE **Chapter Review**, pp. 30–31 GENERAL
CRF **Chapter Review*** GENERAL
CRF **Chapter Tests A*** GENERAL, **B*** ADVANCED, **C*** SPECIAL NEEDS
SE **Standardized Test Preparation**, pp. 32–33 GENERAL
CRF **Standardized Test Preparation*** GENERAL
CRF **Performance-Based Assessment*** GENERAL
OSP **Test Generator** GENERAL
CRF **Test Item Listing*** GENERAL

Online and Technology Resources

go.hrw.com Holt Online Learning

Visit **go.hrw.com** for access to Holt Online Learning, or enter the keyword **HS7 Home** for a variety of free online resources.

One-Stop Planner® CD-ROM

This CD-ROM package includes:
• Lab Materials QuickList Software
• Holt Calendar Planner
• Customizable Lesson Plans
• Printable Worksheets
• ExamView® Test Generator
• Interactive Teacher's Edition
• Holt PuzzlePro®
• Holt PowerPoint® Resources

SKILLS DEVELOPMENT RESOURCES	SECTION REVIEW AND ASSESSMENT	STANDARDS CORRELATIONS
SE **Pre-Reading Activity**, p. 2 GENERAL OSP **Science Puzzlers, Twisters & Teasers** GENERAL SS **Science Skills** Reading a Science Textbook* ADVANCED		**National Science Education Standards** HNS 2; SAI 1
CRF **Directed Reading A*** BASIC, **B*** SPECIAL NEEDS CRF **Vocabulary and Section Summary*** GENERAL SE **Reading Strategy** Reading Organizer, p. 4 GENERAL TE **Reading Strategy** Reading Organizer, p. 5 GENERAL SE **Connection to Biology** Technology and Aging, p. 7 GENERAL TE **Inclusion Strategies**, p. 8	SE **Reading Checks**, pp. 4, 7, 9 GENERAL TE **Homework**, p. 7 ADVANCED TE **Reteaching**, p. 8 BASIC TE **Quiz**, p. 8 GENERAL TE **Alternative Assessment**, p. 8 GENERAL SE **Section Review,*** p. 9 GENERAL CRF **Section Quiz*** GENERAL	SAI 1; ST 2; SPSP 3, 4; HNS 1
CRF **Directed Reading A*** BASIC, **B*** SPECIAL NEEDS CRF **Vocabulary and Section Summary*** GENERAL SE **Reading Strategy** Reading Organizer, p. 10 GENERAL TE **Reading Strategy** Mnemonics, p. 11 BASIC SE **Connection to Environmental Science** Minnesota's Deformed Frogs, p. 12 GENERAL SE **Connection to Language Arts** "Leading Doctors Say…", p. 13 GENERAL SE **Math Practice** Averages, p. 16 GENERAL MS **Math Skills for Science** What Is an Average?* GENERAL CRF **Reinforcement Worksheet** The Mystery of the Bubbling Top* BASIC CRF **Critical Thinking** The Case of the Bulge* ADVANCED	SE **Reading Checks**, pp. 10, 12, 14, 16 GENERAL TE **Homework**, p. 13 GENERAL TE **Reteaching**, p. 16 BASIC TE **Quiz**, p. 16 GENERAL TE **Alternative Assessment**, p. 16 ADVANCED SE **Section Review,*** p. 17 GENERAL CRF **Section Quiz*** GENERAL	SAI 1, 2; HNS 2
CRF **Directed Reading A*** BASIC, **B*** SPECIAL NEEDS CRF **Vocabulary and Section Summary*** GENERAL SE **Reading Strategy** Reading Organizer, p. 18 GENERAL SE **Connection to Environmental Science** Samples, p. 19 GENERAL TE **Reading Strategy** Paired Reading, p. 19 BASIC SE **Connection to Chemistry** Model Cocaine in the Brain, p. 21 GENERAL SS **Science Skills** Study Habits GENERAL MS **Math Skills for Science** Arithmetic with Decimals* GENERAL	SE **Reading Checks**, pp. 19, 20 GENERAL TE **Reteaching**, p. 20 BASIC TE **Quiz**, p. 20 GENERAL TE **Homework**, p. 20 ADVANCED TE **Alternative Assessment**, p. 20 GENERAL SE **Section Review,*** p. 21 GENERAL CRF **Section Quiz*** GENERAL	UCP 2; SAI 1; SPSP 3, 4; HNS 2
CRF **Directed Reading A*** BASIC, **B*** SPECIAL NEEDS CRF **Vocabulary and Section Summary*** GENERAL SE **Reading Strategy** Reading Organizer, p. 22 GENERAL TE **Inclusion Strategies**, p. 23 ◆ MS **Math Skills for Science** A Formula for SI Catch-up* GENERAL MS **Math Skills for Science** What Is SI?* GENERAL MS **Math Skills for Science** Finding Perimeter and Area* GENERAL MS **Math Skills for Science** Finding Volume* GENERAL SS **Science Skills** Safety Rules! GENERAL	SE **Reading Checks**, pp. 22, 25, 27 GENERAL TE **Reteaching**, p. 26 BASIC TE **Quiz**, p. 26 GENERAL TE **Alternative Assessment**, p. 26 BASIC TE **Homework**, p. 24 BASIC SE **Section Review,*** p. 27 GENERAL CRF **Section Quiz*** GENERAL	UCP 3; SPSP 1, HNS 3

SCI LINKS.
NSTA
www.scilinks.org
Maintained by the **National Science Teachers Association.** See Chapter Enrichment pages that follow for a complete list of topics.

Current Science®

Check out **Current Science** articles and activities by visiting the HRW Web site at **go.hrw.com.** Just type in the keyword **HL5CS04T.**

Classroom Videos

• **Lab Videos** demonstrate the chapter lab.
• **Brain Food Video Quizzes** help students review the chapter material.

Classroom CD-ROMs

• **Guided Reading Audio CD** (Also in Spanish)
• **Interactive Explorations**
• **Virtual Investigations**
• **Visual Concepts**
• **Science Tutor**

Holt Lab Generator CD-ROM

Search for any lab by topic, standard, difficulty level, or time. Edit any lab to fit your needs, or create your own labs. Use the Lab Materials QuickList software to customize your lab materials list.

Visual Resources

CHAPTER STARTER TRANSPARENCY

Imagine . . .

BELLRINGER TRANSPARENCIES

Section: Asking About Life
Have you ever wondered how homing pigeons find their way home? Do you know why the dinosaurs went extinct? Write five questions about the natural world that you hope to have answered in this class.

Record your questions in your **science journal.**

Section: Scientific Methods
Which do you think is more important: imagination or knowledge? Can one exist without the other?

Reflect on this in your **science journal.** You may want to think of some famous scientists to write about in your answer. Then share your answer with the class and have a debate.

TEACHING TRANSPARENCIES

Scientific Methods

Common SI Units and Conversions

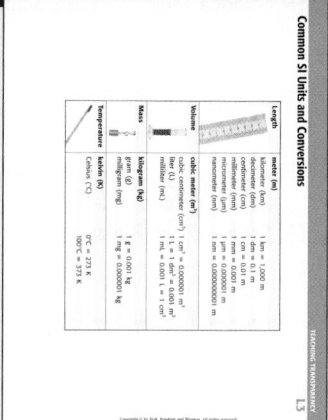

TEACHING TRANSPARENCIES

Three Temperature Scales

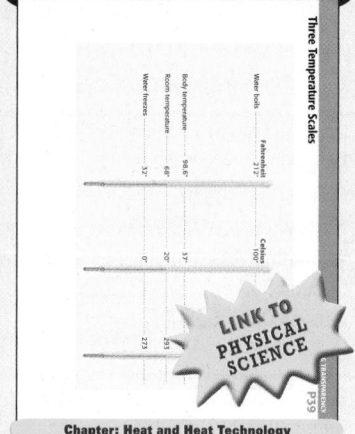

LINK TO PHYSICAL SCIENCE

Chapter: Heat and Heat Technology

CONCEPT MAPPING TRANSPARENCY

Use the following terms to complete the concept map below:
scientific methods, observations, controlled experiments, drawing conclusions, scientists, questions

Planning Resources

LESSON PLANS

Lesson Plan   SAMPLE

Section: Waves

Pacing
Regular Schedule: with lab(s):2 days   without lab(s):2 days
Block Schedule: with lab(s):1 1/2 days   without lab(s):1 day

Objectives
1. Relate the seven properties of life to a living organism.
2. Describe seven themes that can help you to organize what you learn about biology.
3. Identify the tiny structures that make up all living organisms.
4. Differentiate between reproduction and heredity and between metabolism and homeostasis.

National Science Education Standards Covered
LSInter1:Cells have particular structures that underlie their functions.
LSMat1:Most cell functions involve chemical reactions.
LSBeh1:Cells store and use information to guide their functions.
UCP1:Cell functions are regulated.
SF1: Cells can differentiate and form complete multicellular organisms.
PS1: Species evolve over time.
ESS1: The great diversity of organisms is the result of more than 3.5 billion years of evolution.
ESS2: Natural selection and its evolutionary consequences provide a scientific explanation for the fossil record of ancient life forms as well as for the striking molecular similarities observed among the diverse species of living organisms.
ST1: The millions of different species of plants, animals, and microorganisms that live on Earth today are related by descent from common ancestors.
ST2: The energy for life primarily comes from the sun.
SPSP1: The complexity and organization of organisms accommodates the need for obtaining, transforming, transporting, releasing, and eliminating the matter and energy used to sustain the organism.
SPSP2: As matter and energy flows through different levels of organization of living systems—cells, organs, communities—and between living systems and the physical environment, chemical elements are recombined in different ways.
HNS1: Organisms have behavioral responses to internal changes and to external stimuli.

PARENT LETTER

SAMPLE

Dear Parent,

Your son's or daughter's science class will soon begin exploring the chapter entitled "The World of Physical Science." In this chapter, students will learn about how the scientific method applies to the world of physical science and the role of physical science in the world. By the end of the chapter, students should demonstrate a clear understanding of the chapter's main ideas and be able to discuss the following topics:

1. physical science is the study of energy and matter (Section 1)
2. the role of physical science in the world around them (Section 1)
3. careers that rely on physical science (Section 1)
4. the steps used in the scientific method (Section 2)
5. examples of technology (Section 2)
6. how the scientific method is used to answer questions and solve problems (Section 2)
7. how our knowledge of science changes over time (Section 2)
8. how models represent real objects or systems (Section 3)
9. examples of different ways models are used in science (Section 3)
10. the importance of the International System of Units (Section 4)
11. the appropriate units to use for particular measurements (Section 4)
12. how area and density are derived quantities (Section 4)

Questions to Ask Along the Way

You can help your son or daughter learn about these topics by asking interesting questions such as the following:

• What are some surprising careers that use physical science?
• What is a characteristic of a good hypothesis?
• When is it a good idea to use a model?
• Why do Americans measure things in terms of inches and yards instead of centimeters and meters ?

ALSO IN SPANISH

TEST ITEM LISTING

TEST ITEM LISTING
The World of Science   SAMPLE

MULTIPLE CHOICE

1. A limitation of models is that
   a. they are large enough to see.
   b. they do not act exactly like the things that they model.
   c. they are smaller than the things that they model.
   d. they model unfamiliar things.
   Answer: B   Difficulty: 1   Section: 3   Objective: 2

2. The length 10 m is equal to
   a. 100 cm.   c. 10,000 mm.
   b. 1,000 cm.   d. Both (b) and (c)
   Answer: B   Difficulty: 3   Section: 3   Objective: 2

3. To be valid, a hypothesis must be
   a. testable.   c. made into a law.
   b. supported by evidence. d. Both (a) and (b)
   Answer: B   Difficulty: 3   Section: 3   Objective: 2 · 1

4. The statement "Sheila has a stain on her shirt" is an example of a(n)
   a. law.   c. observation.
   b. hypothesis.   d. prediction.
   Answer: B   Difficulty: 1   Section: 3   Objective: 2

5. A hypothesis is often developed out of
   a. observations.   c. laws.
   b. experiments.   d. Both (a) and (b)
   Answer: B   Difficulty: 1   Section: 3   Objective: 2

6. How many milliliters are in 3.5 kL?
   a. 3,500 mL.   c. 3,500, 000 mL.
   b. 0.0035 mL.   d. 35,000 mL.
   Answer: B   Difficulty: 1   Section: 3   Objective: 2

7. A map of Seattle is an example of a
   a. law.   c. model.
   b. theory.   d. unit.
   Answer: B   Difficulty: 1   Section: 3   Objective: 2

8. A lab has the safety icons shown below. These icons mean that you should wear
   a. only safety goggles.   c. safety goggles and a lab apron.
   b. only a lab apron.   d. safety goggles, a lab apron, and gloves.
   Answer: B   Difficulty: 1   Section: 3   Objective: 2

9. The law of conservation of mass says the lot of mass before a chemical change is
   a. more than the total mass after the change.
   b. less than the total mass after the change.
   c. the same as the total mass before the change.
   d. not the same as the total mass after the change.
   Answer: B   Difficulty: 1   Section: 3   Objective: 2

10. In which of the following areas might you find a geochemist at work?
    a. studying the chemistry of rocks   c. studying fishes
    b. studying forestry   d. studying the atmosphere
    Answer: B   Difficulty: 1   Section: 3   Objective: 2

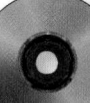

One-Stop Planner® CD-ROM

This CD-ROM includes all of the resources shown here and the following time-saving tools:

• *Lab Materials QuickList Software*
• *Customizable lesson plans*
• *Holt Calendar Planner*
• *The powerful ExamView® Test Generator*

Meeting Individual Needs

DIRECTED READING A
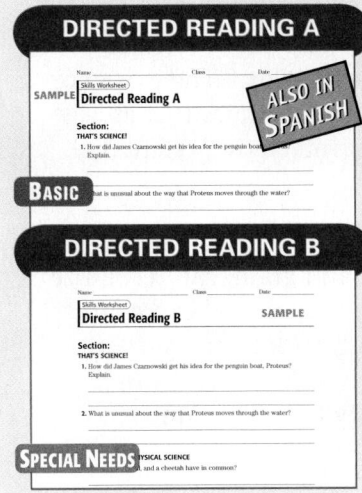

DIRECTED READING B

VOCABULARY ACTIVITY
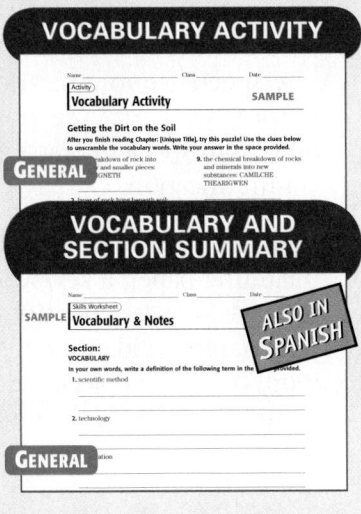

VOCABULARY AND SECTION SUMMARY

REINFORCEMENT
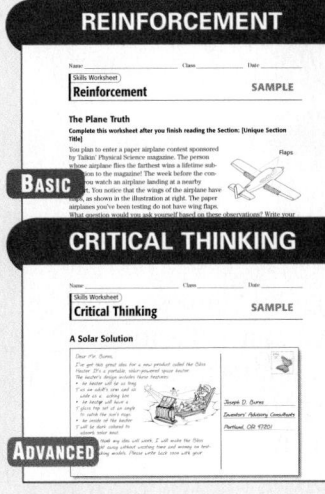

CRITICAL THINKING

SCILINKS ACTIVITY

SCIENCE PUZZLERS, TWISTERS & TEASERS

Labs and Activities

LONG-TERM PROJECTS & RESEARCH IDEAS
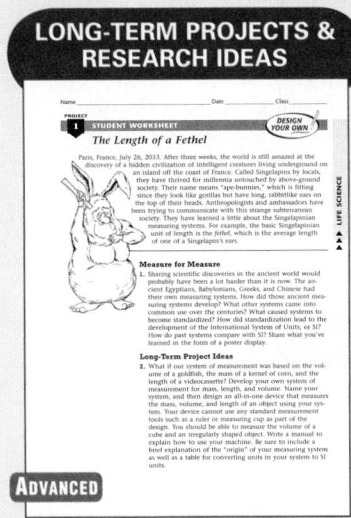

WHIZ-BANG DEMONSTRATIONS
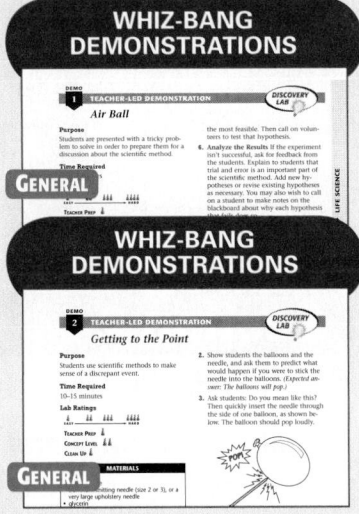

WHIZ-BANG DEMONSTRATIONS

INQUIRY LABS
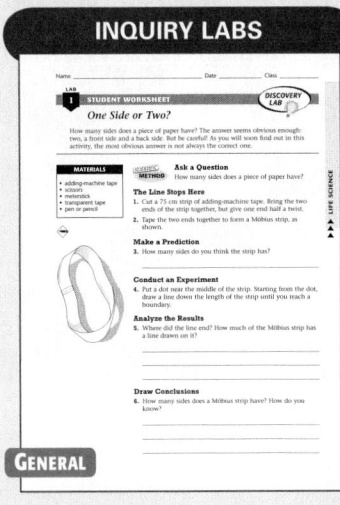

DATASHEETS FOR QUICK LABS

DATASHEETS FOR CHAPTER LABS

DATASHEETS FOR LABBOOK

Review and Assessments

SECTION QUIZ
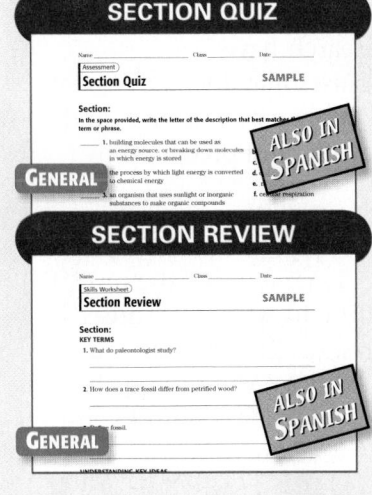

SECTION REVIEW

CHAPTER REVIEW
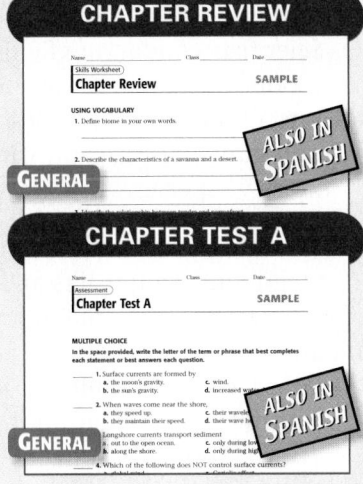

CHAPTER TEST A

CHAPTER TEST B
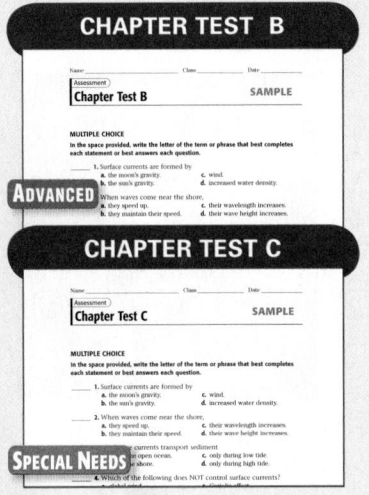

CHAPTER TEST C

STANDARDIZED TEST PREPARATION
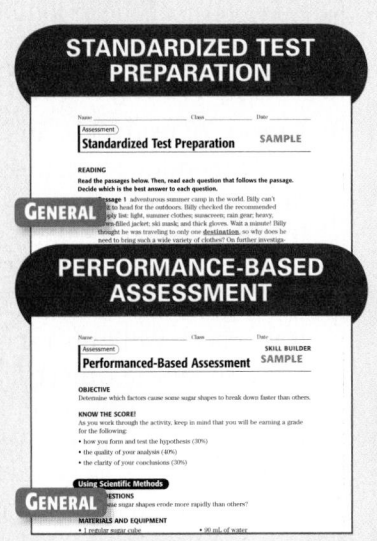

PERFORMANCE-BASED ASSESSMENT

This Chapter Enrichment provides relevant and interesting information to expand and enhance your presentation of the chapter material.

Section 1

Science and Scientists

Deformed Frogs

- The discovery of deformed frogs by Minnesota middle school students in 1995 sparked much attention around the country. Since that summer, reports of amphibian deformations have poured into agencies from many parts of the continent.

- The reported deformities include extra limbs, malformed or missing limbs, and facial malformations. Deformities have been documented in 44 states and involve nearly 60 species. In some local populations, up to 60% of the amphibians exhibit deformities.

Dr. Pepperberg's Studies on Parrots

- Parrots, or psittacids, are rarely mentioned during discussions of animal intelligence, but recent studies indicate that they are intelligent animals. Dr. Irene Pepperberg, while an associate professor at the University of Arizona's Department of Ecology and Evolutionary Biology, demonstrated that African gray parrots can process information and make decisions.

- Pepperberg has studied Alex, an African gray parrot, for more than 20 years. Pepperberg says that she has used a variety of techniques to establish a form of interspecies communication with Alex. "The existence of such behavior," she says, "demonstrates that at least one avian species is capable of interactive, referential communication."

- Alex can count and identify more than 35 objects, including paper, a key, wood, and grain; can recognize seven colors; can identify five shapes; and can combine names to identify, request, refuse, and categorize more than 100 objects. Alex even learned to boss around lab assistants to modify his environment.

Is That a Fact!

- ◆ In this century, the Siberian, or Amur, tiger has survived wars, revolutions, and deforestation in eastern Asia. Its numbers in the wild were below 100 in the 1940s, but conservation efforts have brought numbers to around 400. There are now more than 4,500 km^2 of protected areas for these tigers in Russia. About 500 additional Siberian tigers live in captivity.

Section 2

Scientific Methods

Vanishing Amphibians

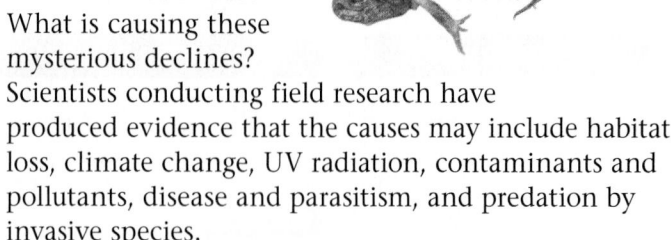

- Scientists are perplexed by steady declines in the world's amphibian populations since the mid-1980s. What is causing these mysterious declines? Scientists conducting field research have produced evidence that the causes may include habitat loss, climate change, UV radiation, contaminants and pollutants, disease and parasitism, and predation by invasive species.

- Alarmingly, declines are not simply occurring in places where human impacts are obvious; some of the most dramatic declines are happening in wilderness areas and parks. In the United States, declines are particularly serious in California, the Rocky Mountains, the Southwest, and Puerto Rico. Worldwide, areas of concern include Australia and Central America.

- The scientific community suspects that there is no single reason for the declines. Different possible causes seem to be at work in different parts of the world. The cause is clear in some cases but not in others. Many researchers believe that multiple causes are adding up to endanger the world's amphibians.

Is That a Fact!

◆ The continental United States is home to at least 230 amphibian species.

Section 3

Scientific Models

Modeling Dinosaurs

- In 1995, the unearthing of a rare fossil *Parasaurolophus* skull prompted a unique form of computer-based modeling. Scientists hypothesized that the cavity-filled crest atop the skull might have been used to produce a low-frequency sound that could vary in pitch. In 1997, scientists in New Mexico used computed tomography scans and powerful computers to simulate the sounds that the crest could have produced. The same techniques may be used in other engineering applications, such as predicting the strength of structural materials.

A Model Birthday

- In 1953, scientists James Watson and Francis Crick assembled the first accurate model of a DNA molecule. Their discovery of DNA's structure was celebrated as one of the key scientific achievements of the 20th century. Fifty years later, the anniversary of this event was marked by a variety of commemorative events. Art historian Martin Kemp dubbed the double helix "the Mona Lisa of modern science."

Section 4

Tools, Measurement, and Safety

Masses of Precious Gems

- The carat is a unit of mass used only for expressing the mass of precious gems. The masses of diamonds, rubies, emeralds, sapphires, aquamarines, zircons, spinels, opals, and pearls are expressed carats. The carat is equal to 4 grains. The grain is also a unit of mass, but its definition differs from country to country. For example, an English grain is approximately 64.8 g, but a French grain is approximately 53.1 g. Because this difference could cause confusion and disputes among jewelers and their customers, the metric carat was defined in 1907 as exactly 0.200 g.

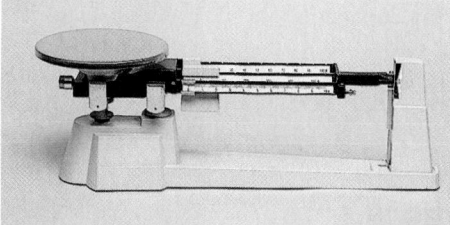

Is That a Fact!

◆ Very few countries have not officially adopted the International System of Units (SI). Among these countries are the United States, Bangladesh, and Liberia. Other countries either use the SI or are in the process of making the transition.

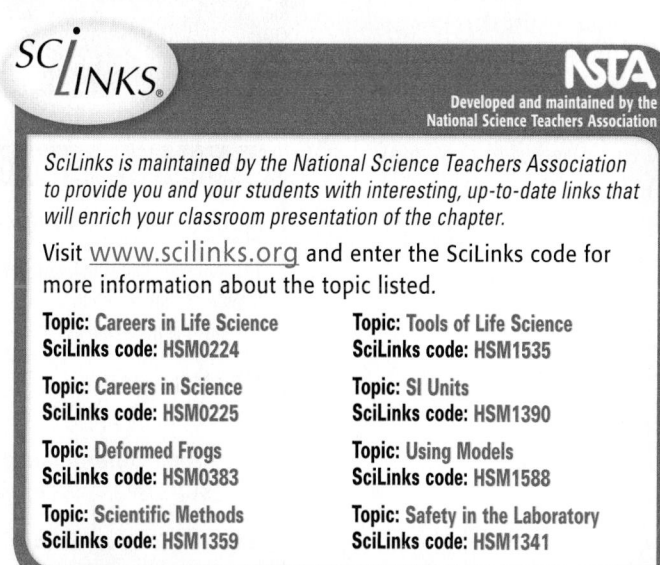

SciLinks is maintained by the National Science Teachers Association to provide you and your students with interesting, up-to-date links that will enrich your classroom presentation of the chapter.

Visit www.scilinks.org and enter the SciLinks code for more information about the topic listed.

Topic: Careers in Life Science
SciLinks code: HSM0224

Topic: Careers in Science
SciLinks code: HSM0225

Topic: Deformed Frogs
SciLinks code: HSM0383

Topic: Scientific Methods
SciLinks code: HSM1359

Topic: Tools of Life Science
SciLinks code: HSM1535

Topic: SI Units
SciLinks code: HSM1390

Topic: Using Models
SciLinks code: HSM1588

Topic: Safety in the Laboratory
SciLinks code: HSM1341

Overview

Tell students that this chapter will introduce them to the world of science around them—the world of plants and animals, volcanoes and earthquakes, television and cell phones. Students will see that science is about asking questions and using scientific methods to find answers and build knowledge. Science is also about using models and tools to investigate questions and share answers.

Assessing Prior Knowledge

Students should be familiar with the following topics:
- measurement
- basic arithmetic

Identifying Misconceptions

Students may have limited ideas about what "science" is. Even after significant amounts of direct instruction, students often maintain misconceptions, such as the idea that science is just facts to be memorized. Also, students may have prior conceptions that science is boring or hard or that it involves conducting elaborate experiments in a lab. As you begin this chapter, query students about their conceptions of science. Help students recognize that science is a body of knowledge that may change over time.

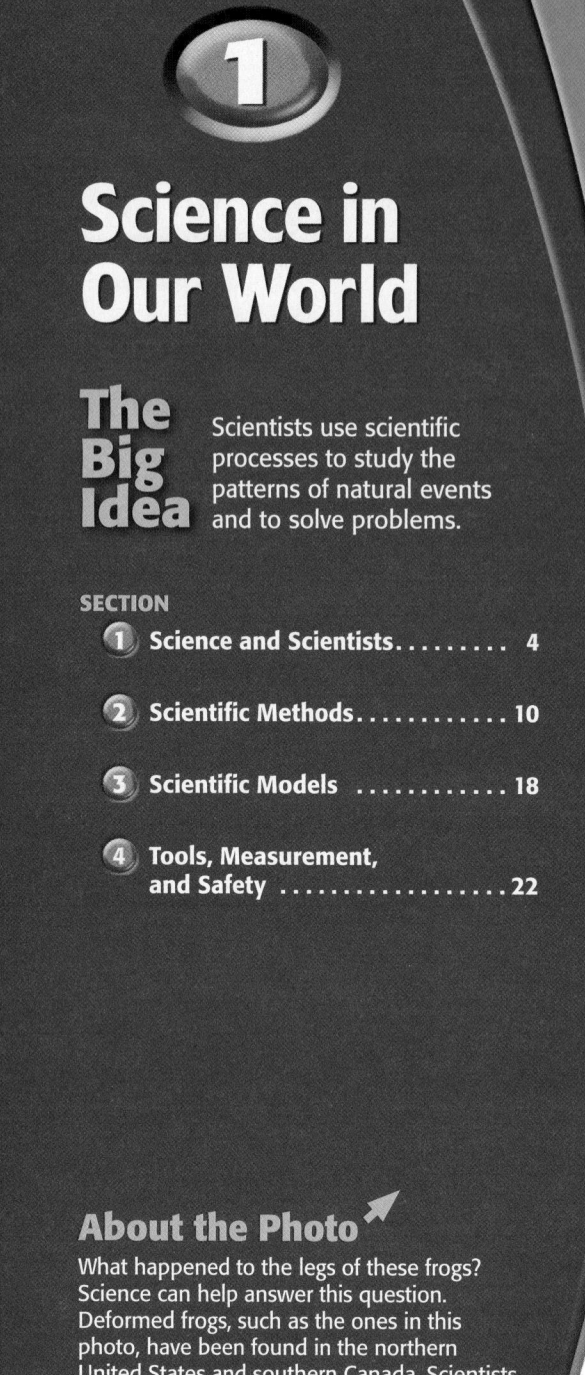

Science in Our World

The Big Idea Scientists use scientific processes to study the patterns of natural events and to solve problems.

About the Photo

What happened to the legs of these frogs? Science can help answer this question. Deformed frogs, such as the ones in this photo, have been found in the northern United States and southern Canada. Scientists and students like you have been using science to find out how frogs may develop deformities.

PRE-READING ACTIVITY

FOLDNOTES **Layered Book** Before you read the chapter, create the FoldNote entitled "Layered Book" described in the **Study Skills** section of the Appendix. Label the tabs of the layered book with "Examples of life scientists," "Scientific methods," "Scientific models," and "Tools, measurement, and safety." As you read the chapter, write information you learn about each category under the appropriate tab.

Standards Correlations

National Science Education Standards

The following codes indicate the National Science Education Standards that correlate to this chapter. The full text of the standards is at the front of the book.

Chapter Opener
HNS 2; SAI 1

Section 1 Science and Scientists
SAI 1; ST 2; SPSP 3, 4; HNS 1

Section 2 Scientific Methods
SAI 1, 2; HNS 2

Section 3 Scientific Models
UCP 2; SAI 1; SPSP 3, 4; HNS 2

Section 4 Tools, Measurement, and Safety
UCP 3; SPSP 1, HNS 3

Chapter Lab
UCP 2; SAI 1; ST 2

Chapter Review
UCP 2, 3; SAI 2; SPSP 3, 4

Science in Action
UCP 5; ST 2; SPSP 5; HNS 1

- can, coffee, 1/2–1 lb size, empty
- objects, various, small (such as rocks, nuts, washers, pencils, silverware, small toys, dried fruit, crumpled paper, or paper clips)
- sock, sport, long

Safety Caution: Cover any sharp edges around the rim of the coffee cans with tape. Be sure that the objects placed in the cans are safe to handle. Students should wear safety gloves.

Teacher's Notes: You must prepare this activity ahead of time. Fill the cans with four or five small objects. Try to choose some common and some uncommon objects that would require more than one of the senses to identify. To assemble each setup, cut the toe out of a sport sock, stretch the open toe around the open end of the coffee can, and use duct tape to secure the sock to the can.

Answers

1. Students may guess wrong based on assumptions made from the first thing they notice (such as the sound or shape of the object).

2. Students are likely to make observations using hearing, touch (including sensing weight), and perhaps smell but not sight or taste.

START-UP ACTIVITY

A Little Bit of Science

In this activity, you'll find out that you can learn about the unknown without having to see it.

Procedure

1. Your teacher will give you a **coffee can** to which a **sock** has been attached. Do not look into the can.
2. Reach through the opening in the sock. You will feel **several objects** inside the can.
3. Record observations you make about the objects by feeling them, shaking the can, and so on.
4. What do you think is in the can? List your guesses. State some reasons for your guesses.
5. Pour the contents of the can onto your desk. Compare your list with what was in the can.

Analysis

1. Did you guess the contents of the can correctly? What might have caused you to guess wrongly?
2. What observations did you make about each of the objects while they were in the can? Which of your senses did you use?

Imagine . . .

You are walking through a field with some classmates. Suddenly you notice that there are frogs hopping around all over the place! You and your classmates start catching the frogs with a net. As you lift the first frog from the net, you notice something. Its legs seem to be broken. You look at your friend's frog. It seems to be injured, too. You look at another. A frog with no eyes? Wait a minute! These frogs aren't injured. They're deformed! What are these, aliens from outer space?

exposed to some sort of chemical? The students gathered more information on the frogs and alerted local scientists. Students and scientists from all over the country are now working together to

Chapter Starter Transparency
Use this transparency to help students begin thinking about the world of life science and using scientific methods.

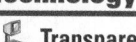

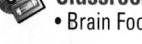

Focus

Overview

This section defines science and explains that science often starts with a question. Students learn that scientists use several types of investigations to find answers to their questions. Students also learn about some ways that science affects their lives and about some jobs that use science.

🔊 Bellringer

Have students write five questions about the natural world. (Sample answers: How do homing pigeons find their way home? Why do volcanoes erupt? Why doesn't dry ice melt?)

Ask several students to share their questions with the class.

Motivate

Group ACTiViTY — GENERAL

Scientists in Your Town
Organize the class into groups. Have the groups brainstorm about what types of people in the community use science in their jobs. Have each group choose a scientist to interview by phone or e-mail. Encourage students to consider a variety of professions. Invite a person who uses science to visit the class.
LS Verbal

What You Will Learn

- Describe three methods of investigation.
- Identify benefits of science in the world around you.
- Describe five jobs that use science.

Vocabulary
science

READING STRATEGY

Prediction Guide Before reading this section, write the title of each heading in this section. Next, under each heading, write what you think you will learn.

science the knowledge obtained by observing natural events and conditions in order to discover facts and formulate laws or principles that can be verified or tested

Science and Scientists

You are enjoying a picnic on a summer day. Crumbs from your sandwich fall to the ground, and ants carry the crumbs away. You wonder, Why do ants show up at picnics?

Congratulations! You just took one of the first steps of being a scientist. How did you do it? You observed the world around you. Then, you asked a question about your observations. And asking a question is part of what science is all about.

Start with a Question

The world around you is full of amazing things. Single-celled algae float unseen in ponds. Volcanoes erupt with explosive force. Mars may have had water in the past. And 40-ton whales glide through the oceans. These things or others, such as those shown in **Figure 1,** may lead you to ask a question. A question is the beginning of science. **Science** is the knowledge obtained by observing the natural world in order to discover facts and to formulate laws and principles that can be verified or tested.

✔ **Reading Check** What is science? (*See the Appendix for answers to Reading Checks.*)

In Your Own Neighborhood

Take a look around your home, school, and neighborhood. Often, you take things that you use or see every day for granted. But one day you might look at something in a new way. That's when a question hits you! The student in **Figure 1** didn't have to look very far to realize that he had some questions to ask.

The World and Beyond

You don't have to stop at questions about things in your neighborhood. Ask questions about atoms or galaxies, pandas and bamboo, or earthquakes. A variety of plants and animals live in a variety of places. And each place has a unique combination of rocks, soil, and water.

You can even ask questions about places other than those on Earth. Look outward to the moon, the sun, and the planets in our solar system. Beyond that, you have the rest of the universe! There are enough questions to keep scientists busy for a long time.

Figure 1 *Part of science is asking questions about the world around you.*

CHAPTER RESOURCES

Chapter Resource File

- Lesson Plan
- Directed Reading A **BASIC**
- Directed Reading B **SPECIAL NEEDS**

Technology

Transparencies
- Bellringer

Workbooks

Science Skills
- Reading a Science Textbook **GENERAL**

Answer to Reading Check

Science is the knowledge obtained by observing natural events and conditions in order to discover facts and formulate laws or principles that can be verified or tested.

Investigation: The Search for Answers

After you ask a question, it's time to look for an answer. But how do you start your investigation? Several methods may be used.

Research

You can find answers to some of your questions by doing research, as **Figure 2** shows. You can ask someone who knows a lot about the subject of your question. You can find information in textbooks, encyclopedias, and magazines. You can search on the Internet. You might read a report of an experiment that someone did. But be sure to think about the sources of your information. Use information only from reliable sources.

Observation

You can also find answers to questions by making careful observations. For example, if you want to know how spiders spin their webs, look for a web. When you find one, return to observe the spider as it spins. But be careful in making observations. Sometimes, what people expect to observe affects what they do observe. For example, most plants need light to grow. Does that mean that all plants need bright sunlight? Do some plants prefer shade? Some people might "observe" that bright light is the only answer. To test an observation, you may have to do an experiment.

Experimentation

You might answer the question about light and shade by doing a simple experiment, such as the one shown in **Figure 3.** Your research and your observations can help you plan your experiment. What should you do if your experiment needs something that is hard to get? For example, what do you do if you want to know whether a certain plant grows in space? Don't give up! Try to find results from someone else's experiment!

Figure 2 *A library is a good place to begin your search for answers.*

SCHOOL to HOME

Ask a Question

The next time you're outside, look carefully around you. Think of a science-related question that you would like to answer. Write the question in your **science journal.** Discuss with a parent which methods of investigation would be most likely to help you answer your question.

ACTIVITY

Figure 3 *This student is doing an experiment to find out whether this type of plant grows better in shade or in direct sunlight.*

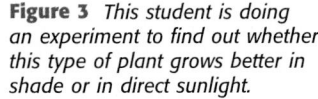
INTERNET ACTIVITY

Essay — **GENERAL**

For an internet activity related to this chapter, have students go to **go.hrw.com** and type in the keyword **HL5LIVW.**

SCIENCE HUMOR

Q: What's the difference between a friendly dog and a marine biologist?

A: One's a tail wagger; the other's a whale tagger!

Spreading Disease Before class, make a phenolphthalein solution (dissolve 2 g in 100 mL of 95% ethanol, then add 100 mL of water) and a sodium hydroxide solution (dissolve 20 g in 1 L of water). Prepare a test tube and a plastic eyedropper for each student. Fill one of the test tubes halfway with sodium hydroxide solution and all the rest halfway with water. Have students wear safety goggles, a lab apron, and protective gloves for this activity. Tell students that one classmate is "infected." Have students exchange 10 drops of the liquid in their test tube with four different partners. Place one drop of phenolphthalein in each test tube. Anyone whose liquid turns pink is now "infected."

Disposal Information: Add 0.1 M HCl until the pH is between 5 and 9; pour down the drain. LS Intrapersonal

Using the Figure — GENERAL

Recycling Have students measure the mass of an empty aluminum soft-drink can. (The mass of one can should be close to 14.7 g.) Have students estimate the number of cans the class uses in 30 days. Finally, have students calculate the amount of each resource shown in **Figure 5** that would be saved by recycling these cans. (Sample answer: If each of 25 students uses 60 cans in 30 days, the resources saved are 0.0864 metric tons of chemical products, 302.4 kWh of energy, and 0.0864 metric tons of ore.) LS Logical

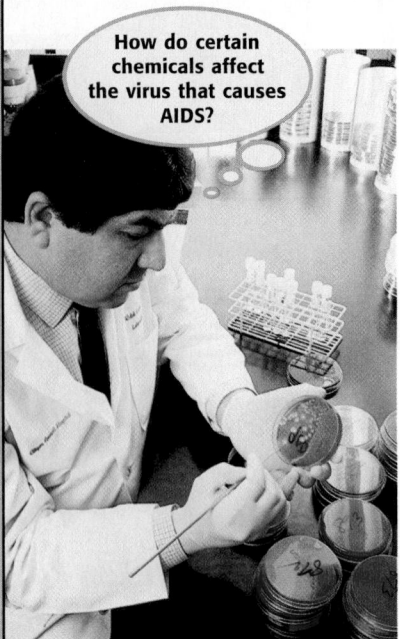

Figure 4 *Abdul Lakhani studies AIDS to find a cure for the disease.*

Why Ask Questions?

Although scientists cannot answer every question immediately, they do find some interesting answers. Do any of the answers really matter? Absolutely! As you study science, you will see how science affects you and society around you.

Fighting Diseases

Polio is a disease that can cause paralysis by affecting the brain and nerves. Do you know anyone who has had polio? You probably don't. But in 1952, polio infected 58,000 Americans. Fortunately, vaccines developed in 1955 and 1956 have eliminated polio in the United States. In fact, the virus that causes polio has been wiped out in most of the world.

Today, scientists are searching for cures for diseases such as mad cow disease, tuberculosis, and acquired immune deficiency syndrome (AIDS). The scientist in **Figure 4** is learning more about AIDS, which kills millions of people every year.

Saving Resources

Science also helps answer the question, How can we make resources last longer? Recycling is one answer. Think about the last time that you recycled an aluminum can. By recycling that can, you saved more than just the aluminum, as **Figure 5** shows. Using science, people have developed more-efficient methods and better equipment for recycling aluminum, paper, steel, glass, and even some plastics. In this way, science helps make resources last longer.

Figure 5 **Resources Saved Through Recycling**

Compared with producing aluminum from its ore, recycling 1 metric ton (1.1 tons) of aluminum:

 produces 95% less air pollution

 saves 4 metric tons (4.4 tons) of ore

 produces 4 metric tons (4.4 tons) fewer chemical products

 uses 14,000 kWh less energy

 produces 97% less water pollution

Cultural Awareness ADVANCED

Fighting Disease Shisaburo Kitasato, born in 1852, was a Japanese scientist who was one of the first to discover the bacteria that cause tetanus, diphtheria, and bubonic plague. Kitasato developed a procedure to grow pure tetanus bacteria. This procedure enabled him to develop treatments for tetanus infections and led him to discover techniques and materials that he would later use to fight diphtheria and the plague.

WEIRD SCIENCE

In an attempt to help endangered animals, researchers at the Texas A&M Reproductive Sciences Laboratory in College Station, Texas, have begun Project Noah's Ark. This project collects the eggs, sperm, embryos, and DNA of endangered animals and stores them in liquid nitrogen.

Answering Society's Questions

Sometimes, society faces a question that does not seem to have an immediate answer. For example, at one time, the question of how to reduce air pollution did not have any obvious, reasonable answers. The millions of people who depended on their cars could not just stop driving. As the problem of air pollution became more important to people, scientists developed different technologies to address it. For example, one source of air pollution is exhaust from cars. Through science, people have developed cleaner-burning gasoline. People have even developed new ways to clean up exhaust before it leaves the tailpipe of a car!

Reading Check How can society influence the types of technologies that are developed?

Scientists All Around You

Believe it or not, scientists work in many different places. If you think about it, any person who asks questions and looks for answers could be called a scientist! Keep reading to learn about just a few people who use science in their jobs.

Zoologist

A *zoologist* (zoh AHL uh jist) is a person who studies the lives of animals. Dale Miquelle, shown in **Figure 6,** is part of a team of Russian and American zoologists studying the Siberian tiger. The tigers have almost become extinct after being hunted and losing their homes. By learning about the tigers' living space and food needs, zoologists hope to make a plan that will help the tigers survive better in the wild.

Figure 6 *To learn how much land a Siberian tiger covers, Dale Miquelle tracks a tiger that is wearing a radio-transmitting collar.*

Science Involves Processes Ask students how the processes of asking questions, doing research, making observations, and doing experiments work together to increase scientific knowledge. You may need to remind students of the definition of *science*. LS Logical

Quiz — GENERAL

1. What are three ways that a scientist can investigate a question? (research, observation, and experimentation)

2. Why is science important to you and the world around you? (Science helps save lives, resources, and the environment.)

3. What do you think is the most important technological development in the last 10 years? Explain why you think so. (Answers may vary. The key is how the student connects the technological development to a need in society.)

Alternative Assessment — BASIC

Animal Aid Have students research what is being done to preserve animal habitats in their area. Have students also find out what they can do to promote animal preservation. Students can determine what types of scientists are involved in preservation efforts. Have students make a poster or do a presentation to show what they learned. LS Verbal

Figure 7 *This geochemist may work outdoors when collecting rock samples from the field. Then, he may work indoors as he analyzes the samples in his laboratory.*

Geochemist

Some scientists work outdoors most of the time. Other scientists spend much of their time in the laboratory. A geochemist (JEE oh KEM ist), such as the one shown in **Figure 7,** may work in both places. A *geochemist* is a person who specializes in the chemistry of rocks, minerals, and soil.

Geochemists determine the economic value of these materials. They also try to find out what the environment was like when these materials formed and what has happened to the materials since they first formed.

Mechanic

Do you have a machine that needs repairs? Call a mechanic, such as Gene Webb in **Figure 8.** Mechanics work on everything from cars to the space shuttle. Mechanics use science to solve problems. Mechanics must find answers to questions about why a machine is not working. Then, they must find a way to make it work. Mechanics also think of ways to improve the machine, to make it work faster or more efficiently.

Figure 8 *A mechanic can help keep a car's engine running smoothly.*

Oceanographer

An *oceanographer* studies the ocean. Some oceanographers study waves and ocean currents. Others study plants and animals that live in the ocean. Still others study the ocean floor, including how it forms.

While studying the ocean floor, oceanographers discovered black smokers. Black smokers are cracks where hot water (around 300°C!) from beneath Earth's surface comes up. These vents in the ocean floor are home to some strange animals, including red-tipped tube worms and blind white crabs.

INCLUSION Strategies

• **Gifted and Talented**
Ask students to extend their understanding of polio and other diseases by researching these questions:

• How does polio affect the body?

• When was polio common?

• Why did people stop getting polio?

• What other diseases used to be more serious threats than they are now?
LS Logical

CONNECTION ACTIVITY
Language Arts — BASIC

"The Tyger" Have students read William Blake's poem "The Tyger," and read the poem aloud to the class. Ask students what the author of the poem thinks about tigers and what comes to students' minds when they read the poem. Have students write a poem about their favorite animal. LS Verbal

Volcanologist

If black smokers aren't hot enough for you, perhaps you would like to become a volcanologist (VAHL kuh NAHL uh jist). A *volcanologist* studies one of Earth's most interesting processes—volcanoes. The volcanologist shown in **Figure 9** is photographing lava flowing from Mt. Etna, a volcano in Italy. Mt. Etna's lava may reach temperatures of 1,050°C. By learning more about volcanoes, volcanologists hope to get better at predicting when a volcano will erupt. Being able to predict eruptions would help save lives.

 **Reading Check** What does a volcanologist do?

Figure 9 *Volcanologists gain a better understanding of the inside of the Earth by studying the makeup of lava.*

SECTION Review

Summary

- Science is a process of gathering knowledge about the natural world by making observations and asking questions.
- Science begins by asking a question.
- Even if science cannot answer the question right away, the answers that scientists find may be very important.
- A question may lead to a scientific investigation, including research, observations, and experimentation.
- Science can help save lives, fight diseases, save resources, and protect the environment.
- A variety of people may become scientists for a variety of reasons.

Using Key Terms

1. In your own words, write a definition for the term *science*.

Understanding Key Ideas

2. A zoologist might study any of the following EXCEPT
   a. shellfish living in ponds.
   b. the reason that mole rats live in large groups underground.
   c. environmental threats to sea turtles.
   d. rocks and minerals in the Painted Desert.

3. Describe five careers that use science.

4. How are observation and experimentation different?

5. How may what people expect to observe affect what they do observe? How can people avoid this problem?

Math Skills

6. Students in a science class collected 50 frogs from a pond. They found that 15 of the frogs had serious deformities. What percentage of the frogs had deformities?

Critical Thinking

7. **Making Inferences** An ad for deluxe garbage bags says that the bags are 30% stronger than regular garbage bags. Describe how science can help you find out if this claim is true.

8. **Identifying Relationships** Make a list of three things that you consider to be a problem in society. Give an example of how new technology might solve these problems.

9. **Applying Concepts** Look at Figure 9. Write five questions about what you see. Describe how science might help you answer your questions. Share your questions with your classmates.

SCILINKS
Developed and maintained by the National Science Teachers Association

For a variety of links related to this chapter, go to www.scilinks.org

Topic: Careers in Science
SciLinks code: HSM0244

CHAPTER RESOURCES

Chapter Resource File
- Section Quiz GENERAL
- Section Review GENERAL
- Vocabulary and Section Summary GENERAL

Focus

Overview

This section introduces scientific methods used by scientists through a case study of an actual investigation of deformed frogs. The section also demonstrates the development of testable hypotheses and the importance of sharing information among scientists.

 **Bellringer**

Ask students to write a brief response to this question:

"Which is more important, imagination or knowledge?"

Have students share their responses and then debate this question. Raise the point that many important scientists were known for their original thinking and sometimes faced resistance to their new ideas.

Motivate

ACTIVITY ———— GENERAL

Now You See It As an exercise in observation, display a collection of assorted shapes on the overhead projector. Allow the students to look at the shapes for 15 seconds. Turn the projector off, and have the students spend 5 minutes describing or drawing as many of the shapes as they can in their **science journal.** **LS** Visual/Intrapersonal

What You Will Learn

- Explain why scientists use scientific methods.
- Determine the appropriate design of a controlled experiment.
- Use information in tables and graphs to analyze experimental results.
- Explain how scientific knowledge can change.

Vocabulary
scientific methods
hypothesis
controlled experiment
variable

READING STRATEGY

Reading Organizer As you read this section, make a flowchart of the possible steps in scientific methods.

scientific methods a series of steps followed to solve problems

Scientific Methods

Imagine that your class is on a field trip to a wildlife refuge. You discover several deformed frogs. You wonder what could be causing the frogs' deformities.

A group of students from Le Sueur, Minnesota, actually made this discovery! By making observations and asking questions about the observations, the students used scientific methods.

What Are Scientific Methods?

When scientists observe the natural world, they often think of a question or problem. But scientists don't just guess at answers. They use scientific methods. **Scientific methods** are the ways in which scientists follow steps to answer questions and solve problems. The steps used for all investigations are the same. But the order in which the steps are followed may vary, as shown in **Figure 1.** Scientists may use all of the steps or just some of the steps during an investigation. They may even repeat some of the steps. The order depends on what works best to answer the question. No matter where scientists work or what questions they try to answer, all scientists have two things in common. They are curious about the natural world, and they use similar methods to investigate it.

Reading Check What are scientific methods? (*See the Appendix for answers to Reading Checks.*)

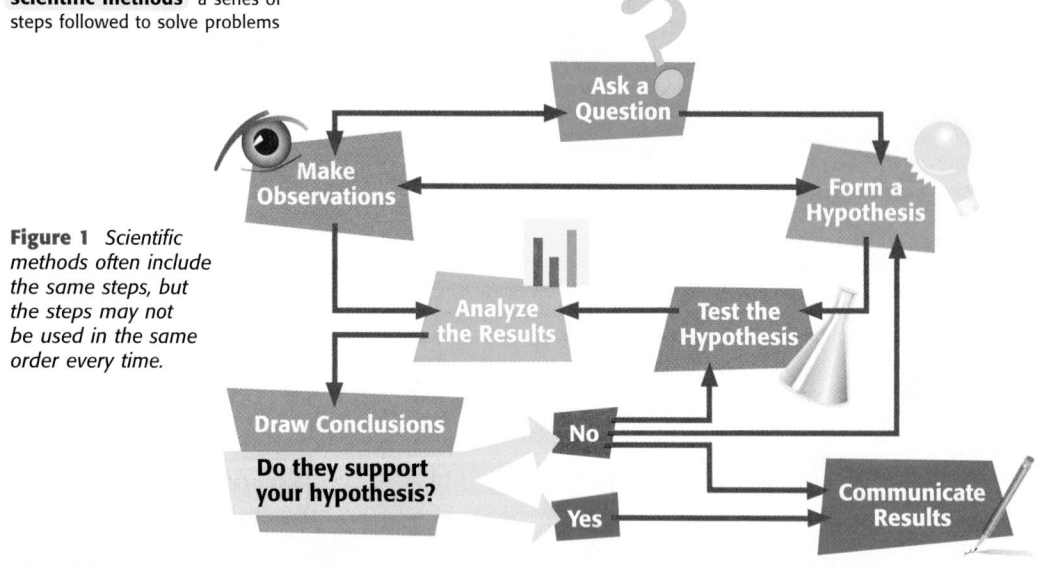

Figure 1 *Scientific methods often include the same steps, but the steps may not be used in the same order every time.*

Make Observations · Ask a Question · Form a Hypothesis · Test the Hypothesis · Analyze the Results · Draw Conclusions · Do they support your hypothesis? · No · Yes · Communicate Results

CHAPTER RESOURCES

Chapter Resource File

- **Lesson Plan**
- **Directed Reading A** BASIC
- **Directed Reading B** SPECIAL NEEDS

Technology

Transparencies
- Bellringer
- Scientific Methods

Answer to Reading Check

a series of steps used by scientists to solve problems

Ask a Question

Have you ever observed something out of the ordinary or difficult to explain? Such an observation usually raises questions. For example, about the deformed frogs you might ask, "Could something in the water be causing the frog deformities?" Looking for answers may include making more observations.

Make Observations

After the students in Minnesota realized something was wrong with the frogs, they decided to make additional, careful observations, as shown in **Figure 2.** They counted the number of deformed frogs and the number of normal frogs they caught. They also photographed the frogs, took measurements, and wrote a thorough description of each frog.

In addition, the students collected data on other organisms living in the pond. They also conducted many tests on the pond water and measured things such as the level of acidity. The students carefully recorded their data and observations.

Accurate Observations

Any information that you gather through your senses is an observation. Observations can take many forms. They may be measurements of length, volume, time, speed, or loudness. They may describe the color or shape of an organism. Or they may record the behavior of organisms in an area. The range of observations that a scientist can make is endless. But no matter what observations reveal, they are useful only if they are accurately made and recorded. Scientists use many standard tools and methods to make and record observations. Examples of these tools are shown in **Figure 3.**

Figure 2 *Making careful observations is often the first step in an investigation.*

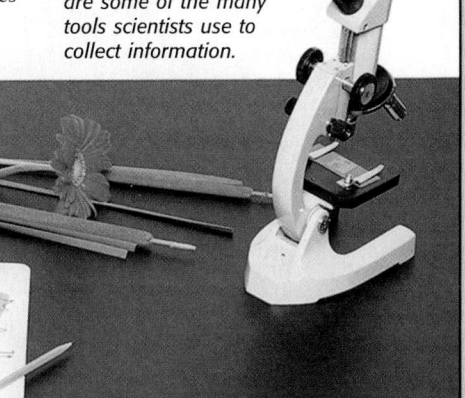

Figure 3 *Microscopes, rulers, and thermometers are some of the many tools scientists use to collect information.*

WEIRD SCIENCE

In 1786, Luigi Galvani noted that the legs of a dead frog jerked when he touched them with a brass hook. The hook created a small electric current, which stimulated the nerve. The nerve in turn stimulated the muscle. With these observations, Galvani helped establish the fields of neurophysiology and clinical neurology.

BRAIN FOOD

Albert Einstein said, "Imagination is more important than knowledge. Knowledge is limited. Imagination encircles the world." He also said, "Logic will get you from A to B. Imagination will take you everywhere."

Demonstration — GENERAL

Frog Call Scientists who study frogs often locate the frogs by their calls. The northern leopard frog, which inhabits the pond that was studied by the Minnesota students, has quite a peculiar call—a mixture of grunts, snores, and squeaks that sounds like a wet palm being rubbed across an inflated balloon. Ask a volunteer to use a balloon to demonstrate the frog's call for the class.
LS Auditory

Answer to Reading Check

A hypothesis is testable if an experiment can be designed to test the hypothesis.

Discussion — BASIC

Testing Hypotheses Answers to questions in many areas of life can be found by forming and testing a hypothesis. Have students form a hypothesis based on the following observation:

The black pavement is hotter than the concrete sidewalk.

Ask students how such a hypothesis might be tested. (Sample hypothesis: A dark surface heats up under the sun more quickly than a light surface. Sample test: Place dark and light paper in sunlight at the same time and measure temperature over time.)
LS Verbal/Logical • English Language Learners

CONNECTION TO Environmental Science

WRITING SKILL **Minnesota's Deformed Frogs**
Deformed frogs were first noticed in Minnesota in 1995. In 1996, the Minnesota Pollution Control Agency (MPCA) began studying the problem. It funded and coordinated studies searching for the causes of the deformities. Find out what the MPCA is doing about the deformed frogs today, and write a short summary of what the MPCA has discovered.

hypothesis an explanation that is based on prior scientific research or observations and that can be tested

---

Form a Hypothesis

After asking questions and making observations, scientists may form a hypothesis. A **hypothesis** (hie PAHTH uh sis) is a possible explanation or answer to a question. A good hypothesis is based on observation and can be tested. When scientists form hypotheses, they think logically and creatively and consider what they already know.

To be useful, a hypothesis must be testable. A hypothesis is testable if an experiment can be designed to test the hypothesis. Yet if a hypothesis is not testable, it is not always wrong. An untestable hypothesis is simply one that cannot be supported or disproved. Sometimes, it may be impossible to gather enough observations to test a hypothesis.

Scientists may form different hypotheses for the same problem. In the case of the Minnesota frogs, scientists formed the hypotheses shown in **Figure 4.** Were any of these explanations correct? To find out, scientists had to test each hypothesis.

✓ **Reading Check** What makes a hypothesis testable?

Figure 4
More than one hypothesis can be made for a single question.

> *Hypothesis 1:*
> The deformities were caused by one or more chemical pollutants in the water.
>
> *Hypothesis 2:*
> The deformities were caused by attacks from parasites or other frogs.
>
> *Hypothesis 3:*
> The deformities were caused by an increase in exposure to ultraviolet light from the sun.

Answer to Connection to Environmental Science

Answers may vary. Students should find the MPCA site on the Internet and should be able to write a brief history of Minnesota's deformed frogs. Although the MPCA funded several studies of the frogs in the 1990s, it is no longer doing so. Students may also find updated information (from 2001) at the USGS "Malformed Frogs" Web site. The final conclusion appears to be that several factors in the waters of Minnesota caused the frogs' deformities.

ACTIVITY — ADVANCED

PORTFOLIO **Test a Hypothesis** Encourage students to come up with a very simple hypothesis that they can easily test themselves. Require students to have you approve the design of their experiment before they begin. **LS** Logical/Intrapersonal

Predictions

Before scientists can test a hypothesis, they must first make predictions. A prediction is a statement of cause and effect that can be used to set up a test for a hypothesis. Predictions are usually stated in an if-then format, as shown in **Figure 5.**

Figure 5 lists the predictions made for the hypotheses shown in **Figure 4.** More than one prediction may be made for each hypothesis. After predictions are made, scientists can conduct experiments to see which predictions, if any, prove to be true and support the hypotheses.

Figure 5 *More than one prediction may be made for a single hypothesis.*

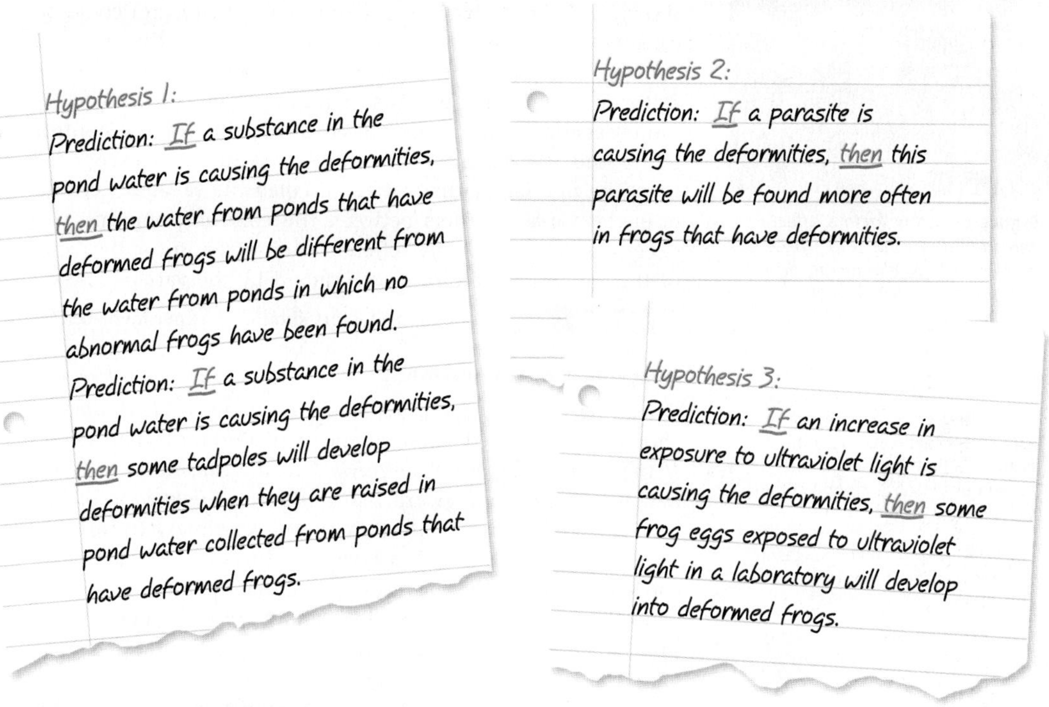

Hypothesis 1:
Prediction: If a substance in the pond water is causing the deformities, then the water from ponds that have deformed frogs will be different from the water from ponds in which no abnormal frogs have been found.
Prediction: If a substance in the pond water is causing the deformities, then some tadpoles will develop deformities when they are raised in pond water collected from ponds that have deformed frogs.
Hypothesis 2:
Prediction: If a parasite is causing the deformities, then this parasite will be found more often in frogs that have deformities.
Hypothesis 3:
Prediction: If an increase in exposure to ultraviolet light is causing the deformities, then some frog eggs exposed to ultraviolet light in a laboratory will develop into deformed frogs.

CONNECTION TO Language Arts

WRITING SKILL **"Leading doctors say . . ."** Suppose that you and a friend see an ad for a cold remedy on TV. According to the ad, "Leading doctors recommend this product for their patients." Then, a famous actor comes on and says that he or she uses the product, too. Write a dialogue of the debate you might have with your friend about whether these claims are believable.

MISCONCEPTION ALERT

It Never Fails Students may believe that an experiment is a failure if the hypothesis is not supported by the results. Remind them that the point of conducting experiments is to investigate the hypothesis and to learn from the data. Often, much can be learned when an experiment disproves a hypothesis or creates new questions. Experiments to advance science would be pointless if the outcome were known.

Answer to Connection to Language Arts

Answers may vary. Students' dialogues should include a discussion of topics such as who the doctors are, what they are "leaders" of, what relationship (if any) they have with the drug manufacturer, and what exactly this remedy does. Students should question what expertise the actor has to talk about medication, what the actor actually says about the product, and why a drug company would hire an actor to sell medicines.

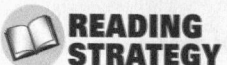

READING STRATEGY — BASIC

Roots of Words Have students use a dictionary to find the definition and root origins of the word *hypothesis*. Have volunteers write on the board the information that they find. Small groups of students could then compile lists of words that contain the word roots *hypo-* or *-thesis* as an alternative or additional activity. Example words include *hypothermia, hypoallergenic, synthesis, prosthesis,* and *photosynthesis.* English Language Learners

LS Verbal/Auditory

ACTIVITY — GENERAL

Writing **Writing Predictions** Have students practice writing predictions as "if-then" statements. Some questions that they can consider when writing their predictions are the following:

- Is an unknown liquid water or rubbing alcohol? (Sample prediction: If the liquid is rubbing alcohol, then it will have an odor.)
- Can plants sense which way is up? (Sample prediction: If the plant is laid on its side for several days, then the stem will begin to curve upward.)
- Do cardinals prefer sunflower seeds to millet? (Sample prediction: If cardinals are offered both sunflower seeds and millet and they prefer sunflower seeds, then they will eat the sunflower seeds first.)

LS Verbal/Logical English Language Learners

Homework — GENERAL

Writing **Investigate Your Area** Have students observe the daily activities in and around a local pond, woods, or garden over a period of several weeks. Tell students to record their observations in their science journal. PORTFOLIO

LS Visual/Intrapersonal

Discussion — GENERAL

Are We Next? At the forefront of the deformed-frog situation are these concerns: Is human health at risk? Do the malformed frogs signal a widespread environmental problem?

Discuss these concerns with students, and pose this question: "What steps can scientists take to find out whether humans are also at risk?" **LS** Verbal

Using the Table — BASIC

Experimental Factors Have students study the table on this page. Ask them the following questions:

- What is the only factor that differs between the control group and the experimental groups? (the variable, which is exposure time to UV light)

- What would happen if the temperature varied for each of the groups? (The experiment would not be controlled, because there is more than one variable.)

- How should the experiment be altered if we wanted to test the effect of temperature? (Have a different temperature of water for each group, but do not expose any of them to UV light. Leave the other factors the same.) **LS** Verbal/Logical

Answer to Reading Check

only one

Figure 6 *Many factors affect this tadpole in the wild. These factors include chemicals, light, temperature, and parasites.*

controlled experiment an experiment that tests only one factor at a time by using a comparison of a control group with an experimental group

variable a factor that changes in an experiment in order to test a hypothesis

Test the Hypothesis

After scientists make a prediction, they test the hypothesis. Scientists try to design experiments that will clearly show whether a particular factor caused an observed outcome. In an experiment, a *factor* is anything that can influence the experiment's outcome. Factors can be anything from temperature to the type of organism being studied.

Under Control

Scientists studying the frogs in Minnesota observed many factors that affect the development of frogs in the wild, as shown in **Figure 6.** But it was hard to tell which factor could be causing the deformities. To sort factors out, scientists perform controlled experiments. A **controlled experiment** tests only one factor at a time and consists of a control group and one or more experimental groups. All of the factors for the control group and the experimental groups are the same except for one. The one factor that differs is called the **variable.** Because only the variable differs between the control group and the experimental groups, any differences observed in the outcome of the experiment are probably caused by the variable.

✔ **Reading Check** How many factors should an experiment test?

Designing an Experiment

Designing a good experiment requires planning. Every factor should be considered. Examine the prediction for Hypothesis 3: *If an increase in exposure to ultraviolet light is causing the deformities, then some frog eggs exposed to ultraviolet light in a laboratory will develop into deformed frogs.* An experiment to test this hypothesis is summarized in **Table 1.** In this case, the variable is the length of time the eggs are exposed to ultraviolet (UV) light. All other factors, such as the temperature of the water, are the same in the control group and in the experimental groups.

Table 1 Experiment to Test Effect of UV Light on Frogs				
	Control factors			**Variable**
Group	**Kind of frog**	**Number of Eggs**	**Temperature of water**	**UV light exposure**
#1 (control)	leopard frog	100	25°C	0 days
#2 (experimental)	leopard frog	100	25°C	15 days
#3 (experimental)	leopard frog	100	25°C	24 days

Is That a Fact!

Evidence suggests that UV light levels are highest in late spring and early summer, the time of year when Minnesota's frog population is laying eggs. Such evidence points to a need for UV experiments in natural environments at various times of the year.

MISCONCEPTION ALERT

Exciting Experiments Students often assume that worthwhile experiments should be dazzling—something must explode or change color or sizzle with electric discharges. However, as the frog-egg example shows, many good experiments are not so dramatic. In addition, they often take time to yield results. A point to emphasize is that anyone can perform experiments.

Figure 7 · UV Light Experiment

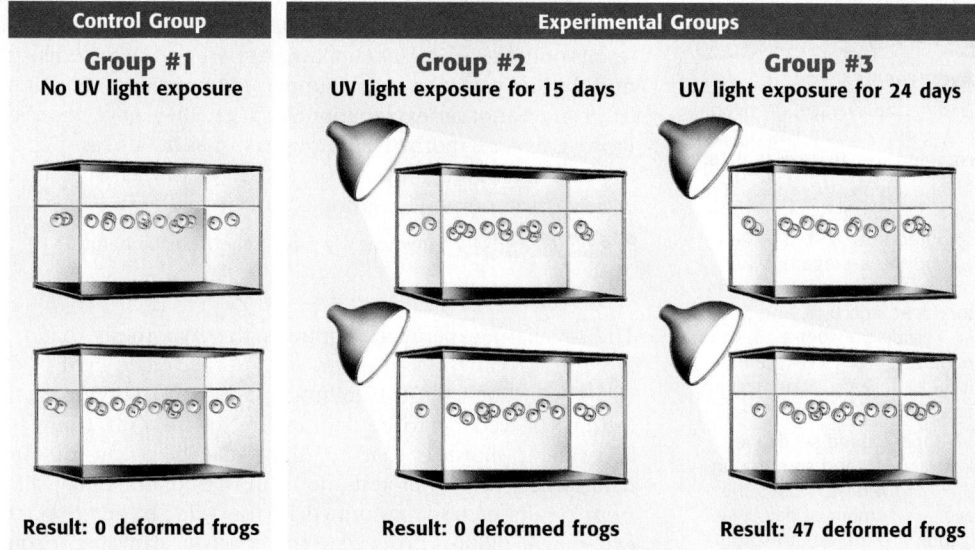

Control Group	Experimental Groups	
Group #1 No UV light exposure	**Group #2** UV light exposure for 15 days	**Group #3** UV light exposure for 24 days
Result: 0 deformed frogs	**Result: 0 deformed frogs**	**Result: 47 deformed frogs**

Collecting Data

Figure 7 shows the experimental setup to test Hypothesis 3. As **Table 1** shows, there are 100 eggs in each group. Scientists always try to test many individuals. They want to be sure that differences between control and experimental groups are caused by the variable and not by differences between individuals. The larger the groups are, the smaller the effect of a difference between individual frogs will be. The larger the groups are, the more likely it is that the variable is responsible for any changes and the more accurate the data collected are likely to be.

Scientists test a result by repeating the experiment. If an experiment gives the same results each time, scientists are more certain about the variable's effect on the outcome. Scientists keep clear, accurate, honest records of their data so that other scientists can repeat the experiment and verify the results.

Analyze the Results

After scientists finish their tests, they must organize their data and analyze the results. Scientists may organize data in a table or a graph. The data collected from the UV light experiment are shown in the bar graph in **Figure 8.** Analyzing the results helps scientists explain and focus on the effect of the variable. For example, the graph shows that the length of UV exposure has an effect on the development of frog deformities.

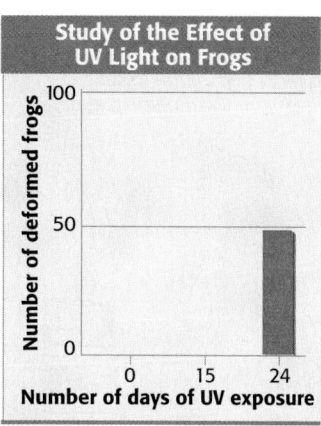

Figure 8 *This graph shows that 24 days of UV exposure had an effect on frog deformities, while less exposure had no effect.*

Reteaching — **BASIC**

Experimental Setup Have students propose other experiments that scientists could use to test the effect of UV light on frogs. Discuss how such an experiment might be set up. **LS** Logical/Verbal

Quiz — **GENERAL**

1. Why is it important to have a control group when doing an experiment? (Data from the experimental groups are compared with data from the control group to see the effect caused by changes to the variable.)

2. Why should a hypothesis be testable? (If a hypothesis is not testable, there is no way to support it or to show it to be wrong.)

Alternative Assessment — **ADVANCED**

Using Scientific Methods Have students use scientific methods to answer a simple, everyday question. The students should set up experiments, keep careful records, and then summarize their results and present them to the class. **LS** Logical/Intrapersonal

MATH PRACTICE

Averages

Finding the average, or mean, of a group of numbers is a common way to analyze data.

For example, three seeds were kept at 25°C and sprouted in 8, 8, and 5 days. To find the average number of days that it took the seeds to sprout, add 8, 8, and 5 and divide the sum by 3, the number of subjects (seeds). It took these seeds an average of 7 days to sprout.

Suppose three seeds were kept at 30°C and sprouted in 6, 5, and 4 days. What's the average number of days that it took these seeds to sprout?

Figure 9 *This student scientist is communicating the results of his investigation at a science fair.*

CONNECTION ACTIVITY Math — **BASIC**

Averages Remind students how to calculate the average (or *mean*) of a group of numbers by using the following formula:

*average =
sum of all data points ÷
total number of data points*

Emphasize that averages are often used to summarize or look for trends in data. Have students answer the following questions:

Draw Conclusions

After scientists have analyzed the data from several experiments, they can draw conclusions. They decide whether the results of the experiments support a hypothesis. When scientists find that a hypothesis is not supported by the tests, they must try to find another explanation for what they have observed. Proving that a hypothesis is wrong is just as helpful as supporting it. Why? Either way, the scientist has learned something, which is the purpose of using scientific methods.

✓ **Reading Check** How can a wrong hypothesis be helpful?

Is It the Answer?

The UV light experiment supports the hypothesis that frog deformities can be caused by exposure to UV light. Does this mean that UV light definitely caused frogs living in the Minnesota wetland to be deformed? No, the only thing this experiment shows is that UV light may be a cause of frog deformities. Results of tests done in a laboratory may differ from results of tests performed in the wild. In addition, the experiment did not investigate the effects of parasites or some other substance on the frogs. In fact, many scientists now think that more than one factor could be causing the deformities.

Sometimes, similar investigations or experiments give different results. For example, another research team may have had results that did not support the UV light hypothesis. In such a case, scientists must work together to decide if the differences in the results are scientifically significant. Often, making that decision takes more experiments and more evidence.

Communicate Results

Scientists form a global community. After scientists complete their investigations, they communicate their results to other scientists. The student in **Figure 9** is explaining the results of a science project.

Scientists regularly share their results for several reasons. First, other scientists may then repeat the experiments to see if they get the same results. Second, the information can be considered by other scientists with similar interests. The scientists can then compare hypotheses and form consistent explanations. New data may strengthen existing hypotheses or show that the hypotheses need to be altered. There are many paths from observations and questions to communicating results.

1. Four students ran a 100 m race in the following times: 15 s, 19 s, 21 s, and 25 s. What was the average time? ([15 + 19 + 21 + 25] ÷ 4 = 20 s)

2. Three children were picking berries. One picked 51 berries, the second picked 64 berries, and the third picked 68 berries. What was the average number of berries picked? ([51 + 64 + 68] ÷ 3 = 61 berries)

LS Logical

English Language Learners

SECTION Review

Summary

- Scientific methods are the ways in which scientists follow steps to answer questions and solve problems.
- Any information you gather through your senses is an observation. Observations often lead to the formation of questions and hypotheses.
- A hypothesis is a possible explanation or answer to a question. A well-formed hypothesis is testable by experiment.
- A controlled experiment tests only one factor at a time and consists of a control group and one or more experimental groups.
- After testing a hypothesis, scientists analyze the results and draw conclusions about whether the hypothesis is supported.
- Communicating results allows others to check the results, add to their knowledge, and design new experiments.

Using Key Terms

1. Use the following terms in the same sentence: *hypothesis, controlled experiment,* and *variable.*

Understanding Key Ideas

2. The steps of scientific methods
   a. are exactly the same in every investigation.
   b. must be used in the same order every time.
   c. are not used in the same order every time.
   d. always end with a conclusion.

3. What is the appropriate design of a controlled experiment?

4. What causes scientific knowledge to change?

Math Skills

5. Calculate the average of the following values: 4, 5, 6, 6, and 9.

Critical Thinking

6. **Analyzing Methods** Why was UV light chosen to be the variable in the frog experiment?

7. **Analyzing Processes** Why are there many ways to follow the steps of scientific methods?

8. **Making Inferences** Why might two scientists working on the same problem draw different conclusions?

9. **Making Inferences** Why do scientists use scientific methods?

Interpreting Graphics

10. The table below shows how long it takes for bacteria to double. Plot the information on a graph. Put temperature on the *x*-axis and the time to double on the *y*-axis. Do not graph values for which there is no growth. At what temperature do the bacteria multiply the fastest?

Temperature (°C)	Time to double (min)
10	130
20	60
25	40
30	29
37	17
40	19
45	32
50	no growth

11. What would happen if you changed the scale of the graph by using values of 0 to 300 minutes on the *y*-axis? How might that change affect your interpretation of the data?

Developed and maintained by the National Science Teachers Association

For a variety of links related to this chapter, go to www.scilinks.org

Topic: Scientific Methods; Deformed Frogs
SciLinks code: HSM1359; HSM0383

---

5. $[(4 + 5 + 6 + 6 + 9) \div 5]$
   $= [30 \div 5] = 6$

6. Sample answer: Because the scientists were trying to test the hypothesis that UV light causes deformities, UV light was the factor that needed to be varied—the variable.

7. Sample answer: because sometimes scientists need to go back and change a step and sometimes not every step is important to an investigation

8. Sample answer: They may have tested different variables, and other factors in the control and experimental groups may have differed.

9. Sample answer: Scientists use scientific methods because one or more of the steps are used in every experiment, which helps ensure that experimental results are accurate.

10. See sample graph below. The temperature at which bacteria multiply most quickly is 37°C.

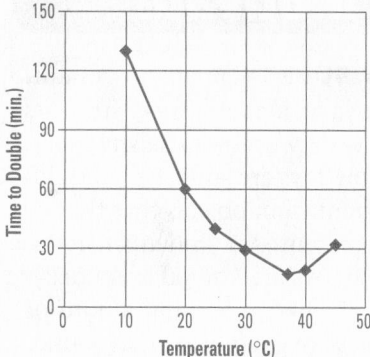

11. Data on the graph would not change, but the shape of the curve would change, which might cause errors.

Answers to Section Review

1. Sample answer: One way to test a hypothesis is to conduct a controlled experiment that tests only one variable.

2. c

3. A controlled experiment is properly designed if it tests only one factor at a time and it consists of a control group and one or more experimental groups.

4. Scientific knowledge changes because scientists conduct experiments to test new hypotheses. Their results build upon existing knowledge.

CHAPTER RESOURCES

Chapter Resource File

- Section Quiz `GENERAL`
- Section Review `GENERAL`
- Vocabulary and Section Summary `GENERAL`
- Reinforcement Worksheet `BASIC`
- Critical Thinking `ADVANCED`

Workbooks

Math Skills for Science
- What Is an Average? `BASIC`

Focus

Overview

This section discusses the role of models in science and defines three types of models. Students learn that models are important tools despite their limitations. Students learn about theories and laws and the differences between theories and laws.

 Bellringer

Ask students to write answers to the following questions:

- What is a model?
- Name several types of models.
- What models have you used?

LS Verbal

Motivate

Discussion —————— GENERAL

Toys as Models Show students a variety of toys. Ask students how toys are similar to and different from objects that the toys represent. Ask students whether the toys are limited as models, and whether any limitations of toys are good or bad. Introduce the idea of scale models. (The toys are similar to the objects that they represent, but toys are usually smaller. A limitation of toys is that they do not act like the objects represented. The limitations may be good or bad—a teddy bear won't hurt you, but you can't drive a toy car to the store.) **LS** Verbal

What You Will Learn

- Give examples of three types of models.
- Identify the benefits and limitations of models.
- Compare the ways that scientists use hypotheses, theories, and laws.

Vocabulary

model
theory
law

READING STRATEGY

Reading Organizer As you read this section, create an outline of the section. Use the headings from the section in your outline.

model a pattern, plan, representation, or description designed to show the structure or workings of an object, system, or concept

Scientific Models

How can you see the parts of a cell? Unless you had superhuman eyesight, you couldn't see inside most cells without using a microscope.

What would you do if you didn't have a microscope? Looking at a model of a cell would help! A model of a cell can help you understand what the parts of a cell look like.

Types of Scientific Models

A **model** is a representation of an object or system. Scientific models are used to help explain how something works or to describe the structure of something. A model may be used to predict future events. However, models have limitations. A model is never exactly like the real thing. If it were, it would not be a model. Three major kinds of scientific models are physical, mathematical, and conceptual models.

Physical Models

A model volcano and a miniature steam engine are examples of physical models. Some physical models, such as a model of a cell, look like the thing that they model. But a limitation of the model of a cell is that the model is not alive and doesn't act exactly like a cell. Other physical models, such as the model of a skyscraper in **Figure 1,** look and act at least somewhat like the thing that they model. Scientists often use the model that is simplest to use but that still serves their purpose.

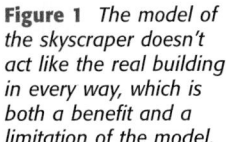

Figure 1 *The model of the skyscraper doesn't act like the real building in every way, which is both a benefit and a limitation of the model.*

CHAPTER RESOURCES

Chapter Resource File

 • **Lesson Plan**
- **Directed Reading A** BASIC
- **Directed Reading B** SPECIAL NEEDS

Technology

 Transparencies
- Bellringer

Workbooks

 Math Skills for Science
- Using Proportions and Cross-Multiplication GENERAL
- Punnett Square Popcorn GENERAL

Is That a Fact!

All animals are made of cells, and most animal cells are only 10 to 20 μm long—too small to see with the naked eye. However, some cells may be seen easily without the aid of a microscope. The yolk of an ostrich egg is the largest single cell. An ostrich egg can be 25 cm in diameter!

Figure 2 Mathematical Model: A Punnett Square

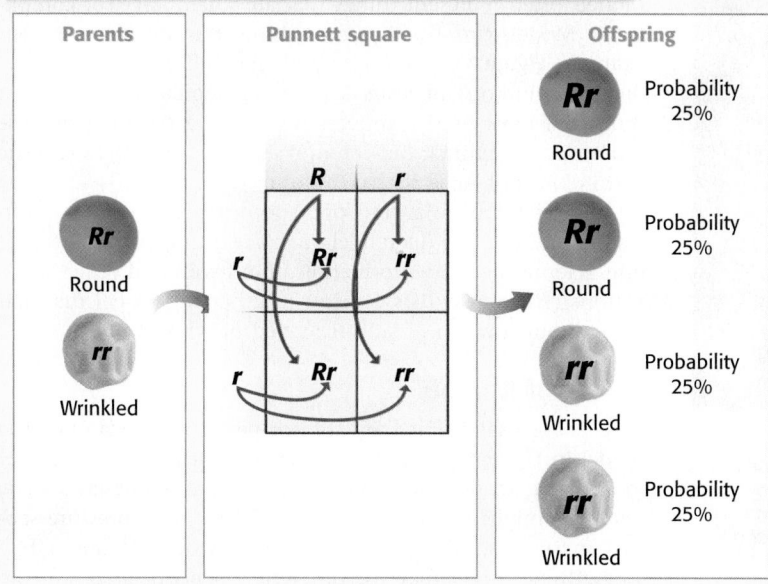

Parents	Punnett square	Offspring

Rr Round
rr Wrinkled

R r
r **Rr** **rr**
r **Rr** **rr**

Rr Round — Probability 25%
Rr Round — Probability 25%
rr Wrinkled — Probability 25%
rr Wrinkled — Probability 25%

Mathematical Models

A mathematical model may be made up of numbers, equations, and other forms of data. Some mathematical models are simple and can be used easily. The Punnett square shown in **Figure 2** helps scientists study the passing of traits from parents to offspring. Using this model, scientists can predict how often certain traits will appear in the offspring of certain parents.

Computers are useful for creating and manipulating mathematical models. They make fewer mistakes and can keep track of more variables than a person can. But a computer model can also be incorrect in many ways. The more complex a model is, the more carefully scientists must build and test the model.

✓ Reading Check What type of model is a Punnett square? (*See the Appendix for answers to Reading Checks.*)

Conceptual Models

The third type of model is the conceptual model. Some conceptual models are systems of ideas. Others compare unfamiliar things with familiar things to help explain unfamiliar ideas. The idea that the solar system formed from a spinning disk of gas is a conceptual model. Scientists also use conceptual models to classify behaviors of animals. Scientists can then predict how an animal might respond to a certain action based on behaviors that have already been observed.

CONNECTION TO Environmental Science

Samples Scientists studying deformed frogs in Minnesota wanted to know at what stage in the frogs' development the deformities happened. So, the scientists collected a large sample of frogs in all stages of development.

The larger a sample is, the more accurately it represents the whole population. If, for example, a sample of frogs is too small, one unusual frog may make the results of the study inaccurate. If the sample has too many old frogs or too many tadpoles, the sample is unrepresentative of the whole population. Give an example of an unrepresentative sample. Make a poster describing how that sample might make the experimental results inaccurate.

ACTIVITY

Teach

📖 READING STRATEGY — GENERAL

Paired Reading Pair each student with a partner. Instruct students to read the Types of Scientific Models section silently and to make note of any passages that seem confusing. After students finish reading, ask one student to summarize the section and the second student to add any ideas that were omitted. Each reader should help his or her partner with any parts that the partner did not understand. Ask the students prepare a list of questions (with answers) to ask the class.
LS Interpersonal — English Language Learners

Group ACTIVITY — BASIC

Writing **Classifying** Biologists have developed a system of classifying all living things. This classification system is a conceptual model. Provide students with objects or pictures of objects such as buttons, paper clips, screws, rubber bands, and pencils. Have students develop their own classification scheme for these items. Ask students to illustrate their classification system by using some type of visual organizer. **LS** Logical — English Language Learners

Answer to Reading Check
a mathematical model

Answer to Connection to Environmental Science

Answers may vary. Sample answer: If the sample of frogs contains too many tadpoles relative to the whole frog population and the deformities happen later in the frogs' development, the scientists might conclude that not many frogs become deformed. The unrepresentative sample makes the results inaccurate and unreliable.

Out with the Old? Have students debate the following question: "As new theories and models are developed, should older theories and models be thrown out and forgotten?"

Many current models and theories have developed out of older models and theories. Often, older models and theories are still useful for understanding certain aspects of science. On the other hand, it is often difficult for science to progress if many people refuse to accept the newer models and theories.

LS Logical/Verbal

Quiz — GENERAL

1. How does a theory differ from a law? (A theory is an explanation that ties together many hypotheses and observations. A law is a summary of many experimental results and observations.)

2. Name three types of models. (physical models, mathematical models, and conceptual models)

Alternative Assessment — ADVANCED

Scale Models Introduce students to scale models, such as maps. For scale models, the ratio between the model's dimensions and the dimensions of the object represented by the model is constant. Organize students into groups, and challenge the groups to make a scale drawing of the classroom. **LS** Logical

Figure 3 *This computer-generated model doesn't just look like a dinosaur. It may also open and close its jaws in much the same way that a dinosaur does.*

theory an explanation that ties together many hypotheses and observations

law a summary of many experimental results and observations; a law tells how things work

Benefits of Models

Models often represent things that are small, large, or complicated. Models can also represent things that do not exist. For example, **Figure 3** is a model of one type of dinosaur. Dinosaurs died out millions of years ago. Some popular movies about dinosaurs have used computer models like this one because dinosaurs are extinct. But the movies would not be as realistic if they did not have the scientific models.

A model can be a kind of hypothesis, and scientists can test a model. To build a model of an organism, even an extinct one, scientists gather information from fossils and other observations. Then, scientists can test whether the model fits their ideas about how an organism moved or what it ate.

Limits of Models

Models are useful, but they are not perfect. For example, the model in **Figure 3** gives scientists an idea of how the dinosaur looked. But to find out how strong the dinosaur's jaws were, scientists might build a physical model that has pressure sensors in the jaw. That model would provide data about bite strength. Scientists may use different models to represent the same thing, such as the dinosaur's jaw. But the kind of model and the model's complexity depend on the model's purpose.

Even a model jaw that has pressure sensors is not perfect. Scientists can compare the dinosaur bite with the bite of a crocodile. Next, scientists use their model to conduct tests. Scientists might then estimate how hard the dinosaur could bite. But without a live dinosaur, the result is still a hypothesis.

Building Scientific Knowledge

Sometimes, scientists draw different conclusions from the same data. Other times, new results show that old conclusions are wrong. Scientists are always asking new questions or looking at old questions from a different angle. As scientists find new answers, scientific knowledge continues to grow and change.

Scientific Theories

For every hypothesis, more than one prediction can be made. Each time another prediction is proven true, the hypothesis gains more support. Over time, scientists tie together everything that they have learned. An explanation that ties together many related observations, facts, and tested hypotheses is called a **theory.** Theories are conceptual models that help organize scientific thinking. Theories are used to explain observations and to predict what might happen in the future.

✔ **Reading Check** How do scientists use theories?

Answer to Reading Check

to explain a broad range of observations, facts, and tested hypotheses, to predict what might happen, and to organize scientific thinking

Computer-Generated Models Have students search the Internet for computer-generated, three-dimensional models (animated or not animated), such as models of molecules, future airplanes or cars, and prehistoric organisms. Have students find out how the models were made and who made them. (Often, scientists, artists, and computer programmers work together to make these models. They use a variety of techniques and experiment as they work.) **LS** Visual/Logical

Scientific Laws

What happens when a theory and its models correctly predict the results of many experiments? A scientific law may be formed. In science, a **law** is a summary of many experimental results and observations. A scientific law is a statement of what *will* happen in a specific situation. A law tells you how things work.

Scientific laws are at work around you every day. For example, the law of gravity states that objects will always fall toward the center of Earth. And inside your cells, many laws of chemistry are at work to keep you alive.

Scientific Change

New scientific ideas may take time to be accepted as facts, scientific theories, or scientific laws. Scientists should be open to new ideas but should always test new ideas by using scientific methods. If new evidence challenges an accepted idea, scientists must reexamine the old evidence and reevaluate the old idea. In this way, the process of building scientific knowledge never ends.

CONNECTION TO Chemistry

Model Cocaine in the Brain
Analyze and evaluate information from a scientifically literate viewpoint by reading scientific texts, magazine articles, and newspaper articles about how drugs, such as cocaine, affect brain chemistry. Create a model to show what you have learned. Use your model to describe possible treatments for drug addiction.

SECTION Review

Summary

- Models represent objects or systems. Often, they use familiar things to represent unfamiliar things. Three main types of models are physical, mathematical, and conceptual models. Models have limitations but are useful and can be changed based on new evidence.

- Scientific knowledge is built as scientists form and revise scientific hypotheses, models, theories, and laws.

Using Key Terms

In each of the following sentences, replace the incorrect term with the correct term from the word bank.

theory   law   hypothesis

1. A conclusion is an explanation that matches many hypotheses but may still change.

2. A model tells you exactly what to expect in certain situations.

Understanding Key Ideas

3. A limitation of models is that
   a. they are large enough to see.
   b. they do not act exactly like the things that they model.
   c. they are smaller than the things that they model.
   d. they model unfamiliar things.

4. What type of model would you use to test the hypothesis that global warming is causing polar icecaps to melt? Explain.

Math Skills

5. If Jerry is 2.1 m tall, how tall is a scale model of Jerry that is 10% of his size?

Critical Thinking

6. **Applying Concepts** You want to make a model of an extinct plant. What are two kinds of models that you might use? Describe the advantages and disadvantages of each type of model.

SCiLINKS.

NSTA
Developed and maintained by the National Science Teachers Association

For a variety of links related to this chapter, go to www.scilinks.org

Topic: Using Models
SciLinks code: HSM1588

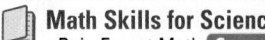

CHAPTER RESOURCES

Chapter Resource File
- Section Quiz GENERAL
- Section Review GENERAL
- Vocabulary and Section Summary GENERAL

Workbooks

Math Skills for Science
- Rain Forest Math GENERAL
- Scale of Organisms GENERAL

Science Skills
- Using Models to Communicate GENERAL
- Introduction to Graphs GENERAL

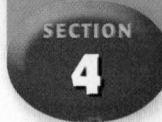

SECTION
4

Focus

Overview

This section describes several tools that scientists use to gather information. Students also learn about the International System of Units (SI). Students learn the units and tools associated with quantities such as mass and volume. Finally, students learn about lab safety and safety symbols.

🔔 Bellringer

Have students write an answer to the following question:

> Why do you think scientists use tools such as graduated cylinders and stopwatches?

Ask students to share their answers with the class, and briefly discuss their responses. **LS** Logical

Motivate

Demonstration — GENERAL

Tools of the Trade Demonstrate the use and care of a graduated cylinder and a balance to the class. **LS** Visual/Verbal

---

What You Will Learn

● Collect, record, and analyze information by using various tools.
● Explain the importance of the International System of Units.
● Calculate area and density.
● Identify lab safety symbols, and demonstrate safe practices during lab investigations.

Vocabulary

meter	volume
area	temperature
mass	density

READING STRATEGY

Reading Organizer As you read this section, make a concept map by using the terms above.

Tools, Measurement, and Safety

Would you use a hammer to tighten a bolt on a bicycle? No, you wouldn't. You need the right tools to fix a bike.

Scientists use a variety of tools in their experiments. A tool is anything that helps you do a task.

Tools for Measuring

You might remember that one way to collect data is to take measurements. To get the best measurements, you need the proper tools. Stopwatches, metersticks, and balances are tools that you can use to make measurements. Thermometers, spring scales, and graduated cylinders are also helpful tools. Some of the uses of these tools are shown in **Figure 1.**

✓ **Reading Check** Name six tools used for taking measurements. (*See the Appendix for answers to Reading Checks.*)

Tools for Analyzing

After you collect data, you need to analyze them. Perhaps you need to find the average of your data. Calculators are handy tools to help you do calculations quickly. Or you might show your data in a graph or a figure. A computer that has the correct software can help you make neat, colorful figures. Of course, even a pencil and graph paper are tools that you can use to graph your data.

Figure 1 Measurement Tools

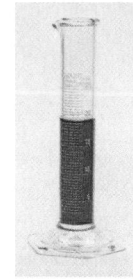
You can use a **graduated cylinder** to measure volume.

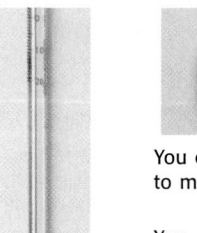
You can use a **thermometer** to measure temperature.

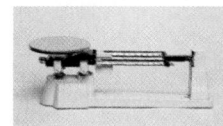
You can use a **meterstick** to measure length.

You can use a **balance** to measure mass.

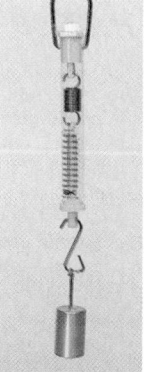
You can use a **spring scale** to measure force.

You can use a **stopwatch** to measure time.

CHAPTER RESOURCES

Chapter Resource File

 • Lesson Plan
• Directed Reading A **BASIC**
• Directed Reading B **SPECIAL NEEDS**

Technology

 Transparencies
• Bellringer
• Common SI Units

Workbooks

 Math Skills for Science
• Creating Exponents **GENERAL**

Answer to Reading Check

stopwatch, graduated cylinder, meterstick, spring scale, balance, and thermometer

Units of Measurement

The ability to make accurate and reliable measurements is an important skill in science. Many systems of measurement are used throughout the world. At one time in England, the standard for an inch was three grains of barley placed end to end. Other modern standardized units were originally based on parts of the body, such as the foot. Such systems were not very reliable. Their units were based on objects that had different sizes.

The International System of Units

In the late 1700s, the French Academy of Sciences began to form a global measurement system now known as the *International System of Units,* or SI. Today, most scientists and almost all countries use this system. One advantage of using SI measurements is that doing so helps scientists share and compare their observations and results.

Another advantage of SI units is that all units are based on the number 10, which makes conversions from one unit to another easy. The table in **Table 1** contains commonly used SI units for length, volume, mass, and temperature.

No Rulers Allowed

1. Measure the width of your desk, but don't use a ruler.
2. Select another object to use as your unit of measurement.
3. Compare your measurement with those of your classmates.
4. Explain why it is important to use standard units of measurement.

Table 1 Common SI Units and Conversions

Length	meter (m) kilometer (km) decimeter (dm) centimeter (cm) millimeter (mm) micrometer (μm) nanometer (nm)	1 km = 1,000 m 1 dm = 0.1 m 1 cm = 0.01 m 1 mm = 0.001 m 1 μm = 0.000001 m 1 nm = 0.000000001 m
Volume	cubic meter (m³) cubic centimeter (cm³) liter (L) milliliter (mL)	1 cm³ = 0.000001 m³ 1 L = 1 dm³ = 0.001 m³ 1 mL = 0.001 L = 1 cm³
Mass	kilogram (kg) gram (g) milligram (mg)	1 g = 0.001 kg 1 mg = 0.000001 kg
Temperature	Kelvin (K) Celsius (°C)	0°C = 273 K 100°C = 373 K

Science Bloopers

The second is the SI unit for time. The second was originally defined as $\frac{1}{86,400}$ of a mean solar day. Later, astronomers discovered that a day is not a constant interval of time: the gravitational attraction of the moon slows Earth's rotation, so each day is about 40 ns longer than the previous day! Now, the definition of a *second* is based on the movement of an electron between energy levels in a cesium atom.

Cultural Awareness ADVANCED

It All Adds Up! Devices that assist in calculations have been around for a long time. A variety of cultures have used many variations of the computer, including the "pebble computer" and the abacus. Have students research and prepare presentations about some of these early "computers," including how they work.

English Language Learners

LS Verbal

Teach

Answer to Quick Lab

Measurements may vary depending on the unit of measurement chosen. Units might include hand width, hand length, finger width, or pencil length. (By comparing their units and measurements with those of others, students should recognize that a standard of measurement is important in order to communicate data and to be understood.)

CONNECTION ACTIVITY
Math ─────────── GENERAL

International System of Units

To help students understand SI conversions, instruct them to answer the following questions:

1. How many meters are there in 2.5 km? (2,500 m)
2. How many centimeters are there in 3.1 m? (310 cm)
3. How do you express 20 km in millimeters? (20,000,000 mm)

LS Logical

INCLUSION Strategies

- *Developmentally Delayed*
- *Hearing Impaired*
- *Visually Impaired*

Many students can best understand information when it is presented in physical ways. Use this activity to help students understand the term *irregular shape.* Gather a group of items that have regular and irregular shapes, such as the following:

regular: textbook, cardboard box, container of three tennis balls, cylindrical food box or plastic container, shoe box, and round ball

irregular: shoe, phone, watch, coffee mug, chair, backpack, and stapler

Place the items on a desk or table. Ask students to separate the items into regular and irregular shapes.

LS Kinesthetic

Research ── GENERAL

The SI in the United States The United States is the only industrialized nation in the world that does not officially use the SI. Talk about some of the reasons the country has had such a hard time changing systems. Then, ask students to research the history of the English system and the SI. Suggest that they also investigate English measurements, such as the furlong and the stone. **LS** Verbal/Logical

Answers to MathFocus

1. 125.5 km $\times$ 8.225 km = 1,032 km^2

Teacher's Note: There are several rules for determining significant digits and for using significant digits in calculations. One rule is given in the activity. Another rule is that in the addition and subtraction of numbers, the result can be no more certain than the least certain number in the calculation.

CONNECTION to Physical Science ── GENERAL

How Hot? Although students may be most familiar with the Fahrenheit scale, remind them that they will be using the Celsius scale in their science class. Use the teaching transparency "Three Temperature Scales" to demonstrate the importance of paying attention to the units in which a temperature is given. **LS** Logical/Visual

Figure 2 *This scientist is using a metric ruler to measure a lizard's length. The unit chosen to describe an object, such as this lizard, depends on the size of the object being measured.*

meter the basic unit of length in the SI (symbol, m)

area a measure of the size of a surface or a region

Measurement

Scientists report measured quantities in a way that shows the precision of the measurement. To do so, they use significant figures. *Significant figures* are the digits in a measurement that are known with certainty. The Math Focus below will help you understand significant figures and will teach you how to use the correct number of digits. Now that you have a standardized system of units for measuring things, you can use the system to measure length, area, mass, volume, and temperature.

Length

How long is a lizard? Well, a **meter** (m) is the basic SI unit of length. However, a scientist, such as the one in **Figure 2,** would use centimeters (cm) to describe a small lizard's length. If you divide 1 m into 100 parts, each part equals 1 cm. So, 1 cm is one-hundredth of a meter. Even though 1 cm seems small, some things are even smaller. Scientists describe the length of very small objects in micrometers (μm) or nanometers (nm). To see these small objects, scientists use powerful microscopes.

Area

How much paper would you need to cover the top of your desk? To answer this question, you must find the area of the desk. **Area** is a measure of the size of the surface of an object. To calculate the area of a square or a rectangle, measure the length and width. Then, use the following equation:

$$area = length \times width$$

Units for area are square units, such as square meters (m^2), square centimeters (cm^2), and square kilometers (km^2).

Significant Figures Calculate the area of a carpet that is 3.145 m long (four significant figures) and 5.75 m (three significant figures) wide. (Hint: In multiplication and division problems, the answer cannot have more significant figures than the measurement that has the smallest number of significant figures does.)

Step 1: Write the equation for area.

$$area = length \times width$$

Step 2: Replace *length* and *width* with the measurements given, and solve.

$$area = 3.125 \text{ m} \times 5.75 \text{ m} = 18.08375 \text{ m}^2$$

Step 3: Round the answer to get the correct number of significant figures. Here, the correct number of significant figures is three, because the value with the smallest number of significant figures has three significant figures.

$$area = 18.1 \text{ m}^2$$

Now Its Your Turn

1. Use a calculator to perform the following calculation: 125.5 km $\times$ 8.225 km. Write the answer with the correct number of significant figures.

CHAPTER RESOURCES

Technology

 Transparencies
- **LINK TO PHYSICAL SCIENCE** Three Temperature Scales

Workbooks

 Math Skills for Science
- What Is SI? **GENERAL**
- A Formula for SI Catch-Up **GENERAL**
- Finding Perimeter and Area **GENERAL**
- Finding Volume **GENERAL**

 Science Skills
- Recognizing Bias in Graphs **GENERAL**
- Interpreting Your Data **GENERAL**

Is That a Fact!

The International System of Units is abbreviated *SI* because it stands for *Système International d'Unités,* which is French.

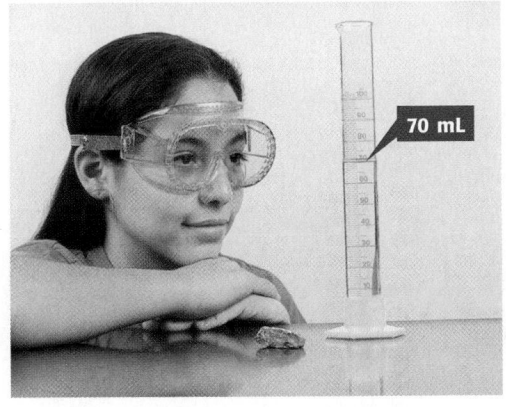

Figure 3 *Adding the rock changes the water level from 70 mL to 80 mL. So, the rock displaces 10 mL of water. Because 1 mL = 1 cm³, the volume of the rock is 10 cm³.*

Mass

How large a rock can a rushing stream move? The answer depends on the energy of the stream and the mass of the rock. **Mass** is a measure of the amount of matter in an object. The kilogram (kg) is the basic unit for mass in the SI. Kilograms are used to describe the mass of a large rock. Grams are used to measure the mass of smaller objects. One thousand grams equals 1 kg. For example, a medium-sized apple has a mass of about 100 g. Masses of very large objects are given in metric tons. A metric ton equals 1,000 kg.

✓ **Reading Check** What is the basic SI unit for mass?

Volume

Think about moving some magnets to a laboratory. How many magnets will fit into a box? The answer depends on the volume of the box and the volume of each magnet. **Volume** is a measure of the size of a body in three-dimensional space. In this case, you need the volumes of the box and of the magnets.

The volume of a liquid is often given in liters (L). Liters are based on the meter. A cubic meter (1 m³) is equal to 1,000 L. So, 1,000 L will fit into a box measuring 1 m on each side. A milliliter (mL) will fit into a box measuring 1 cm on each side. So, 1 mL = 1 cm³. Graduated cylinders are used to measure the volume of liquids.

The volume of a large, solid object is given in cubic meters (m³). The volumes of smaller objects can be given in cubic centimeters (cm³) or cubic millimeters (mm³). The volume of a box can be calculated by multiplying the object's length, width, and height. The volume of an irregularly shaped object can be found by measuring the volume of liquid that the object displaces. You can see how this works in **Figure 3.**

mass a measure of the amount of matter in an object

volume a measure of the size of a body or region in three-dimensional space

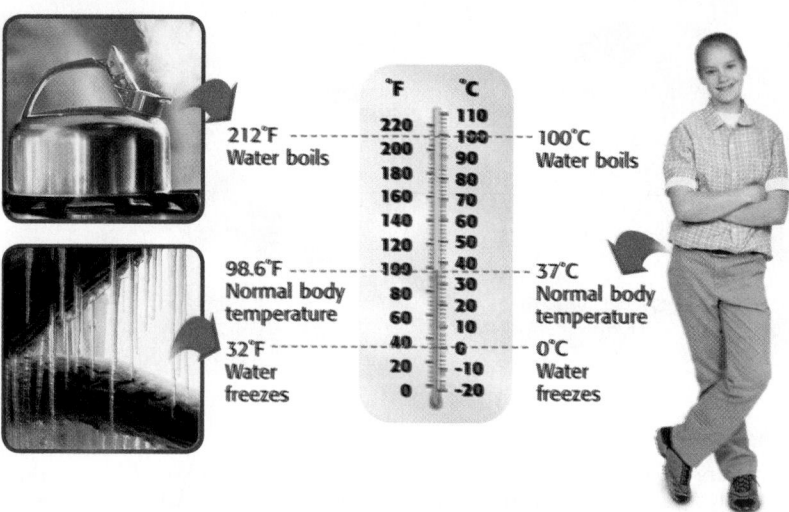

Figure 4 This thermometer shows the relationship between degrees Fahrenheit and degrees Celsius.

temperature the measure of how hot (or cold) something is

density the ratio of the mass of a substance to the volume of the substance

Temperature

How hot is melted iron? To answer this question, a scientist would measure the temperature of the liquid metal. **Temperature** is a measure of how hot or cold something is. You probably use degrees Fahrenheit (°F) to describe temperature. Scientists commonly use degrees Celsius (°C), although the kelvin (K) is the official SI base unit for temperature. You will use degrees Celsius in this book. The thermometer in **Figure 4** compares the Fahrenheit and Celsius scales.

Density

If you measure the mass and volume of an object, you have the measurements that you need to find the density of the object. **Density** is the amount of matter in a given volume. You cannot measure density directly. But after you have measured the mass and the volume, you can use the following equation to calculate density:

$$density = \frac{mass}{volume}$$

Density is the ratio of mass to volume, so units often used for density are grams per milliliter (g/mL) and grams per cubic centimeter (g/cm³). Density may be difficult to understand. Think of a table-tennis ball and a golf ball. They have similar volumes. But a golf ball has more mass than a table-tennis ball does. So the golf ball has a greater density.

Safety Rules!

Science is exciting and fun, but it can also be dangerous. Don't take any chances! Always follow your teacher's instructions. Don't take shortcuts—even when you think there is no danger. Before starting an experiment, get your teacher's permission. Read the lab procedures carefully. Pay special attention to safety information and caution statements. **Figure 5** shows the safety symbols used in this book. Get to know these symbols and their meanings. Do so by reading the safety information in the front of this book. **This is important!** If you are still unsure about what a safety symbol means, ask your teacher.

Reading Check Why are safety symbols important?

Figure 5   Safety Symbols

Eye Protection   Clothing Protection   Hand Safety

Heating Safety   Electric Safety   Sharp Object

Chemical Safety   Animal Safety   Plant Safety

SECTION Review

Summary

- Scientists use a variety of tools to measure and analyze the world around them.
- The International System of Units (SI) is a simple, reliable, and uniform system of measurement that is used by most scientists.
- The basic units of measurement in the SI are the meter (for length), the kilogram (for mass), and the kelvin (for temperature).
- Before starting any science activity or science lab, review the safety symbols and the safety rules for that activity or lab. Don't take chances with your health and safety.

Using Key Terms

Complete each of the following sentences by choosing the correct term from the word bank.

mass   area
volume   temperature

1. A measure of the size of a surface or a region is called ___.

2. Scientists use kilograms when measuring an object's ___.

3. The ___ of a liquid is usually described in liters.

Understanding Key Ideas

4. SI units are
   a. based on standardized measurements of body parts.
   b. almost always based on the number 10.
   c. used to measure only length.
   d. used only in France.

5. What is temperature?

6. If you wanted to measure the mass of a fly, which SI unit would be most appropriate?

Math Skills

7. What is the area of a soccer field that is 110 m long and 85 m wide?

8. What is the density of silver if a 6 cm³ piece of silver has a mass of 63 g?

Critical Thinking

9. **Applying Concepts** Some people are thinking about sending humans to the moon and then to the planet Mars. Why is it important for scientists around the world to use the International System of Units as they make these plans?

10. **Making Inferences** Give an example of something that can happen if you do not follow safety rules.

11. **Applying Concepts** What tool would you use to measure the mass of the air in a basketball?

SCI LINKS.

NSTA
Developed and maintained by the National Science Teachers Association

For a variety of links related to this chapter, go to www.scilinks.org

Topic: Tools of Science; SI Units
SciLinks code: HSM1535; HSM1390

Answer to Reading Check

Safety symbols alert you to particular safety concerns or specific dangers in a lab.

CHAPTER RESOURCES

Chapter Resource File

- Section Quiz **GENERAL**
- Section Review **GENERAL**
- Vocabulary and Section Summary **GENERAL**
- SciLinks Activity **GENERAL**
- Datasheet for Quick Lab

Technology

- Interactive Explorations CD-ROM
  - Something's Fishy **GENERAL**

Workbooks

Science Skills
- Safety Rules! **GENERAL**

Writing **More on Density** Because dense materials, such as rock, tend to sink, sometimes we forget that huge, seaworthy ships are made of very dense materials, such as steel. Ships have even been made of concrete. Have students conduct research on the Internet on any of the following topics:

- why ships float
- what materials have been used in the history of ship building
- how ships are designed
- how ships are constructed
- concrete-canoe competitions (held at many universities)

Students should report their findings in a short paper.

LS Verbal/Logical

Answers to Section Review

1. area
2. mass
3. volume
4. b
5. Temperature is a measure of how hot or cold something is.
6. the gram or the milligram
7. 110 m × 85 m = 9,350 m²
8. 63 g ÷ 6 cm³ = 10.5 g/cm³
9. Sample answer: The importance of the SI can be seen in space travel. If one person is using one system of measurements and another person is using a different system, one person might forget to indicate that he or she is using a different system. As a result, the spaceship could go way off course or could be traveling too fast to land safely.
10. Sample answer: You could get hurt by an unknown chemical.
11. The tool for measuring mass, even the mass of air, is a balance.

Using Scientific Methods

Skills Practice Lab

Does It All Add Up?

Teacher's Notes

Time Required

One 45-minute class period

Lab Ratings

EASY ———————————→ HARD

Teacher Prep 🧪🧪
Student Set-Up 🧪
Concept Level 🧪🧪
Clean Up 🧪

MATERIALS

The materials listed on the student page are enough for a group of 2–3 students. Prepare a jug of plain water labeled "Liquid A" and a jug of either isopropyl alcohol (2-propanol, $CH_3CH(OH)CH_3$) or denatured ethyl alcohol (95% ethanol, CH_3CH_2OH) labeled "Liquid B." Safety thermometers are recommended.

Safety Caution

Remind students to review all safety cautions and icons before beginning this lab activity. Caution students to handle thermometers with care and to treat all unknown chemicals as dangerous. Alcohol is flammable and poisonous. Students should wear goggles and aprons at all times. A fire extinguisher and fire blanket should be nearby. Know how to use them. The room should be well ventilated, and students should be familiar with evacuation procedures.

OBJECTIVES

Apply scientific methods to predict, measure, and observe the mixing of two unknown liquids.

MATERIALS

- beakers, 100 mL (2)
- Celsius thermometer
- glass-labeling marker
- graduated cylinders, 50 mL (3)
- liquid A, 75 mL
- liquid B, 75 mL
- protective gloves

SAFETY

Does It All Add Up?

Your math teacher won't tell you this, but did you know that sometimes 2 + 2 does not appear to equal 4?! In this experiment, you will use scientific methods to predict, measure, and observe the mixing of two unknown liquids. You will learn that a scientist does not set out to prove a hypothesis but to test it and that sometimes the results just don't seem to add up!

Make Observations

1 Put on your safety goggles, gloves, and lab apron. Examine the beakers of liquids A and B provided by your teacher. Write down as many observations as you can about each liquid. **Caution:** Do not taste, touch, or smell the liquids.

2 Pour exactly 25 mL of liquid A from the beaker into each of two 50 mL graduated cylinders. Combine these samples in one of the graduated cylinders. Record the final volume. Pour the liquid back into the beaker of liquid A. Rinse the graduated cylinders. Repeat this step for liquid B.

Form a Hypothesis

3 Based on your observations and on prior experience, formulate a testable hypothesis that states what you expect the volume to be when you combine 25 mL of liquid A with 25 mL of liquid B.

4 Make a prediction based on your hypothesis. Use an if-then format. Explain the basis for your prediction.

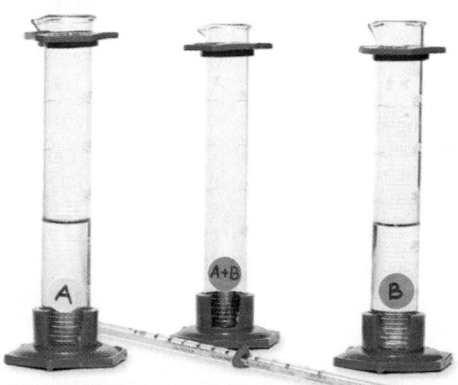

 **Holt Lab Generator CD-ROM**

Search for any lab by topic, standard, difficulty level, or time. Edit any lab to fit your needs, or create your own labs. Use the Lab Materials QuickList software to customize your lab materials list.

CHAPTER RESOURCES

Chapter Resource File

 • Datasheet for Chapter Lab
• Lab Notes and Answers

Technology

• Classroom Videos
• Lab Video

Kevin McCurdy
Elmwood Junior High School
Rogers, Arkansas

Data Table				
	Contents of cylinder A	Contents of cylinder B	Mixing results: predictions	Mixing results: observations
Volume				
Appearance		DO NOT WRITE IN BOOK		
Temperature				

Test the Hypothesis

5. Make a data table like the one above.

6. Mark one graduated cylinder "A." Carefully pour exactly 25 mL of liquid A into this cylinder. In your data table, record its volume, appearance, and temperature.

7. Mark another graduated cylinder "B." Carefully pour exactly 25 mL of liquid B into this cylinder. Record its volume, appearance, and temperature in your data table.

8. Mark the empty third cylinder "A + B."

9. In the "Mixing results: predictions" column in your table, record the prediction you made earlier. Each classmate may have made a different prediction.

10. Carefully pour the contents of both cylinders into the third graduated cylinder.

11. Observe and record the total volume, appearance, and temperature in the "Mixing results: observations" column of your table.

Analyze the Results

1. **Analyzing Data** Discuss your predictions as a class. How many different predictions were there? Which predictions were supported by testing? Did any measurements surprise you?

Draw Conclusions

2. **Drawing Conclusions** Was your hypothesis supported or disproven? Either way, explain your thinking. Describe everything that you think you learned from this experiment.

3. **Analyzing Methods** Explain the value of incorrect predictions.

Disposal Information

Set out a disposal container. Have students pour their water-alcohol mix and any alcohol they have left over into the container at the end of the procedure. Make sure the pH is between 5 and 9, dilute it with 10 times as much water, and pour it down the drain.

Lab Notes

Do not reveal the identity of the liquids until the end of the lab! In this lab, students will likely be surprised to discover that 25 mL of liquid A (water) plus 25 mL of liquid B (an alcohol) do not make 50 mL of the mixture. Spaces between molecules of alcohol become filled with water molecules, resulting in a lower total volume. The water-alcohol mixture will be cloudy and bubbly for a brief time after mixing and may emit some heat. Have students record observations until the mixture becomes clear and then make their final measurements and observations.

Try the following demonstration in order to model the mixing of water and alcohol molecules for your students. Mix 25 mL of marbles with 25 mL of round BB-gun pellets. The BBs will settle between the marbles, and the result will be a total volume less than 50 mL.

Analyze the Results

Note: All answers in this lab are based on student observations and may vary.

1. Students may make some unusual predictions. You may want to lead them into questions about volume. Encourage them to think of many ways to observe and characterize the two liquids. Avoid giving away the explanation too quickly.

Draw Conclusions

2. Check that students are clear about whether or not their hypothesis was supported and in what ways their observations supported or disproved their hypothesis.

3. Incorrect predictions can lead to new questions and a new understanding of the way things work.

Assignment Guide

SECTION	QUESTIONS
1	13
2	2, 4, 7–8, 14, 19–22
3	3, 6, 15–17
4	5, 9–12, 18, 23–25
1 and 2	1

ANSWERS

Using Key Terms

1. Sample answer: You can use scientific methods to study science.

2. Sample answer: A variable is the only factor that should change during a controlled experiment.

3. Sample answer: A theory is an explanation for a broad range of observations and hypotheses. A hypothesis is an explanation for a specific set of observations and can be tested.

4. Sample answer: A controlled experiment tests one factor at a time by comparing a control group with an experimental group. A variable is a factor that changes in an experiment.

5. Sample answer: Area is a measure of a flat surface. Volume is a measure of space or size in three dimensions.

6. Sample answer: A physical model, such as a car, is a physical representation of an object, a real automobile. A conceptual model is a system of ideas. It may compare an idea with something familiar.

USING KEY TERMS

1 Use the following terms in the same sentence: *science* and *scientific methods*.

2 Use the following terms in the same sentence: *controlled experiment* and *variable*.

For each pair of terms, explain how the meanings of the terms differ.

3 *theory* and *hypothesis*

4 *controlled experiment* and *variable*

5 *area* and *volume*

6 *physical model* and *conceptual model*

UNDERSTANDING KEY IDEAS

Multiple Choice

7 The steps of scientific methods
  a. must all be used in every scientific investigation.
  b. must always be used in the same order.
  c. often start with a question.
  d. always result in the development of a theory.

8 In a controlled experiment,
  a. a control group is compared with one or more experimental groups.
  b. there are at least two variables.
  c. all factors should be different.
  d. a variable is not needed.

9 Which of the following tools is best for measuring 100 mL of water?
  a. 10 mL graduated cylinder
  b. 150 mL graduated cylinder
  c. 250 mL beaker
  d. 500 mL beaker

10 Which of the following is NOT an SI unit?
  a. meter
  b. foot
  c. liter
  d. kilogram

11 A pencil is 14 cm long. How many millimeters long is it?
  a. 1.4 mm
  b. 140 mm
  c. 1,400 mm
  d. 1,400,000 mm

12 The directions for a lab include the safety icons shown below. These icons mean that

  a. you should be careful.
  b. you are going into the laboratory.
  c. you should wash your hands first.
  d. you should wear safety goggles, a lab apron, and gloves during the lab.

Short Answer

13 List three ways that science is beneficial to living things.

14 Why do hypotheses need to be testable?

Understanding Key Ideas

7. c
8. a
9. b
10. b
11. b
12. d

13. Sample answer: Science can be used to find cures for diseases, to create new power sources, and to predict earthquakes.

14. Hypotheses need to be testable in order to be useful. If no information can be gathered to either support or disprove a hypothesis, the hypothesis is merely an idea that cannot be built upon scientifically.

15. Sample answer: A scientist studying animals might use a radio collar to track the animal's location, a computer database program to record data, and a computer mapping program to draw maps.

15 Give an example of how a scientist might use computers and technology.

16 List three types of models, and give an example of each.

17 What are some advantages and limitations of models?

18 Which SI units can be used to describe the volume of an object? Which SI units can be used to describe the mass of an object?

19 In a controlled experiment, why should there be several individuals in the control group and in each of the experimental groups?

20 Concept Mapping Use the following terms to create a concept map: *observations, predictions, questions, controlled experiments, variable,* and *hypothesis.*

21 Making Inferences Investigations often begin with observation. What limits the observations that scientists can make?

22 Forming Hypotheses A scientist who studies mice makes the following observation: On the day the mice are fed vitamins with their meals, they perform better in mazes. What hypothesis would you form to explain this phenomenon? Write a testable prediction based on your hypothesis.

INTERPRETING GRAPHICS

The pictures below show how an egg can be measured by using a beaker and water. Use the pictures below to answer the questions that follow.

Before: 125 mL   After: 200 mL

23 What kind of measurement is being taken?

a. area

b. length

c. mass

d. volume

24 Which of the following is an accurate measurement of the egg in the picture?

a. 75 cm³

b. 125 cm³

c. 125 mL

d. 200 mL

25 Make a double line graph using the data in the table below.

Number of Frogs		
Date	**Normal**	**Deformed**
1995	25	0
1996	21	0
1997	19	1
1998	20	2
1999	17	3
2000	20	5

18. The SI units used to describe volume are liters (L), units based on the liter, and units based on the cubic meter. The SI units used to describe the mass of an object are kilograms (kg) and other units based on the gram.

19. The more individuals there are in the groups, the more confident scientists can be that differences between the groups were caused by the variable and not by natural differences between individual organisms.

Critical Thinking

20. An answer to this exercise can be found at the end of this book.

21. Sample answer: Observations are limited by human senses or by technology. Things that cannot be observed may exist.

22. Sample answer: Vitamins help the mice remember the maze. A testable prediction might be "I predict that if I give some mice vitamins before they run the maze and I do not give vitamins to other mice before they run the maze, the mice who get the vitamins will perform better on the maze.

Interpreting Graphics

23. d

24. a
(200 mL − 125 mL = 75 mL = 75 cm³)

25. See the graph below.

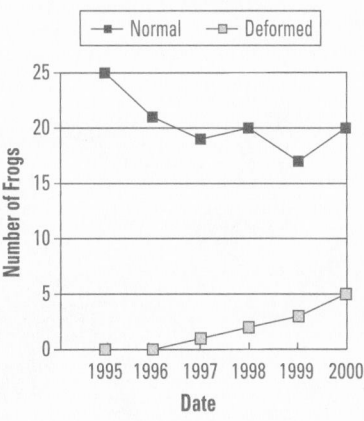

16. Sample answer: Physical models include toys and a model of a cell or a human body. Mathematical models include a Punnett square and equations to calculate physical forces. Conceptual models include theories about how the solar system formed or how life evolved on Earth.

17. Sample answer: advantages of models: they are easier to see and manipulate than the real thing might be, and they can simplify concepts; limitations: models do not behave exactly like the real thing, so they may not accurately predict results

CHAPTER RESOURCES

Chapter Resource File

- Chapter Review **GENERAL**
- Chapter Test A **GENERAL**
- Chapter Test B **ADVANCED**
- Chapter Test C **SPECIAL NEEDS**
- Vocabulary Activity **GENERAL**

Workbooks

Study Guide
- Study Guide is also available in Spanish.

Standardized Test Preparation

Teacher's Notes

To provide practice under more realistic conditions, give students 20 minutes to answer all of the questions in this Standardized Test Preparation.

Answer Key

Question	Answer
1	D
2	D
3	A
4	B
5	D
6	B
7	B
8	C
9	A
10	*
11	*

*See Test Doctor.

Multiple Choice

Use the diagram below to answer question 1.

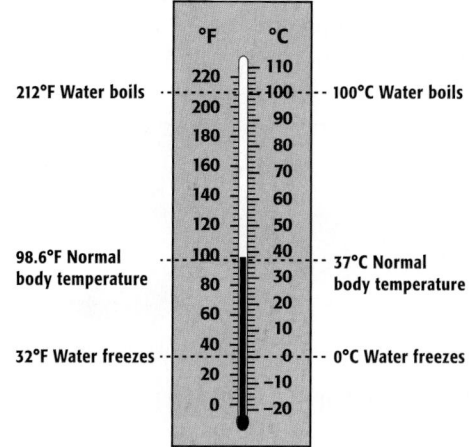

1. **The thermometer above correlates Fahrenheit and Celsius temperature scales. According to the thermometer, which of the following sentences is true?**

   A. You can swim in water that is 100°C.

   B. You can boil eggs in water that is 150°F.

   C. You can skate on water that is 10°C.

   D. Your body temperature is about 37°C.

2. **What is the purpose of scientific investigation?**

   A. to demonstrate how science works

   B. to ask questions and make observations

   C. to perform experiments

   D. to answer certain kinds of questions about the world

3. **Which of the following is a tool for measuring the volume of a liquid?**

   A. graduated cylinder

   B. cubic centimeter

   C. liter

   D. meterstick

4. **Which of the following is a feature of a scale model?**

   A. an unfamiliar thing is explained by comparing the unfamiliar thing to something that is familiar

   B. the measurements of the model are proportional to the measurements of the real object

   C. the mass of an object is measured using a scale or balance and represented on the model through labels

   D. numbers, equations, and data are used to find patterns within combinations of variables

5. **A scientist hypothesizes new factories are raising pollution levels in several nearby lakes. What is the best way to test the hypothesis?**

   A. to do library research on the harmful effects of acid precipitation in lakes

   B. to experiment with how pollution affects water plants that are native to Georgia

   C. to count the number of water plant species found in a Georgia lake

   D. to collect lake water samples and test each sample for pollution level

TEST DOCTOR

Question 1 A: It would be dangerous to swim in water that is 100°C, the temperature at which water boils. B: Water boils at 215°F, so an egg in water at 150°F, would not be boiled. C: Water that is 10°C is above the freezing point of water, which is 0°C, so it would not be solid. D: Correct.

Question 2 A: A scientific method is a means to an end. It is not an end in itself. B, C: Asking questions, making observations, and performing experiments are steps within scientific investigations. D: Correct.

Question 3 A: Correct. B, C: Cubic centimeters and liters are units of volume. D: A meterstick is used to measure length. When finding the volume of a solid, you may use a meterstick to find the length, width, and height of an object.

Question 4 A: This is a feature of a conceptual model. B: Correct. C: The term *scale* in scale model does not indicate that a scale or balance is used. However, some physical models may include labels, such as mass or height. D: This is a feature of a mathematical model.

Use the table below to answer question 6.

Testing Matrix: Effect of UV Light on Leopard Frogs

Group	Number of eggs	Temperature of water (°C)	UV light exposure (days)
#1 (control)	100	25	0
#2 (experimental)	100	25	15
#3 (experimental)	100	25	24

6. The data in the table above were collected during an experiment to test the effects of ultraviolet (UV) light on frogs. What is the independent variable in the experiment?

   A. water temperature

   B. length of exposure to UV light

   C. number of eggs

   D. kind of frog

7. Which of these common steps in a scientific inquiry involves coming up with a possible answer to a question about the world?

   A. communication of results

   B. formation of a hypothesis

   C. making observations

   D. testing a hypothesis

8. How many grams are in 1.2 kg?

   A. 12 g

   B. 120 g

   C. 1,200 g

   D. 12,000 g

9. Which of the following is a symbol for an SI unit of length?

   A. m

   B. cm^3

   C. L

   D. kg

Open Response

10. A biologist designs an experiment to determine the eating habits of cardinals. She performs her tests on 20 captured birds that live in identical cages. She feeds half of the cardinals a set amount of food each day. She lets the other half of the birds eat as much as they would like. All other aspects of their care are the same. Is this a controlled experiment? What is the variable in the experiment? Explain your answer.

11. From a scientific point of view, what is the problem with the following claim about an animal that is native to Kentucky? "Slender Glass Lizards are happy for eight hours each day."

Standardized Test Preparation

Question 10 Full-credit answers should include the following points:

- It is a controlled experiment because all aspects of the experiment are identical except for the variable.
- The variable is the amount of food that the cardinals get to eat, because each of the test groups have different feeding opportunities.

Question 11 Full-credit answers should include the following points:

- To be usable, scientific claims (including hypotheses) must be testable.
- It is not clear how you could design an experiment to test whether a lizard is happy.

Question 5 A: By doing library research, the scientist might be able to find information on pollution in the lakes, but she will not be able to test her hypothesis directly. B, C: The scientist's hypothesis is that the amount of pollution is reaching high levels; it is not about how the pollution levels affect plants or the population of plants. D: Correct.

Question 6 A, C, D: Only one factor, the variable, is changed within each group during a controlled experiment. All other factors, control factors, are the same within each group. Water temperature, the number of eggs, and the kind of frog are control factors. B: Correct.

Question 7 B: Correct. Students struggling with this question should review all the steps of scientific inquiry.

Question 8 A: 12 g = 0.012 kg. B: 120 g = 0.12 kg. C: Correct. D: 12,000 g = 12 kg.

Question 9 A: Correct. B: Cubic centimeters are units of volume. C: Liters are units of volume. D: Kilograms are units of mass.

Science in Action

Science in Action

Scientific Debate

Background

There are three main ingredients of a fire: oxygen, heat, and fuel. Firefighters call this the *fire triangle*, and their goal is to eliminate at least one ingredient. Two groups of firefighters are sent into a forest fire: *hotshots* and *smokejumpers*. Hotshots build a *firebreak* in order to stop the spread of the fire. They clear an area of land of anything that could become fuel for the fire, such as trees, bushes, and grass. The smokejumpers jump from airplanes into remote places to fight small blazes or to start *backfires* in order to eliminate fuel from an oncoming fire.

Science Fiction

AcTiViTy — GENERAL

Further Reading If students liked this story, recommend other stories by Edward D. Hoch, such as the following:

- *The Monkey's Clue*
- *The Stolen Sapphire*
- *The Night, My Friend: Stories of Crime & Suspense*

Scientific Debate

Should We Stop All Forest Fires?

Since 1972, the policy of the National Park Service has been to manage the national parks as naturally as possible. Because fire is a natural event in forests, this policy includes allowing most fires caused by lightning to burn. The only lightning-caused fires that are put out are those that threaten lives, property, uniquely scenic areas, or endangered species. All human-caused fires are put out. However, this policy has caused some controversy. Some people want this policy followed in all public forests and even grasslands. Others think that all fires should be put out.

Social Studies AcTiViTy

WRITING SKILL Research a location where there is a debate about controlling forest fires. You might look into national forests or parks. Write a newspaper article about the issue. Be sure to present all sides of the debate.

Science Fiction

"The Homesick Chicken" by Edward D. Hoch

Why did the chicken cross the road? You think you know the answer to this old riddle, don't you? But "The Homesick Chicken," by Edward D. Hoch, may surprise you. That old chicken may not be exactly what it seems.

You see, one of the chickens at the high-tech Tangaway Research Farms has escaped. Then, it was found in a vacant lot across the highway from Tangaway, pecking away contentedly. Why did it bother to escape? Barnabus Rex, a specialist in solving scientific riddles, is called in to work on this mystery. As he investigates, he finds clues and forms a hypothesis. Read the story, and see if you can explain the mystery before Mr. Rex does.

Language Arts AcTiViTy

WRITING SKILL Write your own short story about a chicken crossing a road for a mysterious reason. Give clues (evidence) to the reader about the mysterious reason but do not reveal the truth until the end of the story. Be sure the story makes sense scientifically.

Answer to Social Studies Activity
Student articles should reflect objective, journalistic style and present more than one perspective on the issue. Encourage students to research areas that are close to where they live.

Answer to Language Arts Activity
Student stories should include logical clues and have a logical ending. Encourage students to read each other's stories and give each other feedback on the use of scientific reasoning in the story.

George Archibald

Dancing with Cranes Imagine a man flapping his arms in a dance with a whooping crane. Does this sound funny? When Dr. George Archibald danced with a crane named Tex, he wasn't joking around. To help this endangered species survive, Archibald wanted cranes to mate in captivity so that he could release cranes into the wild. But the captive cranes wouldn't do their courtship dance. Archibald's cranes had imprinted on the humans that raised them. *Imprinting* is a process in which birds learn to recognize their species by looking at their parents. The birds saw humans as their own species, and could only reproduce if a human did the courtship dance. So, Archibald decided to dance. His plan worked! After some time, Tex hatched a baby crane.

After that, Archibald found a way to help the captive cranes imprint on other cranes. He and his staff now feed baby cranes with hand puppets that look like crane heads. They play recordings of real crane sounds for the young cranes. They even wear crane suits when they are near older birds. These cranes are happy to do their courtship dance with each other instead of with Archibald.

Math ACTIVITY

Suppose you want to drive a group of cranes from Madison, Wisconsin, to Orlando, Florida. Find and measure this distance on a map. If your truck goes 500 km per gas tank and a tank costs $30, how much would gas cost on your trip?

go.hrw.com

To learn more about these Science in Action topics, visit go.hrw.com and type in the keyword HZ5SW7F.

Current Science

Check out Current Science® articles related to this chapter by visiting go.hrw.com. Just type in the keyword HZ5CS01.

Answer to Math Activity
664.5 km ÷ 16 days = 41.53 km/day.

Big Idea:
Unity and Diversity

All living things on Earth are united by certain common characteristics. Every organism is composed of one or more cells, each of which is composed of the same basic elements. Cells perform the functions that are necessary to maintain the life of the organism. All organisms are also able to sense and respond to a stimulus, to reproduce, to use energy, and to grow and develop. Despite these shared characteristics, the living things on Earth are very diverse in terms of habit, habitat, and appearance. This diversity can be attributed to differences in both learned behaviors and inherited traits.

This unit demonstrates the unity found in life on Earth. **The Cell in Action** describes some common processes that occur at the cellular level, such as cellular respiration and cell division. The same chapter introduces the process of photosynthesis, which has provided the basis for a significant portion of the diversity of life on Earth. Plants, which employ photosynthesis are an important form of life on Earth. Plants also have other unique characteristics, which are discussed in detail in **Plant Processes.** These two chapters help establish the foundation for a greater understanding of the unity and dependence among the diverse forms of life on Earth.

TIMELINE

Life Processes

Life science is the study of living things—from the tiniest bacterium to the largest tree! In this unit, you will discover the similarities of all living things. You will learn about important processes such as cellular respiration and photosynthesis. These life processes make life possible on Earth.

This timeline includes a few of the many people who have studied living things and a few events that have shaped the history of life science. And there's always more to be learned, so keep your eyes open.

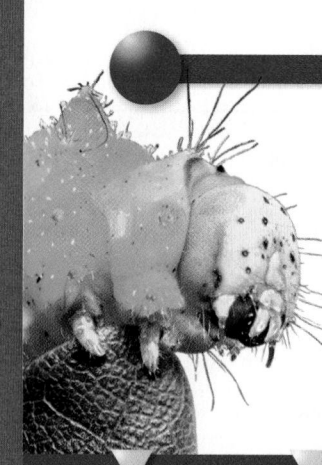

Around 2700 BCE

Si Ling-Chi, empress of China, observes silkworms in her garden and develops a process to cultivate them and make silk.

1931

The first electron microscope is developed.

1934

Dorothy Crowfoot Hodgkin uses X-ray techniques to determine the protein structure of insulin.

1970

Floppy disks for computer data storage are introduced.

1983

Dian Fossey writes *Gorillas in the Mist*, a book about her research on mountain gorillas in Africa and her efforts to save them from poachers.

Around 1000

Arab mathematician and physicist Ibn al Haytham discovers that vision is caused by the reflection of light from objects into the eye.

1684

Improvements to microscopes allow the first observation of red blood cells.

1914

His studies on agriculture and soil conservation lead George Washington Carver to perform research on peanuts.

1944

Oswald T. Avery demonstrates that DNA is the material that carries genetic properties in living organisms.

1946

ENIAC, the first entirely electronic computer, is built. It weighs 30 tons.

1967

Dr. Christiaan Barnard performs the first successful human heart transplant.

1984

A process known as DNA fingerprinting is developed by Alec Jeffreys.

1998

In China, scientists discover a fossil of a dinosaur that had feathers.

2001

A team of scientists led by Philippa Uwins announces that tiny nanobes that are 20 to 150 nanometers wide have been found in Australia. Scientists debate whether these particles are living.

Group ACTiViTY
Unity and Diversity

MATERIALS

- construction paper, assorted colors
- glue
- markers, assorted colors
- paper
- pipe cleaners, assorted colors
- scissors
- straws
- string
- tape

Teacher's Note: Provide students with an assortment of materials that may be useful for building models. Allow students to develop features that may not be correct or functional so that you can assess student's prior knowledge. Such features will also provide students with greater opportunities to make modifications that may not have otherwise been possible.

Building an Organism Divide the class into groups of six and ask each group to create a new kind of plant. Ask each group to build a labeled model of the organism. Instruct each group to prepare a five-minute presentation describing the plants that they have created and give the presentation to the class. Keep these models on display in the class, and allow students to refer to their models as they study the content in this unit. Once your instruction on this unit is complete, you may choose to allow students to modify their models based on what they have learned in this unit. Have students write a brief paragraph explaining the modifications that they chose to make.

The Cell in Action
Chapter Planning Guide

Compression guide:
To shorten instruction because of time limitations, omit the Chapter Lab.

OBJECTIVES	LABS, DEMONSTRATIONS, AND ACTIVITIES	TECHNOLOGY RESOURCES
PACING • 135 min pp. 38–43 **Chapter Opener**	**SE** Start-up Activity, p. 39 ◆ GENERAL	**OSP** Parent Letter ▪ **CD** Student Edition on CD-ROM **CD** Guided Reading Audio CD ▨ **TR** Chapter Starter Transparency* **VID** Brain Food Video Quiz
Section 1 Exchange with the Environment • Explain the process of diffusion. • Describe how osmosis occurs. • Compare passive transport with active transport. • Explain how large particles get into and out of cells.	**TE** Demonstration Membrane Model, p. 40 ◆ GENERAL **SE** Quick Lab Bead Diffusion, p. 41 ◆ GENERAL **CRF** Datasheet for Quick Lab* **SE** Inquiry Lab The Perfect Taters Mystery, p. 52 ◆ GENERAL **CRF** Datasheet for Chapter Lab* **LB** Inquiry Labs Fish Farms in Space* ◆ GENERAL **LB** Whiz-Bang Demonstrations It's in the Bag!* ◆ BASIC	**OSP** Lesson Plans (also in print) **TR** Bellringer Transparency* **TR** L9 Passive and Active Transport* **TR** L10 Endocytosis; Exocytosis* **CRF** SciLinks Activity* GENERAL **VID** Lab Videos for Life Science **CD** Interactive Explorations CD-ROM The Nose Knows GENERAL
PACING • 45 min pp. 44–47 **Section 2 Cell Energy** • Describe photosynthesis and cellular respiration. • Compare cellular respiration with fermentation.	**TE** Demonstration Leaves and Light, p. 44 GENERAL **SE** Connection to Chemistry, Earth's Early Atmosphere p. 45 GENERAL **TE** Group Activity Recycling Carbon, p. 45 GENERAL **TE** Group Activity Photosynthesis and Cellular Respiration, p. 46 GENERAL **SE** Skills Practice Lab Stayin' Alive!, p. 704 GENERAL **CRF** Datasheet for LabBook*	**OSP** Lesson Plans (also in print) **TR** Bellringer Transparency* **TR** L11 The Connection Between Photosynthesis and Respiration* **TR** LINK TO PHYSICAL SCIENCE P44 Solar Heating Systems*
PACING • 45 min pp. 48–51 **Section 3 The Cell Cycle** • Explain how cells produce more cells. • Describe the process of mitosis. • Explain how cell division differs in animals and plants.	**TE** Activity Making Models, p. 48 GENERAL **SE** Connection to Language Arts Picking Apart Vocabulary, p. 49 GENERAL **TE** Connection Activity Math, p. 49 ADVANCED **LB** Labs You Can Eat The Mystery of the Runny Gelatin* ◆ GENERAL **LB** Whiz-Bang Demonstrations Stop Picking on My Enzyme* ◆ BASIC **LB** Long-Term Projects & Research Ideas Taming the Wild Yeast* ◆ ADVANCED **SE** Science in Action Math, Social Studies, and Language Arts Activities, pp. 58–59 GENERAL	**OSP** Lesson Plans (also in print) **TR** Bellringer Transparency* **TR** L12 The Cell Cycle* **TE** Internet Activity, p. 50 GENERAL

PACING • 90 min

CHAPTER REVIEW, ASSESSMENT, AND STANDARDIZED TEST PREPARATION

CRF Vocabulary Activity* GENERAL
SE Chapter Review, pp. 54–55 GENERAL
CRF Chapter Review* ▪ GENERAL
CRF Chapter Tests A* ▪ GENERAL, B* ADVANCED, C* SPECIAL NEEDS
SE Standardized Test Preparation, pp. 56–57 GENERAL
CRF Standardized Test Preparation* GENERAL
CRF Performance-Based Assessment* GENERAL
OSP Test Generator, Test Item Listing

Online and Technology Resources

Holt Online Learning

Visit go.hrw.com for access to Holt Online Learning, or enter the keyword **HS7 Home** for a variety of free online resources.

One-Stop Planner® CD-ROM

This CD-ROM package includes:
• Lab Materials QuickList Software
• Holt Calendar Planner
• Customizable Lesson Plans
• Printable Worksheets
• ExamView® Test Generator
• Interactive Teacher's Edition
• Holt PuzzlePro®
• Holt PowerPoint® Resources

SKILLS DEVELOPMENT RESOURCES	SECTION REVIEW AND ASSESSMENT	CORRELATIONS
SE Pre-Reading Activity, p. 38 `GENERAL` **OSP** Science Puzzlers, Twisters & Teasers `GENERAL`		**National Science Education Standards** UCP 3; SAI 1; SPSP 5; LS 1b
CRF Directed Reading A* ■ `BASIC`, B* `SPECIAL NEEDS` **WB** Workbook* `Struggling Readers` **CRF** Vocabulary and Section Summary* ■ `GENERAL` **SE** Reading Strategy Reading Organizer, p. 40 `GENERAL` **TE** Inclusion Strategies, p. 41 **TE** Support for English Language Learners, p. 41 **CRF** Reinforcement Worksheet Into and Out of the Cell* `BASIC` **SS** Science Skills Doing a Lab Write-Up* `BASIC` **SS** Science Skills Taking Notes* `BASIC` **MS** Math Skills for Science Multiplying Whole Numbers* `BASIC` **MS** Math Skills for Science Dividing Whole Numbers with Long Division* `BASIC`	**SE** Reading Checks, pp. 41, 43 `GENERAL` **TE** Reteaching, p. 42 `BASIC` **TE** Quiz, p. 42 `GENERAL` **TE** Alternative Assessment, p. 42 `ADVANCED` **TE** Homework, p. 42 `GENERAL` **SE** Section Review,* p. 43 ■ `GENERAL` **CRF** Section Quiz* ■ `GENERAL`	UCP 1, 2, 3, 4; LS 1c; *Chapter Lab:* UCP 2; SAI 1
CRF Directed Reading A* ■ `BASIC`, B* `SPECIAL NEEDS` **WB** Workbook* `Struggling Readers` **CRF** Vocabulary and Section Summary* ■ `GENERAL` **SE** Reading Strategy Discussion, p. 44 `GENERAL` **TE** Support for English Language Learners, p. 45 **CRF** Reinforcement Worksheet Activities of the Cell* `BASIC` **SS** Science Skills Using Logic* `BASIC` **SS** Science Skills Identifying Bias* `GENERAL`	**SE** Reading Checks, pp. 45, 47 `GENERAL` **TE** Reteaching, p. 46 `BASIC` **TE** Quiz, p. 46 `GENERAL` **TE** Alternative Assessment, p. 46 `GENERAL` **TE** Homework, p. 46 `ADVANCED` **SE** Section Review,* p. 47 `GENERAL` **CRF** Section Quiz* ■ `GENERAL`	UCP 1, 3, 4, 5; SAI 2; ST 2; SPSP 4; LS 1c, 4c; *LabBook:* SAI 1; SPSP 1; LS 1c
CRF Directed Reading A* ■ `BASIC`, B* `SPECIAL NEEDS` **WB** Workbook* `Struggling Readers` **CRF** Vocabulary and Section Summary* ■ `GENERAL` **SE** Reading Strategy Paired Summarizing, p. 48 `GENERAL` **TE** Connection to Math Cell Multiplication, p. 48 `BASIC` **TE** Reading Strategy Prediction Guide, p. 49 `GENERAL` **TE** Support for English Language Learners, p. 49 **TE** Inclusion Strategies, p. 50 **MS** Math Skills for Science Multiplying Whole Numbers* `BASIC` **MS** Math Skills for Science Grasping Graphing* `GENERAL` **SS** Science Skills Organizing Your Research* `GENERAL` **SS** Science Skills Researching on the Web* `BASIC` **CRF** Reinforcement Worksheet This Is Radio KCEL* `BASIC` **CRF** Critical Thinking A Celluloid Thriller* `ADVANCED`	**SE** Reading Checks, pp. 49, 50 `GENERAL` **TE** Reteaching, p. 50 `BASIC` **TE** Quiz, p. 50 `GENERAL` **TE** Alternative Assessment, p. 50 `GENERAL` **SE** Section Review,* p. 51 ■ `GENERAL` **CRF** Section Quiz* ■ `GENERAL`	SAI 1; LS 1c, 2d

Visual Resources

CHAPTER STARTER TRANSPARENCY

The Cell in Action — CHAPTER STARTER

Happy 140th Birthday!

What If . . . ?

How long would you like to live? What if you could live to be 120 years old? or 150 and beyond? Since ancient times, people have searched in vain for a magical fountain or potion that could give them eternal youth. No one has yet found the secret of immortality, but scientists have recently made a startling discovery that may help extend people's lives.

In January of 1998, researchers at the University of Texas reported that they had found an enzyme in the body that acts like a cellular "fountain of youth." In the laboratory, the enzyme enables human cells to stay young and multiply long past the time when cells would normally stop dividing and die. Researchers hope that the enzyme can someday be used to understand and treat certain cancers and other incurable diseases. Although the so-called immortalizing enzyme won't help people live forever, it may help them live longer, healthier lives.

Every living thing is made of cells. In this chapter you will learn how cells grow and how they make more cells. You will also learn how cells transport materials and obtain the energy they need to survive.

BELLRINGER TRANSPARENCIES

The Cell in Action — BELLRINGER TRANSPARENCY

Section: Exchange with the Environment
Which of the following best describes a living cell:
a) building block
b) a living organism
c) a complex factory
d) all of the above

Write a paragraph in your **science journal** defending your choice.

Section: Cell Energy
Make a list of all the different types of cells that you can think of and the jobs they do. Then make a list of all the reasons that a cell needs energy.

Write your answers in your **science journal**.

TEACHING TRANSPARENCIES

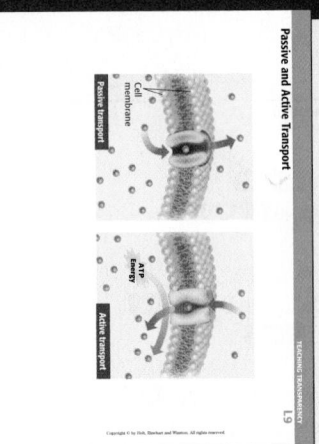

Passive and Active Transport

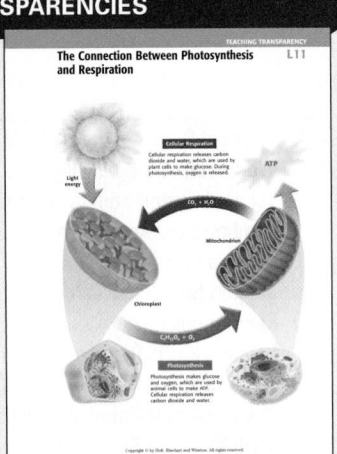

The Connection Between Photosynthesis and Respiration — L11

TEACHING TRANSPARENCIES

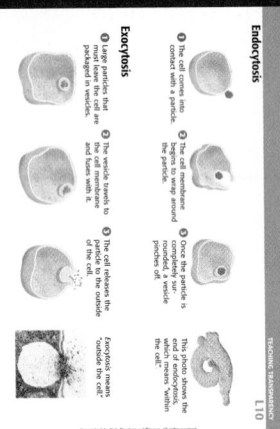

Exocytosis / Endocytosis — L10

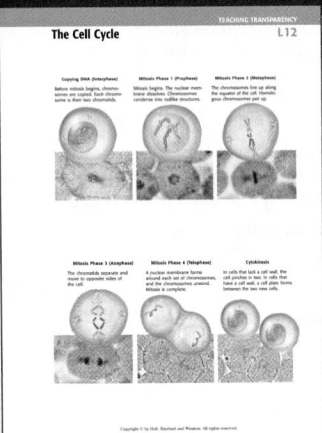

The Cell Cycle — L12

Solar Heating Systems — P44

Chapter: Heat and Heat Technology

LINK TO PHYSICAL SCIENCE

CONCEPT MAPPING TRANSPARENCY

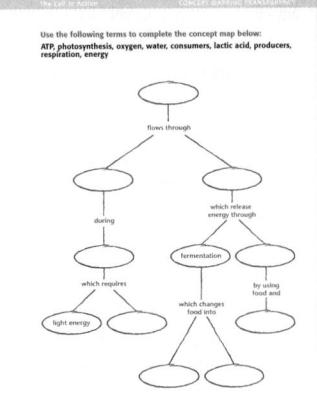

The Cell in Action — CONCEPT MAPPING TRANSPARENCY

Use the following terms to complete the concept map below:
ATP, photosynthesis, oxygen, water, consumers, lactic acid, producers, respiration, energy

Planning Resources

LESSON PLANS

Lesson Plan SAMPLE

Section: Waves

Pacing
Regular Schedule: with lab(s):2 days without lab(s):2 days
Block Schedule: with lab(s):1 1/2 days without lab(s):1 day

Objectives
1. Relate the seven properties of life to a living organism.
2. Describe seven themes that can help you to organize what you learn about biology.
3. Identify the tiny structures that make up all living organisms.
4. Differentiate between reproduction and heredity and between metabolism and homeostasis.

National Science Education Standards Covered
LSInter1:Cells have particular structures that underlie their functions.
LSMat1:Most cell functions involve chemical reactions.
LSBeh1:Cells store and use information to guide their functions.
UCP1:Cell functions are regulated.
SI1: Cells can differentiate and form complete multicellular organisms.
PS1: Species evolve over time.
ESS1: The great diversity of organisms is the result of more than 3.5 billion years of evolution.
ESS2: Natural selection and its evolutionary consequences provide a scientific explanation for the fossil record of ancient life forms as well as for the striking molecular similarities observed among the diverse species of living organisms.
ST1: The millions of different species of plants, animals, and microorganisms that live on Earth today are related by descent from common ancestors.
ST2: The energy for life primarily comes from the sun.
SPSP1: The complexity and organization of organisms accommodates the need for obtaining, transforming, transporting, releasing, and eliminating the matter and energy used to sustain the organism.
SPSP6: As matter and energy flows through different levels of organization of living systems—cells, organs, communities—and between living systems and the physical environment, chemical elements are recombined in different ways.
HNS1: Organisms have behavioral responses to internal changes and to external stimuli.

PARENT LETTER

SAMPLE

Dear Parent,

Your son's or daughter's science class will soon begin exploring the chapter entitled "The World of Physical Science." In this chapter, students will learn about how the scientific method applies to the world of physical science and the role of physical science in the world. By the end of the chapter, students should demonstrate a clear understanding of the chapter's main ideas and be able to discuss the following topics:

1. physical science as the study of energy and matter (Section 1)
2. the role of physical science in the world around them (Section 1)
3. careers that rely on physical science (Section 1)
4. the steps used in the scientific method (Section 2)
5. examples of technology (Section 2)
6. how the scientific method is used to answer questions and solve problems (Section 2)
7. how our knowledge of science changes over time (Section 2)
8. how models represent real objects or systems (Section 3)
9. examples of different ways models are used in science (Section 3)
10. the importance of the International System of Units (Section 4)
11. the appropriate units to use for particular measurements (Section 4)
12. how area and density are derived quantities (Section 4)

Questions to Ask Along the Way

You can help your son or daughter learn about these topics by asking interesting questions such as the following:

- What are some surprising careers that use physical science?
- What is a characteristic of a good hypothesis?
- When is a good idea to use a model?
- Why do Americans measure things in terms of inches and yards and meters?

ALSO IN SPANISH

TEST ITEM LISTING

TEST ITEM LISTING
The World of Science SAMPLE

MULTIPLE CHOICE

1. A limitation of models is that
   a. they are large enough to see
   b. they do not act exactly like the things that they model.
   c. they are smaller than the things that they model.
   d. they model unfamiliar things.
   Answer: B Difficulty: 1 Section: 3 Objective: 2

2. The length 10 m is equal to
   a. 100 cm. c. 10,000 mm.
   b. 1,000 cm. d. Both (b) and (c.)
   Answer: B Difficulty: 1 Section: 3 Objective: 2

3. To be valid, a hypothesis must be
   a. testable. c. made into a law.
   b. supported by evidence. d. Both (a) and (b)
   Answer: D Difficulty: 1 Section: 3 Objective: 2 1

4. The statement "Sheila has a stain on her shirt" is an example of a(n)
   a. law. c. observation.
   b. hypothesis. d. prediction.
   Answer: B Difficulty: 1 Section: 3 Objective: 2

5. A hypothesis is often developed out of
   a. observations. c. laws.
   b. experiments. d. Both (a) and (b)
   Answer: B Difficulty: 1 Section: 3 Objective: 2

6. How many milliliters are in 3.5 kL?
   a. 3,500 mL c. 3,500,000 mL
   b. 3.0035 mL d. 35,000 mL
   Answer: B Difficulty: 1 Section: 3 Objective: 2

7. A map of Seattle is an example of a
   a. law. c. model.
   b. theory. d. unit.
   Answer: B Difficulty: 1 Section: 3 Objective: 2

8. A lab has the safety icons shown below. These icons mean that you should wear
   a. only safety goggles c. safety goggles and a lab apron.
   b. only a lab apron. d. safety goggles, a lab apron, and gloves.
   Answer: B Difficulty: 1 Section: 3 Objective: 2

9. The law of conservation of mass says the tot al mass before a chemical change is
   a. more than the total mass after the change.
   b. less than the total mass after the change.
   c. the same as the total mass after the change.
   d. not the same as the total mass after the change.
   Answer: B Difficulty: 1 Section: 3 Objective: 2

10. In which of the following areas might you find a geochemist at work?
    a. studying the chemistry of rocks c. studying fabric
    b. studying forestry d. studying the atmosphere
    Answer: B Difficulty: 1 Section: 3 Objective: 2

One-Stop Planner® CD-ROM

This CD-ROM includes all of the resources shown here and the following time-saving tools:

- *Lab Materials QuickList Software*
- *Customizable lesson plans*
- *Holt Calendar Planner*
- *The powerful ExamView® Test Generator*

Meeting Individual Needs

DIRECTED READING A
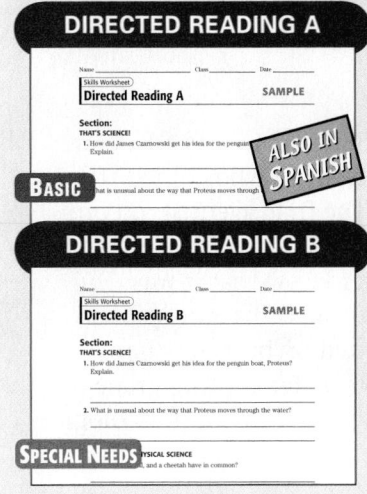
BASIC · **ALSO IN SPANISH**

DIRECTED READING B
SPECIAL NEEDS

VOCABULARY ACTIVITY
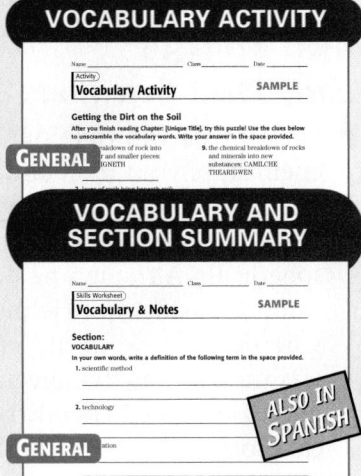
GENERAL

VOCABULARY AND SECTION SUMMARY
GENERAL · **ALSO IN SPANISH**

REINFORCEMENT
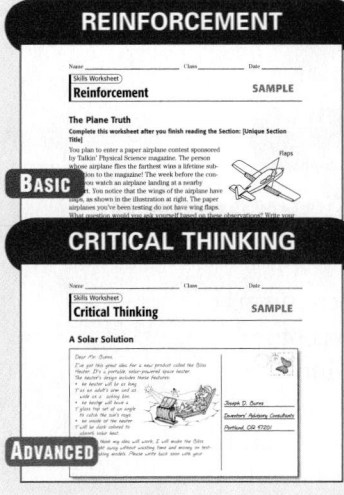
BASIC

CRITICAL THINKING
ADVANCED

SCILINKS ACTIVITY

GENERAL

SCIENCE PUZZLERS, TWISTERS & TEASERS
GENERAL

Labs and Activities

LONG-TERM PROJECTS & RESEARCH IDEAS
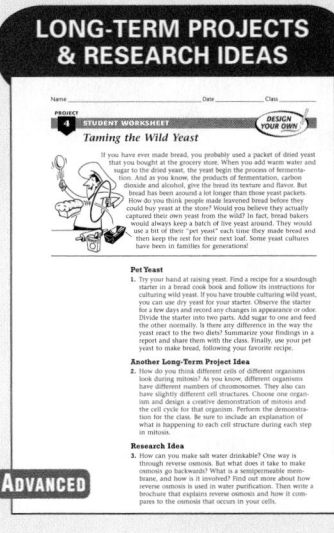
ADVANCED

WHIZ-BANG DEMONSTRATIONS
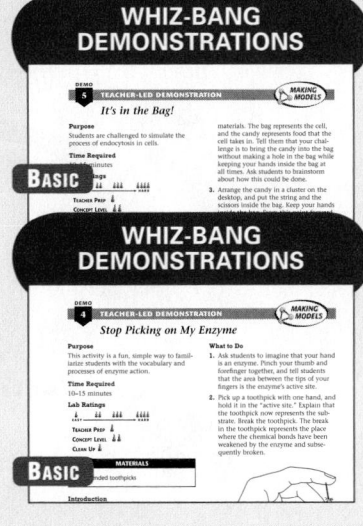
BASIC

WHIZ-BANG DEMONSTRATIONS
BASIC

INQUIRY LABS
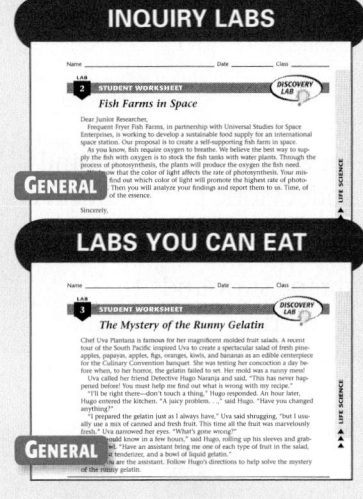
GENERAL

LABS YOU CAN EAT
GENERAL

DATASHEETS FOR QUICK LABS

DATASHEETS FOR CHAPTER LABS

DATASHEETS FOR LABBOOK

Review and Assessments

SECTION QUIZ
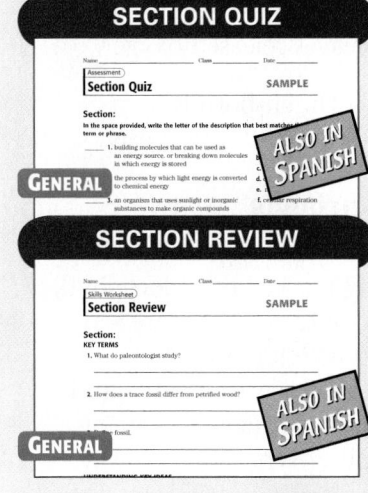
GENERAL · **ALSO IN SPANISH**

SECTION REVIEW
GENERAL · **ALSO IN SPANISH**

CHAPTER REVIEW
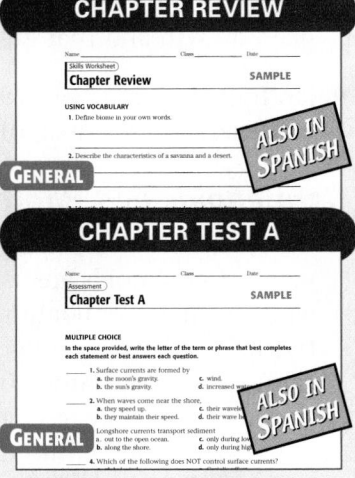
GENERAL · **ALSO IN SPANISH**

CHAPTER TEST A
GENERAL · **ALSO IN SPANISH**

CHAPTER TEST B
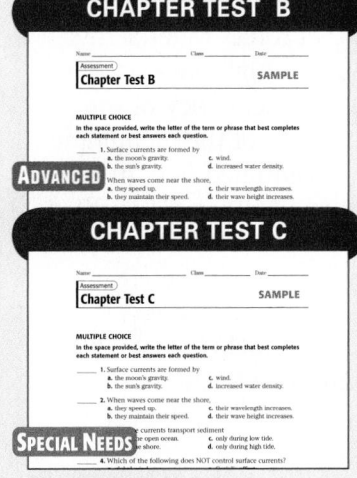
ADVANCED

CHAPTER TEST C
SPECIAL NEEDS

STANDARDIZED TEST PREPARATION
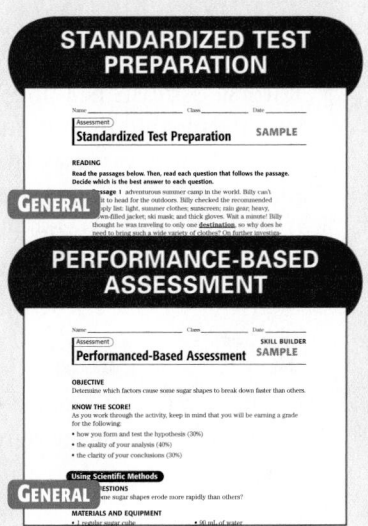
GENERAL

PERFORMANCE-BASED ASSESSMENT
GENERAL

This Chapter Enrichment provides relevant and interesting information to expand and enhance your presentation of the chapter material.

Section 1

Exchange with the Environment

Endocytosis

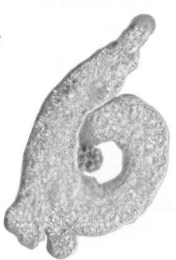

- There are three different mechanisms of endocytosis: phagocytosis, receptor-mediated endocytosis, and pinocytosis. These processes allow a substance to enter a cell without passing through the cell membrane. The substance involved determines which method is used.

- Large particles such as bacteria enter the cell by phagocytosis. The host cell changes shape, and the membrane sends out projections called *pseudopods*, meaning "false feet," which surround the particle, bringing it inside the cell.

- In receptor-mediated endocytosis, receptors on the membrane that are specific for a given substance bind to the substance before the endocytotic process begins. This method is used during cholesterol metabolism.

- In pinocytosis, the cell membrane surrounds the substance and forms a vesicle to bring the material into the cell. Pinocytosis usually involves material that is dissolved in water.

 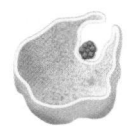 

Reverse Osmosis

- Reverse osmosis is a process that forces water across semipermeable membranes under high pressure. The high pressure reverses the natural tendency of the solutes on the more concentrated side of the membrane to pass through to the less-concentrated side. In this way, water passing through the membrane is purified.

Is That a Fact!

◆ The largest single-celled organism that ever lived was a protozoan that measured 20 cm in diameter. It is now extinct.

Section 2

Cell Energy

Early Plant Scientists

- Jan Baptista Van Helmont (1580–1644) was a Belgian chemist, physiologist, and physician who coined the word *gas*. Van Helmont was the first scientist to comprehend the existence of gases separate from the atmospheric air. Although he didn't know that it was carbon dioxide, van Helmont stated that the *spiritus sylvestre,* or "wild spirit," emitted by burning charcoal was the same as that given off by fermenting grape juice. He applied chemistry to the study of physiological processes, and for this he is known as the "father of biochemistry."

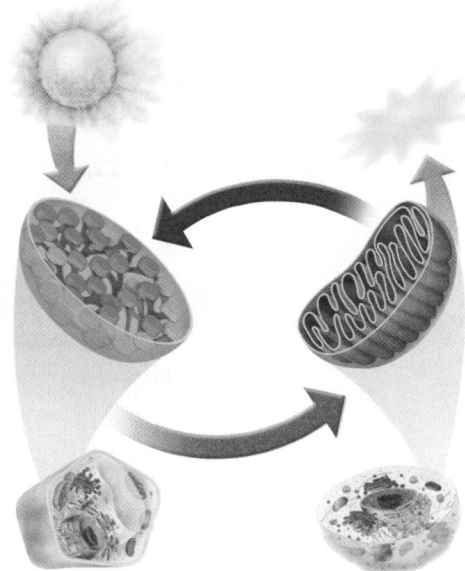

- Joseph Priestley (1733–1804) was an English clergyman and physical scientist who was one of the discoverers of oxygen. He also observed that light was vital for plant growth and that green leaves released oxygen.

- Jan Ingenhousz (1730–1799), a Dutch-born British physician and scientist, discovered photosynthesis.

Carotenoids and Photosynthesis

- Carotenoids are responsible for the orange colors in plants. Carotenoids are usually masked by chlorophyll, which is more abundant until autumn. They are sensitive to wavelengths of light to which chlorophyll cannot respond. Carotenoids absorb wavelengths and transfer the energy to chlorophyll, which then incorporates that energy into the photosynthetic pathway.

Section 3

The Cell Cycle

Cytogenetics

- Cytogeneticists study the role of human chromosomes in health and disease. Chromosome studies can reveal abnormalities such as whether a person is carrying the genetic material for a genetically linked disease.

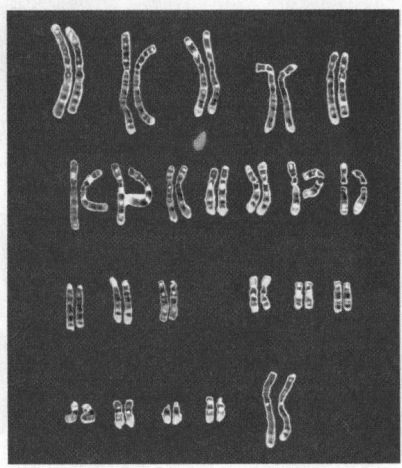

Cell Division

- The frequency of cell division varies a great deal. Fruit-fly embryo cells divide about every eight minutes. Human liver cells may not divide for up to one year. Scientists are still trying to determine what orchestrates growth and regulates cell division. This information would help scientists understand diseases of unregulated cell division, such as cancer.

- DNA and chromosomes are related but are not the same thing. A chromosome is made up of DNA that has been wound up and organized with proteins that hold it all together. For much of the cell cycle, DNA is loose and not very visible.

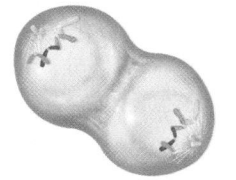 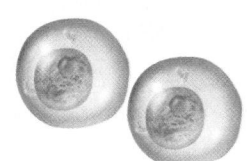

Is That a Fact!

- In an adult human body, cell division happens at least 10 million times every second.

Cell Adhesion

- Blood cells exist individually in the body, but most other cells are connected to each other. Usually this involves special adhesion proteins, such as adherins, cadherins, catenins, and integrins. These proteins connect adjoining cells by physically locking the cells together, fastening one cell to the next. Sometimes these junctions are outside the cell, and sometimes they are inside. Adhesion proteins can span the cell membranes and connect the inside of one cell to the inside of its neighbor cell.

Is That a Fact!

- In a healthy body, cells reproduce at exactly the same rate at which cells die. However, some agents make cells reproduce uncontrollably, causing a disease known as cancer. One of these carcinogenic agents is ultraviolet radiation, which is emitted by the sun and ultraviolet lamps. People who spend excessive amounts of time in the sun run the risk of developing skin cancer.

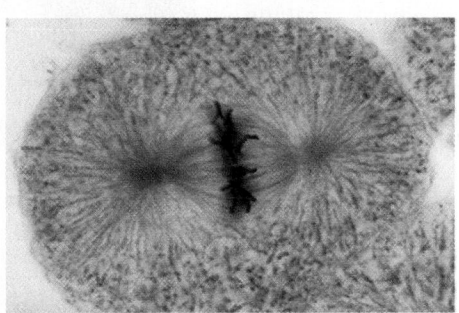

SciLinks is maintained by the National Science Teachers Association to provide you and your students with interesting, up-to-date links that will enrich your classroom presentation of the chapter.

Visit www.scilinks.org and enter the SciLinks code for more information about the topic listed.

Topic: Diffusion	Topic: Photosynthesis
SciLinks code: HSM0406	SciLinks code: HSM1140
Topic: Osmosis	Topic: Cell Cycle
SciLinks code: HSM1090	SciLinks code: HSM0235
Topic: Cell Energy	Topic: Cell Structures
SciLinks code: HSM0237	SciLinks code: HSM0240

Overview

In this chapter, students will learn about how cells interact with their environment, how cells get nutrients and get rid of wastes, and where cells get the energy from to carry out all the activities of life. Students will also learn about how cells produce more cells.

Assessing Prior Knowledge

Students should be familiar with the following topic:

• cells as the basic units of life

Identifying Misconceptions

Students may not think of cells as self-contained units of life. It is important for students to realize that cells, just like multicellular organisms, live in an environment and must perform all the activities—such as taking in nutrients, using energy, and getting rid of wastes—necessary to stay alive and reproduce. Students may also be confused about the difference between cells and molecules. Emphasize the relationship between cells and molecules, and that proteins, carbohydrates, and other substances are made of molecules. These molecules must be smaller than the cells they enter and leave. Many students believe that proteins and other molecules are bigger than cells.

The Cell in Action

The Big Idea

Cells carry out important life functions including taking in nutrients and releasing materials, obtaining energy, and growing.

About the Photo

This adult katydid is emerging from its last immature, or nymph, stage. As the katydid changed from a nymph to an adult, every structure of its body changed. To grow and change, an organism must produce new cells. When a cell divides, it makes a copy of its genetic material.

PRE-READING ACTIVITY

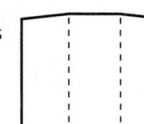

FOLDNOTES **Tri-Fold** Before you read the chapter, create the FoldNote entitled "Tri-Fold" described in the **Study Skills** section of the Appendix. Write what you know about the actions of cells in the column labeled "Know." Then, write what you want to know in the column labeled "Want." As you read the chapter, write what you learn about the actions of cells in the column labeled "Learn."

Standards Correlations

National Science Education Standards

The following codes indicate the National Science Education Standards that correlate to this chapter. The full text of the standards is at the front of the book.

Chapter Opener
UCP 3; SAI 1; SPSP 5; LS 1b

Section 1 Exchange with the Environment
UCP 1, 2, 3, 4; LS 1c

Section 2 Cell Energy
UCP 1, 3, 4, 5; SAI 2; ST 2; SPSP 4; LS 1c, 4c;
LabBook: SAI 1; SPSP1; LS 1c

Section 3 The Cell Cycle
SAI 1; LS 1c, 2d

Chapter Lab
UCP 2; SAI 1

Chapter Review
UCP 1, 2, 3, 4, 5; SAI 1, 2; ST 2; SPSP 4, 5; LS 1b, 1c, 2d, 4c

Science in Action
UCP 1, 2, 3, 5; SAI 1, 2; ST 1, 2; SPSP 5; LS 1d, 1e, 1f

START-UP ACTIVITY
MATERIALS

FOR EACH STUDENT
- cup, small plastic
- ruler
- stirring rod
- sugar solution
- test tube, large plastic
- test-tube rack
- test tube, small plastic
- yeast-and-water mixture

Safety Caution: Remind students to review all safety cautions and icons before beginning this lab activity. Students should wear safety goggles at all times and wash their hands when they are finished. Students should not taste the solutions.

Teacher's Notes: The yeast suspension is prepared by mixing one package of dry yeast in 250 mL of water. The sugar solution is prepared by dissolving 30 mL (2 tbsp) of sugar in 100 mL of water.

Answers

1. Answers may vary. Students should subtract the first measurement from the second measurement.

2. When the yeast cells released the energy in sugar, the CO_2 that the cells produced increased the volume of air in the smaller tube and pushed more yeast-and-sugar mixture into the larger tube, increasing the height of the liquid in the larger tube.

START-UP ACTIVITY

Cells in Action

Yeast are single-celled fungi that are an important ingredient in bread. Yeast cells break down sugar molecules to release energy. In the process, carbon dioxide gas is produced, which causes bread dough to rise.

Procedure

1. Add **4 mL of a sugar solution** to **10 mL of a yeast-and-water mixture**. Use a **stirring rod** to thoroughly mix the two liquids.

2. Pour the stirred mixture into a small test tube.

3. Place a slightly **larger test tube** over the **small test tube**. The top of the small test tube should touch the bottom of the larger test tube.

4. Hold the test tubes together, and quickly turn both test tubes over. Place the test tubes in a test-tube rack.

5. Use a **ruler** to measure the height of the fluid in the large test tube. Wait 20 min, and then measure the height of the liquid again.

Analysis

1. What is the difference between the first height measurement and the second height measurement?

2. What do you think caused the change in the fluid's height?

What If . . . ?

How long would you like to live? What if you could live to be 120 years old? What if 150 and beyond? Since ancient times, people have searched in vain for a magical fountain or potion that could give them eternal youth. No one has yet found the secret of immortality, but scientists

past the time when cells would normally stop dividing and die. Researchers hope that the enzyme can someday be used to understand and treat certain cancers and other incurable diseases. Although the so-called immortalizing enzyme won't help people live forever, it may

Chapter Starter Transparency
Use this transparency to help students begin thinking about the relationship between cells and their environment.

CHAPTER RESOURCES

Technology

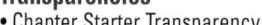

Transparencies — READING SKILLS
- Chapter Starter Transparency

Student Edition on CD-ROM

Guided Reading Audio CD
- English or Spanish

Classroom Videos
- Brain Food Video Quiz

Workbooks

Science Puzzlers, Twisters & Teasers
- The Cell in Action GENERAL

Focus

Overview

This section explains the processes of diffusion and osmosis. Students will compare the passive and active transport of particles into and out of cells.

Bellringer

Write the following on the board:

Which of the following best describes a living cell: a building block, a living organism, a complex factory, or all of the above? Explain your choice.

Motivate

Demonstration — GENERAL

Membrane Model Blow soap bubbles for the class. Explain that soap bubbles have properties, such as flexibility, that are similar to biological membranes. Components of soap film and of cell membranes move around freely. Soap bubbles and membranes are self-sealing. If two bubbles or membranes collide, they fuse. If one is cut in half, two smaller but whole bubbles or membranes form.

English Language Learners

LS Visual

What You Will Learn

- Explain the process of diffusion.
- Describe how osmosis occurs.
- Compare passive transport with active transport.
- Explain how large particles get into and out of cells.

Vocabulary

diffusion
osmosis
passive transport
active transport
endocytosis
exocytosis

READING STRATEGY

Reading Organizer As you read this section, make a table comparing active transport and passive transport.

Exchange with the Environment

What would happen to a factory if its power were shut off or its supply of raw materials never arrived? What would happen if the factory couldn't get rid of its garbage?

Like a factory, an organism must be able to obtain energy and raw materials and get rid of wastes. An organism's cells perform all of these functions. These functions keep cells healthy so that they can divide. Cell division allows organisms to grow and repair injuries.

The exchange of materials between a cell and its environment takes place at the cell's membrane. To understand how materials move into and out of the cell, you need to know about diffusion.

What Is Diffusion?

What happens if you pour dye on top of a layer of gelatin? At first, it is easy to see where the dye ends and the gelatin begins. But over time, the line between the two layers will blur, as shown in **Figure 1.** Why? Everything, including the gelatin and the dye, is made up of tiny moving particles. Particles travel from where they are crowded to where they are less crowded. This movement from areas of high concentration (crowded) to areas of low concentration (less crowded) is called **diffusion** (di FYOO zhuhn). Dye particles diffuse from where they are crowded (near the top of the glass) to where they are less crowded (in the gelatin). Diffusion also happens within and between living cells. Cells do not need to use energy for diffusion.

diffusion the movement of particles from regions of higher density to regions of lower density

Figure 1 *The particles of the dye and the gelatin slowly mix by diffusion.*

CONNECTION to

Math ——— GENERAL

Gas Diffusion Have students solve the following problem in class or as part of their homework:

Gases diffuse about 10,000 times faster in air than in water. If a gas diffuses to fill a room completely in 6 min, how long would it take the gas to fill a similar volume of still water? (60,000 min) How many hours would that be? (1,000 h) How many days? (41.67 days) LS Logical

Figure 2 Osmosis

❶ The side that holds only pure water has the higher concentration of water particles.

❷ During osmosis, water particles move to where they are less concentrated.

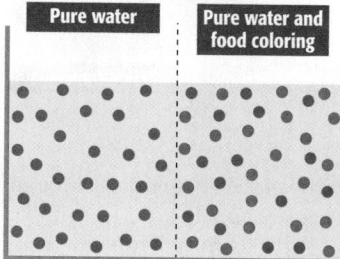

Pure water | Pure water and food coloring

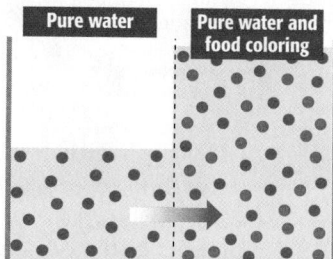

Pure water | Pure water and food coloring

Diffusion of Water

The cells of organisms are surrounded by and filled with fluids that are made mostly of water. The diffusion of water through cell membranes is so important to life processes that it has been given a special name—**osmosis** (ahs MOH sis).

Water is made up of particles, called *molecules*. Pure water has the highest concentration of water molecules. When you mix something, such as food coloring, sugar, or salt, with water, you lower the concentration of water molecules. **Figure 2** shows how water molecules move through a membrane that is semipermeable (SEM i PUHR mee uh buhl). *Semipermeable* means that only certain substances can pass through. The picture on the left in **Figure 2** shows liquids that have different concentrations of water. Over time, the water molecules move from the liquid with the high concentration of water molecules to the liquid with the lower concentration of water molecules.

The Cell and Osmosis

Osmosis is important to cell functions. For example, red blood cells are surrounded by plasma. Plasma is made up of water, salts, sugars, and other particles. The concentration of these particles is kept in balance by osmosis. If red blood cells were in pure water, water molecules would flood into the cells and cause them to burst. When red blood cells are put into a salty solution, the concentration of water molecules inside the cell is higher than the concentration of water outside. This difference makes water move out of the cells, and the cells shrivel up. Osmosis also occurs in plant cells. When a wilted plant is watered, osmosis makes the plant firm again.

Reading Check Why would red blood cells burst if you placed them in pure water? (*See the Appendix for answers to Reading Checks.*)

osmosis the diffusion of water through a semipermeable membrane

Bead Diffusion

1. Put three groups of **colored beads** on the bottom of a **plastic bowl**. Each group should be made up of five beads of the same color.

2. Stretch some **clear plastic wrap** tightly over the top of the bowl. Gently shake the bowl for 10 seconds while watching the beads.

3. How is the scattering of the beads like the diffusion of particles? How is it different from the diffusion of particles?

MATERIALS

FOR EACH GROUP
• colored beads, 3 groups
• plastic bowl
• plastic wrap, clear

Answers

3. Beads moved from areas of more-concentrated colors to areas of less-concentrated colors. Eventually, different-colored beads were mixed somewhat evenly. Mixing beads required the use of students' energy and occurred more quickly than diffusion normally occurs.

Answer to Reading Check

Red blood cells would burst in pure water because water particles move from outside, where particles were dense, to inside the cell, where particles were less dense. This movement of water would cause red blood cells to fill up and burst.

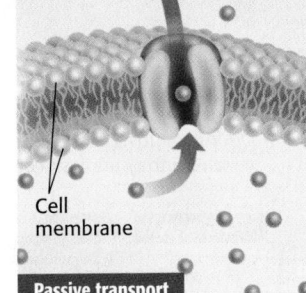
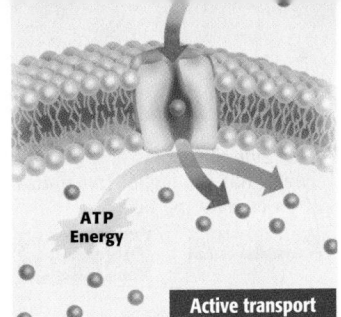

Cell membrane

ATP Energy

Passive transport

Active transport

Figure 3 *In passive transport, particles travel through proteins to areas of lower concentration. In active transport, cells use energy to move particles, usually to areas of higher concentration.*

passive transport the movement of substances across a cell membrane without the use of energy by the cell

active transport the movement of substances across the cell membrane that requires the cell to use energy

endocytosis the process by which a cell membrane surrounds a particle and encloses the particle in a vesicle to bring the particle into the cell

Moving Small Particles

Small particles, such as sugars, cross the cell membrane through passageways called *channels*. These channels are made up of proteins in the cell membrane. Particles travel through these channels by either passive or active transport. The movement of particles across a cell membrane without the use of energy by the cell is called **passive transport**, and is shown in **Figure 3.** During passive transport, particles move from an area of high concentration to an area of low concentration. Diffusion and osmosis are examples of passive transport.

A process of transporting particles that requires the cell to use energy is called **active transport.** Active transport usually involves the movement of particles from an area of low concentration to an area of high concentration.

Moving Large Particles

Small particles cross the cell membrane by diffusion, passive transport, and active transport. Large particles move into and out of the cell by processes called *endocytosis* and *exocytosis*.

Endocytosis

The active-transport process by which a cell surrounds a large particle, such as a large protein, and encloses the particle in a vesicle to bring the particle into the cell is called **endocytosis** (EN doh sie TOH sis). *Vesicles* are sacs formed from pieces of cell membrane. **Figure 4** shows endocytosis.

Figure 4 **Endocytosis**

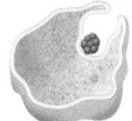

1 The cell comes into contact with a particle.

2 The cell membrane begins to wrap around the particle.

3 Once the particle is completely surrounded, a vesicle pinches off.

This photo shows the end of *endocytosis*, which means "within the cell."

Homework ——— GENERAL

 Transport Ask students to describe how each of the following materials would get through a cell membrane and into a cell.

a. pure water (osmosis)

b. sugar entering a cell that already contains a high concentration of particles (active transport)

c. sugar entering a cell that has a low concentration of particles (diffusion or passive transport)

d. a protein (active transport or endocytosis)

LS Logical

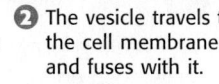 **Figure 5** **Exocytosis**

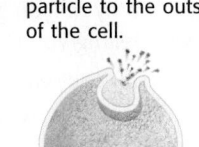

❶ Large particles that must leave the cell are packaged in vesicles.

❷ The vesicle travels to the cell membrane and fuses with it.

❸ The cell releases the particle to the outside of the cell.

Exocytosis means "outside the cell."

 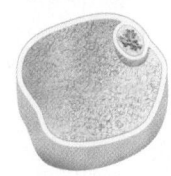 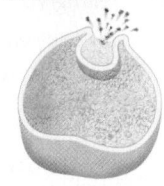 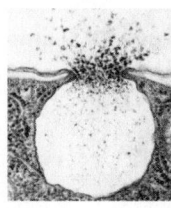

Exocytosis

When large particles, such as wastes, leave the cell, the cell uses an active-transport process called **exocytosis** (EK soh sie TOH sis). During exocytosis, a vesicle forms around a large particle within the cell. The vesicle carries the particle to the cell membrane. The vesicle fuses with the cell membrane and releases the particle to the outside of the cell. **Figure 5** shows exocytosis.

exocytosis the process in which a cell releases a particle by enclosing the particle in a vesicle that then moves to the cell surface and fuses with the cell membrane

✓ **Reading Check** What is exocytosis?

SECTION Review

Summary

- Diffusion is the movement of particles from an area of high concentration to an area of low concentration.

- Osmosis is the diffusion of water through a semi-permeable membrane.

- Cells move small particles by diffusion, which is an example of passive transport, and by active transport.

- Large particles enter the cell by endocytosis, and exit the cell by exocytosis.

Using Key Terms

For each pair of terms, explain how the meanings of the terms differ.

1. *diffusion* and *osmosis*

2. *active transport* and *passive transport*

3. *endocytosis* and *exocytosis*

Understanding Key Ideas

4. The movement of particles from a less crowded area to a more crowded area requires

   a. sunlight.   **c.** a membrane.
   b. energy.   **d.** osmosis.

5. What structures allow small particles to cross cell membranes?

Math Skills

6. The area of particle 1 is 2.5 mm². The area of particle 2 is 0.5 mm². The area of particle 1 is how many times as big as the area of particle 2?

Critical Thinking

7. **Predicting Consequences** What would happen to a cell if its channel proteins were damaged and unable to transport particles? What would happen to the organism if many of its cells were damaged in this way? Explain your answer.

8. **Analyzing Ideas** Why does active transport require energy?

SCiLINKS **NSTA**
Developed and maintained by the National Science Teachers Association

For a variety of links related to this chapter, go to www.scilinks.org

Topics: Diffusion; Osmosis
SciLinks code: HSM0406; HSM1090

Answers to Section Review

1. Sample answer: Diffusion is when any kind of particles move from a crowded area to a less crowded area. Osmosis is diffusion of water through a semipermeable membrane.

2. Sample answer: Active transport requires energy, while passive transport does not require energy.

3. Sample answer: Endocytosis is the process that brings things into a cell, and exocytosis takes things out of a cell.

4. b

5. Small particles move through channels in the cell membrane.

6. 5

7. Sample answer: If a cell were unable to transport particles, it could not get the materials that it needs or remove wastes. The cell would most likely die. If many of an organism's cells were damaged in this way, the organism would become sick and might die.

8. Active transport requires energy because the cell must work against the flow of particles.

Answer to Reading Check

Exocytosis is the process by which a cell moves large particles to the outside of the cell.

CHAPTER RESOURCES

Chapter Resource File

 • Section Quiz **GENERAL**
• Section Review **GENERAL**
• Vocabulary and Section Summary **GENERAL**
• Reinforcement Worksheet **BASIC**
• SciLinks Activity **GENERAL**
• Datasheet for Quick Lab

Technology

 Interactive Explorations CD-ROM
• The Nose Knows **GENERAL**

Focus

Overview

This section introduces energy and the cell. Students learn about solar energy and the process of photosynthesis. Finally, students learn about cellular respiration and fermentation.

🔊 Bellringer

Ask students to make a list of all the reasons why a cell might need energy. Remind students that there are many types of cells doing many different jobs.

Motivate

Demonstration — GENERAL

Leaves and Light Ask students what they think would happen if a plant could not get sunlight. A few days before teaching this section, cut out a square from black construction paper. Fold the square over a leaf of any common plant, such as a geranium. Affix the square with a paper clip. Be sure the leaf does not receive any sunlight. Leave the leaf covered for about one week. Remove the black square. The leaf will be paler than the other leaves. In the absence of sunlight, chlorophyll is depleted and not replenished. The leaf's green color will have faded.

English Language Learners

LS Visual

What You Will Learn

● Describe photosynthesis and cellular respiration.
● Compare cellular respiration with fermentation.

Vocabulary

photosynthesis
cellular respiration
fermentation

READING STRATEGY

Discussion Read this section silently. Write down questions that you have about this section. Discuss your questions in a small group.

photosynthesis the process by which plants, algae, and some bacteria use sunlight, carbon dioxide, and water to make food

Cell Energy

Why do you get hungry? Feeling hungry is your body's way of telling you that your cells need energy.

All cells need energy to live, grow, and reproduce. Plant cells get their energy from the sun. Many animal cells get the energy they need from food.

From Sun to Cell

Nearly all of the energy that fuels life comes from the sun. Plants capture energy from the sun and change it into food through a process called **photosynthesis.** The food that plants make supplies them with energy. This food also becomes a source of energy for the organisms that eat the plants.

Photosynthesis

Plant cells have molecules that absorb light energy. These molecules are called *pigments*. Chlorophyll (KLAWR uh FIL), the main pigment used in photosynthesis, gives plants their green color. Chlorophyll is found in chloroplasts.

Plants use the energy captured by chlorophyll to change carbon dioxide and water into food. The food is in the form of the simple sugar glucose. Glucose is a carbohydrate. When plants make glucose, they convert the sun's energy into a form of energy that can be stored. The energy in glucose is used by the plant's cells. Photosynthesis also produces oxygen. Photosynthesis is summarized in **Figure 1.**

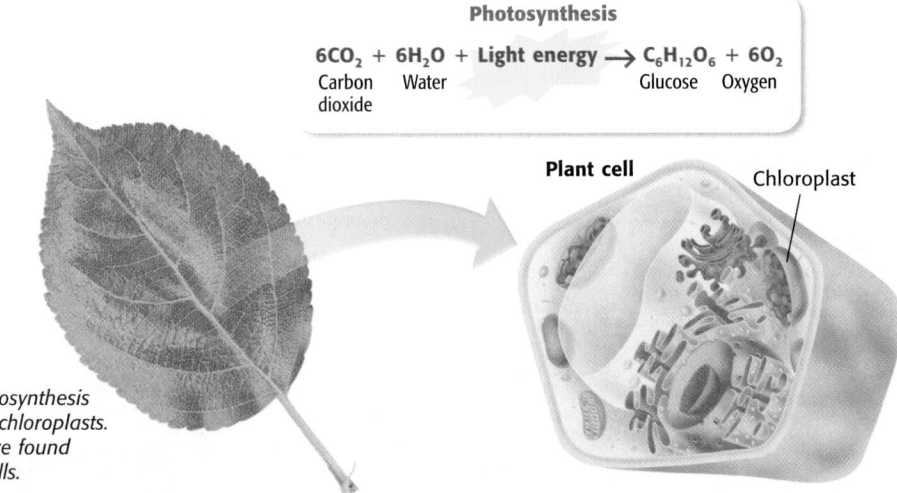

Photosynthesis

$$6CO_2 + 6H_2O + \text{Light energy} \longrightarrow C_6H_{12}O_6 + 6O_2$$

Carbon dioxide · Water · Glucose · Oxygen

Plant cell · Chloroplast

Figure 1 *Photosynthesis takes place in chloroplasts. Chloroplasts are found inside plant cells.*

CHAPTER RESOURCES

Chapter Resource File

 • **Lesson Plan**
 • **Directed Reading A** BASIC, **B** SPECIAL NEEDS

Technology

 Transparencies
 • Bellringer
 • *LINK TO* **PHYSICAL SCIENCE** P44 Solar Heating Systems

Workbooks

 Interactive Textbook Struggling Readers

 Science Skills
 • Using Logic BASIC
 • Identifying Bias GENERAL

MISCONCEPTION ALERT

Not the Only Steps The processes of photosynthesis and respiration are complex chemical reactions that involve several steps shown by many chemical reactions. The much simpler equations shown for the processes of respiration and photosynthesis in this chapter are the *net* equations for those reactions.

Getting Energy from Food

Animal cells have different ways of getting energy from food. One way, called **cellular respiration,** uses oxygen to break down food. Many cells can get energy without using oxygen through a process called **fermentation.** Cellular respiration will release more energy from a given food than fermentation will.

Cellular Respiration

The word *respiration* means "breathing," but cellular respiration is different from breathing. Breathing supplies the oxygen needed for cellular respiration. Breathing also removes carbon dioxide, which is a waste product of cellular respiration. But cellular respiration is a chemical process that occurs in cells.

Most complex organisms, such as plants and animals, obtain energy through cellular respiration. During cellular respiration, food (such as glucose) is broken down into CO_2 and H_2O, and energy is released. In animals, most of the energy released maintains body temperature. Some of the energy is used to form adenosine triphosphate (ATP). ATP supplies energy that fuels cell activities.

Most of the process of cellular respiration takes place in the cell membrane of prokaryotic cells. But in the cells of eukaryotes, cellular respiration takes place mostly in the mitochondria. The process of cellular respiration is summarized in **Figure 2.** Does the equation in the figure remind you of the equation for photosynthesis? **Figure 3** on the next page shows how photosynthesis and respiration are related.

Reading Check What is the difference between cellular respiration and breathing? (*See the Appendix for answers to Reading Checks.*)

Cellular Respiration

$$C_6H_{12}O_6 + 6O_2 \rightarrow 6CO_2 + 6H_2O + \text{energy (ATP)}$$
Glucose   Oxygen   Carbon   Water
                     dioxide

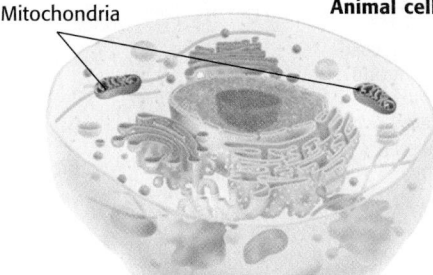

Mitochondria   **Animal cell**

CONNECTION TO Chemistry

Earth's Early Atmosphere

Scientists think that Earth's early atmosphere lacked oxygen. Because of this lack of oxygen, early organisms used fermentation to get energy from food. When organisms began to photosynthesize, the oxygen they produced entered the atmosphere. How do you think this oxygen changed how other organisms got energy?

cellular respiration the process by which cells use oxygen to produce energy from food

fermentation the breakdown of food without the use of oxygen

Figure 2 *The mitochondria in the cells of this cow will use cellular respiration to release the energy stored in the grass.*

Reteaching — BASIC

Concept Mapping Have students draw a concept map of energy transfer using the following images:

sunshine; tree, for firewood; sugar cane; yeast consuming sugar, making bread rise; person chopping firewood, for baking oven; person eating bread

Students should note on their maps which organisms use photosynthesis, which use respiration, and which use fermentation. **LS** Visual

Quiz — GENERAL

Ask students whether the following statements are true or false.

1. Plants and animals capture their energy from the sun. (false)

2. Cellular respiration describes how a cell breathes. (false)

3. Fermentation in animals produces ATP and lactic acid. (true)

Alternative Assessment — GENERAL

Lungs of the Earth Tell students that plants are sometimes called the "lungs of the Earth." Ask students to think about this and to prepare an illustrated presentation for the class. Students may want to research the role that rain forests play as Earth's "lungs" and explain the contributions rain forests make to the health of the planet. **LS** Verbal/Visual

Figure 3 The Connection Between Photosynthesis and Respiration

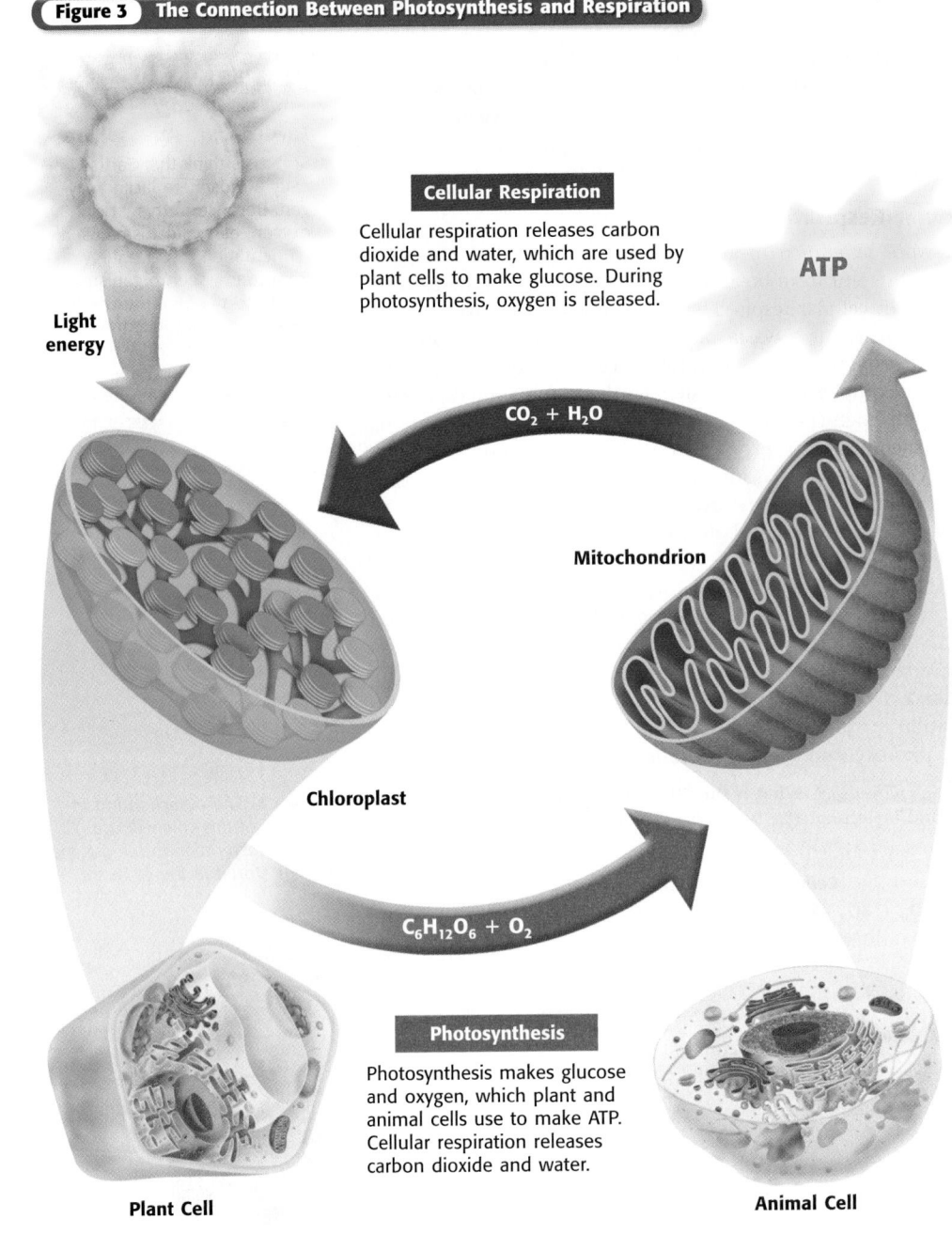

Light energy

Cellular Respiration

Cellular respiration releases carbon dioxide and water, which are used by plant cells to make glucose. During photosynthesis, oxygen is released.

ATP

$CO_2 + H_2O$

Mitochondrion

Chloroplast

$C_6H_{12}O_6 + O_2$

Photosynthesis

Photosynthesis makes glucose and oxygen, which plant and animal cells use to make ATP. Cellular respiration releases carbon dioxide and water.

Plant Cell

Animal Cell

Group Activity — GENERAL

Photosynthesis and Cellular Respiration Have students work in pairs and refer to the diagram on this page. Have each pair compare and contrast photosynthesis and respiration. Ask students to answer the following questions: "What happens to the ATP? Where does the ATP go? How is ATP used by the cell? How is the cell's use of CO_2 and H_2O similar to people's recycling of paper and glass bottles?" **LS** Interpersonal/Logical

Homework — ADVANCED

Comparing Cell Processes Newer kinds of solar cells simulate photosynthesis more closely than older solar cells do. Just as plant cells use energy from the sun to change water and carbon dioxide into energy-rich sugars, these new solar cells use the sun's energy to convert water into energy-rich hydrogen gas, which can be used as fuel. The byproduct of this process is oxygen. Have students research these newer solar cells and make a poster showing how they work. **LS** Visual

Connection Between Photosynthesis and Respiration

As shown in **Figure 3,** photosynthesis transforms energy from the sun into glucose. During photosynthesis, cells use CO_2 to make glucose, and the cells release O_2. During cellular respiration, cells use O_2 to break down glucose and release energy and CO_2. Each process makes the materials that are needed for the other process to occur elsewhere.

Fermentation

Have you ever felt a burning sensation in your leg muscles while you were running? When muscle cells can't get the oxygen needed for cellular respiration, they use the process of fermentation to get energy. One kind of fermentation happens in your muscles and produces lactic acid. The buildup of lactic acid contributes to muscle fatigue and causes a burning sensation. This kind of fermentation also happens in the muscle cells of other animals and in some fungi and bacteria. Another type of fermentation occurs in some types of bacteria and in yeast as described in **Figure 4.**

✓ Reading Check What are two kinds of fermentation?

Figure 4 *Yeast forms carbon dioxide during fermentation. The bubbles of CO_2 gas cause the dough to rise and leave small holes in bread after it is baked.*

SECTION Review

Summary

- Most of the energy that fuels life processes comes from the sun.
- The sun's energy is converted into food by the process of photosynthesis.
- Cellular respiration breaks down glucose into water, carbon dioxide, and energy.
- Fermentation is a way that cells get energy from their food without using oxygen.

Using Key Terms

1. In your own words, write a definition for the term *fermentation*.

Understanding Key Ideas

2. O_2 is released during
   a. cellular respiration.
   b. photosynthesis.
   c. breathing.
   d. fermentation.

3. How are photosynthesis and cellular respiration related?

4. How are respiration and fermentation similar? How are they different?

Math Skills

5. Cells of plant A make 120 molecules of glucose an hour. Cells of plant B make half as much glucose as plant A does. How much glucose does plant B make every minute?

Critical Thinking

6. **Analyzing Relationships** Why are plants important to the survival of all other organisms?

7. **Applying Concepts** You have been given the job of restoring life to a barren island. What types of organisms would you put on the island? If you want to have animals on the island, what other organisms must you bring? Explain your answer.

SCiLINKS.

Developed and maintained by the
National Science Teachers Association

For a variety of links related to this chapter, go to www.scilinks.org

Topic: Cell Energy; Photosynthesis
SciLinks code: HSM0237; HSM1140

Answers to Section Review

1. Sample answer: Fermentation is the process by which some organisms get energy from food without using oxygen.

2. b

3. Photosynthesis uses the waste materials of cellular respiration, CO_2 and H_2O, to generate glucose. Cellular respiration uses the waste material of photosynthesis, O_2, to break down glucose.

4. Cellular respiration and fermentation both release the energy stored in food. Fermentation does not use oxygen, and cellular respiration does use oxygen.

5. The cells of plant B make an average of 1 glucose molecule per minute.

6. Sample answer: Plants turn energy from the sun into chemical energy. Animals that eat the plants use the stored energy. Plants also produce O_2.

7. Sample answer: Animals such as birds, insects, and mammals would be good on the island. Plants must be on the island in order to provide a source of food for the animals.

Answer to Reading Check

One kind of fermentation produces CO_2, and the other kind produces lactic acid.

CHAPTER RESOURCES

Chapter Resource File

- Section Quiz **GENERAL**
- Section Review **GENERAL**
- Vocabulary and Section Summary **GENERAL**
- Reinforcement Worksheet **BASIC**

Technology

Transparencies
- L11 The Connection Between Photosynthesis and Respiration

SECTION

3

Focus

Overview

This section introduces the life cycle of a cell. Students will learn how cells reproduce and how mitosis is important. Finally, students will learn how cell division differs between plants and animals.

Bellringer

On the board, write the following:

> Biology is the only science in which multiplication means the same thing as division.

Have students write an explanation of this sentence. (When cells divide, they are multiplying. Some students may point out that multiplying a number by a fraction is the same as division.)

Motivate

ACTIVITY ——————— GENERAL

Making Models Have pairs of students use string for the cell membrane and pieces of pipe cleaners for chromosomes to demonstrate the basic steps of mitosis, as described in this section. **LS** Visual/Interpersonal

---

What You Will Learn

● Explain how cells produce more cells.
● Describe the process of mitosis.
● Explain how cell division differs in animals and plants.

Vocabulary

cell cycle
chromosome
homologous chromosomes
mitosis
cytokinesis

READING STRATEGY

Paired Summarizing Read this section silently. In pairs, take turns summarizing the material. Stop to discuss ideas that seem confusing.

cell cycle the life cycle of a cell

chromosome in a eukaryotic cell, one of the structures in the nucleus that are made up of DNA and protein; in a prokaryotic cell, the main ring of DNA

The Cell Cycle

In the time that it takes you to read this sentence, your body will have made millions of new cells! Making new cells allows you to grow and replace cells that have died.

The environment in your stomach is so acidic that the cells lining your stomach must be replaced every few days. Other cells are replaced less often, but your body is constantly making new cells.

The Life of a Cell

As you grow, you pass through different stages in life. Your cells also pass through different stages in their life cycle. The life cycle of a cell is called the **cell cycle.**

The cell cycle begins when the cell is formed and ends when the cell divides and forms new cells. Before a cell divides, it must make a copy of its deoxyribonucleic acid (DNA). DNA is the hereditary material that controls all cell activities, including the making of new cells. The DNA of a cell is organized into structures called **chromosomes.** Copying chromosomes ensures that each new cell will be an exact copy of its parent cell. How does a cell make more cells? It depends on whether the cell is prokaryotic (with no nucleus) or eukaryotic (with a nucleus).

Making More Prokaryotic Cells

Prokaryotic cells are less complex than eukaryotic cells are. Bacteria, which are prokaryotes, have ribosomes and a single, circular DNA molecule but don't have membrane-enclosed organelles. Cell division in bacteria is called *binary fission,* which means "splitting into two parts." Binary fission results in two cells that each contain one copy of the circle of DNA. A few of the bacteria in **Figure 1** are undergoing binary fission.

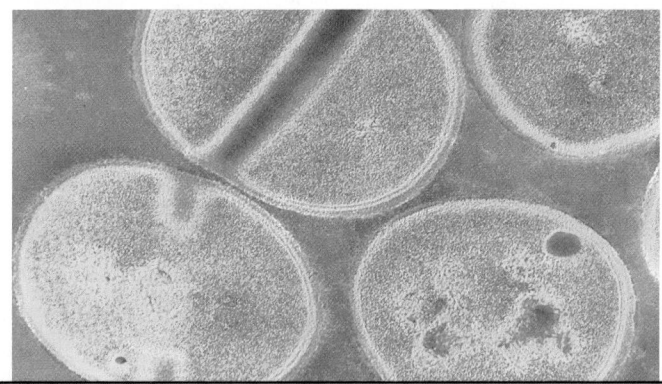

Figure 1 *Bacteria reproduce by binary fission.*

CHAPTER RESOURCES

Chapter Resource File

▪ **Lesson Plan**
▪ **Directed Reading A** BASIC, **B** SPECIAL NEEDS

Technology

▪ **Transparencies**
  • Bellringer
  • L12 The Cell Cycle

Workbooks

▪ **Interactive Textbook** Struggling Readers

▪ **Math Skills for Science**
  • Multiplying Whole Numbers BASIC
  • Grasping Graphing GENERAL

CONNECTION to Math ——————— BASIC

Cell Multiplication It takes Cell A 1 h to complete its cell cycle and produce two cells. The cell cycle of Cell B takes 2 h. How many more cells would be formed from Cell A than from Cell B in 6 h?

(After 6 h, Cell A would have formed 64 cells, and Cell B would have formed 8 cells. Cell A would have formed 56 cells more than Cell B.)
LS Logical/Verbal

Eukaryotic Cells and Their DNA

Eukaryotic cells are more complex than prokaryotic cells are. The chromosomes of eukaryotic cells contain more DNA than those of prokaryotic cells do. Different kinds of eukaryotes have different numbers of chromosomes. More-complex eukaryotes do not necessarily have more chromosomes than simpler eukaryotes do. For example, fruit flies have 8 chromosomes, potatoes have 48, and humans have 46. **Figure 2** shows the 46 chromosomes of a human body cell lined up in pairs. These pairs are made up of similar chromosomes known as **homologous chromosomes** (hoh MAHL uh guhs KROH muh SOHMZ).

✔ *Reading Check* Do more-complex organisms always have more chromosomes than simpler organisms do? (*See the Appendix for answers to Reading Checks.*)

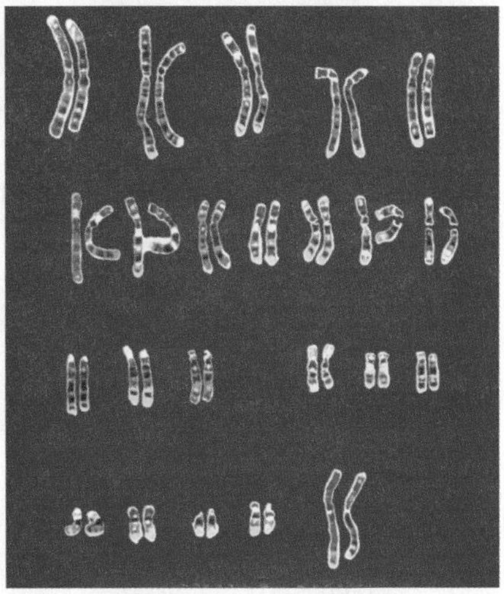

Figure 2 *Human body cells have 46 chromosomes, or 23 pairs of chromosomes.*

Making More Eukaryotic Cells

The eukaryotic cell cycle includes three stages. In the first stage, called *interphase,* the cell grows and copies its organelles and chromosomes. After each chromosome is duplicated, the two copies are called *chromatids*. Chromatids are held together at a region called the *centromere.* The joined chromatids twist and coil and condense into an X shape, as shown in **Figure 3.** After this step, the cell enters the second stage of the cell cycle.

In the second stage, the chromatids separate. The complicated process of chromosome separation is called **mitosis.** Mitosis ensures that each new cell receives a copy of each chromosome. Mitosis is divided into four phases, as shown on the following pages.

In the third stage, the cell splits into two cells. These cells are identical to each other and to the original cell.

homologous chromosomes chromosomes that have the same sequence of genes and the same structure

mitosis in eukaryotic cells, a process of cell division that forms two new nuclei, each of which has the same number of chromosomes

Figure 3 *This duplicated chromosome consists of two chromatids. The chromatids are joined at the centromere.*

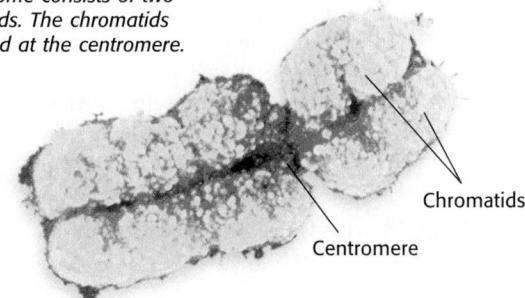

Chromatids

Centromere

CONNECTION TO Language Arts

Picking Apart Vocabulary

Brainstorm what words are similar to the parts of the term *homologous chromosome.* What can you guess about the meaning of the term's root words? Look up the roots of the words, and explain how they help describe the concept. **ACTIVITY**

Is That a Fact!
Before sophisticated microscopes were available, scientists could not see cells pinching and dividing. Many scientists believed that cells came into existence spontaneously—as though crystallizing out of bodily fluids.

Writing **Biography of a Cell**
Have students write and illustrate the biography of a cell. It can be humorous or serious, but it should include accurate descriptions of how materials are transported into and out of the cell and how cells reproduce. **LS** Visual/Verbal

Quiz —— GENERAL

1. What is cell division? (It is the process by which cells reproduce themselves.)

2. How do prokaryotic cells make more cells? (binary fission)

3. How do eukaryotic cells make more cells? (mitosis and cytokinesis)

Alternative Assessment —— GENERAL

Writing **Mitosis and Cancer**
Have students research the role of mitosis in cancer and write a report or create a poster or other visual presentation on what they learn. Students' reports should include information about various cancer treatments, such as radiation, chemotherapy, and surgery. **LS** Verbal/Visual

Answer to Reading Check

During cytokinesis in plant cells, a cell plate is formed. During cytokinesis in animal cells, a cell plate does not form.

Figure 4 **The Cell Cycle**

Copying DNA (Interphase)	Mitosis Phase 1 (Prophase)	Mitosis Phase 2 (Metaphase)
Before mitosis begins, chromosomes are copied. Each chromosome is then two chromatids.	Mitosis begins. The nuclear membrane dissolves. Chromosomes condense into rodlike structures.	The chromosomes line up along the equator of the cell. Homologous chromosomes pair up.

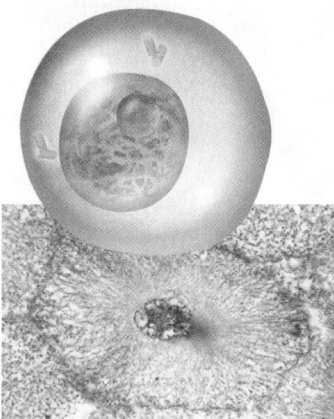 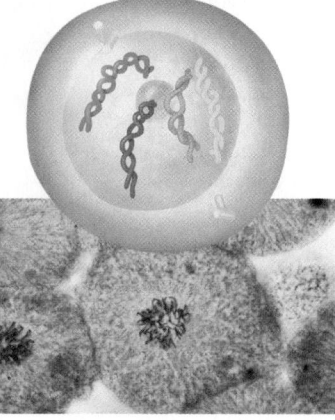 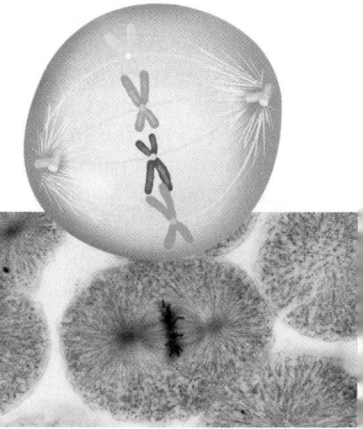

cytokinesis the division of the cytoplasm of a cell

Mitosis and the Cell Cycle

Figure 4 shows the cell cycle and the phases of mitosis in an animal cell. Mitosis has four phases that are shown and described above. This diagram shows only four chromosomes to make it easy to see what's happening inside the cell.

Cytokinesis

In animal cells and other eukaryotes that do not have cell walls, division of the cytoplasm begins at the cell membrane. The cell membrane begins to pinch inward to form a groove, which eventually pinches all the way through the cell, and two daughter cells form. The division of cytoplasm is called **cytokinesis** and is shown at the last step of **Figure 4.**

Eukaryotic cells that have a cell wall, such as the cells of plants, algae, and fungi, reproduce differently. In these cells, a *cell plate* forms in the middle of the cell. The cell plate contains the materials for the new cell membranes and the new cell walls that will separate the new cells. After the cell splits into two, a new cell wall forms where the cell plate was. The cell plate and a late stage of cytokinesis in a plant cell are shown in **Figure 5.**

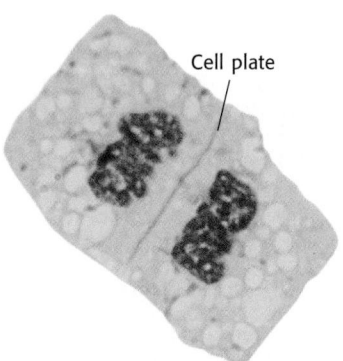

Cell plate

Figure 5 *When a plant cell divides, a cell plate forms and the cell splits into two cells.*

✓ *Reading Check* What is the difference between cytokinesis in an animal cell and cytokinesis in a plant cell?

Mitosis Phase 3 (Anaphase)

The chromatids separate and move to opposite sides of the cell.

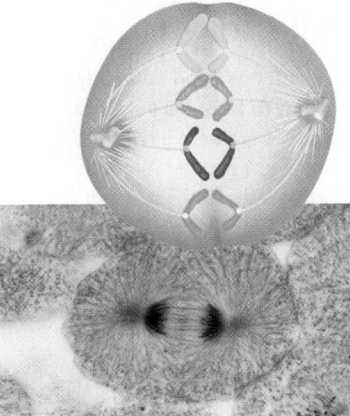

Mitosis Phase 4 (Telophase)

A nuclear membrane forms around each set of chromosomes, and the chromosomes unwind. Mitosis is complete.

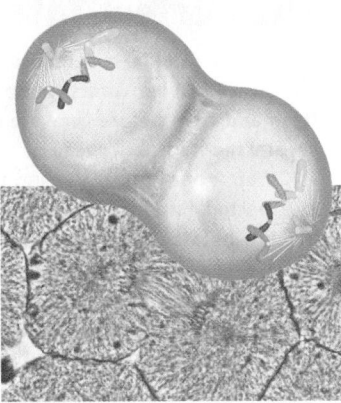

Cytokinesis

In cells that lack a cell wall, the cell pinches in two. In cells that have a cell wall, a cell plate forms between the two new cells.

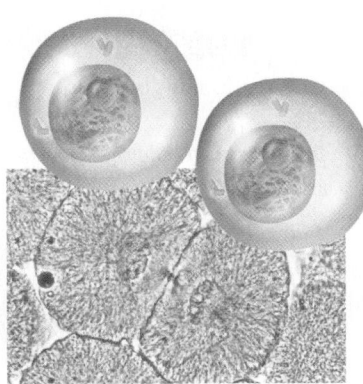

SECTION Review

Summary

- A cell produces more cells by first copying its DNA.
- Eukaryotic cells produce more cells through the four phases of mitosis.
- Mitosis produces two cells that have the same number of chromosomes as the parent cell.
- At the end of mitosis, a cell divides the cytoplasm by cytokinesis.
- In plant cells, a cell plate forms between the two new cells during cytokinesis.

Using Key Terms

1. In your own words, write a definition for each of the following terms: *cell cycle* and *cytokinesis*.

Understanding Key Ideas

2. Eukaryotic cells
   a. do not divide.
   b. undergo binary fission.
   c. undergo mitosis.
   d. have cell walls.

3. Why is it important for chromosomes to be copied before cell division?

4. Describe mitosis.

Math Skills

5. Cell A takes 6 h to complete division. Cell B takes 8 h to complete division. After 24 h, how many more copies of cell A would there be than cell B?

Critical Thinking

6. **Predicting Consequences** What would happen if cytokinesis occurred without mitosis?

7. **Applying Concepts** How does mitosis ensure that a new cell is just like its parent cell?

8. **Making Comparisons** Compare the processes that animal cells and plant cells use to make new cells. How are the processes different?

Developed and maintained by the National Science Teachers Association

For a variety of links related to this chapter, go to www.scilinks.org

Topic: Cell Cycle
SciLinks code: HSM0235

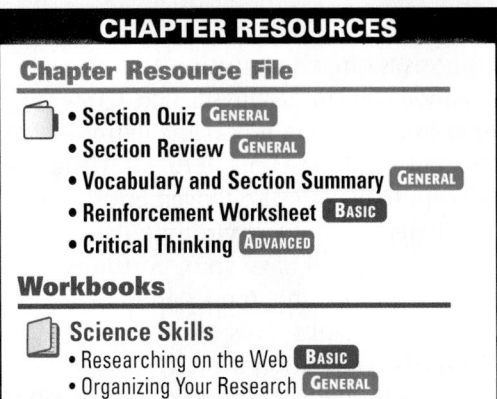

CHAPTER RESOURCES

Chapter Resource File

- Section Quiz **GENERAL**
- Section Review **GENERAL**
- Vocabulary and Section Summary **GENERAL**
- Reinforcement Worksheet **BASIC**
- Critical Thinking **ADVANCED**

Workbooks

Science Skills
- Researching on the Web **BASIC**
- Organizing Your Research **GENERAL**

The Perfect Taters Mystery

Teacher's Notes

Time Required

Two 45-minute class periods

Lab Ratings

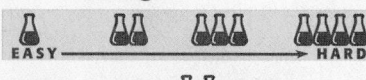

EASY ——————→ HARD

Teacher Prep 🧪🧪

Student Set-Up 🧪🧪

Concept Level 🧪🧪🧪

Clean Up 🧪

MATERIALS

The materials listed on the student pages are enough for one class of students. You will need one or two potatoes per class. Do not allow students to cut or peel potatoes. You will need to do this ahead of time. Allow students to choose the number of containers they will need for the experiment. They may wish to test several salt concentrations.

Safety Caution

Remind students to review all safety cautions and icons before beginning this lab activity.

Avoid including green or discolored parts of the potato in the pieces students work with. These could cause illness.

Lab Notes

Osmosis is often a confusing and misunderstood concept in life science. Quite often, students can repeat the definition of the process but are unable to apply the concept to explain the movement of water in different osmotic environments. In this lab, students will have an opportunity to observe osmosis in a model and obtain measurable results. This lab can be done as a class demonstration if materials and space are limited. The purpose of this lab is to reinforce comprehension of osmosis and to practice the scientific method.

Using Scientific Methods

Inquiry Lab

The Perfect Taters Mystery

You are the chief food detective at Perfect Taters Food Company. The boss, Mr. Fries, wants you to find a way to keep his potatoes fresh and crisp before they are cooked. His workers have tried several methods, but these methods have not worked. Workers in Group A put the potatoes in very salty water, and something unexpected happened to the potatoes. Workers in Group B put the potatoes in water that did not contain any salt, and something else happened! Workers in Group C didn't put the potatoes in any water, and that didn't work either. Now, you must design an experiment to find out what can be done to make the potatoes stay crisp and fresh.

OBJECTIVES

Examine osmosis in potato cells.

Design a procedure that will give the best results.

MATERIALS

- cups, clear plastic, small
- potato pieces, freshly cut
- potato samples (A, B, and C)
- salt
- water, distilled

SAFETY

- Before you plan your experiment, review what you know. You know that potatoes are made of cells. Plant cells contain a large amount of water. Cells have membranes that hold water and other materials inside and keep some things out. Water and other materials must travel across cell membranes to get into and out of the cell.

- Mr. Fries has told you that you can obtain as many samples as you need from the workers in Groups A, B, and C. Your teacher will have these samples ready for you to observe.

- Make a data table like the one below. List your observations in the data table. Make as many observations as you can about the potatoes tested by workers in Groups A, B, and C.

Observations	
Group A	
Group B	
Group C	

Ask a Question

❶ Now that you have made your observations, state Mr. Fries's problem in the form of a question that can be answered by your experiment.

CHAPTER RESOURCES

Chapter Resource File

- Datasheet for Chapter Lab
- Lab Notes and Answers

Technology

Classroom Videos
- Lab Video

LabBook

- Stayin' Alive!

Form a Hypothesis

2 Form a hypothesis based on your observations and your questions. The hypothesis should be a statement about what causes the potatoes not to be crisp and fresh. Based on your hypothesis, make a prediction about the outcome of your experiment. State your prediction in an if-then format.

Test the Hypothesis

3 Once you have made a prediction, design your investigation. Check your experimental design with your teacher before you begin. Mr. Fries will give you potato pieces, water, salt, and no more than six containers.

4 Keep very accurate records. Write your plan and procedure. Make data tables. To be sure your data is accurate, measure all materials carefully and make drawings of the potato pieces before and after the experiment.

Analyze the Results

1 **Explaining Events** Explain what happened to the potato cells in Groups A, B, and C in your experiment. Include a discussion of the cell membrane and the process of osmosis.

Draw Conclusions

2 **Analyzing Results** Write a letter to Mr. Fries that explains your experimental method, results, and conclusion. Then, make a recommendation about how he should handle the potatoes so that they will stay fresh and crisp.

Analyze the Results

1. The potato cells in Group A were placed in very salty water. The potatoes shriveled up because water moved out of the cell and into the salty water (from an area of high concentration of water to an area of low concentration of water). This may be confusing to some students who may think that because the concentration of salt is high outside the potato, the salt should move to the area of lower concentration. Explain that although water can move through a cell membrane by osmosis, salt must be moved across a cell membrane by a process that requires energy.

The potato cells in Group B were placed in water with no salt. The potatoes swelled because the concentration of water was lower inside the cell. (The concentration of salt and other molecules was higher inside the potato cell.)

The potato cells in Group C turned brown and dried up because the water concentration outside the cell was low. In fact, there wasn't any water at all. The water evaporated as soon as it left the cell membrane. The potato cells turned brown because of chemical reactions with the air.

Draw Conclusions

2. Letters to Mr. Fries will vary according to each student's results. However, all students should explain that through trial and error they found one salt concentration that was closest to the concentration of salt and other molecules inside the potato. This is the concentration that should be used to maintain an osmotic balance in the potato. Furthermore, some students will realize that the potatoes must be kept in water to prevent them from turning brown.

CHAPTER RESOURCES
Workbooks

- **Whiz-Bang Demonstrations**
  - It's in the Bag! **BASIC**
  - Stop Picking on My Enzyme **BASIC**
- **Labs You Can Eat**
  - The Mystery of the Runny Gelatin **GENERAL**
- **Inquiry Labs**
  - Fish Farms in Space **GENERAL**
- **Long-Term Projects & Research Ideas**
  - Taming the Wild Yeast **ADVANCED**

 Holt Lab Generator CD-ROM

Search for any lab by topic, standard, difficulty level, or time. Edit any lab to fit your needs, or create your own labs. Use the Lab Materials QuickList software to customize your lab materials list.

CLASSROOM TESTED & APPROVED

Susan Gorman
North Ridge Middle School
North Richland Hills, Texas

Assignment Guide

Section	Questions
1	1, 2, 6, 8, 12, 16
2	3, 4, 7, 10, 13, 17
3	5, 9, 11, 14, 15, 18–22

ANSWERS

Using Key Terms

1. Sample answer: Osmosis is the diffusion of water through a semipermeable membrane.

2. Sample answer: Exocytosis is the process cells use to remove large particles; endocytosis is the process cells use to move large particles into a cell

3. photosynthesis

4. cellular respiration

5. Cytokinesis is the division of just the cytoplasm. Mitosis is the process in eukaryotic cells in which the nuclear material splits to form two new nuclei.

6. Active transport requires the cell to use energy to move substances. Passive transport does not require the cell to use any energy.

7. Cellular respiration releases stored energy by using oxygen. Fermentation releases stored energy without using oxygen.

Understanding Key Ideas

8. c

9. a

10. d

11. c

USING KEY TERMS

1 Use the following terms in the same sentence: *diffusion* and *osmosis*.

2 In your own words, write a definition for each of the following terms: *exocytosis* and *endocytosis*.

Complete each of the following sentences by choosing the correct term from the word bank.

> cellular respiration
> photosynthesis
> fermentation

3 Plants use ___ to make glucose.

4 During ___, oxygen is used to break down food molecules releasing large amounts of energy.

For each pair of terms, explain how the meanings of the terms differ.

5 *cytokinesis* and *mitosis*

6 *active transport* and *passive transport*

7 *cellular respiration* and *fermentation*

UNDERSTANDING KEY IDEAS

Multiple Choice

8 The process in which particles move through a membrane from a region of low concentration to a region of high concentration is

a. diffusion.

b. passive transport.

c. active transport.

d. fermentation.

9 What is the result of mitosis and cytokinesis?

a. two identical cells

b. two nuclei

c. chloroplasts

d. two different cells

10 Before the energy in food can be used by a cell, the energy must first be transferred to molecules of

a. proteins.

b. carbohydrates.

c. DNA.

d. ATP.

11 Which of the following cells would form a cell plate during the cell cycle?

a. a human cell

b. a prokaryotic cell

c. a plant cell

d. All of the above

Short Answer

12 Are exocytosis and endocytosis examples of active or passive transport? Explain your answer.

13 Name the cell structures that are needed for photosynthesis and the cell structures that are needed for cellular respiration.

14 Describe the three stages of the cell cycle of a eukaryotic cell.

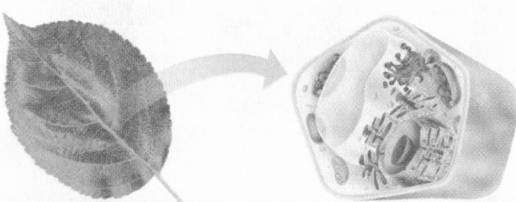

12. Endocytosis and exocytosis are examples of active transport. In both processes the cell must change shape, wrap around a particle, and make other movements that require the cell to use energy.

13. Chloroplasts are needed for photosynthesis. Cellular respiration requires mitochondria.

14. The first stage is cell growth and copying of DNA (duplication). The second stage is mitosis, which involves separating the duplicated chromosomes. The third stage is cytokinesis (cell division), which results in two separate, identical cells.

CRITICAL THINKING

15 Concept Mapping Use the following terms to create a concept map: *chromosome duplication, cytokinesis, prokaryote, mitosis, cell cycle, binary fission,* and *eukaryote.*

16 Making Inferences Which one of the plants pictured below was given water mixed with salt, and which one was given pure water? Explain how you know, and be sure to use the word *osmosis* in your answer.

17 Identifying Relationships Why would your muscle cells need to be supplied with more food when there is a lack of oxygen than when there is plenty of oxygen present?

18 Applying Concepts A parent cell has 10 chromosomes.

a. Will the cell go through binary fission or mitosis and cytokinesis to produce new cells?

b. How many chromosomes will each new cell have after the parent cell divides?

INTERPRETING GRAPHICS

The picture below shows a cell. Use the picture below to answer the questions that follow.

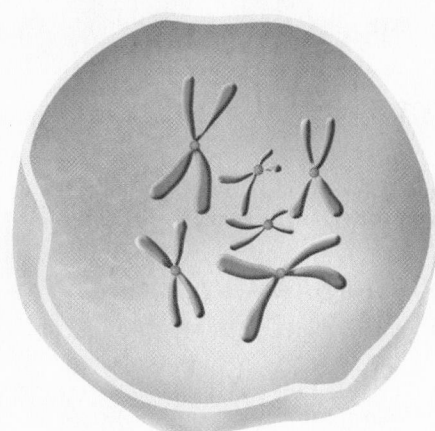

19 Is the cell prokaryotic or eukaryotic?

20 Which stage of the cell cycle is this cell in?

21 How many chromatids are present? How many pairs of homologous chromosomes are present?

22 How many chromosomes will be present in each of the new cells after the cell divides?

Critical Thinking

15. 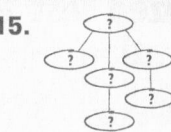 An answer to this exercise can be found at the end of this book.

16. The plant on the left was given pure water. The plant on the right was given salt water. Osmosis occurred in both plants. In the plant on the left, water moved into the plant because the concentration of water was lower in the plant than in the soil. So, the plant on the left did not wilt. In the plant on the right, the water in the plant moved into the soil, where the concentration of water was lower. The concentration of water in the soil was lower because the water contained salt. As a result, the plant on the right wilted.

17. When there is plenty of oxygen, the cells can get energy from cellular respiration. When there is a lack of oxygen, the cells must use fermentation, which doesn't produce as much energy. For fermentation to produce more energy, more food would be required.

18. a. The cell is a eukaryotic cell and will go through mitosis and cytokinesis. Prokaryotic cells have only one chromosome.

b. Each new cell will receive a copy of each chromosome, so each new cell will have 10 chromosomes.

Interpreting Graphics

19. The cell is eukaryotic because it shows chromatids held together at a centromere. Prokaryotic cells do not have chromatids.

20. The cell is in mitosis because the chromosomes have already duplicated.

21. There are 12 chromatids. There are three pairs of homologous chromosomes.

22. There will be six chromosomes in each new cell.

CHAPTER RESOURCES

Chapter Resource File

- Chapter Review GENERAL
- Chapter Test A GENERAL
- Chapter Test B ADVANCED
- Chapter Test C SPECIAL NEEDS
- Vocabulary Activity GENERAL

Workbooks

Study Guide
- Study Guide is also available in Spanish.

Teacher's Notes

To provide practice under more realistic conditions, give students 20 minutes to answer all of the questions in this Standardized Test Preparation.

Answer Key

Question	Answer
1	C
2	A
3	C
4	D
5	A
6	B
7	C
8	B
9	C
10	*
11	*

*See Test Doctor.

Multiple Choice

1. What is the primary source of energy for all organisms?

A. carbohydrates

B. ATP

C. sunlight

D. glucose

2. In eukaryotic organisms, which cell part converts the energy stored in food to ATP?

A. mitochondrion

B. chromosome

C. cell membrane

D. chloroplast

3. Plants are producers. Which of the following statements best describes producers?

A. They obtain their food by eating other organisms.

B. They use a process known as cellular respiration to make their own food.

C. They capture light energy from the sun and use it to make food.

D. They take in oxygen and produce carbon dioxide.

Use the diagram below to answer question 4.

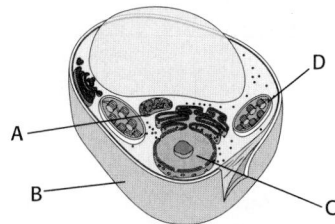

4. What structure in the cell above can convert energy from the sun into chemical energy that can be used by plants and animals?

A. structure A

B. structure B

C. structure C

D. structure D

5. Which of the following correctly displays the cell cycle?

A. interphase, prophase, metaphase, anaphase, telophase, cytokinesis

B. interphase, cytokinesis, anaphase, mitosis, telophase

C. prophase, metaphase, interphase, anaphase, telophase

D. prophase, mitosis, interphase, metaphase, cytokinesis

6. When plants make glucose, they are converting the sun's radiant energy

A. into ATP.

B. into chemical energy that can be stored.

C. in a process known as cellular respiration.

D. into chlorophyll.

✚ TEST DOCTOR

Question 1 A, D: Organisms store energy in carbohydrates. Glucose is a simple carbohydrate that is made by plants during photosynthesis. B: ATP supplies energy for cell activities. It is formed through processes such as respiration and fermentation. C: Correct.

Question 2 A: Correct. B: Chromosomes are cell structures made of DNA. They have nothing to do with converting energy. C: Energy stored in food is converted into ATP in the cell membranes of prokaryotic organisms. D: Chloroplasts are the organelles that make food through photosynthesis.

Question 3 A: Consumers obtain food by eating other organisms. B: Cellular respiration is used to break down food, not to make food. C: Correct. D: Most producers use photosynthesis, which requires carbon dioxide as a reactant and releases oxygen as a product.

Question 4 A: Mitochondria break down glucose to provide energy to cells. B: The cell wall provides support and protection for the cell. C: The nucleus holds the chromosomes of eukaryotic cells. D: Correct.

Use the illustration below to answer question 7.

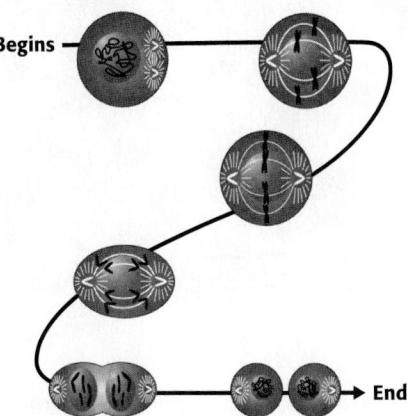

Begins

Ends

7. **Based on the process shown in Katie's sketches of cell division, which of the following is a valid conclusion?**

A. Cytokinesis occurs right after the chromosomes are copied.

B. Two identical new cells form during mitosis.

C. Chromosomes are condensed throughout the process of mitosis.

D. The cells shown in the diagram are prokaryotic cells.

8. **How is the process of cellular respiration in eukaryotic cells different than cellular respiration in prokaryotic cells? Cellular respiration**

A. requires oxygen in eukaryotic cells but not in prokaryotic cells.

B. occurs in mitochondria in eukaryotic cells, but in the cell membrane in prokaryotic cells.

C. produces lactic acid in eukaryotic cells, but carbon dioxide gas in prokaryotic cells.

D. Cellular respiration is not possible in prokaryotic cells.

9. **During mitosis, chromosomes condense from long strands into rodlike structures. What must happen before this stage of the cell cycle?**

A. The paired chromatids separate and move to opposite sides of the cell.

B. The paired chromatids align at the cell's equator.

C. The cell grows and copies its organelles.

D. The nuclear membrane dissolves.

Open Response

10. **Kudzu is a vine that was planted during the Great Depression in order to control soil erosion. This fast-growing plant is now considered a weed. In the southeastern United States, kudzu can grow up to 20 m in one year. Kudzu cells undergo rapid cell division. Draw a diagram and describe the cell cycle for kudzu cells.**

11. **The Longleaf Pine Forest is a fire-adapted ecosystem that once covered 70–90 million acres along the coast of the southeastern U.S. Less than 5% of this forest now remains. Plants in this ecosystem include longleaf pine, wiregrass, and native legumes. Animals include scarab beetles and other invertebrates, striped newts, dusky gopher frogs, indigo snakes, and bobwhite quail. Describe how energy would move through organisms in this ecosystem.**

Some prokaryotes and some eukaryotes can carry out each of these types of fermentation. D: Prokaryotic cells are capable of respiration, but they do not have mitochondria. Instead, they perform respiration in the cell membrane.

Question 9 A: Chromosomes are replicated during interphase, before they condense into rodlike structures, which occurs during prophase. Paired chromatids separate and move to opposite sides of the cell during anaphase, which occurs after interphase, prophase, and metaphase. B: Paired chromatids also align at the cell's equator during anaphase. C: Correct. D: The nuclear membrane dissolves during metaphase, which occurs after interphase and prophase.

Question 10 Full-credit answers should include diagrams and descriptions of interphase, prophase, metaphase, anaphase, telophase, and cytokinesis for the eukaryotic cell. Students should also include the following:

- Each cell has a cell wall.
- A cell plate forms between the two new cells during cytokinesis.
- A new cell wall forms where the cell plate was.

Question 11 Full-credit answers should show an understanding of photosynthesis, cellular respiration, and how energy moves through some of the plants and animals of this ecosystem. Answers should include the following:

- Energy enters the forest when plants perform photosynthesis, converting the sun's energy into chemical energy (glucose) that can be stored in plant tissues.
- Cellular respiration releases stored chemical energy, most of which is converted to heat. Some is used for cell processes and some is stored.
- Chemical energy stored in plants is obtained by animals when they eat the plants.
- The chemical energy stored in plant-eating animals is obtained by animals that eat the plant-eaters. Energy in animals that eat plant-eaters is passed to the animals that eat them.

Question 5 A: Correct. B: Chromosomes are replicated during interphase, a stage that precedes mitosis. C: A parent cell splits completely to become two new cells during cytokinesis, a stage that follows mitosis. D: Chromatids line up during a phase of mitosis called *metaphase.* Mitosis is not complete until the chromatids have split and two new nuclei have formed.

Question 6 A: The sun's energy is not directly converted into ATP during photosynthesis. Rather, the energy is converted into stored chemical energy in the form of glucose. The glucose is later broken down into ATP, which is the form of energy used within the cell. B: Correct. C: Cellular respiration is one of the methods used by cells to convert the stored energy contained in glucose into usable energy in the form of ATP. D: Chlorophyll is the pigment that absorbs light energy for photosynthesis.

Question 7 A: Mitosis occurs right after the chromosomes are copied. Cytokinesis occurs after mitosis. B: Two identical cells form during cytokinesis. C: Correct. D: Only eukaryotic cells undergo the cell cycle shown in the diagram.

Question 8 A: All cellular respiration involves oxygen. Fermentation breaks down food without oxygen. B: Correct. C: Lactic acid and carbon dioxide are products of two types of fermentation.

Scientific Discovery

Background

The release of energy from food is called *cellular respiration*. Cellular respiration takes place in two stages. The end result of the process is that energy is stored in the cell in the form of ATP (adenosine triphosphate) molecules.

In the microbial battery, scientists harvest some of this energy and transfer it into electricity that can be readily used.

One of the benefits of the microbial battery is its ability to make use of waste products. Ask students to consider the effect this might have on the energy demands of nations that have limited access to fossil fuels.

Science Fiction

Teaching Strategy— BASIC

This is a relatively long story, containing quite a few medical terms. Students may find it easier to read if the class discusses some of the unfamiliar terms before they start reading the story.

Science in Action

Scientific Discoveries

Electrifying News About Microbes

Your car is out of fuel, and there isn't a service station in sight. This is not a problem! Your car's motor runs on electricity supplied by trillions of microorganisms. Some chemists think that "living" batteries will someday operate everything from watches to entire cities. A group of scientists at King's College in London have demonstrated that microorganisms can convert food into usable electrical energy. The microorganisms convert foods such as table sugar and molasses most efficiently. An efficient microorganism can convert more than 90% of its food into compounds that will fuel an electric reaction. A less efficient microbe will only convert 50% of its food into these types of compounds.

Math ACTIVITY

An efficient microorganism converts 90% of its food into fuel compounds, and an inefficient microorganism converts only 50%. If the inefficient microorganism makes 60 g of fuel out of a possible 120 g of food, how much fuel would an efficient microorganism make out of the same amount of food?

Science Fiction

"Contagion" by Katherine MacLean

A quarter mile from their spaceship, the *Explorer*, a team of doctors walk carefully along a narrow forest trail. Around them, the forest looks like a forest on Earth in the fall—the leaves are green, copper, purple, and fiery red. But it isn't fall. And the team is not on Earth.

Minos is enough like Earth to be the home of another colony of humans. But Minos might also be home to unknown organisms that could cause severe illness or death among the crew of *Explorer*. These diseases might be enough like diseases on Earth to be contagious, but they might be different enough to be very difficult to treat.

Something large moves among the shadows—it looks like a man. What happens next? Read Katherine's MacLean's "Contagion" in the *Holt Anthology of Science Fiction* to find out.

Language Arts ACTIVITY

WRITING SKILL Write two to three paragraphs that describe what you think might happen next in the story.

Answer to Math Activity

An efficient microbe converts 90% of its food to fuel compounds; 90% of 120 g is 108 g of fuel compounds.

Answer to Language Arts Activity

Students' predictions will vary. Whatever a student predicts, the prediction should be reasonably related to the information that the student has from reading this introductory paragraph.

Jerry Yakel

Neuroscientist Jerry Yakel credits a sea slug for making him a neuroscientist. In a college class studying neurons, or nerve cells, Yakel got to see firsthand how ions move across the cell membrane of *Aplysia californica*, also known as a sea hare. He says, "I was totally hooked. I knew that I wanted to be a neurophysiologist then and there. I haven't wavered since."

Today, Yakel is a senior investigator for the National Institutes of Environmental Health Sciences, which is part of the U.S. government's National Institutes of Health. "We try to understand how the normal brain works," says Yakel of his team. "Then, when we look at a diseased brain, we train to understand where the deficits are. Eventually, someone will have an idea about a drug that will tweak the system in this or that way."

Yakel studies the ways in which nicotine affects the human brain. "It is one of the most prevalent and potent neurotoxins in the environment," says Yakel. "I'm amazed that it isn't higher on the list of worries for the general public."

Social Studies ACTiViTY

WRITING SKILL Research a famous or historical figure in science. Write a short report that outlines how he or she became interested in science.

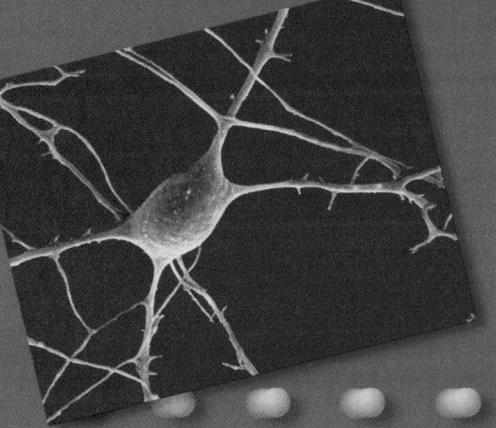

go.hrw.com

To learn more about these Science in Action topics, visit go.hrw.com and type in the keyword **HL5ACTF.**

Current Science

Check out Current Science® articles related to this chapter by visiting go.hrw.com. Just type in the keyword **HL5CS04.**

Plant Processes
Chapter Planning Guide

Compression guide:
To shorten instruction because of time limitations, omit Section 3.

OBJECTIVES	LABS, DEMONSTRATIONS, AND ACTIVITIES	TECHNOLOGY RESOURCES
PACING • 135 min pp. 60–65 **Chapter Opener**	SE **Start-up Activity,** p. 61 GENERAL	OSP **Parent Letter** CD **Student Edition on CD-ROM** CD **Guided Reading Audio CD** TR **Chapter Starter Transparency*** VID **Brain Food Video Quiz**
Section 1 Photosynthesis • Describe photosynthesis. • Compare photosynthesis and cellular respiration. • Describe how gas is exchanged in the leaves of plants. • Describe two ways in which photosynthesis is important.	TE **Group Activity** Modeling Molecules, p. 63 GENERAL SE **Connection to Chemistry** Transpiration, p. 64 GENERAL SE **Skills Practice Lab** Food Factory Waste, p. 64 GENERAL CRF **Datasheet for Chapter Lab*** SE **Skills Practice Lab** Weepy Weeds, p. 706 GENERAL CRF **Datasheet for LabBook*** LB **Calculator-Based Labs** Power of the Sun* ADVANCED	OSP **Lesson Plans** (also in print) TR **Bellringer Transparency*** TR **L46 Photosynthesis*** TR **L47 Gas Exchange in Leaves*** TR *LINK TO PHYSICAL SCIENCE* P57 Balancing a Chemical Equation* VID **Lab Videos for Life Science**
PACING • 45 min pp. 66–69 **Section 2 Reproduction of Flowering Plants** • Describe pollination and fertilization in flowering plants. • Explain how fruits and seeds are formed from flowers. • List three reasons why a seed might be dormant. • List three examples of asexual reproduction in plants.	TE **Demonstration** Parts of a Flower, p. 66 GENERAL TE **Group Activity** Concept Mapping, p. 67 GENERAL TE **Activity** Germination, p. 67 BASIC SE **Quick Lab** Thirsty Seeds, p. 68 GENERAL CRF **Datasheet for Quick Lab*** LB **Labs You Can Eat** Not Just Another Nut* GENERAL	OSP **Lesson Plans** (also in print) TR **Bellringer Transparency*** TR **L48 Pollination and Fertilization*** TR **L49 Seed Production***
PACING • 45 min pp. 70–73 **Section 3 Plant Responses to the Environment** • Describe how plants may respond to light and gravity. • Explain how some plants respond to night length. • Describe how some plants respond to changes of season.	SE **School-to-Home Activity** Earth's Orbit and the Seasons, p. 72 GENERAL SE **Science in Action** Math, Social Studies, and Language Arts Activities, pp. 80–81 GENERAL LB **EcoLabs & Field Activities** Recycle! Make Your Own Paper* GENERAL LB **Long-Term Projects & Research Ideas** Plant Partners* ADVANCED LB **Calculator-Based Labs** What Causes the Seasons?* ADVANCED	OSP **Lesson Plans** (also in print) TR **Bellringer Transparency*** TR **L50 Night Length and Blooming; Amount of Pigment Based on Season*** SE **Internet Activity,** p. 71 GENERAL CRF **SciLinks Activity*** GENERAL CD **Interactive Explorations CD-ROM** How's It Growing? GENERAL

PACING • 90 min

CHAPTER REVIEW, ASSESSMENT, AND STANDARDIZED TEST PREPARATION

CRF **Vocabulary Activity*** GENERAL
SE **Chapter Review,** pp. 76–77 GENERAL
CRF **Chapter Review*** GENERAL
CRF **Chapter Tests A*** GENERAL, **B*** ADVANCED, **C*** SPECIAL NEEDS
SE **Standardized Test Preparation,** pp. 78–79 GENERAL
CRF **Standardized Test Preparation*** GENERAL
CRF **Performance-Based Assessment*** GENERAL
OSP **Test Generator, Test Item Listing**

Online and Technology Resources

 Holt Online Learning

Visit **go.hrw.com** for access to Holt Online Learning, or enter the keyword **HS7 Home** for a variety of free online resources.

 **One-Stop Planner® CD-ROM**

This CD-ROM package includes:
• Lab Materials QuickList Software
• Holt Calendar Planner
• Customizable Lesson Plans
• Printable Worksheets

• ExamView® Test Generator
• Interactive Teacher's Edition
• Holt PuzzlePro®
• Holt PowerPoint® Resources

SKILLS DEVELOPMENT RESOURCES	SECTION REVIEW AND ASSESSMENT	CORRELATIONS
SE Pre-Reading Activity, p. 60 `GENERAL` **OSP** Science Puzzlers, Twisters & Teasers `GENERAL`		**National Science Education Standards** UCP 1, 2, 5; SAI 1, 2; LS 1c, 3a, 3b
CRF Directed Reading A* ■ `BASIC`, B* `SPECIAL NEEDS` **WB** Workbook* `Struggling Readers` **CRF** Vocabulary and Section Summary* ■ `GENERAL` **SE** Reading Strategy Discussion, p. 62 `GENERAL` **SE** Connection to Social Studies Sugar, p. 63 `GENERAL` **TE** Support for English Language Learners, p. 63 **TE** Inclusion Strategies, p. 63 **CRF** Reinforcement Worksheet A Leaf's Work Is Never Done* `BASIC` **MS** Math Skills for Science Balancing Chemical Equations* `GENERAL`	**SE** Reading Checks, pp. 62, 65 `GENERAL` **TE** Reteaching, p. 64 `BASIC` **TE** Quiz, p. 64 `GENERAL` **TE** Alternative Assessment, p. 64 `GENERAL` **SE** Section Review,* p. 65 ■ `GENERAL` **CRF** Section Quiz* ■ `GENERAL`	UCP 1, 2, 3, 4, 5; SAI 1, 2; SPSP 3; HNS 1, 2; LS 1a, 1c, 3c, 4c; *LabBook:* UCP 2, 3, 5; SAI 1, 2; LS 3a; *Chapter Lab:* UCP 2, 3, 5; SAI 1, 2; LS 1c, 1d, 3a, 4c
CRF Directed Reading A* ■ `BASIC`, B* `SPECIAL NEEDS` **WB** Workbook* `Struggling Readers` **CRF** Vocabulary and Section Summary* ■ `GENERAL` **SE** Reading Strategy Reading Organizer, p. 66 `GENERAL` **TE** Support for English Language Learners, p. 67 **CRF** Reinforcement Worksheet Fertilizing Flowers* `BASIC`	**SE** Reading Checks, pp. 67, 68 `GENERAL` **TE** Reteaching, p. 68 `BASIC` **TE** Quiz, p. 68 `GENERAL` **TE** Alternative Assessment, p. 68 `GENERAL` **SE** Section Review,* p. 69 ■ `GENERAL` **CRF** Section Quiz* ■ `GENERAL`	UCP 2, 3, 4, 5; SAI 1, 2; SPSP 4; HNS 1; LS 1a, 2a, 2b, 2d, 5b
CRF Directed Reading A* ■ `BASIC`, B* `SPECIAL NEEDS` **WB** Workbook* `Struggling Readers` **CRF** Vocabulary and Section Summary* ■ `GENERAL` **SE** Reading Strategy Discussion, p. 70 `GENERAL` **SE** Math Practice Bending by Degrees, p. 71 `GENERAL` **TE** Support for English Language Learners, p. 72 **TE** Inclusion Strategies, p. 72 **CRF** Reinforcement Worksheet How Plants Respond to Change* `BASIC` **CRF** Critical Thinking Space Plants* `ADVANCED`	**SE** Reading Checks, pp. 70, 71, 72 `GENERAL` **TE** Homework, p. 71 `ADVANCED` **TE** Reteaching, p. 72 `BASIC` **SE** Section Review,* p. 73 ■ `GENERAL` **TE** Quiz, p. 73 `GENERAL` **TE** Alternative Assessment, p. 73 `GENERAL` **CRF** Section Quiz* ■ `GENERAL`	UCP 1, 2, 3; SAI 1, 2; SPSP 2, 3, 5; HNS 2; LS 2b, 2c, 3a, 3c, 3d, 5b

www.scilinks.org
Maintained by the **National Science Teachers Association.** See Chapter Enrichment pages that follow for a complete list of topics.

Check out *Current Science* articles and activities by visiting the HRW Web site at **go.hrw.com.** Just type in the keyword **HL5CS13T.**

Classroom Videos
• **Lab Videos** demonstrate the chapter lab.
• **Brain Food Video Quizzes** help students review the chapter material.

Classroom CD-ROMs
• **Guided Reading Audio CD** (Also in Spanish)
• **Interactive Explorations**
• **Virtual Investigations**
• **Visual Concepts**
• **Science Tutor**

Holt Lab Generator CD-ROM
Search for any lab by topic, standard, difficulty level, or time. Edit any lab to fit your needs, or create your own labs. Use the Lab Materials QuickList software to customize your lab materials list.

Visual Resources

CHAPTER STARTER TRANSPARENCY

Strange but True!

It's war every day in the cornfield. When beet armyworm caterpillars attack the corn, the corn fights back. The corn somehow manages to send out SOS signals. Soon, parasitic wasps swoop in, attack the caterpillars, and save the day!

How can a plant send out a distress signal? When a corn plant is being munched on by a caterpillar, chemicals in the mouth of the caterpillar cause the corn plant to release a second chemical into the air. Wasps sense the corn's response and make a beeline for the infested plant. Like an airborne cavalry, the wasps dive for the caterpillars and lay eggs under their skin. The eggs hatch in a short time, and the wasp larvae devour the insides of the caterpillars.

Jim Tumlinson, the scientist who discovered this partnership between corn and wasps, says it probably occurred by chance. Many plants release special chemicals when attacked by pests. The wasps have a natural attraction to the chemical released by corn plants.

Tumlinson hopes to breed other plants so that they release insect-attracting chemicals. Attracting plant-friendly wasps could decrease the need for poisonous pesticides.

Making and releasing special chemicals are processes that occur in many plants. In this chapter you will learn about other plant processes.

BELLRINGER TRANSPARENCIES

Section: Photosynthesis
Where do you get the energy you need to stay alive? Where do the things you get your energy from get their energy? Is there an ultimate source of energy for most life on earth?

Write your response in your **science journal.**

Section: Reproduction of Flowering Plants
What are pollination and fertilization? Draw a diagram in your **science journal** of a flowering plant's reproductive system. Do you think there are plants with only male reproductive parts and plants with only female reproductive parts? Explain your answer.

Write your answers in your **science journal.**

TEACHING TRANSPARENCIES

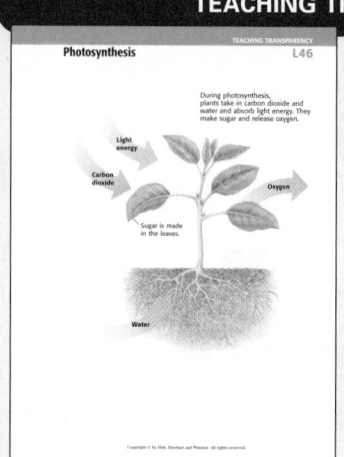

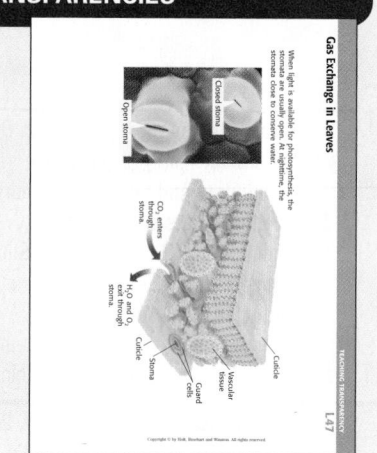

TEACHING TRANSPARENCIES

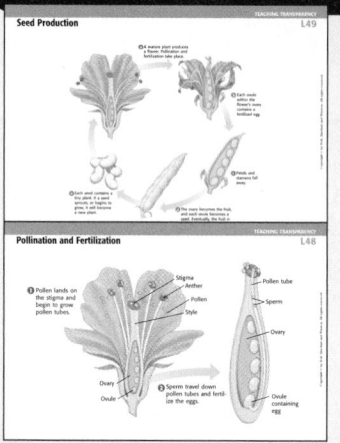

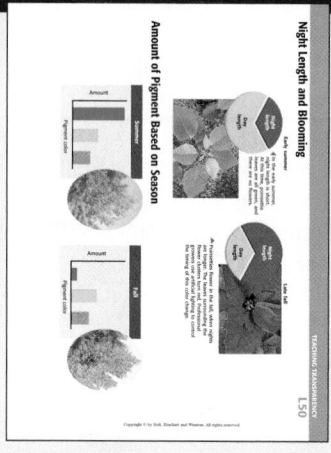

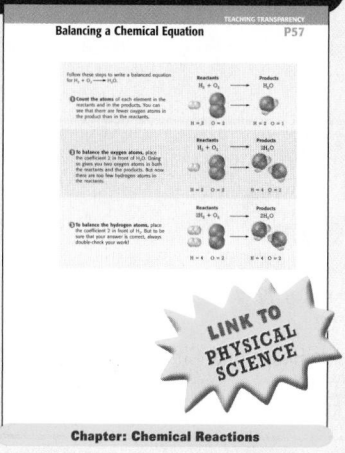

CONCEPT MAPPING TRANSPARENCY

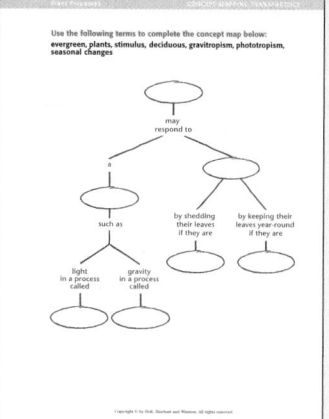

Planning Resources

LESSON PLANS

Lesson Plan SAMPLE

Section: Waves

Pacing
Regular Schedule: with lab(s):2 days without lab(s)1 days
Block Schedule: with lab(s):1 1/2 days without lab(s)1 days

Objectives
1. Relate the seven properties of life to a living organism.
2. Describe seven themes that can help you to organize what you learn about biology.
3. Identify the tiny structures that make up all living organisms.
4. Differentiate between reproduction and heredity and between metabolism and homeostasis.

National Science Education Standards Covered
LSInter1c:Cells have particular structures that underlie their functions.
LSMat1:Most cell functions involve chemical reactions.
LSBeh1:Cells store and use information to guide their functions.
UCP1:Cell functions are regulated.
SI1: Cells can differentiate and form complete multicellular organisms.
PS1:Species evolve over time.
ESS1: The great diversity of organisms is the result of more than 3.5 billion years of evolution.
ESS2: Natural selection and its evolutionary consequences provide a scientific explanation for the fossil record of ancient life forms as well as for the striking molecular similarities observed among the diverse species of living organisms.
ST3: The millions of different species of plants, animals, and microorganisms that live on Earth today are related by descent from common ancestors.
ST2: The energy for life primarily comes from the sun.
SPSP5: The complexity and organization of organisms accommodate the need for obtaining, transforming, transporting, releasing, and eliminating the matter and energy used to sustain the organism.
SPSP6: As matter and energy flows through different levels of organization of living systems, cells, organs, communities—and between living systems and the physical environment, chemical elements are recombined in different ways.
HNS1: Organisms have behavioral responses to internal change and to external stimuli.

PARENT LETTER

SAMPLE

Dear Parent,

Your son's or daughter's science class will soon begin exploring the chapter entitled "The World of Physical Science." In this chapter, students will learn about how the scientific method applies to the world of physical science and the role of physical science in the world. By the end of the chapter, students should demonstrate a clear understanding of the chapter's main ideas and be able to discuss the following topics:

1. physical science is the study of energy and matter (Section 1)
2. the role of physical science in the world around them (Section 1)
3. careers that rely on physical science (Section 1)
4. the steps used in the scientific method (Section 2)
5. examples of technology (Section 2)
6. how the scientific method is used to answer questions and solve problems (Section 2)
7. how our knowledge of science changes over time (Section 2)
8. how models represent real objects or systems (Section 3)
9. examples of different ways models are used in science (Section 3)
10. the importance of the International System of Units (Section 4)
11. the appropriate units to use for particular measurements (Section 4)
12. how area and density are derived quantities (Section 4)

Questions to Ask Along the Way

You can help your son or daughter learn about these topics by asking interesting questions such as the following:

• What are some surprising careers that use physical science?
• What is a characteristic of a good hypothesis?
• When is it a good idea to use a model?
• Why do Americans measure things in terms of inches and yards and meters ?

ALSO IN SPANISH

TEST ITEM LISTING

TEST ITEM LISTING
The World of Science SAMPLE

MULTIPLE CHOICE

1. A limitation of models is that
a. they are large enough to see
b. they do not exactly like the things that they model.
c. they are smaller than the things that they model.
d. they model unfamiliar things.
Answer: B   Difficulty: 1   Section: 3   Objective: 2

2. The length 10 m is equal to
a. 100 cm.   c. 10,000 mm.
b. 1000 cm.   d. Both (b) and (c)
Answer: B   Difficulty: 1   Section: 3   Objective: 2

3. To be valid, a hypothesis must be
a. testable   c. made into a law.
b. supported by evidence.   d. Both (a) and (b)
Answer: B   Difficulty: 1   Section: 3   Objective: 2 1

4. The statement "Sheila has a stain on her shirt" is an example of a(n)
a. observation.   c. law.
b. hypothesis.   d. prediction.
Answer: B   Difficulty: 1   Section: 3   Objective: 2

5. A hypothesis is often developed out of
a. observations.   c. laws.
b. experiments.   d. Both (a) and (b)
Answer: B   Difficulty: 1   Section: 3   Objective: 2

6. How many milliliters are in 3.5 kL?
a. 3,500 mL   c. 3,500, 000 mL
b. 0.0035 mL   d. 35,000 mL
Answer: B   Difficulty: 1   Section: 3   Objective: 2

7. A map of Seattle is an example of a
a. law.   c. model.
b. theory.   d. unit.
Answer: B   Difficulty: 1   Section: 3   Objective: 2

8. It a lab has safety icons shown below. These icons mean that you should wear
a. only safety goggles.   c. safety goggles and a lab apron.
b. only a lab apron.   d. safety goggles, a lab apron, and gloves.
Answer: B   Difficulty: 1   Section: 3   Objective: 2

9. The law of conservation of mass says the tot al mass before a chemical change is
a. more than the total mass after the change.
b. less than the total mass after the change.
c. the same as the total mass after the change.
d. not the same as the total mass after the change.
Answer: B   Difficulty: 1   Section: 3   Objective: 2

10. In which of the following areas might you find a geochemical at work?
a. studying the chemistry of rocks   c. studying fabric
b. studying forestry   d. studying the atmosphere

One-Stop Planner® CD-ROM

This CD-ROM includes all of the resources shown here and the following time-saving tools:

• *Lab Materials QuickList Software*
• *Customizable lesson plans*
• *Holt Calendar Planner*
• *The powerful ExamView® Test Generator*

Meeting Individual Needs

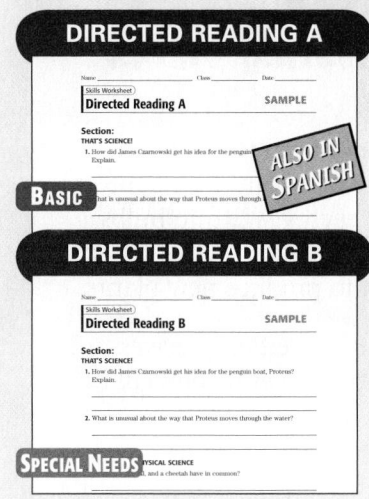

DIRECTED READING A
BASIC

DIRECTED READING B
SPECIAL NEEDS

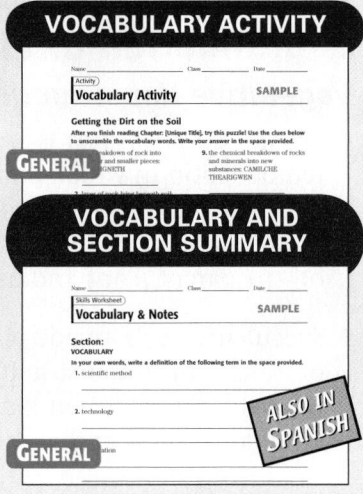

VOCABULARY ACTIVITY
GENERAL

VOCABULARY AND SECTION SUMMARY
GENERAL

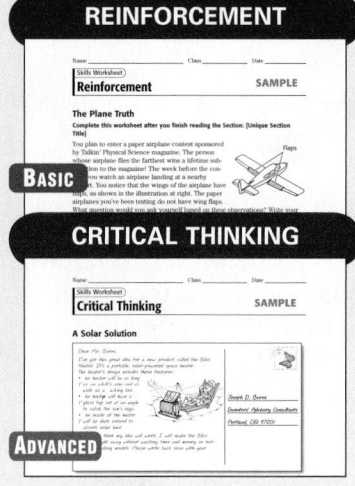

REINFORCEMENT
BASIC

CRITICAL THINKING
ADVANCED

SCILINKS ACTIVITY
GENERAL

SCIENCE PUZZLERS, TWISTERS & TEASERS
GENERAL

Labs and Activities

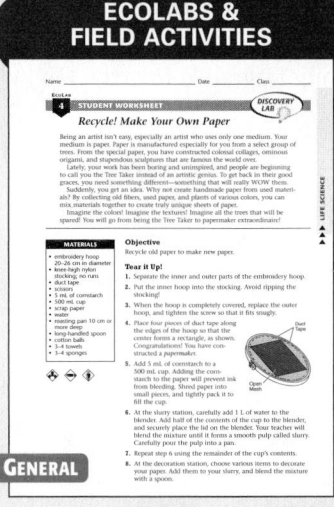

ECOLABS & FIELD ACTIVITIES
GENERAL

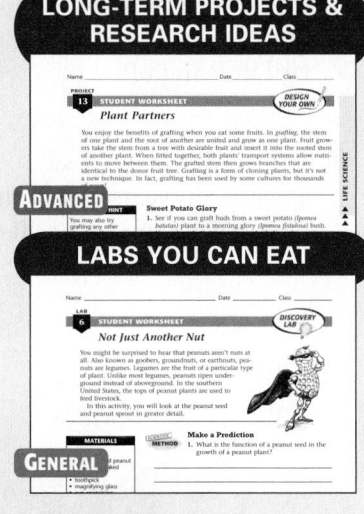

LONG-TERM PROJECTS & RESEARCH IDEAS
ADVANCED

LABS YOU CAN EAT
GENERAL

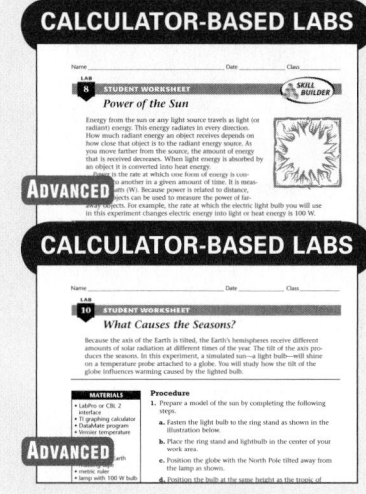

CALCULATOR-BASED LABS
ADVANCED

CALCULATOR-BASED LABS
ADVANCED

DATASHEETS FOR QUICK LABS

DATASHEETS FOR CHAPTER LABS

DATASHEETS FOR LABBOOK

Review and Assessments

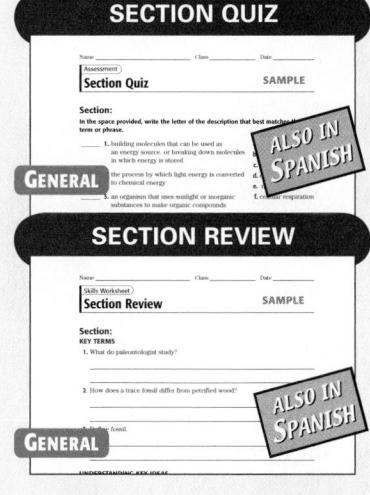

SECTION QUIZ
GENERAL

SECTION REVIEW
GENERAL

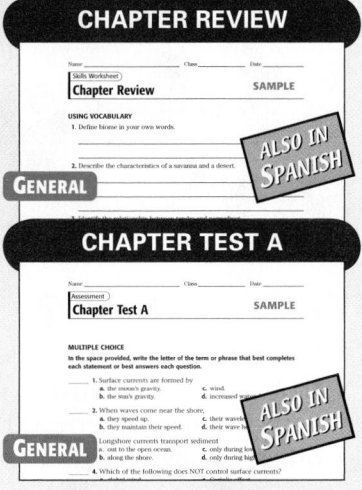

CHAPTER REVIEW
GENERAL

CHAPTER TEST A
GENERAL

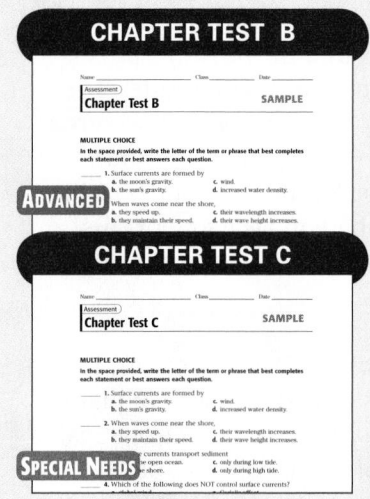

CHAPTER TEST B
ADVANCED

CHAPTER TEST C
SPECIAL NEEDS

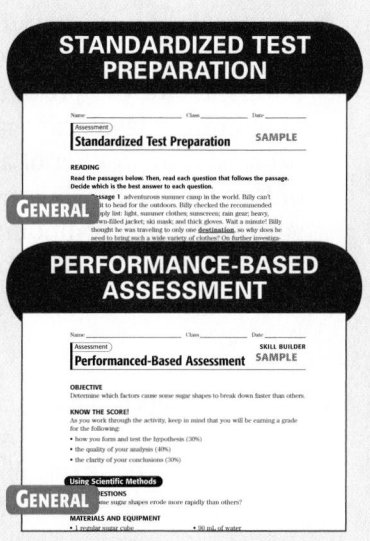

STANDARDIZED TEST PREPARATION
GENERAL

PERFORMANCE-BASED ASSESSMENT
GENERAL

This Chapter Enrichment provides relevant and interesting information to expand and enhance your presentation of the chapter material.

Section 1

Photosynthesis

Sunlight

- While sunlight is used for photosynthesis, too much sunlight—specifically, too much ultraviolet radiation—can damage a plant. Ultraviolet radiation damages plant DNA, bleaches leaves yellow, and stunts growth.

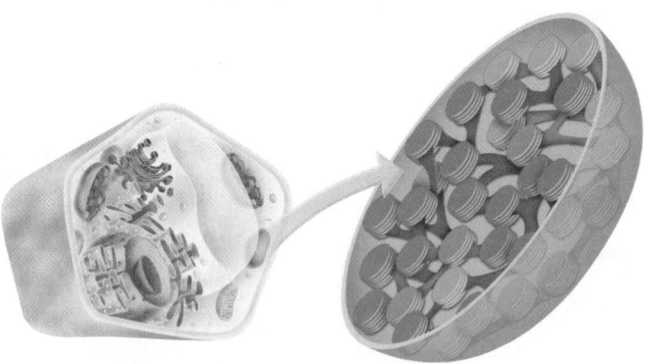

Water

- Water conservation is as important for alpine plants as it is for cactuses. In the Alps, the mountain aven and the mountain kidney vetch have hairlike coverings on their leaves to reduce water loss. These coverings also provide insulation.

Air

- Ozone, O_3, is a gas found in Earth's atmosphere. Ozone in the stratosphere protects Earth from harmful UV light. However, ozone found in the troposphere, or at ground level, can harm plants. Ground-level ozone is a byproduct of a reaction between two types of human-made pollutants—nitrogen oxides and volatile organic compounds. Sunlight and heat facilitate the reaction between these molecules. For this reason, there is often more ground-level ozone on hot days.

- Ground-level ozone damages the leaves of plants. It reduces the yield of crops, stunts the growth of plants, and reduces the survivability of seedlings. Ozone makes some plants more susceptible to disease and pests.

Section 2

Reproduction of Flowering Plants

Vegetative Reproduction

- *Vegetative reproduction* is another term for asexual reproduction in which a piece of a plant grows into a complete plant. For example, each year, tulip bulbs produce one or two new bulbs, which can be broken off the parent plant and used to produce new plants.

- Succulents, such as jade plants, have fleshy leaves full of water. This water sustains the leaves if they fall off the parent plant, often long enough for the leaves to send down roots and develop into new plants.

Is That a Fact!

- Night-blooming flowers rely on nocturnal animals, such as bats and hawkmoths, to pollinate their flowers. The flowers are usually white for increased visibility and often have a strong fragrance to attract pollinators.

- The oldest known fossil seeds are approximately 350 million years old, from the late Devonian period. They belong to plants called *seed ferns*.

The Perfect Flower?

- Flowers can be either perfect or imperfect. Perfect flowers have both male parts (stamens) and female parts (pistils). Imperfect flowers have one or the other—stamens or pistils—but not both.

Section 3

Plant Responses to the Environment

Plant Pigments

- In addition to containing the green pigment chlorophyll, plants contain other pigments that account for the colorful changes in autumn leaves. Xanthophylls are yellow, carotenes are yellowish orange, anthocyanins are red and purple, and tannins are brown.

- Carotenes and xanthophylls are always present in leaves. Anthocyanins are synthesized in late summer and autumn. They are not always present in leaves.

- In some years, the autumn colors of leaves—especially reds—are bright and colorful; in other years, they are dull. Two factors affect autumn leaf color: warm, sunny days followed by cool nights and the amount of moisture in the soil contribute to the production of bright colors.

Is That a Fact!

- In 2001, the U.S. Department of Agriculture reported that more than 67 million poinsettias (*Euphorbia pulcherrima*) were sold in the United States. Even though poinsettias are sold only during the late fall and early winter, poinsettias are the country's most popular potted plants.

Discovery of Auxins

- Charles Darwin (1809–1882) is credited with making the first recorded observations that led to the discovery of plant hormones called *auxins*. Auxins control the elongation of plant cells. In 1881, Darwin and his son, Francis, described phototropism, the bending of a plant toward a light source. The Darwins placed caps on the growing tips of grass seedlings and noted that the growing tips did not bend. When the caps were removed, the tips bent toward the light source. Other scientists furthered Darwin's research and discovered auxins in the early 1900s.

Is That a Fact!

- Plant hormones occur in very small quantities. In a pineapple plant, for example, only 6 μg of auxins are present for 1 kg of plant material. In terms of weight, this is equivalent to a needle in a truckload of hay that weighs 20 metric tons.

SciLinks is maintained by the National Science Teachers Association to provide you and your students with interesting, up-to-date links that will enrich your classroom presentation of the chapter.

Visit www.scilinks.org and enter the SciLinks code for more information about the topic listed.

Topic: Photosynthesis
SciLinks code: HSM1140

Topic: Reproduction of Plants
SciLinks code: HSM1295

Topic: Plant Tropisms
SciLinks code: HSM1166

Topic: Plant Growth
SciLinks code: HSM1159

Overview

Tell students that this chapter will help them learn about photosynthesis, reproduction in flowering plants, and plant responses to the environment. The chapter describes pollination, fertilization, asexual reproduction, and tropisms in plants.

Assessing Prior Knowledge

Students should be familiar with the following topics:

- seed plants
- asexual reproduction

Identifying Misconceptions

Students may have several misconceptions about photosynthesis and the way that plants get energy. First, help students understand that while plants produce glucose during photosynthesis, most of this glucose is immediately converted to sucrose or starch for storage. Then, help students understand that plants produce oxygen as a byproduct of photosynthesis but that plants also need oxygen. Plants use oxygen for cellular respiration, which releases energy from glucose and other food molecules. During this process, plants give off carbon dioxide. This carbon dioxide can exit the plant in the same way that oxygen and water vapor exit the plant—through the stomata.

Plant Processes

The Big Idea

Like all living things, plants need nourishment, reproduce, and respond to stimuli.

SECTION

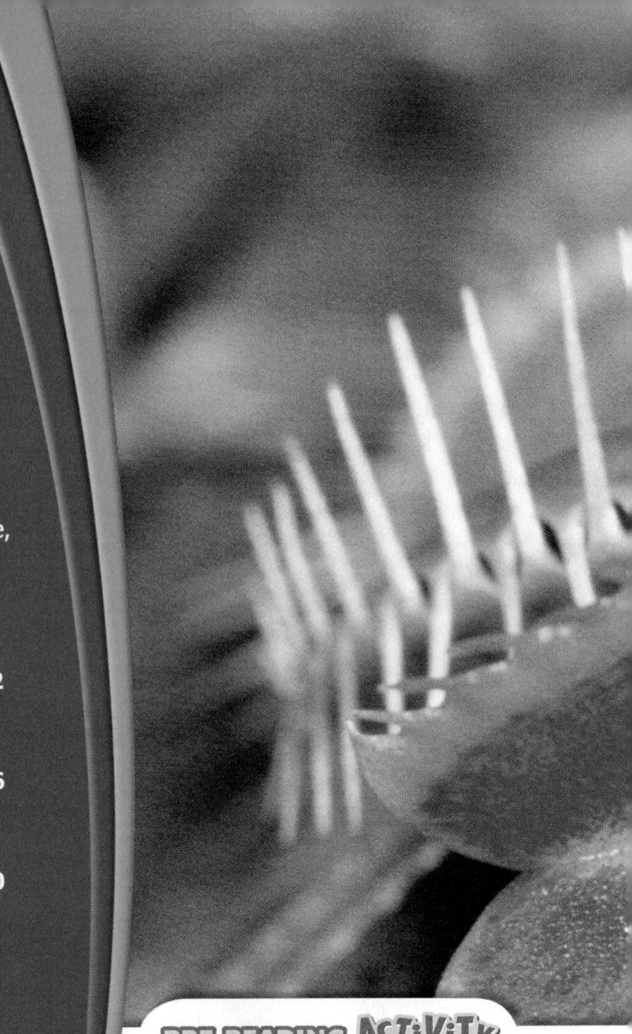

About the Photo

The plant in this photo is a Venus' flytrap. Those red and green spiny pads are its leaves. Like other plants, Venus' flytraps rely on photosynthesis to get energy. What is so unusual about the Venus' flytrap? Unlike most plants, the Venus' flytrap gets important nutrients, such as nitrogen, by capturing and digesting insects or other small animals.

PRE-READING ACTIVITY

FOLDNOTES Booklet Before you read the chapter, create the FoldNote entitled "Booklet" described in the **Study Skills** section of the Appendix. Label each page of the booklet with a main idea from the chapter. As you read the chapter, write what you learn about each main idea on the appropriate page of the booklet.

Standards Correlations

National Science Education Standards

The following codes indicate the National Science Education Standards that correlate to this chapter. The full text of the standards is at the front of the book.

Chapter Opener
UCP 1, 2, 5; SAI 1, 2; LS 1c, 3a, 3b

Section 1 Photosynthesis
UCP 1, 2, 3, 4, 5; SAI 1, 2; SPSP 3; HNS 1, 2; LS 1a, 1c, 3c, 4c; *LabBook:* UCP 2, 3, 5; SAI 1, 2; LS 3a

Section 2 Reproduction of Flowering Plants
UCP 2, 3, 4, 5; SAI 1, 2; SPSP 4; HNS 1; LS 1a, 2a, 2b, 2d, 5b

Section 3 Plant Responses to the Environment
UCP 1, 2, 3; SAI 1, 2; SPSP 2, 3, 5; HNS 2; LS 2b, 2c, 3a, 3c, 3d, 5b

Chapter Lab
UCP 2, 3, 5; SAI 1, 2; LS 1c, 1d, 3a, 4c

START-UP ACTIVITY

MATERIALS

FOR EACH GROUP
- corn seeds (5–6)
- cup, clear plastic, medium-sized
- marker
- paper towels
- water

Teacher's Notes: To minimize the effect of light on the growth of the stems, students should rotate the cups every day. Students can also wrap the sides of the cups in aluminum foil.

Be sure that students keep the paper towels moist throughout the activity.

To further emphasize the effect of gravity on plant growth, have students turn their cups upside down after the plants have grown for several days.

Answers

1. Students should observe that the stems of all the germinating seeds grow upward, or away from the force of gravity, no matter what the original orientation of the seeds was.

2. Sample answer: The shoots grew upward because plants grow away from the force of gravity.

START-UP ACTIVITY

Which End Is Up?

If you plant seeds with their "tops" facing in different directions, will their stems all grow upward? Do this activity to find out.

Procedure

1. Pack a **clear, medium-sized plastic cup** with slightly moistened **paper towels.**

2. Place **five or six corn seeds,** equally spaced, around the cup between the side of the cup and the paper towels. Point the tip of each seed in a different direction.

3. Using a **marker,** draw arrows on the outside of the cup to show the direction each seed tip points.

4. Place the cup in a well-lit location for 1 week. Keep the seeds moist by adding **water** to the paper towels as needed.

5. After 1 week, observe the seeds. Record the direction in which each shoot grew.

Analysis

1. In which direction did each of your shoots grow?

2. What might explain why your shoots grew the way they did?

Chapter Review

UCP 1, 2, 3, 4, 5; SAI 1, 2; SPSP 2, 3, 4, 5; HNS 1, 2; LS 1a, 1c, 2a, 2b, 2c, 2d, 3a, 3c, 3d, 4c, 5b

Science in Action

UCP 5; HNS 1, 2, 3; LS 1d, 2a, 2b, 4d, 5c

Strange but True!

It's war every day in the cornfield. When beet armyworm caterpillars attack the corn, the corn fights back. The corn somehow manages to send out SOS signals. Soon, parasitic wasps swoop in, attack the caterpillars, and save the day!

How can a plant send out a distress signal? When a corn plant is being munched on by a caterpillar, chemicals in the mouth of the caterpillar cause the corn plant to release a second chemical into the air. Wasps sense the corn's response and make a beeline for the infested plant.

Like an airborne cavalry, the wasps dive for the caterpillars and lay eggs under their skin. The eggs hatch in a short time, and the wasp larvae devour the insides of the caterpillars.

Jim Tumlinson, the scientist who discovered this partnership between corn and wasps, says it probably occurred by chance. Many plants release special chemicals when attacked by pests. The wasps have a natural attraction for the chemical released by corn plants.

Tumlinson hopes to breed other plants so that they release insect-attracting chemicals. Attracting plant-friendly wasps could decrease the need for poisonous pesticides.

Making and releasing special chemicals are processes that occur in many plants. In this chapter you will learn about other plant processes.

Chapter Starter Transparency
Use this transparency to help students begin thinking about plant processes.

CHAPTER RESOURCES

Technology

Transparencies
- Chapter Starter Transparency

READING SKILLS

Student Edition on CD-ROM

Guided Reading Audio CD
- English or Spanish

Classroom Videos
- Brain Food Video Quiz

Workbooks

Science Puzzlers, Twisters & Teasers
- Plant Processes GENERAL

Focus

Overview

This section describes photosynthesis. Students will learn about the relationship between photosynthesis and cellular respiration. In addition, they will learn about the importance of stomata in transpiration.

 Bellringer

Write the following question on the board or overhead projector: "Where do you get the energy you need to stay alive?" (Students will likely answer that they get their energy from the foods that they eat.) **LS** Verbal

Motivate

Discussion —————— GENERAL

Food and Energy Before students begin reading this section, ask them the following questions:

• Where do the animals that are used for food get their energy to survive? (Sample answer: The animals eat plants or other animals that eat plants.)

• Where do plants get their energy to survive? (Plants get their energy from sunlight.)

Explain to students that plants use energy from the sun to make their own food in a process called *photosynthesis*. **LS** Verbal

What You Will Learn

● Describe photosynthesis.
● Compare photosynthesis and cellular respiration.
● Describe how gas is exchanged in the leaves of plants.
● Describe two ways in which photosynthesis is important.

Vocabulary

photosynthesis   stoma
chlorophyll   transpiration
cellular respiration

READING STRATEGY

Discussion Read this section silently. Write down questions that you have about this section. Discuss your questions in a small group.

Photosynthesis

Plants don't have lungs. But like you, plants need air. Air contains oxygen, carbon dioxide, and other gases. Your body needs oxygen, and plants need oxygen. But what other gas is important to plants?

If you guessed *carbon dioxide*, you are correct. Plants use carbon dioxide for photosynthesis (FOHT oh SIN thuh sis). **Photosynthesis** is the process by which plants make their own food. Plants capture energy from sunlight during photosynthesis. This energy is used to make the sugar glucose ($C_6H_{12}O_6$) from carbon dioxide (CO_2) and water (H_2O).

Capturing Light Energy

Plant cells have organelles called *chloroplasts* (KLAWR uh PLASTS), shown in **Figure 1**. Chloroplasts are surrounded by two membranes. Inside the chloroplast, another membrane forms stacks called *grana* (GRAY nuh). Grana contain a green pigment, called **chlorophyll** (KLAWR uh FIL), that absorbs light energy.

Sunlight is made up of many different wavelengths of light. Chlorophyll absorbs many of these wavelengths. But it reflects more wavelengths of green light than wavelengths of other colors of light. So, most plants look green.

✓ **Reading Check** Why are most plants green? (*See the Appendix for answers to Reading Checks.*)

Figure 1   **Chloroplast Structure**

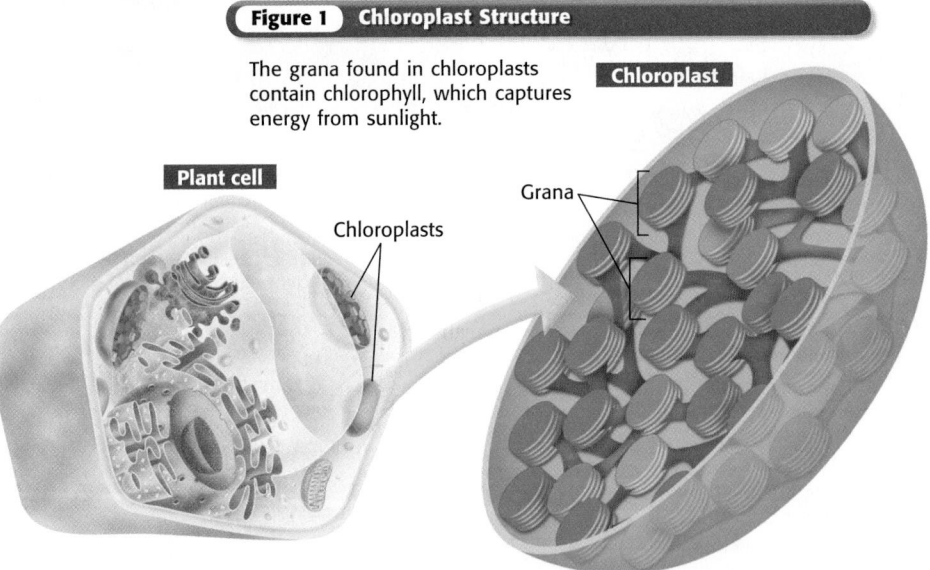

The grana found in chloroplasts contain chlorophyll, which captures energy from sunlight.

Plant cell

Chloroplasts

Chloroplast

Grana

CHAPTER RESOURCES

Chapter Resource File

  • **Lesson Plan**
  • **Directed Reading A** BASIC
  • **Directed Reading B** SPECIAL NEEDS

Technology

  Transparencies
  • Bellringer
  • L46 Photosynthesis
  • *LINK TO PHYSICAL SCIENCE* P57 Balancing a Chemical Equation

Workbooks

  Interactive Textbook Struggling Readers

Answer to Reading Check

Chlorophyll reflects more wavelengths of green light than wavelengths of other colors of light. So, most plants look green.

Making Sugar

The light energy captured by chlorophyll is used to help form glucose molecules. In turn, oxygen gas (O_2) is given off by plant cells. Photosynthesis is a complicated process made up of many steps. But photosynthesis can be summarized by the following chemical equation:

$$6CO_2 + 6H_2O \xrightarrow{\text{light energy}} C_6H_{12}O_6 + 6O_2$$

Six molecules of carbon dioxide and six molecules of water are needed to form one molecule of glucose and six molecules of oxygen. **Figure 2** shows where plants get the materials for photosynthesis.

Getting Energy from Sugar

Glucose molecules store energy. Plant cells use this energy for their life processes. To get energy, plant cells break down glucose and other food molecules in a process called **cellular respiration.** During this process, plant cells use oxygen. The cells give off carbon dioxide and water. Excess glucose is converted to another sugar called *sucrose* or stored as starch.

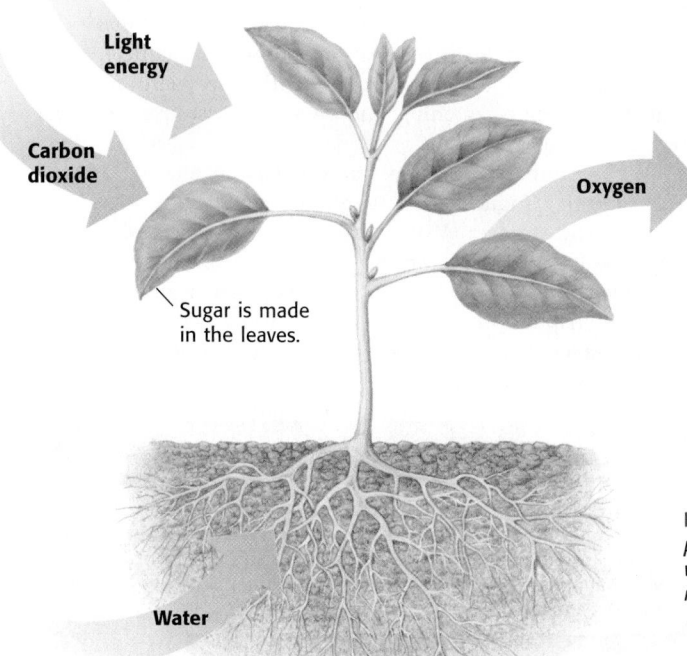

Light energy

Carbon dioxide

Oxygen

Sugar is made in the leaves.

Water

Figure 2 *During photosynthesis, plants take in carbon dioxide and water and absorb light energy. They make sugar and release oxygen.*

photosynthesis the process by which plants, algae, and some bacteria use sunlight, carbon dioxide, and water to make food

chlorophyll a green pigment that captures light energy for photosynthesis

cellular respiration the process by which cells use oxygen to produce energy from food

Definitions Have students read the definitions of *photosynthesis, cellular respiration,* and *transpiration* aloud and then write a definition of each term in their own words. **English Language Learners**

LS Verbal

Quiz — GENERAL

1. What molecules do plants use to make sugar? (carbon dioxide and water)

2. What substances enter and exit a leaf through the stomata? (Sample answer: Carbon dioxide enters the leaf while oxygen and water exit the leaf.)

3. How is oxygen an important byproduct of photosynthesis? (Sample answer: The oxygen produced by photosynthesis is used by animals and plants for cellular respiration.)

Alternative Assessment — GENERAL

Writing **Stomata** Have students write about stomata. Students should describe the appearance of stomata and the passage of materials through the stomata. **LS** Verbal

---

Figure 3 **Gas Exchange in Leaves**

When light is available for photosynthesis, the stomata are usually open. At nighttime, the stomata close to conserve water.

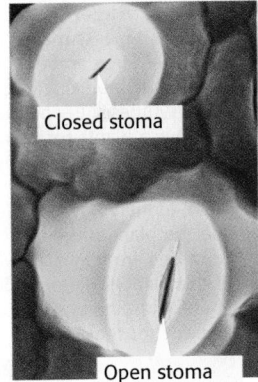

Closed stoma

Open stoma

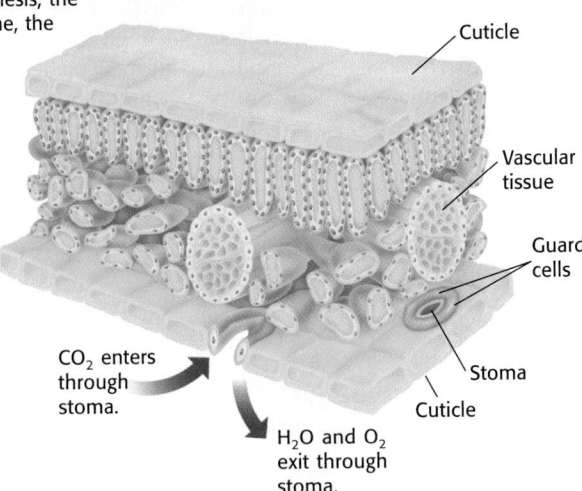

Cuticle

Vascular tissue

Guard cells

Stoma

Cuticle

CO_2 enters through stoma.

H_2O and O_2 exit through stoma.

stoma one of many openings in a leaf or a stem of a plant that enable gas exchange to occur (plural, *stomata*)

transpiration the process by which plants release water vapor into the air through stomata

Gas Exchange

Many above-ground plant surfaces are covered by a waxy cuticle. The cuticle protects the plant from water loss. How does a plant get carbon dioxide through this barrier? Carbon dioxide enters the plant's leaves through stomata (singular, *stoma*). A **stoma** is an opening in the leaf's epidermis and cuticle. Each stoma is surrounded by two *guard cells*. The guard cells act like double doors, opening and closing the stoma. You can see stomata in **Figure 3.**

When stomata are open, carbon dioxide enters the leaf. The oxygen produced during photosynthesis exits the leaf through the stomata. Water vapor also exits the leaf in this way. The loss of water from leaves is called **transpiration.** Most of the water absorbed by a plant's roots replaces the water lost during transpiration. Sometimes, more water is lost through a plant's leaves than is absorbed by the plant's roots. When this happens, the plant wilts.

CONNECTION TO Chemistry

Transpiration Wrap a plastic bag around the branch of a tree or a portion of a potted plant. Secure the bag closed with a piece of tape or a rubber band, but be sure not to injure the plant. Record what happens over the next few days. What happened to the bag? How does this illustrate transpiration?

ACTIVITY

Answer to Connection to Chemistry

Students should note that water droplets form on the inside of the plastic bag. These water droplets demonstrate transpiration because the water comes from the plant. The water vapor that exits the leaves through the stomata condenses on the inside of the bag.

WEIRD SCIENCE

Some leaves have more than 100,000 stomata per square centimeter of leaf surface.

The Importance of Photosynthesis

Plants and other photosynthetic organisms, such as some bacteria and many protists, form the base of nearly all food chains on Earth. An example of one food chain is shown in **Figure 4.** During photosynthesis, plants store light energy as chemical energy. Some animals use this chemical energy when they eat plants. Other animals get energy from plants indirectly. These animals eat animals that eat plants. Most organisms could not survive without photosynthetic organisms.

Plants, animals, and most other organisms rely on cellular respiration to get energy. Cellular respiration requires oxygen. Oxygen is a byproduct of photosynthesis. So, photosynthesis provides the oxygen that animals and plants need for cellular respiration.

Reading Check What are two ways in which photosynthesis is important?

Figure 4 *Mice rely on plants for food. In turn, cats get energy from mice.*

SECTION Review

Summary

- During photosynthesis, plants use energy from sunlight, carbon dioxide, and water to make food.

- Plants get energy from food by cellular respiration, which uses oxygen and releases carbon dioxide and water.

- Transpiration, or the loss of water through the leaves, happens when stomata are open.

- Photosynthesis provides oxygen. Most animals rely on photosynthetic organisms for food.

Using Key Terms

1. In your own words, write a definition for each of the following terms: *photosynthesis*, *chlorophyll*, and *cellular respiration*.

Understanding Key Ideas

2. During photosynthesis, plants
   a. absorb energy from sunlight.
   b. use carbon dioxide and water.
   c. make food and oxygen.
   d. All of the above

3. How is cellular respiration related to photosynthesis?

4. Describe gas exchange in plants.

Math Skills

5. Plants use 6 carbon dioxide molecules and 6 water molecules to make 1 glucose molecule. How many carbon dioxide and water molecules would be needed to make 12 glucose molecules?

Critical Thinking

6. **Predicting Consequences** Predict what might happen if plants and other photosynthetic organisms disappeared.

7. **Applying Concepts** Light filters let through certain colors of light. Predict what would happen if you grew a plant under a green light filter.

For a variety of links related to this chapter, go to www.scilinks.org

Topic: Photosynthesis
SciLinks code: HSM1140

CHAPTER RESOURCES

Chapter Resource File

- Section Quiz GENERAL
- Section Review GENERAL
- Vocabulary and Section Summary GENERAL
- Reinforcement Worksheet BASIC

Technology

Transparencies
- L47 Gas Exchange in Leaves

Workbooks

Math Skills for Science
- Balancing Chemical Equations GENERAL

Focus

Overview

This section describes pollination and fertilization. Students will be able to explain how fruits are formed from flowers and differentiate between sexual and asexual reproduction in flowering plants.

🔊 Bellringer

Ask students the following question: "What are pollination and fertilization?" (Sample answer: Pollination happens when a pollen grain reaches the stigma. Fertilization happens when a sperm joins with an egg.)

Motivate

Demonstration — GENERAL

Parts of a Flower Show students a variety of fresh flowers, and ask them to compare the flowers. Point out the stamens, stigmas, petals, and sepals in each flower. Remove the petals, and shake the flower over paper. (Pollen can stain skin and clothing. You may wish to wear protective gloves.) Ask students to identify the powder on the paper. (pollen) Explain that pollen contain the flower's male reproductive cells.
English Language Learners
LS Visual

SECTION 2

What You Will Learn

- Describe pollination and fertilization in flowering plants.
- Explain how fruits and seeds are formed from flowers.
- List three reasons why a seed might be dormant.
- List three examples of asexual reproduction in plants.

Vocabulary
dormant

READING STRATEGY

Reading Organizer As you read this section, make a table comparing sexual reproduction and asexual reproduction in plants.

Reproduction of Flowering Plants

Imagine you are standing in a field of wildflowers. You're surrounded by bright colors and sweet fragrances. You can hear bees buzzing from flower to flower.

Flowering plants are the largest and most diverse group of plants. Their success is partly due to their flowers. Flowers are adaptations for sexual reproduction. During sexual reproduction, an egg is fertilized by a sperm.

Fertilization

In flowering plants, fertilization takes place within flowers. *Pollination* happens when pollen is moved from anthers to stigmas. Usually, wind or animals move pollen from one flower to another flower. Pollen contains sperm. After pollen lands on the stigma, a tube grows from each pollen grain. The tube grows through the style to an ovule. Ovules are found inside the ovary. Each ovule contains an egg. Sperm from the pollen grain move down the pollen tube and into an ovule. Fertilization happens when a sperm fuses with the egg inside an ovule. **Figure 1** shows pollination and fertilization.

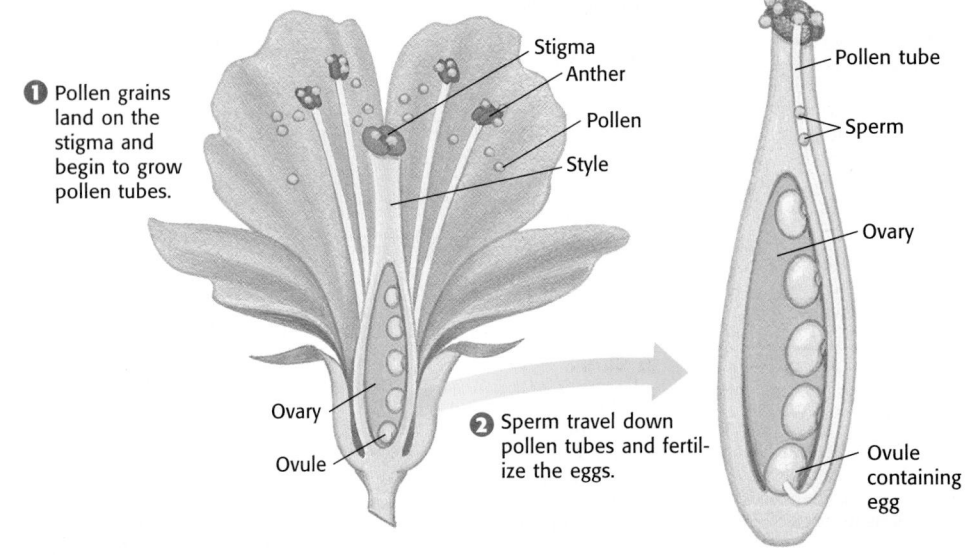

Figure 1 Pollination and Fertilization

① Pollen grains land on the stigma and begin to grow pollen tubes.

Stigma
Anther
Pollen
Style
Ovary
Ovule

Pollen tube
Sperm
Ovary
Ovule containing egg

② Sperm travel down pollen tubes and fertilize the eggs.

CHAPTER RESOURCES

Chapter Resource File

 • Lesson Plan
- Directed Reading A BASIC
- Directed Reading B SPECIAL NEEDS

Technology

 Transparencies
- Bellringer
- L48 Pollination and Fertilization
- L49 Seed Production

Workbooks

 Interactive Textbook Struggling Readers

CONNECTION to History — GENERAL

Cacao In 1519, the explorer Hernando Cortez brought cacao beans and a recipe from Montezuma's court back to Spain. The recipe was for a new drink called *xocoatl*, or chocolate. Invite students to research the history of chocolate. Have students make posters of their findings. **LS Verbal/Visual**

Figure 2 Seed Production

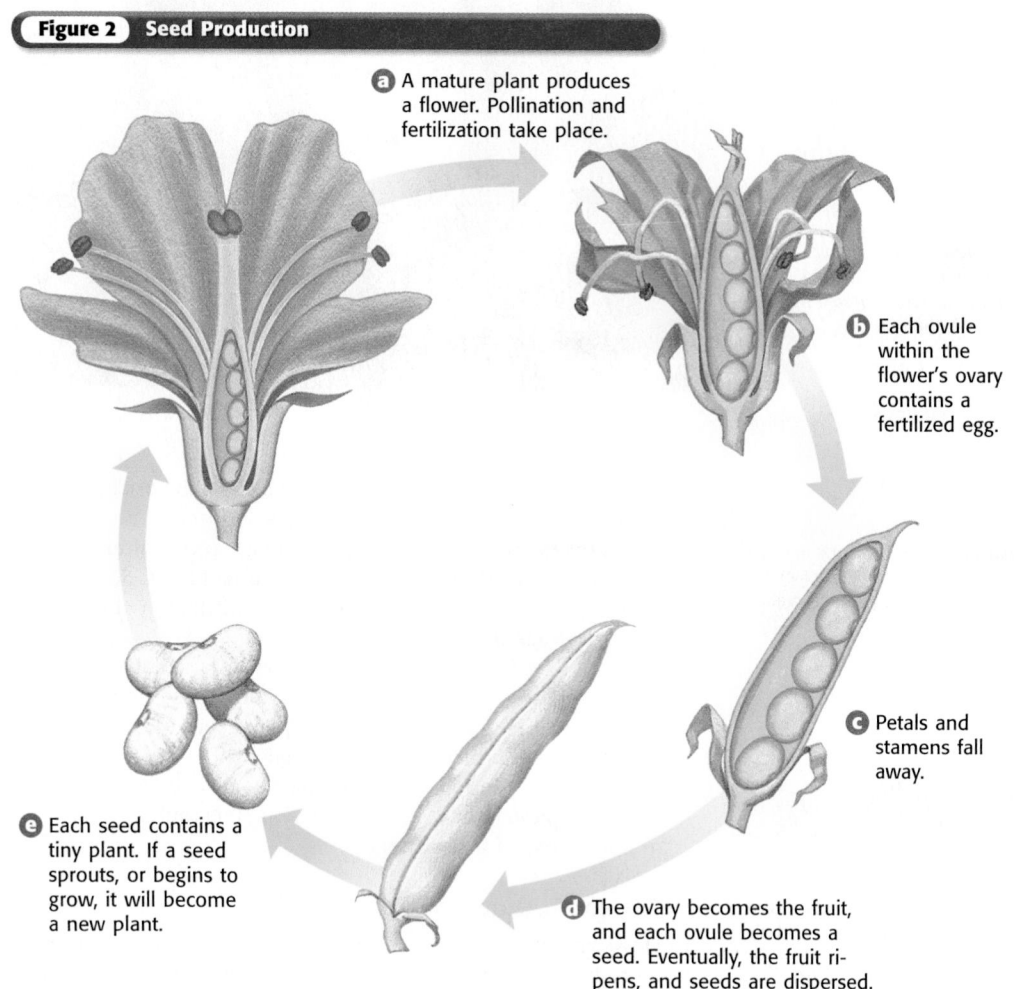

a A mature plant produces a flower. Pollination and fertilization take place.

b Each ovule within the flower's ovary contains a fertilized egg.

c Petals and stamens fall away.

d The ovary becomes the fruit, and each ovule becomes a seed. Eventually, the fruit ripens, and seeds are dispersed.

e Each seed contains a tiny plant. If a seed sprouts, or begins to grow, it will become a new plant.

From Flower to Fruit

After fertilization takes place, the ovule develops into a seed. The seed contains a tiny, undeveloped plant. The ovary surrounding the ovule becomes a fruit, as shown in **Figure 2.**

As a fruit swells and ripens, it protects the developing seeds. **Figure 3** shows a common fruit. Fruits often help a plant spread its seeds. Many fruits are edible. Animals may eat these fruits. Then, the animals discard the seeds away from the parent plant. Other fruits, such as burrs, get caught in an animal's fur. Some fruits are carried by the wind.

Reading Check How do fruits help a plant spread its seeds? (*See the Appendix for answers to Reading Checks.*)

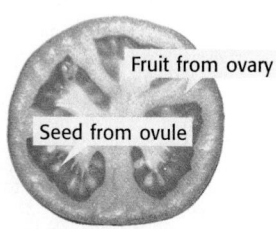

Fruit from ovary

Seed from ovule

Figure 3 *Tomatoes develop from a flower's ovary and ovules.*

English Language Learners

Ovary vs. ovule Students may find these two words confusing. Tell students they both come from ovum (Latin for egg), but that they identify different plant parts with different functions. Then, ask students to fill in a T-chart comparing ovary and ovule. They should include appearance, location in the plant, and role in fertilization. Have students exchange charts and check their answers. Ask spot questions to check understanding. **LS** Verbal

Answer to Reading Check

Sample answer: Animals may eat fruits and discard the seeds away from the parent plant. Other fruits, such as burrs, get caught in an animal's fur. Some fruits are carried by the wind.

Teach

Group ACTIVITY — GENERAL

Concept Mapping Have students work together in groups of four to create a concept map that details the process of sexual reproduction in plants from the time that pollen grains reach the stigma until a seed develops inside a fruit. Encourage students to illustrate their work. **LS** Verbal/Logical Co-op Learning

ACTIVITY ———— BASIC

MATERIALS

FOR EACH GROUP
• bean seeds (1 packet)
• container, plastic, small, with snap-on caps (2)
• water

Germination Show students that plant germination can push the caps off bottles. This demonstration will take a few days. Fill a container, such as a plastic film canister, with bean seeds. Fill another container with bean seeds and water. Snap the caps onto the bottles. (Don't use child-proof bottles that lock.) Place the bottles where they can be observed. In a few days, the germinating bean seeds will knock the caps off or even split the bottles apart. Ask students to note which beans are more powerful—the beans with water or the beans without water. (The beans with water are expanding as they absorb water for germination. They are producing CO_2 because they have begun cellular respiration.) English Language Learners **LS** Visual

Close

Reteaching ——— BASIC

Making Comparisons Ask students to compare sexual and asexual reproduction in flowering plants. Students should recognize the structures involved and the ways in which pollination and fertilization differ from asexual reproduction. **LS** Logical

Quiz ——— GENERAL

Ask students whether each of the following statements is true or false.

1. Pollination happens when a sperm joins with an egg. (false)

2. Tubers, plantlets, and runners are structures used for asexual reproduction. (true)

3. *Dormant* describes the active state of a seed or other plant part. (false)

Alternative Assessment ——— GENERAL

Drawing Flowers Have students make a drawing of a flower and label the anthers, stigmas, style, ovary, and ovule. Students should also show pollination and fertilization. English Language Learners
LS Visual

Answer to Reading Check
plantlets, tubers, and runners

Figure 4 *Seeds grow into new plants. The roots begin to grow first. Then, the shoot grows up through the soil.*

dormant describes the inactive state of a seed or other plant part when conditions are unfavorable to growth

Thirsty Seeds

1. Fill a **Petri dish** two-thirds full of **water**, and add **six dry bean seeds**. Using a **wax pencil**, label the dish "Water."

2. Add **six dry bean seeds** to a dry **Petri dish**. Label this dish "Control."

3. The next day, compare the size of the two sets of seeds. Record your observations.

4. What caused the size of the seeds to change? Why might this be important to the seed's survival?

From Seed to Plant

Once a seed is fully developed, the young plant inside the seed stops growing. The seed may become dormant. When seeds are **dormant**, they are inactive. Dormant seeds often survive long periods of drought or freezing temperatures. Some seeds need extreme conditions, such as cold winters or forest fires, to break their dormancy.

When seeds are dropped or planted in a suitable environment, the seeds sprout. To sprout, most seeds need water, air, and warm temperatures. Each plant species has an ideal temperature at which most of its seeds will begin to grow. For many plants, the ideal temperature for growth is about 27°C (80.6°F). **Figure 4** shows the *germination* (JUHR muh NAY shuhn), or sprouting, of a bean seed.

Other Methods of Reproduction

Flowering plants may also reproduce asexually. For asexual reproduction, plants do not need flowers. Part of a plant, such as a stem or root, produces a new plant. The following are three structures plants use to reproduce asexually:

- **Plantlets** Tiny plants grow along the edges of a plant's leaves. These plantlets fall off and grow on their own.

- **Tubers** Underground stems, or tubers, can produce new plants after a dormant season.

- **Runners** Above-ground stems from which new plants can grow are called *runners*.

You can see an example of each kind of asexual reproduction in **Figure 5.**

✓ **Reading Check** What are three structures plants use to reproduce asexually?

MATERIALS

FOR EACH GROUP
- bean seed (12)
- marker or wax pencil
- Petri dish (2)
- water

Answers

3. Students should note that the seeds in water increased in size or cracked open.

4. The seeds swell because they are absorbing water. Once a seed absorbs enough water, the seed coat ruptures, which allows the root and shoot to emerge.

Figure 5 Three Structures for Asexual Reproduction

Kalanchoe plants produce **plantlets** along the edges of their leaves. The plantlets eventually fall off and root in the soil to grow on their own.

A potato is a **tuber,** or underground stem. The "eyes" of potatoes are buds that can grow into new plants.

The strawberry plant produces **runners,** or stems that grow horizontally along the ground. Buds along the runners take root and grow into new plants.

SECTION Review

Summary

- After pollination, a pollen tube forms from the stigma to an ovule. This tube allows a sperm to fertilize an egg.
- After fertilization, seeds and fruit form. The seeds are protected by fruit.
- A dormant seed can survive drought and freezing temperatures. Some seeds need extreme conditions to break their dormancy.
- Some plants use plantlets, tubers, or runners to reproduce asexually.

Using Key Terms

1. In your own words, write a definition for the term *dormant*.

Understanding Key Ideas

2. Pollination happens when
   a. a pollen tube forms.
   b. a sperm cell fuses with an egg.
   c. pollen is transferred from the anther to the stigma.
   d. None of the above

3. Which part of a flower develops into a fruit? into a seed?

4. Why do seeds become dormant?

5. Describe how plants reproduce asexually.

Math Skills

6. A seed sprouts when the temperature is 27°C. If the temperature is now 20°C and it rises 1.5°C per week, in how many weeks will the seed sprout?

Critical Thinking

7. **Making Inferences** What do flowers and runners have in common? How do they differ?

8. **Identifying Relationships** When might asexual reproduction be important for the survival of some flowering plants?

9. **Analyzing Ideas** Sexual reproduction produces more genetic variety than asexual reproduction. Why is variety important?

SCLINKS ®   **NSTA**
Developed and maintained by the National Science Teachers Association

For a variety of links related to this chapter, go to www.scilinks.org

Topic: Reproduction of Plants
SciLinks code: HSM1295

CHAPTER RESOURCES

Chapter Resource File
- Section Quiz **GENERAL**
- Section Review **GENERAL**
- Vocabulary and Section Summary **GENERAL**
- Reinforcement Worksheet **BASIC**
- Datasheet for Quick Lab

Answers to Section Review

1. Sample answer: A seed or plant part that doesn't grow when conditions are unfavorable is dormant.

2. c

3. ovary; ovule

4. Sample answer: Dormant seeds can survive unfavorable conditions, such as long periods of drought and freezing temperatures. Some seeds need extreme conditions, such as cold winters or forest fires, to break their dormancy.

5. Sample answer: Plantlets are tiny plants that grow along the edges of a plant's leaves, fall to the ground, and grow on their own. Tubers are underground stems that can produce new plants. Runners are above-ground stems from which new plants can grow.

6. in about 5 weeks
   (27°C − 20°C = 7°C;
   7°C ÷ 1.5°C/week = 4.7 weeks)

7. Sample answer: Both flowers and runners are used for reproduction, but flowers are involved in sexual reproduction, whereas runners are used for asexual reproduction.

8. Sample answer: A flowering plant produces seeds, but conditions may not be favorable for the seeds to grow. However, these same conditions may not affect asexual reproduction, so the plant can continue reproducing in this way. Also, if there are no pollinators in an area, sexual reproduction would be difficult for some plants. So, these plants may reproduce asexually.

9. Sample answer: Genetic variety may improve the ability of the plant to survive. For example, the offspring produced by asexual reproduction have the same weaknesses that the parent plant does. The offspring of sexual production differ from a parent plant, so the offspring may survive diseases or unfavorable conditions that would have affected the parent plant.

Overview

This section describes how plants respond to light and gravity and how some plants flower in response to night length.

 **Bellringer**

Have students answer the following questions:

• How does the direction of light affect the growth of plants? (Sample answer: Plants may grow toward light.)

• How does gravity affect the growth of plants? (Sample answer: A plant's shoots grow away from the force of gravity, and a plant's roots grow toward the force of gravity.)

Motivate

Discussion ——— GENERAL

Plant Responses Bring to class a touch-sensitive plant, such as *Mimosa pudica*. Show students how the leaves of the plant "fold up" when they are touched. You also can demonstrate plant movement with a Venus' flytrap. Explain to students that while these movements are plant responses, they are not tropisms. They are nastic movements. Nastic movements are plant responses that happen independently of the direction of a stimulus. **LS** Visual

---

SECTION

3

Plant Responses to the Environment

What happens when you get really cold? Do your teeth chatter? Or do you shiver? Anything that causes a reaction in your body is a **stimulus** (plural, **stimuli**). But would a plant respond to a stimulus?

Plants do respond to stimuli! For example, they respond to light, gravity, and changing seasons.

Plant Tropisms

Some plants respond to an environmental stimulus by growing in a particular direction. Growth in response to a stimulus is called a **tropism** (TROH PIZ uhm). Tropisms are either positive or negative. Plant growth toward a stimulus is a positive tropism. Plant growth away from a stimulus is a negative tropism.

Light

What happens if you place a houseplant so that it gets light from only one direction, such as from a window? The shoot tips probably bend toward the light. Bending toward the light is a positive tropism. A change in the direction a plant grows that is caused by light is called *phototropism* (FOH toh TROH PIZ uhm). The result of phototropism is shown in **Figure 1.** Shoots bend because cells on one side of the shoot grow longer than cells on the other side of the shoot.

✓ *Reading Check* What happens when a plant gets light from only one direction? (*See the Appendix for answers to Reading Checks.*)

What You Will Learn

● Describe how plants may respond to light and gravity.
● Explain how some plants respond to night length.
● Describe how some plants respond to the changes of season.

Vocabulary
tropism

READING STRATEGY

Discussion Read this section silently. Write down questions that you have about this section. Discuss your questions in a small group.

tropism the growth of all or part of an organism in response to an external stimulus, such as light

Figure 1 *The plant cells on the dark side of the shoot grow longer than the cells on the other side. So, the shoot bends toward the light.*

Answer to Reading Check

Sample answer: The shoot tips will probably bend toward the light.

Figure 2 Gravitropism

▼ To grow away from the pull of gravity, this plant has grown upward.

▼ This plant has recently been upside down.

Bending by Degrees

Suppose a plant has a positive phototropism and bends toward light at a rate of 0.3° per minute. In how many hours will the plant bend 90°?

Gravity

Plant growth also changes in response to the direction of gravity. This change is called *gravitropism* (GRAV i TROH piz uhm). The effect of gravitropism is demonstrated by the plants in **Figure 2.** A few days after a plant is placed on its side or turned upside down, the roots and shoots change direction of growth. Most shoot tips have negative gravitropism. They grow upward, away from the center of the Earth. In contrast, most root tips have positive gravitropism. Roots grow downward, toward the center of the Earth.

Seasonal Responses

What would happen if a plant living in an area that has very cold winters flowered in December? Would the plant be able to successfully produce seeds and fruits? Probably not. The plant's flowers would likely freeze and die. So, the flowers would never produce mature seeds.

Plants living in regions with cold winters can detect the change in seasons. How do plants do this? As fall and winter approach, the days get shorter, and the nights get longer. The opposite happens when spring and summer approach. Plants respond to the change in the length of day.

 **Reading Check** How do plants detect seasonal changes?

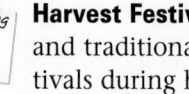

For another activity related to this chapter, go to **go.hrw.com** and type in the keyword **HL5PL2W.**

Answer to Reading Check

Sample answer: Plants respond to the change in the length of day.

Cultural Awareness GENERAL

Writing **Harvest Festivals** Many ancient and traditional cultures have festivals during harvest time, often in the fall. Ask interested students to research a harvest festival. Have students write a magazine article about their findings. LS Verbal

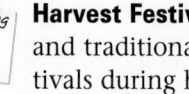

Teach

Answer to Math Practice

5 h (90° ÷ 0.3°/min = 300 min; 300 min ÷ 60 min/h = 5 h)

Using the Figure— GENERAL

Phototropism and Gravitropism

Have students look closely at **Figure 1** and **Figure 2.** Point out that after a few days, the leaves of the plants in the photos grow toward light or away from the force of gravity. Roots are not affected by light, but they grow toward the force of gravity. Ask students to describe these tropisms as positive or negative. (Growth toward a stimulus is a positive tropism, while growth away from a stimulus is a negative tropism. Growth by shoots toward light and growth by roots toward gravity are positive tropisms. The growth of shoots away from gravity is a negative tropism.) LS Verbal   English Language Learners

Homework —— ADVANCED

Investigating Plant Growth

Have students research how the lifespan of a plant is measured in one-year growing seasons. Ask students to describe the life cycle of plants in each of the following categories and to give examples of each:

• annuals (plants whose life cycle is completed in one growing season; corn, marigolds, beans, and sunflowers)

• biennials (plants that require two growing seasons to complete their life cycle; hollyhocks, foxgloves, carrots, and onions)

• perennials (plants that live year after year for more than two years; trees, roses, asparagus, and irises)

Encourage students to include drawings that illustrate when each plant begins to grow, produces seeds, and dies. LS Verbal/Visual

INCLUSION Strategies

- *Developmentally Delayed*
- *Learning Disabled*

The idea that leaves do not turn colors but that one of the colors is removed is probably in opposition to what most students think. Using a leaf pattern, trace two leaves onto green construction paper and one each onto yellow and orange construction paper. Cover each of the yellow and orange leaves with a green leaf. Discuss and show that the yellow and orange colors are there but are covered by the green. Then, remove the green leaf and discuss that the other colors in leaves become visible when the green color decreases in the fall. You may want to explain to students that red pigments are an exception—these pigments are made in the fall.

LS Visual

Close

Reteaching — BASIC

Organizing Information Write the following heads on the board: "Phototropism," "Gravitropism," and "Seasonal responses." Ask student volunteers to add information under the appropriate head.

LS Verbal/Logical

Figure 3 Night Length and Flower Color

Early summer

Night length

Day length

◀ In the early summer, night length is short. At this time, poinsettia leaves are all green, and there are no flowers.

Late fall

Night length

Day length

▲ Poinsettias flower in the fall, when nights are longer. The leaves surrounding the flower clusters turn red. Professional growers use artificial lighting to control the timing of this color change.

Length of Day

The difference between day length and night length is an important environmental stimulus for many plants. This stimulus can cause plants to begin reproducing. For example, some plants flower in fall or winter. At this time, night length is long. These plants are called *short-day plants*. Poinsettias, such as those shown in **Figure 3,** are short-day plants. Chrysanthemums are also short-day plants. Other plants flower in spring or early summer, when night length is short. These plants are called *long-day plants*. Clover, spinach, and lettuce are examples of long-day plants.

Seasons and Leaf Loss

All trees lose their leaves. Some trees, such as pine and holly, shed some of their leaves year-round so that some leaves are always on the tree. These trees are called *evergreen trees*. Evergreen trees have leaves adapted to survive throughout the year. The leaves are often covered with a thick cuticle. This cuticle protects the leaves from cold and dry weather.

Other trees, such as maple, oak, and elm trees, are called *deciduous* (dee SIJ oo uhs) *trees*. These trees lose all of their leaves around the same time each year. In colder areas, deciduous trees usually lose their leaves before winter begins. In warmer climates that have wet and dry seasons, deciduous trees lose their leaves before the dry season. The loss of leaves helps plants survive low temperatures or long periods without rain.

✓ **Reading Check** Compare evergreen trees and deciduous trees.

SCHOOL to HOME

Earth's Orbit and the Seasons

The seasons are caused by Earth's tilt and its orbit around the sun. Research how Earth's orbit determines the seasons. With a parent, make a model of the Earth's orbit around the sun to illustrate your findings.

ACTIVITY

Answer to Reading Check

Sample answer: Evergreen trees always have some leaves on them. Deciduous trees lose all of their leaves around the same time each year.

Answer to School-to-Home Activity

Students' models should illustrate an understanding of how Earth's orbit and tilt affect the amount of sunlight that an area receives at a particular time of year.

SUPPORT FOR

English Language Learners

Seasons Tell students that in some places in the United States the leaves of deciduous trees don't turn color when seasons change; they simply drop off. These areas are mostly in the southern United States, where the temperatures remain high. Ask students if the weather gets cold enough for leaves to turn in their first countries. If not, how do trees react to changing weather? (Answers may include flowering or dropping leaves without changing color.) **LS** Verbal

---

Figure 4 Amount of Pigment Based on Season

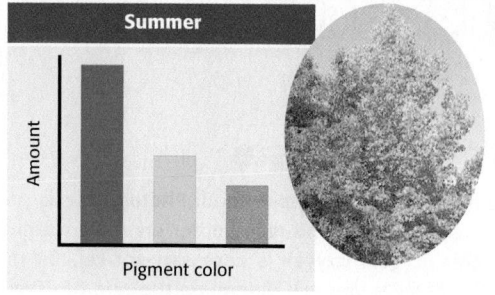

Summer

Amount

Pigment color

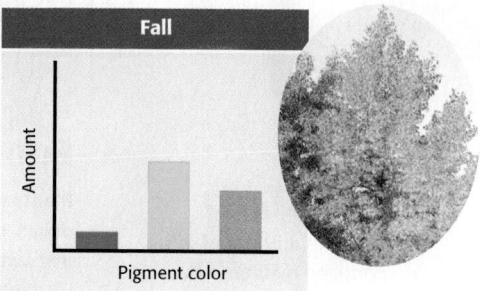

Fall

Amount

Pigment color

Seasons and Leaf Color

As shown in **Figure 4,** the leaves of deciduous trees may change color before they are lost. As fall approaches, green chlorophyll breaks down. Orange or yellow pigments in the leaves are then revealed. These pigments were always present in the leaves. But they were hidden by green chlorophyll.

SECTION Review

Summary

- Plant growth in response to a stimulus is called a tropism. Tropisms are positive or negative.
- Plants react to light, gravity, and changing seasons.
- Short-day plants flower when night length is long. Long-day plants flower when night length is short.
- Evergreen trees do not lose all their leaves at one time. Deciduous trees lose their leaves at the same time each year.

Using Key Terms

1. In your own words, write a definition for the term *tropism*.

Understanding Key Ideas

2. Deciduous trees lose their leaves
   a. to conserve water during the dry season.
   b. around the same time each year.
   c. to survive low winter temperatures.
   d. All of the above

3. How do light and gravity affect plants?

4. Describe how day length can affect the flowering of plants.

Math Skills

5. A certain plant won't bloom until it is dark for 70% of a 24 h period. How long is the day when the plant will bloom?

Critical Thinking

6. **Making Inferences** Many evergreen trees live in areas with long, cold winters. Why might these evergreen trees keep their leaves all year?

7. **Analyzing Ideas** Some short-day plants bloom during the winter. If cold weather reduces the chances that a plant will produce seeds, what might you conclude about where these short-day plants are found?

SciLINKS

NSTA
Developed and maintained by the National Science Teachers Association

For a variety of links related to this chapter, go to www.scilinks.org

Topic: Plant Tropisms; Plant Growth
SciLinks code: HSM1166; HSM1159

CHAPTER RESOURCES

Chapter Resource File

- Section Quiz GENERAL
- Section Review GENERAL
- Vocabulary and Section Summary GENERAL
- Reinforcement Worksheet BASIC
- Critical Thinking ADVANCED
- SciLinks Activity GENERAL

Technology

Transparencies
- L50 Night Length and Blooming; Amount of Pigment Based on Season

Food Factory Waste

Teacher's Notes

Time Required

One 45-minute class period and about 5 minutes per day for 5 days

Lab Ratings

EASY —————————————— HARD

Teacher Prep 🧪🧪
Student Set-Up 🧪🧪🧪
Concept Level 🧪🧪🧪
Clean Up 🧪🧪

MATERIALS

The materials listed on the student page are enough for a pair or small group of students. *Elodea* (whose common name is *waterweed*) is a common aquarium plant and can be found at some pet stores and most places that sell aquarium fish. A 5% solution of baking soda and water can be made by adding water to 5 g of baking soda until the volume is 100 mL. (You would add about 95 mL of water.)

Safety Caution

Remind students to review all safety cautions and icons before beginning this lab activity.

OBJECTIVES

Measure the amount of gas produced over time by photosynthesis.

Draw a graph of the amount of gas produced versus time.

MATERIALS

- baking-soda-and-water solution, 5% (500 mL)
- beaker (600 mL)
- *Elodea* sprigs, 20 cm long (2–3)
- funnel
- gloves, protective
- ruler, metric
- test tube

SAFETY

Food Factory Waste

Plants use photosynthesis to make food. Photosynthesis produces oxygen gas. Humans and many other organisms cannot live without this oxygen. Oxygen is necessary for cellular respiration. In this activity, you will determine the rate of oxygen production for an *Elodea* plant.

Procedure

1. Add 450 mL of baking-soda-and-water solution to a beaker.

2. Put two or three sprigs of *Elodea* in the beaker. The baking soda will provide the *Elodea* with the carbon dioxide it needs for photosynthesis.

3. Place the wide end of the funnel over the *Elodea*. The small end of the funnel should be pointing up. The *Elodea* and the funnel should be completely under the solution.

4. Fill a test tube with the remaining baking-soda-and-water solution. Place your thumb over the end of the test tube, and turn the test tube upside down. Make sure no air enters the test tube. Hold the opening of the test tube under the solution. Place the test tube over the small end of the funnel. Try not to let any solution out of the test tube.

Holt Lab Generator CD-ROM

Search for any lab by topic, standard, difficulty level, or time. Edit any lab to fit your needs, or create your own labs. Use the Lab Materials QuickList software to customize your lab materials list.

David Sparks
Redwater Junior High School
Redwater, Texas

CHAPTER RESOURCES

Chapter Resource File

 • Datasheet for Chapter Lab
• Lab Notes and Answers

Technology

 Classroom Videos
• Lab Video

 LabBook

• Weepy Weeds

5. Place the beaker setup in a well-lit area.

6. Prepare a data table similar to the one below.

Amount of Gas Present in the Test Tube

Days of exposure to light	Total amount of gas present (mm)	Amount of gas produced per day (mm)
0		
1		
2		
3		
4		
5		

DO NOT WRITE IN BOOK

7. If no air entered the test tube, record that there was 0 mm of gas in the test tube on day 0. If air got into the tube while you were placing it, measure the height of the column of air in the test tube in millimeters. Measure the gas in the test tube from the middle of the curve on the bottom of the upside-down test tube to the level of the solution. Record this number for day 0.

8. As described in the previous step, measure the amount of gas in the test tube each day for the next 5 days. Record your measurements in the second column of your data table.

9. Calculate the amount of gas produced each day. Subtract the amount of gas present on the previous day from the amount of gas present on the current day. Record these amounts in the third column of your data table.

Analyze the Results

1. **Constructing Graphs** Make a graph similar to the one below. Based on your measurements, your graph should show the amount of gas produced versus time.

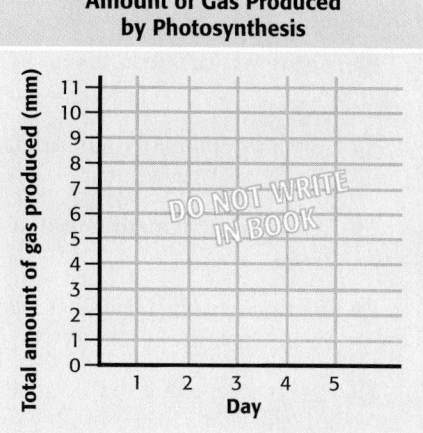

Amount of Gas Produced by Photosynthesis

DO NOT WRITE IN BOOK

2. **Describing Events** Based on your graph, what happened to the amount of gas in the test tube?

Draw Conclusions

3. **Interpreting Information** Write the equation for photosynthesis. Then, relate each part of your experiment to the part of the equation it represents.

Applying Your Data

As you can see from your results, *Elodea* produces oxygen gas as a byproduct of photosynthesis. Research photosynthesis. Find out if there are factors that affect the rate of photosynthesis. Then, predict what would happen to the production of oxygen gas.

CHAPTER RESOURCES
Workbooks

Labs You Can Eat
• Not Just Another Nut GENERAL

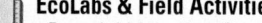
EcoLabs & Field Activities
• Recycle! Make Your Own Paper GENERAL

Long-Term Projects & Research Ideas
• Plant Partners ADVANCED

Calculator Based Labs
• Power of the Sun ADVANCED
• What Causes the Seasons? ADVANCED

Lab Notes
You may want to have students practice placing the test tube over the inverted funnel using water before students do so with the baking-soda solution. It may take two or three tries to get the test tube over the funnel stem without letting any air into the tube. Tell students the following: "First, fill the test tube with the solution. Place your thumb over the opening tightly so that air cannot get in. Submerge your thumb and the top of the test tube. Once the top of the test tube is underwater, you can remove your thumb from the opening of the test tube and maneuver the test tube over the stem of the funnel. Be sure that you have the *Elodea* in place under the funnel before you begin!"

Analyze the Results

1. Students' graphs should show a gradual increase in the amount of gas in the test tube.

2. Sample answer: The amount of gas in the test tube increased over time.

Draw Conclusions

3. $6CO_2 + 6H_2O + \text{light energy} \rightarrow C_6H_{12}O_6 + 6O_2$

CO_2 is carbon dioxide, which comes from the baking-soda-and-water solution. H_2O is water, which is also found in the baking-soda-and-water solution. Light energy comes from the sun. $C_6H_{12}O_6$ is glucose, and O_2 is oxygen. Glucose and oxygen are products of photosynthesis. The oxygen is released by *Elodea* and fills the test tube. The glucose is stored by the *Elodea*.

Applying Your Data

Students should demonstrate an understanding of the factors that affect the rate of photosynthesis. Students will find that among those factors, color of light and the amount of carbon dioxide and water present can affect the rate of photosynthesis. Students should indicate that factors that increase the rate of photosynthesis lead to the production of more oxygen while factors that decrease the rate of photosynthesis decrease the amount of oxygen produced.

Assignment Guide

SECTION	QUESTIONS
1	1, 3–5, 7–8, 16–18
2	6, 10, 13–15, 19, 22–25
3	2, 9, 11–12, 20–21

ANSWERS

Using Key Terms

1. transpiration
2. tropism
3. Chlorophyll
4. cellular respiration
5. stoma
6. dormant
7. Photosynthesis

Understanding Key Ideas

8. b
9. b
10. c
11. Sample answer: Short-day plants bloom when nights are long, during the fall and winter. Long-day plants bloom when nights are short, during the spring and summer.
12. Sample answer: The shoots would bend upward, away from the force of gravity, while the roots would bend downward, toward the force of gravity.

Chapter Review

USING KEY TERMS

Complete each of the following sentences by choosing the correct term from the word bank.

stoma	photosynthesis
dormant	cellular respiration
tropism	chlorophyll
transpiration	

1 The loss of water from leaves is called ___.

2 A plant's response to light or gravity is called a ___.

3 ___ is a green pigment found in plant cells.

4 To get energy from the food made during photosynthesis, plants use ___.

5 A ___ is an opening in the epidermis and cuticle of a leaf.

6 An inactive seed is ___.

7 ___ is the process by which plants make their own food.

UNDERSTANDING KEY IDEAS

Multiple Choice

8 During gas exchange in plants,
  a. carbon dioxide exits while oxygen and water enter the leaf.
  b. oxygen and water exit while carbon dioxide enters the leaf.
  c. carbon dioxide and water enter while oxygen exits the leaf.
  d. carbon dioxide and oxygen enter while water exits the leaf.

9 Plants often respond to light from one direction by
  a. bending away from the light.
  b. bending toward the light.
  c. wilting.
  d. None of the above

10 Which of the following is NOT a way that plants reproduce asexually?
  a. runners
  b. tubers
  c. flowers
  d. plantlets

Short Answer

11 Compare short-day plants and long-day plants.

12 How do potted plants respond to gravity if placed on their sides?

13 Describe the pollination and fertilization of flowering plants.

14 What three things do seeds need before they will sprout?

15 Explain how fruits and seeds form from flowers.

16 Compare photosynthesis and cellular respiration.

17 What are two ways in which photosynthesis is important?

---

13. Sample answer: Pollination happens when pollen is transferred from the anthers to the stigma. After the pollen lands on the stigma, a tube grows from each pollen grain. The tube grows through the style to an ovule. A sperm travels down the tube and fertilizes an egg in the ovule.

14. water, air, and warm temperatures

15. Sample answer: After the egg is fertilized, the ovule forms a seed. The ovary becomes a fruit, which protects the seeds.

16. Sample answer: Photosynthesis is the process by which plants make glucose. It uses carbon dioxide and water and produces oxygen. Cellular respiration is the process by which plants get energy from glucose and other food molecules. Cellular respiration uses oxygen and gives off carbon dioxide and water.

17. Sample answer: Photosynthetic organisms form the base of nearly all food chains on Earth. Photosynthesis also produces the oxygen that animals and plants need for cellular respiration.

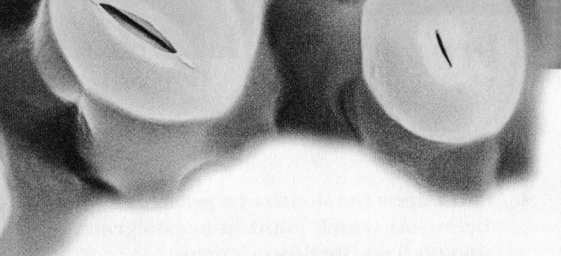

18 **Concept Mapping** Use the following terms to create a concept map: *plants, cellular respiration, light energy, photosynthesis, chemical energy, carbon dioxide,* and *oxygen.*

19 **Making Inferences** Many plants live in areas that have severe winters. Some of these plants have seeds that will not germinate unless the seeds have first been exposed to a long period of cold. How might this characteristic help new plants survive?

20 **Analyzing Ideas** Most plant shoots have positive phototropism. Plant roots have positive gravitropism. What might be the benefits of each of these characteristics?

21 **Applying Concepts** If you wanted to make poinsettias bloom and the leaves turn red in the summer, what would you have to do?

22 **Making Inferences** Imagine that someone discovered a new flowering plant. The plant has yellow flowers and underground stems. How might this plant reproduce asexually?

INTERPRETING GRAPHICS

The graph below shows seed germination rates for different seed companies. Use the graph below to answer the questions that follow.

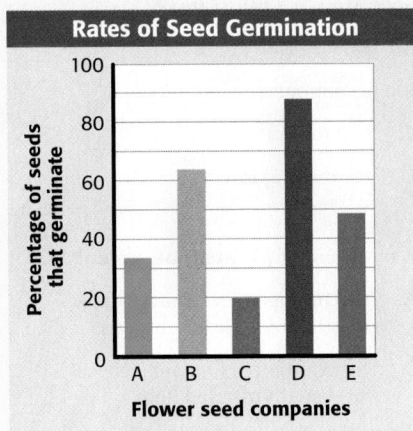

Rates of Seed Germination

Percentage of seeds that germinate vs *Flower seed companies* (A, B, C, D, E)

23 Which seed company had the highest rate of seed germination? the lowest rate of seed germination?

24 Which seed companies had seed germination rates higher than 50%?

25 If Elaine wanted to buy seeds that had a germination rate higher than 60%, which seed companies would she buy seeds from? Why might Elaine want to buy seeds with a higher germination rate?

Critical Thinking

18. An answer to this exercise can be found at the end of this book.

19. Sample answer: If the seeds germinate before they have been exposed to a long period of cold, they may germinate too early. The cold temperatures may not be over, so the young plants may be exposed to freezing temperatures that may kill the plants.

20. Sample answer: Positive phototropism can ensure that plant shoots get the sunlight that they need for photosynthesis. The positive gravitropism of plant roots ensures that the roots can reach water.

21. Sample answer: I would have to grow the poinsettias under controlled lights. Instead of exposing the poinsettias to long periods of darkness during the winter, I would expose the poinsettias to short periods of darkness and long periods of light. To bloom in the summer, the poinsettias should be exposed to long nights and short days during the summer.

22. Sample answer: Underground stems, such as tubers, can grow into new plants, so the plant likely reproduces asexually in this way.

Interpreting Graphics

23. D; C

24. B and D

25. B and D; More seeds will grow if Elaine buys seeds that have higher germination rates.

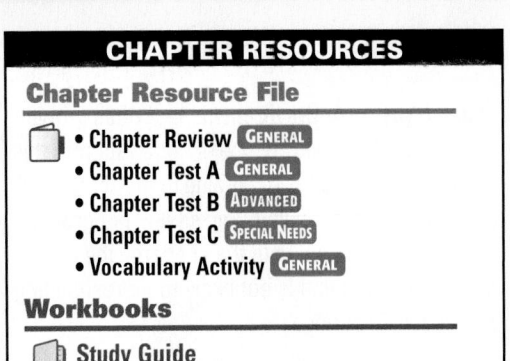

CHAPTER RESOURCES

Chapter Resource File

- **Chapter Review** GENERAL
- **Chapter Test A** GENERAL
- **Chapter Test B** ADVANCED
- **Chapter Test C** SPECIAL NEEDS
- **Vocabulary Activity** GENERAL

Workbooks

Study Guide
- Study Guide is also available in Spanish.

Teacher's Notes

To provide practice under more realistic conditions, give students 20 minutes to answer all of the questions in this Standardized Test Preparation.

Answer Key

Question	Answer
1	B
2	B
3	C
4	D
5	B
6	A
7	D
8	A
9	C
10	A
11	B
12	*
13	*

*See Test Doctor.

Multiple Choice

1. Shawn recently placed his houseplant next to a window. After a week, Shawn noticed that the shoot tips of the plant started to bend toward the light coming from the window. What kind of tropism does Shawn's plant have?

   A. gravitropism

   B. phototropism

   C. thigmotropism

   D. seasonal tropism

2. Why do most plants look green?

   A. The chlorophyll in plants captures green light for photosynthesis.

   B. The chlorophyll in plants reflects wavelengths of green light.

   C. The chloroplasts in plants are surrounded by two green membranes.

   D. The chloroplasts in plants make green sugar during photosynthesis.

3. What must happen for sexual reproduction to occur in flowering plants?

   A. Plantlets must fall from the parent.

   B. The fruit of the plant must be edible.

   C. An egg must be fertilized by a sperm.

   D. Pollen must be produced.

4. Carla drew the sketch of a peach blossom below. At which point in her diagram do you find the flower's ovary?

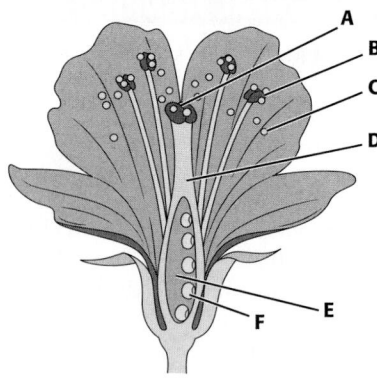

   A. point A

   B. point B

   C. point C

   D. point D

5. The chemical equation for cellular respiration is shown below. What happens on the right side of the arrow?

$$C_6H_{12}O_6 + 6O_2 \longrightarrow 6CO_2 + 6H_2O$$

   A. Sugar is produced.

   B. Carbon dioxide and water are produced.

   C. Six carbon atoms combine with six oxygen atoms.

   D. Carbon dioxide and oxygen are produced.

6. What kind of energy is transferred into chemical energy by photosynthesis?

   A. radiant energy from the sun

   B. potential energy of the ground

   C. kinetic energy of a plant's leaves

   D. kinetic energy from wind

 TEST DOCTOR

Question 1 A: Gravitropism describes growth in response to gravity, which is not a factor in this scenario. B: Correct. C: According to the scenario, the plant is not touching anything, so it is not growing in response to touch. D: In the scenario, the plant is growing indoors and is not likely to be responding to a seasonal change.

Question 2 A: Chlorophyll reflects wavelengths of green light and absorbs wavelengths of other colors of light. B: Correct. C: Chloroplasts contain chlorophyll, which reflects green light. The other structures of the cell play no part in the green color. D: The sugar produced in the process of photosynthesis has no color.

Question 3 A: Plantlets fall from a parent in one form of asexual reproduction. B: Edible fruit is a way of distributing seeds in plants that produce fruit. It is not a requirement for sexual reproduction. C: Correct. D: In order for sexual reproduction to occur, an egg must be fertilized by a sperm.

Question 4 A: The stigma is shown at point A. B: Pollen is found at point B. C: An ovule is shown at point C. D: Correct.

7. Why do the leaves of some deciduous trees change color in the fall?

A. More of the colored pigments enter the leaves in the fall.

B. Cold weather causes chlorophyll to change color.

C. Chlorophyll changes into different colors in cold weather.

D. Chlorophyll breaks down, revealing pigments that were always there.

8. At what point does a young plant inside a seed stop growing?

A. when the seed is fully developed

B. when the seed becomes dormant

C. when the seed is eaten by an animal

D. when the seed germinates

9. In photosynthesis, what energy source is converted into chemical energy and stored as glucose ($C_6H_{12}O_6$)?

A. chemical energy

B. H_2O

C. light energy

D. CO_2

10. Pollination occurs in angiosperms when

A. pollen moves from anthers to stigmas.

B. the ovule develops into a seed.

C. the ovary becomes the fruit.

D. sperm moves down the pollen tube.

Use the table below to answer question 11.

$6CO_2 + 6H_2O$	Light Energy $\longrightarrow$	$C_6H_{12}O_6 + 6O_2$

11. Analyze the equation for photosynthesis above and identify which of the following is a valid conclusion.

A. The process of photosynthesis produces carbon dioxide.

B. Carbon dioxide combines with the hydrogen in the water.

C. Six hydrogen atoms disappear during photosynthesis.

D. Six oxygen atoms are destroyed during photosynthesis.

Open Response

12. Wetlands, such as Kentucky's bald cypress swamps, are often thick with vegetation. Such locations are usually much more humid than cities. One cause is greater evaporation from the open water found in wetlands. What is another cause?

13. In Kentucky, strawberries are planted in the early spring. In the first year, blooms are removed to encourage the growth of runners. Would these runners work in another garden? How could a strawberry plant be exactly reproduced in this way?

Standardized Test Preparation

the point at which the young plant stops growing. C: Seeds may be distributed by animals, but this has nothing to do with the development of the young plant. D: When the seed germinates, or sprouts, the young plant is growing from the seed. The young plant is no longer inside the seed.

Question 9 A: The product of photosynthesis is chemical energy. Chemical energy is not converted into chemical energy during photosynthesis. B: Water is not an energy source in photosynthesis. C: Correct. D: Like water, carbon dioxide is used during photosynthesis. It is not an energy source.

Question 10 A: Correct. B: Pollination occurs when pollen moves from the anthers of a flower to the stigmas of a flower. Fertilization leads to the development of a plant's seeds. C: Fertilization, not pollination, leads to the development of fruit. D: Fertilization, not pollination, occurs when sperm moves down a plant's pollen tube.

Question 11 A: The process of photosynthesis produces glucose and oxygen, not carbon dioxide. B: Correct. C: No hydrogen (or any other) atoms disappear in the process of photosynthesis. D: No oxygen atoms are destroyed in the process of photosynthesis.

Question 12 Full-credit answers should include the following points:

• In the process of transpiration, plants release water vapor.

• Lush vegetation in a wetland produces more water vapor from plant transpiration than in a city, where there is less plant matter.

Question 13 Full-credit answers should include the following points:

• Yes, the runners could be planted in another garden.

• Under good growing conditions, the runners could succeed in producing new plants because strawberries are able to reproduce asexually.

• Asexually produced offspring are identical to the "mother" plant.

Question 5 A: Sugar is produced in the process of photosynthesis. During cellular respiration, carbon dioxide and water are expelled from the cell. B: Correct. C: In cellular respiration, 6 carbon atoms combine with 12 oxygen atoms to form 6 carbon dioxide molecules. D: During cellular respiration, carbon dioxide and water are expelled from the cell. No oxygen is expelled.

Question 6 A: Correct. B: Potential energy is the energy of position and cannot be converted into chemical energy by plants. C: Kinetic energy is the energy of movement and cannot be converted

into chemical energy by plants. D: Plants cannot convert kinetic energy into chemical energy.

Question 7 A: The change in color is due to chlorophyll breaking down, which reveals pigments that were always present in the leaves. No new pigment enters the leaves. B: Chlorophyll reflects wavelengths of green light, which is not affected by temperature. C: Chlorophyll does not "change" color at any time. It reflects green wavelengths of light regardless of temperature. D: Correct.

Question 8 A: Correct. B: A developed seed might or might not become dormant. Dormancy occurs once the seed is fully developed, which is

Weird Science

Background

The corpse flower, or titan arum (*Amorphophallus titanum*), generates heat to disperse malodorous sulfuric compounds across a great distance. This metabolic burn of the plant's stored carbohydrates uses up an enormous amount of energy. This is one reason that the titan arum seldom blooms—in the wild, it may bloom only three to four times within 40 years.

Scientific Debate

ACTiViTY ———— GENERAL

Have an ecologist or a landscaper come to the classroom and talk to your class about how to plan, plant, and take care of a native plant garden. Then, have students research and design a native plant garden. After students design their native plant gardens, consider choosing one of the designs and having the class plant the garden in the schoolyard or on an empty lot. Be sure to get the appropriate permission before planting the garden. Your community may have other native plant gardens that your class can visit for inspiration.

Science in Action

Weird Science

What's That Smell?

Imagine that you are walking through a tropical rain forest. You're surrounded by green—green leaves, green vines, and green trees. You can hear monkeys and birds calling to each other. When you touch the plants nearby, they are wet from a recent rain shower. But what's that horrible smell? You don't see any rotting garbage around, but you do see a huge flower spike. As you get closer, the smell gets stronger. Then, you realize the flower is what smells so bad! The flower is called a *corpse flower*. The corpse flower is just one plant that uses bad odors to attract pollinators.

Math ACTiViTY

A corpse flower sprouts and grows to a maximum height of 2.35 m in 28 days. In centimeters, what is the average growth of the corpse flower per day?

Scientific Debate

Are Exotic Species Helpful or Harmful?

Have you visited the coast of California? If so, you may have seen large eucalyptus trees. You may be surprised to know that those trees are an exotic species. An *exotic species* is an organism that makes a new home for itself in a new place. People brought eucalyptus trees to California to use them in their yards and gardens. Since then, eucalyptus trees have spread to other areas. Exotic species often take over areas. Exotic species may compete with native species. Sometimes, exotic species keep native species from surviving. But in urban areas, exotic species are sometimes the only plants that will grow. So, are exotic species helpful or harmful?

Social Studies ACTiViTY

Identify an exotic species that people imported to grow in their gardens. Find out where the exotic species came from and the effect it is having on the environment.

Answer to Math Activity

8.4 cm per day (2.35 m × 100 cm/m = 235 cm; 235 cm ÷ 28 days = 8.4 cm/day)

Answer to Social Studies Activity

Students may be surprised to discover that many of the plants that they are familiar with are exotic species. Some of these plants include alfalfa, bamboo, catnip, kudzu, and dandelion. Students should recognize that exotic species can have an adverse effect on native species.

Nalini Nadkarni

Canopy Scientist As a child, Nalini Nadkarni loved to climb trees. She still does. Nadkarni is a biologist who studies the forest canopy. The canopy is the uppermost layer of the trees. It includes leaves, twigs, and branches and the air among them. Far above the ground, the canopy is home to many different plants, birds, insects, and other animals.

Canopy science was a new field of study when Nadkarni started her research 20 years ago. Because most canopies are tall, few scientists visited them. Most field biologists did their research with both feet planted firmly on the ground. Today, scientists know that the canopy is an important habitat for wildlife.

Nadkarni tells others about the importance of forests. As she puts it, "I can have a real impact in raising public awareness of the need to save forests." Nadkarni has invited artists and musicians to visit the canopy. "In my job, I try to understand the science of the canopy, but artists and musicians help capture the aesthetic value of the canopy."

Language Arts ACTIVITY

WRITING SKILL Imagine that you are a canopy scientist. Then, write a creative story about something that you would like to study in the canopy.

To learn more about these Science in Action topics, visit go.hrw.com and type in the keyword **HL5PL2F.**

Current Science

Check out Current Science® articles related to this chapter by visiting go.hrw.com. Just type in the keyword **HL5CS13.**

UNIT 2

Big Idea:
Biological Change

As Earth has changed over its long history, the organisms that live on Earth have also changed. Fossils provide evidence that many species that were alive in the past are no longer alive. Fossil evidence also shows that at various points in Earth's past, new species have emerged. Biological change has resulted in the biodiversity that we see today. Although species of organisms on Earth differ, they also share many characteristics. For example, all living things are made of cells and carry genetic information in their DNA.

The chapters in this unit introduce students to the concept of biological change by first describing how genetic information is inherited by individuals and then explaining how populations change over time. **Heredity** provides information about how genes are passed from one generation to the next. **Genes and DNA** extends this discussion to the cellular level. The chapter explains the relationship between genes and DNA. In **Evolution and Living Things**, students are introduced to the theory of evolution, which describes how populations change over time in response to their environment. Finally, **History of Life on Earth** presents information about the organisms that have lived on Earth.

UNIT 2

TIMELINE

Heredity and Evolution

The differences and similarities between living things are the subject of this unit. You will learn how characteristics are passed from one generation to another, how living things are classified based on their characteristics, and how these characteristics help living things survive.

Scientists have not always understood these topics, and there is still much to be learned. This timeline will give you an idea of some things that have been learned so far.

1753
Carolus Linnaeus publishes the first of two volumes containing the classification of all known species.

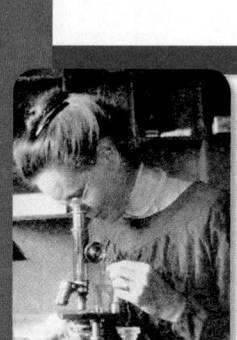

1905
Nettie Stevens describes how human gender is determined by the X and Y chromosomes.

1930
The planet Pluto is discovered.

1969
Apollo 11 lands on the moon. Neil Armstrong becomes the first person to walk on the lunar surface.

1859
Charles Darwin suggests that natural selection is a mechanism of evolution.

1860
Abraham Lincoln is elected the 16th president of the United States.

1865
Gregor Mendel publishes the results of his studies of genetic inheritance in pea plants.

1951
Rosalind Franklin photographs DNA.

1953
James Watson and Francis Crick figure out the structure of DNA.

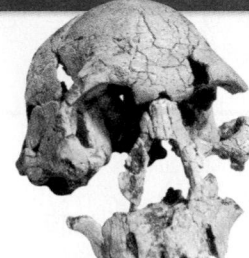

1960
Mary and Jonathan Leakey discover fossil bones of the human ancestor *Homo habilis* in Olduvai Gorge, Tanzania.

1974
Donald Johanson discovers a fossilized skeleton of one of the first hominids, *Australopithecus afarensis,* also called "Lucy."

1990
Ashanti DeSilva's white blood cells are genetically engineered to treat her immune deficiency disease.

2003
The Human Genome Project is completed. Scientists spent 13 years mapping out the 3 billion DNA subunits of chromosomes.

Group ACTIVITY
Biological Change

MATERIALS

- paper
- pencils
- photos of various organisms (optional)

Counting Generations Divide the class into small groups of two to three students. Tell the students that a bald eagle can reproduce about 6 years after it hatches, which means that the time between generations of bald eagles is about 6 years. Explain that the average age between one generation and the next is about 25 years for humans, 10 weeks for mice (about five generations per year), and 3 years for octopuses. Ask the students to estimate how many generations of humans, bald eagles, mice and octopuses have existed in the last 100 years. Ask students to estimate how many generations of humans, bald eagles, mice, and octopuses have existed in the last 1,000 years. Ask students to estimate how many generations of octopuses have existed in the last 1 million years. Challenge students to think of ways to represent this large number. For example, students could use grains of salt to represent generations. First, ask students to measure 0.1 of table salt, and estimate the number of salt grains in the 0.1. Dividing the total number of generations of octopuses by the number of salt grains that 0.1g represents yields the mass of salt that contains the number of generations. Have students measure this amount, and place it in a large, flat container.

Compression guide:
To shorten instruction because of time limitations, omit the Chapter Lab.

OBJECTIVES	LABS, DEMONSTRATIONS, AND ACTIVITIES	TECHNOLOGY RESOURCES
PACING • 90 min pp. 84–91 **Chapter Opener**	**SE** Start-up Activity, p. 85 ◆ GENERAL	**OSP** Parent Letter ■ **CD** Student Edition on CD-ROM **CD** Guided Reading Audio CD ■ **TR** Chapter Starter Transparency* **VID** Brain Food Video Quiz
Section 1 Mendel and His Peas • Explain the relationship between traits and heredity. • Describe the experiments of Gregor Mendel. • Explain the difference between dominant and recessive traits.	**TE** Activity Trait Trends, p. 86 GENERAL **SE** School-to-Home Activity Describing Traits, p. 87 GENERAL **TE** Demonstration Flower Dissection, p. 88 ◆ BASIC **TE** Activity Mendelian Crosses, p. 88 ADVANCED **SE** Science in Action Math, Science, and Social Studies Activities, pp. 112–113 GENERAL	**OSP** Lesson Plans (also in print) **TR** Bellringer Transparency* **CRF** SciLinks Activity* GENERAL
PACING • 90 min pp. 92–97 **Section 2 Traits and Inheritance** • Explain how genes and alleles are related to genotype and phenotype. • Use the information in a Punnett square. • Explain how probability can be used to predict possible genotypes in offspring. • Describe three exceptions to Mendel's observations.	**TE** Demonstration Ratios, p. 92 ◆ BASIC **SE** Quick Lab Making a Punnett Square, p. 93 GENERAL **CRF** Datasheet for Quick Lab* **SE** Quick Lab Taking Your Chances, p. 94 ◆ GENERAL **CRF** Datasheet for Quick Lab* **TE** Connection Activity Math, p. 94 ADVANCED **SE** Connection to Chemistry Round and Wrinkled, p. 95 GENERAL **SE** Model-Making Lab Bug Builders, Inc., p. 106 ◆ GENERAL **CRF** Datasheet for Chapter Lab*	**OSP** Lesson Plans (also in print) **TR** Bellringer Transparency* **TR** L13 Punnett Squares **TR** *LINK TO PHYSICAL SCIENCE* P109 The Periodic Table of the Elements* **VID** Lab Videos for Life Science
PACING • 45 min pp. 98–105 **Section 3 Meiosis** • Explain the difference between mitosis and meiosis. • Describe how chromosomes determine sex. • Explain why sex-linked disorders occur in one sex more often than in the other. • Interpret a pedigree.	**TE** Activity Crosses, p. 98 GENERAL **TE** Connection Activity Math, p. 98 ADVANCED **TE** Activity Describing Meiosis, p. 101 BASIC **TE** Connection Activity Math, p. 101 GENERAL **TE** Group Activity Comparing Mitosis and Meiosis, p. 102 GENERAL **TE** Connection Activity Language Arts, p. 103 GENERAL **SE** Inquiry Lab Tracing Traits, p. 708 GENERAL **CRF** Datasheet for LabBook* **LB** Long-Term Projects & Research Ideas Portrait of a Dog* ADVANCED	**OSP** Lesson Plans (also in print) **TR** Bellringer Transparency* **TR** L14 The Steps of Meiosis: A* **TR** L15 The Steps of Meiosis: B* **TR** L16 Meiosis and Dominance* **SE** Internet Activity, p.102 GENERAL **TE** Internet Activity, p.105 GENERAL

PACING • 90 min

CHAPTER REVIEW, ASSESSMENT, AND STANDARDIZED TEST PREPARATION

CRF Vocabulary Activity* GENERAL
SE Chapter Review, pp. 108–109 GENERAL
CRF Chapter Review* ■ GENERAL
CRF Chapter Tests A* ■ GENERAL, B* ADVANCED, C* SPECIAL NEEDS
SE Standardized Test Preparation, pp. 110–111 GENERAL
CRF Standardized Test Preparation* GENERAL
CRF Performance-Based Assessment* GENERAL
OSP Test Generator, Test Item Listing

Online and Technology Resources

 Holt Online Learning

Visit **go.hrw.com** for access to Holt Online Learning, or enter the keyword **HS7 Home** for a variety of free online resources.

 **One-Stop Planner® CD-ROM**

This CD-ROM package includes:
• Lab Materials QuickList Software
• Holt Calendar Planner
• Customizable Lesson Plans
• Printable Worksheets
• ExamView® Test Generator
• Interactive Teacher's Edition
• Holt PuzzlePro®
• Holt PowerPoint® Resources

SKILLS DEVELOPMENT RESOURCES	SECTION REVIEW AND ASSESSMENT	CORRELATIONS
SE **Pre-Reading Activity**, p. 84 `GENERAL` OSP **Science Puzzlers, Twisters & Teasers*** `GENERAL`		**National Science Education Standards** UCP 2, 3; LS 1d, 2c
CRF **Directed Reading A*** ■ `BASIC`, **B*** `SPECIAL NEEDS` WB **Workbook*** Struggling Readers CRF **Vocabulary and Section Summary*** ■ `GENERAL` SE **Reading Strategy** Brainstorming, p. 86 `GENERAL` TE **Support for English Language Learners**, p. 87 SE **Math Practice** Understanding Ratios, p. 90 `GENERAL` TE **Reading Strategy** Paired Reading, p. 87 `BASIC` TE **Inclusion Strategies**, p. 89 ◆ MS **Math Skills for Science** What Is a Ratio?* `GENERAL` SS **Science Skills** Finding Useful Sources* `GENERAL`	SE **Reading Checks**, pp. 86, 89, 90 `GENERAL` TE **Reaching**, p. 90 `BASIC` TE **Quiz**, p. 90 `GENERAL` TE **Alternative Assessment**, p. 90 `ADVANCED` SE **Section Review**,* p. 91 `GENERAL` TE **Homework**, p. 91 `GENERAL` CRF **Section Quiz*** ■ `GENERAL`	UCP 1, 2; SAI 1, 2; ST 2; SPSP 5; HNS 1, 2, 3; LS 2b, 2e
CRF **Directed Reading A*** ■ `BASIC`, **B*** `SPECIAL NEEDS` WB **Workbook*** Struggling Readers CRF **Vocabulary and Section Summary*** ■ `GENERAL` SE **Reading Strategy** Paired Summarizing, p. 92 `GENERAL` TE **Support for English Language Learners**, p. 94 SE **Math Focus** Probability, p. 95 `GENERAL` MS **Math Skills for Science** Punnett Square Popcorn* `GENERAL` CRF **Reinforcement Worksheet** Dimples and DNA* `BASIC`	SE **Reading Checks**, pp. 92, 94, 96 `GENERAL` TE **Homework**, p. 95 `GENERAL` TE **Reaching**, p. 96 `BASIC` TE **Quiz**, p. 96 `GENERAL` TE **Alternative Assessment**, p. 97 `GENERAL` SE **Section Review**,* p. 97 ■ `GENERAL` CRF **Section Quiz*** ■ `GENERAL`	UCP 2, 3; LS 2a, 2b, 2c, 2d, 2e; *Chapter Lab:* SAI 1; HNS 2; LS 2c, 2e
CRF **Directed Reading A*** ■ `BASIC`, **B*** `SPECIAL NEEDS` WB **Workbook*** Struggling Readers CRF **Vocabulary and Section Summary*** ■ `GENERAL` SE **Reading Strategy** Reading Organizer, p. 98 `GENERAL` SE **Connection to Language Arts** Greek Roots, p. 99 `GENERAL` TE **Reading Strategy** Prediction Guide, p. 100 `GENERAL` TE **Support for English Language Learners**, p. 100 TE **Inclusion Strategies**, p. 102 CRF **Critical Thinking** A Bittersweet Solution* `ADVANCED`	SE **Reading Checks**, pp. 99, 100 `GENERAL` TE **Reaching**, p. 104 `BASIC` TE **Quiz**, p. 104 `GENERAL` TE **Alternative Assessment**, p. 104 `GENERAL` TE **Homework**, p. 104 `ADVANCED` SE **Section Review**,* p. 105 ■ `GENERAL` CRF **Section Quiz*** ■ `GENERAL`	UCP 4, 5; SAI 1; SPSP 5; HNS 2, 3; LS 1c, 1d, 2a, 2b, 2c, 2d; *LabBook:* UCP 2; SAI 1; HNS 2; LS 2b, 2c, 2e

www.scilinks.org

Maintained by the **National Science Teachers Association.** See Chapter Enrichment pages that follow for a complete list of topics.

Check out *Current Science* articles and activities by visiting the HRW Web site at go.hrw.com. Just type in the keyword **HL5CS05T**.

 Classroom Videos

- **Lab Videos** demonstrate the chapter lab.
- **Brain Food Video Quizzes** help students review the chapter material.

Classroom CD-ROMs

- **Guided Reading Audio CD** (Also in Spanish)
- **Interactive Explorations**
- **Virtual Investigations**
- **Visual Concepts**
- **Science Tutor**

 Holt Lab Generator CD-ROM

Search for any lab by topic, standard, difficulty level, or time. Edit any lab to fit your needs, or create your own labs. Use the Lab Materials QuickList software to customize your lab materials list.

Visual Resources

CHAPTER STARTER TRANSPARENCY

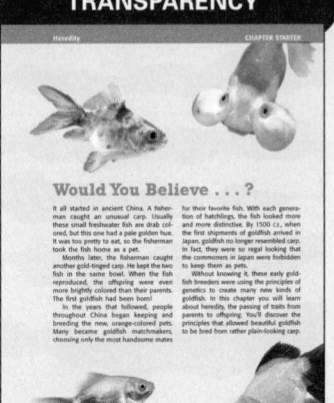

BELLRINGER TRANSPARENCIES

Section: Mendel and His Peas

You have probably noticed that different people have different characteristics, such as eye color, hair color, or whether or not their ear lobes attach directly to their head or hang down loosely. These characteristics are called traits. Where do you think people get these different traits? How do you think they are passed from one generation to the next?

Write your answers in your **science journal.**

Section: Traits and Inheritance

If you flip a coin, what are the chances that it will land on heads? tails? Suppose that you flip the coin, get heads, and then flip again. What are the chances that you will get heads again? What are the chances you will get heads two times in a row? five times?

Record your answers in your **science journal.**

TEACHING TRANSPARENCIES

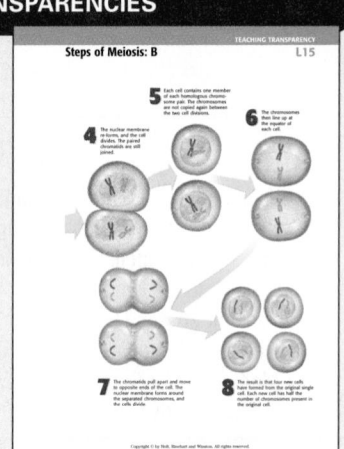

TEACHING TRANSPARENCIES

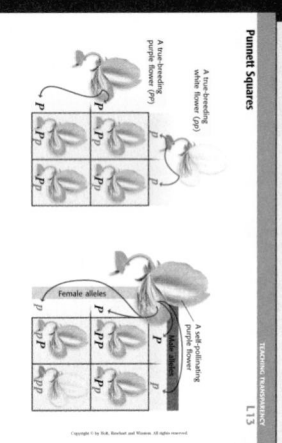

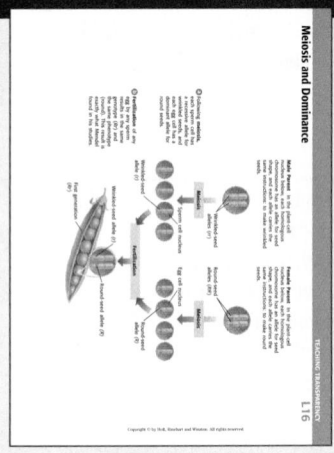

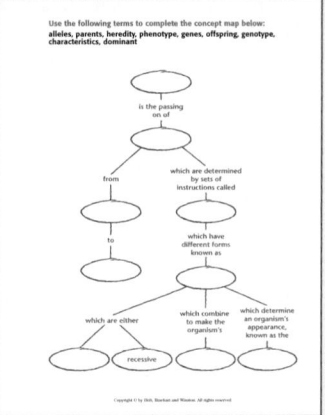

Chapter: The Periodic Table

CONCEPT MAPPING TRANSPARENCY

Use the following terms to complete the concept map below:
alleles, parents, heredity, phenotype, genes, offspring, genotype, characteristics, dominant.

Planning Resources

LESSON PLANS

Lesson Plan   SAMPLE

Section: Waves

Pacing
Regular Schedule: with lab(s):2 days   without lab(s):2 days
Block Schedule: with lab(s):1 1/2 days   without lab(s):1 day

Objectives
1. Relate the seven properties of life to a living organism.
2. Describe seven themes that can help you to organize what you learn about biology.
3. Identify the tiny structures that make up all living organisms.
4. Differentiate between reproduction and heredity and between metabolism and homeostasis.

National Science Education Standards Covered
LSInter4: Cells have particular structures that underlie their functions.
LSMat1: Most cell functions involve chemical reactions.
LSBeh1: Cells store and use information to guide their functions.
UCP1: Cell functions are regulated.
SI1: Cells can differentiate and form complete multicellular organisms.
PS1: Species evolve over time.
ESS1: The great diversity of organisms is the result of more than 3.5 billion years of evolution.
ESS2: Natural selection and its evolutionary consequences provide a scientific explanation for the fossil record of ancient life forms as well as for the striking molecular similarities observed among the diverse species of living organisms.
ST1: The millions of different species of plants, animals, and microorganisms that live on Earth today are related by descent from common ancestors.
ST2: The energy for life glows from the sun.
SPSP1: The complexity and organization of organisms accommodates the need for obtaining, transforming, transporting, releasing, and eliminating the matter and energy used to sustain the organism.
SPSP6: As matter and energy flows through different levels of organization of living systems—cells, organs, communities—and between living systems and the physical environment, chemical elements are recombined in different ways.
HNS1: Organisms have behavioral responses to internal changes and to external stimuli.

PARENT LETTER

SAMPLE

Dear Parent,

Your son's or daughter's science class will soon begin exploring the chapter entitled "The World of Physical Science." In this chapter, students will learn about how the scientific method applies to the world of physical science and the role of physical science in the world. By the end of the chapter, students should demonstrate a clear understanding of the chapter's main ideas and be able to discuss the following topics:

1. physical science is the study of energy and matter (Section 1)
2. the role of physical science in the world around them (Section 1)
3. careers that rely on physical science (Section 1)
4. the steps used in the scientific method (Section 2)
5. examples of technology (Section 2)
6. how the scientific method is used to answer questions and solve problems (Section 2)
7. how our knowledge of science changes over time (Section 2)
8. how models represent real objects or systems (Section 3)
9. examples of different ways models are used in science (Section 3)
10. the importance of the International System of Units (Section 4)
11. the appropriate units to use for particular measurements (Section 4)
12. how area and density are derived quantities (Section 4)

Questions to Ask Along the Way

You can help your son or daughter learn about these topics by asking interesting questions such as the following:

• What are some surprising careers that use physical science?
• What is a characteristic of a good hypothesis?
• When is it a good idea to use a model?
• Why do Americans measure things in terms of inches and yards and meters?

TEST ITEM LISTING

TEST ITEM LISTING
The World of Science   SAMPLE

MULTIPLE CHOICE

1. A limitation of models is that
   a. they are large enough to see
   b. they do not act exactly like the things that they model.
   c. they are smaller than the things that they model.
   d. they model submicroscopic things.
   Answer: B   Difficulty: 1   Section: 3   Objective: 2
2. The length 10 m is equal to
   a. 100 cm.   c. 10,000 mm.
   b. 100 cm.   d. Both (b) and (c)
   Answer: D   Difficulty: 1   Section: 3   Objective: 2
3. To be valid, a hypothesis must be
   a. testable.   c. made into a law.
   b. supported by evidence.   d. Both (a) and (b)
   Answer: D   Difficulty: 1   Section: 3   Objective: 2
4. The statement "Sheila has a stain on her shirt" is an example of a(n)
   a. law.   c. observation.
   b. hypothesis.   d. prediction.
   Answer: B   Difficulty: 1   Section: 2   Objective: 2
5. A hypothesis is often developed out of
   a. observations.   c. laws.
   b. experiments.   d. Both (a) and (b)
   Answer: A   Difficulty: 1   Section: 2   Objective: 2
6. How many milliliters are in 3.5 kL?
   a. 3500 mL   c. 3,500, 000 mL
   b. 0.0035 mL   d. 35,000 mL
   Answer: B   Difficulty: 1   Section: 3   Objective: 2
7. A map of Seattle is an example of a
   a. law   c. model.
   b. theory   d. unit.
   Answer: C   Difficulty: 1   Section: 3   Objective: 2
8. A lab has the safety icons shown below. These icons mean that you should wear
   a. only safety goggles.   c. safety goggles and a lab apron.
   b. only a lab apron.   d. safety goggles, a lab apron, and gloves.
   Answer: D   Difficulty: 1   Section: 1   Objective: 2
9. The law of conservation of mass says the total mass before a chemical change is
   a. less than the total mass after the change.
   b. the same as the total mass after the change.
   c. more than the total mass after the change.
   d. not the same as the total mass after the change.
   Answer: B   Difficulty: 1   Section: 3   Objective: 2
10. In which of the following areas might you find a geochemist at work?
   a. studying the chemistry of rocks   c. studying babies
   b. studying forestry   d. studying the atmosphere
   Answer: B   Difficulty: 1   Section: 3   Objective: 2

One-Stop Planner® CD-ROM

This CD-ROM includes all of the resources shown here and the following time-saving tools:

• *Lab Materials QuickList Software*
• *Customizable lesson plans*
• *Holt Calendar Planner*
• *The powerful ExamView® Test Generator*

Meeting Individual Needs

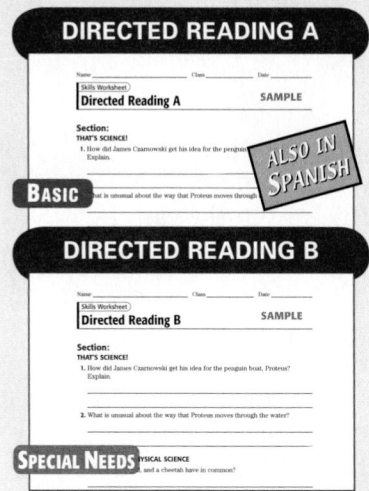

DIRECTED READING A

Skills Worksheet
Directed Reading A — SAMPLE

Section:
THAT'S SCIENCE!

1. How did James Czarnowski get idea for the penguin boat, Proteus? Explain.

BASIC · ALSO IN SPANISH

DIRECTED READING B

Skills Worksheet
Directed Reading B — SAMPLE

Section:
THAT'S SCIENCE!

1. How did James Czarnowski get idea for the penguin boat, Proteus? Explain.

2. What is unusual about the way that Proteus moves through the water?

SPECIAL NEEDS

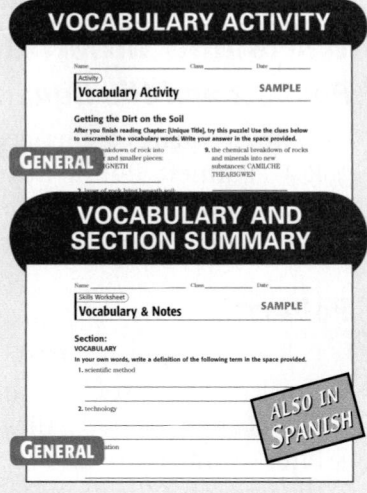

VOCABULARY ACTIVITY

Activity
Vocabulary Activity — SAMPLE

Getting the Dirt on the Soil
After you finish reading Chapter: [Unique Title], try this puzzle! Use the clues below to unscramble the vocabulary words. Write your answer in the space provided.

GENERAL

VOCABULARY AND SECTION SUMMARY

Skills Worksheet
Vocabulary & Notes — SAMPLE

Section:
VOCABULARY
In your own words, write a definition of the following term in the space provided.
1. scientific method

2. technology

GENERAL · ALSO IN SPANISH

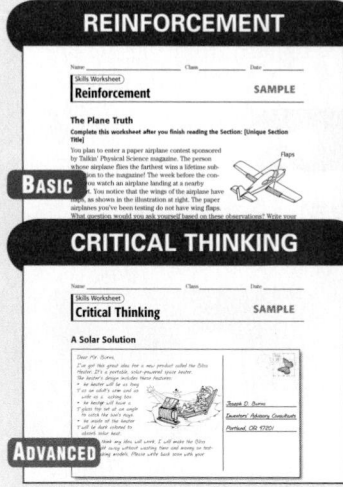

REINFORCEMENT

Skills Worksheet
Reinforcement — SAMPLE

The Plane Truth
Complete this worksheet after you finish reading the Section: [Unique Section Title]

BASIC

CRITICAL THINKING

Skills Worksheet
Critical Thinking — SAMPLE

A Solar Solution

ADVANCED

SCILINKS ACTIVITY

Activity
SciLinks Activity — SAMPLE

MARINE ECOSYSTEMS
Go to www.scilinks.com. To find links related to marine ecosystems, type in the keyword

GENERAL

SCIENCE PUZZLERS, TWISTERS & TEASERS

CHAPTER 5 SCIENCE PUZZLERS, TWISTERS & TEASERS
Heredity

Put on Your Rhyming Genes
1. Fill in the blanks in each of the following rhymes to complete these catchy jingles about heredity.

GENERAL

Labs and Activities

LONG-TERM PROJECTS & RESEARCH IDEAS

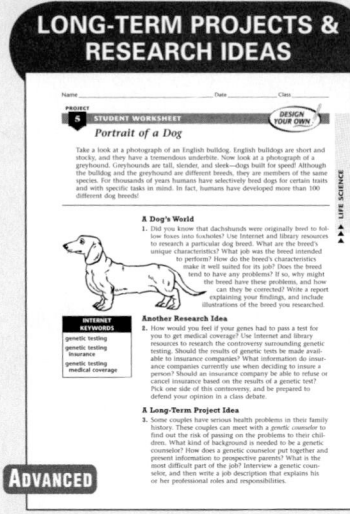

PROJECT
5 STUDENT WORKSHEET — DESIGN YOUR OWN
Portrait of a Dog

A Dog's World
Another Research Idea
A Long-Term Project Idea

ADVANCED

DATASHEETS FOR QUICK LABS

TEACHER RESOURCE PAGE
Quick Lab — DATASHEET FOR QUICK LAB
Reaction to Stress — SAMPLE

Background

DATASHEETS FOR CHAPTER LABS

TEACHER RESOURCE PAGE
Skills Practice Lab — DATASHEET FOR CHAPTER LAB
Using Scientific Methods — SAMPLE

Teacher's Notes
TIME REQUIRED
One 45-minute class period.

DATASHEETS FOR LABBOOK

TEACHER RESOURCE PAGE
Skills Practice Lab — DATASHEET FOR LABBOOK LAB
Does It All Add Up? — SAMPLE

Teacher's Notes
TIME REQUIRED
One 45-minute class period.

Review and Assessments

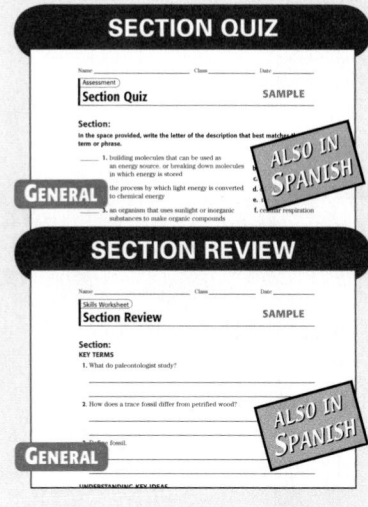

SECTION QUIZ

Assessment
Section Quiz — SAMPLE

Section:
In the space provided, write the letter of the description that best matches the term or phrase.

GENERAL · ALSO IN SPANISH

SECTION REVIEW

Skills Worksheet
Section Review — SAMPLE

Section:
KEY TERMS
1. What do paleontologist study?

2. How does a trace fossil differ from petrified wood?

GENERAL · ALSO IN SPANISH

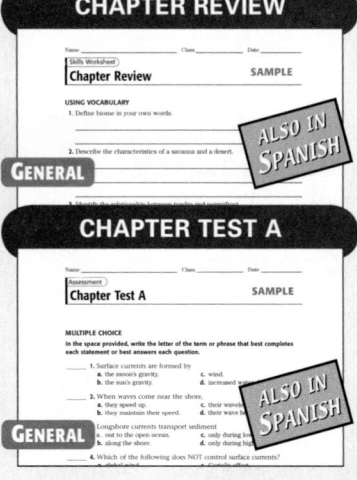

CHAPTER REVIEW

Skills Worksheet
Chapter Review — SAMPLE

USING VOCABULARY
1. Define biome in your own words.

2. Describe the characteristics of a savanna and a desert.

GENERAL · ALSO IN SPANISH

CHAPTER TEST A

Assessment
Chapter Test A — SAMPLE

MULTIPLE CHOICE
In the space provided, write the letter of the term or phrase that best completes each statement or best answers each question.

GENERAL · ALSO IN SPANISH

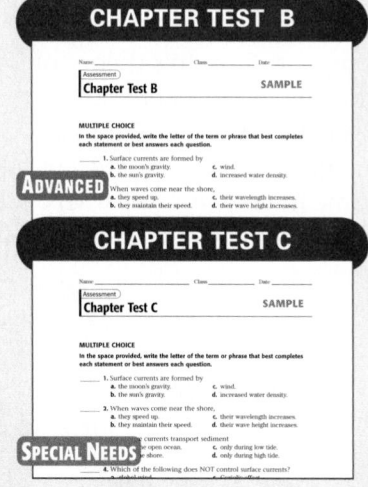

CHAPTER TEST B

Assessment
Chapter Test B — SAMPLE

MULTIPLE CHOICE
In the space provided, write the letter of the term or phrase that best completes each statement or best answers each question.

ADVANCED

CHAPTER TEST C

Assessment
Chapter Test C — SAMPLE

MULTIPLE CHOICE
In the space provided, write the letter of the term or phrase that best completes each statement or best answers each question.

SPECIAL NEEDS

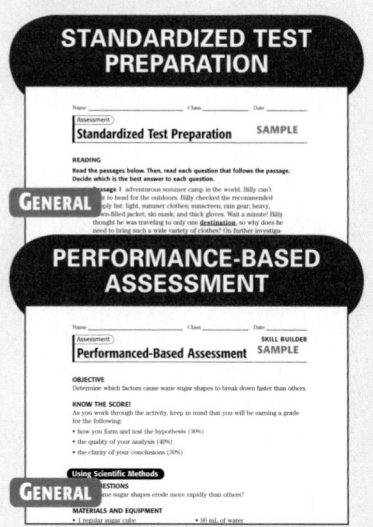

STANDARDIZED TEST PREPARATION

Assessment
Standardized Test Preparation — SAMPLE

READING
Read the passages below. Then, read each question that follows the passage.

GENERAL

PERFORMANCE-BASED ASSESSMENT

Assessment
Performanced-Based Assessment — SKILL BUILDER SAMPLE

OBJECTIVE

KNOW THE SCORE!

Using Scientific Methods

MATERIALS AND EQUIPMENT

GENERAL

This Chapter Enrichment provides relevant and interesting information to expand and enhance your presentation of the chapter material.

Section 1

Mendel and His Peas

Gregor Mendel

- In 1843, in the city of Brünn, Austria (which is now Brno, a city in the Czech Republic), Gregor Mendel (1822–1884) entered a monastery. In 1865, Mendel published the results of his garden-pea experiments. Although Mendel's ideas are widespread today, few scientists learned of his work during his lifetime because there were few ways to distribute information. Mendel presented his findings in two lectures, and only 40 copies of his work were printed in his lifetime.

- When Mendel was elected abbot of the monastery in 1868, his duties prevented him from visiting other scientists or attending conferences where he could have discussed his results. Not until 1900, when Mendel's work was rediscovered by scientists in Holland, Germany, and Austria-Hungary, were his theories spread through the scientific community.

- Mendel's work was used to support Darwin's theory of evolution by natural selection and is considered to be the foundation of modern genetics. Mendel also made contributions to beekeeping, horticulture, and meteorology. In 1877, Mendel became interested in weather and began issuing weather reports to local farmers.

Is That a Fact!
- From 1856 to 1863, while studying inheritance, Mendel grew almost 30,000 pea plants!

Section 2

Traits and Inheritance

Punnett and His Squares

- Punnett squares are named after their inventor, R. C. Punnett. Punnett explored inheritance by crossing different breeds of chickens in the early 1900s, soon after Mendel's work was rediscovered.

Pollination

- Pollen can be transferred between plants by wind, insects, and a variety of animals. Some common pollinators are bees, butterflies, moths, flies, bats, and birds. Animals are attracted to the color of the flower, the patterns found on the petals, or the flower's fragrance. Pollen is an excellent food for some animals.

Is That a Fact!
- Male bees have only half the number of chromosomes that female bees have.

Section 3

Meiosis

Chromosomes

- Chromosomes are composed of genes, the sequences of DNA that provide the instructions for making all the proteins in an organism. During cell division, the duplicated chromosomes separate so that one copy of each chromosome is present in the two new cells.

Walther Flemming

- Walther Flemming (1843–1905), a German physician and anatomist, was the first to use a microscope and special dyes to study cell division. Flemming used the term *mitosis* to describe the process he observed.

Mitosis

- In mitosis, a cell divides to form two identical cells. The steps of the process are similar in almost all living organisms. In addition to enabling growth, mitosis allows organisms to replace cells that have died or malfunctioned. Mitosis can take anywhere from a few minutes to a few hours, and it may be affected by characteristics of the environment, such as light and temperature.

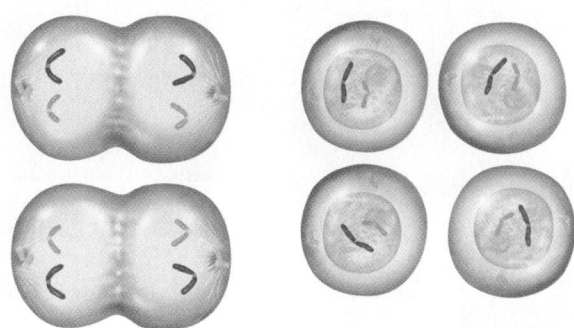

Meiosis

- Meiosis is not the same in all organisms. In humans, meiosis is very different in males and females. In males, meiosis results in four similar sperm cells. In females, however, only one functional egg is produced. The other resulting cells, which are known as *polar bodies,* are formed during the division of the original cell but do not mature.

Genetic Disorders

- A genetic disorder results from an inherited disruption in an organism's DNA. These inherited disruptions can take several forms, including a change in the number of chromosomes and the deletion or duplication of entire chromosomes or parts of chromosomes. Often, the change responsible for a disorder is the alteration of a single specific gene. However, some genetic disorders result from several of these genetic alterations occurring simultaneously. Diseases resulting from these alterations cause a wide variety of physical malfunctions and developmental problems.

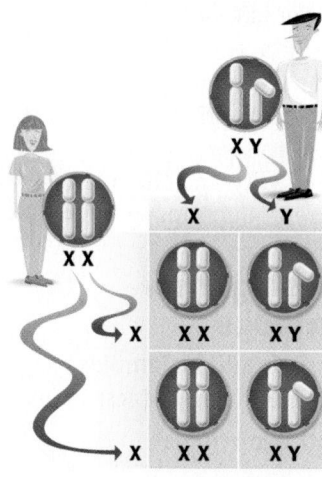

- Cystic fibrosis (CF) is a disease for which one in 31 Americans carries a recessive trait. If two of these people have children together, there is a 25% chance that any child born to them will have the disease. CF affects the intestinal, bronchial, and sweat glands. In people with CF, these glands secrete thick, sticky fluids that are difficult for the body to process, impeding breathing and digestion. Due to improvements in diagnosis and treatment, median life expectancy for those with CF has improved from under 10 years in 1960 to an estimated 40 years for those born in 1990.

- Rubinstein-Taybi syndrome (RTS) is a complex genetic disorder whose characteristics include broad thumbs and toes, mental retardation, and distinctive facial features. This wide range of characteristics is believed to be linked to any one of a number of mutations in a gene responsible for providing the body with a protein called *CBP*. CBP is thought to be vital to the body's delicate metabolism. Because CBP greatly influences body processes, people with a problem producing CBP have a wide range of difficulties. Children with RTS can benefit from proper nutrition and early intervention with therapies and special education.

SCiLINKS®

NSTA
Developed and maintained by the
National Science Teachers Association

SciLinks is maintained by the National Science Teachers Association to provide you and your students with interesting, up-to-date links that will enrich your classroom presentation of the chapter.

Visit www.scilinks.org and enter the SciLinks code for more information about the topic listed.

Topic: Heredity
SciLinks code: HSM0738

Topic: Phenotypes
SciLinks code: HSM1135

Topic: Dominant and Recessive Traits
SciLinks code: HSM0423

Topic: Meiosis
SciLinks code: HSM0935

Topic: Genotypes
SciLinks code: HSM0664

Topic: Genetic Diseases, Screening, Counseling
SciLinks code: HSM0651

Overview

Tell students that this chapter will introduce heredity—the ways that traits are passed from parents to offspring. The chapter describes the ways scientists study heredity and the role of sexual reproduction.

Assessing Prior Knowledge

Students should be familiar with the following topics:

• scientific methods

• cells

• mitosis

Identifying Misconceptions

Students often hold onto misconceptions about inheritance, even after instruction. For example, they may believe that traits are inherited from only one parent or that environmentally caused characteristics may be passed on to offspring. Students tend to understand phenotype (physical traits) more easily than genotype. Finally, the process of meiosis, as it relates to the structure and location of chromosomes, is very complex. Most students require time and repeated exposure in order to comprehend all the parts and steps of meiosis. Assure students that the concepts of heredity are a foundation that will be built upon throughout their studies of life science.

Heredity

The Big Idea

Heredity is the passage of traits from one generation to the next.

About the Photo

The guinea pig in the middle has dark fur, and the other two have light orange fur. The guinea pig on the right has longer hair than the other two. Why do these guinea pigs look different from one another? The length and color of their fur was determined before they were born. These are just two of the many traits determined by genetic information. Genetic information is passed on from parents to their offspring.

PRE-READING ACTIVITY

FOLDNOTES **Key-Term Fold** Before you read the chapter, create the FoldNote entitled "Key-Term Fold" described in the **Study Skills** section of the Appendix. Write a key term from the chapter on each tab of the key-term fold. Under each tab, write the definition of the key term.

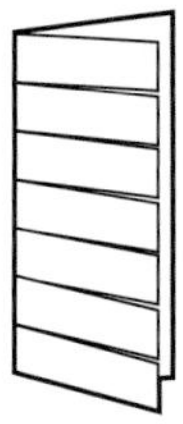

Standards Correlations

National Science Education Standards

The following codes indicate the National Science Education Standards that correlate to this chapter. The full text of the standards is at the front of the book.

Chapter Opener
UCP 2, 3; LS 1d, 2c

Section 1 Mendel and His Peas
UCP 1, 2; SAI 1, 2; ST 2; SPSP 5; HNS 1, 2, 3; LS 2b, 2e

Section 2 Traits and Inheritance
UCP 2, 3; LS 2a, 2b, 2c, 2d, 2e

Section 3 Meiosis
UCP 4, 5; SAI 1; SPSP 5; HNS 2, 3; LS 1c, 1d, 2a, 2b, 2c, 2d; *Lab Book*: UCP 2; SAI 1; HNS 2; LS 2b, 2c, 2e

Chapter Lab
SAI 1; HNS 2; LS 2c, 2e

Chapter Review
LS 1c, 2a, 2b, 2c, 2d, 2e

Science in Action
ST 2; SPSP 5

START-UP ACTiViTY

MATERIALS

FOR EACH GROUP
• boxes large, (3)
• gloves different types, (5)
• hats different types, (5)
• scarves different types, (5)

Safety Caution: Infestations of head lice are a common problem in schools. Sharing hats should be avoided during such a period. Jackets or sweatshirts could be substituted for hats in this exercise.

Answers

1. Answers may vary. There should be many different combinations. It is not likely that students will see all of the possible combinations.

2. Sample answer: eight new combinations (taken from the outfits of the two "parents") would be possible for the third person ("offspring"). This process is like inheritance because you are choosing combinations of hats, scarves, and gloves randomly. Traits are also passed from parent to offspring randomly. By combining the traits (outfits) of two "parents" (partners), there are many possible combinations of traits in the "offspring" (third person).

3. Sample answer: The number of possible genetic combinations is huge because we have so many genes.

START-UP ACTiViTY

Clothing Combos

How do the same parents have children with many different traits?

Procedure

1. Gather **three boxes**. Put **five hats** in the first box, **five gloves** in the second, and **five scarves** in the third.

2. Without looking in the boxes, select one item from each box. Repeat this process, five students at a time, until the entire class has picked "an outfit." Record what outfit each student chooses.

Analysis

1. Were any two outfits exactly alike? Did you see all possible combinations? Explain your answer.

2. Choose a partner. Using your outfits, how many different combinations could you make by giving a third person one hat, one glove, and one scarf? How is this process like parents passing traits to their children?

3. After completing this activity, why do you think parents often have children who look very different from each other?

Would You Believe . . . ?

It all started in ancient China. A fisherman caught an unusual carp. Usually these small freshwater fish are drab colored, but this one had a pale golden hue. It was too pretty to eat, so the fisherman took the fish home as a pet.

Months later, the fisherman caught another gold-tinged carp. He kept the two fish in the same bowl. When the fish reproduced, the offspring were even more brightly colored than their parents. The first goldfish had been born!

In the years that followed, people throughout China began keeping and breeding the new, orange-colored pets. Many became goldfish matchmakers, choosing only the most handsome mates

for their favorite fish. With each generation of hatchlings, the fish looked more and more distinctive. By 1500 C.E., when the first shipments of goldfish arrived in Japan, goldfish no longer resembled carp. In fact, they were so regal looking that the commoners in Japan were forbidden to keep them as pets.

Without knowing it, these early goldfish breeders were using the principles of genetics to create many new kinds of goldfish. In this chapter you will learn about heredity, the passing of traits from parents to offspring. You'll discover the principles that allowed beautiful goldfish to be bred from rather plain-looking carp.

Chapter Starter Transparency
Use this transparency to help students begin thinking about heredity.

CHAPTER RESOURCES

Technology

 **Transparencies**
• Chapter Starter Transparency

READING SKILLS

Student Edition on CD-ROM

Guided Reading Audio CD
• English or Spanish

Classroom Videos
• Brain Food Video Quiz

Workbooks

Science Puzzlers, Twisters & Teasers
• Heredity GENERAL

Focus

Overview

This section introduces the genetic experiments of Gregor Mendel. Students explore how crosses between different parent plants produce different offspring. Students are also introduced to genetic probability.

 **Bellringer**

Present the following prompt to your students: "You have probably noticed that different people have different traits, such as eye color, hair color, and ear lobes that do or do not attach directly to their head. Where do people get these different traits?" (Many traits are inherited from parents and passed from parents to offspring through genes.)

Motivate

ACTIVITY ————— GENERAL

Trait Trends Create a large table to record the number of students with the following traits: widow's peak, ability to roll tongue, and attached earlobes. Have pairs of students enter data for each other by adding tick marks on the table. Ask students if they can see any trends in the class data. If possible, compile data from several classes. **LS Kinesthetic/Interpersonal**

What You Will Learn

● Explain the relationship between traits and heredity.
● Describe the experiments of Gregor Mendel.
● Explain the difference between dominant and recessive traits.

Vocabulary

heredity
dominant trait
recessive trait

READING STRATEGY

Brainstorming The key idea of this section is heredity. Brainstorm words and phrases related to heredity.

Figure 1 *Gregor Mendel discovered the principles of heredity while studying pea plants.*

CHAPTER RESOURCES

Chapter Resource File

 • **Lesson Plan**
• **Directed Reading A** BASIC
• **Directed Reading B** SPECIAL NEEDS

Technology

 Transparencies
• Bellringer

Workbooks

 Interactive Textbook Struggling Readers

Mendel and His Peas

Why don't you look like a rhinoceros? The answer to this question seems simple: Neither of your parents is a rhinoceros. But there is more to this answer than meets the eye.

As it turns out, **heredity,** or the passing of traits from parents to offspring, is more complicated than you might think. For example, you might have curly hair, while both of your parents have straight hair. You might have blue eyes even though both of your parents have brown eyes. How does this happen? People have investigated this question for a long time. About 150 years ago, Gregor Mendel performed important experiments. His discoveries helped scientists begin to find some answers to these questions.

✓ **Reading Check** What is heredity? (*See the Appendix for answers to Reading Checks.*)

Who Was Gregor Mendel?

Gregor Mendel, shown in **Figure 1,** was born in 1822 in Heinzendorf, Austria. Mendel grew up on a farm and learned a lot about flowers and fruit trees.

When he was 21 years old, Mendel entered a monastery. The monks taught science and performed many scientific experiments. From there, Mendel was sent to Vienna where he could receive training in teaching. However, Mendel had trouble taking tests. Although he did well in school, he was unable to pass the final exam. He returned to the monastery and put most of his energy into research. Mendel discovered the principles of heredity in the monastery garden.

Unraveling the Mystery

From working with plants, Mendel knew that the patterns of inheritance were not always clear. For example, sometimes a trait that appeared in one generation (parents) was not present in the next generation (offspring). In the generation after that, though, the trait showed up again. Mendel noticed these kinds of patterns in several other living things, too. Mendel wanted to learn more about what caused these patterns.

To keep his investigation simple, Mendel decided to study only one kind of organism. Because he had studied garden pea plants before, they seemed like a good choice.

Answer to Reading Check

the passing of traits from parents to offspring

Self-Pollinating Peas

In fact, garden peas were a good choice for several reasons. Pea plants grow quickly, and there are many different kinds available. They are also able to self-pollinate. A *self-pollinating plant* has both male and female reproductive structures. So, pollen from one flower can fertilize the ovule of the same flower or the ovule of another flower on the same plant. The flower on the right side of **Figure 2** is self-pollinating.

Why is it important that pea plants can self-pollinate? Because eggs (in an ovule) and sperm (in pollen) from the same plant combine to make a new plant, Mendel was able to grow true-breeding plants. When a *true-breeding plant* self-pollinates, all of its offspring will have the same trait as the parent. For example, a true-breeding plant with purple flowers will always have offspring with purple flowers.

Pea plants can also cross-pollinate. In *cross-pollination,* pollen from one plant fertilizes the ovule of a flower on a different plant. There are several ways that this can happen. Pollen may be carried by insects to a flower on a different plant. Pollen can also be carried by the wind from one flower to another. The left side of **Figure 2** shows these kinds of cross-pollination.

heredity the passing of genetic traits from parent to offspring

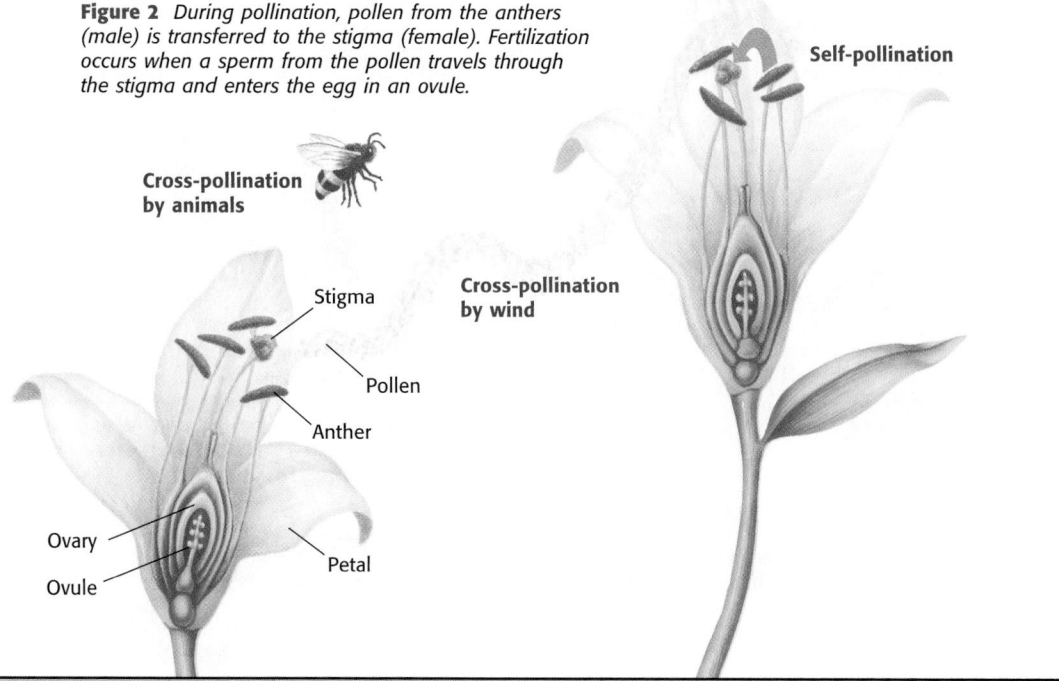

Figure 2 *During pollination, pollen from the anthers (male) is transferred to the stigma (female). Fertilization occurs when a sperm from the pollen travels through the stigma and enters the egg in an ovule.*

Cross-pollination by animals

Cross-pollination by wind

Self-pollination

Stigma

Pollen

Anther

Ovary

Ovule

Petal

Discussion ——— GENERAL

Scientific Methods Have students identify the use of scientific methods in Mendel's work.

- **Ask a question:** How are traits inherited?
- **Form a hypothesis:** Inheritance has a pattern.
- **Test the hypothesis:** Cross true-breeding plants and offspring.
- **Analyze the results:** Identify patterns in inherited traits.
- **Draw conclusions:** Traits are inherited in predictable patterns.
- **Communicate the results:** Publish the results for peer review.

Ask students, "Why weren't Mendel's ideas accepted for so many years?" (because of problems with the last step—other scientists could not easily read or understand his findings)

LS Logical/Verbal

Demonstration ——— BASIC

Flower Dissection Obtain a flower that has anthers and a stigma, such as a pea flower, a tulip, or a lily. Be careful because pollen can stain clothing and cause allergic reactions. Dissect the flower, and show students the anthers and the stigma. Ask students if this flower could self-pollinate. (yes, because it has both anthers and a stigma) Demonstrate how Mendel removed the anthers of his flowers and then used a small brush to transfer pollen from plant to plant.

LS Kinesthetic English Language Learners

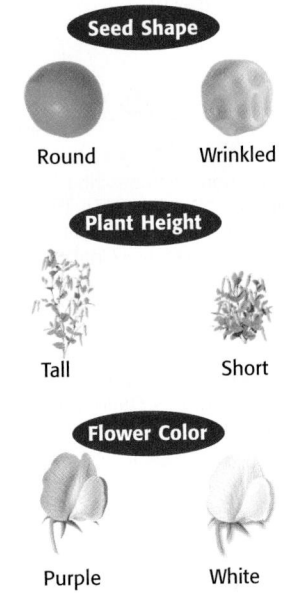

Seed Shape

Round   Wrinkled

Plant Height

Tall   Short

Flower Color

Purple   White

Figure 3 *These are some of the plant characteristics that Mendel studied.*

Characteristics

Mendel studied only one characteristic at a time. A *characteristic* is a feature that has different forms in a population. For example, hair color is a characteristic in humans. The different forms, such as brown or red hair, are called *traits*. Mendel used plants that had different traits for each of the characteristics he studied. For instance, for the characteristic of flower color, he chose plants that had purple flowers and plants that had white flowers. Three of the characteristics Mendel studied are shown in **Figure 3**.

Mix and Match

Mendel was careful to use plants that were true breeding for each of the traits he was studying. By doing so, he would know what to expect if his plants were to self-pollinate. He decided to find out what would happen if he bred, or crossed, two plants that had different traits of a single characteristic. To be sure the plants cross-pollinated, he removed the anthers of one plant so that the plant could not self-pollinate. Then, he used pollen from another plant to fertilize the plant, as shown in **Figure 4**. This step allowed Mendel to select which plants would be crossed to produce offspring.

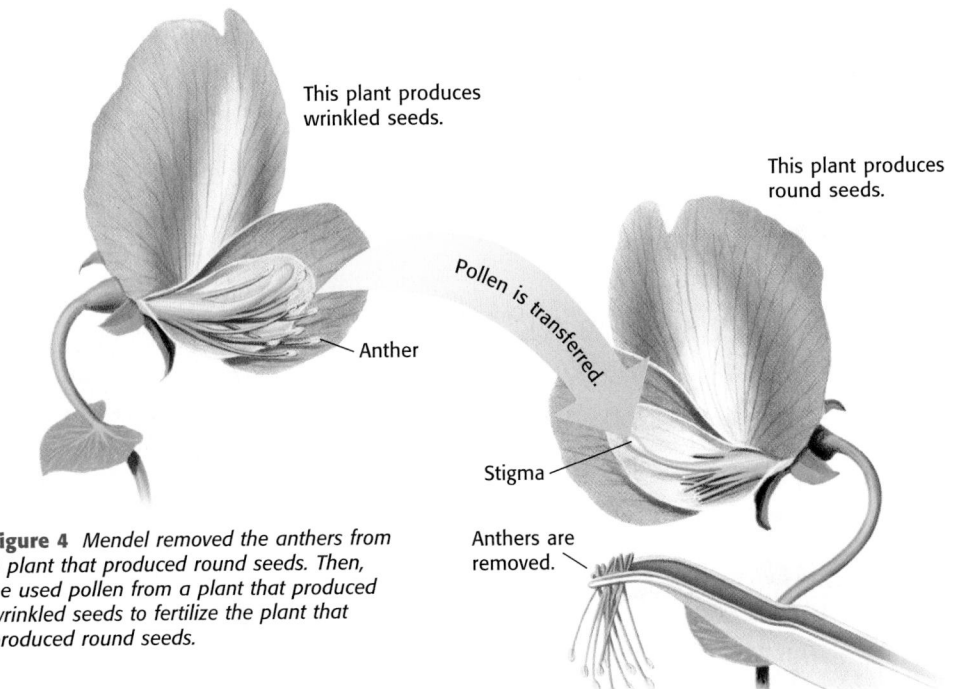

This plant produces wrinkled seeds.

This plant produces round seeds.

Pollen is transferred.

Anther

Stigma

Anthers are removed.

Figure 4 *Mendel removed the anthers from a plant that produced round seeds. Then, he used pollen from a plant that produced wrinkled seeds to fertilize the plant that produced round seeds.*

ACTiViTY ——— ADVANCED

Mendelian Crosses Give each student a purple bead (*P*) and a white bead (*p*), and ask students to perform a Mendelian cross. Tell students to begin the first generation with the allele combination *Pp*. Have students randomly "pollinate" with 10 other members of the class. To pollinate, one student should hide one bead in each hand. The partner should pick a hand. That hand holds the allele from one parent. Partners should switch roles and repeat this step to determine the allele from the second parent. Students should record the genotype for each pollination. Have students tally the results and determine the ratio of white-flowering plants to purple-flowering plants that results from the matches.

LS Kinesthetic/Interpersonal Co-op Learning

Mendel's First Experiments

In his first experiments, Mendel crossed pea plants to study seven different characteristics. In each cross, Mendel used plants that were true breeding for different traits for each characteristic. For example, he crossed plants that had purple flowers with plants that had white flowers. This cross is shown in the first part of **Figure 5.** The offspring from such a cross are called *first-generation plants*. All of the first-generation plants in this cross had purple flowers. Are you surprised by the results? What happened to the trait for white flowers?

Mendel got similar results for each cross. One trait was always present in the first generation, and the other trait seemed to disappear. Mendel chose to call the trait that appeared the **dominant trait.** Because the other trait seemed to fade into the background, Mendel called it the **recessive trait.** (To *recede* means "to go away or back off.") To find out what might have happened to the recessive trait, Mendel decided to do another set of experiments.

Mendel's Second Experiments

Mendel allowed the first-generation plants to self-pollinate. **Figure 5** also shows what happened when a first-generation plant with purple flowers was allowed to self-pollinate. As you can see, the recessive trait for white flowers reappeared in the second generation.

Mendel did this same experiment on each of the seven characteristics. In each case, some of the second-generation plants had the recessive trait.

✓ Reading Check Describe Mendel's second set of experiments.

dominant trait the trait observed in the first generation when parents that have different traits are bred

recessive trait a trait that reappears in the second generation after disappearing in the first generation when parents with different traits are bred

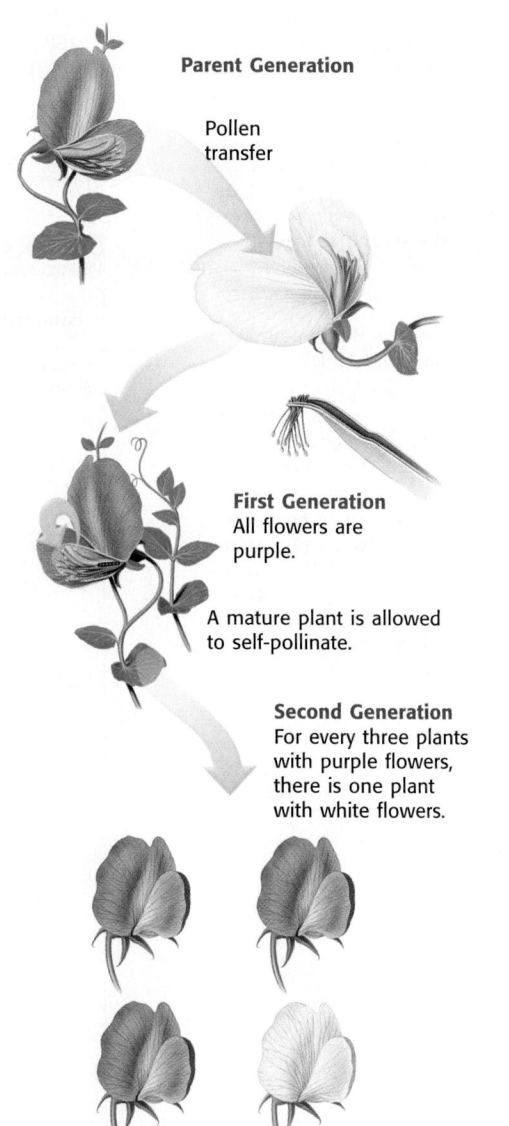

Parent Generation

Pollen transfer

First Generation
All flowers are purple.

A mature plant is allowed to self-pollinate.

Second Generation
For every three plants with purple flowers, there is one plant with white flowers.

Figure 5 *Mendel used the pollen from a plant with purple flowers to fertilize a plant with white flowers. Then, he allowed the offspring to self-pollinate.*

Answer to Reading Check

During his second set of experiments, Mendel allowed the first-generation plants, which resulted from his first set of experiments, to self-pollinate. The recessive trait reappeared in the second generation.

INCLUSION Strategies

- *Learning Disabled*
- *Attention Deficit Disorder*
- *Developmentally Delayed*

Use this activity to physically model the abstract concepts of *recessive* and *dominant*. To prepare, gather sheets of two kinds of transparent film: clear and purple. Cut the sheets into rectangles that are small enough to handle. Make one rectangle of each type for each student in the class.

1. Tell students that they are going to serve as models of Mendel's experiment in **Figure 5.** Give half of the students two purple rectangles each. Announce that these students have purple flowers. Give the other half of the students two clear rectangles each. Announce that these students have white flowers. Announce that the class now represents Mendel's parent generation.

2. Have each student trade one rectangle with another student. Announce that these new combinations represent Mendel's first generation. Tell students to hold the rectangles together in front of a light. Tell students that the purple gene is dominant and that those who see purple through the rectangles have purple flowers. This generation all has purple flowers.

3. Finally, have students trade one rectangle randomly with another student. Announce that the class now represents Mendel's second generation. Have students count the number of "flowers" of each type, and compare these results to Mendel's.
   L Kinesthetic   English Language Learners

Close

Answers for Table 1 Ratios

Seed color	3.00:1
Seed shape	2.96:1
Pod color	2.82:1
Pod shape	2.95:1
Flower position	3.14:1
Plant height	2.84:1

Reteaching — BASIC

Mendel's Experiments Have students re-enact Mendel's experiments using cups (to represent a plant), colored buttons or chips (to represent various alleles or genotypes), and colored strips of paper (to represent visible traits or phenotypes). Have students perform crosses by taking alleles from "parent" cups and creating "offspring" cups, deciding which traits would then become visible. **English Language Learners**

LS Kinesthetic/Logical

Quiz — GENERAL

1. What did Mendel call the trait that appeared in all of his first-generation plants? (the dominant trait)

2. What is the probability of getting heads in a coin toss? (1/2)

Alternative Assessment — ADVANCED

Story of a Scientist Have students create a comic book or short video drama about Mendel's life and work. Tell students to highlight his use of the scientific method and his habits as a scientist. **LS Interpersonal**

Ratios in Mendel's Experiments

Mendel then decided to count the number of plants with each trait that turned up in the second generation. He hoped that this might help him explain his results. Take a look at Mendel's results, shown in **Table 1.**

As you can see, the recessive trait did not show up as often as the dominant trait. Mendel decided to figure out the ratio of dominant traits to recessive traits. A *ratio* is a relationship between two different numbers that is often expressed as a fraction. Calculate the dominant-to-recessive ratio for each characteristic. (If you need help, look at the Math Practice at left.) Do you notice anything interesting about the ratios? Round to the nearest whole number. Are the ratios all the same, or are they different?

✓ **Reading Check** What is a ratio?

Understanding Ratios

A ratio is a way to compare two numbers. Look at **Table 1.** The ratio of plants with purple flowers to plants with white flowers can be written as 705 to 224 or 705:224. This ratio can be reduced, or simplified, by dividing the first number by the second as follows:

$$\frac{705}{224} = \frac{3.15}{1}$$

which is the same thing as a ratio of 3.15:1.

For every 3 plants with purple flowers, there will be roughly 1 plant with white flowers. Try this problem:

In a box of chocolates, there are 18 nougat-filled chocolates and 6 caramel-filled chocolates. What is the ratio of nougat-filled chocolates to caramel-filled chocolates?

Table 1 Mendel's Results

Characteristic	Dominant traits		Recessive traits		Ratio
Flower color	705 purple		224 white		3.15:1
Seed color	6,002 yellow		2,001 green		?
Seed shape	5,474 round		1,850 wrinkled		?
Pod color	428 green		152 yellow		?
Pod shape	882 smooth		299 bumpy		?
Flower position	651 along stem		207 at tip		?
Plant height	787 tall		277 short		?

Answer to Math Practice

The ratio of nougat-filled chocolates to caramel-filled chocolates is 18:6, or 18/6, which can be reduced to 3/1. This fraction can be rewritten as 3:1 or 3 to 1.

Answers to questions on student page

All the ratios are about the same. They can be rounded to 3:1.

Answer to Reading Check

A ratio is a relationship between two different numbers that is often expressed as a fraction.

Gregor Mendel—Gone but Not Forgotten

Mendel realized that his results could be explained only if each plant had two sets of instructions for each characteristic. Each parent would then donate one set of instructions. In 1865, Mendel published his findings. But good ideas are sometimes overlooked or misunderstood at first. It wasn't until after his death, more than 30 years later, that Mendel's work was widely recognized. Once Mendel's ideas were rediscovered and understood, the door was opened to modern genetics. Genetic research, as shown in **Figure 6,** is one of the fastest changing fields in science today.

Figure 6 *This researcher is continuing the work started by Gregor Mendel more than 100 years ago.*

SECTION Review

Summary

- Heredity is the passing of traits from parents to offspring.
- Gregor Mendel made carefully planned experiments using pea plants that could self-pollinate.
- When parents with different traits are bred, dominant traits are always present in the first generation. Recessive traits are not visible in the first generation but reappear in the second generation.
- Mendel found a 3:1 ratio of dominant-to-recessive traits in the second generation.

Using Key Terms

1. Use each of the following terms in a separate sentence: *heredity*, *dominant trait,* and *recessive trait*.

Understanding Key Ideas

2. A plant that has both male and female reproductive structures is able to
   a. self-replicate.
   b. self-pollinate.
   c. change colors.
   d. None of the above

3. Explain the difference between self-pollination and cross-pollination.

4. What is the difference between a trait and a characteristic? Give one example of each.

5. Describe Mendel's first set of experiments.

6. Describe Mendel's second set of experiments.

Math Skills

7. In a bag of chocolate candies, there are 21 brown candies and 6 green candies. What is the ratio of brown to green? What is the ratio of green to brown?

Critical Thinking

8. **Predicting Consequences** Gregor Mendel used only true-breeding plants. If he had used plants that were not true breeding, do you think he would have discovered dominant and recessive traits? Explain.

9. **Applying Concepts** In cats, there are two types of ears: normal and curly. A curly-eared cat mated with a normal-eared cat, and all of the kittens had curly ears. Are curly ears a dominant or recessive trait? Explain.

10. **Identifying Relationships** List three other fields of study that use ratios.

For a variety of links related to this chapter, go to www.scilinks.org
Topic: Heredity; Dominant and Recessive Traits
SciLinks code: HSM0738; HSM0423

Homework ——— GENERAL

Poster Project Have students create posters to illustrate Mendel's first and second experiments. Have each student demonstrate one of the seven traits that Mendel studied. Encourage students to use materials such as flowers, yellow and green seeds, or wrinkled and round peas. Each project should clearly identify the parents, the first generation, and the second generation. Visual/Logical

CHAPTER RESOURCES

Chapter Resource File
- Section Quiz GENERAL
- Section Review GENERAL
- Vocabulary and Section Summary GENERAL
- SciLinks Activity GENERAL

Workbooks
- Science Skills
  - Finding Useful Sources GENERAL
- Math Skills for Science
  - What is Ratio? GENERAL

Focus

Overview

In this section, students distinguish between genotype and phenotype and use mathematical models to predict the results of genetic crosses. They also learn some exceptions to Mendel's rules of inheritance.

 Bellringer

Have students respond to the following prompts: "If you flip a coin, what are the chances that it will land on heads?" (1/2 or 50%) "tails?" (same) "Suppose you flip the coin once, get heads, and then flip it again. What are the chances that you will get heads again?" (still 1/2 or 50%) "Explain." (Each flip of the coin is independent of the last. The chances are the same on each flip.)

Motivate

Demonstration ——— BASIC

Ratios To review fractions and ratios, display three pennies and one nickel, and then ask students the following questions: "How many coins are there in all?" (4) "What fraction of the coins are pennies?" (3/4) "What fraction of the coins are nickels?" (1/4) "What is the ratio of pennies to nickels?" (3 to 1)

LS Visual/Verbal

What You Will Learn

- Explain how genes and alleles are related to genotype and phenotype.
- Use the information in a Punnett square.
- Explain how probability can be used to predict possible genotypes in offspring.
- Describe three exceptions to Mendel's observations.

Vocabulary

gene
allele
phenotype
genotype
probability

READING STRATEGY

Paired Summarizing Read this section silently. In pairs, take turns summarizing the material. Stop to discuss ideas that seem confusing.

gene one set of instructions for an inherited trait

allele one of the alternative forms of a gene that governs a characteristic, such as hair color

phenotype an organism's appearance or other detectable characteristic

Figure 1 *Albinism is an inherited disorder that affects a person's phenotype in many ways.*

Traits and Inheritance

Mendel calculated the ratio of dominant traits to recessive traits. He found a ratio of 3:1. What did this tell him about how traits are passed from parents to offspring?

A Great Idea

Mendel knew from his experiments with pea plants that there must be two sets of instructions for each characteristic. The first-generation plants carried the instructions for both the dominant trait and the recessive trait. Scientists now call these instructions for an inherited trait **genes.** Each parent gives one set of genes to the offspring. The offspring then has two forms of the same gene for every characteristic—one from each parent. The different forms (often dominant and recessive) of a gene are known as **alleles** (uh LEELZ). Dominant alleles are shown with a capital letter. Recessive alleles are shown with a lowercase letter.

✓ *Reading Check* **What is the difference between a gene and an allele?** (*See the Appendix for answers to Reading Checks.*)

Phenotype

Genes affect the traits of offspring. An organism's appearance is known as its **phenotype** (FEE noh TIEP). In pea plants, possible phenotypes for the characteristic of flower color would be purple flowers or white flowers. For seed color, yellow and green seeds are the different phenotypes.

Phenotypes of humans are much more complicated than those of peas. Look at **Figure 1** below. The man has an inherited condition called *albinism* (AL buh NIZ uhm). Albinism prevents hair, skin, and eyes from having normal coloring.

CHAPTER RESOURCES

Chapter Resource File

- Lesson Plan
- Directed Reading A BASIC
- Directed Reading B SPECIAL NEEDS

Technology

Transparencies
- Bellringer
- L13 Punnett Squares
- *LINK TO PHYSICAL SCIENCE* P109 The Periodic Table of the Elements

Workbooks

Interactive Textbook Struggling Readers

Answer to Reading Check

A gene contains the instructions for an inherited trait. the different versions of a gene are called *alleles.*

Genotype

Both inherited alleles together form an organism's **genotype.** Because the allele for purple flowers (*P*) is dominant, only one *P* allele is needed for the plant to have purple flowers. A plant with two dominant or two recessive alleles is said to be *homozygous* (HOH moh ZIE guhs). A plant that has the genotype *Pp* is said to be *heterozygous* (HET uhr oh ZIE guhs).

Punnett Squares

A Punnett square is used to organize all the possible combinations of offspring from particular parents. The alleles for a true-breeding, purple-flowered plant are written as *PP*. The alleles for a true-breeding, white-flowered plant are written as *pp*. The Punnett square for this cross is shown in **Figure 2.** All of the offspring have the same genotype: *Pp*. The dominant allele, *P*, in each genotype ensures that all of the offspring will be purple-flowered plants. The recessive allele, *p*, may be passed on to the next generation. This Punnett square shows the results of Mendel's first experiments.

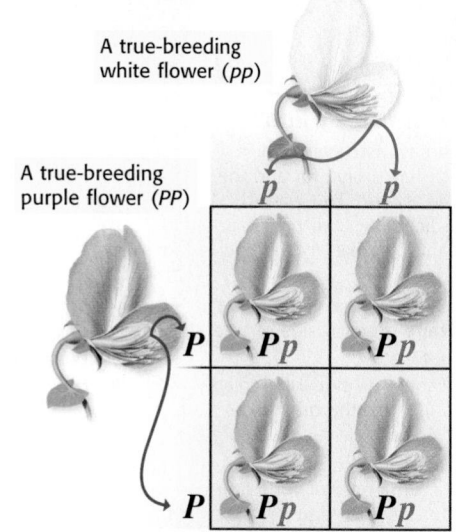

A true-breeding white flower (*pp*)

A true-breeding purple flower (*PP*)

Figure 2 *All of the offspring for this cross have the same genotype—Pp.*

genotype the entire genetic makeup of an organism; also the combination of genes for one or more specific traits

Making a Punnett Square

1. Draw a square, and divide it into four sections.
2. Write the letters that represent alleles from one parent along the top of the box.
3. Write the letters that represent alleles from the other parent along the side of the box.
4. The cross shown at right is between two plants that produce round seeds. The genotype for each is *Rr*. Round seeds are dominant, and wrinkled seeds are recessive. Follow the arrows to see how the inside of the box was filled. The resulting alleles inside the box show all the possible genotypes for the offspring from this cross. What would the phenotypes for these offspring be?

SCIENCE HUMOR

Q: What do you get when you cross a bridge with a bicycle?

A: to the other side

Teach

CONNECTION to Physical Science—ADVANCED

Mathematical Models The Punnett square and the periodic Table are both mathematical models that were developed by scientists who observed numerical patterns. These models are used to organize scientific understanding of patterns and to make predictions. Show students the teaching transparency entitled "The Periodic Table of the Elements." Discuss the ways that a Punnett square is similar.
LS Visual/Logical

MISCONCEPTION ALERT

Invisible Phenotypes Students may overgeneralize the idea that a phenotype can be a visible trait. This idea may help students to differentiate phenotype from genotype, but remind students that phenotype is any trait that is inherited (in other words, a result of the genotype). However, not all such traits may be visible. Most traits are fundamentally expressed as chemicals produced by cells.

Answer to Quick Lab

Three of the offspring would have round seeds, and one would have wrinkled seeds.

Answers to Quick Lab

4. Students should get *bb* on average 1/4 or 25% of the time.

5. 1/4 or 25%

6. 1/4 (If brown fur results from genotype *Bb*, then brown fur is dominant, and white fur will result from the genotype *bb*.)

CONNECTION ACTIVITY
Math ———————— ADVANCED

Probability of Independent Events The probability of two or more independent events is the product of the individual probabilities. For example, the probability of getting heads in a coin toss is 1/2, but the probability of getting heads twice in a row is $1/2 \times 1/2$, or 1/4. Have students consider the following parent genotypes for pea plants: *PpRr* and *Pprr*. Work out and discuss the probability of each possible combined phenotype. (For example, the probability of a plant with white flowers and round seeds is $1/4 \times 1/2 = 1/8$.) **LS Logical**

Answer to Reading Check
Probability is the mathematical chance that something will happen.

Quick Lab

Taking Your Chances

You have two guinea pigs. Each has brown fur and the genotype *Bb*. You want to predict what their offspring might look like. Try this to find out.

1. Stick a **piece of masking tape** on each side of **two quarters.**

2. Label one side with a capital *B* and the other side with a lowercase *b*.

3. Toss both coins 10 times, making note of your results each time.

4. How many times did you get the *bb* combination?

5. What is the probability that the next toss will result in *bb*?

6. What are the chances that the guinea pigs' offspring will have white fur (with the genotype *bb*)?

probability the likelihood that a possible future event will occur in any given instance of the event

---

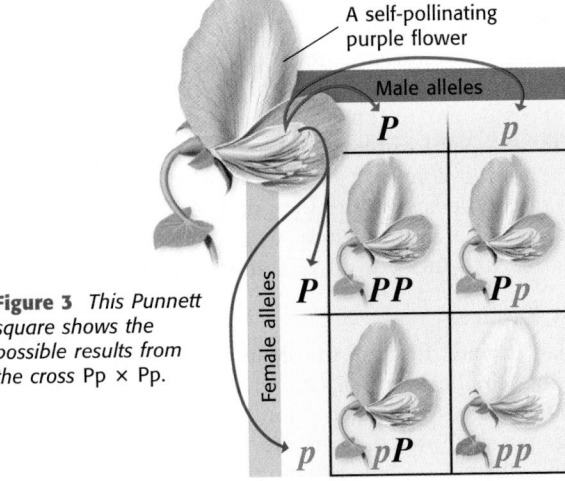

Figure 3 *This Punnett square shows the possible results from the cross Pp × Pp.*

More Evidence for Inheritance

In Mendel's second experiments, he allowed the first generation plants to self-pollinate. **Figure 3** shows a self-pollination cross of a plant with the genotype *Pp*. What are the possible genotypes of the offspring?

Notice that one square shows the genotype *Pp*, while another shows *pP*. These are exactly the same genotype. The other possible genotypes of the offspring are *PP* and *pp*. The combinations *PP*, *Pp*, and *pP* have the same phenotype—purple flowers. This is because each contains at least one dominant allele (*P*).

Only one combination, *pp*, produces plants that have white flowers. The ratio of dominant to recessive is 3:1, just as Mendel calculated from his data.

What Are the Chances?

Each parent has two alleles for each gene. When these alleles are different, as in *Pp*, offspring are equally likely to receive either allele. Think of a coin toss. There is a 50% chance you'll get heads and a 50% chance you'll get tails. The chance of receiving one allele or another is as random as a coin toss.

Probability

The mathematical chance that something will happen is known as **probability.** Probability is most often written as a fraction or percentage. If you toss a coin, the probability of tossing tails is 1/2—you will get tails half the time.

✓ **Reading Check** What is probability?

MISCONCEPTION ALERT

The Role of Chance Students' lack of understanding of mathematical probability may block their understanding of the random and independent sorting of genes that occurs during meiosis. Be careful that students do not overextend mathematical probabilities to predict the outcome of single events. It is correct to predict that an average of many outcomes will be similar to, but not exactly match, a probability ratio.

SUPPORT FOR

English Language Learners
Language of Probabilities When probabilities are discussed in English, specific language is used to convey how much chance there is that something could actually happen. Point out words such as *possible, probable, chance, likely,* and *random* as students are reading. Ask what they mean or provide examples if students do not know. Emphasize that these words have some subtle linguistic differences in meaning. **LS Verbal**

MATH FOCUS

Probability If you roll a pair of dice, what is the probability that you will roll 2 threes?

Step 1: Count the number of faces on a single die. Put this number in the denominator: 6.

Step 2: Count how many ways you can roll a three with one die. Put this number in the numerator: 1/6.

Step 3: To find the probability that you will throw 2 threes, multiply the probability of throwing the first three by the probability of throwing the second three: 1/6 × 1/6 = 1/36.

Now It's Your Turn

If you roll a single die, what is the probability that you will roll an even number?

Calculating Probabilities

To find the probability that you will toss two heads in a row, multiply the probability of tossing the first head (1/2) by the probability of tossing the second head (1/2). The probability of tossing two heads in a row is 1/4.

Genotype Probability

To have white flowers, a pea plant must receive a *p* allele from each parent. Each offspring of a *Pp* × *Pp* cross has a 50% chance of receiving either allele from either parent. So, the probability of inheriting two *p* alleles is 1/2 × 1/2, which equals 1/4, or 25%. Traits in pea plants are easy to predict because there are only two choices for each trait, such as purple or white flowers and round or wrinkled seeds. Look at **Figure 4.** Do you see only two distinct choices for fur color?

Figure 4 These kittens inherited one allele from their mother for each trait.

CONNECTION TO Chemistry

Round and Wrinkled Round seeds may look better, but wrinkled seeds taste sweeter. The dominant allele for seed shape, *R*, causes sugar to be changed into starch (which is a storage molecule for sugar). This change makes the seed round. Seeds with the genotype *rr* do not make or store this starch. Because the sugar has not been changed into starch, the seed tastes sweeter. If you had a pea plant with round seeds (*Rr*), what would you cross it with to get some offspring with wrinkled seeds? Draw a Punnett square showing your cross.

ACTIVITY

Homework —— **GENERAL**

Punnett Squares Have students create Punnett squares for each of the different crosses in Mendel's experiments. Students should include the genotype and phenotype of each parent and each set of possible offspring. **LS** Visual/Logical

WEIRD SCIENCE

Many ordinary fruits and vegetables carry recessive genes for bizarre traits. For instance, a recessive gene in tomatoes causes the skin to be covered with fuzzy hair!

Answer to Math Focus
3/6 or 1/2

Answer to Connection to Chemistry

You would cross it with a plant with wrinkled seeds (*rr*). Students should draw a Punnett square showing this cross.

	R	r
r	Rr	rr
r	Rr	rr

MISCONCEPTION ALERT

Exception to Mendel's Rules Caution students not to assume that all inherited traits follow the examples studied by Mendel. For instance, a cross between a red-haired horse and a white-haired horse can produce a horse with both red and white hair. Such a horse is said to have a roan coat. This is an example of *codominance*—the expression of two phenotypes at the same time within the same organism. As in the case of incomplete dominance (which is when a heterozygote shows a phenotype that is intermediate between the homozygous traits), both alleles are visible in the offspring, and therefore neither allele is purely dominant.

Reteaching ———— BASIC

Writing **Exceptions** Have students describe three exceptions to Mendel's heredity principles in their **science journal.** LS Verbal

Quiz ———————— GENERAL

In rabbits, the allele for black fur, *B*, is dominant over the allele for white fur, *b*. Suppose two black parents produce one white and three black bunnies.

1. What are the genotypes of the parents? (The parents must both have the recessive allele, so they are both genotype *Bb*.)

2. What are the possible genotypes of all four siblings? (White has genotype *bb*, and black may have *BB* or *Bb*.)

Alternative Assessment ———— GENERAL

Tracing Traits Ask students to imagine two true-breeding animal parents that have different genetic traits. Have them assign three characteristics, such as tall or short and red nosed or blue nosed, to each parent. Have students label each characteristic as either dominant or recessive. Then, have students use Punnett squares to determine the possible genotypes and phenotypes for each trait in the parents' offspring and in a possible second generation.

LS Logical/ Interpersonal

English Language Learners

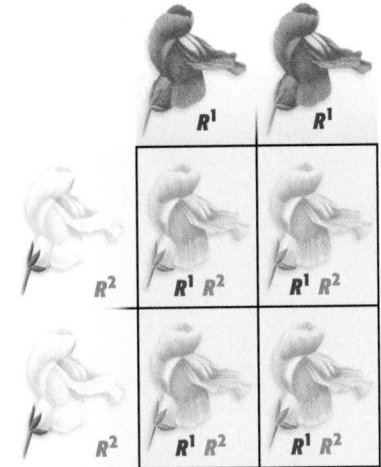

Figure 5 *Cross-breeding two true-breeding snapdragons provides a good example of incomplete dominance.*

More About Traits

As you may have already discovered, things are often more complicated than they first appear to be. Gregor Mendel uncovered the basic principles of how genes are passed from one generation to the next. But as scientists learned more about heredity, they began to find exceptions to Mendel's principles. A few of these exceptions are explained below.

Incomplete Dominance

Since Mendel's discoveries, researchers have found that sometimes one trait is not completely dominant over another. These traits do not blend together, but each allele has its own degree of influence. This is known as *incomplete dominance*.

One example of incomplete dominance is found in the snapdragon flower. **Figure 5** shows a cross between a true-breeding red snapdragon (R^1R^1) and a true-breeding white snapdragon (R^2R^2). As you can see, all of the possible phenotypes for their offspring are pink because both alleles of the gene have some degree of influence.

✔ **Reading Check** What is incomplete dominance?

One Gene, Many Traits

Sometimes one gene influences more than one trait. An example of this phenomenon is shown by the white tiger in **Figure 6.** The white fur is caused by a single gene, but this gene influences more than just fur color. Do you see anything else unusual about the tiger? If you look closely, you'll see that the tiger has blue eyes. Here, the gene that controls fur color also influences eye color.

Figure 6 *The gene that gave this tiger white fur also influenced its eye color.*

 **BRAIN FOOD**

Round Peas Mendel found that round seeds were dominant over wrinkled seeds. However, at the microscopic level, this is a case of incomplete dominance. The *R* and *r* alleles actually seem to affect the amount of starch produced in the pea. *RR* seeds have many starch grains that give them a full, round shape, but *rr* seeds have few starch grains and a wrinkled shape. *Rr* seeds have an intermediate number of starch grains—but enough for the pea to be full and round.

Many Genes, One Trait

Some traits, such as the color of your skin, hair, and eyes, are the result of several genes acting together. Therefore, it's difficult to tell if some traits are the result of a dominant or a recessive gene. Different combinations of alleles result in different eye-color shades, as shown in **Figure 7.**

The Importance of Environment

Genes aren't the only influences on traits. A guinea pig could have the genes for long fur, but its fur could be cut. In the same way, your environment influences how you grow. Your genes may make it possible that you will grow to be tall, but you need a healthy diet to reach your full potential height.

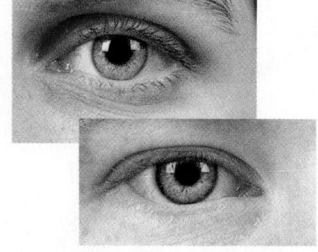

Figure 7 At least two genes determine human eye color. That's why many shades of a single color are possible.

SECTION Review

Summary

- Instructions for an inherited trait are called *genes*. For each gene, there are two alleles, one inherited from each parent. Both alleles make up an organism's genotype. Phenotype is an organism's appearance.

- Punnett squares show all possible offspring genotypes.

- Probability can be used to describe possible outcomes in offspring and the likelihood of each outcome.

- Incomplete dominance occurs when one allele is not completely dominant over the other allele.

- Some genes influence more than one trait.

Using Key Terms

1. Use the following terms in the same sentence: *gene* and *allele*.

2. In your own words, write a definition for each of the following terms: *genotype* and *phenotype*.

Understanding Key Ideas

3. Use a Punnett square to determine the possible genotypes of the offspring of a *BB* × *Bb* cross.
   a. all *BB*   c. *BB, Bb, bb*
   b. *BB, Bb*   d. all *bb*

4. How are genes and alleles related to genotype and phenotype?

5. Describe three exceptions to Mendel's observations.

Math Skills

6. What is the probability of rolling a five on one die three times in a row?

Critical Thinking

7. **Applying Concepts** The allele for a cleft chin, *C*, is dominant among humans. What are the results of a cross between parents with genotypes *Cc* and *cc*?

Interpreting Graphics

The Punnett square below shows the alleles for fur color in rabbits. Black fur, *B*, is dominant over white fur, *b*.

	?	?
?	*Bb*	*Bb*
?	*Bb*	*Bb*

8. Given the combinations shown, what are the genotypes of the parents?

9. If black fur had incomplete dominance over white fur, what color would the offspring be?

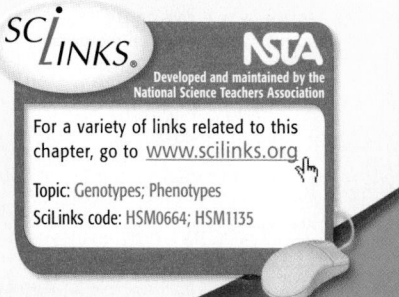

SCiLINKS®

NSTA
Developed and maintained by the
National Science Teachers Association

For a variety of links related to this chapter, go to www.scilinks.org

Topic: Genotypes; Phenotypes
SciLinks code: HSM0664; HSM1135

Focus

Overview

In this section, students are introduced to meiosis and relate it to Mendel's findings. Students also learn about sex chromosomes and hereditary disorders.

 Bellringer

Ask students to write a sentence for each of the following terms: *heredity, genotype, phenotype.* (Sample answer: Heredity is the passing of traits from parents to offspring. The combination of an organism's alleles is its genotype. All of an organism's physical traits are its phenotype.)

Motivate

ACTiViTY ———— GENERAL

Crosses Have students model a cross between an organism with one pair of chromosomes and a member of the opposite sex of its species. Show the chromosomes in the cross as "$F_1F_2 \times M_1M_2$." Explain that F_1 and F_2 represent the father's chromosomes, and M_1 and M_2 represent the mother's chromosomes. Ask students, "If each parent contributes only one chromosome from his or her own pair to the offspring, what are the possible combinations in the offspring?" (F_1M_1, F_1M_2, F_2M_1, and F_2M_2) **LS** Logical/Visual

What You Will Learn

- Explain the difference between mitosis and meiosis.
- Describe how chromosomes determine sex.
- Explain why sex-linked disorders occur in one sex more often than in the other.
- Interpret a pedigree.

Vocabulary

homologous chromosomes
meiosis
sex chromosome
pedigree

READING STRATEGY

Reading Organizer As you read this section, make a flowchart of the steps of meiosis.

homologous chromosomes chromosomes that have the same sequence of genes and the same structure

meiosis a process in cell division during which the number of chromosomes decreases to half the original number by two divisions of the nucleus, which results in the production of sex cells

Meiosis

Where are genes located, and how do they pass information? Understanding reproduction is the first step to finding the answers.

There are two kinds of reproduction: asexual and sexual. Asexual reproduction results in offspring with genotypes that are exact copies of their parent's genotype. Sexual reproduction produces offspring that share traits with their parents but are not exactly like either parent.

Asexual Reproduction

In *asexual reproduction,* only one parent cell is needed. The structures inside the cell are copied, and then the parent cell divides, making two exact copies. This type of cell reproduction is known as *mitosis.* Most of the cells in your body and most single-celled organisms reproduce in this way.

Sexual Reproduction

In sexual reproduction, two parent cells join together to form offspring that are different from both parents. The parent cells are called *sex cells.* Sex cells are different from ordinary body cells. Human body cells have 46, or 23 pairs of, chromosomes. One set of human chromosomes is shown in **Figure 1.** Chromosomes that carry the same sets of genes are called **homologous** (hoh MAHL uh guhs) **chromosomes.** Imagine a pair of shoes. Each shoe is like a homologous chromosome. The pair represents a homologous pair of chromosomes. But human sex cells are different. They have 23 chromosomes—half the usual number. Each sex cell has only one of the chromosomes from each homologous pair. Sex cells have only one "shoe."

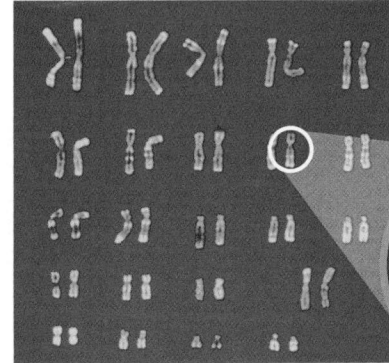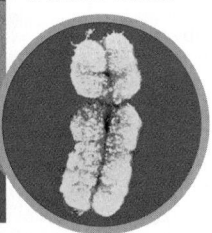

Figure 1 *Human body cells have 23 pairs of chromosomes. One member of a pair of homologous chromosomes is shown below.*

CHAPTER RESOURCES

Chapter Resource File

- **Lesson Plan**
- **Directed Reading A** BASIC
- **Directed Reading B** SPECIAL NEEDS

Technology

Transparencies
- Bellringer

Workbooks

Interactive Textbook Struggling Readers

CONNECTION ACTiViTY
Math ———— ADVANCED

Crosses In algebraic multiplication, some students use the mnemonic device FOIL (**f**irst, **o**uter, **i**nner, **l**ast). This device can be used to calculate genotype crosses. For example, the cross $X_1X_2 \times Y_1Y_2$ yields:

First: X_1X_2

Outer: X_1Y_2

Inner: X_2Y_1

Last: Y_1Y_2

LS Logical/Auditory

Meiosis

Sex cells are made during meiosis (mie OH sis). **Meiosis** is a copying process that produces cells with half the usual number of chromosomes. Each sex cell receives one-half of each homologous pair. For example, a human egg cell has 23 chromosomes, and a sperm cell has 23 chromosomes. The new cell that forms when an egg cell and a sperm cell join has 46 chromosomes.

Reading Check How many chromosomes does a human egg cell have? (*See the Appendix for answers to Reading Checks.*)

Genes and Chromosomes

What does all of this have to do with the location of genes? Not long after Mendel's work was rediscovered, a graduate student named Walter Sutton made an important observation. Sutton was studying sperm cells in grasshoppers. Sutton knew of Mendel's studies, which showed that the egg and sperm must each contribute the same amount of information to the offspring. That was the only way the 3:1 ratio found in the second generation could be explained. Sutton also knew from his own studies that although eggs and sperm were different, they did have something in common: Their chromosomes were located inside a nucleus. Using his observations of meiosis, his understanding of Mendel's work, and some creative thinking, Sutton proposed something very important:

Genes are located on chromosomes!

Understanding meiosis was critical to finding the location of genes. Before you learn about meiosis, review mitosis, shown in **Figure 2.** Meiosis is outlined in **Figure 3** on the next two pages.

CONNECTION TO Language Arts

Greek Roots The word *mitosis* is related to a Greek word that means "threads." Threadlike spindles are visible during mitosis. The word *meiosis* comes from a Greek word that means "to make smaller." How do you think meiosis got its name?

Figure 2 Mitosis Revisited

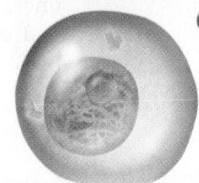
① Each chromosome is copied.

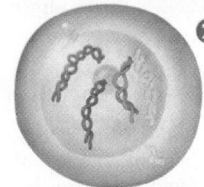
② The chromosomes thicken and shorten. Each chromosome consists of two identical copies, called *chromatids.*

③ The nuclear membrane dissolves. The chromatids line up along the equator (center) of the cell.

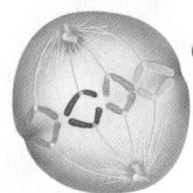
④ The chromatids pull apart.

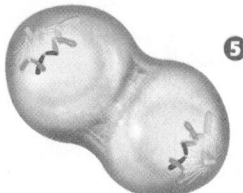
⑤ The nuclear membrane forms around the separated chromatids. The chromosomes unwind, and the cell divides.

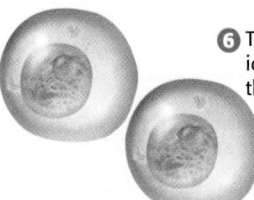
⑥ The result is two identical copies of the original cell.

Answer to Connection to Language Arts
Sample answer: Meiosis makes each of the daughter cells smaller than the parent cell. Also, there are fewer chromosomes in the daughter cells than in the parent cell.

Science Bloopers

Wrong Number In 1918, a prominent scientist miscounted the number of chromosomes in a human cell. He counted 48. For almost 40 years, scientists thought this number was correct. In fact, not until 1956 were chromosomes counted correctly and found to number only 46.

Prediction Guide Before students read the passage about meiosis, ask them whether the following statements are true or false. Students will discover the answers as they explore the rest of the section.

• Mitosis is the only type of cell division. (false)

• Only cells that produce sex cells undergo meiosis. (true)

• Sex cells contain half the number of chromosomes that other body cells do. (true)

🅛🅢 **Verbal/Auditory**

Answer to Reading Check

During meiosis, one parent cell makes four new cells.

Discussion — GENERAL

Predicting Problems Ask students what they think would happen if something went wrong during cell division and the sperm or egg cell ended up with either too few or too many chromosomes? (The fertilized egg, with too few or too many chromosomes, may die, or the growing embryo may have birth defects. Down syndrome occurs in humans when the offspring receives an extra twenty-first chromosome.)

🅛🅢 **Verbal/Logical**

The Steps of Meiosis

During mitosis, chromosomes are copied once, and then the nucleus divides once. During meiosis, chromosomes are copied once, and then the nucleus divides twice. The resulting sperm and eggs have half the number of chromosomes of a normal body cell. **Figure 3** shows all eight steps of meiosis. Read about each step as you look at the figure. Different types of living things have different numbers of chromosomes. In this illustration, only four chromosomes are shown.

✓ **Reading Check** How many cells are made from one parent cell during meiosis?

Figure 3 **Steps of Meiosis**

Read about each step as you look at the diagram. Different types of living things have different numbers of chromosomes. In this diagram, only four chromosomes are shown.

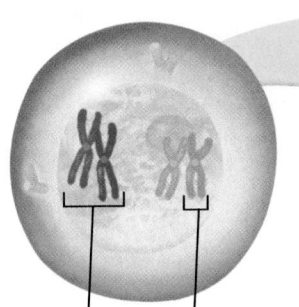

One pair of homologous chromosomes

Two chromatids

1 Before meiosis begins, the chromosomes are in a threadlike form. Each chromosome makes an exact copy of itself, forming two halves called *chromatids*. The chromosomes then thicken and shorten into a form that is visible under a microscope. The nuclear membrane disappears.

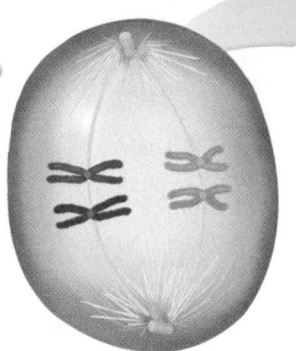

2 Each chromosome is now made up of two identical chromatids. Similar chromosomes pair with one another, and the paired homologous chromosomes line up at the equator of the cell.

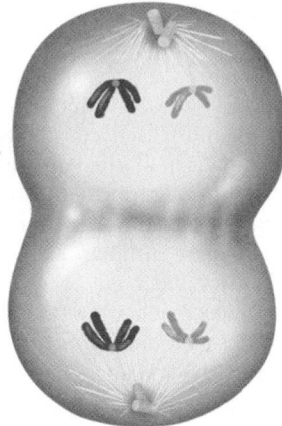

3 The chromosomes separate from their homologous partners and then move to opposite ends of the cell.

---

5 Each cell contains one member of each homologous chromosome pair. The chromosomes are not copied again between the two cell divisions.

6 The chromosomes then line up at the equator of each cell.

4 The nuclear membrane re-forms, and the cell divides. The paired chromatids are still joined.

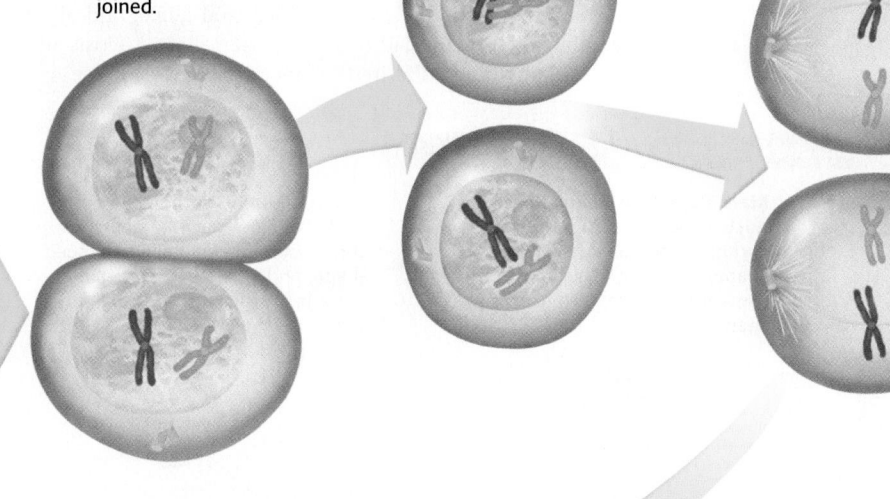

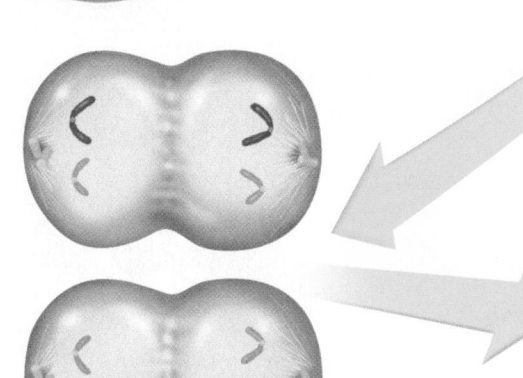

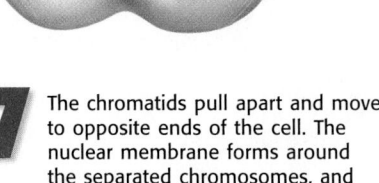

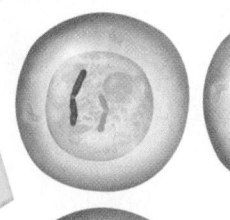

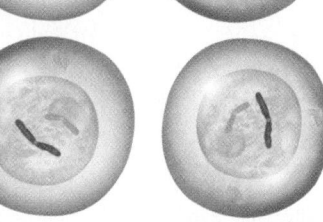

7 The chromatids pull apart and move to opposite ends of the cell. The nuclear membrane forms around the separated chromosomes, and the cells divide.

8 The result is that four new cells have formed from the original single cell. Each new cell has half the number of chromosomes present in the original cell.

MISCONCEPTION ALERT

Chromatids and Chromosome Pairing Students often have difficulty keeping track of the differences between the way that chromatids and chromosome pairs move during mitosis as compared to meiosis. Caution students to note these differences as they compare mitosis and meiosis, and to analyze the ways that these differences are critical to each process.

ACTIVITY ——— **BASIC**

Describing Meiosis Have students write their own captions for the steps of meiosis illustrated here. They should use language and descriptions that will help them understand and remember the material.

LS Verbal/Visual

CONNECTION ACTIVITY
Math ——— **GENERAL**

Chromosome Number Meiosis and sexual reproduction have benefits for organisms because these processes maintain a variety of traits within a population. Meiosis and sexual recombination reshuffle the genetic material in each generation. Furthermore, the division of chromosomes during meiosis ensures that when the egg and sperm combine, the new organism has the same number of chromosomes as its parents. To explore these concepts, ask students the following questions:

• If the normal number of chromosomes for a certain organism is 30, how many chromosomes would be found in the egg or sperm cells? (15)

• What would happen if eggs and sperm were produced by mitosis instead of by meiosis? (The organism would produce sex cells with a full set of 30 chromosomes.)

• If the organism described above were to have offspring that also produced sex cells by mitosis, how many chromosomes would be found in the descendants after four generations? (first generation: 60; second generation: 120; third generation: 240; fourth generation: 480)

LS Verbal/Logical

- *Learning Disabled*
- *Attention Deficit Disorder*

Have students make a flip book that animates the phases of meiosis. First, have students draw the events of meiosis in at least 15 sketches on sturdy cards. Explain that each drawing should vary only slightly from the one before it. When the book is flipped through quickly, the images should appear to be in motion, and students will be able to watch meiosis in action. This activity could be repeated to demonstrate mitosis.

LS Visual   English Language Learners

Group ACTIVITY — GENERAL

Comparing Mitosis and Meiosis Organize the class into small groups. Instruct each group to create a table listing the similarities and differences between mitosis and meiosis. Challenge groups to make the longest list possible in a limited time period. After their time is up, have groups report items from their lists. Discuss and correct items as you compile a single, large table for display in the classroom.   English Language Learners

LS Visual/Verbal

INTERNET ACTIVITY

For another activity related to this chapter, go to **go.hrw.com** and type in the keyword **HL5HERW**.

Meiosis and Mendel

As Walter Sutton figured out, the steps in meiosis explained Mendel's results. **Figure 4** shows what happens to a pair of homologous chromosomes during meiosis and fertilization. The cross shown is between a plant that is true breeding for round seeds and a plant that is true breeding for wrinkled seeds.

Each fertilized egg in the first generation had one dominant allele and one recessive allele for seed shape. Only one genotype was possible because all sperm formed by the male parent during meiosis had the wrinkled-seed allele, and all of the female parent's eggs had the round-seed allele. Meiosis also helped explain other inherited characteristics.

Figure 4   Meiosis and Dominance

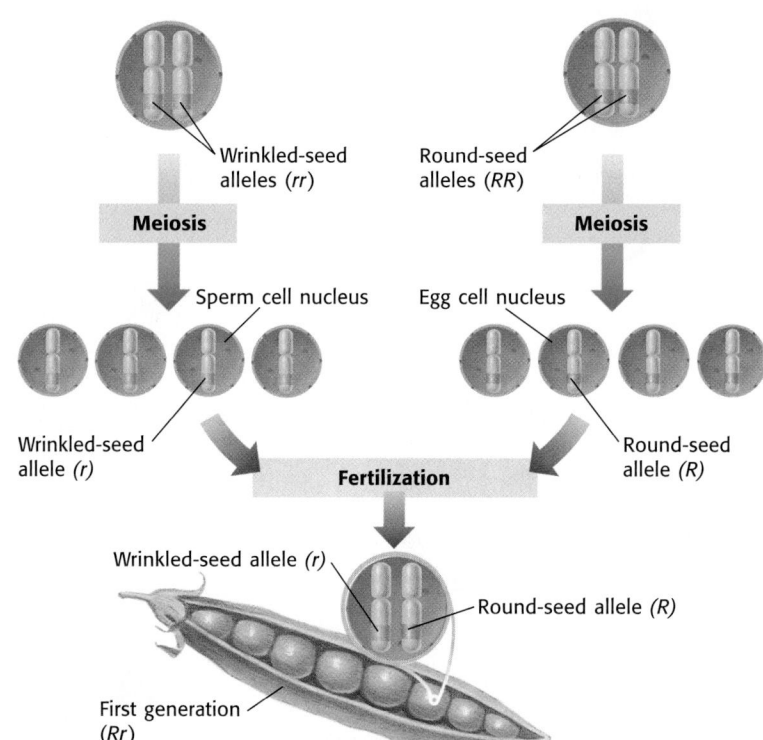

Male Parent In the plant-cell nucleus below, each homologous chromosome has an allele for seed shape, and each allele carries the same instructions: to make wrinkled seeds.

Female Parent In the plant-cell nucleus below, each homologous chromosome has an allele for seed shape, and each allele carries the same instructions: to make round seeds.

Wrinkled-seed alleles (rr)

Round-seed alleles (RR)

Meiosis

Meiosis

ⓐ Following **meiosis,** each sperm cell has a recessive allele for wrinkled seeds, and each egg cell has a dominant allele for round seeds.

Sperm cell nucleus

Egg cell nucleus

Wrinkled-seed allele (r)

Round-seed allele (R)

ⓑ **Fertilization** of any egg by any sperm results in the same genotype (Rr) and the same phenotype (round). This result is exactly what Mendel found in his studies.

Fertilization

Wrinkled-seed allele (r)

Round-seed allele (R)

First generation (Rr)

CHAPTER RESOURCES

Technology

 Transparencies
- L16 Meiosis and Dominance

Is That a Fact!

Martin-Bell syndrome is a genetic disorder also known as *Fragile X syndrome.* It is one of the most common forms of inherited mental retardation. This disorder is a genetic condition associated with mental retardation and autism. The disorder is identified by flaws apparent in the long arm of the X chromosome.

Sex Chromosomes

Information contained on chromosomes determines many of our traits. **Sex chromosomes** carry genes that determine sex. In humans, females have two X chromosomes. But human males have one X chromosome and one Y chromosome.

During meiosis, one of each of the chromosome pairs ends up in a sex cell. Females have two X chromosomes in each body cell. When meiosis produces the egg cells, each egg gets one X chromosome. Males have both an X chromosome and a Y chromosome in each body cell. Meiosis produces sperm with either an X or a Y chromosome. An egg fertilized by a sperm with an X chromosome will produce a female. If the sperm contains a Y chromosome, the offspring will be male, as shown in **Figure 5.**

Sex-Linked Disorders

The Y chromosome does not carry all of the genes of an X chromosome. Females have two X chromosomes, so they carry two copies of each gene found on the X chromosome. This makes a backup gene available if one becomes damaged. Males have only one copy of each gene on their one X chromosome. The genes for certain disorders, such as colorblindness, are carried on the X chromosome. These disorders are called *sex-linked disorders.* Because the gene for such disorders is recessive, men are more likely to have sex-linked disorders.

People who are colorblind can have trouble distinguishing between shades of red and green. To help the colorblind, some cities have added shapes to their street lights, as shown in **Figure 6.** Hemophilia (HEE moh FIL ee uh) is another sex-linked disorder. Hemophilia prevents blood from clotting, and people with hemophilia bleed for a long time after small cuts. Hemophilia can be fatal.

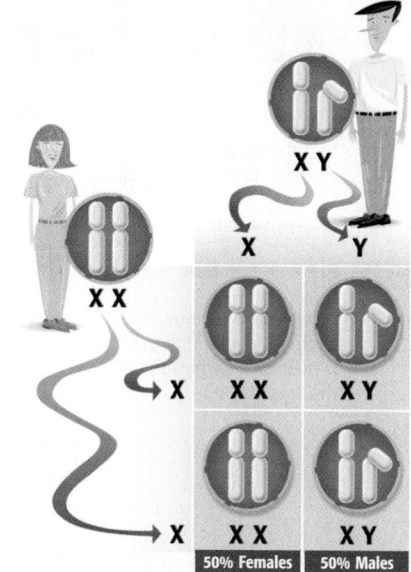

Figure 5 *Egg and sperm combine to form either the XX or XY combination.*

sex chromosome one of the pair of chromosomes that determine the sex of an individual

Figure 6 *This stoplight in Canada is designed to help the colorblind see signals easily. This photograph was taken over a few minutes to show all three shapes.*

BRAIN FOOD

In human males, meiosis and sperm production take about nine weeks and occur continuously after puberty begins. In females, meiosis and egg production begin before birth and then stop until puberty. From puberty until menopause, one egg each month resumes meiosis and finishes developing. So, production of a mature egg may take up to 50 years!

Reteaching — BASIC

Modeling Mates Have students use Punnett squares to model several possible combinations of parents with sex-linked traits that are variously dominant and recessive.

LS Logical/ Kinesthetic   English Language Learners

Quiz — GENERAL

Are the following statements true or false?

1. Every one of the chromosomes is different between men and women. (false)

2. Men and women each have different numbers of chromosomes in their sex cells. (false)

3. If you looked inside a cell during mitosis and you could see the chromosomes lining up, you could tell whether the cell belongs to a man or a woman. (true)

Alternative Assessment — GENERAL

Writing

Meiosis versus Mitosis Tell students that there will be a mock debate to decide whether mitosis or meiosis is "better." First, have the class discuss and agree upon a definition of "better." Then, have students choose a "side" and prepare a written argument that is supported by scientific facts. You may wish to allow volunteers to act out such a debate. LS Verbal

Figure 7 Pedigree for a Recessive Disease

☐ Males   ○ Females

Vertical lines connect children to their parents.

■ or ● A solid square or circle indicates that the person has a certain trait.

◩ or ◖ A half-filled square or circle indicates that the person is a carrier of the trait.

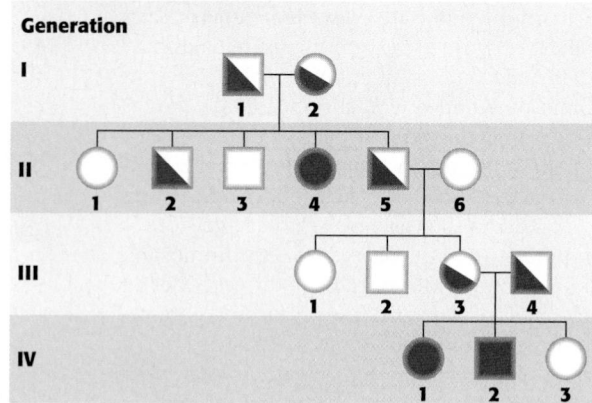

pedigree a diagram that shows the occurrence of a genetic trait in several generations of a family

Figure 8 Roses have been selectively bred to create large, bright flowers.

Genetic Counseling

Hemophilia and other genetic disorders can be traced through a family tree. If people are worried that they might pass a disease to their children, they may consult a genetic counselor. These counselors often make use of a diagram known as a **pedigree,** which is a tool for tracing a trait through generations of a family. By making a pedigree, a counselor can often predict whether a person is a carrier of a hereditary disease. The pedigree shown in **Figure 7** traces a disease called *cystic fibrosis* (SIS tik FIE broh sis). Cystic fibrosis causes serious lung problems. People with this disease have inherited two recessive alleles. Both parents need to be carriers of the gene for the disease to show up in their children.

Pedigrees can be drawn up to trace any trait through a family tree. You could even draw a pedigree that would show how you inherited your hair color. Many different pedigrees could be drawn for a typical family.

Selective Breeding

For thousands of years, humans have seen the benefits of the careful breeding of plants and animals. In *selective breeding,* organisms with desirable characteristics are mated. You have probably enjoyed the benefits of selective breeding, although you may not have realized it. For example, you have probably eaten an egg from a chicken that was bred to produce more eggs. Your pet dog may be a result of selective breeding. Roses, like the one shown in **Figure 8,** have been selectively bred to produce large flowers. Wild roses are much smaller and have fewer petals than roses that you could buy at a nursery.

WEIRD SCIENCE

Gene therapy is an experimental field of medical research in which defective genes are replaced with healthy genes. One way to insert healthy genes involves using a delivery system called a *gene gun* to inject microscopic gold bullets coated with genetic material.

Homework — ADVANCED

Pet Pedigrees Have students obtain a copy of the pedigree of a thoroughbred animal from a professional breeder of dogs, cats, horses, or other animals. Ask students to write a paragraph explaining what information the pedigree provides about the animal and its ancestors. LS Verbal/Interpersonal

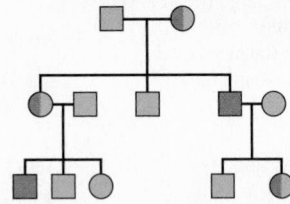

Summary

- In mitosis, chromosomes are copied once, and then the nucleus divides once. In meiosis, chromosomes are copied once, and then the nucleus divides twice.
- The process of meiosis produces sex cells, which have half the number of chromosomes. These two halves combine during reproduction.
- In humans, females have two X chromosomes. So, each egg contains one X chromosome. Males have both an X and a Y chromosome. So, each sperm cell contains either an X or a Y chromosome.
- Sex-linked disorders occur in males more often than in females. Colorblindness and hemophilia are examples of sex-linked disorders.
- A pedigree is a diagram used to trace a trait through many generations of a family.

Using Key Terms

1. Use each of the following terms in the same sentence: *meiosis* and *sex chromosomes*.

In each of the following sentences, replace the incorrect term with the correct term from the word bank.

pedigree	homologous chromosomes
meiosis	mitosis

2. During fertilization, chromosomes are copied, and then the nucleus divides twice.

3. A Punnett square is used to show how inherited traits move through a family.

4. During meiosis, sex cells line up in the middle of the cell.

Understanding Key Ideas

5. Genes are found on
   a. chromosomes.
   b. proteins.
   c. alleles.
   d. sex cells.

6. If there are 14 chromosomes in pea plant cells, how many chromosomes are present in a sex cell of a pea plant?

7. Draw the eight steps of meiosis. Label one chromosome, and show its position in each step.

Interpreting Graphics

Use this pedigree to answer the question below.

8. Is this disorder sex linked? Explain your reasoning.

Critical Thinking

9. **Identifying Relationships** Put the following in order of smallest to largest: chromosome, gene, and cell.

10. **Applying Concepts** A pea plant has purple flowers. What alleles for flower color could the sex cells carry?

SCLINKS

NSTA

Developed and maintained by the
National Science Teachers Association

For a variety of links related to this chapter, go to www.scilinks.org
Topic: Meiosis; Genetic Diseases, Screening, Counseling
SciLinks code: HSM0935; HSM0651

Answers to Section Review

1. Sample answer: At the end of meiosis, each sex cell will contain only one sex chromosome (either X or Y).

2. During meiosis, chromosomes are copied, and then the nucleus divides twice.

3. A pedigree is used to show how inherited traits move through a family.

4. During meiosis, homologous chromosomes line up in the middle of the cell.

5. a

6. 7

7. Answers may vary. Students' drawings should be similar to the diagram of meiosis in the student text.

8. Sample answer: yes; The disorder seems to be sex linked because the females are carriers of the disease but only males have the disease itself.

9. gene, chromosome, cell

10. Sample answer: Because the purple gene (*P*) is dominant over the white gene (*p*), the genotype of the purple-flowered pea plant could be either *PP* or *Pp*. Thus, the possible alleles carried by the sex cells would be *P* or *p*.

INTERNET ACTIVITY
Essay ——— GENERAL

For an internet activity related to this chapter, have students goto **go.hrw.com** and type in the keyword **HL5DNAW**.

CHAPTER RESOURCES

Chapter Resource File

- Section Quiz GENERAL
- Section Review GENERAL
- Vocabulary and Section Summary GENERAL
- Critical Thinking ADVANCED

Bug Builders, Inc.

Teacher's Notes

Time Required
Two 45-minute class periods

Lab Ratings

EASY ————————————→ HARD

Teacher Prep 🧪🧪🧪
Student Set-Up 🧪🧪
Concept Level 🧪🧪🧪
Clean Up 🧪

MATERIALS

The materials listed on the student page are enough for a group of 3–4 students. For step 3, prepare 14 small paper sacks—representing paired parent alleles for each of seven characteristics—as follows:

1. Use the table in step 6 to decide the genotypes for each of the parent bugs' characteristics.

2. Cut 1 in. squares of paper to represent alleles. Use seven colors of paper—a different color for each characteristic. Cut enough squares so that each student will receive two alleles for each characteristic.

3. Label the alleles for each characteristic according to the genotypes you chose.

4. Label each pair of sacks with one of the seven characteristics. Place an equal number of alleles in each sack.

5. For each characteristic, label one sack "Mom" and the other sack "Dad." Have students draw one allele from each sack.

Safety Caution

Remind students to review all safety cautions and icons before beginning this lab activity. Students should use caution with toothpicks and should not eat any of the materials used.

Bug Builders, Inc.

Imagine that you are a designer for a toy company that makes toy alien bugs. The president of Bug Builders, Inc., wants new versions of the wildly popular Space Bugs, but he wants to use the bug parts that are already in the warehouse. It's your job to come up with a new bug design. You have studied how traits are passed from one generation to another. You will use this knowledge to come up with new combinations of traits and assemble the bug parts in new ways. Model A and Model B, shown below, will act as the "parent" bugs.

Ask a Question

1 If there are two forms of each of the seven traits, then how many possible combinations are there?

Form a Hypothesis

2 Write a hypothesis that is a possible answer to the question above. Explain your reasoning.

Test the Hypothesis

3 Your teacher will display 14 allele sacks. The sacks will contain slips of paper with capital or lowercase letters on them. Take one piece of paper from each sack. (Remember: Capital letters represent dominant alleles, and lowercase letters represent recessive alleles.) One allele is from "Mom," and one allele is from "Dad." After you have recorded the alleles you have drawn, place the slips of paper back into the sack.

 OBJECTIVES

Build models to further your understanding of inheritance.

Examine the traits of a population of offspring.

 MATERIALS

- allele sacks (14) (supplied by your teacher)
- gumdrops, green and black (feet)
- map pins (eyes)
- marshmallows, large (head and body segments)
- pipe cleaners (tails)
- pushpins, green and blue (noses)
- scissors
- toothpicks, red and green (antennae)

SAFETY

Model A ("Mom")
- red antennae
- 3 body segments
- curly tail
- 2 pairs of legs
- green nose
- black feet
- 3 eyes

Model B ("Dad")
- green antennae
- 2 body segments
- straight tail
- 3 pairs of legs
- blue nose
- green feet
- 2 eyes

CHAPTER RESOURCES

Chapter Resource File

 • **Datasheet for Chapter Lab**
• **Lab Notes and Answers**

Technology

 Classroom Videos
• Lab Video

• Tracing Traits

Bug Family Traits				
Trait	Model A "Mom" allele	Model B "Dad" allele	New model "Baby" genotype	New model "Baby" phenotype
Antennae color				
Number of body segments				
Tail shape				
Number of leg pairs		*DO NOT WRITE IN BOOK*		
Nose color				
Foot color				
Number of eyes				

4 Create a table like the one above. Fill in the first two columns with the alleles that you selected from the sacks. Next, fill in the third column with the genotype of the new model ("Baby").

5 Use the information below to fill in the last column of the table.

Genotypes and Phenotypes	
RR or *Rr*—red antennae	*rr*—green antennae
SS or *Ss*—3 body segments	*ss*—2 body segments
CC or *Cc*—curly tail	*cc*—straight tail
LL or *Ll*—3 pairs of legs	*ll*—2 pairs of legs
BB or *Bb*—blue nose	*bb*—green nose
GG or *Gg*—green feet	*gg*—black feet
EE or *Ee*—2 eyes	*ee*—3 eyes

6 Now that you have filled out your table, you are ready to pick the parts you need to assemble your bug. (Toothpicks can be used to hold the head and body segments together and as legs to attach the feet to the body.)

Analyze the Results

1 **Organizing Data** Take a poll of the traits of the offspring. What are the ratios for each trait?

2 **Examining Data** Do any of the new models look exactly like the parents? Explain.

Draw Conclusions

3 **Interpreting Information** What are the possible genotypes of the parent bugs?

4 **Making Predictions** How many different genotypes are possible in the offspring?

Applying Your Data

Find a mate for your "Baby" bug. What are the possible genotypes and phenotypes of the offspring from this match?

Ask a Question

1. There are 128 possible combinations. (Calculation: There are two forms of each of seven characteristics, so, $2 \times 2 \times 2 \times 2 \times 2 \times 2 \times 2 = 2^7 = 128$)

Analyze the Results

1. Student ratios should be similar to the ratios determined when the alleles were selected by the teacher.

2. If any students have offspring bugs that look like one of the parents, have students compare the genotype of the offspring with the genotype of the parents. The offspring and parents look alike but still have different genotypes for some traits.

Draw Conclusions

3. Student answers should reflect the data on parent alleles that were recorded in step 5.

4. Students' answers should include Punnett squares based on the parental traits. Except for the results obtained by parental genotypes that are all homozygous recessive, students will see other possibilities for genotypes and phenotypes from the same parents.

Applying Your Data

Students should create Punnett squares to show the possible genotypes and describe phenotypes that follow the rules of dominance for each characteristic.

Chapter Review

Assignment Guide

Section	Questions
1	7, 13, 18
2	2, 4, 5, 8, 9, 11, 19–23
3	1, 3, 6, 10, 12, 14–17

ANSWERS

Using Key Terms

1. sex cells
2. phenotype, genotype
3. Meiosis
4. alleles

Understanding Key Ideas

5. d
6. c
7. b
8. b
9. c
10. c
11. b

USING KEY TERMS

Complete each of the following sentences by choosing the correct term from the word bank.

sex cells	genotype
sex chromosomes	alleles
phenotype	meiosis

❶ Sperm and eggs are known as _____.

❷ The _____ is the expression of a trait and is determined by the combination of alleles called the _____.

❸ _____ produces cells with half the normal number of chromosomes.

❹ Different versions of the same genes are called _____.

UNDERSTANDING KEY IDEAS

Multiple Choice

❺ Genes carry information that determines
- a. alleles.
- b. ribosomes.
- c. chromosomes.
- d. traits.

❻ The process that produces sex cells is
- a. mitosis.
- b. photosynthesis.
- c. meiosis.
- d. probability.

❼ The passing of traits from parents to offspring is called
- a. probability.
- b. heredity.
- c. recessive.
- d. meiosis.

❽ If you cross a white flower with the genotype *pp* with a purple flower with the genotype *PP*, the possible genotypes in the offspring are
- a. *PP* and *pp*.
- b. all *Pp*.
- c. all *PP*.
- d. all *pp*.

❾ For the cross in item 8, what would the phenotypes be?
- a. all white
- b. 3 purple and 1 white
- c. all purple
- d. half white, half purple

❿ In meiosis,
- a. chromosomes are copied twice.
- b. the nucleus divides once.
- c. four cells are produced from a single cell.
- d. two cells are produced from a single cell.

⓫ When one trait is not completely dominant over another, it is called
- a. recessive.
- b. incomplete dominance.
- c. environmental factors.
- d. uncertain dominance.

Short Answer

12 Which sex chromosomes do females have? Which do males have?

13 In one or two sentences, define the term *recessive trait* in your own words.

14 How are sex cells different from other body cells?

15 What is a sex-linked disorder? Give one example of a sex-linked disorder that is found in humans.

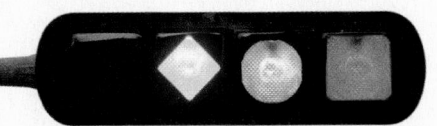

16 **Concept Mapping** Use the following terms to create a concept map: *meiosis, eggs, cell division, X chromosome, mitosis, Y chromosome, sperm,* and *sex cells.*

17 **Identifying Relationships** If you were a carrier of one allele for a certain recessive disorder, how could genetic counseling help you prepare for the future?

18 **Applying Concepts** If a child has blond hair and both of her parents have brown hair, what does that tell you about the allele for blond hair? Explain.

19 **Applying Concepts** What is the genotype of a pea plant that is true-breeding for purple flowers?

INTERPRETING GRAPHICS

Use the Punnett square below to answer the questions that follow.

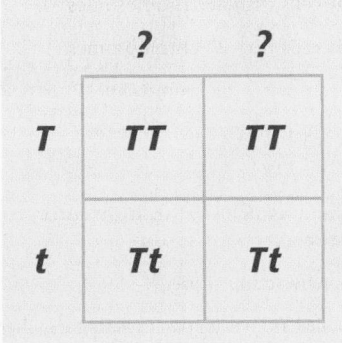

	?	**?**
T	**TT**	**TT**
t	**Tt**	**Tt**

20 What is the unknown genotype?

21 If *T* represents the allele for tall pea plants and *t* represents the allele for short pea plants, what is the phenotype of each parent and of the offspring?

22 If each of the offspring were allowed to self-fertilize, what are the possible genotypes in the next generation?

23 What is the probability of each genotype in item 22?

Critical Thinking

16. An answer to this exercise can be found at the end of this book.

17. Sample answer: A genetic counselor could test my spouse to see if my spouse is also a carrier of the recessive allele. The counselor could then predict what the chances are that we could have a child with the recessive disorder.

18. The allele for blond hair is recessive.

19. *PP*

Interpreting Graphics

20. *TT*

21. All the parents and offspring are tall pea plants.

22. Students should make two new Punnett squares. Self-fertilization of *TT* (*TT* × *TT*) will yield offspring that are all *TT*. Self fertilization of *Tt* (*Tt* × *Tt*) will yield offspring that are *TT*, *Tt*, and *tt*.

23. *TT* has a 100% probability with a *TT* parent and a 25% probability with a *Tt* parent. *Tt* has a 50% probability with a *Tt* parent and a 0% probability with a *TT* parent. The genotype *tt* has a 25% probability with a *Tt* parent and a 0% probability with a *TT* parent.

12. Females have two X chromosomes. Males have one X and one Y chromosome.

13. Sample answer: A recessive trait is a genetic trait that is expressed only if there is not a dominant allele present.

14. Sex cells have half the number of chromosomes as other body cells.

15. Sample answer: A sex-linked disorder is a disorder that is caused by a gene on one of the sex chromosomes and so is expressed in one sex more than the other. Color blindness is a sex-linked disorder found in humans.

Standardized Test Preparation

Teacher's Notes

To provide practice under more realistic conditions, give students 20 minutes to answer all of the questions in this Standardized Test Preparation.

Answer Key

Question	Answer
1	D
2	C
3	C
4	A
5	B
6	C
7	C
8	B
9	A
10	D
11	*
12	*

*See Test Doctor.

Multiple Choice

1. **What kind of cells are created during meiosis in humans?**

   A. body cells with 46 chromosomes

   B. body cells with 23 chromosomes

   C. sex cells with 46 chromosomes

   D. sex cells with 23 chromosomes

2. **Traits such as skin color, hair color, and eye color result from**

   A. one gene acting alone.

   B. one allele from each parent acting together.

   C. several genes acting together.

   D. one dominant allele.

3. **The allele for freckles, _F_, is dominant. If a woman with freckles _(FF)_ and a man without freckles _(ff)_ have children, what are the possible genotypes of the children?**

   A. _Ff, ff_

   B. _FF, Ff, ff_

   C. _Ff_

   D. _ff_

4. **Which of the following is the process that allows humans to mate organisms, such as dogs or roses, with the goal of producing desirable traits?**

   A. selective breeding

   B. sexual reproduction

   C. genetic typing

   D. genetic counseling

5. **Homologous chromosomes contain**

   A. the same alleles, but no genes.

   B. the same genes, but possibly different alleles for the genes.

   C. the same genes and the same alleles for the genes.

   D. different genes and different alleles.

Use the chart below to answer question 6.

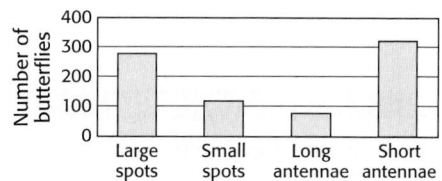

6. **Mai-lin created the chart above as part of a field experiment studying traits of Viceroy butterflies. Based on the data in the graph, which traits are dominant?**

   A. large spots and long antennae

   B. small spots and long antennae

   C. large spots and short antennae

   D. small spots and short antennae

TEST DOCTOR

Question 1 A, B: The result of meiosis is sex cells. Body cells have a paired set of chromosomes, whereas sex cells have an unpaired set of chromosomes. C: A human cell has 46 chromosomes, or 23 pairs of chromosomes. Meiosis results in 23 unpaired chromosomes per cell. D: Correct.

Question 2 A, B: The color of skin, hair, and eyes are the results of different combinations of many alleles. This explains the large diversity among the traits. C: Correct. D: A dominant allele would result in less diversity of color. Usually the

dominant allele would be indicated by the most prevalent skin, hair, or eye color.

Question 3 A, B, D: The only possible genotype for this cross is _Ff_. The children can only inherit an _F_ allele from the mother and an _f_ allele from the father. C: Correct.

Question 4 A: Correct. B: Organisms use sexual reproduction in order to produce offspring, but not necessarily with the intention of producing certain traits. C, D: Genetic typing and genetic counseling are activities that a genetic counselor may engage in. They involve finding out which traits and diseases a person or family may display or carry.

7. Which of the following statements is true?

A. A phenotype is the entire genetic makeup of an organism, whereas a genotype is the combination of genes for one specific trait.

B. A phenotype is the result of the environment on appearance, whereas a genotype is the result of genes on appearance.

C. A phenotype is the appearance of an organism, whereas a genotype is the genetic makeup of the organism.

D. A phenotype is the result of heterozygous alleles, whereas a genotype is the result of homozygous alleles.

Use the diagram below to answer question 8.

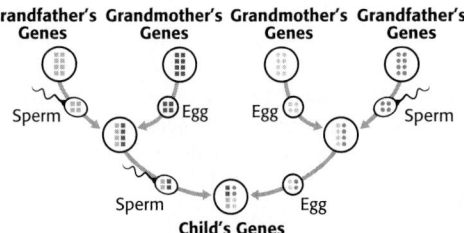

INHERITING GENES

8. If the grandfather on the mother's side is colorblind (and no one else is), how likely is it that the mother's child will be colorblind?

A. more likely than not

B. more likely if the child is a boy

C. more likely if the child is a girl

D. highly unlikely: colorblindness is not hereditary

9. Why do identical twins have the same genotype?

A. They have the same sets of alleles.

B. They come from two similar eggs.

C. They look exactly alike.

D. They have heterozygous genotypes.

10. When Mendel crossed true-breeding tall pea plants with true-breeding short pea plants, all of the offspring were tall. When he allowed the first-generation pea plants to self-pollinate, some of the offspring were tall and some were short. What should Mendel have concluded from these results?

A. Only dominant traits appear in every generation.

B. Both dominant and recessive traits appear in every generation.

C. Dominant and recessive traits appear at random from one generation to the next.

D. Dominant and recessive traits appear in predictable patterns from one generation to the next.

Open Response

11. Suppose a grower bred a blackberry bush that produces more fruit than a normal blackberry bush, but it also becomes susceptible to disease. If this bush self-pollinates, what are the chances (25%, 50%, 75%, or 100%) that its seedlings will also be susceptible to the disease? Explain your answer.

12. What are the differences between the sexual and asexual reproduction of cells?

the overall likelihood that a child of the mother in the diagram would be color-blind is one to three (twenty-five percent). B: Correct. C: A female child would not be colorblind since she would inherit a non-defective back-up X chromosome from her father. Depending on which X chromosome she inherited from her mother, she will or will not have colorblindness as a recessive trait. D: Colorblindness is a hereditary, sex-linked disorder.

Question 9 A: Correct. B: A geno-type is determined by the fertilization of a single egg and a single sperm. Each sex cell contributes one set of alleles. In order for two humans to have identical genotypes, they must result from the same egg and sperm. C: Looking exactly alike is a result of having the same genotype. D: A heterozygous genotype refers to the different alleles of a gene. Identical twins will have identical geno-types, whether they are heterozygous or homozygous genotypes.

Question 10 A, B, C: Recessive traits appear when offspring inherit two copies of the recessive allele. Dominant traits appear when offspring inherit two dominant alleles or one dominant allele and one recessive allele. D: Correct.

Question 11 Full-credit answers should include the following points:

- A self-pollinating plant produces offspring that have the same traits as the parent plant.
- All of its seedlings would thus be susceptible to the disease.
- The chance is 100%.

Question 12 Full-credit answers should include at least most of these points (first asexual/second sexual):

- cell reproduction process: mitosis/meiosis
- number of parent cells: one/two
- kind of parent cells: ordinary/unusual (egg and sperm sex cells with half the usual chromosomes)
- times nucleus divides: once/twice
- offspring cell–parent cell(s) similarity: identical/not identical (different chromosomes from each parent)

Question 5 A, C, D: Homologous chromosomes contain the same genes, but they may contain different alleles. B: Correct.

Question 6 A. According to the table, more butterflies have short antennae than have long antennae. Thus, having long antennae is not a dominant trait. B: According to the table, more butterflies have large spots than have small spots, and more butterflies have short antennae than have long antennae. Thus, both small spots and long antennae are not dominant traits. C: Correct. D: According to the table, more butterflies have large spots on their wings than have small spots. Thus, having small spots is not a dominant trait.

Question 7 A: A genotype is both the entire genetic makeup of an organism and a combination of genes for one specific trait. B: Though environment does affect phenotype, a genotype results in more than appearance. A genotype also determines traits that are not visible, such as colorblindness and hemophilia in humans or egg production in chickens. C: Correct. D: A genotype may be heterozygous or homozygous.

Question 8 A: The student may not have taken into account the likelihood that the child is male. Since there is about a fifty-fifty chance that the child would be a boy, and a fifty-fifty chance that a boy (with the specified grandfather) would be colorblind,

Chapter 4 • Standardized Test Preparation

Science, Technology, and Society

Background

Genetic research has spawned a flurry of debate over ethical, social, and legal issues surrounding the use of genetic information. These issues include the privacy and ownership of personal genetic information and the possibility that people will selectively breed or control the birth of their children based on genetic knowledge.

Weird Science

Teaching Strategy—GENERAL

Offer the following analogies to help students grasp the concepts discussed in this article.

- Blueprints: Show students sample construction blueprints. Explain that genes are like these plans for a building and that mutations are like mistakes in copying, reading, or building from the blueprints.

- Recipes: Show students a book of cake recipes. Genes are like recipes, and an organism is like a cake made according to a recipe. A mutation is like using a different ingredient or a different amount of an ingredient. The mutation may or may not "ruin" the "cake."

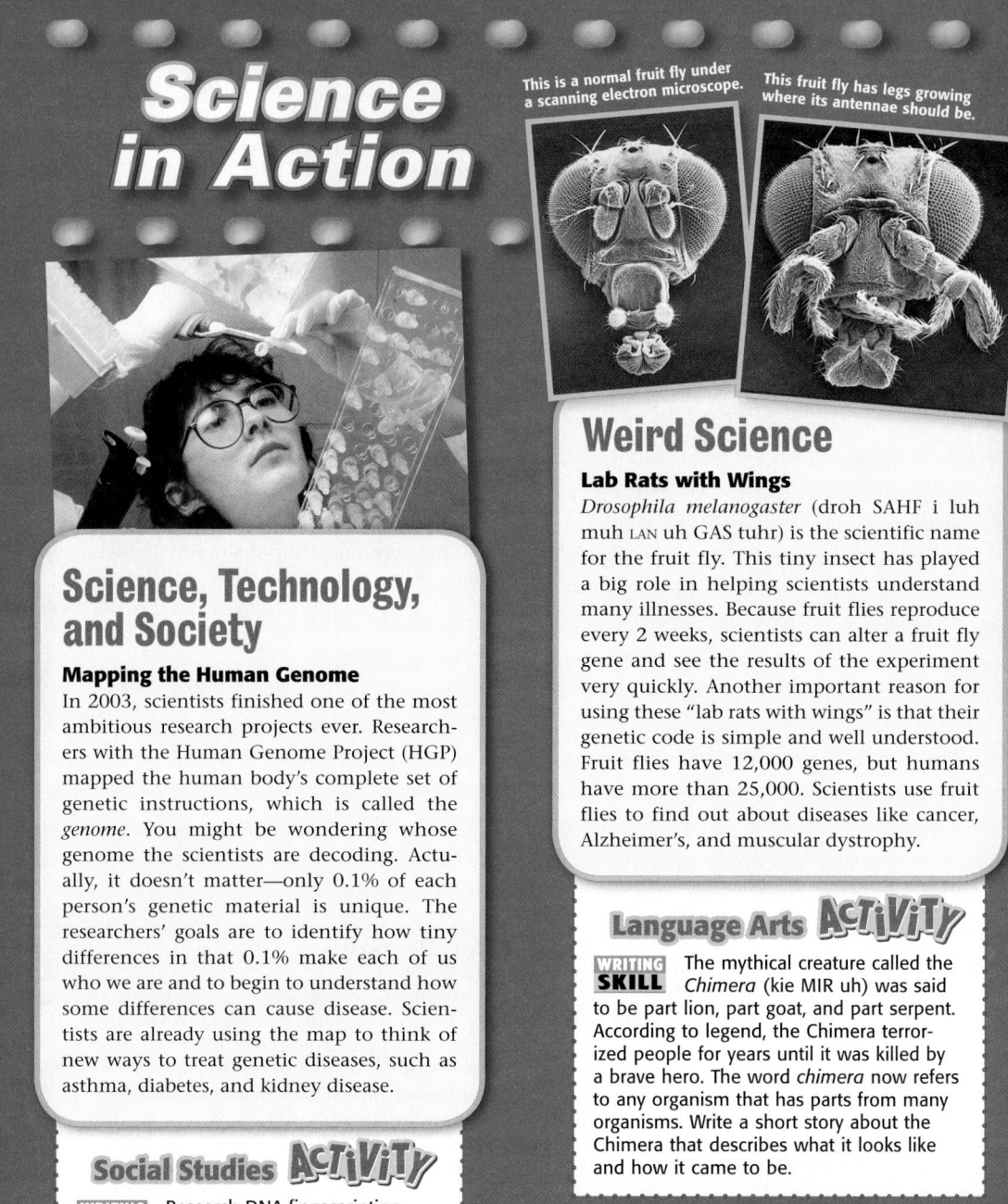

Science in Action

This is a normal fruit fly under a scanning electron microscope.

This fruit fly has legs growing where its antennae should be.

Science, Technology, and Society

Mapping the Human Genome

In 2003, scientists finished one of the most ambitious research projects ever. Researchers with the Human Genome Project (HGP) mapped the human body's complete set of genetic instructions, which is called the *genome*. You might be wondering whose genome the scientists are decoding. Actually, it doesn't matter—only 0.1% of each person's genetic material is unique. The researchers' goals are to identify how tiny differences in that 0.1% make each of us who we are and to begin to understand how some differences can cause disease. Scientists are already using the map to think of new ways to treat genetic diseases, such as asthma, diabetes, and kidney disease.

Social Studies ACTiViTY

WRITING SKILL Research DNA fingerprinting. Write a short report describing how DNA fingerprinting has affected the way criminals are caught.

Weird Science

Lab Rats with Wings

Drosophila melanogaster (droh SAHF i luh muh LAN uh GAS tuhr) is the scientific name for the fruit fly. This tiny insect has played a big role in helping scientists understand many illnesses. Because fruit flies reproduce every 2 weeks, scientists can alter a fruit fly gene and see the results of the experiment very quickly. Another important reason for using these "lab rats with wings" is that their genetic code is simple and well understood. Fruit flies have 12,000 genes, but humans have more than 25,000. Scientists use fruit flies to find out about diseases like cancer, Alzheimer's, and muscular dystrophy.

Language Arts ACTiViTY

WRITING SKILL The mythical creature called the *Chimera* (kie MIR uh) was said to be part lion, part goat, and part serpent. According to legend, the Chimera terrorized people for years until it was killed by a brave hero. The word *chimera* now refers to any organism that has parts from many organisms. Write a short story about the Chimera that describes what it looks like and how it came to be.

Answer to Social Studies Activity

Sample answer: DNA fingerprinting has made it much easier to match genetic material (evidence) at a crime scene to the genetic information of one particular individual. DNA can be found in hair, saliva, blood, and small skin cells. The DNA is analyzed and then compared to the DNA fingerprint of particular individuals. When the DNA fingerprints match, police can be sure that the person was at the scene of the crime.

Answer to Language Arts Activity

The Chimera (or Chimaera) was said to be a savage beast that spat fire from its mouth. In classical Greco-Roman stories, it wreaked havoc on the ancient lands until it was killed by the hero Bellerophon, who rode his winged horse Pegasus. This basic story is among the most ancient myths and appears in many texts from Homer's *Iliad* to traditional fairy tales.

Stacey Wong

Genetic Counselor If your family had a history of a particular disease, what would you do? Would you eat healthier foods, get more exercise, or visit your doctor regularly? All of those are good ideas, but Stacey Wong went a step farther. Her family's history of cancer helped her decide to become a genetic counselor. "Genetic counselors are usually part of a team of health professionals," she says, which can include physicians, nurses, dieticians, social workers, laboratory personnel, and others. "If a diagnosis is made by the geneticist," says Wong, "then I provide genetic counseling." When a patient visits a genetic counselor, the counselor asks many questions and builds a family medical history. Although counseling involves discussing what it means to have a genetic condition, Wong says "the most important part is to get to know the patient or family we are working with, listen to their concerns, gain an understanding of their values, help them to make decisions, and be their advocate."

Math ACTIVITY

The probability of inheriting genetic disease *A* is 1/10,000. The probability of inheriting genetic disease *B* is also 1/10,000. What is the probability that one person would inherit both genetic diseases *A* and *B*?

To learn more about these Science in Action topics, visit **go.hrw.com** and type in the keyword **HL5HERF**.

Current Science

Check out Current Science® articles related to this chapter by visiting go.hrw.com. Just type in the keyword **HL5CS05**.

Careers

Background

Stacey Wong was born in Oakland, California, and grew up in the nearby suburb of Alameda. She received a B.S. in cell and molecular biology from UCLA and an M.S. in genetic counseling from California State University Northridge. More information about genetic-counseling careers can be obtained from the National Society of Genetic Counselors.

Answer to Math Activity

1/10,000 × 1/10,000 = 1/100,000,000

Genes and DNA
Chapter Planning Guide

Compression guide:
To shorten instruction
because of time limitations,
omit the Chapter Lab.

OBJECTIVES	LABS, DEMONSTRATIONS, AND ACTIVITIES	TECHNOLOGY RESOURCES
PACING • 135 min pp. 114–119 **Chapter Opener**	**SE Start-up Activity,** p. 115 ◆ `GENERAL`	**OSP Parent Letter** ■ **CD Student Edition on CD-ROM** **CD Guided Reading Audio CD** ■ **TR Chapter Starter Transparency*** **VID Brain Food Video Quiz**
Section 1 What Does DNA Look Like? • List three important events that led to understanding the structure of DNA. • Describe the basic structure of a DNA molecule. • Explain how DNA molecules can be copied.	**TE Activity** Modeling Code, p. 116 `GENERAL` **TE Group Activity** A Place in History, p. 117 `GENERAL` **SE Quick Lab** Making a Model of DNA, p. 118 ◆ `GENERAL` **CRF Datasheet for Quick Lab*** **SE Science in Action** Math, Social Studies, and Language Arts Activities, pp. 134–135 `GENERAL` **SE Model-Making Lab** Base-Pair Basics, p. 128 ◆ `GENERAL` **CRF Datasheet for Chapter Lab*** **LB Whiz-Bang Demonstrations** Grand Strand* `GENERAL`	**OSP Lesson Plans** (also in print) **TR Bellringer Transparency*** **TR L17 DNA Structure*** **CRF SciLinks Activity*** `GENERAL` **VID Lab Videos for Life Science**
PACING • 45 min pp. 120–127 **Section 2 How DNA Works** • Explain the relationship between DNA, genes, and proteins. • Outline the basic steps in making a protein. • Describe three types of mutations, and provide an example of a gene mutation. • Describe two examples of uses of genetic knowledge.	**TE Demonstration** A Tight Fit, p. 120 ◆ `GENERAL` **TE Connection Activity** Chemistry, p. 122 `ADVANCED` **TE Group Activity** Skit, p. 122 `GENERAL` **TE Connection Activity** Math, p. 123 ◆ `GENERAL` **TE Activity** Complementary Code, p. 124 `BASIC` **SE School-to-Home Activity** An Error in the Message, p. 125 `GENERAL` **TE Connection Activity** Social Studies, p. 126 `ADVANCED` **LB Long-Term Projects & Research Ideas** The Antifreeze Protein* `ADVANCED` **LB Long-Term Projects & Research Ideas** Ewe Again, Dolly?* `ADVANCED`	**OSP Lesson Plans** (also in print) **TR Bellringer Transparency*** **TR L18 Unraveling DNA*** **TR L19 The Making of a Protein: A*** **TR L20 The Making of a Protein: B*** **TR** *LINK TO EARTH SCIENCE* E66 The Formation of Smog* **TR L21 How Sickle Cell Anemia Results from a Mutation*** **SE Internet Activity,** p. 122 `GENERAL` **CD Interactive Explorations CD-ROM** DNA Pawprints `GENERAL`

PACING • 90 min

CHAPTER REVIEW, ASSESSMENT, AND STANDARDIZED TEST PREPARATION

CRF Vocabulary Activity* `GENERAL`
SE Chapter Review, pp. 130–131 `GENERAL`
CRF Chapter Review* ■ `GENERAL`
CRF Chapter Tests A* ■ `GENERAL`, **B*** `ADVANCED`, **C*** `SPECIAL NEEDS`
SE Standardized Test Preparation, pp. 132–133 `GENERAL`
CRF Standardized Test Preparation* `GENERAL`
CRF Performance-Based Assessment* `GENERAL`
OSP Test Generator, Test Item Listing

Online and Technology Resources

Visit **go.hrw.com** for access to Holt Online Learning, or enter the keyword **HS7 Home** for a variety of free online resources.

This CD-ROM package includes:
• Lab Materials QuickList Software
• Holt Calendar Planner
• Customizable Lesson Plans
• Printable Worksheets
• ExamView® Test Generator
• Interactive Teacher's Edition
• Holt PuzzlePro®
• Holt PowerPoint® Resources

SKILLS DEVELOPMENT RESOURCES	SECTION REVIEW AND ASSESSMENT	CORRELATIONS
SE Pre-Reading Activity, p. 114 `GENERAL` **OSP** Science Puzzlers, Twisters & Teasers `GENERAL`		**National Science Education Standards** UCP 5; SAI 1, 2; ST 2; LS 2e
CRF Directed Reading A* ■ `BASIC`, B* `SPECIAL NEEDS` **WB** Workbook* `Struggling Readers` **CRF** Vocabulary and Section Summary* ■ `GENERAL` **SE** Reading Strategy Prediction Guide, p. 116 `GENERAL` **SE** Connection to Chemistry Linus Pauling, p. 117 `GENERAL` **TE** Reading Strategy Mnemonics, p. 117 `BASIC` **TE** Inclusion Strategies, p. 117 **TE** Support for English Language Learners, p. 117 **MS** Math Skills for Science A Shortcut for Multiplying Large Numbers* `GENERAL` **SS** Science Skills Science Drawing* `GENERAL`	**SE** Reading Checks, pp. 117, 119 `GENERAL` **TE** Reteaching, p. 118 `BASIC` **TE** Quiz, p. 119 `GENERAL` **TE** Alternative Assessment, p. 119 `GENERAL` **SE** Section Review,* p. 119 ■ `GENERAL` **CRF** Section Quiz* ■ `GENERAL`	UCP 2, 5; SAI 1, 2; ST 1, 2; SPSP 5; HNS 1, 2, 3; LS 1a, 2d, 5a; *Chapter Lab:* UCP 2, 5; SAI 1, 2; HNS 1; LS 1a
CRF Directed Reading A* ■ `BASIC`, B* `SPECIAL NEEDS` **WB** Workbook* `Struggling Readers` **CRF** Vocabulary and Section Summary* ■ `GENERAL` **SE** Reading Strategy Reading Organizer, p. 120 `GENERAL` **SE** Math Practice Code Combinations, p. 123 `GENERAL` **TE** Support for English Language Learners, p. 124 **TE** Inclusion Strategies, p. 125 **SE** Connection to Social Studies Genetic Property, p. 126 `GENERAL` **CRF** Reinforcement Worksheet DNA Mutations* `BASIC` **CRF** Critical Thinking The Perfect Parrot* `ADVANCED`	**SE** Reading Checks, pp. 120, 123, 124, 125, 126 `GENERAL` **TE** Homework, p. 122 `GENERAL` **TE** Homework, p. 125 `GENERAL` **TE** Reteaching, p. 126 `BASIC` **SE** Section Review,* p. 127 ■ `GENERAL` **TE** Quiz, p. 126 `GENERAL` **TE** Alternative Assessment, p. 126 `GENERAL` **CRF** Section Quiz* ■ `GENERAL`	UCP 1, 4, 5; SAI 1, 2; ST 2; SPSP 4, 5; LS 1c, 1e, 1f, 2b, 2c, 2d, 2e, 5b

SCLINKS.
NSTA
www.scilinks.org
Maintained by the **National Science Teachers Association**. See Chapter Enrichment pages that follow for a complete list of topics.

Check out *Current Science* articles and activities by visiting the HRW Web site at **go.hrw.com.** Just type in the keyword **HL5CS06T.**

 **Classroom Videos**
- **Lab Videos** demonstrate the chapter lab.
- **Brain Food Video Quizzes** help students review the chapter material.

 Classroom CD-ROMs
- **Guided Reading Audio CD** (Also in Spanish)
- **Interactive Explorations**
- **Virtual Investigations**
- **Visual Concepts**
- **Science Tutor**

Holt Lab Generator CD-ROM

Search for any lab by topic, standard, difficulty level, or time. Edit any lab to fit your needs, or create your own labs. Use the Lab Materials QuickList software to customize your lab materials list.

Visual Resources

CHAPTER STARTER TRANSPARENCY

BELLRINGER TRANSPARENCIES

TEACHING TRANSPARENCIES

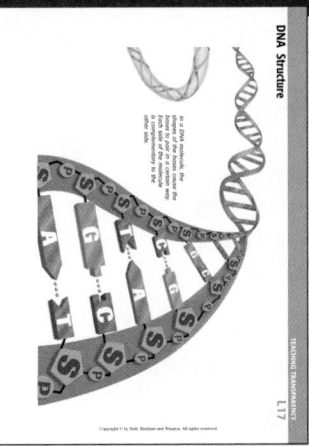

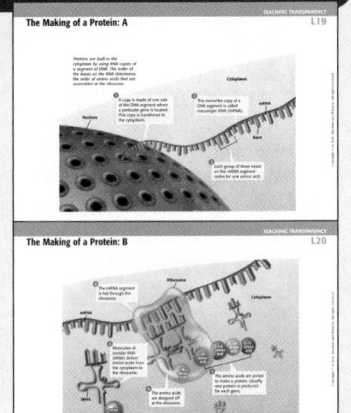

TEACHING TRANSPARENCIES

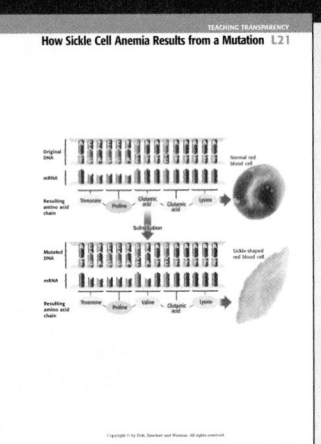

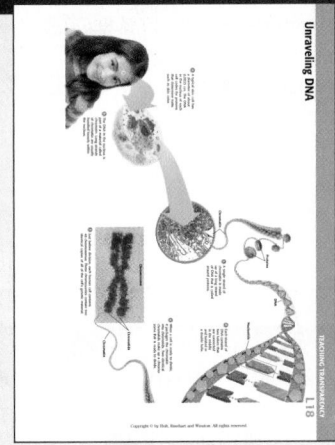

CONCEPT MAPPING TRANSPARENCY

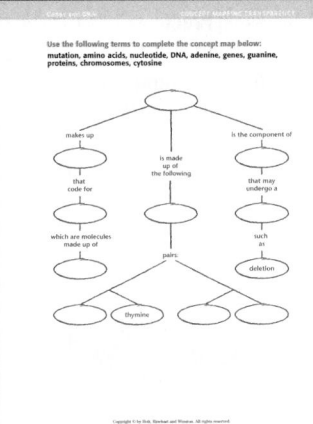

Planning Resources

LESSON PLANS

PARENT LETTER

TEST ITEM LISTING

One-Stop Planner® CD-ROM

This CD-ROM includes all of the resources shown here and the following time-saving tools:

- *Lab Materials QuickList Software*
- *Customizable lesson plans*
- *Holt Calendar Planner*
- *The powerful ExamView® Test Generator*

Meeting Individual Needs

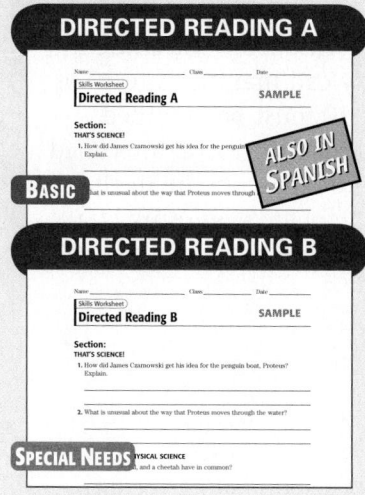

DIRECTED READING A

BASIC

ALSO IN SPANISH

DIRECTED READING B

SPECIAL NEEDS

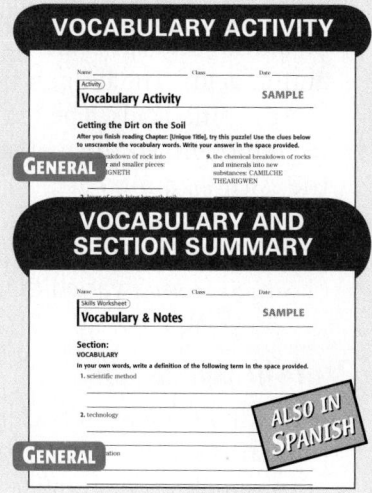

VOCABULARY ACTIVITY

GENERAL

VOCABULARY AND SECTION SUMMARY

GENERAL

ALSO IN SPANISH

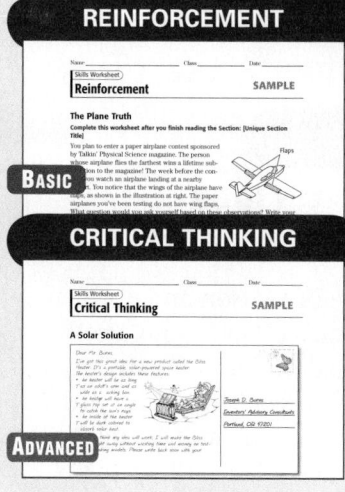

REINFORCEMENT

BASIC

CRITICAL THINKING

ADVANCED

SCILINKS ACTIVITY

GENERAL

SCIENCE PUZZLERS, TWISTERS & TEASERS

GENERAL

Labs and Activities

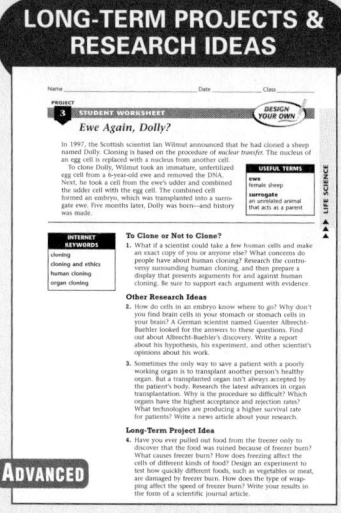

LONG-TERM PROJECTS & RESEARCH IDEAS

ADVANCED

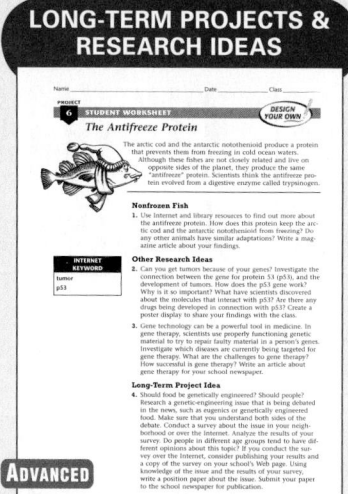

LONG-TERM PROJECTS & RESEARCH IDEAS

ADVANCED

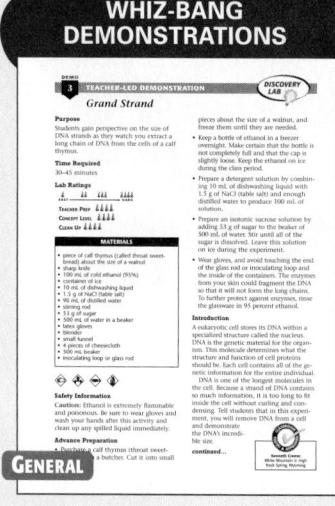

WHIZ-BANG DEMONSTRATIONS

GENERAL

DATASHEETS FOR QUICK LABS

DATASHEETS FOR CHAPTER LABS

DATASHEETS FOR LABBOOK

Review and Assessments

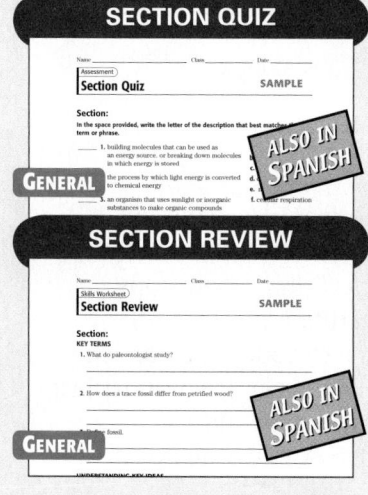

SECTION QUIZ

GENERAL

ALSO IN SPANISH

SECTION REVIEW

GENERAL

ALSO IN SPANISH

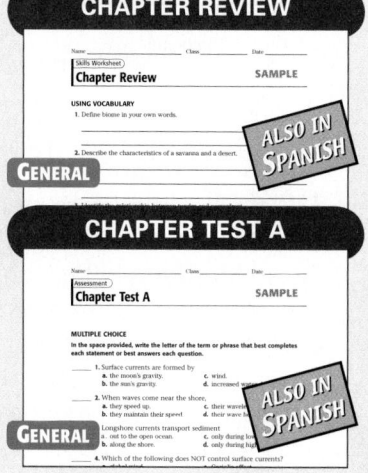

CHAPTER REVIEW

GENERAL

ALSO IN SPANISH

CHAPTER TEST A

GENERAL

ALSO IN SPANISH

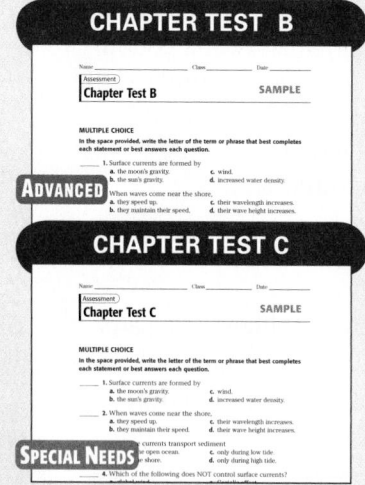

CHAPTER TEST B

ADVANCED

CHAPTER TEST C

SPECIAL NEEDS

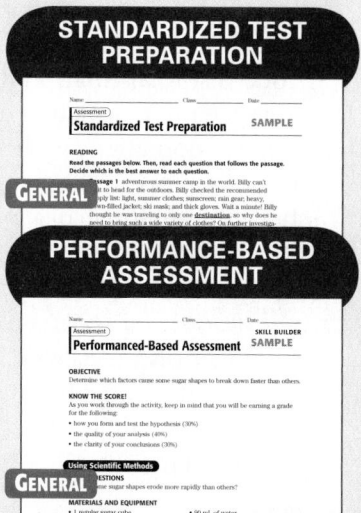

STANDARDIZED TEST PREPARATION

GENERAL

PERFORMANCE-BASED ASSESSMENT

GENERAL

This Chapter Enrichment provides relevant and interesting information to expand and enhance your presentation of the chapter material.

Section 1

What Does DNA Look Like?

Discovering DNA

- In 1869, long before the time of Watson and Crick, a 22-year-old Swiss scientist isolated DNA from a cell nucleus. Unfortunately, he had no idea of its function, much less of its role in inheritance. It was not until 75 years later, in 1944, that an American geneticist named Oswald T. Avery found evidence that DNA is the carrier of genetic information.

Section 2

How DNA Works

Cracking the Genetic Code

- In the 1960s, scientists cracked the genetic code—the translation between codons (sequences of three bases) and amino acids. They have found that the genetic code is similar in all living organisms. If a codon aligns with a particular amino acid in humans, the same codon aligns with the same amino acid in bacteria. This similarity suggests that all life-forms have a common evolutionary ancestor.

Is That a Fact!

- Human DNA consists of about 3 billion base pairs. If you could print a book with all the genetic information carried in just one human cell, it would be 500,000 pages long.

Amino Acids

- All known organisms produce proteins using only 20 amino acids as building blocks (some use a rare 21st amino acid). The human body can manufacture 10 of these amino acids. The other 10 must be obtained from proteins in the diet and for this reason are called the *essential* amino acids. Foods that contain all the essential amino acids at once include eggs, milk, seafood, and meat. However, all amino acids can be obtained from a varied diet.

Protein Synthesis

- It took many years for scientists to determine how protein is synthesized in the cell. The discovery that DNA's nucleotide sequence corresponds to a certain amino acid sequence was a key step in unlocking this mystery. This link was conclusively proven by Charles Yanofsky and Sydney Brenner in 1964.

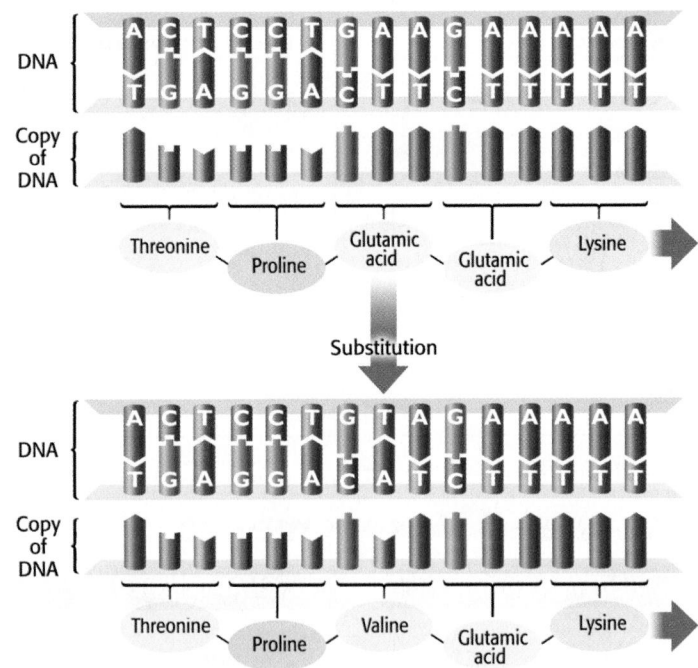

- The genetic sequences used to make proteins can be compared to sentences. Where each three-letter "word" in the genetic "sentence" starts and stops is very important for constructing a protein. For example, suppose the sentence to code for a particular protein read "PAT SAW THE FAT CAT." If you start just one base pair too late, the sentence would read "ATS AWT HEF ATC AT," which is meaningless.

Is That a Fact!

◆ If uncoiled, the DNA in the 46 chromosomes of a human body cell is about 2 m long. Within chromosomes, this DNA is so tightly coiled that if all 46 chromosomes were lined up end to end, they would span less than 0.5 cm.

Genetic Engineering

● Genetically engineered hybrid organisms are often called *chimeras*. The word *chimera* comes from Greek mythology, in which the Chimera was a fire-breathing monster, usually depicted as a composite of a lion, a goat, and a serpent.

● Scientists often disagree about the ethics of genetic engineering and about the safety risks involved. Dr. Maxine Frank Singer was one of the first scientists to warn the National Academy of Science of the potential hazards of genetic engineering. Because of the efforts of Dr. Singer and her colleagues, the National Institute of Health began to develop specific guidelines for genetic research as early as 1976. These guidelines, now regularly amended, continue to regulate the production and use of DNA and genetically engineered organisms.

The Human Genome Project

● The Human Genome Project (HGP) was started in 1990 as an international collaboration of scientists with the goal of mapping the entire sequence of DNA found in humans. In April 2003, in conjunction with the anniversary of the historic publication by Watson and Crick of DNA's molecular structure, the HGP announced that its work was mostly done. The HGP had completed mapping 99% of the human genetic code. Some mystery remained about the area of chromosomes called the *centromere*.

● Many potential benefits are predicted to result from the Human Genome Project, and some benefits have already been realized. Scientists working on the HGP have developed faster methods of determining the sequences within DNA samples. Also, scientists have improved methods of finding and tracking the functions of specific genes within cells. Such advances have made it easier to study the genetics of all kinds of organisms and to find the genetic indicators of specific kinds of cancer and other diseases.

DNA Fingerprints

● DNA fingerprints are frequently used in criminal investigations. The DNA can come from hair, skin cells, blood, or other body fluids left at the crime scene by the perpetrator. Scientists use enzymes to make copies of specific DNA sections from different locations on different chromosomes. The copied fragments are separated by size and other characteristics on a gel, and they are stained to yield a unique set of dark bands on the gel. This set of bands is known as a *DNA fingerprint*. The fingerprint is then compared with the DNA fingerprint of the suspect to help determine innocence or guilt.

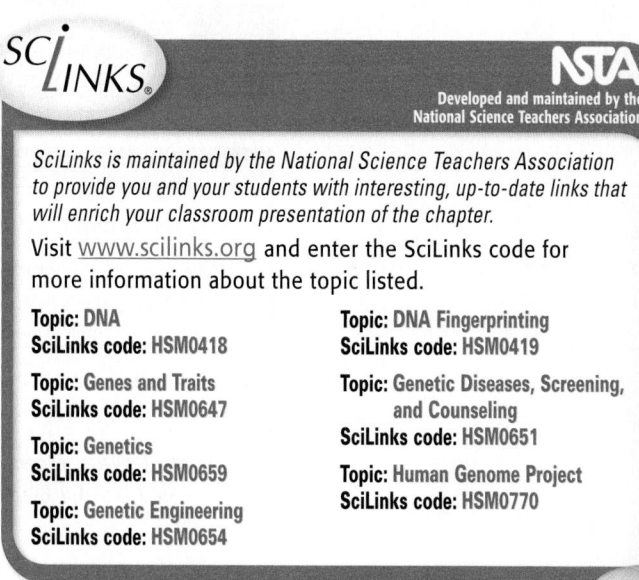

SciLinks is maintained by the National Science Teachers Association to provide you and your students with interesting, up-to-date links that will enrich your classroom presentation of the chapter.

Visit www.scilinks.org and enter the SciLinks code for more information about the topic listed.

Topic: DNA
SciLinks code: HSM0418

Topic: Genes and Traits
SciLinks code: HSM0647

Topic: Genetics
SciLinks code: HSM0659

Topic: Genetic Engineering
SciLinks code: HSM0654

Topic: DNA Fingerprinting
SciLinks code: HSM0419

Topic: Genetic Diseases, Screening, and Counseling
SciLinks code: HSM0651

Topic: Human Genome Project
SciLinks code: HSM0770

Overview

Tell students that this chapter is about DNA—the substance that makes up genes—and about how DNA works within cells to direct the growth and functioning of every organism.

Assessing Prior Knowledge

Students should be familiar with the following topics:

• cell structure

• mitosis and meiosis

• basic rules of heredity

• chromosomes

Identifying Misconceptions

The roles of DNA, RNA, and proteins in cells are very complex, and many puzzles remain. Students may tend to simplify their concept of the "rules" as they learn them. Students may remain unconvinced of the role of chance and probability in heredity. Also, students may have difficulty linking their knowledge of the functions of DNA at the cellular level to what they have learned and will learn about the functioning of tissues and organs within an entire organism.

Genes and DNA

The Big Idea DNA is the genetic material of living organisms and is located in the chromosomes of each cell.

About the Photo ↗

These adult mice have no hair—not because their hair was shaved off but because these mice do not grow hair. In cells of these mice, the genes that normally cause hair to grow are not working. The genes were "turned off" by scientists who have learned to control the function of some genes. Scientists changed the genes of these mice to research medical problems such as cancer.

PRE-READING ACTIVITY

Graphic Organizer

Concept Map Before you read the chapter, create the graphic organizer entitled "Concept Map" described in the **Study Skills** section of the Appendix. As you read the chapter, fill in the concept map with details about DNA.

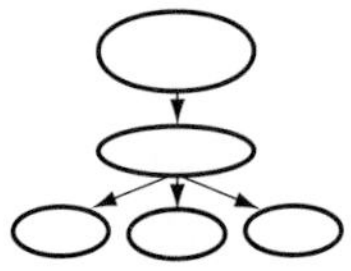

Standards Correlations

National Science Education Standards

The following codes indicate the National Science Education Standards that correlate to this chapter. The full text of the standards is at the front of the book.

Chapter Opener
UCP 5; SAI 1, 2; ST 2; LS 2e

Section 1 What Does DNA Look Like?
UCP 2, 5; SAI 1, 2; ST 1, 2; SPSP 5; HNS 1, 2, 3;
LS 1a, 2d, 5a

Section 2 How DNA Works
UCP 1, 4, 5; SAI 1, 2; ST 2; SPSP 4, 5; LS 1c, 1e, 1f, 2b, 2c, 2d, 2e, 5b

Chapter Lab
UCP 2, 5; SAI 1, 2; HNS 1; LS 1a

Chapter Review
UCP 1, 2, 5; SAI 1, 2; ST 2; SPSP 4; HNS 2, 3; LS 1a, 1c, 1e, 1f, 2c, 2d, 2e, 5a, 5b

Science In Action
UCP 1, 2, 5; ST 2; SPSP 4 ,5; HNS 1, 2, 3; LS 1f

START-UP **ACTIVITY**

MATERIALS

FOR EACH GROUP
- magnifying lens
- paper, tracing (1 sheet)
- paper, white (1 sheet for each student)
- pencil or piece of charcoal
- tape, transparent

Safety Caution: Remind students to review all safety cautions and icons before beginning this lab activity. Charcoal is nontoxic, but it can stain clothes.

Teacher's Notes: The loop pattern is found in about 65% of the population, the whorl in about 30%, and the arch in about 5%.

Answers

1. The number of fingerprint types will vary for each class. No two students should have the same fingerprint (those of identical twins may be similar but still unique). Accept any reasonable explanation that incorporates variation in inherited traits among populations.

START-UP **ACTIVITY**

Fingerprint Your Friends

One way to identify people is by taking their fingerprints. Does it really work? Are everyone's fingerprints unique? Try this activity to find out.

Procedure

1. Rub the tip of a **pencil** back and forth across a **piece of tracing paper.** Make a large, dark mark.
2. Rub the tip of one of your fingers on the pencil mark. Then place a small **piece of transparent tape** over the darkened area on your finger.
3. Remove the tape, and stick it on **a piece of white paper.** Repeat steps 1–3 for the rest of your fingers.
4. Look at the fingerprints with a **magnifying lens.** What patterns do you see? Is the pattern the same on every finger?

Analysis

1. Compare your fingerprints with those of your classmates. Do any two people in your class have the same prints? Try to explain your findings.

Chapter Starter Transparency
Use this transparency to help students begin thinking about genes and DNA.

CHAPTER RESOURCES

Technology

Transparencies
- Chapter Starter Transparency

READING **SKILLS**

Student Edition on CD-ROM

Guided Reading Audio CD
- English or Spanish

Classroom Videos
- Brain Food Video Quiz

Workbooks

Science Puzzlers, Twisters & Teasers
- Genes and DNA GENERAL

SECTION
1

Focus

Overview

This section introduces students to the structure and function of DNA and to the process of DNA replication.

 Bellringer

To test prior knowledge, have students answer the following questions:

1. Give an example of the difference between traits and characteristics. (Sample answer: Eye color is a characteristic, while having blue eyes is a trait.)

2. Where are genes found in cells? (in chromosomes; in cells that have nuclei, chromosomes are within the nucleus)

Motivate

ACTIVITY ———— GENERAL

Modeling Code Create a code by pairing each letter of the alphabet with a numeral. For example, the numeral 1 could represent the letter *a*. Have students encode a brief message. Then, have students exchange and decode the message. Explain that a code is simply another way to represent information and that there are many types of codes. The genetic code is based on sequences of the four nucleotide bases of DNA. **English Language**
LS Logical **Learners**

What You Will Learn

● List three important events that led to understanding the structure of DNA.
● Describe the basic structure of a DNA molecule.
● Explain how DNA molecules can be copied.

Vocabulary
DNA
nucleotide

READING STRATEGY

Prediction Guide Before reading this section, write the title of each heading in this section. Next, under each heading, write what you think you will learn.

DNA **d**eoxyribo**n**ucleic **a**cid, a molecule that is present in all living cells and that contains the information that determines the traits that a living thing inherits and needs to live

nucleotide in a nucleic-acid chain, a subunit that consists of a sugar, a phosphate, and a nitrogenous base

What Does DNA Look Like?

For many years, the structure of a DNA molecule was a puzzle to scientists. In the 1950s, two scientists deduced the structure while experimenting with chemical models. They later won a Nobel Prize for helping solve this puzzle!

Inherited characteristics are determined by genes, and genes are passed from one generation to the next. Genes are parts of chromosomes, which are structures in the nucleus of most cells. Chromosomes are made of protein and DNA. **DNA** stands for *deoxyribonucleic acid* (dee AHKS ee RIE boh noo KLEE ik AS id). DNA is the genetic material—the material that determines inherited characteristics. But what does DNA look like?

The Pieces of the Puzzle

Scientists knew that the material that makes up genes must be able to do two things. First, it must be able to give instructions for building and maintaining cells. Second, it must be able to be copied each time a cell divides, so that each cell contains identical genes. Scientists thought that these things could be done only by complex molecules, such as proteins. They were surprised to learn how much the DNA molecule could do.

Nucleotides: The Subunits of DNA

DNA is made of subunits called nucleotides. A **nucleotide** consists of a sugar, a phosphate, and a base. The nucleotides are identical except for the base. The four bases are *adenine, thymine, guanine,* and *cytosine.* Each base has a different shape. Scientists often refer to a base by the first letter of the base, *A, T, G,* and *C.* **Figure 1** shows models of the four nucleotides.

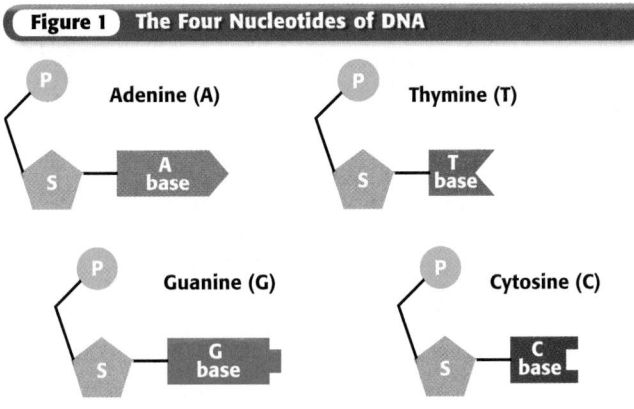

Figure 1 The Four Nucleotides of DNA

Adenine (A)
Thymine (T)
Guanine (G)
Cytosine (C)

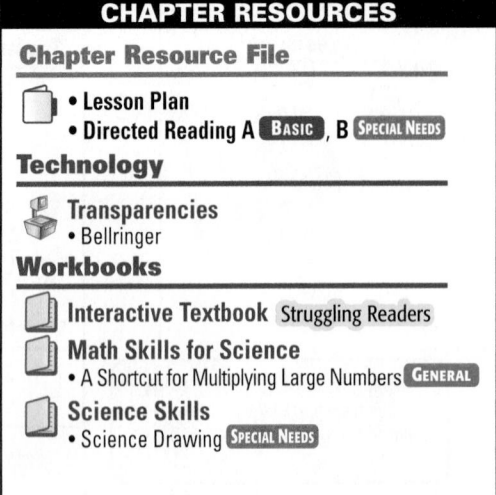

CHAPTER RESOURCES

Chapter Resource File

📁 • Lesson Plan
• Directed Reading A **BASIC**, B **SPECIAL NEEDS**

Technology

💻 **Transparencies**
• Bellringer

Workbooks

📓 **Interactive Textbook** Struggling Readers

📓 **Math Skills for Science**
• A Shortcut for Multiplying Large Numbers **GENERAL**

📓 **Science Skills**
• Science Drawing **SPECIAL NEEDS**

Chargaff's Rules

In the 1950s, a biochemist named Erwin Chargaff found that the amount of adenine in DNA always equals the amount of thymine. And he found that the amount of guanine always equals the amount of cytosine. His findings are known as *Chargaff's rules*. At the time of his discovery, no one knew the importance of these findings. But Chargaff's rules later helped scientists understand the structure of DNA.

✓ **Reading Check** Summarize Chargaff's rules. (*See the Appendix for answers to Reading Checks.*)

Franklin's Discovery

More clues about the structure of DNA came from scientists in Britain. There, chemist Rosalind Franklin, shown in **Figure 2,** was able to make images of DNA molecules. She used a process known as *X-ray diffraction* to make these images. In this process, X rays are aimed at the DNA molecule. When an X ray hits a part of the molecule, the ray bounces off. The pattern made by the bouncing rays is captured on film. Franklin's images suggested that DNA has a spiral shape.

Watson and Crick's Model

At about the same time, two other scientists were also trying to solve the mystery of DNA's structure. They were James Watson and Francis Crick, shown in **Figure 3.** After seeing Franklin's X-ray images, Watson and Crick concluded that DNA must look like a long, twisted ladder. They were then able to build a model of DNA by using simple materials from their laboratory. Their model perfectly fit with both Chargaff's and Franklin's findings. The model eventually helped explain how DNA is copied and how it functions in the cell.

CONNECTION TO Chemistry

WRITING SKILL **Linus Pauling** Many scientists contributed to the discovery of DNA's structure. In fact, some scientists competed to be the first to make the discovery. One of these competitors was a chemist named Linus Pauling. Research and write a paragraph about how Pauling's work helped Watson and Crick.

Figure 2 *Rosalind Franklin used X-ray diffraction to make images of DNA that helped reveal the structure of DNA.*

Figure 3 *This photo shows James Watson (left) and Francis Crick (right) with their model of DNA.*

Teach

📖 READING STRATEGY — BASIC

Mnemonics Have students create a mnemonic device that will remind them of the names of the bases and the way the bases form pairs. Examples such as "**A**toms are **T**iny" or "**A**dam is **T**errific" might help remind students that **a**denine pairs with **t**hymine. "**C**athy is **G**reat" might remind them that **c**ytosine pairs with **g**uanine.
LS Verbal/Logical

Answer to Reading Check

Guanine and cytosine are always found in DNA in equal amounts, as are adenine and thymine.

⊙ INCLUSION Strategies

- *Learning Disabled*
- *Attention Deficit Disorder*
- *Behavior Control Issues*

Give students a chance to move around while they learn. Have students group themselves by eye color: all blues together, etc. Then, have students within each eye color group line up from lightest shade to darkest shade. Assign a spokesman within each group to explain how they decided the order for their line up. Also, ask each team to tell the number of unique eye colors within the team.
LS Kinesthetic
English Language Learners

SUPPORT FOR

English Language Learners

Visualization To check comprehension of Chargaff's rules and Franklin's discovery, ask students how they would create a visual of each without actual words. (Chargaff's rules: A = T, C = G; Franklin's discovery: diagram showing rays bouncing off a DNA molecule) Invite volunteers to write or draw the visuals on the board. Point out any errors in content or spelling, and have students make corrections. Then, have students copy the visuals into their science journals.
LS Visual/Verbal

Answer to Connection to Chemistry

Linus Pauling was an innovator in the use of models to deduce chemical behavior. Whereas some scientists belittled the practice of "playing" with chemical models, Pauling inspired other scientists, such as Watson and Crick, to try this strategy. Watson and Crick's deduction of DNA's ladder structure was partly brought about by manipulating models of nucleotides.

Group ACTiViTY — GENERAL

A Place in History Have students imagine that they have just discovered the structure of DNA and must present their findings to a group of scientists. Have small groups of students use a model of DNA, a poster, or another visual aid to briefly describe the structure of DNA to their classmates. **LS** Verbal

DNA's Complementary Strands

To help students understand how the term *complementary* relates to the structure of DNA, point out that the term means "completing." Using **Figure 4** and **Figure 5,** explain that complementary base pairs join to *complete* each rung on the spiral-staircase structure of DNA. Then, point out that complementary strands of DNA join to complete one DNA molecule.

LS Visual/Verbal

Quiz — GENERAL

1. When is DNA copied? (every time a cell divides)

2. Name the four types of nucleotides. (adenine, thymine, guanine, and cytosine)

Alternative Assessment — GENERAL

 **Custom Code** Have students create an alternative code that functions like DNA in the following ways:

• The code is based on four letters or symbols.

• Coded information can be split up and then reassembled.

Have students draw and explain their coding system. **LS** Logical

Making a Model of DNA

1. Gather assorted simple materials that you could use to build a basic model of DNA. You might use **clay, string, toothpicks, paper, tape, plastic foam,** or **pieces of food.**

2. Work with a partner or a small team to build your model. Use your book and other resources to check the details of your model.

3. Show your model to your classmates. Give your classmates feedback about the scientific aspects of their models.

DNA's Double Structure

The shape of DNA is shown in **Figure 4.** As you can see, a strand of DNA looks like a twisted ladder. This shape is known as a *double helix* (DUB uhl HEE liks). The two sides of the ladder are made of alternating sugar parts and phosphate parts. The rungs of the ladder are made of a pair of bases. Adenine on one side of a rung always pairs with thymine on the other side. Guanine always pairs with cytosine.

Notice how the double helix structure matches Chargaff's observations. When Chargaff separated the parts of a sample of DNA, he found that the matching bases were always present in equal amounts. To model how the bases pair, Watson and Crick tried to match Chargaff's observations. They also used information from chemists about the size and shape of each of the nucleotides. As it turned out, the width of the DNA ladder matches the combined width of the matching bases. Only the correct pairs of bases fit within the ladder's width.

Making Copies of DNA

The pairing of bases allows the cell to *replicate*, or make copies of, DNA. Each base always bonds with only one other base. Thus, pairs of bases are *complementary* to each other, and both sides of a DNA molecule are complementary. For example, the sequence CGAC will bond to the sequence GCTG.

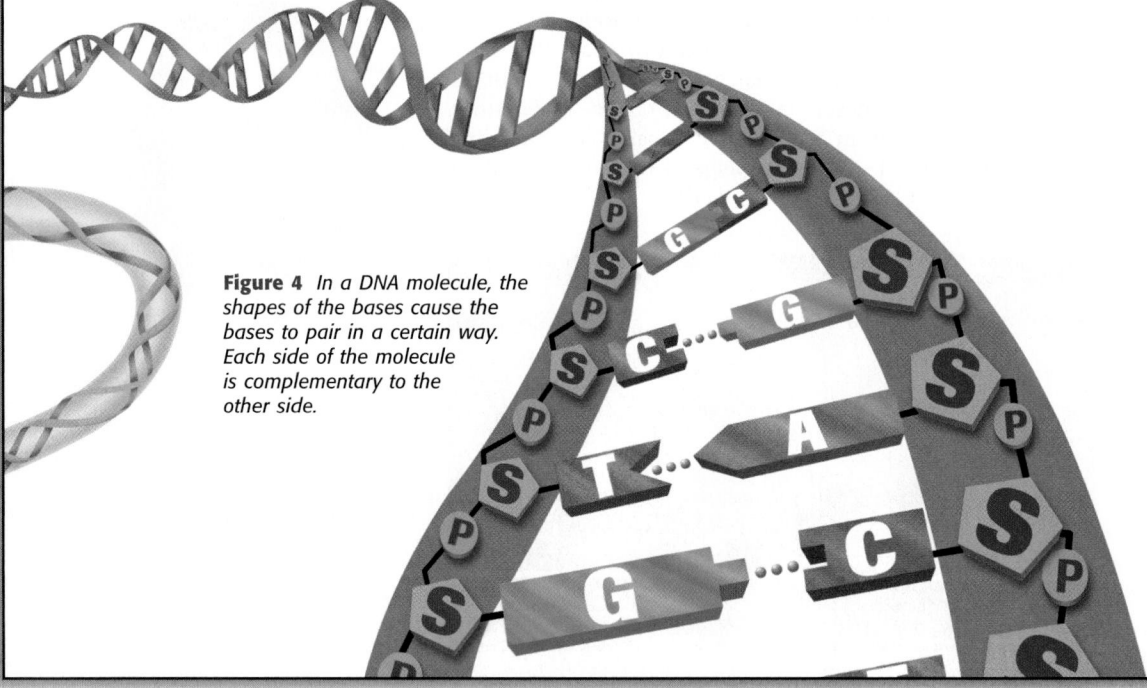

Figure 4 *In a DNA molecule, the shapes of the bases cause the bases to pair in a certain way. Each side of the molecule is complementary to the other side.*

MATERIALS

FOR EACH GROUP

• variety of materials, such as clay, string, toothpicks, paper, tape, plastic foam, beads or buttons and pipe cleaners or wire.

• food or candy items could be another option

Teacher's Note: Display student models within the school. Have students reevaluate or improve upon them later.

Safety Caution: Advise students to keep the area around them uncluttered. Students should exercise caution with sharp objects. Any food items used should not be eaten and should be disposed of.

Answers

2. Student models should resemble **Figure 4** in basic structure but may vary in size, color, and construction.

3. Students should suggest ways to make each model more accurate.

How Copies Are Made

During replication, as shown in **Figure 5,** a DNA molecule is split down the middle, where the bases meet. The bases on each side of the molecule are used as a pattern for a new strand. As the bases on the original molecule are exposed, complementary nucleotides are added to each side of the ladder. Two DNA molecules are formed. Half of each of the molecules is old DNA, and half is new DNA.

When Copies Are Made

DNA is copied every time a cell divides. Each new cell gets a complete copy of all the DNA. The job of unwinding, copying, and re-winding the DNA is done by proteins within the cell. So, DNA is usually found with several kinds of proteins. Other proteins help with the process of carrying out the instructions written in the code of the DNA.

✓ **Reading Check** How often is DNA copied?

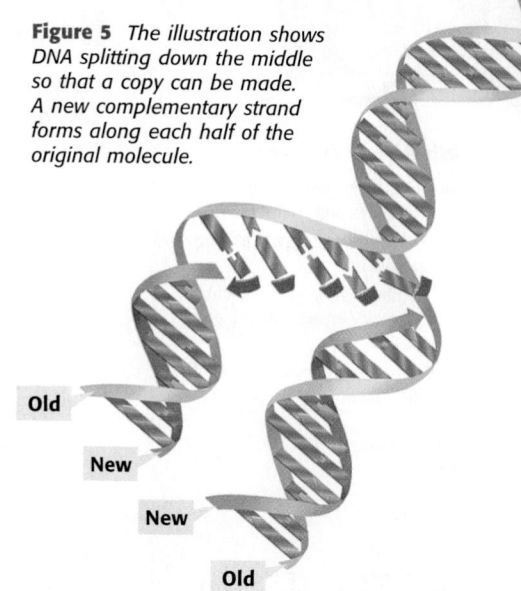

Figure 5 *The illustration shows DNA splitting down the middle so that a copy can be made. A new complementary strand forms along each half of the original molecule.*

Old

New

New

Old

Answers to Section Review

1. Sample answer: DNA is the material that makes up genes and is found in all cells.

2. Sample answer: A nucleotide is a subunit of a DNA molecule and consists of a sugar, a phosphate, and a base; there are four kinds of bases and thus four kinds of nucleotides.

3. Sample answers: Scientists thought only complex materials such as proteins could make up genes; Erwin Chargaff discovered the rules of nucleotide base pairing; Rosalind Franklin made images of DNA molecules; Watson and Crick made a correct model of DNA's structure.

4. c

5. 20% guanine, because it should be equal to the amount of cytosine; 30% adenine, because the remaining 60% of the DNA should be made up of equal amounts of adenine and thymine

6. Sample answer: DNA is found in the cells of all organisms.

7. GAATCCGAATGGT

8. DNA copies are made by splitting the molecule down the middle and then adding new nucleotides to each side. (Students' drawings should resemble **Figure 5.**)

SECTION Review

Summary

- DNA is the material that makes up genes. It carries coded information that is copied in each new cell.

- The DNA molecule looks like a twisted ladder. The two halves are long strings of nucleotides. The rungs are complementary pairs of bases.

- Because each base has a complementary base, DNA can be replicated accurately.

Using Key Terms

1. Use the term *DNA* in a sentence.

2. In your own words, write a definition for the term *nucleotide*.

Understanding Key Ideas

3. List three important events that led to understanding the structure of DNA.

4. Which of the following is NOT part of a nucleotide?
   a. base
   b. sugar
   c. fat
   d. phosphate

Math Skills

5. If a sample of DNA contained 20% cytosine, what percentage of guanine would be in this sample? What percentage of adenine would be in the sample? Explain.

Critical Thinking

6. **Making Inferences** Explain what is meant by the statement "DNA unites all organisms."

7. **Applying Concepts** What would the complementary strand of DNA be for the sequence of bases below?

   C T T A G G C T T A C C A

8. **Analyzing Processes** How are copies of DNA made? Draw a picture as part of your answer.

For a variety of links related to this chapter, go to www.scilinks.org

Topic: DNA; Genes and Traits
SciLinks code: HSM0418; HSM0647

Answer to Reading Check

every time a cell divides

CHAPTER RESOURCES

Chapter Resource File

- Section Quiz **GENERAL**
- Section Review **GENERAL**
- Vocabulary and Section Summary **GENERAL**
- SciLinks Activity **GENERAL**
- Datasheet for Quick Lab

Technology

Transparencies
- L17 DNA Structure

Focus

Overview

This section shows how DNA is a part of chromosomes, how DNA is used as a template for making proteins, and how errors in DNA can lead to mutations and genetic disorders.

 Bellringer

Have students unscramble the following words and use them both in one sentence:

tpsoneir (proteins)

neesg (genes)

(Sample answer: Genes contain instructions for making proteins.)

Motivate

Demonstration — GENERAL

A Tight Fit To illustrate the way that DNA is *supercoiled* within chromosomes and cells, hold up a long rubber band or thick piece of string. Begin to twist each end in opposite directions until coils form. Continue twisting until the band is highly compacted. Then, challenge students to fit 2 m of fine thread into a thimble or an empty gelatin capsule. **English Language Learners**

LS Kinesthetic

Answer to Reading Check

a string of nucleotides that give the cell information about how to make a specific trait

---

What You Will Learn

● Explain the relationship between DNA, genes, and proteins.
● Outline the basic steps in making a protein.
● Describe three types of mutations, and provide an example of a gene mutation.
● Describe two examples of uses of genetic knowledge.

Vocabulary
RNA
ribosome
mutation

READING STRATEGY

Reading Organizer As you read this section, make a flowchart of the steps of how DNA codes for proteins.

How DNA Works

Almost every cell in your body contains about 2 m of DNA. How does all of the DNA fit in a cell? And how does the DNA hold a code that affects your traits?

DNA is found in the cells of all organisms, including bacteria, mosquitoes, and humans. Each organism has a unique set of DNA. But DNA functions the same way in all organisms.

Unraveling DNA

DNA is often wound around proteins, coiled into strands, and then bundled up even more. In a cell that lacks a nucleus, each strand of DNA forms a loose loop within the cell. In a cell that has a nucleus, the strands of DNA and proteins are bundled into chromosomes, as shown in **Figure 1.**

The structure of DNA allows DNA to hold information. The order of the bases on one side of the molecule is a code that carries information. A *gene* consists of a string of nucleotides that give the cell information about how to make a specific trait. There is an enormous amount of DNA, so there can be a large variety of genes.

✓ **Reading Check** What makes up a gene? (*See the Appendix for answers to Reading Checks.*)

Figure 1 Unraveling DNA

a A typical skin cell has a diameter of about 0.0025 cm. The DNA in the nucleus of each cell codes for proteins that determine traits such as skin color.

b The DNA in the nucleus is part of a material called *chromatin*. Long strands of chromatin are usually bundled loosely within the nucleus.

CHAPTER RESOURCES

Chapter Resource File

• Lesson Plan
• Directed Reading A **BASIC**
• Directed Reading B **SPECIAL NEEDS**

Technology

Transparencies
• Bellringer
• L18 Unraveling DNA

Workbooks

Interactive Textbook **Struggling Readers**

MISCONCEPTION ALERT

DNA from the Dead Can ancient DNA be used to produce dinosaurs? In some science fiction, scientists make dinosaurs by combining fragments of ancient DNA with DNA from modern organisms. In reality, less-ancient fragments of DNA have indeed been found. However, a fragment of DNA is not enough information to make an entire organism. And identifying the owner of a given DNA fragment is difficult.

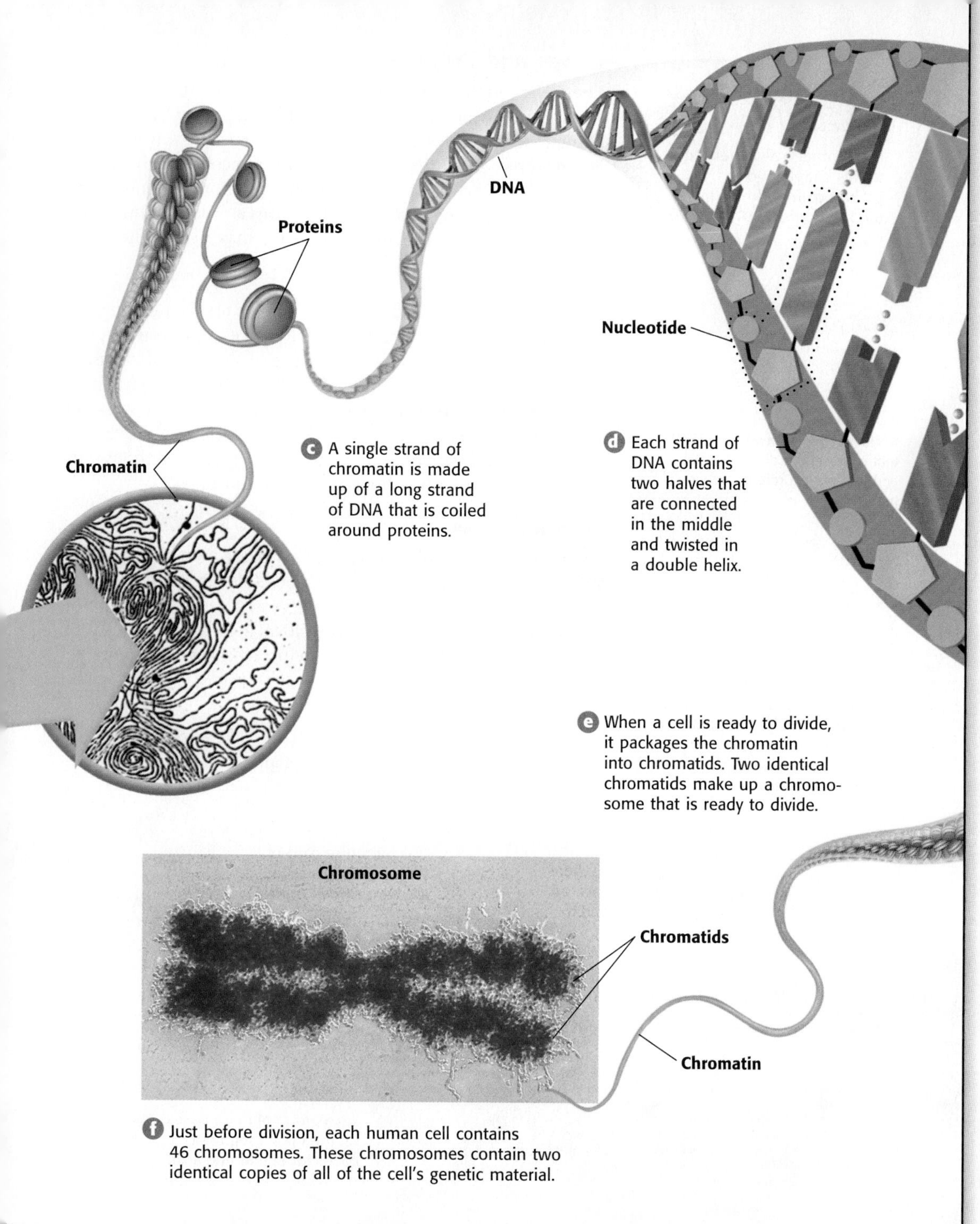

DNA

Proteins

Chromatin

Nucleotide

c A single strand of chromatin is made up of a long strand of DNA that is coiled around proteins.

d Each strand of DNA contains two halves that are connected in the middle and twisted in a double helix.

e When a cell is ready to divide, it packages the chromatin into chromatids. Two identical chromatids make up a chromosome that is ready to divide.

Chromosome

Chromatids

Chromatin

f Just before division, each human cell contains 46 chromosomes. These chromosomes contain two identical copies of all of the cell's genetic material.

Teach

Using the Figure — BASIC

Unraveling DNA Have students carefully study **Figure 1.** Remind them that each chromosome is a pair of chromatids, and each chromatid is one long strand of DNA. This DNA strand is usually somewhat wound up around proteins in the form of chromatin. The chromatin may be tightly bundled (and visible) or loose (and not visible) within the nucleus. Most of the time, the chromatin is loose. Ask students the following questions:

• Where is the DNA in your cells? (in the nucleus)

• How does so much DNA fit into the nucleus? (It is coiled up tightly around proteins.)

• What is the name for strands of DNA wound around proteins? (chromatin)

• When do chromosomes become visible in cells? (when the cell is about to divide)

• What are chromatids? (two identical copies of a chromosome that is about to divide)

LS Visual/Auditory

BRAIN FOOD

Hereditary Hearing
Researchers are trying to find out if a gene is responsible for "perfect pitch," the ability to determine any musical note upon hearing it. It is a rare ability—possessed by one in every 2,000 people—found most often among musicians. People with perfect pitch can easily tell the musical note of a dial tone, the hum of a refrigerator, or of any sound they hear. The researchers think that people with perfect pitch may inherit the ability, but an early education in music may also be necessary.

WEIRD SCIENCE

In 2003, the Human Genome Project had successfully mapped 99% of the 3 billion base pairs that make up a set of human DNA. But the project has raised new questions as well. For example, only about 3% of those base pairs are used in making proteins; the other 97% are regulatory sequences, nonfunctioning genes, and sequences with no known function.

Additionally, scientists originally expected to find over 50,000 human genes because human cells produce at least that many proteins. Instead, latest estimates indicate that there are about 25,000 human genes, and many genes code for multiple proteins. In this and other ways, human genes appear to be unique among organisms.

Proteins' Roles
Have the students pair up. Then, have each pair of students select an important human protein to research. Suggest proteins such as insulin, hemoglobin, dopamine, somatostatin, erythropoetin (EPO), Alpha-1 antitrypsin (AAT), and Factor V (blood-clotting protein). Tell students to summarize the role the protein plays in the human body and to find out a disease that is caused by a mutation in the gene that codes for this protein. Have each pair of students present their findings on small placards that can be displayed in the classroom or school. **LS** Logical/Verbal

Group ACTIVITY — **GENERAL**

Skit Have groups of students write and perform a short skit to demonstrate the formation of a protein. For example, students could play the roles of a ribosome, an amino acid, a transfer RNA, and a DNA copy.
LS Kinesthetic/ Interpersonal   English Language Learners

INTERNET ACTIVITY
For another activity related to this chapter, go to **go.hrw.com** and type in the keyword **HL5DNAW.**

RNA ribonucleic acid, a molecule that is present in all living cells and that plays a role in protein production

Figure 2 *Proteins are built in the cytoplasm by using RNA copies of a segment of DNA. The order of the bases on the RNA determines the order of amino acids that are assembled at the ribosome.*

Genes and Proteins

The DNA code is read like a book—from one end to the other and in one direction. The bases form the alphabet of the code. Groups of three bases are the codes for specific amino acids. For example, the three bases CCA form the code for the amino acid proline. The bases AGC form the code for the amino acid serine. A long string of amino acids forms a protein. Thus, each gene is usually a set of instructions for making a protein.

Proteins and Traits

How are proteins related to traits? Proteins are found throughout cells and cause most of the differences that you can see among organisms. Proteins act as chemical triggers and messengers for many of the processes within cells. Proteins help determine how tall you grow, what colors you can see, and whether your hair is curly or straight. Proteins exist in an almost limitless variety. A single organism may have thousands of genes that code for thousands of proteins.

Help from RNA

Another type of molecule that helps make proteins is called **RNA,** or *ribonucleic acid* (RIE boh noo KLEE ik AS id). RNA is so similar to DNA that RNA can serve as a temporary copy of a DNA sequence. Several forms of RNA help in the process of changing the DNA code into proteins, as shown in **Figure 2.**

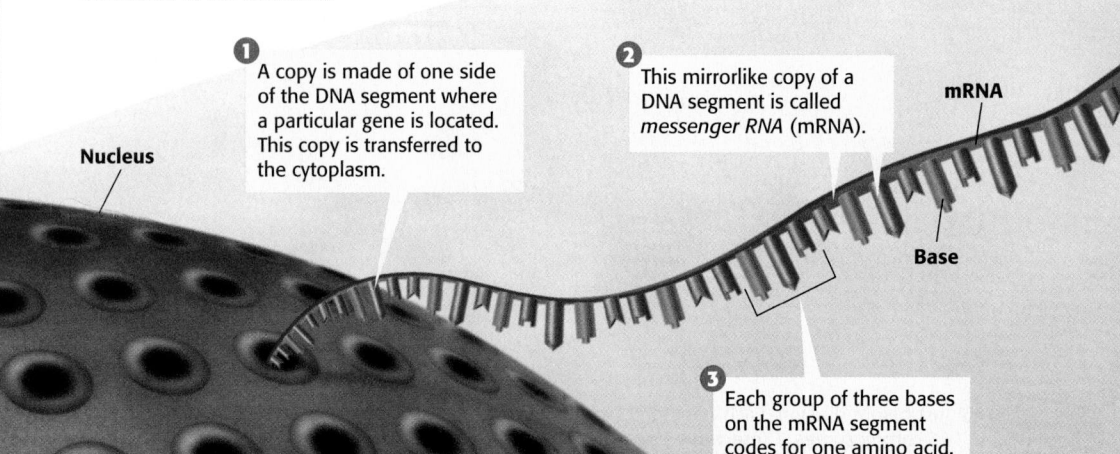

Cytoplasm

1 A copy is made of one side of the DNA segment where a particular gene is located. This copy is transferred to the cytoplasm.

Nucleus

2 This mirrorlike copy of a DNA segment is called *messenger RNA* (mRNA).

mRNA

Base

3 Each group of three bases on the mRNA segment codes for one amino acid.

Homework ——————— **GENERAL**

Research Have students collect information on the use of amino acids to gain muscle. Suggest that they look at ads for amino acid supplements in health-food or fitness magazines or at labels of amino acid powdered drinks at the supermarket. Use these materials to discuss issues such as the expense of such supplements and how they might be used by the body. Discuss how amino acids might be acquired in a balanced diet. **LS** Logical

SCIENCE HUMOR

Q: What happens when an amateur-tein gets paid?

A: It becomes a pro-tein.

The Making of a Protein

The first step in making a protein is to copy one side of the segment of DNA containing a gene. A mirrorlike copy of the DNA segment is made out of RNA. This copy of the DNA segment is called *messenger RNA* (mRNA). It moves out of the nucleus and into the cytoplasm of the cell.

In the cytoplasm, the messenger RNA is fed through a protein assembly line. The "factory" that runs this assembly line is known as a ribosome. A **ribosome** is a cell organelle composed of RNA and protein. The messenger RNA is fed through the ribosome three bases at a time. Then, molecules of *transfer RNA* (tRNA) translate the RNA message. Each transfer RNA molecule picks up a specific amino acid from the cytoplasm. Inside the ribosome, bases on the transfer RNA match up with bases on the messenger RNA like pieces of a puzzle. The transfer RNA molecules then release their amino acids. The amino acids become linked in a growing chain. As the entire segment of messenger RNA passes through the ribosome, the growing chain of amino acids folds up into a new protein molecule.

Reading Check What do the transfer RNA molecules transfer?

Math Practice

Code Combinations

A given sequence of three bases codes for one amino acid. For example, AGT is one possible sequence. How many different sequences of the four DNA base types are possible? (Hint: Make a list.)

ribosome a cell organelle composed of RNA and protein; the site of protein synthesis

CONNECTION ACTIVITY
Math ———— GENERAL

Redundant Code Mathematics has a lot to do with how DNA codes for amino acids. Each combination of three nucleotides that codes for one amino acid is called a *codon*. Yet cells use only 20 different amino acids to build proteins. Thus, most amino acids have several, redundant corresponding codons. This redundancy is another reason that mutations in genes do not always result in changes in proteins. To physically model the possible base combinations that make up codons, organize the class into small groups. Give each group four pieces of paper, with one of the following four letters printed on each piece: *A, T, C,* or *G*. Ask students to come up with as many different three-letter "words" as possible by using the four different bases. (There are 4^3, or 64, possible three-letter "words"—or codons. For example, the four possible combinations that would start with the bases AA are AAA, AAT, AAG, and AAC.) Check that students realize that the order of letters in each combination also matters. For example, *ATA* is not the same "word" as *AAT*. **LS Kinesthetic/Logical**

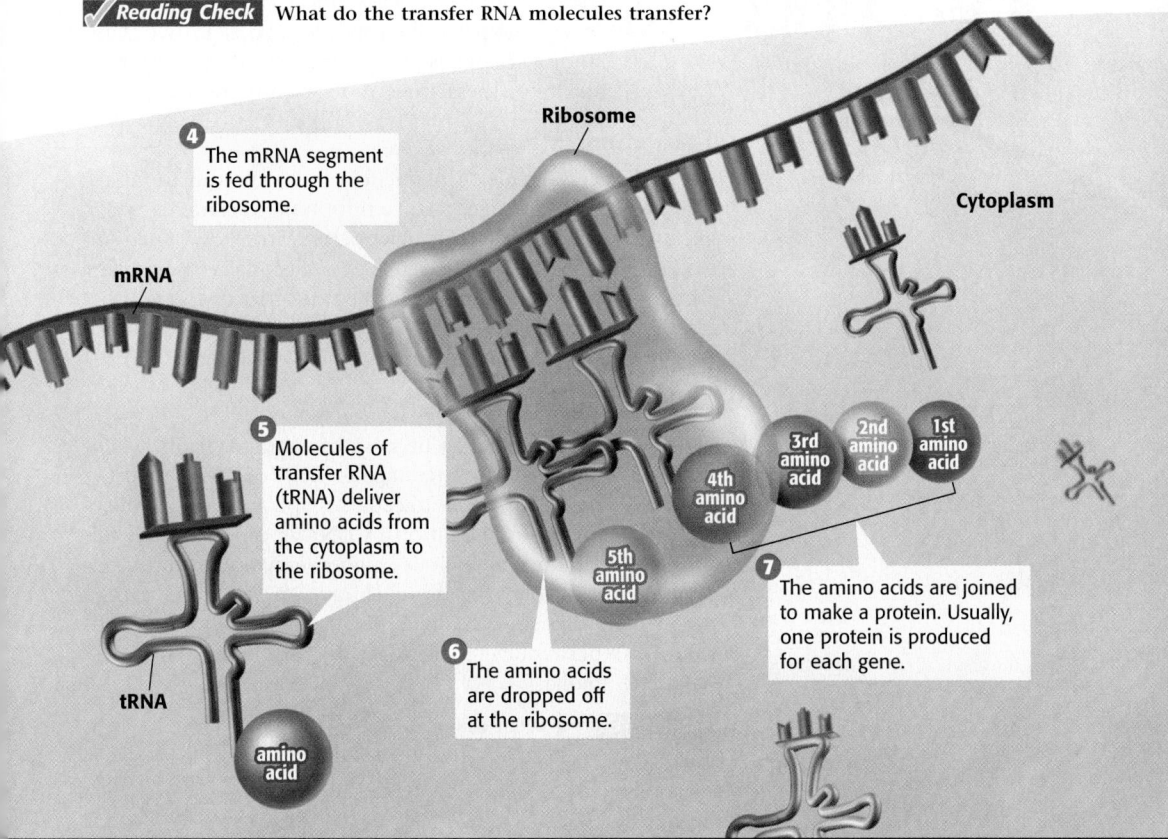

4 The mRNA segment is fed through the ribosome.

Ribosome

Cytoplasm

mRNA

5 Molecules of transfer RNA (tRNA) deliver amino acids from the cytoplasm to the ribosome.

tRNA

amino acid

4th amino acid

5th amino acid

3rd amino acid · 2nd amino acid · 1st amino acid

6 The amino acids are dropped off at the ribosome.

7 The amino acids are joined to make a protein. Usually, one protein is produced for each gene.

WEIRD SCIENCE

There is a gene located on the X chromosome that causes thick hair to grow on the upper body and face, including the ears, nose, cheeks, forehead, and even eyelids of people who have the gene. This condition is sometimes called *werewolf syndrome* because people who have the condition resemble fictional werewolves. This condition affects only appearance, however, not behavior.

CHAPTER RESOURCES

Technology

Transparencies
• L19 The Making of a Protein: A
• L20 The Making of a Protein: B

Complementary Code Write a sequence of DNA bases, such as AACTACGGT, on the board. Ask students to write the complementary base sequence by using base-pairing rules. (TTGATGCCA) Then, ask students to give examples of deletions, insertions, and substitutions.

English Language Learners

LS Visual/Verbal

MISCONCEPTION ALERT

Mutants Among Us? Students may think mutations occur rarely, because organisms that are visibly "mutated" appear infrequently. However, scientists estimate that mistakes are made during DNA replication in approximately one out of every 10,000 base pairs. With cellular proofing mechanisms, the final error rate is as low as one in a billion. Still, we inherit hundreds of mutations from our parents' gametes. Many mutations have no apparent effect. For example, a mutation may occur in a cell that does not produce a particular protein or in a "junk" region of DNA that does not code for anything.

Answer to Reading Check

a physical or chemical agent that can cause a mutation in DNA

Original sequence

Base pair replaced

b Base pair added

c Base pair removed

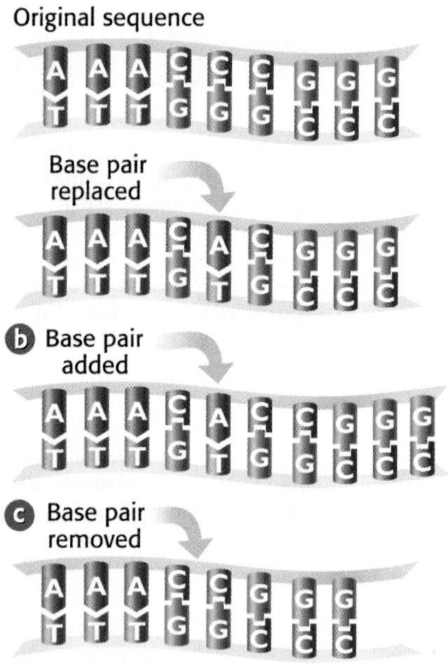

Figure 3 *The original base sequence on the top has been changed to illustrate (a) a substitution, (b) an insertion, and (c) a deletion.*

mutation a change in the nucleotide-base sequence of a gene or DNA molecule

---

Changes in Genes

Imagine that you have been invited to ride on a new roller coaster at the state fair. Before you climb into the front car, you are told that some of the metal parts on the coaster have been replaced by parts made of a different substance. Would you still want to ride this roller coaster? Perhaps a strong metal was used as a substitute. Or perhaps a material that is not strong enough was used. Imagine what would happen if cardboard were used instead of metal!

Mutations

Substitutions like the ones in the roller coaster can accidentally happen in DNA. Changes in the number, type, or order of bases on a piece of DNA are known as **mutations.** Sometimes, a base is left out. This kind of change is known as a *deletion*. Or an extra base might be added. This kind of change is known as an *insertion*. The most common change happens when the wrong base is used. This kind of change is known as a *substitution*. **Figure 3** illustrates these three types of mutations.

Do Mutations Matter?

There are three possible consequences to changes in DNA: an improved trait, no change, or a harmful trait. Fortunately, cells make some proteins that can detect errors in DNA. When an error is found, it is usually fixed. But occasionally the repairs are not accurate, and the mistakes become part of the genetic message. If the mutation occurs in the sex cells, the changed gene can be passed from one generation to the next.

How Do Mutations Happen?

Mutations happen regularly because of random errors when DNA is copied. In addition, damage to DNA can be caused by abnormal things that happen to cells. Any physical or chemical agent that can cause a mutation in DNA is called a *mutagen*. Examples of mutagens include high-energy radiation from X rays and ultraviolet radiation. Ultraviolet radiation is one type of energy in sunlight. It is responsible for suntans and sunburns. Other mutagens include asbestos and the chemicals in cigarette smoke.

Reading Check What is a mutagen?

CHAPTER RESOURCES

Technology

 Transparencies
- *LINK TO EARTH SCIENCE* E66 The Formation of Smog
- L21 How Sickle Cell Anemia Results from a Mutation

SUPPORT FOR

English Language Learners

Mutation and Genes Students may have trouble following the mutation process using only language. As they read about deletions, insertions, and substitutions, model them with a diagram on the board. Draw and label three small original sequences with three pairs of genes. Use carats to show insertion, arrows for substitution, and cross-out for deletion. After students have seen the models, recreate the basic diagrams on the board, and ask volunteers to show the processes. LS Visual/Verbal

An Example of a Substitution

A mutation, such as a substitution, can be harmful because it may cause a gene to produce the wrong protein. Consider the DNA sequence GAA. When copied as mRNA, this sequence gives the instructions to place the amino acid glutamic acid into the growing protein. If a mistake happens and the original DNA sequence is changed to GTA, the sequence will code for the amino acid valine instead.

This simple change in an amino acid can cause the disease *sickle cell disease*. Sickle cell disease affects red blood cells. When valine is substituted for glutamic acid in a blood protein, as shown in **Figure 4,** the red blood cells are changed into a sickle shape.

The sickle cells are not as good at carrying oxygen as normal red blood cells are. Sickle cells are also likely to get stuck in blood vessels and cause painful and dangerous clots.

✓ *Reading Check* What causes sickle cell disease?

An Error in the Message

The sentence below is the result of an error similar to a DNA mutation. The original sentence was made up of three-letter words, but an error was made in this copy. Explain the idea of mutations to your parent or guardian. Then, work together to find the mutation, and write the sentence correctly.

THE IGB ADC ATA TET HEB IGR EDR AT.

Figure 4 How Sickle Cell Disease Results from a Mutation

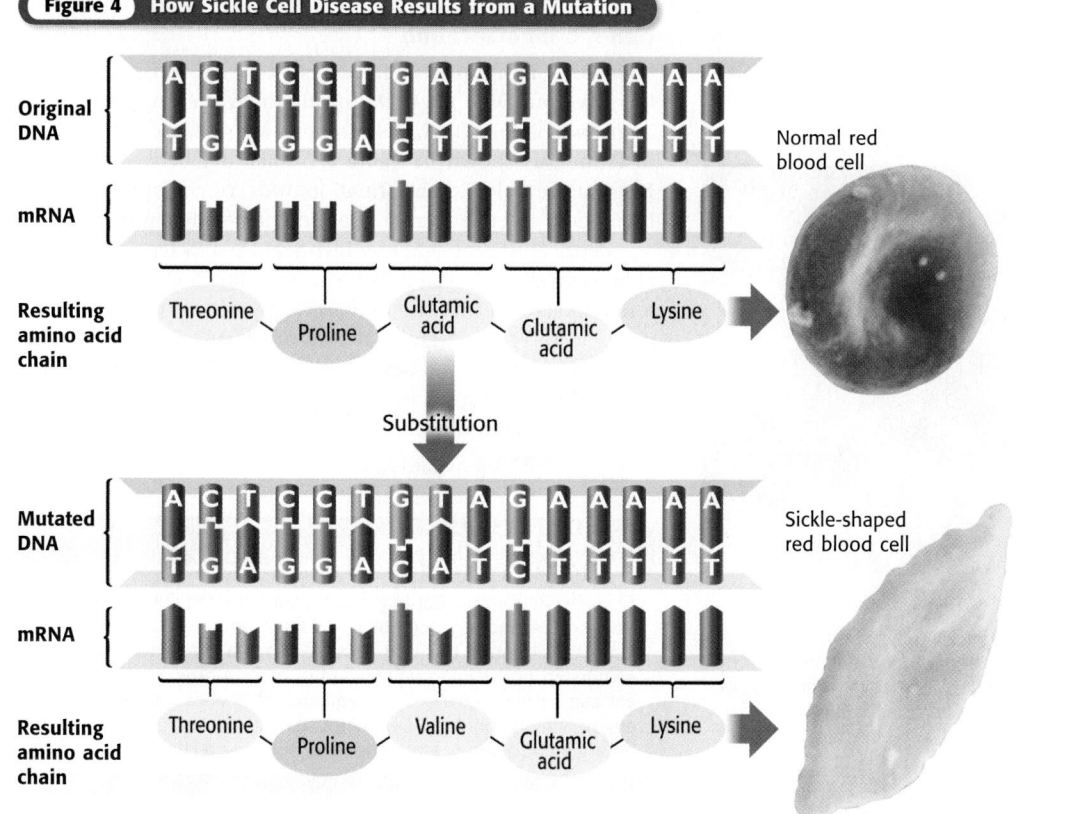

Original DNA

mRNA

Resulting amino acid chain: Threonine — Proline — Glutamic acid — Glutamic acid — Lysine

Normal red blood cell

Substitution

Mutated DNA

mRNA

Resulting amino acid chain: Threonine — Proline — Valine — Glutamic acid — Lysine

Sickle-shaped red blood cell

CONNECTION to Real Life — GENERAL

Misunderstood Disease A person who carries a single allele for sickle cell disease is said to have *sickle cell trait*. Only persons with two of these alleles usually develop the disease. In the past, many people did not understand that sickle cell trait and sickle cell disease are not contagious. In some areas, children with the trait were banned from public schools. 🅛 **Verbal**

Answer to Reading Check

Sickle cell disease is caused by a mutation in a single nucleotide of DNA, which then causes a different amino acid to be assembled in a protein used in blood cells.

Answer to School-to-Home Activity

The mutation is a deletion. THE BIG BAD CAT ATE THE BIG RED RAT.

INCLUSION Strategies

• *Behavior Control Issues*
• *Attention Deficit Disorder*
• *Visually Impaired*

Many students benefit from small-group work and learn well when actively involved. Divide all but four students into groups of three. Assign a DNA combination to each team (AT, CG, TA, or GC). Have students identify their DNA pairs by taping construction paper to their shirts. Ask students to line up to create a "human" DNA chain. Assign each of the remaining four students one of the four combinations. Have the four "extras" move around to create the three types of mutations: deletions, insertions, and substitutions. 🅛 **Intrapersonal**

Homework — GENERAL

Writing **Genetic Diseases** Have students select a genetic disease about which to conduct research and write a report. Suggest diseases such as hemophilia, diabetes, Familial ALS (Amyotrophic Lateral Sclerosis, or Lou Gehrig's Disease), SCID (Severe Combined Immunodeficiency Syndrome, or "Plastic Bubble" syndrome), Huntington's disease, and neurofibromatosis ("elephantitis"). Suggest that their reports focus on historical occurrence of the disease, famous persons that had or have the disease, and treatments that have been tried. 🅛 **Verbal**

Mutations Write a sequence of DNA on the board, and invite students to come up to the board and change the sequence. Then, ask the class to discuss the possible consequences of such a mutation in DNA. (It might cause a different amino acid to be substituted in a protein. This substitution could result in a genetic disorder, an improvement, or no change at all.) Ask how the mutation could be corrected. (Special proteins may find and repair the error.) **LS** Auditory

Quiz — GENERAL

1. What is the function of the ribosome? (In the ribosome, the mRNA code is translated into proteins.)

2. List some causes of DNA mutations. (Answers may include UV radiation, cigarette smoke, or X rays.)

Alternative Assessment — GENERAL

DNA How-To Have students prepare an instruction manual for their DNA. The manual should include instructions for copying their DNA and translating it into proteins. It should also include information about protecting their DNA from mutations by avoiding mutagens and correcting any mutations that occur. **LS** Intrapersonal

English Language Learners · PORTFOLIO

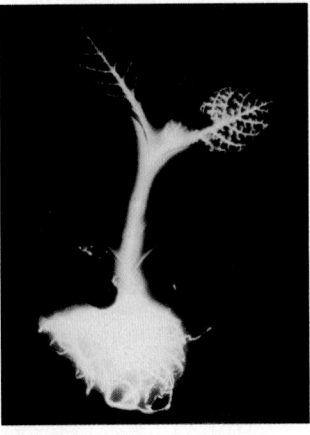

Figure 5 *This genetically engineered tobacco plant contains firefly genes.*

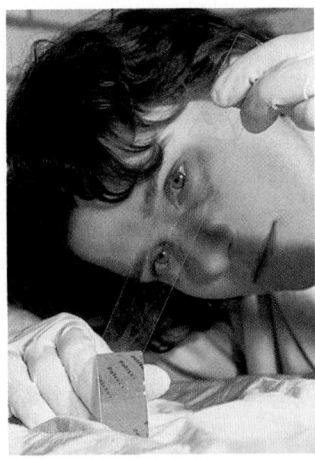

Figure 6 *This scientist is gathering dead skin cells from a crime scene. DNA from the cells could be used as evidence of a criminal's identity.*

Uses of Genetic Knowledge

In the years since Watson and Crick made their model, scientists have learned a lot about genetics. This knowledge is often used in ways that benefit humans. But some uses of genetic knowledge also cause ethical and scientific debates.

Genetic Engineering

Scientists can manipulate individual genes within organisms. This kind of manipulation is called *genetic engineering*. In some cases, genes may be transferred from one type of organism to another. An example of a genetically engineered plant is shown in **Figure 5.** Scientists added a gene from fireflies to this plant. The gene produces a protein that causes the plant to glow.

Scientists may use genetic engineering to create new products, such as drugs, foods, or fabrics. For example, bacteria may be used to make the proteins found in spider's silk. Or cows may be used to produce human proteins. In some cases, this practice could produce a protein that is needed by a person who has a genetic disease. However, some scientists worry about the dangers of creating genetically engineered organisms.

Genetic Identification

Your DNA is unique, so it can be used like a fingerprint to identify you. *DNA fingerprinting* identifies the unique patterns in an individual's DNA. DNA samples are now used as evidence in crimes, as shown in **Figure 6.** Similarities between people's DNA can reveal other information, too. For example, DNA can be used to identify family relations or hereditary diseases.

Identical twins have truly identical DNA. Scientists are now able to create something like a twin, called a clone. A *clone* is a new organism that has an exact copy of another organism's genes. Clones of several types of organisms, including some mammals, have been developed by scientists. However, the possibility of cloning humans is still being debated among both scientists and politicians.

✓ **Reading Check** What is a clone?

CONNECTION TO Social Studies

Genetic Property Could you sell your DNA code? Using current laws and technology, someone could sell genetic information like authors sell books. It is also possible to file a patent to establish ownership of the information used to make a product. Thus, a patent can be filed for a unique sequence of DNA or for new genetic engineering technology. Conduct research to find an existing patent on a genetic sequence or genetic engineering technology.

Answer to Connection to Social Studies

Students should be able to find examples of patents for specially bred or genetically engineered plants and seeds or for procedures that rely on genetic technologies to produce drugs or treat genetic diseases.

Answer to Reading Check

a near-identical copy of another organism, created with the original organism's genes

CONNECTION ACTIVITY Social Studies — ADVANCED

Ethics Debate Have interested students stage a debate about what kinds of regulations should be placed on the practices of genetic manipulation. Suggest students consider issues such as tranferring genes between different species, DNA fingerprinting, cloning, and genetic patents. **LS** Interpersonal

SECTION Review

Summary

- A gene is a set of instructions for assembling a protein. DNA is the molecular carrier of these genetic instructions.
- Every organism has DNA in its cells. Humans have about 2 m of DNA in each cell.
- Within a gene, each group of three bases codes for one amino acid. A sequence of amino acids is linked to make a protein.
- Proteins are fundamental to the function of cells and the expression of traits.

- Proteins are assembled within the cytoplasm through a multi-step process that is assisted by several forms of RNA.
- Genes can become mutated when the order of the bases is changed. Three main types of mutations are possible: insertion, deletion, and substitution.
- Genetic knowledge has many practical uses. Some applications of genetic knowledge are controversial.

Using Key Terms

1. Use each of the following terms in the same sentence: *ribosome* and *RNA*.

2. In your own words, write a definition for the term *mutation*.

Understanding Key Ideas

3. Explain the relationship between genes and proteins.

4. List three possible types of mutations.

5. Which type of mutation causes sickle cell anemia?

   a. substitution
   b. insertion
   c. deletion
   d. mutagen

Math Skills

6. A set of 23 chromosomes in a human cell contains 3.2 billion pairs of DNA bases in sequence. On average, about how many pairs of bases are in each chromosome?

Critical Thinking

7. **Applying Concepts** In which cell type might a mutation be passed from generation to generation? Explain.

8. **Making Comparisons** How is genetic engineering different from natural reproduction?

Interpreting Graphics

The illustration below shows a sequence of bases on one strand of a DNA molecule. Use the illustration below to answer the questions that follow.

 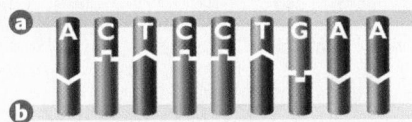

9. How many amino acids are coded for by the sequence on one side (A) of this DNA strand?

10. What is the order of bases on the complementary side of the strand (B), from left to right?

11. If a G were inserted as the first base on the top side (A), what would the order of bases be on the complementary side (B)?

For a variety of links related to this chapter, go to www.scilinks.org

Topic: Genetic Engineering
SciLinks code: HSM0654

Answers to Section Review

1. Sample answer: A ribosome is made of RNA and protein.

2. Sample answer: A mutation is a mistake in the DNA code.

3. Genes are sequences of DNA that code for particular proteins.

4. substitution, insertion, deletion

5. a

6. about 139 million
   (3,200,000,000 ÷ 23 = 139,130,435)

7. A sex cell (germ cell, sperm cell, or egg cell), because these cells contain the genes from which a new organism is formed.

8. Sample answer: Genetic engineering is deliberately controlled by humans and may involve processes that are rare or impossible in nature.

9. 3

10. TGAGGACTT

11. CTGAGGACTT

 **SCIENCE**

Gene therapy is an experimental field of medical research in which defective genes are replaced with healthy genes. One way to insert healthy genes involves using a delivery system called a gene gun to inject microscopic gold bullets coated with genetic material.

CHAPTER RESOURCES

Chapter Resource File

- Section Quiz **GENERAL**
- Section Review **GENERAL**
- Vocabulary and Section Summary **GENERAL**
- Reinforcement Worksheet **BASIC**
- Critical Thinking **ADVANCED**

Technology

- Interactive Explorations CD-ROM
  - DNA Pawprints **GENERAL**

Base-Pair Basics

Teacher's Notes

Time Required

One 45-minute class period

Lab Ratings

Teacher Prep 🧪

Student Set-Up 🧪🧪

Concept Level 🧪

Clean Up 🧪

MATERIALS

The materials listed on the student page are enough for a group of 4–5 students. You may want to provide additional materials for the Applying Your Data section.

Safety Caution

Remind students to review all safety cautions and icons before beginning this lab activity. Students should always exercise care when using scissors.

Model-Making Lab

OBJECTIVES

Construct a model of a DNA strand.

Model the process of DNA replication.

MATERIALS

- bag, large paper
- paper, colored (4 colors)
- paper, white
- scissors

SAFETY

Base-Pair Basics

You have learned that DNA is shaped something like a twisted ladder. The side rails of the ladder are made of sugar parts and phosphate parts. The two side rails are connected to each other by parts called *bases*. The bases join in pairs to form the rungs of the ladder. Within DNA, each base can pair with only one other base. Each of these pairs is called a *base pair*. When DNA replicates, enzymes separate the base pairs, which breaks the rungs of the ladder in half. Then, each half of the DNA ladder can be used as a template for building a new half. In this activity, you will construct a paper model of DNA and use it to model the replication process.

Procedure

1. Trace the models of nucleotides below onto white paper. Label the pieces "A" (**a**denine), "T" (**t**hymine), "C" (**c**ytosine), and "G" (**g**uanine). Draw the pieces again on colored paper. Use a different color for each type of base. Draw the pieces as large as you want, and draw as many of the white pieces and as many of the colored pieces as time will allow.

2. Carefully cut out all of the pieces.

3. Put all of the colored pieces in the classroom into a large paper bag. Spread all of the white pieces in the classroom onto a large table.

4. Remove nine colored pieces from the bag. Arrange the colored pieces in any order in a straight column so that the letters *A, T, C,* and *G* are right side up. Be sure to fit the sugar notches to the phosphate tabs. Draw this arrangement.

5. Find the white bases that correctly pair with the nine colored bases. Remember the base-pairing rules, and pair the bases according to those rules.

6. Pair the pieces by fitting tabs to notches. The letters on the white pieces should be upside down. You now have a model of a double-stranded piece of DNA. The strand contains nine pairs of complementary nucleotides. Draw your model.

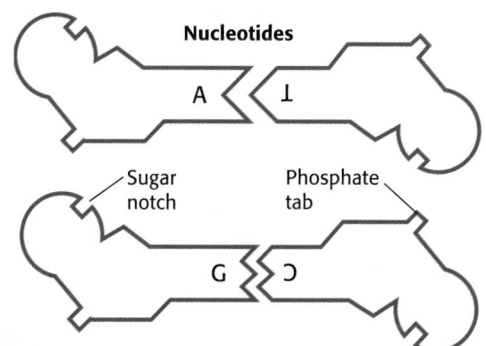

Nucleotides

Sugar notch

Phosphate tab

Lab Notes

You may wish to enlarge the nucleotide template for your students so that the models will be easier to cut out. Explain to students that the white pieces and the colored pieces represent the complementary sides of DNA strands. Also, suggest that students refer to the figure depicting DNA replication in their text. Remind students that this is a model of the parts of a DNA molecule and that the parts of real DNA molecules are three-dimensional and have a more complex shape.

CHAPTER RESOURCES

Chapter Resource File

- **Datasheet for Chapter Lab**
- **Lab Notes and Answers**

Technology

Classroom Videos
- Lab Video

Workbooks

Whiz-Bang Demonstrations
- Grand Strand

Long-Term Projects & Research Ideas
- The Antifreeze Protein ADVANCED
- Ewe Again, Dolly?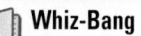

Analyze the Results

① Identifying Patterns Now, separate the two halves of your DNA strand along the middle of the base pair rungs of the ladder. Keep the side rails together by keeping the sugar notches fitted to the phosphate tabs. Draw this arrangement.

② Recognizing Patterns Look at the drawing made in the previous step. Along each strand in the drawing, write the letters of the bases that complement the bases in that strand.

③ Examining Data Find all of the bases that you need to complete replication. Find white pieces to pair with the bases on the left, and find colored pieces to pair with the bases on the right. Be sure that the tabs and notches fit and the sides are straight. You have now replicated your model of DNA. Are the two models identical? Draw your results.

Draw Conclusions

④ Interpreting Information State the correct base-pairing rules. How do these rules make DNA replication possible?

⑤ Evaluating Models What happens when you attempt to pair thymine with guanine? Do they fit together? Are the sides straight? Do all of the tabs and notches fit? Explain.

Applying Your Data

Construct a 3-D model of a DNA molecule that shows DNA's twisted-ladder structure. Use your imagination and creativity to select materials. You may want to use licorice, gum balls, and toothpicks or pipe cleaners and paper clips.

1. Display your model in your classroom.
2. Take a vote to decide which models are the most accurate and the most creative.

Analyze the Results
1. Student drawings should show an "unzipped" DNA strand.
2. Student responses should always show A matched with T and C matched with G.
3. The two new molecules should exactly match each other and match the original molecule.

Draw Conclusions
4. G and C always pair, and A and T always pair. These pairings allow the two halves of a DNA molecule to be separated and replicated and ensure that identical new molecules can be formed.
5. The joining areas of guanine and thymine don't match up. They don't fit together well. The sides of the DNA molecule would not be straight and the parts would not line up if the bases were forced together in this way.

Applying Your Data
1. Student models should be more accurate than any models of DNA that they have previously constructed. Check for the correct "right-handed" orientation of the double-helix spiral, representation of the four base types, correct matching of the base-pairs and subunits, and overall uniformity of the helix.
2. Before voting, have students brainstorm their criteria for "accurate" and "creative." Take a separate vote for each category.

● Holt Lab Generator CD-ROM

Search for any lab by topic, standard, difficulty level, or time. Edit any lab to fit your needs, or create your own labs. Use the Lab Materials QuickList software to customize your lab materials list.

Debra Sampson
Booker T. Washington
Middle School
Elgin, Texas

Assignment Guide

Section	Questions
1	4, 5, 10, 13, 15, 16, 20–22
2	1–3, 6–9, 11, 12, 14, 17–19

ANSWERS

Using Key Terms

1. A mutagen is a substance that can cause a mutation in DNA.
2. nucelotides
3. ribosome

Understanding Key Ideas

4. d
5. b
6. b
7. b
8. a
9. b

USING KEY TERMS

1 Use the following terms in the same sentence: *mutation* and *mutagen*.

The statements below are false. For each statement, replace the underlined term to make a true statement.

2 The information in DNA is coded in the order of <u>amino acids</u> along one side of the DNA molecule.

3 The "factory" that assembles proteins based on the DNA code is called a <u>gene</u>.

UNDERSTANDING KEY IDEAS

Multiple Choice

4 James Watson and Francis Crick

　a. took X-ray pictures of DNA.

　b. discovered that genes are in chromosomes.

　c. bred pea plants to study heredity.

　d. made models to figure out DNA's shape.

5 In a DNA molecule, which of the following bases pair together?

　a. adenine and cytosine

　b. thymine and adenine

　c. thymine and guanine

　d. cytosine and thymine

6 A gene can be all of the following EXCEPT

　a. a set of instructions for a trait.

　b. a complete chromosome.

　c. instructions for making a protein.

　d. a portion of a strand of DNA.

7 Which of the following statements about DNA is NOT true?

　a. DNA is found in all organisms.

　b. DNA is made up of five subunits.

　c. DNA has a structure like a twisted ladder.

　d. Mistakes can be made when DNA is copied.

8 Within the cell, where are proteins assembled?

　a. the cytoplasm

　b. the nucleus

　c. the amino acids

　d. the chromosomes

9 Changes in the type or order of the bases in DNA are called

　a. nucleotides.

　b. mutations.

　c. RNA.

　d. genes.

Short Answer

10 What would be the complementary strand of DNA for the following sequence of bases?

　C T T A G G C T T A C C A

11 If the DNA sequence TGAGCCATGA is changed to TGAGCACATGA, what kind of mutation has occurred?

12 Explain how the DNA in genes relates to the traits of an organism.

13 Why is DNA frequently found associated with proteins inside of cells?

14 What is the difference between DNA and RNA?

10. GAATCCGAATGGT
11. an insertion
12. The DNA in genes codes for specific proteins, and proteins control cells and result in traits.
13. because proteins do much of the work of copying and handling the DNA

14. DNA is deoxyribonucleic acid, and exact copies of a set of DNA are found in each cell of an organism. RNA is ribonucleic acid, which is similar to DNA but is used to carry copies of DNA code around the cell and to build proteins based on this code.

15 **Concept Mapping** Use the following terms to create a concept map: *bases, adenine, thymine, nucleotides, guanine, DNA,* and *cytosine.*

16 **Analyzing Processes** Draw and label a picture that explains how DNA is copied.

17 **Analyzing Processes** Draw and label a picture that explains how proteins are made.

18 **Applying Concepts** The following DNA sequence codes for how many amino acids?

T C A G C C A C C T A T G G A

19 **Making Inferences** Why does the government make laws about the use of chemicals that are known to be mutagens?

The illustration below shows the process of replication of a DNA strand. Use this illustration to answer the questions that follow.

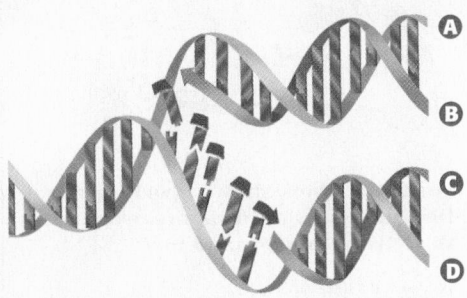

20 Which strands are part of the original molecule?

a. A and B

b. A and C

c. A and D

d. None of the above

21 Which strands are new?

a. A and B

b. B and C

c. C and D

d. None of the above

22 Which strands are complementary?

a. A and C

b. B and C

c. All of the strands

d. None of the strands

Critical Thinking

15. 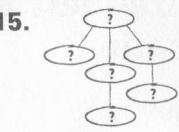 An answer to this exercise can be found at the end of this book.

16. Student drawings should resemble the diagram of replication in their student text and should have appropriate labels.

17. Student drawings should resemble the diagram of protein assembly in their student text and should have appropriate labels.

18. This sequence codes for five amino acids.

19. Sample answer: The government is trying to protect people from the risk of mutagens causing harmful mutations in people's cells—mutations could cause a disease such as cancer.

Interpreting Graphics

20. c

21. b

22. b

CHAPTER RESOURCES

Chapter Resource File

- Chapter Review GENERAL
- Chapter Test A GENERAL
- Chapter Test B ADVANCED
- Chapter Test C SPECIAL NEEDS
- Vocabulary Activity GENERAL

Workbooks

Study Guide
- Study Guide is also available in Spanish.

Standardized Test Preparation

Teacher's Notes

To provide practice under more realistic conditions, give students 20 minutes to answer all of the questions in this Standardized Test Preparation.

Answer Key

Question	Answer
1	C
2	B
3	D
4	C
5	A
6	A
7	C
8	D
9	C
10	*
11	*

*See Test Doctor.

Multiple Choice

Use the figure below to answer question 1.

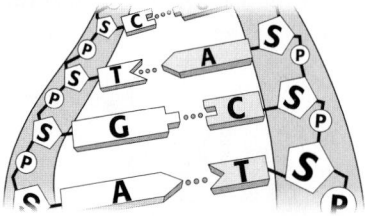

1. **The figure above shows a portion of a DNA molecule. In the figure, what do the letters S and P stand for?**

   A. sugars and proteins

   B. sodium and proteins

   C. sugars and phosphates

   D. sodium and phosphates

2. **Which of the following is the best description of the structure of DNA?**

   A. DNA has two strands that form a branched chain called a *branched helix*.

   B. DNA is in the shape of a twisted ladder called a *double helix*.

   C. DNA is in the shape of a straight ladder called a *straight helix*.

   D. DNA has three strands that form a *triple helix*.

3. **What three components make up a nucleotide?**

   A. a sugar, a protein, and a nitrogenous base

   B. a sucrose, a protein, and a nitrogenous base

   C. a sugar, a proton, and a nitrogenous base

   D. a sugar, a phosphate, and a nitrogenous base

4. **Which pattern shows how bases pair in complementary strands of DNA?**

   A. A–A and C–C

   B. A–G and T–C

   C. A–T and C–G

   D. A–C and T–G

5. **How are copies of DNA made?**

   A. DNA strands unwind and complementary nucleotides are added.

   B. DNA strands unwind and amino acids are joined together to form the copies.

   C. DNA strands are assembled by ribosomes.

   D. DNA strands are made using mRNA templates.

✚ TEST DOCTOR

Question 1 A, B, D: The backbone of DNA is made up of sugars and phosphate groups. C: Correct.

Question 2 A: DNA does not form a branched chain. B: Correct. C: DNA has a twisted ladder shape, not a straight ladder shape. D: DNA has two complementary strands, not three strands.

Question 3 A: DNA is not made up of proteins. B: DNA is not made up of sucrose or proteins. C: Protons are subatomic particles of atoms. Protons are much smaller than atoms or molecules. D: Correct.

Question 4 A, B, D: In DNA, A pairs with T and C pairs with G. C: Correct.

Question 5 A: Correct. B: Amino acids are used to make proteins, not DNA. C: Ribosomes assemble proteins, not DNA. D: mRNA strands are copies of DNA segments that are used to make proteins, not DNA.

Use the figure below to answer question 6.

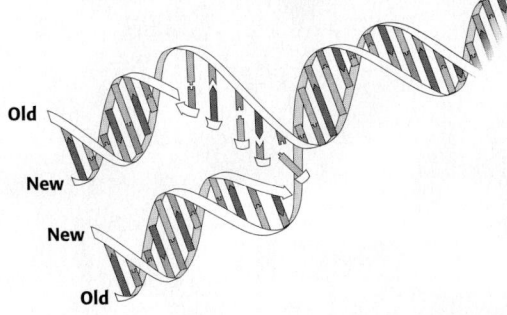

Old

New

New

Old

6. DNA replication results in the formation of two molecules of DNA, as shown in the figure above. Based on the figure, which of the following statements is true?

A. Both molecules of DNA have one new strand and one strand from the original DNA molecule.

B. One molecule is made up of two new strands and the other molecule is made up of old strands.

C. Each strand in the new DNA molecule is made up of portions of old strands and portions of the new strands.

D. Both molecules of DNA can have one new and one old strand, or they can have two new or two old strands.

7. What are the structures that are in the nuclei of most cells and that are made of protein and DNA?

A. cytosine

B. molecules

C. chromosomes

D. nucleotides

8. A scientist conducts research on a sample of DNA that contains 200 nucleotides. Her results show that adenine makes up 30% of the sample and cytosine makes up 20% of the sample. The remaining 50% of the sample is made up of thymine and guanine. How many of the nucleotides are thymine?

A. 30

B. 40

C. 50

D. 60

9. How are proteins formed?

A. Amino acids assemble to form proteins along strands of genes in the nucleus.

B. Genes are fed through ribosomes where amino acids assemble to form proteins.

C. Mirrorlike copies of genes are fed through ribosomes where amino acids assemble to form proteins.

D. Mirrorlike copies of a gene, called tRNA, are made. tRNA is fed through ribosomes where amino acids assemble to form proteins.

Open Response

10. Starting and ending with chromosomes, describe the replication of DNA.

11. How do the genes in DNA determine the characteristics of living things?

Question 9 A, B: Messenger RNA (mRNA) works inside ribosomes within the cytoplasm to carry out protein synthesis. C: Correct. D: mRNA, not tRNA, are mirror-image copies of DNA segments.

Question 10 Full-credit answers should include the following points:

• Chromosomes are made up of chromatin.

• A single strand of chromatin is made up of DNA.

• Chromatin unwinds, and the strands of DNA separate.

• Complementary nucleotides are added to each strand.

• The resulting DNA molecules have one old strand and one new strand.

• The DNA coils again, forming a chromosome.

Question 11 Full-credit answers should include the following points:

• Genes consist of three base pairs.

• A series of genes codes for a specific protein.

• Proteins determine the characteristics of living things.

Question 6 A: Correct. B: Because of the way DNA replicates, it is impossible for one molecule to have only new strands of nucleotides and for the other molecule to have only old strands of nucleotides. C: During DNA replication, it is not possible for a single strand of nucleotides to be made up of both the old strand and the new strand. D: Because of the way DNA replicates, it is impossible for one molecule to have only new strands of nucleotides and for the other molecule to have only old strands of nucleotides.

Question 7 A, D: Nucleotides, including cytosine, are subunits of a nucleic-acid chain, such as DNA. B: *Molecules* is a general term that describes a structure that is made up of atoms, not specifically the structures that are made of protein and DNA. C: Correct.

Question 8 A: Thymine, which pairs with adenine, accounts for 30% of the sample. B: There are 40 nucleotides each of cytosine and guanine. C: Thirty percent of 200 nucleotides is 60 nucleotides. D: Correct.

Scientific Debate

Background

The U.S. Food and Drug Administration began approving genetically modified organisms (GMOs) for consumer use in the 1990s. Some consumer groups have protested and boycotted such foods. Several countries around the world have banned the creation, sale, or importation of GMOs. Some consumer groups have asked that all GMO foods be clearly labeled. The majority of GMO foods being sold in the United States are made with corn or soybeans that contain bacterial genes.

Scientists have mixed opinions about GMOs. However, most scientists recognize that the potential to create new and unknown types of organisms should be undertaken with careful scientific scrutiny, should involve ethical considerations, and should be regulated by governments.

Science Fiction

ACTIVITY —————— **ADVANCED**

Further Reading If students liked this story, encourage them to read more of McKillip's stories, such as the following:

• *Fool's Run*, Warner, 1987

• *Something Rich and Strange*, Bantam, 1994

• *Winter Rose*, Ace, 1996

Science in Action

Scientific Debate

Supersquash or Frankenfruit?

Some food that you buy may have been developed in a new way. Food producers may use genetic engineering to make food crops easier to grow or sell, more nutritious, or resistant to pests and disease. More than half of the packaged foods sold in the United States are likely to contain ingredients from genetically modified organisms.

The U.S. government has stated that research shows that these foods are safe. But some scientists are concerned that genes introduced into crop plants could cause new environmental or health problems. For example, people who are allergic to peanuts might also be allergic to tomato plants that contain peanut genes.

Math ACTIVITY

Write a survey about genetically altered foods. Ask your teacher to approve your questions. Ask at least 15 people to answer your survey. Create graphs to summarize your results.

Science Fiction

"Moby James" by Patricia A. McKillip

Rob Trask and his family live on a space station. Rob thinks that his real brother was sent back to Earth. The person who claims to be his brother, James, is really either some sort of mutated plant or a mutant pair of dirty sweat socks.

Now, Rob has another problem—his class is reading Herman Melville's novel *Moby Dick*. As he reads the novel, Rob becomes convinced that his brother is a great white mutant whale—Moby James. To see how Rob solves his problems, read "Moby James" in the *Holt Anthology of Science Fiction*.

Language Arts ACTIVITY

WRITING SKILL Read "Moby James" by Patricia A. McKillip. Then, write your own short science-fiction story about a mutant organism. Be sure to incorporate some science into your science fiction.

Answer to Math Activity

Check that student surveys ask questions for which answers can be easily tallied, such as "Do you think that genetically modified foods should be labeled in the store?" Check that students have kept records and summarized their results accurately. Give them feedback about how well their graphs communicate the data they gathered.

Answer to Language Arts Activity

Instead of collecting and grading students' stories, you may want to have them read their stories to each other or to a family member, and then ask for feedback about how much science is included in their fiction.

Lydia Villa-Komaroff

Genetic Researcher When Lydia Villa-Komaroff was young, science represented "a kind of refuge" for her. She grew up in a very large family that lived in a very small house. "I always wanted to find things out. I was one of those kids who took things apart."

In college, Villa-Komaroff became very interested in the process of embryonic development—how a simple egg grows into a complex animal. This interest led her to study genes and the way that genes code for proteins. For example, insulin is a protein that is normally produced by the human body. Often, people who suffer from diabetes lack the insulin gene, so their bodies can't make insulin. These people may need to inject insulin into their blood as a drug treatment.

Before the research by Villa-Komaroff's team was done, insulin was difficult to produce. Villa-Komaroff's team isolated the human gene that codes for insulin. Then, the scientists inserted the normal human insulin gene into the DNA of bacteria. This inserted gene caused the bacteria to produce insulin. This technique was a new and more efficient way to produce insulin. Now, most of the insulin used for diabetes treatment is made in this way. Many genetic researchers dream of making breakthroughs like the one that Villa-Komaroff made in her work with insulin.

Social Studies ACTIVITY

WRITING SKILL Do some research about several women, such as Marie Curie, Barbara McClintock, or Maxine Frank Singer, who have done important scientific research. Write a short biography about one of these women.

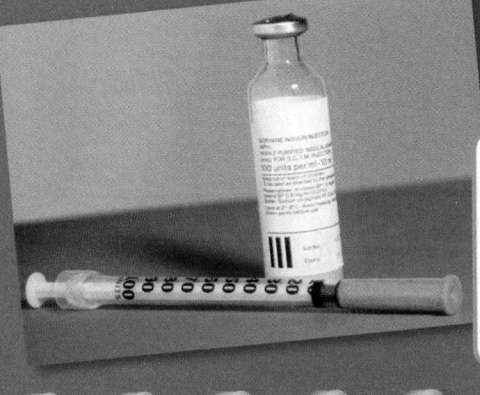

go.hrw.com

To learn more about these Science in Action topics, visit **go.hrw.com** and type in the keyword **HL5DNAF**.

Current Science

Check out Current Science® articles related to this chapter by visiting **go.hrw.com. Just type in the keyword HL5CS06.**

Answer to Social Studies Activity

Suggest that students do research in the library or on the Internet for information. Additional women scientists to consider are as follows:

- Jewel Plummer Cobb
- Ruth Fulton Benedict
- Emma Perry Carr
- Rosalyn Yalow

Check student biographies for accuracy, and comment on any interesting facts.

Lydia Villa-Komaroff grew up in Santa Fe, New Mexico, in a household that loved to tell family stories. One favorite was the story of Villa-Komaroff's grandfather, Encarnacion Villa, and his brush with the Mexican revolutionary Pancho Villa. Encarnacion was going to be killed by Pancho Villa's soldiers when he refused to join their fight. But when Pancho Villa heard the captive's name, he ordered his release but told him he must have many sons. Pancho Villa probably could not imagine that a granddaughter of his former captive would someday become the third Mexican-American woman to earn a Ph.D. in the United States and would go on to make many important contributions to science.

When Lydia Villa-Komaroff and her colleagues inserted the human gene that directs the production of insulin into the DNA of bacteria, they were using recombinant DNA technology. In recombinant DNA technology, researchers identify which segment of DNA is the gene that directs the production of the desired substance, cut this section out of the DNA with special enzymes, and make copies, or clones. The researchers then take one of these clones and insert it, again using special enzymes, into the correct spot on the host DNA. The researchers look for a location on the host DNA that will ensure that the host organism will read the DNA and produce the substance.

The Evolution of Living Things
Chapter Planning Guide

Compression guide:
To shorten instruction because of time limitations, omit Section 3.

OBJECTIVES	LABS, DEMONSTRATIONS, AND ACTIVITIES	TECHNOLOGY RESOURCES
PACING • 90 min pp. 136–145 **Chapter Opener**	**SE** Start-up Activity, p. 137 ◆ `GENERAL`	**OSP** Parent Letter ■ **CD** Student Edition on CD-ROM **CD** Guided Reading Audio CD ■ **TR** Chapter Starter Transparency* **VID** Brain Food Video Quiz
Section 1 Change over Time • Identify two kinds of evidence that show that organisms have evolved. • Describe one pathway through which a modern whale could have evolved from an ancient mammal. • Explain how comparing organisms can provide evidence that they have ancestors in common.	**SE** Connection to Geology Sedimentary Rock, p. 141 ◆ `GENERAL` **TE** Connection Activity Math, p. 141 `ADVANCED` **TE** Connection Activity Art, p. 142 ◆ `ADVANCED` **TE** Connection Activity Geography, p. 143 `ADVANCED`	**OSP** Lesson Plans (also in print) **TR** Bellringer Transparency* **TR** *LINK TO EARTH SCIENCE* E8 The Rock Cycle* **TR** L22 Evidence of Whale Evolution: A* **TR** L23 Evidence of Whale Evolution: B* **TR** L24 Comparing Skeletal Structures*
PACING • 90 min pp. 146–151 **Section 2 How Does Evolution Happen?** • List four sources of Charles Darwin's ideas about evolution. • Describe the four parts of Darwin's theory of evolution by natural selection. • Relate genetics to evolution.	**TE** Demonstration Form and Function, p. 147 ◆ `GENERAL` **TE** Connection Activity Social Studies, p. 147 `ADVANCED` **TE** Connection Activity Geography, p. 148 `GENERAL` **SE** Quick Lab Population Growth Versus Food Supply, p. 149 ◆ `GENERAL` **CRF** Datasheet for Quick Lab* **TE** Activity Natural Selection, p. 150 `BASIC` **SE** Inquiry Lab Survival of the Chocolates, p. 156 `GENERAL` **CRF** Datasheet for Chapter Lab*	**OSP** Lesson Plans (also in print) **TR** Bellringer Transparency* **TR** L25 Four Parts of Natural Selection* **CRF** SciLinks Activity* `GENERAL` **VID** Lab Videos for Life Science
PACING • 45 min pp. 152–155 **Section 3 Natural Selection in Action** • Give three examples of natural selection in action. • Outline the process of speciation.	**TE** Connection Activity Real World, p. 153 `GENERAL` **TE** Group Activity Amazing Adaptations, p. 153 `ADVANCED` **SE** Science in Action Math, Social Studies, and Language Arts Activities, p. 162–163 `GENERAL` **LB** Whiz-Bang Demonstrations Adaptation Behooves You* ◆ `GENERAL` **LB** Long-Term Projects & Research Ideas Evolution's Explosion* `ADVANCED`	**OSP** Lesson Plans (also in print) **TR** Bellringer Transparency* **TR** L26 Evolution of the Galápagos Finches* **TE** Internet Activity, p. 153 `GENERAL`

PACING • 90 min

CHAPTER REVIEW, ASSESSMENT, AND STANDARDIZED TEST PREPARATION

CRF Vocabulary Activity* `GENERAL`
SE Chapter Review, pp. 158–159 `GENERAL`
CRF Chapter Review* ■ `GENERAL`
CRF Chapter Tests A* ■ `GENERAL`, B* `ADVANCED`, C* `SPECIAL NEEDS`
SE Standardized Test Preparation, pp. 160–161 `GENERAL`
CRF Standardized Test Preparation* `GENERAL`
CRF Performance-Based Assessment* `GENERAL`
OSP Test Generator, Test Item Listing

Online and Technology Resources

 Holt Online Learning

Visit **go.hrw.com** for access to Holt Online Learning, or enter the keyword **HS7 Home** for a variety of free online resources.

 One-Stop Planner® CD-ROM

This CD-ROM package includes:
- Lab Materials QuickList Software
- Holt Calendar Planner
- Customizable Lesson Plans
- Printable Worksheets
- ExamView® Test Generator
- Interactive Teacher's Edition
- Holt PuzzlePro®
- Holt PowerPoint® Resources

SKILLS DEVELOPMENT RESOURCES | SECTION REVIEW AND ASSESSMENT | CORRELATIONS

SE Pre-Reading Activity, p. 136 `GENERAL`
OSP Science Puzzlers, Twisters & Teasers* `GENERAL`

National Science Education Standards

UCP 2, 5; SAI 1, 2; LS 1a, 5a

CRF Directed Reading A* ■ `BASIC`**, B*** `SPECIAL NEEDS`
WB Workbook* `Struggling Readers`
CRF Vocabulary and Section Summary* ■ `GENERAL`
SE Reading Strategy Paired Summarizing, p. 138 `GENERAL`
TE Connection to Earth Science Rock Layers, p. 140 `GENERAL`
TE Support for English Language Learners, p. 142
SE Math Practice The Weight of Whales, p. 143 `GENERAL`
TE Inclusion Strategies, p. 143

SE Reading Checks, pp. 138, 140, 142, 144 `GENERAL`
TE Reteaching, p. 144 `BASIC`
TE Quiz, p. 144 `GENERAL`
TE Alternative Assessment, p. 144 `ADVANCED`
TE Homework, p. 145 `GENERAL`
SE Section Review,* p. 145 ■ `GENERAL`
CRF Section Quiz* ■ `GENERAL`

UCP 2, 4, 5; SAI 2; HNS 2; LS 2e, 3a, 3d, 4a, 5a, 5b, 5c

CRF Directed Reading A* ■ `BASIC`**, B*** `SPECIAL NEEDS`
WB Workbook* `Struggling Readers`
CRF Vocabulary and Section Summary* ■ `GENERAL`
SE Reading Strategy Brainstorming, p. 146 `GENERAL`
TE Connection to Geography Galápagos, p. 147 `GENERAL`
TE Support for English Language Learners, p. 147
TE Reading Strategy Prediction Guide, p. 148 `GENERAL`
MS Math Skills for Science Multiplying Whole Numbers* `GENERAL`
CRF Reinforcement Worksheet Bicentennial Celebration* `BASIC`

SE Reading Checks, pp. 147, 149, 150 `GENERAL`
TE Homework, p. 146 `GENERAL`
TE Homework, p. 148 `ADVANCED`
TE Reteaching, p. 150 `BASIC`
TE Quiz, p. 150 `GENERAL`
TE Alternative Assessment, p. 150 `ADVANCED`
SE Section Review,* p. 151 ■ `GENERAL`
CRF Section Quiz* ■ `GENERAL`

UCP 1, 2, 4, 5; SAI 1, 2; SPSP 2, 5; HNS 1, 2, 3; LS 2a, 2b, 2d, 2e, 3d, 5a, 5b; *Chapter Lab:* UCP 2, 4; SAI 1, 2

CRF Directed Reading A* ■ `BASIC`**, B*** `SPECIAL NEEDS`
WB Workbook* `Struggling Readers`
CRF Vocabulary and Section Summary* ■ `GENERAL`
SE Reading Strategy Prediction Guide, p. 152 `GENERAL`
TE Support for English Language Learners, p. 153
TE Inclusion Strategies, p. 154 ◆
CRF Critical Thinking Taking the Earth's Pulse* `ADVANCED`

SE Reading Checks, pp. 153, 154 `GENERAL`
TE Reteaching, p. 154 `BASIC`
TE Quiz, p. 154 `GENERAL`
TE Alternative Assessment, p. 154 `ADVANCED`
SE Section Review,* p. 155 ■ `GENERAL`
CRF Section Quiz* ■ `GENERAL`

UCP 1, 3, 4; SPSP 4, 5; LS 2a, 2e, 3d, 4d, 5b

SCiLINKS.
NSTA
www.scilinks.org
Maintained by the **National Science Teachers Association.** See Chapter Enrichment pages that follow for a complete list of topics.

Current Science®

Check out *Current Science* articles and activities by visiting the HRW Web site at **go.hrw.com.** Just type in the keyword **HL5CS07T.**

Classroom Videos

- **Lab Videos** demonstrate the chapter lab.
- **Brain Food Video Quizzes** help students review the chapter material.

Classroom CD-ROMs

- **Guided Reading Audio CD** (Also in Spanish)
- **Interactive Explorations**
- **Virtual Investigations**
- **Visual Concepts**
- **Science Tutor**

Holt Lab Generator CD-ROM

Search for any lab by topic, standard, difficulty level, or time. Edit any lab to fit your needs, or create your own labs. Use the Lab Materials QuickList software to customize your lab materials list.

Chapter Resources

Visual Resources

CHAPTER STARTER TRANSPARENCY

BELLRINGER TRANSPARENCIES

Section: Change Over Time

The cockroach originated on Earth over 250 million years ago and is thriving today all over the world. A giant deer that was 2 m tall first appeared less than 1 million years ago and became extinct around 11,000 years ago. Why do you think one animal thrived and the other one perished?

Record your answer in your **science journal**.

Section: How Does Evolution Happen?

The following are characteristics that almost all humans have in common: upright walking, hair, fingerprints, binocular vision, speech. List the advantages and disadvantages of each characteristic. Do you think the advantages are greater than the disadvantages? Why or why not?

Record your responses in your **science journal**.

TEACHING TRANSPARENCIES

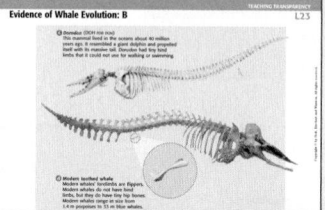
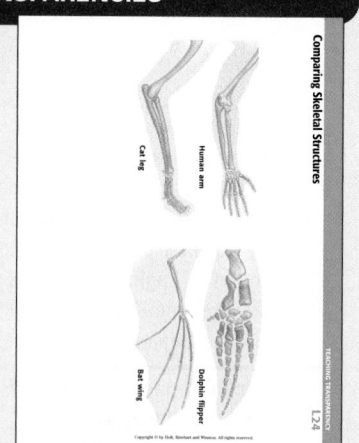

TEACHING TRANSPARENCIES

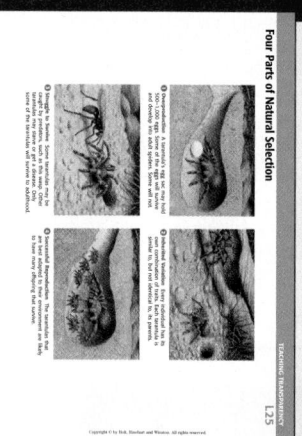
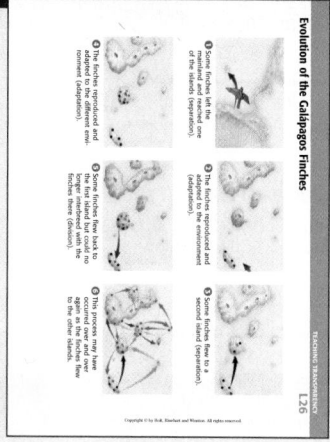
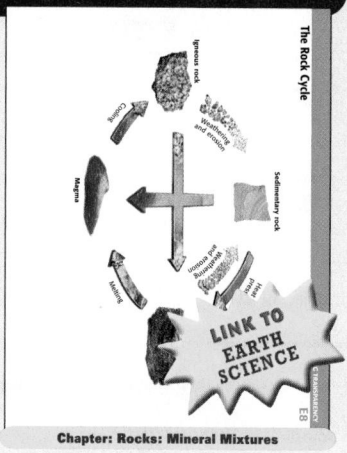

CONCEPT MAPPING TRANSPARENCY

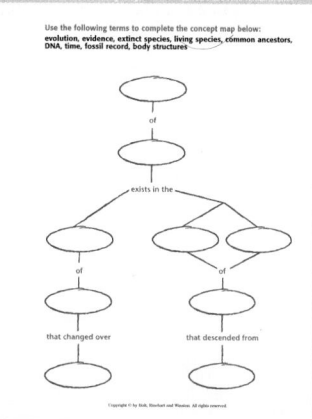

Planning Resources

LESSON PLANS

PARENT LETTER

TEST ITEM LISTING

One-Stop Planner® CD-ROM

This CD-ROM includes all of the resources shown here and the following time-saving tools:

- Lab Materials QuickList Software
- Customizable lesson plans
- Holt Calendar Planner
- The powerful ExamView® Test Generator

Meeting Individual Needs

DIRECTED READING A
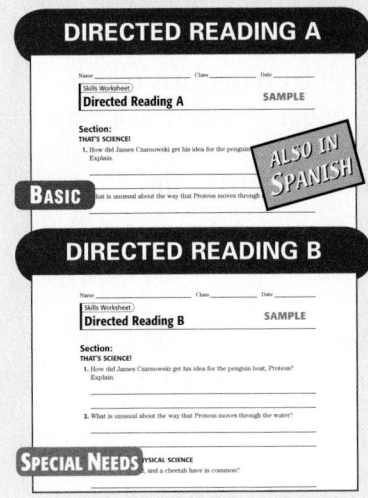
BASIC

VOCABULARY ACTIVITY
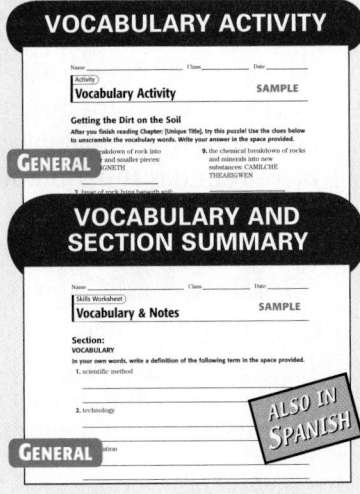
GENERAL

REINFORCEMENT
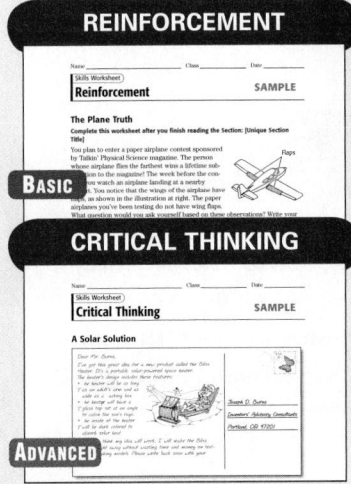
BASIC

SCILINKS ACTIVITY

GENERAL

DIRECTED READING B
SPECIAL NEEDS

VOCABULARY AND SECTION SUMMARY
GENERAL

CRITICAL THINKING
ADVANCED

SCIENCE PUZZLERS, TWISTERS & TEASERS
GENERAL

Labs and Activities

WHIZ-BANG DEMONSTRATIONS
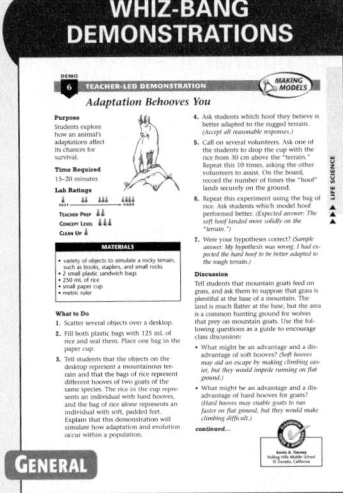
GENERAL

LONG-TERM PROJECTS & RESEARCH IDEAS
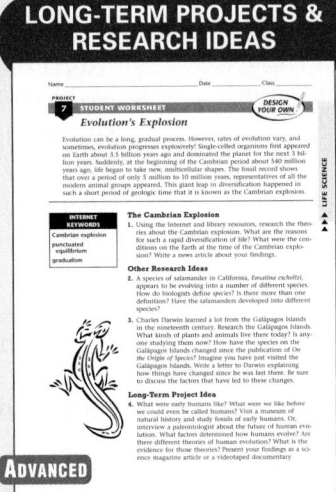
ADVANCED

DATASHEETS FOR QUICK LABS

DATASHEETS FOR CHAPTER LABS

DATASHEETS FOR LABBOOK

Review and Assessments

SECTION QUIZ
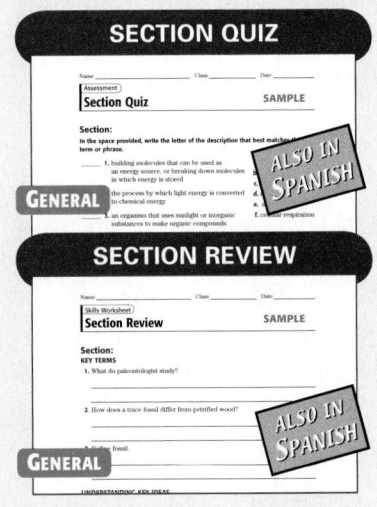
GENERAL

CHAPTER REVIEW
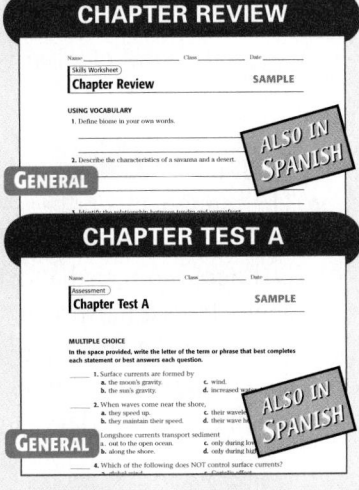
GENERAL

CHAPTER TEST B
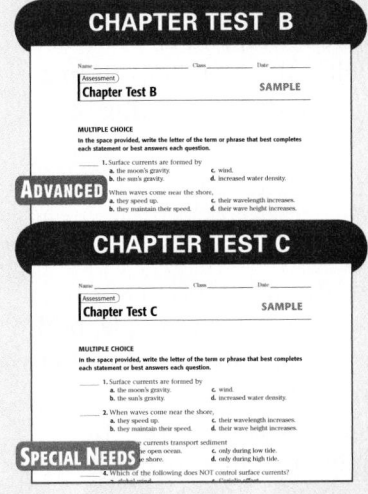
ADVANCED

STANDARDIZED TEST PREPARATION
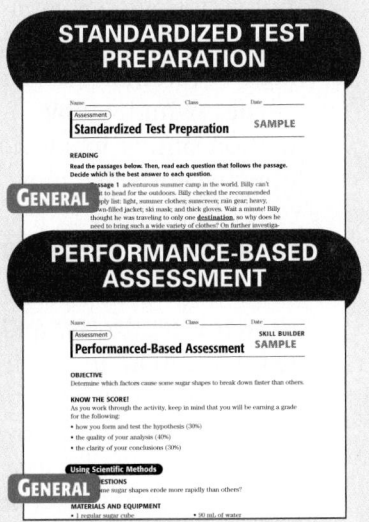
GENERAL

SECTION REVIEW
GENERAL

CHAPTER TEST A
GENERAL

CHAPTER TEST C
SPECIAL NEEDS

PERFORMANCE-BASED ASSESSMENT
GENERAL

This Chapter Enrichment provides relevant and interesting information to expand and enhance your presentation of the chapter material.

Section 1

Change over Time

Evolution of Whales and Other Mammals

- Scientists think that all mammals evolved from a shrewlike ancestor. This ancestor survived the mass extinction that wiped out the dinosaurs about 65 million years ago. This hypothesis is supported by fossils formed during and after the time of the dinosaurs.

- The first ocean-dwelling mammals appeared in the fossil record about 50 million years ago. Scientists think that these mammals were the ancestors of whales and shared an ancestor with the artiodactyl group (even-toed, hoofed mammals). However, other types of aquatic mammals, such as dugongs, manatees, and sea lions, probably evolved separately and from later branches of the mammal lineage.

- In many ways, whales are more similar to their hoofed mammal relatives than they are to fish. Similarities include internal structures, behavior, and DNA. Also, whales swim by moving their tails up and down, in a motion similar to a gallop and to the swimming of an otter, whereas fish move their tails sideways.

Homologous Structures

- *Homologous structures* are anatomical features that have similar evolutionary and embryological origins and exhibit similar anatomical patterns. For example, bird wings, human arms, whale flippers, and deer forelimbs are all homologous. However, bird wings and butterfly wings are *analogous structures* because they function similarly but are anatomically dissimilar.

- Cellular components and biochemicals may also be homologous. For example, hemoglobin molecules from different vertebrate species have similar amino-acid sequences. But hemocyanin, which transports oxygen in crabs, has a very different sequence and is therefore analogous to hemoglobin; that is, the two molecules have a similar function but different structure.

Is That a Fact!

- ◆ The California halibut belongs to the family Bothidae, also known as the *left-eyed flounders*. Despite the name, about 40% of California halibut adults have both eyes on the right side of their body.

Convergent Evolution

- When scientists study the fossils, skeletons, and DNA of species thought to be related, the scientists sometimes find that the organisms are not related at all. For example, the jerboa and the kangaroo rat look almost identical, but scientists have concluded that they have different ancestors. Such cases illustrate *convergent evolution*, where different species developed similar adaptations to similar environmental conditions and roles.

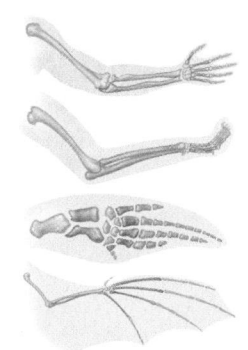

Frozen Fossils

- In some cases, scientists can obtain DNA from ancient tissues that have not completely decomposed or fossilized. Two Japanese geneticists are hoping to create a mammoth-elephant hybrid by using tissue from a Siberian mammoth that died and was frozen thousands of years ago. However, the chances of finding intact DNA are small, and the genetic structures of mammoths and elephants are not fully compatible.

Is That a Fact!

- ◆ The human appendix is a *vestigial organ,* or an organ that performs little or no apparent function but that is thought to have had a function in ancestors. The appendix is a narrow tube attached to the large intestine. In chimpanzees, gorillas, and orangutans, the appendix is an intestinal sac that helps them digest tough plant material.

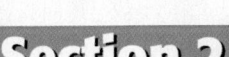

Section 2

How Does Evolution Happen?

Alfred Russel Wallace

- Alfred Wallace (1823–1913) was born in England. He came from a poor family and had no formal scientific education. Though originally interested in botany, he began to study insects with the encouragement of British naturalist Henry Walter Bates, whom Wallace met when he was about 20 years old. Bates and Wallace explored the Amazon from 1848 to 1852 and found much evidence to support a theory of evolution by natural selection.

- From 1854 to 1862, Wallace traveled in the Malay Archipelago to find more evidence of evolution. In 1855, he published a preliminary essay, "On the Law Which Has Regulated the Introduction of New Species." Meanwhile, nearly 20 years after Charles Darwin's voyage on the HMS *Beagle,* Darwin was still mulling over his data. In 1858, Wallace mailed an essay to Darwin that explained Wallace's theory that natural selection pressures species to change.

- In July 1858, Wallace's essay was presented along with a paper by Darwin at a meeting of the Linnean Society in London. In the following year, after nearly two decades of delay (because of his doubts and repeated analysis), Darwin published *On the Origin of Species by Means of Natural Selection.*

Charles Lyell

- Charles Lyell (1797–1875), the eldest of 10 children, was born in Scotland and raised in England. He traveled with his father, who was a naturalist, to collect butterflies and aquatic insects. Lyell continued this informal research throughout college. Lyell's research in geology led him to the belief that natural processes occurring over millions of years have shaped Earth's features. This idea was known as *uniformitarianism.* Lyell's work influenced Darwin's formulation of the theory of natural selection.

Section 3

Natural Selection in Action

Adaptive Coloration

- Penguins, puffins, killer whales, and blue sharks are just some of the ocean animals that have white bellies and black or dark blue dorsal surfaces. This type of coloration is called *countershading.* When seen from below, the white underside helps the animal blend into the lighter sky above the water. When viewed from above, the dark coloration makes the animal difficult to see against the ocean depths.

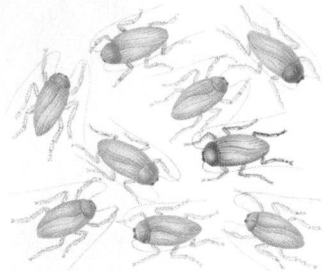

Sexual Selection

- *Sexual selection* is the term for the selection of traits that is brought about by a specific pattern of mating. In many sexual organisms, members of one sex must compete with each other for access to mates. Biologists think this behavior results when one sex's investment in the next generation is greater than the other sex's. At an extreme, the "choosiness" of one sex may drive the evolution of traits that confer no apparent advantage to the opposite sex. The long tails and colorful plumage of many male birds are considered examples of such "runaway sexual selection."

SC*i*LINKS®

NSTA
Developed and maintained by the
National Science Teachers Association

SciLinks is maintained by the National Science Teachers Association to provide you and your students with interesting, up-to-date links that will enrich your classroom presentation of the chapter.

Visit www.scilinks.org and enter the SciLinks code for more information about the topic listed.

Topic: Species and Adaptation
SciLinks code: HSM1433

Topic: Fossil Record
SciLinks code: HSM0615

Topic: Galápagos Islands
SciLinks code: HSM0631

Topic: Darwin and Natural Selection
SciLinks code: HSM0378

Overview

Tell students that this chapter will introduce them to *evolution* —the process by which populations on Earth change over time. Evolution helps explain the variations and adaptations that we see in organisms around us and in evidence of the past.

Assessing Prior Knowledge

Students should be familiar with the following topics:

- scientific methods and models
- heredity and genetics

Identifying Misconceptions

Students may have heard that evolution is "just a theory." But in academic biology, evolution (defined as the process by which species change over time) is accepted in the way that "cell theory" is now accepted. Furthermore, the theory of evolution by natural selection (integrated with modern genetic knowledge) is considered to be strongly supported and widely accepted. Specific models, mechanisms, rates, and other aspects of evolution continue to be investigated and debated among scientists, but few biologists doubt that evolution happens.

The Evolution of Living Things

The Big Idea

Biological evolution explains how populations change over time.

About the Photo

Can you find two eyes and a mouth in this photo? The eyes and mouth belong to an adult flounder. Adult flounders swim on their sides and have both eyes on one side of their body. These characteristics allow flounders to lie flat and still see all of their surroundings. Flounders also look like the sandy bottoms of coastal areas. These adaptations help flounders survive in their environment.

PRE-READING ACTIVITY

Graphic Organizer

Concept Map Before you read the chapter, create the graphic organizer entitled "Concept Map" described in the **Study Skills** section of the Appendix. As you read the chapter, fill in the concept map with details about evolution and natural selection.

Standards Correlations

National Science Education Standards

The following codes indicate the National Science Education Standards that correlate to this chapter. The full text of the standards is at the front of the book.

Chapter Opener
UCP 2, 5; SAI 1, 2; LS 1a, 5a

Section 1 Change over Time
UCP 2, 4, 5; SAI 2; HNS 2; LS 2e, 3a, 3d, 4a, 5a, 5b, 5c

Section 2 How Does Evolution Happen?
UCP 1, 2, 4, 5; SAI 1, 2; SPSP 2, 5; HNS 1, 2, 3; LS 2a, 2b, 2d, 2e, 3d, 5a, 5b

Section 3 Natural Selection in Action
UCP 1, 3, 4; SPSP 4, 5; LS 2a, 2e, 3d, 4d, 5b

Chapter Lab
UCP 2, 4; SAI 1, 2

Chapter Review
SAI 2; SPSP 4; HNS 1, 2, 3; LS 2e, 3d, 4a, 5a, 5b, 5c

Science in Action
SPSP 2, 4, 5; HNS 1, 3

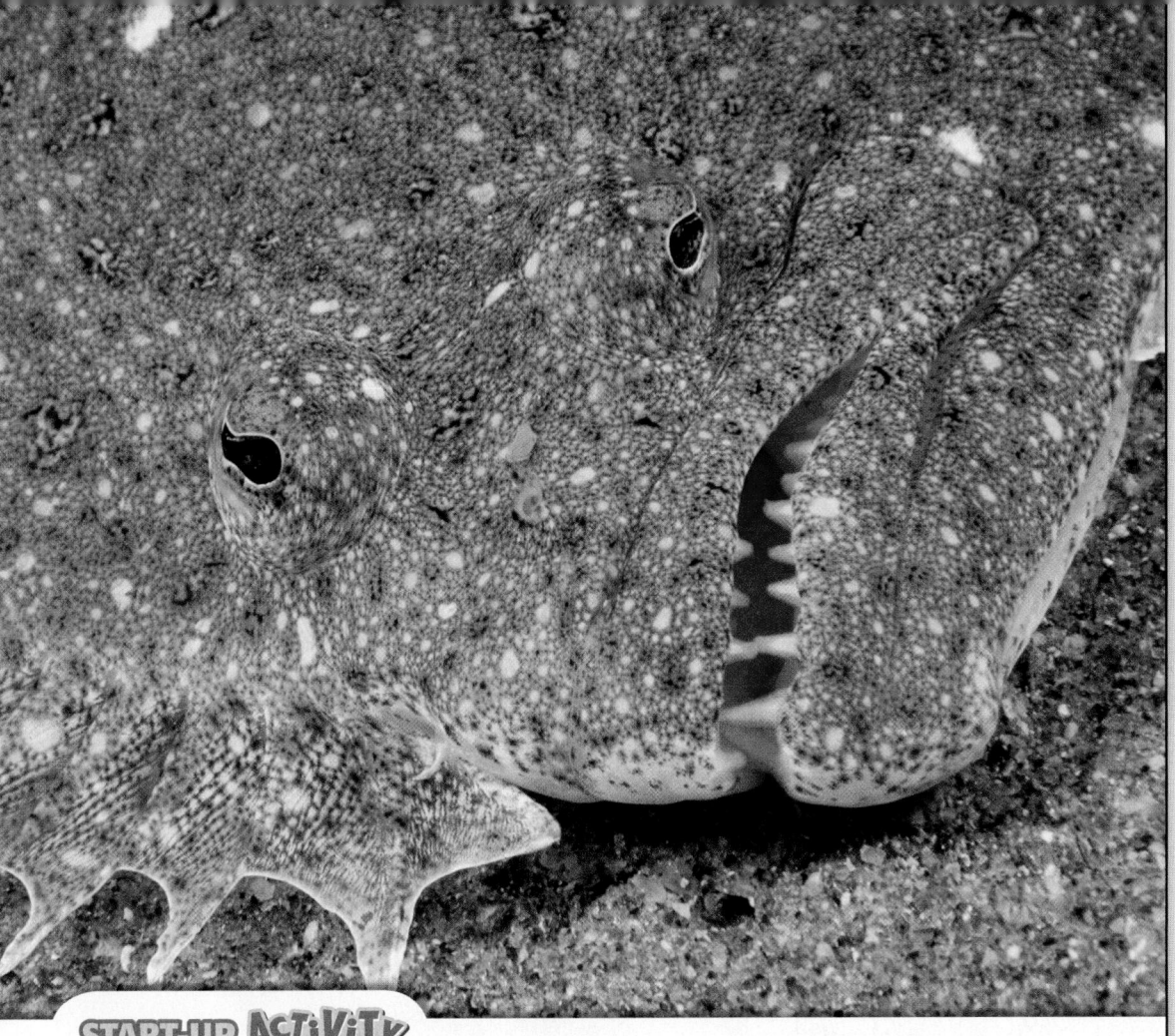

START-UP ACTIVITY

MATERIALS

FOR EACH PAIR
- cloth, white, approximately 20 cm × 20 cm
- marshmallows, colored (all same color), miniature (25)
- marshmallows, white, miniature (25)

Teacher's Note: Newspaper can be used as an alternative to marshmallows in this activity. Instead of using marshmallows, punch 25 holes from the classified section of a newspaper and 25 holes from newsprint in multiple colors, such as the Sunday comics. Instead of using cloth, use the newspaper for the background. Spread the holes on the paper, and have the "hunter" pick up as many as he or she can in 15 s. Tally the results.

Answers

1. Answers may vary, but students are likely to pick up more colored marshmallows than white ones.

2. Sample answer: The marshmallows represent organisms that could be eaten; the cloth represents the area where they live.

3. Sample answer: Many organisms in the wild blend into their surroundings by having colors or patterns that make them hard to see. This might help them hide from things trying to eat them. A weakness of this model is that it's very simple—a real "wild" environment would be more than two colors and would contain a variety of organisms.

START-UP ACTIVITY

Out of Sight, Out of Mind

In this activity, you will see how traits can affect the success of an organism in a particular environment.

Procedure

1. Count out **25 colored marshmallows** and **25 white marshmallows.**

2. Ask your partner to look away while you spread the marshmallows out on a **white cloth.** Do not make a pattern with the marshmallows. Now, ask your partner to turn around and pick the first marshmallow that he or she sees.

3. Repeat step 2 ten times.

Analysis

1. How many white marshmallows did your partner pick? How many colored marshmallows did he or she pick?

2. What did the marshmallows and the cloth represent in your investigation? What effect did the color of the cloth have?

3. When an organism blends into its environment, the organism is *camouflaged.* How does this activity model camouflaged organisms in the wild? What are some weaknesses of this model?

Chapter Starter Transparency
Use this transparency to help students begin thinking about changes in species over time.

CHAPTER RESOURCES

Technology

 Transparencies
- Chapter Starter Transparency

 READING SKILLS

 Student Edition on CD-ROM

Guided Reading Audio CD
- English or Spanish

 **Classroom Videos**
- Brain Food Video Quiz

Workbooks

 Science Puzzlers, Twisters & Teasers
- The Evolution of Living Things GENERAL

Focus

Overview

This section introduces the concept of evolution as change over time in populations of organisms. Students will survey evidence used to understand evolution and determine ancestry, including the fossil record and comparisons of organisms' physical and genetic traits.

🔊 Bellringer

Have students respond to the following prompt: "The cockroach originated on Earth more than 250 million years ago and is thriving today all over the world. A giant deer (more than 2 m tall!) evolved less than 1 million years ago and became extinct around 11,000 years ago. Why do you think one animal thrived and the other perished?" (Accept all reasonable answers.)

Motivate

Discussion ——— GENERAL

Adaptation Ask students if a polar bear could live comfortably in Hawaii. Ask if a fish could survive in a forest. Why or why not? Discuss various characteristics of animals, such as physical adaptations, that make the animals well suited for a specific environment. Verbal

---

What You Will Learn

● Identify two kinds of evidence that show that organisms have evolved.

● Describe one pathway through which a modern whale could have evolved from an ancient mammal.

● Explain how comparing organisms can provide evidence that they have ancestors in common.

Vocabulary

adaptation   fossil
species   fossil record
evolution

READING STRATEGY

Paired Summarizing Read this section silently. In pairs, take turns summarizing the material. Stop to discuss ideas that seem confusing.

Change over Time

If someone asked you to describe a frog, you might say that a frog has long hind legs, has bulging eyes, and croaks. But what color skin would you say that a frog has?

Once you start to think about frogs, you realize that frogs differ in many ways. These differences set one kind of frog apart from another. The frogs in **Figures 1, 2,** and **3** look different from each other, yet they may live in the same areas.

Differences Among Organisms

As you can see, each frog has a different characteristic that might help the frog survive. A characteristic that helps an organism survive and reproduce in its environment is called an **adaptation.** Adaptations may be physical, such as a long neck or striped fur. Or adaptations may be behaviors that help an organism find food, protect itself, or reproduce.

Living things that have the same characteristics may be members of the same species. A **species** is a group of organisms that can mate with one another to produce fertile offspring. For example, all strawberry poison arrow frogs are members of the same species and can mate with each other to produce more strawberry poison arrow frogs. Groups of individuals of the same species living in the same place make up a *population*.

✓ Reading Check How can you tell that organisms are members of the same species? (*See the Appendix for answers to Reading Checks.*)

◀ **Figure 2** The bright coloring of the strawberry poison arrow frog warns predators that the frog is poisonous.

▼ **Figure 1** The red-eyed tree frog hides among a tree's leaves during the day and comes out at night.

Figure 3 The smokey jungle frog blends into the forest floor. ▶

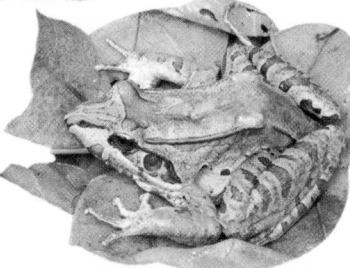

CHAPTER RESOURCES

Chapter Resource File

- Lesson Plan
- Directed Reading A BASIC
- Directed Reading B SPECIAL NEEDS

Technology

Transparencies
• Bellringer

Workbooks

Interactive Textbook Struggling Readers

Answer to Reading Check

Organisms are members of the same species if they mate with each other and produce fertile offspring.

Do Species Change over Time?

In a single square mile of rain forest, there may be dozens of species of frogs. Across the Earth, there are millions of different species of organisms. The species that live on Earth today range from single-celled bacteria, which lack cell nuclei, to multicellular fungi, plants, and animals. Have these species always existed on Earth?

Scientists think that Earth has changed a great deal during its history, and that living things have changed, too. Scientists estimate that the planet is 4.6 billion years old. Since life first appeared on Earth, many species have died out, and many new species have appeared. **Figure 4** shows some of the species that have existed during Earth's history.

Scientists observe that species have changed over time. They also observe that the inherited characteristics in populations change over time. Scientists think that as populations change over time, new species form. Thus, newer species descend from older species. The process in which populations gradually change over time is called **evolution.** Scientists continue to develop theories to explain exactly how evolution happens.

adaptation a characteristic that improves an individual's ability to survive and reproduce in a particular environment

species a group of organisms that are closely related and can mate to produce fertile offspring

evolution the process in which inherited characteristics within a population change over generations such that new species sometimes arise

Figure 4 *This diagram shows some of the many kinds of organisms that have lived on Earth since the planet formed 4.6 billion years ago.*

Is That a Fact!

There are more than 100,000 living mollusk species, and at least 35,000 extinct forms are known from the fossil record. As a group, mollusks are very successful—there have been mollusks on Earth for nearly 600 million years.

WEIRD SCIENCE

The gastric brooding frogs of Australia, now extinct, incubated their tadpoles in their stomachs and gave birth to their young through their mouths!

Using the Figure—GENERAL

Species and Change Ask students to compare the frogs in **Figures 1, 2,** and **3** and discuss the unique adaptations of each. Ask students: "If you see a frog that looks like one of these frogs, can you assume that they are both the same species? (no, not necessarily) How can you tell? (by whether they breed with each other or not.) Next, have students look at **Figure 4.** Ask them how they think changes in the planet could have affected the appearance and disappearance of so many types of organisms over time. (Sample answer: Temperature fluctuations due to ice ages and other climatic changes would have affected which plants and animals could survive. Climate changes caused changes in the vegetation and in the availability of food for animals. Until the planet was able to support a lot of vegetation, there wouldn't have been much food for animals to eat.) **LS** Visual/Verbal

Discussion——BASIC

Populations Versus Species Understanding evolution requires understanding that changes in populations can lead to changes in species. Thus, students must be able to distinguish between populations and species. Reinforce these meanings with the following examples: All domestic cats are the same species. Those that live in one city may be a population, but cats that live in other cities are probably not part of the same population. All of the lizards of a given species that live on an island may be a single population and may be the only population of that species on the island. All humans are the same species, but they have many populations. (Note that even biologists are sometimes unsure about the designation of closely related groups of organisms.) **LS** Verbal

Historic Paleontologist
Mary Anning (1799–1847) made some of the most important fossil discoveries of her time. She was born in Lyme Regis in southern Great Britain, an area with many fossils. Her father, a cabinet-maker and amateur fossil collector, died when Anning was 11 years old, leaving the family in debt. Anning's fossil-finding skills provided the family with needed income. Even before she reached her teens, Anning had discovered part of the first *Ichthyosaurus* to be recognized by scientists in London.

In the early 1820s, a professional fossil collector sold his private collection and gave the proceeds to the Anning family. He recognized that they had contributed many specimens for scientific investigation. Soon after, Mary Anning took charge of the family fossil business. However, many of Anning's finds ended up uncredited. Many scientists could not accept that a person of her financial and educational background could have acquired such expertise. Have students research to find out one of Anning's significant fossil finds (For example, she discovered the first plesiosaur fossil.) **LS** Verbal

Answer to Reading Check

by their estimated ages and physical similarities

Figure 5 *The fossil on the left is of a trilobite, an ancient aquatic animal. The fossils on the right are of seed ferns.*

fossil the trace or remains of an organism that lived long ago, most commonly preserved in sedimentary rock

fossil record a historical sequence of life indicated by fossils found in layers of the Earth's crust

Evidence of Changes over Time

Evidence that organisms have changed over time is buried within Earth's crust. The layers are made up of different kinds of rock and soil stacked on top of each other. These layers form when *sediments*, particles of sand, dust, or soil, are carried by wind and water and are deposited in an orderly fashion. Older layers are deposited before newer layers and are buried deeper within Earth.

Fossils

The remains or imprints of once-living organisms found in layers of rock called **fossils.** Examples of fossils are shown in **Figure 5.** Fossils can be complete organisms, parts of organisms, or just a set of footprints. Fossils usually form when a dead organism is covered by a layer of sediment. Over time, more sediment settles on top of the organism. Minerals in the sediment may seep into the organism and gradually replace the organism with stone. If the organism rots away completely after being covered, it may leave an imprint of itself in the rock.

The Fossil Record

By studying fossils, scientists have made a timeline of life known as the **fossil record.** The fossil record organizes fossils by their estimated ages and physical similarities. Fossils found in newer layers of Earth's crust tend to be similar to present-day organisms. This similarity indicates that the fossilized organisms were close relatives of present-day organisms. Fossils from older layers are less similar to present-day organisms than fossils from newer layers are. The older fossils are of earlier life-forms, which may not exist anymore.

✔ **Reading Check** How does the fossil record organize fossils?

CONNECTION to *Earth Science* —— GENERAL

Rock Layers Using sedimentary layers as reference points, scientists can find the relative age of a fossil. Use the teaching transparency entitled "The Rock Cycle" to illustrate the ways that sedimentary rock is continually formed on Earth. Tell students that a common way for fossils to form is for an organism to be buried under sediment that becomes sedimentary rock. Point out that a layer of sedimentary rock can form only on top of older rock. **LS** Visual

Evidence of Ancestry

The fossil record provides evidence about the order in which species have existed. Scientists observe that all living organisms have characteristics in common and inherit characteristics in similar ways. So, scientists think that all living species descended from common ancestors. Evidence of common ancestors can be found in fossils and in living organisms.

Drawing Connections

Scientists examine the fossil record to figure out the relationships between extinct and living organisms. Scientists draw models, such as the one shown in **Figure 6,** that illustrate their hypotheses. The short horizontal line at the top left in the diagram represents a species that lived in the past. Each branch in the diagram represents a group of organisms that descended from that species.

Scientists think that whales and some types of hoofed mammals have a common ancestor, as **Figure 6** shows. This ancestor was probably a mammal that lived on land between 50 million and 70 million years ago. During this time period, the dinosaurs died out and a variety of mammals appeared in the fossil record. The first ocean-dwelling mammals appeared about 50 million years ago. Scientists think that all mammal species alive today evolved from common ancestors.

Scientists have named and described hundreds of thousands of living and ancient species. Scientists use information about these species to sketch out a "tree of life" that includes all known organisms. But scientists know that their information is incomplete. For example, parts of Earth's history lack a fossil record. In fact, fossils are rare because specific conditions are necessary for fossils to form.

CONNECTION TO Geology

Sedimentary Rock Fossils are most often found in sedimentary rock. *Sedimentary rock* usually forms when rock is broken into sediment by wind, water, and other means. The wind and water move the sediment around and deposit it. Over time, layers of sediment pile up. Lower layers are compressed and changed into rock. Find out if your area has any sedimentary rocks that contain fossils. Mark the location of such rocks on a copy of a local map.

ACTIVITY

Figure 6 *This diagram is a model of the proposed relationships between ancient and modern mammals that have characteristics similar to whales.*

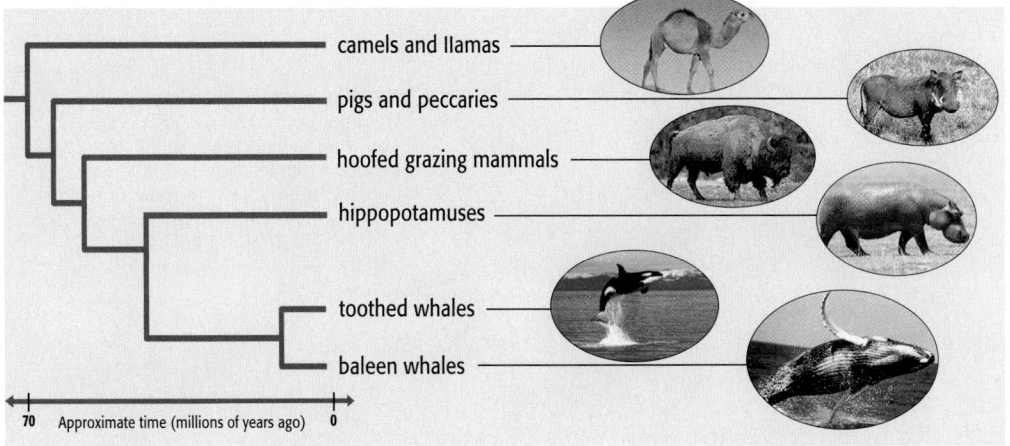

- camels and llamas
- pigs and peccaries
- hoofed grazing mammals
- hippopotamuses
- toothed whales
- baleen whales

70 — Approximate time (millions of years ago) — 0

CONNECTION ACTIVITY Math — ADVANCED

Species Countdown Present the following scenario to students: Imagine that you are a scientific time traveler assigned to count the species in your home state 1,000 years from now. You know that, at present, your home state contains 2,300 animal species and 4,500 plant species. But many species are becoming endangered or extinct. Only 55% of the state's species are expected to remain in existence after 1,000 years. How many species should you expect to count during your visit to the future? (Tip: Round your answer to two significant figures.) (animals: 2,300 × 0.55 = approximately 1,300; plants: 4,500 × 0.55 = approximately 2,500) **LS Logical**

MISCONCEPTION ALERT

Adaptation on Purpose? Students commonly confuse evolutionary adaptation with intentional change. For example, a student might say that an organism "learns" to adapt or "grows" an adaptation to a changing environment. Explain to students that the evolution of adaptations happens to populations over many generations. Evolution never happens within a single individual. And new traits arise by chance and become adaptations in a population only if those traits are both advantageous to individuals and inherited by individuals' offspring. Students may also confuse evolutionary adaptation with acclimation, such as adjustment to seasonal changes. Adaptations that enable a type of organism to adjust to changing conditions can evolve, but adaptations evolve only if traits conferring the adaptations are passed on to future generations.

How Many Toes? Hoofed mammals, or *ungulates*, are classified into two major groups. The even-toed *artiodactyls* have either two or four toes on each foot. Examples are pigs, deer, and cows. The odd-toed *perissodactyls* carry their weight on a middle toe. Examples are horses, zebras, tapirs, and rhinoceroses. All ungulates have similar foot and ankle bones.

SCIENCE HUMOR

Q: How did the dinosaurs listen to music?

A: on their fossil records

Using the Figure—GENERAL

Evidence of Whale Evolution
Have students examine each of the skeletons in **Figure 7** carefully. Ask them to describe one similarity and one difference between each successive species. (Sample answer: *Pakicetus* and *Ambulocetus* have similar limbs and feet, but the limbs of *Ambulocetus* are shorter in proportion to its body.)
LS Visual/Logical   English Language Learners

CONNECTION ACTIVITY
Art——————ADVANCED

Scientific Illustration The role of a scientific illustrator is to create accurate pictures of organisms and objects that scientists study. In the case of long-extinct species, such as dinosaurs, artists must sometimes fill in where science leaves off. Have students look for and compare several examples of illustrations of a specific extinct organism. Have students try to identify ways in which artistic interpretation is used. For comparison, show students examples of similar illustrations from hundreds of years ago, when much less was known about many fossil organisms.   English Language Learners
LS Visual

Answer to Reading Check
a four-legged land mammal

Examining Organisms

Examining an organism carefully can give scientists clues about its ancestors. For example, whales seem similar to fish. But unlike fish, whales breathe air, give birth to live young, and produce milk. These traits show that whales are *mammals*. Thus, scientists think that whales evolved from ancient mammals.

Case Study: Evolution of the Whale

Scientists think that the ancient ancestor of whales was probably a mammal that lived on land and that could run on four legs. A more recent ancestor was probably a mammal that spent time both on land and in water. Comparisons of modern whales and a large number of fossils have supported this hypothesis. **Figure 7** illustrates some of this evidence.

✓ **Reading Check** What kind of organism do scientists think was an ancient ancestor of whales?

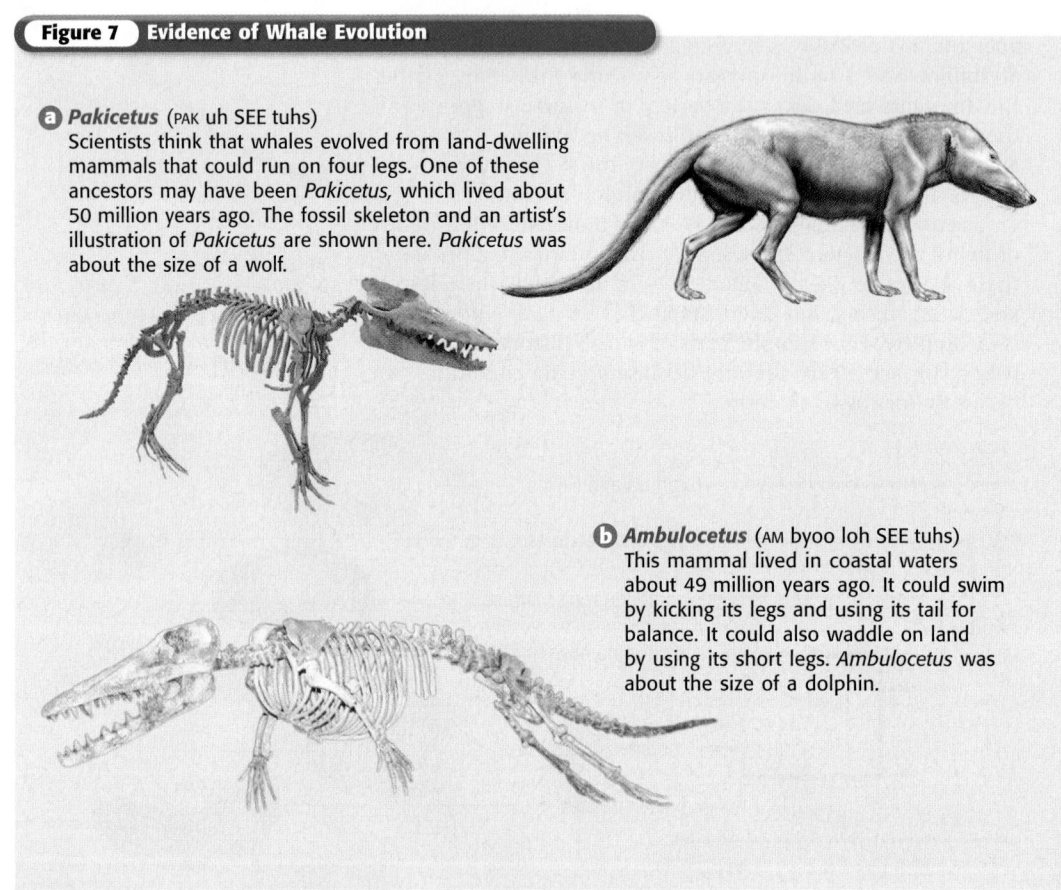

Figure 7 **Evidence of Whale Evolution**

ⓐ *Pakicetus* (PAK uh SEE tuhs)
Scientists think that whales evolved from land-dwelling mammals that could run on four legs. One of these ancestors may have been *Pakicetus,* which lived about 50 million years ago. The fossil skeleton and an artist's illustration of *Pakicetus* are shown here. *Pakicetus* was about the size of a wolf.

ⓑ *Ambulocetus* (AM byoo loh SEE tuhs)
This mammal lived in coastal waters about 49 million years ago. It could swim by kicking its legs and using its tail for balance. It could also waddle on land by using its short legs. *Ambulocetus* was about the size of a dolphin.

CHAPTER RESOURCES

Technology

📦 **Transparencies**
- L22 Evidence of Whale Evolution: A
- L23 Evidence of Whale Evolution: B

SUPPORT FOR

English Language Learners

Evidence Students may not understand the word evidence. Help students define the word. Then, have them read the diagram on whale evolution and, in a discussion setting, list the evidence that whale ancestors lived on land. They may combine what they know about whales with information from the diagram to fill out the list. (live births, milk-producing, air breathing, tiny hip bones for legs not needed in water)
LS Verbal

Walking Whales

The organisms in **Figure 7** form a sequence between ancient four-legged mammals and modern whales. Several pieces of evidence indicate that these species are related by ancestry. Each species shared some traits with an earlier species. However, some species had new traits that were shared with later species. Yet, each species had traits that allowed it to survive in a particular time and place in Earth's history.

Further evidence can be found inside the bodies of living whales. For example, although modern whales do not have hind limbs, inside their bodies are tiny hip bones, as shown in **Figure 7**. Scientists think that these hip bones were inherited from the whales' four-legged ancestors. Scientists often look at this kind of evidence when they want to determine the relationships between organisms.

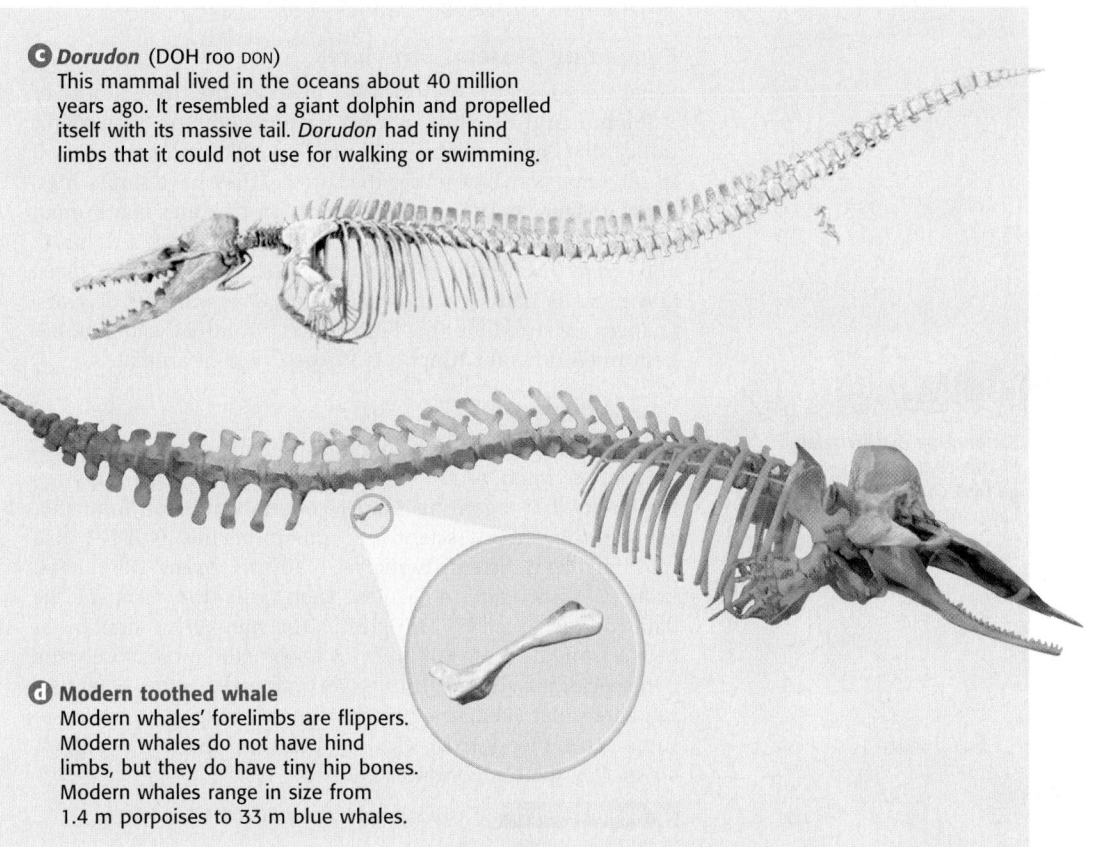

c *Dorudon* (DOH roo DON)
This mammal lived in the oceans about 40 million years ago. It resembled a giant dolphin and propelled itself with its massive tail. *Dorudon* had tiny hind limbs that it could not use for walking or swimming.

d Modern toothed whale
Modern whales' forelimbs are flippers. Modern whales do not have hind limbs, but they do have tiny hip bones. Modern whales range in size from 1.4 m porpoises to 33 m blue whales.

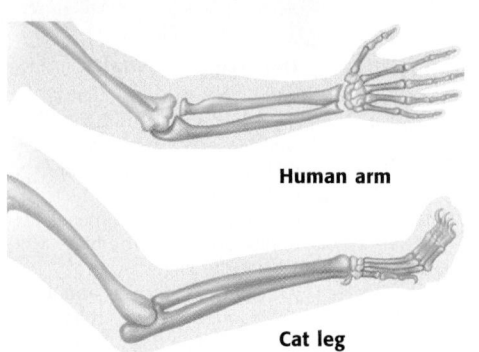

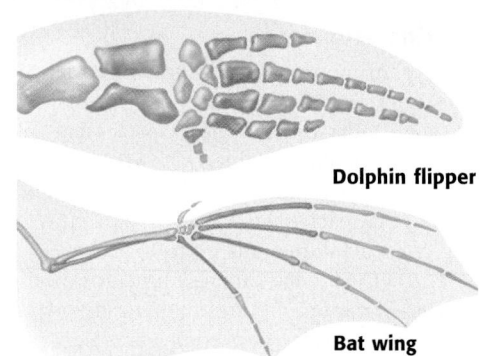

Human arm

Cat leg

Dolphin flipper

Bat wing

Figure 8 *The bones in the front limbs of these animals are similar. Similar bones are shown in the same color. These limbs are different sizes in life.*

Comparing Organisms

Evidence that groups of organisms have common ancestry can be found by comparing the groups' DNA. Because every organism inherits DNA, every organism inherits the traits determined by DNA. Organisms contain evidence that populations and species undergo changes in traits and DNA over time.

Comparing Skeletal Structures

What do your arm, the front leg of a cat, the front flipper of a dolphin, and the wing of a bat have in common? You might notice that these structures do not look alike and are not used in the same way. But under the surface, they have similarities. Look at **Figure 8.** The structure and order of bones of a human arm are similar to those of the front limbs of a cat, a dolphin, and a bat. These similarities suggest that cats, dolphins, bats, and humans had a common ancestor. Over millions of years, changes occurred in the limb bones. Eventually, the bones performed different functions in each type of animal.

Comparing DNA

When scientists compare organism's traits, such as skeletal structures, much of the information that they get supports the theory that organisms share a common ancestor. To further support this theory, scientists compare organisms' DNA at a molecular level. Scientists analyze many organisms' DNA, RNA, proteins, and other molecules. Then, scientists compare the data for each species. The greater the number of similarities between the data sets for any two species, the more closely the two species are related through a common ancestor. Scientists use molecular data, the comparison of traits, and fossils to support the theory that because all existing species have DNA, all species share a common ancestor.

✔ **Reading Check** If two species have similar DNA, what hypothesis is supported?

INTERNET ACTIVITY

For another activity related to this chapter, go to **go.hrw.com** and type in the keyword **HL5EVOW.**

Answer to Reading Check
that they have common ancestry

Is That a Fact!

In the late 1990s, analysis of genetic and hereditary molecular material from a variety of mammals showed that whales share more genetic similarities to hippopotamuses than to any other living mammal group.

SECTION Review

Summary

- Evolution is the process in which inherited characteristics within a population change over generations, sometimes giving rise to new species. Scientists continue to develop theories to explain how evolution happens.

- Evidence that organisms evolve can be found by comparing living organisms to each other and to the fossil record. Such comparisons provide evidence of common ancestry.

- Scientists think that modern whales evolved from an ancient, land-dwelling mammal ancestor. Fossil organisms that support this hypothesis have been found.

- Evidence of common ancestry among living organisms is provided by comparing DNA and inherited traits. Species that have a common ancestor will have traits and DNA that are more similar to each other than to those of distantly related species.

Using Key Terms

Complete each of the following sentences by choosing the correct term from the word bank.

adaptation	species
fossil	evolution

1. Members of the same ___ can mate with one another to produce offspring.

2. A(n) ___ helps an organism survive.

3. When populations change over time, ___ has occurred.

Understanding Key Ideas

4. A human's arm, a cat's front leg, a dolphin's front flipper, and a bat's wing
   a. have similar kinds of bones.
   b. are used in similar ways.
   c. are very similar to insect wings and jellyfish tentacles.
   d. have nothing in common.

5. How does the fossil record show that species have changed over time?

6. What evidence do fossils provide about the ancestors of whales?

Critical Thinking

7. **Making Comparisons** Other than the examples provided in the text, how are whales different from fishes?

8. **Forming Hypotheses** Is a person's DNA likely to be more similar to the DNA of his or her biological parents or to the DNA of one of his or her cousins? Explain your answer.

Interpreting Graphics

9. The photograph below shows the layers of sedimentary rock exposed during the construction of a road. Imagine that a species that lived 200 million years ago is found in layer **b**. Would the species' ancestor, which lived 250 million years ago, most likely be found in layer **a** or in layer **c**? Explain your answer.

For a variety of links related to this chapter, go to www.scilinks.org
Topic: Species and Adaptation; Fossil Record
SciLinks code: HSM1433; HSM0615

Answers to Section Review

1. species
2. adaptation
3. evolution
4. a
5. Sample answer: Fossils of types of organisms that no longer exist are found. These fossils form a sequence of change and adaptation of populations of organisms over time.
6. Sample answer: There are fossils of four-legged land mammals that share some characteristics with modern whales and other hoofed mammals. Also, there is a sequence of fossil organisms that have characteristics in between those of the ancient fossils and modern whales.
7. Sample answer: Whales breathe air with lungs (not gills) and breathe through a spout that is like a nasal passage. Whales swim in an up-and-down "galloping" motion, as otters do (not side to side as fish do).
8. Sample answer: A person's DNA is likely to be most similar to that of his or her biological parents, because the parents are most closely related to the person by birth.
9. layer c; That layer is under layer b, so layer c was probably deposited earlier than layer b and is thus older.

Homework ⎯⎯ GENERAL

Horse Evolution Report Have students research to find the four main ancestors of the horse known from the fossil record. (Eohippus, Mesohippus, Merychippus, Pliohippus) Ask students to make a poster that shows each ancestral horse in order of appearance and to write a paragraph about each one, explaining its unique physical characteristics. Students should conclude their reports with an explanation of the origin of wild horses in North America. **LS Verbal**

CHAPTER RESOURCES

Chapter Resource File

- Section Quiz GENERAL
- Section Review GENERAL
- Vocabulary and Section Summary GENERAL

Technology

Transparencies
- L24 Comparing Skeletal Structures

Focus

Overview

This section introduces students to Charles Darwin and his famous life history. Students will learn the observations and ideas that helped Darwin formulate his theory of natural selection. Finally, students will connect concepts of genetics to explanations of evolution.

 **Bellringer**

Have students respond to the following prompt: "The following are characteristics that almost all humans have in common: upright walking, hair, fingerprints, binocular vision, and speech. List the advantages and disadvantages of each characteristic." (Accept all reasonable answers.)

Motivate

Discussion ——— GENERAL

Dinosaurs Ask students to describe a dinosaur. Ask them to explain why there are no dinosaurs alive today. Ask why they think dinosaurs became extinct. (Sample answer: Dinosaurs were well adapted to their environment and lived over 150 million years on Earth. But a catastrophic event changed the environment faster than the dinosaurs could adapt, and they became extinct.) **LS** Verbal

How Does Evolution Happen?

Imagine that you are a scientist in the 1800s. Fossils of some very strange animals have been found. And some familiar fossils have been found where you would least expect them. How did seashells end up on the tops of mountains?

In the 1800s, geologists began to realize that the Earth is much older than anyone had previously thought. Evidence showed that gradual processes had changed the Earth's surface over millions of years. Some scientists saw evidence of evolution in the fossil record. However, no one had been able to explain *how* evolution happens—until Charles Darwin.

Charles Darwin

In 1831, 21-year-old Charles Darwin, shown in **Figure 1,** graduated from college. Like many young people just out of college, Darwin didn't know what he wanted to do with his life. His father wanted him to become a doctor, but seeing blood made Darwin sick. Although he eventually earned a degree in theology, Darwin was most interested in the study of plants and animals.

So, Darwin signed on for a five-year voyage around the world. He served as the *naturalist*—a scientist who studies nature—on the British ship the HMS *Beagle,* similar to the ship in **Figure 2.** During the trip, Darwin made observations that helped him form a theory about how evolution happens.

What You Will Learn

- List four sources of Charles Darwin's ideas about evolution.
- Describe the four parts of Darwin's theory of evolution by natural selection.
- Relate genetics to evolution.

Vocabulary

trait
selective breeding
natural selection

READING STRATEGY

Brainstorming The key idea of this section is natural selection. Brainstorm words and phrases related to natural selection.

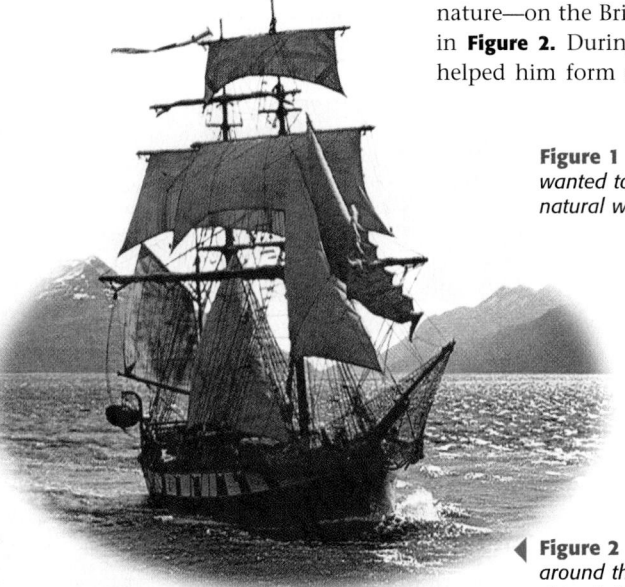

Figure 1 *Charles Darwin wanted to understand the natural world.*

Figure 2 *Darwin sailed around the world on a ship similar to this one.*

Homework ——— GENERAL

 Poster Project Have students research the natural history and current status of a specific sea turtle species to find examples for each of the four steps of natural selection. Have them construct a display to present their findings. Require them to include information about the turtle's reproductive habits, physical adaptations, and factors in its environment that affect its success. **LS** Verbal/Visual

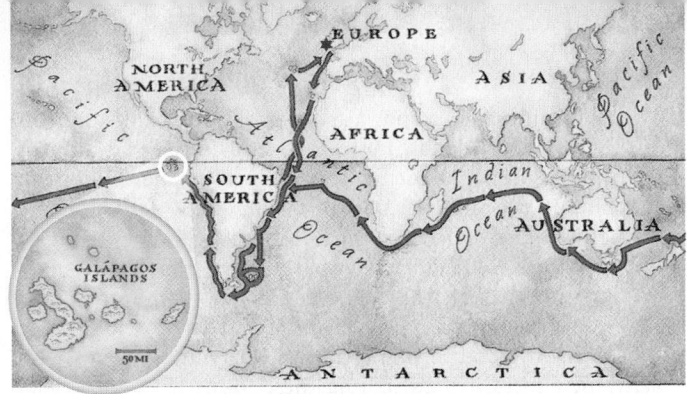

Figure 3 *The course of the HMS* Beagle *is shown by the red line. The journey began and ended in England.*

Darwin's Excellent Adventure

The *Beagle*'s journey is charted in **Figure 3.** Along the way, Darwin collected thousands of plant and animal samples. He kept careful notes of his observations. One interesting place that the ship visited was the Galápagos Islands. These islands are found 965 km (600 mi) west of Ecuador, a country in South America.

✔️ **Reading Check** **Where are the Galápagos Islands?** (*See the Appendix for answers to Reading Checks.*)

Darwin's Finches

Darwin noticed that the animals and plants on the Galápagos Islands were a lot like those in Ecuador. However, they were not exactly the same. The finches of the Galápagos Islands, for example, were a little different from the finches in Ecuador. And the finches on each island differed from the finches on the other islands. As **Figure 4** shows, the beak of each finch is adapted to the way the bird usually gets food.

| **Figure 4** Some Finches of the Galápagos Islands |

The **large ground finch** has a wide, strong beak that it uses to crack open big, hard seeds. This beak works like a nutcracker.

The **cactus finch** has a tough beak that it uses for eating cactus parts and insects. This beak works like a pair of needle-nose pliers.

The **warbler finch** has a small, narrow beak that it uses to catch small insects. This beak works like a pair of tweezers.

READING STRATEGY — GENERAL

Prediction Guide Before students read this page, have them answer the following questions:

• Why did the finches Darwin saw on the Galápagos Islands look similar to those he saw in South America?

• Why did they look a little different?

Have students share and evaluate their answers with a partner after they read the page.

LS Verbal/Intrapersonal

Homework — ADVANCED

Writing | **Island Biogeography Report** *Biogeography* is the study of where animals and plants are found and how they came to live in their particular location. Biogeography uses information from the fossil record and integrates ideas from biology, geology, paleontology, and chemistry. Encourage interested students to write a report about island biogeography. Have them include information about how biogeography is used to design and manage terrestrial wildlife refuges.

LS Verbal/ Intrapersonal

PORTFOLIO

Darwin's Thinking

After returning to England, Darwin puzzled over the animals of the Galápagos Islands. He tried to explain why the animals seemed so similar to each other yet had so many different adaptations. For example, Darwin hypothesized that the island finches were descended from South American finches. The first finches on the islands may have been blown from South America by a storm. Over many generations, the finches may have evolved adaptations for the various island environments.

During the course of his travels, Darwin came up with many new ideas. Before sharing these ideas, he spent several years analyzing his evidence and gathering ideas from other people.

Ideas About Breeding

In Darwin's time, farmers and breeders had produced many kinds of farm animals and plants. These plants and animals had traits that were desired by the farmers and breeders. A **trait** is a characteristic that can be passed from parent to offspring through genes. The process in which humans select which plants or animals to reproduce based on certain desired traits is called **selective breeding.** Most pets, such as the dogs in **Figure 5,** have been bred for various desired traits.

You can see the results of selective breeding in many kinds of organisms. For example, people have bred horses that are particularly fast or strong. And farmers have bred crops that produce large fruit or that grow in specific climates.

trait a genetically determined characteristic

selective breeding the human practice of breeding animals or plants that have certain desired traits

Figure 5 *Over the past 12,000 years, dogs have been selectively bred to produce more than 150 breeds.*

CONNECTION ACTIVITY
Geography — GENERAL

Bird Barrier Locate the Rocky Mountains on a map. Explain to students that bird-identification guides for North America usually classify birds into two groups: birds that are east of the Rocky Mountains and birds that are west of the Rocky Mountains. Brainstorm why ornithologists might use this system. (Sample answer: because the Rockies form a large geographical barrier)

LS Visual/Logical

Is That a Fact!

As a result of selective breeding, the smallest horse is the Falabella, which is only about 76 cm tall. The largest is the Shire, originally bred in England. The Shire can grow to more than 1.73 m high at the shoulder and weigh as much as 910 kg.

Population Growth Versus Food Supply

1. Get an **egg carton** and a **bag of rice**. Use a **marker** to label one row of the carton "Food supply." Then, label the second row "Human population."

2. In the row labeled "Food supply," place one grain of rice in the first cup. Place two grains of rice in the second cup, and place three grains of rice in the third cup. In each subsequent cup, place one more grain than you placed in the previous cup. Imagine that each grain represents enough food for one person's lifetime.

3. In the row labeled "Human population," place one grain of rice in the first cup. Place two grains in the second cup, and place four grains in the third cup. In each subsequent cup, place twice as many grains as you placed in the previous cup. This rice represents people.

4. How many units of food are in the sixth cup? How many "people" are in the sixth cup? If this pattern continued, what would happen?

5. Describe how the patterns in the food supply and in the human population differ. Explain how the patterns relate to Malthus's hypothesis.

MATERIALS

FOR EACH STUDENT
- egg carton, 12-egg size, empty (2)
- marker
- rice (about 1 cup) (or lentils or small pebbles)

Answers

4. There are 32 "people" and 6 units of "food." If this pattern continued, there would be a lot more people than food and not enough food to keep the people alive.

5. The human population is growing much faster than the food supply is. This growth pattern is similar to that in Malthus's prediction.

Ideas About Population

During Darwin's time, Thomas Malthus wrote a famous book entitled *An Essay on the Principle of Population.* Malthus noted that humans have the potential to reproduce rapidly. He warned that food supplies could not support unlimited population growth. **Figure 6** illustrates this relationship. However, Malthus pointed out that human populations are limited by choices that humans make or by problems such as starvation and disease.

After reading Malthus's work, Darwin realized that any species can produce many offspring. He also knew that the populations of all species are limited by starvation, disease, competition, and predation. Only a limited number of individuals survive to reproduce. Thus, there is something special about the survivors. Darwin reasoned that the offspring of the survivors inherit traits that help the offspring survive in their environment.

Malthus's Description of Unlimited Population Growth

Figure 6 *Malthus thought that the human population could increase more quickly than the food supply, with the result that there would not be enough food for everyone.*

Ideas About Earth's History

Darwin had begun to think that species could evolve over time. But most geologists at the time did not think that Earth was old enough to allow for slow changes. Darwin learned new ideas from *Principles of Geology,* a book by Charles Lyell. This book presented evidence that Earth had formed by natural processes over a long period of time. It became clear to Darwin that Earth was much older than anyone had imagined.

Reading Check What did Darwin learn from Charles Lyell?

Using the Figure—**ADVANCED**

Two Kinds of Growth Have students examine **Figure 6.** Ask students to describe the behavior of the graph for food supply. (It rises steadily in a straight line.) Explain that the line representing food supply indicates *linear growth* in which food supply increases by the *addtion of* a given amount of food in each time interval. Next, ask students to describe the behavior of the graph for human population. (It rises quickly in a curved line.) Explain that the line representing human population indicates *exponential growth,* in which human population increases by *multiplication* by a given percentage in each time interval. Ask students to suggest alternative titles for this graph. (Sample answer: "Human Population Growth Vs. Food Supply") **LS Visual/Logical**

Answer to Reading Check

that Earth had been formed by natural processes over a long period of time

Is That a Fact!

The full title of Thomas Malthus's famous essay was "An Essay on the Principle of Population, as it Affects the Future Improvement of Society with Remarks on the Speculations of Mr. Godwin, M. Condorcet, and Other Writers."

Science **Bloopers**

Malthus's work was important in influencing ecological scientists and prompting social planners to consider the potential problems of rapid population growth. However, Malthus was wrong in his projections of the growth of food supplies. The use of machinery, fossil fuels, and chemicals since his time enabled food production to increase more rapidly than Malthus thought possible.

Close

Reteaching — BASIC

 Terms Have students list the key terms and any unfamiliar terms from this chapter. For each term, they should write a definition and then write sample sentences using the term. **LS Verbal**

Quiz — GENERAL

1. Who was Charles Lyell? (He was a British geologist.)

2. What did Darwin learn from Lyell's data about the age of Earth? (Darwin learned from Lyell that Earth was old enough for slow changes to happen in a population.)

Alternative Assessment — ADVANCED

Writing **Darwin's Journal**
Charles Darwin's journals contain notes and records from his travels. Ask students to imagine that they are traveling with Darwin and keeping their own journals. Their notes and drawings should reflect what they see, what questions arise from their observations, and what hypotheses that they form. Encourage students to write journal entries about animals on the Galápagos Islands other than the finches, such as the Galápagos tortoise and marine iguanas. **LS Verbal/Intrapersonal**

Answer to Reading Check
Natural Selection is the process by which organisms that are better adapted to their environment survive and reproduce more successfully than less well adapted organisms do.

Darwin's Theory of Natural Selection

After his voyage on the HMS *Beagle*, Darwin privately struggled with his ideas for about 20 years. Then, in 1858, Darwin received a letter from a fellow naturalist named Alfred Russel Wallace. Wallace had arrived at the same ideas about evolution that Darwin had. In 1859, Darwin published a famous book called *On the Origin of Species by Means of Natural Selection*. In his book, Darwin proposed the theory that evolution happens through *natural selection*. **Natural selection** is the process by which organisms that are better adapted to their environment survive and reproduce more successfully than less well adapted organisms do. The process has four parts and is explained in **Figure 7.**

natural selection the process by which individuals that are better adapted to their environment survive and reproduce more successfully than less well adapted individuals do; a theory to explain the mechanism of evolution

✓ **Reading Check** What is natural selection?

Figure 7 Four Parts of Natural Selection

❶ **Overproduction** A tarantula's egg sac may hold 500–1,000 eggs. Some of the eggs will survive and develop into adult spiders. Some will not.

❷ **Inherited Variation** Every individual has its own combination of traits. Each tarantula is similar to, but not identical to, its parents.

❸ **Struggle to Survive** Some tarantulas may be caught by predators, such as this wasp. Other tarantulas may starve or get a disease. Only some of the tarantulas will survive to adulthood.

❹ **Successful Reproduction** The tarantulas that are best adapted to their environment are likely to have many offspring that survive.

ACTIVITY — BASIC

Natural Selection Have students carefully study **Figure 7** and begin to create their own table, concept map, or other graphic organizer about the four parts of natural selection. For each part of the figure, call on several students to restate the meaning in their own words, and then ask students to write their own version of the explanation on their graphic organizer. Finally, for each part, ask students to describe an additional example of the same process with another organism besides a tarantula. **LS Visual**

Science Bloopers

In 1809, French naturalist Jean Baptiste Lamarck's theory of evolution by *acquired characteristics* stated that if an animal changed a body part through use or nonuse, that change would be inherited by its offspring. For example, larger leg muscles as a result of extensive running would be passed on to the next generation. However, genetic studies in the 1930s and 1940s disproved this mechanism for inheriting traits.

Genetics and Evolution

Darwin lacked evidence for parts of his theory. For example, he knew that organisms inherit traits, but not *how* they inherit traits. He knew that there is great variation among organisms, but not *how* that variation occurs. Today, scientists have found most of the evidence that Darwin lacked. They know that variation happens as a result of differences in genes. Changes in genes may happen whenever organisms produce offspring. Some genes make an organism more likely to survive to reproduce. The process called *selection* happens when only organisms that carry these genes can survive to reproduce. New fossil discoveries and new information about genes add to scientists' understanding of natural selection and evolution.

SECTION Review

Summary

- Darwin explained that evolution occurs through natural selection. His theory has four parts:

  1. Each species produces more offspring than will survive to reproduce.
  2. Individuals within a population have slightly different traits.
  3. Individuals within a population compete with each other for limited resources.
  4. Individuals that are better equipped to live in an environment are more likely to survive to reproduce.

- Modern genetics helps explain the theory of natural selection.

Using Key Terms

1. In your own words, write a definition for the term *trait*.

2. Use the following terms in the same sentence: *selective breeding* and *natural selection*.

Understanding Key Ideas

3. Modern scientific explanations of evolution
   a. have replaced Darwin's theory.
   b. rely on genetics instead of natural selection.
   c. fail to explain how traits are inherited.
   d. combine the principles of natural selection and genetic inheritance.

4. Describe the observations that Darwin made about the species on the Galápagos Islands.

5. Summarize the ideas that Darwin developed from books by Malthus and Lyell.

6. Describe the four parts of Darwin's theory of evolution by natural selection.

7. What knowledge did Darwin lack that modern scientists now use to explain evolution?

Math Skills

8. In a sample of 80 beetles, 50 beetles had 4 spots each, and the rest had 6 spots each. What was the average number of spots per beetle?

Critical Thinking

9. **Making Comparisons** In selective breeding, humans influence the course of evolution. What determines the course of evolution in natural selection?

10. **Predicting Consequences** Suppose that an island in the Pacific Ocean was just formed by a volcano. Over the next million years, how might species evolve on this island?

For a variety of links related to this chapter, go to www.scilinks.org
Topic: Galápagos Islands;
Darwin and Natural Selection
SciLinks code: HSM0631; HSM0378

SCIENTISTS AT ODDS

Rate Debate Evolutionary scientists do not yet agree on how often new species arise. *Gradualism*, the theory that Darwin supported, holds that changes in species occur slowly and steadily over thousands of years. In the 1970s, Stephen Jay Gould and others proposed the theory of *punctuated equilibrium*, which holds that species can remain unchanged for millions of years until dramatic environmental changes prompt speciation.

CHAPTER RESOURCES

Chapter Resource File

- Section Quiz **GENERAL**
- Section Review **GENERAL**
- Vocabulary and Section Summary **GENERAL**
- Reinforcement Worksheet **BASIC**
- SciLinks Activity **GENERAL**
- Datasheet for Quick Lab

Technology

Transparencies
- L25 Four Parts of Natural Selection

Focus

Overview

In this section, students will see examples of natural selection at work. They will relate a species' generation time to its ability to adapt. Students will also examine the process of speciation.

Bellringer

Have students respond to the following prompt: "Write the four parts of natural selection, and create a mnemonic device to remember each part by using the first letter of the words." (Sample answer: Overproduction, genetic Variation, Struggle to survive, successful Reproduction; Olga's Vacation Seemed Relaxing.)

Motivate

Debate——————— GENERAL

People and Nature During the past several hundred years, a rapidly expanding human population has caused some species to become extinct either from habitat destruction or overhunting. Have students takes sides and debate the following issue: If people are as much a part of the environment as trees and birds are, are people's actions just parts of natural processes?
LS Verbal/Intrapersonal

What You Will Learn

● Give three examples of natural selection in action.
● Outline the process of speciation.

Vocabulary
generation time
speciation

READING STRATEGY

Prediction Guide Before reading this section, write the title of each heading in this section. Next, under each heading, write what you think you will learn.

Natural Selection in Action

Have you ever had to take an antibiotic? Antibiotics are supposed to kill bacteria. But sometimes, bacteria are not killed by the medicine. Do you know why?

A population of bacteria might develop an adaptation through natural selection. Most bacteria are killed by the chemicals in antibiotics. But a few of the bacteria have an adaptation that makes them naturally *resistant to,* or not killed by, the antibiotic. These few bacteria survive antibiotic treatment, continue to reproduce, and pass the adaptation to their offspring. After several generations, almost all the bacteria in the population carry the adaptation of antibiotic resistance.

Changes in Populations

The theory of natural selection explains how a population changes in response to its environment. Through ongoing natural selection, a population adapts to its environment. Well-adapted individuals will likely survive and reproduce.

Adaptation to Hunting

Changes in populations are sometimes observed when a new force affects the survival of individuals. Scientists think that hunting in Uganda is affecting Uganda's elephant population. In 1930, about 99% of the male elephants in one area had tusks. Only 1% of the elephants were born without tusks. Today, as many as 15% of the male elephants in that area lack tusks. What happened?

A male African elephant that has tusks is shown in **Figure 1.** The ivory of an elephant's tusks is very valuable. People hunt the elephants for their tusks. As a result, fewer of the elephants that have tusks survive to reproduce, and more of the tuskless elephants survive. When the tuskless elephants reproduce, they pass the tuskless trait to their offspring.

Figure 1 *The ivory tusks of African elephants are very valuable. Some elephants are born without tusks.*

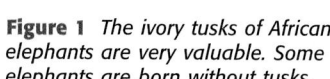

CHAPTER RESOURCES

Chapter Resource File

 • Lesson Plan
• Directed Reading A **BASIC**
• Directed Reading B **SPECIAL NEEDS**

Technology

 Transparencies
• Bellringer

Workbooks

Interactive Textbook Struggling Readers

MISCONCEPTION
///ALERT\\\

Tuskless Elephants It is important to understand that there were always some tuskless elephants in the wild populations. These animals were naturally tuskless—they were born without tusks and never developed tusks. Because the tuskless elephants are not hunted, they are more likely to pass their traits to future generations.

Figure 2 Natural Selection of Insecticide Resistance

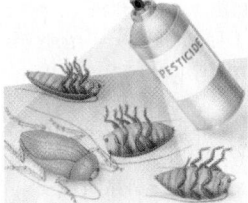

① An insecticide will kill most insects, but a few may survive. These survivors have genes that make them resistant to the insecticide.

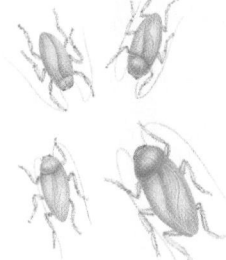

② The survivors then reproduce, passing the insecticide-resistance genes to their offspring.

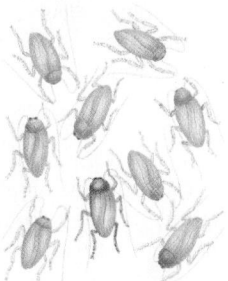

③ In time, the replacement population of insects is made up mostly of individuals that have the insecticide-resistance genes.

④ When the same kind of insecticide is used on the insects, only a few are killed because most of them are resistant to that insecticide.

Insecticide Resistance

To control insect pests, many people use insecticides, chemicals that kill insects. Sometimes, an insecticide that used to work well no longer affects an insect population. The reason is that a few insects in the population are resistant to the chemical. These insects survive insecticide treatment and pass the resistance trait to their offspring. **Figure 2** shows how an insect population becomes resistant to some insecticides.

Insect populations can evolve quickly because insects produce many offspring and have a short generation time. **Generation time** is the average time between one generation and the next.

✔**Reading Check** Why do insects quickly develop resistance to insecticides? (*See the Appendix for answers to Reading Checks.*)

generation time the period between the birth of one generation and the birth of the next generation

Competition for Mates

For organisms that reproduce sexually, competition for mates can select for adaptations. For example, in many bird species, females prefer to mate with colorful males. So, colorful males have more offspring than noncolorful males do. Because colorful males are more likely to pass on their genes to the next generation, the proportion of colorful males is likely to increase from generation to generation.

Section 3 • Natural Selection in Action 153

Reteaching — BASIC

Selection Have students place 20 black beans and 20 red beans on a piece of black paper. Call the display *Generation 1*. Tell students that the beans are fish and ask which would most likely be eaten first by the bean shark. Then tell them to add 5 black beans and take away 5 red ones. Call this *Generation 2*. Have students predict and model *Generation 3*. **LS** Visual

Quiz — GENERAL

Concept Mapping Construct a concept map that shows how a population of mosquitoes can develop resistance to a pesticide.

Alternative Assessment — ADVANCED

Species Report Have each student research and give an oral presentation on how the three steps of speciation (separation, adaptation, and division) worked in providing a particular animal with a distinctive feature. Species of the Galapágos Islands are good examples. **LS** Verbal

Answer to Reading Check

Sample answer: A newly formed canyon, mountain range, or lake could separate the members of a population.

Forming a New Species

Sometimes, drastic changes that can form a new species take place. In the animal kingdom, a *species* is a group of organisms that can mate with each other to produce fertile offspring. A new species may form after a group becomes separated from the original population. This group forms a new population. Over time, the new population adapts to its new environment. Eventually, the new population and the original population differ so greatly that they can no longer mate successfully. The new population may then be considered a new species. The formation of a new species as a result of evolution is called **speciation** (SPEE shee AY shuhn). **Figure 3** shows how new species of Galápagos finches may have formed. Speciation may happen in other ways as well.

speciation the formation of new species as a result of evolution

Separation

Speciation often begins when a part of a population becomes separated from the rest. The process of separation can happen in several ways. For example, a newly formed canyon, mountain range, or lake can divide the members of a population.

✓ **Reading Check** How can parts of a population become separated?

Figure 3 **The Evolution of Galápagos Finch Species**

❶ Some finches left the mainland and reached one of the islands (separation).

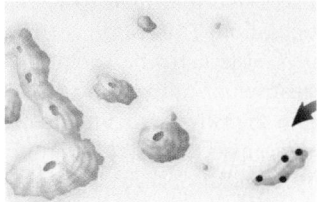

❷ The finches reproduced and adapted to the environment (adaptation).

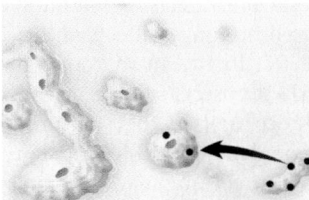

❸ Some finches flew to a second island (separation).

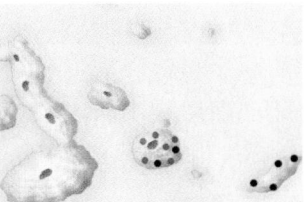

❹ The finches reproduced and adapted to the different environment (adaptation).

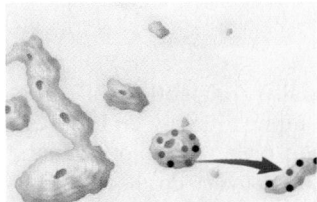

❺ Some finches flew back to the first island but could no longer interbreed with the finches there (division).

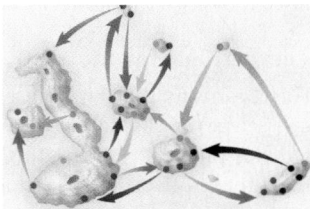

❻ This process may have occurred over and over again as the finches flew to the other islands.

INCLUSION Strategies

- *Learning Disabled*
- *Attention Deficit Disorder*
- *Behavior Control Issues*

Guide students through a simulation. Trace nine rabbit outlines on a single page, and place an X on five of them. For each student, make one copy on each of three colors of paper. Have each student label his or her rabbits. Prompt students through the following stages:

1. Overproduction: Cut out the rabbits.

2. Genetic variation: Spread the rabbits on your desk. Notice the colors.

3. Struggle to survive: For 1 min, try to take rabbits from each other. Yours are "safe" if you are touching them.

4. Successful reproduction: Look at your surviving rabbits. Suppose only those that have an X will reproduce.

As a class, tally and discuss the results.

LS Visual
Co-op Learning

English Language Learners

Adaptation

Populations constantly undergo natural selection. After two groups have separated, natural selection may act on each group in different ways. Over many generations, the separated groups may evolve different sets of traits. If the environmental conditions for each group differ, the adaptations in the groups will also differ.

Division

Over many generations, two separated groups of a population may become very different. Even if a geographical barrier is removed, the groups may not be able to interbreed anymore. At this point, the two groups are no longer the same species.

Figure 4 shows another way that populations may stop interbreeding. Leopard frogs and pickerel frogs probably had the same ancestor species. Then, at some point, some of these frogs began to mate at different times during the year.

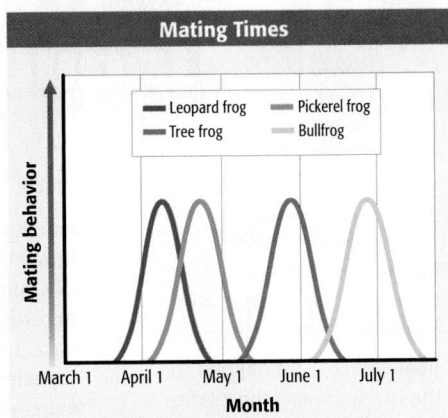

Mating Times

Leopard frog ■ Pickerel frog
Tree frog ■ Bullfrog

Mating behavior (y-axis)

March 1 April 1 May 1 June 1 July 1
Month

Figure 4 *The leopard frog and the pickerel frog are similar species. However, leopard frogs do not search for mates at the same time of year that pickerel frogs do.*

SECTION Review

Summary

- Natural selection explains how populations adapt to changes in their environment. A variety of examples of such adaptations can be found.
- Natural selection also explains how one species may evolve into another. Speciation occurs as populations undergo separation, adaptation, and division.

Using Key Terms

1. In your own words, write a definition for the term *speciation*.

Understanding Key Ideas

2. Two populations have evolved into two species when
   a. the populations are separated.
   b. the populations look different.
   c. the populations can no longer interbreed.
   d. the populations adapt.

3. Explain why the number of tuskless elephants in Uganda may be increasing.

Math Skills

4. A female cockroach can produce 80 offspring at a time. If half of the offspring produced by a certain female are female and each female produces 80 offspring, how many cockroaches are there in the third generation?

Critical Thinking

5. **Forming Hypotheses** Most kinds of cactus have leaves that grow in the form of spines. The stems or trunks become thick, juicy pads or barrels. Explain how these cactus parts might have evolved.

6. **Making Comparisons** Suggest an organism other than an insect that might evolve an adaptation to human activities.

SCiLINKS **NSTA**
Developed and maintained by the
National Science Teachers Association

For a variety of links related to this chapter, go to www.scilinks.org

Topic: Species and Adaptation
SciLinks code: HSM1433

Is That a Fact!

Some species that have adapted to live in total darkness no longer even have eyes! Just as whales have evolved into legless forms, these species have completely adapted to life without light, and some have evolved forms lacking eyes altogether. There are blind cave fish, eels, salamanders, worms, shrimp, crayfish, spiders, beetles, and crickets.

CHAPTER RESOURCES

Chapter Resource File

- Section Quiz **GENERAL**
- Section Review **GENERAL**
- Vocabulary and Section Summary **GENERAL**
- Critical Thinking **ADVANCED**

Technology

Transparencies
- L26 Evolution of the Galápagos Finches

Survival of the Chocolates

Teacher's Notes

Time Required

One or two 45-minute class periods

Lab Ratings

EASY ——————→ HARD

Teacher Prep ⚗
Student Set-Up ⚗⚗
Concept Level ⚗⚗
Clean Up ⚗

Safety Caution

Safety concerns will vary with each design.

Preparation Notes

Be prepared for a variety of experimental designs. For example, students may wish to test which color will crack easiest under physical stress or which color will dissolve more quickly in water. This lab is an opportunity to reinforce scientific methods and practice designing experiments. Encourage students to brainstorm a variety of possible hypotheses and ways of testing the hypotheses. Have students identify scientific methods in their experiments.

Using Scientific Methods
Inquiry Lab

Survival of the Chocolates

Imagine a world populated with candy, and hold that delicious thought in your head for just a moment. Try to apply the idea of natural selection to a population of candy-coated chocolates. According to the theory of natural selection, individuals who have favorable adaptations are more likely to survive. In the "species" of candy-coated chocolates you will study in this experiment, the characteristics of individual chocolates may help them "survive." For example, shell strength (the strength of the candy coating) could be an adaptive advantage. Plan an experiment to find out which characteristics of the chocolates are favorable "adaptations."

OBJECTIVES

Form a hypothesis about the fate of the candy-coated chocolates.

Predict what will happen to the candy-coated chocolates.

Design and conduct an experiment to test your hypothesis.

MATERIALS

- chocolates, candy-coated, small, in a variety of colors (about 100)
- items to be determined by the students and approved by the teacher

SAFETY

Ask a Question

1 What might "survival" mean for a candy-coated chocolate? What are some ways you can test which chocolates are the "strongest" or "most fit" for their environment? Also, write down any other questions that you could ask about the "survival" of the chocolates.

Form a Hypothesis

2 Form a hypothesis, and make a prediction. For example, if you chose to study candy color, your prediction might be similar to this: If the ___ colored shell is the strongest, then fewer of the chocolates with this color of shell will ___ when ___.

 Holt Lab Generator CD-ROM

Search for any lab by topic, standard, difficulty level, or time. Edit any lab to fit your needs, or create your own labs. Use the Lab Materials QuickList software to customize your lab materials list.

CHAPTER RESOURCES

Chapter Resource File

 • Datasheet for Chapter Lab
• Lab Notes and Answers

Technology

 Classroom Videos
• Lab Video

 **Karma Houston-Hughes**
Kyrene Middle School
Tempe, Arizona

Test the Hypothesis

3 Design a procedure to determine which type of candy-coated chocolate is most likely to survive. In your plan, be sure to include materials and tools you may need to complete this procedure.

4 Check your experimental design with your teacher before you begin. Your teacher will supply the candy and assist you in gathering materials and tools.

5 Record your results in a data table. Be sure to organize your data in a clear and understandable way.

Analyze the Results

1 **Describing Events** Write a report that describes your experiment. Be sure to include tables and graphs of the data you collected.

Draw Conclusions

2 **Evaluating Data** In your report, explain how your data either support or do not support your hypothesis. Include possible errors and ways to improve your procedure.

Applying Your Data

Can you think of another characteristic of the chocolates that can be tested to determine which type is best adapted to survive? Explain your idea, and describe how you might test it.

CHAPTER RESOURCES

Workbooks

Whiz-Bang Demonstrations
• Adaptation Behooves You GENERAL

Long-Term Projects & Research Ideas
• Evolution's Explosion ADVANCED

Chapter Review

Chapter Review

Assignment Guide

Section	Questions
1	2–4, 6, 8, 9, 12, 13, 21, 22
2	5, 10, 11, 14, 15, 17, 23
3	1, 7, 16, 18, 19, 20

ANSWERS

Using Key Terms

1. speciation
2. natural selection
3. species
4. fossil record
5. selective breeding
6. adaptation
7. generation time

Understanding Key Ideas

8. a
9. b
10. b
11. c

USING KEY TERMS

Complete each of the following sentences by choosing the correct term from the word bank.

adaptation
evolution
generation time
species
speciation
fossil record
selective breeding
natural selection

1 When a single population evolves into two populations that cannot interbreed anymore, ___ has occurred.

2 Darwin's theory of ___ explained the process by which organisms become well-adapted to their environment.

3 A group of organisms that can mate with each other to produce offspring is known as a(n) ___.

4 The ___ provides information about organisms that have lived in the past.

5 In ___, humans select organisms with desirable traits that will be passed from one generation to another.

6 A(n) ___ helps an organism survive better in its environment.

7 Populations of insects and bacteria can evolve quickly because they usually have a short ___.

UNDERSTANDING KEY IDEAS

Multiple Choice

8 Fossils are commonly found in
 a. sedimentary rock.
 b. all kinds of rock.
 c. granite.
 d. loose sand.

9 The fact that all organisms have DNA as their genetic material is evidence that
 a. all organisms undergo natural selection.
 b. all organisms may have descended from a common ancestor.
 c. selective breeding takes place every day.
 d. genetic resistance rarely occurs.

10 Charles Darwin puzzled over differences in the ___ of the different species of Galápagos finches.
 a. webbed feet
 b. beaks
 c. bone structure of the wings
 d. eye color

11 Darwin observed variations among individuals within a population, but he did not realize that these variations were caused by
 a. interbreeding.
 b. differences in food.
 c. differences in genes.
 d. selective breeding.

---

12. Sample answer: Living organisms can be compared in terms of body structures with other living organisms and with organisms from the fossil record. Also, the DNA of living organisms can be compared.

Short Answer

12 Identify two ways that organisms can be compared to provide evidence of evolution from a common ancestor.

13 Describe evidence that supports the hypothesis that whales evolved from land-dwelling mammals.

14 Why are some animals more likely to survive to adulthood than other animals are?

15 Explain how genetics is related to evolution.

16 Outline an example of the process of speciation.

CRITICAL THINKING

17 **Concept Mapping** Use the following terms to create a concept map: *struggle to survive, theory, genetic variation, Darwin, overpopulation, natural selection,* and *successful reproduction.*

18 **Making Inferences** How could natural selection affect the songs that birds sing?

19 **Forming Hypotheses** In Australia, many animals look like mammals from other parts of the world. But most of the mammals in Australia are marsupials, which carry their young in pouches after birth. Few kinds of marsupials are found anywhere else in the world. What is a possible explanation for the presence of so many of these unique mammals in Australia?

20 **Analyzing Relationships** Geologists have evidence that the continents were once a single giant continent. This giant landform eventually split apart, and the individual continents moved to their current positions. What role might this drifting of continents have played in evolution?

INTERPRETING GRAPHICS

The graphs below show information about the infants that are born and the infants that have died in a population. The weight of each infant was measured at birth. Use the graphs to answer the questions that follow.

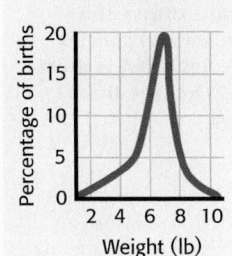
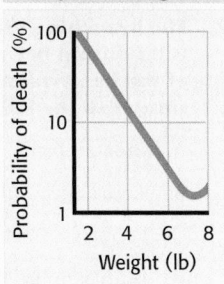

21 What is the most common birth weight?

22 At which birth weight is an infant most likely to survive?

23 How do the principles of natural selection help explain why there are more deaths among babies whose birth weights are low than among babies whose birth weights are average?

14. Sample answer: Those animals that are better adapted to the conditions of their environment, including the condition of competition with other organisms, are more likely to survive to adulthood.

15. Sample answer: Genetics provides a tool with which to analyze and explain what happens inside cells as organisms evolve.

16. Answers may vary. Student answers may resemble the description of the speciation of the Galápagos finches given in the student text.

Critical Thinking

17. 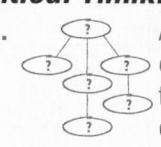 An answer to this exercise can be found at the end of this book.

18. Sample answer: A bird's song could be an advantage if the song helps the bird find mates or food, but the song could be a disadvantage if it attracts predators. So, natural selection would mean that birds whose songs were not an advantage might not survive, and songs would evolve that gave birds some kind of advantage.

19. Sample answer: Australia is an island, so the marsupials there could have evolved separately from other mammals around the world.

20. Sample answer: As the continents drifted apart, populations of species would have been separated and may have had to adapt to new environmental conditions. The separated populations would likely have evolved into separate species over time.

Interpreting Graphics

21. about 7 lb

22. about 7 lb

23. Sample answer: The infants who are best adapted to survive birth are those that weigh about 7 lb at birth.

---

13. Sample answer: Whales share many internal similarities with hoofed land mammals. Ancient fossils of four-legged land mammals exist from times when whales did not exist, but some of these fossils shared characteristics with modern whales and other hoofed mammals. A sequence of fossil organisms shows how the characteristics of modern whales could have evolved from those of ancient land mammals.

CHAPTER RESOURCES

Chapter Resource File

- Chapter Review GENERAL
- Chapter Test A GENERAL
- Chapter Test B ADVANCED
- Chapter Test C SPECIAL NEEDS
- Vocabulary Activity GENERAL

Workbooks

Study Guide
- Study Guide is also available in Spanish.

Standardized Test Preparation

Teacher's Notes

To provide practice under more realistic conditions, give students 20 minutes to answer all of the questions in this Standardized Test Preparation.

Answer Key

Question	Answer
1	A
2	B
3	C
4	A
5	B
6	D
7	B
8	B
9	A
10	*
11	*

*See Test Doctor.

Multiple Choice

1. **Which of the following factors is necessary for natural selection to occur in a species?**

   A. genetic variation within a population

   B. an abundance of food resources

   C. a hospitable environment

   D. a strong family structure

Use the diagram below to answer question 2.

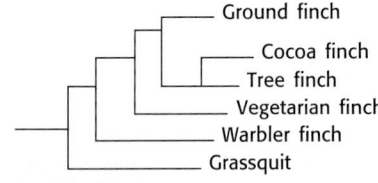

- Ground finch
- Cocoa finch
- Tree finch
- Vegetarian finch
- Warbler finch
- Grassquit

2. **The branching diagram shows the relationship between several species of finches. Which species' DNA is most similar to the DNA of the tree finch?**

   A. Ground finch

   B. Cocoa finch

   C. Vegetarian finch

   D. Warbler finch

3. **Which of the following is an example of natural selection?**

   A. Bears moving into a new part of a forest over many generations.

   B. A tree growing toward sunlight.

   C. Shrubs growing longer thorns over many generations.

   D. A plant growing between rocks.

4. **Charles Darwin noticed that finches on different islands of the Galápagos Islands were similar but that their beaks differed. What explanation for these differences did he propose?**

   A. The beaks of the finches are adapted to the way the bird usually gets food.

   B. The beaks of the finches are a randomly selected trait caused by genetic mutation.

   C. The different beaks of the finches would one day evolve into identical beaks.

   D. Beak size is related to the size of the finch.

5. **A scientist is studying fossils from different layers of sedimentary rock. From which rock layer would the fossils tend to resemble present-day organisms most closely?**

   A. older rock layers

   B. newer rock layers

   C. all rock layers would contain the same fossils

   D. none of the fossils would resemble present-day organisms

6. **A population of organisms is separated into two groups for many years. When would the two populations be considered two different species?**

   A. When the populations live in different habitats.

   B. When the populations eat different food.

   C. When the populations behave differently.

   D. When the populations can no longer interbreed.

 TEST DOCTOR

Question 1 A: Correct. B, C: Individuals in a species that are more adapted to their environment will be better able to thrive in their environments and to compete for available food resources than less adapted individuals. Therefore, a hospitable environment and an abundance of food resources are not necessary for natural selection. D: Natural selection does not depend on family structure.

Question 2 A, C, D: The diagram indicates that cocoa finches and tree finches share the most recent common ancestor. These species are con-nected by the shortest lines on the diagram. B: Correct.

Question 3 A: Bears moving into a new habitat is most likely an example of a learned behavior, not an inherited trait. B, D: Natural selection does not occur over a single generation. C: Correct.

Question 4 A: Correct. B: Genetic mutations made it possible for the beaks to adapt. Successful individuals had beaks that were most suited to the food available, not beaks with random changes. C: Evolution changes organisms to become more specialized to their environments, so the beaks will likely become even more different from each other

7. Which of the following is an example of selective breeding?

A. populations of lizards with a certain trait become more numerous after a change in climate

B. farmers allow only sheep that produce the best wool to breed

C. a population of bacteria develops resistance to an antibiotic

D. a population of insects develops resistance to a pesticide after farmers repeatedly use the same pesticide to kill the insects

8. Alia purchased fruit flies from a biological supply company. One population of fruit flies had straight wings. The other population had wrinkled wings. The fruit flies with straight wings were able to fly, but the flies with wrinkled wings could not fly. Which is the best prediction about what would happen if all the flies were allowed to live in the same environment?

A. The two types of flies would interbreed and produce flies with only slightly wrinkled wings.

B. The flies with straight wings would survive, but the flies with wrinkled wings would die out.

C. All of the flies would survive.

D. None of the flies would survive.

Use the diagram below to answer question 9.

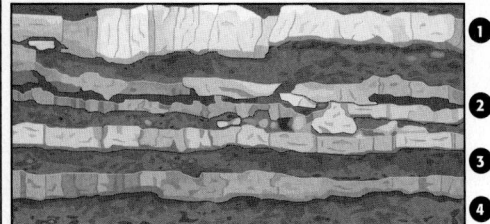

9. The diagram above shows the layers of sedimentary rock exposed during an archaeological dig. In layer 2, archaeologists discovered the fossil of a *Pakicetus*, a mammal that lived around 50 million years ago. In what layer would you expect to find the remains of an *Ambulocetus*, which existed after *Pakicetus* did?

A. layer 1

B. layer 2

C. layer 3

D. layer 4

Open Response

10. What is the relationship between genetics and evolution?

11. A scientist is studying several layers of rock at Big Black Mountain, the highest point in Kentucky. He finds several fossils in each layer. How can these fossils provide evidence of evolution?

Question 8 A: Alia has no evidence to support this prediction. B: Correct. C: Because flies with wrinkled wings cannot fly, wrinkled wings are not a favorable trait. Those flies would probably be unable to find food and would die. D: Straight wings are a favorable trait that contributes to the flies' survival, so those flies would probably survive.

Question 9 A: Correct. In rock layers, more recently living organisms are typically found in the layers toward the top. B: Because *Ambulocetus* existed after *Pakicetus*, it would not be found in the same layer. C: An organism in layer 3 would be older than an organism in layer 2. D: An organism in layer 4 would be older than an organism in layer 2.

Question 10 Full-credit answers should include the following points:

• Genes determine the characteristics or traits of an organism.

• Sometimes, an organism that has certain traits makes the organism more likely to survive.

• The surviving organism reproduces.

• The trait is passed on to offspring.

• Over a very long period of time, the passing on of various successful genes may lead to evolution.

Question 11 Full-credit answers should include the following points:

• A rough estimate of when an organism existed can be determined from the relative positions of fossils in rock layers.

• The fossils can resemble each other, even if they are from different time period.

• Similarities are evidence of a possible evolutionary relationship between older organisms and more recent organisms.

over time. D: Beak shape and size are related to the type of food available, not the size of the finch.

Question 5 A: Older rock layers contain fossils that are less closely related to present-day organisms than newer rock layers do. B: Correct. C: Rock layers may contain some of the same fossils, but each layer will likely be different from one another in some way. D: Newer rock layers contain fossils that tend to be similar to present-day organisms.

Question 6 A, B, C: Speciation occurs when populations can no longer interbreed. Two populations may live in different habitats, eat different foods, and behave differently and still be part of the same species. D: Correct.

Question 7 A: A change in the populations of lizards after a change in climate would be an example of natural selection rather than an example of selective breeding. B: Correct. C: A population of bacteria develops antibiotic resistance through natural selection. D: A population of insects develops pesticide resistance through natural selection.

Science in Action

Science, Technology, and Society

Teaching Strategy—GENERAL

To help students understand changes in agriculture, create a table that contrasts traditional and industrial farming practices. Under "Traditional," list phrases such as *smaller scale, few machines, manual labor, more plant varieties,* and m*ainly for sustenance.* Under "Industrial," list phrases such as *larger scale, more mechanized, fewer plant varieties,* and *primarily for profit.* Point out that a shrinking number of farmers practice some form of traditional agriculture. Scientists at seed banks try to obtain samples of traditionally farmed seeds.

Science Fiction

Background

About the Author Scott Sanders (1945–) writes many different kinds of stories. Early in life, he chose to become a writer rather than a scientist, although he still has an interest science. Sanders has written about folklore, physics, the naturalist John James Audubon, and settlers of Indiana. Much of his work is nonfiction. His writing has been published in books and periodicals, such as the *Chicago Sun-Times, Harper's,* and *Omni.*

Science, Technology, and Society

Seed Banks

All over the world, scientists are making deposits in a special kind of bank. These banks are not for money, but for seeds. Why should seeds be saved? Saving seeds saves plants that may someday save human lives. These plants could provide food or medicine in the future. Throughout human history, many medicines have been developed from plants. And scientists keep searching for new chemicals among the incredible variety of plants in the world. But time is running out. Many plant species are becoming extinct before they have even been studied.

Math ACTIVITY

Many drugs were originally developed from plants. Suppose that 100 plants are used for medicines this year, but 5% of plant species become extinct each year. How many of the medicinal plants would be left after 1 year? after 10 years? Round your answers to whole numbers.

Science Fiction

"The Anatomy Lesson" by Scott Sanders

Do you know the feeling you get when you have an important test? A medical student faces a similar situation in this story. The student needs to learn the bones of the human body for an anatomy exam the next day. The student goes to the anatomy library to study. The librarian lets him check out a box of bones that are supposed to be from a human skeleton. But something is wrong. There are too many bones. They are the wrong shape. They don't fit together correctly. Somebody must be playing a joke! Find out what's going on and why the student and the librarian will never be the same after "The Anatomy Lesson." You can read it in the *Holt Anthology of Science Fiction.*

Language Arts ACTIVITY

WRITING SKILL Before you read this story, predict what you think will happen. Write a paragraph that "gives away" the ending that you predict. After you have read the story, listen to some of the predictions made by your classmates. Discuss your opinions about the possible endings.

Answer to Math Activity

year	number of plants
0	100
1	95
5	77
10	60

Answer to Language Arts Activity

Student paragraphs may vary. Have students compare their predictions to the story's ending and to other students' predictions.

People in Science

Raymond Pierotti

Canine Evolution Raymond Pierotti thinks that it's natural that he became an evolutionary biologist. He grew up exploring the desert around his home in New Mexico. He was fascinated by the abundant wildlife surviving in the bleak landscape. "One of my earliest memories is getting coyotes to sing with me from my backyard," he says.

Pierotti now studies the evolutionary relationships between wolves, coyotes, and domestic dogs. Some of his ideas come from the traditions of the Comanches. According to the Comanche creation story, humans came from wolves. Although Pierotti doesn't believe that humans evolved from wolves, he sees the creation story as a suggestion that humans and wolves have evolved together. "Wolves are very similar to humans in many ways," says Pierotti. "They live in family groups and hunt together. It is possible that wolves actually taught humans how to hunt in packs, and there are ancient stories of wolves and humans hunting together and sharing the food. I think it was this relationship that inspired the Comanche creation stories."

Social Studies ACTIVITY

WRITING SKILL Research a story of creation that comes from a Greek, Roman, or Native American civilization. Write a paragraph summarizing the myth, and share it with a classmate.

go.hrw.com
To learn more about these Science in Action topics, visit go.hrw.com and type in the keyword **HL5EVOF**.

Current Science
Check out Current Science® articles related to this chapter by visiting go.hrw.com. Just type in the keyword **HL5CS07**.

ACTIVITY — GENERAL

Have every student write or present a report on a breed of dog. The report should focus on the origin and evolution of the breed, with particular attention paid to the culture that bred it and why those characteristics were chosen. The report could also explore whether these breeds make good household pets and why. Students can easily find information on dog breeds on the Internet by searching for either the name of a breed or for "dog breeds" and visiting any of several sites that collect information on different breeds.

Answer to Social Studies Activity

Student summaries may vary. Have students share their summaries with each other or with the entire class, and then discuss similarities between the myths.

The History of Life on Earth
Chapter Planning Guide

Compression guide:
To shorten instruction because of time limitations, omit Section 3.

OBJECTIVES	LABS, DEMONSTRATIONS, AND ACTIVITIES	TECHNOLOGY RESOURCES
PACING • 90 min pp. 164–171 **Chapter Opener**	**SE** Start-up Activity, p. 165 ◆ GENERAL	**OSP** Parent Letter ■ **CD** Student Edition on CD-ROM **CD** Guided Reading Audio CD ■ **TR** Chapter Starter Transparency* **VID** Brain Food Video Quiz
Section 1 Evidence of the Past • Explain how fossils can be formed and how their age can be estimated. • Describe the geologic time scale and the way that scientists use it. • Compare two ways that conditions for life on Earth have changed over time.	**TE** Activity Newspaper Layers, p. 167 ◆ GENERAL **SE** Connection to Social Studies A Place in Time, p. 168 ◆ GENERAL **TE** Group Activity Detailed Geologic Timeline, p. 168 ADVANCED **SE** Quick Lab Making a Geologic Timeline, p. 169 ◆ GENERAL **CRF** Datasheet for Quick Lab* **TE** Activity Rock Collectors, p. 169 GENERAL **SE** Skills Practice Lab The Half-Life of Pennies, p. 710 ◆ GENERAL **CRF** Datasheet for LabBook*	**OSP** Lesson Plans (also in print) **TR** Bellringer Transparency* **TR** L27 Using Half-Lives to Date Fossils* **TR** L117 The Geologic Time Scale* **TR** L29 Moving Continents and Tectonic Plates*
PACING • 45 min pp. 172–177 **Section 2 Eras of the Geologic Time Scale** • Outline the major developments that allowed life to exist on Earth. • Describe the types of organisms that arose during the four major divisions of the geologic time scale.	**TE** Connection Activity Earth Science, p. 173 ◆ GENERAL **TE** Activity Using Maps, p. 173 ◆ GENERAL **TE** Group Activity Ancient Plants, p. 174 GENERAL **TE** Connection Activity Real World, p. 174 ◆ GENERAL **LB** Long-Term Projects & Research Ideas A Horse is a Horse* ADVANCED	**OSP** Lesson Plans (also in print) **TR** Bellringer Transparency* **SE** Internet Activity, p. 173 GENERAL **CRF** SciLinks Activity* GENERAL **CD** Interactive Explorations CD-ROM Rock On! GENERAL
PACING • 90 min pp. 178–183 **Section 3 Humans and Other Primates** • Describe two characteristics that all primates share. • Describe three major groups of hominids.	**TE** Activity Exploring Vision, p. 179 GENERAL **TE** Activity Primate Characteristics, p. 180 ◆ BASIC **TE** Group Activity Comparing Hominids, p. 180 ◆ GENERAL **SE** School-to-Home Activity Thumb Through This, p. 181 GENERAL **TE** Connection Activity Art, p. 181 ◆ GENERAL **TE** Activity Classifying Primates, p. 183 ADVANCED **SE** Inquiry Lab Mystery Footprints, p. 184 ◆ GENERAL **CRF** Datasheet for Chapter Lab* **SE** Science in Action Math, Social Studies, and Language Arts Activities, pp. 190–191 GENERAL	**OSP** Lesson Plans (also in print) **TR** Bellringer Transparency* **TR** L30 Comparison of Primate Skeletons* **VID** Lab Videos for Life Science

PACING • 90 min

CHAPTER REVIEW, ASSESSMENT, AND STANDARDIZED TEST PREPARATION

CRF Vocabulary Activity* GENERAL
SE Chapter Review, pp. 186–187 GENERAL
CRF Chapter Review* ■ GENERAL
CRF Chapter Tests A* ■ GENERAL, B* ADVANCED, C* SPECIAL NEEDS
SE Standardized Test Preparation, pp. 188–189 GENERAL
CRF Standardized Test Preparation* GENERAL
CRF Performance-Based Assessment* GENERAL
OSP Test Generator, Test Item Listing

Online and Technology Resources

go.hrw.com Holt Online Learning

Visit **go.hrw.com** for access to Holt Online Learning, or enter the keyword **HS7 Home** for a variety of free online resources.

 **One-Stop** Planner® CD-ROM

This CD-ROM package includes:
• Lab Materials QuickList Software
• Holt Calendar Planner
• Customizable Lesson Plans
• Printable Worksheets
• ExamView® Test Generator
• Interactive Teacher's Edition
• Holt PuzzlePro®
• Holt PowerPoint® Resources

SKILLS DEVELOPMENT RESOURCES	SECTION REVIEW AND ASSESSMENT	CORRELATIONS
SE Pre-Reading Activity, p. 164 `GENERAL` **OSP** Science Puzzlers, Twisters & Teasers `GENERAL`		**National Science Education Standards** UCP 2, 3; SAI 1, 2; SPSP 5; HNS 3
CRF Directed Reading A* ■ `BASIC`, B* `SPECIAL NEEDS` **WB** Workbook* `Struggling Readers` **CRF** Vocabulary and Section Summary* ■ `GENERAL` **SE** Reading Strategy Reading Organizer, p. 166 `GENERAL` **SE** Math Practice Fractions of Fractions, p. 167 `GENERAL` **TE** Support for English Language Learners, p. 167 **TE** Inclusion Strategies, p. 170 **SE** Connection to Geology Mid-Atlantic Ridge, p. 171 `GENERAL` **MS** Math Skills for Science Radioactive Decay and the Half-Life* `GENERAL` **MS** Math Skills for Science Geologic Time Scale* `GENERAL` **CRF** Reinforcement Worksheet Earth Timeline* `BASIC`	**SE** Reading Checks, pp. 167, 169, 170 `GENERAL` **TE** Homework, p. 169 `GENERAL` **TE** Reteaching, p. 170 `BASIC` **TE** Quiz, p. 170 `GENERAL` **TE** Alternative Assessment, p. 171 `GENERAL` **SE** Section Review,* p. 171 `GENERAL` **CRF** Section Quiz* ■ `GENERAL`	UCP 1, 2, 4; SAI 1, 2; HNS 1, 2, 3; LS 1a, 3d, 5b, 5c; *LabBook:* UCP 1, 3; SAI 1; LS 5c
CRF Directed Reading A* ■ `BASIC`, B* `SPECIAL NEEDS` **WB** Workbook* `Struggling Readers` **CRF** Vocabulary and Section Summary* ■ `GENERAL` **SE** Reading Strategy Mnemonics, p. 172 `GENERAL` **TE** Support for English Language Learners, p. 173 **SE** Connection to Oceanography Prehistoric Marine Organisms, p. 174 `GENERAL` **TE** Inclusion Strategies, p. 174 **SE** Math Focus Relative Scale, p. 176 `GENERAL` **TE** Connection to Math Another Time Scale, p. 176 `ADVANCED` **MS** Math Skills for Science Subtraction Review* `GENERAL` **CRF** Reinforcement Worksheet Condensed History* `BASIC`	**SE** Reading Checks, pp. 172, 175, 176 `GENERAL` **TE** Reteaching, p. 176 `BASIC` **TE** Quiz, p. 176 `GENERAL` **TE** Alternative Assessment, p. 176 `GENERAL` **SE** Section Review,* p. 177 ■ `GENERAL` **CRF** Section Quiz* ■	UCP 1, 2, 3, 4; SAI 1; LS 1a, 1b, 3d, 5a, 5b, 5c
CRF Directed Reading A* `BASIC`, B* `SPECIAL NEEDS` **WB** Workbook* `Struggling Readers` **CRF** Vocabulary and Section Summary* ■ `GENERAL` **SE** Reading Strategy Discussion, p. 178 `GENERAL` **TE** Support for English Language Learners, p. 179 **CRF** Critical Thinking Fossil Revelations* `ADVANCED`	**SE** Reading Checks, pp. 179, 180, 183 `GENERAL` **TE** Homework, p. 182 `GENERAL` **TE** Reteaching, p. 182 `BASIC` **TE** Quiz, p. 182 `GENERAL` **TE** Alternative Assessment, p. 182 `ADVANCED` **SE** Section Review,* p. 183 ■ `GENERAL` **CRF** Section Quiz* ■ `GENERAL`	UCP 2, 4, 5; SAI 1, 2; ST 1, 2; HNS 2, 3; LS 1a, 3d, 5a, 5b, 5c; *Chapter Lab:* UCP 2, 5; SAI 1; HNS 2

SCLINKS.
NSTA
www.scilinks.org
Maintained by the **National Science Teachers Association.** See Chapter Enrichment pages that follow for a complete list of topics.

Current Science®

Check out *Current Science* articles and activities by visiting the HRW Web site at **go.hrw.com**. Just type in the keyword **HL5CS08T**.

Classroom Videos

- **Lab Videos** demonstrate the chapter lab.
- **Brain Food Video Quizzes** help students review the chapter material.

Classroom CD-ROMs

- **Guided Reading Audio CD** (Also in Spanish)
- **Interactive Explorations**
- **Virtual Investigations**
- **Visual Concepts**
- **Science Tutor**

Holt Lab Generator CD-ROM

Search for any lab by topic, standard, difficulty level, or time. Edit any lab to fit your needs, or create your own labs. Use the Lab Materials QuickList software to customize your lab materials list.

Visual Resources

CHAPTER STARTER TRANSPARENCY

The History of Life on Earth — CHAPTER STARTER

Imagine . . .

One day you and your friends learn about a secret underground passage that leads into an old abandoned mansion, and you set out to find it. In your walk around a field in search of the passage, you stumble across a large hole in the ground. Could this be it?

One by one, you and your friends squeeze down into the hole. You slide down the sloping tunnel and finally land. Dusting yourself off, you turn on your flashlight. Instead of finding a passage to an abandoned mansion, you and your friends find yourselves in an immense cavern. Painted high on the cavern's walls are pictures of bulls, cows, horses, and stags. You get the feeling these images have been here for a very long time. Who made these paintings?

This adventure actually occurred in southern France in the late 1940s. Four teenage boys went hunting for a passageway to the old manor of Lascaux. Instead of finding a passageway, they stumbled onto a 17,000-year-old connection with our ancestors, the Cro-Magnons. Three of the adventurers are shown below talking to their teacher.

BELLRINGER TRANSPARENCIES

The History of Life on Earth — BELLRINGER TRANSPARENCY

Section: Evidence of the Past
Imagine that you haven't cleaned your room for 30 years and you finally decide to sort through the 2 m pile of stuff on your floor. What might you find on the top of the pile? in the middle? on the bottom?

Write your responses in your **science journal.**

Section: Eras of the Geologic Time Scale
Suppose that electrical energy had never been developed. How would your life differ from what it is like now? What do you do every day that requires electricity?

Write your answers in your **science journal.**

TEACHING TRANSPARENCIES

Using Half-Lives to Date Fossils — L27

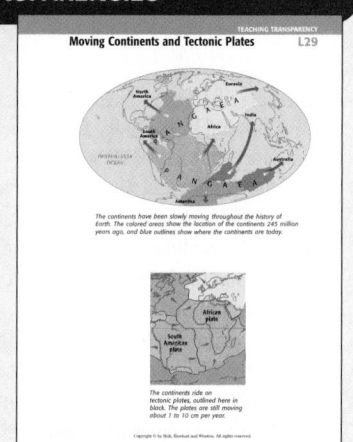

Moving Continents and Tectonic Plates — TEACHING TRANSPARENCY L29

The continents have been slowly moving throughout the history of Earth. The colored areas show the location of the continents 245 million years ago, and blue outlines show where the continents are today.

The continents ride on tectonic plates, outlined here in black. The plates are still moving about 1 to 10 cm per year.

TEACHING TRANSPARENCIES

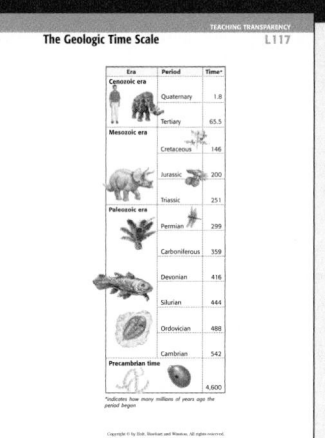

The Geologic Time Scale — TEACHING TRANSPARENCY L117

Era	Period	Time*
Cenozoic era	Quaternary	1.8
	Tertiary	65.5
Mesozoic era	Cretaceous	146
	Jurassic	200
	Triassic	251
Paleozoic era	Permian	299
	Carboniferous	359
	Devonian	416
	Silurian	444
	Ordovician	488
	Cambrian	542
Precambrian time		4,600

*indicates how many millions of years ago the period began.

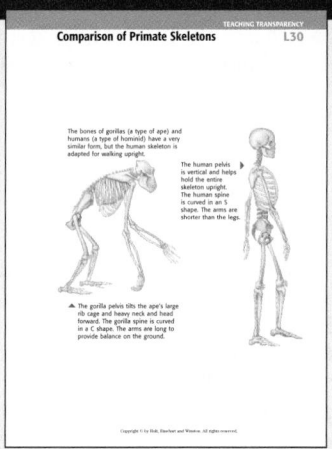

Comparison of Primate Skeletons — TEACHING TRANSPARENCY L30

The bones of gorillas (a type of ape) and humans (a type of hominid) have a very similar form, but the human skeleton is adapted for walking upright.

The human pelvis helps hold the entire skeleton upright. The human spine is curved in an S shape. The arms are shorter than the legs.

▲ The gorilla pelvis is vertical and helps support the ape's large rib cage and heavy neck and head forward. The gorilla spine is curved in a C shape. The arms are long to provide balance on the ground.

The Tectonic Plates; Close-up of a Tectonic Plate — E20

Continental crust

Mantle

Andes mountain

LINK TO EARTH SCIENCE

Chapter: Plate Tectonics

CONCEPT MAPPING TRANSPARENCY

The History of Life on Earth — CONCEPT MAPPING

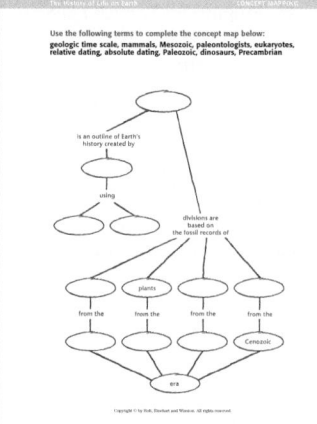

Use the following terms to complete the concept map below:
geologic time scale, mammals, Mesozoic, paleontologists, eukaryotes, relative dating, absolute dating, Paleozoic, dinosaurs, Precambrian

Planning Resources

LESSON PLANS

Lesson Plan — SAMPLE

Section: Waves

Pacing
Regular Schedule: with lab(s):2 days   without lab(s)2 days
Block Schedule: with lab(s): 1 1/2 days   without lab(s)1 day

Objectives
1. Relate the seven properties of life to a living organism.
2. Describe seven themes that can help you to organize what you learn about biology.
3. Identify the tiny structures that make up all living organisms.
4. Differentiate between reproduction and heredity and between metabolism and homeostasis.

National Science Education Standards Covered
LSInter6:Cells have particular structures that underlie their functions.
LSMat1:Most cell functions involve chemical reactions.
LSBeh1:Cells store and use information to guide their functions.
UCP1:Cell functions are regulated.
SI1: Cells can differentiate and form complete multicellular organisms.
PS1: Species evolve over time.
ESS1: The great diversity of organisms is the result of more than 3.5 billion years of evolution.
ESS2: Natural selection and its evolutionary consequences provide a scientific explanation for the fossil record of ancient life forms as well as for the striking molecular similarities observed among the diverse species of living organisms.
ST1: The complexity and organization of organisms accommodates the need for obtaining, transforming, transporting, releasing, and eliminating the matter and energy used to sustain the organism.
ST2: The energy for life primarily comes from the sun.
SPSP1: The complexity and organization of organisms accommodates the need for obtaining, transforming, transporting, releasing, and eliminating the matter and energy used to sustain the organism.
SPSP6: As matter and energy flows through different levels of organization of living systems—cells, organs, communities—and between living systems and the physical environment, chemical elements are recombined in different ways.
HNS1: Organisms have behavioral responses to internal changes and to external stimuli.

PARENT LETTER

SAMPLE

Dear Parent,

Your son's or daughter's science class will soon begin exploring the chapter entitled "The World of Physical Science." In this chapter, students will learn about how the scientific method applies to the world of physical science and the role of physical science in the world. By the end of the chapter, students should demonstrate a clear understanding of the chapter's main ideas and be able to discuss the following topics:

1. physical science is the study of energy and matter (Section 1)
2. the role of physical science in the world around them (Section 1)
3. careers that rely on physical science (Section 1)
4. the steps used in the scientific method (Section 2)
5. examples of technology (Section 2)
6. how the scientific method is used to answer questions and solve problems (Section 2)
7. how our knowledge of science changes over time (Section 2)
8. how models represent real objects or systems (Section 3)
9. examples of different ways models are used in science (Section 3)
10. the importance of the International System of Units (Section 4)
11. the appropriate units to use for particular measurements (Section 4)
12. how area and density are derived quantities (Section 4)

Questions to Ask Along the Way

You can help your son or daughter learn about these topics by asking interesting questions, such as the following:

* What are some surprising careers that use physical science?
* What is a characteristic of a good hypothesis?
* When is it a good idea to use a model?
* Why do Americans measure things in terms of inches and yards and meters ?

ALSO IN SPANISH

TEST ITEM LISTING

TEST ITEM LISTING
The World of Science — SAMPLE

MULTIPLE CHOICE

1. A limitation of models is that
   a. they are large enough to see.
   b. they do not act exactly like the things that they model.
   c. they are smaller than the things that they model.
   d. they model unfamiliar things.
   Answer: B   Difficulty: 1   Section: 3   Objective: 2

2. The length 10 m is equal to:
   a. 100 cm.   c. 10,000 mm.
   b. 1,000 cm.   d. Both (b) and (c)
   Answer: B   Difficulty: 1   Section: 4   Objective: 2

3. To be valid, a hypothesis must be
   a. testable.   c. made into a law.
   b. supported by evidence.   d. Both (a) and (b)
   Answer: B   Difficulty: 1   Section: 2   Objective: 1

4. The statement "Sheila has a stain on her shirt" is an example of a(n)
   a. law.   c. observation.
   b. hypothesis.   d. prediction.
   Answer: B   Difficulty: 1   Section: 2   Objective: 2

5. A hypothesis is often developed out of
   a. observations.   c. laws.
   b. experiments.   d. Both (a) and (b)
   Answer: D   Difficulty: 1   Section: 2   Objective: 2

6. How many milliliters are in 3.5 kL?
   a. 3,500 mL   c. 3,500, 000 mL
   b. 0.0035 mL   d. 35,000 mL
   Answer: C   Difficulty: 1   Section: 4   Objective: 2

7. A map of Seattle is an example of a
   a. law.   c. model.
   b. theory.   d. unit.
   Answer: C   Difficulty: 1   Section: 3   Objective: 2

8. A lab has the safety icons shown below. These icons mean that you should wear
   a. only safety goggles.   c. safety goggles and a lab apron.
   b. only a lab apron.   d. safety goggles, a lab apron, and gloves.
   Answer: D   Difficulty: 1   Section: 1   Objective: 2

9. The law of conservation of mass says the sum of mass before a chemical change is
   a. more than the total mass after the change
   b. less than the total mass after the change
   c. the same as the total mass after the change
   d. not the same as the total mass after the change
   Answer: C   Difficulty: 1   Section: 3   Objective: 2

10. In which of the following areas might you find a geochemist at work?
    a. studying the chemistry of rocks   c. studying fishes
    b. studying forestry   d. studying the atmosphere
    Answer: A   Difficulty: 1   Section: 3

One-Stop Planner® CD-ROM

This CD-ROM includes all of the resources shown here and the following time-saving tools:

* Lab Materials QuickList Software
* Customizable lesson plans
* Holt Calendar Planner
* The powerful ExamView® Test Generator

Meeting Individual Needs

DIRECTED READING A

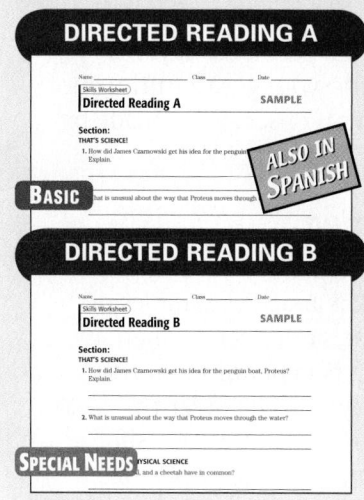

Directed Reading A — SAMPLE

Section: THAT'S SCIENCE!
1. How did James Czarnowski get his idea for the penguin boat, Proteus? Explain.

ALSO IN SPANISH

BASIC

DIRECTED READING B

Directed Reading B — SAMPLE

Section: THAT'S SCIENCE!
1. How did James Czarnowski get his idea for the penguin boat, Proteus? Explain.

2. What is unusual about the way that Proteus moves through the water?

SPECIAL NEEDS

VOCABULARY ACTIVITY

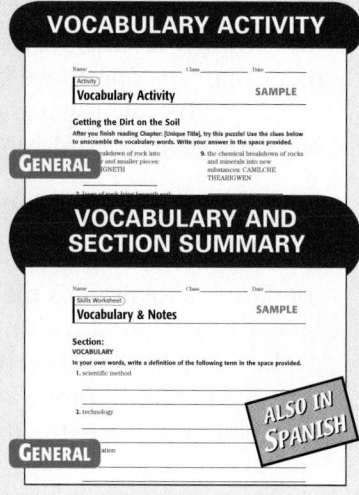

Vocabulary Activity — SAMPLE

Getting the Dirt on the Soil

After you finish reading Chapter: [Unique Title], try this puzzle! Use the clues below to unscramble the vocabulary words. Write your answer in the space provided.

GENERAL

VOCABULARY AND SECTION SUMMARY

Vocabulary & Notes — SAMPLE

Section: VOCABULARY
In your own words, write a definition of the following term in the space provided.
1. scientific method
2. technology

ALSO IN SPANISH

GENERAL

REINFORCEMENT

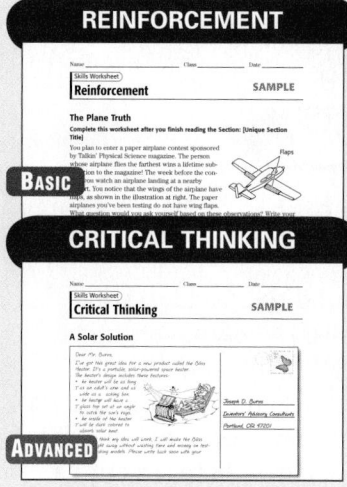

Reinforcement — SAMPLE

The Plane Truth
Complete this worksheet after you finish reading the Section: [Unique Section Title]

BASIC

CRITICAL THINKING

Critical Thinking — SAMPLE

A Solar Solution

ADVANCED

SCILINKS ACTIVITY

SciLinks Activity — SAMPLE

MARINE ECOSYSTEMS
Go to www.scilinks.com. To find links related to marine ecosystems, type in the keyword HL5400. Then, use the links to answer the questions about marine ecosys-

GENERAL

SCIENCE PUZZLERS, TWISTERS & TEASERS

SCIENCE PUZZLERS, TWISTERS & TEASERS
The History of Life on Earth

Scientific Sleuthing
1. Each of the statements below was made by an organism during the era in which it evolved. Write the correct era in the space provided. The organisms evolved during the following eras: Precambrian, Paleozoic, Mesozoic, or Cenozoic.
a. I've seen the greatest swimmers of my generation destroyed.
b. People often accuse me of monkeying around.
c. Oxygen? What is that?

GENERAL

Labs and Activities

LONG-TERM PROJECTS & RESEARCH IDEAS

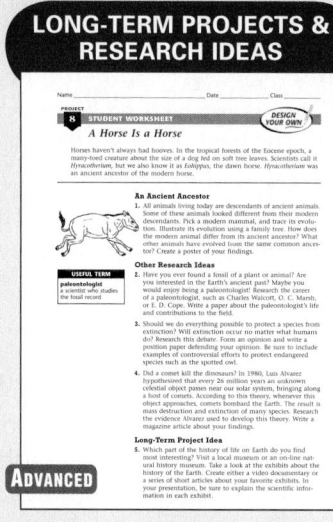

STUDENT WORKSHEET — DESIGN YOUR OWN
A Horse Is a Horse

Horses haven't always had hooves. In the tropical forests of the Eocene epoch, a many-toed creature about the size of a dog fed on soft tree leaves. Scientists call it *Hyracotherium*, but we also know it as *Eohippus*, the dawn horse. *Hyracotherium* was an ancient ancestor of the modern horse.

An Ancient Ancestor
1. All animals living today are descendants of ancient animals. Some of these animals looked different from their modern descendants. Pick a modern mammal, and trace its evolution. Illustrate its evolution using a family tree. How does the modern animal differ from its ancient ancestor? What other animals have evolved from the same common ancestor? Create a poster of your findings.

USEFUL TERM
paleontologist
a scientist who studies the fossil record

Other Research Ideas
2. Have you ever found a fossil of a plant or animal? Are you interested in the Earth's ancient past? Maybe you would enjoy being a paleontologist. Research the career of a paleontologist, such as Charles Walcott, O. C. Marsh, or E. D. Cope. Write a paper about the paleontologist's life and contributions to the field.

3. Should we do everything possible to protect a species from extinction? Will extinction occur no matter what humans do? Research this debate. Form an opinion and write a position paper defending your opinion. Be sure to include examples of controversial efforts to protect endangered species such as the spotted owl.

4. Did a comet kill the dinosaurs? In 1980, Luis Alvarez hypothesized that every 26 million years an unknown celestial object passes near our solar system, bringing along a host of comets. According to the theory, whenever this object approaches, comets bombard the Earth. The result is mass destruction and extinction of many species. Research the evidence Alvarez used to develop this theory. Write a magazine article about your findings.

Long-Term Project Idea
5. Which part of the history of life on Earth do you find most interesting? Visit a local museum or an on-line natural history museum. Take a look at the exhibits about the history of the Earth. Create either a video documentary or a series of short articles about your favorite exhibits. In your presentation, be sure to explain the scientific information in each exhibit.

ADVANCED

DATASHEETS FOR QUICK LABS

TEACHER RESOURCE PAGE
Quick Lab
Reaction to Stress — DATASHEET FOR QUICK LAB — SAMPLE

Background
The graph below illustrates changes that occur in the membrane potential of a neuron during an action potential. Use the graph to answer the following questions. Refer to Figure 3 as needed.

DATASHEETS FOR CHAPTER LABS

TEACHER RESOURCE PAGE
Skills Practice Lab
Using Scientific Methods — DATASHEET FOR CHAPTER LAB — SAMPLE

Teacher's Notes
TIME REQUIRED
One 45-minute class period.

DATASHEETS FOR LABBOOK

TEACHER RESOURCE PAGE
Skills Practice Lab
Does It All Add Up? — DATASHEET FOR LABBOOK LAB — SAMPLE

Teacher's Notes
TIME REQUIRED
One 45-minute class period.

Review and Assessments

SECTION QUIZ

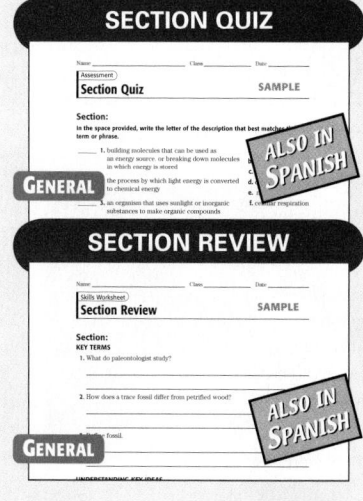

Assessment
Section Quiz — SAMPLE

Section:
In the space provided, write the letter of the description that best matches the term or phrase.
1. building molecules that can be used as an energy source or breaking down molecules in which energy is stored
2. the process by which light energy is converted to chemical energy
3. an organism that uses sunlight or inorganic substances to make organic compounds

a.
b.
c.
d.
e.
f. cellular respiration

ALSO IN SPANISH

GENERAL

SECTION REVIEW

Skills Worksheet
Section Review — SAMPLE

Section:
KEY TERMS
1. What do paleontologist study?
2. How does a trace fossil differ from petrified wood?

ALSO IN SPANISH

GENERAL

CHAPTER REVIEW

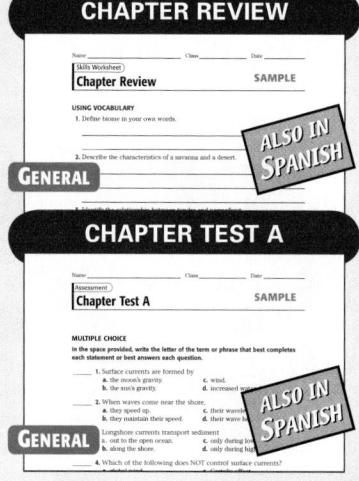

Skills Worksheet
Chapter Review — SAMPLE

USING VOCABULARY
1. Define biome in your own words.
2. Describe the characteristics of a savanna and a desert.

ALSO IN SPANISH

GENERAL

CHAPTER TEST A

Assessment
Chapter Test A — SAMPLE

MULTIPLE CHOICE
In the space provided, write the letter of the term or phrase that best completes each statement or best answers each question.
1. Surface currents are formed by
a. the moon's gravity.   c. wind.
b. the sun's gravity.   d. increased water density.
2. When waves come near the shore,
a. they speed up.   c. their wavelength increases.
b. they maintain their speed. d. their wave height increases.
Longshore currents transport sediment
a. to the open ocean.   c. only during low tide.
b. along the shore.   d. only during high tide.
4. Which of the following does NOT control surface currents?

ALSO IN SPANISH

GENERAL

CHAPTER TEST B

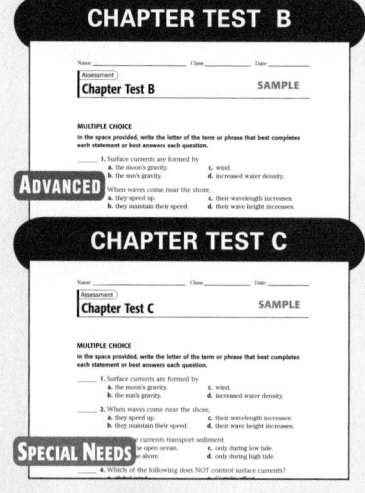

Assessment
Chapter Test B — SAMPLE

MULTIPLE CHOICE
1. Surface currents are formed by
a. the moon's gravity.   c. wind.
b. the sun's gravity.   d. increased water density.
When waves come near the shore,
a. they speed up.   c. their wavelength increases.
b. they maintain their speed. d. their wave height increases.

ADVANCED

CHAPTER TEST C

Assessment
Chapter Test C — SAMPLE

MULTIPLE CHOICE
In the space provided, write the letter of the term or phrase that best completes each statement or best answers each question.
1. Surface currents are formed by
a. the moon's gravity.   c. wind.
b. the sun's gravity.   d. increased water density.
2. When waves come near the shore,
a. they speed up.   c. their wavelength increases.
b. they maintain their speed. d. their wave height increases.
Longshore currents transport sediment
a. to the open ocean.   c. only during low tide.
b. along the shore.   d. only during high tide.
4. Which of the following does NOT control surface currents?

SPECIAL NEEDS

STANDARDIZED TEST PREPARATION

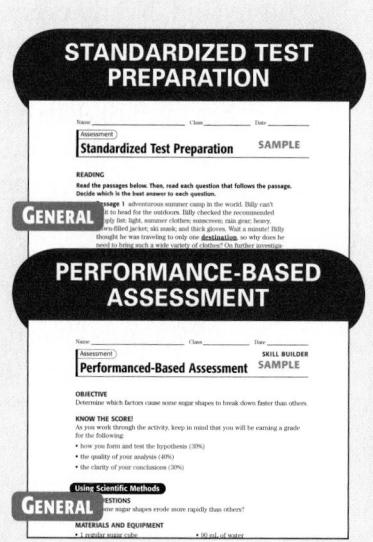

Assessment
Standardized Test Preparation — SAMPLE

READING
Read the passages below. Then, read each question that follows the passage. Decide which is the best answer to each question.

Passage 1 adventurous summer camp in the world. Billy can't wait to head for the outdoors. Billy checked the recommended supply list: light, summer clothes; sunscreen; rain gear; heavy-down-filled jacket; ski mask; and thick gloves. Wait a minute! Billy thought he was traveling to only one destination, so why does he need to bring such a wide variety of clothes? On further investiga-

GENERAL

PERFORMANCE-BASED ASSESSMENT

Assessment
Performance-Based Assessment — SKILL BUILDER SAMPLE

OBJECTIVE
Determine which factors cause some sugar shapes to break down faster than others?

KNOW THE SCORE!
As you work through the activity, keep in mind that you will be earning a grade for the following:
• how you form and test the hypothesis (30%)
• the quality of your analysis (40%)
• the clarity of your conclusions (30%)

Using Scientific Methods
MATERIALS AND EQUIPMENT
• 1 regular sugar cube   • 50 mL of water

GENERAL

This Chapter Enrichment provides relevant and interesting information to expand and enhance your presentation of the chapter material.

Section 1

Evidence of the Past

Paul Sereno

- Paul Sereno has traveled around the world to study and document dinosaur fossils. He teaches at the University of Chicago and also involves his students in searching museum collections and combing deserts for new fossils. Sereno's teams have made many important finds. One of the first was in 1988 in Argentina, where his team unearthed the skeletons of a primitive 12-foot-long dinosaur called *Herrerasaurus*. The fossils in that area shed light on how and when the Age of Reptiles began. Sereno has continued to map the dinosaur family tree by studying fossils in the Sahara, in Niger, and in Morocco.

Fossils

- Fossils may be mere traces of organisms. Preserved footprints, feces, gnaw marks, and dug-out holes can all be considered fossils. Also, traces or remains of organisms can be preserved in materials other than sedimentary rock, such as amber, tar, or lava.

- Despite what many people think, fossils are not difficult to find. Nearly every state in the United States contains an abundance of fossils. However, scientists think that only a tiny fraction of the countless organisms that lived on Earth has been preserved as fossils. Many organisms have lived and died without leaving evidence of their existence in the fossil record.

Is That a Fact!

◆ The oldest fossils known are structures called *stromatolites* that are more than 3.5 billion years old. These structures are bands of sedimentary rock that are very similar to layered mats formed today by colonies of bacteria and cyanobacteria.

Law of Superposition

- The law of superposition states that in a series of undisturbed sedimentary rock layers, each layer is older than the one above it and younger than the one below it. This law is based on an observation made by Nicolaus Steno, a Danish physician, in 1669.

Methods of Absolute Dating

- Radioisotope dating is the most widely used method for dating a fossil. This method analyzes samples of igneous rock found within the same rock formation as the fossil. The method differs depending on the type of chemical isotope analyzed. The older the rocks are, the less accurate the dating. Isotopes with shorter half-lives provide a more accurate range of possible ages for younger rocks and fossils. Radiocarbon dating by accelerator mass spectrometry (AMS) has become a preferred method to date with high accuracy carbon-based fossils less than 60,000 years old.

Is That a Fact!

◆ The beginning of the Paleozoic era is sometimes called the *Cambrian explosion*. Within the first 100 million years of this period, a large variety of multicellular organisms appeared for the first time on Earth, including most of the major groups of animals.

Modern Mass Extinction

- Because of natural selection, there will always be some extinctions of species within any given time period. Mass extinctions, however, are periods of acceleration of the average rate of extinction. Many scientists think that our planet has entered another era of mass extinction and that human activities are prompting these extinctions. Species all over the Earth are threatened by habitat destruction, pollution, and invasive nonnative species. During the last 200 years, more than 50 species of birds, more than 75 species of mammals, and hundreds of other species have become extinct.

Section 2

Eras of the Geologic Time Scale

Experiment About the Origin of Life

- In 1953, American scientist Stanley Miller devised a famous experiment to simulate life-forming conditions on the early Earth. He mixed together hydrogen, ammonia, and methane (to represent the air) and water (to represent the oceans) in a flask. When he applied electricity to the mixture, amino acids were produced. His experiment demonstrated that the building blocks of life could be created on Earth through simple chemistry. Scientists have since found amino acids in meteorites, confirming that conditions favorable for their formation also exist elsewhere.

Dinosaur Whodunit

- Scientists continue to debate various hypotheses about the cause of the mass extinction that wiped out the dinosaurs at the end of the Cretaceous period of the Mesozoic era. The prime suspect for many scientists is an asteroid that created the 185 km wide Chicxulub crater in the Yucatán area of the Gulf of Mexico. Seismology studies support this hypothesis. However, a sample of rock from the core of this crater contains evidence that the Chicxulub asteroid did not result in sudden climate change. An alternative hypothesis is that a series of asteroid impacts eventually caused climate changes that led to the mass extinction.

Is That a Fact!

- ◆ Dinosaurs are not the biggest animals ever to have lived on Earth. Blue whales are bigger than the largest known dinosaur.

Section 3

Humans and Other Primates

Clues to Migration Route

- Scientists think that people passed through the Nile Valley of Egypt when they migrated from Africa, perhaps as early as 100,000 years ago. The first evidence supporting this idea was an adundance of fossil tools and other artifacts in the Nile Valley area. Then, in 1994, the team of Belgian archaeologist Pierre Vermeersch found an ancient—but clearly human—skeleton in the area. The skeleton appears to have been a child that was ritually buried over 80,000 years ago. The skull and teeth show similarities to those of equally old human remains from East Africa and the Middle East. These similarities show a link between the African and the Middle Eastern populations.

Dawn of Language

- Scientists Matt Cartmill and Richard Kay examined fossil hominid skulls and measured the hole through which the hypoglossal nerve passes in its course from the brain to the tongue. The hypoglossal nerve enables precise control over the tongue movements needed for speech. A large hole suggests a larger nerve. Chimpanzees have much smaller holes in their skulls than do modern humans. Because australopithecine skulls have small holes, like the skulls of chimpanzees, Cartmill and Kay think that australopithecines were unable to form words.

Developed and maintained by the National Science Teachers Association

SciLinks is maintained by the National Science Teachers Association to provide you and your students with interesting, up-to-date links that will enrich your classroom presentation of the chapter.

Visit www.scilinks.org and enter the SciLinks code for more information about the topic listed.

Topic: Evidence of the Past
SciLinks code: HSM0545

Topic: Geologic Time Scale
SciLinks code: HSM0669

Topic: Fossil Record
SciLinks code: HSM0615

Topic: Birds and Dinosaurs
SciLinks code: HSM0169

Topic: Mass Extinctions
SciLinks code: HSM0916

Topic: Human Evolution
SciLinks code: HSM0769

Overview

In this chapter, students will learn about the evidence of the history of life on earth. Students will study the geologic time scale and theories about the evolution of hominids.

Assessing Prior Knowledge

Students should be familiar with the following topics:

- cells
- the basic chemistry of life
- classification
- evolution

Identifying Misconceptions

As students learn the material in this chapter, they may have misconceptions about the length of time living organisms have been on Earth and the length of time needed for geologic processes. For example, mass extinctions are "sudden" on a geologic time scale but may take thousands of years. Furthermore, students may have misconceptions about how long humans have been on Earth. Students may also be unaware of the large amount of evidence scientists have gathered in order to determine the time and order of events in Earth's history.

The History of Life on Earth

The Big Idea

Geologic evidence allows us to understand the evolution of life on Earth.

About the Photo

What is 23,000 years old and 9 ft tall? The partial remains of the woolly mammoth in this picture! The mammoth was found in the frozen ground in Siberia in 1999. Scientists think that several types of woolly mammoths roamed the northern hemisphere until about 4,000 years ago.

FOLDNOTES **Layered Book** Before you read the chapter, create the Foldnote entitled "Layered Book" described in the **Study Skills** section of the Appendix. Label the tabs of the layered book with "Precambrian time," "Paleozoic era," "Mesozoic era," and "Cenozoic era." As you read the chapter, write information you learn about each category under the appropriate tab.

Standards Correlations

National Science Education Standards

The following codes indicate the National Science Education Standards that correlate to this chapter. The full text of the standards is at the front of the book.

Chapter Opener
UCP 2, 3; SAI 1, 2; SPSP 5; HNS 3

Section 1 Evidence of the Past
UCP 1, 2, 4; SAI 1, 2; HNS 1, 2, 3; LS 1a, 3d, 5b, 5c;
LabBook: UCP 1, 3; SAI 1; LS 5c

Section 2 Eras of the Geologic Time Scale
UCP 1, 2, 3, 4; SAI 1; LS 1a, 1b, 3d, 5a, 5b, 5c

Section 3 Humans and Other Primates
UCP 2, 4, 5; SAI 1, 2; ST 1, 2; HNS 2, 3; LS 1a, 3d, 5a, 5b, 5c

Chapter Lab
UCP 2, 5; SAI 1; HNS 2

Chapter Review
LS 1a, 1b, 3d, 5a, 5b, 5c

Science in Action
UCP 2; ST 2; SPSP 5; HNS 1, 3

START-UP ACTIVITY

MATERIALS

FOR EACH STUDENT
• clay, modeling
• leaf or shell
• plaster of Paris
• plate, paper

Teacher's Note: Coating the leaves or shells with a light vegetable oil will help prevent the clay and plaster from sticking.

Answers

1. Sample answer: The crab, the clam, and perhaps the seed will make the best fossils because they have hard parts that would decay slowly and leave clear impressions. The softer objects—the jellyfish, the leaf, and the mushroom—are less likely to make impressions in the sediment and more likely to decay quickly, so they are less likely to form fossils.

2. Sample answer: Like all models, this model cannot encompass all real possibilities. This model does not exactly duplicate the way most fossils are formed. For example, this model does not show how fossils of softer organisms can be formed. Also, in this model, oxygen is present, but the plaster forms into rock quickly, so the objects are not given time to decay. Finally, in this model, the objects do not move on their own, but moving organisms might leave fossils of traces such as footprints.

START-UP ACTIVITY

Making a Fossil

In this activity, you will make a model of a fossil.

Procedure

1. Get a **paper plate,** some **modeling clay,** and a **leaf** or a **shell** from your teacher.

2. Flatten some of the modeling clay on the paper plate. Push the leaf or shell into the clay. Be sure that your leaf or shell has made a mark in the clay. Remove the leaf or shell carefully.

3. Ask your teacher to cover the clay with **plaster of Paris.** Allow the plaster to dry overnight.

4. Carefully remove the paper plate and the clay from the plaster the next day.

Analysis

1. Consider the following objects—a clam, a seed, a jellyfish, a crab, a leaf, and a mushroom. Which of the objects do you think would make good fossils? Explain your answers.

2. In nature, fossils form only under certain conditions. For example, fossils may form when a dead organism is covered by tiny bits of sand or dirt for a long period of time. The presence of oxygen can prevent fossils from forming. Considering these facts, what are some limitations of your model of how a fossil is formed?

Chapter Starter Transparency
Use this transparency to help students begin thinking about evidence of past life on Earth.

CHAPTER RESOURCES

Technology

Transparencies
• Chapter Starter Transparency

READING SKILLS

Student Edition on CD-ROM

Guided Reading Audio CD
• English or Spanish

Classroom Videos
• Brain Food Video Quiz

Workbooks

Science Puzzlers, Twisters & Teasers
• The History of Life on Earth **GENERAL**

Focus

Overview

This section introduces students to fossils and how they provide clues to Earth's past. Students learn how fossils most commonly form in sedimentary rock. They explore the methods scientists use to determine the age of fossils. They learn how scientists place events in the Earth's history in the correct order and how mass extinctions mark the boundaries of eras. Finally, they learn how plate tectonics has moved continents slowly and affected life over time.

Bellringer

Ask students to imagine that they haven't cleaned their room for 30 years. After 30 years, they finally decide to sort through the 2 m pile of stuff on their floor. Ask students, "What might you find on the top of the pile? in the middle? on the bottom?" (The items on the bottom are most likely to be those that were left on the floor at an earlier time than were the items above them.)

What You Will Learn

- Explain how fossils can be formed and how their age can be estimated.
- Describe the geologic time scale and the way that scientists use it.
- Compare two ways that conditions for life on Earth have changed over time.

Vocabulary

fossil
relative dating
absolute dating
geologic time scale
extinct
plate tectonics

READING STRATEGY

Reading Organizer As you read this section, make a concept map by using the terms above.

fossil the trace or remains of an organism that lived long ago, most commonly preserved in sedimentary rock

---

Evidence of the Past

In 1995, scientist Paul Sereno found a dinosaur skull that was 1.5 m long in the Sahara, a desert in Africa. The dinosaur may have been the largest land predator that has ever existed!

Scientists such as Paul Sereno look for clues to help them reconstruct what happened in the past. These scientists, called *paleontologists* (PAY lee uhn TAHL uh jists), use fossils to reconstruct the history of life before humans existed. Fossils show us that life on Earth has changed a great deal. They also provide us clues about how those changes happened.

Fossils

Fossils are traces or imprints of living things—such as animals, plants, bacteria, and fungi—that are preserved by geological processes. Fossils sometimes form when a dead organism is covered by a layer of sediment. The sediment may later be pressed together to form sedimentary rock. **Figure 1** shows one way that fossils can form in sedimentary rock.

| **Figure 1** | **One Way Fossils Can Form** |

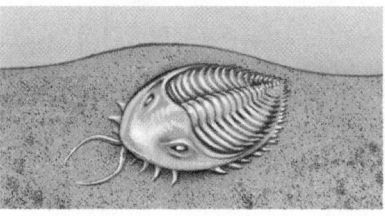

❶ Fossils can form in several ways. The most common way is when an organism dies and becomes buried in sediment.

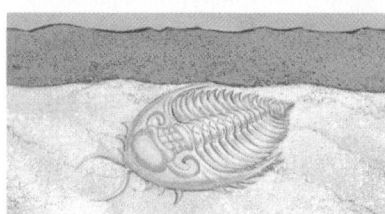

❷ The organism gradually decomposes and leaves a hollow impression, or *mold*, in the sediment.

❸ Over time, the mold fills with sediment, which forms a *cast* of the organism.

CHAPTER RESOURCES

Chapter Resource File

- **Lesson Plan**
- **Directed Reading A** BASIC
- **Directed Reading B** SPECIAL NEEDS

Technology

Transparencies
- Bellringer
- L27 Using Half-Lives to Date Fossils

Workbooks

Interactive Textbook Struggling Readers

SCIENTISTS AT ODDS

Fossil Finds In the 1870s, two American scientists, Edward Drinker Cope and Othniel Charles Marsh, studied dinosaur fossils. They became bitter rivals and often argued. In 1878, Marsh and Cope were both excavating fossils in Wyoming. They had separate excavations and didn't want to share their findings. Both groups found more fossils than they could carry. To prevent the other group from taking their fossils, each group smashed all the fossils that couldn't be carried away.

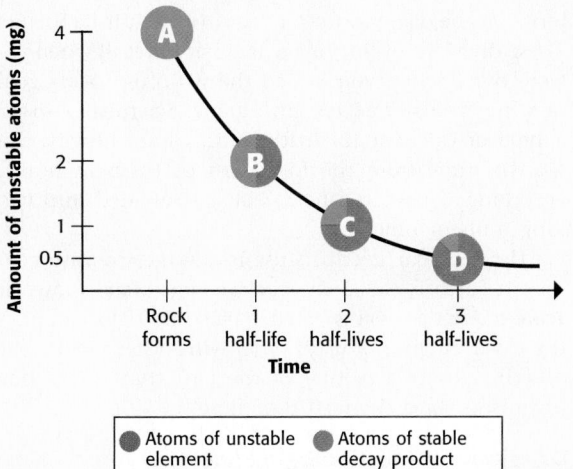

Figure 2 Using Half-Lives to Date Fossils

A The unstable atoms in this sample of rock have a half-life of 1.3 billion years. The sample contained 4 mg of unstable atoms when it formed.

B After 1.3 billion years, (one half-life for this type of unstable atom), 2 mg of the unstable atoms have decayed to become stable atoms, and 2 mg of unstable atoms remain.

C After 2.6 billion years (two half-lives for this sample), the rock sample contains 3 mg of stable decay atoms and 1 mg of unstable atoms.

D After three half-lives, only 0.5 mg of unstable atoms remain in the rock sample. This is equal to one-eighth of the original amount.

The Age of Fossils

Sedimentary rock has many layers. The oldest layers are usually on the bottom. The newest layers are usually on the top. The layers can tell a scientist the relative age of fossils. Fossils found in the bottom layers are usually older than the fossils in the top layers. So, scientists can determine whether a fossil is older or younger than other fossils based on its position in sedimentary rock. Estimating the age of rocks and fossils in this way is called **relative dating.**

In addition, scientists can determine the age of a fossil more precisely. **Absolute dating** is a method that measures the age of fossils or rocks in years. In one type of absolute dating, scientists examine atoms. *Atoms* are the particles that make up all matter. Atoms, in turn, are made of smaller particles. Some atoms are unstable and will decay by releasing energy, particles, or both. When an atom decays it becomes a different, and more stable, kind of atom. Each kind of unstable atom decays at its own rate. As shown in **Figure 2,** the time it takes for half of the unstable atoms in a sample to decay is the *half-life* of that type of unstable atom. By measuring the ratio of unstable atoms to stable atoms, scientists can determine the approximate age of a sample of rock.

Reading Check Which type of fossil dating is more precise?
(*See the Appendix for answers to Reading Checks.*)

relative dating any method of determining whether an event or object is older or younger than other events or objects

absolute dating any method of measuring the age of an object or event in years

Fractions of Fractions
Find the answer to each of the following problems. Be sure to show your work. You may want to draw pictures.
1. $1/2 \times 1/2 \times 1/2 \times 1/2$
2. $1/2 \times 1/8$
3. $1/4 \times 1/4$

Group ACTIVITY —ADVANCED

Detailed Geologic Timeline
Table 1 shows that geologic time is divided into *eras*, which are broken into smaller divisions called *periods*. But periods can be divided into *epochs*, and scientists continue to add many more details to this table. Challenge students to construct a giant geologic timeline that identifies all of these divisions. Direct them to scale the size of the divisions relative to time. Allow them to do research in the library or on the Internet for information. LS Visual

Research ——— GENERAL

Extinct Species Students could research plant and animal species that have become extinct within the last 200 years. Many of the extinctions were caused by human activities. Extinct birds include the dodo, great auk, Labrador duck, moa, and passenger pigeon. Extinct mammals include the Steller's sea cow and the quagga. LS Verbal

Discussion ——— GENERAL

Abbreviations In geological and paleontological literature, students may encounter the abbreviations *MYA* and *BYA*. Explain to students that *MYA* means "million years ago." Likewise, *BYA* means "billion years ago." Ask students why they think geologists use this form of dating. LS Verbal

Table 1	Geologic Time Scale	
Era	**Period**	**Time***
Cenozoic era	Quaternary	1.8
	Tertiary	65.5
Mesozoic era	Cretaceous	146
	Jurassic	200
	Triassic	251
Paleozoic era	Permian	299
	Carboniferous	359
	Devonian	416
	Silurian	444
	Ordovician	488
	Cambrian	542
Precambrian time		4,600

*indicates how many millions of years ago the period began

The Geologic Time Scale

Think about important events that have happened during your lifetime. You usually recall each event in terms of the day, month, or year in which it happened. These divisions of time make it easier to recall when you were born, when you kicked the winning soccer goal, or when you started the fifth grade. Scientists also use a type of calendar to divide Earth's long history. The span of time from the formation of Earth to now is very long. Therefore, the calendar is divided into very long units of time.

The calendar scientists use to outline the history of life on Earth is called the **geologic time scale,** shown in **Table 1.** After a fossil is dated, a paleontologist can place the fossil in chronological order with other fossils. This ordering forms a picture of the past that shows how organisms have changed over time.

Divisions in the Geologic Time Scale

Paleontologists have divided the geologic time scale into large blocks of time. Each block may be divided into smaller blocks of time as scientists continue to find more fossil information.

The divisions known as *era*s are characterized by the type of organism that dominated Earth at the time. For instance, the Mesozoic era—dominated by dinosaurs and other reptiles—is referred to as the *Age of Reptiles*. Eras began with a change in the type of organism that was most dominant.

Paleontologists sometimes adjust and add details to the geologic time scale. The early history of Earth has been poorly understood because fossils from this period are rare. So, the earliest part of the geologic time scale is not named as an era. But more evidence of life before the Paleozoic era is being gathered. Scientists have proposed using this evidence to name new eras before the Paleozoic era.

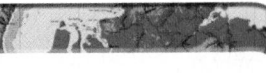

CONNECTION TO Social Studies

A Place in Time Most of the periods of the Paleozoic era were named by geologists for places where rocks from that period are found. Research the name of each period of the Paleozoic era listed in **Table 1.** On a copy of a world map, label the locations related to each name.

ACTIVITY

BRAIN FOOD

Private Fossil Collectors In 1997, the most complete skeleton ever found of a *Tyrannosaurus rex* was auctioned. The winning bid was $8.36 million, made by the Field Museum of Natural History in Chicago. Scientists were relieved that a museum won the bid; their fear was that a private collector would buy the skeleton fossil and not allow scientists to study it.

Answer to Connection to Social Studies

Cambrian: for Cambria, the Latin name for Wales in Great Britain; Ordovician: after the Ordivices, a Celtic tribe; Silurian: after the Silures, a Celtic tribe; Devonian: for Devonshire, England; Carboniferous: for coal-bearing rocks in England; Permian: for the Russian province of Perm

Figure 3 Scientists think that a meteorite hit Earth about 65 million years ago and caused major climate changes.

Mass Extinctions

Some of the important divisions in the geologic time scale mark times when rapid changes happened on Earth. During these times, many species died out completely, or became **extinct**. When a species is extinct, it does not reappear. At certain points in the Earth's history, a large number of species disappeared from the fossil record. These periods when many species suddenly become extinct are called *mass extinctions*.

Scientists are not sure what caused each of the mass extinctions. Most scientists think that the extinction of the dinosaurs happened because of extreme changes in the climate on Earth. These changes could have resulted from a giant meteorite hitting the Earth, as shown in **Figure 3.** Or, forces within the Earth could have caused many volcanoes and earthquakes.

Reading Check What are mass extinctions?

geologic time scale the standard method used to divide the Earth's long natural history into manageable parts

extinct describes a species that has died out completely

Making a Geologic Timeline

1. Use a **metric ruler** to mark 10 cm sections on a **strip of paper** that is 46 cm long.

2. Label each 10 cm section in order from top to bottom as follows: 1 bya (billion years ago), 2 bya, etc. The timeline begins at 4.6 bya.

3. Divide each 10 cm section into 10 equal subsections. Divide the top 1 cm into 10 subsections. Calculate the number of years that are represented by 1 mm on this scale.

4. On your timeline, label the following events:
   a. Earth forms. (4.6 billion years ago)
   b. First animals appear. (600 million years ago)
   c. Dinosaurs appear. (251 million years ago)
   d. Dinosaurs are extinct. (65 million years ago)
   e. Humans appear. (160,000 years ago)

5. Label other events from the chapter.

6. Describe what most of the timeline looks like.

7. Compare the length of time dinosaurs existed with the length of time humans have existed.

CHAPTER RESOURCES

Chapter Resource File

 • **Datasheet for Quick Lab** GENERAL

Workbooks

Math Skills for Science
• Geologic Time Scale GENERAL
• Radioactive Decay and the Half-Life GENERAL

Technology

 Transparencies
• L117 The Geologic Time Scale

Illustrating Drift Have students cut out each continent from a copy of an area-proportionate world map. Have them try to fit the cut-out continents together into one landmass, using **Figure 4** as a model. Then, ask students to model the movements of the continents into their current locations. Finally, ask them to predict where the continents might be in the future if they keep moving in a similar way. (Predictions might include a wider Atlantic Ocean and a shift northward of Africa, Australia, and South America.) **LS** **Visual/Kinesthetic**

Quiz ———— GENERAL

1. How are fossils most commonly formed? (An organism is buried in sediments that harden into rock.)

2. What can scientists learn about Earth's past from fossils? (how life on Earth has changed over time)

3. Why would fossils found at the top of a canyon probably be younger than those found at the bottom of the canyon? (The upper layers were deposited more recently.)

Answer to Reading Check

the idea that the Earth's continents once formed a single landmass surrounded by oceans

---

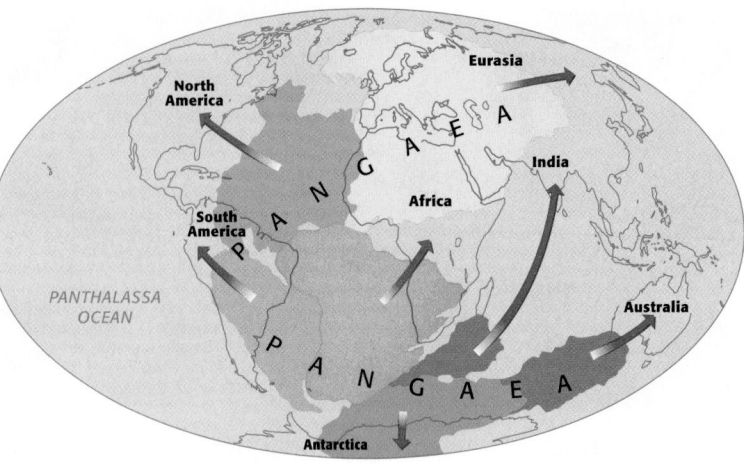

Figure 4 *The continents have been slowly moving throughout the history of Earth. The colored areas show the location of the continents 245 million years ago, and blue outlines show where the continents are today.*

plate tectonics the theory that explains how large pieces of the Earth's outermost layer, called *tectonic plates,* move and change shape

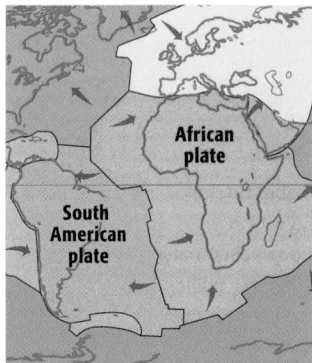

Figure 5 *The continents ride on tectonic plates, outlined here in black. The plates are still moving about 1 to 10 cm per year.*

The Changing Earth

Did you know that fossils of tropical plants have been found in Antarctica? Antarctica, now frozen, must have once had a warm climate to support these plants. The fossils provide evidence that Antarctica was once located near the equator!

Pangaea

Have you ever noticed that the continents look like pieces of a puzzle? German scientist Alfred Wegener had a similar thought in the early 1900s. He proposed that long ago the continents formed one landmass surrounded by a gigantic ocean. Wegener called that single landmass *Pangaea* (pan JEE uh), which means "all Earth." **Figure 4** shows how the continents may have formed from Pangaea.

 **Reading Check** What idea did Alfred Wegener propose?

Do the Continents Move?

In the mid-1960s, J. Tuzo Wilson of Canada came up with the idea that the continents were not moving by themselves. Wilson thought that huge pieces of the Earth's crust were pushed around by forces within the planet. Each huge piece of crust is called a *tectonic plate.* Wilson's theory of how these huge pieces of crust move around the Earth is called **plate tectonics.**

According to Wilson, the outer crust of the Earth is broken into seven large, rigid plates and several smaller ones. The continents and oceans ride on top of these plates. The motion of the plates causes the continents to move. For example, the plates that carry South America and Africa are slowly moving apart, as shown in **Figure 5.**

Adaptation to Slow Changes

When conditions on the Earth change, organisms may become extinct. A rapid change, such as a meteorite impact, may cause a mass extinction. But slow changes, such as moving continents, allow time for adaptation.

Anywhere on Earth, you are able to see living things that are well adapted to the location where they live. Yet in the same location, you may find evidence of organisms that lived there in the past that were very different. For example, the animals currently living in Antarctica are able to survive very cold temperatures. But under the frozen surface of Antarctica are the remains of tropical forests. Conditions on Earth have changed many times in history, and life has changed, too.

CONNECTION TO Geology

Mid-Atlantic Ridge In 1947, scientists examined rock from a ridge that runs down the middle of the Atlantic Ocean, between Africa and the Americas. They found that this rock was much younger than the rock on the continents. Explain what this finding indicates about the tectonic plates.

SECTION Review

Summary

- Fossils are formed most often in sedimentary rock. The age of a fossil can be determined using relative dating and absolute dating.

- The geologic time scale is a timeline that is used by scientists to outline the history of Earth and life on Earth.

- Conditions for life on Earth have changed many times. Rapid changes, such as a meteorite impact, might have caused mass extinctions. But many groups of organisms have adapted to changes such as the movement of tectonic plates.

Using Key Terms

1. Use the following terms in the same sentence: *fossil* and *extinct*.

2. In your own words, write a definition for the term *plate tectonics*.

Understanding Key Ideas

3. Explain how a fossil forms in sedimentary rock.

4. What kind of information does the geologic time scale show?

5. About how many years of Earth's history was Precambrian time?

6. What are two possible causes of mass extinctions?

Math Skills

7. The Earth formed 4.6 billion years ago. Modern humans have existed for about 160,000 years. Simple worms have existed for at least 500 million years. For what fraction of the history of Earth have humans existed? have worms existed?

Critical Thinking

8. **Identifying Relationships** Why are both absolute dating and relative dating used to determine the age of fossils?

9. **Making Inferences** Fossils of *Mesosaurus*, the small aquatic reptile shown below, have been found only in Africa and South America. Using what you know about plate tectonics, how would you explain this finding?

SCI LINKS. **NSTA**
Developed and maintained by the National Science Teachers Association

For a variety of links related to this chapter, go to www.scilinks.org

Topic: Evidence of the Past
SciLinks code: HSM0545

CONNECTION to Earth Science —— GENERAL

The South American Plate Have students identify the boundaries of the South American tectonic plate on a map. Ask students, "What kinds of features mark the east side of the plate?" (a rift or canyon down the middle of the Atlantic Ocean) Ask, "Which direction is the plate drifting?" (to the west, away from Africa.) Ask, "What is happening on the west side of the plate?" (the plate is crashing into another plate and pushing up the Andes mountains) **LS Visual**

CHAPTER RESOURCES

Chapter Resource File

- Section Quiz GENERAL
- Section Review GENERAL
- Vocabulary and Section Summary GENERAL
- Reinforcement Worksheet BASIC
- Datasheet for Quick Lab

Technology

Transparencies
- L29 Moving Continents and Tectonic Plates

Alternative Assessment —— GENERAL

Geologic Time Scale Each student in a group receives three blank cards. The group looks at **Table 1** in this section and thinks of questions that could be answered using information from the table. Students write a question on one side of a card. They stack the cards with the blank sides up. In turn, each student draws a card, reads the question on it, and attempts to answer the question. Group members determine if the answer is correct by consulting the table. **LS Visual/Interpersonal**

Answer to Connection to Geology

This finding indicates that the plates are spreading apart as newer rock forms at the center.

Answers to Section Review

1. Sample answer: Scientists can learn about extinct organisms from fossils.

2. Sample answer: Plate tectonics is a theory about how the plates of the Earth's crust move around.

3. A fossil may form when a dead organism is covered by a layer of sediment. Then, these sediments are slowly pressed together to form sedimentary rock.

4. how organisms and Earth have changed over time

5. about 4 billion years

6. meteorite impacts and forces within the Earth

7. Humans have existed for 16/460,000 of the history of Earth. Worms have existed for 5/46 of Earth's history.

8. Sample answer: to compare the results of each method so there can be greater confidence in the conclusions

9. Sample answer: Perhaps *Mesosaurus* evolved after Pangaea broke up but before South America and Africa split apart.

Focus

Overview

This section discusses current theories regarding the origin of life. Students are introduced to the four major divisions of geologic time in chronological order: Precambrian time, the Paleozoic era, the Mesozoic era, and the Cenozoic era. They learn about the organisms that characterize each era.

🔊 Bellringer

Ask students to respond to the following question:

> Suppose that electrical energy had never been developed. How would your life differ from what it is like now?

Discuss with students the consequences of great changes over time.

Answer to Reading Check

The early Earth was very different from Earth as it is today. There were violent events and a harsh atmosphere.

What You Will Learn

- Outline the major developments that allowed life to exist on Earth.
- Describe the types of organisms that arose during the four major divisions of the geologic time scale.

Vocabulary

Precambrian time
Paleozoic era
Mesozoic era
Cenozoic era

READING STRATEGY

Mnemonics As you read this section, create a mnemonic device to help you remember the eras of geologic time.

Precambrian time the period in the geologic time scale from the formation of the Earth to the beginning of the Paleozoic era, from about 4.6 billion to 542 million years ago

---

Eras of the Geologic Time Scale

The walls of the Grand Canyon are layered with different kinds and colors of rocks. The deeper down into the canyon you go, the older the layers of rocks. Try to imagine a time when the bottom layer was the only layer that existed.

Each layer of rock tells a story about what was happening on Earth when that layer was on top. The rocks and fossils in each layer tell the story. Scientists have compared the stories told by fossils and rocks all over the Earth. From these stories, scientists have divided geologic history into four major parts. These divisions are Precambrian time, the Paleozoic era, the Mesozoic era, and the Cenozoic era.

Precambrian Time

The layers at the bottom of the Grand Canyon are from the oldest part of the geologic time scale. **Precambrian time** (pree KAM bree ʊʜɴ TIEM) is the time from the formation of Earth 4.6 billion years ago to about 542 million years ago. Life on Earth began during this time.

Scientists think that the early Earth was very different than it is today. The atmosphere was made of gases such as water vapor, carbon dioxide, and nitrogen. Also, the early Earth was a place of great turmoil, as illustrated in **Figure 1.** Volcanic eruptions, meteorite impacts, and violent storms were common. Intense radiation from the sun bombarded Earth's surface.

✔️ **Reading Check** Describe the early Earth. (*See the Appendix for answers to Reading Checks.*)

Figure 1 *This illustration shows the conditions under which the first life on Earth may have formed.*

CHAPTER RESOURCES

Chapter Resource File

- **Lesson Plan**
- **Directed Reading A** BASIC
- **Directed Reading B** SPECIAL NEEDS

Technology

Transparencies
- Bellringer

Workbooks

Interactive Textbook Struggling Readers

Is That a Fact!

Throughout Earth's history, the forces of erosion have been altering the planet's surface, making it almost impossible to find rocks older than 3.5 billion years. However, a number of rocks dating from about 3.5 billion to 3.9 billion years ago have been found in Canada and Greenland. The oldest was found in the Northwest Territories of Canada in 1989.

How Did Life Begin?

Scientists think that life developed from simple chemicals in the oceans and in the atmosphere. Energy from radiation and storms could have caused these chemicals to react. Some of these reactions formed the complex molecules that made life possible. Eventually, these molecules may have joined to form structures such as cells.

The early atmosphere of the Earth did not contain oxygen gas. The first organisms did not need oxygen to survive. These organisms were *prokaryotes* (proh KAR ee OHTS), or single-celled organisms that lack a nucleus.

Photosynthesis and Oxygen

There is evidence that *cyanobacteria,* a new kind of prokaryotic organism, appeared more than 3 billion years ago. Some cyanobacteria are shown in **Figure 2.** Cyanobacteria use sunlight to produce their own food. Along with doing other things, this process releases oxygen. The first cyanobacteria began to release oxygen gas into the oceans and air.

Eventually, some of the oxygen formed a new layer of gas in the upper atmosphere. This gas, called *ozone,* absorbs harmful radiation from the sun, as shown in **Figure 3.** Before ozone formed, life existed only in the oceans and underground. The new ozone layer reduced the radiation on Earth's surface.

Multicellular Organisms

After about 1 billion years, organisms that were larger and more complex than prokaryotes appeared in the fossil record. These organisms, known as *eukaryotes* (yoo KAR ee OHTS), contain a nucleus and other complex structures in their cells. Eventually, eukaryotic cells may have evolved into organisms that are composed of many cells.

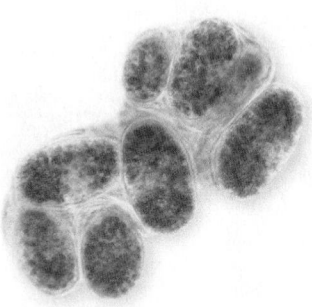

Figure 2 *Cyanobacteria are the simplest living organisms that use the sun's energy to produce their own food.*

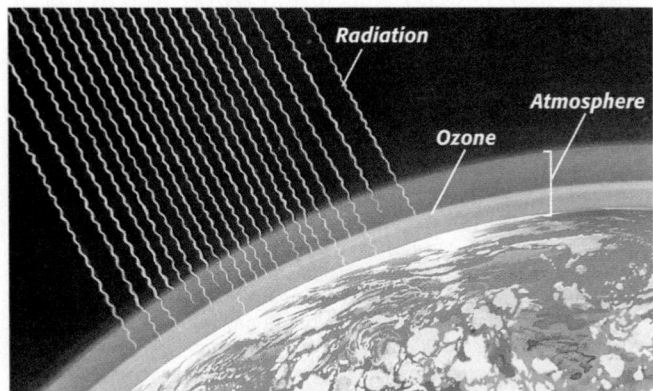

Figure 3 *Oxygen in the atmosphere formed a layer of ozone, which helps to absorb harmful radiation from the sun.*

INTERNET ACTIVITY

For another activity related to this chapter, go to **go.hrw.com** and type in the keyword **HL5HISW.**

CONNECTION ACTIVITY
Earth Science ——— GENERAL

Ancient Mountains Provide a large wall map of the world, and provide map pins or tacks in three colors. Have students locate the following mountain ranges on a map. Have students place pins on the map for each range to match the eras when each range was formed. Use the following list for reference:

Blue (Paleozoic):
• Caledonian (Scandinavia), Acadian (New York), Appalachian (eastern North America), Ural (Russia)

Green (Mesozoic):
• Palisades (New Jersey), Rockies (western North America)

Red (Cenozoic):
• Andes (South America), Alps (Europe), Himalayas (Asia)

LS Visual/Kinesthetic

Motivate

Discussion ——— GENERAL

Historical Perspective Have students pretend that they are in a time-travel machine. What scientifically significant events would they witness as they travel back in time to Earth's origin? List the events on the board in the order that they are suggested. Ask students how they can determine whether the events are in chronological order. (Students can consult the geologic time scale or other scientific materials.) LS Verbal/Logical

Teach

ACTIVITY ——— GENERAL

Using Maps Have students locate the following three earthquake and volcano zones on a world map. One zone extends nearly all the way around the edge of the Pacific Ocean. A second zone is located near the Mediterranean Sea and extends across Asia into India. The third zone extends through Iceland to the middle of the Atlantic Ocean. LS Visual

SUPPORT FOR

English Language Learners

Timeline Mural Students will better understand the division of time if they can see the differences between the periods or eras covered in this section. Give groups of 4 students a four-foot piece of butcher paper, marked off in one-foot sections. Each group member should re-create one of the time periods in its correct position on the mural. Each period should include the name and time span of the period, descriptions of the world at that time, and labeled drawings of plant and animal life as appropriate. LS Visual/Verbal

Ancient Plants Organize the class into five groups, and assign each group one of the following groups of paleozoic plants: club mosses, ferns, horsetails, ginkos, or conifers.

Have each group use encyclopedias or botany books to look up the plant group and prepare a poster about it. Have students include diagrams of key features of the plant group and pictures of fossils and living examples of the group. **LS** Interpersonal/Visual
Co-op Learning

CONNECTION ACTiViTY
Real World——— GENERAL

Fossil Fuels The huge plants that grew in forests during the Paleozoic era later became coal. Ask students to research the locations of the world's coal deposits and to mark them on a world map. (Most of the known coal reserves are in Australia, China, Germany, Poland, Great Britain, India, Russia, South Africa, the United States, and Canada.)
LS Visual

Answer to Connection to Oceanography

Descriptions may vary.

Figure 4 *Organisms that first appeared in the Paleozoic era include reptiles, amphibians, fishes, worms, and ferns.*

Paleozoic era the geologic era that followed Precambrian time and that lasted from 542 million to 251 million years ago

The Paleozoic Era

The **Paleozoic era** (PAY lee OH ZOH ik ER uh) began about 542 million years ago and ended about 251 million years ago. Considering the length of Precambrian time, you can see that the Paleozoic era was relatively recent. Rocks from the Paleozoic era are rich in fossils of animals such as sponges, corals, snails, clams, squids, and trilobites. Fishes, the earliest animals with backbones, appeared during this era, and sharks became abundant. **Figure 4** shows an artist's depiction of life in the Paleozoic era.

The word *Paleozoic* comes from Greek words that mean "ancient life." When scientists first named this era, they thought it held the earliest forms of life. Scientists now think that earlier forms of life existed, but less is known about those life-forms. Before the Paleozoic era, most organisms lived in the oceans and left few fossils.

Life on Land

During the 300 million years of the Paleozoic era, plants, fungi, and air-breathing animals slowly colonized land. By the end of the era, forests of giant ferns, club mosses, horsetails, and conifers covered much of the Earth. All major plant groups except for flowering plants appeared during this era. These plants provided food and shelter for animals.

Fossils indicate that crawling insects were some of the first animals to live on land. They were followed by large salamander-like animals. Near the end of the Paleozoic era, reptiles and winged insects appeared.

The largest mass extinction known took place at the end of the Paleozoic era. By 251 million years ago, as many as 90% of marine species had become extinct. The mass extinction wiped out entire groups of marine organisms, such as trilobites. The oceans were completely changed.

CONNECTION TO Oceanography

Prehistoric Marine Organisms Find a variety of pictures and descriptions of marine organisms from the Cambrian period of the Paleozoic era. Choose three organisms that you find interesting. Draw or write a description of each organism. Find out whether scientists think the organism is related to any living group of organisms, and add this information to your description.

INCLUSION Strategies

• *Hearing Impaired* • *Learning Disabled*
• *Visually Impaired*

Demonstrate the superposition of geologic layers. Have student teams each use a different color of modeling clay to create a 3 in diameter circle, representing a piece of land. Ask teams to use other pieces of clay to add organisms to the land. Choose one team's model to represent early organisms, and place it where all students can see it. Then, choose a different team's model, and place it on top of the first, squashing the bottom organisms. Continue in this manner until all circles have been stacked. Slice a cross section through the stack for all to see. **LS** Kinesthetic

English Language Learners

The Mesozoic Era

The **Mesozoic era** (MES oh ZOH ik ER uh) began about 251 million years ago and lasted about 185.5 million years. *Mesozoic* comes from Greek words that mean "middle life." Scientists think that the surviving reptiles evolved into many different species after the Paleozoic era. Therefore, the Mesozoic era is commonly called the *Age of Reptiles.*

Life in the Mesozoic Era

Dinosaurs are the most well known reptiles that evolved during the Mesozoic era. Dinosaurs dominated the Earth for about 150 million years. A great variety of dinosaurs lived on Earth. Some had unique adaptations, such as ducklike bills for feeding or large spines on their bodies for defense. In addition to dinosaurs roaming the land, giant marine lizards swam in the ocean. The first birds also appeared during the Mesozoic era. In fact, scientists think that some of the dinosaurs became the ancestors of birds.

The most important plants during the early part of the Mesozoic era were conifers, which formed large forests. Flowering plants appeared later in the Mesozoic era. Some of the organisms of the Mesozoic era are illustrated in **Figure 5.**

The Extinction of Dinosaurs

At the end of the Mesozoic era, 65.5 million years ago, dinosaurs and many other animal and plant species became extinct. What happened to the dinosaurs? According to one hypothesis, a large meteorite hit the Earth and generated giant dust clouds and enough heat to cause worldwide fires. The dust and smoke from these fires blocked out much of the sunlight and caused many plants to die out. Without enough plants to eat, the plant-eating dinosaurs died out. And the meat-eating dinosaurs that fed on the plant-eating dinosaurs died. Global temperatures may have dropped for many years. However, some mammals and birds survived.

 **Reading Check** What kind of event happened at the end of both the Paleozoic and Mesozoic eras?

Figure 5 *The Mesozoic era was dominated by dinosaurs. The era ended with the mass extinction of many species.*

Mesozoic era the geologic era that lasted from 251 million to 65.5 million years ago; also called the *Age of Reptiles*

Answer to Reading Check

a mass extinction

Comparing Organisms Have students compare the characteristics of each of the Paleozoic, Mesozoic, and Cenozoic organisms described in this section with those of a living descendant (if one exists) of each of the organisms. Students can organize the information in the form of a chart. **LS** Visual

Quiz ———— GENERAL

On index cards, write the names of several types of organisms that appeared in each the four major divisions of geologic time mentioned in this section. Then, on paper strips, write the names of the geologic time divisions, and place the strips on a tabletop. Direct students to classify each organism named on a card by placing the card under the appropriate paper strip.

Alternative Assessment ———— GENERAL

Diorama Organize students into groups of three or four. Groups should use boxes with covers and art materials to make a diorama of one of the four major divisions of geologic time mentioned in this section. **LS** Interpersonal/Kinesthetic

Answer to Reading Check
"recent life"

Figure 6 *Many types of mammals evolved during the Cenozoic era.*

The Cenozoic Era

The **Cenozoic era** (SEN uh ZOH ik ER uh) began about 65 million years ago and continues today. *Cenozoic* comes from Greek words that mean "recent life." Scientists have more information about the Cenozoic era than about any of the previous eras. Fossils from the Cenozoic era formed recently in geologic time, so they are found in rock layers closer to the Earth's surface. The closer the fossils are to the surface, the easier they are to find.

During the Cenozoic era, many kinds of mammals, birds, insects, and flowering plants appeared. Some organisms that appeared in the Cenozoic era are shown in **Figure 6**.

✓ **Reading Check** What does *Cenozoic* mean?

The Age of Mammals

The Cenozoic era is sometimes called the *Age of Mammals*. Mammals have dominated the Cenozoic era the way reptiles dominated the Mesozoic era. Early Cenozoic mammals were small, forest dwellers. Larger mammals appeared later in the era. Some of these larger mammals had long legs for running, teeth that were specialized for eating different kinds of food, and large brains. Cenozoic mammals have included mastodons, saber-toothed cats, camels, giant ground sloths, and small horses.

MATH FOCUS

Relative Scale It's hard to imagine 4.6 billion years. One way is to use a *relative scale*. For example, we can represent all of Earth's history by using the 12 h shown on a clock. The scale would begin at noon, representing 4.6 billion years ago, and end at midnight, representing the present. Because 12 h represent 4.6 billion years, 1 h represents about 383 million years. (Hint: 4.6 billion ÷ 12 = 383 million) So, what time on the clock represents the beginning of the Paleozoic era, 543 million years ago?

Step 1: Write the ratio.

$$\frac{x}{543{,}000{,}000 \text{ years}} = \frac{1 \text{ h}}{383{,}000{,}000 \text{ years}}$$

Step 2: Solve for *x*.

$$x = \frac{543{,}000{,}000 \text{ years} \times 1 \text{ h}}{383{,}000{,}000 \text{ years}} = 1.42 \text{ h}$$

Step 3: Convert the answer to the clock scale.

1.42 h = 1 h + (0.42 × 60 min/h)

1.42 h = 1 h 25 min

So, the Paleozoic era began 1 h 25 min before midnight, at about 10:35.

Now It's Your Turn

1. Use this method to calculate the relative times at which the Mesozoic and Cenozoic eras began.

Answer to Math Focus

Mesozoic:
    12 h − [(348 ÷ 383) × 60] min = 11:21
Cenozoic:
    12 h − [(65 ÷ 383) × 60] min = 11:50

CONNECTION to Math ———— ADVANCED

Another Time Scale Have students calculate the length of the major divisions of geologic time relative to a 365-day calendar. They should state the month and day that each of the eras began. Use the Math Focus as an example, and provide a calendar for reference. Also, have students calculate the day that humans appeared (about 150,000 years ago). (Precambrian: Jan. 1; Paleozoic: Nov. 16; Mesozoic: Dec. 12; Cenozoic: Dec. 26; humans appeared: Dec. 31) **LS** Logical

The Cenozoic Era Today

We are currently living in the Cenozoic era. Modern humans appeared during this era. The environment and landscapes that we see around us today are part of this era.

However, the climate has changed many times during the Cenozoic era. Earth's history includes some periods called *ice ages,* during which the climate was very cold. During the ice ages, ice sheets and glaciers extended from the Earth's poles. To survive, many organisms migrated toward the equator. Other organisms adapted to the cold or became extinct.

When will the Cenozoic era end? No one knows. In the future, geologists might draw the line at a time when life on Earth again undergoes major changes.

Cenozoic era the most recent geologic era, beginning 65 million years ago; also called the *Age of Mammals*

SECTION Review

Summary

- The Earth is about 4.6 billion years old. Life formed from nonliving matter long ago.
- Precambrian time includes the formation of the Earth and the appearance of simple organisms.
- The first cells did not need oxygen. Later, photosynthetic cells evolved and released oxygen into the atmosphere.
- During the Paleozoic era, animals appeared in the oceans and on land, and plants grew on land.
- Dinosaurs dominated the Earth during the Mesozoic era.
- Mammals have dominated the Cenozoic era. This era continues today.

Using Key Terms

1. Use each of the following terms in a separate sentence: *Precambrian time, Paleozoic era, Mesozoic era,* and *Cenozoic era.*

Understanding Key Ideas

2. Unlike the atmosphere today, the atmosphere 3.5 billion years ago did not contain
   a. carbon dioxide.
   b. nitrogen.
   c. gases.
   d. ozone.

3. How do prokaryotic cells and eukaryotic cells differ?

4. Explain why cyanobacteria were important to the development of life on Earth.

5. Place in chronological order the following events on Earth:
   a. The first cells appeared that could make their own food from sunlight.
   b. The ozone layer formed.
   c. Simple chemicals reacted to form the molecules of life.
   d. Animals appeared.
   e. The first organisms appeared.
   f. Humans appeared.
   g. The Earth formed.

Math Skills

6. Calculate the total number of years that each of the geologic eras lasted, rounding to the nearest 100 million. Then, calculate each of these values as a percentage of the total 4.6 billion years of Earth's history. Round your answer to the units place.

Critical Thinking

7. **Making Inferences** Which chemicals probably made up the first cells on Earth?

8. **Forming Hypotheses** Think of your own hypothesis to explain the disappearance of the dinosaurs. Explain your hypothesis.

SCI LINKS. **NSTA**
Developed and maintained by the
National Science Teachers Association

For a variety of links related to this chapter, go to www.scilinks.org

Topic: Geologic Time Scale
SciLinks code: HSM0669

SCIENTISTS AT ODDS

Fire or Ice Scientists continue to debate whether another ice age is coming soon or whether the Earth is overheating. During Earth's history, the climate has changed many times, slowly switching between icy cold and lush warmth. Scientists call the warmer periods *interglacial* because each is usually followed by another ice age. However, in recent decades average temperatures on Earth seem to keep getting warmer.

CHAPTER RESOURCES

Chapter Resource File

 • Section Quiz GENERAL
• Section Review GENERAL
• Vocaulary and Section Summary GENERAL
• Reinforcement Worksheet BASIC
• SciLinks Activity GENERAL

Technology

 Interactive Explorations CD-ROM
• Rock On! GENERAL

Workbooks

 **Math Skills for Science**
• Subtraction Review BASIC

SECTION
3

Focus

Overview

In this section, students will learn that scientists think humans share a common ancestor and common characteristics with other primates, such as apes and monkeys. This section describes the characteristics of hominids and examines trends in their evolution that could have led to modern humans.

Bellringer

Ask students to write an answer to the following question:

What makes you unique among your family members? (Responses might include food preferences, health condition, physical appearance, and talents.)

Point out that understanding human ancestry requires recognizing similarities and differences, such as those seen in families.

What You Will Learn

- Describe two characteristics that all primates share.
- Describe three major groups of hominids.

Vocabulary

primate
hominid
Homo sapiens

READING STRATEGY

Discussion Read this section silently. Write down questions that you have about this section. Discuss your questions in a small group.

Humans and Other Primates

Have you ever heard someone say that humans descended from monkeys or apes? Well, scientists would not exactly say that. The scientific theory is that humans, apes, and monkeys share a common ancestor. This common ancestor probably lived more than 45 million years ago.

Most scientists agree that there is enough evidence to support this theory. Many fossils of organisms have been found that show traits of both humans and apes. Also, comparisons of modern humans and apes support this theory.

Primates

What characteristics make us human? Humans are classified as primates. **Primates** are a group of mammals that includes humans, apes, monkeys, and lemurs. Primates have the characteristics illustrated in **Figure 1**.

The First Primates

The ancestors of primates may have co-existed with the dinosaurs. These ancestors were probably mouselike mammals that were active at night, lived in trees, and ate insects. The first primates did not exist until after the dinosaurs died out. About 45 million years ago, primates that had larger brains appeared. These were the first primates that had traits similar to monkeys, apes, and humans.

Figure 1 **Characteristics of Primates**

Both eyes are located at the front of the head, and they provide binocular, or three-dimensional, vision.

Almost all primates, such as these orangutans, have five flexible fingers—four fingers and an opposable thumb. This thumb enables primates to grip objects. Most primates besides humans also have opposable big toes.

CHAPTER RESOURCES

Chapter Resource File

- **Lesson Plan**
- **Directed Reading A** BASIC
- **Directed Reading B** SPECIAL NEEDS

Technology

Transparencies
- Bellringer
- L30 Comparison of Primate Skeletons

Workbooks

Interactive Textbook Struggling Readers

Is That a Fact!

Although the skulls of a human and a chimpanzee appear similar, there are significant differences. The cranium of a human skull is domed, whereas the chimpanzee's cranium is flattened. Also, canine teeth in humans do not overlap as they do in chimpanzees. And because humans walk upright, the place where the spine connects to the skull is more centered under the skull in humans.

Apes and Chimpanzees

Scientists think that the chimpanzee, a type of ape, is the closest living relative of humans. This theory does not mean humans descended from chimpanzees. It means that humans and chimpanzees share a common ancestor. Sometime between 6 million and 30 million years ago, the ancestors of humans, chimpanzees, and other apes began to evolve along different lines.

primate a type of mammal characterized by opposable thumbs and binocular vision

Hominids

Humans are in a family separate from other primates. This family, called **hominids,** includes only humans and their human-like ancestors. The main characteristic that separates hominids from other primates is bipedalism. *Bipedalism* means "walking primarily upright on two feet." Evidence of bipedalism can be seen in a primate's skeletal structure. **Figure 2** shows a comparison of the skeletal features of apes and hominids.

hominid a type of primate characterized by bipedalism, relatively long lower limbs, and lack of a tail

✓ **Reading Check** In which family are humans classified? (*See the Appendix for answers to Reading Checks.*)

Figure 2 **Comparison of Primate Skeletons**

The bones of gorillas (a type of ape) and humans (a type of hominid) have a very similar form, but the human skeleton is adapted for walking upright.

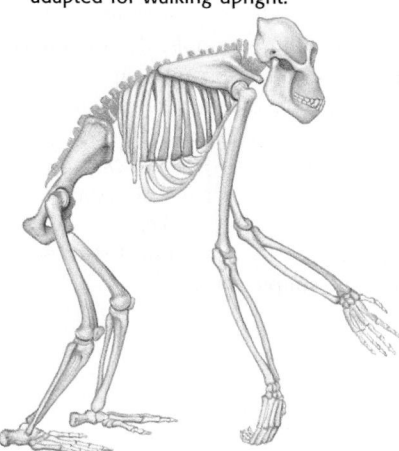

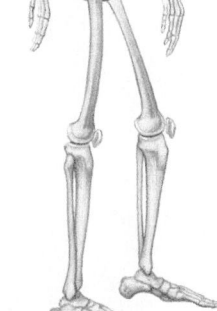

The human pelvis is vertical and helps hold the entire skeleton upright. The human spine is curved in an S shape. The arms are shorter than the legs.

▲ The gorilla pelvis tilts the ape's large rib cage and heavy neck and head forward. The gorilla spine is curved in a C shape. The arms are long to provide balance on the ground.

CONNECTION to Anthropology — ADVANCED

Bipedalism The tendency to walk fully upright distinguishes us from apes. But how do our physical features relate to our posture? Thomas Greiner, a physical anthropologist, developed a computer model that shows how muscle action relates to bone shape. Greiner concluded that in order to regularly walk upright, an ape would need larger gluteus maximus muscles and a larger ileum. These attributes are seen in human bodies.

Primate Characteristics Help students identify the characteristics that distinguish primates from other mammal groups. Show them pictures of primate and nonprimate mammals. Ask students to describe how the primates differ from the other animals. (Sample answer: Primates generally have flatter faces than nonprimates. Their eyes are located at the front of the head rather than at the sides, their snouts are small, and their fingers are flexible.) **LS Visual/Logical**

Answer to Reading Check
Africa

Group ACTIVITY ━ **GENERAL**

Comparing Hominids Create and display a large table to compare the distinguishing characteristics of the primates and hominids discussed in this section. Column heads might include "Binocular vision," "Bipedalism," "Brain size," "Tool use," "Known locations," and "Estimated dates." Call on students to make additions to the table. **LS Logical/Verbal**

Figure 3 *This skull was found in the Sahel desert in Chad, Africa. The skull is estimated to be 6 million to 7 million years old.*

Hominids Through Time

Scientists are constantly filling in pieces of the hominid family picture. They have found many different fossils of ancient hominids and have named at least 18 types of hominids. However, scientists do not agree on the classification of every fossil. Fossils are classified as hominids when they share some of the characteristics of modern humans. But each type of hominid was unique in terms of size, the way it walked, the shape of its skull, and other characteristics.

The Earliest Hominids

The earliest hominids had traits that were more humanlike than apelike. These traits include the ability to walk upright as well as smaller teeth, flatter faces, and larger brains than earlier primates. The oldest hominid fossils have been found in Africa. So, scientists think hominid evolution began in Africa. **Figure 3** shows a fossil that may be from one of the earliest hominids. It is 6 million to 7 million years old.

✓ Reading Check Where are the earliest hominid fossils found?

Australopithecines

Many early hominids are classified as *australopithecines* (AW struh LOH PITH uh SEENS). Members of this group were similar to apes but were different from apes in several ways. For example, their brains were slightly larger than the brains of apes. Some of them may have used stone tools. They climbed trees but also walked on two legs.

Fossil evidence of australopithecines has been found in several places in Africa. The fossilized footprints in **Figure 4** were probably made by a member of this group over 3 million years ago. Some skeletons of australopithecines have been found near what appear to be simple tools.

Figure 4 *Anthropologist Mary Leakey discovered these 3.6 million year old footprints in Tanzania, Africa.*

SCIENTISTS AT ODDS

In 1975, fossils of 13 hominids were found in Ethiopia by Donald Johansen, a contemporary of Mary Leakey. These fossils differed in body size and jaw shape. Some anthropologists think that the larger fossils represent the males and the smaller fossils represent the females of a particular species. Johansen and others believe that the differences indicate that the fossils are of two distinct species of australopithecines.

Is That a Fact!

One of the most famous skeletons of an australopithecine was found by Donald Johansen in Ethiopia 1974 and was nicknamed "Lucy." This nickname came from the Beatles' hit song "Lucy in the Sky with Diamonds," which was playing around the time when the fossil was discovered.

A Variety of Early Hominids

Many australopithecines and other types of hominids lived at the same time. Some australopithecines had slender bodies. They had humanlike jaws and teeth but had small, apelike skulls. They probably lived in forests and grasslands and ate a vegetarian diet. Scientists think that some of these types of hominids may have been the ancestors of modern humans.

Some early hominids had large bodies and massive teeth and jaws. They had a unique skull structure and relatively small brains. Most of these types of hominids lived in tropical forests and probably ate tough plant material, such as roots. Scientists do not think that these large-bodied hominids are the ancestors of modern humans.

Global Hominids

About 2.4 million years ago, a new group of hominids appeared. These hominids were similar to the slender australopithecines but were more humanlike. These new hominids had larger and more complex brains, rounder skulls, and flatter faces than early hominids. They showed advanced tool-making abilities and walked upright.

These new hominids were members of the group *Homo,* which includes modern humans. Fossil evidence indicates that several members of the *Homo* group existed at the same time and on several continents. Members of this group were probably scavengers that ate a variety of foods. Some of these hominids may have adapted to climate change by migrating and changing the way they lived.

An early member of this new group was *Homo habilis* (HOH moh HAB uh luhs), which lived about 2.4 million years ago. About 1.8 million years ago, a hominid called *Homo erectus* (HOH moh i REK tuhs) appeared. This type of hominid could grow as tall as modern humans do. A museum creation of a member of *Homo erectus* is shown in **Figure 5.** No one knows what early hominids looked like. Scientists construct models based on skulls and other evidence.

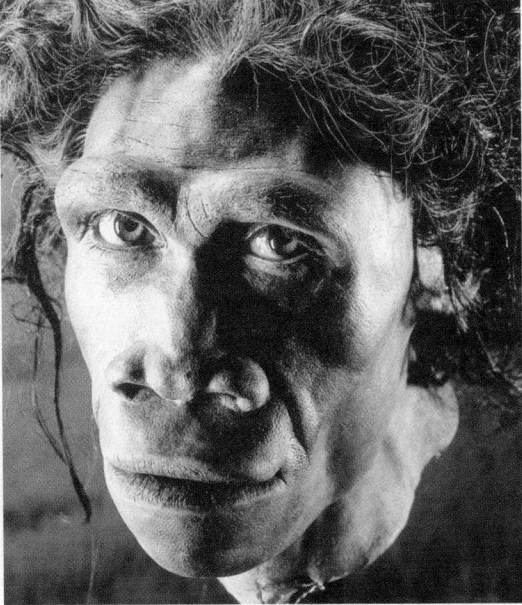

Figure 5 *Fossils of a hominid known as* Homo erectus *have been found in Africa, Europe, and Asia.*

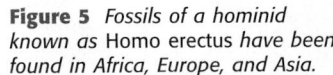
Answers to School-to-Home Activity

3. a. Answers may vary. Most of the tasks will probably be more difficult without the use of the thumb.
   b. Answers may vary. Some people would not like to carry out such a difficult task on a regular basis.

Discussion ─── GENERAL

Analyzing Tools *Homo habilis* is thought to have made one of the oldest recognizable stone tools. The tool was a pebble with some sharp edges. Ask students how they think the tool was made. (Sample answer: Flakes were chipped off the pebble to sharpen it.) **LS** Verbal/Logical

CONNECTION ACTIVITY ART ─── GENERAL

Sculpting Sculptors probably helped paleoanthropologists determine the physical appearance of the hominid shown in **Figure 5.** Sculptors can apply their knowledge of anatomy to reconstruct body features. Have students research how sculptors are called upon to reconstruct hominid faces and heads, based on skulls. Then, have interested students use clay to sculpt a model of the head of a hominid. **LS** Kinesthetic — English Language Learners

---

MISCONCEPTION ALERT

Students often misunderstand the meaning of the scientific name of the genus *Homo.* This word comes from the greek word for "earth" or "ground" and was later used to mean "man" or "human being" in latin. In some other words, the word root *homo-* comes from the greek word meaning "same."

CONNECTION to History ─── GENERAL

Insulting Apes? Many cartoons in the 19th century satirized the idea that humans are related to apes. In one such cartoon, Henry Bergh, the founder of the Society for the Prevention of Cruelty to Animals, chided Charles Darwin for insulting apes by suggesting that they are related to humans. Suggest that students look for examples of these historical cartoons. **LS** Visual/Interpersonal

Reteaching ———— BASIC

Timeline Have students make a timeline that shows the order of appearance of the primates discussed in the chapter. When students have finished their timelines, have them review the timeline of another student. [LS] **Visual**

Quiz ———— GENERAL

Among primates, what is distinctive about hominids? (The main characteristic that distinguishes hominids from other primates is walking upright on two legs as their main way of moving around.)

Alternative Assessment ———— ADVANCED

Hominid Poster Have students construct a poster with a detailed timeline of the appearance of different types of primates and hominids. Ask students to include pictures and information about the distinguishing characteristics of each group. Encourage students to conduct additional research to find the latest discoveries. [LS] **Visual/Logical**

Homo sapiens the species of hominids that includes modern humans and their closest ancestors and that first appeared about 100,000 to 160,000 years ago

Figure 6 *These photos show museum recreations of early* Homo sapiens.

Recent Hominids

As recently as 30,000 years ago, two types of hominids may have lived in the same areas at the same time. Both had the largest brains of any hominids and made advanced tools, clothing, and art. Scientists think that modern humans may have descended from one of these two types of hominids.

Neanderthals

One recent hominid is known as *Neanderthal* (nee AN duhr TAWL). Neanderthals lived in Europe and western Asia. They may have lived as early as 230,000 years ago. They hunted large animals, made fires, and wore clothing. They also may have cared for the sick and elderly and buried their dead with cultural rituals. About 30,000 years ago, Neanderthals disappeared. No one knows what caused their extinction.

Early and Modern Humans

Modern humans are classified as the species **Homo sapiens** (HOH moh SAY pee UHNZ). The earliest *Homo sapiens* existed in Africa 100,000 to 160,000 years ago. The group migrated out of Africa sometime between 40,000 and 100,000 years ago. Compared with Neanderthals, *Homo sapiens* has a smaller and flatter face, and has a skull that is more rounded. Of all known hominids, only *Homo sapiens* still exists.

Early *Homo sapiens* created large amounts of art. Early humans produced sculptures, carvings, paintings, and clothing such as that shown in **Figure 6.** The preserved villages and burial grounds of early humans show that they had an organized and complex society.

Homework ———— GENERAL

Writing **Future Scientists** Have students write a page from an anthropologist's journal that will be written 100,000 years in the future. Tell students that the anthropologist is studying an archaeological site that contains the remains or traces of people from today. Suggest that students describe the scientist's thoughts and hypotheses about the site. [LS] **Visual**

Science Bloopers

A skull of a *Homo sapiens* who had dental problems was found in Zambia. There was a hole in one side of the skull and signs of a partially healed abscess. This skull was made famous by a writer who imagined that the hole was caused by a bullet shot from an interplanetary visitor's gun 120,000 years ago.

Drawing the Hominid Family Tree

Scientists review their hypotheses when they learn something new about a group of organisms and their related fossils. As more hominid fossils are discovered, there are more features to compare. Sometimes, scientists add details to the relationships they see between each group. Sometimes, new groups of hominids are recognized. Human evolution was once thought to be a line of descent from ancient primates to modern humans. But scientists now speak of a "tree" or even a "bush" to describe the evolution of various hominids in the fossil record.

✓ Reading Check What is likely to happen when a new hominid fossil is discovered?

SECTION Review

Summary

- Humans, apes, and monkeys are primates. Almost all primates have opposable thumbs and binocular vision.
- Hominids, a subgroup of primates, include humans and their humanlike ancestors. The oldest known hominid fossils may be 7 million years old.
- Early hominids included australopithecines and the *Homo* group.
- Early *Homo sapiens* did not differ very much from present-day humans. *Homo sapiens* is the only type of hominid living today.

Using Key Terms

1. Use each of the following words in the same sentence: *primate, hominid,* and *Homo sapiens.*

Understanding Key Ideas

2. The unique characteristics of primates are
   a. bipedalism and thumbs.
   b. opposable thumbs.
   c. opposable thumbs and binocular vision.
   d. opposable toes and thumbs.

3. Describe the major evolutionary developments from early hominids to modern humans.

4. Compare members of the *Homo* group with australopithecines.

Critical Thinking

5. **Forming Hypotheses** Suggest some reasons why Neanderthals might have become extinct.

6. **Making Inferences** Imagine you are a scientist excavating an ancient campsite. What might you infer about the people who used the site if you found the charred bones of large animals and various stone blades among human fossils?

Interpreting Graphics

The figure below shows a possible ancestral relationships between humans and some modern apes. Use this figure to answer the questions that follow.

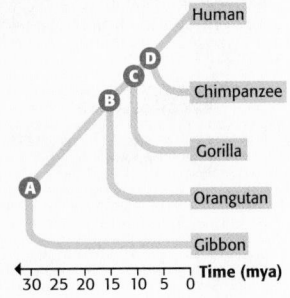

7. Which letter represents the ancestor of all the apes?

8. To which living ape are gorillas most closely related?

For a variety of links related to this chapter, go to www.scilinks.org

Topic: Human Evolution
SciLinks code: HSM0769

ACTIVITY — ADVANCED

Classifying Primates Have students find out the family or genus of the apes and hominids mentioned in this section.

- Apes: family Pongidae (great apes; includes orangutans, gorillas, chimpanzees)
- Hominids: family Hominidae
- Australopithecines: genus *Australopithecus* (slender) and genus *Paranthropus* (robust)
- Homo group: genus *Homo* (includes species *Homo habilis, Homo erectus, Homo neanderthalensis,* and *Homo sapiens*)

LS Verbal

Mystery Footprints

Teacher's Notes

Time Required
Two 45-minute class periods

Lab Ratings

EASY ———————————→ HARD

Teacher Prep 🧪🧪🧪
Student Set-Up 🧪🧪
Concept Level 🧪🧪
Clean Up 🧪🧪

Preparation Notes

To set up this lab, you will need to either find a sandy area outside or construct a long, shallow sandbox out of wood or cardboard. You may prefer to perform this activity outside because it is likely to be messy. Ask a boy and a girl (preferably students who are not in your science class) or two adults, one male and one female, to walk through the sand with their bare feet. The sand should be about 16 cm deep, and the area to be walked through should be long enough that three or four footprints can be seen in the sand. Slightly moistened sand will hold the best footprints. You may want to make the footprints more permanent by using plaster of Paris. If you do not have access to sand, look for a type of soil that will hold a footprint.

OBJECTIVES

Form a hypothesis to explain observations of traces left by other organisms.

Design and **conduct** an experiment to test one of these hypotheses.

Analyze and **communicate** the results in a scientific way.

MATERIALS

- ruler, metric or meterstick
- sand, slightly damp
- large box, at least 1 m² or large enough to contain 3 or 4 footprints

SAFETY

Mystery Footprints

Sometimes, scientists find clues preserved in rocks that are evidence of the activities of organisms that lived thousands of years ago. Evidence such as preserved footprints can provide important information about an organism. Imagine that your class has been asked by a group of scientists to help study some human footprints. These footprints were found embedded in rocks in an area just outside of town.

Ask a Question

① Your teacher will give you some mystery footprints in sand. Examine the mystery footprints. Brainstorm what you might learn about the people who walked on this patch of sand.

Form a Hypothesis

② As a class, formulate several testable hypotheses about the people who left the footprints. Form groups of three people, and choose one hypothesis for your group to investigate.

Test the Hypothesis

③ Draw a table for recording your data. For example, if you have two sets of mystery footprints, your table might look similar to the one below.

Mystery Footprints		
	Footprint set 1	**Footprint set 2**
Length		
Width		
Depth of toe		
Depth of heel		
Length of stride		

DO NOT WRITE IN BOOK

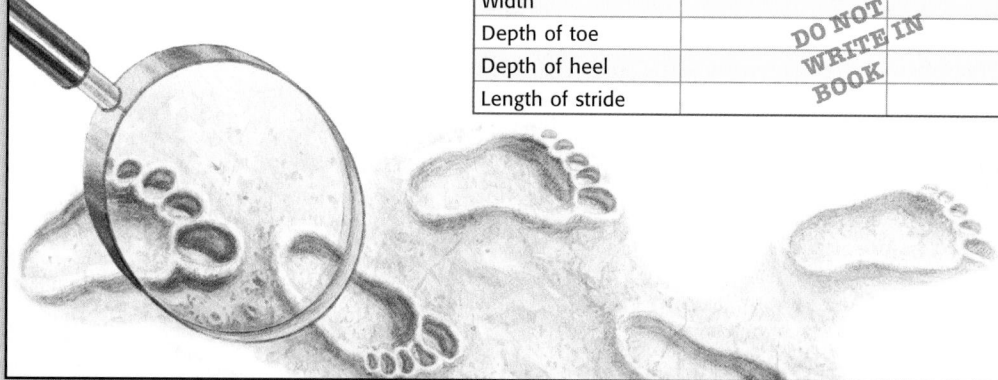

Holt Lab Generator CD-ROM

Search for any lab by topic, standard, difficulty level, or time. Edit any lab to fit your needs, or create your own labs. Use the Lab Materials QuickList software to customize your lab materials list.

Maurine Marchani
Raymond Park Middle School
Indianapolis, Indiana

CHAPTER RESOURCES

Chapter Resource File
- • Datasheet for Chapter Lab
- • Lab Notes and Answers

Technology

 Classroom Videos
  • Lab Video

• The Half-Life of Pennies

④ With the help of your group, you may first want to analyze your own footprints to help you draw conclusions about the mystery footprints. For example, use a meterstick to measure your stride when you are running. Is your stride different when you are walking? What part of your foot touches the ground first when you are running? When you are running, which part of your footprint is deeper?

⑤ Make a list of the kind of footprint each different activity produces. For example, you might write, "When I am running, my footprints are deep near the toe area and 110 cm apart."

Analyze the Results

① **Classifying** Compare the data from your footprints with the data from the mystery footprints. How are the footprints alike? How are they different?

② **Identifying Patterns** How many people do you think made the mystery footprints? Explain your interpretation.

③ **Analyzing Data** Can you tell if the mystery footprints were made by men, women, children, or a combination? Can you tell if they were standing still, walking, or running? Explain your interpretation.

Draw Conclusions

④ **Drawing Conclusions** Do your data support your hypothesis? Explain.

⑤ **Evaluating Methods** How could you improve your experiment?

Communicating Your Data

WRITING SKILL Summarize your group's conclusions in a report for the scientists who asked for your help. Begin by stating your hypothesis. Then, summarize the methods you used to study the footprints. Include the comparisons you made between your footprints and the mystery footprints. Add pictures if you wish. State your conclusions. Finally, offer some suggestions about how you could improve your investigation.

CHAPTER RESOURCES

Workbooks

📖 **Long-Term Projects & Research Ideas**
• A Horse Is a Horse **ADVANCED**

Answers

The answers for this activity will depend on the footprints your students observe. Students should be able to compare their own activities with variations in the footprints they leave. Then, they should be able to apply what they've learned to the mystery footprints.

Safety Caution

Remind students to review all safety cautions and icons before beginning this lab activity. Supervise students during this activity. Provide students with ample space and a safe location to test walking and running on the sandy area. Remind each group of students to keep out of the way of others. Have students keep shoes, or at least socks, on while walking on the sandy area.

Lab Notes

Tell the students to imagine that a group of scientists wish to analyze human footprints found in the rocks near fossilized remains and that the scientists have contacted the class to help with the investigation. The scientists want to know how the students intend to gather information to make inferences about the humans who left the prints. Explain that a scientist should be able to make the same type of inferences about an organism from fresh tracks as from preserved tracks. Use the mystery footprints in the sand to help students design investigations for gathering data. From the data, students can learn to draw inferences.

A large proportion of research on evolution depends on making scientific inferences and checking for corroboration among different sources of data. To conclude the laboratory experience, lead the students in a discussion about the importance of large sets of data in helping scientists make inferences.

Chapter Review

Assignment Guide

Section	Questions
1	5, 7, 11, 12, 20–22, 26, 27
2	1–4, 8, 9, 13–16, 19, 23, 24
3	6, 10, 17–19, 25

ANSWERS

Using Key Terms

1. Precambrian time
2. Cenozoic era
3. Mesozoic era
4. Paleozoic era
5. Absolute dating tries to determine a specific range of dates, while relative dating determines the order of events but not specific dates.
6. Hominids are a type of primate, but not all primates are hominids.

Understanding Key Ideas

7. d
8. a
9. d
10. d

USING KEY TERMS

Complete each of the following sentences by choosing the correct term from the word bank.

Precambrian time   Paleozoic era
Mesozoic era   Cenozoic era

1. During ___, life is thought to have originated from nonliving matter.

2. The Age of Mammals refers to the ___.

3. The Age of Reptiles refers to the ___.

4. Plants colonized land during the ___.

For each pair of terms, explain how the meanings of the terms differ.

5. *relative dating* and *absolute dating*

6. *primates* and *hominids*

UNDERSTANDING KEY IDEAS

Multiple Choice

7. If the half-life of an unstable element is 5,000 years, what percentage of the parent material will be left after 10,000 years?
   a. 100%
   b. 75%
   c. 50%
   d. 25%

8. The first cells on Earth appeared in
   a. Precambrian time.
   b. the Paleozoic era.
   c. the Mesozoic era.
   d. the Cenozoic era.

9. In which era are we currently living?
   a. Precambrian time
   b. Paleozoic era
   c. Mesozoic era
   d. Cenozoic era

10. Scientists think that the closest living relatives of humans are
    a. lemurs.
    b. monkeys.
    c. gorillas.
    d. chimpanzees.

Short Answer

11. Describe how plant and animal remains can become fossils.

12. What information do fossils provide about the history of life?

13. List three important steps in the early development of life on Earth.

14. List two important groups of organisms that appeared during each of the three most recent geologic eras.

15. Describe the event that scientists think caused the mass extinction at the end of the Mesozoic era.

11. Sample answer: The remains of organisms can become fossils when geologic processes preserve them or their traces. An example is sediment covering an organism and the shape becoming hardened into rock.

12. Fossils tell us about the kinds of organisms that existed and the way they changed over time.

13. Simple chemicals reacted to form the molecules that make up life. Simple cells formed. Photosynthetic cells developed and began to produce oxygen.

14. Sample answer: Precambrian: prokaryotes and eukaryotes; Paleozoic: multicellular organisms, plants, insects, and amphibians; Mesozoic: dinosaurs and other reptiles, birds, and small mammals; Cenozoic: large mammals, including humans, and more-diverse birds and insects

15. A giant meteorite hit the Earth, disturbing ecosystems and causing climate change.

16. From which geologic era are fossils most commonly found?

17. Describe two characteristics that are shared by all primates.

18. Which hominid species is alive today?

CRITICAL THINKING

19. **Concept Mapping** Use the following terms to create a concept map: *Earth's history, humans, Paleozoic era, dinosaurs, Precambrian time, land plants, Mesozoic era, cyanobacteria,* and *Cenozoic era.*

20. **Applying Concepts** Can footprints be fossils? Explain your answer.

21. **Making Inferences** If you find rock layers containing fish fossils in a desert, what can you infer about the history of the desert?

22. **Applying Concepts** Explain how an environmental change can threaten the survival of a species. Give two examples.

23. **Analyzing Ideas** Why do scientists think the first cells did not need oxygen to survive?

24. **Identifying Relationships** How does the extinction that occurred at the end of the Mesozoic era relate to the Age of Mammals?

25. **Making Comparisons** Make a table listing the similarities and differences between australopithecines, early members of the group *Homo,* and modern members of the species *Homo sapiens.*

INTERPRETING GRAPHICS

The graph below shows data about fossilized teeth that were found within a series of rock layers. Use this graph to answer the questions that follow.

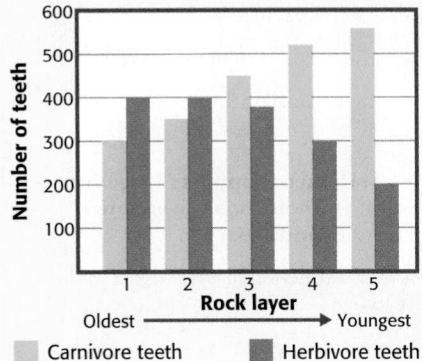

Oldest ⟶ Youngest

☐ Carnivore teeth ☐ Herbivore teeth

26. Which of the following statements best describes the information presented in the graph?

a. Over time, the number of carnivores decreased and the number of herbivores increased.

b. Over time, the number of carnivores increased and the number of herbivores increased.

c. Over time, the number of carnivores and herbivores remained the same.

d. Over time, the number of carnivores increased and the number of herbivores decreased.

27. At what point did carnivore teeth begin to outnumber herbivore teeth?

a. between layer 1 and layer 2

b. between layer 2 and layer 3

c. between layer 3 and layer 4

d. between layer 4 and layer 5

16. Fossils in the Cenozoic era are most common because they are closer to the surface of Earth and were formed more recently.

17. Primates have opposable thumbs that allow them to grasp objects, and they have eyes positioned at the front of their heads that allow them to tell how far away something is.

18. *Homo sapiens*

Critical Thinking

19. 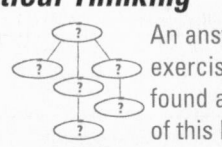 An answer to this exercise can be found at the end of this book.

20. yes; A footprint is a trace left by an organism.

21. that the rocks there may have once been underwater

22. Sample answer: If an environment changes suddenly, species may not be adapted to survive the change. Examples might be a sudden change from a hot to a cold climate or a sudden change from a wet to a dry environment.

23. There was no oxygen available when the first cells developed.

24. After the dinosaurs were wiped out (with the exception of birds), mammals were able to take their place in ecosystems.

25. Sample answer:

	Australo-pithecines	Early homo	Homo sapiens
Bipedalism	yes	yes	yes
Brains	medium	larger	largest
Tools	none	some	many
Art	none	none	a lot
Known locations	Africa	several continents	world-wide

Interpreting Graphics

26. d

27. b

CHAPTER RESOURCES

Chapter Resource File

- Chapter Review GENERAL
- Chapter Test A GENERAL
- Chapter Test B ADVANCED
- Chapter Test C SPECIAL NEEDS
- Vocabulary Activity GENERAL

Workbooks

Study Guide
- Study Guide also available in Spanish.

Standardized Test Preparation

Teacher's Notes

To provide practice under more realistic conditions, give students 20 minutes to answer all of the questions in this Standardized Test Preparation.

Answer Key

Question	Answer
1	C
2	C
3	B
4	A
5	B
6	B
7	D
8	B
9	A
10	*
11	*

*See Test Doctor.

Multiple Choice

1. Which of the following events provides evidence that environmental conditions on Earth have changed?

   A. a fossilized footprint in lava rock

   B. an insect fossil in amber

   C. a marine fossil on a mountaintop

   D. a dinosaur fossil in sedimentary rock

2. Which statement supports Wegener's idea that the continents were once part of one landmass?

   A. A mass extinction happened 251 million years ago.

   B. Fossils of marine animals are found on mountaintops.

   C. Fossils of tropical plants have been found in Antarctica.

   D. The half-lives of unstable elements throughout Earth are the same.

3. A scientist is trying determine the age of a fossil. If the scientist wants to find the fossil's age in years, which method should she use?

   A. The scientist should examine the rock layers.

   B. The scientist should examine atoms in the rock.

   C. The scientist should examine the fossil's position in the rock.

   D. The scientist should examine how deep in the rock the fossil was located.

4. Based on the fossil record, which of the following statements describes a way in which primates changed over time?

   A. Primate brains became larger.

   B. Humans evolved from Neanderthals.

   C. Fewer primates exist today than before.

   D. Primates arose with the dinosaurs.

5. Mesosaurus was a small, aquatic reptile and Glossopteris was an ancient plant species. Based on the map below, which of the following statements is true?

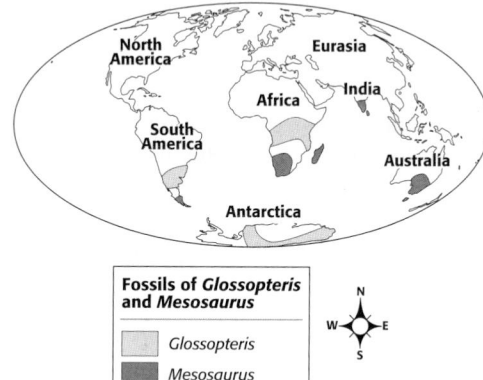

Fossils of *Glossopteris* and *Mesosaurus*

   Glossopteris

   Mesosaurus

   A. Australia was once much colder.

   B. Antarctica was once much warmer.

   C. Central Africa was once covered by water.

   D. North America was once covered by water.

➕ TEST DOCTOR

Question 1 A, B, D: A fossilized footprint, an insect in amber, or fossilized bones are all evidence of life, but not evidence of environmental change. C: Correct.

Question 2 A: Mass extinctions occur as a result of rapid processes, not slow processes such as continental drift. B: Fossils of marine animals on mountaintops indicate that the environment of an area changed, but this change may have to do with factors other than continental drift, such as volcanic activity or uplift. C: Correct. D: Half-lives vary depending on the unstable atom. Earth's crust is similar in all parts of the world, but this characteristic does not prove continental drift.

6. Which of the following organisms will most likely become a fossil?

A. a plant covered by a lava flow

B. a small lizard covered by tree sap

C. a deer killed and eaten by predators

D. a bacterium dead on the bottom of the ocean

7. Why are fossils from the Cenozoic Era, which began 65 million years ago, the easiest fossils to find?

A. Fossils of the largest creatures are from this era.

B. The number of species greatly increased during this era.

C. Life on Earth, in the form of cyanobacteria, began during this era.

D. Fossils from this era are found in layers closest to Earth's surface.

8. A mass extinction occurs when a large number of species become extinct. Which of the following events might lead to a mass extinction?

A. A volcano erupts.

B. A comet strikes Earth.

C. An island forms in the ocean.

D. Two continents move away from each other.

9. The figure below shows the ozone layer, which became part of the upper atmosphere as Earth developed. Based on the figure, which of the following statements about ozone is true?

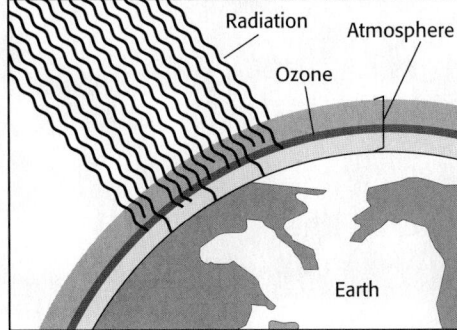

A. The ozone layer absorbs radiation, which can harm organisms, making life possible.

B. The ozone layer reflects radiation, which can harm organisms, making life possible.

C. The ozone layer allows large amounts of radiation to warm Earth, making life possible.

D. The ozone layer made the atmosphere thicker, blocking radiation and making life possible.

Open Response

10. What changes in Earth's atmosphere made life on Earth possible?

11. What fossil evidence indicates a mass extinction?

Question 6 A: The hot lava would likely burn all evidence of the plant before a fossil could form. B: Correct. C: Predators and scavengers will likely leave little behind of the deer to form a fossil. D: Because they lack hard parts, bacteria do not often from fossils.

Question 7 A: There is evidence of large creatures from eras before the Cenozoic Era. B: The number of species has increased during several eras in Earth's history. C: Cyanobacteria leave few fossils behind. Additionally, these organisms arose well before 65 million years ago. D: Correct.

Question 8 A: A volcanic eruption might lead to the death of organisms near the volcano, but it would probably not affect organisms around the world. B: Correct. C: An island formed through volcanic activity could affect organisms, but only local ones. D: Continental drift would affect long-term adaptations, but it would not cause mass extinctions.

Question 9 A: Correct. B: The figure does not indicate that the ozone layer reflects radiation. C. The figure clearly shows that radiation stops at the ozone layer and does not reach Earth's surface. D. Based on the figure, the ozone layer makes up a very small portion of the atmosphere. Additionally, the figure does not indicate that the thickness of the atmosphere plays a role in blocking radiation.

Question 10 Full-credit answers should include the following points:

• The amount of oxygen in the atmosphere increased due to photosynthetic organisms.

• The ozone layer formed, absorbing harmful radiation.

• The formation of the ozone layer allowed the survival of new organisms on Earth's surface.

Question 11 Full-credit answers should include the following points:

• A mass extinction is the extinction of many species within a short time.

• Fossil evidence of a mass extinction would include a single layer of rock that has many species in it.

• The species that died out do not appear later in the fossil record.

Question 3 A: Rock layers can provide relative age, but not absolute age. B: Correct. C: The fossil's position in the rock might be used to determine relative age. D: Again, the depth of the fossil might be used to determine relative age.

Question 4 A: Correct. B: Humans and Neanderthals coexisted for a short period of time, which means humans are not descended from Neanderthals. C: Primates have become more diverse over time, not less diverse. D: Primate ancestors may have arisen during the age of the dinosaurs, but fossil evidence of primates has not been found during this period of time.

Question 5 A: The evidence of *Mesosaurus* in Australia indicates part of it was once under water but does not provide evidence about Australia's climate. B: Correct. C: Central Africa has fossils of *Glossopteris*, indicating it was not under water. D: There is no evidence of either *Mesosaurus* or *Glossopteris* in North America, so it cannot be determined if it was once under water from this map.

Science, Technology, and Society

Background

The computer-generated skull image is reconstructed from the fossil skull of a Neanderthal child. The fossil find is named *Le Moustier 1*; it was excavated from a cave in Le Moustier, France. This site is also important because of the unique types of tools found there. The tools indicate a different form of tool-making than is found in many other Neanderthal sites. One theory related to this finding is that Neanderthals learned new toolmaking techniques from *Homo sapiens* at some point when the two groups came in contact.

Scientific Debate

Discussion —————— GENERAL

Ask students to discuss what they might do if human fossils were discovered in their backyard. Then, discuss a scenario in which a company is prevented or delayed from conducting business when human fossils are discovered on their property. Brainstorm other similar scenarios or research and discuss real scenarios with which the students might be familiar. Ask students to think of ways that these conflicts might be resolved.

Science in Action

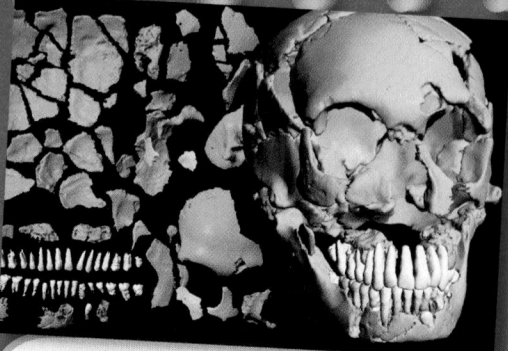

Residents of this neighborhood in Jerusalem, Israel, objected when anthropologists started to dig in the area.

Science, Technology, and Society

Using Computers to Examine Fossils

Paleontologists want to examine fossils without taking apart or damaging the fossils. Fortunately, they can now use a technology called *computerized axial tomography*, or *CAT scanning*, which provides views inside objects without touching the objects. A CAT scan is a series of cross-section pictures of an object. A computer can assemble these "slices" to create a three-dimensional picture of the entire object. Computer graphic programs can also be used to move pictures of fossil pieces around to see how the pieces fit together. The fossil skull above was reconstructed using CAT scans and computers.

Math ACTiViTY

The average volume of a Neanderthal adult's brain was about 1,400 cm³, while that of an adult gorilla is about 400 cm³. Calculate how much larger a Neanderthal brain was than a gorilla brain. Express your answer as a percentage.

Scientific Debate

Who Owns the Past?

Does a piece of land include all the layers below it? If you start digging, you may find evidence of past life. In areas that have been inhabited by human ancestors, you may find artifacts that they left behind. But who has the right to dig up these "leftovers" from the past? And who owns them?

In areas that contain many remains of the past, digging up land often leads to conflicts. Landowners may want to build on their own land. But when remains of ancient human cultures are found, living relatives of those cultures may lay claim to the remains. Scientists are often caught in the middle, because they want to study and preserve evidence of past life.

Social Studies ACTiViTY

WRITING SKILL Research an area where there is a debate over what to do with fossils or remains of human ancestors. Write a newspaper article about the issue. Be sure to present all sides of the debate.

Answer to Math Activity

350%

Sample calculation:

$1,400 \div 400 = 3.5$

$3.5 \times 100\% = 350\%$

Answer to Social Studies Activity

Student articles should reflect journalistic style, being both interesting and objective. Check that students have presented more than one side of the issue they have chosen. Almost any large urban area will have some notable archaeological or paleontological sites, and efforts to excavate the sites are often inconvenient to someone. However, if students need help selecting an area, suggest one of the following locations: New York City, New York; Miami, Florida; Rome, Italy; Athens, Greece; Island of Brac, Croatia; Jerusalem, Israel; Ayodhya, India; Kathmandhu, Nepal; or Yangtze River, China.

The Leakey Family

A Family of Fossil Hunters In some families, a business is passed down from one generation to the next. For the Leakey's, the family business is paleoanthropology (PAY lee OH AN thruh PAWL uh jee)—the study of the origin of humans. The first famous Leakey was Dr. Louis Leakey, who was known for his hominid fossil discoveries in Africa in the 1950s. Louis formed many important hypotheses about human evolution. Louis' wife, Mary, made some of the most-important hominid fossil finds of her day.

Louis and Mary's son, Richard, carried on the family tradition of fossil hunting. He found his first fossil, which was of an extinct pig, when he was six years old. As a young man, he went on safari expeditions in which he collected photographs and specimens of African wildlife. Later, he met and married a zoologist named Meave. The photo at right shows Richard (right), Meave (left), and their daughter Louise (middle) Each of the Leakeys has contributed important finds to the study of ancient hominids.

Language Arts ACTIVITY

WRITING SKILL Visit the library and look for a book by or about the Leakey family and other scientists who have worked with them. Write a short book review to encourage your classmates to read the book.

go.hrw.com

To learn more about these Science in Action topics, visit **go.hrw.com** and type in the keyword **HL5HISF**.

Current Science

Check out Current Science® articles related to this chapter by visiting **go.hrw.com**. Just type in the keyword **HL5CS08**.

Answer to Language Arts Activity

Students can find numerous books about members of the Leakey family, books written by some of the Leakeys, and books about their colleagues, such as Dian Fossey, Jane Goodall, Birute Galdikas, and Donald Johanson.

People In Science

Background

In Africa, Richard Leakey may be more widely known for his strong beliefs in political rather than scientific arenas. He has organized and raised money for campaigns against the poaching of wildlife in Kenya. And in 1995, he founded a political party that opposes corruption in the Kenyan government. His political work has been controversial and at times dangerous, as he has received death threats and beatings from opponents.

ACTIVITY ——— GENERAL

Have interested students research and make timelines of major discoveries in hominid evolution. Suggest that they include a map that pinpoints the location of each major discovery. They may wish to present their findings in a poster or Web page.

Big Idea:
The Earth and Universe

The universe is always changing. On Earth, changes can be seen on land, in the atmosphere, and in oceans and fresh water. Systems, such as the rock cycle and weather patterns, can be studied to understand past events and predict what may occur in the future. Yet these systems are not closed. For example, changes in the atmosphere affect the oceans. And changes in Earth's land, water, and atmosphere also affect the organisms that live on the planet.

The chapters in this unit develop students' understandings of how changes on Earth occur. **Maps as Models of the Earth** begins the unit by describing how maps are used in Earth Science. Next, **Minerals of the Earth's Crust** examines the minerals found on Earth and describes how they are formed. **Rocks: Mineral Mixtures** continues this study of the composition of Earth while emphasizing the different transformations that occur to the materials that make rocks. Finally, **The Rock and Fossil Record** explains how scientists study fossils in or on Earth's crust in order to understand the changes that have occurred on Earth.

UNIT 3

TIMELINE

Earth's Resources

In this unit, you will learn about the basic components of the solid Earth—rocks and the minerals from which they are made. You will also learn about other resources the Earth contains. The ground beneath your feet is a treasure-trove of interesting materials, some of which are very valuable. Secrets of Earth's history are also hidden within the ground's depths. This timeline shows some of the events that have occurred through human history as scientists have come to understand more about our planet.

1543

Nicolaus Copernicus argues that the sun rather than the Earth is the center of the universe.

1860

Fossil remains of *Archaeopteryx*, a species that may link reptiles and birds, are discovered in Germany.

1936

Hoover Dam is completed. This massive hydroelectric dam, standing more than 221 m, required 3.25 million cubic yards of concrete to build.

1975

Tabei Junko of Japan becomes the first woman to successfully climb Mount Everest, 22 years after Edmund Hillary and Tenzing Norgay first conquered the mountain in 1953.

1681
The dodo, a flightless bird, is driven to extinction by the actions of humans.

1739
Georg Brandt identifies a new element and names it cobalt.

1848
James Marshall discovers gold at Sutter's Mill, in California, beginning the California gold rush. Prospectors during the gold rush of the following year are referred to as "forty-niners."

1947
Willard F. Libby develops a method of dating prehistoric objects by using radioactive carbon.

1955
Using 1 million pounds of pressure per square inch and temperatures of more than 1,700°C, General Electric creates the first artificial diamonds from graphite.

1969
Apollo 11 astronauts Neil Armstrong and Edwin "Buzz" Aldrin bring 22 kg of moon rocks and soil back to the Earth.

1989
Russian engineers drill a borehole 12 km into the Earth's crust. The borehole is more than 3 times deeper than the deepest mine shaft.

1997
Sojourner, a roving probe on Mars, investigates a Martian boulder nicknamed Yogi.

1999
A Japanese automaker introduces the first hybrid car into the U.S. market.

Group ACTiViTy
The Earth and Universe

MATERIALS
- hand lens
- microscope
- microscope slides
- pipettes
- table salt
- water

Teacher's Note: This activity helps students understand how crystals form. Learning about crystals is helpful because minerals, the basis of rocks, have crystalline structures. Also, this experiment replicates how salt water evaporates to form the mineral halite. Displaying samples or pictures of halite may help in the discussion.

Observing Crystals Mix about 2 teaspoons of salt with 20 mL of warm water. Use a pipette or a dropper to transfer one drop of the solution to a slide. Streaking the drop across the slide will cause evaporation to occur more quickly, which may lead to better results. Use a hand lens to observe the slide. Use a microscope to observe the solution. As the solution evaporates, crystals will form. Have students draw pictures of their observations. For a size comparison, use microscopes or hand lens to observe table salt that has not been diluted and evaporated.

Maps as Models of the Earth
Chapter Planning Guide

Compression guide:
To shorten instruction because of time limitations, omit the Chapter Lab.

OBJECTIVES	LABS, DEMONSTRATIONS, AND ACTIVITIES	TECHNOLOGY RESOURCES
PACING • 135 min pp. 194–201 **Chapter Opener**	SE **Start-up Activity,** p. 195 GENERAL	OSP **Parent Letter** ■ CD **Student Edition on CD-ROM** CD **Guided Reading Audio CD** ■ TR **Chapter Starter Transparency*** VID **Brain Food Video Quiz**
Section 1 You Are Here • Explain how a magnetic compass can be used to find directions on Earth. • Explain the difference between true north and magnetic north. • Compare latitude and longitude. • Explain how latitude and longitude are used to locate places on Earth.	TE **Group Activity** Using Directions, p. 196 GENERAL SE **School-to-Home Activity** Columbus's Voyage, p. 197 GENERAL SE **Quick Lab** Making a Compass, p. 198 ◆ GENERAL CRF **Datasheet for Quick Lab*** TE **Group Activity** Finding True North, p. 199 GENERAL SE **Connection to Social Studies** Global Addresses, p. 200 GENERAL SE **Skills Practice Lab** Round or Flat?, p. 214 ◆ GENERAL CRF **Datasheet for Chapter Lab*** SE **Inquiry Lab** Orient Yourself!, p. 711 GENERAL CRF **Datasheet for LabBook***	OSP **Lesson Plans** (also in print) TR **Bellringer Transparency*** TR **E3 The North and South Poles*** TR **E4 Lines of Longitude; Lines of Latitude*** VID **Lab Videos for Earth Science**
PACING • 45 min pp. 202–209 **Section 2 Mapping the Earth's Surface** • Explain why maps of the Earth show distortion. • Describe four types of map projections. • Identify five pieces of information that should be shown on a map. • Describe four methods modern mapmakers use to make accurate maps.	SE **Science in Action** Math, Social Studies, and Language Arts Activities, pp. 220–221 GENERAL TE **Group Activity** Comparing Map Projections, p. 205 BASIC TE **Connection Activity** Math, p. 206 GENERAL TE **Connection Activity** Language Arts, p. 207 ADVANCED TE **Activity** Remote-Sensing Technology, p. 207 GENERAL TE **Connection to Physical Science** Landsat Satellites, p. 207 ADVANCED	OSP **Lesson Plans** (also in print) TR **Bellringer Transparency*** TR **E5 Cylindrical Projection; Conic Projection; Azimuthal Projection*** TR **LINK TO PHYSICAL SCIENCE** P92 The Electromagnetic Spectrum* TE **Internet Activity,** p. 203 CRF **SciLinks Activity*** GENERAL
PACING • 45 min pp. 210–213 **Section 3 Topographic Maps** • Explain how contour lines show elevation and landforms on a map. • Explain how the relief of an area determines the contour interval used on a map. • List the rules of contour lines.	TE **Activity** Investigate Your Area, p. 210 ◆ GENERAL TE **Group Activity** Model Terrain, p. 211 BASIC SE **Skills Practice Lab** Topographic Tuber, p. 713 GENERAL CRF **Datasheet for LabBook*** LB **Inquiry Labs** Looking for Buried Treasure* ADVANCED LB **Long-Term Projects & Research Ideas** Globe Trotting* ADVANCED	OSP **Lesson Plans** (also in print) TR **Bellringer Transparency***

PACING • 90 min

CHAPTER REVIEW, ASSESSMENT, AND STANDARDIZED TEST PREPARATION

CRF **Vocabulary Activity*** GENERAL
SE **Chapter Review,** pp. 216–217 GENERAL
CRF **Chapter Review*** ■ GENERAL
CRF **Chapter Tests A*** ■ GENERAL, **B*** ADVANCED, **C*** SPECIAL NEEDS
SE **Standardized Test Preparation,** pp. 218–219 GENERAL
CRF **Standardized Test Preparation*** GENERAL
CRF **Performance-Based Assessment*** GENERAL
OSP **Test Generator, Test Item Listing**

Online and Technology Resources

Holt Online Learning

Visit **go.hrw.com** for access to Holt Online Learning, or enter the keyword **HS7 Home** for a variety of free online resources.

One-Stop Planner® CD-ROM

This CD-ROM package includes:
• Lab Materials QuickList Software
• Holt Calendar Planner
• Customizable Lesson Plans
• Printable Worksheets
• ExamView® Test Generator
• Interactive Teacher's Edition
• Holt PuzzlePro®
• Holt PowerPoint® Resources

SKILLS DEVELOPMENT RESOURCES	SECTION REVIEW AND ASSESSMENT	CORRELATIONS
SE **Pre-Reading Activity**, p. 194 GENERAL OSP **Science Puzzlers, Twisters & Teasers** GENERAL		**National Science Education Standards** ST 1, 2; SAI 1; SPSP 5; HNS 1, 3
CRF **Directed Reading A*** ■ BASIC, **B*** SPECIAL NEEDS WB **Workbook*** Struggling Readers CRF **Vocabulary and Section Summary*** ■ GENERAL SE **Reading Strategy** Reading Organizer, p. 196 GENERAL TE **Reading Strategy** Prediction Guide, p. 198 GENERAL TE **Support for English Language Learners**, p. 198 TE **Inclusion Strategies**, p. 199 ◆ CRF **Reinforcement Worksheet** Where on Earth?* BASIC	SE **Reading Checks**, pp. 197, 198, 200 GENERAL TE **Reteaching**, p. 200 BASIC TE **Quiz**, p. 200 GENERAL TE **Alternative Assessment**, p. 200 GENERAL SE **Section Review,*** p. 201 ■ GENERAL CRF **Section Quiz*** ■ GENERAL	UCP 2, 3, 5; SAI 1; ST 1, 2; SPSP 5; HNS 1, 3 *Chapter Lab:* UCP 2, 3; SAI 1; ST 1; HNS1
CRF **Directed Reading A*** ■ BASIC, **B*** SPECIAL NEEDS WB **Workbook*** Struggling Readers CRF **Vocabulary and Section Summary*** ■ GENERAL SE **Reading Strategy** Discussion, p. 202 GENERAL SE **Connection to Social Studies** Mapmaking and Ship Navigation, p. 204 GENERAL TE **Reading Strategy** Making an Outline, p. 203 BASIC TE **Support for English Language Learners**, p. 203 TE **Reading Strategy** Mnemonics, p. 204 GENERAL TE **Inclusion Strategies**, p. 206 ◆ MS **Math Skills for Science** Using Proportions and Cross-Multiplication* GENERAL	SE **Reading Checks**, pp. 202, 205, 206, 208 GENERAL TE **Homework**, p. 204 GENERAL TE **Homework**, p. 205 ADVANCED TE **Reteaching**, p. 208 BASIC TE **Quiz**, p. 208 GENERAL TE **Alternative Assessment**, p. 208 GENERAL SE **Section Review,*** p. 209 ■ GENERAL CRF **Section Quiz*** ■ GENERAL	UCP 2, 3, 5; SAI 1; ST 2; SPSP 5; HNS 3
CRF **Directed Reading A*** ■ BASIC, **B*** SPECIAL NEEDS WB **Workbook*** Struggling Readers CRF **Vocabulary and Section Summary*** ■ GENERAL SE **Reading Strategy** Paired Summarizing, p. 210 GENERAL TE **Support for English Language Learners**, p. 211 CRF **Reinforcement Worksheet** Interpreting a Topographic Map* BASIC CRF **Critical Thinking** Shaping the World* ADVANCED MS **Math Skills for Science** Mapping and Surveying GENERAL	SE **Reading Checks**, p. 211 GENERAL TE **Reteaching**, p. 212 BASIC TE **Quiz**, p. 212 GENERAL TE **Alternative Assessment**, p. 212 GENERAL SE **Section Review,*** p. 213 ■ GENERAL CRF **Section Quiz*** ■ GENERAL	UCP 2, 3, 5; SAI 1; ST 2; SPSP 2, 5; HNS 1 *LabBook:* UCP 2, 3; SAI 1; ST 1

www.scilinks.org

Maintained by the **National Science Teachers Association.** See Chapter Enrichment pages that follow for a complete list of topics.

Check out *Current Science* articles and activities by visiting the HRW Web site at **go.hrw.com.** Just type in the keyword **HZ5CS02T.**

 **Classroom Videos**

- **Lab Videos** demonstrate the chapter lab.
- **Brain Food Video Quizzes** help students review the chapter material.

 Classroom CD-ROMs

- **Guided Reading Audio CD** (Also in Spanish)
- **Interactive Explorations**
- **Virtual Investigations**
- **Visual Concepts**
- **Science Tutor**

Holt Lab Generator CD-ROM

Search for any lab by topic, standard, difficulty level, or time. Edit any lab to fit your needs, or create your own labs. Use the Lab Materials QuickList software to customize your lab materials list.

Visual Resources

CHAPTER STARTER TRANSPARENCY

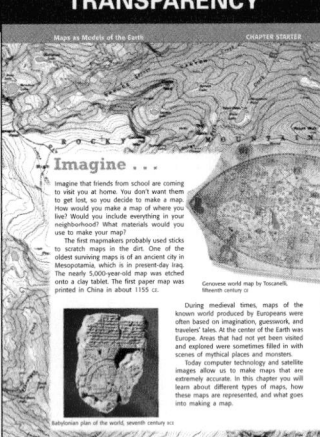

BELLRINGER TRANSPARENCIES

Section: You Are Here
Everyone uses maps. Some maps are very formal with lots of detail, compass points, and drawn to perfect scale. Some maps are just useful memories you use to know the quickest way to class or to the cafeteria. Draw a map from your house to one of your favorite places. Clearly label all landmarks, and include information that might be useful to someone using the map.

Draw your map in your **science journal.**

Section: Mapping the Earth's Surface
Compare the world map, the state map, and the community map. Make a chart of the similarities and differences between each map. You might use the world map to plan a big trip, or to look up a place you heard of on the news. Can you think of three uses for each kind of map? Can you think of three improvements you could make to each of these maps?

Record your answers in your **science journal.**

TEACHING TRANSPARENCIES

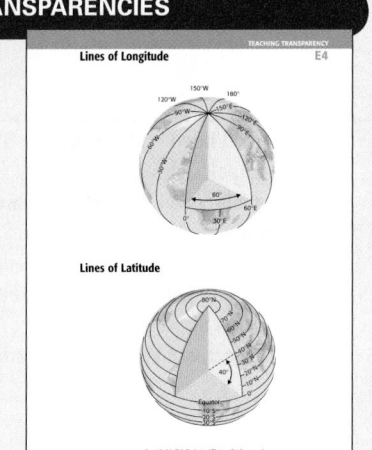

The North and South Poles

Lines of Longitude

Lines of Latitude

TEACHING TRANSPARENCIES

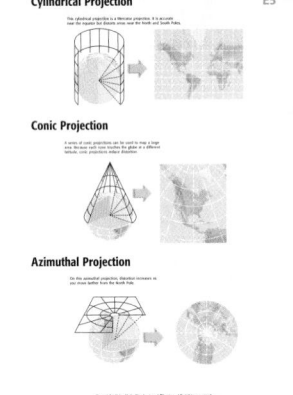

Cylindrical Projection

Conic Projection

Azimuthal Projection

The Electromagnetic Spectrum

LINK TO PHYSICAL SCIENCE

Chapter: The Nature of Light

CONCEPT MAPPING TRANSPARENCY

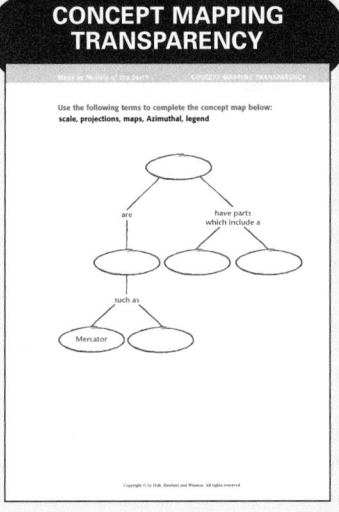

Use the following terms to complete the concept map below:
scale, projections, maps, Azimuthal, legend

Planning Resources

LESSON PLANS

Lesson Plan   SAMPLE

Section: Waves

Pacing
Regular Schedule: with lab(s):2 days   without lab(s)2 days
Block Schedule: with lab(s):1 1/2 days without lab(s)1 day

Objectives
1. Relate the seven properties of life to a living organism.
2. Describe seven themes that can help you to organize what you learn about biology.
3. Identify the tiny structures that make up all living organisms.
4. Differentiate between reproduction and heredity and between metabolism and homeostasis.

National Science Education Standards Covered
LSInter1:Cells have particular structures that underlie their functions.
LSMat1: Most cell functions involve chemical reactions.
LSBeh1:Cells store and use information to guide their functions.
UCP1:Cell functions are regulated.
SI1: Cells can differentiate and form complete multicellular organisms.
PS1:Species evolve over time.
ESS1: The great diversity of organisms is the result of more than 3.5 billion years of evolution.
ESS2: Natural selection and its evolutionary consequences provide a scientific explanation for the fossil record of ancient life forms as well as for the striking molecular similarities observed among the diverse species of living organisms.
ST1: The millions of different species of plants, animals, and microorganisms that live on Earth today are related by descent from common ancestors.
ST2: The energy for life primarily comes from the sun.
SPSP1: The complexity and organization of organisms accommodates the need for obtaining, transforming, transporting, releasing, and eliminating the matter and energy used to sustain the organism.
SPSP6: As matter and energy flows through different levels of organization of living systems—cells, organs, communities—and between living systems and the physical environment, chemical elements are recombined in different ways.
HNS1: Organisms have behavioral responses to internal changes and to external stimuli.

PARENT LETTER

SAMPLE

Dear Parent,

Your son's or daughter's science class will soon begin exploring the chapter entitled "The World of Physical Science." In this chapter, students will learn about how the scientific method applies to the world of physical science and the role of physical science in the world. By the end of the chapter, students should demonstrate a clear understanding of the chapter's main ideas and be able to discuss the following topics:

1. physical science is the study of energy and matter (Section 1)
2. the role of physical science in the world around them (Section 1)
3. careers that rely on physical science (Section 1)
4. the steps used in the scientific method (Section 2)
5. examples of technology (Section 2)
6. how the scientific method is used to answer questions and solve problems (Section 2)
7. how our knowledge of science changes over time (Section 2)
8. how models represent real objects or systems (Section 3)
9. examples of different ways models are used in science (Section 3)
10. the importance of the International System of Units (Section 4)
11. the appropriate units to use for particular measurements (Section 4)
12. how area and density are derived quantities (Section 4)

Questions to Ask Along the Way

You can help your son or daughter learn about these topics by asking interesting questions such as the following:

• What are some surprising careers that use physical science?
• What is a characteristic of a good hypothesis?
• When is it a good idea to use a model?
• Why do Americans measure things in terms of inches and yards and meters ?

ALSO IN SPANISH

TEST ITEM LISTING

TEST ITEM LISTING
The World of Earth Science   SAMPLE

MULTIPLE CHOICE

1. A limitation of models is that
   a. they are large enough to see.
   b. they do not act exactly like the things that they model.
   c. they are smaller than the things that they model.
   d. they model unfamiliar things.
   Answer: B   Difficulty: 1   Section: 3   Objective: 2
2. The length 10 m is equal to
   a. 100 cm.   c. 10,000 mm.
   b. 1,000 cm.   d. Both (b) and (c)
   Answer: B   Difficulty: 1   Section: 3   Objective: 2
3. To be valid, a hypothesis must be
   a. testable.   c. made into a law.
   b. supported by evidence.   d. Both (a) and (b)
   Answer: B   Difficulty: 1   Section: 2   Objective: 1
4. The statement "Sheila has a stain on her shirt" is an example of a(n)
   a. law.   c. observation.
   b. hypothesis.   d. prediction.
   Answer: B   Difficulty: 1   Section: 2   Objective: 2
5. A hypothesis is often developed out of
   a. observations.   c. laws.
   b. experiments.   d. Both (a) and (b)
   Answer: B   Difficulty: 1   Section: 2   Objective: 2
6. How many milliliters are in 3.5 kL?
   a. 3,500 mL   c. 3,300,000 mL
   b. 0.0035 mL   d. 35,000 mL
   Answer: B   Difficulty: 1   Section: 3   Objective: 2
7. A map of Seattle is an example of a
   a. law.   c. model.
   b. theory.   d. unit.
   Answer: B   Difficulty: 1   Section: 3   Objective: 2
8. A lab has the safety icons shown below. These icons mean that you should wear
   a. only safety goggles c. safety goggles and a lab apron.
   b. only a lab apron.   d. safety goggles, a lab apron, and gloves
   Answer: B   Difficulty: 1   Section: 3   Objective: 2
9. The law of conservation of mass states that the lot of mass before a chemical change is
   a. more than the total mass after the change
   b. less than the total mass after the change
   c. the same as the total mass after the change.
   d. not the same as the total mass after the change
   Answer: B   Difficulty: 1   Section: 3   Objective: 2
10. In which of the following areas might you find a geochemist at work?
    a. studying volcanoes   c. studying fishes
    b. studying forestry   d. studying the atmosphere
    Answer: B   Difficulty: 1   Section: 3   Objective: 2

One-Stop Planner® CD-ROM

This CD-ROM includes all of the resources shown here and the following time-saving tools:

• *Lab Materials QuickList Software*
• *Customizable lesson plans*
• *Holt Calendar Planner*
• *The powerful ExamView® Test Generator*

Meeting Individual Needs

DIRECTED READING A
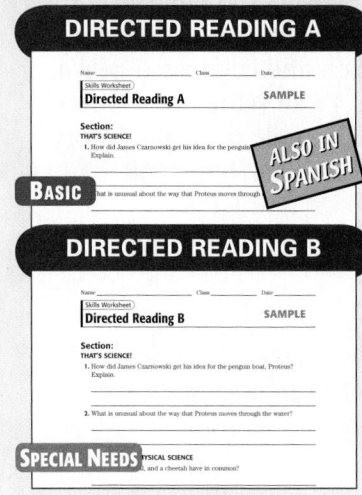
BASIC · ALSO IN SPANISH

VOCABULARY ACTIVITY
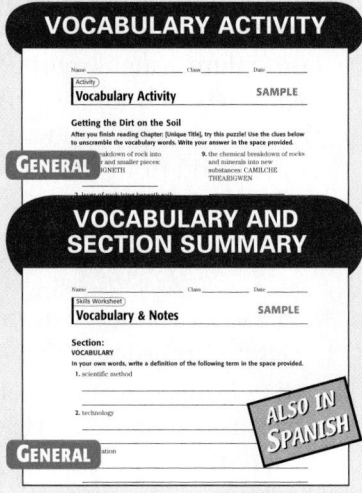
GENERAL

REINFORCEMENT
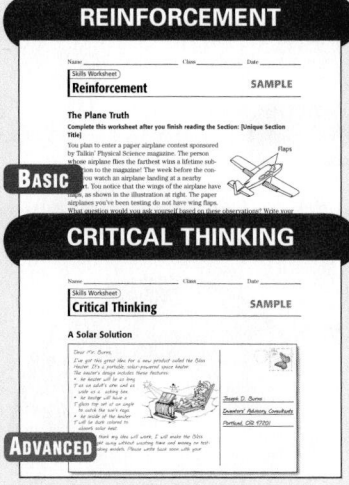
BASIC

SCILINKS ACTIVITY

GENERAL

DIRECTED READING B
SPECIAL NEEDS

VOCABULARY AND SECTION SUMMARY
GENERAL · ALSO IN SPANISH

CRITICAL THINKING
ADVANCED

SCIENCE PUZZLERS, TWISTERS & TEASERS
GENERAL

Labs and Activities

LONG-TERM PROJECTS & RESEARCH IDEAS
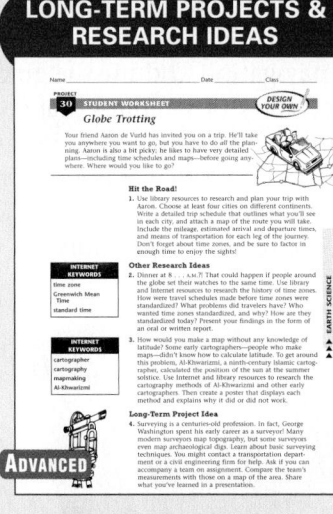
ADVANCED

INQUIRY LABS
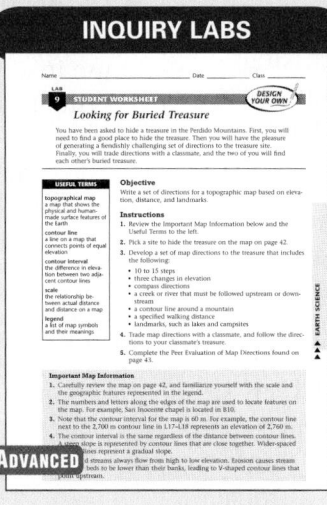
ADVANCED

DATASHEETS FOR QUICK LABS

DATASHEETS FOR CHAPTER LABS

DATASHEETS FOR LABBOOK

Review and Assessments

SECTION QUIZ
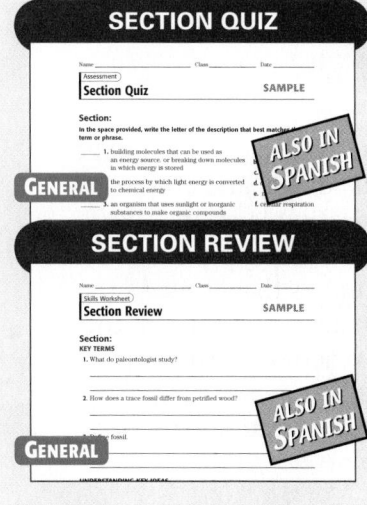
GENERAL · ALSO IN SPANISH

CHAPTER REVIEW
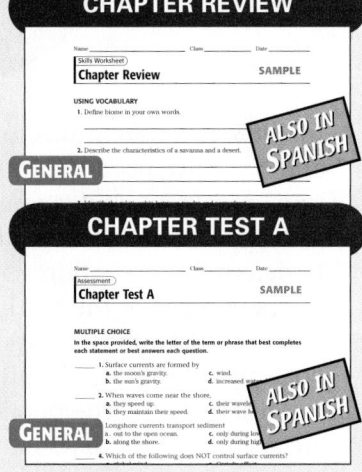
GENERAL · ALSO IN SPANISH

CHAPTER TEST B
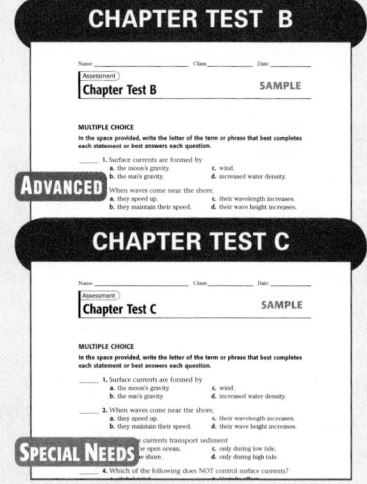
ADVANCED

STANDARDIZED TEST PREPARATION
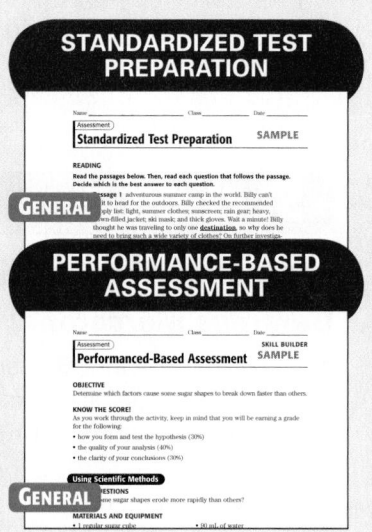
GENERAL

SECTION REVIEW
GENERAL · ALSO IN SPANISH

CHAPTER TEST A
GENERAL · ALSO IN SPANISH

CHAPTER TEST C
SPECIAL NEEDS

PERFORMANCE-BASED ASSESSMENT
GENERAL

This Chapter Enrichment provides relevant and interesting information to expand and enhance your presentation of the chapter material.

Section 1

You Are Here

Longitude

- Because Earth rotates 360° every 24 h, it turns 15° every hour. Therefore, longitude can be determined at any place on the globe if the local time and the time at the prime meridian are known. Before the mid-18th century, the unreliability of clocks—especially those aboard ships, where motion, temperature variation, and moisture could wreak havoc with a timepiece's workings—thwarted calculations of longitude. Many shipwrecks occurred because the ship captains could not accurately calculate their location.

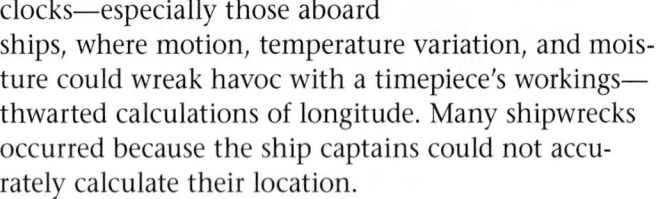

- In 1707, inaccurate longitudinal information caused four ships in a British fleet to run aground, and 2,000 sailors died. The British Parliament addressed the problem by offering a large reward to anyone who could develop a method to accurately calculate longitude within half a degree. John Harrison (1693–1776), a self-taught clockmaker, developed a chronometer that remained accurate on rough seas, and he won the prize in 1763. More than 200 years later, astronaut Neil Armstrong gave credit to Harrison for the role he played in enabling exploration of Earth and in inspiring future generations to venture toward exploration of the moon.

Section 2

Mapping the Earth's Surface

Gerardus Mercator

- Gerardus Mercator was born Gerhard Kremer in 1512 in Rupelmonde, Flanders (present-day Belgium). At age 24, Mercator was a highly skilled engraver, calligrapher, and scientific-instrument maker. With two of his teachers, he made the first globe of the Earth

in 1536–1537. A true Renaissance man, Mercator was a highly esteemed cartographer, who also published a treatise on italic lettering, designed a grammar-school curriculum, taught mathematics, and conducted genealogical research for his patron, Duke Wilhelm of Cleve. He even attempted to write a chronology of the history of the world from the formation of Earth to 1568.

Is That a Fact!

- ◆ In 1544, Gerardus Mercator was imprisoned on charges of treason. Apparently, his frequent absences from Flanders to gather map data aroused the suspicions of authorities. He remained imprisoned for 7 months before his friends succeeded in clearing his name.

The Global Positioning System

- During the 1970s, the U.S. Department of Defense developed the Global Positioning System (GPS) for use in aircraft navigation and missile guidance. The system uses a network of satellites that continuously transmit positioning information to receivers on Earth. The distance between a receiver and at least four satellites is used to compute the latitude and longitude coordinates of the receiver's position.

- In 1983, the system was made available to the public and has since been used for land, sea, and air navigation, surveying, and geophysical exploration. The system can be highly accurate, making it possible to determine a position within less than 1 m. As the prices of some of the receivers have plummeted, the use of the GPS for recreational activities, such as boating, hiking, and hunting, has increased. Most receivers used by the public for recreational purposes are accurate only to about 10 m.

Landsat

- Since the Landsat program began in 1972, a number of satellites have been deployed that carry remote-sensing equipment. The equipment is designed to detect radiation in different bands of the electromagnetic spectrum. The most recent satellites, *Landsat 4, 5,* and *7,* orbit Earth from pole to pole every 16 days. Landsat data are particularly useful for thematic mapping. For example, data from the blue-green spectral region are useful for distinguishing between coniferous and deciduous plants, and data from the thermal infrared range supply information about soil moisture.

Section 3

Topographic Maps
Inuit Relief Maps

- The Inuit of Baffin Island were skilled mapmakers. They made permanent relief maps by carving coastal features into pieces of wood and walrus ivory. The Inuit also sewed small pieces of fur or driftwood to sealskin to represent islands. They measured distance on their maps not by miles but by "sleeps." The distance to a hunting ground, for example, would be measured by how many rest stops would be taken before reaching it.

John Wesley Powell (1834–1902)

- American geologist and surveyor John Wesley Powell headed an official expedition to the Grand Canyon in 1871. His purpose was to conduct a topographic survey to map "as broad a belt of country as it was possible" on both sides of the Colorado and Green Rivers. The expedition yielded meticulously detailed topographic maps for an area that had previously been described as the "great unknown." Those maps were instrumental to Powell's appointment in 1881 as director of the U.S. Geological Survey (USGS).

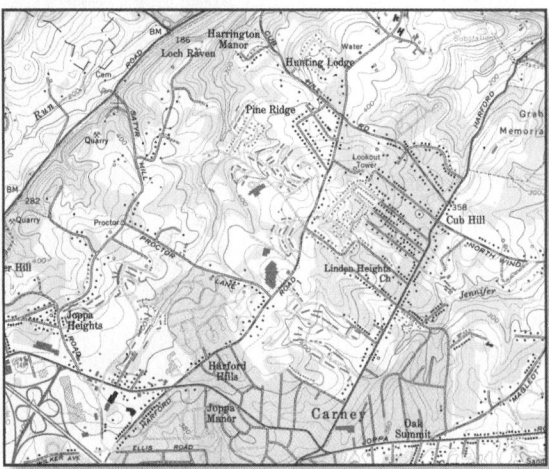

- As director, Powell aimed to create topographic maps for the entire country by using large scales, ranging from 1:250,000 for desert regions to 1:62,500 for densely populated areas. Powell insisted on including data concerning soils, springs, and other natural resources, which he felt were essential for making land-use decisions. The high-quality topographical maps created during Powell's administration set the standard for published topographic maps in the United States for many years to come.

SciLinks is maintained by the National Science Teachers Association to provide you and your students with interesting, up-to-date links that will enrich your classroom presentation of the chapter.

Visit www.scilinks.org and enter the SciLinks code for more information about the topic listed.

Topic: Latitude and Longitude
SciLinks code: HSM0854

Topic: Topographic Maps
SciLinks code: HSM1536

Topic: Mapmaking
SciLinks code: HSM0909

Overview

This chapter will help students learn basic map-reading skills. Students will also learn how a compass is used to find directions and how lines of latitude and longitude are used to identify points on the Earth's surface.

Assessing Prior Knowledge

Students should be familiar with the following topic:

• scientific models

Identifying Misconceptions

As students learn the material in this chapter, some of them may be confused about how a compass is used to determine direction. Some students may think that a compass can keep a person from getting lost. Stress to students that a compass is usually used in conjunction with a map. Also, some students may be confused about the distortion that occurs when information on a sphere is transferred to a flat surface. Students may not recognize that all maps have some degree of distortion.

8

Maps as Models of the Earth

The Big Idea

Maps are models of Earth that are important tools in both science and society.

About the Photo

No ordinary camera took this picture! In fact, a camera wasn't used at all. This image is a radar image of a mountainous area of Tibet. It was taken from the space shuttle. Radar imaging is a method that scientists use to map areas of the Earth from far above the Earth's surface.

PRE-READING ACTIVITY

FOLDNOTES **Three-Panel Flip Chart**
Before you read the chapter, create the FoldNote entitled "Three-Panel Flip Chart" described in the **Study Skills** section of the Appendix. Label the flaps of the three-panel flip chart with "Cylindrical projection," "Conical projection," and "Azimuthal projection." As you read the chapter, write information you learn about each category under the appropriate flap.

Standards Correlations

The following codes indicate the National Science Education Standards that correlate to this chapter. The full text of the standards is at the front of the book.

Chapter Opener
SAI 1; SPSP 5; HNS 1, 3

Section 1 You Are Here
UCP 2, 3, 5; SAI 1; ST 1, 2; SPSP 5; HNS 1, 3

Section 2 Mapping Earth's Surface
UCP 2, 3, 5; SAI 1; ST 2; SPSP 5; HNS 3

Section 3 Topographic Maps
UCP 2, 3, 5; SAI 1; ST 2; SPSP 2, 5, HNS 1; *LabBook:* UCP 2, 3; SAI 1; ST 1

Chapter Lab
UCP 2, 3; SAI 1; ST 1; HNS 1

Chapter Review
UCP 2; SAI 2; HNS 3

Science in Action
ST1; SPSP 5; HNS 1, 3

START-UP ACTIVITY
MATERIALS
FOR EACH STUDENT
• computer (optional)
• paper
• pencils, colored

Teacher's Note: Before students start their maps, have them brainstorm a list of school landmarks, and suggest that they use the location of these landmarks as reference points in their maps.

Answers

1. Answers may vary. Accept all reasonable responses.
2. Answers may vary. Accept all reasonable responses.
3. Answers may vary.

START-UP ACTIVITY

Follow the Yellow Brick Road

In this activity, you will not only learn how to read a map but you will also make a map that someone else can read.

Procedure

1. Use a **computer drawing program or colored pencils and paper** to draw a map that shows how to get from your classroom to another place in your school, such as the gym. Make sure you include enough information for someone unfamiliar with your school to find his or her way.

2. After you finish drawing your map, switch maps with a partner. Examine your classmate's map, and try to figure out where the map is leading you.

Analysis

1. Is your map an accurate picture of your school? Explain your answer.

2. What could you do to make your map better? What are some limitations of your map?

3. Compare your map with your partner's map. How are your maps alike? How are they different?

Chapter Starter Transparency
Use this transparency to help students begin thinking about the history of mapmaking.

CHAPTER RESOURCES

Technology

• Transparencies
  • Chapter Starter Transparency   READING SKILLS

• Student Edition on CD-ROM

• Guided Reading Audio CD
  • English or Spanish

• Classroom Videos
  • Brain Food Video Quiz

Workbooks

• Science Puzzlers, Twisters & Teasers
  • Maps as Models of the Earth   GENERAL

Focus

Overview

This section opens with a discussion of the history of mapmaking. Students learn how to find directions on a globe by using reference points such as the North and South Poles. Students learn how a compass is used to find directions and how true north differs from magnetic north. The section closes with a discussion of lines of latitude and longitude and the way they can be used to locate points on the Earth's surface.

 **Bellringer**

Ask students to draw a map from their home to one of their favorite places. Have them clearly label all landmarks and include information that might be useful to someone using the map.

Motivate

 — **GENERAL**

Using Directions Have students write a description of the route they take as they travel between home and school. Then, have them rewrite the description using cardinal directions. Have pairs of students trade descriptions and use a map to check the accuracy of each other's maps. **LS** Verbal

English Language Learners

What You Will Learn

● Explain how a magnetic compass can be used to find directions on Earth.
● Explain the difference between true north and magnetic north.
● Compare latitude and longitude.
● Explain how latitude and longitude are used to locate places on Earth.

Vocabulary

map	latitude
true north	equator
magnetic declination	longitude
	prime meridian

READING STRATEGY

Reading Organizer As you read this section, create an outline of the section. Use the headings from the section in your outline.

map a representation of the features of a physical body such as Earth

Figure 1 *This map shows what explorers thought the world looked like 1,800 years ago.*

You Are Here

Have you ever noticed the curve of the Earth's surface? You probably haven't. When you walk across the Earth, it does not appear to be curved. It looks flat.

Over time, ideas about Earth's shape have changed. Maps reflected how people saw the world and what technology was available. A **map** is a representation of the features of a physical body such as Earth. If you look at Ptolemy's (TAHL uh meez) world map from the second century, as shown in **Figure 1,** you might not know what you are looking at. Today satellites give us more accurate images of the Earth. In this section, you will learn how early scientists knew Earth was round long before pictures from space were taken. You will also learn how to find location and direction on Earth's surface.

What Does Earth Really Look Like?

The Greeks thought of Earth as a sphere almost 2,000 years before Christopher Columbus made his voyage in 1492. The observation that a ship sinks below the horizon as it sails into the distance supported the idea of a spherical Earth. If Earth were flat, the ship would not sink below the horizon.

Eratosthenes (ER uh TAHS thuh NEEZ), a Greek mathematician, wanted to know the size of Earth. In about 240 BCE, he calculated Earth's circumference using math and observations of the sun. There were no satellites or computers back then. We now know his calculation was wrong by only 6,250 km!

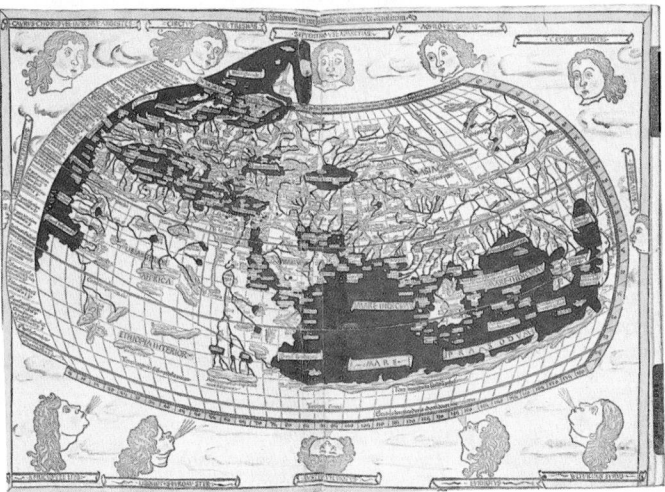

CHAPTER RESOURCES

Chapter Resource File

- **Lesson Plan**
- **Directed Reading A** **BASIC**
- **Directed Reading B** **SPECIAL NEEDS**

Technology

Transparencies
- Bellringer
- E3 The North and South Poles

Workbooks

Interactive Textbook Struggling Readers

Is That a Fact!

The orientation of maps with north at the top is arbitrary. For many centuries, European maps placed east at the top to emphasize the importance of Jerusalem to the Europeans' faith. The Chinese put south at the top of their maps because nothing to the north held any interest for them.

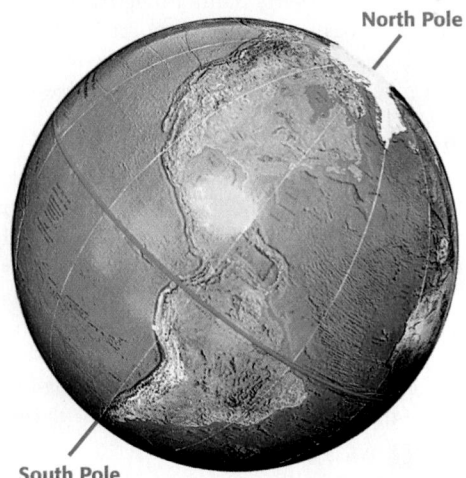

Figure 2 *The North Pole is a good reference point for describing locations in North America.*

North Pole

South Pole

WRITING SKILL **Columbus's Voyage**

Did Christopher Columbus discover that Earth was a sphere only after he completed his voyage in 1492? Or did he know before he left? With a parent or guardian, use the Internet or the library to find out more information about Columbus's voyage. Then, write a paragraph describing what you learned.

ACTIVITY

Finding Direction on Earth

When giving directions to your home, you might name a landmark, such as a grocery store, as a reference point. A *reference point* is a fixed place on the Earth's surface from which direction and location can be described.

The Earth is spherical, so it has no top, bottom, or sides for people to use as reference points for determining locations on its surface. However, the Earth does rotate, or spin, on its axis. The Earth's axis is an imaginary line that runs through the Earth. At either end of the axis is a geographic pole. The North and South Poles are used as reference points when describing direction and location on the Earth, as shown in **Figure 2.**

✔ *Reading Check* What is a reference point? (*See the Appendix for answers to Reading Checks.*)

Cardinal Directions

A reference point alone will not help you give good directions. You will need to be able to describe how to get to your home from the reference point. You will need to use the directions north, south, east, and west. These directions are called *cardinal directions*. Using cardinal directions is much more precise than saying "Turn left," "Go straight," or "Turn right." So, you may tell a friend to walk a block north of the gas station to get to your home. To use cardinal directions properly, you will need a compass, shown in **Figure 3.**

Figure 3 *A compass shows the cardinal directions north, south, east and west, as well as combinations of these directions.*

Prediction Guide Before students read these pages, ask them if the following statements are true or false:

• Earth has four poles. (true)

• A compass is the only thing you need to find a location. (false)

• Imaginary lines drawn around Earth can be used to pinpoint locations. (true)

English Language Learners

LS Verbal

MATERIALS

FOR EACH STUDENT
• compass
• magnet
• needle, sewing, steel
• paper, tissue, 1 cm x 3 cm
• water, in a bowl

Answers

4. Answers may vary. Both compasses should be pointing in the same direction.

5. Answers may vary.

Answer to Reading Check

True north is the direction to the geographic North Pole.

Using a Compass

A magnetic compass will show you which direction is north. A *compass* is a tool that uses the natural magnetism of the Earth to show direction. A compass needle points to the magnetic north pole. Earth has two different sets of poles—the geographic poles and the magnetic poles, as shown in **Figure 4.**

True North and Magnetic Declination

Remember that the Earth's geographic poles are on either end of the Earth's axis. Earth has its own magnetic field, which produces magnetic poles. Earth's magnetic poles are not lined up exactly with Earth's axis. So, there is a difference between the locations of Earth's magnetic and geographic poles. **True north** is the direction to the geographic North Pole. When using a compass, you need to make a correction for the difference between the geographic North Pole and the magnetic north pole. The angle of correction is called **magnetic declination.**

Reading Check What is true north?

true north the direction to the geographic North Pole

magnetic declination the difference between the magnetic north and the true north

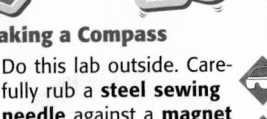

Making a Compass

1. Do this lab outside. Carefully rub a **steel sewing needle** against a **magnet** in the same direction 40 times.

2. Float a **1 cm × 3 cm piece of tissue paper** in a **bowl of water.**

3. Place the needle in the center of the tissue paper.

4. Compare your compass with a **regular compass.** Are both compasses pointing in the same direction?

5. How would you improve your compass?

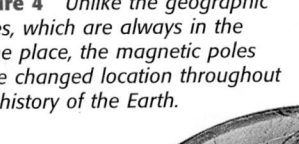

Figure 4 *Unlike the geographic poles, which are always in the same place, the magnetic poles have changed location throughout the history of the Earth.*

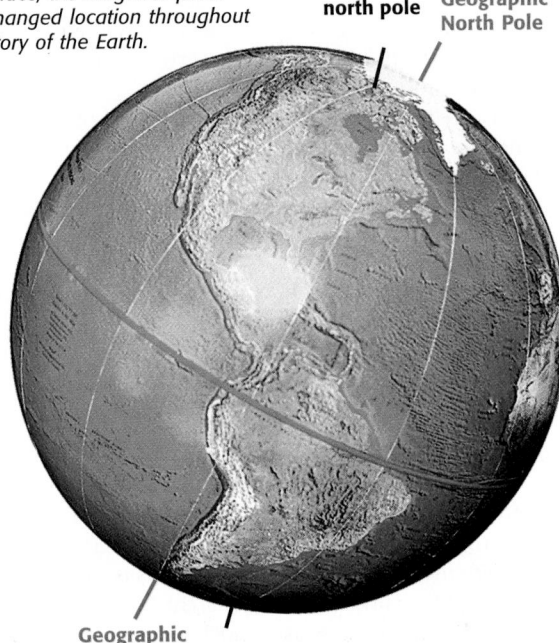

Magnetic north pole

Geographic North Pole

Geographic South Pole

Magnetic south pole

English Language Learners

Map Evolution Some students may not have had much exposure to maps and globes. For a review, have students look at the map from 1,800 years ago and the modern globe on the preceding pages. Ask them to write answers to the following questions.

• What color is land on each?
• What color is water?
• In what other ways are the globe and map the same?

• In what other ways are they different? (Similarities may include a rounded shape for Earth and gridlines for navigation. Differences may include rivers and human representations on the map, and Earth as from space and relief representations on the globe.)

Mark language and content errors, and have students correct their work. **LS Visual/Verbal**

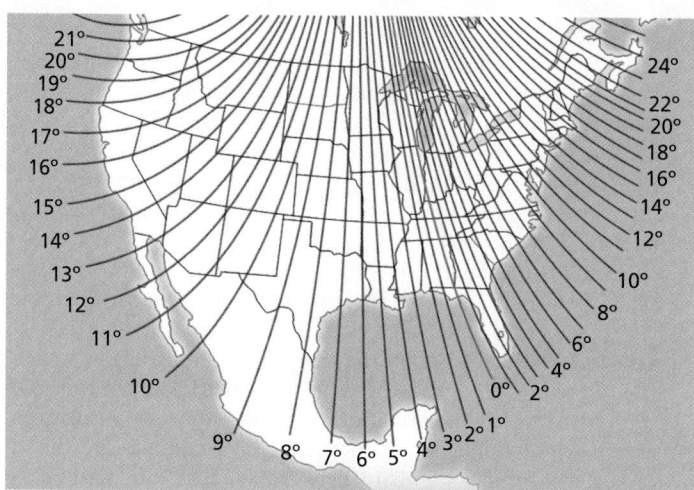

Figure 5 *The lines on the map connect points that have the same magnetic declination.*

Using Magnetic Declination

Magnetic declination is measured in degrees east or west of true north. Magnetic declination has been determined for different points on the Earth's surface. Once you know the declination for your area, you can use a compass to determine true north. This correction is like the correction you would make to the handlebars of a bike with a bent front wheel. You have to turn the handlebars a certain amount to make the bicycle go straight. **Figure 5** shows a map of the magnetic declination of the United States. What is the approximate magnetic declination of your city or town?

Finding Locations on the Earth

All of the houses and buildings in your neighborhood have addresses that give their location. But how would you find the location of something such as a city or an island? These places can be given an "address" using *latitude* and *longitude*. Latitude and longitude are shown by intersecting lines on a globe or map that allow you to find exact locations.

Latitude

Imaginary lines drawn around the Earth parallel to the equator are called lines of latitude, or *parallels*. **Latitude** is the distance north or south from the equator. Latitude is expressed in degrees, as shown in **Figure 6.** The **equator** is a circle halfway between the North and South Poles that divides the Earth into the Northern and Southern Hemispheres. The equator represents 0° latitude. The North Pole is 90° north latitude, and the South Pole is 90° south latitude.

latitude the distance north or south from the equator; expressed in degrees

equator the imaginary circle halfway between the poles that divides the Earth into the Northern and Southern Hemispheres

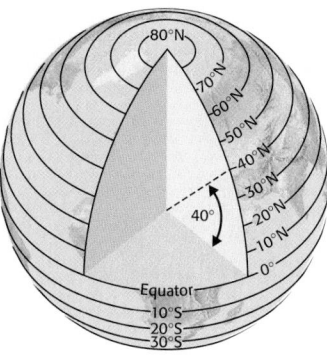

Figure 6 *Degrees latitude are a measure of the angle made by the equator and the location on the Earth's surface, as measured from the center of the Earth.*

CHAPTER RESOURCES

Technology

Transparencies
• E4 Lines of Longitude; Lines of Latitude

Finding True North Without a Compass To complete this activity, you will need a stake that is approximately 30 cm long, a ball of string, a dull pencil, and a straight edge. This activity will take several hours, it must be performed on a sunny day, and you must start before noon. Insert the stake into level ground where it will receive direct sunlight for several hours. Tie a loop in one end of the string, place it over the stake, and pull the string out to the end of the stake's shadow. Mark this point on the string and on the ground. Use a dull pencil placed at the mark on the string to scribe a circle around the stake. When the shadow of the stake touches this circle again, mark this point. Connect the two marks where the shadow touched the circle with the straight edge. A perpendicular line made from the straight edge away from the direction of the stake will be true North.

LS Visual/Kinesthetic

INCLUSION Strategies

• *Learning Disabled*
• *Developmentally Delayed*
• *Hearing Impaired*

Have students create a "human globe." You will need a variety of colored yarns. Establish direction in the classroom by hanging place cards marked North, South, East, and West. Have students form a circle around the room. Ask them to use red yarn to mark the equator. Next, ask students to begin to mark some additional parallels of latitude with black yarn. Next, create the prime meridian. Finally, use the black yarn to add more lines of longitude. Have tall students push up on the center of the circle to create the rounded effect you see on a globe.

LS Kinesthetic   English Language Learners

Latitude and Longitude On the board, draw two columns. Label one column "Latitude" and the other column "Longitude." Ask students to call out characteristics of latitude and longitude as you write their answers on the board. Students can copy the information on the board and use it as a study tool. **LS** Verbal

Quiz — GENERAL

1. List two reference points that can be used to describe direction and location on Earth. (Sample answer: North Pole, South Pole)

2. What are lines of latitude and lines of longitude? (Lines of latitude are imaginary lines around Earth parallel to the equator that are used to measure a location's distance north or south of the equator. Lines of longitude are imaginary lines that run between the Earth's geographic poles, and they are used to measure a location's distance east or west of the prime meridian.)

Alternative Assessment — GENERAL

Planning a Trip Have students use a world map to plan a trip in which they give their various destinations only in degrees of latitude and longitude. Have pairs of students trade their itineraries, and have each student "decode" the other's trip. **LS** Logical

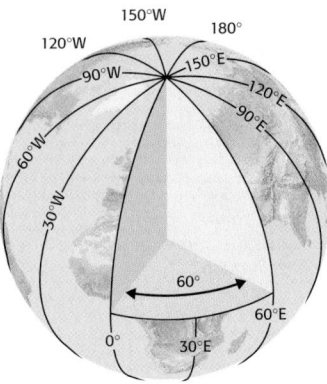

Figure 7 *Degrees longitude are a measure of the angle made by the prime meridian and the location on the Earth's surface, as measured from the center of the Earth.*

longitude the distance east and west from the prime meridian; expressed in degrees

prime meridian the meridian, or line of longitude, that is designated as 0° longitude

Longitude

Lines of longitude, or *meridians*, are imaginary lines that pass through both poles. **Longitude** is the distance east and west from the prime meridian. Like latitude, longitude is expressed in degrees, as shown in **Figure 7.** The **prime meridian** is the line that represents 0° longitude. Unlike lines of latitude, lines of longitude are not parallel. Lines of longitude touch at the poles and are farthest apart at the equator.

Unlike the equator, the prime meridian does not completely circle the globe. The prime meridian runs from the North Pole through Greenwich, England, to the South Pole. The 180° meridian lies on the opposite side of the Earth from the prime meridian. Together, the prime meridian and the 180° meridian divide the Earth into two equal halves—the Eastern and Western Hemispheres. East lines of longitude are found east of the prime meridian, between 0° and 180° longitude. West lines of longitude are found west of the prime meridian, between 0° and 180° longitude.

Using Latitude and Longitude

Points on the Earth's surface can be located by using latitude and longitude. Lines of latitude and lines of longitude cross and form a grid system on globes and maps. This grid system can be used to find locations north or south of the equator and east or west of the prime meridian.

Figure 8 shows you how latitude and longitude can be used to find the location of your state capital. First, locate the star representing your state capital on the appropriate map. Then, use the lines of latitude and longitude closest to your state capital to estimate its approximate latitude and longitude.

✓ *Reading Check* Which set of imaginary lines are referred to as meridians: lines of latitude or lines of longitude?

CONNECTION TO Social Studies

Global Addresses You can find the location of any place on Earth by finding the coordinates of the place, or latitude and longitude, on a globe or a map. Using a globe or an atlas, find the coordinates of the following cities:

New York, New York   Madrid, Spain
Sao Paulo, Brazil   Paris, France
Sydney, Australia   Cairo, Egypt

Then, find the latitude and longitude coordinates of your own city. Can you find another city that shares the same latitude as your city? Can you find another city that shares the same longitude?

ACTIVITY

Answer to Connection to Social Studies

New York, New York: 40°N, 74°W

Sao Paulo, Brazil: 23°S, 47°W

Sydney, Australia: 33°S, 151°E

Madrid, Spain: 40°N, 4°W

Paris, France: 42°N, 2°E

Cairo, Egypt: 30°N, 31°E

Answer to Reading Check

lines of longitude

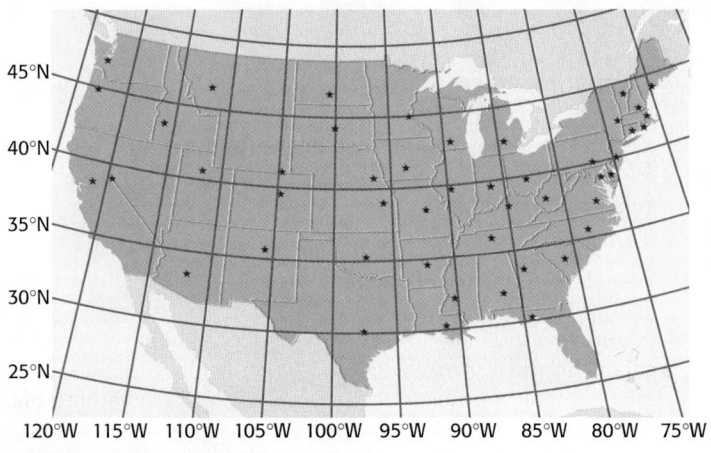

45°N
40°N
35°N
30°N
25°N

120°W 115°W 110°W 105°W 100°W 95°W 90°W 85°W 80°W 75°W

Figure 8 *The grid pattern formed by lines of latitude and longitude allows you to pinpoint any location on the Earth's surface.*

SECTION Review

Summary

- Magnetic compasses are used to find direction on Earth's surface. A compass needle points to the magnetic north pole.

- True north is the direction to the geographic North Pole, which never changes. The magnetic north pole may change over time. Magnetic declination is the difference between true north and magnetic north.

- Latitude and longitude help you find locations on a map or a globe. Lines of latitude run east and west. Lines of longitude run north and south through the poles. These lines cross and form a grid system on globes and maps.

Using Key Terms

1. Use each of the following terms in a separate sentence: *latitude, longitude, equator,* and *prime meridian.*

2. In your own words, write a definition for the term *true north.*

Understanding Key Ideas

3. The geographic poles are
   a. used as reference points when describing direction and location on Earth.
   b. formed because of the Earth's magnetic field.
   c. at either end of the Earth's axis.
   d. Both (a) and (c)

4. How are lines of latitude and lines of longitude alike? How are they different?

5. How can you use a magnetic compass to find directions on Earth?

6. What is the difference between true north and magnetic north?

7. How do lines of latitude and longitude help you find locations on the Earth's surface?

Math Skills

8. The distance between 40°N latitude and 41°N latitude is 69 mi. What is this distance in km? (Hint: 1 km = 0.621 mi)

Critical Thinking

9. **Applying Concepts** While exploring the attic, you find a treasure map. The map shows that the treasure is buried at 97°N and 188°E. Explain why this location is incorrect.

10. **Making Inferences** When using a compass to explore an area, why do you need to know an area's magnetic declination?

For a variety of links related to this chapter, go to www.scilinks.org

Topic: Latitude and Longitude
SciLinks code: HSM0854

MISCONCEPTION ////ALERT\\\\

Compasses and GPS Students may believe that a compass or GPS is all you need to keep from getting lost outdoors. Point out that compasses and GPS are useful only when combined with the ability to read maps and to observe land features. Compasses and GPS can be used for orienting oneself and for taking bearings on landmarks for map triangulation.

CHAPTER RESOURCES

Chapter Resource File

- Section Quiz **GENERAL**
- Section Review **GENERAL**
- Vocabulary and Section Summary **GENERAL**
- Reinforcement Worksheet **BASIC**
- Datasheet for Quick Lab

Overview

In this section, students compare maps and globes as models of the Earth and identify their limitations. Students explore the features of four common map projections. In addition, they discover some of the technological advances that have influenced recent trends in cartography.

 Bellringer

Display a world map, a map of your state, and a map of your community. Have students make a chart in which they list the similarities and differences between each map. Then, have them suggest three uses and three improvements for each map.

Motivate

Discussion ——— GENERAL

Map Distortion Have students examine a globe and a Mercator projection of a world map. Tell students that both are representations of Earth. Ask students to find ways in which the two representations differ. Point out the difference in the size and shape of Greenland. Ask students how they might account for the discrepancies. Tell them that in this section they will learn about the difficulties involved in making flat representations of Earth's curved surface. **LS** Visual/Verbal

---

What You Will Learn

- Explain why maps of the Earth show distortion.
- Describe four types of map projections.
- Identify five pieces of information that should be shown on a map.
- Describe four methods modern mapmakers use to make accurate maps.

Vocabulary

cylindrical projection
conic projection
azimuthal projection
remote sensing

READING STRATEGY

Discussion Read this section silently. Write down questions that you have about this section. Discuss your questions in a small group.

Mapping the Earth's Surface

What do a teddy bear, a toy airplane, and a plastic doll have in common besides being toys? They are all models that represent real things.

Scientists also use models to represent real things, but their models are not toys. Globes and maps are examples of models that scientists use to study the Earth's surface.

Because a globe is a sphere, a globe is the most accurate model of the Earth. A globe accurately shows the sizes and shapes of the continents and oceans in relation to one another. But a globe is not always the best model to use when studying the Earth's surface. A globe is too small to show many details, such as roads and rivers. It is much easier to show details on maps. But how do you show the Earth's curved surface on a flat surface? Keep reading to find out.

A Flat Sphere?

A map is a flat representation of the Earth's curved surface. However, when you move information from a curved surface to a flat surface, you lose some accuracy. Changes called *distortions* happen in the shapes and sizes of landmasses and oceans on maps. Direction and distance can also be distorted. Consider the example of the orange peel shown in **Figure 1.**

✓ **Reading Check** What are distortions on maps? (*See the Appendix for answers to Reading Checks.*)

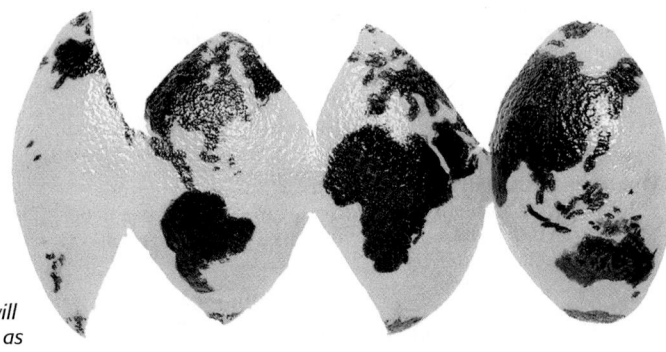

Figure 1 *If you remove and flatten the peel from an orange, the peel will stretch and tear. Notice how shapes as well as distances between points on the peel are distorted.*

CHAPTER RESOURCES

Chapter Resource File

- **Lesson Plan**
- **Directed Reading A** BASIC
- **Directed Reading B** SPECIAL NEEDS

Technology

Transparencies
- Bellringer
- E5 Cylindrical Projection; Conic Projection; Azimuthal Projection

Workbooks

Interactive Textbook Struggling Readers

Answer to Reading Check

Distortions are inaccuracies produced when information is transferred from a curved surface to a flat surface.

Map Projections

Mapmakers use map projections to move the image of Earth's curved surface onto a flat surface. No map projection of Earth can show the surface of a sphere in the correct proportions. All flat maps have distortion. However, a map showing a smaller area, such as a city, has less distortion than a map showing a larger area, such as the world.

To understand how map projections are made, think of Earth as a translucent globe that has a light inside. If you hold a piece of paper against the globe, shadows appear on the paper. These shadows show marks on the globe, such as continents, oceans, and lines of latitude and longitude. The way the paper is held against the globe determines the kind of map projection that is made. The most common map projections are based on three shapes—cylinders, cones, and planes.

Cylindrical Projection

A map projection that is made when the contents of the globe are moved onto a cylinder of paper is called a **cylindrical projection** (suh LIN dri kuhl proh JEK shuhn). The most common cylindrical projection is called a *Mercator projection* (muhr KAYT uhr proh JEK shuhn). The Mercator projection shows the globe's latitude and longitude lines as straight lines. Equal amounts of space are used between longitude lines. Latitude lines are spaced farther apart north and south of the equator. Because of the spacing, areas near the poles look wider and longer on the map than they look on the globe. In **Figure 2,** Greenland appears almost as large as Africa!

cylindrical projection a map projection that is made by moving the surface features of the globe onto a cylinder

INTERNET ACTIVITY

For another activity related to this chapter, go to **go.hrw.com** and type in the keyword **HZ5MAPW.**

Figure 2 **Cylindrical Projection**

This cylindrical projection is a Mercator projection. It is accurate near the equator but distorts areas near the North and South Poles.

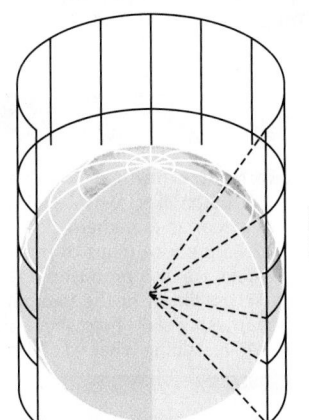  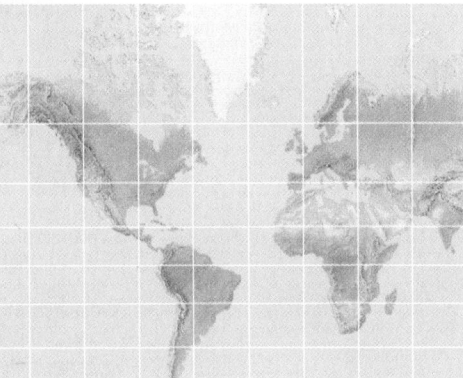

SUPPORT FOR

English Language Learners

Map Projections Students may have trouble processing the complex ideas on map projections using language alone. To give students tangible examples of where errors might occur in map projections, give groups of three students a globe and 3 pieces of white paper. Each student recreates one of the 3 types of map projection by wrapping a sheet of paper around the globe as shown in the figures on this and the following 2 pages and, then,

copying the map for two minutes. Ask students who tried each type of projection to share the problems they found. (Answers should approximate the information from the text, but language will be simpler.) Allow students to demonstrate the problems on the globes to help them express their ideas. **LS Visual/Kinesthetic**

Teach

READING STRATEGY ——— **BASIC**

Making an Outline As students read about map projections, have them write down the name of each type of projection and a brief description of how the projection is made. Have students list the advantages or disadvantages of each type of projection. **LS Verbal**   English Language Learners

MISCONCEPTION ALERT

Map Inaccuracies The distortions of landmasses are not the only inaccuracies that occur on maps. When making maps, such as road maps, for popular use, mapmakers routinely generalize them for both practical and aesthetic reasons. For example, when the size of a map's scale is reduced, two features (such as two lakes or two towns) might appear to be adjacent to each other. In this case, the mapmaker might move them slightly apart. Mapmakers sometimes also add details that may not really exist; for instance, meander loops might be added to a river or stream to make it look more realistic. Topographic maps, however, are made from aerial photographs and are extremely accurate.

INTERNET ACTIVITY
Short Story ——— **GENERAL**

For an internet activity related to this chapter, have students go to **go.hrw.com** and type in the keyword **HZ5MAPW.**

Mnemonics Have students think of some rhymes to help them remember key points about the projections discussed in the text. You might suggest the following to help students get started:

- "If you're traveling to the equator, you'll do well with Mercator."

- "For east to west, conic is best."

- "For a stroll at a pole, an azimuthal will help you stay in control."
LS Verbal/Auditory   English Language Learners

Homework —— GENERAL

Map Projections Have students make a chart listing the strengths and weaknesses of cylindrical, conic, azimuthal, and equal-area projections. Then, have students research another projection, such as the Robinson projection. Have them add the strengths and weaknesses of that projection to their charts. Have them explain at the bottom of the chart why none of the projections is entirely free of distortions and inaccuracies. LS Verbal

Figure 3 Conic Projection

A series of conic projections can be used to map a large area. Because each cone touches the globe at a different latitude, conic projections reduce distortion.

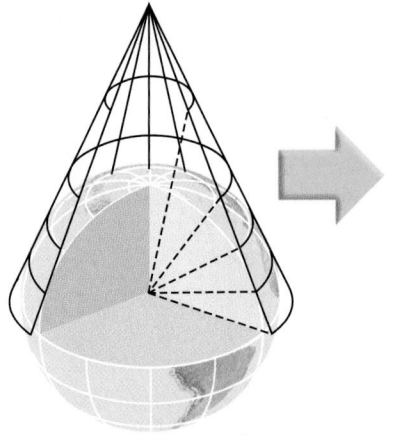
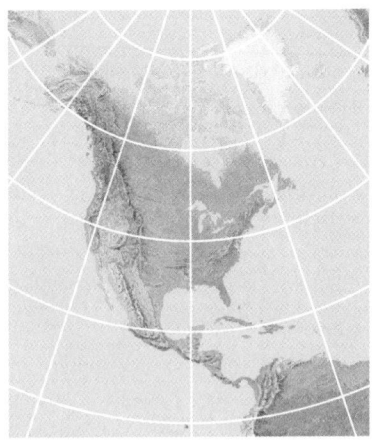

conic projection a map projection that is made by moving the surface features of the globe onto a cone

Conic Projection

A map projection that is made by moving the contents of the globe onto a cone is a **conic projection,** shown in **Figure 3.** This cone is then unrolled to form a flat plane.

The cone touches the globe at each line of longitude but at only one line of latitude. There is no distortion along the line of latitude where the globe touches the cone. Areas near this line of latitude are distorted less than other areas are. Because the cone touches many lines of longitude and only one line of latitude, conic projections are best for mapping large masses of land that have more area east to west. For example, a conic projection is often used to map the United States.

CONNECTION TO Social Studies

WRITING SKILL **Mapmaking and Ship Navigation** Gerardus Mercator is the cartographer (or mapmaker) who developed the Mercator projection. During his career as a mathematician and cartographer, Mercator worked hard to produce maps of many parts of Europe, including Great Britain. He also produced a terrestrial globe and a celestial globe. Use the library or the Internet to research Mercator. How did his mapmaking skills help ship navigators in the 1500s? Write a paragraph describing what you learn.

Science Bloopers

During the process of compiling data from a number of different sources, mistakes are sometimes made. Cartographers have wiped entire cities off maps accidentally! For example, Canada's capital, Ottawa, was once omitted from a Canadian tourist-office map. An official explanation that there was no direct air service between New York City and Ottawa failed to satisfy one Ottawa tourist bureau executive, who remarked irately, "Ottawa should be shown in any case, even if the only point of entry was by two-man kayak."

Figure 4 Azimuthal Projection

On this azimuthal projection, distortion increases as you move farther from the North Pole.

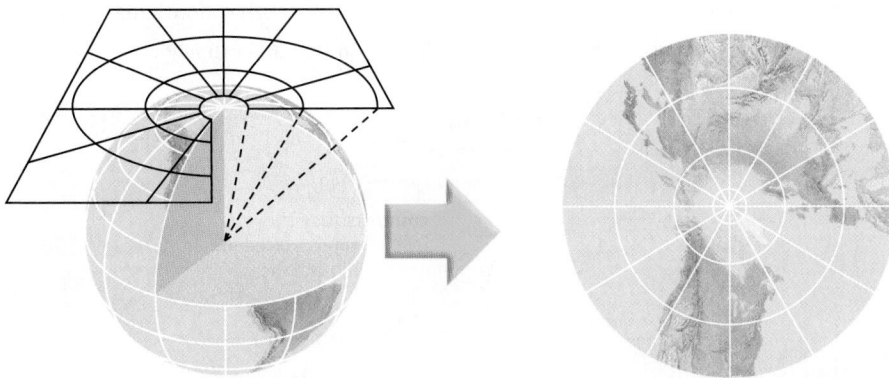

Azimuthal Projection

An **azimuthal projection** (AZ uh MYOOTH uhl proh JEK shuhn) is a map projection that is made by moving the contents of the globe onto a flat plane. Look at **Figure 4.** On an azimuthal projection, the plane touches the globe at only one point. There is little distortion at this point of contact. The point of contact for an azimuthal projection is usually one of the poles. However, distortion of direction, distance, and shape increases as you move away from the point of contact. Azimuthal projections are most often used to map areas of the globe that are near the North and South Poles.

azimuthal projection a map projection that is made by moving the surface features of the globe onto a plane

✓ *Reading Check* How are azimuthal and conic projections alike? How are they different?

Equal-Area Projection

A map projection that shows the area between the latitude and longitude lines the same size as that area on a globe is called an *equal-area projection.* Equal-area projections can be made by using cylindrical, conic, or azimuthal projections. Equal-area projections are often used to map large land areas, such as continents. The shapes of the continents and oceans are distorted on equal-area projections. But because the scale used on equal-area projections is constant throughout the map, this type of projection is good for determining distance on a map. **Figure 5** is an example of an equal-area projection.

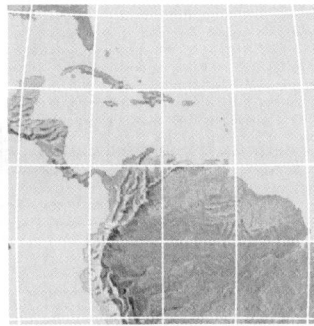

Figure 5 *Equal-area projections are useful for determining distance on a map.*

Answer to Reading Check

Azimuthal and conic projections are similar because they are both ways to represent the curved surface of the Earth on a flat map. Azimuthal projections show the surface of a globe transferred to a flat plane, whereas conic projections show the surface of a globe transferred to a cone.

- *Learning Disabled*
- *Attention Deficit Disorder*
- *Gifted and Talented*

Organize students into pairs or groups of three. Hand out to each group a map of their town or city and brightly colored sticky dots. Ask students to identify and mark with sticky dots on the map the title of the map, map scale, compass rose, and legend. Ask them to find their school, home, and an additional landmark and indicate these sites as well. Next, ask each team to calculate the distance from their school to the various landmarks. For gifted and talented students, ask them to do additional calculations, such as distance between points and direction in degrees using a compass.

English Language Learners

LS Visual

Answer to Reading Check

Every map should have a title, a compass rose, a scale, the date, and a legend.

Information Shown on Maps

Regardless of the kind of map you are reading, the map should contain the information shown in **Figure 6.** This information includes a title, a compass rose, a scale, a legend, and a date. Unfortunately, not all maps have all this information. The more of this information a map has, the more reliable the map is.

Reading Check What information should every map have?

Figure 6 *This Texas road map includes all of the information that a map should contain.*

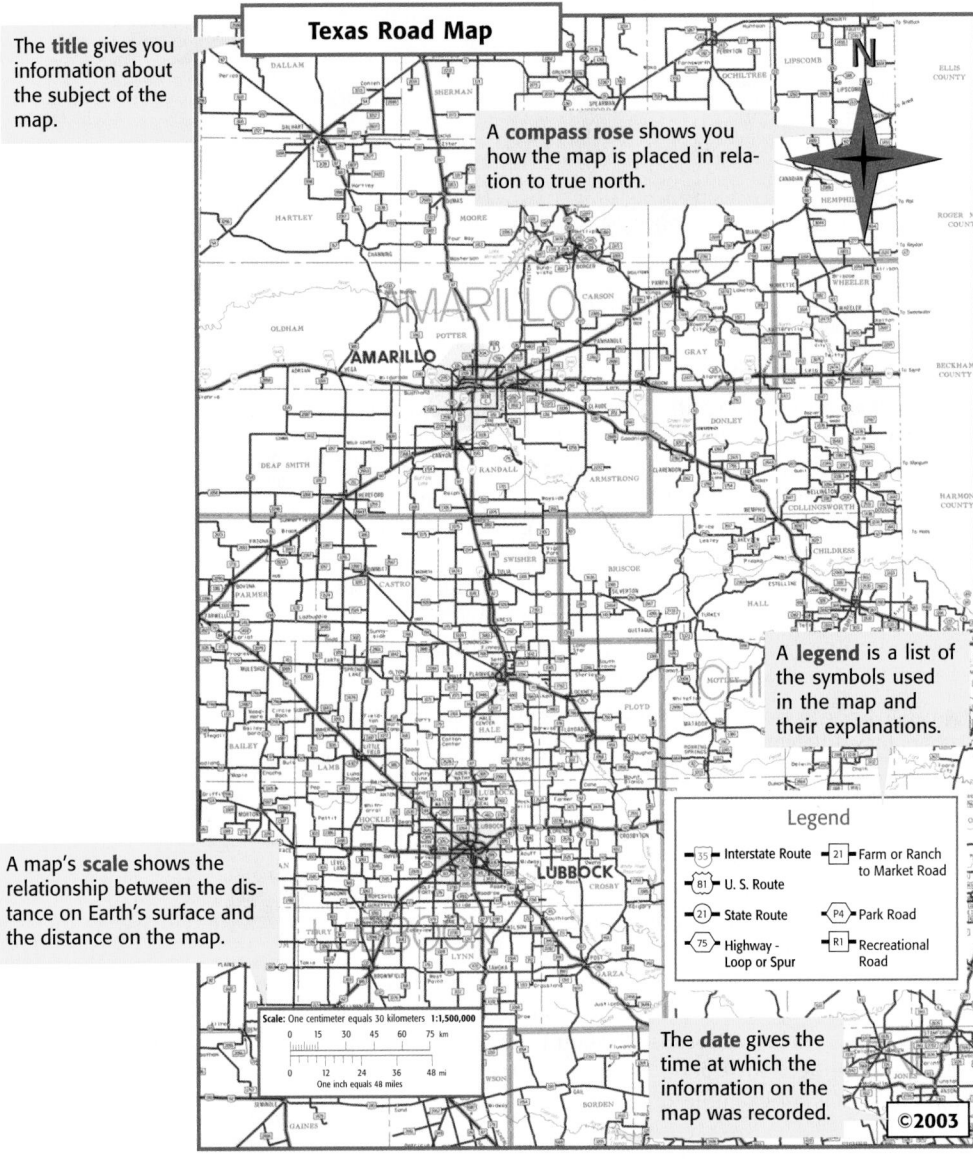

The **title** gives you information about the subject of the map.

A **compass rose** shows you how the map is placed in relation to true north.

A **legend** is a list of the symbols used in the map and their explanations.

A map's **scale** shows the relationship between the distance on Earth's surface and the distance on the map.

The **date** gives the time at which the information on the map was recorded.

Texas Road Map

Legend
- 35 — Interstate Route
- 81 — U. S. Route
- 21 — State Route
- 75 — Highway - Loop or Spur
- 21 — Farm or Ranch to Market Road
- P4 — Park Road
- R1 — Recreational Road

Scale: One centimeter equals 30 kilometers 1:1,500,000
0 15 30 45 60 75 km
0 12 24 36 48 mi
One inch equals 48 miles

©2003

CONNECTION ACTIVITY
Math — GENERAL

Taking a Hike Have students imagine that they want to use a map with a scale of 1:24,000 to estimate the length of a hike. On the map, the route measures 20 cm. Have students calculate the length of the hike in kilometers.
(20 cm × 24,000 = 480,000 cm;
480,000 cm ÷ 100 cm/m = 4,800 m;
4,800 ÷ 1,000 m/km = 4.8 km)
LS Logical

Is That a Fact!

In an attempt to keep foreigners and even Soviet citizens from knowing the exact geography of their country, mapmakers in the Soviet Union printed maps with deliberate mistakes. Roads, rivers, and even cities would be misplaced or omitted. These revisions were especially true of Moscow street maps. Although these maps were made with national security in mind, the end result was that the country operated much less efficiently.

Modern Mapmaking

For many centuries mapmakers relied on the observations of explorers to make maps. Today, however, mapmakers have far more technologically advanced tools for mapmaking.

Many of today's maps are made by remote sensing. **Remote sensing** is a way to collect information about something without physically being there. Remote sensing can be as basic as putting cameras on airplanes. However, many mapmakers rely on more sophisticated technology, such as satellites.

remote sensing the process of gathering and analyzing information about an object without physically being in touch with the object

Remote Sensing and Satellites

The image shown in **Figure 7** is a photograph taken by a satellite. Satellites can also detect energy that your eyes cannot. Remote sensors gather data about energy coming from Earth's surface and send the data back to receiving stations on Earth. A computer is then used to process the information to make a picture you can see.

Remote Sensing Using Radar

Radar is a tool that uses waves of energy to map Earth's surface. Waves of energy are sent from a satellite to the area being observed. The waves are then reflected from the area to a receiver on the satellite. The distance and the speed in which the waves travel to the area and back are measured and analyzed to create a map of the area. The waves used in radar can move through clouds and water. Because of this ability, radar has been used to map the surface of Venus, whose atmosphere is thick and cloudy.

Figure 7 *Satellites can produce very detailed images of the Earth's surface. The satellite that took this picture was 423 mi above the Earth's surface!*

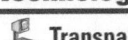

Close

Reteaching — BASIC

Demonstration To reinforce students' understanding of GPS technology, show students how a GPS unit operates. Using a hand-held GPS unit, take students to various locations outside, and have them observe the unit as it updates the coordinates of your location. **LS** Visual

Quiz — GENERAL

1. Equal-area projections are used to map what type of area? (Equal-area projections are used to map large areas of land.)

2. How has remote-sensing technology contributed to the science of mapmaking? (Remote sensing has allowed people to view Earth's surface from above, which enables mapmakers to make more accurate maps.)

3. Why is it important for a road map to show the date the map was made? (The date allows the user to determine if the map is accurate because the location and names of streets and roads may change over time.)

Alternative Assessment — GENERAL

Analyzing Maps Maps made by a noncartographer using a computer often omit crucial elements, such as a scale, a date, or a compass rose. Have students bring in a map from a newspaper, a magazine, or an advertisement, and have them write a critique of the map. **LS** Visual

Figure 8 *This tiny GPS unit may come in handy if you are ever lost.*

Global Positioning System

Did you know that satellite technology can actually help you from getting lost? The *global positioning system* (GPS) can help you find where you are on Earth. GPS is a system of orbiting satellites that send radio signals to receivers on Earth. The receivers calculate a given place's latitude, longitude, and elevation.

GPS was invented in the 1970s by the U.S. Department of Defense for military use. However, during the last 30 years, GPS has made its way into people's daily lives. Mapmakers use GPS to verify the location of boundary lines between countries and states. Airplane and boat pilots use GPS for navigation. Businesses and state agencies use GPS for mapping and environmental planning. Many new cars have GPS units that show information on a screen on the dashboard. Some GPS units are small enough to wear on your wrist, as shown in **Figure 8,** so you can know your location anywhere you go!

Geographic Information Systems

Mapmakers now use geographic information systems to store, use, and view geographic information. A *geographic information system*, or GIS, is a computerized system that allows a user to enter different types of information about an area. This information is entered and stored as layers. The user can then use the stored information to make complex analyses or display maps. **Figure 9** shows three GIS images of Seattle, Washington.

Reading Check Explain how information is stored using GIS.

Figure 9 *The images at right show the location of sewer lines, roads, and parks in Seattle, Washington.*

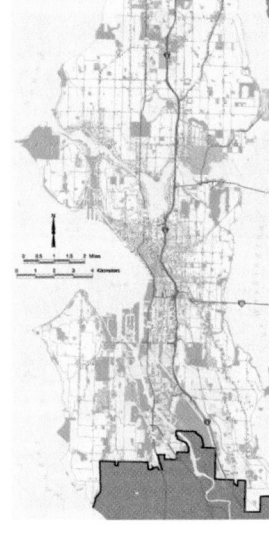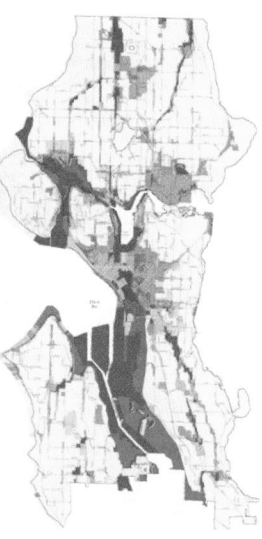

Answer to Reading Check
A GIS system stores information in layers.

Summary

- When information is moved from a curved surface to a flat surface, distortion occurs.
- Three main types of projections are used to show Earth's surface on a flat map: cylindrical, conic, and azimuthal projections.
- Equal-area maps are used to show the area of a piece of land in relation to the area of other landmasses and oceans.
- Maps should contain a title, a scale, a legend, a compass rose, and a date.

- Modern mapmakers use remote sensing technology, such as satellites and radar.
- The Global positioning system, or GPS, is a system of satellites that can help you determine your location no matter where you are.
- Geographical information systems, or GIS, are computerized systems that allow mapmakers to store and use many types of data about an area.

Using Key Terms

1. In your own words, write a definition for each of the following terms: *cylindrical projection, azimuthal projection,* and *conic projection.*

Understanding Key Ideas

2. Which of the following map projections is most often used to map the United States?
   a. cylindrical projection
   b. conic projection
   c. azimuthal projection
   d. equal-area projection

3. List five things found on maps. Explain how each thing is important to reading a map.

4. Describe how GPS can help you find your location on Earth.

5. Why is radar useful when mapping areas that tend to be covered in clouds?

Critical Thinking

6. **Analyzing Ideas** Imagine you are a mapmaker. You have been asked to map a landmass that has more area from east to west than from north to south. What type of map projection would you use? Explain.

7. **Making Inferences** Imagine looking at a map of North America. Would this map have a large scale or a small scale? Would a map of your city have a large scale or a small scale? Explain.

Interpreting Graphics

Use the map below to answer the questions that follow.

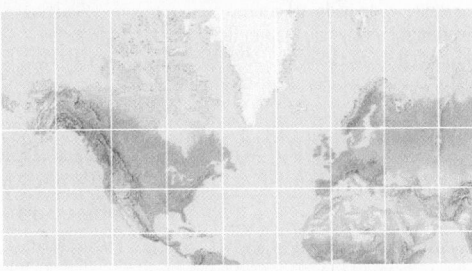

8. What type of projection was used to make this map?

9. Which areas of this map are the most distorted? Explain.

10. Which areas of this map are the least distorted? Explain.

Developed and maintained by the
National Science Teachers Association

For a variety of links related to this chapter, go to www.scilinks.org

Topic: Mapmaking
SciLinks code: HSM0909

Answers to Section Review

1. Sample answer: A cylindrical projection transfers information from a curved surface onto a cylinder. An azimuthal projection transfers information from a curved surface onto a flat plane. A conic projection transfers information from a curved surface onto a cone.

2. b

3. Maps should include a title, a scale, a legend, a compass rose, and a date. The title describes the subject of the map; the scale, legend, and compass rose help the reader use the map; and the date describes the age of the map.

4. A GPS unit uses satellite technology to pinpoint the latitude, longitude, and elevation of the area you are in.

5. Radar is useful when mapping cloudy areas because radar waves can travel through clouds.

6. Sample answer: A conic projection would be the best map projection to use when mapping a landmass that has more area from east to west than from north to south.

7. Sample answer: A map of North America would most likely have a small scale, because a map of a large area would not show much detail. A map of my city would have a larger scale, because this map would show more detail.

8. cylindrical projection

9. The areas near the North Pole are most distorted.

10. The areas nearest the equator is the least distorted.

Focus

Overview

In this section, students investigate how contour lines are used to show elevation and landforms on a topographic map. In addition, they learn how to read and interpret the features of a topographic map.

 Bellringer

Have students examine the topographic map shown on this page. Have them imagine that they are standing on the top of Campbell Hill. Students should describe in their **science journal** what they see in each direction. Tell students that they will learn to read topographic maps, such as the ones in this section.

Motivate

ActiViTY ——— GENERAL

Investigate Your Area If possible, obtain topographic maps of your area. You may be able to find these maps at camping stores or on the Internet. As a class, locate different landforms in your area. Discuss with students how contour intervals indicate changes in elevation. If possible, take a class field trip to one of the areas. **LS** Visual   English Language Learners

What You Will Learn

- Explain how contour lines show elevation and landforms on a map.
- Explain how the relief of an area determines the contour interval used on a map.
- List the rules of contour lines.

Vocabulary

topographic map
elevation
contour line
contour interval
relief
index contour

READING STRATEGY

Paired Summarizing Read this section silently. In pairs, take turns summarizing the material. Stop to discuss ideas that seem confusing.

topographic map a map that shows the surface features of Earth

elevation the height of an object above sea level

contour line a line that connects points of equal elevation

Topographic Maps

Imagine you are going on a camping trip in the wilderness. To be prepared, you want to take a compass and a map. But what kind of map should you take? Because there won't be any roads in the wilderness, you can forget about a road map. Instead, you will need a topographic map.

A **topographic map** (TAHP uh GRAF ik MAP) is a map that shows surface features, or topography (tuh PAHG ruh fee), of the Earth. Topographic maps show both natural features, such as rivers, lakes, and mountains, and features made by humans, such as cities, roads, and bridges. Topographic maps also show elevation. **Elevation** is the height of an object above sea level. The elevation at sea level is 0. In this section, you will learn how to read a topographic map.

Elements of Elevation

The United States Geological Survey (USGS), a federal government agency, has made topographic maps for most of the United States. These maps show elevation in feet (ft) rather than in meters, the SI unit usually used by scientists.

Contour Lines

On a topographic map, *contour lines* are used to show elevation. **Contour lines** are lines that connect points of equal elevation. For example, one contour line would connect points on a map that have an elevation of 100 ft. Another line would connect points on a map that have an elevation of 200 ft. **Figure 1** illustrates how contour lines appear on a map.

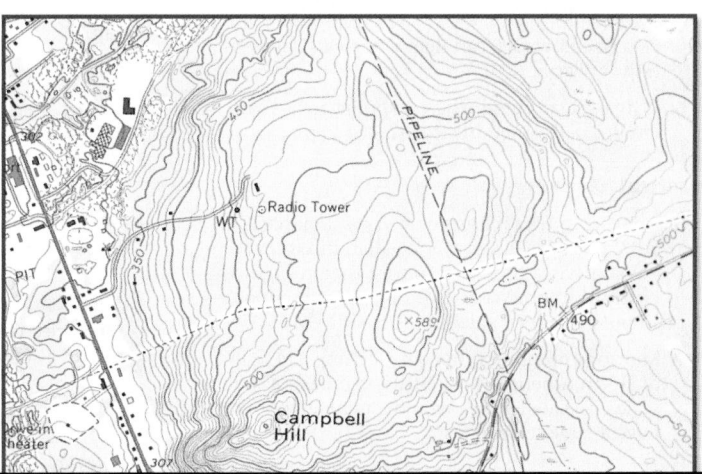

Figure 1 *Because contour lines connect points of equal elevation, the shape of the contour lines reflects the shape of the land.*

Is That a Fact!

The Ordnance Survey of Great Britain produces topographic maps with very large scales, ranging from 1:10,000 to 1:1,250. Such large scales permit a level of detail that shows the location of public telephones, windmills, and even large boulders!

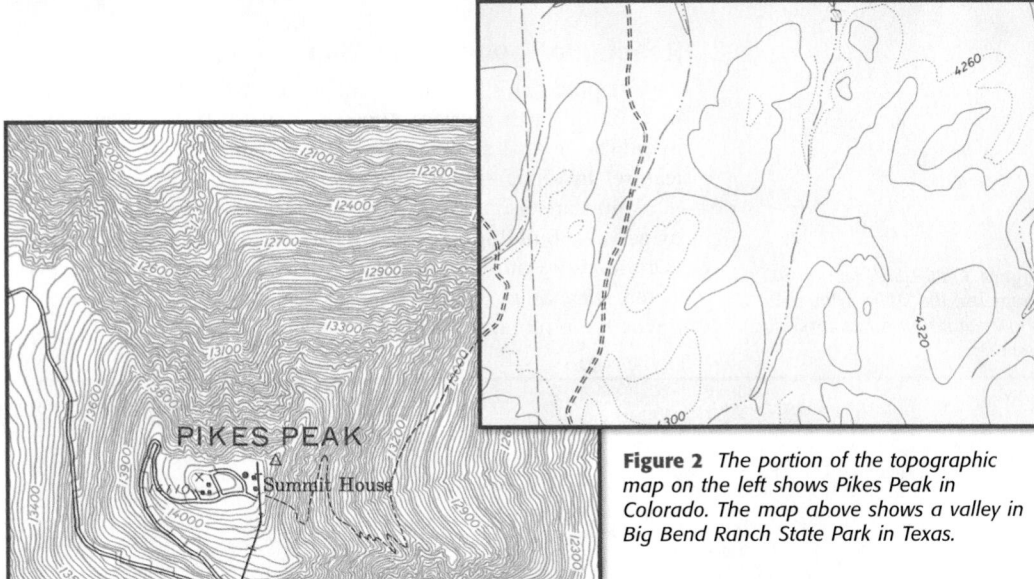

Figure 2 *The portion of the topographic map on the left shows Pikes Peak in Colorado. The map above shows a valley in Big Bend Ranch State Park in Texas.*

Contour Interval

The difference in elevation between one contour line and the next is called the **contour interval.** For example, a map with a contour interval of 20 ft would have contour lines every 20 ft of elevation change, such as 0 ft, 20 ft, 40 ft, and 60 ft. A mapmaker chooses a contour interval based on the area's relief. **Relief** is the difference in elevation between the highest and lowest points of the area being mapped. Because the relief of an area with mountains is large, the relief might be shown on a map using a large contour interval, such as 100 ft. However, a flat area has small relief and might be shown on a map by using a small contour interval, such as 10 ft.

The spacing of contour lines also indicates slope, as shown in **Figure 2.** Contour lines that are close together show a steep slope. Contour lines that are spaced far apart show a gentle slope.

Index Contour

On USGS topographic maps, an index contour is used to make reading the map easier. An **index contour** is a darker, heavier contour line that is usually every fifth line and that is labeled by elevation. Find an index contour on both of the topographic maps shown in **Figure 2.**

✓ *Reading Check* What is an index contour? (*See the Appendix for answers to Reading Checks.*)

contour interval the difference in elevation between one contour line and the next

relief the variations in elevation of a land surface

index contour on a map, a darker, heavier contour line that is usually every fifth line and that indicates a change in elevation

---

CONNECTION TO
Oceanography

Mapping the Ocean Floor
Oceanographers use topographic maps to map the topography of the ocean floor. Use the Internet or the library to find a topographic map of the ocean floor. How are maps of the ocean floor similar to maps of the continents? How are they different?

Reteaching — BASIC

Rules of Contour Lines Using a topographic map, show students examples of the rules of contour lines. Discuss how contour lines never cross, and show specific areas of steep slope, gentle slope, rivers or streams, and hills and depressions. **LS** Visual

Quiz — GENERAL

1. What is a contour interval on a topographic map? (the difference in elevation between one contour line and the next)

2. What do closely spaced contour lines on a topographic map indicate? (a steep area)

3. How does a topographic map indicate the direction that a stream flows? (Streams flow downhill, or in the direction that elevation decreases. The Vs point toward higher elevations.)

Alternative Assessment — GENERAL

Using Maps Photocopy a portion of a topographic map that shows a mountain. Indicate the scale of the map on the photocopy. Distribute copies to students, and ask them to trace a route to the top. Then, have them write a description of their "trail" that includes the length of the hike, the elevations where the trail is the steepest, and the points where the slope is gentle. Have students also note other features, such as streams, power lines, or road crossings. **LS** Verbal

Reading a Topographic Map

Topographic maps, like other maps, use symbols to represent parts of the Earth's surface. **Figure 3** shows a USGS topographic map. The legend shows some of the symbols that represent features in topographic maps.

Colors are also used to represent features of Earth's surface. In general, buildings, roads, bridges, and railroads are black. Contour lines are brown. Major highways are red. Bodies of water, such as rivers, lakes, and oceans are blue. Cities and towns are pink, and wooded areas are green.

Figure 3 *All USGS topographic maps use the same symbols to show natural and human-made features.*

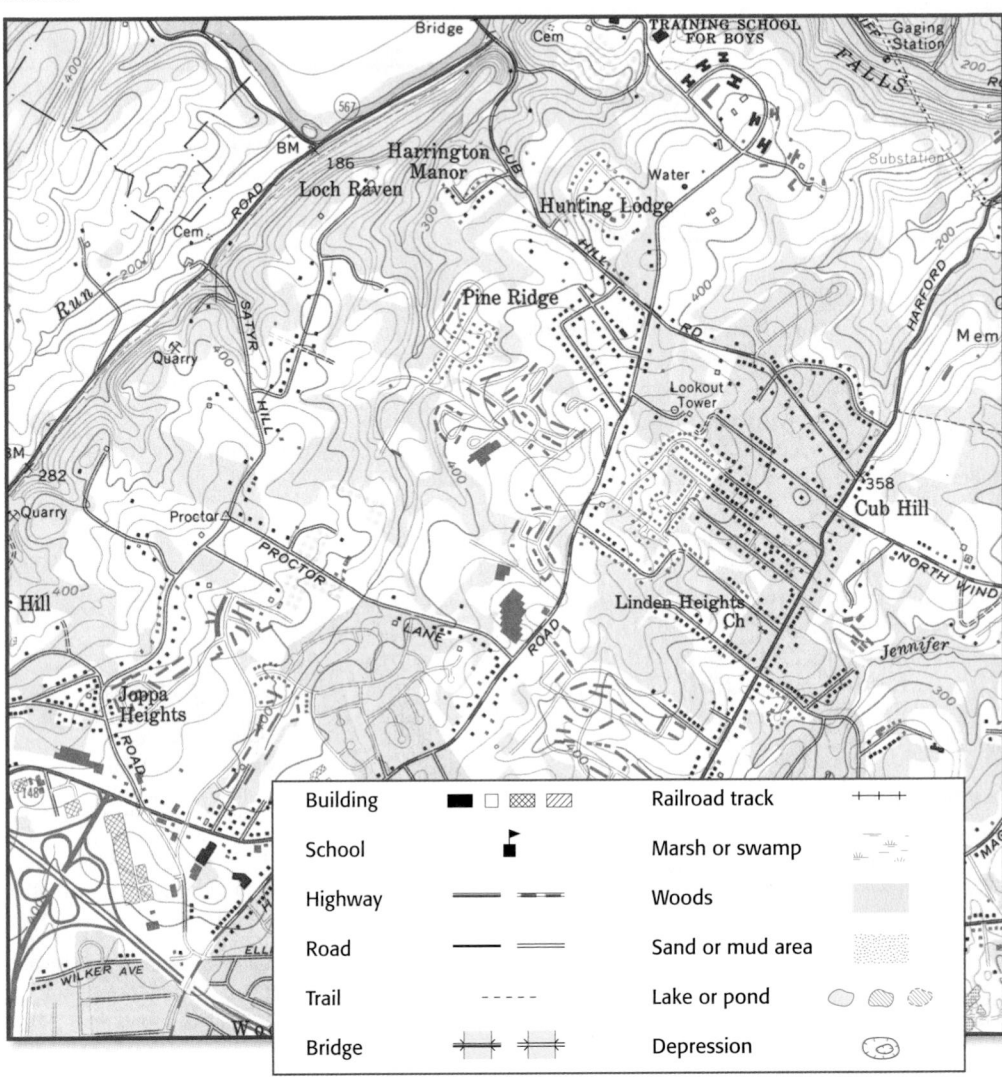

The Golden Rules of Contour Lines

Contour lines are the key to explaining the size and shape of landforms on a topographic map. Reading a topographic map takes training and practice. The following rules will help you understand how to read topographic maps:

- Contour lines never cross. All points along a contour line represent one elevation.
- The spacing of contour lines depends on slope characteristics. Contour lines that are close together show a steep slope. Contour lines that are far apart show a gentle slope.
- Contour lines that cross a valley or stream are V shaped. The V points toward the area of highest elevation. If a stream or river flows through the valley, the V points upstream.
- The tops of hills, mountains, and depressions are shown by closed circles. Depressions are marked with short, straight lines inside the circle that point downslope to the depression.

CONNECTION TO Environmental Science

Endangered Species State agencies, such as the Texas Parks and Wildlife Department, use topographic maps to mark where endangered plant and animal species are. By marking the location of the endangered plants and animals, these agencies can record and protect these places. Use the Internet or another source to find out if there is an agency in your state that tracks endangered species by using topographic maps.

SECTION Review

Summary

- Contour lines are used to show elevation and landforms by connecting points of equal elevation.
- The contour interval is determined by the relief of an area.
- Contour lines never cross. Contour lines that cross a valley or a stream are V shaped and point upstream. The tops of hills, mountains, and depressions are shown by closed circles.

Using Key Terms

1. In your own words, write a definition for each of the following terms: *topographic map, contour interval,* and *relief.*

Understanding Key Ideas

2. An index contour
   a. is a heavier contour line that shows a change in elevation.
   b. points in the direction of higher elevation.
   c. indicates a depression.
   d. indicates a hill.

3. How do topographic maps represent the Earth's surface?

4. How does the relief of an area determine the contour interval used on a map?

5. What are the rules of contour lines?

Math Skills

6. The contour line at the base of a hill reads 90 ft. There are five contour lines between the base of the hill and the top of the hill. If the contour interval is 30 ft, what is the elevation of the highest contour line?

Critical Thinking

7. **Making Inferences** Why isn't the highest point on a hill represented by a contour line?

SCi LINKS.

NSTA
Developed and maintained by the National Science Teachers Association

For a variety of links related to this chapter, go to www.scilinks.org

Topic: Topographic Maps
SciLinks code: HSM1536

Answers to Section Review

1. Sample answer: A topographic map shows the surface features of the Earth. A contour interval is the difference in elevation between two adjacent contour lines. Relief is the difference in elevation between the highest and lowest points of the area being mapped.

2. a

3. Topographic maps use contour lines to show the surface features of Earth. Symbols indicate other features.

4. If the relief of an area is large, a topographic map of the area will have a large contour interval. If the relief of an area is small, a topographic map of the area will have a small contour interval.

5. Contour lines never cross. The spacing of contour lines depends on the slope characteristics of an area. Contour lines that cross a valley or a stream are V shaped, and the V points upstream. The tops of mountains and the bottoms of depressions are shown by closed circles. Depressions are marked with short, straight lines inside the circle that point downslope.

6. 30 ft × 5 = 150 ft; 90 ft + 150 ft = 240 ft

7. The highest point on a hill or mountain is a single point, not a group of points with the same elevation.

Round or Flat?

Teacher's Notes

Time Required

One 45-minute class period

Lab Ratings

EASY —————→ HARD

Teacher Prep 🧪🧪
Student Set-Up 🧪🧪🧪
Concept Level 🧪🧪🧪
Clean Up 🧪

MATERIALS

The materials listed on the student page are enough for a group of 3 or 4 students.

Safety Caution

Remind students to review all safety cautions and icons before beginning this lab activity.

Preparation Notes

Obtain inflated basketballs from your school's physical education instructor. Asking students to bring basketballs from home may be necessary. Begin the activity by reminding students that circumference is the distance around a circle or sphere.

You may also need to review the use of protractors with students before performing this activity.

OBJECTIVES

Construct a tool to measure the circumference of the Earth.

Calculate the circumference of the Earth.

MATERIALS

- basketball
- books or notebooks (2)
- calculator (optional)
- clay, modeling
- flashlight or small lamp
- meterstick
- pencils, unsharpened (2)
- protractor
- ruler, metric
- string, 10 cm long
- tape, masking
- tape measure

SAFETY

Round or Flat?

Eratosthenes thought of a way to measure the circumference of Earth. He came up with the idea when he read that a well in southern Egypt was entirely lit by the sun at noon once each year. He realized that to shine on the entire surface of the well water, the sun must be directly over the well. At the same time, in a city just north of the well, a tall monument cast a shadow. Thus, Eratosthenes reasoned that the sun could not be directly over both the monument and the well at noon on the same day. In this experiment, you will see how Eratosthenes' way of measuring works.

Ask a Question

1. How could I use Eratosthenes' method of investigation to measure the size of the Earth?

Form a Hypothesis

2. Formulate a hypothesis that answers the question above. Record your hypothesis.

Test the Hypothesis

3. Set the basketball on a table. Place a book or notebook on either side of the basketball to hold the ball in place. The ball represents Earth.

Lab Notes

Explain that Eratosthenes' experiment worked because he set up a ratio. It may be necessary to review ratios before performing this activity. The formula Eratosthenes used is as follows:

$$\frac{distance\ around\ ball}{distance\ between\ sticks} = \frac{360°\ in\ the\ sphere}{angle\ of\ shadow\ with\ stick}$$

Students may be interested to learn that they can calculate the circumference of the Earth by performing Eratosthenes' experiment in partnership with other schools around the world. The experiment is conducted twice a year during the fall and spring equinoxes. To find out more, have students search for "Eratosthenes' experiment" on the Internet.

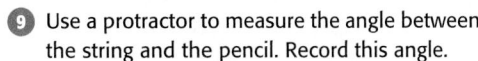

4 Use modeling clay to attach a pencil to the "equator" of the ball so that the pencil points away from the ball.

5 Attach the second pencil to the ball at a point that is 5 cm above the first pencil. This second pencil should also point away from the ball.

6 Use a meterstick to measure 1 m away from the ball. Mark the 1 m position with masking tape. Label the position "Sun." Hold the flashlight so that its front edge is above the masking tape.

7 When your teacher turns out the lights, turn on your flashlight and point it so that the pencil on the equator does not cast a shadow. Ask a partner to hold the flashlight in this position. The second pencil should cast a shadow on the ball.

8 Tape one end of the string to the top of the second pencil. Hold the other end of the string against the ball at the far edge of the shadow. Make sure that the string is tight. But be careful not to pull the pencil over.

9 Use a protractor to measure the angle between the string and the pencil. Record this angle.

10 Use the following formula to calculate the experimental circumference of the ball.

$$Circumference = \frac{360° \times 5 \text{ cm}}{\text{angle between pencil and string}}$$

11 Record the experimental circumference you calculated in step 10. Wrap the tape measure around the ball's equator to measure the actual circumference of the ball. Record this circumference.

Analyze the Results

1 **Examining Data** Compare the experimental circumference with the actual circumference.

2 **Analyzing Data** What could have caused your experimental circumference to differ from the actual circumference?

3 **Analyzing Data** What are some of the advantages and disadvantages of taking measurements this way?

Draw Conclusions

4 **Evaluating Methods** Was Eratosthenes' method an effective way to measure Earth's circumference? Explain your answer.

Analyze the Results

1. Students will likely find that the experimental and actual circumferences are not equal. The two values should be close, however.

2. Answers may vary. Factors that affect this measurement include the angle of the pencils and human error.

3. Sample answer: Because it is impossible to use a tape measure to determine the circumference of the Earth, this procedure offers a good approximation. One disadvantage is that the measurements are not exact.

Draw Conclusions

4. Sample answers: yes; It gives a value that is close to the actual value.

CHAPTER RESOURCES

Chapter Resource File

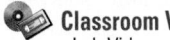
- **Datasheet for Chapter Lab**
- **Lab Notes and Answers**

Technology

- **Classroom Videos**
  - Lab Video

LabBook

- Orient Yourself!
- Topographic Tuber

CHAPTER RESOURCES

Workbooks

Inquiry Labs

- Looking for Buried Treasure **ADVANCED**

Long-Term Projects & Research Ideas
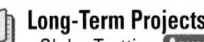
- Globe Trotting **ADVANCED**

Holt Lab Generator CD-ROM

Search for any lab by topic, standard, difficulty level, or time. Edit any lab to fit your needs, or create your own labs. Use the Lab Materials QuickList software to customize your lab materials list.

Barry L. Bishop
San Rafael
Junior High
Ferron, Utah

Assignment Guide

SECTION	QUESTIONS
1	1–3, 7, 8
2	4, 6, 10, 11, 12, 14–16, 18–22, 24
3	5, 9, 13, 17, 23, 25–29

ANSWERS

Using Key Terms

1. Sample answer: True north is the geographic North Pole. Magnetic north refers to the magnetic north pole, which changes.

2. Sample answer: Latitude is the distance north or south from the equator. Longitude is the distance east and west from the prime meridian. Both latitude and longitude are measured in degrees.

3. Sample answer: The equator is the imaginary circle halfway between the poles that divides the Earth into Northern and Southern Hemispheres and represents 0° latitude. The prime meridian represents 0° longitude. It runs from the North to South Poles through Greenwich, England.

USING KEY TERMS

For each pair of terms, explain how the meanings of the terms differ.

1. *true north* and *magnetic north*

2. *latitude* and *longitude*

3. *equator* and *prime meridian*

4. *cylindrical projection* and *azimuthal projection*

5. *contour interval* and *index contour*

6. *global positioning system* and *geographic information system*

UNDERSTANDING KEY IDEAS

Multiple Choice

7. A point whose latitude is 0° is located on the
   a. North Pole.
   b. equator.
   c. South Pole.
   d. prime meridian.

8. The distance in degrees east or west of the prime meridian is
   a. latitude.
   b. declination.
   c. longitude.
   d. projection.

9. Widely spaced contour lines indicate a
   a. steep slope.
   b. gentle slope.
   c. hill.
   d. river.

10. The most common map projections are based on three geometric shapes. Which of the following geometric shapes is NOT one of the three geometric shapes?
    a. cylinder
    b. square
    c. cone
    d. plane

11. A cylindrical projection is distorted near the
    a. equator.
    b. poles.
    c. prime meridian.
    d. date line.

12. What is the relationship between the distance on a map and the actual distance on Earth called?
    a. legend
    b. elevation
    c. relief
    d. scale

13. ___ is the height of an object above sea level.
    a. Contour interval
    b. Elevation
    c. Declination
    d. Index contour

Short Answer

14. List four methods that modern mapmakers use to make accurate maps.

15. Why is a map legend important?

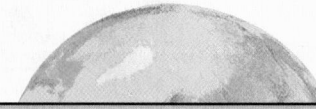

---

4. Sample answer: A cylindrical projection is a map projection made by transferring the surface of the globe onto a cylinder. An azimuthal projection is a map projection made by projecting the surface of the globe onto a plane.

5. Sample answer: Contour interval is the difference in elevation between one contour line and the next. An index contour is a darker, heavier contour line that usually occurs every fifth line.

6. Sample answer: The global positioning system is a system of satellites that send radio signals to receivers on Earth. The receivers calculate a given place's latitude, longitude, and elevation. A geographic information system is a computer system that stores data about an area in layers.

Understanding Key Ideas

7. b	11. b
8. c	12. d
9. b	13. b
10. b	

16 Why does Greenland appear so large in relation to other landmasses on a map made using a cylindrical projection?

17 What is the function of contour lines on a topographic map?

18 How can GPS help you find your location on Earth?

19 What is GIS?

20 Concept Mapping Use the following terms to create a concept map: *maps, legend, map projection, map parts, scale, cylinder, title, cone, plane, date,* and *compass rose.*

21 Making Inferences One of the important parts of a map is its date. Why is the date important?

22 Analyzing Ideas Why is it important for maps to have scales?

23 Applying Concepts Imagine that you are looking at a topographic map of the Grand Canyon. Would the contour lines be spaced close together or far apart? Explain your answer.

24 Analyzing Processes How would a GIS system help a team of engineers plan a new highway system for a city?

25 Making Inferences If you were stranded in a national park, what kind of map of the park would you want to have with you? Explain your answer.

INTERPRETING GRAPHICS

Use the topographic map below to answer the questions that follow.

26 What is the elevation change between two adjacent lines on this map?

27 What type of relief does this area have?

28 What surface features are shown on this map?

29 What is the elevation at the top of Ore Hill?

18. A GPS unit receives signals from a system of satellites and then calculates the latitude and longitude of your location.

19. GIS is a computerized system that allows a user to enter different types of information about an area, this information is then stored in layers.

Critical Thinking

20.  An answer to this exercise can be found at the end of this book.

21. Sample answer: A date on a map is important because the Earth's surface is constantly changing. The date shows you how old the information is.

22. Sample answer: It is important that maps have scales because a map scale allows the user to determine distances on the map.

23. Sample answer: A topographic map of the Grand Canyon would show contour lines close together, indicating steep slopes.

24. Sample answer: A GIS system would allow the team of engineers to access information about current roads and streets, as well as power lines, sewer lines, natural features, and any other information they may need when building a highway.

25. Sample answer: I would want to have a topographic map because this type of map shows the relief of the area rather than only roads and streets.

14. Modern mapmakers use satellite and radar technology, GPS, and GIS to make accurate maps.

15. A map legend is important because it defines the set of symbols used in the map.

16. Greenland appears large on a map created with a cylindrical projection because of distortion. Maps created with a cylindrical projection are increasingly distorted as the distance from the equator increases.

17. Contour lines on a topographic map show the elevation, the relief, and the shape of landforms.

CHAPTER RESOURCES

Chapter Resource File

- Chapter Review GENERAL
- Chapter Test A GENERAL
- Chapter Test B ADVANCED
- Chapter Test C SPECIAL NEEDS
- Vocabulary Activity GENERAL

Workbooks

Study Guide
- Study Guide is also available in Spanish.

Interpreting Graphics

26. 20 ft

27. It has very large relief.

28. Answers may vary. Sample answer: Two hills are shown on this map.

29. 2,025 ft

Teacher's Notes

To provide practice under more realistic conditions, give students 20 minutes to answer all of the questions in this Standardized Test Preparation.

Answer Key

Question	Answer
1	C
2	D
3	A
4	C
5	C
6	B
7	D
8	C
9	D
10	D
11	B
12	*
13	*

*See Test Doctor.

Multiple Choice

1. **Which of the following shapes most accurately represents Earth?**

   A. a cone

   B. a plane

   C. a sphere

   D. a pyramid

2. **Which of the following types of projections is best for determining distance on a map?**

   A. azimuthal projection

   B. conic projection

   C. cylindrical projection

   D. equal-area projection

3. **Which of the following types of projections shows increasing distortion as you move away from the poles?**

   A. azimuthal projection

   B. conic projection

   C. cylindrical projection

   D. equal-area projection

4. **Which of the following types of projections shows increasing distortion as you move away from the equator?**

   A. azimuthal projection

   B. conic projection

   C. cylindrical projection

   D. equal-area projection

Use the table below to answer question 5.

	Scale
Map A	1 cm = 0.5 mile
Map B	1 cm = 25 miles
Map C	1 cm = 250 miles

5. **Ayanna is using Map B to plan a trip from her house in Cleveland, Ohio, to another location. Based on the map's scale, for which of the following trips would Map B be most useful?**

   A. to go to a restaurant 4 miles away

   B. to go to a mall 10 miles away

   C. to go to a stadium 75 miles away

   D. to go to a university 2530 miles away

6. **Which of the following observations led the ancient Greeks to think that Earth was a sphere?**

   A. Winds and ocean currents travel in curved paths over Earth's surface.

   B. A ship sinks below the horizon as it sails into the distance.

   C. Gravity keeps the moon in orbit around Earth.

   D. High tides occur on the side of Earth facing the moon.

7. **Topographic maps are primarily used to show which of the following features?**

   A. the shapes of continents and oceans

   B. lines of latitude and longitude

   C. highways and other roads

   D. the shape and size of surface features

✚ TEST DOCTOR

Question 1 A: A cone is a three-dimensional figure with one vertex and one circular base. B: A plane is a flat surface that extends forever. C: Correct. D: A pyramid has a polygonal base and triangular sides that all meet at a common vertex.

Question 2 A: Distance is distorted on an azimuthal projection. Little distortion occurs at the plane's point of contact, but distortion of distance increases away from the point of contact. B: A conic projection is least distorted along the line of latitude where the cone touches the globe, but distortion of distance

increases away from the point of contact. C: On a cylindrical projection, lines of latitude are spaced farther apart as you move farther north and south of the equator, which distorts distance. D: Correct.

Question 3 A: Correct. B: On conic projections, distortion occurs along all lines of latitude other than the line of latitude that touches the cone. C: A cylindrical projection shows increasing distortion as you move away from the equator, toward the poles. D: The shapes of continents and oceans are distorted on an equal-area projection.

Question 4 A: An azimuthal projection shows increasing distortion as you move away from the

8. Lines that connect points of equal elevation on topographic maps are called

   A. index contours.

   B. contour intervals.

   C. contour lines.

   D. relief.

9. Which of the following statements regarding contour lines on topographic maps is true?

   A. Contour lines that are far apart show a steep slope.

   B. If a stream flows through a valley, the V of a contour line points downstream.

   C. The highest point of a hill or mountain is shown by a contour line.

   D. All points along a contour line represent equal elevation.

Use the map below to answer question 10.

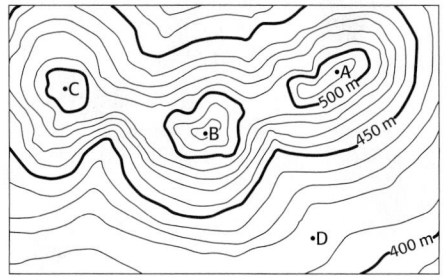

10. Which of the points on the topographic map has the lowest elevation?

   A. point A

   B. point B

   C. point C

   D. point D

11. Which of the following types of information would GIS be most likely to store?

   A. the location of boundary lines

   B. a city's infrastructure

   C. navigation at sea or in the air

   D. navigation across a state

Open Response

12. An area that has one of the highest earthquake risks in the country might surprise you: It's the New Madrid seismic zone that is almost in the center of the country. An earthquake there will immediately affect southeast Missouri, the southern tip of Illinois, northeast Arkansas, and parts of Tennessee and Kentucky. In which layer of the Earth do earthquakes occur? What structures in the layer cause many earthquakes?

13. The coordinates of Frankfort, Kentucky, are 38°, 12 minutes North latitude and 84°, 52 minutes West longitude. Carson City, Nevada, is about 55° west of Frankfort. Each degree of latitude is about 69 miles. At the equator, each degree of longitude is also about 69 miles. At the coordinates of Frankfort, which distance is greater, 55° of longitude or 55° of latitude? Why?

one contour line and the next. C: Correct. D: Relief is the difference in elevation between the highest and lowest points of a mapped area.

Question 9 A: Contour lines that are far apart show a gentle slope. B: If a stream flows through a valley, the V of a contour line points upstream. C: Because the top of a hill or mountain is a single point, this location cannot be a contour line. D: Correct.

Question 10 A: The elevation at point A is 510 m. B: The elevation at point B is 520 m. C: The elevation at point C is 500 m. D: Correct.

Question 11 A: GPS would be useful for obtaining information about the location for boundary lines. B: Correct. C: GPS would be useful for obtaining information about navigation at sea and in the air. D: GPS can be used.

Question 12 Full-credit answers should include the following points:

- Earthquakes occur in the outermost layer, the crust.
- The crust is made up of hard, brittle rock that does not bend or flow easily.
- Faults, or cracks, occur in the rock of the crust.
- Many earthquakes are caused by the movements of these faults.

Question 13 Full-credit answers should include the following points:

- The distance in miles for 55° of latitude is greater at Frankfort than 55° of longitude.
- The parallel lines of latitude are always the same distance apart —approximately 69 miles.
- The lines of longitude are not the same distance apart because they originate at the poles.
- Frankfort, Kentucky, is more than 38° north of the equator, or more than 2600 miles north.
- The closer the measurement is to either pole, the closer together the lines of longitude will be.
- Therefore, each degree of longitude is less than 69 miles.

poles, toward the equator. B: In conic projections, distortion occurs along all lines of latitude other than the line of latitude that touches the cone. C: Correct. D: The shapes of continents and oceans are distorted on an equal-area projection.

Question 5 A, B: The larger scale of Map A would be more useful for these trips. C: Correct. D: This trip requires a map with a smaller scale—Map C.

Question 6 A: Gustave-Gaspard Coriolis first described the Coriolis effect in 1835, after the time of the ancient Greeks. B: Correct C: Sir Isaac Newton's law of universal gravitation was published in 1687, after the time of the ancient Greeks. D: Sir Isaac

Newton's equilibrium theory of tides was published in 1687, after the time of the ancient Greeks.

Question 7 A: Globes are used to show the shapes of continents and oceans. B: Lines of longitude and latitude may be present on topographic maps, but they are used to show location and direction on Earth. C: Highways and other roads may be shown on topographic maps, but they are not the main focus of topographic maps. D: Correct.

Question 8 A: An index contour is a darker, heavier contour line that is usually every fifth line and is labeled by elevation. B: A contour interval is the difference in elevation between

Science, Technology, and Society

ACTiViTY ——————— **GENERAL**

If you have access to a GPS unit, try taking your class on a geo-cache treasure hunt. You can find geocaches posted at many different sites on the Internet. Simply enter in the keyword *geocaching*. Choose a geocache that is relatively easy to find. You may want to find the cache first before taking your class with you to ensure that the cache is still there and that your students can safely access the area.

Scientific Discoveries

Background

According to legend, Allah became displeased with the wickedness of the citizens of Ubar and buried the city under a wave of sand. Ubar was lost for millennia until filmmaker Nicholas Clapp, NASA scientist Dr. Ronald Blom, and a team of explorers uncovered the ruins in 1991.

Discussion ——————— **GENERAL**

Discuss with students the myth of the lost city of Atlantis. Have students suggest different ways that archeologists might search for a city that was covered by water instead of by sand.

Science in Action

Scientific Discoveries

The Lost City of Ubar

According to legend, the city of Ubar was a prosperous ancient city. Ubar was most famous for its frankincense, a tree sap that had many uses. As Ubar was in its decline, however, something strange happened. The city disappeared! It was a great myth that Ubar was swallowed up by the desert. It wasn't until present-day scientists used information from a Shuttle Imaging Radar system aboard the space shuttle that this lost city was found! Using radar, scientists were able to "see" beneath the huge dunes of the desert, where they finally found the lost city of Ubar.

Roads appear as purple lines on this computer-generated remote-sensing image.

Science, Technology, and Society

Geocaching

Wouldn't it be exciting to go on a hunt for buried treasure? Thousands of people around the world participate in geocaching, which is an adventure game for GPS users. In this adventure game, individuals and groups of people put caches, or hidden treasures, in places all over the world. Once the cache is hidden, the coordinates of the cache's location are posted on the Internet. Then, geocaching teams compete to find the cache. Geocaching should only be attempted with parental supervision.

Language Arts ACTiViTY

Why was the word *geocaching* chosen for this adventure game? Use the Internet or another source to find the origin and meaning of the word *geocaching*.

Social Studies ACTiViTY

WRITING SKILL Ubar was once a very wealthy, magnificent city. Its riches were built on the frankincense trade. Research the history of frankincense, and write a paragraph describing how frankincense was used in ancient times and how it is used today.

Answer to Language Arts Activity

The word *geocaching* comes from the Greek root *geo*, meaning "Earth," and the word *cache*, which is a type of hiding place for money, food, or other necessities.

Answer to Social Studies Activity

Sample answer: Frankincense was used to treat illnesses and disguise body odor. Ancient civilizations from Rome to India treasured frankincense. Today, frankincense is used mainly as an incense or an herbal scent in some commercial products.

People in Science

Matthew Henson

Arctic Explorer Matthew Henson was born in Maryland in 1866. His parents were freeborn sharecroppers. When Henson was a young boy, his parents died. He then went to look for work as a cabin boy on a ship. Several years later, Henson had traveled around the world and had become educated in the areas of geography, history, and mathematics. In 1898, Henson met U.S. Naval Lieutenant Robert E. Peary. Peary was the leader of Arctic expeditions between 1886 and 1909.

Peary asked Henson to accompany him as a navigator on several trips, including trips to Central America and Greenland. One of Peary's passions was to be the first person to reach the North Pole. It was Henson's vast knowledge of mathematics and carpentry that made Peary's trek to the North Pole possible. In 1909, Henson was the first person to reach the North Pole. Part of Henson's job as navigator was to drive ahead of the party and blaze the first trail. As a result, he often arrived ahead of everyone else. On April 6, 1909, Henson reached the approximate North Pole 45 minutes ahead of Peary. Upon his arrival, he exclaimed, "I think I'm the first man to sit on top of the world!"

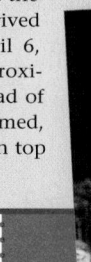

Math ACTiViTY

On the last leg of their journey, Henson and Peary traveled 664.5 km in 16 days! On average, how far did Henson and Peary travel each day?

To learn more about these Science in Action topics, visit go.hrw.com and type in the keyword HZ5MAPF.

Current Science Check out Current Science® articles related to this chapter by visiting go.hrw.com. Just type in the keyword HZ5CS02.

Answer to Math Activity
664.5 km ÷ 16 days = 41.53 km/day.

People in Science

Background

Apart from enduring subfreezing temperatures, sudden snowstorms, and slow starvation, Peary's team had to deal with the unique conditions of ice sheets that cover the Arctic Ocean. Movements of water currents under the ice cause constant changes on its surface. These changes include "pressure ridges," or small, steep mountains of ice that well up on the surface, and "leads," or open lanes of water caused from drifts or rents in the ice. Twice, Henson saved Peary's life by pulling him out of the freezing water of a suddenly formed lead.

ACTiViTY ———— GENERAL

The Explorers Club has been an international meeting place for explorers and scientists since 1904. Some of the most famous and influential field researchers in the world have been invited to join its ranks. Have students research past members of this organization. Then, have them plot on a map all the places these members have explored or discovered. (Students will find that some of the famous members of the Explorers Club include Tenzing Norgay and Sir Edmund Hillary, the first people to climb Mount Everest, Theodore Roosevelt, 26th President and founding member, Roald Amundsen, the first to reach the South Pole and sail the Northwest Passage, Herbert Hoover, 34th President, and Richard Byrd, the first aviator to fly over the Antarctic.)

Minerals of the Earth's Crust
Chapter Planning Guide

Compression guide: To shorten instruction because of time limitations, omit the Chapter Lab.

OBJECTIVES	LABS, DEMONSTRATIONS, AND ACTIVITIES	TECHNOLOGY RESOURCES
PACING • 90 min pp. 222–227 **Chapter Opener**	SE **Start-up Activity**, p. 223 `GENERAL`	OSP **Parent Letter** ■ CD **Student Edition on CD-ROM** CD **Guided Reading Audio CD** ■ TR **Chapter Starter Transparency*** VID **Brain Food Video Quiz**
Section 1 What Is a Mineral? • Describe the structure of minerals. • Describe the two major groups of minerals.	TE **Group Activity** Identifying Minerals, p. 224 ◆ `GENERAL` TE **Group Activity** Mineral Identification, p. 225 `GENERAL` SE **Science in Action** Math, Social Studies, and Language Arts Activities, pp. 244–245 `GENERAL`	OSP **Lesson Plans** (also in print) TR **Bellringer Transparency***
PACING • 90 min pp. 228–231 **Section 2 Identifying Minerals** • Identify seven ways to determine the identity of minerals. • Explain special properties of minerals.	TE **Group Activity** Mineral Classification, p. 228 `GENERAL` TE **Connection Activity** Real World, p. 229 ◆ `GENERAL` SE **Quick Lab** Scratch Test, p. 230 `GENERAL` CRF **Datasheet for Quick Lab*** SE **Skills Practice Lab** Is It Fool's Gold?—A Dense Situation, p. 238 `GENERAL` CRF **Datasheet for Chapter Lab*** SE **Skills Practice Lab** Mysterious Minerals, p. 715 `GENERAL` CRF **Datasheet for LabBook***	OSP **Lesson Plans** (also in print) TR **Bellringer Transparency*** TR *LINK TO **PHYSICAL SCIENCE*** P8 The Three Major Categories of Elements* TR **E6 Mohs' Hardness Scale*** TR **E7 Special Properties of Some Minerals*** CRF **SciLinks Activity*** `GENERAL` VID **Lab Videos for Earth Science**
PACING • 45 min pp. 232–237 **Section 3 The Formation, Mining, and Use of Minerals** • Describe the environments in which minerals form. • Compare the two types of mining. • Describe two ways to reduce the effects of mining. • Describe different uses for metallic and nonmetallic minerals.	TE **Connection Activity** History, p. 233 `GENERAL` SE **School-to-Home Activity** Recycling Minerals at Home, p. 235 `GENERAL` TE **Connection Activity** Life Science, p. 236 `GENERAL` LB **Long-Term Projects & Research Ideas** What's Yours is Mined* `ADVANCED`	OSP **Lesson Plans** (also in print) TR **Bellringer Transparency*** SE **Internet Activity**, p. 233 `GENERAL`

PACING • 90 min

CHAPTER REVIEW, ASSESSMENT, AND STANDARDIZED TEST PREPARATION

CRF **Vocabulary Activity*** `GENERAL`
SE **Chapter Review**, pp. 240–241 `GENERAL`
CRF **Chapter Review*** ■ `GENERAL`
CRF **Chapter Tests A*** ■ `GENERAL`, **B*** `ADVANCED`, **C*** `SPECIAL NEEDS`
SE **Standardized Test Preparation**, pp. 242–245 `GENERAL`
CRF **Standardized Test Preparation*** `GENERAL`
CRF **Performance-Based Assessment*** `GENERAL`
OSP **Test Generator, Test Item Listing**

Online and Technology Resources

 Holt Online Learning

Visit go.hrw.com for access to Holt Online Learning, or enter the keyword **HS7 Home** for a variety of free online resources.

 One-Stop Planner® CD-ROM

This CD-ROM package includes:
• Lab Materials QuickList Software
• Holt Calendar Planner
• Customizable Lesson Plans
• Printable Worksheets
• ExamView® Test Generator
• Interactive Teacher's Edition
• Holt PuzzlePro®
• Holt PowerPoint® Resources

SKILLS DEVELOPMENT RESOURCES	SECTION REVIEW AND ASSESSMENT	CORRELATIONS
SE Pre-Reading Activity, p. 222 `GENERAL` **OSP** Science Puzzlers, Twisters & Teasers `GENERAL`		National Science Education Standards UCP 5; SAI 1
CRF Directed Reading A* ■ `BASIC`, B* `SPECIAL NEEDS` **WB** Workbook* `Struggling Readers` **CRF** Vocabulary and Section Summary* ■ `GENERAL` **SE** Reading Strategy Paired Summarizing, p. 224 `GENERAL` **TE** Support for English Language Learners, p. 225 **SE** Connection to Biology Magnetic, p. 226 `GENERAL` **TE** Inclusion Strategies, p. 226 ◆ **CRF** Reinforcement Worksheet Mystery Mineral* `BASIC` **CRF** Reinforcement Worksheet The Mineral Quiz Show* `BASIC`	**TE** Homework, p. 224 `GENERAL` **SE** Reading Checks, pp. 225, 226 `GENERAL` **TE** Reteaching, p. 226 `BASIC` **TE** Quiz, p. 226 `GENERAL` **TE** Alternative Assessment, p. 226 `GENERAL` **SE** Section Review,* p. 227 ■ `GENERAL` **CRF** Section Quiz* ■ `GENERAL`	UCP 1, 5
CRF Directed Reading A* ■ `BASIC`, B* `GENERAL` **WB** Workbook* `Struggling Readers` **CRF** Vocabulary and Section Summary* ■ `GENERAL` **SE** Reading Strategy Reading Organizer, p. 228 `GENERAL` **TE** Support for English Language Learners, p. 229 **MS** Math Skills for Science Percentages, Fractions, and Decimals* `GENERAL`	**SE** Reading Checks, pp. 229, 230 `GENERAL` **TE** Reteaching, p. 230 `BASIC` **TE** Quiz, p. 230 `GENERAL` **TE** Alternative Assessment, p. 230 `GENERAL` **SE** Section Review,* p. 231 ■ `GENERAL` **CRF** Section Quiz* ■ `GENERAL`	UCP 1, 5; SAI 1 *Chapter Lab:* SAI 1, 2 *LabBook:* SAI 1
CRF Directed Reading A* ■ `BASIC`, B* `SPECIAL NEEDS` **WB** Workbook* `Struggling Readers` **CRF** Vocabulary and Section Summary* ■ `GENERAL` **SE** Reading Strategy Discussion, p. 232 `GENERAL` **SE** Math Practice Surface Coal Mining, p. 234 `GENERAL` **TE** Inclusion Strategies, p. 233 **TE** Support for English Language Learners, p. 235 **CRF** Critical Thinking Mineral Hunt* `ADVANCED`	**SE** Reading Checks, pp. 235, 237 `GENERAL` **TE** Reteaching, p. 236 `BASIC` **TE** Quiz, p. 236 `GENERAL` **TE** Alternative Assessment, p. 236 `GENERAL` **SE** Section Review,* p. 237 ■ `GENERAL` **CRF** Section Quiz* ■ `GENERAL`	UCP 5; SAI 1; SPSP 2, 4

SCi LINKS. NSTA

www.scilinks.org

Maintained by the **National Science Teachers Association.** See Chapter Enrichment pages that follow for a complete list of topics.

Current Science®

Check out *Current Science* articles and activities by visiting the HRW Web site at **go.hrw.com.** Just type in the keyword **HZ5CS03T**.

Classroom Videos

• **Lab Videos** demonstrate the chapter lab.
• **Brain Food Video Quizzes** help students review the chapter material.

Classroom CD-ROMs

• **Guided Reading Audio CD** (Also in Spanish)
• **Interactive Explorations**
• **Virtual Investigations**
• **Visual Concepts**
• **Science Tutor**

Holt Lab Generator CD-ROM

Search for any lab by topic, standard, difficulty level, or time. Edit any lab to fit your needs, or create your own labs. Use the Lab Materials QuickList software to customize your lab materials list.

Visual Resources

CHAPTER STARTER TRANSPARENCY

BELLRINGER TRANSPARENCIES

TEACHING TRANSPARENCIES

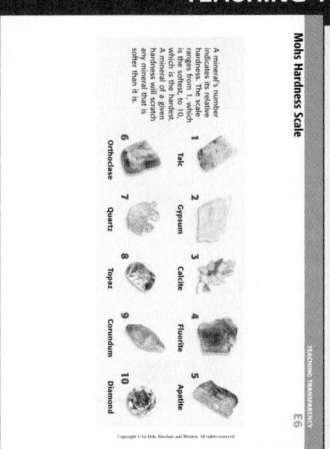

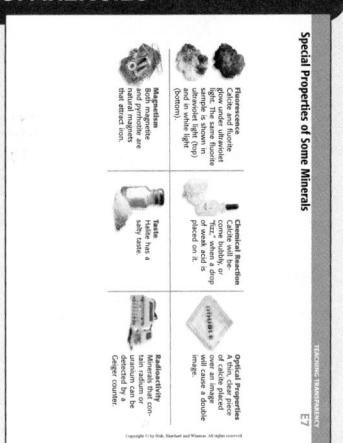

TEACHING TRANSPARENCIES

CONCEPT MAPPING TRANSPARENCY

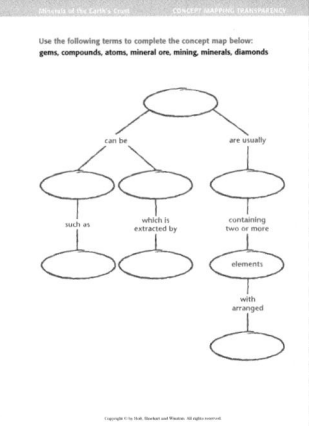

Planning Resources

LESSON PLANS

PARENT LETTER

TEST ITEM LISTING

One-Stop Planner® CD-ROM

This CD-ROM includes all of the resources shown here and the following time-saving tools:

- *Lab Materials QuickList Software*
- *Customizable lesson plans*
- *Holt Calendar Planner*
- *The powerful ExamView® Test Generator*

Meeting Individual Needs

DIRECTED READING A

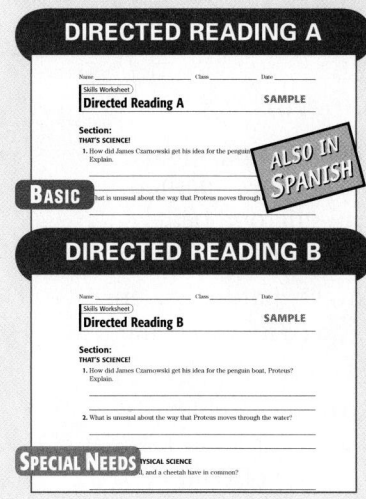

BASIC · ALSO IN SPANISH

DIRECTED READING B

SPECIAL NEEDS

VOCABULARY ACTIVITY

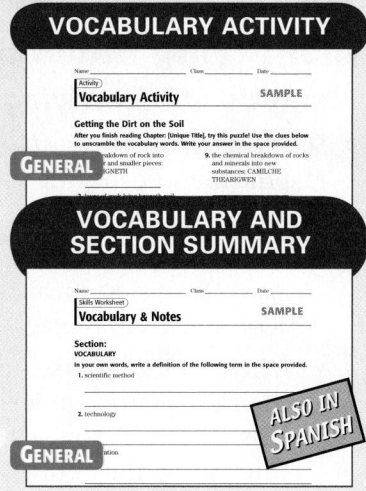

GENERAL

VOCABULARY AND SECTION SUMMARY

GENERAL · ALSO IN SPANISH

REINFORCEMENT

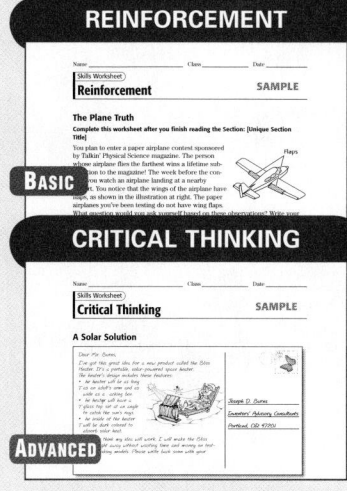

BASIC

CRITICAL THINKING

ADVANCED

SCILINKS ACTIVITY

GENERAL

SCIENCE PUZZLERS, TWISTERS & TEASERS

GENERAL

Labs and Activities

LONG-TERM PROJECTS & RESEARCH IDEAS

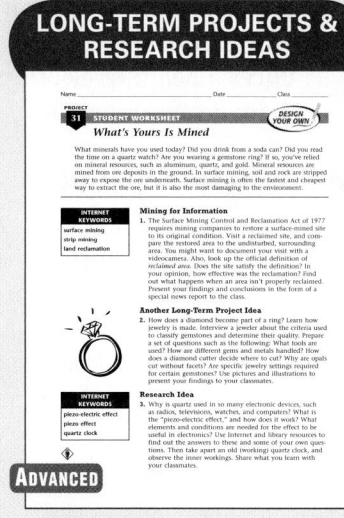

ADVANCED

DATASHEETS FOR QUICK LABS

DATASHEETS FOR CHAPTER LABS

DATASHEETS FOR LABBOOK

Review and Assessments

SECTION QUIZ

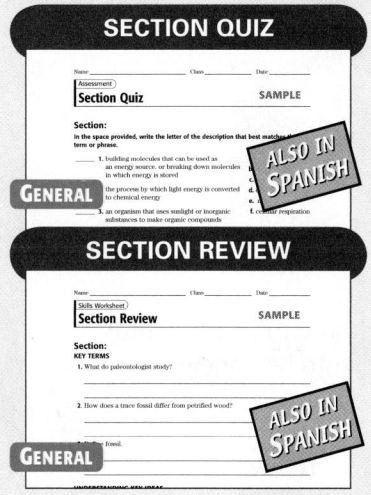

GENERAL · ALSO IN SPANISH

SECTION REVIEW

GENERAL · ALSO IN SPANISH

CHAPTER REVIEW

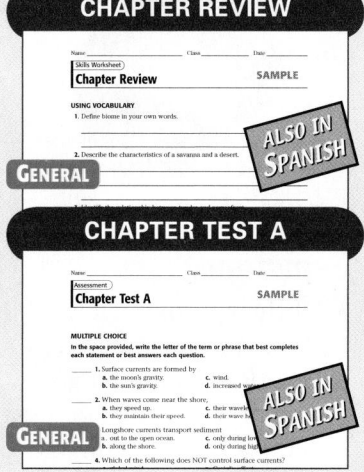

GENERAL · ALSO IN SPANISH

CHAPTER TEST A

GENERAL · ALSO IN SPANISH

CHAPTER TEST B

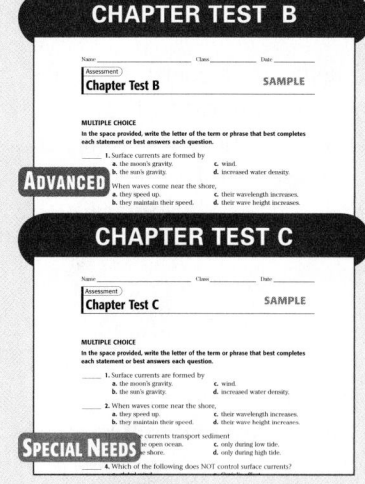

ADVANCED

CHAPTER TEST C

SPECIAL NEEDS

STANDARDIZED TEST PREPARATION

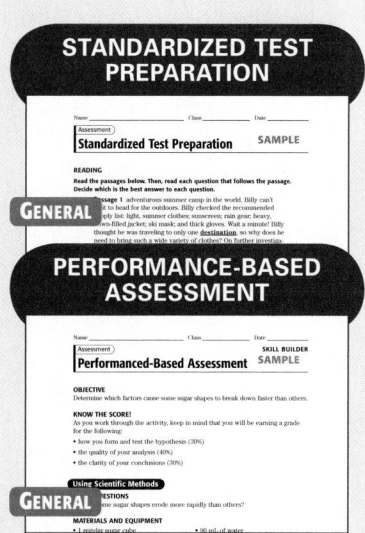

GENERAL

PERFORMANCE-BASED ASSESSMENT

GENERAL

This Chapter Enrichment provides relevant and interesting information to expand and enhance your presentation of the chapter material.

Section 1

What Is a Mineral?

Crystal Structures

- Minerals are composed of atoms that are arranged in repeating three-dimensional patterns. The basic building block of a mineral crystal is called a unit cell. A *unit cell* is the smallest three-dimensional arrangement of atoms that displays the basic form, or symmetry, of the crystal. Many unit cells stacked together form a crystal. For example, a crystal of halite is composed of unit cells of sodium and chlorine atoms arranged in a unique three-dimensional structure.

The Origins of Mineralogy

- The founder of mineralogy is considered to be Georgius Agricola. His treatise on minerals, *De Re Metallica* (1556), recorded most of what was known about minerals at that time. The science of mineralogy advanced greatly when Romé de l'Isle, a French scientist, proposed the concept of the unit cell in 1772. He argued that the characteristics of mineral crystals could be explained only if they were composed of identical unit cells organized in a predictable way. Crystals are composed of unit cells much like a wall might be composed of bricks. After that discovery, the composition of mineral crystals was actively studied by many scientists.

Industrial Uses of Crystals

- The properties of crystals make crystals useful in many ways. The electronics industry uses quartz in the manufacture of radios, watches, microphones, and sonar transducers. Rubies are used in lasers and as styluses in record players, and diamonds are used in industrial drills and saws.

Is That a Fact!

- Currently, about 4,000 minerals have been identified, and 50 to 100 new minerals are discovered each year.

Section 2

Identifying Minerals

Methods of Identifying Minerals

- Scientists usually identify minerals using a petrographic microscope, the hand-specimen method, X-ray diffraction, or an electron microprobe.

  - The hand-specimen method involves determining the color, luster, streak, cleavage, hardness, density, fluorescence, and magnetic qualities of a mineral.

  - When geologists take samples back to the lab, they often use petrographic microscopes to identify minerals. These microscopes make it easier to identify minerals by the optical properties of their crystals.

  - Geologists can analyze minerals at the atomic level by using X-ray diffraction, which measures the way crystal structures diffract X rays. The chemical composition of minerals can also be determined by using an electron microprobe. An electron microprobe produces a beam of electrons that focuses on a sample diameter that may be as small as .001 to .002 mm.

Mohs Hardness Scale

- Friedrich Mohs (1773–1839) was a mineralogist who lived in Vienna, Austria. In 1812, Mohs developed a method for identifying minerals based on their relative hardness. He proposed that a mineral's identity can be determined by comparing the mineral with several minerals of known hardness. A mineral can scratch another mineral of equal or lesser hardness, but it cannot scratch a mineral of greater hardness.

Gemstones

- Of the approximately 4,000 known minerals, only about 100 are cut and polished to become gemstones. One definition of a gemstone is any naturally occurring mineral, rock, or organic material that, when cut and polished, is suitable for use as jewelry.

- Diamond, emerald, ruby, and topaz are usually referred to as precious stones. Amethyst, garnet, and jade are considered semiprecious. Materials such as coral, pearls, and amber are also considered gemstones, even though they form by organic processes.

- Many gems used in jewelry are imitations. For example, glass can be colored green to look like an emerald. Scientists also create some gems artificially. Synthetic rubies, for example, have the same chemical structure as natural rubies. However, a gemologist can identify synthetic rubies by the presence of curved growth striations and air pockets, which do not occur in natural rubies.

Is That a Fact!

◆ The Cullinan diamond is the world's largest diamond. It was found in the Premier mine in Pretoria, Transvaal in 1905. Before being cut, the Cullinan weighed 3,106 carats, or a little more than .5 kg.

◆ The largest gold nugget ever found was the "Welcome Stranger." It had a mass of 71 kg (156.5 pounds) and was found in Australia on February 5, 1869.

Section 3

The Formation, Mining, and Use of Minerals

Ancient Mines

- The earliest evidence of mining dates to a 43,000-year-old iron mine in South Africa. Early miners were probably interested in the pigments associated with iron ores. The earliest metals used by neolithic people were probably gold and copper. Archaeological evidence indicates that the Egyptians mined copper and turquoise around 3400 BCE. Although most of the earliest mining was conducted on the surface, underground mining did occur by 1300 BCE in Africa.

Intrusions and Mineral Formation

- Plutons are intrusive bodies of igneous rock that cool beneath the Earth's surface. A large body of exposed intrusive rock (greater than 100 km²) is called a *batholith*. Large batholiths occur in British Columbia, Alaska, and in the Sierra Nevada.

- A pegmatite is a very coarse-grained intrusive rock formed from the fluid-rich magma that remains after the rest of a pluton has solidified. Pegmatites may contain minerals such as tourmaline, topaz, or beryl.

The Hope Diamond

- The Hope diamond is a 45.5-carat blue diamond owned by the Smithsonian Institution since 1958. The gem was thought to be cursed because it was allegedly stolen from a statue of the Hindu goddess Sita. Misfortune and tragedy seemed to befall those who came in contact with the stone. The fabled gem was originally 112 carats. It was sold to King Louis XIV in 1668, and named the French Blue. The French Blue was stolen in 1792 from Louis XVI and may have been depicted in an 1800 portrait of a Spanish queen. In 1830, a 45.5-carat cut diamond surfaced in London. Experts declared that it was the French Blue recut to hide its identity. The American Henry Hope bought it, and it has since been called the Hope diamond.

Is That a Fact!

◆ At 215 m deep and 1.6 km in circumference, the Kimberley Mine in Kimberley, Union of South Africa, is the largest hand-dug excavation in the world.

Overview

Tell students that this chapter will help them learn about the minerals found in the rocks of the Earth's crust. The chapter describes the structure of minerals, mineral identification, environments in which minerals form, the mining of minerals, and mineral uses.

Assessing Prior Knowledge

Students should be familiar with the following topics:

- fundamental geologic processes
- the periodic table

Identifying Misconceptions

Before teaching the material in this chapter, make sure that students understand the difference between minerals and rocks. Often, these two words are used interchangeably. Emphasize that minerals are the building blocks of rocks and that different rocks are composed of different minerals or different combinations of minerals. For example, the sedimentary rock limestone is composed mostly of calcium carbonate in the form of the mineral calcite. The igneous rock granite is composed of a combination of the minerals quartz, orthoclase, and mica, and often has accessory minerals.

9
Minerals of the Earth's Crust

The Big Idea

Minerals have characteristic physical and chemical properties that determine how each mineral is used by humans.

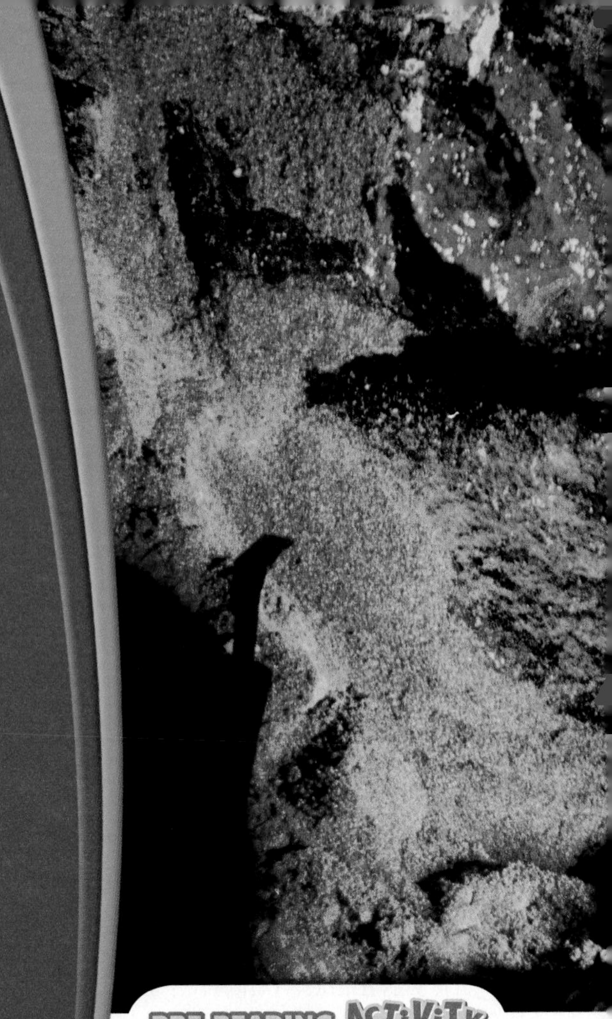

About the Photo

Fluorescence is the ability that some minerals have to glow under ultraviolet light. The beauty of mineral fluorescence is well represented at the Sterling Hill Mine in Franklin, New Jersey. In this picture taken at the mine, minerals in the rock glow as brightly as if they had been freshly painted by an artist.

PRE-READING ACTIVITY

Graphic Organizer

Concept Map Before you read the chapter, create the graphic organizer entitled "Concept Map" described in the **Study Skills** section of the Appendix. As you read the chapter, fill in the concept map with details about minerals.

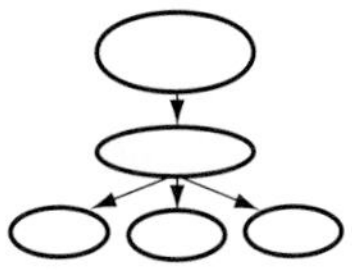

Standards Correlations

National Science Education Standards

The following codes indicate the National Science Education Standards that correlate to this chapter. The full text of the standards is at the front of the book.

Chapter Opener
SAI 1; UCP 5

Section 1 What Is a Mineral?
UCP 1, 5

Section 2 Identifying Minerals
SAI 1; UCP 1, 5; LabBook: SAI 1

Section 3 The Formation, Mining, and Use of Minerals
SAI 1; UCP 5; SPSP 2, 4

Chapter Lab
SAI 1, 2

Chapter Review
SAI 1; UCP 1, 5; SPSP 2, 4

Science in Action
HNS 1

START-UP ACTIVITY

MATERIALS

FOR EACH GROUP
• paper, notebook (one sheet)

Teacher's Notes: Make students aware that most of the materials in the classroom will be made from nonliving things. Exceptions are items that are made of wood or plant fiber and items that are made of plastic, which are made from petroleum. You may want to go further and have students attempt to differentiate between items that are made of metallic minerals and those made of nonmetallic minerals.

Answers

1. Most of the materials in the classroom will most likely be made of nonliving materials. Materials that are made of minerals include graphite in pencils, clay in paper products, metal in desks, gypsum in wallboard, silica in glass, and cement (calcite) in the concrete-slab foundation.

START-UP ACTIVITY

What Is Your Classroom Made Of?

One of the properties of minerals is that minerals are made from nonliving material. Complete the following activity to see if you can determine whether items in your classroom are made from living or nonliving materials.

Procedure

1. On a **sheet of paper,** make two columns. Label one column "Materials made from living things." Label the second column "Materials made from nonliving things."

2. Look around your classroom. Choose a variety of items to put on your list. Some items that you might select are your clothing, your desk, books, notebook paper, pencils, the classroom windows, doors, walls, the ceiling, and the floor.

3. With a partner, discuss each item that you have chosen. Decide into which column each item should be placed. Write down the reason for your decision.

Analysis

1. Are most of the items that you chose made of living or nonliving materials?

Imagine . . .

If you owned all of the jewels shown on this page, you would be a millionaire. These precious gems—diamonds, rubies, sapphires, and emeralds—are valued at anywhere from $1,000 to $50,000 per carat (1 carat = 200 mg).

however, a few handfuls of pencils will not make you rich.

Gems are valuable not because of the elements they contain but because of how their atoms are arranged. Under certain conditions, common atoms can

Chapter Starter Transparency
Use this transparency to help students begin thinking about the diversity of minerals.

CHAPTER RESOURCES

Technology

Transparencies
• Chapter Starter Transparency

READING SKILLS

Student Edition on CD-ROM

Guided Reading Audio CD
• English or Spanish

Classroom Videos
• Brain Food Video Quiz

Workbooks

Science Puzzlers, Twisters & Teasers
• Minerals of the Earth's Crust GENERAL

Focus

Overview

This section explores the nature of minerals by describing their four characteristics. Students learn that mineral crystals are generated by atomic structures, and they learn how to classify minerals into two major compositional groups—silicates and nonsilicates.

 **Bellringer**

Display a piece of pencil lead (graphite) and a photograph of a diamond. Explain that both substances are composed of carbon. Ask students to brainstorm how two substances with such different properties can form from atoms of the same element.

Motivate

Group **ACTiViTY** — **GENERAL**

Identifying Minerals Place an assortment of objects on a table. Possibilities include a piece of wood, a fossil, a piece of bone, a piece of granite, and a quartz crystal. Organize the class into groups of two or three students. Tell the students to examine the objects and to determine which ones are minerals by using the four questions in **Figure 1** on this page. **LS** Logical/Verbal

What You Will Learn

● Describe the structure of minerals.
● Describe the two major groups of minerals.

Vocabulary

mineral
element
compound
crystal
silicate mineral
nonsilicate mineral

READING STRATEGY

Paired Summarizing Read this section silently. In pairs, take turns summarizing the material. Stop to discuss ideas that seem confusing.

What Is a Mineral?

You may think that all minerals look like gems. But, in fact, most minerals look more like rocks. Does this mean that minerals are the same as rocks? Well, not really. So, what's the difference?

For one thing, rocks are made of minerals, but minerals are not made of rocks. A **mineral** is a naturally formed, inorganic solid that has a definite crystalline structure.

Mineral Structure

By answering the four questions in **Figure 1,** you can tell whether an object is a mineral. If you cannot answer "yes" to all four questions, you don't have a mineral. Three of the four questions may be easy to answer. The question about crystalline structure may be more difficult. To understand what crystalline structure is, you need to know a little about the elements that make up a mineral. **Elements** are pure substances that cannot be broken down into simpler substances by ordinary chemical means. All minerals contain one or more of the 92 naturally occurring elements.

Is it nonliving material?
A mineral is inorganic, meaning it isn't made of living things.

Is it a solid?
Minerals can't be gases or liquids.

Does it have a crystalline structure?
Minerals are crystals, which have a repeating inner structure that is often reflected in the shape of the crystal. Minerals generally have the same chemical composition throughout.

Is it formed in nature?
Crystalline materials made by people aren't classified as minerals.

Figure 1 *The answers to these four questions will determine whether an object is a mineral.*

CHAPTER RESOURCES

Chapter Resource File

 • Lesson Plan
• Directed Reading A **BASIC**
• Directed Reading B **SPECIAL NEEDS**

Technology

 Transparencies
• Bellringer

Workbooks

 Interactive Textbook Struggling Readers

Homework ——— **GENERAL**

At Home with Minerals Ask students to find four items in their home that are derived from minerals. Have them add labels to identify the minerals that are contained in different products. Have students share their findings with the class. (Examples include table salt, which is composed of halite; pencil lead, which is composed of graphite; and cooking pots, which are composed of iron, copper, or aluminum.) **LS** Visual

Atoms and Compounds

Each element is made of only one kind of atom. An *atom* is the smallest part of an element that has all the properties of that element. Like other substances, minerals are made up of atoms of one or more elements.

Most minerals are made of compounds of several different elements. A **compound** is a substance made of two or more elements that have been chemically joined, or bonded. Halite, NaCl, for example, is a compound of sodium, Na, and chlorine, Cl, as shown in **Figure 2**. A few minerals, such as gold and silver, are composed of only one element. A mineral that is composed of only one element is called a *native element*.

✓ **Reading Check** How does a compound differ from an element? (*See the Appendix for answers to Reading Checks.*)

Crystals

Solid, geometric forms of minerals produced by a repeating pattern of atoms or molecules that is present throughout the mineral are called **crystals.** A crystal's shape is determined by the arrangement of the atoms or molecules within the crystal. The arrangement of atoms or molecules in turn is determined by the kinds of atoms or molecules that make up the mineral. Each mineral has a definite crystalline structure. All minerals can be grouped into crystal classes according to the kinds of crystals they form. **Figure 3** shows how the arrangement of atoms in gold may form cubic crystals.

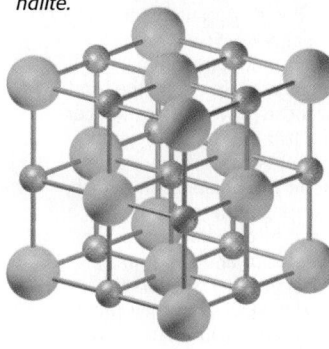

Figure 2 When atoms of sodium (purple) and chlorine (green) join, they form a compound commonly known as rock salt, or the mineral halite.

mineral a naturally formed, inorganic solid that has a definite crystalline structure

element a substance that cannot be separated or broken down into simpler substances by chemical means

compound a substance made up of atoms of two or more different elements joined by chemical bonds

crystal a solid whose atoms, ions, or molecules are arranged in a definite pattern

---

Figure 3	Composition of the Mineral Gold

The mineral gold is composed of gold atoms arranged in a crystalline structure.

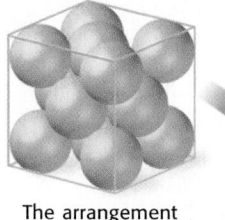

The arrangement of gold atoms

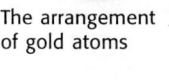

The shape of a gold crystal

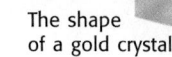

Crystals of the mineral gold

MISCONCEPTION ALERT

Crystal Form and Mineral Identification
In much the same way that color is a deceptive guide to identifying minerals, crystal form is often a misleading physical property. The unit cells of halite and gold are shown in **Figure 2** and **Figure 3**. When different unit cells are combined, however, they can generate crystal forms that look nothing like their atomic structure. A large variety of complex crystal shapes can be generated by starting with a simple polyhedron, such as a cube. For example, the mineral fluorite belongs in the isometric (cubic) class but commonly forms octahedral-shaped crystals.

Close

Reteaching — BASIC

Elements and Compounds Have students prepare a set of cards for 10 common minerals. Give students the chemical formula for each mineral, and have them write the chemical formula next to the mineral name. This exercise will reinforce the difference between minerals that are composed of a single element and minerals that are composed of multiple elements. **LS Visual**

Quiz — GENERAL

1. What is a mineral? (a naturally formed, inorganic solid that has a crystalline structure)

2. What does a crystal's shape depend on? (the arrangement of the atoms within the crystal)

Alternative Assessment — GENERAL

Classifying Minerals Write the following mineral-group names on the board: silicates, native elements, carbonates, halides, oxides, sulfates, and sulfides. Have students match the following items with the mineral group from which they are derived: a copper penny (native elements); cement (carbonates); rock salt (halides); toothpaste (sulfates); batteries (sulfides); sand (silicates). **LS Logical**

Answer to Reading Check

Answers may vary. Silicate minerals contain a combination of silicon and oxygen; nonsilicate minerals do not contain a combination of silicon and oxygen.

CONNECTION TO Biology

WRITING SKILL **Magnetite** The mineral magnetite has a special property—it is magnetic. Scientists have found that some animals' brains contain magnetite. And scientists have shown that certain fish can sense magnetic fields because of the magnetite in the brains of these fish. The magnetite gives the fish a sense of direction. Using the Internet or another source, research other animals that have magnetite in their brains. Summarize your findings in a short essay.

silicate mineral a mineral that contains a combination of silicon, oxygen, and one or more metals

nonsilicate mineral a mineral that does not contain compounds of silicon and oxygen

---

Two Groups of Minerals

The most common classification of minerals is based on chemical composition. Minerals are divided into two groups based on their chemical composition. These groups are the silicate minerals and the nonsilicate minerals.

Silicate Minerals

Silicon and oxygen are the two most common elements in the Earth's crust. Minerals that contain a combination of these two elements are called **silicate minerals.** Silicate minerals make up more than 90% of the Earth's crust. The rest of the Earth's crust is made up of nonsilicate minerals. Silicon and oxygen usually combine with other elements, such as aluminum, iron, magnesium, and potassium, to make up silicate minerals. Some of the more common silicate minerals are shown in **Figure 4.**

Nonsilicate Minerals

Minerals that do not contain a combination of the elements silicon and oxygen form a group called the **nonsilicate minerals.** Some of these minerals are made up of elements such as carbon, oxygen, fluorine, and sulfur. **Figure 5** on the following page shows the most important classes of nonsilicate minerals.

✔️ **Reading Check** How do silicate minerals differ from nonsilicate minerals?

Figure 4   Common Silicate Minerals

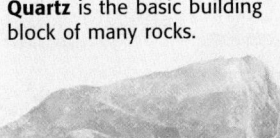

Quartz is the basic building block of many rocks.

Feldspar minerals are the main component of most rocks on the Earth's surface.

Mica minerals separate easily into sheets when they break. Biotite is one of several kinds of mica.

INCLUSION Strategies

- *Learning Disabilities*
- *Developmentally Delayed*

Organize students into pairs or groups of three. Give each group some common mineral samples. Pass out paint sample strips from a hardware store, and have students identify each mineral's color. Students should record their observations in their **science journal.** Next, hand out materials that serve as examples of luster. A candle could demonstrate waxy luster, and a jar top is an example of metallic luster. Have students use these examples to determine the luster of each mineral sample. The teams should perform all of the mineral tests in a similar way and share their findings with the class. **LS Visual/Kinesthetic**   English Language Learners

---

Figure 5 Classes of Nonsilicate Minerals

Native elements are minerals that are composed of only one element. Some examples are copper, Cu, gold, Au, and silver, Ag. Native elements are used in communications and electronics equipment.

Copper

Oxides are compounds that form when an element, such as aluminum or iron, combines chemically with oxygen. Oxide minerals are used to make abrasives, aircraft parts, and paint.

Corundum

Carbonates are minerals that contain combinations of carbon and oxygen in their chemical structure. We use carbonate minerals in cement, building stones, and fireworks.

Calcite

Sulfates are minerals that contain sulfur and oxygen, SO_4. Sulfates are used in cosmetics, toothpaste, cement, and paint.

Gypsum

Halides are compounds that form when fluorine, chlorine, iodine, or bromine combine with sodium, potassium, or calcium. Halide minerals are used in the chemical industry and in detergents.

Fluorite

Sulfides are minerals that contain one or more elements, such as lead, iron, or nickel, combined with sulfur. Sulfide minerals are used to make batteries, medicines, and electronic parts.

Galena

SECTION Review

Summary

- A mineral is a naturally formed, inorganic solid that has a definite crystalline structure.
- Minerals may be either elements or compounds.
- Mineral crystals are solid, geometric forms that are produced by a repeating pattern of atoms.
- Minerals are classified as either silicate minerals or nonsilicate minerals based on the elements of which they are composed.

Using Key Terms

1. In your own words, write a definition for each of the following terms: *element, compound,* and *mineral.*

Understanding Key Ideas

2. Which of the following minerals is a nonsilicate mineral?
   a. mica
   b. quartz
   c. gypsum
   d. feldspar

3. What is a crystal, and what determines a crystal's shape?

4. Describe the two major groups of minerals.

Math Skills

5. If there are approximately 3,600 known minerals and about 20 of the minerals are native elements, what percentage of all minerals are native elements?

Critical Thinking

6. **Applying Concepts** Explain why each of the following is not considered a mineral: water, oxygen, honey, and teeth.

7. **Applying Concepts** Explain why scientists consider ice to be a mineral.

8. **Making Comparisons** In what ways are sulfate and sulfide minerals the same. In what ways are they different?

SCI LINKS®

NSTA

Developed and maintained by the National Science Teachers Association

For a variety of links related to this chapter, go to www.scilinks.org

Topic: Gems
SciLinks code: HSM0640

Focus

Overview

In this section, students will learn common techniques used to identify minerals. They will also examine some of the interesting properties of minerals, such as fluorescence, radioactivity, and magnetism.

🎵 Bellringer

Show students a variety of mineral samples. Have students list as many phrases as they can to describe each sample. Have students organize these phrases into categories. Students can use these categories to determine whether or not each sample is a different mineral.

Motivate

Group **ACTIVITY** — GENERAL

Mineral Classification Have students develop a classification system for minerals based on observable physical properties. Give groups a variety of minerals or photographs of minerals. Students should create a classification system based on observable differences and similarities between the samples. After the groups have developed a classification system, give them several new samples. Have them place the samples in their classification scheme.

LS Visual/Logical

What You Will Learn

● Identify seven ways to determine the identity of minerals.
● Explain special properties of minerals.

Vocabulary

luster	fracture
streak	hardness
cleavage	density

READING STRATEGY

Reading Organizer As you read this section, create an outline of the section. Use the headings from the section in your outline.

---

luster the way in which a mineral reflects light

Identifying Minerals

If you closed your eyes and tasted different foods, you could probably determine what the foods are by noting properties such as saltiness or sweetness. You can also determine the identity of a mineral by noting different properties.

In this section, you will learn about the properties that will help you identify minerals.

Color

The same mineral can come in a variety of colors. For example, in its purest state quartz is clear. Samples of quartz that contain various types of and various amounts of impurities, however, can be a variety of colors.

Besides impurities, other factors can change the appearance of minerals. The mineral pyrite, often called fool's gold, normally has a golden color. But if pyrite is exposed to air and water for a long period, it can turn brown or black. Because of factors such as impurities, color usually is not the best way to identify a mineral.

Luster

The way a surface reflects light is called **luster.** When you say an object is shiny or dull, you are describing its luster. Minerals have metallic, submetallic, or nonmetallic luster. If a mineral is shiny, it has a metallic luster. If the mineral is dull, its luster is either submetallic or nonmetallic. The different types of lusters are shown in **Figure 1.**

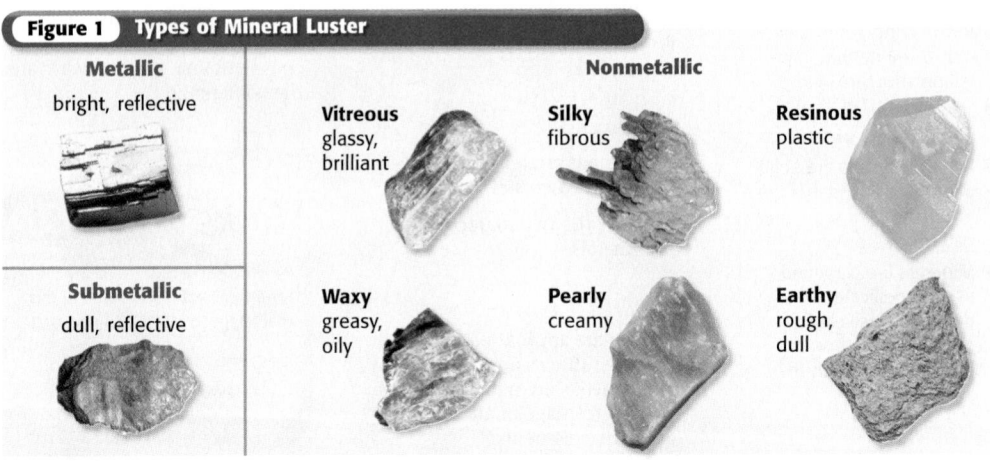

Figure 1 Types of Mineral Luster

Metallic
bright, reflective

Submetallic
dull, reflective

Nonmetallic

Vitreous glassy, brilliant

Silky fibrous

Resinous plastic

Waxy greasy, oily

Pearly creamy

Earthy rough, dull

CHAPTER RESOURCES

Chapter Resource File

- • Lesson Plan
- • Directed Reading A BASIC, B SPECIAL NEEDS

Technology

- Transparencies
  - • Bellringer
  - • *LINK TO PHYSICAL SCIENCE* P8 The Three Major Categories of Elements

Workbooks

- Interactive Textbook Struggling Readers

- Math Skills for Science
  - • Percentages, Fractions, and Decimals GENERAL

⚛ WEIRD SCIENCE

How can you tell a real diamond from a fake? A gem specialist uses specialized tools to distinguish real diamonds from impostors. But there are some tests that even an untrained person can conduct. One of the simplest tests is to try to pick up the stone in question with a moistened fingertip. Diamonds can be picked up this way; most other stones cannot.

Streak

The color of a mineral in powdered form is called the mineral's **streak**. A mineral's streak can be found by rubbing the mineral against a piece of unglazed porcelain called a *streak plate*. The mark left on the streak plate is the streak. The streak is a thin layer of powdered mineral. The color of a mineral's streak is not always the same as the color of the mineral sample. The difference between color and streak is shown in **Figure 2.** Unlike the surface of a mineral sample, the streak is not affected by air or water. For this reason, using streak is more reliable than using color in identifying a mineral.

✓ Reading Check Why is using streak more reliable in identifying a mineral than using color is? (*See the Appendix for answers to Reading Checks.*)

Figure 2 *The color of the mineral hematite may vary, but hematite's streak is always red-brown.*

Cleavage and Fracture

Different types of minerals break in different ways. The way a mineral breaks is determined by the arrangement of its atoms. **Cleavage** is the tendency of some minerals to break along smooth, flat surfaces. **Figure 3** shows the cleavage patterns of the minerals mica and halite.

Fracture is the tendency of some minerals to break unevenly along curved or irregular surfaces. One type of fracture is shown in **Figure 4.**

streak the color of the powder of a mineral

cleavage the splitting of a mineral along smooth, flat surfaces

fracture the manner in which a mineral breaks along either curved or irregular surfaces

Figure 3 *Cleavage varies with mineral type.*

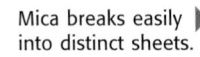

Mica breaks easily into distinct sheets. ▶

Halite breaks at 90° angles in three directions. ▼

Figure 4 *This sample of quartz shows a curved fracture pattern called* conchoidal fracture *(kahn KOYD uhl FRAK chuhr).*

Answer to Reading Check
A mineral's streak is not affected by air or water, but a mineral's color may be affected by air or water.

CONNECTION ACTIVITY
Real World ———— GENERAL

Class Visit Invite a jeweler to visit the class, and ask the jeweler to explain how gemstones are made into jewelry. The jeweler could bring in visual aids to help students understand how gems are located, mined, and prepared for commercial use.
LS Visual

Close

Reteaching — BASIC

Mnemonics Have students create a mnemonic device that will help them learn the Mohs hardness scale. One example is **T**errible **G**iants **C**an **F**ind **A**lligators **O**r **Q**uaint **T**igers **C**onveniently **D**igestible. This will help students remember the minerals in order of hardness: talc, gypsum, calcite, fluorite, apatite, orthoclase, quartz, topaz, corundum, and diamond. **LS** Auditory

Quiz — GENERAL

1. Why is color not always a reliable way of identifying a mineral? (Factors such as weathering and the inclusion of impurities can affect the mineral's color.)

2. What property do minerals that glow under ultraviolet light display? (fluorescence)

Alternative Assessment — GENERAL

Mineral Identification Cards
Have students prepare mineral identification cards for some of the most common minerals. They can list the words color, luster, hardness, streak, cleavage and fracture, and density on each card. For each card, ask them to fill in the properties of a common mineral. Students should write the name of the mineral on the back of the card and use the cards as study aids or assessment tools. **LS** Visual

---

Figure 5 Mohs Hardness Scale

A mineral's number indicates its relative hardness. The scale ranges from 1, which is the softest, to 10, which is the hardest. A mineral of a given hardness will scratch any mineral that is softer than it is.

1 Talc 2 Gypsum 3 Calcite 4 Fluorite 5 Apatite
6 Orthoclase 7 Quartz 8 Topaz 9 Corundum 10 Diamond

hardness a measure of the ability of a mineral to resist scratching

density the ratio of the mass of a substance to the volume of the substance

Scratch Test
1. You will need a **penny**, a **pencil**, and your **fingernail**. Which one of these three materials is the hardest?
2. Use your fingernail to try to scratch the graphite at the tip of a pencil.
3. Now try to scratch the penny with your fingernail.
4. Rank the three materials in order from softest to hardest.

Hardness

A mineral's resistance to being scratched is called **hardness**. To determine the hardness of minerals, scientists use *Mohs hardness scale*, shown in **Figure 5**. Notice that talc has a rating of 1 and diamond has a rating of 10. The greater a mineral's resistance to being scratched is, the higher the mineral's rating is. To identify a mineral by using Mohs scale, try to scratch the surface of a mineral with the edge of one of the 10 reference minerals. If the reference mineral scratches your mineral, the reference mineral is harder than your mineral.

✓ **Reading Check** How would you determine the hardness of an unidentified mineral sample?

Density

If you pick up a golf ball and a table-tennis ball, which will feel heavier? Although the balls are of similar size, the golf ball will feel heavier because it is denser. **Density** is the measure of how much matter is in a given amount of space. In other words, density is a ratio of an object's mass to its volume. Density is usually measured in grams per cubic centimeter. Because water has a density of 1 g/cm^3, it is used as a reference point for other substances. The ratio of an object's density to the density of water is called the object's *specific gravity*. The specific gravity of gold, for example, is 19. So, gold has a density of 19 g/cm^3. In other words, 1 cm^3 of gold contains 19 times as much matter than 1 cm^3 of water contains.

Answer to Reading Check

Scratch the mineral with a series of 10 reference minerals. If the reference mineral scratches the unidentified mineral, the reference mineral is harder than the unidentified mineral.

MATERIALS

FOR EACH GROUP
• pencil
• penny

Answers

4. The mineral graphite is the softest material of the three, followed by the fingernail and, then, the penny.

Special Properties

Some properties are particular to only a few types of minerals. The properties shown in **Figure 6** can help you quickly identify the minerals shown. To identify some properties, however, you will need specialized equipment.

Figure 6 Special Properties of Some Minerals

Fluorescence
Calcite and fluorite glow under ultraviolet light. The same fluorite sample is shown in ultraviolet light (top) and in white light (bottom).

Chemical Reaction
Calcite will become bubbly, or "fizz," when a drop of weak acid is placed on it.

Optical Properties
A thin, clear piece of calcite placed over an image will cause a double image.

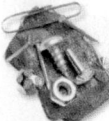
Magnetism
Both magnetite and pyrrhotite are natural magnets that attract iron.

Taste
Halite has a salty taste.

Radioactivity
Minerals that contain radium or uranium can be detected by a Geiger counter.

SECTION Review

Summary

- Properties that can be used to identify minerals are color, luster, streak, cleavage, fracture, hardness, and density.
- Some minerals can be identified by special properties they have, such as taste, magnetism, fluorescence, radioactivity, chemical reaction, and optical properties.

Using Key Terms

1. Use each of the following terms in a separate sentence: *luster, streak,* and *cleavage.*

Understanding Key Ideas

2. Which of the following properties of minerals is expressed in numbers?
   a. fracture
   b. cleavage
   c. hardness
   d. streak

3. How do you determine a mineral's streak?

4. Briefly describe the special properties of minerals.

Math Skills

5. If a mineral has a specific gravity of 5.5, how much more matter is there in 1 cm^3 of this mineral than in 1 cm^3 of water?

Critical Thinking

6. **Applying Concepts** What properties would you use to determine whether two mineral samples are different minerals?

7. **Applying Concepts** If a mineral scratches calcite but is scratched by apatite, what is the mineral's hardness?

8. **Analyzing Methods** What would be the easiest way to identify calcite?

SCiLINKS®
NSTA
Developed and maintained by the National Science Teachers Association

For a variety of links related to this chapter, go to www.scilinks.org

Topic: Identifying Minerals
SciLinks code: HSM0782

CHAPTER RESOURCES

Chapter Resource File

- Section Quiz GENERAL
- Section Review GENERAL
- Vocabulary and Section Summary GENERAL
- Datasheet for Quick Lab
- SciLinks Activity GENERAL

Technology

Transparencies
- E6 Mohs Hardness Scale
- E7 Special Properties of Some Minerals

SECTION
3

Focus

Overview

This section discusses how minerals form deep within Earth's crust and how they form at or close to the Earth's surface. Students will learn about different techniques used to mine minerals. This section concludes with a discussion of the value of mineral resources and the importance of environmentally responsible mining and reclamation.

🔊 Bellringer

Show students a mineral resource map of your state. Have students locate mines that are closest to where they live and discuss the mineral commodities that are mined at these locations.

Motivate

Discussion ——— GENERAL

Simulating a Gold Rush To simulate the excitement of the gold rush of 1849, make up a flyer that tells of a rich gold deposit found in a nearby area. Make copies, and pass them out to students. Have students discuss their reactions to such an announcement. Then, discuss the chaotic enthusiasm of the gold rush. Note that from 1848 to 1860, the population in California grew from 14,000 to 380,000 people! **LS** Visual/Verbal

What You Will Learn

● Describe the environments in which minerals form.
● Compare the two types of mining.
● Describe two ways to reduce the effects of mining.
● Describe different uses for metallic and nonmetallic minerals.

Vocabulary

ore
reclamation

READING STRATEGY

Discussion Read this section silently. Write down questions that you have about this section. Discuss your questions in a small group.

The Formation, Mining, and Use of Minerals

If you wanted to find a mineral, where do you think you would look?

Minerals form in a variety of environments in the Earth's crust. Each of these environments has a different set of physical and chemical conditions. Therefore, the environment in which a mineral forms determines the mineral's properties. Environments in which minerals form may be on or near the Earth's surface or deep beneath the Earth's surface.

Limestones Surface water and ground-water carry dissolved materials into lakes and seas, where they crystallize on the bottom. Minerals that form in this environment include calcite and dolomite.

Evaporating Salt Water When a body of salt water dries up, minerals such as gypsum and halite are left behind. As the salt water evaporates, these minerals crystallize.

Metamorphic Rocks When changes in pressure, temperature, or chemical makeup alter a rock, *metamorphism* takes place. Minerals that form in metamorphic rock include calcite, garnet, graphite, hematite, magnetite, mica, and talc.

CHAPTER RESOURCES

Chapter Resource File

• Lesson Plan
• Directed Reading A **BASIC**
• Directed Reading B **SPECIAL NEEDS**

Technology

Transparencies
• Bellringer

Workbooks

Interactive Textbook Struggling Readers

WEIRD SCIENCE

Some of the greatest untapped sources of minerals are hydrothermal vents deep under the sea. These hydrothermal vents are called *black smokers* because they spew out hot, mineral-rich water that is almost black. As the hot water mixes with the cool ocean water, minerals crystallize on the ocean floor. But no one has found an economical way to mine them yet.

INTERNET ACTIVITY

For another activity related to this chapter, go to go.hrw.com and type in the keyword **HZ5MINW**.

Hot-Water Solutions
Groundwater works its way downward and is heated by magma. It then reacts with minerals to form a hot liquid solution. Dissolved metals and other elements crystallize out of the hot fluid to form new minerals. Gold, copper, sulfur, pyrite, and galena form in such hot-water environments.

Pegmatites As magma moves upward, it can form teardrop-shaped bodies called *pegmatites.* The mineral crystals in pegmatites become extremely large, sometimes growing to several meters across! Many gemstones, such as topaz and tourmaline, form in pegmatites.

Plutons As magma rises upward through the crust, it sometimes stops moving before it reaches the surface and cools slowly, forming millions of mineral crystals. Eventually, the entire magma body solidifies to form a *pluton.* Mica, feldspar, magnetite, and quartz are some of the minerals that form from magma.

Teach

CONNECTION ACTIVITY
History ———————— GENERAL

The History of Mining Communities

Encourage students to learn more about the social and environmental effects of mining by having each student create a scrapbook detailing the history of a mining community. Students should research the history of a community from the discovery of ore to the present. Students' scrapbooks should include drawings and photographs showing changes in the community as well as text describing the history of the area. Have students focus on the types of ore extracted, the use and value of the ore in the world market, and the impact mining has had on the people and environment of the area. Possible communities include the following: Bodie, California; Calico, California; Johannesburg, California; Randsburg, California; Bullfrog, Nevada; Goldfield, Nevada; Manhattan, Nevada; Rhyolite, Nevada; Tonopah, Nevada; Silver City, Utah; Bisbee, Arizona; Gleeson, Arizona; Silverbell, Arizona; Tombstone, Arizona; Kelly, New Mexico; Terlingua, Texas; Leadville, Colorado; Butte, Montana; and the Yanomami Indian tribes of Brazil and Venezuela. Have students share their scrapbooks with the class. **LS** Visual/Intrapersonal

INCLUSION Strategies

- **Learning Disabled**
- **Attention Deficit Disorder**
- **Behavior Control Issues**

Organize students into small teams to play a mineral quiz game. Each team should choose a category that relates to a heading in the section and write five questions and answers for the category on separate index cards. The difficulty and point value of the questions should increase incrementally. Review each team's questions and answers before you start the game. If a team cannot answer a question, the team should work with another team to answer the question. If teams cooperate, they should share the points earned. When the game is over, hand out a review sheet that contains the questions and answers. **LS** Interpersonal

English Language Learners

Debate ———————— GENERAL

Surface Versus Subsurface Mining Tell the class that both surface and subsurface mining have positive and negative aspects. Divide the class into two groups. Assign each group a type of mining, and ask the students in the groups to list the advantages of their type of mining. Also have the groups list the disadvantages of the other group's type of mining. Then, have the groups debate their points. (Some advantages of surface mining include that miners are safer when working above ground and have easier access to ore. On the other hand, surface mining alters the landscape and has a greater potential for contaminating the environment. Subsurface mining does not necessarily affect the landscape, and with this type of mining, it is easier to contain potentially harmful wastes. However, subsurface mining has a greater potential for miners to be trapped underground and has the possibility of underground fires and explosions.) Ask each student to write a brief summary of his or her team's viewpoint. Students should include reasons they personally agree or disagree with the opinion. **LS** Verbal/Interpersonal
Co-op Learning

Surface Coal Mining

Producing 1 metric ton of coal requires that up to 30 metric tons of earth be removed first. Some surface coal mines produce up to 50,000 metric tons of coal per day. How many metric tons of earth might have to be removed in order to mine 50,000 metric tons of coal?

ore a natural material whose concentration of economically valuable minerals is high enough for the material to be mined profitably

Mining

Many kinds of rocks and minerals must be mined to extract the valuable elements they contain. Geologists use the term **ore** to describe a mineral deposit large enough and pure enough to be mined for profit. Rocks and minerals are removed from the ground by one of two methods—surface mining or subsurface mining. The method miners choose depends on how close to the surface or how far down in the Earth the mineral is located.

Surface Mining

When mineral deposits are located at or near the surface of the Earth, surface-mining methods are used to remove the minerals. Types of surface mines include open pits, surface coal mines, and quarries.

Open-pit mining is used to remove large, near-surface deposits of economically important minerals such as gold and copper. As shown in **Figure 1,** ore is mined downward, layer by layer, in an open-pit mine. Explosives are often used to break up the ore. The ore is then loaded into haul trucks and transported from the mine for processing. Quarries are open pits that are used to mine building stone, crushed rock, sand, and gravel. Coal that is near the surface is removed by surface coal mining. Surface coal mining is sometimes known as strip mining because the coal is removed in strips that may be as wide as 50 m and as long as 1 km.

Figure 1 *In open-pit mines, the ore is mined downward in layers. The stair-step excavation of the walls keeps the sides of the mine from collapsing. Giant haul trucks (inset) are used to transport ore from the mine.*

 GENERAL

The Empire of Great Zimbabwe The mining of gold, copper, and iron in southeastern Africa helped build the empire of Great Zimbabwe, which arose during the mid-thirteenth century and lasted until about the middle of the fifteenth century. Invite students to find out more about mining techniques in Great Zimbabwe and about the Karanga people who ruled the empire. **LS** Logical

Mining on Other Planets Some scientists speculate that there are valuable deposits of minerals on other bodies in our solar system. Ask students to think about what issues should be considered before staking claims and mining other planets.

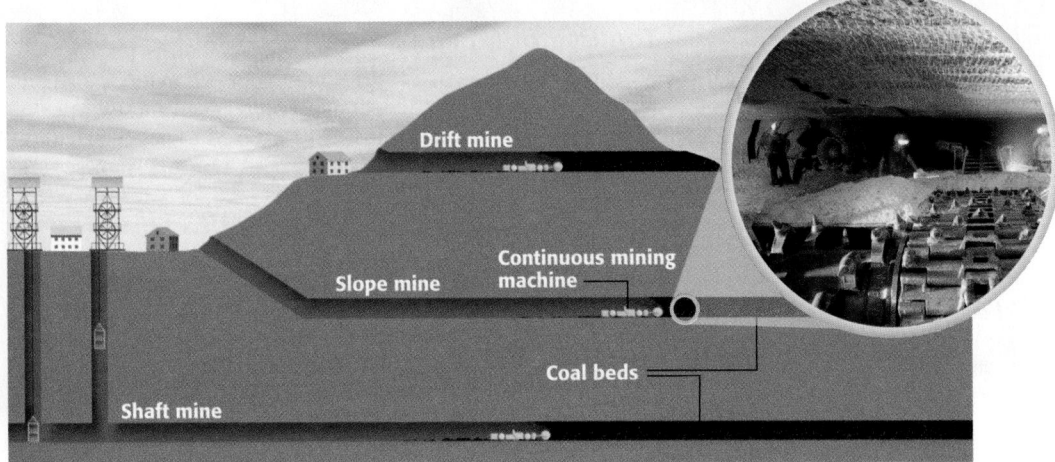

Drift mine

Slope mine

Continuous mining machine

Coal beds

Shaft mine

Subsurface Mining

Subsurface mining methods are used when mineral deposits are located too deep within the Earth to be surface mined. Subsurface mining often requires that passageways be dug into the Earth to reach the ore. As shown in **Figure 2,** these passageways may be dug horizontally or at an angle. If a mineral deposit extends deep within the Earth, however, a vertical shaft is sunk. This shaft may connect a number of passageways that intersect the ore at different levels.

✔ **Reading Check** Compare surface and subsurface mining. *(See the Appendix for answers to Reading Checks.)*

Responsible Mining

Mining gives us the minerals we need, but it may also create problems. Mining can destroy or disturb the habitats of plants and animals. Also, the waste products from a mine may get into water sources, which pollutes surface water and groundwater.

Mine Reclamation

One way to reduce the potential harmful effects of mining is to return the land to its original state after the mining is completed. The process by which land used for mining is returned to its original state or better is called **reclamation.** Reclamation of mined public and private land has been required by law since the mid-1970s. Another way to reduce the effects of mining is to reduce our need for minerals. We reduce our need for minerals by recycling many of the mineral products that we currently use, such as aluminum.

Figure 2 *Subsurface mining is the removal of minerals or other materials from deep within the Earth. Passageways must be dug underground to reach the ore. Machines such as continuous mining machines (inset) are used to mine ore in subsurface mines.*

reclamation the process of returning land to its original condition after mining is completed

Recycling Minerals at Home

With a parent or guardian, locate products in your home that are made of minerals. Decide which of these products could be recycled. In your **science journal,** make a list of the products that could be recycled to save minerals.

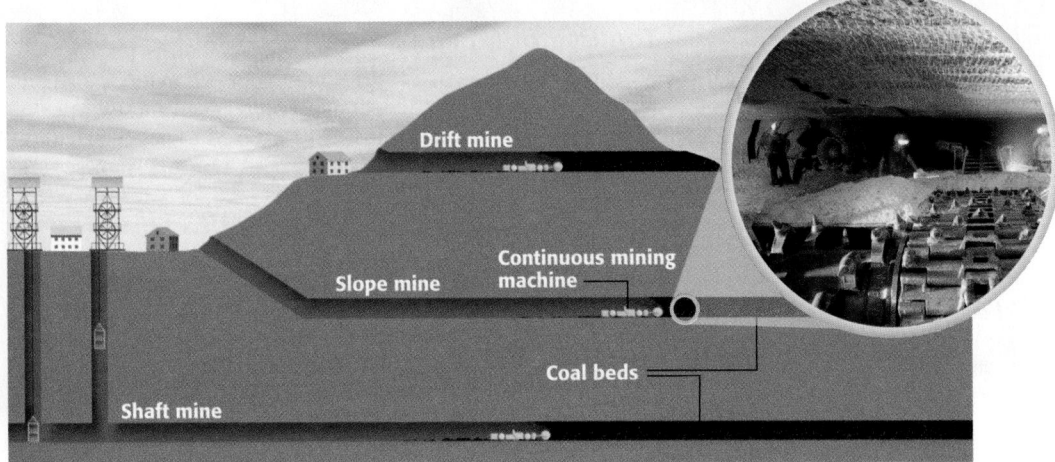
SUPPORT FOR

English Language Learners

Mine Reclamation Visual aids help students articulate complex ideas. Therefore, download "before mining" and "after reclamation" photos of reclaimed mines from around the world from the Internet. Have pairs of students compare what they see in the photos for each site and, then, describe how the land has changed over time. Ask students to summarize their observations in short paragraphs. Identify errors in their writing, and ask students to correct and resubmit their work. **LS Visual/Verbal**

CONNECTION to Real Life ——— GENERAL

Mineral Collecting Mineral collecting is a popular pastime for many people around the world. The practitioners are commonly referred to as "rockhounds." The tools of the mineral-collecting trade include pickaxes, sledgehammers, pry bars, chisels, hand lenses, and paint brushes. Mineral collectors are often members of local mineralogical societies. Contact a mineralogical society that is located near you, and find out if one of its members can speak to your class about different aspects of mineralogy.

MISCONCEPTION ///ALERT\\\

What Is a Carat? The mass of a gem is measured using a unit called the *carat*. This should not be confused with the karat used to measure the purity of gold. A 1-carat diamond crystal has a mass of 200 mg. This is approximately the same as the mass of one children's aspirin. A 1-karat gold nugget is 1/24 pure gold.

Reteaching — BASIC

Concept Mapping Have students make a concept map in their **science journal** of one mining process discussed in this section. Make sure students include each step in the mining process. The first step should be the search for mineral or ore deposits. The final step should include information about the products that are manufactured from the mineral and information about the cleanup of the mine wastes. **LS** Visual

Quiz — GENERAL

1. List three minerals that form in metamorphic rock. (sample answers: garnet, mica, and talc)

2. What is ore? (mineral deposits large enough and pure enough to be mined for profit)

3. How can mining cause water pollution? (The waste products from a mine can introduce toxic concentrations of elements into rivers, lakes, and groundwater.)

Alternative Assessment — GENERAL

Designing a Spacecraft Tell students to design a spacecraft that will carry astronauts to another planet in our solar system. Have students create a diagram of their spacecraft that includes labels that indicate the minerals used to make the spacecraft. **LS** Logical

Table 1	Common Uses of Minerals
Mineral	**Uses**
Copper	electrical wire, plumbing, coins
Diamond	jewelry, cutting tools, drill bits
Galena	batteries, ammunition
Gibbsite	cans, foil, appliances, utensils
Gold	jewelry, computers, spacecraft, dentistry
Gypsum	wallboards, plaster, cement
Halite	nutrition, highway de-icer, water softener
Quartz	glass, computer chips
Silver	photography, electronics products, jewelry
Sphalerite	jet aircraft, spacecraft, paints

The Use of Minerals

As shown in **Table 1,** some minerals are of major economic and industrial importance. Some minerals can be used just as they are. Other minerals must be processed to get the element or elements that the minerals contain. **Figure 3** shows some processed minerals used to make the parts of a bicycle.

Metallic Minerals

Some minerals are metallic. Metallic minerals have shiny surfaces, do not let light pass through them, and are good conductors of heat and electricity. Metallic minerals can be processed into metals that are strong and do not rust. Other metals can be pounded or pressed into various shapes or stretched thinly without breaking. These properties make metals desirable for use in aircraft, automobiles, computers, communications and electronic equipment, and spacecraft. Examples of metallic minerals that have many industrial uses are gold, silver, and copper.

Nonmetallic Minerals

Other minerals are nonmetals. Nonmetallic minerals have shiny or dull surfaces, may let light pass through them, and are good insulators of electricity. Nonmetallic minerals are some of the most widely used minerals in industry. For example, calcite is a major component of concrete, which is used in building roads, buildings, bridges, and other structures. Industrial sand and gravel, or silica, have uses that range from glassmaking to producing computer chips.

Figure 3 Some Materials Used in the Parts of a Bicycle

Handlebars
titanium from ilmenite

Frame
aluminum from bauxite

Spokes
iron from magnetite

Pedals
beryllium from beryl

CONNECTION ACTIVITY
Life Science — GENERAL

The SEAM Project The Surface Environment and Mining (SEAM) program was established by the U.S. Forest Service in 1973 to address the issue of land reclamation in the wake of mining operations. Since then, this highly successful program has returned vast areas of land formerly used for mining to its original condition. The most recent SEAM projects can be researched on the Internet. To research local reclamation efforts, students could contact mining companies and local conservation groups listed in the phone directory. **LS** Logical

Gemstones

Some nonmetallic minerals, called *gemstones*, are highly valued for their beauty and rarity rather than for their usefulness. Important gemstones include diamond, ruby, sapphire, emerald, aquamarine, topaz, and tourmaline. An example of a diamond is shown in **Figure 4.** Color is the most important characteristic of a gemstone. The more attractive the color is, the more valuable the gem is. Gemstones must also be durable. That is, they must be hard enough to be cut and polished. The mass of a gemstone is expressed in a unit known as a *carat*. One carat is equal to 200 mg.

✔ *Reading Check* In your own words, define the term *gemstone*.

Figure 4 *The Cullinan diamond, at the center of this scepter, is part of the largest diamond ever found.*

SECTION
Review

Summary

- Environments in which minerals form may be located at or near the Earth's surface or deep below the surface.

- The two types of mining are surface mining and subsurface mining.

- Two ways to reduce the effects of mining are the reclamation of mined land and the recycling of mineral products.

- Some metallic and nonmetallic minerals have many important economic and industrial uses.

Using Key Terms

Complete each of the following sentences by choosing the correct term from the word bank.

ore   reclamation

1. _____ is the process of returning land to its original condition after mining is completed.

2. _____ is the term used to describe a mineral deposit that is large enough and pure enough to be mined for profit.

Understanding Key Ideas

3. Which of the following conditions is NOT important in the formation of minerals?
   a. presence of groundwater
   b. evaporation
   c. volcanic activity
   d. wind

4. What are the two main types of mining, and how do they differ?

5. List some uses of metallic minerals.

6. List some uses of nonmetallic minerals.

Math Skills

7. A diamond cutter has a raw diamond that weighs 19.5 carats and from which two 5-carat diamonds will be cut. How much did the raw diamond weigh in milligrams? How much will each of the two cut diamonds weigh in milligrams?

Critical Thinking

8. **Analyzing Ideas** How does reclamation protect the environment around a mine?

9. **Applying Concepts** Suppose you find a mineral crystal that is as tall as you are. What kinds of environmental factors would cause such a crystal to form?

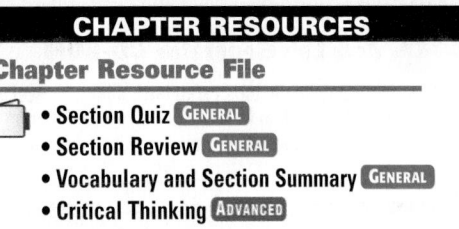

For a variety of links related to this chapter, go to www.scilinks.org

Topic: Mining Minerals
SciLinks code: HSM0968

SCiLINKS®
NSTA
Developed and maintained by the National Science Teachers Association

Answer to Reading Check

CHAPTER RESOURCES

Chapter Resource File

- • Section Quiz `GENERAL`
- • Section Review `GENERAL`
- • Vocabulary and Section Summary `GENERAL`
- • Critical Thinking `ADVANCED`

Is It Fool's Gold? A Dense Situation

Teacher's Notes

Time Required

One 45-minute class period

Lab Ratings

EASY ———————————— HARD

Teacher Prep 🧪🧪
Student Set-Up 🧪🧪🧪
Concept Level 🧪🧪
Clean Up 🧪🧪

MATERIALS

Materials listed on the student page are sufficient for a group of 2 to 4 students. If your mineral samples are small, the change in volume may be difficult to detect. In that case, replace the beaker in steps 7–10 with a graduated cylinder.

Safety Caution

Remind students to review all safety cautions and icons before beginning this lab activity.

Preparation Notes

Students may need to review the concepts of density and specific gravity prior to performing this activity.

Using Scientific Methods
Skills Practice Lab

Is It Fool's Gold? A Dense Situation

Have you heard of fool's gold? Maybe you've seen a piece of it. This mineral is actually pyrite, and it was often passed off as real gold. However, there are simple tests that you can do to keep from being tricked. Minerals can be identified by their properties. Some properties, such as color, vary from sample to sample. Other properties, such as density and specific gravity, remain consistent across samples. In this activity, you will try to verify the identity of some mineral samples.

OBJECTIVES

Calculate the density and specific gravity of a mineral.

Explain how density and specific gravity can be used to identify a mineral specimen.

MATERIALS

- balance
- beaker, 400 mL
- galena sample
- pyrite sample
- ring stand
- spring scale
- string
- water, 400 mL

SAFETY

Ask a Question

1️⃣ How can I determine if an unknown mineral is not gold or silver?

Form a Hypothesis

2️⃣ Write a hypothesis that is a possible answer to the question above. Explain your reasoning.

Test the Hypothesis

3️⃣ Copy the data table. Use it to record your observations.

Observation Chart		
Measurement	Galena	Pyrite
Mass in air (g)		
Weight in air (N)		
Volume of mineral (mL)	DO NOT WRITE IN BOOK	
Weight in water (N)		

4️⃣ Find the mass of each sample by laying the mineral on the balance. Record the mass of each sample in your data table.

5️⃣ Attach the spring scale to the ring stand.

6️⃣ Tie a string around the sample of galena, and leave a loop at the loose end. Suspend the galena from the spring scale, and find its mass and weight in air. Do not remove the sample from the spring scale yet. Enter these data in your data table.

Galena

Pyrite

Holt Lab Generator CD-ROM

Search for any lab by topic, standard, difficulty level, or time. Edit any lab to fit your needs, or create your own labs. Use the Lab Materials QuickList software to customize your lab materials list.

Norman Holcomb
Marion Local Schools
Maria Stein, Ohio

CLASSROOM TESTED & APPROVED

CHAPTER RESOURCES

Chapter Resource File

 • Datasheet for Chapter Lab
• Lab Notes and Answers

Technology

 Classroom Videos
• Lab Video

 LabBook
• Mysterious Minerals

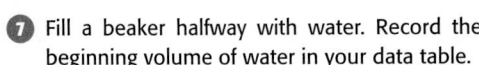

7 Fill a beaker halfway with water. Record the beginning volume of water in your data table.

8 Carefully lift the beaker around the galena until the mineral is completely submerged. Be careful not to splash any water out of the beaker! Do not allow the mineral to touch the beaker.

9 Record the new volume and weight in your data table.

10 Subtract the original volume of water from the new volume to find the amount of water displaced by the mineral. This is the volume of the mineral sample itself. Record this value in your data table.

11 Repeat steps 6—10 for the sample of pyrite.

Analyze the Results

1 **Constructing Tables** Copy the data table below. (Note: 1 mL = 1 cm³)

Density Data Table		
Mineral	**Density (g/cm³)**	**Specific gravity**
Silver	10.5	10.5
Galena	DO NOT WRITE IN BOOK	
Pyrite		
Gold	19.0	19.0

2 **Organizing Data** Use the following equations to calculate the density and specific gravity of each mineral, and record your answers in your data table.

$$density = \frac{mass\ in\ air}{volume}$$

$$specific\ gravity = \frac{weight\ in\ air}{weight\ in\ air - weight\ in\ water}$$

Draw Conclusions

3 **Drawing Conclusions** The density of pure gold is 19 g/cm³. How can you use this information to prove that your sample of pyrite is not gold?

4 **Drawing Conclusions** The density of pure silver is 10.5 g/cm³. How can you use this information to prove that your sample of galena is not silver?

5 **Applying Conclusions** If you found a gold-colored nugget, how could you find out if the nugget was real gold or fool's gold?

Analyze the Results

2.

Mineral	Density (g/cm³)	Specific gravity
Silver	10.5	10.5
Galena	7.4 to 7.6	7.4 to 7.6
Pyrite	5.0	5.0
Gold	19.0	19.0

Lab Notes

• Density is conventionally described as g/cm³, not g/mL.

• Because specific gravity is the ratio of a substance's density to the density of water (1 g/cm³), the value will be the same for density. The difference is that specific gravity is a number, and density is a number with the units grams per cubic centimeter (g/cm³).

• Because of impurities, the density of some minerals is given in ranges. The density of pure gold is 19.0 g/cm³; lower numbers indicate the presence of impurities. The density of pure silver is 10.5 g/cm³; depending on impurities, that number can be higher or lower.

• Ideally, the values for specific gravity and density obtained in this lab will be identical. Discrepancies will likely result from differences in precision. Students should learn that all scientific measurements involve some margin of error.

Draw Conclusions

3. Because the density of the sample is not 19.0 g/cm³, the sample is not gold.

4. Because the density of the sample is not 10.5 g/cm³, the sample is not pure silver. (The sample could contain silver mixed with other minerals.)

5. Sample answer: You could find the density and specific gravity of the nugget. If it was pure gold, the density would be 19.0 g/cm³ and the specific gravity would be 19.0, but you would have to perform more tests. If the sample had a density of 5.0 g/cm³ and a specific gravity of 5.0, then it would likely be pyrite (fool's gold).

Chapter Review

Assignment Guide

Section	Questions
1	1, 4, 6, 8, 12, 19
2	2, 5, 7, 16, 18–20, 22–25
3	9–11, 13–15, 21
1 and 3	3

ANSWERS

Using Key Terms

1. Sample answer: An element is a pure substance that cannot be broken into simpler substances by normal chemical means. A compound is a substance made of two or more bonded elements. A mineral is an inorganic solid that formed naturally and has a crystalline structure.

2. Sample answer: Streak is the color of a mineral in powdered form. The color of a mineral may change due to air or water, but the mineral's streak is always the same.

3. Sample answer: A mineral is a naturally formed, inorganic solid with a crystalline structure. An ore is a deposit of minerals that is large enough and pure enough to be mined for a profit.

4. Sample answer: Silicate minerals contain compounds of silicon and oxygen; nonsilicate minerals do not contain compounds of silicon and oxygen.

USING KEY TERMS

1. Use each of the following terms in a separate sentence: *element, compound,* and *mineral.*

For each pair of terms, explain how the meanings of the terms differ.

2. *color* and *streak*

3. *mineral* and *ore*

4. *silicate mineral* and *nonsilicate mineral*

UNDERSTANDING KEY IDEAS

Multiple Choice

5. Which of the following properties of minerals does Mohs scale measure?
   a. luster
   b. hardness
   c. density
   d. streak

6. Pure substances that cannot be broken down into simpler substances by ordinary chemical means are called
   a. molecules.
   b. elements.
   c. compounds.
   d. crystals.

7. Which of the following properties is considered a special property that applies to only a few minerals?
   a. luster
   b. hardness
   c. taste
   d. density

8. Silicate minerals contain a combination of the elements
   a. sulfur and oxygen.
   b. carbon and oxygen.
   c. iron and oxygen.
   d. silicon and oxygen.

9. The process by which land used for mining is returned to its original state is called
   a. recycling.
   b. regeneration.
   c. reclamation.
   d. renovation.

10. Which of the following minerals is an example of a gemstone?
    a. mica
    b. diamond
    c. gypsum
    d. copper

Short Answer

11. Compare surface and subsurface mining.

12. Explain the four characteristics of a mineral.

13. Describe two environments in which minerals form.

14. List two uses for metallic minerals and two uses for nonmetallic minerals.

15. Describe two ways to reduce the effects of mining.

16. Describe three special properties of minerals.

Understanding Key Ideas

5. b
6. b
7. c
8. d
9. c
10. b
11. Surface mining is used to mine mineral deposits that are at or near the Earth's surface. Subsurface mining is used to mine mineral deposits that are too deep in the Earth to be surface mined.

12. A mineral is inorganic, meaning its origin is not living things. A mineral is a solid, not a liquid or gas. A mineral is formed in nature and is not made by people. A mineral has a crystalline structure and has the same chemical structure throughout.

13. Sample answer: Two environments in which minerals form are plutons, in which a magma body solidifies before it reaches the Earth's surface, and hot-water solutions, from which dissolved metals and other elements crystallize out of a hot fluid to form minerals.

CRITICAL THINKING

17. Concept Mapping Use the following terms to create a concept map: *minerals, calcite, silicate minerals, gypsum, carbonates, nonsilicate minerals, quartz,* and *sulfates.*

18. Making Inferences Imagine that you are trying to determine the identity of a mineral. You decide to do a streak test. You rub the mineral across the streak plate, but the mineral does not leave a streak. Has your test failed? Explain your answer.

19. Applying Concepts Why would cleavage be important to gem cutters, who cut and shape gemstones?

20. Applying Concepts Imagine that you work at a jeweler's shop and someone brings in some gold nuggets for sale. You are not sure if the nuggets are real gold. Which identification tests would help you decide whether the nuggets are gold?

21. Identifying Relationships Suppose you are in a desert. You are walking across the floor of a dry lake, and you see crusts of cubic halite crystals. How do you suppose the halite crystals formed? Explain your answer.

INTERPRETING GRAPHICS

The table below shows the temperatures at which various minerals melt. Use the table below to answer the questions that follow.

Melting Points of Various Minerals	
Mineral	**Melting Point (°C)**
Mercury	−39
Sulfur	+113
Halite	801
Silver	961
Gold	1,062
Copper	1,083
Pyrite	1,171
Fluorite	1,360
Quartz	1,710
Zircon	2,500

22. According to the table, what is the approximate difference in temperature between the melting points of the mineral that has the lowest melting point and the mineral that has the highest melting point?

23. Which of the minerals listed in the table do you think is a liquid at room temperature?

24. Pyrite is often called *fool's gold.* Using the information in the table, how could you determine if a mineral sample is pyrite or gold?

25. Convert the melting points of the minerals shown in the table from degrees Celsius to degrees Fahrenheit. Use the formula $°F = (9/5 × °C) + 32$.

16. Sample answer: chemical reaction: some minerals, such as calcite, bubble when a drop of weak acid is placed on them; fluorescence: some minerals glow under ultraviolet light; radioactivity: minerals that contain radium or uranium can be detected by a Geiger counter.

Critical Thinking

17. An answer to this exercise can be found at the end of this book.

18. No, the test was successful. I learned that the unknown mineral has no streak and that the mineral is harder than the streak plate. This clue will help me identify the mineral.

19. Sample answer: Gem cutters can cut along cleavage surfaces to shape gemstones. Gem cutters also want to avoid cutting across cleavage surfaces.

20. Students should suggest performing several tests to see whether the mineral is gold. Gold is very dense and soft, so one would start with density and hardness tests.

21. Sample answer: Because halite is salt (sodium chloride), the crusts of halite crystals formed when a body of salt water evaporated and left the halite behind.

Interpreting Graphics

22. The difference between the highest and lowest melting points is 2,539°C, the difference between the melting points of mercury and zircon. (2,500°C − −39°C = 2,539°C)

23. Mercury would be a liquid at room temperature because its melting point is −39°C.

24. Pyrite has a higher melting point than gold does (1,171°C > 1,062°C).

25. mercury: −38°F; sulfur: 235°F; halite: 1,474°F; silver: 1,762°F; gold: 1,944°F; copper: 1,981°F; pyrite: 2,140°F; fluorite: 2,480°F; quartz: 3,110°F; zircon: 4,532°F (Answers are rounded.)

14. Sample answer: Metallic minerals such as gold are used in the manufacture of computers and spacecraft. Nonmetallic minerals such as quartz are used to manufacture computer chips and glass.

15. Two ways to reduce the effects of mining are the reclamation of mined land and the recycling of mineral products.

Teacher's Notes

To provide practice under more realistic conditions, give students 20 minutes to answer all of the questions in this Standardized Test Preparation.

Answer Key

Question	Answer
1	C
2	B
3	B
4	C
5	D
6	D
7	C
8	A
9	C
10	B
11	D
12	*
13	*

*See Test Doctor.

Multiple Choice

1. **Which of the following statements best defines a mineral?**

   A. a substance that cannot by chemical means be separated or broken down into simpler substances

   B. a substance made up of the atoms of two or more elements that are joined by chemical bonds

   C. a naturally formed inorganic solid that has a regular crystalline structure

   D. a solid whose atoms, ions, or molecules are arranged in a regular pattern

2. **Which of the following substances is a mineral?**

   A. coal, which is formed with the remains of living things

   B. fluorite, which is a crystalline solid with the chemical formula CaF_2

   C. obsidian, which is a volcanic glass and is not crystalline

   D. brass, which is a metal that is made by humans

3. **Minerals that contain one or more elements combined with silicon and oxygen are called**

   A. sulfides.

   B. silicates.

   C. oxides.

   D. halides.

Use the table below to answer Question 4.

Chemical symbol	Mineral	Mineral Class
Au	gold	native element
$CaCO_3$	calcite	_____
FeS_2	pyrite	sulfide
SiO_2	quartz	silicate

4. **Which of the following terms correctly completes the table above?**

   A. sulfate

   B. oxide

   C. carbonate

   D. halide

5. **Which of the following is a nonsilicate mineral?**

   A. orthoclase, $KAlSi_3O_8$

   B. talc, $Mg_3Si_4O_{10}(OH)_2$

   C. almandine, $Fe_3Al_2(SiO_4)_3$

   D. magnetite, Fe_3O_4

6. **Which of the following minerals can be identified by taste?**

   A. magnetite

   B. fluorite

   C. calcite

   D. halite

✚ TEST DOCTOR

Question 1 A: This statement defines an element. B: This statement defines a compound. C: Correct. D: This statement defines a crystal.

Question 2 A: Minerals are inorganic; they are not formed from living things. B: Correct. C: Minerals have ordered internal structures, or are crystalline. D: Minerals are naturally occurring; they are not man-made.

Question 3 A: Sulfides are nonsilicate minerals that contain one or more elements that are combined with sulfur. B: Correct. C: Oxide minerals contain an element other than silicon that is combined chemically with oxygen. D: Halides are nonsilicate minerals that contain fluorine, chlorine, iodine, or bromine combined with sodium, potassium, or calcium.

Question 4 A: Sulfates are minerals that contain sulfur and oxygen. Calcite does not contain sulfur. B: Oxides are compounds that form when an element combines with oxygen. While calcite contains oxygen, it contains two other elements as well. C: Correct. D: Halides are nonsilicate minerals that contain fluorine, chlorine, iodine, or bromine combined with sodium, potassium, or calcium. Calcite does not contain fluorine, chlorine, iodine, or bromine.

7. Minerals such as gypsum and halite form

A. from hot-water solutions.

B. when a rock is altered by metamorphism.

C. when bodies of salt water evaporate.

D. from the cooling of magma that rises upward through the crust.

8. Which of the following statements about metallic minerals is true?

A. Metallic minerals can be pounded or pressed into various shapes.

B. Metallic minerals have dull lusters.

C. Metallic minerals let light pass through them.

D. Metallic minerals are poor conductors of electricity.

9. Why are gemstones valuable?

A. They can be used to strengthen concrete and to build buildings.

B. They are good conductors of heat and electricity.

C. They are beautiful and rare.

D. They taste good.

10. Which of the following would be considered an ore?

A. a small deposit of a mineral that is rare and has no known use

B. a large deposit of a mineral that has many uses and costs little to mine

C. a small deposit of a mineral that is rare, valuable, and very expensive to mine

D. a large deposit of a mineral that is abundant but that has no known use

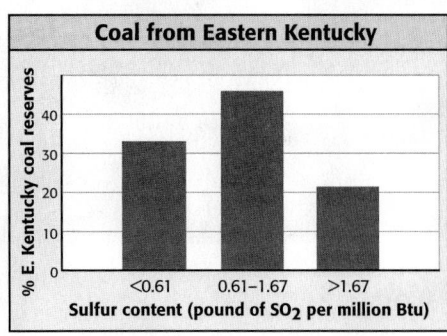

Coal from Eastern Kentucky

% E. Kentucky coal reserves (y-axis): 0, 10, 20, 30, 40

Sulfur content (pound of SO$_2$ per million Btu) (x-axis): <0.61, 0.61–1.67, >1.67

11. Eastern Kentucky's coal fields contain large amounts of coal, but not all of it has a low enough sulfur content to meet government pollution-reduction goals. If the emissions limit was set at a maximum of 1.67 pounds of SO$_2$ per million Btu, how much of Eastern Kentucky's coal could be used?

A. 13.6%

B. 32.3%

C. 45.9%

D. 78.2%

Open Response

12. What is the difference between an element and a mineral?

13. The state rock of Kentucky happens to be a mineral, Kentucky agate. Its chemical composition is SiO$_2$. In what group of minerals does agate belong? How do you know?

Question 9 A: While many nonmetallic minerals are used in concrete and building materials, gemstones are too valuable for that use. B: Because gemstones are typically nonmetallic minerals, they generally do not conduct electricity or heat well. C: Correct. D: Most gemstones do not have a taste.

Question 10 A: A mineral that has no known use is not worth mining. B: Correct. C: This deposit may be too small and expensive to mine for the company to make a profit. D: A mineral that has no known use is not worth mining.

Question 11 A: This figure is the result of subtracting the percentage of low-sulfur coal from the percentage of medium-sulfur coal. B: This is the percentage of low-sulfur coal found in Kentucky, which is only part of the total that will meet the emissions limit of 1.67 lb/mm Btu. C: This is the percentage of medium-sulfur coal found in Kentucky, which is only part of the total that will meet the emissions limit of 1.67 lb/mm Btu. D: Correct.

Question 12 Full-credit answers should include the following points:

- Elements are a single substance, chemically speaking.
- Some elements, such as gold, aluminum, or iron, can be minerals because they are solid, crystalline, and naturally formed by inorganic processes.
- All minerals are made of one or more elements.

Question 13 Full-credit answers should include the following points:

- Agate is a silicate mineral.
- Agate is made of silica and oxygen, which are found in all silicate minerals.
- Non-silicate minerals do not contain silica or oxygen.

Question 5 A, B, C: Orthoclase, talc, and almandine all contain combinations of silicon and oxygen. D: Correct.

Question 6 A: Magnetite can be identified by its magnetic property. B: Fluorite can be identified by its ability to fluoresce under ultraviolet light. C: Calcite can be identified by its ability to fluoresce under ultraviolet light, its ability to react with acids, and its ability to form a double image. D: Correct.

Question 7 A: Minerals such as gold, copper, sulfur, pyrite, and galena form from hot water solutions. B: Minerals such as calcite, garnet, graphite, hematite, magnetite, mica, and talc form during metamorphism. C: Correct. D: Minerals such as feldspar, magnetite, and quartz form in igneous plutons.

Question 8 A: Correct. B: Metallic minerals have shiny, metallic lusters. C: Metallic minerals do not let light pass through them. D: Metallic minerals are good conductors of electricity.

Science Fiction

Background

Few people have had as long-lasting an impact on science fiction as Jack Williamson. This story, "The Metal Man," was first published in 1928—over 70 years ago! Although it was his very first short story, it is still a classic. Since then, Williamson has written dozens of science fiction novels, short-stories, other novels, and books about writing. The term *science fiction* did not exist when Williamson began writing. Known as one of the great pioneers of science fiction, Williamson was the first to write about antimatter. And, he coined the terms *terraform* (in 1941) and *genetic engineering* (in 1951). Williamson is also credited for making science fiction a field worthy of literary attention. For this accomplishment, Williamson has received several awards. In 1976, he became the second person to win the Grand Nebula Award. In 1994, he earned a lifetime achievement award from World Fantasy.

Science in Action

Science Fiction

"The Metal Man" by Jack Williamson

In a dark, dusty corner of Tyburn College Museum stands a life-sized statue of a man. Except for its strange greenish color, the statue looks quite ordinary. But if you look closely, you will see the perfect detail of the hair and skin. On the statue's chest, you will also see a strange mark—a dark crimson shape with six sides. No one knows how the statue ended up in the dark corner. But most people in Tyburn believe that the metal man is, or once was, Professor Thomas Kelvin of Tyburn College's geology department. Read for yourself the strange story of Professor Kelvin and the Metal Man, which is in the *Holt Anthology of Science Fiction*.

Language Arts ACTIVITY

WRITING SKILL Read "The Metal Man" by Jack Williamson. Write a short essay explaining how the ideas in the story are related to what you are learning.

Weird Science

Wieliczka Salt Mine

Imagine an underground city that is made entirely of salt. Within the city are churches, chapels, rooms of many kinds, and salt lakes. Sculptures of biblical scenes, saints, and famous historical figures carved from salt are found throughout the city. Even chandeliers of salt hang from the ceilings. Such a city is located 16 km southeast of Krakow, Poland, inside the Wieliczka (VEE uh LEETS kuh) Salt Mine. As the mine grew over the past 700 years, it turned into an elaborate underground city. Miners constructed chapels to patron saints so they could pray for a safe day in the mine. Miners also developed superstitions about the mine. So, images that were meant to bring good luck were carved in salt. In 1978, the mine was added to UNESCO's list of endangered world heritage sites. Many of the sculptures in the mine have begun to dissolve because of the humidity in the air. Efforts to save the treasures in the mine from further damage were begun in 1996.

Social Studies ACTIVITY

WRITING SKILL Research some aspect of the role of salt in human history. For example, subjects might include the Saharan and Tibetan salt trade or the use of salt as a form of money in ancient Poland. Report your findings in a one-page essay.

Answer to Language Arts Activity
Have students present short essays on "The Metal Man" in front of the class.

Answer to Social Studies Activity
Answers may vary.

People in Science

Jamie Hill

The Emerald Man Jamie Hill was raised in the Brushy Mountains of North Carolina. While growing up, Hill gained firsthand knowledge of the fabulous green crystals that could be found in the mountains. These green crystals were emeralds. Emerald is the green variety of the silicate mineral beryl and is a valuable gemstone. Emerald crystals form in pockets, or openings, in rock known as *pegmatite*.

Since 1985, Hill has been searching for pockets containing emeralds in rock near the small town of Hiddenite, North Carolina. He has been amazingly successful. Hill has discovered some spectacular emerald crystals. The largest of these crystals weighs 858 carats and is on display at the North Carolina Museum of Natural Science. Estimates of the total value of the emeralds that Hill has discovered so far are well in the millions of dollars. Hill's discoveries have made him a celebrity, and he has appeared both on national TV and in magazines.

Math ACTIVITY

An emerald discovered by Jamie Hill in 1999 was cut into a 7.85-carat stone that sold for $64,000 per carat. What was the total value of the cut stone?

go.hrw.com
To learn more about these Science in Action topics, visit go.hrw.com and type in the keyword **HZ5MINF.**

Current Science
Check out Current Science® articles related to this chapter by visiting go.hrw.com. Just type in the keyword **HZ5CS03.**

Answer to Math Activity
$64,000 × 7.85 = $502,400

Weird Science

Background

On September 9, 1978, the Wieliczka Salt Mine was entered into UNESCO's 1st World List of Cultural and Natural Heritage. An important reason for the mine's inclusion in the list was the fact that the mine illustrates most of the stages of the development of mining technology over time. This developmental progression began in the Middle Ages, when salt was obtained from brine springs by the process of heating the brine and vaporizing the water. During the 14th and early 15th centuries, technological developments included the sinking of shafts and the use of pulley systems to transport salt to the surface. By the mid-15th century, horse gear was used to transport salt to the surface. In the 18th century, steam lifts began to be used for transporting salt. Similarly, the excavation of the salt progressed from the use of simple hand-tools to hand drills and then to pneumatic drills.

People in Science

Teaching Strategy—BASIC

Have students research minerals that can be found in the area in which they live. This information may be obtained from the United States Geological Survey or from a state entity, such as a state bureau of mines and geology. Have students put together a mineral list and, if possible, locations where specific minerals might be found.

If the option is practical, you may wish to lead the class on a rock hunt around the schoolyard. Have students discuss which minerals they think make up the rocks they found.

Rocks: Mineral Mixtures
Chapter Planning Guide

Compression guide:
To shorten instruction because of time limitations, omit the Chapter Lab.

OBJECTIVES	LABS, DEMONSTRATIONS, AND ACTIVITIES	TECHNOLOGY RESOURCES
PACING • 90 min pp. 246–255 **Chapter Opener**	SE **Start-up Activity,** p. 247 ◆ GENERAL	OSP **Parent Letter** ▪ CD **Student Edition on CD-ROM** CD **Guided Reading Audio CD** ▪ TR **Chapter Starter Transparency*** VID **Brain Food Video Quiz**
Section 1 The Rock Cycle • Describe two ways rocks have been used by humans. • Describe four processes that shape Earth's features. • Describe how each type of rock changes into another type as it moves through the rock cycle. • List two characteristics of rock that are used to help classify it.	TE **Group Activity** Rates of Weathering, p. 249 GENERAL TE **Activity** Rock Dictionary, p. 251 BASIC TE **Connection Activity** Language Arts, p. 251 BASIC TE **Group Activity** Describing Rocks, p. 253 BASIC LB **Labs You Can Eat** Famous Rock Groups* ◆ GENERAL LB **Calculator-Based Labs** A Hot and Cool Lab ◆ ADVANCED TE **Using the Figure** Diagramming the Rock Cycle, p. 250 GENERAL	OSP **Lesson Plans** (also in print) TR **Bellringer Transparency*** TR **E8 The Rock Cycle*** TR LINK TO LIFE SCIENCE L65 The Water Cycle*
PACING • 45 min pp. 256–259 **Section 2 Igneous Rock** • Describe three ways that igneous rock forms. • Explain how the cooling rate of magma affects the texture of igneous rock. • Distinguish between igneous rock that cools within Earth's crust and igneous rock that cools at Earth's surface.	SE **Science in Action** Math, Social Studies, and Language Arts Activities, pp. 276–277 GENERAL SE **Skills Practice Lab** Crystal Growth, p. 717 ◆ GENERAL TE **Using the Figure** Making Inferences, p. 257 BASIC TE **Connection to Life Science** Life Along a Rift, p. 257 ADVANCED	OSP **Lesson Plans** (also in print) TR **Bellringer Transparency*** TR **E9 Intrusive Igneous Rock Bodies*** SE **Internet Activity,** p. 258 GENERAL
PACING • 90 min pp. 260–263 **Section 3 Sedimentary Rock** • Describe the origin of sedimentary rock. • Describe the three main categories of sedimentary rock. • Describe three types of sedimentary structures.	TE **Demonstration** Dissolution of Minerals, p. 260 GENERAL SE **Connection to Language Arts** Salty Expressions, p. 261 GENERAL TE **Activity** Sedimentary Rock, p. 261 BASIC TE **Connection Activity** Real World, p. 262 GENERAL SE **Skills Practice Lab** Let's Get Sedimental, p. 270 ◆ GENERAL LB **Whiz-Bang Demonstrations** Settling Down* ◆ BASIC	OSP **Lesson Plans** (also in print) TR **Bellringer Transparency*** VID **Lab Videos for Earth Science**
PACING • 45 min pp. 264–269 **Section 4 Metamorphic Rock** • Describe two ways a rock can undergo metamorphism. • Explain how the mineral composition of rock changes as the rocks undergo metamorphism. • Describe the difference between foliated and nonfoliated metamorphic rock. • Explain how metamorphic rock structures are related to deformation.	TE **Activity** Modeling Metamorphism, p. 264 GENERAL SE **Quick Lab** Stretching Out, p. 265 GENERAL SE **School-to-Home Activity** Making a Rock Collection, p. 266 GENERAL TE **Connection Activity** Real World, p. 267 ADVANCED SE **Connection to Biology** Metamorphosis, p. 268 GENERAL SE **Model-Making Lab** Metamorphic Mash, p. 720 ◆ GENERAL LB **Long-Term Projects & Research Ideas** Home-Grown Crystals* ADVANCED	OSP **Lesson Plans** (also in print) TR **Bellringer Transparency*** TR **E10 Regional and Contact Metamorphism*** CD **Interactive Explorations CD-ROM** "Rock On!"* GENERAL

PACING • 90 min

CHAPTER REVIEW, ASSESSMENT, AND STANDARDIZED TEST PREPARATION

CRF **Vocabulary Activity*** GENERAL
SE **Chapter Review,** pp. 272–273 GENERAL
CRF **Chapter Review*** ▪ GENERAL
CRF **Chapter Tests A*** ▪ GENERAL, **B*** ADVANCED, **C*** SPECIAL NEEDS
SE **Standardized Test Preparation,** pp. 274–275 GENERAL
CRF **Standardized Test Preparation*** GENERAL
CRF **Performance-Based Assessment*** GENERAL
OSP **Test Generator, Test Item Listing**

Online and Technology Resources

 Holt Online Learning

Visit go.hrw.com for access to Holt Online Learning, or enter the keyword **HS7 Home** for a variety of free online resources.

 **One-Stop Planner® CD-ROM**

This CD-ROM package includes:
• Lab Materials QuickList Software
• Holt Calendar Planner
• Customizable Lesson Plans
• Printable Worksheets

• ExamView® Test Generator
• Interactive Teacher's Edition
• Holt PuzzlePro®
• Holt PowerPoint® Resources

SKILLS DEVELOPMENT RESOURCES	SECTION REVIEW AND ASSESSMENT	CORRELATIONS
SE Pre-Reading Activity, p. 246 GENERAL **OSP** Science Puzzlers, Twisters & Teasers* GENERAL		National Science Education Standards SAI 1, 2
CRF Directed Reading A* ■ BASIC, B* SPECIAL NEEDS **WB** Workbook* Struggling Readers **CRF** Vocabulary and Section Summary* ■ GENERAL **SE** Reading Strategy Reading Organizer, p. 248 GENERAL **TE** Inclusion Strategies, p. 250 ◆ **TE** Support for English Language Learners, p. 250 **MS** Math Skills for Science Parts of 100: Calculating Percentages* GENERAL **CRF** SciLinks Activity, The Rock Cycle* GENERAL	**SE** Reading Checks, pp. 248, 252, 253, 254 GENERAL **TE** Homework, p. 251 GENERAL **TE** Reteaching, p. 254 BASIC **TE** Quiz, p. 254 GENERAL **TE** Alternative Assessment, p. 254 GENERAL **SE** Section Review,* p. 255 ■ GENERAL **CRF** Section Quiz* ■ GENERAL	UCP 1; SAI 1, 2; ST 2; SPSP 5; HNS 1; ES 1c, 1d
CRF Directed Reading A* ■ BASIC, B* SPECIAL NEEDS **WB** Workbook* Struggling Readers **CRF** Vocabulary and Section Summary* ■ GENERAL **SE** Reading Strategy Reading Organizer, p. 256 GENERAL **TE** Support for English Language Learners, p. 257	**SE** Reading Checks, pp. 257, 259 GENERAL **TE** Reteaching, p. 258 BASIC **TE** Quiz, p. 258 GENERAL **TE** Alternative Assessment, p. 258 GENERAL **TE** Homework, p. 258 ADVANCED **SE** Section Review,* p. 259 ■ GENERAL **CRF** Section Quiz* ■ GENERAL	UCP 1, 2; SAI 1, 2; ES 1c, 1d; *LabBook:* SAI 1, 2
CRF Directed Reading A* ■ BASIC, B* SPECIAL NEEDS **WB** Workbook* Struggling Readers **CRF** Vocabulary and Section Summary* ■ GENERAL **SE** Reading Strategy Reading Organizer, p. 260 GENERAL **TE** Support for English Language Learners, p. 261	**SE** Reading Checks, pp. 261, 263 GENERAL **TE** Reteaching, p. 262 BASIC **TE** Quiz, p. 262 GENERAL **TE** Alternative Assessment, p. 262 GENERAL **SE** Section Review,* p. 263 ■ GENERAL **CRF** Section Quiz* ■ GENERAL	UCP 1, 2; SAI 1, 2; ES 1c, 1d, 1k, 2b; *Chapter Lab:* SAI 1, 2
CRF Directed Reading A* ■ BASIC, B* SPECIAL NEEDS **WB** Workbook* Struggling Readers **CRF** Vocabulary and Section Summary* ■ GENERAL **SE** Reading Strategy Discussion, p. 264 GENERAL **TE** Support for English Language Learners, p. 266 **TE** Inclusion Strategies, p. 267 **MS** Math Skills for Science The Unit Factor and Dimensional Analysis* GENERAL **CRF** Reinforcement Worksheet What Is It?* BASIC **CRF** Critical Thinking Between a Rock and a Hard Place* ADVANCED	**SE** Reading Checks, pp. 265, 266, 269 GENERAL **TE** Reteaching, p. 268 BASIC **TE** Quiz, p. 268 GENERAL **TE** Alternative Assessment, p. 268 GENERAL **TE** Homework, p. 268 ADVANCED **SE** Section Review,* p. 269 ■ GENERAL **CRF** Section Quiz* ■ GENERAL	UCP 1, 2; SAI 1, 2; ES 1c; *LabBook:* SAI 1, 2

SCILINKS.
NSTA
www.scilinks.org
Maintained by the **National Science Teachers Association.** See Chapter Enrichment pages that follow for a complete list of topics.

Check out *Current Science* articles and activities by visiting the HRW Web site at **go.hrw.com.** Just type in the keyword **HZ5CS04T.**

 **Classroom Videos**

• **Lab Videos** demonstrate the chapter lab.
• **Brain Food Video Quizzes** help students review the chapter material.

 Classroom CD-ROMs

• **Guided Reading Audio CD** (Also in Spanish)
• **Interactive Explorations**
• **Virtual Investigations**
• **Visual Concepts**
• **Science Tutor**

Holt Lab Generator CD-ROM

Search for any lab by topic, standard, difficulty level, or time. Edit any lab to fit your needs, or create your own labs. Use the Lab Materials QuickList software to customize your lab materials list.

Visual Resources

CHAPTER STARTER TRANSPARENCY

Imagine . . .

BELLRINGER TRANSPARENCIES

Section: The Rock Cycle
Many of us work hard to recycle the items we use in our daily lives to reduce the impact we have on the environment. In a way, the Earth also recycles through the rock cycle. Can you imagine what rock might look like through each stage of the rock cycle? How long do you think it takes to recycle a soda can? What about a piece of granite?

Record your thoughts in your **science journal.**

Section: Igneous Rock
Do you think rocks that cooled and solidified from lava on Earth's surface would look different from those that cooled and solidified from magma inside the Earth? To answer this question, ask yourself how the Hawaiian Islands differ from the Rocky Mountains.

Explain your answer in your **science journal.**

TEACHING TRANSPARENCIES

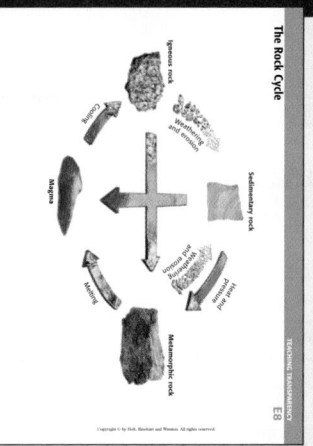

The Rock Cycle

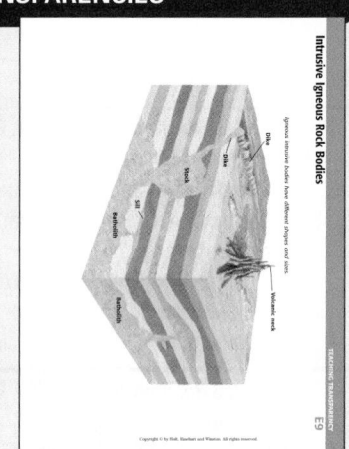

Intrusive Igneous Rock Bodies

TEACHING TRANSPARENCIES

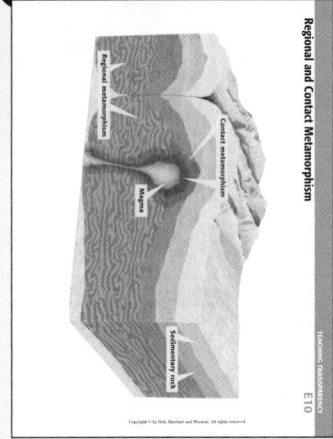

Regional and Contact Metamorphism

The Digestive System of a Bird

Chapter: Birds and Mammals

CONCEPT MAPPING TRANSPARENCY

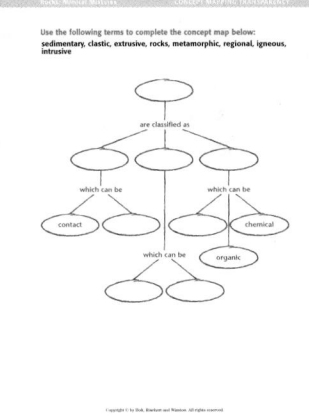

Use the following terms to complete the concept map below:
sedimentary, clastic, extrusive, rocks, metamorphic, regional, igneous, intrusive

Planning Resources

LESSON PLANS

Lesson Plan   SAMPLE

Section: Waves

Pacing
Regular Schedule: with lab(s):2 days   without lab(s):1 days
Block Schedule: with lab(s):1 1/2 days   without lab(s):1 day

Objectives
1. Relate the seven properties of life to a living organism.
2. Describe seven themes that can help you to organize what you learn about biology.
3. Identify the tiny structures that make up all living organism.
4. Differentiate between reproduction and heredity and between metabolism and homeostasis.

National Science Education Standards Covered
LSInter6:Cells have particular structures that underlie their functions.
LSMat1:Most cell functions involve chemical reactions.
LSBeh1:Cells store and use information to guide their functions.
UCP1:Cell functions are regulated.
SI1: Cells can differentiate and form complete multicellular organisms.
PS1: Species evolve over time.
ESS1: The great diversity of organisms is the result of more than 3.5 billion years of evolution.
ESS2: Natural selection and its evolutionary consequences provide a scientific explanation for the fossil record of ancient life forms as well as for the striking molecular similarities observed among the diverse species of living organisms.
ST1: The millions of different species of plants, animals, and microorganisms that live on Earth today are related by descent from common ancestors.
ST2: The energy for life primarily comes from the sun.
SPSP1: The complexity and organization of organisms accommodate the need for obtaining, transforming, transporting, releasing, and eliminating the matter and energy used to sustain the organism.
SPSP6: As matter and energy flows through different levels of organization of living systems—cells, organs, communities—and between living systems and the physical environment, chemical elements are recombined in different ways.
HNS1: Organisms have behavioral responses to internal changes and to external stimuli.

PARENT LETTER

Dear Parent,   SAMPLE

Your son's or daughter's science class will soon begin exploring the chapter entitled "The World of Physical Science." In this chapter, students will learn about how the scientific method applies to the world of physical science and the role of physical science in the world. By the end of the chapter, students should demonstrate a clear understanding of the chapter's main ideas and be able to discuss the following topics:

1. physical science is the study of energy and matter (Section 1)
2. the role of physical science in the world around them (Section 1)
3. careers that rely on physical science (Section 1)
4. the steps used in the scientific method (Section 2)
5. examples of technology (Section 2)
6. how the scientific method is used to answer questions and solve problems (Section 2)
7. how our knowledge of science changes over time (Section 2)
8. how models represent real objects or systems (Section 3)
9. examples of different ways models are used in science (Section 3)
10. the importance of the International System of Units (Section 4)
11. the appropriate units to use for particular measurements (Section 4)
12. how area and density are derived quantities (Section 4)

Questions to Ask Along the Way

You can help your son or daughter learn about these topics by asking interesting questions such as the following:

- What are some surprising careers that use physical science?
- What is a characteristic of a good hypothesis?
- When is it a good idea to use a model?
- Why do Americans measure things in terms of inches and yards and meters?

ALSO IN SPANISH

TEST ITEM LISTING

TEST ITEM LISTING
The World of Earth Science   SAMPLE

MULTIPLE CHOICE

1. A limitation of models is that
   a. they are large enough to see.
   b. they do not act exactly like the things that they model.
   c. they are smaller than the things that they model.
   d. they model unfamiliar things.
   Answer: B   Difficulty: 1   Section: 3   Objective: 2

2. The length 10 m is equal to
   a. 100 cm.   c. 10,000 mm.
   b. 1,000 cm.   d. Both (a) and (c)
   Answer: B   Difficulty: 1   Section: 3   Objective: 2

3. To be valid, a hypothesis must be
   a. testable.   c. made into a law.
   b. supported by evidence.   d. Both (a) and (b)
   Answer: B   Difficulty: 1   Section: 3   Objective: 2

4. The statement "Sheila has a stain on her shirt" is an example of a(n)
   a. law.   c. observation.
   b. hypothesis.   d. prediction.
   Answer: B   Difficulty: 1   Section: 3   Objective: 2

5. A hypothesis is often developed out of
   a. observations.   c. laws.
   b. experiments.   d. Both (a) and (b)
   Answer: B   Difficulty: 1   Section: 3   Objective: 2

6. How many milliliters are in 3.5 kL?
   a. 3,500 mL   c. 3,500, 000 mL
   b. 0.0035 mL   d. 35,000 mL.
   Answer: B   Difficulty: 1   Section: 3   Objective: 2

7. A map of Seattle is an example of a
   a. law.   c. model.
   b. theory.   d. unit.
   Answer: B   Difficulty: 1   Section: 3   Objective: 2

8. A lab has the safety icons shown below. These icons mean that you should wear
   a. only hand protection.   c. safety goggles and a lab apron.
   b. only a lab apron.   d. safety goggles, a lab apron, and gloves
   c. only a lab apron.   d. safety goggles, a lab apron, and gloves
   Answer: B   Difficulty: 1   Section: 3   Objective: 2

9. The law of conservation of mass says the lot of mass before is chemical change is
   a. more than the total mass after the change.
   b. less than the total mass after the change.
   c. the same as the total mass after the change.
   d. not the same as the total mass after the change.
   Answer: B   Difficulty: 1   Section: 3   Objective: 2

10. In which of the following areas might you find a geochemist at work?
    a. studying the chemistry of rocks   c. studying fishes
    b. studying forestry   d. studying the atmosphere
    Answer: B   Difficulty: 1   Section: 3   Objective: 2

One-Stop Planner® CD-ROM

This CD-ROM includes all of the resources shown here and the following time-saving tools:

- *Lab Materials QuickList Software*
- *Customizable lesson plans*
- *Holt Calendar Planner*
- *The powerful ExamView® Test Generator*

Meeting Individual Needs

DIRECTED READING A
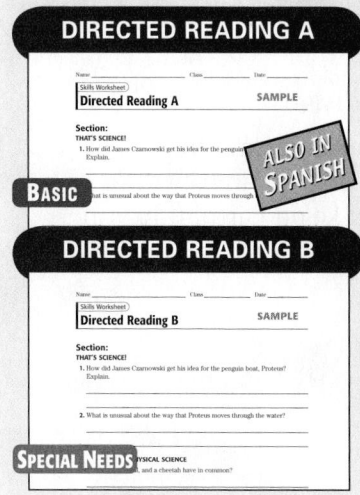

VOCABULARY ACTIVITY
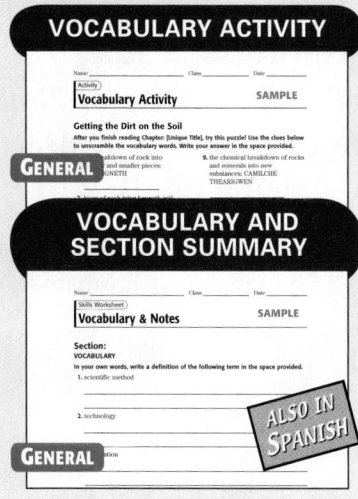

REINFORCEMENT
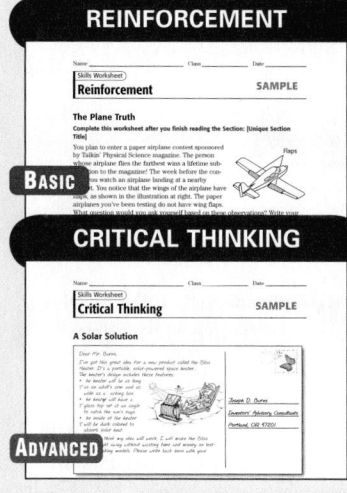

SCILINKS ACTIVITY

Labs and Activities

LONG-TERM PROJECTS & RESEARCH IDEAS
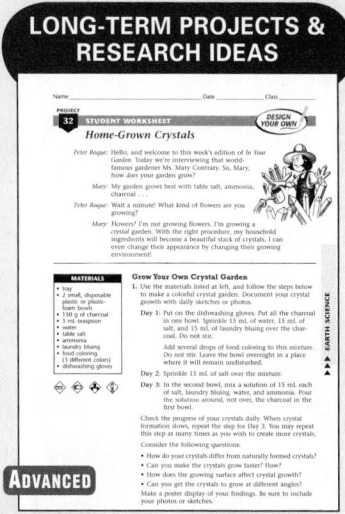

WHIZ-BANG DEMONSTRATIONS
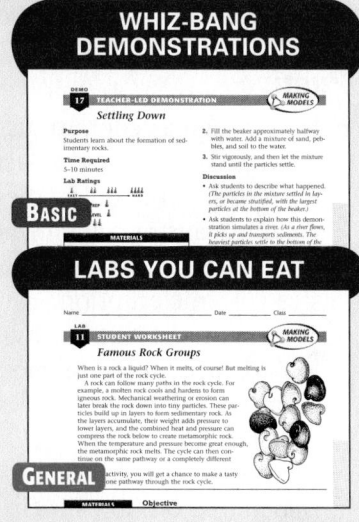

CALCULATOR-BASED LABS
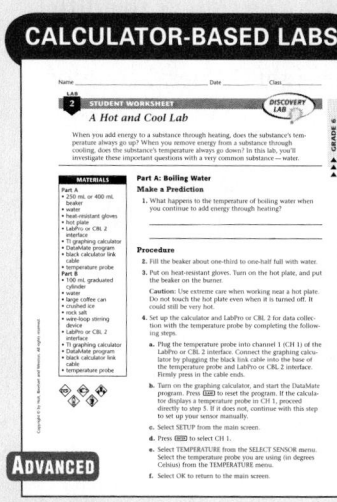

DATASHEETS FOR QUICK LABS

Review and Assessments

SECTION QUIZ
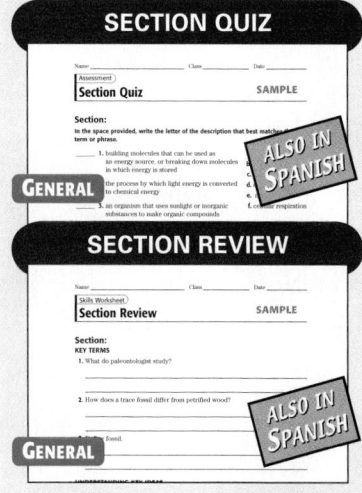

CHAPTER REVIEW
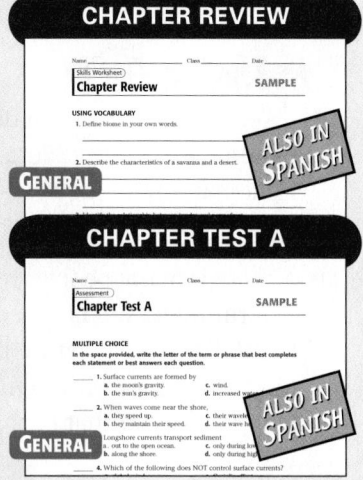

CHAPTER TEST B
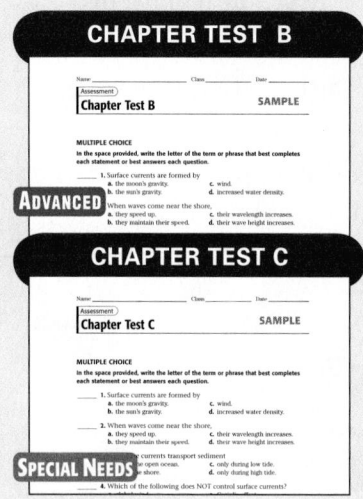

STANDARDIZED TEST PREPARATION
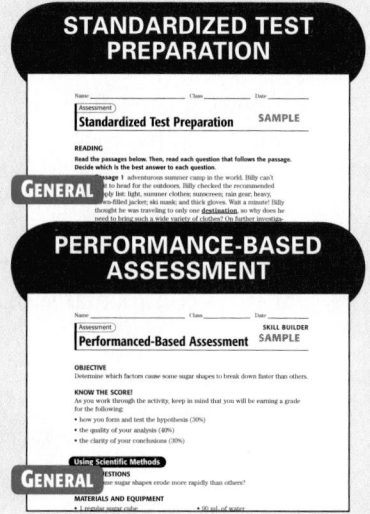

This Chapter Enrichment provides relevant and interesting information to expand and enhance your presentation of the chapter material.

Section 1

The Rock Cycle

Rock Composition

- This chapter focuses on the mineral composition of rock, not its bulk composition. These are two very different means of measuring rock composition.

- The *mineral composition* of a rock refers to the proportions of the different minerals in the rock and is usually expressed in percentages by volume. Even coal, a sedimentary rock made of organic matter, contains clay minerals or pyrite.

- The *bulk composition* of a rock is the sum of the different elements that make up the rock and is usually expressed in percentages by weight. Mineral composition is affected by bulk composition.

Is That a Fact!

◆ Although rocks contain many elements, the rocks in Earth's crust are nearly 94% oxygen by number of atoms.

◆ Approximately 92% of the Earth's crust is igneous and metamorphic rock.

◆ Although sedimentary rock makes up about 8% of the Earth's crust, it is spread thinly over much of the planet's surface. Sedimentary rock covers 75% of the Earth's continental surfaces!

Section 2

Igneous Rock

The Great Dike of Zimbabwe

- Dikes can range in width from a few millimeters to many kilometers. The Great Dike of Zimbabwe, in Africa, is the largest known dike on Earth. It has an average width of 6 to 8 km and extends for almost 500 km across Zimbabwe.

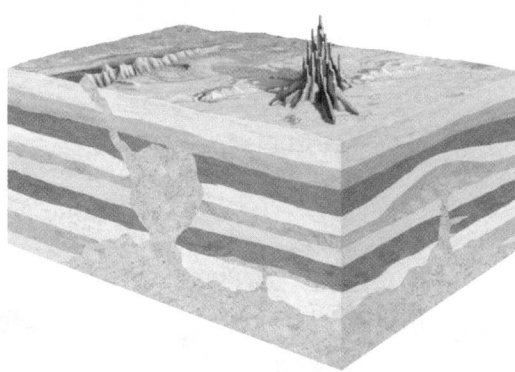

Pumice

- Some magmas contain dissolved gases, such as carbon dioxide. When these gases come out of magma in the form of small bubbles, the magma greatly increases its volume, causing an enormous buildup of pressure. This can result in an explosive volcanic eruption. The result can be a frothy-looking rock called *pumice*. Pumice is full of small holes, called *vesicles*, where the trapped gases used to be. Depending on how much space is taken up by vesicles, some types of pumice can float in water!

Is That a Fact!

◆ Igneous rocks that form deep underground are called plutonic rocks, after Pluto, the god of the underworld in Roman mythology. Volcanic rocks are named after Vulcan, the Roman god of metalworking and fire.

◆ Although many people think of lava as a thin and runny liquid, lava flows are often quite viscous. Usually, the temperature has cooled enough for crystals to begin forming, which can give lava a consistency similar to that of thick oatmeal.

Section 3

Sedimentary Rock

Working with Clay

● Clay is composed primarily of silicate minerals. Clays are easy to work with when they are wet because the tiny plate-shaped silicate crystals are surrounded by water molecules. As the water evaporates, the silicates are cemented into place, and the clay becomes brittle and difficult to work with.

Is That a Fact!

◆ Bentonite, a form of clay composed of very fine silicate crystals, has a wide variety of industrial applications. Some forms of bentonite can expand as much as 300% when mixed with water. Bentonite is used to make cat litter, to line artificial ponds, to remove impurities from wines and juices, to treat wastewater, and in a variety of applications for oil drilling.

Section 4

Metamorphic Rock

Metamorphosis in a Lab

● Geologists can estimate the temperature and pressure that metamorphosed a rock by simulating the process of metamorphosis in a laboratory. When geologists know the chemical composition of certain minerals within a rock, they can subject a similar compound to a range of temperatures and pressures. By observing the laboratory results, they can make predictions about how similar materials behave in metamorphic environments. Geologists can determine the temperature at which metamorphism occurred within 20°C and the pressure within a fraction of a kilobar.

Carrara Marble

● In the mountains around Carrara, Italy, a marble prized for its purity and beauty has been quarried for at least 2,000 years. Its whiteness is due to the lack of organic materials in the limestone from which it recrystallized. Carrara marble was used in the interior of the Pantheon, in Rome. It is also found in the Leaning Tower of Pisa, in the pavement of Saint Peter's Basilica, in Vatican City, and in the Kennedy Center, in Washington, D.C.

Is That a Fact!

◆ Metamorphic rocks are a challenge to study because they form within a wide range of temperature and pressure. Scientists must distinguish between the geologic history of the metamorphic rock and the history of the igneous, sedimentary, or previously metamorphosed rocks it formed from. For the same reason, however, metamorphic rocks offer many important clues about tectonic activity in the Earth's past.

◆ Metamorphism occurs quickly at high temperatures, but it also occurs at temperatures that are surprisingly low. For example, clay minerals in mudstone and shale can begin to metamorphose at temperatures as low as 50°C! This reaction, however, takes many millions of years to occur.

SciLINKS®

NSTA

Developed and maintained by the National Science Teachers Association

SciLinks is maintained by the National Science Teachers Association to provide you and your students with interesting, up-to-date links that will enrich your classroom presentation of the chapter.

Visit www.scilinks.org and enter the SciLinks code for more information about the topic listed.

Topic: Composition of Rock
SciLinks code: HSM0327

Topic: Sedimentary Rock
SciLinks code: HSM1365

Topic: Igneous Rock
SciLinks code: HSM0783

Topic: Metamorphic Rock
SciLinks code: HSM0949

Overview

Tell students that this chapter will teach them about the rock cycle. They will learn about igneous, sedimentary, and metamorphic rocks. Students will find out how each rock type is formed and how each rock type is classified.

Assessing Prior Knowledge

Students should be familiar with the following topics:

• mineral environments

Identifying Misconceptions

Students may not realize that rock, like other substances on Earth, is part of a cycle. Within this cycle, a variety of geological processes act on rock to change and ultimately recycle it. These processes occur on the Earth's surface, in the shallow subsurface, or deep within the Earth and may be continuous or occur in a series of steps. The time in which processes act to change or recycle rock often happen over millions or tens of millions of years.

10

Rocks: Mineral Mixtures

The Big Idea

Rock changes through the rock cycle and is classified by how it formed, by its composition, and by its texture.

PRE-READING ACTIVITY

Graphic Organizer

Spider Map Before you read the chapter, create the graphic organizer entitled "Spider Map" described in the **Study Skills** section of the Appendix. Label the circle "Rock." Create a leg for each of the sections in this chapter. As you read the chapter, fill in the map with details about the material presented in each section of the chapter.

About the Photo

Irish legend claims that the mythical hero Finn MacCool built the Giant's Causeway, shown here. But this rock formation is the result of the cooling of huge amounts of molten rock. As the molten rock cooled, it formed tall pillars separated by cracks called *columnar joints*.

Standards Correlations

National Science Education Standards

The following codes indicate the National Science Education Standards that correlate to this chapter. The full text of the standards is at the front of the book.

Chapter Opener
SAI 1, 2

Section 1 The Rock Cycle
ES 1c, 1d; HNS 1; SAI 1, 2; SPSP 5; ST 2; UCP 1

Section 2 Igneous Rock
ES 1c, 1d; SAI 1, 2; UCP 1, 2; LabBook: SAI 1, 2

Section 3 Sedimentary Rock
ES 1c, 1d, 1k, 2b; SAI 1, 2; UCP 1, 2

Section 4 Metamorphic Rock
ES 1c; SAI 1, 2; UCP 1, 2; LabBook: SAI 1, 2

Chapter Lab
SAI 1, 2

Chapter Review
ES 1c, 1d, 2b; HNS 1; SAI 1, 2; SPSP 5; ST 2; UCP 1, 2

Science in Action
ES 1c, 2a; HNS 1, 2, 3; SAI 1, 2; SPSP 3, 5; ST 2

START-UP ACTIVITY
MATERIALS

FOR EACH GROUP
• bag containing several different and varied objects

Answers

1. Answers may vary. Sample answer: I sorted the objects by color, size, and composition.

2. Answers may vary. Sample answer: Yes, there were objects that could fit into more than one group. I solved this problem by deciding which characteristics were more important and then sorting the object into a corresponding group.

3. Answers may vary. Accept all reasonable responses. Students may mention color, texture, composition, and hardness.

START-UP ACTIVITY

Classifying Objects

Scientists use the physical and chemical properties of rocks to classify rocks. Classifying objects such as rocks requires looking at many properties. Do this exercise for some classification practice.

Procedure

1. Your teacher will give you a **bag** containing **several objects.** Examine the objects, and note features such as size, color, shape, texture, smell, and any unique properties.

2. Develop three different ways to sort these objects.

3. Create a chart that organizes objects by properties.

Analysis

1. What properties did you use to sort the items?

2. Were there any objects that could fit into more than one group? How did you solve this problem?

3. Which properties might you use to classify rocks? Explain your answer.

Chapter Starter Transparency
Use this transparency to help students begin thinking about the importance of rock to human societies.

CHAPTER RESOURCES

Technology

Transparencies
• Chapter Starter Transparency

READING SKILLS

Student Edition on CD-ROM

Guided Reading Audio CD
• English or Spanish

Classroom Videos
• Brain Food Video Quiz

Workbooks

Science Puzzlers, Twisters & Teasers
• Rocks: Mineral Mixtures GENERAL

Focus

Overview

This section introduces the rock cycle and the processes that shape the surface of the Earth. The processes of weathering, erosion, deposition, uplift, melting, cooling, and metamorphism are explained, in the context of the rock cycle.

 Bellringer

Pose the following questions to students:

• How can rock be recycled?

• How long would recycling a rock take?

• What would the rock look like before, during, and after the process of recycling?

Motivate

Discussion ——— GENERAL

Geologic Time Some students may not realize how long changes in the rock cycle take. The processes that shape rock can take millions to tens of millions of years. Discuss the geologic time scale with students to give them a perspective of how long the Earth has existed and how long these processes have been affecting the Earth.
LS Logical

What You Will Learn

● Describe two ways rocks have been used by humans.
● Describe four processes that shape Earth's features.
● Describe how each type of rock changes into another type as it moves through the rock cycle.
● List two characteristics of rock that are used to help classify it.

Vocabulary

rock cycle   deposition
rock   composition
erosion   texture

READING STRATEGY

Reading Organizer As you read this section, make a flowchart of the steps of the rock cycle.

The Rock Cycle

You know that paper, plastic, and aluminum can be recycled. But did you know that the Earth also recycles? And one of the things that Earth recycles is rock.

Scientists define **rock** as a naturally occurring solid mixture of one or more minerals and organic matter. It may be hard to believe, but rocks are always changing. The continual process by which new rock forms from old rock material is called the **rock cycle.**

The Value of Rock

Rock has been an important natural resource as long as humans have existed. Early humans used rocks as hammers to make other tools. They discovered that they could make arrowheads, spear points, knives, and scrapers by carefully shaping rocks such as chert and obsidian.

Rock has also been used for centuries to make buildings, monuments, and roads. **Figure 1** shows how rock has been used as a construction material by both ancient and modern civilizations. Buildings have been made out of granite, limestone, marble, sandstone, slate, and other rocks. Modern buildings also contain concrete and plaster, in which rock is an important ingredient.

✓ **Reading Check** Name some types of rock that have been used to construct buildings. (*See the Appendix for answers to Reading Checks.*)

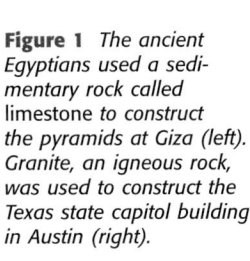

Figure 1 *The ancient Egyptians used a sedimentary rock called* limestone *to construct the pyramids at Giza (left). Granite, an igneous rock, was used to construct the Texas state capitol building in Austin (right).*

CHAPTER RESOURCES

Chapter Resource File

 • **Lesson Plan**
    • **Directed Reading A** BASIC
    • **Directed Reading B** SPECIAL NEEDS

Technology

 Transparencies
    • Bellringer

Workbooks

 Interactive Textbook Struggling Readers

Answer to Reading Check

Types of rock that have been used by humans to construct buildings include granite, limestone, marble, sandstone, and slate.

Processes That Shape the Earth

Certain geological processes make and destroy rock. These processes shape the features of our planet. These processes also influence the type of rock that is found in a certain area of Earth's surface.

Weathering, Erosion, and Deposition

The process in which water, wind, ice, and heat break down rock is called *weathering*. Weathering is important because it breaks down rock into fragments. These rock and mineral fragments are the sediment of which much sedimentary rock is made.

The process by which sediment is removed from its source is called **erosion.** Water, wind, ice, and gravity can erode and move sediments and cause them to collect. **Figure 2** shows an example of the way land looks after weathering and erosion.

The process in which sediment moved by erosion is dropped and comes to rest is called **deposition.** Sediment is deposited in bodies of water and other low-lying areas. In those places, sediment may be pressed and cemented together by minerals dissolved in water to form sedimentary rock.

Heat and Pressure

Sedimentary rock made of sediment can also form when buried sediment is squeezed by the weight of overlying layers of sediment. If the temperature and pressure are high enough at the bottom of the sediment, the rock can change into metamorphic rock. In some cases, the rock gets hot enough to melt. This melting creates the magma that eventually cools to form igneous rock.

How the Cycle Continues

Buried rock is exposed at the Earth's surface by a combination of uplift and erosion. *Uplift* is movement within the Earth that causes rocks inside the Earth to be moved to the Earth's surface. When uplifted rock reaches the Earth's surface, weathering, erosion, and deposition begin.

rock a naturally occurring solid mixture of one or more minerals or organic matter

rock cycle the series of processes in which a rock forms, changes from one type to another, is destroyed, and forms again by geological processes

erosion the process by which wind, water, ice, or gravity transports soil and sediment from one location to another

deposition the process in which material is laid down

Figure 2 *Bryce Canyon, in Utah, is an excellent example of how the processes of weathering and erosion shape the face of our planet.*

Using the Figure—GENERAL

Diagramming the Rock Cycle Ask students to use the information in the rock-cycle illustration to draw a diagram of the rock cycle in their **science journal.** The first step in the illustration is the formation of sedimentary rock; ask students to begin their rock cycle with a different step. Encourage them to write a descriptive caption for every stage of the rock cycle. **LS Visual**

SUPPORT FOR

English Language Learners

Cycles Connecting new ideas to what students already know helps them understand concepts and language. Ask students to brainstorm examples of cycles in everyday life, for example, the "life" of an aluminum can. Have them describe specific points in the cycle as volunteers diagram and label them on the board Point out language errors or logical weaknesses as the diagrams develop, and ask students to help improve them. **LS Verbal/Logical**

MISCONCEPTION ALERT

Rock Cycle Misconceptions Rocks rarely undergo the complete process shown in the rock-cycle diagram. Sedimentary rocks can become igneous rocks, and metamorphic rocks can become sedimentary rocks. Also, some students may not realize the length of time it takes for changes to occur in the rock cycle. The process shown in the diagram can take millions to tens of millions of years.

Illustrating the Rock Cycle

You have learned about various geological processes, such as weathering, erosion, heat, and pressure, that create and destroy rock. The diagram on these two pages illustrates one way that sand grains can change as different geological processes act on them. In the following steps, you will see how these processes change the original sand grains into sedimentary rock, metamorphic rock, and igneous rock.

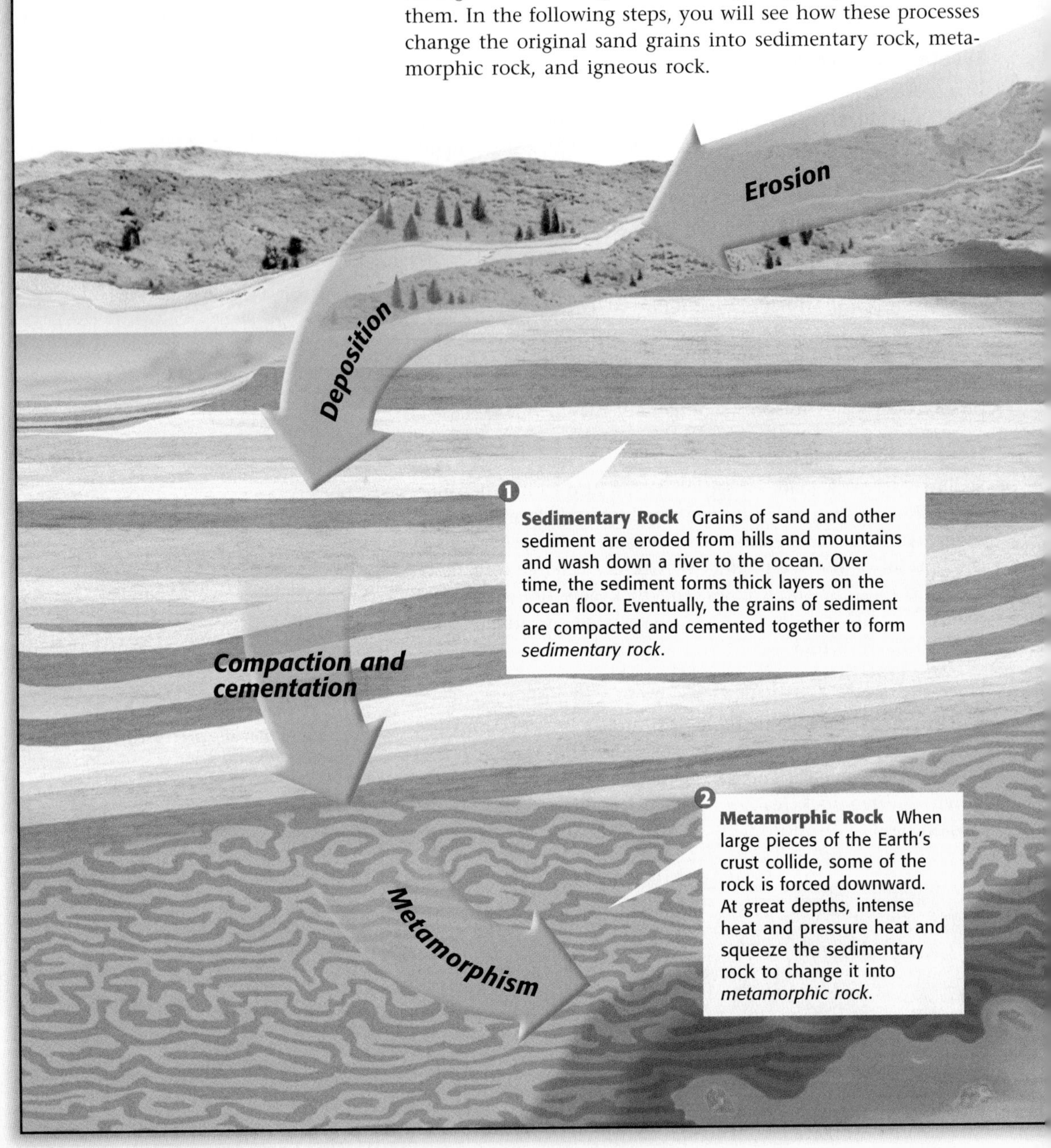

Erosion

Deposition

Compaction and cementation

Metamorphism

1 Sedimentary Rock Grains of sand and other sediment are eroded from hills and mountains and wash down a river to the ocean. Over time, the sediment forms thick layers on the ocean floor. Eventually, the grains of sediment are compacted and cemented together to form *sedimentary rock.*

2 Metamorphic Rock When large pieces of the Earth's crust collide, some of the rock is forced downward. At great depths, intense heat and pressure heat and squeeze the sedimentary rock to change it into *metamorphic rock.*

INCLUSION Strategies

- *Learning Disabled*
- *Attention Deficit Disorder*
- *Hearing Impaired*

Groups will use different foods to model sedimentary, metamorphic, and igneous rocks and minerals. Have real rock samples available (enough for each group). Organize students into groups of three or four students. Give students a chocolate-chip cookie to model granite (igneous), a sugar cube to model marble (metamorphic), a brownie to model shale (sedimentary), a magnifying glass, a large sheet of paper, and magic markers. Ask students to describe and sketch their three samples. To describe each sample, students should note the sample's texture, color, and composition. On the board, compile descriptions for each "rock" from each group. Pass real rock samples to each group, and have the groups match their samples to the real rocks. **LS Visual**  English Language Learners

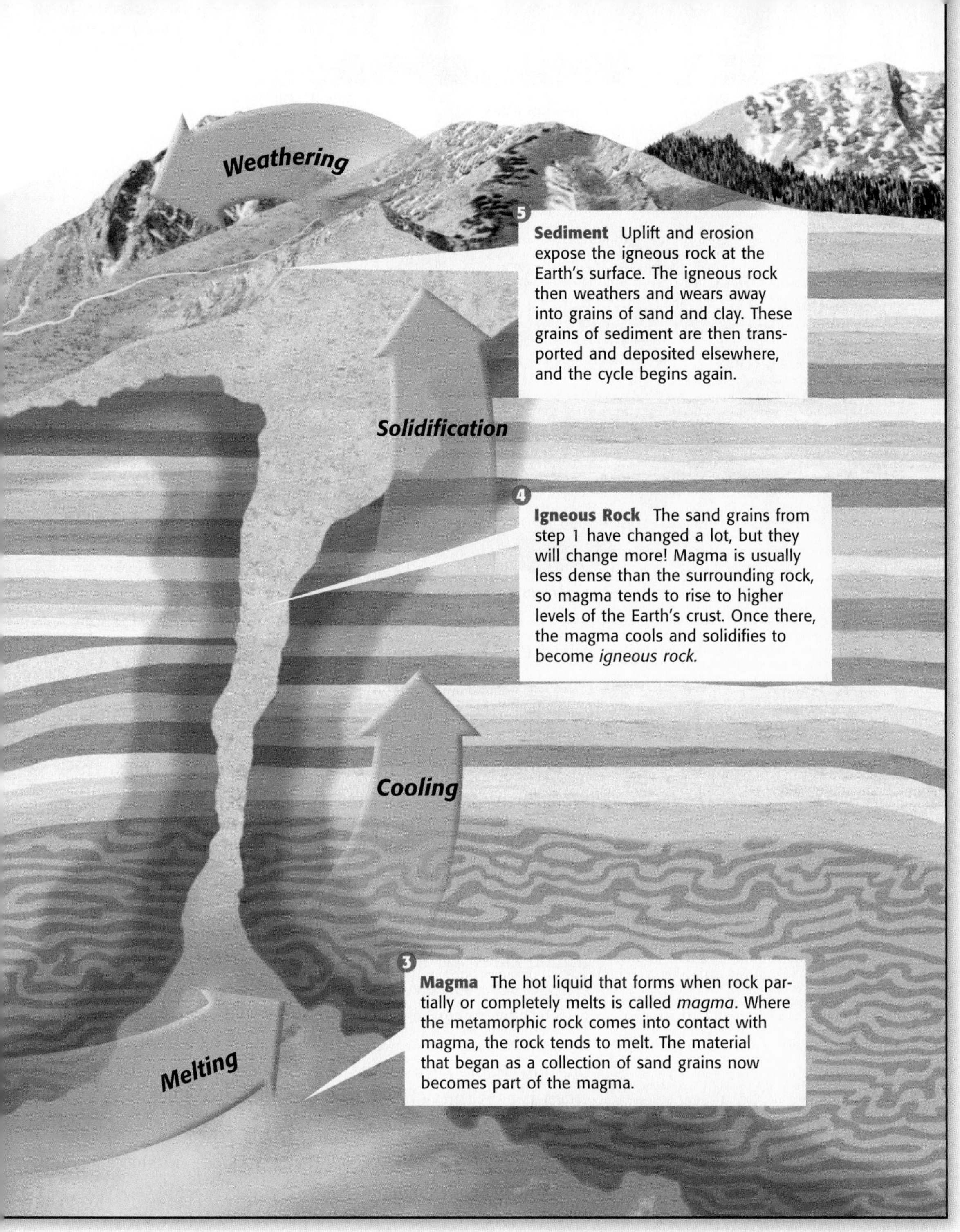
Weathering
5
Sediment Uplift and erosion expose the igneous rock at the Earth's surface. The igneous rock then weathers and wears away into grains of sand and clay. These grains of sediment are then transported and deposited elsewhere, and the cycle begins again.
Solidification
4
Igneous Rock The sand grains from step 1 have changed a lot, but they will change more! Magma is usually less dense than the surrounding rock, so magma tends to rise to higher levels of the Earth's crust. Once there, the magma cools and solidifies to become *igneous rock.*
Cooling
3
Magma The hot liquid that forms when rock partially or completely melts is called *magma*. Where the metamorphic rock comes into contact with magma, the rock tends to melt. The material that began as a collection of sand grains now becomes part of the magma.
Melting

Is That a Fact!

Geologists can use the Earth's magnetic field to determine the approximate age of rocks. They examine both igneous and sedimentary rocks to determine the pattern of magnetic reversals. When these rocks form, the magnetic minerals they contain orient with the direction of the Earth's magnetic field. The pattern of magnetic reversals allows scientists to date the rock layers.

CHAPTER RESOURCES

Technology

Transparencies
- E8 The Rock Cycle

ACTIVITY — BASIC

Rock Dictionary Have students prepare a *Rock Dictionary.* Ask them to list the three types of rock and the processes that occur in the rock cycle. Ask students to record the dictionary definition for each rock type or rock-cycle process and then define it in their own words. Encourage students to make up mnemonic devices, such as jokes or rhymes, to help them remember the meaning of each term. English Language Learners

LS Logical

CONNECTION ACTIVITY
Language Arts — BASIC

Writing **Passing Through**
Ask students to imagine being an ancient grain of sand on a beach. Have them write a letter describing their lifetime in the rock cycle. The grain of sand should pass through several processes in the rock cycle during its lifetime. Students can share their letters with the class. English Language Learners

LS Intrapersonal

Homework — GENERAL

Illustration Have students make a poster that illustrates the rock cycle. Encourage them to cut out pictures from magazines of the different types of rock and processes in the rock cycle. For example, marble is a metamorphic rock that could be represented by a picture of a marble statue. English Language Learners

LS Visual

Teach, *continued*

Figure 3 The Rock Cycle

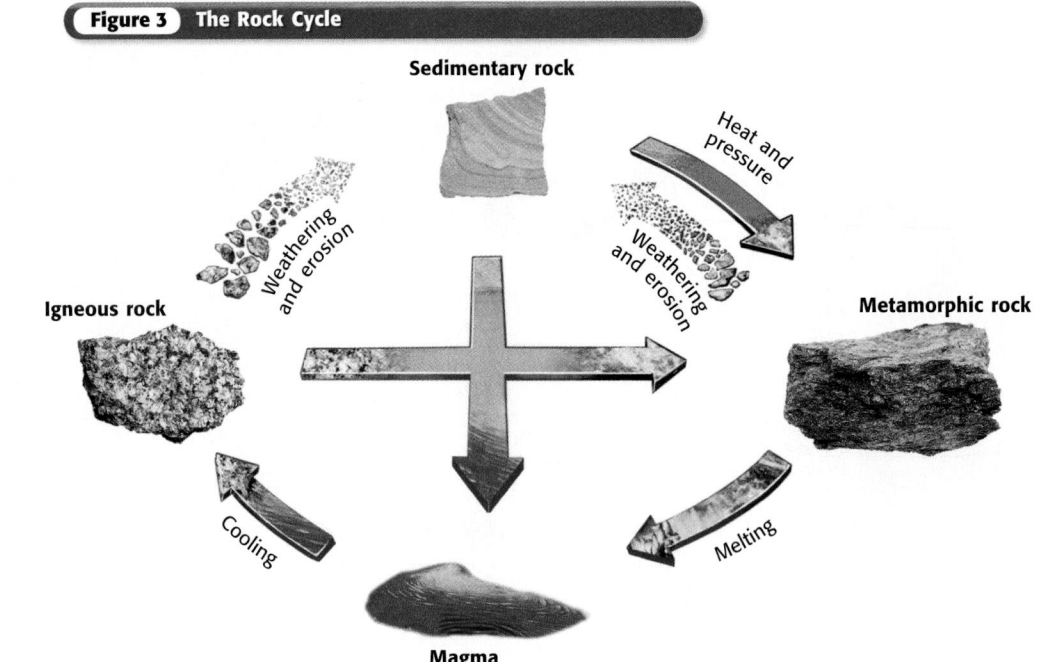

Sedimentary rock
Heat and pressure
Weathering and erosion
Weathering and erosion
Metamorphic rock
Igneous rock
Cooling
Melting
Magma

Round and Round It Goes

You have seen how different geological processes can change rock. Each rock type can change into one of the three types of rock. For example, igneous rock can change into sedimentary rock, metamorphic rock, or even back into igneous rock. This cycle, in which rock is changed by geological processes into different types of rock, is known as the rock cycle.

Rocks may follow various pathways in the rock cycle. As one rock type is changed to another type, several variables, including time, heat, pressure, weathering, and erosion may alter a rock's identity. The location of a rock determines which natural forces will have the biggest impact on the process of change. For example, rock at the Earth's surface is primarily affected by forces of weathering and erosion, whereas deep inside the Earth, rocks change because of extreme heat and pressure. **Figure 3** shows the different ways rock may change when it goes through the rock cycle and the different forces that affect rock during the cycle.

✓ **Reading Check** What processes change rock deep within the Earth?

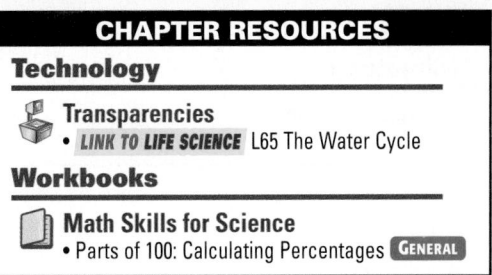
Answer to Reading Check
Rock within the Earth is affected by temperature and pressure.

Rock Classification

You have already learned that scientists divide all rock into three main classes based on how the rock formed: igneous, sedimentary, and metamorphic. But did you know that each class of rock can be divided further? These divisions are also based on differences in the way rocks form. For example, all igneous rock forms when magma cools and solidifies. But some igneous rocks form when magma cools *on* the Earth's surface, and others form when magma cools deep *beneath* the surface. Therefore, igneous rock can be divided again based on how and where it forms. Sedimentary and metamorphic rocks are also divided into groups. How do scientists know how to classify rocks? They study rocks in detail using two important criteria—composition and texture.

Composition

The minerals a rock contains determine the **composition** of that rock, as shown in **Figure 4.** For example, a rock made of mostly the mineral quartz will have a composition very similar to that of quartz. But a rock made of 50% quartz and 50% feldspar will have a very different composition than quartz does.

✓ Reading Check What determines a rock's composition?

composition the chemical makeup of a rock; describes either the minerals or other materials in the rock

What's in It?

Assume that a granite sample you are studying is made of 30% quartz and 55% feldspar by volume. The rest is made of biotite mica. What percentage of the sample is biotite mica?

Figure 4 **Two Examples of Rock Composition**

The composition of a rock depends on the minerals the rock contains.

Limestone

95% Calcite / 5% Aragonite

Granite

10% Biotite mica

35% Quartz / 55% Feldspar

CONNECTION to Math ———— GENERAL

Percentages A percentage is a ratio that is expressed in terms of hundredths. When analyzing pure substances, percentage composition remains the same at any mass. For example, in terms of atomic mass, the percentage of oxygen by weight in water is 88.8%, whether you are describing a single raindrop or an entire ocean. **LS Logical**

Answer to Math Practice

100% of rock — (30% quartz + 55% feldspar) = 15% biotite mica

Group ACTIVITY — BASIC

Describing Rocks Organize the class into small groups. Give each group samples of sandstone, limestone, and conglomerate. Number the samples. Provide a magnifying lens, a mineral identification key, a small dental pick, and paper towels (to capture any pieces of rock that break off during the activity). Write the following instructions on the board:

1. Describe the color and texture of each rock.

2. Using your unaided eye, examine the grains that make up each rock. Describe what you see.

3. Using the magnifying lens, try to identify the mineral composition of each rock.

4. Use the dental pick to test how well each rock is cemented, and record what you discover.

5. Classify each rock by grain size as fine grained, medium grained, or coarse grained.

After groups have analyzed the rocks, have group members discuss their findings. **English Language Learners**
LS Logical/Kinesthetic

Answer to Reading Check

The minerals that a rock contains determine a rock's composition.

Figure 5   **Three Examples of Sedimentary Rock Texture**

Fine-grained

Siltstone

Medium-grained

Sandstone

Coarse-grained

Conglomerate

Reteaching ——— BASIC

Diagramming the Rock Cycle
Have students create a diagram
of the processes that shape
Earth's surface. The diagram
should be a simplified version
of the rock cycle. The diagram
should include the processes of
weathering, erosion, deposition,
and uplift. **LS** Visual

Quiz ——————— GENERAL

1. List four processes that
   change rock from one type to
   another. (weathering, changes
   in pressure, melting, and cooling)

2. What are the three main
   classes of rock? (igneous, sedimentary, and metamorphic)

3. How is a brick similar to a
   metamorphic rock? (Bricks
   are made from clay and then
   baked to become strong and
   resistant to weathering. Bricks
   are "metamorphosed" by high
   temperatures.)

Alternative
Assessment ——— GENERAL

Rock Cycle Skit   Have students
write a skit portraying the rock
cycle. Roles can include the
minerals that make up rock and
the forces that affect them. To
represent the forces—heat, pressure, erosion, and weathering—
suggest that students create
special costumes. **LS** Kinesthetic

texture the quality of a rock that is
based on the sizes, shapes, and positions of the rock's grains

Texture

The size, shape, and positions of the grains that make up a rock
determine a rock's **texture.** Sedimentary rock can have a fine-
grained, medium-grained, or coarse-grained texture, depending
on the size of the grains that make up the rock. Three samples
of textures are shown in **Figure 5.** The texture of igneous rock
can be fine-grained or coarse-grained, depending on how much
time magma has to cool. Based on the degree of temperature
and pressure a rock is exposed to, metamorphic rock can also
have a fine-grained or coarse-grained texture.

The texture of a rock can provide clues as to how and
where the rock formed. Look at the rocks shown in **Figure 6.**
The rocks look different because they formed in very different ways. The texture of a rock can reveal the process that
formed it.

✓**Reading Check**   Give three examples of sedimentary rock
textures.

Figure 6   **Texture and Rock Formation**

Basalt, a fine-grained igneous
rock, forms when lava that
erupts onto Earth's surface
cools rapidly.

Sandstone, a medium-grained
sedimentary rock, forms when
sand grains deposited in dunes,
on beaches, or on the ocean
floor are buried and cemented.

Answer to Reading Check

Fine-grained rocks are made of small grains,
such as silt or clay particles. Medium-grained
rocks are made of medium-sized grains, such
as sand. Coarse-grained rocks are made of
large grains, such as pebbles.

SECTION Review

Summary

- Rock has been an important natural resource for as long as humans have existed. Early humans used rock to make tools. Ancient and modern civilizations have used rock as a construction material.

- Weathering, erosion, deposition, and uplift are all processes that shape the surface features of the Earth.

- The rock cycle is the continual process by which new rock forms from old rock material.

- The sequence of events in the rock cycle depends on processes, such as weathering, erosion, deposition, pressure, and heat, that change the rock material.

- Composition and texture are two characteristics that scientists use to classify rocks.

- The composition of a rock is determined by the minerals that make up the rock.

- The texture of a rock is determined by the size, shape, and positions of the grains that make up the rock.

Using Key Terms

Complete each of the following sentences by choosing the correct term from the word bank.

rock	composition
rock cycle	texture

1. The minerals that a rock is made of determine the ___ of that rock.

2. ___ is a naturally occurring, solid mixture of crystals of one or more minerals.

Understanding Key Ideas

3. Sediments are transported or moved from their original source by a process called
   a. deposition.
   b. erosion.
   c. uplift.
   d. weathering.

4. Describe two ways that rocks have been used by humans.

5. Name four processes that change rock inside the Earth.

6. Describe four processes that shape Earth's surface.

7. Give an example of how texture can provide clues as to how and where a rock formed.

Critical Thinking

8. **Making Comparisons** Explain the difference between texture and composition.

9. **Analyzing Processes** Explain how rock is continually recycled in the rock cycle.

Interpreting Graphics

10. Look at the table below. Sandstone is a type of sedimentary rock. If you had a sample of sandstone that had an average particle size of 2 mm, what texture would your sandstone have?

Classification of Clastic Sedimentary Rocks	
Texture	**Particle size**
coarse grained	> 2 mm
medium grained	0.06 to 2 mm
fine grained	< 0.06 mm

Developed and maintained by the National Science Teachers Association

For a variety of links related to this chapter, go to www.scilinks.org

Topic: Composition of Rock
SciLinks code: HSM0327

Answers to Section Review

1. composition

2. Rock

3. b

4. Rocks have been used by humans to make tools and weapons and to construct buildings.

5. Four processes that change rock inside the Earth are compaction and cementation, metamorphism, melting, and cooling.

6. Weathering is the process by which water, wind, ice, and heat break down rock. Erosion is the process by which sediment is removed from its source. Deposition is the process by which sediment moved by erosion is laid down. Uplift is the process by which rock within the Earth moves to Earth's surface.

7. Answers may vary. Sample answer: Fine grains in an igneous rock indicate that the rock cooled quickly, which means it was likely to have formed at Earth's surface.

8. Composition is the percent of elements that make up a rock. Texture is a quality of a rock that is based on the size, shape, and position of its grains.

9. Answers may vary. Sample answer: Rock is continually recycled by different processes in the rock cycle. Melting of sedimentary, metamorphic, or igneous rock creates new igneous rock. The weathering, erosion, deposition, burial, compression, and cementation of igneous, metamorphic, or sedimentary rock creates new sedimentary rock. Igneous, sedimentary, or metamorphic rock that is subjected to increased heat and pressure can be metamorphosed.

10. a medium-grained texture

Focus

Overview

This section discusses the formation of igneous rock from the cooling of magma. Students learn about the difference between intrusive and extrusive igneous rock. Students also learn about the difference between felsic and mafic igneous rock and how the rate of cooling affects the texture of igneous rock.

🔊 Bellringer

Pose the following question to students: "Do you think rocks that cooled and solidified from lava on Earth's surface would look different from those that cooled and solidified from magma inside the Earth? Why?"

Motivate

Discussion —— GENERAL

Volcanoes Ask students to discuss how volcanoes affect people. Discuss eruptions, lava flows, and ash clouds. Then, ask students about the benefits of volcanoes. Explain that lava and magma form land. Explain that volcanic soil is some of the most fertile soil in the world, which is why many populations are willing to live alongside potentially dangerous volcanoes. **LS** Logical

What You Will Learn

- Describe three ways that igneous rock forms.
- Explain how the cooling rate of magma affects the texture of igneous rock.
- Distinguish between igneous rock that cools within Earth's crust and igneous rock that cools at Earth's surface.

Vocabulary

intrusive igneous rock
extrusive igneous rock

READING STRATEGY

Reading Organizer As you read this section, make a table comparing intrusive rock and extrusive rock.

Igneous Rock

Where do igneous rocks come from? Here's a hint: The word **igneous** comes from a Latin word that means "fire."

Igneous rock forms when hot, liquid rock, or *magma,* cools and solidifies. The type of igneous rock that forms depends on the composition of the magma and the amount of time it takes the magma to cool.

Origins of Igneous Rock

Igneous rock begins as magma. As shown in **Figure 1,** there are three ways magma can form: when rock is heated, when pressure is released, or when rock changes composition.

When magma cools enough, it solidifies to form igneous rock. Magma solidifies in much the same way that water freezes. But there are also differences between the way magma freezes and the way water freezes. One main difference is that water freezes at 0°C. Magma freezes between 700°C and 1,250°C. Also, liquid magma is a complex mixture containing many melted minerals. Because these minerals have different melting points, some minerals in the magma will freeze or become solid before other minerals do.

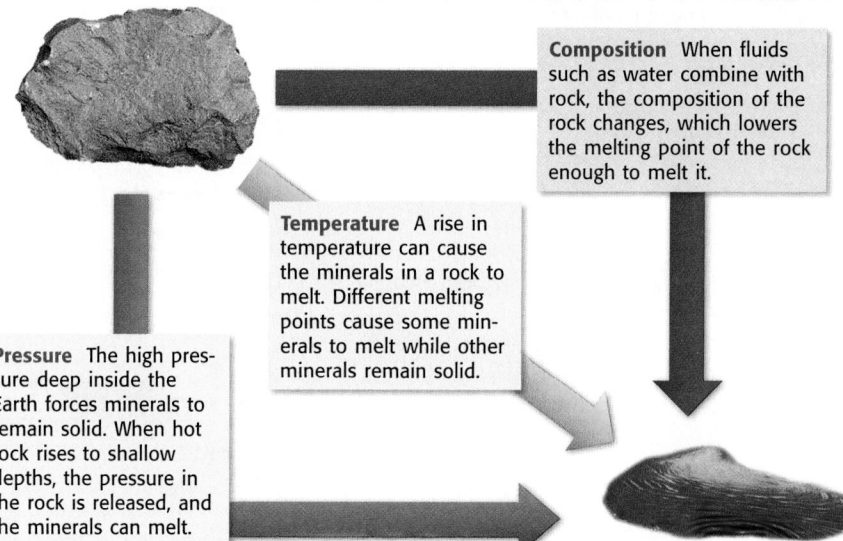

Figure 1 The Formation of Magma

Composition When fluids such as water combine with rock, the composition of the rock changes, which lowers the melting point of the rock enough to melt it.

Temperature A rise in temperature can cause the minerals in a rock to melt. Different melting points cause some minerals to melt while other minerals remain solid.

Pressure The high pressure deep inside the Earth forces minerals to remain solid. When hot rock rises to shallow depths, the pressure in the rock is released, and the minerals can melt.

CHAPTER RESOURCES

Chapter Resource File

- **Lesson Plan**
- **Directed Reading A** BASIC
- **Directed Reading B** SPECIAL NEEDS

Technology

Transparencies
- Bellringer

Workbooks

Interactive Textbook Struggling Readers

⚛ WEIRD SCIENCE

Surtsey is a volcanic island south of Iceland that people actually saw being born! In 1963, fishermen saw jets of spray, steam, and lava shooting more than 30 m out of the ocean. One month later, the volcano broke through the surface to form an island. By the time the eruptions ended, Surtsey covered an area of approximately 2.8 km².

Figure 2 Igneous Rock Texture

	Coarse-grained	Fine-grained
Felsic	Granite	Rhyolite
Mafic	Gabbro	Basalt

Composition and Texture of Igneous Rock

Look at the rocks in **Figure 2.** All of the rocks are igneous rocks even though they look different from one another. These rocks differ from one another in what they are made of and how fast they cooled.

The light-colored rocks are less dense than the dark-colored rocks are. The light-colored rocks are rich in elements such as aluminum, potassium, silicon, and sodium. These rocks are called *felsic rocks.* The dark-colored rocks, called *mafic rocks,* are rich in calcium, iron, and magnesium, and poor in silicon.

Figure 3 shows what happens to magma when it cools at different rates. The longer it takes for the magma or lava to cool, the more time mineral crystals have to grow. The more time the crystals have to grow, the larger the crystals are and the coarser the texture of the resulting igneous rock is.

In contrast, the less time magma takes to cool, the less time crystals have to grow. Therefore, the rock that is formed will be fine grained. Fine-grained igneous rock contains very small crystals, or if the cooling is very rapid, it contains no crystals.

Reading Check Explain the difference between felsic rock and mafic rock. (*See the Appendix for answers to Reading Checks.*)

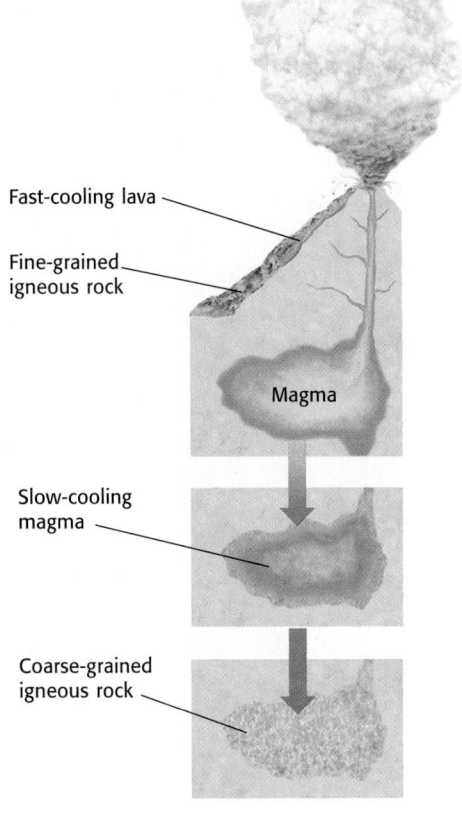

Figure 3 *The amount of time it takes for magma or lava to cool determines the texture of igneous rock.*

Fast-cooling lava

Fine-grained igneous rock

Magma

Slow-cooling magma

Coarse-grained igneous rock

Teach

Using the Figure — BASIC

Making Inferences Have students rank the rocks shown in **Figure 2** by how fast they cooled. Tell students to pay careful attention to the grain size of each rock. (From fastest cooled to slowest cooled, the rocks are basalt, rhyolite, gabbro, and granite.) **LS** Visual/Logical

CONNECTION to Life Science — ADVANCED

Life Along a Rift Until 1977, biologists thought few life-forms lived at ocean depths where sunlight does not reach. When scientists in the submersible *Alvin* explored the bottom of a deep ocean trench called the Galápagos Rift, they discovered structures called black smokers that release dissolved mineral compounds and heat the water. Scientists were amazed to discover an entire ecosystem that did not depend on photosynthesis for energy. This discovery has led some scientists to speculate that life may also have originated in the outer solar system—particularly in the oceans that may exist under the surface of Europa, one of Jupiter's moons. Have students research the bizarre life-forms that scientists found living around black smokers. **LS** Logical

Answer to Reading Check

Felsic rocks are light-colored igneous rocks rich in aluminum, potassium, silicon, and sodium. Mafic rocks are dark-colored igneous rocks rich in calcium, iron, and magnesium.

Close

Reteaching — **BASIC**

Word Meanings Compare the words *intrusive* and *extrusive* with the words *interior* and *exterior.* Have students brainstorm other words that use the prefixes *in-* and *ex-* to help them remember the meanings of the terms *intrusive* and *extrusive.* **LS Logical**   English Language Learners

Quiz — **GENERAL**

1. Name five types of bodies of intrusive igneous rock. (batholiths, stocks, dikes, sills, and volcanic necks)

2. What is a fissure? (A fissure is a long crack in the Earth's crust through which lava erupts and flows.)

Alternative Assessment — **GENERAL**

Modeling Igneous Rock Bodies Have students create a model cross section that shows the formation of both intrusive and extrusive igneous rock. Students can use **Figure 4** as a basis for their models. Supply students with several different colors of clay so that they can color-code different bodies, such as the magma source, dikes, sills, plutons, and the lava that forms extrusive rock.   English Language Learners
LS Kinesthetic/Visual

INTERNET ACTIVITY

For another activity related to this chapter, go to **go.hrw.com** and type in the keyword **HZ5RCKW**.

intrusive igneous rock rock formed from the cooling and solidification of magma beneath the Earth's surface

Figure 4 *Igneous intrusive bodies have different shapes and sizes.*

Igneous Rock Formations

Igneous rock formations are located above and below the surface of the Earth. You may be familiar with igneous rock formations that were caused by lava cooling on the Earth's surface, such as volcanoes. But not all magma reaches the surface. Some magma cools and solidifies deep within the Earth's crust.

Intrusive Igneous Rock

When magma *intrudes,* or pushes, into surrounding rock below the Earth's surface and cools, the rock that forms is called **intrusive igneous rock.** Intrusive igneous rock usually has a coarse-grained texture because it is well insulated by surrounding rock and cools very slowly. The minerals that form are large, visible crystals.

Masses of intrusive igneous rock are named for their size and shape. Common intrusive shapes are shown in **Figure 4.** *Plutons* are large, irregular-shaped intrusive bodies. The largest of all igneous intrusions are *batholiths. Stocks* are intrusive bodies that are exposed over smaller areas than batholiths. Sheetlike intrusions that cut across previous rock units are called *dikes,* whereas *sills* are sheetlike intrusions that are oriented parallel to previous rock units.

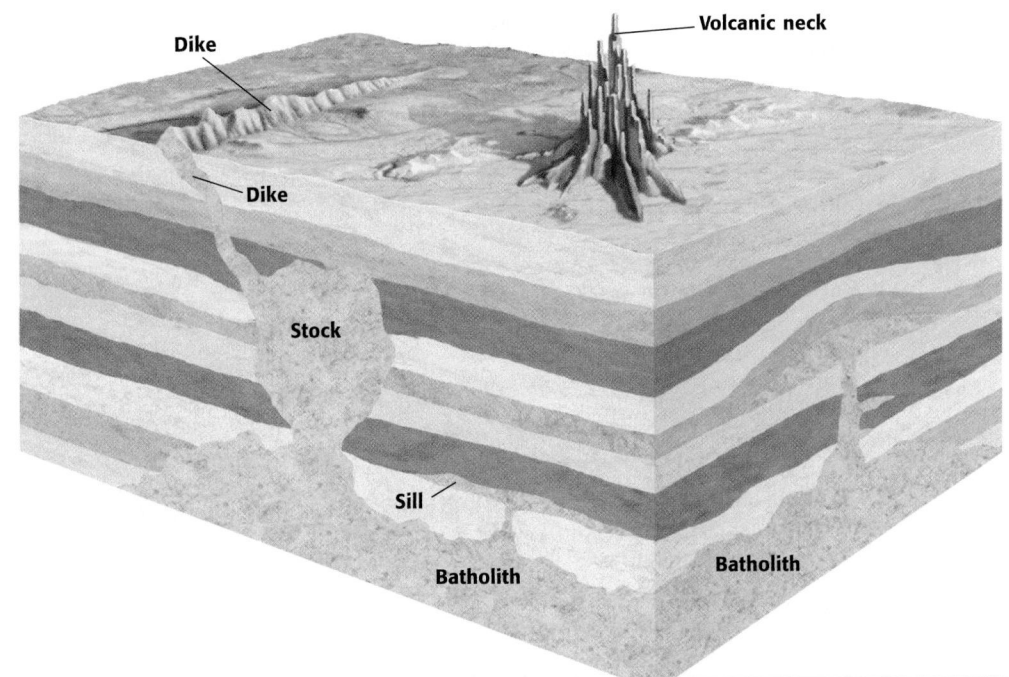

Homework — **ADVANCED**

Writing **Volcanic Necks** A volcanic neck is the hardened core of a volcano that is left behind after the volcano erodes away. Ship Rock, a volcanic neck on a Navajo reservation in New Mexico, soars 518 m above the desert. Devils Tower National Monument, in Wyoming, rises 386 m. Have students research one of these formations to learn how it formed.
LS Logical

Extrusive Igneous Rock

Igneous rock that forms from magma that erupts, or extrudes, onto the Earth's surface is called **extrusive igneous rock.** Extrusive rock is common around volcanoes. It cools quickly on the surface and contains very small crystals or no crystals.

When lava erupts from a volcano, a *lava flow* forms. **Figure 5** shows an active lava flow. Lava does not always flow from volcanoes. Sometimes lava erupts and flows from long cracks in the Earth's crust called *fissures.* Lava flows from fissures on the ocean floor at places where tension is causing the ocean floor to be pulled apart. This lava cools to form new ocean floor. When a large amount of lava flows out of fissures onto land, the lava can cover a large area and form a plain called a *lava plateau.* Pre-existing landforms are often buried by these lava flows.

✓ Reading Check How does new ocean floor form?

Figure 5 *An active lava flow is shown in this photo. When exposed to Earth's surface conditions, lava quickly cools and solidifies to form a fine-grained igneous rock.*

extrusive igneous rock rock that forms as a result of volcanic activity at or near the Earth's surface

---

SECTION Review

Summary

- Igneous rock forms when magma cools and hardens.
- The texture of igneous rock is determined by the rate at which the rock cools.
- Igneous rock that solidifies at Earth's surface is extrusive. Igneous rock that solidifies within Earth's surface is intrusive.
- Shapes of common igneous intrusive bodies include batholiths, stocks, sills, and dikes.

Using Key Terms

1. In your own words, write a definition for each of the following terms: *intrusive igneous rock* and *extrusive igneous rock.*

Understanding Key Ideas

2. ___ is an example of a coarse-grained, felsic, igneous rock.
   a. Basalt
   b. Gabbro
   c. Granite
   d. Rhyolite

3. Explain three ways in which magma can form.

4. What determines the texture of igneous rocks?

Math Skills

5. The summit of a granite batholith has an elevation of 1,825 ft. What is the height of the batholith in meters?

Critical Thinking

6. **Making Comparisons** Dikes and sills are both types of igneous intrusive bodies. What is the difference between a dike and a sill?

7. **Predicting Consequences** An igneous rock forms from slow-cooling magma deep beneath the surface of the Earth. What type of texture is this rock most likely to have? Explain.

SCILINKS® **NSTA**
Developed and maintained by the National Science Teachers Association

For a variety of links related to this chapter, go to www.scilinks.org

Topic: Igneous Rock
SciLinks code: HSM0783

Answer to Reading Check

New sea floor forms when lava that flows from fissures on the ocean floor cools and hardens.

Answers to Section Review

1. Sample answer: Intrusive igneous rock forms from magma that solidifies underground. Extrusive igneous rock forms from magma that solidifies after it has reached the surface.

2. c

3. Temperature, pressure, and a change in the composition of a rock can cause magma to form. A rise in temperature can cause minerals in a rock to melt, forming magma. When pressure in a rock that is hot is released, the minerals in that rock can melt, forming magma. When fluids such as water combine with rock, the composition of the rock changes. This change in composition lowers the melting point of the rock enough to melt it, forming magma.

4. When magma cools slowly, crystals have a longer time to grow, so the igneous rock that forms is coarse grained. When magma cools quickly, crystals have a short time to grow, so the igneous rock that forms is fine grained.

5. 1,825 ft ÷ 3.28 ft/m = 556.4 ft/m

6. A sill intrudes rock parallel to the surrounding rock layers. A dike cuts across the surrounding rock layers.

7. Because the rock formed from slowly cooling magma deep inside the Earth, the crystals had more time to grow. Therefore, the texture of the rock would most likely be coarse grained.

SECTION

3

Focus

Overview

This section explores how sedimentary rock forms and how it accumulates in layers, or strata. Students distinguish between clastic, chemical, and organic sedimentary rocks and learn how each rock type forms.

🔊 Bellringer

Ask students to write about how layers in sedimentary rock are like the rings in a tree. How are they different? What information can geologists infer by examining sedimentary layers?

Motivate

Demonstration — GENERAL

Dissolution of Minerals Limestone forms when calcium carbonate crystallizes out of ocean water. Students may not believe that water contains the chemical components of dissolved minerals. If you live in an area with hard water, have students observe ice melting in warm water. After the ice melts, there is a layer of fluffy calcium carbonate that forms at the bottom of the glass. If you live in an area with soft water, make hard water by dissolving a little baking soda and calcium chloride in water. Then, freeze the water into ice cubes. Use these ice cubes for the demonstration. **LS** Visual

What You Will Learn

● Describe the origin of sedimentary rock.

● Describe the three main categories of sedimentary rock.

● Describe three types of sedimentary structures.

Vocabulary

strata
stratification

READING STRATEGY

Reading Organizer As you read this section, create an outline of this section. Use the headings from the section in your outline.

Figure 1 *The red sandstone "monuments" for which Monument Valley in Arizona has been named are the products of millions of years of erosion.*

Sedimentary Rock

Have you ever tried to build a sand castle at the beach? Did you ever wonder where the sand came from?

Sand is a product of weathering, which breaks rock into pieces. Over time, sand grains may be compacted, or compressed, and then cemented together to form a rock called *sandstone.* Sandstone is just one of many types of sedimentary rock.

Origins of Sedimentary Rock

Wind, water, ice, sunlight, and gravity all cause rock to physically weather into fragments. Through the process of erosion, these rock and mineral fragments, called *sediment*, are moved from one place to another. Eventually, the sediment is deposited in layers. As new layers of sediment are deposited, they cover older layers. Older layers become compacted. Dissolved minerals, such as calcite and quartz, separate from water that passes through the sediment to form a natural cement that binds the rock and mineral fragments together into sedimentary rock.

Sedimentary rock forms at or near the Earth's surface. It forms without the heat and pressure that are involved in the formation of igneous and metamorphic rocks.

The most noticeable feature of sedimentary rock is its layers, or **strata.** A single, horizontal layer of rock is sometimes visible for many miles. Road cuts are good places to observe strata. **Figure 1** shows the spectacular views that sedimentary rock formations carved by erosion can provide.

CHAPTER RESOURCES

Chapter Resource File

📁 • **Lesson Plan**
• **Directed Reading A** BASIC
• **Directed Reading B** SPECIAL NEEDS

Technology

💾 **Transparencies**
• Bellringer

Workbooks

📖 **Interactive Textbook** Struggling Readers

⚛ WEIRD SCIENCE

The Bonneville Salt Flats, in Utah, are the remnants of a vast lake called Lake Bonneville. After the last ice age, most of the lake drained quickly, but much of the remaining water slowly evaporated, which left behind the salt flats. The Great Salt Lake is the largest of the lakes left after Lake Bonneville evaporated.

Figure 2 Classification of Clastic Sedimentary Rock

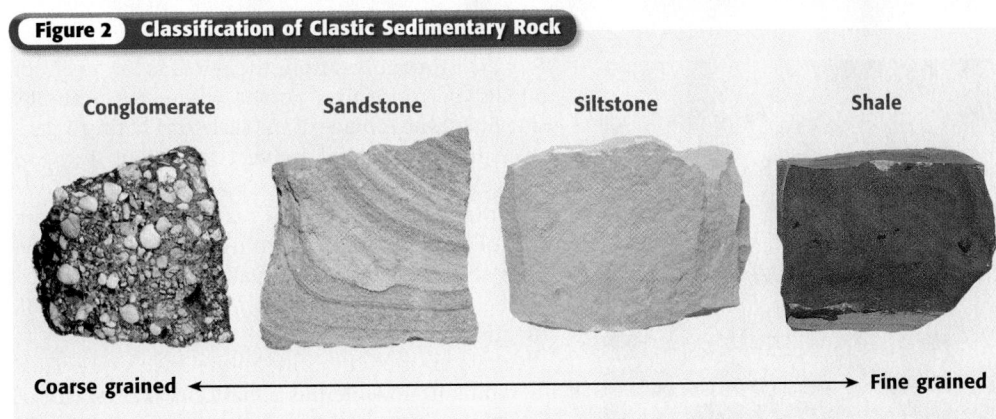

Conglomerate   Sandstone   Siltstone   Shale

Coarse grained ◄——————————————————————► Fine grained

Composition of Sedimentary Rock

Sedimentary rock is classified by the way it forms. *Clastic sedimentary rock* forms when rock or mineral fragments, called *clasts,* are cemented together. *Chemical sedimentary rock* forms when minerals crystallize out of a solution, such as sea water, to become rock. *Organic sedimentary rock* forms from the remains of once-living plants and animals.

Clastic Sedimentary Rock

Clastic sedimentary rock is made of fragments of rocks cemented together by a mineral such as calcite or quartz. **Figure 2** shows how clastic sedimentary rock is classified according to the size of the fragments from which the rock is made. Clastic sedimentary rocks can have coarse-grained, medium-grained, or fine-grained textures.

Chemical Sedimentary Rock

Chemical sedimentary rock forms from solutions of dissolved minerals and water. As rainwater slowly makes its way to the ocean, it dissolves some of the rock material it passes through. Some of this dissolved material eventually crystallizes and forms the minerals that make up chemical sedimentary rock. Halite, one type of chemical sedimentary rock, is made of sodium chloride, $NaCl$, or table salt. Halite forms when sodium ions and chlorine ions in shallow bodies of water become so concentrated that halite crystallizes from solution.

✔ **Reading Check** How does a chemical sedimentary rock such as halite form? (*See the Appendix for answers to Reading Checks.*)

strata layers of rock (singular, *stratum*)

CONNECTION TO Language Arts

WRITING SKILL **Salty Expressions** The word salt is used in many expressions in the English language. Some common examples include "the salt of the earth," "taken with a grain of salt," not worth his salt," "the salt of truth," "rubbing salt into a wound," and "old salt." Use the Internet or another source to research one these expressions. In your research, attempt to find the origin of the expression. Write a short paragraph that summarizes what you found.

Answer to Reading Check

Halite forms when sodium ions and chlorine ions in shallow bodies of water become so concentrated that halite crystallizes from solution.

Reteaching ——— BASIC

Creating a Diagram Have students select one of the three types of sedimentary rock. Ask students to create a diagram that illustrates all of the processes that occur in the formation of the rock type they have selected. **LS** Visual

Quiz ——— GENERAL

1. How does halite form? (It forms when sodium ions and chlorine ions become so concentrated in ocean water that halite crystallizes out of the water.)

2. What is stratification, and why is it important to Earth scientists? (Stratification is the layering of rock. It is important because it records many events in Earth's history, as well as erosion and deposition rates.)

Alternative Assessment ——— GENERAL

Depositional Environments
To review sedimentary rock formation, have students draw a picture of an environment that shows where the sediments come from and where they are deposited. A second drawing should show what the environment might look like millions of years later after sedimentary rock has formed. **LS** Visual

Figure 3 Ocean animals called coral create huge deposits of limestone. As they die, their skeletons collect on the ocean floor.

Organic Sedimentary Rock

Most limestone forms from the remains, or *fossils*, of animals that once lived in the ocean. For example, some limestone is made of the skeletons of tiny organisms called *coral*. Coral are very small, but they live in huge colonies called *reefs*, shown in **Figure 3.** Over time, the skeletons of these sea animals, which are made of calcium carbonate, collect on the ocean floor. These animal remains eventually become cemented together to form *fossiliferous limestone* (FAH suhl IF uhr uhs LIEM STOHN).

Corals are not the only animals whose remains are found in fossiliferous limestone. The shells of mollusks, such as clams and oysters, commonly form fossiliferous limestone. An example of fossiliferous limestone that contains mollusks is shown in **Figure 4.**

Another type of organic sedimentary rock is *coal*. Coal forms underground when partially decomposed plant material is buried beneath sediment and is changed into coal by increasing heat and pressure. This process occurs over millions of years.

Figure 4 **The Formation of Organic Sedimentary Rock**

Marine organisms, such as brachiopods, get the calcium carbonate for their shells from ocean water. When these organisms die, their shells collect on the ocean floor and eventually form fossiliferous limestone (inset). Over time, huge rock formations that contain the remains of large numbers of organisms, such as brachiopods, form.

CONNECTION ACTIVITY
Real World ——— GENERAL

Uses of Organic Sedimentary Rock
Chalk is a sedimentary rock formed from the shells of tiny marine creatures, including diatoms. The shells of diatoms contain silica, which can be used as an abrasive to clean teeth. Have students divide into groups and research other uses of organic sedimentary rock. Have each group prepare a class presentation in which they discuss the benefits and ingredients of a product made from sedimentary rock. **LS** Logical

Is That a Fact!

The Great Barrier Reef, a long coral reef that lies off the northeastern coast of Australia, is the most massive structure ever built by living creatures. It is more than 2,000 km long and covers an area of 207,000 km^2.

Sedimentary Rock Structures

Many features can tell you about the way sedimentary rock formed. The most important feature of sedimentary rock is stratification. **Stratification** is the process in which sedimentary rocks are arranged in layers. Strata differ from one another depending on the kind, size, and color of their sediment.

Sedimentary rocks sometimes record the motion of wind and water waves on lakes, oceans, rivers, and sand dunes in features called *ripple marks*, as shown in **Figure 5**. Structures called *mud cracks* form when fine-grained sediments at the bottom of a shallow body of water are exposed to the air and dry out. Mud cracks indicate the location of an ancient lake, stream, or ocean shoreline. Even raindrop impressions can be preserved in fine-grained sediments, as small pits with raised rims.

✓ **Reading Check** What are ripple marks?

Figure 5 *These ripple marks were made by flowing water and were preserved when the sediments became sedimentary rock. Ripple marks can also form from the action of wind.*

stratification the process in which sedimentary rocks are arranged in layers

---

SECTION Review

Summary

- Sedimentary rock forms at or near the Earth's surface.
- Clastic sedimentary rock forms when rock or mineral fragments are cemented together.
- Chemical sedimentary rock forms from solutions of dissolved minerals and water.
- Organic limestone forms from the remains of plants and animals.
- Sedimentary structures include ripple marks, mud cracks, and raindrop impressions.

Using Key Terms

1. In your own words, write a definition for each of the following terms: *strata* and *stratification*.

Understanding Key Ideas

2. Which of the following is an organic sedimentary rock?
   a. chemical limestone
   b. shale
   c. fossiliferous limestone
   d. conglomerate

3. Explain the process by which clastic sedimentary rock forms.

4. Describe the three main categories of sedimentary rock.

Math Skills

5. A layer of a sedimentary rock is 2 m thick. How many years did it take for this layer to form if an average of 4 mm of sediment accumulated per year?

Critical Thinking

6. **Identifying Relationships** Rocks are classified based on texture and composition. Which of these two properties would be more important for classifying clastic sedimentary rock?

7. **Analyzing Processes** Why do you think raindrop impressions are more likely to be preserved in fine-grained sedimentary rock rather than in coarse-grained sedimentary rock?

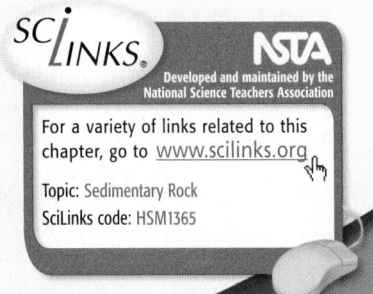

Answer to Reading Check

Ripple marks are the marks left by wind and water waves on lakes, seas, rivers, and sand dunes.

CHAPTER RESOURCES

Chapter Resource File

- Section Quiz GENERAL
- Section Review GENERAL
- Vocabulary and Section Summary GENERAL

Answers to Section Review

1. Sample answer: Strata are layers in sedimentary rock. Stratification is the process in which layers are arranged into sedimentary rock.

2. c

3. Clastic sedimentary rock is formed by the processes of weathering, erosion, deposition, compaction, and cementation. Rocks are physically weathered into fragments called sediment. Sediment is transported by erosion and is deposited in layers. Older layers of sediments are compacted by younger layers of sediments. Sediments in layers that have been compacted are cemented together by minerals that are dissolved in water, such as calcite and quartz, forming clastic sedimentary rock.

4. Clastic sedimentary rock forms when sediments are compacted and cemented together. Chemical sedimentary rock forms when dissolved minerals separate out of solution and crystallize. Organic sedimentary rock is made from the remains of animals that once lived in the ocean.

5. 2 m = 2,000 mm; 2,000 mm ÷ 4 mm/year = 500 years

6. Texture is more useful in classifying clastic sedimentary rock because the size of the grain can provide clues to where and how the rock was formed.

7. Answers may vary. Sample answer: The finer the grains of sediment are, the more likely delicate structures such as raindrop impressions will be preserved in them.

Focus

Overview

This section examines what happens when rock metamorphoses. Changes in heat or pressure can alter a rock's chemical nature and physical structure. Students will learn how different types of metamorphism cause changes in rock texture.

 Bellringer

Ask students to write a brief description of how cookies are made. Ask them to consider how the mixture of raw ingredients is like sedimentary rock. Ask them to describe how cookie dough metamorphoses when it is baked in an oven.

Motivate

ACTiViTY ———— GENERAL

Modeling Metamorphism

Provide each student with pieces of red, yellow, green, and purple modeling clay. Have students flatten each piece, pile the pieces on top of each other, and press down on them firmly. Then, have students push inward on opposite sides of the stack or pull the stack gently so that the clay doesn't break apart. Explain that they will be learning how intense pressure and heat can cause rock to behave in similar ways. **LS** Visual/Kinesthetic

What You Will Learn

- Describe two ways a rock can undergo metamorphism.
- Explain how the mineral composition of rocks changes as the rocks undergo metamorphism.
- Describe the difference between foliated and nonfoliated metamorphic rock.
- Explain how metamorphic rock structures are related to deformation.

Vocabulary

foliated
nonfoliated

READING STRATEGY

Discussion Read this section silently. Write down questions that you have about this section. Discuss your questions in a small group.

Metamorphic Rock

Have you ever watched a caterpillar change into a butterfly? Some caterpillars go through a biological process called metamorphosis in which they completely change their shape.

Rocks can also go through a process called *metamorphism*. The word *metamorphism* comes from the Greek words *meta,* which means "changed," and *morphos,* which means "shape." Metamorphic rocks are rocks in which the structure, texture, or composition of the rock have changed. All three types of rock can be changed by heat, pressure, or a combination of both.

Origins of Metamorphic Rock

The texture or mineral composition of a rock can change when its surroundings change. If the temperature or pressure of the new environment is different from the one in which the rock formed, the rock will undergo metamorphism.

The temperature at which most metamorphism occurs ranges from 50°C to 1,000°C. However, the metamorphism of some rocks takes place at temperatures above 1,000°C. It seems that at these temperatures the rock would melt, but this is not true of metamorphic rock. It is the depth and pressure at which metamorphic rocks form that allows the rock to heat to this temperature and maintain its solid nature. Most metamorphic change takes place at depths greater than 2 km. But at depths greater than 16 km, the pressure can be 4,000 times greater than the pressure of the atmosphere at Earth's surface.

Large movements within the crust of the Earth cause additional pressure to be exerted on a rock during metamorphism. This pressure can cause the mineral grains in rock to align themselves in certain directions. The alignment of mineral grains into parallel bands is shown in the metamorphic rock in **Figure 1.**

Figure 1 *This metamorphic rock is an example of how mineral grains were aligned into distinct bands when the rock underwent metamorphism.*

CHAPTER RESOURCES

Chapter Resource File

 • **Lesson Plan**
• **Directed Reading A** BASIC, **B** SPECIAL NEEDS

Technology

 Transparencies
• Bellringer
• E10 Regional and Contact Metamorphism

Workbooks

 Interactive Textbook Struggling Readers

 **Math Skills for Science**
• The Unit Factor and Dimensional Analysis GENERAL

WEIRD SCIENCE

When rocks metamorphose under high temperature and pressure, they become plastic and can be easily deformed. It is not unusual for spherical pebbles in a conglomerate to be stretched into ellipses more than 30 times their original diameter!

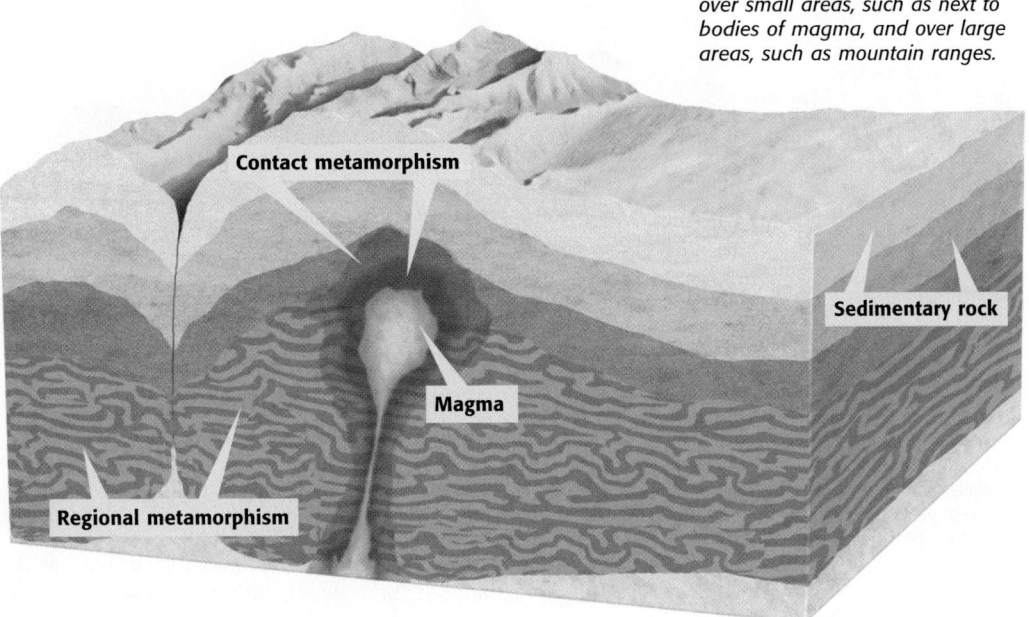

Contact metamorphism

Sedimentary rock

Magma

Regional metamorphism

Contact Metamorphism

One way rock can undergo metamorphism is by being heated by nearby magma. When magma moves through the crust, the magma heats the surrounding rock and changes it. Some minerals in the surrounding rock are changed into other minerals by this increase in temperature. The greatest change takes place where magma comes into direct contact with the surrounding rock. The effect of heat on rock gradually decreases as the rock's distance from the magma increases and as temperature decreases. *Contact metamorphism* occurs near igneous intrusions, as shown in **Figure 2.**

Regional Metamorphism

When pressure builds up in rock that is buried deep below other rock formations or when large pieces of the Earth's crust collide with each other, *regional metamorphism* occurs. The increased pressure and temperature causes rock to become deformed and chemically changed. Unlike contact metamorphism, which happens near bodies of magma, regional metamorphism occurs over thousands of cubic kilometers deep within Earth's crust. Rocks that have undergone regional metamorphism are found beneath most continental rock formations.

Reading Check Explain how and where regional metamorphism takes place. (*See the Appendix for answers to Reading Checks.*)

Answer to Reading Check

Regional metamorphism occurs when pressure builds up in rock that is buried deep below other rock formations or when large pieces of the Earth's crust collide. The increased pressure can cause thousands of square miles of rock to become deformed and chemically changed.

 Quick Lab

Stretching Out

1. Sketch the crystals in granite rock on a **piece of paper** with a **black-ink pen.** Be sure to include the outline of the rock, and fill it in with different crystal shapes.

2. Flatten some **plastic play putty** over your drawing, and slowly peel it off.

3. After making sure that the outline of your granite has been transferred to the putty, squeeze and stretch the putty. What happened to the crystals in the granite? What happened to the granite?

Is That a Fact!

The largest expanse of exposed metamorphic rock in the world is the Canadian Shield, a huge horseshoe-shaped region encircling Hudson Bay. Covering about half of Canada, it is about 4,586,900 km^2 and is the source of more than 70% of the minerals mined in Canada.

Using the Figure— BASIC

Writing **Analogies** Ask students to think of some analogies for contact metamorphism (for example, an egg frying in a skillet). Have students draw a diagram of the process of contact metamorphism. Have the class think of some analogies for regional metamorphism (for example, making toast). Then, have students draw a diagram of the process of regional metamorphism. **LS Logical/Visual**

 **Quick Lab**

MATERIALS

FOR EACH STUDENT
• black-ink pen
• paper
• plastic play putty

Answer

3. The "crystals" become stretched and deformed. The "granite" changed its shape because of the force applied to it.

MISCONCEPTION ALERT

Metamorphism As you discuss **Figure 2,** be sure students understand that the composition of a metamorphic rock and the heat and pressure it is subjected to determine how much it deforms. Students should understand that the bulk composition of rock does not change during metamorphism unless fluids are introduced into the rock. However, the mineral composition of the rock may change as heat and pressure change.

Metamorphic Minerals Several types of minerals found in metamorphic rock, such as garnet, tourmaline, and serpentine, are used in sculpture and in jewelry making. Encourage students to choose one of these minerals, research it, and create a poster illustrating how it forms and what its uses are. **LS Visual**

MISCONCEPTION ALERT

Heat and Temperature Heat and temperature are not the same thing. Heat is the transfer of thermal energy from one object to another. Temperature is a measure of how hot (or cold) something is. Temperature is not a form of energy. When a rock comes into contact with magma, thermal energy is transferred from the magma to the rock because the magma is at a higher temperature than the rock. As a result, the temperature of the rock increases while the temperature of the magma decreases. But heating a rock does not always raise its temperature. If the rock is already so hot that it is on the verge of melting, additional heat will cause the rock to melt (and change state), but will not change the rock's temperature.

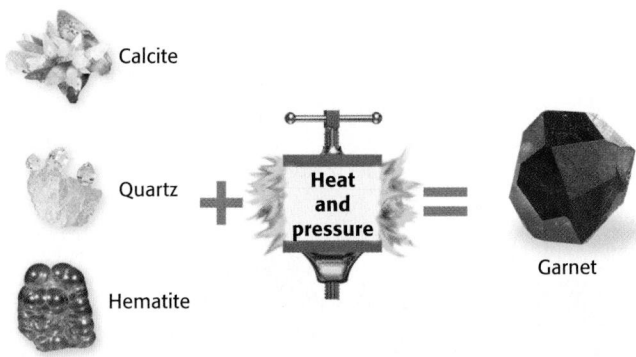

Figure 3 *The minerals calcite, quartz, and hematite combine and recrystallize to form the metamorphic mineral garnet.*

Calcite

Quartz + **Heat and pressure** = Garnet

Hematite

SCHOOL to HOME

Making a Rock Collection
With a parent or guardian, try to collect a sample of each class of rock described in this chapter. You may wish to collect rocks from road cuts or simply collect pebbles from your garden or driveway. Try to collect samples that show the composition and texture of each rock. Classify the rocks in your collection, and bring it to class. With other members of the class, discuss your rock samples and see if they are accurately identified.

Figure 4 *Scientists can understand a metamorphic rock's history by observing the minerals the rock contains. For example, a metamorphic rock that contains garnet formed at a greater depth and under greater heat and pressure than a rock that contains only chlorite.*

Composition of Metamorphic Rock

Metamorphism occurs when temperature and pressure inside the Earth's crust change. Minerals that were present in the rock when it formed may not be stable in the new temperature and pressure conditions. The original minerals change into minerals that are more stable in these new conditions. Look at **Figure 3** to see an example of how this change happens.

Many of these new minerals form only in metamorphic rock. As shown in **Figure 4,** some metamorphic minerals form only at certain temperatures and pressures. These minerals, known as *index minerals,* are used to estimate the temperature, depth, and pressure at which a rock undergoes metamorphism. Index minerals include biotite mica, chlorite, garnet, kyanite, muscovite mica, sillimanite, and staurolite.

✓ Reading Check What is an index mineral?

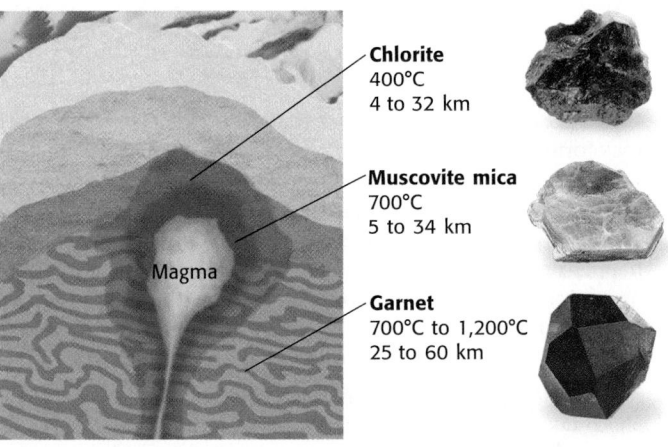

Chlorite
400°C
4 to 32 km

Muscovite mica
700°C
5 to 34 km

Magma

Garnet
700°C to 1,200°C
25 to 60 km

Answer to Reading Check

An index mineral is a metamorphic mineral that forms only at certain temperatures and pressures and therefore can be used by scientists to estimate the temperature, pressure, and depth at which a rock undergoes metamorphosis.

SUPPORT FOR

English Language Learners

Making Models To help students "see" the composition of Earth's crust, have students work in pairs to make a model cross section. The model should include materials that represent magma, contact and regional metamorphic rocks, and sedimentary strata. Students should label each different material with the English word or words for what it represents. Associating sections of the crust with the words that identify them will increase comprehension. **LS Visual/Verbal**

Textures of Metamorphic Rock

You have learned that texture helps scientists classify igneous and sedimentary rock. The same is true of metamorphic rock. All metamorphic rock has one of two textures—foliated or nonfoliated. Take a closer look at each of these types of metamorphic rock to find out how each type forms.

Foliated Metamorphic Rock

The texture of metamorphic rock in which the mineral grains are arranged in planes or bands is called **foliated.** Foliated metamorphic rock usually contains aligned grains of flat minerals, such as biotite mica or chlorite. Look at **Figure 5.** Shale is a sedimentary rock made of layers of clay minerals. When shale is exposed to slight heat and pressure, the clay minerals change into mica minerals. The shale becomes a foliated metamorphic rock called *slate*.

Metamorphic rocks can become other metamorphic rocks if the environment changes again. If slate is exposed to more heat and pressure, the slate can change into rock called *phyllite*. When phyllite is exposed to heat and pressure, it can change into *schist*.

If metamorphism continues, the arrangement of minerals in the rock changes. More heat and pressure cause minerals to separate into distinct bands in a metamorphic rock called *gneiss* (NIES).

Figure 5 *The effects of metamorphism depend on the heat and pressure applied to the rock. Here you can see what happens to shale, a sedimentary rock, when it is exposed to more and more heat and pressure.*

foliated the texture of metamorphic rock in which the mineral grains are arranged in planes or bands

Sedimentary shale

Slate

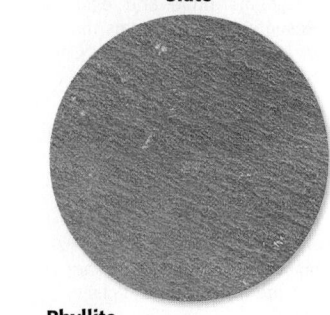

Phyllite

Schist

Gneiss

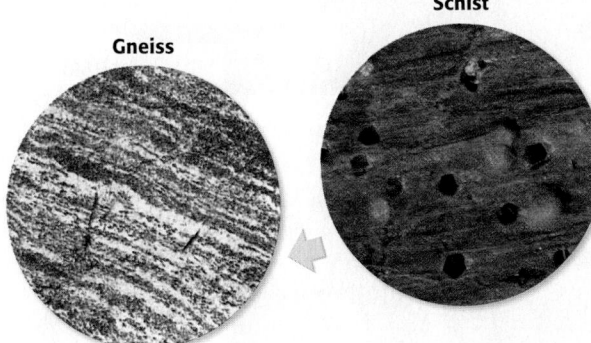

Discussion — BASIC

Predicting Patterns Display metamorphic rocks in groups of foliated rocks (slate, phyllite, schist, and gneiss) and nonfoliated rocks (quartzite, marble, hornfels, and soapstone). Have students compare the rocks according to color, appearance, and composition. Explain that the temperature and pressure of regional metamorphism tend to produce foliated rocks, whereas the temperature of contact metamorphism tends to produce nonfoliated rocks. Ask students to predict what the terms *foliated* and *nonfoliated* mean and then read further to see if they were correct. **LS** Visual/Logical

CONNECTION ACTiViTY Real World — ADVANCED

Asbestos Removal Asbestos is an informal name for a group of fibrous minerals usually found in regionally metamorphosed rock. Manufacturers value these minerals because minerals resist burning and don't readily conduct thermal energy or electric current. However, some kinds of asbestos fracture into tiny needles that can become airborne. This dust is linked to a lung disease called *asbestosis*. As a result, asbestos has been removed from many public places at great expense. Have students find out about the many uses for asbestos and any cleanup projects that are occurring in your area. Have students summarize their findings in the form of a poster. **LS** Logical

INCLUSION Strategies

- *Behavior Control*
- *Attention Deficit Disorder*
- *Gifted and Talented*

Have students conduct a scavenger hunt in their classroom to identify minerals that are used to make items that we use every day. Organize students into groups of 3 to 4 students. Assign each group an area of the classroom, and provide each group with self-stick labels to mark items made out of minerals. Each group should try to label the mineral(s) that make up each item. Items made of minerals that students may identify include light bulbs, electrical wiring, door knobs, locks, hinges, windows, plumbing fixtures, and pencils. Ask students what additional items made of minerals may be found in their homes. Talented and gifted students can do additional research on minerals used to make a light bulb and/or a computer. **LS** Visual/Logical

English Language Learners

Creating an Outline Have students select a type of foliated or nonfoliated metamorphic rock. Ask students to create an outline of the steps that occur in the formation of the rock. Some students may want to write their outline in the form of a recipe for making a metamorphic rock. **LS** Logical

Quiz — GENERAL

1. Why is marble considered a nonfoliated metamorphic rock? (Its mineral grains are not arranged in planes or bands.)

2. What does the composition of a metamorphic rock tell you about the rock's origin and formation? (Different metamorphic minerals indicate the temperature and pressure conditions that existed when the rock formed.)

Alternative Assessment — GENERAL

Preparing a Lesson Have students prepare a lesson about this chapter to present to a second-grade class. They will need to prepare vocabulary lists, illustrations, and worksheets to help the younger students understand the types of rock, the uses of rock, and the way rocks form. **LS** Logical/Visual

---

CONNECTION TO Biology

WRITING SKILL **Metamorphosis** The term *metamorphosis* means "change in form." When some animals undergo a dramatic change in the shape of their body, they are said to have undergone a metamorphosis. As part of their natural life cycle, moths and butterflies go through four stages. After they hatch from an egg, they are in the larval stage in the form of a caterpillar. In the next stage, they build a cocoon or become a chrysalis. This stage is called the *pupal stage*. They finally emerge into the adult stage of their life, in which they have wings, antennae, and legs! Research other animals that undergo a metamorphosis, and summarize your findings in a short essay.

nonfoliated the texture of metamorphic rock in which the mineral grains are not arranged in planes or bands

---

Nonfoliated Metamorphic Rock

The texture of metamorphic rock in which the mineral grains are not arranged in planes or bands is called **nonfoliated**. Notice that the rocks shown in **Figure 6** do not have mineral grains that are aligned. This lack of aligned mineral grains is the reason these rocks are called *nonfoliated rocks*.

Nonfoliated rocks are commonly made of one or only a few minerals. During metamorphism, the crystals of these minerals may change in size or the mineral may change in composition in a process called *recrystallization*. The quartzite and marble shown in **Figure 6** are examples of sedimentary rocks that have recrystallized during metamorphism.

Quartz sandstone is a sedimentary rock made of quartz sand grains that have been cemented together. When quartz sandstone is exposed to the heat and pressure, the spaces between the sand grains disappear as the grains recrystallize to form quartzite. Quartzite has a shiny, glittery appearance. Like quartz sandstone, it is made of quartz. But during recrystallization, the mineral grains have grown larger than the original grains in the sandstone.

When limestone undergoes metamorphism, the same process that happened to the quartz happens to the calcite, and the limestone becomes marble. The calcite crystals in the marble are larger than the calcite grains in the original limestone.

Figure 6 Two Examples of Nonfoliated Metamorphic Rock

Marble and quartzite are nonfoliated metamorphic rocks. As you can see in the views through a microscope, the mineral crystals are not well aligned.

Marble

Quartzite

Homework — ADVANCED

Investigate Your Area Have students look at stone buildings and houses around their town. Ask students to identify the rock used in construction as igneous, sedimentary, or metamorphic. Ask students to consider the following questions: Which rock type was most commonly used? Which rock type was used least? Why was a specific rock type used for a particular application? Encourage students to find out the origin of rock used in buildings in your community. **LS** Visual

Metamorphic Rock Structures

Like igneous and sedimentary rock, metamorphic rock also has features that tell you about its history. In metamorphic rocks, these features are caused by deformation. *Deformation* is a change in the shape of a rock caused by a force placed on it. These forces may cause a rock to be squeezed or stretched.

Folds, or bends, in metamorphic rock are structures that indicate that a rock has been deformed. Some folds are not visible to the naked eye. But, as shown in **Figure 7,** some folds may be kilometers or even hundreds of kilometers in size.

✓ Reading Check How are metamorphic rock structures related to deformation?

Figure 7 *These large folds occur in metamorphosed sedimentary rock along Saglet Fiord in Labrador, Canada.*

SECTION Review

Summary

- Metamorphic rocks are rocks in which the structure, texture, or composition has changed.
- Two ways rocks can undergo metamorphism are by contact metamorphism and regional metamorphism.
- As rocks undergo metamorphism, the original minerals in a rock change into new minerals that are more stable in new pressure and temperature conditions.
- Foliated metamorphic rock has mineral crystals aligned in planes or bands, whereas nonfoliated rocks have unaligned mineral crystals.
- Metamorphic rock structures are caused by deformation.

Using Key Terms

1. In your own words, define the following terms: *foliated* and *nonfoliated.*

Understanding Key Ideas

2. Which of the following is not a type of foliated metamorphic rock?
   a. gneiss
   b. slate
   c. marble
   d. schist

3. Explain the difference between contact metamorphism and regional metamorphism.

4. Explain how index minerals allow a scientist to understand the history of a metamorphic rock.

Math Skills

5. For every 3.3 km a rock is buried, the pressure placed upon it increases 0.1 gigapascal (100 million pascals). If rock undergoing metamorphosis is buried at 16 km, what is the pressure placed on that rock? (Hint: The pressure at Earth's surface is .101 gigapascal.)

Critical Thinking

6. **Making Inferences** If you had two metamorphic rocks, one that has garnet crystals and the other that has chlorite crystals, which one could have formed at a deeper level in the Earth's crust? Explain your answer.

7. **Applying Concepts** Which do you think would be easier to break, a foliated rock, such as slate, or a nonfoliated rock, such as quartzite? Explain.

8. **Analyzing Processes** A mountain range is located at a boundary where two tectonic plates are colliding. Would most of the metamorphic rock in the mountain range be a product of contact metamorphism or regional metamorphism? Explain.

SCLINKS

NSTA
Developed and maintained by the
National Science Teachers Association

For a variety of links related to this chapter, go to www.scilinks.org

Topic: Metamorphic Rock
SciLinks code: HSM0949

Let's Get Sedimental

Teacher's Notes

Time Required
Two 45-minute class periods

Lab Ratings

EASY ——————————→ HARD

Teacher Prep 🧪
Student Set-Up 🧪🧪
Concept Level 🧪🧪
Clean Up 🧪🧪

MATERIALS

The materials listed are enough for a group of three or four students. You may substitute smaller plastic bottles. The amount of sand, gravel, and soil depends on the size of the jar. Each group will need enough of these materials to fill the bottle two-thirds full with a mixture of sand, gravel, and soil.

Safety Caution
Students should be extremely careful when cutting the sides from the plastic bottles.

Preparation Notes
If the students use larger plastic bottles, the sediment may take several days to dry completely. It may be a good idea to ask the students to follow steps 1–5 as an introduction to the chapter. The class can then finish the procedure when the sediment has dried.

Skills Practice Lab

OBJECTIVES

Model the process of sedimentation.

Determine whether sedimentary rock layers are undisturbed.

MATERIALS

- clay
- dropper pipet
- gravel
- magnifying lens
- mixing bowl, 2 qt
- sand
- scissors
- soda bottle with a cap, plastic, 2 L
- soil, clay rich, if available
- water

SAFETY

Lab Notes
This lab illustrates the sedimentary (depositional) process of sorting. When sediment is suspended in water, the largest, heaviest particles will settle out first, followed by the finer, lighter particles. This process can allow scientists and students studying sedimentary rock layers to determine the original orientation of the rock.

Let's Get Sedimental

How do we determine if sedimentary rock layers are undisturbed? The best way to do this is to be sure that fine-grained sediments near the top of a layer lie above coarse-grained sediments near the bottom of the layer. This lab activity will show you how to read rock features that will help you distinguish individual sedimentary rock layers. Then, you can look for the features in real rock layers.

Procedure

1. In a mixing bowl, thoroughly mix the sand, gravel, and soil. Fill the soda bottle about one-third full of the mixture.

2. Add water to the soda bottle until the bottle is two-thirds full. Twist the cap back onto the bottle, and shake the bottle vigorously until all of the sediment is mixed in the rapidly moving water.

3. Place the bottle on a tabletop. Using the scissors, carefully cut the top off the bottle a few centimeters above the water, as shown. The open bottle will allow water to evaporate.

4. Immediately after you set the bottle on the tabletop, describe what you see from above and through the sides of the bottle.

5. Do not disturb the container. Allow the water to evaporate. (You may speed up the process by carefully using the dropper pipet to siphon off some of the clear water after you allow the container to sit for at least 24 hours.) You may also set the bottle in the sun or under a desk lamp to speed up evaporation.

6. After the sediment has dried and hardened, describe its surface.

7. Carefully lay the container on its side, and cut a wide, vertical strip of plastic down the length of the bottle to expose the sediments in the container. You may find it easier if you place pieces of clay on either side of the container to stabilize it. (If the bottle is clear along its length, this step may not be required.)

8. Brush away the loose material from the sediment, and gently blow on the surface until it is clean. Examine the surface, and record your observations.

CHAPTER RESOURCES

Chapter Resource File

 • **Datasheet for Chapter Lab**
• **Lab Notes and Answers**

Technology

 Classroom Videos
• Lab Video

• Crystal Growth
• Metamorphic Mash

Analyze the Results

1. **Identifying Patterns** Do you see anything through the side of the bottle that could help you determine if a sedimentary rock is undisturbed? Explain your answer.

2. **Identifying Patterns** Can you observe a pattern of deposition? If so, describe the pattern of deposition of sediment that you observe from top to bottom.

3. **Explaining Events** Explain how these features might be used to identify the top of a sedimentary layer in real rock and to decide if the layer has been disturbed.

4. **Identifying Patterns** Do you see any structures through the side of the bottle that might indicate which direction is up, such as a change in particle density or size?

5. **Identifying Patterns** Use the magnifying lens to examine the boundaries between the gravel, sand, and silt. Do the size of the particles and the type of sediment change dramatically in each layer?

Draw Conclusions

6. **Making Predictions** Imagine that a layer was deposited directly above the sediment in your bottle. Describe the composition of this new layer. Will it have the same composition as the mixture in steps 1–5 in the Procedure?

Applying Your Data

With your class or with a parent, visit an outcrop of sedimentary rock. Apply the information that you have learned in this lab to see if you can determine whether the sedimentary rock layers are disturbed or undisturbed.

Analyze the Results

1. Answers may vary. Students should understand that the finest sediments should be at the top. This sequence can indicate the top of a layer in a sedimentary outcrop. If the layers are not in this order, the rock may have been disturbed.

2. Students should indicate that in the sorting process, gravel settled out first, followed by sand, and then soil.

3. If features that geologists expect to find only in the top layer are found elsewhere, this finding indicates that the column has been disturbed. Geologists carefully study the layers for these features so that they can determine the original order of the layers.

4. Each layer should show finer particles at the top. This pattern can be seen only from the side.

5. Students should see the same grading effect at the boundaries. The changes within each layer will be gradual, but the changes between layers may be more dramatic.

Draw Conclusions

6. If sediment having the same particle sizes as the mixture in steps 1–5 is deposited on top of the sediment in the bottle, the new layer should have the same composition as the layer in the bottle.

Assignment Guide

SECTION	QUESTIONS
1	1, 2, 10, 12, 15–16, 21–25
2	5, 7, 8, 11, 19
3	4, 6
4	3, 9, 13–14, 18, 20
2, 3, and 4	17

ANSWERS

Using Key Terms

1. Sample answer: The rock cycle is the process in which one rock type changes into another rock type. In this process, rock is continuously recycled.

2. texture

3. Foliated

4. stratification

5. Extrusive igneous rock

Understanding Key Ideas

6. c

7. d

8. c

9. b

10. b

11. d

12. Scientists use differences in composition, or the minerals a rock is made up of, to classify rock. Scientists use differences in texture—the sizes, shapes, and positions of the grains a rock is made up of—to further classify rocks.

USING KEY TERMS

1. In your own words, write a definition for the term *rock cycle*.

Complete each of the following sentences by choosing the correct term from the word bank.

stratification	foliated
extrusive igneous rock	texture

2. The ___ of a rock is determined by the sizes, shapes, and positions of the minerals the rock contains.

3. ___ metamorphic rock contains minerals that are arranged in plates or bands.

4. The most characteristic property of sedimentary rock is ___.

5. ___ forms plains called *lava plateaus*.

UNDERSTANDING KEY IDEAS

Multiple Choice

6. Sedimentary rock is classified into all of the following main categories except
   a. clastic sedimentary rock.
   b. chemical sedimentary rock.
   c. nonfoliated sedimentary rock.
   d. organic sedimentary rock.

7. An igneous rock that cools very slowly has a ___ texture.
   a. foliated
   b. fine-grained
   c. nonfoliated
   d. coarse-grained

8. Igneous rock forms when
   a. minerals crystallize from a solution.
   b. sand grains are cemented together.
   c. magma cools and solidifies.
   d. mineral grains in a rock recrystallize.

9. A ___ is a common structure found in metamorphic rock.
   a. ripple mark   c. sill
   b. fold   d. layer

10. The process in which sediment is removed from its source and transported is called
   a. deposition.   c. weathering.
   b. erosion.   d. uplift.

11. Mafic rocks are
   a. light-colored rocks rich in calcium, iron, and magnesium.
   b. dark-colored rocks rich in aluminum, potassium, silica, and sodium.
   c. light-colored rocks rich in aluminum, potassium, silica, and sodium.
   d. dark-colored rocks rich in calcium, iron, and magnesium.

Short Answer

12. Explain how composition and texture are used by scientists to classify rocks.

13. Describe two ways a rock can undergo metamorphism.

14. Explain why some minerals only occur in metamorphic rocks.

15. Describe how each type of rock changes as it moves through the rock cycle.

13. Two ways in which a rock can undergo metamorphism is by contact metamorphism and regional metamorphism. Contact metamorphism occurs near igneous intrusions, where magma comes in direct contact with the surrounding rock. Regional metamorphism occurs when pressure builds up in deep rock or when large pieces of Earth's crust collide, deforming and chemically changing rock over large areas.

14. Some minerals can form only at specific pressures and temperatures present during metamorphism.

15. Sample answer: When rocks are buried, they are heated and squeezed to create metamorphic rock. Sometimes, the heat is enough to melt the rock and create magma, which cools to form igneous rock. Buried rocks are uplifted, and when rocks at the Earth's surface are eroded, sediments are created. These sediments are buried and later harden into sedimentary rock.

16 Describe two ways rocks were used by early humans and ancient civilizations.

CRITICAL THINKING

17 **Concept Mapping** Use the following terms to construct a concept map: *rocks, metamorphic, sedimentary, igneous, foliated, nonfoliated, organic, clastic, chemical, intrusive,* and *extrusive.*

18 **Making Inferences** If you were looking for fossils in the rocks around your home and the rock type that was closest to your home was metamorphic, do you think that you would find many fossils? Explain your answer.

19 **Applying Concepts** Imagine that you want to quarry, or mine, granite. You have all of the equipment, but you have two pieces of land to choose from. One area has a granite batholith underneath it. The other has a granite sill. If both intrusive bodies are at the same depth, which one would be the better choice for you to quarry? Explain your answer.

20 **Applying Concepts** The sedimentary rock coquina is made up of pieces of seashells. Which of the three kinds of sedimentary rock could coquina be? Explain your answer.

21 **Analyzing Processes** If a rock is buried deep inside the Earth, which geological processes cannot change the rock? Explain your answer.

INTERPRETING GRAPHICS

The bar graph below shows the percentage of minerals by mass that compose a sample of granite. Use the graph below to answer the questions that follow.

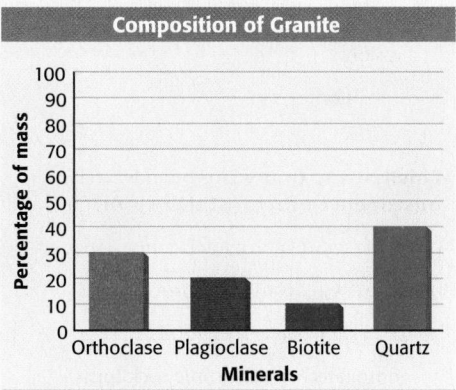

22 Your rock sample is made of four minerals. What percentage of each mineral makes up your sample?

23 Both plagioclase and orthoclase are feldspar minerals. What percentage of the minerals in your sample of granite are not feldspar minerals?

24 If your rock sample has a mass of 10 g, how many grams of quartz does it contain?

25 Use paper, a compass, and a protractor or a computer to make a pie chart. Show the percentage of each of the four minerals your sample of granite contains. (Look in the Appendix of this book for help on making a pie chart.)

16. Two ways rocks were used by early humans and ancient civilizations were as tools and as building materials.

Critical Thinking

17. 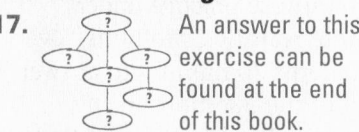 An answer to this exercise can be found at the end of this book.

18. You would not find many—or any—fossils where you live because fossils are usually found in sedimentary rock, not metamorphic rock. (Occasionally, fossils are preserved in metamorphic rock that was once sedimentary rock.)

19. The property with the batholith would be a better buy because batholiths are much bigger than sills.

20. The seashells that make up coquina are made up of the remains of once-living organisms, so coquina is an organic sedimentary rock. (The shells are technically clasts, because they are particles that have been deposited.)

21. A rock buried deep beneath the surface cannot be changed by weathering and erosion, which are geological processes that change Earth's surface features.

Interpreting Graphics

22. orthoclase = 30%, plagioclase = 20%, biotite = 10%, quartz = 40%

23. plagioclase + orthoclase = 30% + 20% = 50%
100% − 50% = 50%
Fifty percent of the minerals in the granite are not feldspars.

24. 10 g × 0.40 = 4 g

25. Accept all reasonable responses. Charts should show the correct percentages of the minerals.

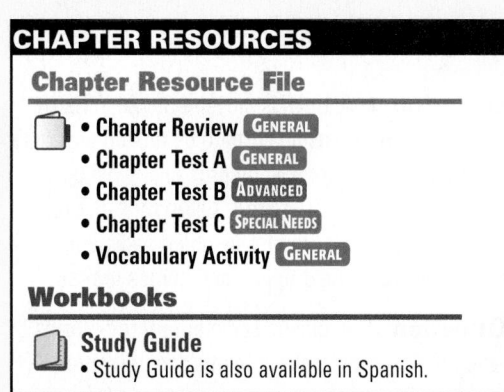

CHAPTER RESOURCES

Chapter Resource File

- Chapter Review GENERAL
- Chapter Test A GENERAL
- Chapter Test B ADVANCED
- Chapter Test C SPECIAL NEEDS
- Vocabulary Activity GENERAL

Workbooks

Study Guide
- Study Guide is also available in Spanish.

Teacher's Notes

To provide practice under more realistic conditions, give students 20 minutes to answer all of the questions in this Standardized Test Preparation.

Answer Key

Question	Answer
1	C
2	D
3	A
4	B
5	A
6	D
7	C
8	B
9	A
10	D
11	A
12	*
13	*

*See Test Doctor.

Multiple Choice

1. **The process by which water, wind, ice, or gravity transports soil and sediment from one location to another is called**

    A. uplift.

    B. weathering.

    C. erosion.

    D. deposition.

2. **Which of the following occurs as a consequence of recrystallization?**

    A. clastic sedimentary rock forms

    B. extrusive igneous rock forms

    C. intrusive igneous rock forms

    D. nonfoliated metamorphic rock forms

3. **Igneous rock forms when**

    A. magma cools and hardens.

    B. minerals crystallize out of sea water.

    C. heat and pressure change the composition and texture of a rock.

    D. natural cement binds rock fragments together.

4. **Volcanic activity on Earth's surface would most likely result in the formation of which of the following types of rock?**

    A. intrusive igneous rock

    B. extrusive igneous rock

    C. clastic sedimentary rock

    D. chemical sedimentary rock

Use the diagram below to answer question 5.

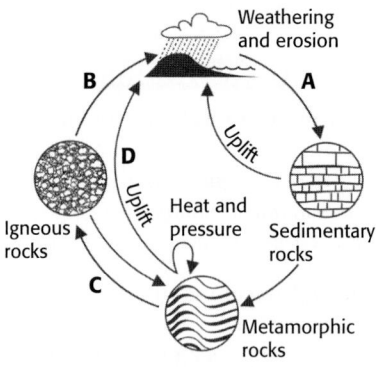

The Rock Cycle

5. **Which of the following processes occurs at point C on the diagram of the rock cycle shown above?**

    A. deposition

    B. uplift

    C. heat and pressure

    D. melting and cooling

6. **During metamorphism, limestone changes to become a metamorphic rock called marble. What happens to the calcite in the limestone during this process?**

    A. The calcite crystals change in chemical composition.

    B. The calcite crystals separate to form bonds.

    C. The calcite crystals become quartz crystals.

    D. The calcite crystals recrystallize and grow larger.

✚ TEST DOCTOR

Question 1 A: Uplift is movement within Earth that causes rocks inside Earth to be moved to Earth's surface. B: Weathering is the process by which wind, water, ice, or heat break down rock. C: Correct. D: Deposition is the process in which sediment moved by erosion is dropped and comes to rest.

Question 2 A: Clastic sedimentary rock forms when rocks or mineral fragments are cemented together. B: Extrusive igneous rock forms from magma that erupts onto Earth's surface. C: Intrusive igneous rock forms from the cooling and solidification of magma beneath Earth's surface. D: Correct.

Question 3 A: Correct. B: Sedimentary rock forms when minerals crystallize out of seawater. C: Metamorphic rock forms when heat and pressure change the texture of a rock. D: Sedimentary rock forms when natural cement binds rock fragments together.

Question 4 A: Intrusive igneous rock forms from the cooling and solidification of magma beneath Earth's surface. B: Correct. C: Clastic sedimentary rock forms when rock or mineral fragments are cemented together. D: Chemical sedimentary rock forms when minerals crystallize out of sea water to become rock.

7. **A rock that forms from the melting and cooling of rock has which of the following characteristics?**

   A. It is made of crystals.

   B. It is made of fragments of other rocks.

   C. It has bands of minerals.

   D. It is dark in color.

8. **Buried rock is exposed at Earth's surface by the combination of which two processes?**

   A. weathering and deposition

   B. uplift and erosion

   C. erosion and deposition

   D. deposition and uplift

9. **How does clastic sedimentary rock form?**

   A. Rock fragments are cemented together by a mineral such as calcite or quartz.

   B. Dissolved minerals crystallize out of solution in water to form solid minerals.

   C. Partially decomposed plant material is turned into rock by heat and pressure.

   D. Skeletons of sea animals that collected on the ocean floor are cemented together.

10. **Stratification would occur as the result of which of the following processes?**

    A. the cooling and solidification of magma

    B. the partial or complete melting of rock

    C. the deformation of rock by heat and pressure

    D. the deposition of sediments in a body of water

Use the table below to answer question 11.

Rock Type

Rock Sample	Texture	Composition
Sample A	coarse-grained	mica, quartz, and feldspar
Sample B	medium-grained	quartz sand in quartz cement
Sample C	foliated	biotite mica
Sample D	fine-grained	olivine, pyroxene, feldspar

11. **Which of the four rock samples in the table above most likely formed through the process of heating and cooling beneath Earth's surface?**

    A. Sample A

    B. Sample B

    C. Sample C

    D. Sample D

Open Response

12. **Kaolin is a white claystone that is composed of kaolinite and other minerals. Kaolin is used as a coating on glossy paper. It is also used in the production of ceramics, paints, plastics, and rubber. What type of rock is kaolin? How is kaolin rock formed?**

13. **Elberton granite can be seen all over the United States, in buildings, monuments, and gravestones. The stone consists of coarse light-gray and dark-gray grains, which give it a speckled appearance. What was the process that formed Elberton granite? What can you infer about the properties of this stone from its uses?**

Uplift is movement within Earth that causes rocks inside Earth to be moved to Earth's surface.

Question 9 A: Correct. B: Chemical sedimentary rock forms when dissolved minerals crystallize out of solution in water to form solid minerals. C: Coal forms when partially decomposed plant material is turned into rock by heat and pressure. D: Organic sedimentary rock forms when skeletons of sea animals collected on the ocean floor are cemented together.

Question 10 A: The cooling and solidification of magma results in the formation of igneous rock. B: The partial or complete melting of rock forms magma. C: The deformation of rock by heat and pressure results in the formation of metamorphic rock. D: Correct.

Question 11 A: Correct. B: Rock B is a clastic sedimentary rock that formed through cementation, not melting and cooling. C: Rock C is a metamorphic rock that formed through heat and pressure, not melting and cooling. D: Rock D is an igneous rock that formed through melting and cooling at Earth's surface.

Question 12 Full-credit answers should include the following points:

- Kaolin is a clastic sedimentary rock.
- Kaolin is formed when kaolinite and other mineral particles become cemented together.
- The particles in kaolin were cemented together by a mineral such as calcite or quartz.

Question 13 Full-credit answers should include the following points:

- Elberton granite is an igneous rock, which formed when melted magma cooled.
- This granite formed from melted quartz, feldspar, and mica.
- It was most likely formed by an intrusion of magma, which cooled slowly below Earth's surface to create the coarse-grained rock.
- Because the rock is used for buildings and monuments, it must be strong and durable outdoors.

Question 5 A: Correct. B: Uplift occurs when any of the rock types move to the surface and are exposed to weathering and erosion. C: Heat and pressure change igneous or sedimentary rock to metamorphic rock. Heat and pressure can also cause further changes to metamorphic rock. D: Melting and cooling change metamorphic rock to igneous rock.

Question 6 A: The calcite crystals have the same composition in limestone as they have in marble. B: Bonds are formed when crystals grow larger, and not when they separate. C: The chemical formula for calcite, $CaCO_3$, is not the same as the chemical formula for quartz, SiO_2. Calcite cannot change into quartz. D: Correct.

Question 7 A: A rock that is made of crystals is an igneous rock. B: A rock that is made of fragments of other rocks is a sedimentary rock. C: Correct. D: The color of a rock that forms from the melting and cooling of rock will vary according to the minerals present in the original rock.

Question 8 A: Weathering breaks down rocks at Earth's surface into sediment, and sediment is laid down in low-lying areas in the process of deposition. B: Correct. C: Sediment is removed from its source by the process of erosion and is laid down in low-lying areas in the process of deposition. D: Sediment is laid down in low-lying areas in the process of deposition.

Science, Technology, and Society

Background

Archaeologists estimate that Easter Island was first settled sometime between 400 CE and 700 CE. The first inhabitants arrived from Polynesia. This was confirmed in 1994, when DNA extracted from 12 Easter Island skeletons was found to be Polynesian. Either Tahiti or the Marquesas islands, which had been reached by Melanesian seafarers by at least 300 CE, were the most likely starting point for these voyages.

Scientific Discoveries

Background

Sixty-five million years ago, an asteroid at least 10 km wide struck the Earth near Yucatán, Mexico. Some scientists think the collision caused the extinction of approximately 15% to 20% of life on Earth, including the dinosaurs. Today, the crater is buried beneath 1,100 m of limestone, so there are few clues to the crater's existence. As scientists drilled into the impact site, they found mineral evidence of shock metamorphism. They confirmed that rocks in the area had been subjected to a high-pressure event.

Science in Action

Science, Technology, and Society

The Moai of Easter Island

Easter island is located in the Pacific Ocean more than 3,200 km from the coast of Chile. The island is home to mysterious statues that were carved from volcanic ash. The statues, called *moai*, have human heads and large torsos. The average moai weighs 14 tons and is more than 4.5 m tall, though some are as tall as 10 m! Altogether, 887 moai have been discovered. How old are the moai? Scientists believe that the moai were built between 500 and 1,000 years ago. What purpose did moai serve for their creators? The moai may have been religious symbols or gods.

Social Studies ACTIVITY

WRITING SKILL Research another ancient society or civilization, such as the ancient Egyptians, who are believed to have used stone to construct monuments to their gods or to important people. Report your findings in a short essay.

Scientific Discoveries

Shock Metamorphism

When a large asteroid, meteoroid, or comet collides with the Earth, extremely high temperatures and pressures are created in Earth's surface rock. These high pressures and temperatures cause minerals in the surface rock to shatter and recrystallize. The new minerals that result from this recrystallization cannot be created under any other conditions. This process is called *shock metamorphism*.

When large objects from space collide with the Earth, craters are formed by the impact. However, impact craters are not always easy to find on Earth. Scientists use shock metamorphism as a clue to locate ancient impact craters.

Language Arts ACTIVITY

WRITING SKILL The impact site caused by the asteroid strike in the Yucatán 65 million years ago has been named the Chicxulub (cheeks OO loob) structure. Research the origin of the name Chicxulub, and report your findings in a short paper.

Answer to Social Studies Activity

Have students report their findings to the class. While reporting their findings, students should pinpoint the location of the monuments they are discussing on a world map.

Answer to Language Arts Activity

Hold a short discussion with the class about the meaning of the name *Chicxulub* (in the local Mayan dialect, *Chicxulub* means "the devil's tail") and the importance of the Chicxulub impact structure. While doing so, point out the location of the Chicxulub impact site on a map. You may also want to discuss other large North American impact structures, such as Sudbury in Ontario, Canada, Manicouagan in Quebec, Canada, and the impact structure in Chesapeake Bay, in Virginia, USA.

Robert L. Folk

Petrologist For Dr. Robert Folk, the study of rock takes place on the microscopic level. Dr. Folk is searching for tiny life-forms he has named nannobacteria, or dwarf bacteria, in rock. *Nannobacteria* may also be spelled *nanobacteria*. Because nannobacteria are so incredibly small, only 0.05 to 0.2 μm in diameter, Folk must use an extremely powerful 100,000× microscope, called a *scanning electron microscope,* to see the shape of the bacteria in rock. Folk's research had already led him to discover that a certain type of Italian limestone is produced by bacteria. The bacteria were consuming the minerals, and the waste of the bacteria was forming the limestone. Further research led Folk to the discovery of the tiny nannobacteria. The spherical or oval-shaped nannobacteria appeared as chains and grapelike clusters. From his research, Folk hypothesized that nannobacteria are responsible for many inorganic reactions that occur in rock. Many scientists are skeptical of Folk's nannobacteria. Some skeptics believe that the tiny size of nannobacteria makes the bacteria simply too small to contain the chemistry of life. Others believe that nannobacteria actually represent structures that do not come from living things.

Math ACTIVITY

If a nannobacterium is 1/10 the length, 1/10 the width, and 1/10 the height of an ordinary bacterium, how many nannobacteria can fit within an ordinary bacterium? (Hint: Draw block diagrams of both a nannobacterium and an ordinary bacterium.)

go.hrw.com

To learn more about these Science in Action topics, visit go.hrw.com and type in the keyword **HZ5RCKF.**

Current Science

Check out Current Science® articles related to this chapter by visiting go.hrw.com. **Just type in the keyword HZ5CS04.**

Answer to Math Activity
$10 \times 10 \times 10 = 10^3 = 1{,}000$ nannobacteria can fit within a normal bacterium.

The Rock and Fossil Record
Chapter Planning Guide

Compression guide:
To shorten instruction because of time limitations, omit Section 1.

OBJECTIVES	LABS, DEMONSTRATIONS, AND ACTIVITIES	TECHNOLOGY RESOURCES
PACING • 90 min pp. 278–283 **Chapter Opener**	SE **Start-up Activity**, p. 279 GENERAL	OSP **Parent Letter** ■ CD **Student Edition on CD-ROM** CD **Guided Reading Audio CD** ■ CRF **Chapter Starter Transparency*** VID **Brain Food Video Quiz**
Section 1 Earth's Story and Those Who First Listened • Compare uniformitarianism and catastrophism. • Describe how the science of geology has changed over the past 200 years. • Explain the role of paleontology in the study of Earth's history.	TE **Activity** Debate Posters, p. 280 GENERAL SE **Connection to Biology** Darwin and Lyell, p. 281 GENERAL TE **Connection Activity** Language Arts, p. 281 GENERAL LB **Inquiry Labs** A Penny for Your Thoughts* GENERAL	OSP **Lesson Plans** (also in print) TR **Bellringer Transparency*** TR **E14 Hutton and the Principle of Uniformitarianism***
PACING • 90 min pp. 284–289 **Section 2 Relative Dating: Which Came First?** • Explain how relative dating is used in geology. • Explain the principle of superposition. • Describe how the geologic column is used in relative dating. • Identify two events and two features that disrupt rock layers. • Explain how physical features are used to determine relative ages.	TE **Demonstration** Superposition, p. 284 GENERAL TE **Activity** Modeling Faults and Intrusions, p. 286 ◆ GENERAL TE **Group Activity** Field Trip, p. 286 GENERAL TE **Activity** Unconformities, p. 287 BASIC SE **Model-Making Lab** How Do You Stack Up?, p. 306 ◆ GENERAL	OSP **Lesson Plans** (also in print) TR **Bellringer Transparency*** TR **E15 Constructing the Geologic Column*** VID **Lab Videos for Earth Science**
PACING • 45 min pp. 290–293 **Section 3 Absolute Dating: A Measure of Time** • Describe how radioactive decay occurs. • Explain how radioactive decay relates to radiometric dating. • Identify four types of radiometric dating. • Determine the best type of radiometric dating to use to date an object.	TE **Activity** Absolute Dating Skit, p. 290 GENERAL TE **Connection Activity** Math, p. 290 GENERAL LB **Long-Term Projects & Research Ideas** The Hard Rock Chronicles* ADVANCED LB **Labs You Can Eat** Geopancakes* BASIC	OSP **Lesson Plans** (also in print) TR **Bellringer Transparency*** TR **LINK TO PHYSICAL SCIENCE** P64 Radioactive Decay and Half-Life*
PACING • 45 min pp. 294–299 **Section 4 Looking at Fossils** • Describe five ways that different types of fossils form. • List three types of fossils that are not part of organisms. • Explain how fossils can be used to determine the history of changes in environments and organisms. • Explain how index fossils can be used to date rock layers.	TE **Group Activity** Carbon Impressions, p. 294 ◆ GENERAL SE **Connection to Environmental Science** Preservation in Ice, p. 295 GENERAL TE **Activity** Making Fossils, p. 295 ◆ GENERAL TE **Group Activity** Imagining Environmental Change, p. 297 GENERAL SE **Quick Lab** Make a Fossil, p. 297 ◆ GENERAL SE **School-to-Home Activity** Fossil Hunt, p. 298 GENERAL	OSP **Lesson Plans** (also in print) TR **Bellringer Transparency***
PACING • 45 min pp. 300–305 **Section 5 Time Marches On** • Explain how geologic time is recorded in rock layers. • Identify important dates on the geologic time scale. • Explain how environmental changes resulted in the extinction of some species.	TE **Connection Activity** Math, p. 300 GENERAL TE **Activity** Learning About the Eons, p. 301 BASIC TE **Connection Activity** Language Arts, p. 302 GENERAL TE **Activity** Prehistoric Illustrations, p. 304 ADVANCED LB **EcoLabs & Field Activities** Rock of Ages* ADVANCED	OSP **Lesson Plans** (also in print) TR **Bellringer Transparency*** TR **E111 The Geologic Time Scale*** SE **Internet Activity**, p. 301 GENERAL CRF **SciLinks Activity*** GENERAL

PACING • 90 min

CHAPTER REVIEW, ASSESSMENT, AND STANDARDIZED TEST PREPARATION

CRF **Vocabulary Activity*** GENERAL
SE **Chapter Review**, pp. 308–309 GENERAL
CRF **Chapter Review*** ■ GENERAL
CRF **Chapter Tests A*** ■ GENERAL, **B*** ADVANCED, **C*** SPECIAL NEEDS
SE **Standardized Test Preparation**, pp. 310–311 GENERAL
CRF **Standardized Test Preparation*** GENERAL
CRF **Performance-Based Assessment*** GENERAL
OSP **Test Generator, Test Item Listing**

Online and Technology Resources

 Holt Online Learning

Visit go.hrw.com for access to Holt Online Learning, or enter the keyword **HS7 Home** for a variety of free online resources.

 **One-Stop Planner® CD-ROM**

This CD-ROM package includes:
• Lab Materials QuickList Software
• Holt Calendar Planner
• Customizable Lesson Plans
• Printable Worksheets

• ExamView® Test Generator
• Interactive Teacher's Edition
• Holt PuzzlePro®
• Holt PowerPoint® Resources

SKILLS DEVELOPMENT RESOURCES	SECTION REVIEW AND ASSESSMENT	CORRELATIONS
SE Pre-Reading Activity, p. 278 `GENERAL` **OSP** Science Puzzlers, Twisters & Teasers* `GENERAL`		**National Science Education Standards** SAI 1, 2
CRF Directed Reading A* ■ `BASIC`, B* `SPECIAL NEEDS` **WB** Workbook* Struggling Readers **CRF** Vocabulary and Section Summary* ■ `GENERAL` **SE** Reading Strategy Reading Organizer, p. 280 `GENERAL` **TE** Support for English Language Learners, p. 281	**SE** Reading Checks, pp. 281, 282 `GENERAL` **TE** Reteaching, p. 282 `BASIC` **TE** Quiz, p. 282 `GENERAL` **TE** Alternative Assessment, p. 282 `GENERAL` **SE** Section Review,* p. 283 ■ `GENERAL` **CRF** Section Quiz* ■ `GENERAL`	UCP 2, 4; SAI 1, 2; SPSP 5; HNS 1, 2, 3; ES 2a
CRF Directed Reading A* ■ `BASIC`, B* `SPECIAL NEEDS` **WB** Workbook* Struggling Readers **CRF** Vocabulary and Section Summary* ■ `GENERAL` **SE** Reading Strategy Reading Organizer, p. 284 `GENERAL` **TE** Support for English Language Learners, p. 285 **TE** Reading Strategy Prediction Guide, p. 286 `BASIC` **CRF** Reinforcement Worksheet A Geologic Column Sandwich* `BASIC`	**SE** Reading Checks, pp. 285, 287, 288 `GENERAL` **TE** Reteaching, p. 288 `BASIC` **TE** Quiz, p. 288 `GENERAL` **TE** Alternative Assessment, p. 288 `GENERAL` **SE** Section Review,* p. 289 ■ `GENERAL` **CRF** Section Quiz* ■ `GENERAL`	UCP 1, 2; HNS 2; ES 2b *Chapter Lab:* SAI 1, 2
CRF Directed Reading A* ■ `BASIC`, B* `SPECIAL NEEDS` **WB** Workbook* Struggling Readers **CRF** Vocabulary and Section Summary* ■ `GENERAL` **SE** Reading Strategy Reading Organizer, p. 290 `GENERAL` **TE** Support for English Language Learners, p. 291 **TE** Reading Strategy Activity, p. 291 `GENERAL` **TE** Inclusion Strategies, p. 291	**SE** Reading Checks, pp. 291, 293 `GENERAL` **TE** Reteaching, p. 293 `BASIC` **TE** Quiz, p. 293 `GENERAL` **TE** Alternative Assessment, p. 293 `GENERAL` **SE** Section Review,* p. 294 ■ `GENERAL` **CRF** Section Quiz* ■ `GENERAL`	UCP 1, 3; SAI 1, 2; ST 2; SPSP 5; HNS 1, 2, 3; ES 2b
CRF Directed Reading A* ■ `BASIC`, B* `SPECIAL NEEDS` **WB** Workbook* Struggling Readers **CRF** Vocabulary and Section Summary* ■ `GENERAL` **SE** Reading Strategy Reading Organizer, p. 294 `GENERAL` **TE** Reading Strategy Activity, p. 295 `GENERAL` **TE** Support for English Language Learners, p. 297	**SE** Reading Checks, pp. 294, 296, 298, 299 `GENERAL` **TE** Reteaching, p. 298 `BASIC` **TE** Quiz, p. 298 `GENERAL` **TE** Alternative Assessment, p. 298 `ADVANCED` **TE** Homework, p. 298 `GENERAL` **SE** Section Review,* p. 299 ■ `GENERAL` **CRF** Section Quiz* ■ `GENERAL`	UCP 1, 2, 3, 4; SAI 1, 2; SPSP 5; ES 1k, 2b
CRF Directed Reading A* ■ `BASIC`, B* `SPECIAL NEEDS` **WB** Workbook* Struggling Readers **CRF** Vocabulary and Section Summary* ■ `GENERAL` **SE** Reading Strategy Brainstorming, p. 300 `GENERAL` **TE** Support for English Language Learners, p. 301 **TE** Reading Strategy Mnemonics, p. 302 `GENERAL` **TE** Inclusion Strategies, p. 303 **CRF** Critical Thinking Adiós Alamosaurus* `ADVANCED`	**SE** Reading Checks, pp. 301, 302, 304 `GENERAL` **TE** Homework, p. 301 `ADVANCED` **TE** Reteaching, p. 304 `BASIC` **TE** Quiz, p. 304 `GENERAL` **TE** Alternative Assessment, p. 304 `GENERAL` **SE** Section Review,* p. 305 ■ `GENERAL` **TE** Homework, p. 305 `GENERAL` **CRF** Section Quiz* ■ `GENERAL`	UCP 1, 3; SAI 1, 2; HNS 2; ES 2b

SCILINKS.
NSTA
www.scilinks.org
Maintained by the **National Science Teachers Association.** See Chapter Enrichment pages that follow for a complete list of topics.

Current Science®
Check out *Current Science* articles and activities by visiting the HRW Web site at go.hrw.com. Just type in the keyword **HZ5CS06T.**

Classroom Videos
- **Lab Videos** demonstrate the chapter lab.
- **Brain Food Video Quizzes** help students review the chapter material.

Classroom CD-ROMs
- **Guided Reading Audio CD** (Also in Spanish)
- **Interactive Explorations**
- **Virtual Investigations**
- **Visual Concepts**
- **Science Tutor**

Holt Lab Generator CD-ROM
Search for any lab by topic, standard, difficulty level, or time. Edit any lab to fit your needs, or create your own labs. Use the Lab Materials QuickList software to customize your lab materials list.

Visual Resources

CHAPTER STARTER TRANSPARENCY

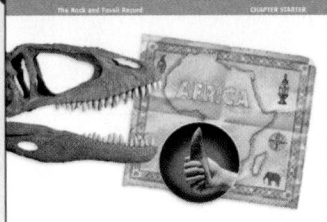

What a Find!

Imagine that you are a scientist looking for fossils. You are climbing up a sandstone cliff in unexplored mountains in North Africa. The sun is scorching. The temperature is 120°F in the shade. You see a tooth in the 90-million-year-old rock. It looks like a shark's tooth, but it is more than 12 cm long! You dig around the tooth and discover that it is attached to a huge skull. Eventually, you uncover the entire skull, which contains a full set of these ferocious teeth. The skull measures about 1.6 m in length, which is about the height of a refrigerator. You realize that this skull with savage teeth belonged to a large dinosaur.

You take the skull back to your lab to study it more closely. Given the size of the skull, you decide the skeleton of the animal it came from must have been about 14 m long—about as big as a school bus. That's even larger than *Tyrannosaurus rex!* This 90-million-year-old giant you have found most likely chased other dinosaurs by running on large, powerful hind legs, and its blade-like teeth meant certain death for its prey. You have discovered a vicious predator from the past!

BELLRINGER TRANSPARENCIES

Section: Earth's Story and Those Who First Listened
"The Present Is the Key to the Past." This phrase was the cornerstone of the uniformitarianist theory developed by geologist James Hutton in the late 1700s.

Write a few sentences in your **science journal** about how studying the present could reveal the story of Earth's history. Use sketches to illustrate processes that occurred millions of years ago that you can still see today.

Section: Relative Dating: Which Came First?
Arrange the following sentences in a logical order to make a short story:
I stood in the checkout line.
I selected two apples.
I walked home from the store.
I gave the cashier money.
I went to the store.
The cashier gave me change.
I was hungry.

Write your story in your **science journal.**

TEACHING TRANSPARENCIES

Hutton and the Principle of Uniformitarianism

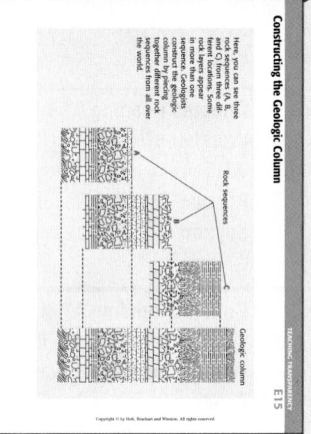

Constructing the Geologic Column

TEACHING TRANSPARENCIES

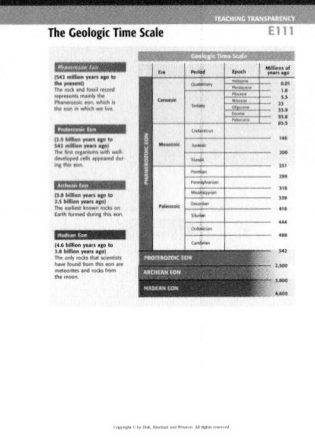

The Geologic Time Scale   E111

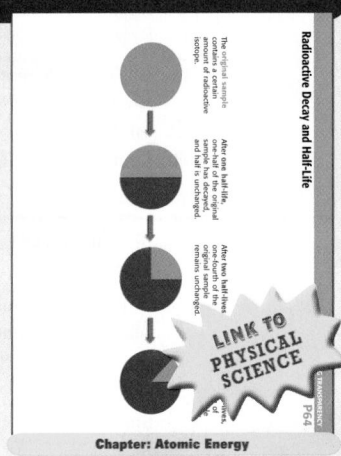

Radioactive Decay and Half-Life

LINK TO PHYSICAL SCIENCE

Chapter: Atomic Energy

CONCEPT MAPPING TRANSPARENCY

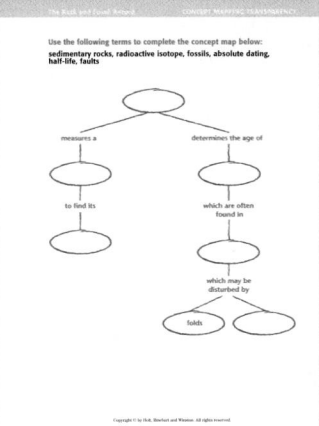

Use the following terms to complete the concept map below:
sedimentary rocks, radioactive isotope, fossils, absolute dating, half-life, faults

Planning Resources

LESSON PLANS

Lesson Plan   SAMPLE

Section: Waves

Pacing
Regular Schedule: with lab(s):2 days   without lab(s):2 days
Block Schedule: with lab(s): 1 1/2 days   without lab(s):1 day

Objectives
1. Relate the seven properties of life to a living organism.
2. Describe seven themes that can help you to organize what you learn about biology.
3. Identify the tiny structures that make up all living things.
4. Differentiate between reproduction and heredity and between metabolism and homeostasis.

National Science Education Standards Covered
LSInter6:Cells have particular structures that underlie their functions.
LSMat1:Most cell functions involve chemical reactions.
LSBeh1:Cells store and use information to guide their functions.
UCP1:Cell functions are regulated.
SI1: Cells can differentiate and form complete multicellular organisms.
PS1: Species evolve over time.
ESS3: The great diversity of organisms is the result of more than 3.5 billion years of evolution.
ESS2: Natural selection and its evolutionary consequences provide a scientific explanation for the fossil record of ancient life forms as well as for the striking molecular similarities observed among the diverse species of living organisms.
ST1: The millions of different species of plants, animals, and microorganisms that live on Earth today are related by descent from common ancestors.
ST2: The energy for life primarily comes from the sun.
SPSP1: The complexity and organization of organisms accommodates the need for obtaining, transforming, transporting, releasing, and eliminating the matter and energy used to sustain the organisms.
SPSP6: As matter and energy flows through different levels of organization of living systems—cells, organs, organisms, communities—and between living systems and the physical environment, chemical elements are recombined in different ways.
HNS1: Organisms have behavioral responses to internal changes and to external stimuli.

PARENT LETTER

SAMPLE

Dear Parent,

Your son's or daughter's science class will soon begin exploring the chapter entitled "The World of Physical Science." In this chapter, students will learn about how the scientific method applies to the world of physical science and the role of physical science in the world. By the end of the chapter, students should demonstrate a clear understanding of the chapter's main ideas and be able to discuss the following topics:

1. physical science as the study of energy and matter (Section 1)
2. the role of physical science in the world around them (Section 1)
3. careers that rely on physical science (Section 1)
4. the steps used in the scientific method (Section 2)
5. examples of technology (Section 2)
6. how the scientific method is used to answer questions and solve problems (Section 2)
7. how our knowledge of science changes over time (Section 2)
8. how models represent real objects or systems (Section 3)
9. examples of different ways models are used in science (Section 3)
10. the importance of the International System of Units (Section 4)
11. the appropriate units to use for particular measurements (Section 4)
12. how area and density are derived quantities (Section 4)

Questions to Ask Along the Way

You can help your son or daughter learn about these topics by asking interesting questions such as the following:

• What are some surprising careers that use physical science?

• What is a characteristic of a good hypothesis?

• When is it a good idea to use a model?

• Why do Americans measure things in terms of inches and yards and meters?

ALSO IN SPANISH

TEST ITEM LISTING

TEST ITEM LISTING
The World of Earth Science   SAMPLE

MULTIPLE CHOICE

1. A limitation of models is that
   a. they are large enough to see.
   b. they do not act exactly like the things that they model.
   c. they are smaller than the things that they model.
   d. they model unfamiliar things.
   Answer: B   Difficulty: 1   Section: 3   Objective: 2

2. The length 10 m is equal to
   a. 100 cm.   c. 10,000 mm.
   b. 1,000 cm.   d. Both (b) and (c)
   Answer: B   Difficulty: 1   Section: 3   Objective: 2

3. To be valid, a hypothesis must be
   a. testable.   c. made into a law.
   b. supported by evidence.   d. Both (a) and (b)
   Answer: B   Difficulty: 1   Section: 3   Objective: 2

4. The statement "Sheila has a stain on her shirt" is an example of a(n)
   a. law.   c. observation.
   b. hypothesis.   d. prediction.
   Answer: B   Difficulty: 1   Section: 3   Objective: 2

5. A hypothesis is often developed out of
   a. observations.   c. laws.
   b. experiments.   d. Both (a) and (b)
   Answer: B   Difficulty: 1   Section: 3   Objective: 2

6. How many milliliters are in 3.5 kL?
   a. 3,500 mL.   c. 3,500,000 mL.
   b. 0.0035 mL.   d. 35,000 mL.
   Answer: B   Difficulty: 1   Section: 3   Objective: 2

7. A map of Seattle is an example of a
   a. law.   c. model.
   b. theory.   d. unit.
   Answer: B   Difficulty: 1   Section: 3   Objective: 2

8. A lab has the safety icons shown below. These icons mean that you should wear
   a. only safety goggles.   c. safety goggles and a lab apron.
   b. only a lab apron.   d. safety goggles, a lab apron, and gloves.
   Answer: B   Difficulty: 1   Section: 3   Objective: 2

9. The loss of composition of mass uses the fat of mass before a chemical change is
   a. more than the total mass after the change.
   b. less than the total mass after the change.
   c. the same as the total mass after the change.
   d. not the same as the total mass after the change.
   Answer: B   Difficulty: 1   Section: 3   Objective: 2

10. In which of the following areas might you find a geochemist at work?
    a. studying the chemistry of rocks   c. studying fishes
    b. studying forestry   d. studying the atmosphere
    Answer: B   Difficulty: 1   Section: 3   Objective: 2

One-Stop Planner® CD-ROM

This CD-ROM includes all of the resources shown here and the following time-saving tools:

• *Lab Materials QuickList Software*

• *Customizable lesson plans*

• *Holt Calendar Planner*

• *The powerful ExamView® Test Generator*

Meeting Individual Needs

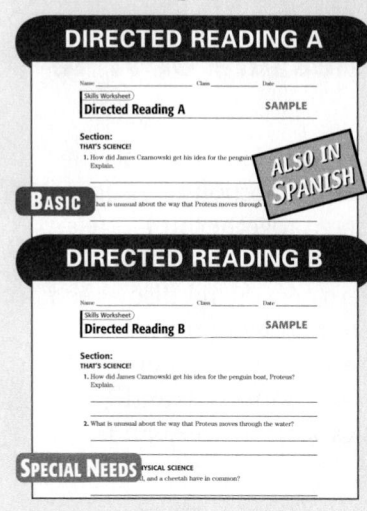

DIRECTED READING A
BASIC · ALSO IN SPANISH

DIRECTED READING B
SPECIAL NEEDS

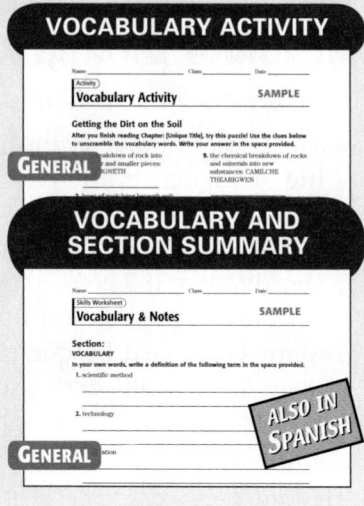

VOCABULARY ACTIVITY
GENERAL

VOCABULARY AND SECTION SUMMARY
GENERAL · ALSO IN SPANISH

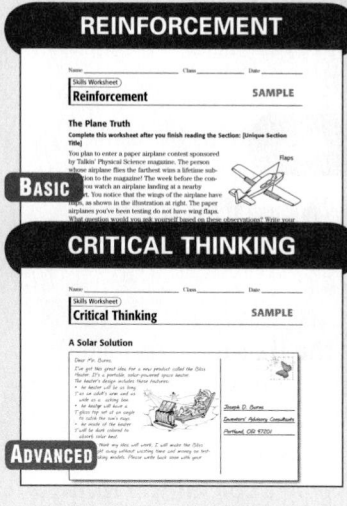

REINFORCEMENT
BASIC

CRITICAL THINKING
ADVANCED

SCILINKS ACTIVITY
GENERAL

SCIENCE PUZZLERS, TWISTERS & TEASERS
GENERAL

Labs and Activities

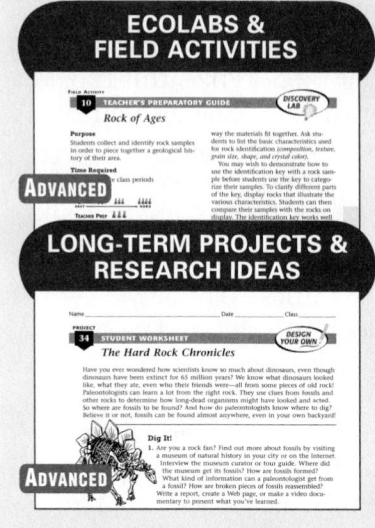

ECOLABS & FIELD ACTIVITIES
ADVANCED

LONG-TERM PROJECTS & RESEARCH IDEAS
ADVANCED

LABS YOU CAN EAT
BASIC

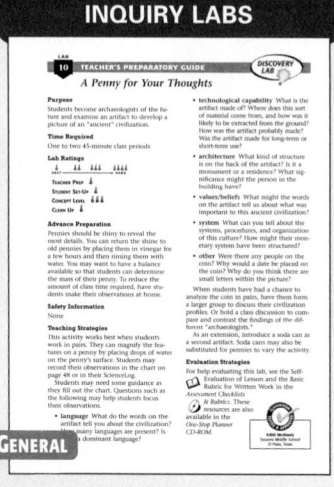

INQUIRY LABS
GENERAL

DATASHEETS FOR QUICK LABS

DATASHEETS FOR CHAPTER LABS

DATASHEETS FOR LABBOOK

Review and Assessments

SECTION QUIZ
GENERAL · ALSO IN SPANISH

SECTION REVIEW
GENERAL · ALSO IN SPANISH

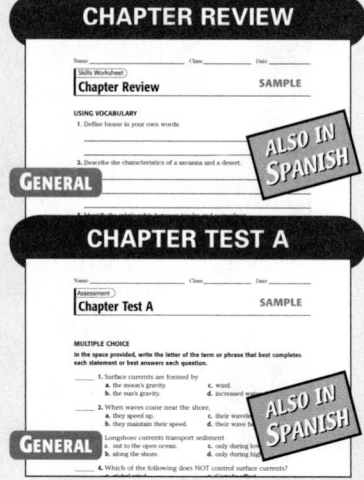

CHAPTER REVIEW
GENERAL · ALSO IN SPANISH

CHAPTER TEST A
GENERAL · ALSO IN SPANISH

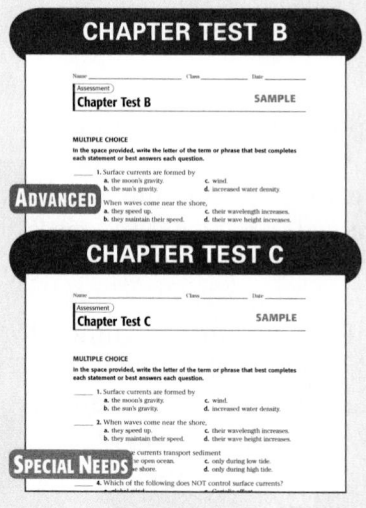

CHAPTER TEST B
ADVANCED

CHAPTER TEST C
SPECIAL NEEDS

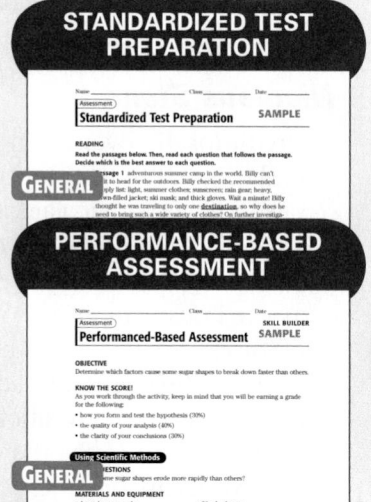

STANDARDIZED TEST PREPARATION
GENERAL

PERFORMANCE-BASED ASSESSMENT
GENERAL

This Chapter Enrichment provides relevant and interesting information to expand and enhance your presentation of the chapter material.

Section 1

Earth's Story and Those Who First Listened

Actualism

- Although James Hutton was the first to introduce the principles of uniformitarianism, he is considered an actualist, not a strict uniformitarianist. He recognized that while many geologic processes happen slowly, some catastrophic events do play a role in the formation of the Earth. Today, geologists accept actualism as a more logical explanation of Earth's history.

Section 2

Relative Dating: Which Came First?

Nicolaus Steno

- Credit for discovering the principles of superposition and original horizontality is given to Niels Stensen (also known as Nicolaus Steno), born in Denmark in 1638. Though originally trained in anatomy and medicine, Steno became interested in geology while serving as the house physician to Grand Duke Ferdinand II of Tuscany. During this period, Steno made significant geologic discoveries. In addition to establishing the principles of superposition and original horizontality, Steno was one of the first Western scientists to argue that fossils are organic.

Section 3

Absolute Dating: A Measure of Time

Marie and Pierre Curie

- The Curies met in spring 1894 while Marie was studying mathematics and physics at the Sorbonne, in Paris. They married in 1895 and worked together in Pierre's laboratory. Marie began work on her doctoral thesis shortly after 1896, the year Henri Becquerel discovered that a strange radiation was emitted by uranium. Marie continued Becquerel's work, obtained her doctorate on radioactive substances in 1903, and won the Nobel Prize for physics with her husband and Becquerel.

- In 1906, Pierre Curie was killed in a wagon accident in Paris. Marie Curie was grief-stricken and dedicated the rest of her life to the work she and her husband had begun. She headed his laboratory at the Sorbonne and became the first woman lecturer at the university. In 1911, Marie received her second Nobel Prize, this time in chemistry for isolating pure radium. She died on July 4, 1934, of leukemia, which was probably caused by her prolonged exposure to radiation.

Radiometric Age-Dating

- The work of Becquerel and the Curies eventually changed the fields of archeology, geology, and paleontology. Before their work, geologists were restricted to using relative methods of dating when trying to determine the age of rocks and minerals. However, after scientists discovered that radioactive elements decay at a constant rate, physicists used this rate to calculate the ages of the rocks that contain these elements.

Section 4

Looking at Fossils

Prehistoric Weevil DNA

- In 1993, research in fossil DNA took a tremendous leap forward when Dr. George Poinar, of the University of California at Berkeley, successfully extracted fragmented DNA from the tissue of a weevil that is 125 million years old and was encased in amber found in Lebanon. In almost all fossils, the DNA has decayed and can no longer be analyzed.

Coelacanths: Living Fossils

- Coelacanths are large, carnivorous, lobe-finned fish. Their fossil record dates back to more than 350 million years ago and, until the 20th century, they were believed to have become extinct about 65 million years ago. In 1938, Marjorie Courtenay-Latimer, a museum curator in a small port village near Cape Town, South Africa, noticed an unusual blue-finned fish among the day's catch at the local docks—it was a coelacanth! A second coelacanth was recovered in 1952 by anglers, again off the African coast. Scientists believe that only a small number of the fish still survive, and in 1995, researchers declared the animal to be in danger of extinction.

- In 1998, Dr. Mark Erdmann confirmed at least two coelacanth specimens from North Sulawesi, Indonesia, 10,000 km from the African coast. The coelacanths were discovered living in volcanic caves below sea level.

Is That a Fact!

- The largest coprolite ever found is a mound of feces that is 65 million years old and was probably left by a *Tyrannosaurus rex*. It is 43 cm across and 15 cm high.

Section 5

Time Marches On

Life in the Precambrian Era

- The period of time from the formation of Earth 4.6 billion years ago to 543 million years ago is called the Precambrian era. Until the discovery of soft-bodied organisms in Australia in 1947, paleontologists believed that only single-celled microorganisms and blue-green algae lived during this period. Now scientists know that a wide variety of animals resembling jellyfish, annelids, and even arthropods evolved in Precambrian seas between 590 million and 700 million years ago. These animals are so far the oldest known multicellular organisms, although traces of possibly earlier ones date back to 1.2 billion years.

SciLinks is maintained by the National Science Teachers Association to provide you and your students with interesting, up-to-date links that will enrich your classroom presentation of the chapter.

Visit www.scilinks.org and enter the SciLinks code for more information about the topic listed.

Topic: Earth's Story
SciLinks code: HSM0450

Topic: Relative Dating
SciLinks code: HSM1288

Topic: Absolute Dating
SciLinks code: HSM0003

Topic: Looking at Fossils
SciLinks code: HSM0886

Topic: Geologic Time
SciLinks code: HSM0668

Overview

Tell students that this chapter will help them learn about the history of the Earth. The chapter describes ways in which scientists use the rock and fossil record to decipher Earth's history.

Assessing Prior Knowledge

Students should be familiar with the following topics:

• basic geological processes

• the classification of life

Identifying Misconceptions

When students think of fossils, they probably think of body fossils—the hard parts of organisms most commonly preserved in rock. Make students aware that organisms can also be preserved in such substances as amber, asphalt, and ice, some of which may preserve soft tissues. The soft tissues of plants and animals can also be replaced by minerals, but this replacement rarely happens. Also inform students that the tracks, trails, and burrows made by organisms are considered fossils.

11

The Rock and Fossil Record

The Big Idea

Studying the rock and fossil record helps us understand Earth's history and the history of life on Earth.

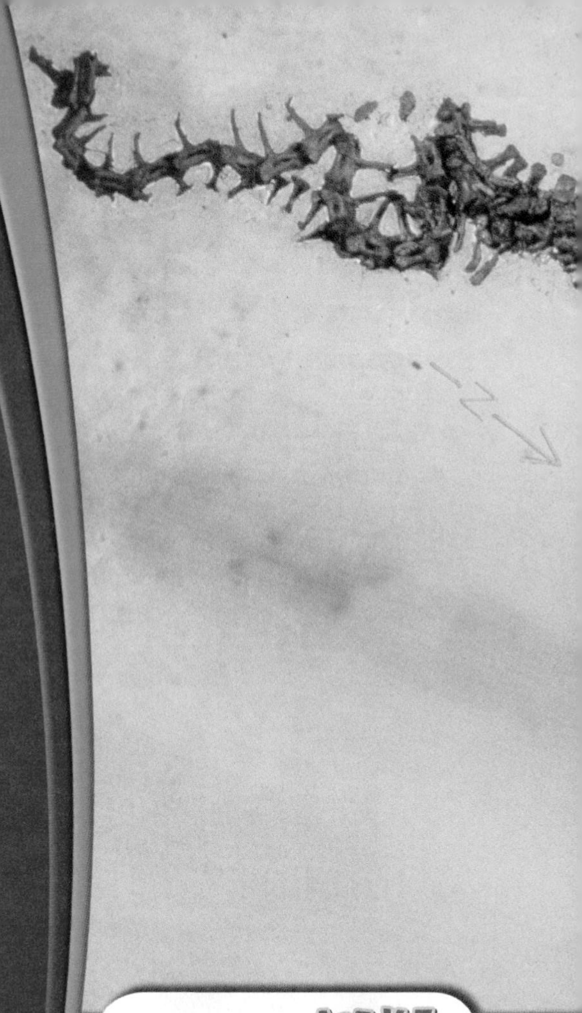

About the Photo

This extremely well preserved crocodile fossil has been out of water for 49 million years. Its skeleton was collected in an abandoned mine pit in Messel, Germany.

PRE-READING ACTIVITY

FOLDNOTES **Layered Book** Before you read the chapter, create the FoldNote entitled "Layered Book" described in the **Study Skills** section of the Appendix. Label the tabs of the layered book with "Earth's history," "Relative dating," "Absolute dating," "Fossils," and "Geologic time." As you read the chapter, write information you learn about each category under the appropriate tab.

Standards Correlations

National Science Education Standards

The following codes indicate the National Science Education Standards that correlate to this chapter. The full text of the standards is in the front of the book.

Chapter Opener
SAI 1, 2

Section 1 Earth's Story and Those Who First Listened
UCP 2, 4; SAI 1, 2; SPSP 5; HNS 1, 2, 3; ES 2a

Section 2 Relative Dating: Which Came First?
UCP 1, 2; HNS 2; ES 2b

Section 3 Absolute Dating: A Measure of Time
UCP 1, 3; SAI 1, 2; ST 2; SPSP 5; HNS 1, 2, 3; ES 2b

Section 4 Looking at Fossils
UCP 1, 2, 3, 4; SAI 1, 2; SPSP 5; ES 1k, 2b

Section 5 Time Marches On
UCP 1, 3; SAI 1, 2; HNS 2; ES 2b

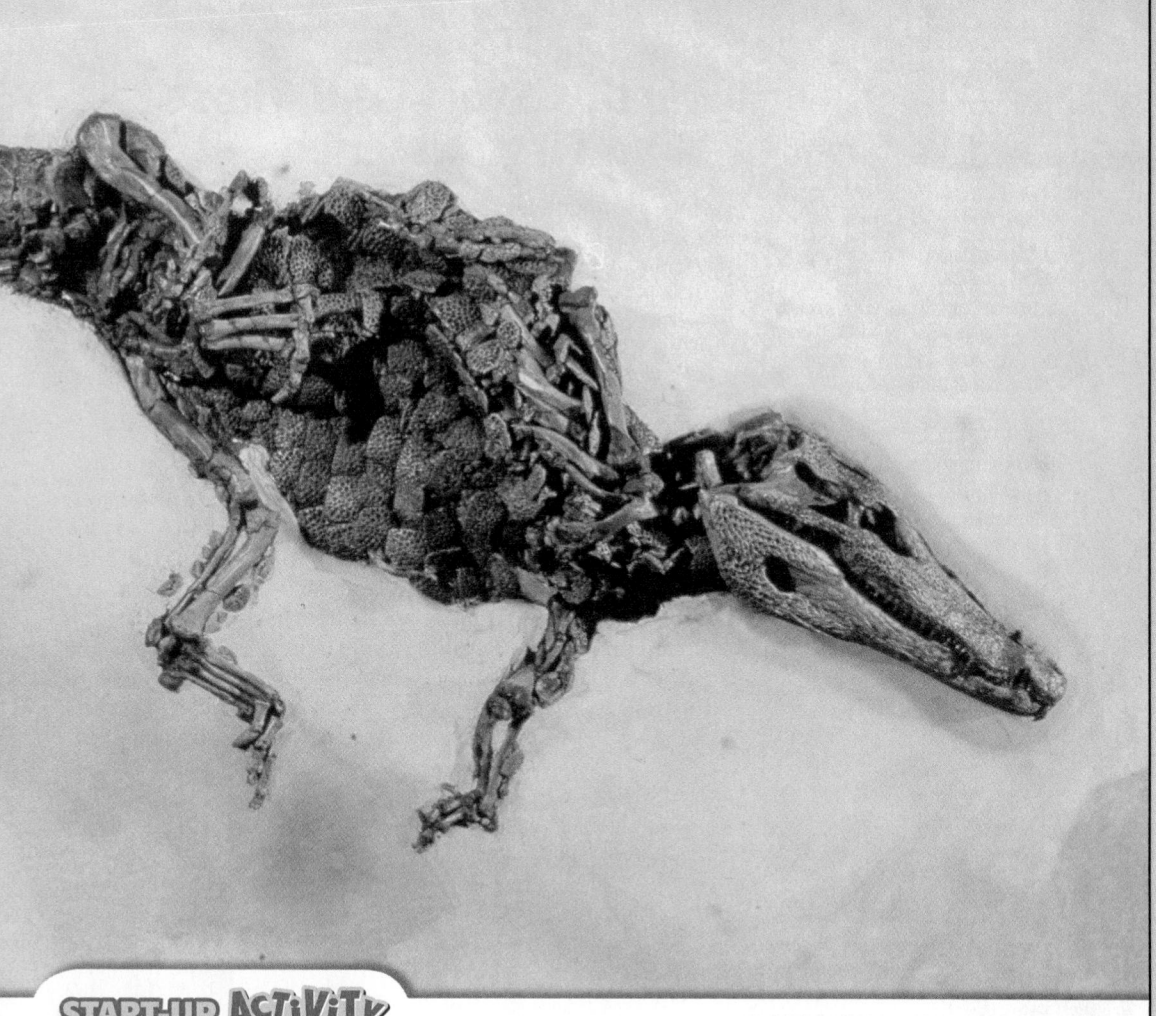

START-UP ACTIVITY

MATERIALS

FOR EACH GROUP
- clay, modeling
- paper sack containing a few small objects, such as shells, coins, paper clips, buttons, toys, or any other objects that have recognizable textures or shapes

Answers

1. Sample answer: Textures and shapes were useful in identifying the model fossils. Small details, colors, and the internal structure of the objects were not preserved.

2. Sample answer: Scientists carefully study fossil remains to determine the characteristics of the organism that became fossilized.

START-UP ACTIVITY

Making Fossils

How do scientists learn from fossils? In this activity, you will study "fossils" and identify the object that made each.

Procedure

1. You and three or four of your classmates will be given **several pieces** of **modeling clay** and a **paper sack** containing a few **small objects.**

2. Press each object firmly into a piece of clay. Try to leave a "fossil" imprint showing as much detail as possible.

3. After you have made an imprint of each object, exchange your model fossils with another group.

4. On a **sheet of paper,** describe the fossils you have received. List as many details as possible. What patterns and textures do you observe?

5. Work as a group to identify each fossil, and check your results. Were you right?

Analysis

1. What kinds of details were important in identifying your fossils? What kinds of details were not preserved in the imprints? For example, can you tell the materials from which the objects are made or their color?

2. Explain how scientists follow similar methods when studying fossils.

Chapter Lab
SAI 1, 2

Chapter Review
UCP 1, 2, 3, 4; ST 2; HNS 2; ES 1k, 2a, 2b

Science in Action
UCP 2, 3, 4, 5; ST 2; SPSP 5; HNS 1, 2, 3; ES 2b

What a Find!

Imagine that you are a scientist looking for fossils. You are climbing up a sandstone cliff in unexplored mountains in North Africa. The sun is scorching. The temperature is 120°F in the shade. You see a tooth in the 90-million-year-old rock. It looks like a shark's tooth, but it is more than 12 cm long! You dig around the tooth and discover that it is attached to a huge skull. Eventually, you uncover

You take the skull back to your lab to study it more closely. Given the size of the skull, you decide the skeleton of the animal it came from must have been about 14 m long—about as big as a school bus. That's even larger than *Tyrannosaurus rex!* This 90-million-year-old giant you have found most likely chased other dinosaurs by running on large, powerful hind legs, and its blade-

Chapter Starter Transparency
Use this transparency to help students begin thinking about the excitement of discovering and studying fossils.

CHAPTER RESOURCES

Technology

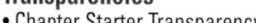 **Transparencies**
- Chapter Starter Transparency

READING SKILLS

 Student Edition on CD-ROM

Guided Reading Audio CD
- English or Spanish

Classroom Videos
- Brain Food Video Quiz

Workbooks

 **Science Puzzlers, Twisters & Teasers**
- The Rock and Fossil Record GENERAL

Focus

Overview

In this section, students will explore the origins of modern geology by comparing and contrasting uniformitarianism and catastrophism. Students will learn that modern geology is a synthesis of both theories and that the forces that shaped the Earth around them are still at work today.

Bellringer

On the board, write the following: "The present is the key to the past." Tell students that this phrase was the cornerstone of the uniformitarianist theory. Have students write a few sentences about how studying the present could reveal the story of Earth's history.

Motivate

ACTiViTY — GENERAL

Debate Posters Have students design a poster announcing a debate between a catastrophist and a uniformitarian. Encourage students to use phrases and illustrations that would attract supporters from both sides. Have them summarize the major points of both sides, and display the finished posters in the classroom. **LS** Visual — English Language Learners

What You Will Learn

● Compare uniformitarianism and catastrophism.
● Describe how the science of geology has changed over the past 200 years.
● Explain the role of paleontology in the study of Earth's history.

Vocabulary
uniformitarianism
catastrophism
paleontology

READING STRATEGY

Reading Organizer As you read this section, make a table comparing uniformitarianism and catastrophism.

Earth's Story and Those Who First Listened

How do mountains form? How is new rock created? How old is the Earth? Have you ever asked these questions? Nearly 250 years ago, a Scottish farmer and scientist named James Hutton did.

Searching for answers to his questions, Hutton spent more than 30 years studying rock formations in Scotland and England. His observations led to the foundation of modern geology.

The Principle of Uniformitarianism

In 1788, James Hutton collected his notes and wrote *Theory of the Earth.* In *Theory of the Earth,* he stated that the key to understanding Earth's history was all around us. In other words, processes that we observe today—such as erosion and deposition—remain uniform, or do not change, over time. This assumption is now called uniformitarianism. **Uniformitarianism** is the idea that the same geologic processes shaping the Earth today have been at work throughout Earth's history. **Figure 1** shows how Hutton developed the idea of uniformitarianism.

Figure 1 *Hutton observed gradual, uniform geologic change.*

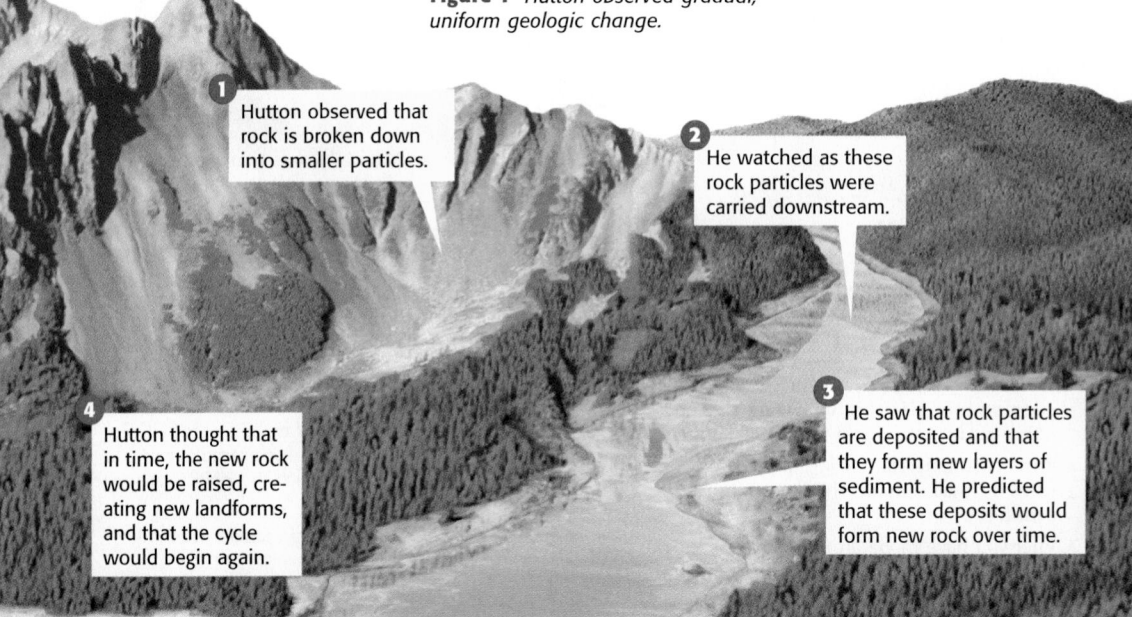

1 Hutton observed that rock is broken down into smaller particles.

2 He watched as these rock particles were carried downstream.

3 He saw that rock particles are deposited and that they form new layers of sediment. He predicted that these deposits would form new rock over time.

4 Hutton thought that in time, the new rock would be raised, creating new landforms, and that the cycle would begin again.

CHAPTER RESOURCES

Chapter Resource File

- **Lesson Plan**
- **Directed Reading A** BASIC
- **Directed Reading B** SPECIAL NEEDS

Technology

Transparencies
- Bellringer
- E14 Hutton and the Principle of Uniformitarianism

Workbooks

Interactive Textbook Struggling Readers

Is That a Fact!

James Hutton's colleague, Sir James Hall, dramatically demonstrated Hutton's theories by melting rock in a furnace and letting it cool, which showed how the rock changed from one form to another form. This demonstration struck a major blow against the catastrophists.

Figure 2 *This photograph shows Siccar Point on the coast of Scotland. Siccar Point is one of the places where Hutton observed results of geologic processes that would lead him to form his principle of uniformitarianism.*

Uniformitarianism Versus Catastrophism

Hutton's theories sparked a scientific debate by suggesting that Earth was much older than previously thought. In Hutton's time, most people thought that Earth was only a few thousand years old. A few thousand years was not nearly enough time for the gradual geologic processes that Hutton described to have shaped our planet. The rocks that he observed at Siccar Point, shown in **Figure 2,** were deposited and folded, indicating a long geological history. To explain Earth's history, most scientists supported catastrophism. **Catastrophism** is the principle that states that all geologic change occurs suddenly. Supporters of catastrophism thought that Earth's features, such as its mountains, canyons, and seas, formed during rare, sudden events called *catastrophes*. These unpredictable events caused rapid geologic change over large areas—sometimes even globally.

✓ **Reading Check** According to catastrophists, what was the rate of geologic change? (*See the Appendix for answers to Reading Checks.*)

A Victory for Uniformitarianism

Despite Hutton's work, catastrophism remained geology's guiding principle for decades. Only after the work of British geologist Charles Lyell did people seriously consider uniformitarianism as geology's guiding principle.

From 1830 to 1833, Lyell published three volumes, collectively titled *Principles of Geology,* in which he reintroduced uniformitarianism. Armed with Hutton's notes and new evidence of his own, Lyell successfully challenged the principle of catastrophism. Lyell saw no reason to doubt that major geologic change happened at the same rate in the past as it happens in the present—gradually.

uniformitarianism a principle that states that geologic processes that occurred in the past can be explained by current geologic processes

catastrophism a principle that states that geologic change occurs suddenly

CONNECTION TO Biology

WRITING SKILL **Darwin and Lyell** The theory of evolution was developed soon after Lyell introduced his ideas, which was no coincidence. Lyell and Charles Darwin were good friends, and their talks greatly influenced Darwin's theories. Similar to uniformitarianism, Darwin's theory of evolution proposes that changes in species occur gradually over long periods of time. Write a short essay comparing uniformitarianism and evolution.

Answer to Connection to Biology
Student essays should include the idea that changes due to uniformitarianism or evolution may occur over very long periods of time.

Answer to Reading Check
Catastrophists believed that all geologic change occurs rapidly.

SUPPORT FOR

English Language Learners

Word Parts Breaking large words into parts may help students assimilate new words faster. First, elicit definitions of *principle* to make sure students understand it; write the word and definition on the board. Next, write *uniformitarian* and *catastrophist* on the board, breaking them up into meaningful parts: *uni-, form-, itarian,* and *catastro-, -phist.* Ask students the meaning of each part, and write their answers on the board. Allow students to consult dictionaries. When both words are completely defined, ask students to write sentences using the words to show comprehension. **LS** Verbal/Logical

CONNECTION ACTIVITY
Language Arts —— **GENERAL**

A Conversation Between Darwin and Lyell Although Charles Darwin and Charles Lyell were avid correspondents and good friends, they did not agree on everything. Darwin was quick to accept the principle of uniformitarianism; he read Lyell's *Principles of Geology* before his famous 1831 voyage on HMS *Beagle.* However, Lyell did not readily embrace Darwin's theories of natural selection. It was not until much later in life that Charles Lyell vigorously supported Darwin's ideas. Ask students to write a script for a conversation that the two scientists might have had. Have them imagine that Darwin has just returned from his journey aboard the HMS *Beagle.* Ask students what questions might Darwin and Lyell have exchanged. Students can present the conversations as short skits. **LS** Verbal

Reteaching ———— BASIC

Summarizing Modern Geology

Have students write a one-paragraph essay that explains how modern geology incorporates catastrophism and uniformitarianism. **LS Verbal**

Quiz ———— GENERAL

1. What is catastrophism?
   (Catastrophism is the idea that geologic change occurred suddenly as a result of infrequent, disastrous events.)

2. Describe uniformitarianism.
   (Uniformitarianism is the principle that the Earth has been shaped by gradual changes throughout history and is shaped by gradual changes that are still occurring today.)

Alternative Assessment ———— GENERAL

Writing **Addressing Mr. Hutton or Mr. Lyell** Have students write a letter to Charles Lyell or James Hutton. The letter should explain why the student agrees or disagrees with the scientist's theories. Suggest that students end the letter with at least two questions that they would like to ask the scientist. Have students exchange letters and answer each other's questions. **LS Verbal/Interpersonal**

Modern Geology—A Happy Medium

During the late 20th century, scientists such as Stephen J. Gould challenged Lyell's uniformitarianism. They believed that catastrophes do, at times, play an important role in shaping Earth's history.

Today, scientists realize that neither uniformitarianism nor catastrophism accounts for all geologic change throughout Earth's history. Although most geologic change is gradual and uniform, catastrophes that cause geologic change have occurred during Earth's long history. For example, huge craters have been found where asteroids and comets are thought to have struck Earth in the past. Some scientists think one such asteroid strike, approximately 65 million years ago, may have caused the dinosaurs to become extinct. **Figure 3** is an imaginary re-creation of the asteroid strike that is thought to have caused the extinction of the dinosaurs. The impact of this asteroid is thought to have thrown debris into the atmosphere. The debris spread around the entire planet and rained down on Earth for decades. This global debris cloud may have blocked the sun's rays, causing major changes in the global climate that doomed the dinosaurs.

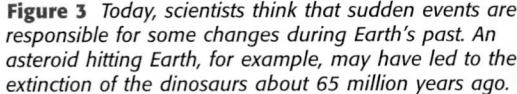 **Reading Check** How can a catastrophe affect life on Earth?

Figure 3 *Today, scientists think that sudden events are responsible for some changes during Earth's past. An asteroid hitting Earth, for example, may have led to the extinction of the dinosaurs about 65 million years ago.*

Answer to Reading Check
A global catastrophe can cause the extinction of species.

Paleontology—The Study of Past Life

The history of the Earth would be incomplete without a knowledge of the organisms that have inhabited our planet and the conditions under which they lived. The science involved with the study of past life is called **paleontology.** Scientists who study this life are called *paleontologists*. The data paleontologists use are fossils. Fossils are the remains of organisms preserved by geologic processes. Some paleontologists specialize in the study of particular organisms. Invertebrate paleontologists study animals without backbones, whereas vertebrate paleontologists, such as the scientist in **Figure 4,** study animals with backbones. Paleobotanists study fossils of plants. Other paleontologists reconstruct past ecosystems, study the traces left behind by animals, and piece together the conditions under which fossils were formed. As you see, the study of past life is as varied and complex as Earth's history itself.

Figure 4 *Edwin Colbert was a 20th-century vertebrate paleontologist who made important contributions to the study of dinosaurs.*

paleontology the scientific study of fossils

SECTION Review

Summary

- Uniformitarianism assumes that geologic change is gradual. Catastrophism is based on the idea that geologic change is sudden.

- Modern geology is based on the idea that gradual geologic change is interrupted by catastrophes.

- Using fossils to study past life is called *paleontology*.

Using Key Terms

1. Use each of the following terms in a separate sentence: *uniformitarianism, catastrophism,* and *paleontology*.

Understanding Key Ideas

2. Which of the following words describes change according to the principle of uniformitarianism?
   a. sudden
   b. rare
   c. global
   d. gradual

3. What is the difference between uniformitarianism and catastrophism?

4. Describe how the science of geology has changed.

5. Give one example of catastrophic global change.

6. Describe the work of three types of paleontologists.

Math Skills

7. An impact crater left by an asteroid strike has a radius of 85 km. What is the area of the crater? (Hint: The area of a circle is πr^2.)

Critical Thinking

8. **Analyzing Ideas** Why is uniformitarianism considered to be the foundation of modern geology?

9. **Applying Concepts** Give an example of a type of recent catastrophe.

Developed and maintained by the
National Science Teachers Association

For a variety of links related to this chapter, go to www.scilinks.org

Topic: Earth's Story
SciLinks code: HSM0450

CHAPTER RESOURCES

Chapter Resource File

- **Section Quiz** GENERAL
- **Section Review** GENERAL
- **Vocabulary and Section Summary** GENERAL

Focus

Overview

In this section, students learn about relative dating techniques and how the geologic column is used to determine the sequence of rock formations.

Bellringer

Ask students to arrange the following sentences in a logical order to make a short story:

1. I stood in the checkout line.

2. I selected two apples.

3. I walked home from the store.

4. I gave the cashier money.

5. I went to the store.

6. The cashier gave me change.

7. I was hungry.

(7, 5, 2, 1, 4, 6, 3)

Motivate

Demonstration —— GENERAL

Superposition Stack several books on your desk. Tell students that the books represent layers of rock that were deposited at different times. Ask students which layer is the oldest. (the one on the bottom) Ask which rock layer is the youngest. (the one on top) Ask students to explain their answers, and tell them that they have just applied a basic geologic concept—the principle of superposition.

LS Visual

What You Will Learn

 Explain how relative dating is used in geology.

 Explain the principle of superposition.

● Describe how the geologic column is used in relative dating.

● Identify two events and two features that disrupt rock layers.

● Explain how physical features are used to determine relative ages.

Vocabulary
relative dating
superposition
geologic column
unconformity

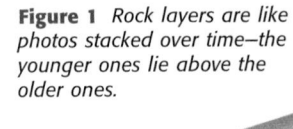
READING STRATEGY

Reading Organizer As you read this section, create an outline of the section. Use the headings from the section in your outline.

Relative Dating: Which Came First?

Imagine that you are a detective investigating a crime scene. What is the first thing you would do?

You might begin by dusting the scene for fingerprints or by searching for witnesses. As a detective, you must figure out the sequence of events that took place before you reached the crime scene.

Geologists have a similar goal when investigating the Earth. They try to determine the order in which events have happened during Earth's history. But instead of relying on fingerprints and witnesses, geologists rely on rocks and fossils to help them in their investigation. Determining whether an object or event is older or younger than other objects or events is called **relative dating.**

The Principle of Superposition

Suppose that you have an older brother who takes a lot of photographs of your family and piles them in a box. Over the years, he keeps adding new photographs to the top of the stack. Think about the family history recorded in those photos. Where are the oldest photographs—the ones taken when you were a baby? Where are the most recent photographs—those taken last week?

Layers of sedimentary rock, such as the ones shown in **Figure 1,** are like stacked photographs. As you move from top to bottom, the layers are older. The principle that states that younger rocks lie above older rocks in undisturbed sequences is called **superposition.**

Figure 1 Rock layers are like photos stacked over time—the younger ones lie above the older ones.

CHAPTER RESOURCES

Chapter Resource File

- Lesson Plan
- Directed Reading A **BASIC**
- Directed Reading B **SPECIAL NEEDS**

Technology

Transparencies
- Bellringer
- E15 Constructing the Geologic Column

Workbooks

Interactive Textbook **Struggling Readers**

Disturbing Forces

Not all rock sequences are arranged with the oldest layers on the bottom and the youngest layers on top. Some rock sequences are disturbed by forces within the Earth. These forces can push other rocks into a sequence, tilt or fold rock layers, and break sequences into movable parts. Sometimes, geologists even find rock sequences that are upside down! The disruptions of rock sequences pose a challenge to geologists trying to determine the relative ages of rocks. Fortunately, geologists can get help from a very valuable tool—the geologic column.

The Geologic Column

To make their job easier, geologists combine data from all the known undisturbed rock sequences around the world. From this information, geologists create the geologic column, as illustrated in **Figure 2**. The **geologic column** is an ideal sequence of rock layers that contains all the known fossils and rock formations on Earth, arranged from oldest to youngest.

Geologists rely on the geologic column to interpret rock sequences. Geologists also use the geologic column to identify the layers in puzzling rock sequences.

Reading Check List two ways in which geologists use the geologic column. (*See the Appendix for answers to Reading Checks.*)

relative dating any method of determining whether an event or object is older or younger than other events or objects

superposition a principle that states that younger rocks lie above older rocks if the layers have not been disturbed

geologic column an arrangement of rock layers in which the oldest rocks are at the bottom

Figure 2 — Constructing the Geologic Column

Here, you can see three rock sequences (A, B, and C) from three different locations. Some rock layers appear in more than one sequence. Geologists construct the geologic column by piecing together different rock sequences from all over the world.

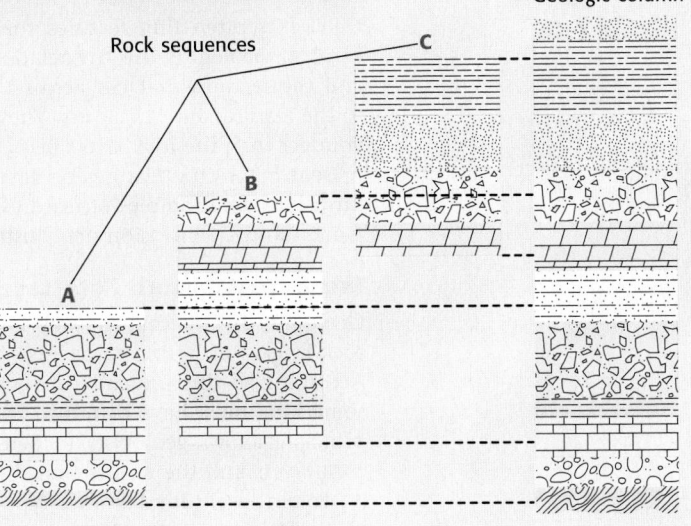

Rock sequences

Geologic column

Teach

Using the Figure — BASIC
Geologic Column Practice
The geologic column is an easy concept for students to understand if they get some hands-on practice. Before the lesson, you may wish to make photocopies of **Figure 2.** Cut out the columns, and have students work independently to piece them together correctly. **Visual/Logical**   English Language Learners

MISCONCEPTION ALERT

The Geologic Column
Students may think that there is a place on Earth that has a continuous sequence of all the rocks formed throughout history. Emphasize to students that no single location on Earth has a continuous sequence of all of the rocks formed throughout geologic history. The geologic column is an idealized sequence of rock layers that have formed around the world since the Earth formed. The geologic column was first pieced together in the mid-19th century, and it is continually being revised as geologists map more of the Earth's rock layers.

SUPPORT FOR

English Language Learners
Relative Dating   Students may not know the meaning of *relative* in this context. To illustrate it, have 4 students of varying heights line up in order of height in front of the class. Point to the second shortest person, and ask, "Is [name] tall?" When students say no, ask, "Is [same name] taller than [name of shortest person]?" When students say yes, point out that height is "relative." Say, "You said that [name] is not tall, but compared to [name], (s)he is. Relative to [name], (s)he is." Repeat the exercise with the word *short* to check comprehension. **Visual/Verbal**

Answer to Reading Check
Geologists use the geologic column to interpret rock sequences and to identify layers in puzzling rock sequences.

Prediction Guide As students explore this section, ask them to answer the following questions:

• If a fault is observed in rock layers, are the rock layers or is the fault older? (the layers)

• If rock layers are deposited horizontally but you see them sharply tilted, did the deposition happen first or did the tilting happen first? (the deposition)

LS Logical

ACTIVITY — GENERAL

Modeling Faults and Intrusions
Show how intrusions and faults disturb rock layers by doing this simple demonstration. Glue several different-colored sponges together to form a model rock sequence. To show a fault, make a straight, diagonal cut through all of the sponge layers. Demonstrate fault movement by sliding the two sponge sections alongside each other. Have students work together to demonstrate intrusions, folding, and tilting. As an extension, have students create a permanent display by gluing their examples to a piece of poster board. **LS Visual**

Figure 3 How Rock Layers Become Disturbed

Fault A *fault* is a break in the Earth's crust along which blocks of the crust slide relative to one another.

Intrusion An *intrusion* is molten rock from the Earth's interior that squeezes into existing rock and cools.

Folding *Folding* occurs when rock layers bend and buckle from Earth's internal forces.

Tilting *Tilting* occurs when internal forces in the Earth slant rock layers.

Disturbed Rock Layers

Geologists often find features that cut across existing layers of rock. Geologists use the relationships between rock layers and the features that cut across them to assign relative ages to the features and the layers. They know that the features are younger than the rock layers because the rock layers had to be present before the features could cut across them. Faults and intrusions are examples of features that cut across rock layers. A fault and an intrusion are illustrated in **Figure 3.**

Events That Disturb Rock Layers

Geologists assume that the way sediment is deposited to form rock layers—in horizontal layers—has not changed over time. According to this principle, if rock layers are not horizontal, something must have disturbed them after they formed. This principle allows geologists to determine the relative ages of rock layers and the events that disturbed them.

Folding and tilting are two types of events that disturb rock layers. These events are always younger than the rock layers they affect. The results of folding and tilting are shown in **Figure 3.**

MISCONCEPTION /// ALERT \\\

Intrusions Students may think that intrusions are vertical penetrations of rock layers. Point out to students that magma, like water, always follows the path of least resistance. Often, intrusions occur at angles or horizontally, between rock layers.

Group ACTIVITY — GENERAL

Field Trip Arrange a field trip to a local area that has exposed rock strata. If possible, contact a geologist from a local university or a museum to accompany the group. In small groups, have students try to locate unconformities and explain the origins of the unconformities. Encourage students to make drawings of the rock formations that they observe, and have them label the features that are described in this chapter. **LS Visual**

Gaps in the Record—Unconformities

Faults, intrusions, and the effects of folding and tilting can make dating rock layers a challenge. Sometimes, layers of rock are missing altogether, creating a gap in the geologic record. To think of this another way, let's say that you stack your newspapers every day after reading them. Now, let's suppose you want to look at a paper you read 10 days ago. You know that the paper should be 10 papers deep in the stack. But when you look, the paper is not there. What happened? Perhaps you forgot to put the paper in the stack. Now, imagine a missing rock layer instead of a missing newspaper.

Missing Evidence

Missing rock layers create breaks in rock-layer sequences called unconformities. An **unconformity** is a surface that represents a missing part of the geologic column. Unconformities also represent missing time—time that was not recorded in layers of rock. When geologists find an unconformity, they must question whether the "missing layer" was never present or whether it was somehow removed. **Figure 4** shows how *nondeposition,* or the stoppage of deposition when a supply of sediment is cut off, and *erosion* create unconformities.

unconformity a break in the geologic record created when rock layers are eroded or when sediment is not deposited for a long period of time

✔ **Reading Check** Define the term unconformity.

Figure 4   How Unconformities Are Created

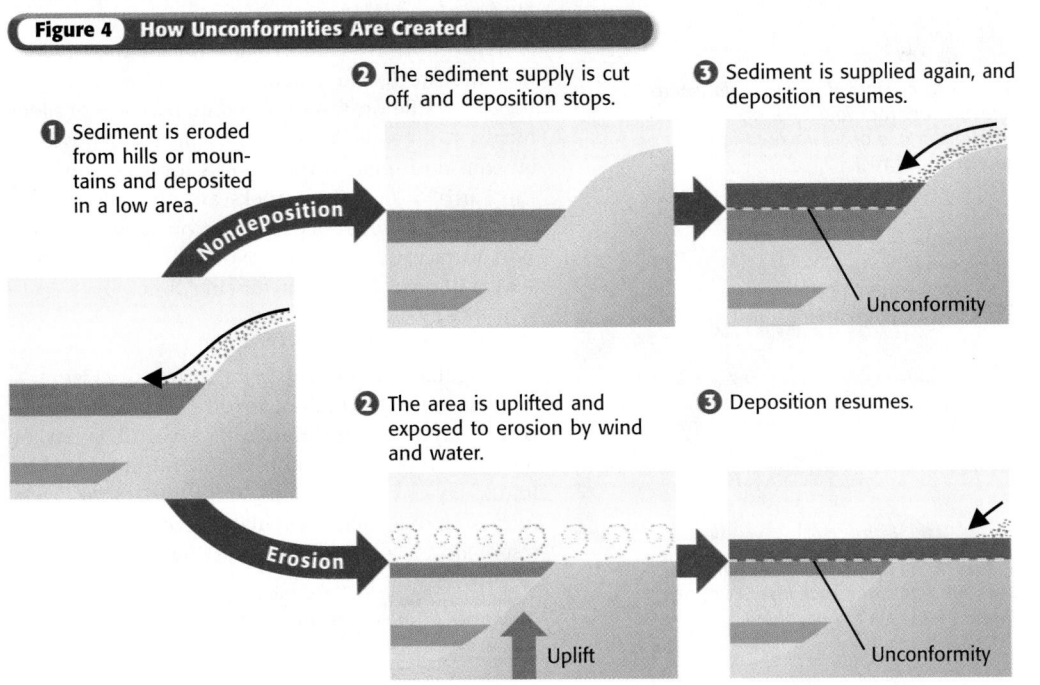

1. Sediment is eroded from hills or mountains and deposited in a low area.

Nondeposition

2. The sediment supply is cut off, and deposition stops.

3. Sediment is supplied again, and deposition resumes.

Unconformity

2. The area is uplifted and exposed to erosion by wind and water.

Erosion

Uplift

3. Deposition resumes.

Unconformity

Is That a Fact!

Unconformities can represent a short gap or a very long gap in the geologic record. The time gap can be as little as a few hundred years or as much as several billion years. Geologists must analyze many different variables to determine the amount of time an unconformity represents.

Using the Figure—ADVANCED

Geologic History Comic Strip
Have students study **Figure 4** and then work independently to create a comic strip that continues the sequence of images in the figure. Students can illustrate geologic events such as intrusions, tilting, folding, faulting, volcanic deposition, or unconformities. Have students share their illustrations with the class and explain the geologic history of their comic strip.
LS Visual

ACTIVITY ——————— BASIC

Unconformities   On the board or overhead projector, use different colors to create a rock formation that consists of five rock layers, an angular unconformity, a nonconformity, and two different fossils located in different layers. Ask students the following:

• Where is the angular unconformity and the nonconformity? How are they different? (An angular unconformity exists between layers that were tilted and horizontal rock layers. The nonconformity is found where nonlayered rock has eroded and where sedimentary rock has been deposited on its surface.)

• Partially erase the top layer of rock; then add two more layers of deposition. Ask students to name this type of unconformity. (disconformity)
LS Visual

Unconformity Review Have students draw a diagram of each type of unconformity on a separate index card. Students can also depict folds, faults, tilting, and intrusions on separate index cards. Have students exchange cards and then try to guess the geologic concept shown on each card. Students can use the index cards as study aids. **LS** Visual

Quiz ——— **GENERAL**

1. What is an unconformity? Name some types of unconformities. (Unconformities are gaps in an area's geologic column. Examples include disconformities, nonconformities, and angular unconformities.)

2. If a folded outcrop features an undeformed intrusion that is interrupted by faulting, in what order did the folding, the faulting, and the intrusion occur? (folding, intrusion, faulting)

Alternative Assessment ——— **GENERAL**

Making Models Have students draw and label disconformities, nonconformities, and angular unconformities in their **science journal.** Ask them to identify the youngest and the oldest rocks and include examples of intrusions, folds, and faults. **LS** Visual

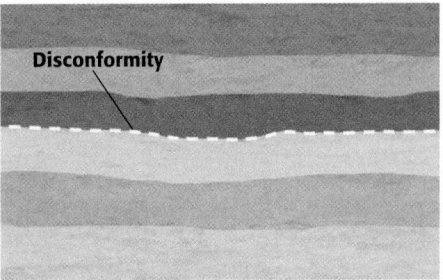

Figure 5 *A disconformity exists where part of a sequence of parallel rock layers is missing.*

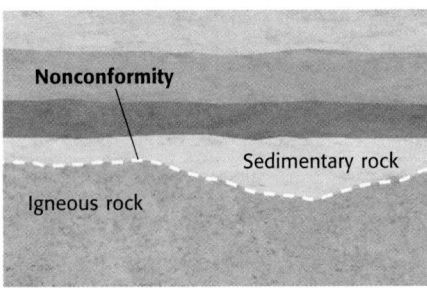

Figure 6 *A nonconformity exists where sedimentary rock layers lie on top of an eroded surface of nonlayered igneous or metamorphic rock.*

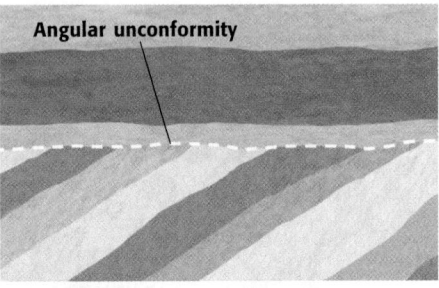

Figure 7 *An angular unconformity exists between horizontal rock layers and rock layers that are tilted or folded.*

Types of Unconformities

Most unconformities form by both erosion and nondeposition. But other factors can complicate matters. To simplify the study of unconformities, geologists place them into three major categories: disconformities, nonconformities, and angular unconformities. The three diagrams at left illustrate these three categories.

Disconformities

The most common type of unconformity is a disconformity, which is illustrated in **Figure 5.** *Disconformities* are found where part of a sequence of parallel rock layers is missing. A disconformity can form in the following way. A sequence of rock layers is uplifted. Younger layers at the top of the sequence are removed by erosion, and the eroded material is deposited elsewhere. At some future time, deposition resumes, and sediment buries the old erosion surface. The disconformity that results shows where erosion has taken place and rock layers are missing. A disconformity represents thousands to many millions of years of missing time.

Nonconformities

A nonconformity is illustrated in **Figure 6.** *Nonconformities* are found where horizontal sedimentary rock layers lie on top of an eroded surface of older intrusive igneous or metamorphic rock. Intrusive igneous and metamorphic rocks form deep within the Earth. When these rocks are raised to Earth's surface, they are eroded. Deposition causes the erosion surface to be buried. Nonconformities represent millions of years of missing time.

Angular Unconformities

An angular unconformity is shown in **Figure 7.** *Angular unconformities* are found between horizontal layers of sedimentary rock and layers of rock that have been tilted or folded. The tilted or folded layers were eroded before horizontal layers formed above them. Angular unconformities represent millions of years of missing time.

✓ *Reading Check* Describe each of the three major categories of unconformities.

Answer to Reading Check

A disconformity is found where part of a sequence of parallel rock layers is missing. A nonconformity is found where horizontal sedimentary rock layers lie on top of an eroded surface of igneous or metamorphic rock. Angular unconformities are found between horizontal sedimentary rock layers and rock layers that have been tilted or folded.

Rock-Layer Puzzles

Geologists often find rock-layer sequences that have been affected by more than one of the events and features mentioned in this section. For example, as shown in **Figure 8,** intrusions may squeeze into rock layers that contain an unconformity. Determining the order of events that led to such a sequence is like piecing together a jigsaw puzzle. Geologists must use their knowledge of the events that disturb or remove rock-layer sequences to help piece together the history of Earth as told by the rock record.

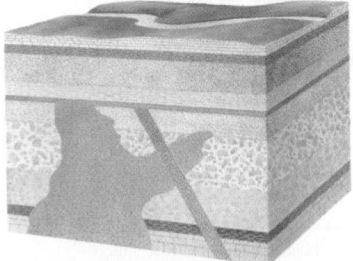

Figure 8 *Rock-layer sequences are often disturbed by more than one rock-disturbing feature.*

SECTION Review

Summary

- Geologists use relative dating to determine the order in which events happen.
- The principle of superposition states that in undisturbed rock sequences, younger layers lie above older layers.
- Folding and tilting are two events that disturb rock layers. Faults and intrusions are two features that disturb rock layers.
- The known rock and fossil record is indicated by the geologic column.
- Geologists examine the relationships between rock layers and the structures that cut across them in order to determine relative ages.

Using Key Terms

1. In your own words, write a definition for each of the following terms: *relative dating, superposition,* and *geologic column.*

Understanding Key Ideas

2. Molten rock that squeezes into existing rock and cools is called a(n)
   a. fold.
   b. fault.
   c. intrusion.
   d. unconformity.

3. List two events and two features that can disturb rock-layer sequences.

4. Explain how physical features are used to determine relative ages.

Critical Thinking

5. **Analyzing Concepts** Is there a place on Earth that has all the layers of the geologic column? Explain.

6. **Analyzing Ideas** Disconformities are hard to recognize because all of the layers are horizontal. How does a geologist know when he or she is looking at a disconformity?

Interpreting Graphics

Use the illustration below to answer the question that follows.

7. If the top rock layer were eroded and deposition later resumed, what type of unconformity would mark the boundary between older rock layers and the newly deposited rock layers?

Developed and maintained by the National Science Teachers Association

For a variety of links related to this chapter, go to www.scilinks.org

Topic: Relative Dating
SciLinks code: HSM1288

Answers to Section Review

1. Sample answer: Relative dating is a method of determining whether an event or object is older or younger than other events or objects. Superposition is a principle that states that younger rocks lie above older rocks in undisturbed rock sequences. The geologic column is an ideal sequence of rock layers that contains all known rock and fossil formations on Earth, arranged from oldest to youngest.

2. c

3. Two events that can disturb rock layers are folding and tilting. Two features that disturb rock layers are faults and intrusions.

4. Geologists can use their knowledge of how physical features form to determine the order in which events occurred and thereby determine relative ages.

5. The geologic column is an ideal sequence of all the rock formations and fossils on Earth. No single location contains all of Earth's rock formations and fossils.

6. Disconformities represent a gap in the geologic column. If part of the column is missing from the layers, then the geologist could be observing a disconformity.

7. an angular unconformity

CHAPTER RESOURCES

Chapter Resource File

- Section Quiz GENERAL
- Section Review GENERAL
- Vocabulary and Section Summary GENERAL
- Reinforcement Worksheet BASIC

Focus

Overview

This section explains how absolute dating can be used to determine the actual age of a fossil or a rock. Students will be able to explain the nature of radioactive decay and describe how radiometric dating measures the radioactive decay of different isotopes to calculate the age of the parent material.

 **Bellringer**

Ask students to write a short paragraph explaining why geologists use both absolute and relative dating to interpret the past.

Motivate

ACTIVITY ——— GENERAL

Absolute Dating Skit Ask two students to be the geologists in this activity. The rest of the class will be radioactive isotopes in a newly formed rock sample. Tell the isotopes to stand up and that they have a half-life of 1 min. Have the geologists go outside the classroom and wait. After 1 min, tell half of the isotopes to sit down. Continue this pattern until one student remains standing. Ask the geologists to determine the age of the sample based on the number of original isotopes and the length of a half-life. LS Visual/Logical

---

SECTION 3

What You Will Learn

● Describe how radioactive decay occurs.
● Explain how radioactive decay relates to radiometric dating.
● Identify four types of radiometric dating.
● Determine the best type of radiometric dating to use to date an object.

Vocabulary

absolute dating
isotope
radioactive decay
radiometric dating
half-life

READING STRATEGY

Reading Organizer As you read this section, make a concept map by using the terms above.

Absolute Dating: A Measure of Time

Have you ever heard the expression "turning back the clock"? With the discovery of the natural decay of uranium in 1896, French physicist Henri Becquerel provided a means of doing just that. Scientists could use radioactive elements as clocks to measure geologic time.

The process of establishing the age of an object by determining the number of years it has existed is called **absolute dating.** In this section, you will learn about radiometric dating, which is the most common method of absolute dating.

Radioactive Decay

To determine the absolute ages of fossils and rocks, scientists analyze isotopes of radioactive elements. Atoms of the same element that have the same number of protons but have different numbers of neutrons are called **isotopes.** Most isotopes are stable, meaning that they stay in their original form. But some isotopes are unstable. Scientists call unstable isotopes *radioactive.* Radioactive isotopes tend to break down into stable isotopes of the same or other elements in a process called **radioactive decay. Figure 1** shows an example of how radioactive decay occurs. Because radioactive decay occurs at a steady rate, scientists can use the relative amounts of stable and unstable isotopes present in an object to determine the object's age.

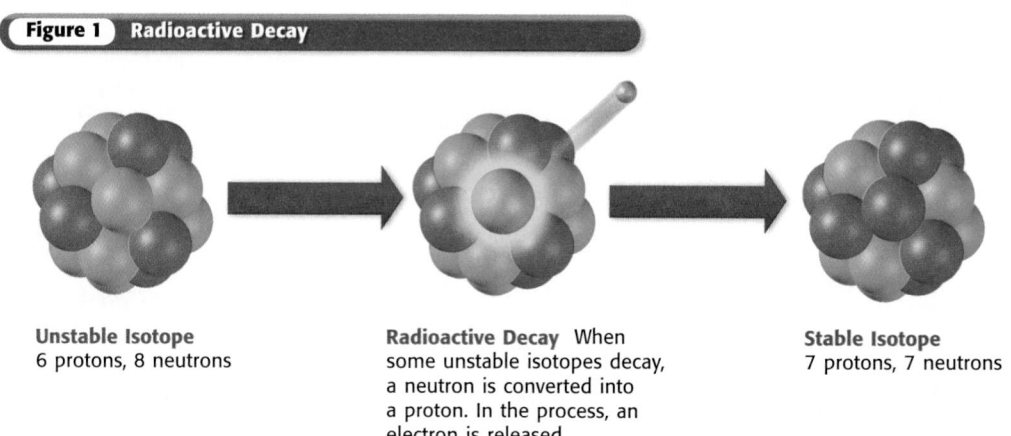

Figure 1 Radioactive Decay

Unstable Isotope
6 protons, 8 neutrons

Radioactive Decay When some unstable isotopes decay, a neutron is converted into a proton. In the process, an electron is released.

Stable Isotope
7 protons, 7 neutrons

CHAPTER RESOURCES

Chapter Resource File

• Lesson Plan
• Directed Reading A BASIC
• Directed Reading B SPECIAL NEEDS

Technology

Transparencies
• Bellringer
• *LINK TO PHYSICAL SCIENCE* P64 Radioactive Decay and Half-Life

Workbooks

Interactive Textbook Struggling Readers

CONNECTION ACTIVITY
Math ——— GENERAL

Calculating Half-Life To help students understand the concept of a half-life, use the transparency entitled "Radioactive Decay and Half-Life." Then, assess the comprehension of the students by asking them to calculate how old an object is when 1/4, 1/8, 1/32, and 1/64 of its carbon-14 remains. The half-life for carbon-14 is 5,730 years. (11,460 years; 17,190 years; 28,650 years; 34,380 years) LS Logical

---

Dating Rocks—How Does It Work?

In the process of radioactive decay, an unstable radioactive isotope of one element breaks down into a stable isotope. The stable isotope may be of the same element or, more commonly, a different element. The unstable radioactive isotope is called the *parent isotope*. The stable isotope produced by the radioactive decay of the parent isotope is called the *daughter isotope*. The radioactive decay of a parent isotope into a stable daughter isotope can occur in a single step or a series of steps. In either case, the rate of decay is constant. Therefore, to date rock, scientists compare the amount of parent material with the amount of daughter material. The more daughter material there is, the older the rock is.

Radiometric Dating

If you know the rate of decay for a radioactive element in a rock, you can figure out the absolute age of the rock. Determining the absolute age of a sample, based on the ratio of parent material to daughter material, is called **radiometric dating**. For example, let's say that a rock sample contains an isotope with a half-life of 10,000 years. A **half-life** is the time that it takes one-half of a radioactive sample to decay. So, for this rock sample, in 10,000 years, half the parent material will have decayed and become daughter material. You analyze the sample and find equal amounts of parent material and daughter material. This means that half the original radioactive isotope has decayed and that the sample must be about 10,000 years old.

What if one-fourth of your sample is parent material and three-fourths is daughter material? You would know that it took 10,000 years for half the original sample to decay and another 10,000 years for half of what remained to decay. The age of your sample would be $2 \times 10{,}000$, or 20,000, years. **Figure 2** shows how this steady decay happens.

✔ **Reading Check** What is a half-life? (*See the Appendix for answers to Reading Checks.*)

absolute dating any method of measuring the age of an event or object in years

isotope an atom that has the same number of protons (or the same atomic number) as other atoms of the same element do but that has a different number of neutrons (and thus a different atomic mass)

radioactive decay the process in which a radioactive isotope tends to break down into a stable isotope of the same element or another element

radiometric dating a method of determining the age of an object by estimating the relative percentages of a radioactive (parent) isotope and a stable (daughter) isotope

half-life the time needed for half of a sample of a radioactive substance to undergo radioactive decay

Figure 2 *After every half-life, the amount of parent material decreases by one-half.*

1/1
0 years

1/2
10,000 years

1/4
20,000 years

1/8
30,000 years

1/16
40,000 years

Reteaching — BASIC

Modeling Have students use two different colors of modeling clay to construct the nuclei of other unstable isotopes. Ask students to identify the protons and neutrons in each model. Discuss the difference between atomic mass and atomic number. Ask students to identify isotopes of the same element, and help them explain radioactive decay by using their model.

LS Logical/Kinesthetic

Quiz — GENERAL

1. When using the carbon-14 dating method, which sample would be older, a sample with a ratio of carbon-14 to carbon-12 of 2 to 1 or a sample with a ratio of 3 to 1? (the sample with a 2 to 1 ratio)

2. What is a half-life? (the time it takes for one-half of a radioactive isotope to decay)

Alternative Assessment — GENERAL

Absolute Dating Display three images of fossils. Tell students that the first fossil is about 30,000 years old, the second is about 1 million years old, and the last came from the Paleozoic era, around 400 million years ago. Ask students to describe how they would determine the absolute age of each fossil.

LS Verbal

Answer to Reading Check

strontium-87

Figure 3 *This burial mound at Effigy Mounds resembles a snake.*

Types of Radiometric Dating

Imagine traveling back through the centuries to a time before Columbus arrived in America. You are standing along the bluffs of what will one day be called the Mississippi River. You see dozens of people building large mounds. Who are these people, and what are they building?

The people you saw in your time travel were Native Americans, and the structures they were building were burial mounds. The area you imagined is now an archaeological site called Effigy Mounds National Monument. **Figure 3** shows one of these mounds.

According to archaeologists, people lived at Effigy Mounds from 2,500 years ago to 600 years ago. How do archaeologists know these dates? They have dated bones and other objects in the mounds by using radiometric dating. Scientists use different radiometric-dating techniques based on the estimated age of an object. As you read on, think about how the half-life of an isotope relates to the age of the object being dated. Which technique would you use to date the burial mounds?

Potassium-Argon Method

One isotope that is used for radiometric dating is potassium-40. Potassium-40 has a half-life of 1.3 billion years, and it decays to argon and calcium. Geologists measure argon as the daughter material. This method is used mainly to date rocks older than 100,000 years.

Uranium-Lead Method

Uranium-238 is a radioactive isotope that decays in a series of steps to lead-206. The half-life of uranium-238 is 4.5 billion years. The older the rock is, the more daughter material (lead-206) there will be in the rock. Uranium-lead dating can be used for rocks more than 10 million years old. Younger rocks do not contain enough daughter material to be accurately measured by this method.

Rubidium-Strontium Method

Through radioactive decay, the unstable parent isotope rubidium-87 forms the stable daughter isotope strontium-87. The half-life of rubidium-87 is 49 billion years. This method is used to date rocks older than 10 million years.

✓ **Reading Check** What is the daughter isotope of rubidium-87?

MISCONCEPTION ALERT

Atomic Decay Students may think that atomic decay is similar to other types of organic decay that they know about. Explain that some elements have forms called *isotopes*. Some isotopes have unstable atomic nuclei that tend to change, or decay. The chance that an atom will decay at any given moment is very small, but that chance is constant. Unstable atoms do not "wear out" or "grow old." From the moment these atoms form to the moment they decay, they always have the same probability of decaying. For example, every potassium-40 atom in a sample has a 50:50 chance of decaying during the course of 1.3 billion years. After 1.3 billion years, half the K-40 atoms will have decayed. Every unstable isotope has a characteristic half-life. Some half-lives are only a ten-thousandth of a second!

Carbon-14 Method

The element carbon is normally found in three forms, the stable isotopes carbon-12 and carbon-13 and the radioactive isotope carbon-14. These carbon isotopes combine with oxygen to form the gas carbon dioxide, which is taken in by plants during photosynthesis. As long as a plant is alive, new carbon dioxide with a constant carbon-14 to carbon-12 ratio is continually taken in. Animals that eat plants contain the same ratio of carbon isotopes.

Once a plant or an animal dies, however, no new carbon is taken in. The amount of carbon-14 begins to decrease as the plant or animal decays, and the ratio of carbon-14 to carbon-12 decreases. This decrease can be measured in a laboratory, such as the one shown in **Figure 4.** Because the half-life of carbon-14 is only 5,730 years, this dating method is used mainly for dating things that lived within the last 50,000 years.

Figure 4 *Some samples containing carbon must be cleaned and burned before their age can be determined.*

SECTION Review

Summary

- During radioactive decay, an unstable isotope decays at a constant rate and becomes a stable isotope of the same or a different element.
- Radiometric dating, based on the ratio of parent to daughter material, is used to determine the absolute age of a sample.
- Methods of radiometric dating include potassium-argon, uranium-lead, rubidium-strontium, and carbon-14 dating.

Using Key Terms

1. Use each of the following terms in a separate sentence: *absolute dating, isotope,* and *half-life.*

Understanding Key Ideas

2. Rubidium-87 has a half-life of
   a. 5,730 years.
   b. 4.5 billion years.
   c. 49 billion years.
   d. 1.3 billion years.

3. Explain how radioactive decay occurs.

4. How does radioactive decay relate to radiometric dating?

5. List four types of radiometric dating.

Math Skills

6. A radioactive isotope has a half-life of 1.3 billion years. After 3.9 billion years, how much of the parent material will be left?

Critical Thinking

7. **Analyzing Methods** Explain why radioactive decay must be constant in order for radiometric dating to be accurate.

8. **Applying Concepts** Which radiometric-dating method would be most appropriate for dating artifacts found at Effigy Mounds? Explain.

Developed and maintained by the National Science Teachers Association

For a variety of links related to this chapter, go to www.scilinks.org

Topic: Absolute Dating
SciLinks code: HSM0003

Answers to Section Review

1. Sample answers: Absolute dating is the process of establishing the age of an object by determining the number of years it has existed. An isotope is an atom that has the same number of protons as other atoms of the same element but has a different number of neutrons. A half-life is the time it takes one-half of a radioactive sample to decay.

2. c

3. Radioactive decay occurs as a radioactive isotope breaks down into a stable isotope. This change happens as the isotope loses an electron and a neutron becomes a proton.

4. Radioactive decay occurs at a constant rate. By determining the ratio between the parent material and the daughter material in an object, scientists can determine how old an object is.

5. potassium-argon, uranium-lead, strontium-rubidium, and carbon-14

6. One-eighth of the parent material will be left. After one half-life, 1/2 of the sample is left. After two half-lives, 1/4 of the sample is left. After three half-lives, 1/8 of the sample is left.

7. If decay rates were inconsistent, scientists would not have a specific half-life number to compare with an object's ratio of parent material to daughter material. Therefore, a precise age could never be determined.

8. Carbon-14 would be the best method to date artifacts from Effigy Mounds. This method is best because carbon-14 has a relatively short half-life of 5,730 years.

BRAIN FOOD

The oldest rock sample on record is a metamorphic gneiss from northern Canada, which is dated at 3.9 billion years old. Zircon crystals from Australia were found to be 4.2 billion years old, but they are part of much younger rock.

CHAPTER RESOURCES

Chapter Resource File

- Section Quiz GENERAL
- Section Review GENERAL
- Vocabulary and Section Summary GENERAL

Focus

Overview

This section describes the formation and preservation of fossils. Students will learn how fossils are used to interpret the past and to date rock layers.

 Bellringer

Ask students to write a few sentences to describe the fossil record of their own lives that might be found 65 million years from now. Tell students that fossils must be naturally preserved.

Motivate

Carbon Impressions Carbon impressions of plants can form when the plants are buried in sediment. As plants decay, a thin film of carbon is left behind. Have students work in groups to make carbon "fossil" imprints. Using plaster of Paris, have students place a flat leaf on the plaster surface. Then, after the plaster has dried, they should cover it with a second layer of plaster. When the plaster has dried, have students split the layers apart. Have students observe the leaf impression. Have them note that a bit of the leaf material sticks to the impression made in the hard material. **LS Visual/Kinesthetic**

What You Will Learn

- Describe five ways that different types of fossils form.
- List three types of fossils that are not part of organisms.
- Explain how fossils can be used to determine the history of changes in environments and organisms.
- Explain how index fossils can be used to date rock layers.

Vocabulary

fossil
trace fossil
mold
cast
index fossil

READING STRATEGY

Reading Organizer As you read this section, create an outline of the section. Use the headings from this section in your outline.

Looking at Fossils

Descending from the top of a ridge in the badlands of Argentina, your expedition team suddenly stops. You look down and realize that you are walking on eggshells—dinosaur eggshells!

A paleontologist named Luis Chiappe had this experience. He had found an enormous dinosaur nesting ground.

Fossilized Organisms

The remains or physical evidence of an organism preserved by geologic processes is called a **fossil.** Fossils are most often preserved in sedimentary rock. But as you will see, other materials can also preserve evidence of past life.

Fossils in Rocks

When an organism dies, it either immediately begins to decay or is consumed by other organisms. Sometimes, however, organisms are quickly buried by sediment when they die. The sediment slows down decay. Hard parts of organisms, such as shells and bones, are more resistant to decay than soft tissues are. So, when sediments become rock, the hard parts of animals are much more commonly preserved than are soft tissues.

Fossils in Amber

Imagine that an insect is caught in soft, sticky tree sap. Suppose that the insect gets covered by more sap, which quickly hardens and preserves the insect inside. Hardened tree sap is called *amber.* Some of our best insect fossils are found in amber, as shown in **Figure 1.** Frogs and lizards have also been found in amber.

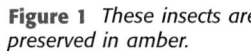 **Reading Check** Describe how organisms are preserved in amber. (*See the Appendix for answers to Reading Checks.*)

Figure 1 *These insects are preserved in amber.*

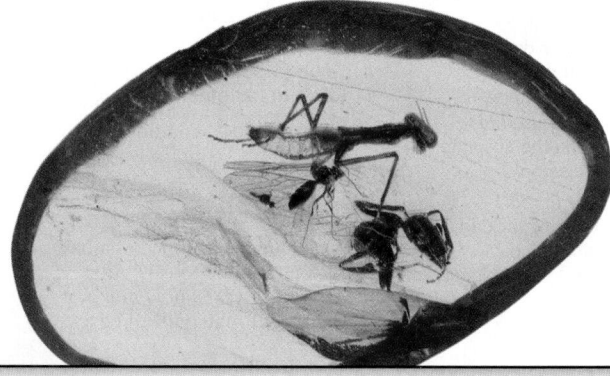

CHAPTER RESOURCES

Chapter Resource File

- **Lesson Plan**
- **Directed Reading A** BASIC
- **Directed Reading B** SPECIAL NEEDS

Technology

Transparencies
- Bellringer

Workbooks

Interactive Textbook Struggling Readers

Answer to Reading Check

An organism is caught in soft, sticky tree sap, which hardens and preserves the organism.

Figure 2 *Scientist Vladimir Eisner studies the upper molars of a 20,000-year-old woolly mammoth found in Siberia, Russia. The almost perfectly preserved male mammoth was excavated from a block of ice in October 1999.*

READING STRATEGY — **GENERAL**

Writing **Activity** Ask students to write short paragraphs exploring possible scenarios for each type of fossilization described in this section. Encourage students to illustrate each scenario and to include details of the paleo-environment at the time of fossilization. **English Language Learners**
LS Logical/Visual

Petrifaction

Another way that organisms are preserved is by petrifaction. *Petrifaction* is a process in which minerals replace an organism's tissues. One form of petrifaction is called *permineralization. Permineralization* is a process in which the pore space in an organism's hard tissue—for example, bone or wood—is filled up with mineral. Another form of petrifaction is called *replacement,* a process in which the organism's tissues are completely replaced by minerals. For example, in some specimens of petrified wood, all of the wood has been replaced by minerals.

Fossils in Asphalt

There are places where asphalt wells up at the Earth's surface in thick, sticky pools. The La Brea asphalt deposits in Los Angeles, California, for example, are at least 38,000 years old. These pools of thick, sticky asphalt have trapped and preserved many kinds of organisms for the past 38,000 years. From these fossils, scientists have learned about the past environment in southern California.

Frozen Fossils

In October 1999, scientists removed a 20,000-year-old woolly mammoth frozen in the Siberian tundra. The remains of this mammoth are shown in **Figure 2.** Woolly mammoths, relatives of modern elephants, became extinct approximately 10,000 years ago. Because cold temperatures slow down decay, many types of frozen fossils are preserved from the last ice age. Scientists hope to find out more about the mammoth and the environment in which it lived.

fossil the remains or physical evidence of an organism preserved by geological processes

CONNECTION TO Environmental Science

WRITING SKILL **Preservation in Ice** Subfreezing climates contain almost no decomposing bacteria. The well-preserved body of John Torrington, a member of an expedition that explored the Northwest Passage in Canada in the 1840s, was uncovered in 1984. His body appeared much as it did at the time he died, more than 160 years earlier. Research another well-preserved discovery, and write a report for your class.

ACTiViTY — **GENERAL**

Making Fossils Distribute the following materials to groups of students: several leaves or small shells, a small amount of petroleum jelly, plaster of Paris, water, waxed paper, a square of heavy cardboard, and a milk carton. Have each group fill the carton halfway with plaster. Have groups add some water, and stir the mixture to form a smooth, thick paste. Have students pour the plaster mixture onto the cardboard square covered by waxed paper. Then, have them coat the leaves or the shells with petroleum jelly, and place the items jelly side down into the plaster. Have students allow the plaster to dry for 24 h before removing the leaves or the shells. Groups may wish to create a fossil record of a mystery environment. Have students exchange and interpret records of other groups. **LS Kinesthetic/Visual**

MISCONCEPTION ALERT

Rancho La Brea Asphalt Pits Students may refer to the Rancho La Brea asphalt pits in Los Angeles, California, as tar pits. Explain to students that the material seeping to the surface is asphalt, not tar. Asphalt is a type of bitumen found in a natural state or obtained by evaporating petroleum. Tar is obtained by the distillation of coal, wood, or shale.

Debate ——————— ADVANCED

Amateur Fossil Collecting
Have students debate the pros and cons of amateur fossil collecting. They should understand that amateur fossil collectors have made some amazing discoveries and have helped to advance the field of paleontology. On the other hand, amateur fossil collectors have lost important information by improperly removing fossils, by not recording data about locations or associated fossils, and by failing to donate specimens to research institutions for study. Point out that it is illegal to collect fossils from state or national parks without a permit that allows you to do so. It is also illegal to remove vertebrate fossils from public lands without a permit. Have students conclude the debate by writing a handbook for amateur fossil collectors.
LS Interpersonal

Answer to Reading Check

A mold is a cavity in rock where a plant or an animal was buried. A cast is an object created when sediment fills a mold and becomes rock.

Figure 3 *These dinosaur tracks are located in Arizona. They leave a trace of a dinosaur that had longer legs than humans do.*

trace fossil a fossilized mark that is formed in soft sediment by the movement of an animal

mold a mark or cavity made in a sedimentary surface by a shell or other body

cast a type of fossil that forms when sediments fill in the cavity left by a decomposed organism

Other Types of Fossils

Besides their hard parts—and in rare cases their soft parts—do organisms leave behind any other clues about their existence? What other evidence of past life do paleontologists look for?

Trace Fossils

Any naturally preserved evidence of animal activity is called a **trace fossil.** Tracks like the ones shown in **Figure 3** are a fascinating example of a trace fossil. These fossils form when animal footprints fill with sediment and are preserved in rock. Tracks reveal a lot about the animal that made them, including how big it was and how fast it was moving. Parallel trackways showing dinosaurs moving in the same direction have led paleontologists to hypothesize that dinosaurs moved in herds.

Burrows are another trace fossil. Burrows are shelters made by animals, such as clams, that bury in sediment. Like tracks, burrows are preserved when they are filled in with sediment and buried quickly. A *coprolite* (KAHP roh LIET), a third type of trace fossil, is preserved animal dung.

Molds and Casts

Molds and casts are two more examples of fossils. A cavity in rock where a plant or animal was buried is called a **mold.** A **cast** is an object created when sediment fills a mold and becomes rock. A cast shows what the outside of the organism looked like. **Figure 4** shows two types of molds from the same organism—and internal mold and an external mold.

✓ **Reading Check** How are a cast and a mold different?

Figure 4 *This photograph shows two molds from an ammonite. The image on the left is the internal mold of the ammonite, which formed when sediment filled the ammonite's shell, which later dissolved away. The image on the right is the external mold of the ammonite, which preserves the external features of the shell.*

MISCONCEPTION ///ALERT\\\

Museum Displays Many people assume that when they see dinosaur bones in a museum, they are looking at the actual bones that made up the dinosaur. In older museums, this may be the case. However, point out that many newer museums do not display the actual fossilized dinosaur bones. They make casts of the bones. Using the casts, they make fiberglass reproductions of the bones. The fiberglass bones are much lighter than the original bones and can stand without support.

Figure 5 *This scientist has found marine fossils on mountaintops in the Yoho National Park in Canada. The fossil of* Marrella, *shown above, tells the scientist that these rocks were pushed up from below sea level millions of years ago.*

Using Fossils to Interpret the Past

Think about your favorite outdoor place. Now, imagine that you are a paleontologist at the same site 65 million years from now. What types of fossils would you dig up? Based on the fossils you found, how would you reconstruct this place?

The Information in the Fossil Record

The fossil record offers only a rough sketch of the history of life on Earth. Some parts of this history are more complete than others. For example, scientists know more about organisms that had hard body parts than about organisms that had soft body parts. Scientists also know more about organisms that lived in environments that favored fossilization. The fossil record is incomplete because most organisms never became fossils. And of course, many fossils have yet to be discovered.

History of Environmental Changes

Would you expect to find marine fossils on the mountaintop shown in **Figure 5**? The presence of marine fossils means that the rocks of these mountaintops in Canada formed in a totally different environment—at the bottom of an ocean.

The fossil record reveals a history of environmental change. For example, marine fossils help scientists reconstruct ancient coastlines and the deepening and shallowing of ancient seas. Using the fossils of plants and land animals, scientists can reconstruct past climates. They can tell whether the climate in an area was cooler or wetter than it is at present.

Close

Reteaching — BASIC

Section Review Have students write two questions for each heading in the section. Then, have students exchange questions and attempt to answer the questions. **LS** Verbal

Quiz — GENERAL

1. Would a shark tooth make a good index fossil? Why or why not? (A shark tooth could make an excellent index fossil if the shark tooth came from a shark that lived during a relatively short, well-defined geologic time span.)

2. Why do the frigid temperatures of Siberia and the sticky asphalt of the La Brea tar pits preserve fossils well? (Both environments slow down the decay of an organism and help preserve it.)

Alternative Assessment — ADVANCED

How-To Guide Have students prepare a how-to guide for the fossilization processes described in this section. Students should imagine that they are teaching an untrained person how to preserve an organism using sedimentation, amber, tar, ice, and petrifaction. Emphasize that this assignment should read like a recipe, so details are important.
LS Intrapersonal

SCHOOL to HOME

Fossil Hunt
Go on a fossil hunt with a parent or guardian. Find out what kinds of rocks in your local area might contain fossils. Take pictures or draw sketches of your trip and any fossils that you find.

ACTIVITY

index fossil a fossil that is found in the rock layers of only one geologic age and that is used to establish the age of the rock layers

History of Changing Organisms

By studying the relationships between fossils, scientists can interpret how life has changed over time. For example, older rock layers contain organisms that often differ from the organisms found in younger rock layers.

Only a small fraction of the organisms that have existed in Earth's history have been fossilized. Because the fossil record is incomplete, it does not provide paleontologists with a continuous record of change. Instead, they look for similarities between fossils, or between fossilized organisms and their closest living relatives, and try to fill in the blanks in the fossil record.

✓ Reading Check How do paleontologists fill in missing information about changes in organisms in the fossil record?

Using Fossils to Date Rocks

Scientists have found that particular types of fossils appear only in certain layers of rock. By dating the rock layers above and below these fossils, scientists can determine the time span in which the organisms that formed the fossils lived. If a type of organism existed for only a short period of time, its fossils would show up in a limited range of rock layers. These types of fossils are called index fossils. **Index fossils** are fossils of organisms that lived during a relatively short, well-defined geologic time span.

Ammonites

To be considered an index fossil, a fossil must be found in rock layers throughout the world. One example of an index fossil is the fossil of a genus of ammonites (AM uh NIETS) called *Tropites*, shown in **Figure 6**. *Tropites* was a marine mollusk similar to a modern squid. It lived in a coiled shell. *Tropites* lived between 230 million and 208 million years ago and is an index fossil for that period of time.

Figure 6 *Tropites is a genus of coiled ammonites. Tropites existed for only about 20 million years, which makes this genus a good index fossil.*

Homework — GENERAL

Modern Index Fossils Which organisms would make good index fossils for marking the end of the 21st century? Have students research species that have become extinct during the last 100 years and illustrate what the fossils of these species might look like.
LS Logical

Answer to Reading Check

To fill in missing information about changes in organisms in the fossil record, paleontologists look for similarities between fossilized organisms or between fossilized organisms and their closest living relatives.

Trilobites

Fossils of a genus of trilobites (TRIE loh BIETS) called *Phacops* are another example of an index fossil. Trilobites are extinct. Their closest living relative is the horseshoe crab. Through the dating of rock, paleontologists have determined that *Phacops* lived approximately 400 million years ago. So, when scientists find *Phacops* in rock layers anywhere on Earth, they assume that these rock layers are also approximately 400 million years old. An example of a *Phacops* fossil is shown in **Figure 7.**

✓ **Reading Check** Explain how fossils of *Phacops* can be used to establish the age of rock layers.

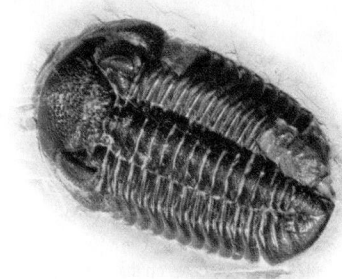

Figure 7 *Paleontologists assume that any rock layer containing a fossil of the trilobite* Phacops *is about 400 million years old.*

SECTION Review

Summary

- Fossils are the remains or physical evidence of an organism preserved by geologic processes.
- Fossils can be preserved in rock, amber, asphalt, and ice and by petrifaction.
- Trace fossils are any naturally preserved evidence of animal activity. Tracks, burrows, and coprolites are examples of trace fossils.
- Scientists study fossils to determine how environments and organisms have changed over time.
- An index fossil is a fossil of an organism that lived during a relatively short, well-defined time span. Index fossils can be used to establish the age of rock layers.

Using Key Terms

Complete each of the following sentences by choosing the correct term from the word bank.

cast   index fossils
mold   trace fossils

1. A ___ is a cavity in rock where a plant or animal was buried.

2. ___ can be used to establish the age of rock layers.

Understanding Key Ideas

3. Fossils are most often preserved in
   a. ice.
   b. amber.
   c. asphalt.
   d. rock.

4. Describe three types of trace fossils.

5. Explain how an index fossil can be used to date rock.

6. Explain why the fossil record contains an incomplete record of the history of life on Earth.

7. Explain how fossils can be used to determine the history of changes in environments and organisms.

Math Skills

8. If a scientist finds the remains of a plant between a rock layer that contains 400 million–year-old *Phacops* fossils and a rock layer that contains 230 million–year-old *Tropites* fossils, how old could the plant fossil be?

Critical Thinking

9. **Making Inferences** If you find rock layers containing fish fossils in a desert, what can you infer about the history of the desert?

10. **Identifying Bias** Because information in the fossil record is incomplete, scientists are left with certain biases concerning fossil preservation. Explain two of these biases.

SCiLINKS®

NSTA
Developed and maintained by the
National Science Teachers Association

For a variety of links related to this chapter, go to www.scilinks.org

Topic: Looking at Fossils
SciLinks code: HSM0886

CHAPTER RESOURCES

Chapter Resource File

- Section Quiz GENERAL
- Section Review GENERAL
- Vocabulary and Section Summary GENERAL
- Datasheet for Quick Lab

Focus

Overview

In this section, students will be introduced to the geologic time scale. The section discusses some important biological and geological events that occurred during each geologic era. The section also informs students about events that result in the sudden appearance or disappearance of species.

 Bellringer

Ask students the following question: "If the history of Earth were the length of 1 calendar year, on what date did modern humans arrive?" (December 31)

Motivate

Discussion ———— GENERAL

Geologic Time After students study the photographs in **Figure 1** and **Figure 2,** ask them how rock layers and fossils record Earth's history. Ask students what kinds of changes in Earth's history might be preserved in the rock and fossil records. Have students summarize their answers in a short essay. **LS Logical**

What You Will Learn

- Explain how geologic time is recorded in rock layers.
- Identify important dates on the geologic time scale.
- Explain how environmental changes resulted in the extinction of some species.

Vocabulary

geologic time scale	period
eon	epoch
era	extinction

READING STRATEGY

Brainstorming The key idea of this section is the geologic time scale. Brainstorm words and phrases related to the geologic time scale.

Time Marches On

How old is the Earth? Well, if the Earth celebrated its birthday every million years, there would be 4,600 candles on its birthday cake! Humans have been around only long enough to light the last candle on the cake.

Try to think of the Earth's history in "fast-forward." If you could watch the Earth change from this perspective, you would see mountains rise up like wrinkles in fabric and quickly wear away. You would see life-forms appear and then go extinct. In this section, you will learn that geologists must "fast-forward" the Earth's history when they write or talk about it. You will also learn about some incredible events in the history of life on Earth.

Geologic Time

Shown in **Figure 1** is the rock wall at the Dinosaur Quarry Visitor Center in Dinosaur National Monument, Utah. Contained within this wall are approximately 1,500 fossil bones that have been excavated by paleontologists. These are the remains of dinosaurs that inhabited the area about 150 million years ago. Granted, 150 million years seems to be an incredibly long period of time. However, in terms of the Earth's history, 150 million years is little more than 3% of the time our planet has existed. It is a little less than 4% of the time represented by the Earth's oldest known rocks.

Figure 1 Bones of dinosaurs that lived about 150 million years ago are exposed in the quarry wall at Dinosaur National Monument in Utah.

CHAPTER RESOURCES

Chapter Resource File

- **Lesson Plan**
- **Directed Reading A** BASIC
- **Directed Reading B** SPECIAL NEEDS

Technology

- **Transparencies**
  - Bellringer

Workbooks

- **Interactive Textbook** Struggling Readers

CONNECTION ACTIVITY
Math ———— GENERAL

Calculating Percentage The dinosaur that had the smallest ratio of brain size to body size was the stegosaurus. The 30 ft long, 3,800 lb stegosaurus had a 2.5 oz brain. Have students calculate the percentage of the stegosaurus's total body weight that its brain represents. (The brain represents 0.004% of its total body weight.) **LS Logical**

Figure 2 *Well-preserved plant and animal fossils are common in the Green River formation. Clockwise from the upper right are a fossil leaf, a dragonfly, a fish, and a turtle.*

The Rock Record and Geologic Time

One of the best places in North America to see the Earth's history recorded in rock layers is in Grand Canyon National Park. The Colorado River has cut the canyon nearly 2 km deep in some places. Over the course of 6 million years, the river has eroded countless layers of rock. These layers represent almost half, or nearly 2 billion years, of Earth's history.

Reading Check How much geologic time is represented by the rock layers in the Grand Canyon? (*See the Appendix for answers to Reading Checks.*)

The Fossil Record and Geologic Time

Figure 2 shows sedimentary rocks that belong to the Green River formation. These rocks, which are found in parts of Wyoming, Utah, and Colorado, are thousands of meters thick. These rocks were once part of a system of ancient lakes that existed for a period of millions of years. Fossils of plants and animals are common in these rocks and are very well preserved. Burial in the fine-grained lake-bed sediments preserved even the most delicate structures.

INTERNET ACTIVITY

For another activity related to this chapter, go to **go.hrw.com** and type in the keyword **HZ5FOSW.**

Homework ——— ADVANCED

Research Before the development of the theory of plate tectonics and the invention of radiometric dating, scientists developed many elaborate experiments to determine the age of the Earth. In the mid-1700s, a French scientist estimated that the Earth was 75,000 years old. He based his estimate on the cooling rate of iron cannonballs. By the 1930s, the estimated age of Earth reached 1 billion years, but it was not until the middle of the 20th century that the current estimate of 4.6 billion years was determined. Have interested students research the different methods that were used in the past to estimate the age of the Earth. **LS Verbal**

READING STRATEGY — GENERAL

Mnemonics Help students devise mnemonic sentences to learn and remember the eons of geologic history. For example, "**Ha**ppy **A**ardvarks **Pr**ance for **Ph**otographers" could be used to recall the **Ha**dean, **A**rchean, **Pr**oterozoic, and **Ph**anerozoic eons. **LS** Auditory

English Language Learners

CONNECTION ACTIVITY
Language Arts — GENERAL

Writing **Geologic Newspapers**
As students read about the geologic time scale, encourage them to consider why scientists chose to divide geologic time in this way. Have them think about the important biological, climatological, and geological differences between each era. After students finish reading about each era, have them work independently to write the front-page headlines for an imaginary newspaper printed at the close of each era. The headlines should detail the important events and characteristics of the era. For example, the front page of the *Mesozoic Times* might herald, "Mammals Appear—Warmblooded" and "Hairy Critters—Can We Trust Them?" If students wish to research more about geologic history, they can write creative articles under each headline.
LS Visual

Phanerozoic Eon

(542 million years ago to the present)
The rock and fossil record represents mainly the Phanerozoic eon, which is the eon in which we live.

Proterozoic Eon

(2.5 billion years ago to 542 million years ago)
The first organisms with well-developed cells appeared during this eon.

Archean Eon

(3.8 billion years ago to 2.5 billion years ago)
The earliest known rocks on Earth formed during this eon.

Hadean Eon

(4.6 billion years ago to 3.8 billion years ago)
The only rocks that scientists have found from this eon are meteorites and rocks from the moon.

Geologic Time Scale

Era	Period	Epoch	Millions of years ago
Cenozoic	Quaternary	Holocene	0.01
		Pleistocene	1.8
	Tertiary	Pliocene	5.3
		Miocene	23
		Oligocene	33.9
		Eocene	55.8
		Paleocene	65.5
Mesozoic	Cretaceous		146
	Jurassic		200
	Triassic		251
Paleozoic	Permian		299
	Pennsylvanian		318
	Mississippian		359
	Devonian		416
	Silurian		444
	Ordovician		488
	Cambrian		542

(PHANEROZOIC EON)

PROTEROZOIC EON	2,500
ARCHEAN EON	3,800
HADEAN EON	4,600

Figure 3 *The geologic time scale accounts for Earth's entire history. It is divided into four major parts called* eons. *Dates given for intervals on the geologic time scale are estimates.*

The Geologic Time Scale

The geologic column represents the billions of years that have passed since the first rocks formed on Earth. Altogether, geologists study 4.6 billion years of Earth's history! To make their job easier, geologists have created the geologic time scale. The **geologic time scale,** which is shown in **Figure 3,** is a scale that divides Earth's 4.6 billion–year history into distinct intervals of time.

 Reading Check Define the term *geologic time scale.*

Answer to Reading Check
The geologic time scale is a scale that divides Earth's 4.6 billion–year history into distinct intervals of time.

Divisions of Time

Geologists have divided Earth's history into sections of time, as shown on the geologic time scale in **Figure 3.** The largest divisions of geologic time are **eons** (EE AHNZ). There are four eons—the Hadean eon, the Archean eon, the Proterozoic eon, and the Phanerozoic eon. The Phanerozoic eon is divided into three **eras,** which are the second-largest divisions of geologic time. The three eras are further divided into **periods,** which are the third-largest divisions of geologic time. Periods are divided into **epochs** (EP uhks), which are the fourth-largest divisions of geologic time.

The boundaries between geologic time intervals represent shorter intervals in which visible changes took place on Earth. Some changes are marked by the disappearance of index fossil species, while others are recognized only by detailed paleontological studies.

The Appearance and Disappearance of Species

At certain times during Earth's history, the number of species has increased or decreased dramatically. An increase in the number of species often comes as a result of either a relatively sudden increase or decrease in competition among species. *Hallucigenia,* shown in **Figure 4,** appeared during the Cambrian period, when the number of marine species greatly increased. On the other hand, the number of species decreases dramatically over a relatively short period of time during a mass extinction event. **Extinction** is the death of every member of a species. Gradual events, such as global climate change and changes in ocean currents, can cause mass extinctions. A combination of these events can also cause mass extinctions.

geologic time scale the standard method used to divide the Earth's long natural history into manageable parts

eon the largest division of geologic time

era a unit of geologic time that includes two or more periods

period a unit of geologic time into which eras are divided

epoch a subdivision of a geologic period

extinction the death of every member of a species

Figure 4 Hallucigenia, named for its "bizarre and dreamlike quality," was one of numerous marine organisms to make its appearance during the early Cambrian period.

Close

Reteaching — BASIC

Geologic Time Scale Have students reproduce **Figure 3** in their **science journal.** Students should leave enough space so that they can add details about the history of life on Earth for each eon and era. **LS Verbal**

Quiz — GENERAL

1. What are the largest divisions of time in the geologic time scale? (eons)

2. During which era did plants start to appear on land? (Paleozoic era)

Alternative Assessment — GENERAL

PORTFOLIO **Making a Geologic History Book** Have students work independently to make construction-paper cutouts of fossils that might be found in each era of Earth's history. Encourage students to create both plant and animal fossils. Students should then paste each era's fossils on rock layers made from construction paper. Students should create five layers for each era and attach all of the layers together so that they fold like an accordion. Students can then annotate each layer by describing the time period the rocks and fossils were deposited, and they can paste in small illustrations of what the environment was like during that time period. Students can display their accordion books for the class to enjoy. **LS Visual**

Figure 5 *Jungles were present during the Paleozoic era, but there were no birds singing in the trees and no monkeys swinging from the branches. Birds and mammals didn't evolve until much later.*

The Paleozoic Era—Old Life

The Paleozoic era lasted from about 542 million to 251 million years ago. It is the first era well represented by fossils.

Marine life flourished at the beginning of the Paleozoic era. The oceans became home to a diversity of life. However, there were few land organisms. By the middle of the Paleozoic, all modern groups of land plants had appeared. By the end of the era, amphibians and reptiles lived on the land, and insects were abundant. **Figure 5** shows what the Earth might have looked like late in the Paleozoic era. The Paleozoic era came to an end with the largest mass extinction in Earth's history. Some scientists believe that ocean changes were a likely cause of this extinction, which killed nearly 90% of all marine species.

The Mesozoic Era—The Age of Reptiles

The Mesozoic era began about 251 million years ago. The Mesozoic is known as the *Age of Reptiles* because reptiles, such as the dinosaurs shown in **Figure 6,** inhabited the land.

During this time, reptiles dominated. Small mammals appeared about the same time as dinosaurs, and birds appeared late in the Mesozoic era. Many scientists think that birds evolved directly from a type of dinosaur. At the end of the Mesozoic era, about 15% to 20% of all species on Earth, including the dinosaurs, became extinct. Global climate change may have been the cause.

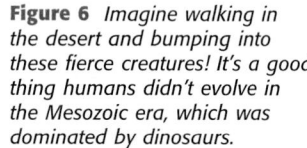 **Reading Check** Why is the Mesozoic known as the *Age of Reptiles*?

Figure 6 *Imagine walking in the desert and bumping into these fierce creatures! It's a good thing humans didn't evolve in the Mesozoic era, which was dominated by dinosaurs.*

ACTIVITY — ADVANCED

Prehistoric Illustrations Encourage advanced learners to use the Internet to research illustrations of prehistoric eras. Students can print the pictures and share them with the class, or students can create their own dioramas. As an extension, challenge students to find inaccuracies in the illustrations. **LS Visual**

Answer to Reading Check

The Mesozoic era is known as the Age of Reptiles because reptiles, including the dinosaurs, were the dominant organisms on land.

The Cenozoic Era–The Age of Mammals

The Cenozoic era, as shown in **Figure 7,** began about 65.5 million years ago and continues to the present. This era is known as the *Age of Mammals.* During the Mesozoic era, mammals had to compete with dinosaurs and other animals for food and habitat. After the mass extinction at the end of the Mesozoic era, mammals flourished. Unique traits, such as regulating body temperature internally and bearing young that develop inside the mother, may have helped mammals survive the environmental changes that probably caused the extinction of the dinosaurs.

Figure 7 *Thousands of species of mammals evolved during the Cenozoic era. This scene shows species from the early Cenozoic era that are now extinct.*

SECTION Review

Summary

- The geologic time scale divides Earth's 4.6 billion–year history into distinct intervals of time. Divisions of geologic time include eons, eras, periods, and epochs.

- The boundaries between geologic time intervals represent visible changes that have taken place on Earth.

- The rock and fossil record represents mainly the Phanerozoic eon, which is the eon in which we live.

- At certain times in Earth's history, the number of life-forms has increased or decreased dramatically.

Using Key Terms

1. Use each of the following terms in the same sentence: *era, period,* and *epoch.*

Understanding Key Ideas

2. The unit of geologic time that began 65.5 million years ago and continues to the present is the
    a. Holocene epoch.
    b. Cenozoic era.
    c. Phanerozoic eon.
    d. Quaternary period.

3. What are the major time intervals represented by the geologic time scale?

4. Explain how geologic time is recorded in rock layers.

5. What kinds of environmental changes cause mass extinctions?

Critical Thinking

6. **Making Inferences** What future event might mark the end of the Cenozoic era?

7. **Identifying Relationships** How might a decrease in competition between species lead to the sudden appearance of many new species?

Interpreting Graphics

8. Look at the illustration below. On the Earth-history clock shown, 1 h equals 383 million years, and 1 min equals 6.4 million years. In millions of years, how much more time is represented by the Proterozoic eon than by the Phanerozoic eon?

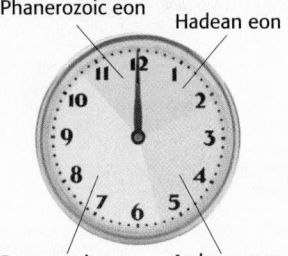

Phanerozoic eon Hadean eon

Proterozoic eon Archean eon

Developed and maintained by the National Science Teachers Association

For a variety of links related to this chapter, go to www.scilinks.org

Topic: Geologic Time
SciLinks code: HSM0668

How Do You Stack Up?

Teacher's Notes

Time Required

Two 45-minute class periods

Lab Ratings

EASY ——————————→ HARD

Teacher Prep
Student Set-Up
Concept Level
Clean Up

MATERIALS

The activity works best if the class is divided into four groups. The materials listed on the student page are enough for each group.

Preparation Notes

Students may need to review the geologic column and the principle of superposition before performing this activity. Also, be certain that your students understand what an index fossil is.

Thicknesses of layers given in the lab are the thicknesses of only the stratigraphic sections. The rock layers represented by the sections would probably be much thicker. However, the relative thicknesses of the layers are represented in the measurements given (i.e., a layer that is 4 cm thick is twice as thick as a layer that is 2 cm thick).

Model-Making Lab

OBJECTIVES

Make a model of a geologic column.

Interpret the geologic history represented by the geologic column you have made.

MATERIALS

- paper, white
- pencil
- pencils or crayons, assorted colors
- ruler, metric
- scissors
- tape, transparent

SAFETY

How Do You Stack Up?

According to the principle of superposition, in undisturbed sequences of sedimentary rock, the oldest layers are on the bottom. Geologists use this principle to determine the relative age of the rocks in a small area. In this activity, you will model what geologists do by drawing sections of different rock outcrops. Then, you will create a part of the geologic column, showing the geologic history of the area that contains all of the outcrops.

Procedure

1. Use a metric ruler and a pencil to draw four boxes on a blank piece of paper. Each box should be 3 cm wide and at least 6 cm tall. (You can trace the boxes shown on the next page.)

2. With colored pencils, copy the illustrations of the four outcrops on the next page. Copy one illustration in each of the four boxes. Use colors and patterns similar to those shown.

3. Pay close attention to the contact between layers—straight or wavy. Straight lines represent bedding planes, where deposition was continuous. Wavy lines represent unconformities, where rock layers may be missing. The top of each outcrop is incomplete, so it should be a jagged line. (Assume that the bottom of the lowest layer is a bedding plane.)

4. Use a black crayon or pencil to add the symbols representing fossils to the layers in your drawings. Pay attention to the shapes of the fossils and the layers that they are in.

5. Write the outcrop number on the back of each section.

6. Carefully cut the outcrops out of the paper, and lay the individual outcrops next to each other on your desk or table.

7. Find layers that have the same rocks and contain the same fossils. Move each outcrop up or down to line up similar layers next to each other.

8. If unconformities appear in any of the outcrops, there may be rock layers missing. You may need to examine other sections to find out what fits between the layers above and below the unconformities. Leave room for these layers by cutting the outcrops along the unconformities (wavy lines).

Lab Notes

Explain that the geologic column for the entire Earth is constructed from smaller columns that are similar to the hypothetical column in this lab. Stratigraphic sections are pieced together to form short columns, and short columns are pieced together to form longer columns. All columns put together make up the geologic column for the entire Earth.

CHAPTER RESOURCES

Chapter Resource File

 • Datasheet for Chapter Lab
• Lab Notes and Answers

Technology

 Classroom Videos
• Lab Video

9 Eventually, you should be able to make a geologic column that represents all four of the outcrops. It will show rock types and fossils for all the known layers in the area.

10 Tape the pieces of paper together in a pattern that represents the complete geologic column.

Analyze the Results

1 **Examining Data** How many layers are in the part of the geologic column that you modeled?

2 **Examining Data** Which is the oldest layer in your column? Which rock layer is the youngest? How do you know? Describe these layers in terms of rock type or the fossils they contain.

3 **Classifying** List the fossils in your column from oldest to youngest. Label the youngest and oldest fossils.

4 **Analyzing Data** Look at the unconformity in outcrop 2. Which rock layers are partially or completely missing? How do you know?

Draw Conclusions

5 **Drawing Conclusions** Which (if any) fossils can be used as index fossils for a single layer? Why are these fossils considered index fossils? What method(s) would be required to determine the absolute age of these fossils?

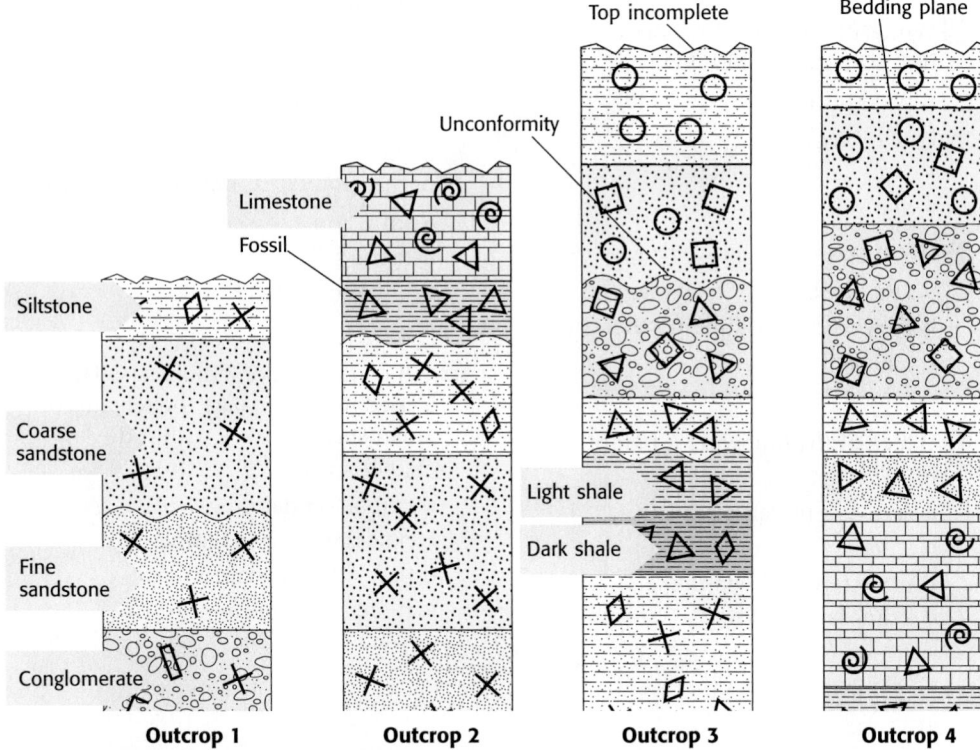

Outcrop 1 — Siltstone, Coarse sandstone, Fine sandstone, Conglomerate

Outcrop 2 — Unconformity, Limestone, Fossil

Outcrop 3 — Top incomplete, Light shale, Dark shale

Outcrop 4 — Bedding plane

Analyze the Results

1. There are 12 layers in this part of the geologic column.

2. The conglomerate that contains rectangles and X fossils is the oldest. The siltstone that contains circle fossils is the youngest.

3. The relative age of the fossils from oldest to youngest is rectangles, X's, diamonds, triangles, spirals, squares, and circles.

4. In Outcrop 2, part of the siltstone and all of the dark shale are missing. This information can be determined by comparing the outcrop with the geologic column.

Draw Conclusions

5. Index fossils include the spirals in the limestone and the rectangles in the conglomerate. These fossils are considered index fossils because they existed for a short range of geologic time. To determine the absolute age of the fossils, you would need to use radiometric dating.

Chapter Review

	Assignment Guide	
SECTION		**QUESTIONS**
1		2, 5, 14, 17
2		6, 9, 11, 22–25
3		10, 12, 15
4		4, 7, 13, 16, 20, 21
5		8, 19
2 and 3		3, 18
2 and 5		1

ANSWERS

Using Key Terms

1. Sample answer: Superposition is the principle that states that younger rocks lie above older rocks in undisturbed sequences. The geologic column is an ideal sequence of rock layers that contains all the known fossil and rock layers on Earth, arranged from oldest to youngest. The geologic time scale is a scale that divides Earth's 4.6 billion year history into distinct intervals of time.

2. Sample answer: Uniformitarianism is the theory that gradual geologic processes that we observe in the present were also active in the past. This theory argues that slow gradual change shapes the Earth. Catastrophism is the theory that past episodes of sudden and drastic change are responsible for the major geologic features that change the Earth.

3. Sample answer: Relative dating is a method of comparing rocks or fossils to each other to determine which ones are older. Absolute dating is a method of determining the age of something in years.

4. Sample answer: A trace fossil is any naturally preserved evidence of animal activity. An index fossil is a fossil of an organism that lived during a relatively short, well-defined geologic time span. It is used to establish the age of rock layers.

USING KEY TERMS

1 In your own words, write a definition for each of the following terms: *superposition, geologic column,* and *geologic time scale.*

For each pair of terms, explain how the meanings of the terms differ.

2 *uniformitarianism* and *catastrophism*

3 *relative dating* and *absolute dating*

4 *trace fossil* and *index fossil*

UNDERSTANDING KEY IDEAS

Multiple Choice

5 Which of the following does not describe catastrophic change?
   a. widespread
   b. sudden
   c. rare
   d. gradual

6 Scientists assign relative ages by using
   a. absolute dating.
   b. the principle of superposition.
   c. radioactive half-lives.
   d. carbon-14 dating.

7 Which of the following is a trace fossil?
   a. an insect preserved in amber
   b. a mammoth frozen in ice
   c. wood replaced by minerals
   d. a dinosaur trackway

8 The largest divisions of geologic time are called
   a. periods.
   b. eras.
   c. eons.
   d. epochs.

9 Rock layers cut by a fault formed
   a. after the fault.
   b. before the fault.
   c. at the same time as the fault.
   d. There is not enough information to determine the answer.

10 Of the following isotopes, which is stable?
   a. uranium-238
   b. potassium-40
   c. carbon-12
   d. carbon-14

11 A surface that represents a missing part of the geologic column is called a(n)
   a. intrusion.
   b. fault.
   c. unconformity.
   d. fold.

12 Which method of radiometric dating is used mainly to date the remains of organisms that lived within the last 50,000 years?
   a. carbon-14 dating
   b. potassium-argon dating
   c. uranium-lead dating
   d. rubidium-strontium dating

Understanding Key Ideas

5. d
6. b
7. d
8. c
9. b
10. c
11. c
12. a

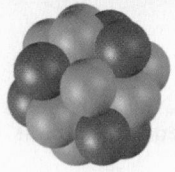  

Short Answer

13 Describe three processes by which fossils form.

14 Identify the role of uniformitarianism in Earth science.

15 Explain how radioactive decay occurs.

16 Describe two ways in which scientists use fossils to determine environmental change.

17 Explain the role of paleontology in the study of Earth's history.

CRITICAL THINKING

18 Concept Mapping Use the following terms to create a concept map: *age, half-life, absolute dating, radioactive decay, radiometric dating, relative dating, superposition, geologic column,* and *isotopes.*

19 Applying Concepts Identify how changes in environmental conditions can affect the survival of a species. Give two examples.

20 Identifying Relationships Why do paleontologists know more about hard-bodied organisms than about soft-bodied organisms?

21 Analyzing Processes Why isn't a 100 million–year-old fossilized tree made of wood?

INTERPRETING GRAPHICS

Use the diagram below to answer the questions that follow.

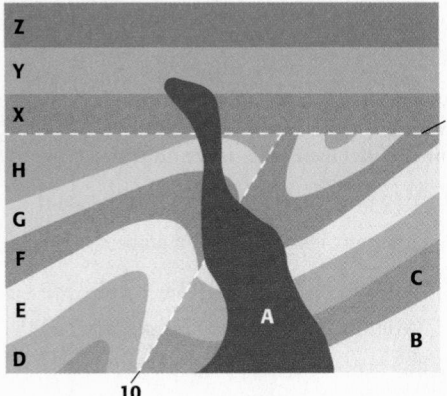

22 Is intrusion **A** younger or older than layer **X**? Explain.

23 What feature is marked by **5**?

24 Is intrusion **A** younger or older than fault **10**? Explain.

25 Other than the intrusion and faulting, what event happened in layers **B, C, D, E, F, G,** and **H**? Number this event, the intrusion, and the faulting in the order that they happened.

15. Radioactive decay occurs as an unstable isotope breaks down into a stable isotope. This change happens as the isotope loses an electron and as a neutron becomes a proton.

16. Paleontologists use fossils to reconstruct past climates and to determine water depth in the oceans.

17. Paleontologists piece together the history of life on Earth by using fossils as their data.

Critical Thinking

18. 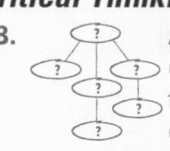 An answer to this exercise can be found at the end of this book.

19. Changes in environmental conditions can change or eliminate a species' habitat, so a species cannot meet its basic needs. Both global climate change and changes in ocean currents can cause the extinction of species.

20. Hard-bodied organisms are more easily preserved, so more of these organisms have been studied.

21. The tree is not made of wood because the wood tissue in the tree was completely replaced by minerals.

Interpreting Graphics

22. younger

23. an angular unconformity

24. Intrusion A is younger than fault 10 because the intrusion is not disturbed by the fault.

25. folding; Folding occurred, and then the fault occurred. After erosion and deposition of layers X and Y, the intrusion occurred.

13. Sample answer: Fossils are formed by the process of petrifaction, in which minerals replace an organism's tissue. Fossils are formed when organisms become trapped in hardened tree sap, or amber. Fossils are formed when an organism is preserved by sediment that slows decay.

14. Uniformitarianism is the guiding principle in Earth science. The geologic processes shaping the Earth today have been at work throughout Earth's history.

CHAPTER RESOURCES

Chapter Resource File

- Chapter Review **GENERAL**
- Chapter Test A **GENERAL**
- Chapter Test B **ADVANCED**
- Chapter Test C **SPECIAL NEEDS**
- Vocabulary Activity **GENERAL**

Workbooks

Study Guide
- Study Guide is also available in Spanish.

Standardized Test Preparation

Teacher's Notes

To provide practice under more realistic conditions, give students 20 minutes to answer all of the questions in this Standardized Test Preparation.

Answer Key

Question	Answer
1	D
2	C
3	A
4	A
5	B
6	A
7	D
8	A
9	C
10	A
11	*
12	*

*See Test Doctor.

Multiple Choice

1. The death of every member of a species is called

   A. catastrophism.

   B. uniformitarianism.

   C. superposition.

   D. extinction.

2. Which of the following provides evidence that environmental conditions on Earth have changed?

   A. A fossilized footprint is found in lava rock.

   B. An insect fossil is found in amber.

   C. A marine fossil is found on a mountaintop.

   D. A dinosaur fossil is found in sedimentary rock.

3. Which of the following animals dominated Earth during the Mesozoic Era?

   A. reptiles

   B. amphibians

   C. mammals

   D. birds

4. The carbon-14 method of radiometric dating would most likely be used to date

   A. archaeological artifacts.

   B. meteorites that have struck Earth.

   C. Earth's oldest rocks.

   D. dinosaur bones and teeth.

5. Which of the following statements best describes present ideas about geologic change?

   A. All geologic change occurs gradually and uniformly.

   B. Most geologic change occurs gradually and uniformly.

   C. All geologic change occurs rapidly and catastrophically.

   D. Most geologic change occurs rapidly and catastrophically.

Use the graph below to answer question 6.

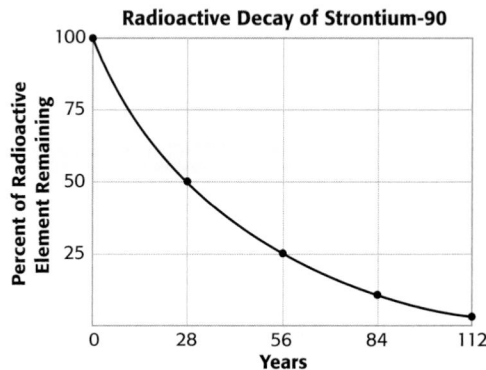

Radioactive Decay of Strontium-90

6. Ramona was studying the radioactive decay of isotopes from the uranium-enrichment facility in Paducah, Kentucky. One isotope she studied was strontium-90. According to the graph, what is the half-life of strontium-90?

   A. 28 years

   B. 56 years

   C. 84 years

   D. 112 years

 TEST DOCTOR

Question 1 A: Catastrophism is the principle that states that geologic change occurs suddenly. B: Uniformitarianism is the principle that states that geologic processes that occurred in the past can be explained by current geologic processes. C: Superposition is the principle that states that younger rock layers lie above older rocks if the layers have not been disturbed. D: Correct.

Question 2 A: A fossilized footprint found in lava rock does not provide evidence that environmental conditions on Earth have changed.

B: Insects are found in amber all over the world. This occurrence alone does not support a theory of environmental change. C: Correct. D: Fossils are found in sedimentary rocks in all kinds of environments. This phenomenon is not evidence that Earth's environments have changed.

Question 3 A: Correct. B: Amphibians were one of the dominant life forms during the Paleozoic Era. C: Mammals were the dominant life form of the Cenozoic Era. D: Birds appeared during the late Mesozoic Era, but birds were not the dominant animals during the Mesozoic Era.

Question 4 A: Correct. B, C, D: Carbon-14 dating can be used to date objects that are less than

Use the diagram below to answer question 7.

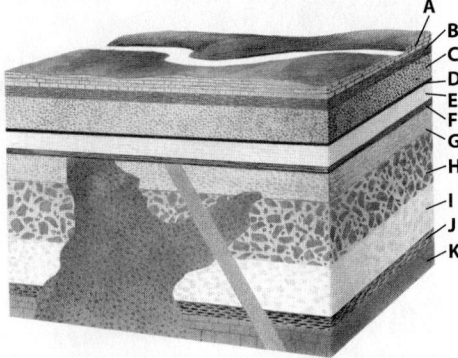

7. **Fossils have been found in layers A, B, C, D, and E. Which fossils are the oldest?**

A. The fossils found in Level A are the oldest.

B. The fossils are all the same age.

C. It is impossible to tell because of the intrusion.

D. The fossils found in Level D are the oldest.

8. **A small reptile called *Mesosaurus* lived 260 million years ago and is now extinct. Fossils of this reptile have been found in both South America and southern Africa. Which of the following statements best explains why the fossils were found on both continents?**

A. At one time, the continents were joined.

B. The reptile swam across the Atlantic Ocean.

C. The reptile traveled across a land bridge.

D. People brought the reptile to South America.

9. **Which of the following would be an example of gradual geologic change?**

A. a volcanic eruption

B. an earthquake-generated tsunami

C. a global rise in sea level

D. an asteroid striking Earth

10. **A fossilized mark that is formed in soft sediment by the movement of an animal is called a(n)**

A. trace fossil.

B. index fossil.

C. mold.

D. cast.

Open Response

11. **Across the Ohio River from Louisville, Kentucky, is the Falls of Ohio State Park. Visitors can walk across acre after acre of fossils of sea creatures from 386 million years ago. What do the fossil beds suggest about the geologic history of the area around Louisville?**

12. **The oldest rocks in Kentucky are found above the surface in the center of the state, but they are far beneath the surface in the western and eastern parts of the state. Yet the elevation at the center of the state is higher than in the western part of the state. How can this be explained?**

has not disturbed the rock layers, and the principle of superposition still applies. D: Correct.

Question 8 A: Correct. B: The Atlantic Ocean is too large for a reptile to swim across. C: There is no evidence that a land bridge existed between the two continents when the reptile lived. D: There is no evidence that people lived on Earth 260 million years ago.

Question 9 A, B, D: A volcanic eruption, a tsunami, and an asteroid striking Earth happen quickly and infrequently. These are all examples of rapid, catastrophic change. C: Correct

Question 10 A: Correct. B: An index fossil is a fossil of an organism that lived during only a short duration of geologic time and that can be used to establish the age of rock layers in which the fossil is found. C: A mold is a mark or cavity in sedimentary rock that forms when a fossil dissolves. D: A cast is a type of fossil that forms when sediments fill in the cavity left by a decomposed organism.

Question 11 Full-credit answers should include the following points:

• Present-day Louisville is located far from any ocean.

• Fossils of sea creatures are located across the river from present-day Louisville.

• The area of present-day Louisville must once have been beneath the sea.

• The age of the fossils suggests that present-day Louisville's location was ocean or inland sea 386 million years ago.

Question 12 Full-credit answers should include the following points:

• The principle of superposition says that older rocks should be lower down than younger rocks.

• For the oldest rocks in Kentucky to be at a higher elevation than younger rocks, the rock layers must have been disturbed.

• Either the center part of the state was lifted up or the western part of the state was pushed down.

• An uplift in the center of the state is more likely.

---

approximately 50,000 years in age. Dating methods such as potassium-argon, rubidium-strontium, and uranium-lead, in which the half-life of the parent isotope is measured in billions of years, would be of more use in dating meteorites, Earth's oldest rocks, and dinosaur fossils.

Question 5 A: Volcanic eruptions and asteroid impacts are examples of rapid, catastrophic changes. B: Correct. C: Erosion and deposition are examples of gradual changes. D: Catastrophic events are fairly rare on a human time scale.

Question 6 A: Correct. B: After 56 years, only 25 percent of the original amount of strontium-90

remained. Thus, the half-life of strontium-90 must be less than 56 years. C: After 84 years, only 12.5 percent of the original amount of strontium-90 remained. Thus, the half-life of strontium-90 must be much less than 84 years. D: After 112 years, only 6.25 percent of the original amount of strontium-90 remained. Thus, the half-life of strontium-90 must be much less than 112 years.

Question 7 A: The principle of superposition states that the bottom layers are oldest; this answer is wrong. B: There are fossils in all of the rock layers, but the layers are different ages; this answer is wrong. C: The intrusion in the illustration

Science in Action

Scientific Debate

Background

Since the 1990s, well-preserved fossils of dinosaurs that have featherlike structures have been found in northern China. For many vertebrate paleontologists, these fossils provide support for the theory that birds are descended from theropods, a group of dinosaurs that include *Tyrannosaurus* and *Velociraptor*. Paleontologists think that the "feathered" dinosaurs were flightless and that the feathers were used for warmth or display.

Science, Technology, and Society

Background

Movies such as *Jurassic Park* may lead some students to believe that DNA extracted from the preserved remains of organisms that have died a long time ago will tell us everything about ancient life. In reality, it is difficult to obtain and study DNA. Large, complex molecules such as DNA are broken down by bacteria and enzymes soon after the death of an organism. The DNA becomes fragmented and cannot be pieced together again. Even the DNA of organisms such as mammoths that have been preserved in ice becomes fragmented.

Scientific Debate

Feathered Dinosaurs

One day in 1996, a Chinese farmer broke open a rock he found in the bed of an ancient dry lake. What he found inside the rock became one of the most exciting paleontological discoveries of the 20th century. Preserved inside were the remains of a dinosaur. The dinosaur had a large head; powerful jaws; sharp, jagged teeth; and, most important of all, a row of featherlike structures along the backbone. Scientists named the dinosaur *Sinosauropteryx*, or "Chinese dragon wing." *Sinosauropteryx* and the remains of other "feathered" dinosaurs recently discovered in China have led some scientists to hypothesize that feathers evolved through theropod (three-toed) dinosaurs. Other paleontologists disagree. They believe the structures along the backbone of these dinosaurs are not feathers but the remains of elongated spines, like those that run down the head and back of an iguana.

Science, Technology, and Society

DNA and a Mammoth Discovery

In recent years, scientists have unearthed several mammoths that had been frozen in ice in Siberia and other remote northern locations. Bones, fur, food in the stomach, and even dung have all been found in good condition. Some scientists hoped that DNA extracted from the mammoths might lead to the cloning of this animal, which became extinct about 10,000 years ago. But the DNA might not be able to be duplicated by scientists. However, DNA samples may nevertheless help scientists understand why mammoths became extinct. One theory about why mammoths became extinct is that they were killed off by disease. Using DNA taken from fossilized mammoth bone, hair, or dung, scientists can check to see if it contains the DNA of a disease-causing pathogen that led to the extinction of the mammoths.

Language Arts ACTIVITY

Paleontologists often give dinosaurs names that describe something unusual about the animal's head, body, feet, or size. These names have Greek or Latin roots. Research the names of some dinosaurs, and find out what the names mean. Create a list of dinosaur names and their meanings.

Math ACTIVITY

The male Siberian mammoth reached a height of about 3 m at the shoulder. Females reached a height of about 2.5 m at the shoulder. What is the ratio of the maximum height of a female Siberian mammoth to the height of a male Siberian mammoth?

Answer to Language Arts Activity
Answers may vary.

Answer to Math Activity
2.5:3.0

Lizzie May

Amateur Paleontologist For Lizzie May, summer vacations have meant trips into the Alaskan wilderness with her stepfather, geologist/paleontologist Kevin May. The purpose of these trips has not been for fun. Instead, Kevin and Lizzie have been exploring the Alaskan wilderness for the remains of ancient life—dinosaurs, in particular.

At age 18, Lizzie May has gained the reputation of being Alaska's most famous teenage paleontologist. It is a reputation that is well deserved. To date, Lizzie has collected hundreds of dinosaur bones and located important sites of dinosaur, bird, and mammal tracks. In her honor and as a result of her hard work in the field, scientists named the skeleton of a dinosaur discovered by the Mays "Lizzie." "Lizzie" is a duckbill dinosaur, or hadrosaur, that lived approximately 90 million years ago. "Lizzie" is the oldest dinosaur ever found in Alaska and one of the earliest known duckbill dinosaurs in North America.

The Mays have made other, equally exciting discoveries. On one summer trip, Kevin and Lizzie located six dinosaur and bird track sites that dated back 97 million to 144 million years. On another trip, the Mays found a fossil marine reptile more than 200 million years old—an ichthyosaur—that had to be removed with the help of a military helicopter. You have to wonder what other exciting adventures are in store for Lizzie and Kevin!

Social Studies ACTIVITY

WRITING SKILL Lizzie May is not the only young person to have made a mark in dinosaur paleontology. Using the Internet or another source, research people such as Bucky Derflinger, Johnny Maurice, Brad Riney, and Wendy Sloboda, who as young people made contributions to the field of dinosaur study. Write a short essay summarizing your findings.

go.hrw.com
To learn more about these Science in Action topics, visit go.hrw.com and type in the keyword HZ5FOSF.

Current Science
Check out Current Science® articles related to this chapter by visiting go.hrw.com. Just type in the keyword HZ5CS06.

Answer to Social Studies Activity
Answers may vary.

Big Idea:
Energy Transformations and Interdependence

Energy transformations are occurring in us, around us, and throughout our universe. Many Earth systems are dependent on solar energy and result from the transformation of solar energy into other forms of energy. For example, solar energy is converted into chemical energy through the process of photosynthesis. Photosynthesis alone provides the basis for much of the interdependence that is evident among living things. Solar energy drives the changes in the weather and climate on Earth. And energy from Earth's interior drives plate tectonics and volcanism.

This unit discusses the importance of energy transformations in ecosystems and large-scale geologic processes. **The Earth's Ecosystems** describes the energy-based interdependence that exists among the organisms that make up different ecosystems. Despite the differences between them, all ecosystems depend on the transformation of energy and matter. These transformations are described in **Earth's Systems and Cycles. Plate Tectonics** discusses the importance of large-scale energy transformations. **Earthquakes** further expands the concept of energy transformations by explaining how earthquakes are the result of movements in Earth's crust that release tremendous amounts of energy. Similarly, **Volcanoes** provides students with a discussion of the mechanisms that cause volcanic eruptions, which occur because of large-scale energy transformations.

UNIT
4

TIMELINE

The Restless Earth

In this unit, you will learn what a dynamic planet the Earth is. Earth's landmasses are changing position continuously as they travel across Earth's surface on tremendous blocks of rock. As these blocks collide with each other, mountain ranges are formed. As these blocks pull apart, magma is released from below, sometimes explosively in volcanic eruptions. When these blocks grind slowly past one another, long breaks in the Earth are created, where devastating earthquakes can take place. This timeline shows some of the events that have occurred as scientists have tried to understand our dynamic Earth.

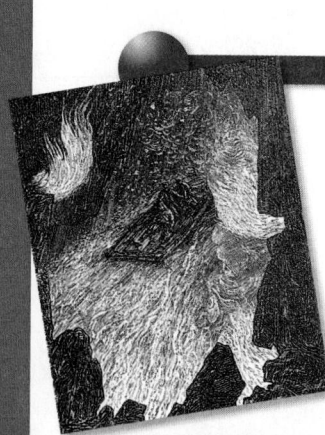

1864
Jules Verne's *A Journey to the Center of the Earth* is published. In this fictional story, the heroes enter and exit the Earth through volcanoes.

1912
Alfred Wegener proposes his theory of continental drift.

1979
Volcanoes are discovered on Io, one of Jupiter's moons.

1980
Mount St. Helens erupts after an earthquake triggers a landslide on the volcano's north face.

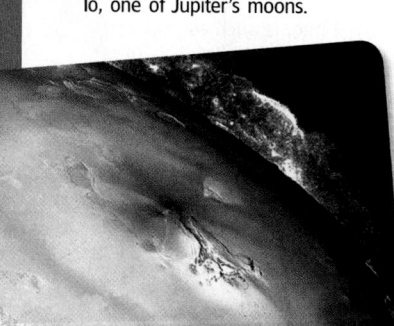

Io, one of Jupiter's moons

1883

When Krakatau erupts, more than 36,000 people are killed.

1896

Henry Ford builds his first car.

The Quadricycle, Henry Ford's first car

1906

San Francisco burns in the aftermath of an earthquake.

1935

Charles Richter devises a system of measuring the magnitude of earthquakes.

1951

Color television programming is introduced in the United States.

1962

A worldwide network of seismographs is established.

1982

Compact discs (CDs) and compact-disc players are made available to the public.

1994

An eight-legged robot named Dante II descends into the crater of an active volcano in Alaska.

Dante II

1997

The population of the Caribbean island of Montserrat dwindles to less than half its original size as frequent eruptions of the Soufriere Hills volcano force evacuations.

2003

An earthquake of magnitude 4.6 strikes Alabama. It is one of the largest earthquakes ever recorded for this area.

Group ACTiViTY
Energy Transformations

MATERIALS

- hard cover textbooks (10)
- marbles

Teacher's Note: On the floor, arrange the textbooks in such a way that their spines are facing each other (five on each side) and so that they create a long, narrow track.

Pass It Along Divide the class into groups so that each group has its own track. In the first round, place one marble at the beginning of the track, and place the second marble in the center of the track, at a point between a row's first and second textbook. Allow each student to flick the first marble toward the second marble so that the first marble hits the second marble and moves it along the track. Ask each group to keep a record of the distances that the last marble reaches. Repeat steps 2–4 for the remaining marbles. Remind students to use the same amount of effort when flicking the first marble. During the activity, encourage students to discuss their observations about energy transformations. At the end of the activity, tell students that Earth's crust is made of plates that are moving around the Earth's surface. Ask students to postulate how this marble activity may relate to the movement of tectonic plates.

The Earth's Ecosystems
Chapter Planning Guide

Compression guide:
To shorten instruction because of time limitations, omit the Chapter Lab.

OBJECTIVES	LABS, DEMONSTRATIONS, AND ACTIVITIES	TECHNOLOGY RESOURCES
PACING • 90 min pp. 316–325 **Chapter Opener**	SE **Start-up Activity**, p. 317 GENERAL	OSP **Parent Letter** ■ CD **Student Edition on CD-ROM** CD **Guided Reading Audio CD** ■ TR **Chapter Starter Transparency*** VID **Brain Food Video Quiz**
Section 1 Land Biomes • Distinguish between abiotic factors and biotic factors in biomes. • Identify seven land biomes on Earth.	TE **Activity** Describing Biomes, p. 318 GENERAL TE **Connection Activity** Language Arts, p. 319 ADVANCED TE **Group Activity** Rainfall and Temperature, p. 320 ADVANCED TE **Connection Activity** Math, p. 320 GENERAL TE **Connection Activity** Real World, p. 321 GENERAL TE **Group Activity** What Biome Am I?, p. 323 BASIC SE **School-to-Home Activity** Local Ecosystems, p. 324 GENERAL SE **Inquiry Lab** Life in the Desert, p. 721 GENERAL CRF **Datasheet for LabBook*** SE **Inquiry Lab** Discovering Mini-Ecosystems, p. 722 GENERAL CRF **Datasheet for LabBook***	OSP **Lesson Plans** (also in print) TR **Bellringer Transparency*** TR **L70 Land Biomes*** TR **L71 Coniferous Forest*** TR **L72 Tropical Rain Forest***
PACING • 45 min pp. 326–331 **Section 2 Marine Ecosystems** • List three abiotic factors that shape marine ecosystems. • Describe four major ocean zones. • Describe five marine ecosystems.	TE **Connection Activity** Real World, p. 328 GENERAL TE **Group Activity** Coral Reef, p. 329 BASIC LB **Calculator-Based Labs** Ocean Floor Mapping* ADVANCED	OSP **Lesson Plans** (also in print) TR **Bellringer Transparency*** TR ***LINK TO EARTH SCIENCE*** E46 Ocean Salinity* TR **L73 Ocean Zones; A*** TR **L74 Ocean Zones; B*** CRF **SciLinks Activity*** GENERAL CD **Interactive Explorations CD-ROM** Sea Sick GENERAL
PACING • 90 min pp. 332–335 **Section 3 Freshwater Ecosystems** • Describe one abiotic factor that affects freshwater ecosystems. • Describe the three zones of a lake. • Describe two wetland ecosystems. • Explain how a lake becomes a forest.	SE **Quick Lab** Pond-Food Relationships, p. 333 GENERAL CRF **Datasheet for Quick Lab*** TE **Activity** Water Distribution, p. 333 GENERAL SE **Skills Practice Lab** Too Much of a Good Thing?, p. 336 GENERAL CRF **Datasheet for Chapter Lab*** SE **Science in Action** Math, Social Studies, and Language Arts Activities, pp. 342–343 GENERAL LB **EcoLabs & Field Activities** Biome Adventure Travel* GENERAL LB **Long-Term Projects & Research Ideas** Tropical Medicine* ADVANCED	OSP **Lesson Plans** (also in print) TR **Bellringer Transparency*** TR **L75 Rivers*** TR **L76 Lake Zones*** SE **Internet Activity**, p. 335 GENERAL VID **Lab Videos for Life Science**

PACING • 90 min

CHAPTER REVIEW, ASSESSMENT, AND STANDARDIZED TEST PREPARATION

CRF **Vocabulary Activity*** GENERAL
SE **Chapter Review**, pp. 338–339 GENERAL
CRF **Chapter Review*** ■ GENERAL
CRF **Chapter Tests A*** ■ GENERAL, **B*** ADVANCED, **C*** SPECIAL NEEDS
SE **Standardized Test Preparation**, pp. 340–341 GENERAL
CRF **Standardized Test Preparation*** GENERAL
CRF **Performance-Based Assessment*** GENERAL
OSP **Test Generator, Test Item Listing**

Online and Technology Resources

 Holt Online Learning

Visit **go.hrw.com** for access to Holt Online Learning, or enter the keyword **HS7 Home** for a variety of free online resources.

 One-Stop Planner® CD-ROM

This CD-ROM package includes:
• Lab Materials QuickList Software
• Holt Calendar Planner
• Customizable Lesson Plans
• Printable Worksheets
• ExamView® Test Generator
• Interactive Teacher's Edition
• Holt PuzzlePro®
• Holt PowerPoint® Resources

SKILLS DEVELOPMENT RESOURCES	SECTION REVIEW AND ASSESSMENT	CORRELATIONS
SE Pre-Reading Activity, p. 316 GENERAL **OSP** Science Puzzlers, Twisters & Teasers GENERAL		**National Science Education Standards** UCP 1, 2; SAI 1, 2; ST 2; SPSP 2; LS 4b, 4c, 4d
CRF Directed Reading A* ■ BASIC, B* SPECIAL NEEDS **WB** Workbook* Struggling Readers **CRF** Vocabulary and Section Summary* ■ GENERAL **SE** Reading Strategy Reading Organizer, p. 318 GENERAL **TE** Support for English Language Learners, p. 319 **SE** Connection to Environmental Science Mountains and Climate, p. 322 GENERAL **TE** Inclusion Strategies, p. 323 **MS** Math Skills for Science Subtraction Review* GENERAL **MS** Math Skills for Science Rain-Forest Math* GENERAL **CRF** Reinforcement Worksheet Know Your Biomes* BASIC	**SE** Reading Checks, pp. 319, 320, 322, 323, 324 GENERAL **TE** Reteaching, p. 324 BASIC **TE** Quiz, p. 324 GENERAL **TE** Alternative Assessment, p. 324 GENERAL **SE** Section Review,* p. 325 ■ GENERAL **CRF** Section Quiz* ■ GENERAL	UCP 2, 4, 5; SAI 1; ST 1; SPSP 2, 3; LS 1a, 3a, 3c, 3d, 4b, 4c, 4d, 5a, 5b; *LabBook:* UCP 1, 2, 4, 5; SAI 1, 2; SPSP 2; LS 3a, 3b, 3c, 4a, 4b, 4d
CRF Directed Reading A* ■ BASIC, B* SPECIAL NEEDS **WB** Workbook* Struggling Readers **CRF** Vocabulary and Section Summary* ■ GENERAL **SE** Reading Strategy Prediction Guide, p. 326 GENERAL **TE** Reading Strategy Prediction Guide, p. 327 GENERAL **TE** Support for English Language Learners, p. 327 **SS** Science Skills Being Flexible* GENERAL	**SE** Reading Checks, pp. 326, 327, 329, 330 GENERAL **TE** Homework, p. 329 GENERAL **TE** Reteaching, p. 330 BASIC **TE** Quiz, p. 330 GENERAL **TE** Alternative Assessment, p. 330 GENERAL **SE** Section Review,* p. 331 ■ GENERAL **CRF** Section Quiz* ■ GENERAL	UCP 2, 3; SAI 1, 2; SPSP 2; LS 1a, 3d, 4a, 4b, 4c, 4d
CRF Directed Reading A* ■ BASIC, B* SPECIAL NEEDS **WB** Workbook* Struggling Readers **CRF** Vocabulary and Section Summary* ■ GENERAL **SE** Reading Strategy Paired Summarizing, p. 332 GENERAL **TE** Support for English Language Learners, p. 333 **SE** Connection to Language Arts Compound Words, p. 334 GENERAL **TE** Inclusion Strategies, p. 334 **CRF** Critical Thinking Risky Development?* ADVANCED	**SE** Reading Checks, pp. 333, 334, 335 GENERAL **TE** Reteaching, p. 334 BASIC **TE** Quiz, p. 334 GENERAL **TE** Alternative Assessment, p. 334 GENERAL **SE** Section Review,* p. 335 ■ GENERAL **CRF** Section Quiz* ■ GENERAL	UCP 2, 3, 4; SAI 1; SPSP 2; LS 1a, 3d, 4a, 4b, 4c, 4d; *Chapter Lab:* UCP 1, 2, 3, 4; SAI 1, 2; ST 2; SPSP 2, 4, 5; LS 4a, 4b, 4c, 4d

sciLINKS
NSTA
www.scilinks.org
Maintained by the **National Science Teachers Association.** See Chapter Enrichment pages that follow for a complete list of topics.

Current Science®

Check out **Current Science** articles and activities by visiting the HRW Web site at **go.hrw.com.** Just type in the keyword **HL5CS20T.**

Classroom Videos

• **Lab Videos** demonstrate the chapter lab.
• **Brain Food Video Quizzes** help students review the chapter material.

Classroom CD-ROMs

• **Guided Reading Audio CD** (Also in Spanish)
• **Interactive Explorations**
• **Virtual Investigations**
• **Visual Concepts**
• **Science Tutor**

Holt Lab Generator CD-ROM

Search for any lab by topic, standard, difficulty level, or time. Edit any lab to fit your needs, or create your own labs. Use the Lab Materials QuickList software to customize your lab materials list.

Visual Resources

CHAPTER STARTER TRANSPARENCY

BELLRINGER TRANSPARENCIES

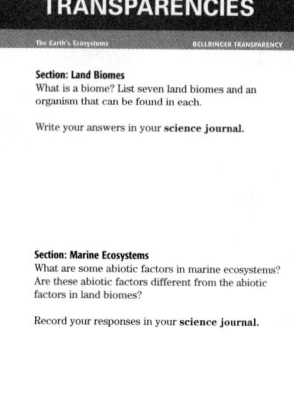

TEACHING TRANSPARENCIES

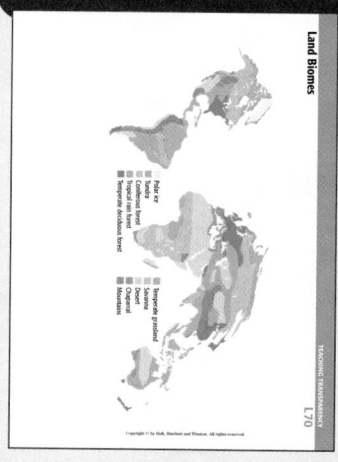

TEACHING TRANSPARENCIES

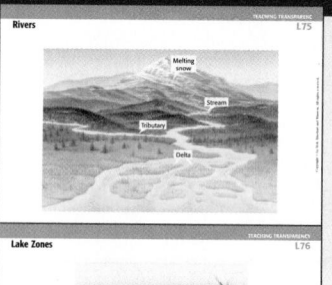

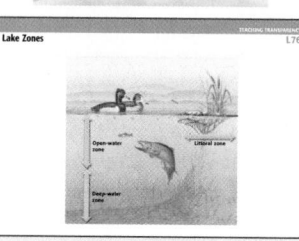

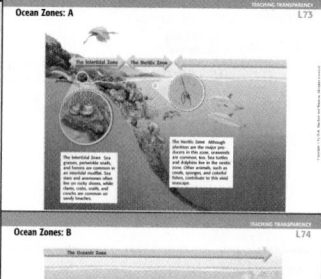

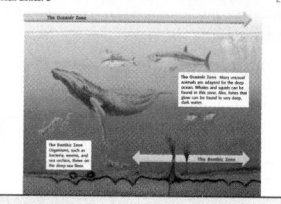

CONCEPT MAPPING TRANSPARENCY

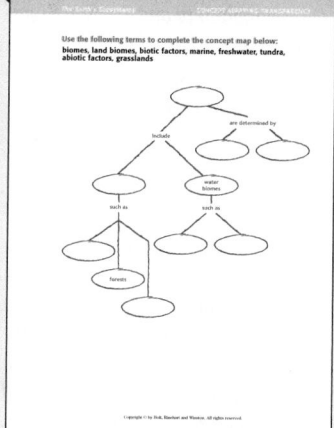

Planning Resources

LESSON PLANS

PARENT LETTER

ALSO IN SPANISH

TEST ITEM LISTING

One-Stop Planner® CD-ROM

This CD-ROM includes all of the resources shown here and the following time-saving tools:

- *Lab Materials QuickList Software*
- *Customizable lesson plans*
- *Holt Calendar Planner*
- *The powerful ExamView® Test Generator*

Meeting Individual Needs

DIRECTED READING A
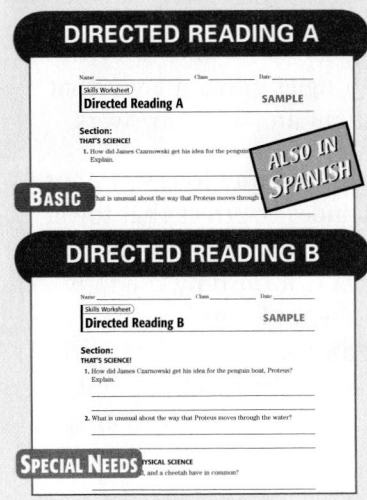
BASIC · **ALSO IN SPANISH**

DIRECTED READING B
SPECIAL NEEDS

VOCABULARY ACTIVITY
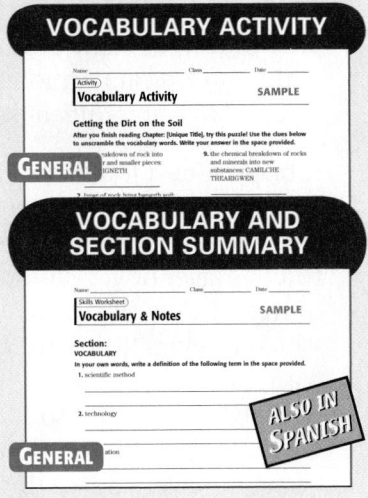
GENERAL

VOCABULARY AND SECTION SUMMARY
GENERAL · **ALSO IN SPANISH**

REINFORCEMENT
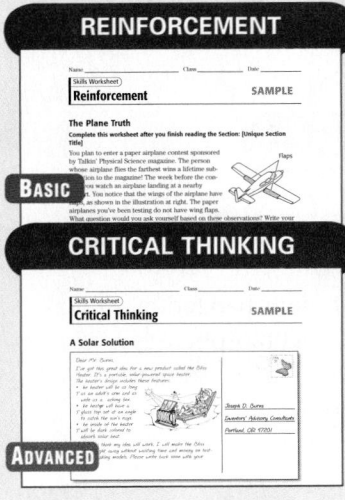
BASIC

CRITICAL THINKING
ADVANCED

SCILINKS ACTIVITY

GENERAL

SCIENCE PUZZLERS, TWISTERS & TEASERS
GENERAL

Labs and Activities

ECOLABS & FIELD ACTIVITIES
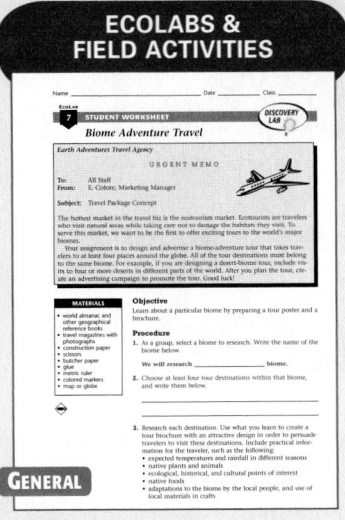
GENERAL

LONG-TERM PROJECTS & RESEARCH IDEAS
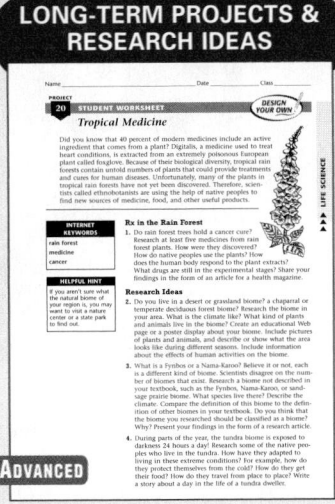
ADVANCED

CALCULATOR-BASED LABS
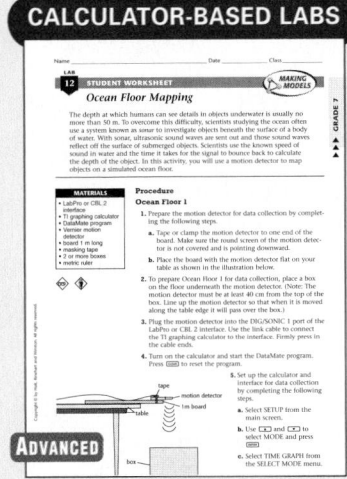
ADVANCED

DATASHEETS FOR QUICK LABS

DATASHEETS FOR CHAPTER LABS

DATASHEETS FOR LABBOOK

Review and Assessments

SECTION QUIZ
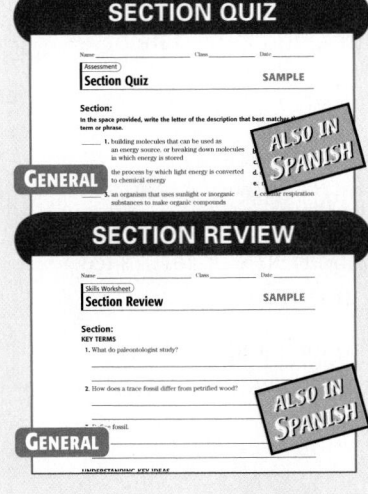
GENERAL · **ALSO IN SPANISH**

SECTION REVIEW
GENERAL · **ALSO IN SPANISH**

CHAPTER REVIEW
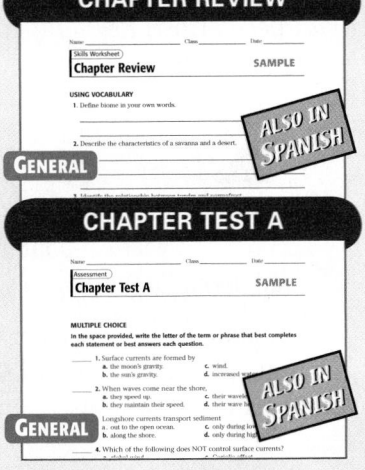
GENERAL · **ALSO IN SPANISH**

CHAPTER TEST A
GENERAL · **ALSO IN SPANISH**

CHAPTER TEST B
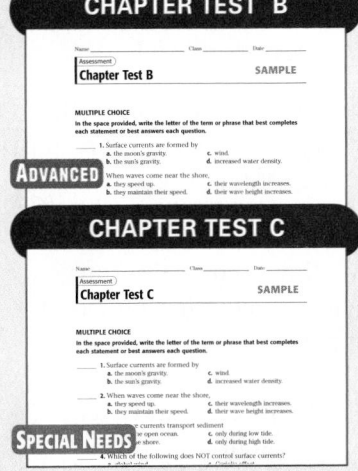
ADVANCED

CHAPTER TEST C
SPECIAL NEEDS

STANDARDIZED TEST PREPARATION
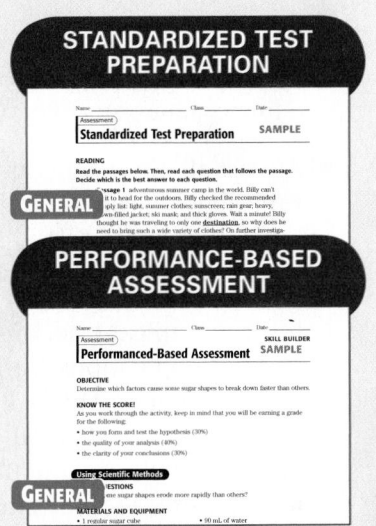
GENERAL

PERFORMANCE-BASED ASSESSMENT
GENERAL

This Chapter Enrichment provides relevant and interesting information to expand and enhance your presentation of the chapter material.

Section 1

Land Biomes

The Biosphere

- All of the parts of Earth that are inhabited by organisms make up the biosphere. The biosphere is a relatively thin layer encircling the planet. Today, aquatic habitats dominate the biosphere.

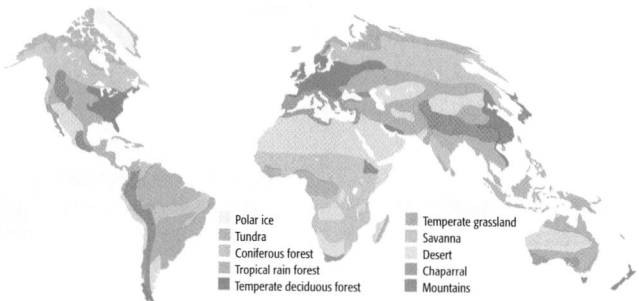

Polar ice
Tundra
Coniferous forest
Tropical rain forest
Temperate deciduous forest
Temperate grassland
Savanna
Desert
Chaparral
Mountains

- Earth can be divided into gas, liquid, and solid parts. The atmosphere is the layer of gases that envelops Earth. The hydrosphere is the portion of Earth's surface that is covered by water. The lithosphere is the soil and rock on Earth's surface.

Biotic and Abiotic Factors

- An ecosystem encompasses all of the biotic and abiotic factors in a particular area. Anything from a rotten log to the entire Earth can be labeled an *ecosystem*, but when discussing very large areas, scientists often use the term *biome* rather than the term *ecosystem*.

- Biotic factors include all organisms—plants, animals, protists, fungi, and bacteria. Abiotic factors include climate, water, sunlight, wind, rocks, and soil.

- Almost all ecosystems are driven by energy from the sun. Thus, the amount of sunlight received by a region has a large effect on the number of producers and consumers that can support an ecosystem.

- Just as chemical reactions are limited by a limiting reagent, populations within ecosystems are limited by limiting factors. The lack of any single abiotic factor can prevent the survival of a population. Limiting factors include the amount of light received, water, temperature, and nutrients in the soil.

Tropical Rain Forests

- Students may think that tropical rain forests are jungles. In fact, a jungle is an area of dense undergrowth within a tropical rain forest. Jungles grow in areas that receive large amounts of sunlight and are near rivers.

- A tropical rain forest can be divided into four strata, or layers. The emergent layer includes the trees that tower over the forest canopy. The canopy layer is the continuous layer of vegetation that is formed by the tops of trees. Below the canopy is the understory layer, which receives little sunlight and is home to leafy plants and young trees. The fourth layer is the forest floor, which receives so little sunlight that few plants grow there. The forest floor is often covered with a very thin layer of decaying matter.

- Tropical rain forests cover about 7% of Earth's surface. This small portion of Earth contains more than 50% of the species that inhabit the planet.

Tundra

- A tundra may receive as little rainfall as a desert does. But the soil in a tundra remains wet because of permafrost, low temperatures, and a low rate of evaporation.

Is That a Fact!

- ◆ Antarctica has been accumulating ice for more than 25 million years. It contains about 90% of Earth's ice and about 70% of Earth's fresh water.

- ◆ In summer, when ice begins to melt and break off into icebergs, Antarctica shrinks. In winter, Antarctica expands to twice its summer size.

Section 2

Marine Ecosystems

Oceans

- The Earth's oceans include the Pacific Ocean, the Atlantic Ocean, the Indian Ocean, and the Arctic Ocean. Although these oceans have different names, they are all connected.

- Because the oceans are connected, a change in one marine environment may eventually affect other marine environments.

Underwater Exploration

- New technology for remote-operated vehicles has broadened scientists' ability to explore ocean depths. Using vehicles equipped with cameras, mechanical arms, and remote sensors, scientists have discovered a new world that includes deep-sea animals, underwater volcanoes, thermal vents, and ecosystems that do not directly depend on light for energy.

- Early diving suits consisted of a hard helmet, a canvas-and-rubber tunic, boots with lead-weighted soles, and 13 kg in weights. This suit, called a *standard diving suit*, was invented by Augustus Siebe in the 1830s.

- In the early 1940s, Jacques-Yves Cousteau invented the Aqua Lung®, the precursor to SCUBA (**S**elf-**C**ontained **U**nderwater **B**reathing **A**pparatus).

Section 3

Freshwater Ecosystems

Wetlands

- Sometimes, wetlands are drained so that the land can be used for agriculture or urban development. Wetlands are breeding grounds for mosquitoes, which can be a health problem. However, wetlands play an important role in flood control, replenish water supplies, and support many organisms.

- Two types of wetlands are introduced in the text: the marsh and the swamp. However, there are many kinds of wetlands, including inland freshwater wetlands, coastal freshwater wetlands, and coastal saltwater wetlands.

Is That a Fact!

- ◆ About 5% of the land in the United States is wetlands.

- ◆ Wetland areas in the contiguous United States have shrunk from about 890,000 km² (in the early 1600s) to about 430,000 km² (in 1997).

Developed and maintained by the National Science Teachers Association

SciLinks is maintained by the National Science Teachers Association to provide you and your students with interesting, up-to-date links that will enrich your classroom presentation of the chapter.

Visit www.scilinks.org and enter the SciLinks code for more information about the topic listed.

Topic: Forests
SciLinks code: HSM0609

Topic: Freshwater Ecosystems
SciLinks code: HSM0621

Topic: Marine Ecosystems
SciLinks code: HSM0911

Overview

Tell students that this chapter will help them learn about Earth's ecosystems. The chapter describes several different land biomes and discusses a variety of marine and freshwater ecosystems.

Assessing Prior Knowledge

Students should be familiar with the following topics:

- interactions of living things
- cycles in nature

Identifying Misconceptions

As students learn the material in this chapter, some of them may be confused about the difference between a biome and an ecosystem. The concept of an *ecosystem* can be used at almost any scale, including the entire Earth. However, applying the concept of ecosystem to Earth and large areas can be confusing. So, scientists often refer to large areas having similar vegetation, animals, and climate as *biomes*. You may want to stress the difference between these two concepts by explaining that a biome is generally larger than areas described as *ecosystems* and that biomes can contain various ecosystems.

12 The Earth's Ecosystems

The Big Idea

Earth's ecosystems are characterized by their living and nonliving parts.

About the Photo

Is this animal a movie monster? No! The thorny devil is a lizard that lives in the desert of Australia. The thorny devil's rough skin is an adaptation that helps it survive in the hot, dry desert. Grooves in the thorny devil's skin collect water that the lizard later drinks. Water lands on its back and runs along the tiny grooves to the thorny devil's mouth.

PRE-READING ACTIVITY

FOLDNOTES **Three-Panel Flip Chart**
Before you read the chapter, create the FoldNote entitled "Three-Panel Flip Chart" described in the **Study Skills** section of the Appendix. Label the flaps of the three-panel flip chart with "Land biomes," "Marine ecosystems," and "Freshwater ecosystems." As you read the chapter, write information you learn about each category under the appropriate flap.

Standards Correlations

National Science Education Standards

The following codes indicate the National Science Education Standards that correlate to this chapter. The full text of the standards is at the front of the book.

Chapter Opener
UCP 1, 2; SAI 1, 2; ST 2; SPSP 2; LS 4b, 4c, 4d

Section 1 Land Biomes
UCP 2, 4, 5; SAI 1; ST 1; SPSP 2, 3; LS 1a, 3a, 3c, 3d, 4b, 4c, 4d, 5a, 5b; *LabBook:* UCP 1, 2, 4, 5; SAI 1, 2; SPSP 2; LS 3a, 3b, 3c, 4a, 4b, 4d

Section 2 Marine Ecosystems
UCP 2 , 3; SAI 1, 2; SPSP 2; LS 1a, 3d, 4a, 4b, 4c, 4d

Section 3 Freshwater Ecosystems
UCP 2, 3, 4; SAI 1; SPSP 2; LS 1a, 3d, 4a, 4b, 4c, 4d

Chapter Lab
UCP 1, 2, 3, 4; SAI 1, 2; ST 2; SPSP 2, 4, 5; LS 4a, 4b, 4c, 4d

Chapter Review
UCP 2, 3, 4, 5; SAI 1, 2; ST 1; SPSP 2, 3; LS 1a, 3a, 3c, 3d, 4a, 4b, 4c, 4d, 5a, 5b

Science in Action
UCP 1, 3; ST 2; SPSP 2, 4, 5; HNS 1, 2, 3; LS 4d, 5c

START-UP ACTIVITY

MATERIALS

FOR EACH GROUP
• gravel
• jar (large, wide-mouthed) or soda
  bottle (2 L)
• lid or plastic wrap
• plants
• soil
• water

Safety Caution: For additional safety, you may want to consider asking students to wear gloves while handling plants. Plants and plant parts should be kept away from the face and eyes because they may cause injury or otherwise cause irritation. Have students wash their hands after handling plants and soil.

Answers

1. Sample answers: gravel, soil, jar (or bottle), lid (or plastic wrap), water, and light

2. plants

3. Sample answer: Like a real eco-system, my mini-ecosystem has biotic and abiotic factors. My mini-ecosystem differs from a real ecosystem because my mini-ecosystem likely doesn't have as many organisms as a real ecosystem does.

START-UP ACTIVITY

A Mini-Ecosystem

In this activity, you will build and observe a minia-ture ecosystem.

Procedure

1. Place a layer of **gravel** at the bottom of a **container,** such as a **large, wide-mouthed jar** or a **2 L soda bottle** with the top cut off. Then, add a layer of **soil.**

2. Add a variety of **plants** that need similar growing conditions. Choose small plants that will not grow too quickly.

3. Spray **water** inside the container to moisten the soil.

4. Loosely cover the container with a **lid** or **plastic wrap.** Place the container in indirect light.

5. Describe the appearance of your ecosystem.

6. Let your mini-ecosystem grow for 6 weeks. Add more water when the soil is dry.

7. Observe your mini-ecosystem every week. Record your observations.

Analysis

1. List the nonliving factors that make up the eco-system that you built.

2. List the living factors that make up your ecosystem.

3. How is your mini-ecosystem similar to a real eco-system? How is it different?

Chapter Starter Transparency
Use this transparency to help students begin thinking about biomes and ecosystems.

CHAPTER RESOURCES

Technology

Transparencies
• Chapter Starter Transparency

READING SKILLS

Student Edition on CD-ROM

Guided Reading Audio CD
• English or Spanish

Classroom Videos
• Brain Food Video Quiz

Workbooks

Science Puzzlers, Twisters & Teasers
• The Earth's Ecosystems GENERAL

SECTION
1

Focus

Overview

This section introduces the concept of a *biome* and describes several land biomes. Students will learn about forests, grass-lands, deserts, and tundras.

🎧 Bellringer

Ask students the following questions about biomes:

• What is a biome? (a large area characterized by climate and the plants and animals that live in the area)

• List seven land biomes. (temperate deciduous forest, coniferous forest, tropical rain forest, temperate grassland, savanna, desert, and tundra)

Motivate

ACTiViTy ———— GENERAL

Describing Biomes Have students work in pairs to brainstorm which characteristics distinguish land biomes from each other. Ask students to write down their ideas and to read them to the class.

LS Verbal/Interpersonal

What You Will Learn

● Distinguish between abiotic factors and biotic factors in biomes.
● Identify seven land biomes on Earth.

Vocabulary

biome   desert
savanna   tundra

READING STRATEGY

Reading Organizer As you read this section, create an outline of the section. Use the headings from the section in your outline.

biome a large region characterized by a specific type of climate and certain types of plant and animal communities

Land Biomes

What do you think of when you think of polar bears? You probably imagine them in a snow-covered setting. Why don't polar bears live in the desert?

Different ecosystems are home to different kinds of organisms. Polar bears don't live in the desert because they are adapted to very cold environments. Polar bears have thick fur. This fur keeps polar bears warm. It also hides them in the snow.

The Earth's Land Biomes

Imagine yourself in a hot, dry, dusty place. You see a cactus on your right. A lizard sits on a rock to your left. Where are you? You may not know exactly, but you probably think you are in a desert.

A desert is different from other places because of its abiotic (AY bie AHT ik) factors and biotic (bie AHT ik) factors. *Abiotic factors* are the nonliving parts of an environment. Soil, water, and climate are abiotic factors. Climate is the average weather conditions for an area over a long period of time. *Biotic factors* are the living parts of an environment. Plants and animals are biotic factors. Areas that have similar abiotic factors usually have similar biotic factors. A **biome** (BIE ohm) is a large area characterized by its climate and the plants and animals that live in the area. A biome contains related ecosystems. For example, a tropical rain forest biome contains treetop ecosystems and forest-floor ecosystems. The major land biomes on Earth are shown in **Figure 1.**

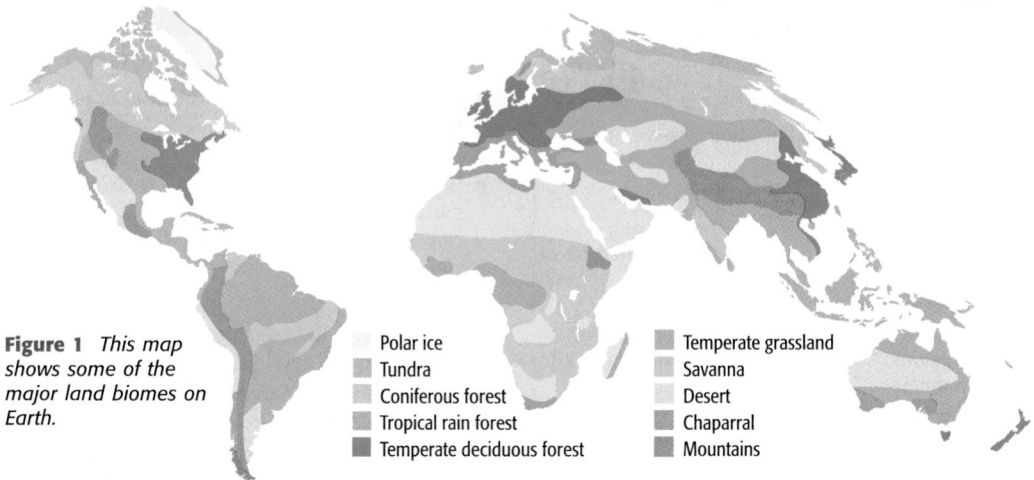

Figure 1 *This map shows some of the major land biomes on Earth.*

Polar ice
Tundra
Coniferous forest
Tropical rain forest
Temperate deciduous forest

Temperate grassland
Savanna
Desert
Chaparral
Mountains

CHAPTER RESOURCES

Chapter Resource File

• **Lesson Plan**
• **Directed Reading A** BASIC , SPECIAL NEEDS

Technology

Transparencies
• Bellringer
• L70 Land Biomes

Workbooks

Interactive Textbook Struggling Readers

Math Skills for Science
• Subtraction Review GENERAL
• Rain-forest Math GENERAL

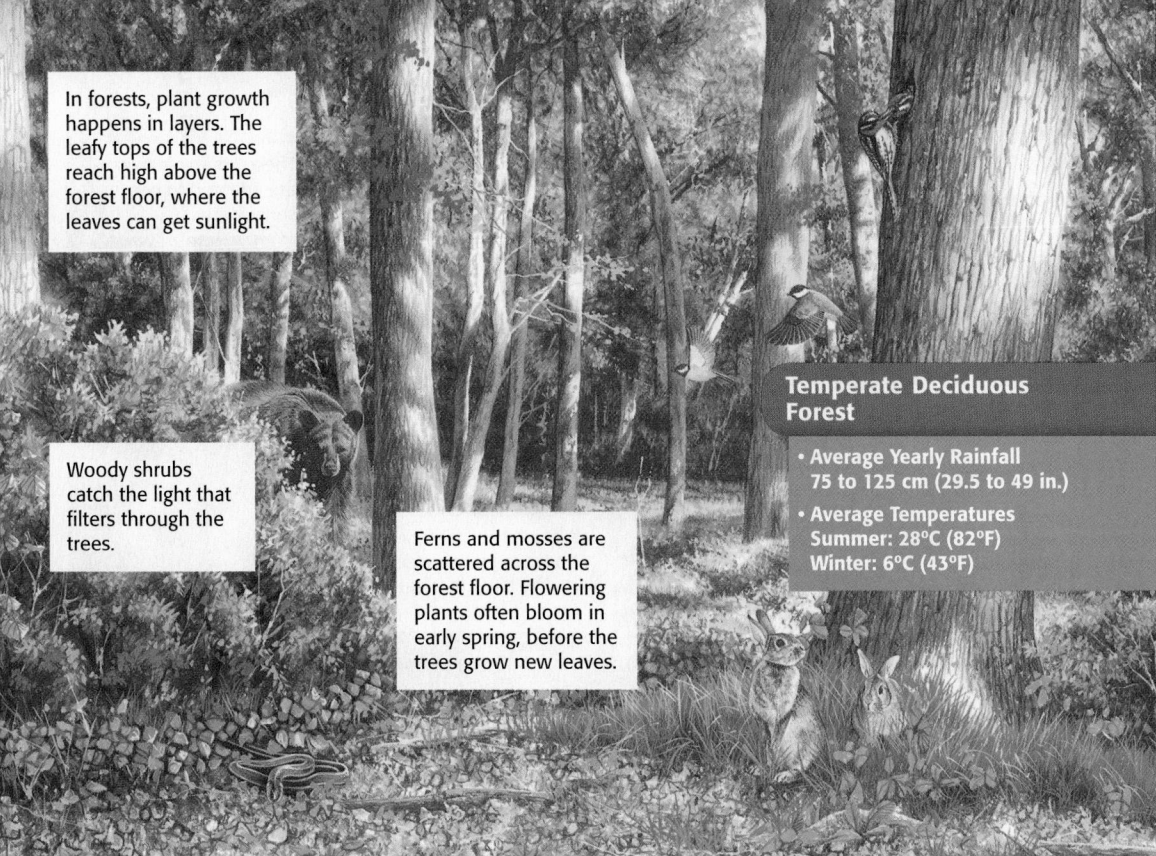

In forests, plant growth happens in layers. The leafy tops of the trees reach high above the forest floor, where the leaves can get sunlight.

Woody shrubs catch the light that filters through the trees.

Ferns and mosses are scattered across the forest floor. Flowering plants often bloom in early spring, before the trees grow new leaves.

Temperate Deciduous Forest

• **Average Yearly Rainfall** 75 to 125 cm (29.5 to 49 in.)
• **Average Temperatures** Summer: 28°C (82°F) Winter: 6°C (43°F)

Figure 2 *In a temperate deciduous forest, mammals, birds, and reptiles thrive on the many leaves, seeds, nuts, and insects.*

Forests

Forest biomes are often found in areas that have mild temperatures and plenty of rain. The kind of forest biome that develops depends on an area's temperatures and rainfall. Three forest biomes are temperate deciduous (dee SIJ oo uhs) forests, coniferous (koh NIF uhr uhs) forests, and tropical rain forests.

Temperate Deciduous Forests

Have you seen leaves change colors in the fall? Have you seen trees lose all of their leaves? If so, you have seen trees that are deciduous. The word *deciduous* comes from a Latin word that means "to fall off." Deciduous trees shed their leaves to save water during the winter or during the dry season. As shown in **Figure 2,** a variety of animals, such as bears, snakes, and woodpeckers, live in temperate deciduous forests.

Reading Check How does the word *deciduous* describe temperate deciduous forests? (*See the Appendix for answers to Reading Checks.*)

Answer to Reading Check

Sample answer: *Deciduous* comes from a Latin word that means "to fall off." In temperate deciduous forests, the trees lose their leaves in the fall.

Rainfall and Temperature

Have students work in groups of four. Give each group an almanac and graph paper. Ask groups to graph the average monthly rainfall and the average monthly temperature for your area. Then, ask students to compare the climate of the region in which you live with the climate of one of the biomes discussed in the section. **LS** Interpersonal/
Logical Co-op Learning

CONNECTION ACTIVITY
Math———————GENERAL

Rainfall Have students compare the amount of rainfall in each of the forest biomes described in the section. Then, ask students the following questions:

• Which forest biome receives the most rain? (tropical rain forest)

• How much more rain than the forest biome that receives the least amount of rain does this biome receive? (The coniferous forest receives a minimum of 35 cm of rain per year. The tropical rain forest receives as much as 400 cm of rain per year. The difference between the two is 365 cm of rain.) **LS** Logical/Auditory

Coniferous Forest

• Average Yearly Rainfall
35 to 75 cm (14 to 29.5 in.)

• Average Temperatures
Summer: 14°C (57°F)
Winter: –10°C (14°F)

These conifer leaves are adapted to conserve water.

A coniferous forest is home to many insects and to birds that eat those insects.

Herbivores that live in the coniferous forest include deer, moose, porcupines, and squirrels.

Figure 3 *Many animals that live in a coniferous forest survive the harsh winters by hibernating or migrating to a warmer climate for the winter.*

Coniferous Forests

Most of the trees in a coniferous forest are called *conifers.* Conifers produce seeds in cones. Conifers also have special leaves that are shaped like needles. The leaves have a thick, waxy coating. This waxy coating has three functions. First, it helps keep conifer leaves from drying out. Second, the waxy coating protects needles from being damaged by cold winter temperatures. Finally, the waxy coating allows most conifers to keep many of their leaves year-round. So, most conifers do not change very much from summer to winter. Trees that stay green all year and do not lose all of their leaves at one time are known as *evergreen trees.*

Figure 3 shows a coniferous forest and some of the animals that live there. Squirrels and insects live in coniferous forests. Birds, such as finches, chickadees, and jays, are common in these forests. Herbivores, such as porcupines, elk, and moose, also live in coniferous forests. The ground beneath large conifers is often covered by a thick layer of needles. Also, very little light reaches the ground. So, few large plants can grow beneath these trees.

✓ Reading Check What is another name for most conifers? What are some animals that live in coniferous forests?

Answer to Reading Check

evergreen trees; squirrels, insects, finches, chickadees, jays, porcupines, elk, and moose

Is That a Fact!

The coniferous forest is also known as *boreal forest* or *taiga.* More land on Earth can be categorized as a coniferous forest biome than can be categorized as any other land biome.

Tropical Rain Forests

Tropical rain forests have more biological diversity than other places on Earth have. This means that rain forests have more kinds of plants and animals than any other land biome. For example, more than 100 different kinds of trees may grow in an area about one-fourth the size of a football field. Many animals live on the ground. But most animals live in the *canopy*, or the treetops. Many different animals live in the canopy. For example, nearly 1,400 species of birds live in the rain-forest canopy. **Figure 4** shows some of the diversity of the tropical rain forest.

Because of its diversity, the rain forest may seem as if it has nutrient-rich soil. But most of the nutrients in the tropical rain forest are found in the plants. The soil is actually very thin and poor in nutrients. Because the soil is so thin, many trees grow above-ground roots for extra support.

Figure 4 *Tropical rain forests have a greater variety of organisms than any other biome.*

Trees form a continuous green roof, or canopy, that may extend 60 m above the forest floor.

Woody vines climb the tree trunks to reach sunlight.

Little light reaches the ground. Low-growing plants in the rain forest don't need a lot of light.

Tropical Rain Forest
- **Average Yearly Rainfall** up to 400 cm (157.5 in.)
- **Average Temperatures** Daytime: 34°C (93°F) Nighttime: 20°C (68°F)

The Greatest Asset Encourage students to read "The Greatest Asset," by Isaac Asimov. It can be found in the *Holt Anthology of Science Fiction*. Ask students to write a short report about the story. [LS] Verbal

Discussion ———— ADVANCED

Eating in the Dry Season
During the dry season, the roots of savanna plants survive but the structures above the ground often die back. Ask students to discuss how herds of large herbivores might survive when savanna vegetation dies back. (Students may suggest that the animals migrate to an area where food and water are more plentiful. Point out that migration is a behavioral adaptation for survival.)
[LS] Verbal/Auditory

Cultural Awareness ———— GENERAL

Farmland Temperate grasslands provide almost ideal growing conditions for most grain crops. For this reason, few temperate grasslands remain today. Ask interested students to identify areas in the United States and in other countries where temperate grasslands are used to grow crops. Have students make a map of their findings. [LS] Visual

---

Temperate Grassland
- **Average Yearly Rainfall**
  25 to 75 cm (10 to 29.5 in.)
- **Average Temperatures**
  Summer: 30°C (86°F)
  Winter: 0°C (32°F)

Figure 5 *Bison once roamed North American temperate grasslands in great herds.*

savanna a grassland that often has scattered trees and that is found in tropical and subtropical areas where seasonal rains, fires, and drought happen

CONNECTION TO Environmental Science

WRITING SKILL **Mountains and Climate**
Mountains can affect the climate of the land around them. Research the ecosystems around a mountain range. In your **science journal,** write a report describing how the mountains affect the climate of the surrounding land.

Grasslands

Grasslands have many names, such as *steppes, prairies,* and *pampas*. Grasslands are found on every continent but Antarctica. They are often flat or have gently rolling hills.

Temperate Grasslands

Temperate grassland plants include grasses and other flowering plants. Temperate grasslands have few trees. Fires, drought, and grazing prevent the growth of trees and shrubs. Temperate grasslands support small seed-eating animals, such as prairie dogs and mice. Large grass eaters, such as the North American bison shown in **Figure 5,** also live in temperate grasslands.

Savannas

A grassland that has scattered clumps of trees and seasonal rains is called a **savanna.** Savannas are found in parts of Africa, India, and South America. During the dry season, savanna grasses dry out and turn yellow. But the grasses' deep roots survive for many months without water. The African savanna is home to many large herbivores, such as elephants, giraffes, zebras, and wildebeests. Some of these animals are shown in **Figure 6.**

✓ **Reading Check** What happens to grasses on a savanna during the dry season?

Savanna
- **Average Yearly Rainfall**
  150 cm (59 in.)
- **Average Temperatures**
  Dry season: 34°C (93°F)
  Wet season: 16°C (61°F)

Figure 6 *In the African savanna, lions and leopards hunt zebras and wildebeests.*

Answer to Connection to Environmental Science

Students should recognize the rain-shadow effect, which causes one side of the mountain range to receive more rain than the other side does. Some students may note that the rain-shadow effect contributes to desertification.

Answer to Reading Check

During the dry season, grasses on the savanna dry out and turn yellow. But their deep roots survive for many months without water.

Cactuses store water in their stems and roots.

Some flowering plants bloom, bear seeds, and die within a few weeks after a heavy rain.

Deep-rooted plants can reach groundwater as deep as 30 m.

Huge ears help jack rabbits get rid of body heat.

Kangaroo rats never need to drink. They recycle water from the foods that they eat.

Figure 7 *The residents of the desert biome have special adaptations to survive in a dry climate.*

Deserts

Biomes that are very dry and often very hot are called **deserts.** Many kinds of plants and animals are found only in deserts. These organisms have special adaptations to live in a hot, dry climate. For example, plants grow far apart so that the plants won't have to compete with each other for water. Some plants have shallow, widespread roots that grow just under the surface. These roots let plants take up water during a storm. Other desert plants, such as cactuses, have fleshy stems and leaves. These fleshy structures store water. The leaves of desert plants also have a waxy coating that helps prevent water loss.

Animals also have adaptations for living in the desert. Most desert animals are active only at night, when temperatures are cooler. Some animals, such as the spadefoot toad, bury themselves in the ground and are dormant during the dry season. Doing so helps these animals escape the heat of summer. Animals such as desert tortoises eat flowers or leaves and store the water under their shells. **Figure 7** shows how some desert plants and animals live in the heat with little water.

desert a region that has little or no plant life, long periods without rain, and extreme temperatures; usually found in hot climates

Reading Check What are some adaptations of desert plants?

Q: Which biome was Elvis's favorite?
A: Grassland

Answer to Reading Check

Sample answer: Desert plants grow far apart. Some plants have shallow, widespread roots to take up water after a storm. Some desert plants have fleshy stems and leaves to store water. They also have waxy coatings to prevent water loss.

Reteaching ——— BASIC

Paired Summarizing Have students work in pairs to review the seven biomes described in the chapter. [LS] Verbal/Interpersonal

Quiz ——— GENERAL

Ask students whether each of the following statements is true or false. Have students correct any false statements.

1. Permafrost thaws only briefly in the summer. (false; Only the top layer of soil thaws; permafrost stays frozen all of the time.)

2. Tropical rain forests have more species than any other land biome. (true)

3. Tropical rain forests have very poor soil. (true)

Alternative Assessment ——— GENERAL

Poster Project Have students choose a biome and make a poster that displays facts about the biome and images of the biome. Posters should indicate where the biome is found. [LS] Visual

Tundra
- Average Yearly Rainfall 30 to 50 cm (12 to 20 in.)
- Average Temperatures Summer: 12°C (54°F) Winter: −26°C (−15°F)

Figure 8 *During winters in the tundra, caribou migrate to grazing grounds that have a more-plentiful supply of food.*

tundra a treeless plain found in the Arctic, in the Antarctic, or on the tops of mountains that is characterized by very low winter temperatures and short, cool summers

SCHOOL to HOME

Local Ecosystems

WRITING SKILL With a family member, explore the ecosystems around your home. What kinds of plants and animals live in your area? In your **science journal**, write a short essay describing the plants and animals in the ecosystems near your home.

Tundra

Imagine a place on Earth where it is so cold that trees do not grow. A biome that has very cold temperatures and little rainfall is called a **tundra.** Two types of tundra are polar tundra and alpine tundra.

Polar Tundra

Polar tundra is found near the North and South Poles. In polar tundra, the layer of soil beneath the surface soil stays frozen all the time. This layer is called *permafrost.* During the short, cool summers, only the surface soil thaws. The layer of thawed soil is too shallow for deep-rooted plants to live. So, shallow-rooted plants, such as grasses and small shrubs, are common. Mosses and lichens (LIE kuhnz) grow beneath these plants. The thawed soil above the permafrost becomes muddy. Insects, such as mosquitoes, lay eggs in the mud. Birds feed on these insects. Other tundra animals include musk oxen, wolves, and caribou, such as the one shown in **Figure 8.**

Alpine Tundra

Alpine tundra is similar to arctic tundra. Alpine tundra also has permafrost. But alpine tundra is found at the top of tall mountains. Above an elevation called the *tree line,* trees cannot grow on a mountain. Alpine tundra is found above the tree line. Alpine tundra gets plenty of sunlight and precipitation.

✓ **Reading Check** What is alpine tundra?

Answer to School-to-Home Activity
Accept all reasonable answers. Students should recognize local flora and fauna.

Answer to Reading Check
Sample answer: Alpine tundra is tundra found at the top of tall mountains, above the tree line.

Summary

- A biome is characterized by abiotic factors, such as climate, and biotic factors, such as plant and animal communities.
- Three forest biomes are temperate deciduous forests, coniferous forests, and tropical rain forests.
- Grasslands are areas where grasses are the main plants. Temperate grasslands have hot summers and cold winters. Savannas have wet and dry seasons.

- Deserts are very dry and often very hot. Desert plants and animals competing for the limited water supply have special adaptations for survival.
- Tundras are cold areas that have very little rainfall. Permafrost, the layer of frozen soil below the surface of arctic tundra, determines the kinds of plants and animals that live on the tundra.

Using Key Terms

1. Use each of the following terms in a separate sentence: *biome* and *tundra*.

2. In your own words, write a definition for each of the following terms: *savanna* and *desert*.

Understanding Key Ideas

3. If you visited a savanna, you would most likely see
   a. large herds of grazing animals, such as zebras, gazelles, and wildebeests.
   b. dense forests stretching from horizon to horizon.
   c. snow and ice throughout most of the year.
   d. trees that form a continuous green roof, called the *canopy*.

4. Components of a desert ecosystem include
   a. a hot, dry climate.
   b. plants that grow far apart.
   c. animals that are active mostly at night.
   d. All of the above

5. List seven land biomes that are found on Earth.

6. What are two things that characterize a biome?

Critical Thinking

7. **Making Inferences** While excavating an area in the desert, a scientist discovers the fossils of very large trees and ferns. What might the scientist conclude about biomes in this area?

8. **Analyzing Ideas** Tundra receives very little rainfall. Could tundra accurately be called a *frozen desert*? Explain your answer.

Interpreting Graphics

Use the bar graph below to answer the questions that follow.

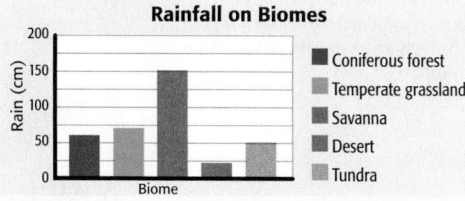
Rainfall on Biomes
- Coniferous forest
- Temperate grassland
- Savanna
- Desert
- Tundra

9. Which biomes receive 50 cm or more of rain each year?

10. Which biome receives the smallest amount of rain? the largest amount of rain?

SCiLINKS®

NSTA
Developed and maintained by the
National Science Teachers Association

For a variety of links related to this chapter, go to www.scilinks.org

Topic: Forests
SciLinks code: HSM0609

CHAPTER RESOURCES

Chapter Resource File

- Section Quiz GENERAL
- Section Review GENERAL
- Vocabulary and Section Summary GENERAL
- Reinforcement Worksheet BASIC

Focus

Overview

This section introduces and describes marine ecosystems. Students will learn about abiotic factors in marine ecosystems and about ocean zones.

 Bellringer

Ask students the following question: "What are abiotic factors in marine ecosystems?" (water temperature, the amount of sunlight that passes into the water, and water depth)

Motivate

Discussion —— GENERAL

Oceans Students may not realize how connected their lives are to the oceans, especially if students live far from the coast. Ask students the following question: "If marine life were to die off, how would humans be affected?" (There would be less food available for human consumption. There would be less oxygen in the atmosphere because marine phytoplankton produce one-third to one-half of atmospheric oxygen. Jobs would be lost. Marine nature preserves would not be available to enjoy for recreation.) **LS Verbal**

What You Will Learn

● List three abiotic factors that shape marine ecosystems.
● Describe four major ocean zones.
● Describe five marine ecosystems.

Vocabulary
plankton
estuary

READING STRATEGY

Prediction Guide Before reading this section, write the title of each heading in this section. Next, under each heading, write what you think you will learn.

plankton the mass of mostly microscopic organisms that float or drift freely in freshwater and marine environments

Figure 1 *Marine ecosystems support a broad diversity of life. Humpback whales rely on plankton for food.*

Marine Ecosystems

What covers almost three-fourths of Earth's surface? What holds both the largest animals and some of the smallest organisms on Earth?

If your answer to both questions is *oceans*, you are correct! Earth's oceans contain many different ecosystems. Scientists call ecosystems in the ocean *marine ecosystems*.

Life in the Ocean

Marine ecosystems are shaped by abiotic factors. These factors include water temperature, water depth, and the amount of sunlight that passes into the water. The animals and plants that live in the ocean come in all shapes and sizes. The largest animals on Earth, blue whales, live in the ocean. So do trillions of tiny plankton. **Plankton** are tiny organisms that float near the surface of the water. Many plankton are producers. They use photosynthesis to make their own food. Plankton form the base of the ocean's food chains. **Figure 1** shows plankton and an animal that relies on plankton for food.

✓ *Reading Check* What are plankton? How are they important to marine ecosystems? (*See the Appendix for answers to Reading Checks.*)

CHAPTER RESOURCES

Chapter Resource File

 • Lesson Plan
• Directed Reading A BASIC
• Directed Reading B SPECIAL NEEDS

Technology

 Transparencies
• Bellringer
• *LINK TO EARTH SCIENCE* E46 Ocean Salinity

Workbooks

 Interactive Textbook Struggling Readers

Answer to Reading Check

Sample answer: Plankton are tiny organisms that float near the surface of the water. They form the base of the ocean's feeding relationships.

Temperature

The temperature of ocean water decreases as the depth of the water increases. However, the temperature change is not gradual. **Figure 2** shows the three temperature zones of ocean water. Notice that the temperature of the water in the surface zone is much warmer than in the rest of the ocean. Temperatures in the surface zone vary with latitude. Areas of the ocean along the equator are warmer than areas closer to the poles. Surface zone temperatures also vary with the time of year. During the summer, the Northern Hemisphere is tilted toward the sun. So, the surface zone is warmer than it is during the winter.

Temperature affects the animals that live in marine ecosystems. For example, fishes that live near the poles have adaptations to live in near-freezing water. In contrast, animals that live in coral reefs need warm water to live. Some animals, such as whales, migrate from cold areas to warm areas of the ocean to reproduce. Water temperature also affects whether some animals, such as barnacles, can eat. If the water is too hot or too cold, these animals may not be able to eat. A sudden change in temperature may cause these animals to die.

Reading Check How does temperature affect marine animals?

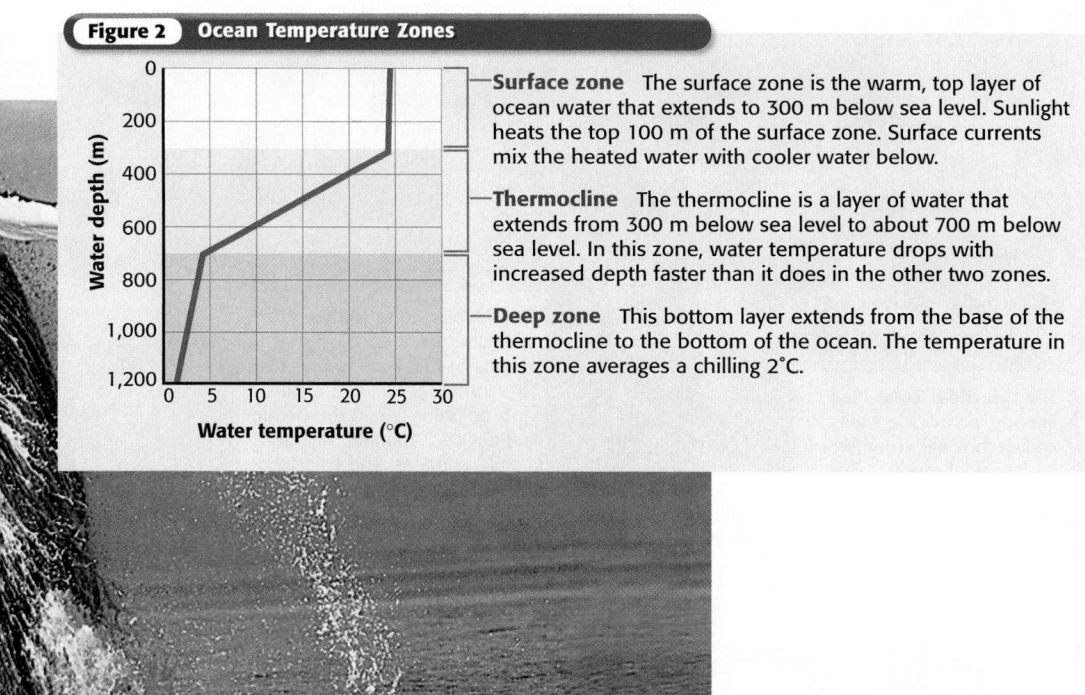

Figure 2 Ocean Temperature Zones

Surface zone The surface zone is the warm, top layer of ocean water that extends to 300 m below sea level. Sunlight heats the top 100 m of the surface zone. Surface currents mix the heated water with cooler water below.

Thermocline The thermocline is a layer of water that extends from 300 m below sea level to about 700 m below sea level. In this zone, water temperature drops with increased depth faster than it does in the other two zones.

Deep zone This bottom layer extends from the base of the thermocline to the bottom of the ocean. The temperature in this zone averages a chilling 2°C.

Answer to Reading Check

Sample answer: Fishes that live near the poles have adaptations for the near-freezing water. Animals in coral reefs need warm water to live. Some animals migrate to warmer waters to reproduce. Water temperature affects whether some animals can eat.

Teach

 GENERAL

Prediction Guide Before students read this page, ask them the following questions:

1. What are three ocean temperature zones? (surface zone, thermocline, and deep zone)

2. How do water temperatures vary in the surface zone? (Sample answer: In the surface zone, water temperature varies with latitude and time of year. Water is warmer near the equator, and water is warmer during the summer.)

3. How does temperature affect marine animals? (Sample answer: Fishes near the poles have adaptations to the near-freezing water. Animals that live in coral reefs need warm water to survive. Some animals migrate to warmer waters to reproduce. Temperature also affects the ability of some animals to eat.)

Have students evaluate their responses after they read about temperature zones in marine ecosystems. **LS** Verbal

Cultural Awareness ADVANCED

Algal Food People in Japan and Korea use brown seaweed to make *kombu* soup. A red alga called *nori* is dried in sheets and wrapped around rice to make sushi. Seaweed provides iodine and other nutrients, but it is often used for the flavor and texture that it adds to foods. Ask interested students to research foods made with algae. Encourage students to prepare some of the dishes that they learn about for the class. **LS** Verbal/Kinesthetic

Using the Figure — BASIC

Ocean Zones Help students understand the information in **Figure 3** by pointing out how it is organized. You may want to point out that the oceanic zone and the benthic zone continue extending into the ocean. Also, point out how the depth of the ocean changes farther away from shore. You may also want to interpret the magnified views of the ocean for students. **LS** Visual — English Language Learners

CONNECTION ACTIVITY
Real World — GENERAL

The Bends A diving condition called the *bends*, or decompression sickness, can occur when a person who is using underwater breathing devices dives very deeply into the water, ascends to the water's surface too quickly after diving, or stays under the water for a long period of time. Ask interested students to research what happens when a person gets decompression sickness. Students should also research ways to prevent and treat decompression sickness. Have students write an informative magazine article about their findings. Ask students to relate their findings to modern SCUBA practices. **LS** Verbal

Depth and Sunlight

In addition to water temperature, life in the ocean is affected by water depth and the amount of sunlight that passes into the water. The major ocean zones are shown in **Figure 3**.

The Intertidal Zone

The intertidal zone is the place where the ocean meets the land. This area is exposed to the air for part of the day. Waves are always crashing on the rock and sand. The animals that live in the intertidal zone have adaptations to survive exposure to air and to keep from being washed away by the waves.

The Neritic Zone

As you move farther away from shore, into the neritic zone (nee RIT ik ZOHN), the water becomes deeper. The ocean floor starts to slope downward. The water is warm and receives a lot of sunlight. Many interesting plants and animals, such as corals, sea turtles, fishes, and dolphins, live in this zone.

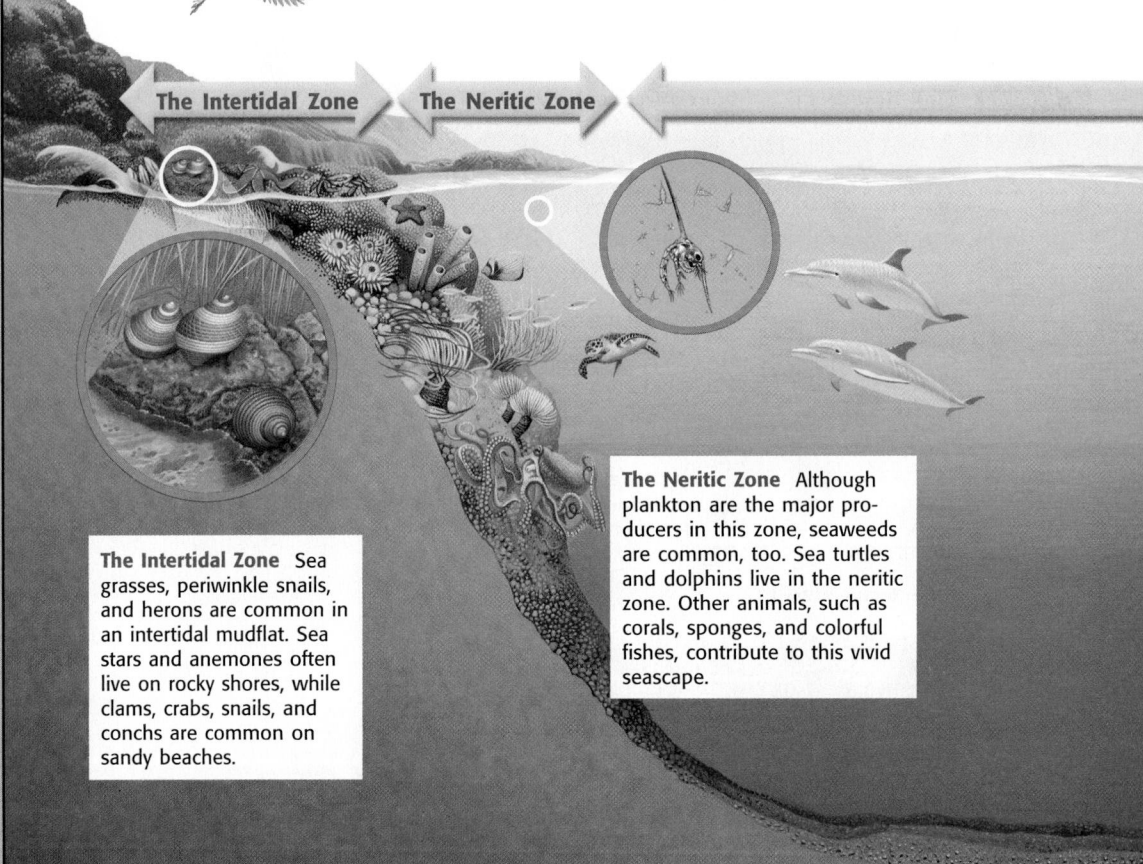

Figure 3 *The life in a marine ecosystem depends on water temperature, water depth, and the amount of sunlight the area receives.*

The Intertidal Zone Sea grasses, periwinkle snails, and herons are common in an intertidal mudflat. Sea stars and anemones often live on rocky shores, while clams, crabs, snails, and conchs are common on sandy beaches.

The Neritic Zone Although plankton are the major producers in this zone, seaweeds are common, too. Sea turtles and dolphins live in the neritic zone. Other animals, such as corals, sponges, and colorful fishes, contribute to this vivid seascape.

CHAPTER RESOURCES

Technology

Transparencies
• L73 Ocean Zones: A
• L74 Ocean Zones: B

CONNECTION to
Physical Science — ADVANCED

Light Red, orange, and yellow wavelengths of light that strike the surface of the water are absorbed more easily than blue and green wavelengths of light are. Blue and green wavelengths can penetrate the water more deeply. Thus, producers that are capable of using blue and green wavelengths of light for photosynthesis can live at greater depths. Ask interested students to research and diagram how light reacts with water. **LS** Visual

The Oceanic Zone

In the oceanic zone, the sea floor drops sharply. This zone contains the deep water of the open ocean. Plankton can be found near the water surface. Animals, such as fishes, whales, and sharks, are found in the oceanic zone. Some animals in this zone live in very deep water. These animals often get food from material that sinks down from the ocean surface.

The Benthic Zone

The benthic zone is the ocean floor. The deepest parts of the benthic zone do not get any sunlight. They are also very cold. Animals, such as fishes, worms, and crabs, have special adaptations to the deep, dark water. Many of these organisms get food by eating material that sinks from above. Some organisms, such as bacteria, get energy from chemicals that escape from thermal vents on the ocean floor. Thermal vents form at cracks in the Earth's crust.

Reading Check How do animals in the benthic zone get food?

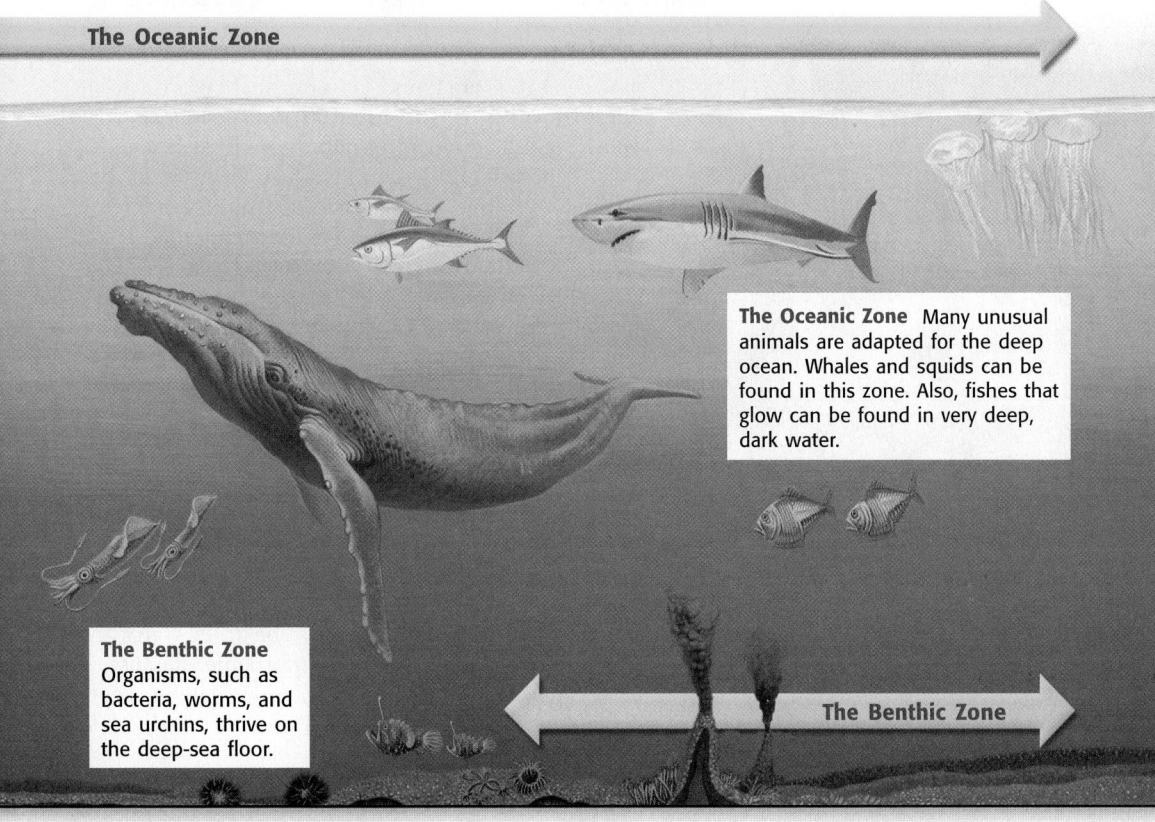

The Oceanic Zone

The Oceanic Zone Many unusual animals are adapted for the deep ocean. Whales and squids can be found in this zone. Also, fishes that glow can be found in very deep, dark water.

The Benthic Zone Organisms, such as bacteria, worms, and sea urchins, thrive on the deep-sea floor.

The Benthic Zone

Group ACTIVITY —— BASIC

Coral Reef Have students research and draw a coral reef. Provide reference materials, a large piece of butcher paper, construction paper, markers, and colored pencils. Have students draw a basic coral reef on the butcher paper. Encourage students to choose an organism that is part of a coral reef, to research the organism, and to draw it. Then, students should place their organism in its habitat on the butcher-paper coral reef. You may want to have one coral reef per class or have all classes contribute to one large coral reef. **LS** Visual/Interpersonal **English Language Learners**

Homework —— GENERAL

Writing **Rigs for Reefs** Tell students that Texas has started a "Rigs for Reefs" program in which oil companies are asked to donate old ocean-platform equipment that would otherwise be taken to shore and sold for scrap metal. The old equipment is easily converted to artificial reefs. Have students imagine that they work for this organization or a similar organization. Then, in a persuasive letter to an oil company, students should explain why the company should participate in the program. **LS** Verbal/Logical

Is That a Fact!

Deep sea vent ecosystems depend on neither sunlight nor photosynthesis for energy. Many of these ecosystems rely on chemicals released by the vents.

Answer to Reading Check

Sample answer: Some animals get food from material that sinks to the bottom from the surface. Other animals get energy from chemicals released by thermal vents.

Reteaching ——— BASIC

Marine Ecosystems On the board, write the following heads: "Intertidal areas," "Coral reefs," "Estuaries," "The Sargasso Sea," and "Polar ice." Ask student volunteers to fill in information about each ecosystem under the appropriate head.
LS Verbal

Quiz ——————— GENERAL

Ask students whether the following statements are true or false.

1. Coral reefs are not very biologically diverse when compared with other marine ecosystems. (false)

2. Oceans provide most of the water for precipitation on Earth. (true)

3. An intertidal area is an area where the ocean meets the land. (true)

4. There is little food available in ecosystems found near polar ice. (false)

Alternative Assessment ——— GENERAL

Concept Mapping Have students create a concept map using the following terms:

benthic zone, marine ecosystems, ocean, neritic zone, coral reef, polar ice, estuaries, intertidal areas, plankton, intertidal zone, and oceanic zone.
LS Verbal/Logical

A Closer Look

Life on Earth depends on the ocean. Through evaporation, the ocean provides most of the water that makes up Earth's precipitation. Ocean temperatures and currents can affect world climates and wind patterns. Humans and many animals depend on the ocean for food.

Many ecosystems exist in the ocean. Some of these ecosystems are found on or near the shore. Other ecosystems are found in the middle of the ocean or near the poles.

Intertidal Areas

estuary an area where fresh water from rivers mixes with salt water from the ocean

Intertidal areas are found near the shore. These areas include mudflats, sandy beaches, and rocky shores. Intertidal organisms must be able to live both underwater and out of water. The organisms that live in mudflats include worms and crabs. Shorebirds feed on these animals. Organisms that live on sandy beaches include worms, clams, crabs, and plankton. On rocky shores, organisms have adaptations to keep from being swept away by crashing waves. Some organisms use rootlike structures called *holdfasts* to attach themselves to the rocks. Other organisms attach themselves to rocks by releasing a special glue.

Coral Reefs

Most coral reefs are found in warm, shallow areas of the neritic zone. The reefs are made up of small animals called *corals*. Corals live in large groups. When corals die, they leave their skeletons behind. New corals grow on these remains. Over time, layers of skeletons build up and form a reef. This reef provides a home for many marine animals and plants. These organisms include algae, brightly colored fishes, sponges, sea stars, and sea urchins. An example of a coral reef is shown in **Figure 4.**

✓ Reading Check How do coral reefs develop?

Estuaries

An area where fresh water from streams and rivers spills into the ocean is called an **estuary** (ES tyoo er ee). In estuaries, the fresh water from rivers and the salt water from the ocean are always mixing. Therefore, the amount of salt in the water is always changing. Plants and animals that live in estuaries must be able to survive the changing concentrations of salt. The fresh water that spills into an estuary is rich in nutrients. Because estuaries are so nutrient rich, they support large numbers of plankton. The plankton, in turn, provide food for many animals.

Figure 4 *A coral reef is one of the most biologically diverse ecosystems on Earth.*

Answer to Reading Check
Sample answer: When corals die, they leave behind their skeletons. Other corals grow on these remains. Over time, the layers build up to form a coral reef.

Is That a Fact!

Reefs The first reef-building organisms on Earth were cyanobacteria that lived about 3.5 billion years ago. Corals have been found in fossil reefs from 500 million years ago. Corals that are similar to modern corals first appeared about 60 million years ago.

The Sargasso Sea

An ecosystem called the *Sargasso Sea* (sahr GAS oh SEE) is found in the middle of the Atlantic Ocean. This ecosystem contains floating rafts of algae called *sargassums* (sahr GAS uhmz). Many of the animals that live in the Sargasso Sea are the same color as sargassums, which helps the animals hide from predators.

Polar Ice

The Arctic Ocean and the ocean around Antarctica make up another marine ecosystem. These icy waters are rich in nutrients, which support large numbers of plankton. Many fishes, birds, and mammals rely on the plankton for food. Animals, such as polar bears and penguins, live on the polar ice.

SECTION Review

Summary

- Abiotic factors that affect marine ecosystems are water temperature, water depth, and the amount of light that passes into the water.
- Plankton form the base of the ocean's food chains.
- Four ocean zones are the intertidal zone, the neritic zone, the oceanic zone, and the benthic zone.
- The ocean contains unique ecosystems, including intertidal areas, coral reefs, estuaries, the Sargasso Sea, and polar ice.

Using Key Terms

1. Use each of the following terms in a separate sentence: *plankton* and *estuary*.

Understanding Key Ideas

2. Water temperature
   a. has no effect on the animals in a marine ecosystem.
   b. affects the types of organisms that can live in a marine ecosystem.
   c. decreases gradually as water gets deeper.
   d. increases as water gets deeper.

3. What are three abiotic factors that affect marine ecosystems?

4. Describe four major ocean zones.

5. Describe five marine ecosystems. For each ecosystem, list an organism that lives there.

Math Skills

6. The ocean covers about 71% of the Earth's surface. If the total surface area of the Earth is about 510 million square kilometers, how many square kilometers are covered by the ocean?

Critical Thinking

7. **Making Inferences** Animals in the Sargasso Sea hide from predators by blending in with the sargassum. Color is only one way to blend in. What is another way that animals can blend in with sargassum?

8. **Identifying Relationships** Many fishes and other organisms that live in the deep ocean produce light. What are two ways in which this light might be useful?

9. **Applying Concepts** Imagine that you are studying animals that live in intertidal zones. You just discovered a new animal. Describe the animal and adaptations the animal has to survive in the intertidal zone.

SCiLINKS.

NSTA
Developed and maintained by the
National Science Teachers Association

For a variety of links related to this chapter, go to www.scilinks.org

Topic: Marine Ecosystems
SciLinks code: HSM0911

Answers to Section Review

1. Sample answer: Plankton are tiny organisms that form the base of many of the ocean's food chains. An estuary is an area where fresh water from rivers mixes with salt water from the ocean.

2. b

3. water temperature, water depth, and the amount of sunlight that passes into the water

4. Sample answer: The intertidal zone is the place where the ocean meets the land. This area is exposed to air for part of the day. The neritic zone is farther from shore, where the water starts to get deeper. This water is often warm and sunny. The oceanic zone starts where the sea floor drops sharply. It includes the deepest part of the ocean. The benthic zone is the ocean floor.

5. Sample answer: Intertidal areas include mudflats, sandy beaches, and rocky shores. Worms live in intertidal areas. Coral reefs are found in the shallow waters of the neritic zone. Corals are small animals that make up the reefs. Estuaries are areas where fresh water meets salt water. Plankton are abundant in estuaries. The Sargasso Sea is found in the middle of the Atlantic Ocean. Sargassum is an alga found in this ecosystem. Polar ice is found at the poles. Plankton thrive on the nutrients found in this near-freezing water.

6. 510,000,000 km² × 0.71 = 362,100,000 km²

7. Sample answer: Animals in the Sargasso Sea could look like or be shaped like the leaves of sargassums.

8. Sample answer: The light may attract prey. The light may also confuse a predator.

9. Accept all reasonable answers. Students should recognize that intertidal organisms must have adaptations for exposure to air and for the effect of surf.

Focus

Overview

This section introduces freshwater ecosystems and the characteristics of rivers, streams, ponds, and lakes. Students will also learn about two types of wetlands and describe how a lake can become a forest.

 Bellringer

Ask students the following question: "What are four freshwater ecosystems?" (Sample answers: streams, rivers, lakes, marshes, ponds, swamps, bogs, and creeks)

Motivate

Discussion ———— GENERAL

Water Sources Ask students, "What is the source for river water?" (Sample answers: springs, melting snow and ice, and rainfall) Tell students that the sources of river water can vary. In addition to springs and precipitation, lakes and ponds can serve as sources for river water.

LS Auditory/Logical

What You Will Learn

- Describe one abiotic factor that affects freshwater ecosystems.
- Describe the three zones of a lake.
- Describe two wetland ecosystems.
- Explain how a lake becomes a forest.

Vocabulary

littoral zone	wetland
open-water zone	marsh
deep-water zone	swamp

READING STRATEGY

Paired Summarizing Read this section silently. In pairs, take turns summarizing the material. Stop to discuss ideas that seem confusing.

Freshwater Ecosystems

A brook bubbles over rocks. A mighty river thunders through a canyon. A calm swamp echoes with the sounds of frogs and birds. What do these places have in common?

Brooks, rivers, and swamps are examples of freshwater ecosystems. The water in brooks and rivers is often fast moving. In swamps, water moves very slowly. Also, water in swamps is often found in standing pools.

Stream and River Ecosystems

The water in brooks, streams, and rivers may flow from melting ice or snow. Or the water may come from a spring. A spring is a place where water flows from underground to the Earth's surface. Each stream of water that joins a larger stream is called a *tributary* (TRIB yoo TER ee). As more tributaries join a stream, the stream contains more water. The stream becomes stronger and wider. A very strong, wide stream is called a *river*. **Figure 1** shows how a river develops.

Like other ecosystems, freshwater ecosystems are characterized by their abiotic factors. An important abiotic factor in freshwater ecosystems is how quickly water moves.

Streams and rivers are full of life. Plants line the edges of streams and rivers. Fish live in the open waters. And clams and snails live in the mud at the bottom of a stream or river. Organisms that live in fast-moving water have adaptations to keep from being washed away. Some producers, such as algae and moss, are attached to rocks. Consumers, such as tadpoles, use suction disks to hold themselves to rocks. Other consumers, such as insects, live under rocks.

Figure 1 *Rivers become larger as more tributaries flow into them.*

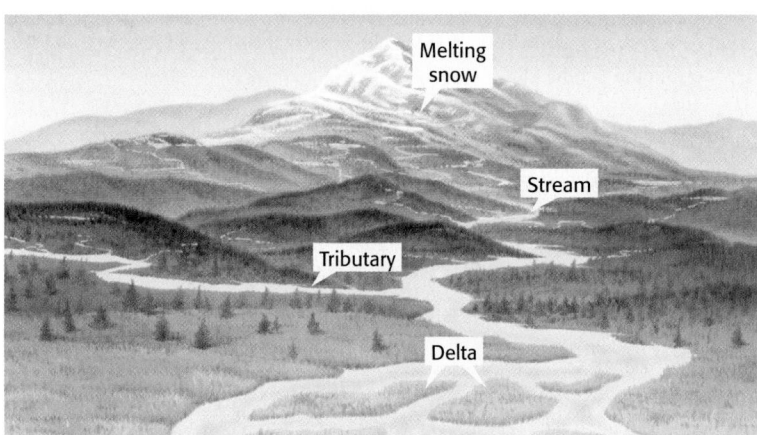

Melting snow

Stream

Tributary

Delta

CHAPTER RESOURCES

Chapter Resource File

- **Lesson Plan**
- **Directed Reading A** BASIC
- **Directed Reading B** SPECIAL NEEDS

Technology

Transparencies
- Bellringer
- L75 Rivers
- L76 Lake Zones

Workbooks

Interactive Textbook Struggling Readers

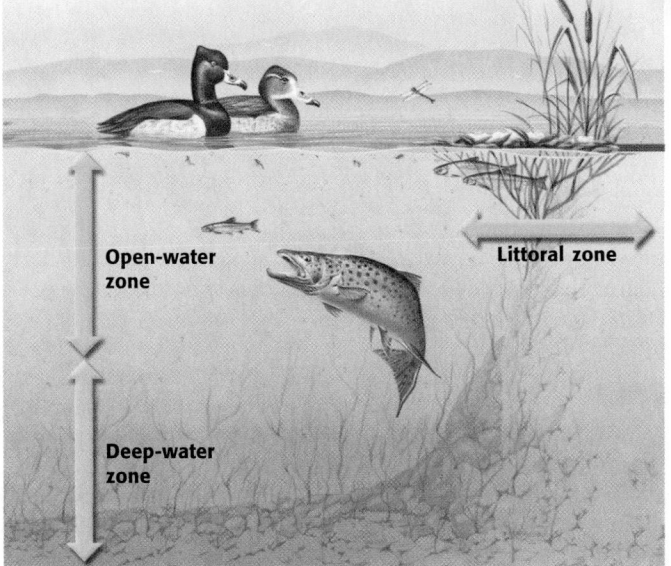

Open-water zone

Littoral zone

Deep-water zone

Figure 2 *Ponds and lakes can be divided into three zones. Each zone has different organisms and abiotic factors.*

Pond and Lake Ecosystems

Ponds and lakes have different ecosystems than streams and rivers do. **Figure 2** shows the zones of a typical lake.

Life near Shore

The area of water closest to the edge of a lake or pond is called the **littoral zone** (LIT uh ruhl ZOHN). Sunlight reaches the bottom of the littoral zone. This sunlight makes it possible for algae and plants to grow in the littoral zone. Algae grow beneath the surface of the water in the littoral zone. Plants that grow near the shore include cattails and rushes. Floating leaf plants, such as water lilies, grow farther from the shore. The plants of the littoral zone are home to small animals, such as snails and insects. Clams and worms bury themselves in the mud. Frogs, salamanders, turtles, fish, and snakes also live in this zone.

Life Away from Shore

The area of a lake or pond that extends from the littoral zone across the top of the water is called the **open-water zone.** The open-water zone goes as deep as sunlight can reach. This zone is home to bass, lake trout, and other fishes. Many photosynthetic plankton also live in this area. Beneath the open-water zone is the **deep-water zone,** where no sunlight reaches. Catfish, carp, worms, crustaceans, fungi, and bacteria live here. These organisms often feed on dead organisms that sink from above.

 **Reading Check** Describe the three zones of a lake. (*See the Appendix for answers to Reading Checks.*)

Quick Lab

Pond-Food Relationships

1. On **index cards,** write the names of some of the plants and animals that live in a typical freshwater pond or small lake. Write one type of organism on each card.

2. Use **yarn** or **string** to connect each organism to its food sources.

3. Describe the food relationships in a pond.

littoral zone the shallow zone of a lake or pond where light reaches the bottom and nurtures plants

open-water zone the zone of a pond or lake that extends from the littoral zone and that is only as deep as light can reach

deep-water zone the zone of a lake or pond below the open-water zone, where no light reaches

Lakes and Ponds Ask students to come up to the board and draw a lake. Students should include the three zones of a lake and some of the organisms found in these zones. Then, ask students to describe how the lake could become a forest.

LS Visual/Verbal

Quiz ————————— **GENERAL**

Ask students the following questions about freshwater ecosystems.

1. What are the three zones of a lake? (littoral zone, open-water zone, deep-water zone)

2. List two kinds of wetlands. How they are different? (marshes and swamps; Marshes do not have trees, but swamps do have trees.)

3. Why do fishes die if a pond or lake contains too many bacterial decomposers? (Sample answer: The bacteria use oxygen in the water. The loss of oxygen results in the death of many fishes.)

Alternative Assessment ——— **GENERAL**

Freshwater Brochure Have students write a travel brochure for one of the freshwater ecosystems described in this section. Brochures should provide information about the ecosystem and the organisms found in it. English Language Learners

LS Verbal

Figure 3 *This painted turtle suns itself on a log in a freshwater marsh.*

wetland an area of land that is periodically underwater or whose soil contains a great deal of moisture

marsh a treeless wetland ecosystem where plants such as grasses grow

swamp a wetland ecosystem in which shrubs and trees grow

CONNECTION TO Language Arts

Compound Words A compound word is a word made up of two or more single words. In your **science journal,** define the two words that make up the word *wetland.* Then, define three more compound words.

INCLUSION Strategies

- *Attention Deficit Disorder*
- *Behavior Control Issues*
- *Learning Disabled*

Students often benefit from hands-on learning. Have students draw a picture of a river that flows into a lake. Ask them to show different ecosystems within the river and lake. Ask students to include organisms found in each ecosystem. English Language Learners

LS Visual

Wetland Ecosystems

An area of land that is sometimes underwater or whose soil contains a great deal of moisture is called a **wetland.** Wetlands support many different plants and animals. Wetlands also play an important role in flood control. During heavy rains or spring snow melt, wetlands soak up large amounts of water. The water in wetlands also moves deeper into the ground. So, wetlands help replenish underground water supplies.

Marshes

A treeless wetland ecosystem where plants, such as grasses, grow is called a **marsh.** A freshwater marsh is shown in **Figure 3.** Freshwater marshes are often found in shallow areas along the shores of lakes, ponds, rivers, and streams. The plants in a marsh vary depending on the depth of the water and the location of the marsh. Grasses, reeds, bulrushes, and wild rice are common marsh plants. Muskrats, turtles, frogs, and birds also live in marshes.

Swamps

A wetland ecosystem in which trees and vines grow is called a **swamp.** Swamps, as shown in **Figure 4,** are found in low-lying areas and beside slow-moving rivers. Most swamps are flooded part of the year, depending on rainfall. Willows, bald cypresses, and oaks are common swamp trees. Vines, such as poison ivy, grow up tree trunks. Plants, such as orchids, may hang from tree branches. Water lilies and other plants grow in standing water. Many fishes, snakes, and birds also live in swamps.

✓ *Reading Check* What is a swamp?

Figure 4 *The trunks of these trees are adapted to give the trees more support in the wet, soft soil of a swamp.*

Answer to Reading Check

A swamp is a wetland ecosystem in which trees and vines grow.

From a Lake to a Forest

Did you know that a lake or pond can disappear? How can this happen? Water entering a standing body of water usually carries nutrients and sediment. These materials settle to the bottom of the pond or lake. Dead leaves from overhanging trees and decaying plant and animal life also settle to the bottom. Then, bacteria decompose this material. This process uses oxygen in the water. The loss of oxygen affects the kinds of animals that can survive in the pond or lake. For example, many fishes would not be able to survive with less oxygen in the water.

Over time, the pond or lake is filled with sediment. Plants grow in the new soil. Shallow areas fill in first. So, plants slowly grow closer and closer to the center of the pond or lake. What is left of the lake or pond becomes a wetland, such as a marsh or swamp. Eventually, the wetland can become a forest.

Reading Check What happens to some of the animals in a pond as the pond becomes a forest?

INTERNET ACTIVITY

For another activity related to this chapter, go to **go.hrw.com** and type in the keyword **HL5ECOW**.

SECTION Review

Summary

- An important abiotic factor in freshwater ecosystems is how quickly water moves.
- The three zones of a pond or lake are the littoral zone, the open-water zone, and the deep-water zone.
- Wetlands include marshes and swamps.
- Sediments and decaying plant and animal matter build up in a pond. Over time, the pond may fill completely and become a forest.

Using Key Terms

1. Use the following terms in the same sentence: *wetland, marsh,* and *swamp.*

Understanding Key Ideas

2. A major abiotic factor in fresh-water ecosystems is the
   a. source of the water.
   b. speed of the water.
   c. width of the stream or river.
   d. None of the above

3. Describe the three zones of a lake.

4. Explain how a lake can become a forest over time.

Math Skills

5. Sunlight can penetrate a certain lake to a depth of 15 m. The lake is five and a half times deeper than the depth to which light can penetrate. In meters, how deep is the lake?

Critical Thinking

6. **Making Inferences** When bacteria decompose material in a pond, the oxygen in the water may be used up. So, fishes in the pond die. How might the absence of fish lead to a pond filling faster?

7. **Applying Concepts** Imagine a steep, rocky stream. What kinds of adaptations might animals living in this stream have? Explain your answer.

SCLINKS **NSTA**
Developed and maintained by the
National Science Teachers Association

For a variety of links related to this chapter, go to www.scilinks.org

Topic: Freshwater Ecosystems
SciLinks code: HSM0621

Answer to Reading Check

Sample answer: Many fishes will die as the pond fills in because bacteria that decompose material in the pond use up the oxygen in the water.

CHAPTER RESOURCES

Chapter Resource File

- Section Quiz **GENERAL**
- Section Review **GENERAL**
- Vocabulary and Section Summary **GENERAL**
- Critical Thinking **ADVANCED**

Too Much of a Good Thing?

Teacher's Notes

Time Required

One 45-minute class period and one 10-minute observation time every 3 days for 3 weeks

Lab Ratings

EASY ———————————→ HARD

Teacher Prep 🧪🧪
Student Set-Up 🧪🧪
Concept Level 🧪🧪🧪
Clean Up 🧪🧪

MATERIALS

The materials listed on the student page are enough for 1–2 students. This lab is a good opportunity to recycle glass jars or clear plastic 2 L soda bottles. Any container that is transparent and will hold at least 1 L of water will do.

Safety Caution

Remind students to review all safety cautions and icons before beginning this lab activity.

Lab Notes

A review of the causes of eutrophication might be helpful before beginning this lab.

Skills Practice Lab

OBJECTIVES

Draw common pond-water organisms.

Observe the effect of fertilizer on pond-water organisms.

Describe how fertilizer affects the number and type of pond-water organisms over time.

MATERIALS

- beaker, 500 mL
- distilled water, 2.25 L
- eyedropper
- fertilizer
- gloves, protective
- graduated cylinder, 100 mL
- jars, 1 qt or 1 L (3)
- microscope
- microscope slides with coverslips
- pencil, wax
- plastic wrap
- pond water containing living organisms, 300 mL
- stirring rod

SAFETY

Too Much of a Good Thing?

Plants need nutrients, such as phosphates and nitrates, to grow. Phosphates are often found in detergents. Nitrates are often found in animal wastes and fertilizers. When large amounts of these nutrients enter rivers and lakes, algae and plants grow rapidly and then die off. Microorganisms that decompose the dead matter use up oxygen in the water. Without oxygen, fish and other animals die. In this activity, you will observe the effect of fertilizers on organisms that live in pond water.

Procedure

1. Label one jar "Control," the second jar "Fertilizer," and the third jar "Excess fertilizer."

2. Pour 750 mL of distilled water into each jar. To the "Fertilizer" jar, add the amount of fertilizer recommended for 750 mL of water. To the "Excess fertilizer" jar, add 10 times the amount recommended for 750 mL of water. Stir the contents of each jar to dissolve the fertilizer.

3. Obtain a sample of pond water. Stir it gently to make sure that the organisms in it are evenly distributed. Pour 100 mL of pond water into each of the three jars.

4. Observe a drop of water from each jar under the microscope. Draw at least four of the organisms. Determine whether the organisms you see are producers, which are usually green, or consumers, which are usually able to move. Describe the number and type of organisms in the pond water.

Common Pond-Water Organisms

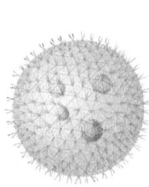   

Volvox (producer)   ***Spirogyra*** (producer)   ***Daphnia*** (consumer)   ***Vorticella*** (consumer)

 Holt Lab Generator CD-ROM

Search for any lab by topic, standard, difficulty level, or time. Edit any lab to fit your needs, or create your own labs. Use the Lab Materials QuickList software to customize your lab materials list.

 **Jason Marsh**
Montevideo High and
Country School
Montevideo, Minnesota

CHAPTER RESOURCES

Chapter Resource File

 • Datasheet for Chapter Lab
• Lab Notes and Answers

Technology

 Classroom Videos
• Lab Video

• Life in the Desert
• Discovering Mini-Ecosystems

---

5 Cover each jar loosely with plastic wrap. Place the jars near a sunny window but not in direct sunlight.

6 Make a prediction about how the pond organisms will grow in each of the three jars.

7 Make three data tables. Title one table "Control," as shown below. Title another table "Fertilizer," and title the third table "Excess fertilizer."

Control			
Date	Color	Odor	Other observations
DO NOT WRITE IN BOOK			

8 Observe the jars when you first set them up and once every 3 days for the next 3 weeks. Note the color, the odor, and the presence of organisms. Record your observations.

9 When organisms become visible in the jars, use an eyedropper to remove a sample from each jar. Observe the sample under the microscope. How have the number and type of organisms changed since you first looked at the pond water?

10 At the end of the 3-week period, observe a sample from each jar under the microscope. Draw at least four of the most abundant organisms, and describe how the number and type of organisms have changed since your last microscope observation.

Analyze the Results

1 **Describing Events** After 3 weeks, which jar has the most abundant growth of algae?

2 **Analyzing Data** Did you observe any effects on organisms (other than algae) in the jar with the most abundant algal growth? Explain your answer.

Draw Conclusions

3 **Drawing Conclusions** What may have caused increased growth in the jars?

4 **Evaluating Results** Did your observations match your predictions? Explain your answer.

5 **Interpreting Information** Decaying plant and animal life contribute to the filling of lakes and ponds. How might the rapid filling of lakes and ponds be prevented or slowed?

Analyze the Results

1. Answers may vary. Students should note increased algal growth in the jars containing fertilizer.

2. Answers may vary. Increased algal growth may lead to increased bacterial growth because of the decomposition of dead algae. The bacteria consume oxygen in the water, which kills organisms that need oxygen to survive. Eventually, this loss of oxygen will also affect algae because algae use oxygen.

Draw Conclusions

3. Sample answer: Algae need nitrates and phosphates to grow. Fertilizer contains nitrates. Adding fertilizer increased the amount of nitrates in the water. So, the algae grew more.

4. Accept all reasonable answers.

5. Sample answer: When more algae grow, they contribute to the filling of the pond. So, preventing detergents and fertilizers from entering a pond will likely prevent algal growth that contributes to the filling of a pond.

CHAPTER RESOURCES

Workbooks

 EcoLabs & Field Activities
• Biome Adventure Travel GENERAL

Long-Term Projects & Research Ideas
• Tropical Medicine GENERAL

Calculator-Based Labs
• Ocean Floor Mapping ADVANCED

Chapter Review

Assignment Guide

Section	Questions
1	1, 3, 6, 10, 12, 16, 19–24
2	2, 7–9, 17
3	4–5, 11, 13–14, 18
1, 2, and 3	15

ANSWERS

Using Key Terms

1. Sample answer: A biome is a large area characterized by climate and the plants and animals that live in the area. Tundra is a biome with cold temperatures, little rainfall, and no trees.

2. Sample answer: Organisms that live in the intertidal zone are exposed to the air for part of the day. In the neritic zone, water is warm and receives a lot of sunlight. The oceanic zone includes the deep areas of the ocean.

3. Sample answer: A savanna is a biome characterized by grasses and seasonal rains. A desert is a biome that is very dry and often very hot.

4. Sample answer: The open-water zone receives sunlight, but the deep-water zone does not receive sunlight.

5. Sample answer: Marshes do not have trees, while swamps do have trees.

USING KEY TERMS

1. In your own words, write a definition for the following terms: *biome* and *tundra*.

2. Use each of the following terms in a separate sentence: *intertidal zone*, *neritic zone*, and *oceanic zone*.

For each pair of terms, explain how the meanings of the terms differ.

3. *savanna* and *desert*

4. *open-water zone* and *deep-water zone*

5. *marsh* and *swamp*

UNDERSTANDING KEY IDEAS

Multiple Choice

6. Trees that lose their leaves in the winter are called
   a. evergreen trees.
   b. coniferous trees.
   c. deciduous trees.
   d. None of the above

7. In which major ocean zone are plants and animals exposed to air for part of the day?
   a. intertidal zone
   b. neritic zone
   c. oceanic zone
   d. benthic zone

8. An abiotic factor that affects marine ecosystems is
   a. the temperature of the water.
   b. the depth of the water.
   c. the amount of sunlight that passes through the water.
   d. All of the above

9. _____ is a marine ecosystem that includes mudflats, sandy beaches, and rocky shores.
   a. An intertidal area
   b. Polar ice
   c. A coral reef
   d. The Sargasso Sea

Short Answer

10. What are seven land biomes?

11. Explain how a small lake can become a forest.

12. What are two factors that characterize biomes?

13. Describe the three zones of a lake.

14. How do rivers form?

15. What are three abiotic factors in land biomes? three abiotic factors in marine ecosystems? an abiotic factor in fresh-water ecosystems?

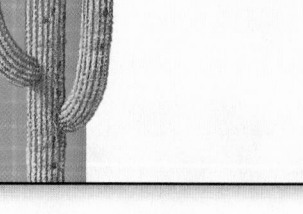

Understanding Key Ideas

6. c 7. a
8. d 9. a

10. temperate deciduous forests, coniferous forests, tropical rain forests, temperate grasslands, savannas, deserts, and tundras

11. Sample answer: Materials that are washed into the lake build up. To decompose these materials, bacteria use oxygen in the water, which affects the animals that live in the lake. The shallow areas fill in, and plants begin to grow. The lake becomes a marsh or swamp. Eventually, the marsh or swamp becomes a forest.

12. Sample answer: climate and the plants and animals that live in an area

13. Sample answer: The littoral zone is the area of a lake closest to shore, where sunlight reaches the bottom of the lake. The open-water zone extends from the littoral zone and is as deep as sunlight can reach. The deep-water zone lies beneath the open-water zone.

14. Sample answer: Water in rivers may come from springs or melting snow. Each stream of water joins another stream. As more water is added, the stream eventually becomes a river.

CRITICAL THINKING

16 Concept Mapping Use the following terms to create a concept map: *plants and animals, tropical rain forest, tundra, biomes, permafrost, canopy, desert,* and *abiotic factors.*

17 Making Inferences Plankton use photosynthesis to make their own food. They need sunlight for photosynthesis. Which of the four major ocean zones can support plankton growth? Explain your answer.

18 Predicting Consequences Wetlands, such as marshes and swamps, play an important role in flood control. Wetlands also help replenish underground water supplies. Predict what might happen if a wetland dries out.

19 Analyzing Ideas A scientist has a new hypothesis. He or she thinks that savannas and deserts are part of one biome rather than two separate biomes. Based on what you've learned, decide if the scientist's hypothesis is correct. Explain your answer.

20 Applying Concepts Imagine that you are a scientist. You are studying an area that gets about 100 cm of rain each year. The average summer temperatures are near 30°C. What biome are you in? What are some plants and animals you will likely encounter? If you stayed in this area for the winter, what kind of preparations might you need to make?

INTERPRETING GRAPHICS

Use the graphs below to answer the questions that follow.

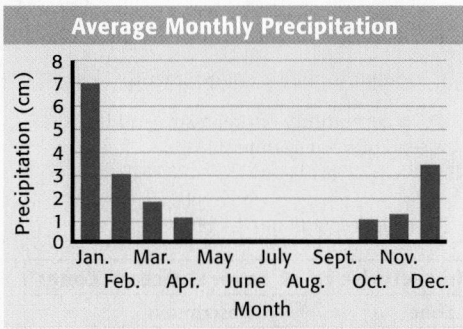

Average Monthly Precipitation

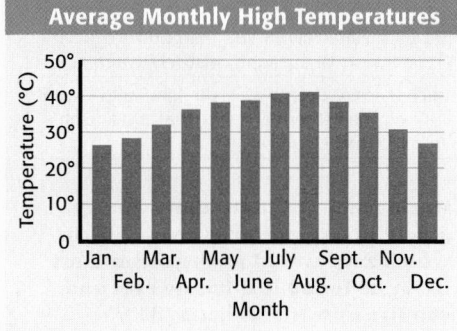

Average Monthly High Temperatures

21 Which biome is most likely found in the region described by the graphs above? Explain your answer.

22 How many centimeters of rain fell in the region during the course of the year?

23 Which month is the hottest in the region? the coolest in the region?

24 What is the average monthly precipitation for the month that has the highest average high temperature?

Critical Thinking

16. An answer to this exercise can be found at the end of this book.

17. Sample answer: Plankton can live in the intertidal zone, the neritic zone, and the oceanic zone. All of these areas receive sunlight, which is necessary for photosynthesis.

18. Sample answer: The area may be more likely to flood if the wetland dries out. Also, because wetlands store water there may be a shortage of water in the area.

19. Sample answer: The hypothesis is incorrect. Savannas and deserts have different climates. Savannas get more rain than deserts do. Also, the plants and animals that live in each area are different. Savannas have grasses and scattered trees, while the plants in the desert grow far apart and are adapted to a very dry climate.

20. Sample answer: The biome is likely a deciduous forest. I would see deciduous trees, bears, deer, and woodpeckers. Winters are likely cold, so I will need warm clothing and shelter.

Interpreting Graphics

21. Sample answer: The biome is likely a desert because the region receives less than 25 cm of rain during the year and is warm.

22. about 19 cm

23. August; January

24. 0 cm

15. climate, water, and rocks; water temperature, water depth, and the amount of sunlight that passes through the water; the speed at which water moves

CHAPTER RESOURCES

Chapter Resource File

- **Chapter Review** GENERAL
- **Chapter Test A** GENERAL
- **Chapter Test B** ADVANCED
- **Chapter Test C** SPECIAL NEEDS
- **Vocabulary Activity** GENERAL

Workbooks

Study Guide
- Study Guide is also available in Spanish.

Standardized Test Preparation

Teacher's Notes

To provide practice under more realistic conditions, give students 20 minutes to answer all of the questions in this Standardized Test Preparation.

Answer Key

Question	Answer
1	D
2	C
3	D
4	B
5	D
6	B
7	B
8	D
9	*
10	*

*See Test Doctor.

Multiple Choice

1. **An ecosystem consists of**

   A. a number of species.

   B. all the places on Earth where life exists.

   C. only the abiotic environment.

   D. a community of organisms and its abiotic environment.

Use the table below to answer question 2.

Characteristics of Several Ocean Zones	
Zone	**Description**
Intertidal	air, sun, and water exposure; crashing waves
Neritic	water depth less than 200 m; lots of sunlight; relatively warm water
Benthic	very deep water; no light; cold except near thermal vents that emit heat and chemicals

2. **Mario made the table above during a field investigation of ocean life. In which zone would an organism most likely be found if it has no eyes and can live in water as hot as 80°C?**

   A. intertidal zone

   B. neritic zone

   C. benthic zone

   D. It would not live in the ocean.

3. **Trout thrive in the oxygen-rich waters of cool, fast-moving streams. Which of the following events might reduce the population of trout in a mountain stream?**

   A. unusually heavy snowfall in the winter

   B. the flow of a tributary stream slows slightly

   C. the movement of a boulder forms a new waterfall

   D. ash and silt from a forest fire cover the surface of the stream

4. **Why are savannas well-suited to supporting large herbivores?**

   A. They have very little biodiversity.

   B. They are areas where grasses are the main plants.

   C. They are dry and hot.

   D. They are cold and dry.

5. **Plants that cannot tolerate water with a constantly changing salt content are NOT likely to be found in**

   A. a freshwater stream

   B. a pond

   C. the neritic zone

   D. an estuary

6. **Tim saw a flock of pelicans flying inland above the Savannah River. What part of an ecosystem did Tim see?**

   A. organism

   B. population

   C. community

   D. abiotic environment

 TEST DOCTOR

Question 1 A: The definition of an ecosystem does not specify the number of species. Some ecosystems do have many species, but not all do. B: An ecosystem is a specific community of organisms and its abiotic environment. This defines the entire biosphere of Earth. C: The abiotic environment is just one component of an ecosystem. D: Correct.

Question 2 A: Without eyes, the animal would have a hard time surviving in the intertidal zone, where there is exposure to bright sunlight and a constant amount of wave motion. Also, the trait of tolerating hot water does not fit well with this zone, as the water temperatures in the intertidal zone are not nearly as high as 80°C. B: The neritic zone is warm and sunny, but these factors would not be useful for an organism with no eyes that could tolerate extremely high temperatures. The animal's lack of eyes would be a disadvantage, as most animals in the neritic zone have eyes and can sense sunlight. C: Correct. D: The animal is well adapted to live in the deep ocean near thermal vents.

Use the charts below to answer question 7.

Biome 1

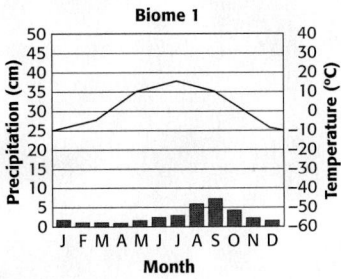

Precipitation (cm) / Temperature (°C)
Month: J F M A M J J A S O N D

Biome 2

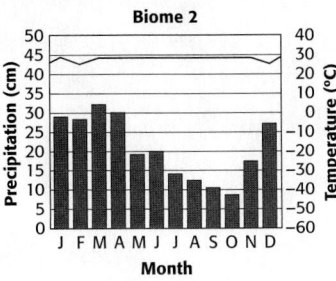

Precipitation (cm) / Temperature (°C)
Month: J F M A M J J A S O N D

7. **Scientists involved in a field study produced the two precipitation and temperature graphs shown above. On each graph, the line represents temperature and the bars represent precipitation. Based on the graph of biome 2, which of the following is a reasonable conclusion?**

   A. Biome 2 is most likely tundra.

   B. Biome 2 is most likely located near the equator.

   C. Biome 2 receives most of its annual rainfall within a three-month period.

   D. Biome 2 has wild temperature swings.

8. **Chantrell is making a terrarium for a praying mantis she wants to study. Praying mantises are carnivores. Chantrell has placed the following in her terrarium: soil, twigs, a rock, a small dish of water, and the praying mantis. What is missing from Chantrell's terrarium?**

   A. plants for the praying mantis to eat

   B. other insects for the praying mantis to eat

   C. a bird for the praying mantis to eat

   D. other insects for the praying mantis to eat, and plants for the other insects to eat

Open Response

9. **Biomes can be used to classify living systems because similar organisms live in a particular biome regardless of where that biome is located. Like all of the eastern United States, Kentucky's biome is temperate deciduous forest. What are the characteristics of temperate deciduous forest?**

10. **Versailles, Kentucky, is in the heart of the state's "bluegrass" region. The average yearly rainfall is 114 cm. The average yearly rainfall in a desert is 25 cm. If a change in global climate causes the average yearly rainfall in Versailles to reduce by 2 cm each year, in how many years would Kentucky's bluegrass region become a desert?**

Only a single population is described. D: The abiotic part of the environment includes all of the physical things that affect organisms living in a certain area. The flock of pelicans represents the biotic part of the environment, which includes organisms.

Question 7 A: The graph indicates that biome 2 has rainfall all year long. The tundra is one of the driest places on Earth. B: Correct. C: The graph indicates that biome 2 receives rainfall all year long. D: The temperature is very consistent.

Question 8 A: Praying mantises are carnivores, which means they eat other animals. They do not eat plants. B: While the praying mantis needs to eat other insects, this is not the best answer. Plants are needed as food for the other insects. Adding only insects does not complete the food chain. C: Praying mantises have been known to eat very small birds, such as hummingbirds. However, birds do not constitute the majority of a praying mantis's diet, and most birds are too big. In fact, many birds would eat the praying mantis. D: Correct.

Question 9 Full-credit answers should include the following points:

- Plant growth happens in layers, with treetops high above the forest floor, leafy shrubs and bushes below, and ferns and mosses on the forest floor.

- Many birds, reptiles, and mammals thrive in a deciduous forest biome.

- Temperatures are moderate, and rainfall is good (specifics: average rainfall 75–125 cm, average temperature extremes: 6–28°C)

- Deciduous trees lose their leaves in the winter.

Question 10 Full-credit answers should include the following points:

- At the rate defined, the region would become desert in about 45 years.

- Students should subtract 25 cm from 114 cm and divide the result by 2 cm.

Standardized Test Preparation

Question 3 A: Greater winter snowfall would increase the rate of flow of cool water in streams. B: A slight change in the flow of a single tributary would probably not alter the flow of the stream. C: A new, small waterfall in a stream would not significantly alter its flow or temperature. D: Correct.

Question 4 A: The amount of biodiversity is correlated with the savanna's ability to support large herbivores. B: Correct. C: Tropical savannas are generally dry and hot. This climate supports grasses, but it is not directly responsible for the savanna's suitability for large herbivores. D: Savannas are not cool and dry.

Question 5 A: Plants that cannot tolerate water with constantly changing salt content could probably survive in a freshwater stream. B: Ponds are water ecosystems. Plants that cannot tolerate water with constantly changing salt content would likely be found in a pond. C: The neritic zone is the deeper water of the ocean near the continental shelf. Plants that are adapted for conditions with constantly salty water would be found here. D: Correct.

Question 6 A: Tim saw a flock of pelicans and thus saw more than a single organism. B: Correct. C: A community is made up of all of the populations of different species that live and interact in an area.

Scientific Debate

ACTIVITY — GENERAL

Invite an ecologist to your classroom to discuss local wetlands. Ask the ecologist to show on a map where local wetlands are located. Also, have the ecologist discuss any pending developments of local wetlands. Afterwards, you may wish to lead students in a debate over whether they support or oppose the proposed developments.

Scientific Discoveries

Background

The first black smoker was found off the Galápagos Islands in 1977. Since then, several black smokers have been found on the floor of the Pacific Ocean. The heat generated by one of these black smokers was so intense that water at the surface was nearly boiling when the chimney was lifted out. While few organisms could survive under such conditions, one species of tubeworms can withstand temperatures up to 80°C (176°F), and some microorganisms can withstand temperatures up to 113°C (235°F)!

Science in Action

Scientific Debate

Developing Wetlands

Wetlands are home to many flowering plants, birds, and turtles. Wetlands also play important roles in flood control and maintaining water quality. However, as more people need homes, grocery stores, and other facilities, some wetlands are being developed for construction. State governments often regulate the development of wetlands. Development is not allowed on many environmentally sensitive wetlands. But it is sometimes allowed on wetlands that are less sensitive. However, some people think that all wetlands should be protected, regardless of how sensitive an area is.

Language Arts ACTIVITY

WRITING SKILL Research wetland development on your own. Then, write a letter in which you describe your opinion about the development of wetlands.

Scientific Discoveries

Ocean Vents

Imagine the deepest parts of the ocean. There is no light at all, and it is very cold. Some of the animals that live here have found a unique place to live—vents on the ocean floor. Water seeps into the Earth between plates on the ocean floor. The water is heated and absorbs sulfuric gases. When the water blasts up through ocean vents, it raises the temperature of the ocean hundreds of degrees! Bacteria use the gases from the ocean vents to survive. In turn, mussels and clams feed on the bacteria. Without ocean vents, it would be much more difficult for these organisms to survive.

Math ACTIVITY

A thermal vent increases the temperature of the water around it to 360°C. If the temperature of the water was 2°C, what is the difference in temperature? By what percentage did the water temperature increase?

Answer to Language Arts Activity
Answers may vary. Accept any response that is well researched, thoughtful, and articulate.

Answer to Math Activity
358°C (360°C − 2°C = 358°C);
17,900% (358°C ÷ 2°C × 100 = 17,900%)

Alfonso Alonso-Mejía

Ecologist During the winter, ecologist Alfonso Alonso-Mejía visits sites in central Mexico where millions of monarch butterflies spend the winter. Unfortunately, the monarchs' winter habitat is threatened by human activity. Only nine of the monarchs' wintering sites remain. Five of the sites are set aside as sanctuaries for monarchs, but these sites are threatened by people who cut down fir trees for firewood or for commercial purposes.

Alonso-Mejía discovered that monarchs depend on understory vegetation, bushlike plants that grow beneath fir trees, to survive. When the temperature is low, monarchs can climb understory vegetation until they are at least 10 cm above the ground. This tiny difference in elevation can ensure that monarchs are warm enough to survive. Because of Alonso-Mejía's discovery, Mexican conservationists are working to protect understory vegetation and monarchs.

Social Studies ACTIVITY

Use your school library or the Internet to research the routes that monarchs use to migrate to Mexico. Draw a map illustrating your findings.

go.hrw.com

To learn more about these Science in Action topics, visit go.hrw.com and type in the keyword **HL5ECOF**.

Current Science

Check out Current Science® articles related to this chapter by visiting go.hrw.com. **Just type in the keyword HL5CS20.**

Earth's Systems and Cycles
Chapter Planning Guide

Compression guide:
To shorten instruction because of time limitations, omit the Chapter Lab.

OBJECTIVES	LABS, DEMONSTRATIONS, AND ACTIVITIES	TECHNOLOGY RESOURCES
PACING • 45 min pp. 344–351 **Chapter Opener**	SE **Start-up Activity**, p. 345 GENERAL	OSP **Parent Letter** ■ TR **Chapter Starter Transparency*** VID **Brain Food Video Quiz**
Section 1 The Geosphere • Identify the four major divisions of Earth. • Identify the layers of Earth based on composition and physical properties. • Describe the rate at which tectonic plates move. • Explain the causes of earthquakes and volcanoes. • Explain how water and wind reshape Earth's surface.	TE **Discussion** How Thick?, p. 346 GENERAL TE **Discussion** Everyday Models, p. 347 BASIC TE **Research** Layer Report, p. 347 ADVANCED TE **Activity** Ring of Fire Tours, p. 348 GENERAL TE **Group Activity** Inside the Volcano, p. 349 GENERAL SE **Science in Action** Math, Social Studies, and Language Arts Activities, pp. 374–375 GENERAL	OSP **Lesson Plans** (also in print) TR **Bellringer Transparency*** TR E107 The Earth System* TR E108 The Structure of Earth* SE **Internet Activity**, p. 349 GENERAL
PACING • 45 min pp. 352–357 **Section 2 The Atmosphere** • Compare the different layers of Earth's atmosphere. • Explain how energy in Earth's atmosphere is transferred by radiation, conduction, and convection. • Explain how the greenhouse effect warms Earth's surface. • Explain how the ozone layer protects Earth from damaging UV radiation.	TE **Discussion** Current Composition, p. 352 GENERAL TE **Activity** UV Index, p. 353 GENERAL SE **Quick Lab** The Heat Is On! p. 354 GENERAL TE **Demonstration** Heated Air, p. 354 BASIC TE **Group Activity** A Local Greenhouse, p. 355 GENERAL TE **Activity** Unbalanced, p. 355 GENERAL SE **Benchmark Activity** Global Warming p. 356 GENERAL LB **Ecolabs & Field Activities** That Greenhouse Effect* BASIC	OSP **Lesson Plans** (also in print) TR **Bellringer Transparency***
PACING • 45 min pp. 358–363 **Section 3 The Hydrosphere and Biosphere** • Describe the global pattern of ocean currents. • Describe how thermal energy is transferred globally and locally by ocean water. • Explain how groundwater is stored in aquifers. • Explain why life on Earth is dependent on energy from the sun. • Describe how energy in the biosphere is cycled by decomposition.	TE **Reading Strategy** Discussion, p. 358 GENERAL TE **Connection to Math** Gulf Stream Travel, p. 359 GENERAL TE **Demonstration** Showing Currents, p. 359 ◆ GENERAL SE **School to Home Activity** Comparing Temperature, p. 360 GENERAL TE **Discussion** Local Currents, p. 360 GENERAL TE **Connection to Real Life** Ocean Monitoring, p. 360 GENERAL TE **Group Activity** Local Currents, p. 360 GENERAL CRF **Datasheets for Labs***	OSP **Lesson Plans** (also in print) TR **Bellringer Transparency*** TR E109 The Ocean Conveyor Belt* TR E110 The Biosphere*
PACING • 90 min pp. 364–367 **Section 4 The Cycling of Matter** • Explain how rock is continuously recycled in the rock cycle. • Identify the steps in the water cycle. • Describe how carbon cycles through the carbon cycle. • Describe how nitrogen cycles through the nitrogen cycle.	TE **Demonstration** Illustrating the Rock Cycle, p. 364 ◆ GENERAL TE **Group Activity** Combining Cycles, p. 365 GENERAL SE **Connection to Biology** Deep-Sea Dining, p. 366 GENERAL SE **Model-Making Lab** Metamorphic Mash, pp. 368–369 GENERAL LB **Whiz-Bang Demonstrations** It's Raining Again; Spin Cycle* BASIC LB **Labs You Can Eat** Famous Rock Groups; Rescue Near the Center of the Earth* GENERAL	OSP **Lesson Plans** (also in print) TR **Bellringer Transparency*** CRF **SciLinks Activity*** GENERAL VID **Lab Videos for Level Blue**

PACING • 90 min

CHAPTER REVIEW, ASSESSMENT, AND STANDARDIZED TEST PREPARATION

CRF **Vocabulary Activity*** GENERAL
SE **Chapter Review**, pp. 370–371 GENERAL
CRF **Chapter Review*** ■ ● GENERAL
CRF **Chapter Tests A*** ■ ● GENERAL, **B*** ADVANCED, **C*** SPECIAL NEEDS
SE **Standardized Test Preparation**, pp. 372–373 GENERAL
CRF **FCAT Preparation*** GENERAL
WKB **FCAT Workbook*** GENERAL
CRF **Performance-Based Assessment*** GENERAL
OSP **Test Generator, Test Item Listing**

Online and Technology Resources

Visit go.hrw.com for access to Holt Online Learning, or enter the keyword **HS7 Home** for a variety of free online resources.

This CD-ROM package includes:
- Lab Materials QuickList Software
- Holt Calendar Planner
- Customizable Lesson Plans
- Printable Worksheets
- ExamView® Test Generator
- Interactive Teacher's Edition
- Holt PuzzlePro®
- Holt PowerPoint® Resources

SKILLS DEVELOPMENT RESOURCES	SECTION REVIEW AND ASSESSMENT	CORRELATIONS
SE Pre-Reading Activity, p. 344 `GENERAL` **OSP** Science Puzzlers, Twisters & Teasers `GENERAL`		**National Science Education Standards** UCP 2, 5; ES 1a, 1b
CRF Directed Reading A* ■ `BASIC`, B* `SPECIAL NEEDS` **CRF** Vocabulary and Section Summary* ■ `GENERAL` **SE** Reading Strategy Paired Summarizing, p. 346 `GENERAL` **TE** Reading Strategy Answering Questions, p. 348 `BASIC` **TE** Cultural Awareness Ancient Beliefs About the Sun, p. 349 `GENERAL`	**SE** Benchmark Checks, pp. 349, 350 `GENERAL` **SE** Reading Check, p. 346 `GENERAL` **TE** Mini-Assessment, p. 350 `GENERAL` **TE** Tutorial, p. 350 `GENERAL` **TE** Enrichment, p. 350 `GENERAL` **SE** Section Review,* p. 351 ■ ● `GENERAL` **CRF** Section Quiz* ● `GENERAL`	UCP 1, 2, 5; ES 1a, 1b, 1c, 1d
CRF Directed Reading A* ■ `BASIC`, B* `SPECIAL NEEDS` **CRF** Vocabulary and Section Summary* ■ `GENERAL` **SE** Reading Strategy Reading Organizer, p. 352 `GENERAL` **TE** Reading Strategy Answering Questions, p. 353 `BASIC` **TE** Homework Alternative Design, p. 354 `ADVANCED` **SE** Math Practice Making Ozone, p. 357 `GENERAL` **CRF** Critical Thinking The Day the Wind Died* `ADVANCED`	**SE** Benchmark Checks, pp. 354, 356 `GENERAL` **SE** Reading Check, p. 353 `GENERAL` **TE** Homework, p. 354 `ADVANCED` **TE** Mini-Assessment, p. 356 `GENERAL` **TE** Tutorial, p. 356 `GENERAL` **TE** Enrichment, p. 356 `GENERAL` **SE** Section Review,* p. 357 ■ ● `GENERAL` **CRF** Section Quiz* ■ ● `GENERAL`	UCP 1; ES 1f, 1h, 1i, 1j
CRF Directed Reading A* ■ `BASIC`, B* `SPECIAL NEEDS` **CRF** Vocabulary and Section Summary* ■ `GENERAL` **SE** Reading Strategy Discussion, p. 358 `GENERAL`	**SE** Benchmark Checks, pp. 359, 362 `GENERAL` **TE** Mini-Assessment, p. 362 `GENERAL` **TE** Tutorial, p. 362 `GENERAL` **TE** Enrichment, p. 362 `GENERAL` **SE** Section Review,* p. 363 ■ ● `GENERAL` **CRF** Section Quiz* ■ ● `GENERAL`	ES 1f, 1g, 1k
CRF Directed Reading A* ■ `BASIC`, B* `SPECIAL NEEDS` **CRF** Vocabulary and Section Summary* ■ `GENERAL` **SE** Reading Strategy Prediction Guide, p. 364 `GENERAL` **TE** Reading Strategy Paired Summarizing, p. 365 `BASIC` **CRF** Reinforcement Worksheet The Cycling of Matter* `BASIC`	**SE** Benchmark Checks, pp. 365, 366 `GENERAL` **TE** Mini-Assessment, p. 366 `GENERAL` **TE** Tutorial, p. 366 `GENERAL` **TE** Enrichment, p. 366 `GENERAL` **SE** Section Review,* p. 367 ■ ● `GENERAL` **CRF** Section Quiz* ■ ● `GENERAL`	ES 1d, 1g, 1k

SC/LINKS.
NSTA
www.scilinks.org
Maintained by the **National Science Teachers Association.** See Chapter Enrichment pages that follow for a complete list of topics.

Current Science®
Check out **Current Science** articles and activities by visiting the HRW Web site at **go.hrw.com.** Just type in the keyword **HL5CS04T.**

Classroom Videos
• **Lab Videos** demonstrate the chapter lab.
• **Brain Food Video Quizzes** help students review the chapter material.

Classroom CD-ROMs
• **Guided Reading Audio CD** (Also in Spanish)
• **Interactive Explorations**
• **Virtual Investigations**
• **Visual Concepts**
• **Science Tutor**

Holt Lab Generator CD-ROM
Search for any lab by topic, standard, difficulty level, or time. Edit any lab to fit your needs, or create your own labs. Use the Lab Materials QuickList software to customize your lab materials list.

Visual Resources

CHAPTER STARTER TRANSPARENCY

BELLRINGER TRANSPARENCIES

Section: The Geosphere
Define the major Earth systems. In which system would you find water recycled? In which system would you find carbon and nitrogen recycled?

Record your response in your **science journal**.

Section: The Atmosphere
Name the major gases that make up Earth's atmosphere. What are the two most abundant gases in the atmosphere? What are some of the less common gases in Earth's atmosphere?

Record your response in your **science journal**.

TEACHING TRANSPARENCIES

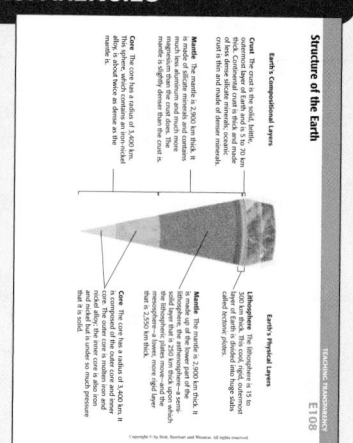

The Earth System

Structure of the Earth

TEACHING TRANSPARENCIES

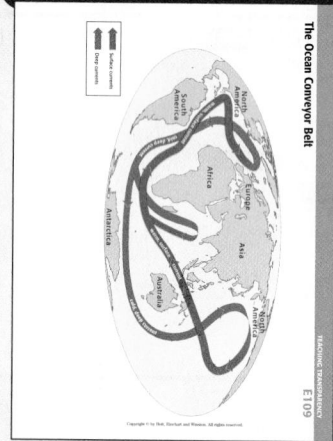

The Ocean Conveyor Belt

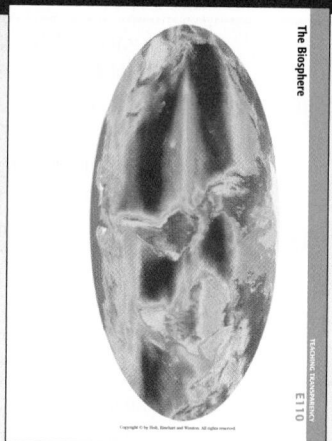

The Biosphere

CONCEPT MAPPING TRANSPARENCY

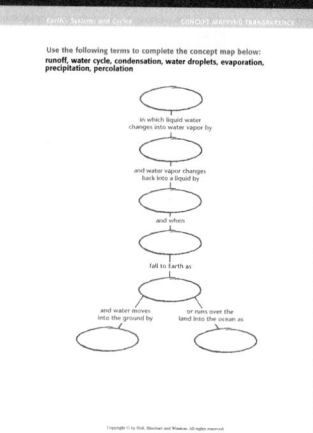

Use the following terms to complete the concept map below:
runoff, water cycle, condensation, water droplets, evaporation, precipitation, percolation

Planning Resources

LESSON PLANS

Lesson Plan   SAMPLE

Section: Waves

Pacing
Regular Schedule: with lab(s):2 days   without lab(s)2 days
Block Schedule: with lab(s):1 1/2 days without lab(s)1 day

Objectives
1. Relate the seven properties of life to a living organism.
2. Describe seven themes that can help you to organize what you learn about biology.
3. Identify the tiny structures that make up all living organisms.
4. Differentiate between reproduction and heredity and between metabolism and homeostasis.

National Science Education Standards Covered
LSInter1:Cells have particular structures that underlie their functions.
LSMat1: Most cell functions involve chemical reactions.
LSBeh1:Cells store and use information to guide their functions.
UCP1:Cell functions are regulated.
SI1: Cells can differentiate and form complete multicellular organisms.
PS1: Species evolve over time.
ESS1: The great diversity of life is the result of more than 3.5 billion years of evolution.
ESS2: Natural selection and its evolutionary consequences provide a scientific explanation for the fossil record of ancient life forms as well as for the striking molecular similarities observed among the diverse species of living organisms.
ST1: The millions of different species of plants, animals, and microorganisms that live on Earth today are related by descent from common ancestors.
ST2: The energy for life primarily comes from the sun.
SPSP1: The complexity and organization of organisms accommodate the need for obtaining, transforming, transporting, releasing, and eliminating the matter and energy used to sustain the organism.
SPSP6: As matter and energy flows through the different levels of organization of living systems—cells, organs, communities—and between living systems and the physical environment, chemical elements are recombined in different ways.
HNS1: Organisms have behavioral responses to internal changes and to external stimuli.

PARENT LETTER

SAMPLE

Dear Parent,

Your son's or daughter's science class will soon begin exploring the chapter entitled "The World of Physical Science." In this chapter, students will learn about how the scientific method applies to the world of physical science and the role of physical science in the world. By the end of the chapter, students should demonstrate a clear understanding of the chapter's main ideas and be able to discuss the following topics:

1. physical science as the study of energy and matter (Section 1)
2. the role of physical science in the world around them (Section 1)
3. careers that rely on physical science (Section 1)
4. the steps used in the scientific method (Section 2)
5. examples of technology (Section 2)
6. how the scientific method is used to answer questions and solve problems (Section 2)
7. how our knowledge of science changes over time (Section 2)
8. how models represent real objects or systems (Section 3)
9. examples of different ways models are used in science (Section 3)
10. the importance of the International System of Units (Section 4)
11. the appropriate units to use for particular measurements (Section 4)
12. how area and density are derived quantities (Section 4)

Questions to Ask Along the Way

You can help your son or daughter learn about these topics by asking interesting questions such as the following:

• What are some surprising careers from the world of physical science?
• What is a characteristic of a good hypothesis?
• When is it a good idea to use a model?
• Why do Americans measure things in terms of inches and yards and meters ?

ALSO IN SPANISH

TEST ITEM LISTING

TEST ITEM LISTING
The World of Science   SAMPLE

MULTIPLE CHOICE

1. A limitation of models is that
   a. they are large enough to seen.
   b. they do not act exactly like the things that they model.
   c. they are smaller than the things that they model.
   d. they model unfamiliar things.
   Answer: B   Difficulty: 1   Section: 3   Objective: 2

2. The length 10 m is equal to
   a. 100 cm.   c. 10,000 mm.
   b. 1,000 cm.   d. Both (b) and (c)
   Answer: B   Difficulty: 1   Section: 3   Objective: 2

3. To be valid, a hypothesis must be
   a. testable.   c. made into a law.
   b. supported by evidence. d. Both (a) and (b)
   Answer: B   Difficulty: 1   Section: 3   Objective: 2 1

4. The statement "Sheila has a stain on her shirt" is an example of a(n)
   a. law.   c. observation.
   b. hypothesis.   d. prediction.
   Answer: B   Difficulty: 1   Section: 3   Objective: 2

5. A hypothesis is often developed out of
   a. observations.   c. laws.
   b. experiments.   d. Both (a) and (b)
   Answer: B   Difficulty: 1   Section: 3   Objective: 2

6. How many milliliters are in 3.5 kL?
   a. 3,500 mL.   c. 3,500,000 mL.
   b. 0.0035 mL.   d. 35,000 mL.
   Answer: B   Difficulty: 1   Section: 3   Objective: 2

7. A map of Seattle is an example of a
   a. law.   c. model.
   b. theory.   d. unit.
   Answer: B   Difficulty: 1   Section: 3   Objective: 2

8. A lab has the safety icons shown below. These icons mean that you should wear
   a. only safety goggles. c. safety goggles and a lab apron.
   b. only a lab apron.   d. safety goggles, a lab apron, and gloves.
   Answer: B   Difficulty: 1   Section: 3   Objective: 2

9. The law of conservation of mass says the total mass before a chemical change is
   a. more than the total mass after the change.
   b. less than the total mass after the change.
   c. the same as the total mass after the change.
   d. Aof the same as the total mass after the change.
   Answer: B   Difficulty: 1   Section: 3   Objective: 2

10. In which of the following areas might you find a geochemist at work?
    a. studying the chemistry of rocks   c. studying fishes
    b. studying forestry   d. studying the atmosphere
    Answer: B   Difficulty: 1   Section: 3   Objective: 2

One-Stop Planner® CD-ROM

This CD-ROM includes all of the resources shown here and the following time-saving tools:

• *Lab Materials QuickList Software*
• *Customizable lesson plans*
• *Holt Calendar Planner*
• *The powerful ExamView® Test Generator*

Meeting Individual Needs

DIRECTED READING A
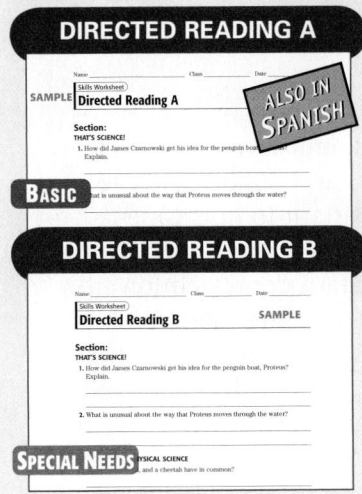
BASIC

DIRECTED READING B
SPECIAL NEEDS

VOCABULARY ACTIVITY
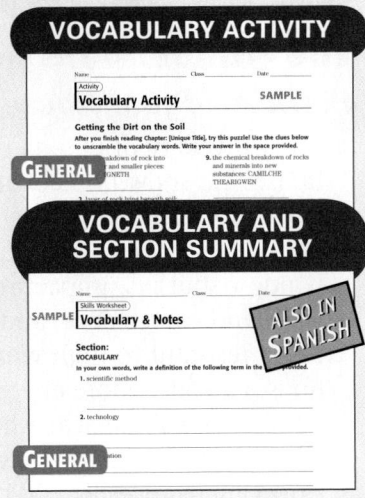
GENERAL

VOCABULARY AND SECTION SUMMARY
GENERAL

REINFORCEMENT
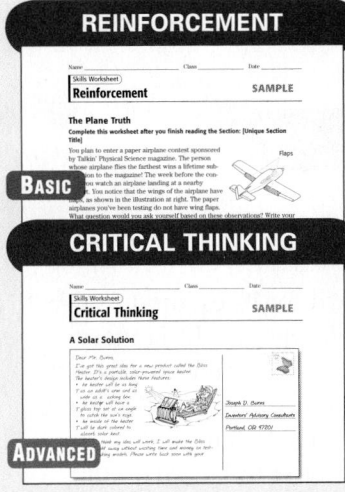
BASIC

CRITICAL THINKING
ADVANCED

SCILINKS ACTIVITY

GENERAL

SCIENCE PUZZLERS, TWISTERS & TEASERS
GENERAL

Labs and Activities

ECOLABS & FIELD ACTIVITIES
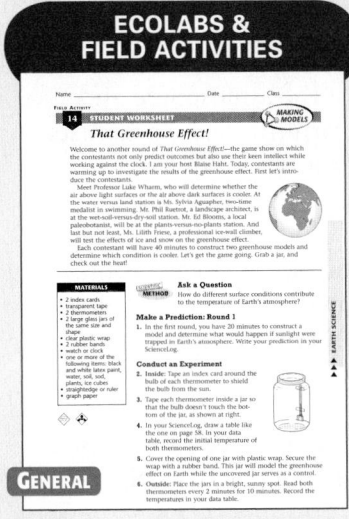
GENERAL

LABS YOU CAN EAT
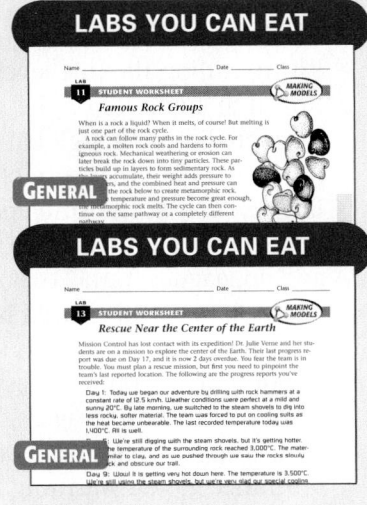
GENERAL

LABS YOU CAN EAT
GENERAL

WHIZ-BANG DEMONSTRATIONS
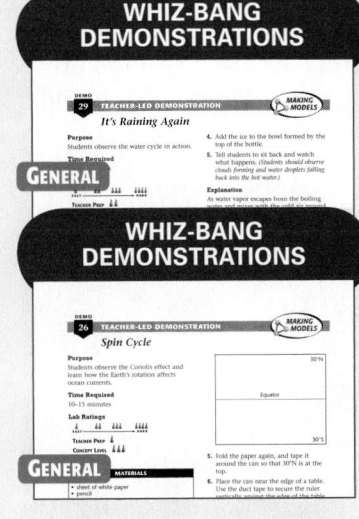
GENERAL

WHIZ-BANG DEMONSTRATIONS
GENERAL

DATASHEETS FOR QUICK LABS

DATASHEETS FOR CHAPTER LABS

DATASHEETS FOR LABBOOK

Review and Assessments

SECTION QUIZ
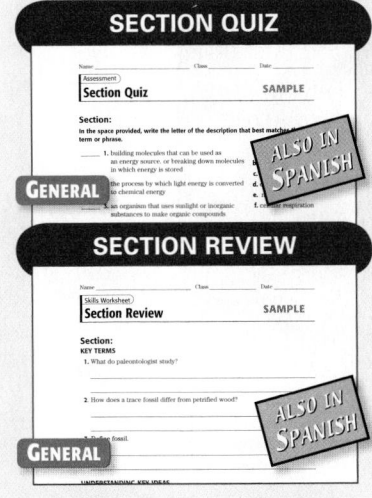
GENERAL

SECTION REVIEW
GENERAL

CHAPTER REVIEW
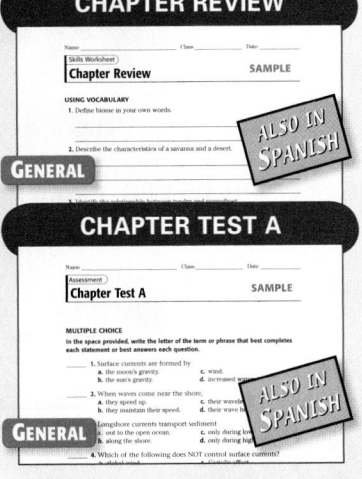
GENERAL

CHAPTER TEST A
GENERAL

CHAPTER TEST B
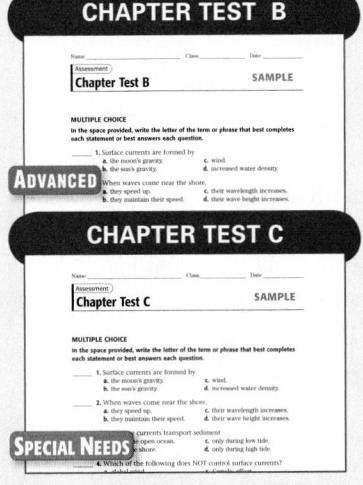
ADVANCED

CHAPTER TEST C
SPECIAL NEEDS

STANDARDIZED TEST PREPARATION
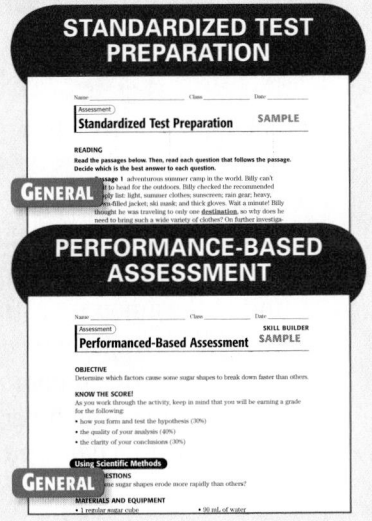
GENERAL

PERFORMANCE-BASED ASSESSMENT
GENERAL

This Chapter Enrichment provides relevant and interesting information to expand and enhance your presentation of the chapter material.

Section 1

The Geosphere

Florida Earthquakes?

- Florida is not generally known for its earthquakes, but there have been a few notable tremors. In January 1879, residents in St. Augustine experienced an earthquake that knocked books from shelves. The quake was also felt in Daytona Beach and Tampa. Two earthquakes in Cuba affected Key West in January 1880. An 1886 earthquake centered in Charleston, South Carolina, rang church bells in St. Augustine. Aftershocks from that quake rocked Jacksonville through the fall of that year. And in 1893 and 1900, Jacksonville was hit by minor quakes. The last two earthquakes recorded in Florida occurred in 1948 on Captiva Island and 1952 in Quincy. Since then, Florida has been seismically silent.

Is That a Fact!

◆ Folklore suggests that animals can predict earthquakes. But this has never been shown scientifically. At this point, even scientists can't predict an earthquake. They can only calculate its probability by studying the history of quakes in an area and monitoring the amount of strain on rocks in a fault. Because earthquake prediction is difficult, scientists have concentrated on improved engineering to make sure buildings and other structures in earthquake zones won't be damaged.

Section 2

The Atmosphere

Hurricane-Proof House

- The University of Florida has built several "hurricane houses" to show homeowners and builders how to make Florida homes more resistant to hurricane damage. Each of these structures features special window shutters, impact-resistant doors, reinforced walls and garage door, and a steel safe room. Besides being resistant to high winds and storm surges, the houses are also more energy efficient than the average home. The UF hurricane homes have already shown their strength. The house in St. Lucie County survived Hurricane Frances in 2004 with little or no damage. The public is welcome to visit the hurricane homes in St. Lucie County, St. Augustine, and Cantonment to learn about bracing structures against mighty winds.

Plants and Excess CO_2

- Rising carbon dioxide levels in the atmosphere are linked to evidence of global warming. Some scientists have predicted that global warming could slow as plants increase their use of this excess carbon dioxide. But research at the University of South Florida (USF) challenges that prediction. USF biologist Peter Stiling and colleagues found that growth of nitrogen-fixing plants actually decreased in an atmosphere of excess carbon dioxide. In a high CO_2 treatment, plants ran out of molybdenum, an essential component of a plant's nitrogen-fixing enzyme. This study suggests that nitrogen-fixers, such as legumes, won't help to minimize global warming.

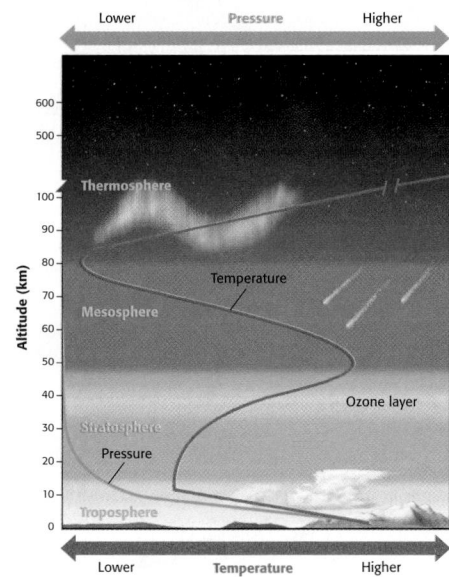

Section 3

The Hydrosphere and Biosphere
Ocean Currents and Jupiter's Atmosphere

- A marine science professor at the University of South Florida has proposed a surprising link between Earth's ocean currents and the cloud bands in Jupiter's atmosphere. No, Jupiter doesn't have a celestial pull on the oceans. But the processes that influence both Earth's oceans and Jupiter's atmosphere may be similar. USF physical oceanographer Boris Galperin studies turbulence and circulation of fluids. He proposes that an underlying turbulence causes a stable system of alternating flows, which form the cloud bands or water currents seen on each planet. Galperin believes that the study of Jupiter's atmosphere may help scientists understand the cause of strong ocean currents on Earth.

Plankton Glow

- Red tides caused by toxic phytoplankton blooms occur each year off Florida's coast. These events kill fish and coral, and contribute to public health problems. Toxic phytoplankton blooms often occur within "black water" runoff—river water full of excess nitrogen and phosphorus (from fertilizer) that pours into the Gulf of Mexico. Scientists were previously unable to determine which black water events might develop into red tides. But oceanographers at the University of South Florida have now developed a prediction tool, using data from two NASA satellites. Instruments on the satellites detect fluorescence or "glow" from phytoplankton chlorophyll. Scientists can examine the amount of fluorescence emitting from black water areas to determine whether runoff contains an abundance of phytoplankton cells that might lead to a red tide event.

Is That a Fact!

- ◆ The world's oceans contain about 50 quadrillion (50,000,000,000,000,000) tons of dissolved salts. If precipitated out of the oceans and spread evenly over Earth's surface, these salts would create a layer about 152 m deep.

Section 4

The Cycling of Materials
Florida Bay and the Nitrogen Cycle

- Researchers at the University of South Florida and the University of Maryland Center for Environmental Studies are studying nitrogen inputs from the Everglades to understand the current nitrogen cycle of Florida Bay. With this research, they hope to predict how a return to freshwater surface flow in the Everglades could affect the Florida Bay ecosystem. From previous coastal studies, scientists know that changes in dissolved inorganic and organic nitrogen inputs can alter phytoplankton communities, affecting higher trophic levels in a coastal food web. Declines in fish populations can result, negatively affecting both commercial and recreational fishing industries. The Florida Bay researchers hope to use current nutrient-cycling data to detect problems that could result from a change in Everglades management.

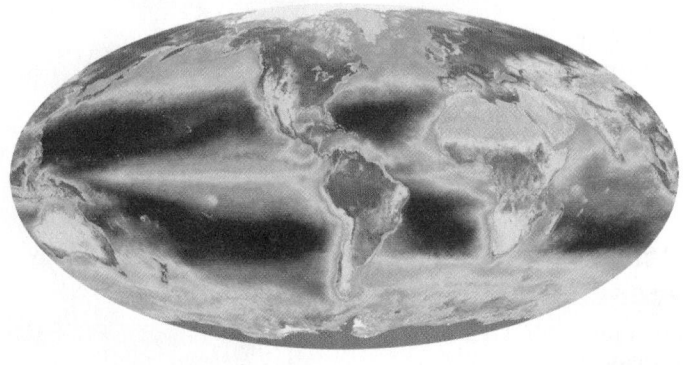

SCi**LINKS**®

N**STA**
Developed and maintained by the
National Science Teachers Association

SciLinks is maintained by the National Science Teachers Association to provide you and your students with interesting, up-to-date links that will enrich your classroom presentation of the chapter.

Visit www.scilinks.org and enter the SciLinks code for more information about the topic listed.

Topic: Earth's Geologic Layers
SciLinks code: HSM0447

Topic: The Atmosphere
SciLinks code: HSM0112

Topic: Water
SciLinks code: HSM1624

Topic: Biosphere
SciLinks code: HSM0162

Topic: Water Cycle
SciLinks code: HSM1626

Topic: Cycles of Matter
SciLinks code: HSM0373

Overview

Earth can be divided into four spheres—the geosphere, the atmosphere, the hydrosphere, and the biosphere. Certain processes in each sphere affect processes in other spheres. Thus, Earth can be regarded as an interrelated system based on the relationships of these processes.

Because little new matter enters the Earth system, the Earth system is closed. Therefore, matter must be recycled. Water, rock, carbon, and nitrogen are different types of matter recycled in the Earth system.

Assessing Prior Knowledge

Students should be familiar with the following topics:

- elements
- rocks
- radiation, conduction, and convection
- saltwater and fresh water
- ecosystems

Identifying Misconceptions

Students may think that each of Earth's spheres exists independently from the others. Explain to students that processes in one sphere affect processes in other spheres. You may wish to use the following examples to make this point:

- Wind and rain from the atmosphere erode soil and sediments on Earth's surface, reshaping the geosphere.
- Partially decomposed plant matter is buried and converted to coal in sedimentary rock beneath Earth's surface.
- Water from the ocean evaporates and condenses in the atmosphere.

Earth's Systems and Cycles

The Big Idea

Processes in the lithosphere, atmosphere, hydrosphere, and biosphere interact to shape Earth.

About the Photo

From space, the land, ocean, and atmosphere appear to be distinct. However, each of these three spheres interact to form a system that sustains life on Earth. Shown here is the Florida Peninsula in the southeastern United States.

PRE-READING **ACTiViTY**

FOLDNOTES **Layered Book** Before you read the chapter, create the FoldNote entitled "Layered Book" described in the **Study Skills** section of the Appendix. Label the tabs of the layered book with "Geosphere," "Atmosphere," "Hydrosphere," and "Biosphere." As you read the chapter, write information you learn about each category under the appropriate tab.

Standards Correlations

National Science Education Standards

The following codes indicate the National Science Education Standards that correlate to this chapter. The full text of the standards is at the front of the book.

Chapter Opener
UCP 2, 5; ES 1a, 1b

Section 1 The Geosphere
UCP 1, 2, 5; ES 1a, 1b, 1c, 1d

Section 2 The Atmosphere
UCP 1; ES 1f, 1h, 1i, 1j

Section 3 The Hydrosphere and Biosphere
ES 1f, 1g, 1k

Section 4 The Cycling of Matter
ES 1d, 1g, 1k

Chapter Lab
UCP 2, 5; SAI 1, 2; ES 1a, 1d

Chapter Review
UCP 2, 5; SAI 1, 2; ES 1a, 1b, 1c, 1d, 1f, 1g, 1h, 1i, 1j, 1k

Science in Action
UCP 2, 5; SAI 1, 2; ES 1b

START-UP ACTIVITY

MATERIALS

FOR EACH GROUP
- large glass container or aquarium
- cold water
- hot water
- small bottle
- piece of string
- food coloring

Safety Caution: Students may want to wear aprons so they do not get food coloring on their clothes.

Answers

1. The hot water and cold water do not mix well.

2. Little thermal energy is transferred from the hot water to the surrounding cold water. On the ocean floor, hot water escaping from a hydrothermal vent probably loses its thermal energy rapidly to the surrounding cold water.

START-UP ACTIVITY

Make a Hydrothermal Vent

In this activity, you will model a hydrothermal vent. Hydrothermal vents are openings in the ocean floor where superhot, mineral-rich waters stream through structures known as *chimneys*. Hydrothermal vents generally occur where large pieces of Earth's lithosphere, called *tectonic plates,* are separating.

Procedure

1. Fill a **large glass container** or **aquarium** with very **cold water.**

2. Tie one end of a **piece of string** around the neck of a **small bottle.**

3. Fill the small bottle with very **hot water,** and add a few drops of **food coloring.**

4. Keep the small bottle upright while you lower it into the glass container until it rests on the bottom.

Analysis

1. Did the food coloring indicate that the hot water and cold water mixed?

2. Based on your results, what do you predict happens to the superhot water from a hydrothermal vent when it encounters the cold water of the ocean floor?

Rocks: Mineral Mixtures   CHAPTER STARTER

Imagine . . .

Imagine that you are an architect who has just been hired to design an amphitheater. The client wants the amphitheater to be big enough to host large concerts. In fact, she wants the amphitheater to seat an audience of 9,200. The client also wants excellent acoustics (sound qualities), and she wants it without a roof so the guests can enjoy the open air. She also wants the audience to be awed by two red sandstone formations that will tower 122 m

Chapter Starter Transparency
Use this transparency to help students begin thinking about Earth's systems and cycles.

CHAPTER RESOURCES

Technology

🖨 **Transparencies**   **READING SKILLS**
- Chapter Starter Transparency

💿 **Student Edition on CD-ROM**

💿 **Guided Reading Audio CD**
- English or Spanish

📹 **Classroom Videos**
- Brain Food Video Quiz

Workbooks

📓 **Science Puzzlers, Twisters & Teasers**
- Cycles in Nature **GENERAL**

Focus

Overview

In this section, students learn about the solid Earth. Students also learn about plate tectonics, and the mountain building, earthquakes, and volcanoes that occur at tectonic boundaries.

Bellringer

Before students begin to read the chapter, have them name and define the major Earth systems.

Motivate

Discussion — GENERAL

How Thick? Tell students that the layers of all of Earth's systems combined are approximately 6,880 km thick. Have them guess the relative thickness of each layer. Then, have them calculate each actual relative thickness from the information in **Figure 1.** Tell them that, although some of the layers overlap with each other, they can compare each layer's thickness to the total to get an approximate value. (Thickness of the geosphere is ~92.7%; the atmosphere, ~7.2%; hydrosphere, <0.1%; and biosphere, <0.1%.) Have students discuss how well their guesses matched the real numbers, and whether they were surprised by the relative size of any of the layers. **LS** Logical

What You Will Learn

● Identify the four major divisions of Earth.
● Identify the layers of Earth based on composition and physical properties.
● Describe the rate at which tectonic plates move.
● Explain the causes of earthquakes and volcanoes.
● Explain how water and wind reshape Earth's surface.

Vocabulary

geosphere	crust
atmosphere	mantle
hydrosphere	core
biosphere	erosion

READING STRATEGY

Paired Summarizing Read this section silently. In pairs, take turns summarizing the material. Stop to discuss ideas that seem confusing.

The Geosphere

Stop and look at the sky above you and the earth beneath your feet. What do they have in common? They are constantly changing.

Some changes on Earth happen slowly, and others happen quickly. Some changes are driven by energy from within Earth. Others are driven by energy from the sun. But these changes are related, because Earth is an interconnected, global system.

Earth as a System

In this chapter, you will learn about the four major divisions, or spheres, of Earth and how they work together as a system. The four divisions of Earth are the geosphere, atmosphere, hydrosphere, and biosphere. The **geosphere** is the solid rocks of Earth. The geosphere is surrounded by the **atmosphere,** which is made up of invisible gases and water vapor. The **hydrosphere** consists of the global ocean, polar ice caps, glaciers, lakes, rivers, water vapor, clouds, and rain. The **biosphere** is the area where all life on Earth exists.

As seen in **Figure 1,** Earth's spheres are overlapping and share some of the same physical space. But each of these spheres has a different composition and different energy relations.

✓ **Reading Check** Briefly define each of the four major divisions of Earth. *(See the Appendix for answers to Reading Checks.)*

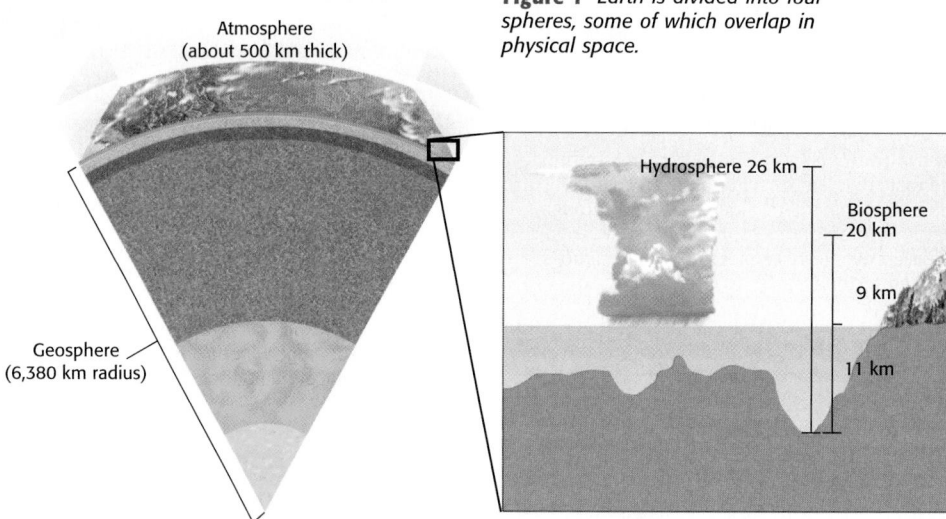

Figure 1 *Earth is divided into four spheres, some of which overlap in physical space.*

Atmosphere (about 500 km thick)

Geosphere (6,380 km radius)

Hydrosphere 26 km

Biosphere 20 km

9 km

11 km

CHAPTER RESOURCES

Chapter Resource File

 • Directed Reading A **BASIC**
• Directed Reading B **SPECIAL NEEDS**

Technology

 Transparencies
• Bellringer
• E107 The Earth System
• E108 The Structure of Earth

● **One-Stop Planner CD-ROM**
• Lesson Plan (also in print)

Answer to Reading Check

The geosphere is the rocky part of Earth that extends from Earth's core to its surface. The atmosphere is the mixture of gases that surrounds Earth. The hydrosphere contains all of Earth's water. The biosphere contains all of Earth's life.

Earth's Compositional Layers

Crust The crust is the solid, brittle, outermost layer of Earth and is 5 to 100 km thick. Continental crust is thick and made of less dense silicate minerals; oceanic crust is thin and made of denser minerals.

Mantle The mantle is 2,900 km thick. It is made of silicate minerals and contains much less aluminum and much more magnesium than the crust does. The mantle is slightly denser than the crust is.

Core The core has a radius of 3,400 km. This sphere, which contains an iron-nickel alloy, is about twice as dense as the mantle is.

Figure 2 *The geosphere is divided into compositional and physical layers.*

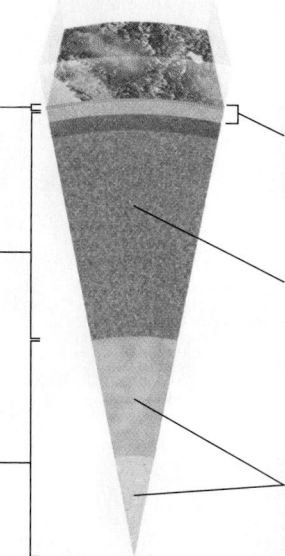

Earth's Physical Layers

Lithosphere The lithosphere is 15 to 300 km thick. This cool, rigid, outermost layer of Earth is divided into huge slabs called *tectonic plates.*

Mantle The mantle is 2,900 km thick. It is made up of the lower part of the lithosphere, the asthenosphere—a semi-solid layer that is 250 km thick upon which the lithospheric plates move—and the mesosphere—a lower, more rigid layer that is 2,550 km thick.

Core The core has a radius of 3,400 km. It is composed of the outer core and inner core. The outer core is molten iron and nickel alloy; the inner core is also iron and nickel but is under so much pressure that it is solid.

The Layers of Earth

The geosphere is the solid Earth, as shown in **Figure 2.** Scientists have learned a lot about Earth's layers by measuring seismic waves generated by earthquakes. They know that Earth's layers differ by chemical composition and physical properties.

The Composition of Earth

Earth is divided into three layers based on chemical composition. The surface layer, or **crust,** is composed largely of silicon, oxygen, and aluminum and represents less than 1% of Earth's mass. The **mantle,** the layer below the crust, is made up largely of silicon, oxygen, and magnesium. Because the mantle contains more magnesium, it is denser than the crust. It accounts for 64% of Earth's mass. In the center of Earth is the **core.** The core is made up mainly of the metal iron, which accounts for the core's high density. Even though the core is the thickest and densest layer, it accounts for only about 35% of Earth's mass.

The Physical Structure of Earth

Earth is also divided into five layers based on physical properties. Earth's rigid, outermost layer, the *lithosphere,* is divided into pieces called *tectonic plates.* These plates move slowly around Earth's surface on the underlying semisolid mantle layer called the *asthenosphere.* The *mesosphere,* the lower layer of the mantle, lies below the asthenosphere. At Earth's center are the *outer core,* which is made of liquid iron and nickel, and the *inner core,* which is made of solid iron and nickel.

geosphere the mostly solid, rocky part of the Earth; extends from the center of the core to the surface of the crust

atmosphere a mixture of gases that surrounds a planet or moon

hydrosphere the portion of Earth that is water

biosphere the part of Earth where life exists

crust the thin and solid outermost layer of the Earth above the mantle

mantle the layer of rock between the Earth's crust and core

core the central part of the Earth below the mantle

Is That a Fact!

The densest part of the Earth, a portion of the inner core, is 13.1 g/cm³. It is almost five times as dense as Earth's continental crust, which is ~2.7 g/cm³.

READING STRATEGY — BASIC

Answering Questions Ask students to study **Figure 3** and write down the name of each plate and the direction in which it is moving. Then, have students answer the following questions: Which direction is the North American plate moving? (southwest) What is happening at the boundary of the Nazca and South American plates? (The plates are colliding, causing mountain formation in western South America.) **LS** Logical

ACTiViTY — GENERAL

Ring of Fire Tours Most of the world's active volcanoes are found along the edge of the Pacific plate. Have each student choose a small portion of this area, called the *Ring of Fire*. Tell them to research their chosen area and then to create a tour brochure that highlights the area's geology, biology, and history. **LS** Visual

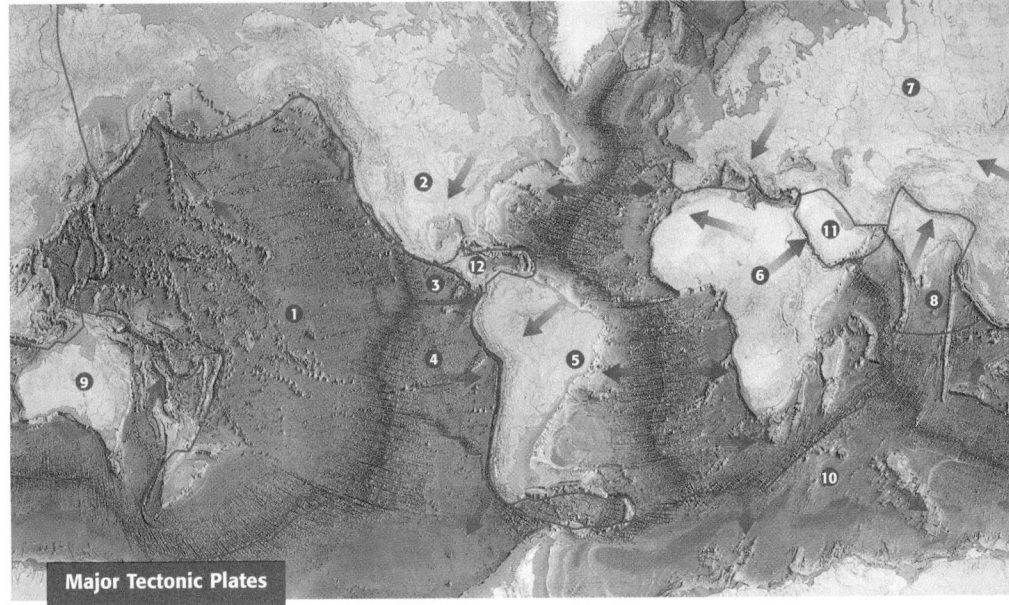

Major Tectonic Plates

- ❶ Pacific plate
- ❷ North American plate
- ❸ Cocos plate
- ❹ Nazca plate
- ❺ South American plate
- ❻ African plate
- ❼ Eurasian plate
- ❽ Indian plate
- ❾ Australian plate
- ❿ Antarctic plate
- ⓫ Arabian plate
- ⓬ Caribbean plate

Figure 3 *Earth's tectonic plates fit together like a giant jigsaw puzzle.*

Plate Tectonics

As you have learned, Earth's lithosphere is divided into tectonic plates. These tectonic plates, which are shown in **Figure 3**, have different sizes, shapes, and thicknesses. A single plate usually includes both continent and ocean. For example, the North American plate includes North America, part of the North Atlantic Ocean, and the island of Greenland. Tectonic plates move around Earth's surface at rates of millimeters to centimeters per year.

Tectonic Plate Boundaries

Plate boundaries are zones of geologic activity at the surface of Earth. Three plate motions are possible at plate boundaries. Plates can separate from each other, such as in the mid-Atlantic Ocean. Plates can also collide with each other and move past each other. The forces generated by these plate motions are responsible for mountain building, earthquakes, and volcanoes.

Mountain Building at Plate Boundaries

Although tectonic plates move slowly, the forces generated in movement are strong enough to cause rock to deform, buckle, and break. These forces are responsible for building major mountain ranges. The Himalaya Mountains were formed during the last 50 million years when the Indian plate moved north and collided with the Eurasian plate.

Is That a Fact!

About 200 million years ago, the tectonic plate containing India began to move north toward the Eurasian plate. India finally joined the Asian landmass approximately 40 to 50 million years ago. The collision formed the Himalayas.

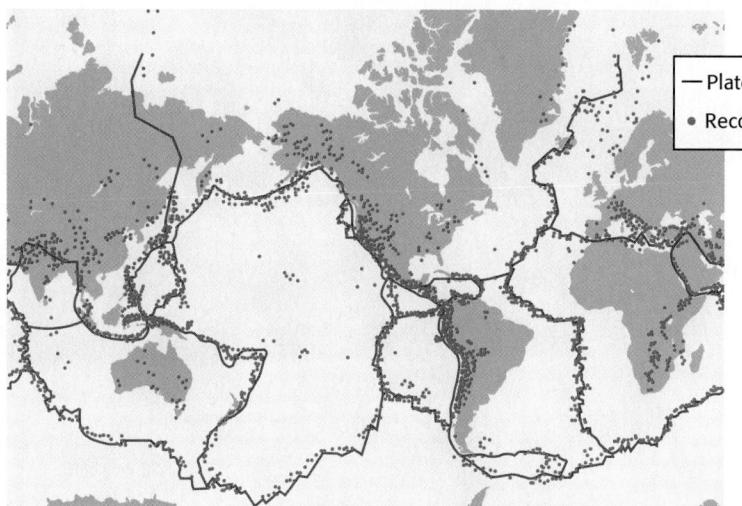

— Plate boundary
• Recorded earthquake

Figure 4 *The red dots in this figure indicate major earthquakes, which mainly occur very close to the tectonic plate boundaries. These boundaries are shown as thick, black lines.*

Earthquakes

Plate boundaries are also where most earthquakes occur. **Figure 4** shows where earthquakes have happened along plate boundaries. When plates move, solid rock is deformed and broken. When this happens, some of the huge amount of energy that is generated is released as vibrations that travel through the ground and shake it. This shaking is an earthquake. Some earthquakes are too small to be felt by humans. Others can be thousands or millions of times stronger. The largest earthquakes can do tremendous damage, as shown in **Figure 5.** These types of earthquakes can be responsible for loss of life and the destruction of buildings and highway overpasses.

✓ Reading Check Explain how earthquakes are caused by the energy released in tectonic plate movement.

Earthquake Zones and Hazards

Earthquake zones are places where large numbers of earthquakes occur. Most earthquake zones are located along plate boundaries. For example, the boundary between the Pacific plate and North American plate along the west coast of North America is an earthquake zone. However, large earthquakes can and do occur in the interior regions of continents. Two large earthquakes occurred within the continental United States in Charleston, South Carolina, in 1886 and in New Madrid, Missouri, in 1812.

Alien Planet Adventure
Create a planet that might be described in a science fiction book. Describe the interactions of the planet's core, mantle, and crust! Go to **go.hrw.com,** and type in the keyword **HZ5TECW.**

Figure 5 *In 1995, a large earthquake shook the area in and around Kobe, Japan. Large sections of the Hanshin Expressway collapsed when the columns supporting the expressway failed.*

Is That a Fact!

In 1994, a magnitude 8.3 earthquake occurred deep in the subduction zone between the Nazca and South American tectonic plates. Although the center of the quake was near La Paz, Bolivia, its effects could be felt all the way to Toronto, Canada. Because the quake was so deep, it caused little damage.

Reteaching — BASIC

Calculating Plate Movement

Students should understand that Earth's processes occur on different scales of time and size. For example, tectonic plate movement occurs very slowly, on a very large scale. Have students calculate yearly movement (in cm/year) for the following tectonic activity:

- The Mid-Atlantic Ridge has spread about 25 km in the last million years. (2.5 cm/yr)

- Near Richmond, Florida, movement of the North American plate was estimated at 18.3 mm/yr using GPS readings. (1.83 cm/yr)

- Over 34 years, the hot spot that created Hawaii migrated about 136 cm. (4.0 cm/yr) **LS** Logical

Quiz — GENERAL

Identify the two processes that can affect Earth's landscape quickly and on a large scale.

A. plate tectonics and erosion

B. an earthquake and a volcanic eruption

C. erosion and an earthquake

D. a volcanic eruption and plate tectonics

Alternative Assessment — GENERAL

Moving Like the Earth Take the class outside or to the gym. Tell them that you are going to shout out a process common in the geosphere, which they should then act out. For example, tell them that they could demonstrate an earthquake by shaking and jumping around very quickly for a few seconds and then becoming still. Encourage students to act out each process together, as a geologic dance. **LS** Kinesthetic

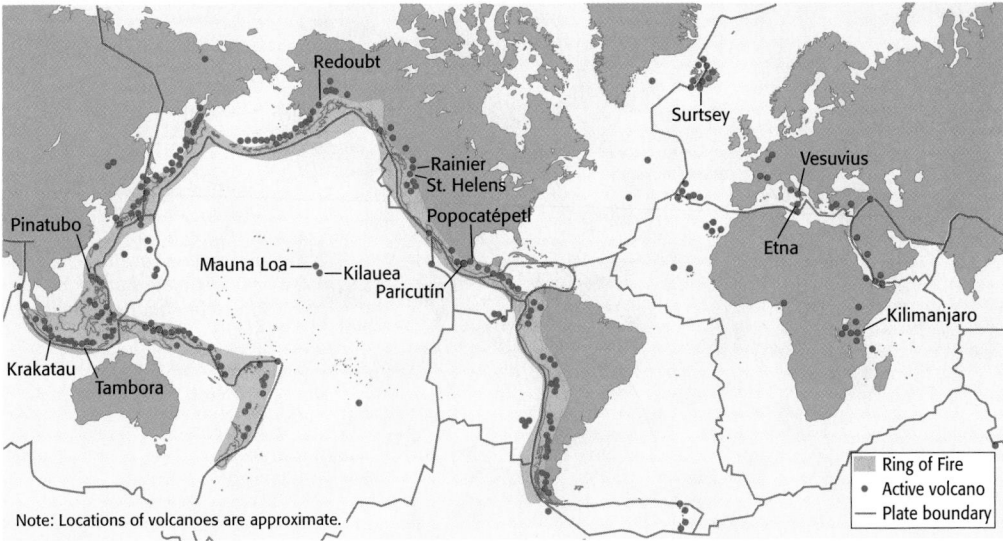

Figure 6 *Tectonic plate boundaries are also areas of volcanic activity. Nearly 75% of the active volcanoes on Earth are located around the Pacific Ocean, which has caused this area to be named the* Ring of Fire.

erosion the process by which wind, water, ice, or gravity transports soil and sediment from one location to another

Volcanoes

Volcanoes are mountains that form when magma rises from Earth's interior to Earth's surface, where the magma cools and solidifies. As shown in **Figure 6,** volcanoes often occur near tectonic plate boundaries. On the ocean floor, volcanoes are located directly on the boundaries where plates pull apart. On continents, volcanoes are often located inland from the plate boundary, where the ocean plate is forced below the continent. Examples of places where volcanoes occur on continents are the west coasts of North America and South America.

Effects of Volcanic Eruptions

Local effects of volcanic eruptions include the loss of lives and property and the destruction of the surrounding environment. Damage can be caused by flowing lava and by volcanic ash that is ejected during an eruption. This wind-carried volcanic ash and dust can also cause problems regionally or even globally.

Large volcanic eruptions can affect Earth's climate when ash blocks sunlight from reaching Earth's surface and sulfur gases reflect sunlight. Both of these effects can lower Earth's temperature. After the eruption of Mount Pinatubo in the Philippines in 1991, the amount of sunlight reaching the surface of the entire Earth was decreased by about 3%. This decrease in sunlight lowered the average global temperature by several tenths of a degree for a few years.

Reading Check Explain how a large volcanic eruption can affect the average global temperature.

Answer to Reading Check

Large volcanic eruptions can lower the average global temperature. This occurs as a result of a decrease in the amount of sunlight that reaches Earth's surface. This decrease is caused by volcanic ash and sulfur gases in Earth's atmosphere, which block and reflect sunlight.

Erosion

The process by which soil and sediment are transported from one location to another is called **erosion.** In the process of erosion, moving water, ice, and wind constantly move soil and sediment and reshape Earth's surface. Water is a very powerful force for reshaping Earth's surface. Although erosion happens over millions of years, moving water can create surface features such as the Grand Canyon, shown in **Figure 7.** Wind can move soil, especially in places where vegetation and roots do not hold the soil in place. Loose, sandy soil is most affected by wind erosion.

Figure 7 *These cliffs in the Grand Canyon were formed by the action of moving water and by wind over millions of years.*

SECTION Review

Summary

- Earth can be divided into four spheres that work together as a global system.
- The solid Earth can be divided into layers based on chemical composition and physical properties.
- Earth's lithosphere is divided into tectonic plates, which move slowly around Earth's surface.
- Tectonic plate movement can release energy in the form of earthquakes.
- Volcanic eruptions can reduce the amount of sunlight that reaches Earth's surface.
- Wind and water are erosional forces that reshape Earth's surface.

Using Key Terms

1. Use *geosphere, atmosphere, hydrosphere,* and *biosphere* in the same sentence.

Understanding Key Ideas

2. Identify the layers of Earth by their composition and physical properties.

3. Describe the rate at which tectonic plates move.

4. Explain what causes earthquakes.

5. Describe local and global effects of volcanic eruptions.

6. Explain how water and wind reshape Earth's surface.

7. Describe a tectonic plate.

8. Identify what kind of measurements helped scientists determine the structure of Earth's interior.

Critical Thinking

9. **Predicting Consequences** How might the lowering of average global temperature over a period of several years affect life on Earth?

10. **Identifying Relationships** Identify two or more of Earth's spheres that overlap in the same physical space.

11. **Making Comparisons** Compare Earth's crust with Earth's mantle.

12. **Analyzing Ideas** A volcanic eruption ejects large quantities of ash and gas into Earth's upper atmosphere. What will be the most likely consequence of this cloud of gas and ash?

Developed and maintained by the National Science Teachers Association

For a variety of links related to this chapter, go to www.scilinks.org

Topic: Earth's Geologic Layers
SciLinks code: HSM0447

7. A tectonic plate is a large piece of the Earth's lithosphere that moves slowly on top of the asthenosphere. Tectonic plates are composed of continental crust, oceanic crust, and both continental and oceanic crust.

8. Scientists can measure the speeds at which seismic waves travel through different parts of the Earth. This measurement helps them calculate the density and thickness of each layer the waves pass through.

9. Answers may vary. Sample answer: The lowering of average global temperature on Earth might kill some crops and reduce the supply of food for humans.

10. Answers may vary. Sample answer: The biosphere and hydrosphere overlap in much of the same physical space.

11. Earth's crust is thin, from 5 to 100 km thick, whereas the mantle, which lies below the crust, is 2,900 km thick. The crust is composed largely of silicon, oxygen, and aluminum, and is less than 1% of Earth's mass. The mantle is composed mainly of silicon, oxygen, and magnesium, is about 10% denser than the crust, and is 64% of Earth's mass.

12. Sample answer: Large amounts of ash and gas in the upper atmosphere can lower Earth's temperature by preventing sunlight from reaching Earth's surface.

Answers to Section Review

1. Answers may vary. Sample answer: The four divisions of Earth are the geosphere, the atmosphere, the hydrosphere, and the biosphere.

2. The compositional layers of Earth are the crust, mantle, and core. The physical layers of Earth are the lithosphere, asthenosphere, mesosphere, outer core, and inner core.

3. Tectonic plates move at rates of millimeters to centimeters per year.

4. Earthquakes happen when rock is deformed and broken, and the energy that is generated is released as vibrations that travel through the ground.

5. Local effects of volcanic eruptions include loss of life and property, and the destruction of the surrounding environment. A global effect of volcanic eruptions may be a lowering of the average global temperature.

6. Water and wind constantly move soil and sediments. These actions constantly reshape Earth's surface.

What You Will Learn

- Compare and contrast the different layers of Earth's atmosphere.
- Explain how energy in Earth's atmosphere is transferred by radiation, conduction, and convection.
- Explain how the greenhouse effect warms Earth's surface.
- Explain how the ozone layer protects Earth from damaging UV radiation.

Vocabulary

radiation
conduction
convection

READING STRATEGY

Reading Organizer As you read this section, create an outline of the section. Use the headings from the section in your outline.

The Atmosphere

When you think of Earth's atmosphere, you probably think of sunlight, clouds, wind, rain, and many other phenomena that you can see. However, Earth's atmosphere affects our planet in very important ways that are not immediately visible.

For example, changes in atmospheric temperature and pressure influence Earth's weather. Atmospheric gases, such as carbon dioxide, water vapor, and methane, absorb energy and keep Earth warm. And ozone—a molecule of oxygen that contains three oxygen atoms, O_3—forms a layer in the atmosphere that absorbs harmful ultraviolet radiation.

Composition of the Atmosphere

Earth is surrounded by a mixture of gases called the *atmosphere*. Earth's atmosphere extends outward some 500 km from the surface of Earth. However, the majority of atmospheric gases are concentrated within 12 km of Earth's surface.

Figure 1 shows the gases that compose the atmosphere. Nitrogen, N_2, makes up 78% of the atmosphere by volume. Nitrogen is put into the atmosphere mostly by microorganisms and volcanic eruptions. Oxygen, O_2, makes up 21% of the atmosphere by volume. Oxygen is released by plants through photosynthesis. Oxygen is used by both plants and animals during respiration. Other important gases in the atmosphere include water vapor, carbon dioxide, and argon. These three gases make up nearly 1% of atmospheric gases. The atmosphere also contains small particles, which include dust, volcanic ash, sea salt, and smoke.

Figure 1 Composition of the Atmosphere

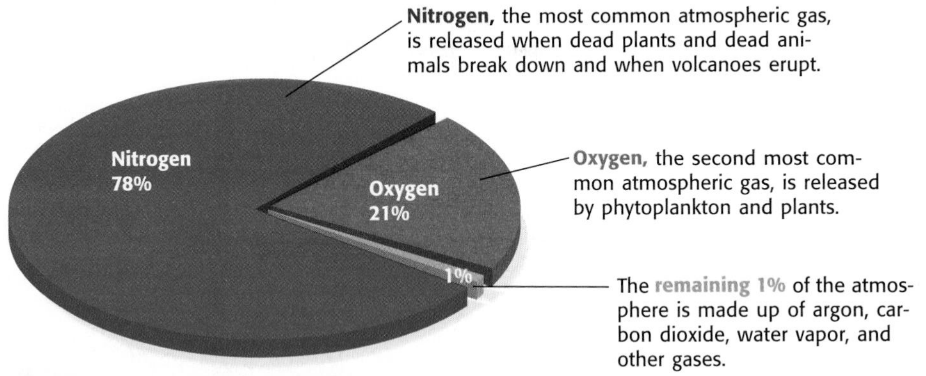

Nitrogen, the most common atmospheric gas, is released when dead plants and dead animals break down and when volcanoes erupt.

Oxygen, the second most common atmospheric gas, is released by phytoplankton and plants.

The remaining 1% of the atmosphere is made up of argon, carbon dioxide, water vapor, and other gases.

Nitrogen 78%

Oxygen 21%

1%

Layers in the Atmosphere

Earth's atmosphere is made up of four layers, which are classified by their altitude and temperature, as shown in **Figure 2.** The major gases, nitrogen and oxygen, occur in the same proportions throughout the atmosphere. Carbon dioxide is also well mixed. Some other gases, such as water vapor and ozone, have varying concentrations.

The Troposphere

The *troposphere* is the atmospheric layer in which we live. It extends from the surface of Earth to an altitude of about 12 km. **Figure 2** shows that as altitude increases in the troposphere, temperature and atmospheric pressure decrease. Water vapor is restricted mainly to the troposphere. Thus, weather, such as rain, snow, and clouds, is also restricted to the troposphere. Depending on location and temperature, water vapor varies from 0.1% to 3% of atmospheric gases in the troposphere.

The Stratosphere

The atmospheric layer immediately above the troposphere is the *stratosphere,* which extends up to about 50 km. Here, temperature rises with altitude. The reason is that incoming solar ultraviolet (UV) radiation interacts with oxygen to form ozone. This stratospheric ozone forms a layer from about 15 km to 40 km in altitude in the middle of the stratosphere. The ozone layer is very important because it absorbs ultraviolet radiation from the sun that can damage or kill organisms.

The Mesosphere

Above the stratosphere is the *mesosphere*. The mesosphere extends up to 80 km. It is the coldest layer of the atmosphere. Temperatures can reach –93°C at the top of the mesosphere.

The Thermosphere

The layer farthest from Earth's surface is the *thermosphere*. This layer extends from 80 km to 500 km. Oxygen molecules in the thermosphere absorb incoming solar UV radiation, causing temperatures to reach 2,000°C. Oxygen and nitrogen also absorb harmful X-ray and gamma-ray radiation from space.

Reading Check Show that you can differentiate the layers of Earth's atmosphere by stating one fact about each layer. (*See the Appendix for answers to Reading Checks.*)

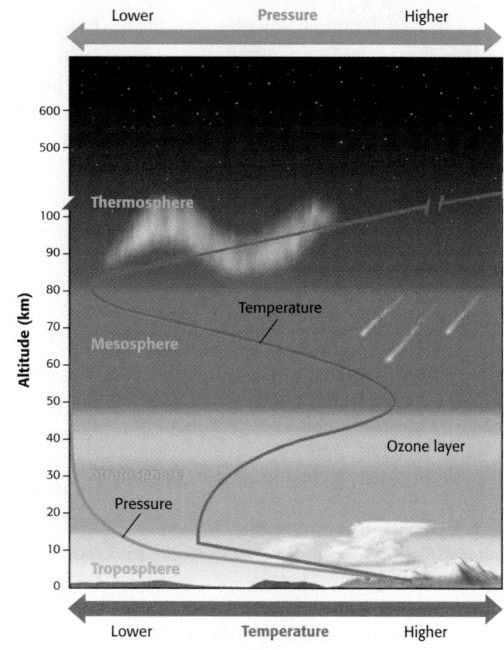

Figure 2 *Scientists divide Earth's atmosphere into four distinct layers. The way temperature varies with altitude is easy to see in this diagram.*

Homework ——— ADVANCED

Alternative Design Passive solar systems use air warmed by the sun to heat buildings. Have students write a pamphlet that explains how passive solar systems work. Have them also include some of the ways people can easily incorporate passive solar principles into their own homes or apartments.

LS Intrapersonal

Demonstration ——— BASIC

Heated Air Demonstrate how heat causes air to move by turning on a hot plate at the front of the room. As the plate warms, have students pass their hands over the top of the plate to observe how the air is moving. They should be able to feel that warm air is rising. Ask them to explain why this is happening. (As the hot plate warms the air above it, the air's density decreases and the air rises.) **LS** Kinesthetic

MATERIALS

FOR EACH GROUP
• beaker, 250 mL (2)
• floodlight, 150 W
• paper, black, one sheet
• paper, white one sheet
• tape
• thermometer
• water

Answer

5. radiation; The light bulb does not touch the beaker, so the energy is not passed by conduction. The energy is transferred through the air but without the movement of the air, so the energy must be transferred by radiation.

Quick Lab

The Heat Is On!

1. Fill **two 250 mL beakers** with **water.** Use a **thermometer** to record the initial temperature of the water in both beakers. The temperature of the water should be the same for both beakers.

2. Wrap one beaker with **white paper,** and wrap one with **black paper.** Secure the paper with a piece of **tape.**

3. Place a **150 W floodlight** 50 cm away from the beakers, and turn the light on.

4. Record the temperature of the water in both beakers at 1 min, 5 min, and 10 min.

5. Is energy being transferred to the beakers by radiation, conduction, or convection? Explain your answer.

Answer to Reading Check

Energy comes to Earth from the sun as electromagnetic waves. These waves include ultraviolet wavelengths, visible light, and infrared wavelengths.

Energy from the Sun to Earth

Even though we live almost 150 million kilometers from the sun, it is the source of 99% of the thermal energy on the surface of Earth. The energy from the sun is transmitted by **radiation** as electromagnetic waves. These waves include ultraviolet, visible light, and infrared (IR). When you are outside on a sunny day, you can feel the radiation from the sun warm the surface of your body.

✓ **Reading Check** Identify the various forms in which energy comes to Earth from the sun.

Heating the Atmosphere and Earth's Surface

Although the sun releases an enormous amount of energy, only a very small percentage of the sun's total energy actually reaches Earth's surface. As shown in **Figure 3,** about 25% of the radiant energy that Earth receives from the sun is *reflected* by the atmosphere. Sources of reflection in Earth's atmosphere include clouds and air. Another 5% of solar energy is *reflected* by the surface of Earth, particularly by ice and snow. Another 25% of the energy that Earth receives from the sun is *absorbed* by the atmosphere—by atmospheric gases, clouds, and ozone. Finally, 45% of the solar energy that Earth receives is *absorbed* by Earth's surface—the land and the oceans.

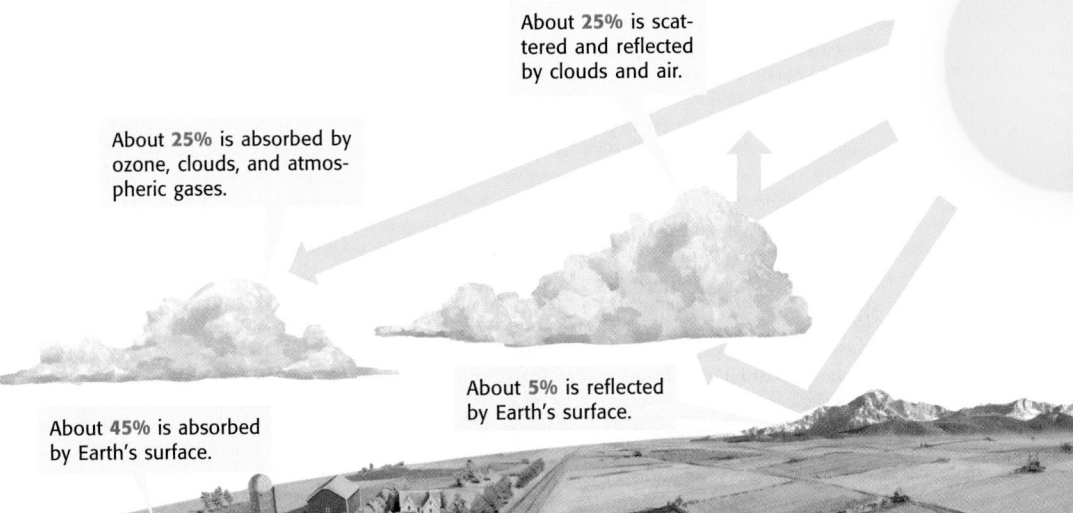

Figure 3 *Energy from the sun is absorbed by the atmosphere, land, and water and is changed into thermal energy.*

About **25%** is scattered and reflected by clouds and air.

About **25%** is absorbed by ozone, clouds, and atmospheric gases.

About **5%** is reflected by Earth's surface.

About **45%** is absorbed by Earth's surface.

Is That a Fact!

Scientists used to assume that the sun emitted a constant amount of solar energy. But, satellite studies beginning in 1978 have shown that solar radiation varies in a 22-year cycle, called the *Hale cycle.* Scientists can used this information to create a more precise model of future climate change.

Energy Transfer

As you have already learned, the energy from the sun is transmitted to Earth in the form of radiation. When this energy reaches Earth, the energy is transferred in two other ways. One way energy is transferred is by conduction. **Conduction** is the transfer of thermal energy through a material. Thermal energy is always transferred from a hotter area to a colder area, such as your warm feet to a cold floor. When air molecules come into direct contact with the warm surface of Earth, thermal energy is transferred to the atmosphere.

The second and more common way energy is transferred in Earth's atmosphere is by convection. **Convection** is the transfer of thermal energy by the circulation of a liquid or a gas.

In Earth's atmosphere, as a general rule, currents of warm, less dense air rise into the atmosphere, and currents of cold, dense air sink toward Earth's surface. As a current of warm air rises into the atmosphere from Earth's surface, the current begins to cool. As the air current cools, it becomes denser than the air that surrounds it. When the current can no longer rise, it begins sinking back toward Earth's surface. As this cool air sinks, it pushes currents of warm air away from Earth's surface. This continuous cycle of warm air rising and cool air sinking is called a *convection current* and is shown in **Figure 4.**

radiation the transfer of energy as electromagnetic waves

conduction the transfer of energy as heat through a material

convection the transfer of thermal energy by the circulation or movement of a liquid or gas

Figure 4 *The processes of radiation, conduction, and convection heat Earth and its atmosphere.*

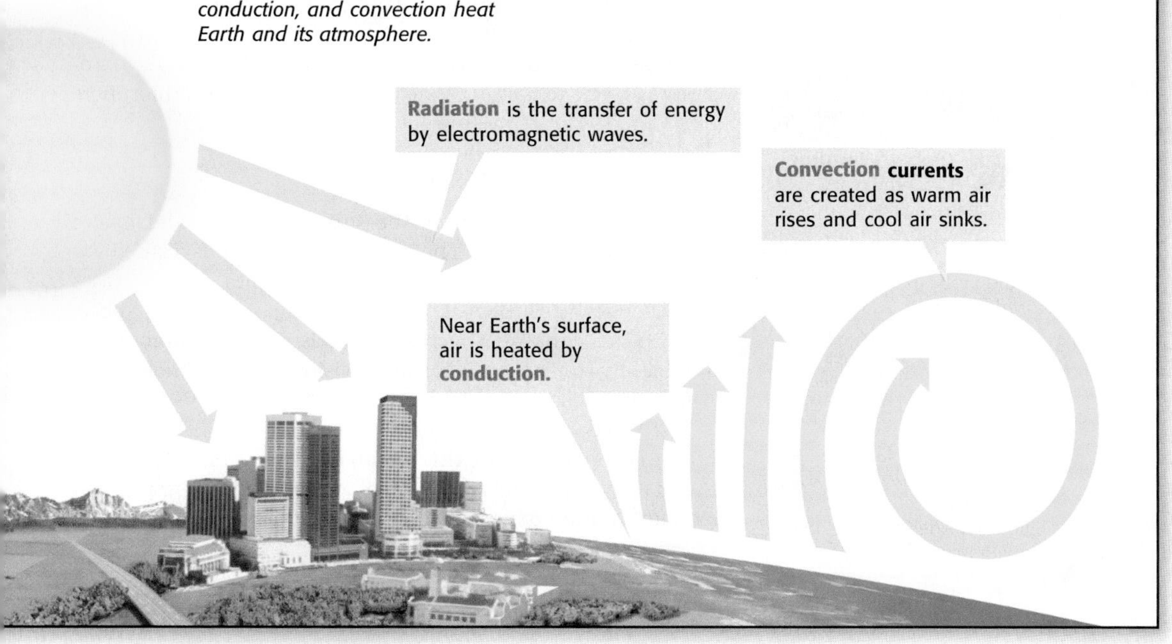

Radiation is the transfer of energy by electromagnetic waves.

Convection currents are created as warm air rises and cool air sinks.

Near Earth's surface, air is heated by **conduction.**

Transfer Examples Students should understand that energy from the sun is transferred within Earth's atmosphere by the processes of radiation, convection, and conduction. On the board, write the headings "Radiation," "Conduction," and "Convection." Ask students to give real-life examples of each type of energy transfer. **LS** Logical

Quiz ——— GENERAL

Energy from the sun travels through space and enters Earth's atmosphere through

A. convection.

B. conduction.

C. radiation.

D. diffraction.

Alternative Assessment ——— GENERAL

Demonstrating Transfer Set up a lamp to represent the sun. Turn the lamp on, and direct the lamp onto a variety of rocks of different colors to represent Earth. Ask students to name the process that transfers energy from this model "sun" to the model "Earth." (radiation) Ask each student to hold a rock and feel how heat transfers between the rock and the hand. Have them name this process of heat transfer. (conduction) Place the rocks back under the light, and allow them to heat up. Then, remove the light, and have students feel how the air moves above the rocks. You may want to put an ice cube next to the rocks to cause differential heating of the air around the rocks. Ask them to name the process that causes transfer of heat by air currents. (convection)

LS Kinesthetic/Logical

Figure 5 **The Greenhouse Effect**

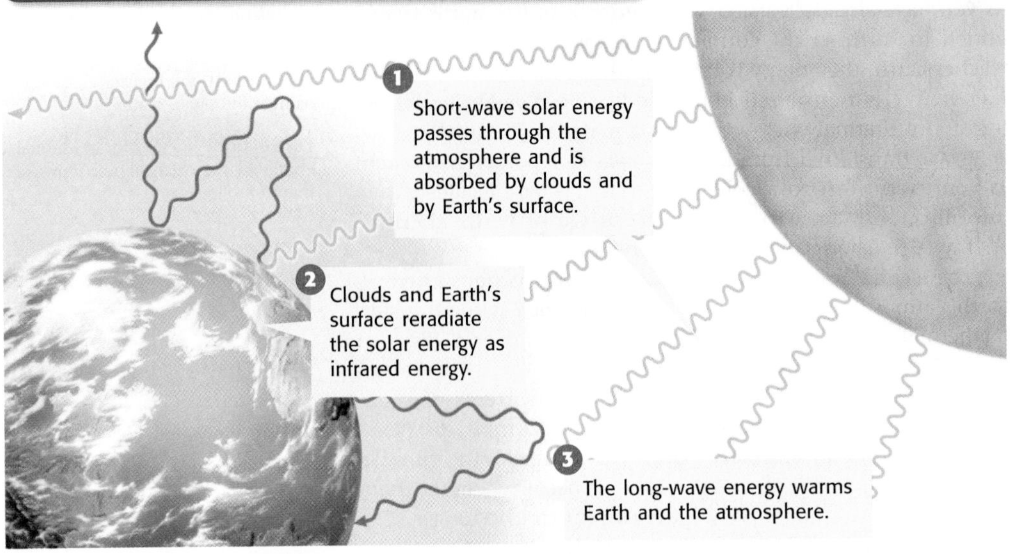

1. Short-wave solar energy passes through the atmosphere and is absorbed by clouds and by Earth's surface.

2. Clouds and Earth's surface reradiate the solar energy as infrared energy.

3. The long-wave energy warms Earth and the atmosphere.

CONNECTION TO Environmental Science

WRITING SKILL **Global Warming** In recent years, many scientists have hypothesized that Earth is getting warmer. These scientists think that the problem may be caused in part by humans, who are adding to the concentrations of greenhouse gases when they burn fossil fuels. Other scientists think that the heating of Earth may simply be part of cyclical climate change. Research global warming. Using the information you collect, argue both sides of the global-warming issue.

Earth's Energy Budget

The 45% of solar energy that is absorbed by Earth's surface is important for Earth's processes. Approximately 20% of this energy causes water to evaporate from the ocean. Evaporation transfers water vapor to the atmosphere. About 6% of the energy is transferred from the land to the atmosphere as rising air masses. Another 5% is reradiated into the atmosphere, and less than 1% produces wind and waves and is used in photosynthesis. The remaining 13% is reabsorbed by the atmosphere in a process called the *greenhouse effect*.

The Greenhouse Effect

The *greenhouse effect* warms the surface of Earth and makes Earth suitable for life. The greenhouse effect is caused by greenhouse gases in the atmosphere. Examples of these gases are water vapor, carbon dioxide, and methane. **Figure 5** shows how the greenhouse effect works. Gases in the atmosphere are mainly transparent to solar visible and UV radiation, which reach Earth's surface. At Earth's surface, this radiation is reradiated as infrared radiation. The greenhouse gases in the atmosphere absorb this infrared energy and retain it as thermal energy in the atmosphere. This thermal energy is then conducted and convected to the surface, warming it.

Reading Check Explain how the reradiation of infrared radiation from Earth's surface affects Earth's temperature.

Answer to Reading Check

Greenhouse gases in Earth's atmosphere absorb reradiated infrared energy from Earth's surface and retain the energy in the atmosphere as thermal energy. This thermal energy is conducted and convected through the atmosphere, warming the atmosphere.

The Ozone Shield

As you have already learned, concentrated ozone forms a layer in the stratosphere. This layer of ozone is found from approximately 15 km to 40 km above Earth's surface. This layer of ozone is very important because it protects life from damage caused by UV radiation from the sun. Ozone forms a shield that absorbs 95% to 99% of this harmful UV radiation.

UV radiation can damage the DNA of an organism. DNA contains the information that determines the traits that an organism inherits and needs to live. The damaging effects of UV light on humans can include skin cancer, wrinkling of the skin, and a weakening of the immune response.

Making Ozone

How many molecules of ozone, O_3, can be made from 12 molecules of oxygen gas, O_2?

SECTION Review

Summary

- The atmosphere is made up of mostly nitrogen gas and oxygen gas.
- Earth's atmosphere is divided into layers based on altitude and temperature.
- The processes of radiation, conduction, and convection heat Earth and its atmosphere.
- The greenhouse effect warms Earth's surface and makes Earth suitable for life.
- The ozone layer protects life on Earth from damage caused by UV radiation from the sun.

Using Key Terms

1. Use *radiation, conduction,* and *convection* in the same sentence.

Understanding Key Ideas

2. What is the best example of thermal conduction?
   a. a light bulb warming a lampshade
   b. an egg cooking on a frying pan
   c. water boiling in a pot
   d. gasses circulating in the atmosphere

3. Identify the gases that compose Earth's atmosphere.

4. Compare and contrast the layers of Earth's atmosphere.

5. Explain how the greenhouse effect warms Earth.

6. Explain the importance of the ozone layer to life on Earth.

Math Skills

7. If an average cloud has a density of 0.5 g/m³ and has a volume of 1,000,000,000 m³. What is the mass of an average cloud?

Critical Thinking

8. **Making Comparisons** Compare the ways in which conduction and convection transfer heat in the atmosphere.

9. **Making Predictions** Predict how the temperatures on Earth might be affected if the percentage of greenhouse gases in the atmosphere were to increase.

For a variety of links related to this chapter, go to www.scilinks.org

Topic: The Atmosphere
SciLinks code: HSM0112

Answer to Math Practice

8 molecules of ozone

Answers to Section Review

1. Thermal energy is transferred in Earth's atmosphere by radiation, conduction, and convection.

2. b

3. The gases that compose Earth's atmosphere include nitrogen, oxygen, argon, carbon dioxide, and water vapor.

4. Answers may vary. Sample answer: The four layers of Earth's atmosphere, from lowest to highest, are the troposphere, stratosphere, mesosphere, and thermosphere. In the troposphere, as altitude increases, temperature and air pressure decrease. In the stratosphere, temperature increases with altitude. The mesosphere is the coldest layer in the atmosphere, with temperatures reaching −93°C. The thermosphere is the hottest layer in the atmosphere, with temperatures as hot as 2,000°C.

5. The greenhouse effect warms Earth because greenhouse gases absorb reradiated infrared energy from Earth's surface and retain the energy as thermal energy in the atmosphere. This thermal energy is convected and conducted through the atmosphere, warming the atmosphere.

6. The ozone layer is important to life on Earth because the ozone layer forms a shield that absorbs 95% to 99% of all harmful incoming ultraviolet radiation from the sun.

7. 0.5 g/m³ × 1,000,000,000 m = 500,000,000 g, or 500,000 kg

8. When air molecules come into direct contact with the warm surface of Earth, thermal energy is transferred to the atmosphere by conduction. Convection transfers thermal energy in the atmosphere when currents of warm air rise into the atmosphere and cool, and currents of cool air sink and push currents of warm air away from Earth's surface.

9. If the percentage of greenhouse gases in the atmosphere increased, more reradiated infrared energy from Earth's surface would be absorbed and retained as thermal energy in the atmosphere. Thus, temperatures on Earth would increase.

CHAPTER RESOURCES

Chapter Resource File

- Section Quiz **GENERAL**
- Section Review **GENERAL**
- Vocabulary and Section Summary **GENERAL**
- Critical Thinking Worksheet **ADVANCED**
- Datasheet for Quick Lab

Focus

Overview

In this section, students will learn about the hydrosphere, including the global ocean, ocean currents, and the transfer of thermal energy by ocean water. Sources of fresh water and groundwater storage in aquifers are discussed, too. Students will also learn about the biosphere and how energy flows in the biosphere.

Bellringer

Ask students to name some differences between a freshwater lake and an ocean. (The water in an ocean contains a greater quantity of salts than the water in a freshwater lake. An ocean is much larger, deeper, and older than a freshwater lake. Oceans and freshwater lakes contain different types of organisms. An ocean has currents that extend for great distances; a freshwater lake generally does not.)

Motivate

Demonstration — BASIC

No Barriers Demonstrate to students that the oceans are truly continuous by having them look at a globe. Ask them to trace sea routes from Florida to a variety of world destinations. **LS** Visual

What You Will Learn

- Describe the global pattern of ocean currents.
- Describe how thermal energy is transferred globally and locally by ocean water.
- Explain how groundwater is stored in aquifers underground.
- Explain why life on Earth is dependent on energy from the sun.
- Describe how energy in the biosphere is cycled by decomposition.

Vocabulary

surface current
deep current
aquifer

READING STRATEGY

Discussion Read this section silently. Write down questions that you have about this section. Discuss your questions in a small group.

The Hydrosphere and Biosphere

"Water, water, everywhere." You have probably heard this expression before, but do you realize how great the amount of water on Earth really is?

Earth's hydrosphere covers 71% of Earth's surface. It includes the water that is visible in the oceans, lakes, rivers, glaciers, and polar ice caps. However, the hydrosphere also includes clouds, rain, and snow in the atmosphere and water in the pores of underground rocks.

The Global Ocean

The global ocean, a portion of which is shown in **Figure 1,** is the largest reservoir of water on Earth. The global ocean contains more than 97% of all water on Earth and covers a surface area of approximately 335 million square kilometers.

As you know, the water in the global ocean is salty. If you evaporate a 1,000 g sample of ocean water, you are left with 35 g of salts. For this reason, ocean water is denser than fresh water. The majority of these salts are table salt, which is made up of the elements sodium and chlorine.

The temperature of surface ocean water varies from warm at the equator to near freezing at the poles. Ocean water temperature also decreases with depth. The surface water located in the top 100 to 200 m of the ocean is much warmer than deeper water.

Figure 1 *In this satellite view of Earth, the Florida Peninsula separates the Gulf of Mexico (above) from the Atlantic Ocean (below).*

CHAPTER RESOURCES

Chapter Resource File

- Directed Reading A **BASIC**
- Directed Reading B **SPECIAL NEEDS**

Technology

Transparencies
- Bellringer
- E109 The Ocean Conveyor Belt

One-Stop Planner CD-ROM
- Lesson Plan (also in print)

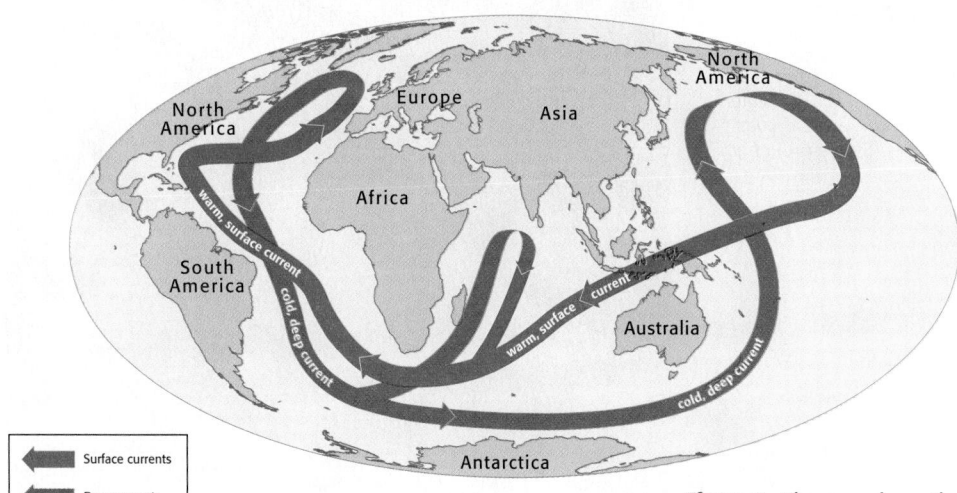

| Surface currents |
| Deep currents |

Gulf Stream Travel At the end of August 2004, the Gulf Stream had a typical velocity of between 0.4 and 1 m/s as its currents traveled along the Atlantic Coast. Calculate how many hours it would take one portion of the current to travel from West Palm Beach, Florida to Jacksonville (about 447 km), if its velocity were 0.6 m/s. (447 km x 1000 m/km = 447,000 m ÷ 0.6 m/s = 745,000 s ÷ 3600 s/hr = about 207 hours) **LS** Logical

Ocean Currents

Ocean water contains streamlike movements of water called *ocean currents*. Ocean currents are either surface currents or deep currents. Both types of currents are part of the global pattern of ocean currents known as the *ocean conveyor belt*.

Figure 2 *The map shows the flow directions of ocean currents— the ocean conveyor belt. Warm-water currents are shown as red arrows; cold-water currents are shown as blue arrows.*

Surface Currents

The surface currents of the global ocean are shown above in **Figure 2. Surface currents** are horizontal, streamlike movements of water that occur at or near the surface of the ocean. Surface currents are driven mainly by winds. They can reach depths of several hundred meters and lengths of several thousand kilometers, and they can travel across oceans.

surface current a horizontal movement of ocean water that is caused by wind and that occurs at or near the ocean's surface

deep current a streamlike movement of ocean water far below the surface

Deep Currents

Deep currents, also shown in **Figure 2,** are streamlike movements of water that are located far below the ocean surface. Because deep currents are located near the ocean bottom, they are not controlled by the wind. Instead, these currents result when cold and, therefore, dense surface water sinks and flows along the bottom of the ocean. As shown in **Figure 2,** deep currents flow from the North Atlantic Ocean to Antarctica and then into the Pacific Ocean. Bottom water then flows northward toward Alaska, where the water rises to the surface again. This journey takes more than a thousand years.

Reading Check Explain how ocean currents form the global pattern known as the *ocean conveyor belt*. (*See the Appendix for answers to Reading Checks.*)

Demonstration ———— GENERAL

Showing Currents Fill a clear pie plate with cold water. Sprinkle a leafy herb, such as basil, on the top of the water. Place some rocks in the plate to represent landmasses. Tell students that this model represents the world and its oceans. Have students blow on the water to simulate surface currents, and discuss how the basil moves. Gently rock the plate to simulate currents affected by the spinning of Earth. Then, fill a measuring cup with very warm water, and slowly pour some of this water into the pie plate to try to simulate convection currents in the ocean. Again, have students observe and discuss what happens to the basil. **LS** Visual

Is That a Fact!

Even though the Arctic Ocean is part of the global ocean, you can't sail from Alaska to Norway across this body of water. That's because most of the surface of the Arctic Ocean is covered by pack ice—frozen seawater pushed together by waves and wind.

Answer to Reading Check

Surface currents and deep currents form the pattern known as the ocean conveyor belt because they transport warm and cold water for thousands of miles throughout the global ocean.

Discussion ——— GENERAL

Local Currents Have students study the figures showing ocean currents on both this page and the previous page. Then, lead a discussion about which surface currents have the greatest effect on the United States, and how these currents influence U.S. climate. **LS** Verbal

CONNECTION to
Real Life ——— GENERAL

Ocean Monitoring Even though the ocean and its currents have a profound effect on weather patterns and climate, few systems are in place for continuous monitoring of ocean characteristics. Scientists in Maine have recognized the potential benefits of continuous monitoring and are working on coordinating a system of buoys, satellites, and land-based radar to record hourly current direction, temperature, salinity, turbidity, dissolved oxygen, wave characteristics, wind information, and surface weather (such as temperature and fog) in the Gulf of Maine. This project, called *GoMOOS*, serves as a pilot project for a national ocean monitoring system. From GoMOOS, scientists hope to gather information that can aid search-and-rescue missions, provide critical information to fishermen and boaters, and provide an understanding of how changes in current patterns can affect fisheries and global climate change. Have interested students look at the GoMOOS Web site for more information. **LS** Visual

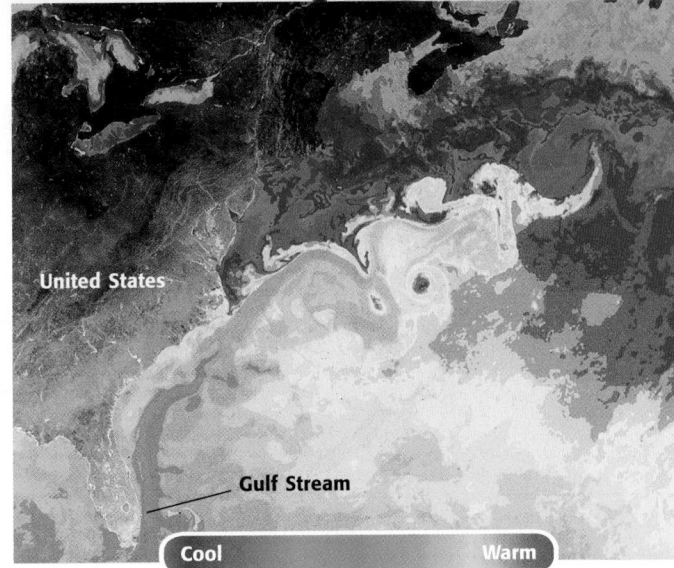

Figure 3 *The Gulf Stream moves warm, equatorial water north along the eastern coast of the United States to higher latitudes.*

SCHOOL to HOME

Comparing Temperature
With a parent or guardian, check your local newspaper for the high and low temperatures in your town on a specific date. Check the same temperatures for another town that is located at the same or a similar latitude. Try to choose a town that is located closer to or farther from the ocean than the town in which you live. Are the temperatures in your town higher or lower than those of the other town? Do the temperatures of the town located nearer to the ocean appear to be influenced by the moderating effect of the ocean?

A Global Temperature Regulator

The global ocean is a reservoir for thermal energy from the sun. Because the global ocean covers such a large area of the surface of Earth, the global ocean absorbs much of the 45% of solar energy that reaches Earth.

Ocean water warms as it absorbs thermal energy near the equator. As the surface currents flow, this energy is transferred to midlatitudes. **Figure 3** shows how a surface current called the *Gulf Stream* transports warm, equatorial water northward. As a result of this thermal energy transfer by the Gulf Stream, Florida and even the British Isles are several degrees warmer than are other coastal areas at similar latitudes.

The transfer of thermal energy by flowing water is much more efficient than the transfer of thermal energy stored on land. The reason for this difference lies in the fact that thermal energy from the land is moved by wind. Unlike ocean water, wind does not distribute thermal energy evenly over Earth's surface.

Local Climate

Ocean water warms and cools more slowly than the land nearby. Therefore, the ocean can keep the summer temperatures of land near the water cooler. It can also make winter temperatures warmer. Coastal areas can be many degrees warmer or cooler than areas that are located 30 or more kilometers inland.

✓ **Reading Check** Explain how heat from the ocean can affect temperatures on land.

Research ——— GENERAL

El Niño Ask students to research how an El Niño or La Niña event can alter global weather patterns. Have them create a research report or poster that summarizes the worldwide effects of an El Niño or La Niña event that occurred in the last 10 years. **LS** Intrapersonal

Answer to Reading Check

The ocean can keep temperatures in coastal areas cooler during the summer and warmer during the winter.

Fresh Water

Only 2.8% of all the water on Earth is fresh water. Fresh water occurs as polar ice caps, glaciers, lakes, rivers, and streams. Polar ice caps and glaciers contain about 77% of Earth's fresh water. Lakes, such as the five Great Lakes of North America, are another reservoir of fresh water. Surprisingly, all lakes account for only about 0.003% of fresh water. Rivers and streams compose another 0.00004% of fresh water.

In Florida, much of the surface fresh water is found in the Everglades. The Everglades is a giant, slow-moving wetland that flows south from Lake Okeechobee to Florida Bay. A small portion of the Everglades is shown in **Figure 4.**

Groundwater

Groundwater is surface water that has seeped into the ground over time. Below ground, groundwater is stored in microscopic cracks in rocks and in the pores between rock grains. Although we cannot see this groundwater, it represents 22% of the fresh water on Earth.

Bodies of rock below the ground that contain groundwater are called **aquifers.** Groundwater aquifers that occur in the continental United States are shown on the map in **Figure 5.** The groundwater from aquifers is made available for human use by pumping from wells. Groundwater that is pumped from aquifers must be replaced. The process by which groundwater seeps back into aquifers from Earth's surface is called *recharge*. Recharge is part of Earth's groundwater cycling process.

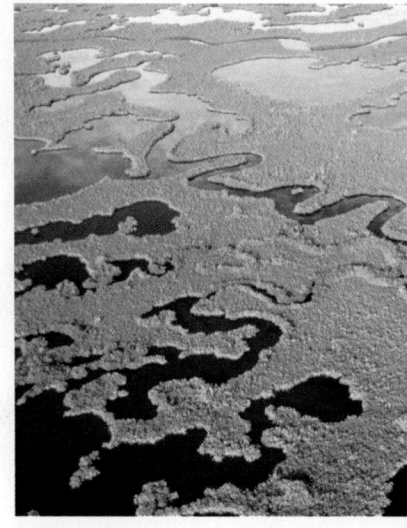

Figure 4 *The wetlands known as the Everglades cover more than 19,000 km² of South Florida.*

aquifer a body of rock or sediment that stores groundwater and allows the flow of groundwater

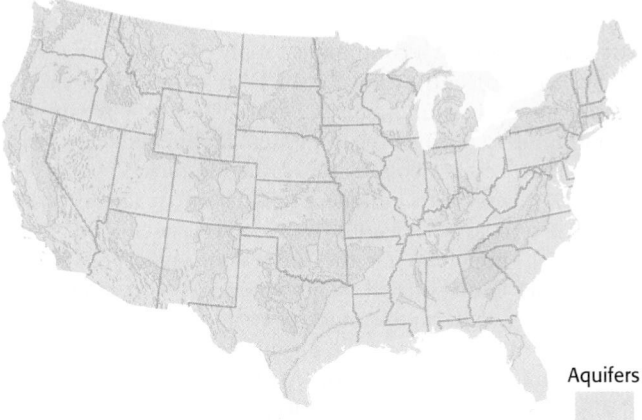

Aquifers

Figure 5 *The continental United States has extensive groundwater aquifers. The water from these aquifers has many agricultural, industrial, and municipal uses.*

WEIRD SCIENCE

Chitin is a natural polymer, produced by insects, crustaceans, worms, and fungi. In insects and crustaceans, chitin forms the hard, armor-like shell that protects the organism's body. Chitosan is a product derived from chitin. This versatile substance has been used to treat burns, reduce serum cholesterol levels, dye fabrics, increase crop yields, and remove excess sediment in ponds! Encourage students to learn more about chitosan's properties and its many uses.

Interactions and Cycling

Students should understand that interactions between living and nonliving components of a system result in the flow of energy and cycling of nutrients within the system. Have students explain how the following organisms and nonliving components could interact within the specified system.

- the sun and shrimp in a coastal seagrass habitat (The sun warms ocean water and creates currents that deliver nutrients to the shrimp.)

- phosphorus and sugar cane in an agricultural field (Phosphorus is a nutrient that helps sugar cane to grow.)
 Logical

Quiz ——— GENERAL

In a typical freshwater ecosystem, energy would flow from

A. aquatic plants to fish and then to algae.

B. wading birds to fish and then to plants.

C. algae to fish and then to wading birds.

D. bacteria to algae and then to fish.

Alternative Assessment ——— GENERAL

Coastal Energy Have students research the components of a typical coastal ecosystem. Then, have each student create a poster that illustrates how energy flows through that system. **LS** Visual

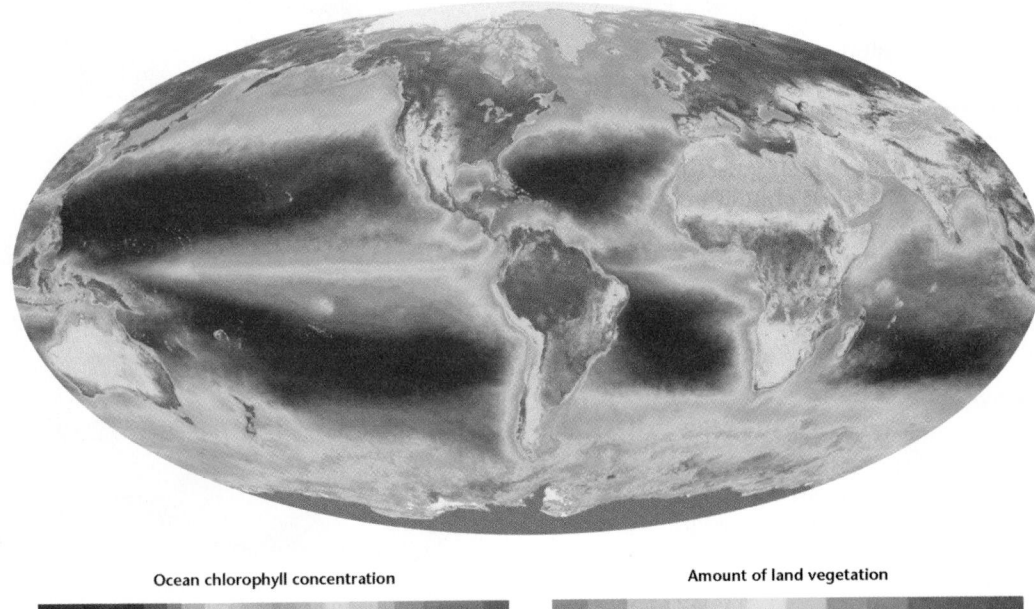

Ocean chlorophyll concentration

Low   High

Amount of land vegetation

Low   High

Figure 6 *The colors in this image of Earth indicate the concentrations of plant life in the oceans and on land.*

The Biosphere

Life on Earth is found in a variety of habitats. These habitats are collectively called *the biosphere.* The biosphere includes the part of the atmosphere that extends from the surface of Earth to approximately 11 km above Earth's surface. Most of the hydrosphere is also part of the biosphere. Most life on Earth is dependent on a continuous supply of energy from the sun. But some organisms have even been found living deep in Earth's crust. This finding is an example of how scientists are continuing to discover life in new environments today and expanding the known boundaries of the biosphere.

The biosphere has a unique combination of factors that organisms need for life. Liquid water and a suitable habitat are extremely important for the survival of organisms. Most organisms are also restricted to environments with moderate temperatures. A continuous source of energy is equally important for organisms. For example, organisms such as plants and algae use sunlight to produce food. As shown in **Figure 6,** plants and algae are found both in the oceans and on land. Other organisms get their food from consuming plants and algae.

✓ *Reading Check* Explain why organisms are dependent on a continuous supply of energy from the sun.

Answer to Reading Check

Animals depend on a continuous supply of energy from the sun in order to obtain the food they need.

The Ozone Shield

As you have already learned, concentrated ozone forms a layer in the stratosphere. This layer of ozone is found from approximately 15 km to 40 km above Earth's surface. This layer of ozone is very important because it protects life from damage caused by UV radiation from the sun. Ozone forms a shield that absorbs 95% to 99% of this harmful UV radiation.

UV radiation can damage the DNA of an organism. DNA contains the information that determines the traits that an organism inherits and needs to live. The damaging effects of UV light on humans can include skin cancer, wrinkling of the skin, and a weakening of the immune response.

Making Ozone

How many molecules of ozone, O_3, can be made from 12 molecules of oxygen gas, O_2?

SECTION Review

Summary

- The atmosphere is made up of mostly nitrogen gas and oxygen gas.
- Earth's atmosphere is divided into layers based on altitude and temperature.
- The processes of radiation, conduction, and convection heat Earth and its atmosphere.
- The greenhouse effect warms Earth's surface and makes Earth suitable for life.
- The ozone layer protects life on Earth from damage caused by UV radiation from the sun.

Using Key Terms

1. Use *radiation, conduction,* and *convection* in the same sentence.

Understanding Key Ideas

2. What is the best example of thermal conduction?
   a. a light bulb warming a lampshade
   b. an egg cooking on a frying pan
   c. water boiling in a pot
   d. gasses circulating in the atmosphere

3. Identify the gases that compose Earth's atmosphere.

4. Compare and contrast the layers of Earth's atmosphere.

5. Explain how the greenhouse effect warms Earth.

6. Explain the importance of the ozone layer to life on Earth.

Math Skills

7. If an average cloud has a density of 0.5 glm³ and has a volume of 1,000,000,000 m³. What is the mass of an average cloud?

Critical Thinking

8. **Making Comparisons** Compare the ways in which conduction and convection transfer heat in the atmosphere.

9. **Making Predictions** Predict how the temperatures on Earth might be affected if the percentage of greenhouse gases in the atmosphere were to increase.

For a variety of links related to this chapter, go to www.scilinks.org

Topic: The Atmosphere
SciLinks code: HSM0112

Answer to Math Practice

8 molecules of ozone

Answers to Section Review

1. Thermal energy is transferred in Earth's atmosphere by radiation, conduction, and convection.

2. b

3. The gases that compose Earth's atmosphere include nitrogen, oxygen, argon, carbon dioxide, and water vapor.

CHAPTER RESOURCES

Chapter Resource File

- Section Quiz GENERAL
- Section Review GENERAL
- Vocabulary and Section Summary GENERAL
- Critical Thinking Worksheet ADVANCED
- Datasheet for Quick Lab

---

4. Answers may vary. Sample answer: The four layers of Earth's atmosphere, from lowest to highest, are the troposphere, stratosphere, mesosphere, and thermosphere. In the troposphere, as altitude increases, temperature and air pressure decrease. In the stratosphere, temperature increases with altitude. The mesosphere is the coldest layer in the atmosphere, with temperatures reaching −93°C. The thermosphere is the hottest layer in the atmosphere, with temperatures as hot as 2,000°C.

5. The greenhouse effect warms Earth because greenhouse gases absorb reradiated infrared energy from Earth's surface and retain the energy as thermal energy in the atmosphere. This thermal energy is convected and conducted through the atmosphere, warming the atmosphere.

6. The ozone layer is important to life on Earth because the ozone layer forms a shield that absorbs 95% to 99% of all harmful incoming ultraviolet radiation from the sun.

7. 0.5 g/m³ × 1,000,000,000 m = 500,000,000 g, or 500,000 kg

8. When air molecules come into direct contact with the warm surface of Earth, thermal energy is transferred to the atmosphere by conduction. Convection transfers thermal energy in the atmosphere when currents of warm air rise into the atmosphere and cool, and currents of cool air sink and push currents of warm air away from Earth's surface.

9. If the percentage of greenhouse gases in the atmosphere increased, more reradiated infrared energy from Earth's surface would be absorbed and retained as thermal energy in the atmosphere. Thus, temperatures on Earth would increase.

Focus

Overview

In this section, students will learn about the hydrosphere, including the global ocean, ocean currents, and the transfer of thermal energy by ocean water. Sources of fresh water and groundwater storage in aquifers are discussed, too. Students will also learn about the biosphere and how energy flows in the biosphere.

 **Bellringer**

Ask students to name some differences between a freshwater lake and an ocean. (The water in an ocean contains a greater quantity of salts than the water in a freshwater lake. An ocean is much larger, deeper, and older than a freshwater lake. Oceans and freshwater lakes contain different types of organisms. An ocean has currents that extend for great distances; a freshwater lake generally does not.)

Motivate

Demonstration — BASIC

No Barriers Demonstrate to students that the oceans are truly continuous by having them look at a globe. Ask them to trace sea routes from Florida to a variety of world destinations. **LS** Visual

What You Will Learn

● Describe the global pattern of ocean currents.

● Describe how thermal energy is transferred globally and locally by ocean water.

● Explain how groundwater is stored in aquifers underground.

● Explain why life on Earth is dependent on energy from the sun.

● Describe how energy in the biosphere is cycled by decomposition.

Vocabulary

surface current
deep current
aquifer

READING STRATEGY

Discussion Read this section silently. Write down questions that you have about this section. Discuss your questions in a small group.

The Hydrosphere and Biosphere

"Water, water, everywhere." You have probably heard this expression before, but do you realize how great the amount of water on Earth really is?

Earth's hydrosphere covers 71% of Earth's surface. It includes the water that is visible in the oceans, lakes, rivers, glaciers, and polar ice caps. However, the hydrosphere also includes clouds, rain, and snow in the atmosphere and water in the pores of underground rocks.

The Global Ocean

The global ocean, a portion of which is shown in **Figure 1,** is the largest reservoir of water on Earth. The global ocean contains more than 97% of all water on Earth and covers a surface area of approximately 335 million square kilometers.

As you know, the water in the global ocean is salty. If you evaporate a 1,000 g sample of ocean water, you are left with 35 g of salts. For this reason, ocean water is denser than fresh water. The majority of these salts are table salt, which is made up of the elements sodium and chlorine.

The temperature of surface ocean water varies from warm at the equator to near freezing at the poles. Ocean water temperature also decreases with depth. The surface water located in the top 100 to 200 m of the ocean is much warmer than deeper water.

Figure 1 *In this satellite view of Earth, the Florida Peninsula separates the Gulf of Mexico (above) from the Atlantic Ocean (below).*

CHAPTER RESOURCES

Chapter Resource File

 • Directed Reading A **BASIC**
• Directed Reading B **SPECIAL NEEDS**

Technology

 Transparencies
• Bellringer
• E109 The Ocean Conveyor Belt

 One-Stop Planner CD-ROM
• Lesson Plan (also in print)

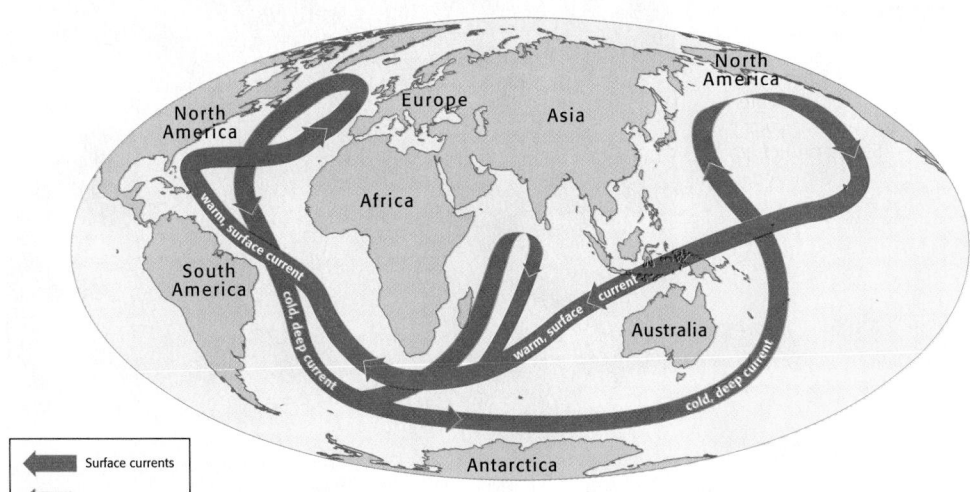

North America

Europe

Asia

North America

Africa

South America

Australia

Antarctica

Surface currents

Deep currents

Figure 2 *The map shows the flow directions of ocean currents—the ocean conveyor belt. Warm-water currents are shown as red arrows; cold-water currents are shown as blue arrows.*

Ocean Currents

Ocean water contains streamlike movements of water called *ocean currents.* Ocean currents are either surface currents or deep currents. Both types of currents are part of the global pattern of ocean currents known as the *ocean conveyor belt.*

Surface Currents

The surface currents of the global ocean are shown above in **Figure 2. Surface currents** are horizontal, streamlike movements of water that occur at or near the surface of the ocean. Surface currents are driven mainly by winds. They can reach depths of several hundred meters and lengths of several thousand kilometers, and they can travel across oceans.

Deep Currents

Deep currents, also shown in **Figure 2,** are streamlike movements of water that are located far below the ocean surface. Because deep currents are located near the ocean bottom, they are not controlled by the wind. Instead, these currents result when cold and, therefore, dense surface water sinks and flows along the bottom of the ocean. As shown in **Figure 2,** deep currents flow from the North Atlantic Ocean to Antarctica and then into the Pacific Ocean. Bottom water then flows northward toward Alaska, where the water rises to the surface again. This journey takes more than a thousand years.

✓ Reading Check Explain how ocean currents form the global pattern known as the *ocean conveyor belt.* (*See the Appendix for answers to Reading Checks.*)

surface current a horizontal movement of ocean water that is caused by wind and that occurs at or near the ocean's surface

deep current a streamlike movement of ocean water far below the surface

Teach

CONNECTION to Math ——— GENERAL

Gulf Stream Travel At the end of August 2004, the Gulf Stream had a typical velocity of between 0.4 and 1 m/s as its currents traveled along the Atlantic Coast. Calculate how many hours it would take one portion of the current to travel from West Palm Beach, Florida to Jacksonville (about 447 km), if its velocity were 0.6 m/s. (447 km x 1000 m/km = 447,000 m ÷ 0.6 m/s = 745,000 s ÷ 3600 s/hr = about 207 hours) **LS** Logical

Demonstration ——— GENERAL

Showing Currents Fill a clear pie plate with cold water. Sprinkle a leafy herb, such as basil, on the top of the water. Place some rocks in the plate to represent landmasses. Tell students that this model represents the world and its oceans. Have students blow on the water to simulate surface currents, and discuss how the basil moves. Gently rock the plate to simulate currents affected by the spinning of Earth. Then, fill a measuring cup with very warm water, and slowly pour some of this water into the pie plate to try to simulate convection currents in the ocean. Again, have students observe and discuss what happens to the basil. **LS** Visual

Answer to Reading Check

Surface currents and deep currents form the pattern known as the ocean conveyor belt because they transport warm and cold water for thousands of miles throughout the global ocean.

Discussion — GENERAL

Local Currents Have students study the figures showing ocean currents on both this page and the previous page. Then, lead a discussion about which surface currents have the greatest effect on the United States, and how these currents influence U.S. climate. **LS** Verbal

CONNECTION to
Real Life — GENERAL

Ocean Monitoring Even though the ocean and its currents have a profound effect on weather patterns and climate, few systems are in place for continuous monitoring of ocean characteristics. Scientists in Maine have recognized the potential benefits of continuous monitoring and are working on coordinating a system of buoys, satellites, and land-based radar to record hourly current direction, temperature, salinity, turbidity, dissolved oxygen, wave characteristics, wind information, and surface weather (such as temperature and fog) in the Gulf of Maine. This project, called *GoMOOS*, serves as a pilot project for a national ocean monitoring system. From GoMOOS, scientists hope to gather information that can aid search-and-rescue missions, provide critical information to fishermen and boaters, and provide an understanding of how changes in current patterns can affect fisheries and global climate change. Have interested students look at the GoMOOS Web site for more information. **LS** Visual

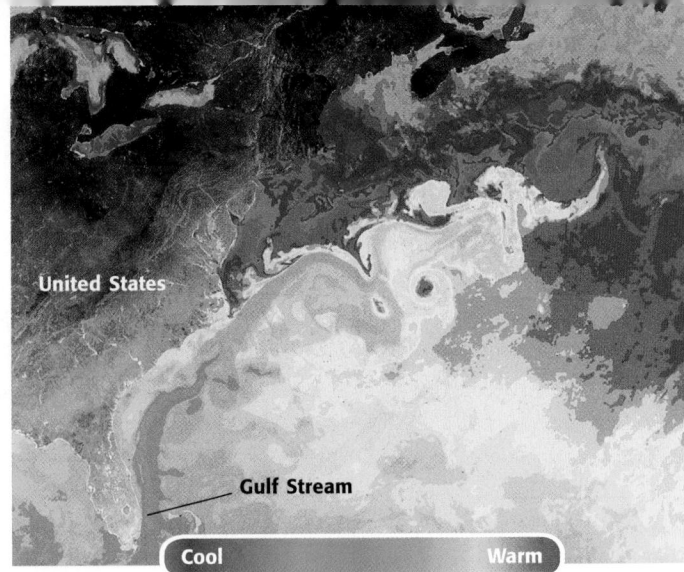

Figure 3 *The Gulf Stream moves warm, equatorial water north along the eastern coast of the United States to higher latitudes.*

United States

Gulf Stream

Cool　　　　　　　　Warm

SCHOOL to HOME

Comparing Temperature
With a parent or guardian, check your local newspaper for the high and low temperatures in your town on a specific date. Check the same temperatures for another town that is located at the same or a similar latitude. Try to choose a town that is located closer to or farther from the ocean than the town in which you live. Are the temperatures in your town higher or lower than those of the other town? Do the temperatures of the town located nearer to the ocean appear to be influenced by the moderating effect of the ocean?

A Global Temperature Regulator

The global ocean is a reservoir for thermal energy from the sun. Because the global ocean covers such a large area of the surface of Earth, the global ocean absorbs much of the 45% of solar energy that reaches Earth.

Ocean water warms as it absorbs thermal energy near the equator. As the surface currents flow, this energy is transferred to midlatitudes. **Figure 3** shows how a surface current called the *Gulf Stream* transports warm, equatorial water northward. As a result of this thermal energy transfer by the Gulf Stream, Florida and even the British Isles are several degrees warmer than are other coastal areas at similar latitudes.

The transfer of thermal energy by flowing water is much more efficient than the transfer of thermal energy stored on land. The reason for this difference lies in the fact that thermal energy from the land is moved by wind. Unlike ocean water, wind does not distribute thermal energy evenly over Earth's surface.

Local Climate

Ocean water warms and cools more slowly than the land nearby. Therefore, the ocean can keep the summer temperatures of land near the water cooler. It can also make winter temperatures warmer. Coastal areas can be many degrees warmer or cooler than areas that are located 30 or more kilometers inland.

✓ **Reading Check** Explain how heat from the ocean can affect temperatures on land.

Research — GENERAL

El Niño Ask students to research how an El Niño or La Niña event can alter global weather patterns. Have them create a research report or poster that summarizes the worldwide effects of an El Niño or La Niña event that occurred in the last 10 years. **LS** Intrapersonal

Answer to Reading Check

The ocean can keep temperatures in coastal areas cooler during the summer and warmer during the winter.

Fresh Water

Only 2.8% of all the water on Earth is fresh water. Fresh water occurs as polar ice caps, glaciers, lakes, rivers, and streams. Polar ice caps and glaciers contain about 77% of Earth's fresh water. Lakes, such as the five Great Lakes of North America, are another reservoir of fresh water. Surprisingly, all lakes account for only about 0.003% of fresh water. Rivers and streams compose another 0.00004% of fresh water.

In Florida, much of the surface fresh water is found in the Everglades. The Everglades is a giant, slow-moving wetland that flows south from Lake Okeechobee to Florida Bay. A small portion of the Everglades is shown in **Figure 4**.

Groundwater

Groundwater is surface water that has seeped into the ground over time. Below ground, groundwater is stored in microscopic cracks in rocks and in the pores between rock grains. Although we cannot see this groundwater, it represents 22% of the fresh water on Earth.

Bodies of rock below the ground that contain groundwater are called **aquifers.** Groundwater aquifers that occur in the continental United States are shown on the map in **Figure 5.** The groundwater from aquifers is made available for human use by pumping from wells. Groundwater that is pumped from aquifers must be replaced. The process by which groundwater seeps back into aquifers from Earth's surface is called *recharge*. Recharge is part of Earth's groundwater cycling process.

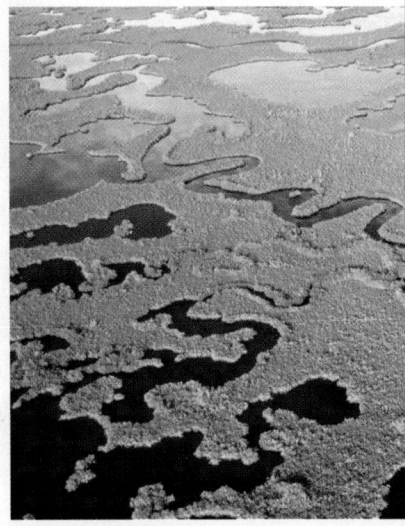

Figure 4 *The wetlands known as the Everglades cover more than 19,000 km² of South Florida.*

aquifer a body of rock or sediment that stores groundwater and allows the flow of groundwater

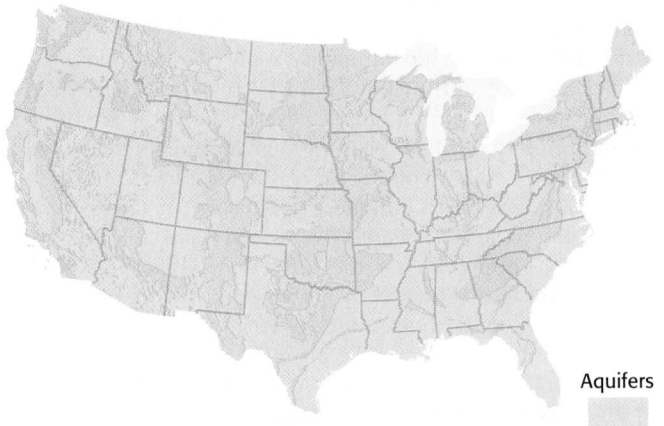

Aquifers

Figure 5 *The continental United States has extensive groundwater aquifers. The water from these aquifers has many agricultural, industrial, and municipal uses.*

Interactions and Cycling

Students should understand that interactions between living and nonliving components of a system result in the flow of energy and cycling of nutrients within the system. Have students explain how the following organisms and nonliving components could interact within the specified system.

- the sun and shrimp in a coastal seagrass habitat (The sun warms ocean water and creates currents that deliver nutrients to the shrimp.)

- phosphorus and sugar cane in an agricultural field (Phosphorus is a nutrient that helps sugar cane to grow.) Logical

Quiz — GENERAL

In a typical freshwater ecosystem, energy would flow from

A. aquatic plants to fish and then to algae.

B. wading birds to fish and then to plants.

C. algae to fish and then to wading birds.

D. bacteria to algae and then to fish.

Alternative Assessment — GENERAL

Coastal Energy Have students research the components of a typical coastal ecosystem. Then, have each student create a poster that illustrates how energy flows through that system. LS Visual

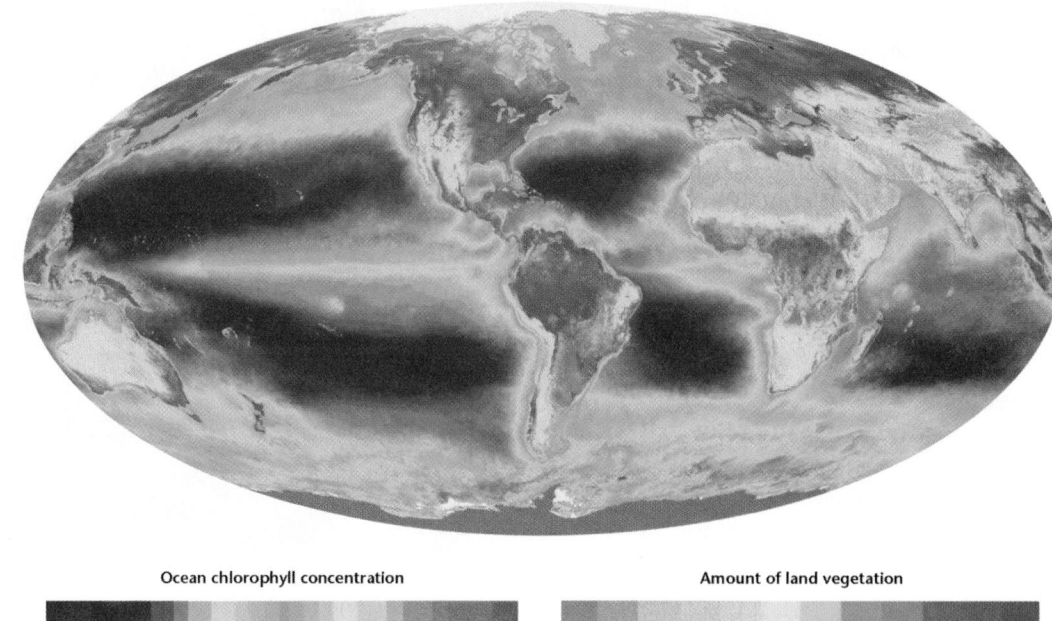

Ocean chlorophyll concentration   Low   High

Amount of land vegetation   Low   High

Figure 6 *The colors in this image of Earth indicate the concentrations of plant life in the oceans and on land.*

The Biosphere

Life on Earth is found in a variety of habitats. These habitats are collectively called *the biosphere.* The biosphere includes the part of the atmosphere that extends from the surface of Earth to approximately 11 km above Earth's surface. Most of the hydrosphere is also part of the biosphere. Most life on Earth is dependent on a continuous supply of energy from the sun. But some organisms have even been found living deep in Earth's crust. This finding is an example of how scientists are continuing to discover life in new environments today and expanding the known boundaries of the biosphere.

The biosphere has a unique combination of factors that organisms need for life. Liquid water and a suitable habitat are extremely important for the survival of organisms. Most organisms are also restricted to environments with moderate temperatures. A continuous source of energy is equally important for organisms. For example, organisms such as plants and algae use sunlight to produce food. As shown in **Figure 6,** plants and algae are found both in the oceans and on land. Other organisms get their food from consuming plants and algae.

✓ *Reading Check* Explain why organisms are dependent on a continuous supply of energy from the sun.

Answer to Reading Check

Animals depend on a continuous supply of energy from the sun in order to obtain the food they need.

Energy Flow in the Biosphere

What happens to plants and animals when they die? Dead organisms are consumed by decomposers, such as bacteria and insects. By breaking down dead plant and animal matter, decomposers obtain the energy that they need to live. The process of decomposition releases carbon dioxide and water. Some of this carbon dioxide will be used by plants during photosynthesis to make sugars. During decomposition, some bacteria release nitrogen into the soil in a form that plants can use. Plants use this form of nitrogen in many activities, such as making new proteins.

✓ Reading Check Explain how energy in the biosphere is cycled by the process of decomposition.

SECTION Review

Summary

- The largest reservoir of water on Earth is the global ocean.
- Ocean currents form a global pattern known as the ocean conveyor belt.
- Thermal energy is transferred both globally and locally by ocean water.
- Fresh water represents 2.8% of all water on Earth. Groundwater for human use is located underground in aquifers.
- The biosphere is the part of Earth where all life is found. Energy in the biosphere is cycled by the process of decomposition.

Using Key Terms

1. Write an original definition for *surface current* and *deep current*.

Understanding Key Ideas

2. Describe the global pattern of ocean currents.

3. Describe how thermal energy is transferred globally and locally by ocean currents.

4. Explain how groundwater is stored underground in aquifers.

5. Explain the importance of energy from the sun to life on Earth.

6. Explain how decomposers recycle energy in the biosphere.

Math Skills

7. Groundwater flows at a speed of 4km/h. At this rate, how long will it take water to flow 10km?

Critical Thinking

8. **Analyzing Processes** Why can the process of aquifer recharge be considered a natural event that occurs in a pattern?

9. **Analyzing Ideas** Identify a new environment on Earth whose discovery would cause scientists to expand the known boundaries of the biosphere. Explain.

10. **Identifing Relationships** Explain how urban growth might affect the recharge of an area's groundwater.

For a variety of links related to this chapter, go to www.scilinks.org

Topic: Water; Biosphere
SciLinks code: HSM1624; HSM0162

Answer to Reading Check

When plants and animals die, decomposers get their energy from converting the remains into carbon dioxide and water. Plants use both of these chemicals during photosynthesis, which is how plants make their energy.

CHAPTER RESOURCES

Chapter Resource File

- **Section Quiz** GENERAL
- **Section Review** GENERAL
- **Vocabulary and Section Summary** GENERAL

Technology

Transparencies
- E110 The Biosphere

Focus

Overview

Matter is continuously cycled through the rock, water, carbon, and nitrogen cycles.

 **Bellringer**

Divide the class into small groups, and give each group a sedimentary rock. Ask the groups to find their rock in the rock cycle diagram and to predict what would happen if the rock was subjected to heat and pressure. (It would become metamorphic rock.)

Motivate

Demonstration— GENERAL

Illustrating the Rock Cycle

Cut a layered candy bar so the class can see its layers. Ask students to indicate which type of rock the candy bar most resembles. (sedimentary) Now place a paper towel on top of the candy bar, and a book or piece of wood over the paper towel. Apply steady downward pressure to the bar, until it flattens. Ask students to name the type of rock the candy bar now most resembles. (metamorphic) Place the candy bar in a glass container, and heat the container, using a hot plate, until the chocolate melts. Pour the chocolate onto a plate, and allow it to cool. Ask students to name the type of rock the cooled chocolate most resembles. (igneous) **LS** Visual

What You Will Learn

- Explain how rock is continuously recycled in the rock cycle.
- Identify the steps in the water cycle.
- Describe how carbon cycles through the carbon cycle.
- Describe how nitrogen cycles through the nitrogen cycle.

Vocabulary

rock cycle   carbon cycle
water cycle   nitrogen cycle

READING STRATEGY

Prediction Guide Before reading this section, write the title of each heading in this section. Next, under each heading, write what you think you will learn.

The Cycling of Matter

Have you ever asked yourself, Why is it that I always have water to drink and air to breathe? Why don't we run out of resources?

The answer is that matter on Earth is recycled. Earth is a closed system into which very little new matter enters. So, existing matter must cycle continuously for this planet to support life. Water, carbon, nitrogen, and even rocks move through cycles. If these materials did not cycle, Earth could not support life.

The Rock Cycle

Rocks in Earth's crust are classified into three types: sedimentary, metamorphic, and igneous. Different geologic processes can change each of these rock types into one of the three types of rocks. This cycle, in which rock is changed by geologic processes into different types of rock, is called the **rock cycle.** As shown in **Figure 1,** rock may cycle through the rock cycle in various ways. As a rock moves through the rock cycle, heat, pressure, weathering, erosion, melting, cooling, or a combination of these variables can change a rock's identity. The process of change a rock goes through next depends on where the rock is in the rock cycle.

Figure 1 The Rock Cycle

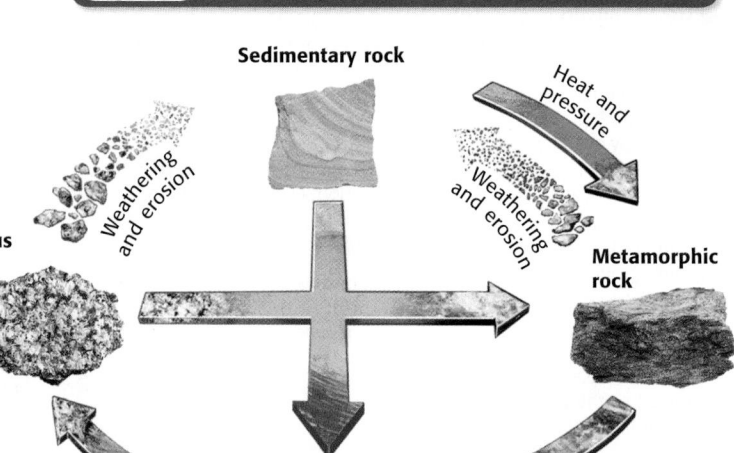

Sedimentary rock
Heat and pressure
Weathering and erosion
Igneous rock
Weathering and erosion
Metamorphic rock
Cooling
Melting
Magma

CHAPTER RESOURCES

Chapter Resource File

- **Directed Reading A** BASIC
- **Directed Reading B** SPECIAL NEEDS

Technology

Transparencies
- Bellringer

One-Stop Planner CD-ROM
- Lesson Plan (also in print)

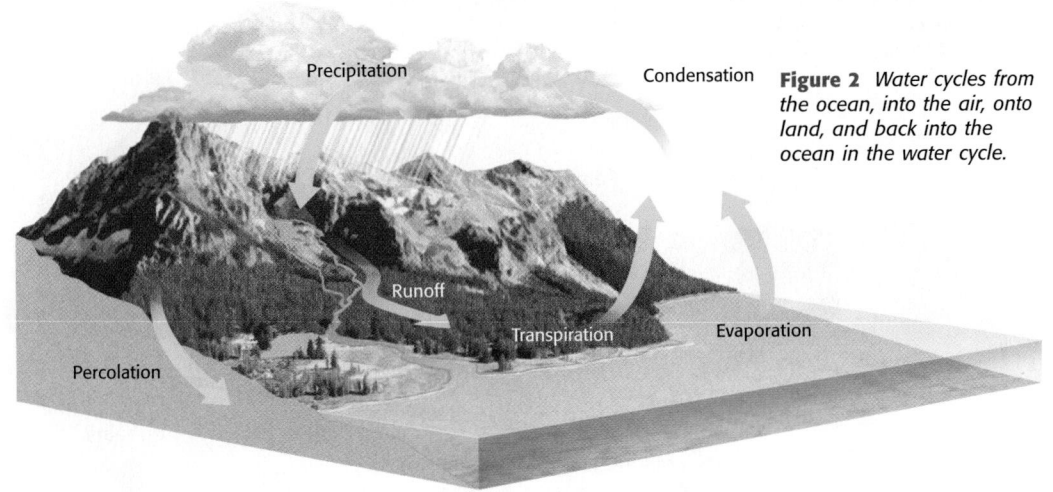

Precipitation

Condensation

Runoff

Transpiration

Evaporation

Percolation

Figure 2 *Water cycles from the ocean, into the air, onto land, and back into the ocean in the water cycle.*

The Water Cycle

Water moves continuously from the ocean, to the atmosphere, to the land, and back to the ocean. This process is called the **water cycle,** and is shown in **Figure 2.**

Steps in the water cycle include evaporation, transpiration, condensation, precipitation, runoff, and percolation. *Evaporation* occurs when liquid water in the ocean and on Earth's surface changes into water vapor, a gas. Water vapor is also released into the air through pores, called *stomata*, on the leaves of plants. This process is known as *transpiration*. After water vapor is released, it rises into the atmosphere. There, it cools and turns into liquid water droplets. This change in water from a gas to a liquid is called *condensation*. When water droplets become heavy enough, gravity causes them to fall back to Earth as *precipitation*. Rain, snow, and hail are all forms of precipitation. The majority of precipitation never reaches the land surface. It falls directly into the ocean.

Precipitation that does reach the land surface may fill lakes, streams, and rivers and eventually return to the ocean. This movement of water over the land surface is called *runoff*. Water moves across Earth's land surface from higher to lower elevations under the influence of gravity.

Some water does not run off the land surface. Gravity may move the water downward through spaces in rock or soil to become groundwater. This downward movement of groundwater is called *percolation*.

✔ **Reading Check** Describe the process by which water moves through the water cycle. (*See the Appendix for answers to Reading Checks.*)

rock cycle the series of processes in which a rock forms, changes from one type to another, is destroyed, and forms again by geologic processes

water cycle the continuous movement of water between the atmosphere, the land, and the oceans

Is That a Fact!
Some trees and shrubs are able to fix nitrogen from the atmosphere. One study showed that red alder trees fixed 320 kg of atmospheric nitrogen per hectare each year. That's about a third of a ton of nitrogen!

Earth System Interactions

Students should understand that conditions in each of Earth's systems can affect the conditions that exist in the other systems. Have students name the two systems interacting in each example:

- Energy from the sun causes ocean currents. (atmosphere, hydrosphere)
- Birds migrate north in the spring. (atmosphere, biosphere)
- Pressure from layers of sediment compresses together the shells of clams and mollusks. (biosphere, geosphere)
   Logical

Quiz ——— GENERAL

In the nitrogen cycle, bacteria in nitrogen-fixing plants convert atmospheric nitrogen to which of the following gases?

A. O_2

B. N_2

C. nitrous oxide

D. ammonia

Alternative Assessment ——— GENERAL

A Patch of Soil Have students research the properties of soil. You may also want to collect soil and encourage students to examine it under a microscope. Then, ask them to create a poster or model showing how all of Earth's systems influence soil's biotic and mineral components. **LS** Logical

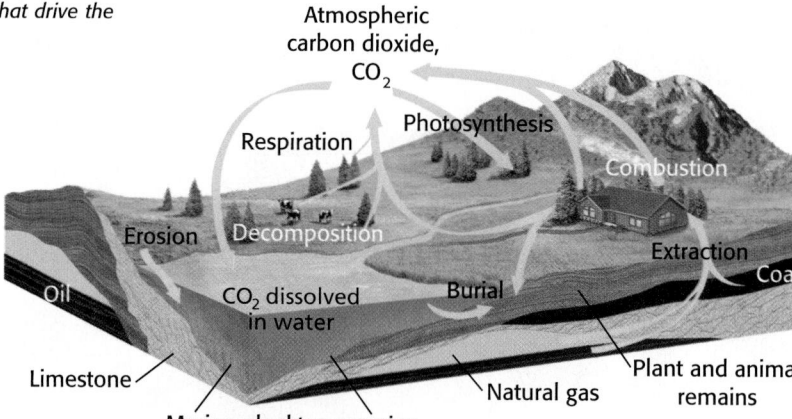

Figure 3 *Photosynthesis, respiration, combustion, and decomposition are important processes that drive the carbon cycle.*

CONNECTION TO Biology

Deep-Sea Dining Some deep-sea tube worms have bacteria living inside them. These bacteria use gases to produce nutrition in the form of organic carbon. Any extra nutrition is transferred to the tube worms. This relationship that is beneficial to the tube worm and the bacteria is called *mutualism*. Research other organisms that benefit from mutualism, and write a report on what you have learned.

The Carbon Cycle

With the exception of water molecules, the most common molecules in organisms are molecules that contain carbon. The cycling of carbon between the atmosphere, land, water, and organisms is called the **carbon cycle.**

Photosynthesis plays a key role in the carbon cycle. During the process of photosynthesis, plants use sunlight, atmospheric carbon dioxide, and water to make sugars for nutrition. Most organisms obtain the carbon and the energy they need by consuming plants or by consuming other organisms. When organisms break down sugar molecules to release energy, carbon is returned to the environment as carbon dioxide. This process, called *respiration,* occurs in the cells of organisms. The byproducts of respiration are carbon dioxide and water. These byproducts can be reused in photosynthesis.

Carbon dioxide is also released into the environment during the process of decomposition. *Decomposition* occurs when organisms such as bacteria, fungi, or insects break down organic matter into simple molecules. When partially decomposed organic matter is deeply buried and heated, it is chemically transformed over millions of years into fuels, such as coal, gas, and oil. When humans burn these fuels, carbon returns to the atmosphere as carbon dioxide. This is an example of *combustion,* the process by which substances are burned to release energy.

✓ *Reading Check* **Explain why the carbon cycle is important to Earth's organisms.**

Answer to Reading Check

The carbon cycle is important to Earth's organisms because carbon is one of the most common molecules in organisms.

The Nitrogen Cycle

The movement of nitrogen between the environment and organisms is called the **nitrogen cycle,** which is shown in **Figure 4.** Certain bacteria in soil change atmospheric nitrogen into forms of nitrogen that plants can use. Other organisms obtain the nitrogen they need from plants. When organisms die, decomposers release this nitrogen back into the soil. Plants then take up some of this nitrogen. Some bacteria in soil change this nitrogen into atmospheric nitrogen, which returns to the atmosphere.

carbon cycle the movement of carbon from the nonliving environment into living things and back

nitrogen cycle the process in which nitrogen circulates among the air, soil, water, plants, and animals in an ecosystem

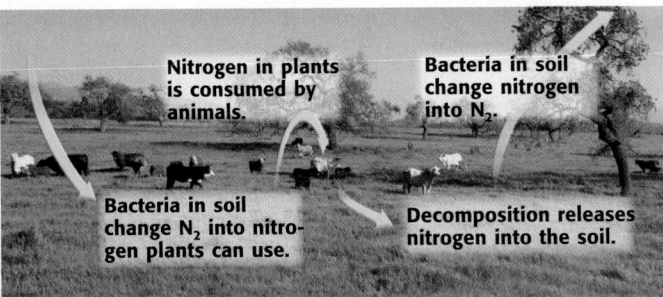

Nitrogen in plants is consumed by animals.

Bacteria in soil change nitrogen into N₂.

Bacteria in soil change N₂ into nitrogen plants can use.

Decomposition releases nitrogen into the soil.

Figure 4 *The nitrogen cycle includes bacteria, plants, and animals.*

5. Some bacteria in the soil change atmospheric nitrogen into a form plants can use. Animals obtain the nitrogen they need by eating plants. When plants and animals die, decomposers release nitrogen back into the soil. Some bacteria change this nitrogen into atmospheric nitrogen, which is returned to the atmosphere.

6. Gravity causes water droplets to fall to Earth as precipitation. Gravity also causes water to percolate into the ground or to flow across Earth's surface from higher to lower elevations.

7. During the process of photosynthesis, plants use atmospheric carbon dioxide to make sugars for nutrition.

SECTION Review

Summary

- The process in which a rock forms, changes from one type to another, is destroyed, and forms again by geologic processes is called the *rock cycle.*

- In the water cycle, water moves continuously from the ocean, to the atmosphere, to land, and back to the ocean.

- Substances that are necessary for life are continuously cycled in the carbon cycle and nitrogen cycle.

Using Key Terms

1. Use *rock cycle, water cycle, carbon cycle,* and *nitrogen cycle* in the same sentence.

Understanding Key Ideas

2. Explain how rock is continuously recycled in the rock cycle.

3. Identify the steps in the water cycle.

4. Describe how carbon cycles through the carbon cycle.

5. Describe how nitrogen cycles through the nitrogen cycle.

Critical Thinking

6. **Analyzing Ideas** What is the importance of gravity in the movement of water in the water cycle?

7. **Identifing Relationships** The processes of photosynthesis, respiration, combustion, and decomposition are all part of the carbon cycle. In which process do organisms take up carbon? Explain.

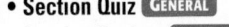

For a variety of links related to this chapter, go to www.scilinks.org

Topic: Water Cycle, Cycles of Matter
SciLinks code: HSM1626; HSM0303

Answers to Section Review

1. Matter continuously cycles through the rock cycle, water cycle, carbon cycle, and nitrogen cycle.

2. In the rock cycle, rock is continuously changed by different processes into different types of rocks.

3. The steps in the water cycle include evaporation, transpiration, condensation, precipitation, percolation, and runoff.

4. Plants use atmospheric carbon dioxide to make sugars for nutrition. Animals obtain the carbon they need by eating other organisms. Through respiration, many organisms release carbon dioxide back into the environment. Decomposers, organisms that break down organic matter into simple molecules, can also release carbon dioxide back into the environment.

Metamorphic Mash
Teacher's Notes

Time Required
One 45-minute class period

Lab Ratings

Teacher Prep ⚗
Student Set-Up ⚗⚗
Concept Level ⚗⚗
Clean Up ⚗⚗

MATERIALS
The materials listed on the student page are enough for 1 student.

Safety Caution
Remind students to review all safety cautions and icons before beginning this lab activity.

Procedure
5. The sequins should be lying in a random pattern. Any layering is the result of rolling the ball.

8. The sequins are all horizontal.

Analyze the Results
1. It represents the pressure that creates metamorphic rock.

2. Before the ball was flattened, the sequins were lying in a random pattern. Once the ball was flattened, they lined up perpendicular to the pressure.

Model-Making Lab

Metamorphic Mash

Metamorphism is a complex process that takes place deep within the Earth, where the temperature and pressure would turn a human into a crispy pancake. The effects of this extreme temperature and pressure are obvious in some metamorphic rocks. One of these effects is the reorganization of mineral grains within the rock. This reorganization of mineral grains can result in a metamorphic rock that has a foliated texture. A foliated metamorphic rock has its mineral grains arranged in planes or bands. Examples of foliated metamorphic rocks are slate, phyllite, schist, and gneiss. In this activity, you will investigate the process of metamorphism without being charred, flattened, or buried.

OBJECTIVES

Model the process of metamorphism.

Describe how the process of metamorphism can reorganize the mineral grains within a rock.

MATERIALS

- cardboard (or plywood), very stiff, small pieces
- clay, modeling
- knife, plastic
- sequins (or other small flat objects)

SAFETY

Procedure

1. Flatten the clay into a layer about 1 cm thick.

2. Sprinkle the surface of the clay with sequins.

3. Roll the corners of the clay toward the middle to form a neat ball.

4. Carefully use the plastic knife to cut the ball in half.

5. On a separate sheet of paper, describe the position and location of the sequins inside the ball that you cut in half.

6. Put the ball back together, and use the sheets of cardboard or plywood to flatten the ball until it is a slab that is about 2 cm thick.

7. Using the plastic knife, slice open the slab of clay in several places.

8. Describe the position and location of the sequins in the slab.

Analyze the Results

1. What physical process does flattening the ball represent?

2. Describe any changes in the position and location of the sequins that occurred as the clay ball was flattened into a slab.

 Holt Lab Generator CD-ROM

Search for any lab by topic, standard, difficulty level, or time. Edit any lab to fit your needs, or create your own labs. Use the Lab Materials QuickList software to customize your lab materials list.

CLASSROOM TESTED & APPROVED

Dwight Patton
Carrol T. Welch Middle School
Horizon City, Texas

Draw Conclusions

Draw Conclusions

3 How are the sequins oriented in relation to the force you put on the ball to flatten it?

4 How does the orientation of the sequins in your clay ball model the reorganization of mineral grains in a metamorphic rock with a foliated texture? Explain your answer.

5 Do you think the orientation of the mineral grains in a foliated metamorphic rock tells you anything about the rock? (Think in terms of temperature and pressure.) Defend your answer.

Applying Your Data

Suppose that you find a foliated metamorphic rock that has grains running in two distinct directions. Use what you have learned in this activity to offer a possible explanation for this observation.

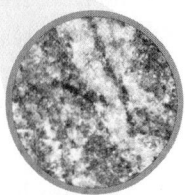

Foliation

Draw Conclusions

3. The sequins are aligned perpendicular to the force.

4. The orientation of the sequins models the alignment of mineral grains in a foliated metamorphic rock in planes and bands.

5. Because the grains line up at right angles to the pressure, they are perpendicular to the strongest stress.

Applying Your Data

Answers may vary. Sample answer: Two pressures acting on the rock at different times must have pushed on the rock in different directions.

CHAPTER RESOURCES

Chapter Resource File

- **Datasheet for Chapter Lab**
- **Lab Notes and Answers**

- Crystal Growth

CHAPTER RESOURCES

Workbooks

Whiz-Bang Demonstrations BASIC
- It's Raining Again
- Spin Cycle

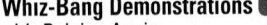
Labs You Can Eat GENERAL
- Famous Rock Groups
- Rescue Near the Center of the Earth

Ecolabs & Field Activities BASIC
- That Greenhouse Effect

Assignment Guide

SECTION	QUESTIONS
1	3, 8, 15, 19, 22
2	4, 9–10, 14, 16, 23–24
3	2, 7, 11, 17–18, 20–21
4	5, 6, 12–13
2 and 3	1

ANSWERS

Using Key Terms

1. The atmosphere is the mixture of gases that surrounds Earth. The hydrosphere is that portion of Earth that is water.

2. A deep current is a stream-like movement of cold ocean water that is located far below the ocean surface. A surface current is a horizontal, stream-like movement of water that occurs at or near the surface of the ocean.

3. The crust is the thin, outer-most compositional layer of Earth. The mantle is the thick, denser compositional layer of Earth below the crust.

4. Convection is the transfer of thermal energy by the circulation or movement of a gas or a liquid. Conduction is the transfer of energy as heat through a material from a hotter to colder area.

5. The rock cycle is the series of processes in which rock forms, changes from one type to another, is destroyed, and forms again by geologic processes. The water cycle is the continuous movement of water between the atmosphere, the land, and the oceans.

6. The carbon cycle is the cycling of carbon between the atmosphere, land, water, and organisms. The nitrogen cycle is the movement of nitrogen between the environment and organisms.

Understanding Key Ideas

7. d	**11.** b
8. c	**12.** c
9. a	**13.** d
10. b	**14.** a

15. Wind and moving water are continuously transporting sediment from one place to another. In doing so, wind and water are continuously reshaping Earth's surface.

16. The greenhouse effect makes life on Earth possible because greenhouse gases in the atmosphere absorb infrared energy reradiated from Earth's surface and retain it as thermal energy in the atmosphere. This thermal energy is conducted and convected through Earth's atmosphere, warming the atmosphere.

USING KEY TERMS

For each pair of terms, explain how the meanings of the terms differ.

1. *atmosphere* and *hydrosphere*
2. *deep current* and *surface current*
3. *crust* and *mantle*
4. *convection* and *conduction*
5. *rock cycle* and *water cycle*
6. *carbon cycle* and *nitrogen cycle*

UNDERSTANDING KEY IDEAS

Multiple Choice

7. The sphere of Earth in which all life is contained is called the
   a. geosphere.
   b. atmosphere.
   c. hydrosphere.
   d. biosphere.

8. At which rate do tectonic plates move around Earth's surface?
   a. meters per year
   b. kilometers per year
   c. centimeters per year
   d. micrometers per year

9. Which of the following types of radiant energy that comes from the sun can damage an organism's DNA?
   a. UV radiation
   b. visible light
   c. infrared radiaton
   d. microwaves

10. How is most thermal energy in the atmosphere transferred?
    a. by radiation
    b. by convection
    c. by conduction
    d. by diffusion

11. Which of the following is a property of deep currents?
    a. Deep currents contain warm water.
    b. Deep currents flow along the ocean bottom.
    c. Deep currents are controlled by the wind.
    d. Deep currents form when cold water rises to the ocean surfaces.

12. Which of the following processes in the water cycle takes place in the geosphere?
    a. condensation
    b. evaporation
    c. percolation
    d. precipitation

13. In which cycle does decomposition release carbon dioxide into the atmosphere?
    a. the water cycle
    b. the nitrogen cycle
    c. the rock cycle
    d. the carbon cycle

14. Only a small fraction of the energy radiated by the sun reaches Earth. What happens to the majority of the sun's energy that reaches Earth?
    a. It is absorbed by the land and ocean.
    b. It is reflected by clouds and air.
    c. It is reflected by Earth's surface.
    d. It is absorbed by ozone, clouds, and atmospheric gases.

Short Answer

15. Describe the way in which wind and moving water reshape Earth's surface.

16. Explain how the greenhouse effect makes life on Earth possible.

17 Describe the way in which thermal energy is transferred globally and locally by ocean water.

18 Explain why animals are dependent on a continuous supply of energy from the sun.

Math Skills

19 If the radius of Earth is 6,500 km and the radius of the core is 3,400 km, what percentage of Earth's radius does the core represent?

CRITICAL THINKING

20 **Concept Mapping** Use the following terms to create a concept map: *geosphere, crust, mantle, inner core, outer core, core, lithosphere, asthenosphere, mesosphere, compositional layer,* and *physical layer.*

21 **Analyzing Ideas** How do differences in density cause currents to flow both in the surface waters of the ocean and in the bottom waters of the ocean?

22 **Predicting Consequences** What might the consequences be for humans if groundwater is pumped from an aquifer at a much faster rate than the aquifer is recharging?

INTERPRETING GRAPHICS

The illustration below shows how temperature and pressure change with altitude in Earth's atmosphere. Use the illustration below to answer the questions that follow.

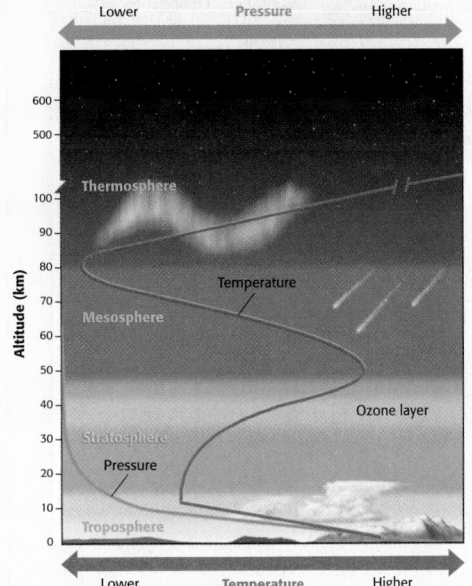

23 In which atmospheric layer is the temperature the coldest?

a. the troposphere

b. the stratosphere

c. the mesophere

d. the thermosphere

24 In which atmospheric layer is the pressure the highest?

a. the troposphere

b. the stratosphere

c. the mesophere

d. the thermosphere

17. Thermal energy is transferred globally by warm surface currents. Locally, the ocean keeps coastal areas cooler during the summer and warmer during the winter.

18. Animals are dependent upon a continuous supply of energy from the sun in order to obtain the food and, therefore, the energy they need.

19. 3,400 ÷ 6,500 × 100 = 52.3%

Critical Thinking

20. 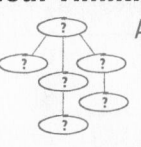 An answer to this exercise can be found at the end of this book.

21. Warm water is less dense than cold water is. Therefore, warm water flows at or near the surface of the ocean as surface currents. Cold water, being denser than warm water, sinks and flows along the bottom of the ocean as deep currents.

22. Answers may vary. Sample answer: If groundwater is being pumped from an aquifer faster than the aquifer is recharging, there would be more competition for the remaining water from industrial, agricultural, and municipal water consumers, and the price of water would become more expensive.

Interpreting Graphics

23. c

24. a

CHAPTER RESOURCES

Chapter Resource File

- **Chapter Review** GENERAL
- **Chapter Test A** GENERAL
- **Chapter Test B** ADVANCED
- **Chapter Test C** SPECIAL NEEDS
- **Vocabulary Activity** GENERAL

Workbooks

Study Guide
- Assessment resources are also available in Spanish and Haitian Creole.

Standardized Test Preparation

Teacher's Notes

To provide practice under more realistic conditions, give students 20 minutes to answer all of the questions in this Standardized Test Preparation.

Answer Key

Question	Answer
1	A
2	C
3	B
4	A
5	C
6	B
7	D
8	D
9	*
10	*

*See Test Doctor.

Multiple Choice

Use the illustration below to answer question 1.

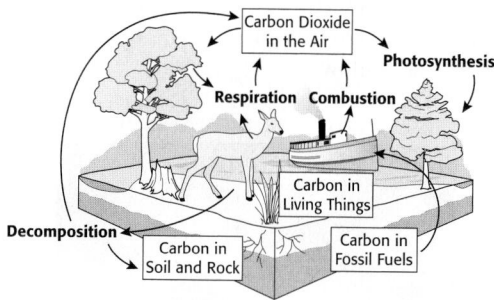

1. **The illustration above shows the carbon cycle. During the carbon cycle, some carbon is released into the atmosphere and some carbon is released into the soil. Which of the following processes is most involved in releasing carbon into the air?**

   A. combustion

   B. decomposition

   C. photosynthesis

   D. transpiration

2. **In which layer of the atmosphere do people live?**

   A. stratosphere

   B. mesosphere

   C. troposphere

   D. thermosphere

3. **Which of the following occurs as a result of the forces generated by plate motion at tectonic plate boundaries?**

   A. erosion

   B. volcanoes

   C. sediment deposition

   D. warm surface currents

4. **Thermal energy flows from hot areas to cold areas. By what process is air near the Earth's surface heated by the surface?**

   A. conduction

   B. convection

   C. diffusion

   D. radiation

5. **Ocean currents are streamlike movements of ocean water. Ocean currents can either be deep currents or surface currents. Which of the following is true of surface currents? They**

   A. contain dense water.

   B. are cold-water currents.

   C. reach depths of several hundred meters.

   D. flow from the North Atlantic Ocean to the Pacific Ocean.

 TEST DOCTOR

Question 1 A: Correct. B: During decomposition, organic material is broken down into simple molecules such as carbon by bacteria or fungi, releasing carbon back into the soil. C: Photosynthesis uses carbon dioxide and releases oxygen into the atmosphere. D: During transpiration, plants release water into the atmosphere. The process is not part of the carbon cycle; transpiration is part of the water cycle.

Question 2 A: The stratosphere is the layer immediately above the troposphere, which is the layer closest to Earth's surface. B: The mesosphere is the layer above the atmosphere. C: Correct. D: The thermosphere is the layer of the atmosphere that is farthest from the Earth's surface.

Question 3 A: Erosion results from the movement of ice, wind, or water. B: Correct. C: Sediment is deposited by moving ice, wind, or water. D: Warm ocean currents receive most of their heat from solar radiation, not from geothermal sources at the plate boundaries.

Use the illustration below to answer question 6.

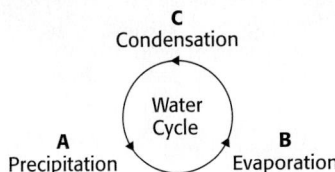

C
Condensation

Water
Cycle

A
Precipitation

B
Evaporation

6. The water cycle depicted above involves energy changes and the continuous movement of water between the ground and the atmosphere. Condensation primarily takes place

A. on land.

B. in the atmosphere.

C. in the oceans.

D. in the polar ice caps.

7. In the rock cycle, which type of rock is formed by heating and pressure?

A. igneous rock

B. sedimentary rock

C. magma

D. metamorphic rock

8. The four divisions of the Earth are the geosphere, the atmosphere, the hydrosphere, and the biosphere. Each sphere has a different composition and different energy relations. However, conditions in one of the Earth's spheres can influence the conditions in one or more of the other three spheres. Which of the following statements is an example of how conditions that exist in the atmosphere directly influence the conditions that exist in the biosphere?

A. Evaporation transfers ocean water to the atmosphere.

B. A volcanic eruption ejects ash and gas into the atmosphere.

C. Partially decomposed organic matter is buried and chemically transformed into fossil fuel over millions of years.

D. The ozone layer blocks much of the harmful ultraviolet radiation that would reach the Earth's surface.

Open Response

9. During the nitrogen cycle, nitrogen-fixing bacteria change nitrogen gas into a form of nitrogen that can be used by plants. Some pesticides that are used on soil can kill these helpful bacteria. How would the nitrogen cycle be affected if nitrogen-fixing bacteria were destroyed?

10. The ozone shield is a layer in the stratosphere. Why is it important to life on Earth?

Standardized Test Preparation

Question 8 A: This is an example of how conditions in the atmosphere influence conditions in the hydrosphere. B: This is an example of how conditions in the geosphere influence conditions in the atmosphere. C: This is an example of how conditions in the geosphere convert once-living organisms in the biosphere. D: Correct.

Question 9 Full-credit answers should include three of the following points:

- If nitrogen-fixing bacteria were destroyed, nitrogen gas would not be converted into nitrates, the form of nitrogen that plants can use.

- Plants would not be able to absorb nitrogen and consumers would not receive nitrogen by eating plants.

- Without nitrogen, plants and consumers would not be able to build proteins and DNA.

Question 10 Full-credit answers should include the following points:

- The ozone layer protects life from damage caused by UV radiation.

- The ozone layer absorbs around 95% to 99% of harmful UV radiation.

- UV radiation can damage an organism's DNA.

- UV radiation harms people by causing skin cancer, wrinkling the skin, and weakening the immune system.

Question 4 A: Correct. B, C, and D: Ninety-nine percent of the thermal energy in the surface of the Earth originates as electromagnetic radiation from the Sun. The surface heats the nearby air by conduction. Within the atmosphere, heat is transferred by convection through the continual rising of warm air and sinking of cool air. Diffusion is not involved in this heat transfer.

Question 5 A: Deep currents contain dense water. B: Deep currents are generally cold. C: Correct. D: Cold currents flow from the North Atlantic Ocean to the Pacific Ocean.

Question 6 A, C: Condensation is the change of water vapor into liquid water, whereas evaporation is the change of liquid water into water vapor. Evaporation, not condensation, occurs primarily on Earth's surface. B: Correct. D: Because the polar ice caps do not contain significant amounts of water vapor, very little condensation occurs there.

Question 7 A: Igneous rock is formed by the cooling of magma. B: Sedimentary rock is formed by deposition on Earth's surface. Pressure plays an important part in its formation, but heat is not required. C: Magma is molten rock in the interior of earth. D: Correct.

Science, Technology, and Society

Background

More than 40 years ago, two scientists named Fred Fisher and Fred Spiess were studying the behavior of sound waves underwater. They needed to study sound waves in a setting that was quieter and more stable than a traditional research ship. So, they created the *Floating Instrument Platform (FLIP)*. Since then, the physical behavior of ocean waves and currents has been studied extensively aboard *FLIP*. The platform is amazingly stable—according to one scientist aboard *FLIP* during a hurricane, the platform barely moved. *FLIP* is operated by the Scripps Institution of Oceanography.

Weird Science

Teaching Strategy- GENERAL

Reports of organisms falling with precipitation are not uncommon. Thousands of maggots fell in Acapulco in 1968. In 2000, a heavy rainstorm in the town of Great Yarmouth, located about half a mile from the east coast of England, dropped 2 in. fish with the rain. Have students research other instances of organisms falling with precipitation.

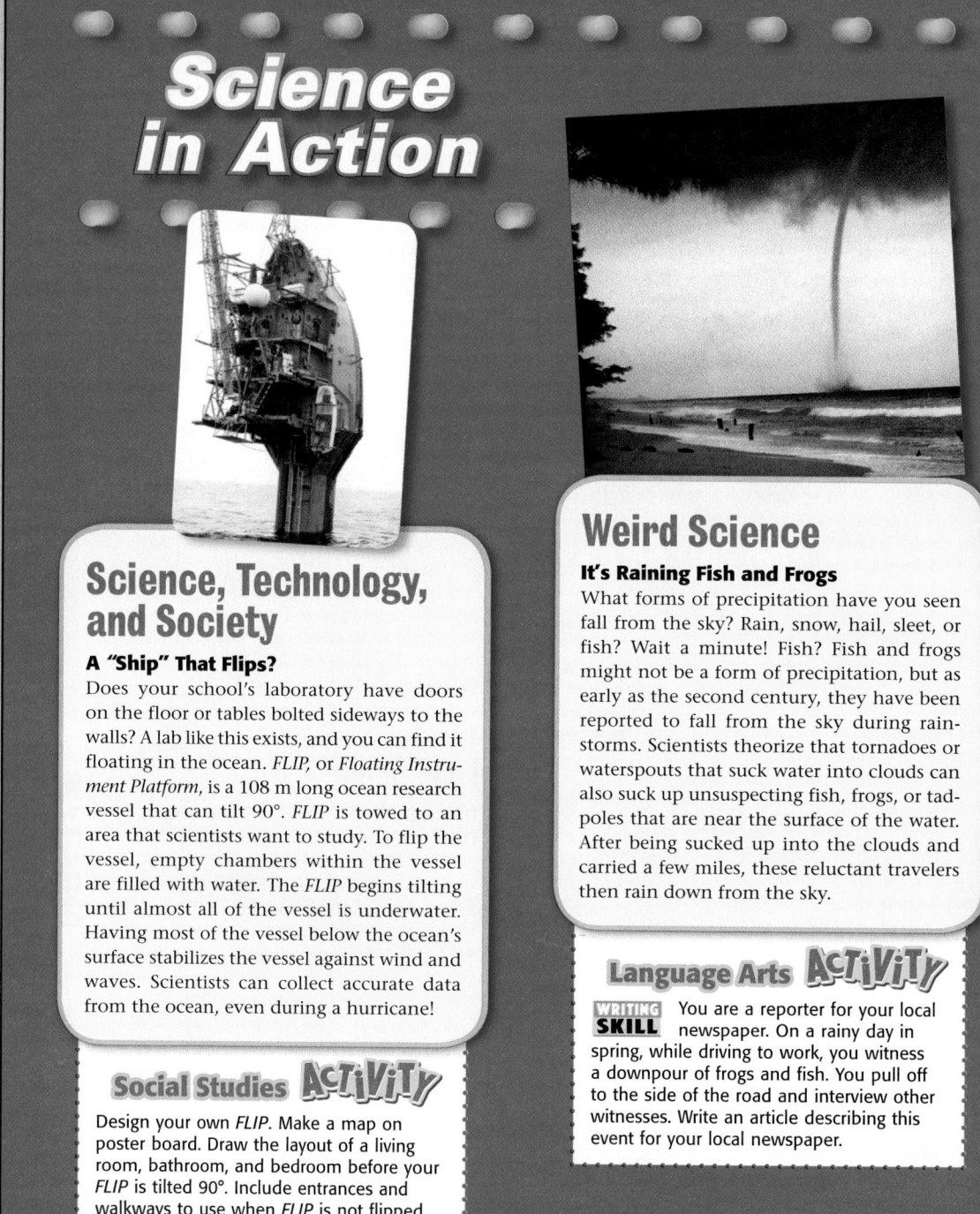

Science in Action

Science, Technology, and Society

A "Ship" That Flips?

Does your school's laboratory have doors on the floor or tables bolted sideways to the walls? A lab like this exists, and you can find it floating in the ocean. *FLIP*, or *Floating Instrument Platform*, is a 108 m long ocean research vessel that can tilt 90°. *FLIP* is towed to an area that scientists want to study. To flip the vessel, empty chambers within the vessel are filled with water. The *FLIP* begins tilting until almost all of the vessel is underwater. Having most of the vessel below the ocean's surface stabilizes the vessel against wind and waves. Scientists can collect accurate data from the ocean, even during a hurricane!

Social Studies ACTiViTY

Design your own *FLIP*. Make a map on poster board. Draw the layout of a living room, bathroom, and bedroom before your *FLIP* is tilted 90°. Include entrances and walkways to use when *FLIP* is not flipped.

Weird Science

It's Raining Fish and Frogs

What forms of precipitation have you seen fall from the sky? Rain, snow, hail, sleet, or fish? Wait a minute! Fish? Fish and frogs might not be a form of precipitation, but as early as the second century, they have been reported to fall from the sky during rainstorms. Scientists theorize that tornadoes or waterspouts that suck water into clouds can also suck up unsuspecting fish, frogs, or tadpoles that are near the surface of the water. After being sucked up into the clouds and carried a few miles, these reluctant travelers then rain down from the sky.

Language Arts ACTiViTY

WRITING SKILL You are a reporter for your local newspaper. On a rainy day in spring, while driving to work, you witness a downpour of frogs and fish. You pull off to the side of the road and interview other witnesses. Write an article describing this event for your local newspaper.

Answer to Social Studies Activity
Answers may vary.

Answer to Language Arts Activity
Answers may vary.

Ashanti Johnson Pyrtle

Chemical Oceanographer Growing up in Dallas, Texas, Ashanti Johnson Pyrtle loved everything associated with science—especially marine science. This interest led her to become the first African American female chemical oceanographer and the first African American to obtain a Ph.D. in oceanography from Texas A&M University.

Pyrtle is now an assistant professor in the College of Marine Science at the University of South Florida. She studies the distribution, transport, and behavior of radionuclides—radioactive particles—found in lakes, rivers, and oceans. Pyrtle's work has focused on a variety of places around the world, including the Lena River estuary in northern Russia. There, she studied sediments taken from the estuary and found evidence of radioactive contamination. Pyrtle's research has shown that currents carry radionuclides from the estuary eastward toward Alaska. The radionuclides could potentially harm fish that are economically important to Alaskan fisherman. Pyrtle has also studied radionuclide distribution in Georgia's Savannah River estuary. The results of these studies will help scientists understand the way in which radionuclides would spread through the aquatic environment if radiation leaked from a nuclear facility.

In addition to working as an oceanographer, Pyrtle participates in programs that help students excel in science. To Pyrtle, research is important, but so is helping others achieve their goals and dreams.

Math

Dr. Pyrtle has discovered the radionuclide cesium-137 in the Savannah River estuary. If half of the cesium-137 decays in 30 years, what percentage of cesium-137 will remain after 150 years?

go.hrw.com

To learn more about these Science in Action topics, visit go.hrw.com and type in the keyword HT6FSYFF.

Current Science

Check out Current Science® articles related to this chapter by visiting go.hrw.com. Just type in the keyword HZ5CS14.

People in Science

ACTIVITY ———— GENERAL

Have students research and make a list of all the possible professions in marine science. Ask each student to pick the one profession that sounds the most interesting to him or her and write a description of it. In the description, have students include educational requirements, job prospects, and research topics associated with this profession. Also encourage students to write a short paragraph that explains why they find this profession interesting.
LS Intrapersonal

Answer to Math Activity

30 yrs = 1/2;
60 yrs = 1/4;
90 yrs = 1/8;
120 yrs = 1/16;
150 yrs = 1/32

Plate Tectonics
Chapter Planning Guide

Compression guide:
To shorten instruction because of time limitations, omit Section 4.

OBJECTIVES	LABS, DEMONSTRATIONS, AND ACTIVITIES	TECHNOLOGY RESOURCES
PACING • 90 min pp. 376–385 **Chapter Opener**	SE **Start-up Activity**, p. 377 GENERAL	OSP **Parent Letter** ■ CD **Student Edition on CD-ROM** CD **Guided Reading Audio CD** ■ TR **Chapter Starter Transparency*** VID **Brain Food Video Quiz**
Section 1 Inside the Earth • Identify the layers of the Earth by their chemical composition. • Identify the layers of the Earth by their physical properties. • Describe a tectonic plate. • Explain how scientists know about the structure of Earth's interior.	TE **Activity** Earth Models, p. 378 GENERAL TE **Connection Activity** Math, p. 379 GENERAL TE **Connection Activity** Language Arts, p. 382 GENERAL SE **Quick Lab** Tectonic Ice Cubes, p. 383 ◆ GENERAL CRF **Datasheet for Quick Lab*** TE **Group Activity** Modeling a Tectonic Plate, p. 383 ◆ GENERAL SE **School-to-Home Activity** Build a Seismograph, p. 384 GENERAL LB **Labs You Can Eat** Rescue Near the Center of the Earth* ◆ GENERAL	OSP **Lesson Plans** (also in print) TR **Bellringer Transparency*** TR **E17** The Composition of the Earth* TR **E18** The Earth's Crust, Lithosphere, and Asthenosphere* TR **E19** The Earth's Mesosphere, Outer Core, and Inner Core* TR **E20** The Tectonic Plates; Close-up of a Tectonic Plate* TR **E21** Discoveries of the Earth's Interior*
PACING • 45 min pp. 386–389 **Section 2 Restless Continents** • Describe Wegener's hypothesis of continental drift. • Explain how sea-floor spreading provides a way for continents to move. • Describe how new oceanic lithosphere forms at mid-ocean ridges. • Explain how magnetic reversals provide evidence for sea-floor spreading.	SE **Science in Action** Math, Social Studies, and Language Arts Activities, pp. 408–409 GENERAL LB **Labs You Can Eat** Cracks in the Hard-Boiled Earth* ◆ BASIC LB **Whiz-Bang Demonstrations** Thar She Blows!* ◆ GENERAL LB **Long-Term Projects & Research Ideas** Legend Has It* ADVANCED	OSP **Lesson Plans** (also in print) TR **Bellringer Transparency*** TR **E22** The Breakup of Pangaea* TR **LINK TO LIFE SCIENCE** L26 Evolution of the Galápagos Finches* TR **E23** Sea-Floor Spreading*
PACING • 90 min pp. 390–393 **Section 3 The Theory of Plate Tectonics** • Describe the three types of tectonic plate boundaries. • Describe the three forces thought to move tectonic plates. • Explain how scientists measure the rate at which tectonic plates move.	TE **Group Activity** Plate Movements, p. 391 ADVANCED TE **Activity** Geologic Features at Tectonic Plate Boundaries, p. 391 GENERAL SE **Model-Making Lab** Convection Connection, p. 402 ◆ GENERAL CRF **Datasheet for Chapter Lab*** LB **Labs You Can Eat** Dough Fault of Your Own* ◆ ADVANCED	OSP **Lesson Plans** (also in print) TR **Bellringer Transparency*** TR **E25** Tectonic Plate Boundaries: A TR **E26** Tectonic Plate Boundaries: B TR **E24** Possible Causes of Tectonic Plate Motion* CRF **SciLinks Activity*** GENERAL VID **Lab Videos for Earth Science**
PACING • 45 min pp. 394–401 **Section 4 Deforming the Earth's Crust** • Describe two types of stress that deform rocks. • Describe three major types of folds. • Explain the differences between the three major types of faults. • Identify the most common types of mountains. • Explain the difference between uplift and subsidence.	TE **Demonstration** Modeling Deformation, p. 394 GENERAL TE **Activity** Folds That Trap Natural Gas, p. 395 ADVANCED TE **Activity** Hanging Walls Versus Footwalls, p. 396 BASIC SE **Quick Lab** Modeling Strike-Slip Faults, p. 397 GENERAL CRF **Datasheet for Quick Lab*** TE **Activity** Making Models, p. 397 GENERAL TE **Activity** Mountain-Building Gallery, p. 399 GENERAL SE **Model-Making Lab** Oh, the Pressure!, p. 723 GENERAL CRF **Datasheet for LabBook***	OSP **Lesson Plans** (also in print) TR **Bellringer Transparency*** SE **Internet Activity**, p. 400 GENERAL

PACING • 90 min

CHAPTER REVIEW, ASSESSMENT, AND STANDARDIZED TEST PREPARATION

CRF **Vocabulary Activity*** GENERAL
SE **Chapter Review**, pp. 404–405 GENERAL
CRF **Chapter Review*** ■ GENERAL
CRF **Chapter Tests A*** ■ GENERAL, **B*** ADVANCED, **C*** SPECIAL NEEDS
SE **Standardized Test Preparation**, pp. 406–407 GENERAL
CRF **Standardized Test Preparation*** GENERAL
CRF **Performance-Based Assessment*** GENERAL
OSP **Test Generator, Test Item Listing**

Online and Technology Resources

 Holt Online Learning

Visit **go.hrw.com** for access to Holt Online Learning, or enter the keyword **HS7 Home** for a variety of free online resources.

 One-Stop Planner® CD-ROM

This CD-ROM package includes:
• Lab Materials QuickList Software
• Holt Calendar Planner
• Customizable Lesson Plans
• Printable Worksheets
• ExamView® Test Generator
• Interactive Teacher's Edition
• Holt PuzzlePro®
• Holt PowerPoint® Resources

SKILLS DEVELOPMENT RESOURCES	SECTION REVIEW AND ASSESSMENT	CORRELATIONS
SE Pre-Reading Activity, p. 376 `GENERAL` **OSP** Science Puzzlers, Twisters & Teasers `GENERAL`		**National Science Education Standards** SAI 1, 2; ES 1b, 2a
CRF Directed Reading A* ■ `BASIC`, B* `SPECIAL NEEDS` **WB** Workbook* `Struggling Readers` **CRF** Vocabulary and Section Summary* ■ `GENERAL` **SE** Reading Strategy Reading Organizer, p. 378 `GENERAL` **SE** Math Practice Using Models, p. 380 `GENERAL` **TE** Reading Strategy Prediction Guide, p. 380 `GENERAL` **TE** Support for English Language Learners, p. 380 **TE** Inclusion Strategies, p. 381 **TE** Reading Strategy Activity, p. 381 `GENERAL` **CRF** Reinforcement Worksheet The Layered Earth* `BASIC`	**SE** Reading Checks, pp. 379, 380, 383, 384 `GENERAL` **TE** Reteaching, p. 384 `BASIC` **TE** Quiz, p. 384 `GENERAL` **TE** Alternative Assessment, p. 384 `GENERAL` **SE** Section Review,* p. 385 `GENERAL` **CRF** Section Quiz* ■ `GENERAL`	UCP 2; SAI 1, 2; ST 2; ES 1a
CRF Directed Reading A* ■ `BASIC`, B* `SPECIAL NEEDS` **WB** Workbook* `Struggling Readers` **CRF** Vocabulary and Section Summary* ■ `GENERAL` **SE** Reading Strategy Paired Summarizing, p. 386 `GENERAL` **TE** Support for English Language Learners, p. 386	**SE** Reading Checks, pp. 386, 389 `GENERAL` **TE** Reteaching, p. 388 `BASIC` **TE** Homework, p. 388 `GENERAL` **TE** Quiz, p. 388 `GENERAL` **TE** Alternative Assessment, p. 388 `GENERAL` **SE** Section Review,* p. 389 `GENERAL` **CRF** Section Quiz* ■ `GENERAL`	UCP 2; SAI 1, 2; ST 2; SPSP 5; HNS 1, 2, 3; ES 1b, 2a
CRF Directed Reading A* ■ `BASIC`, B* `SPECIAL NEEDS` **WB** Workbook* `Struggling Readers` **CRF** Vocabulary and Section Summary* ■ `GENERAL` **SE** Reading Strategy Brainstorming, p. 390 `GENERAL` **TE** Support for English Language Learners, p. 391 **MS** Math Skills for Science A Shortcut for Multiplying Large Numbers* `GENERAL` **CRF** Reinforcement Worksheet A Moving Jigsaw Puzzle* `BASIC`	**SE** Reading Checks, pp. 391, 392 `GENERAL` **TE** Homework, p. 392 `ADVANCED` **TE** Reteaching, p. 392 `BASIC` **TE** Quiz, p. 392 `GENERAL` **TE** Alternative Assessment, p. 392 `GENERAL` **SE** Section Review,* p. 393 ■ `GENERAL` **CRF** Section Quiz* ■ `GENERAL`	UCP 2; SAI 1, 2; SPSP 3, 4, 5; HNS 2; ES 1b, 2a *Chapter Lab:* SAI 1, 2
CRF Directed Reading A* ■ `BASIC`, B* `SPECIAL NEEDS` **WB** Workbook* `Struggling Readers` **CRF** Vocabulary and Section Summary* ■ `GENERAL` **SE** Reading Strategy Discussion, p. 394 `GENERAL` **TE** Support for English Language Learners, p. 395 **SE** Connection to Social Studies The Naming of the Appalachian Mountains, p. 399 `GENERAL` **TE** Inclusion Strategies, p. 400 ◆ **CRF** Critical Thinking Planet of Waves* `ADVANCED`	**SE** Reading Checks, pp. 394, 396, 398 `GENERAL` **TE** Homework, p. 395 `GENERAL` **TE** Reteaching, p. 400 `BASIC` **TE** Quiz, p. 400 `GENERAL` **TE** Alternative Assessment, p. 400 `GENERAL` **SE** Section Review,* p. 401 ■ `GENERAL` **CRF** Section Quiz* ■ `GENERAL`	UCP 2; SAI 1, 2; ES 1b, 2a *LabBook:* SAI 1, 2

sciLINKS.
NSTA
www.scilinks.org
Maintained by the **National Science Teachers Association.** See Chapter Enrichment pages that follow for a complete list of topics.

Current Science®

Check out *Current Science* articles and activities by visiting the HRW Web site at **go.hrw.com.** Just type in the keyword **HZ5CS07T.**

Classroom Videos

- **Lab Videos** demonstrate the chapter lab.
- **Brain Food Video Quizzes** help students review the chapter material.

Classroom CD-ROMs

- **Guided Reading Audio CD** (Also in Spanish)
- **Interactive Explorations**
- **Virtual Investigations**
- **Visual Concepts**
- **Science Tutor**

Holt Lab Generator CD-ROM

Search for any lab by topic, standard, difficulty level, or time. Edit any lab to fit your needs, or create your own labs. Use the Lab Materials QuickList software to customize your lab materials list.

Visual Resources

CHAPTER STARTER TRANSPARENCY

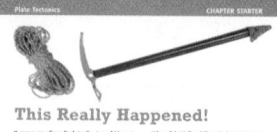

This Really Happened!

BELLRINGER TRANSPARENCIES

Section: Inside the Earth

If you journeyed to the center of the Earth, what do you think you would see along the way?

Draw an illustration of the journey in your **science journal.**

Section: Restless Continents

Judge what is meant by the following statement: "The United States is moving westward." From what you know about geology and plate tectonics explain if you believe this statement to be true or false.

Record your answer in your **science journal.**

TEACHING TRANSPARENCIES

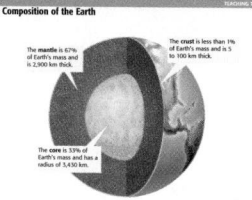

The Composition of the Earth

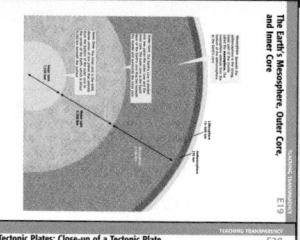

The Earth's Mesosphere, Outer Core, and Inner Core

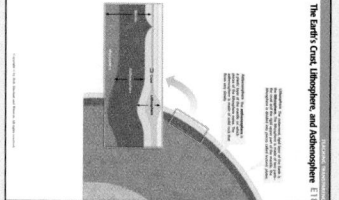

The Earth's Crust, Lithosphere, and Asthenosphere

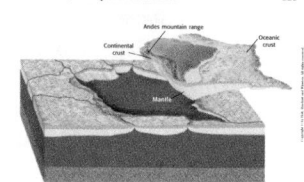

The Tectonic Plates; Close-up of a Tectonic Plate

TEACHING TRANSPARENCIES

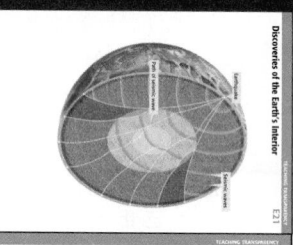

Discoveries of the Earth's Interior

The Breakup of Pangaea

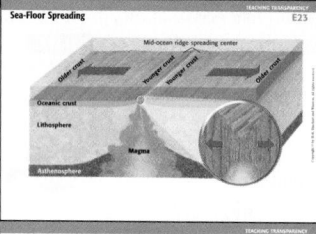

Sea-Floor Spreading

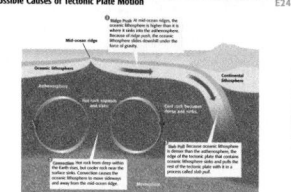

Possible Causes of Tectonic Plate Motion

Evolution of the Galápagos Finches

LINK TO LIFE SCIENCE

Chapter: The Evolution of Living Things

CONCEPT MAPPING TRANSPARENCY

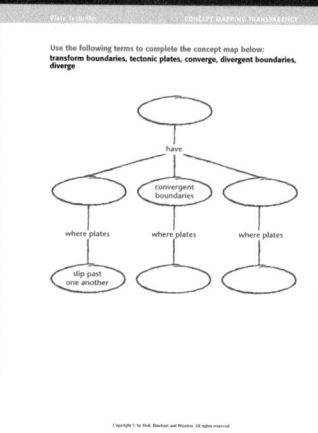

Use the following terms to complete the concept map below: transform boundaries, tectonic plates, converge, divergent boundaries, diverge

Planning Resources

LESSON PLANS

Lesson Plan SAMPLE

Section: Waves

Pacing

Regular Schedule: with lab(s):2 days without lab(s):if days
Block Schedule: with lab(s):1 1/2 days without lab(s):if days

Objectives

1. Relate the seven properties of life to a living organism.
2. Describe seven themes that can help you to organize what you learn about biology.
3. Identify the tiny structures that make up all living organisms.
4. Differentiate between reproduction and heredity and between metabolism and homeostasis.

National Science Education Standards Covered

PARENT LETTER

SAMPLE

Dear Parent,

Your son's or daughter's science class will soon begin exploring the chapter entitled "The World of Physical Science." In this chapter, students will learn about how the scientific method applies to the world of physical science and the role of physical science in the world. By the end of the chapter, students should demonstrate a clear understanding of the chapter's main ideas and be able to discuss the following topics:

ALSO IN SPANISH

TEST ITEM LISTING

TEST ITEM LISTING
The World of Earth Science SAMPLE

MULTIPLE CHOICE

One-Stop Planner® CD-ROM

This CD-ROM includes all of the resources shown here and the following time-saving tools:

- **Lab Materials QuickList Software**
- **Customizable lesson plans**
- **Holt Calendar Planner**
- **The powerful ExamView® Test Generator**

Meeting Individual Needs

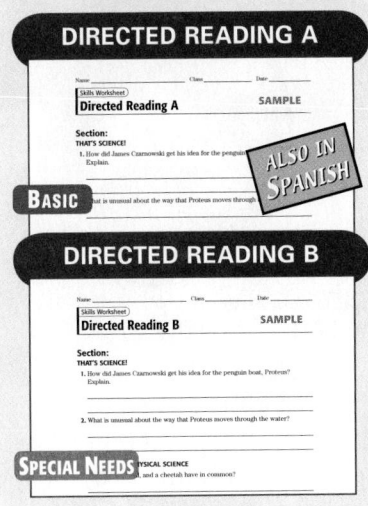

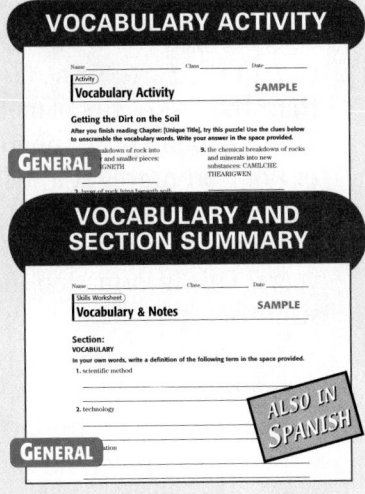

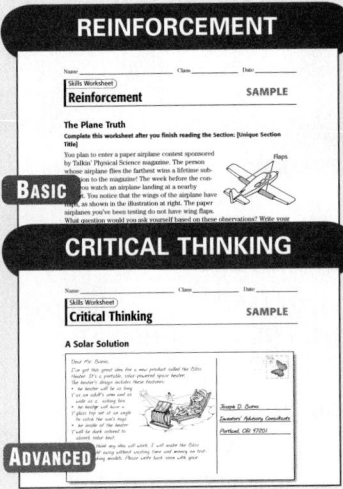

Labs and Activities

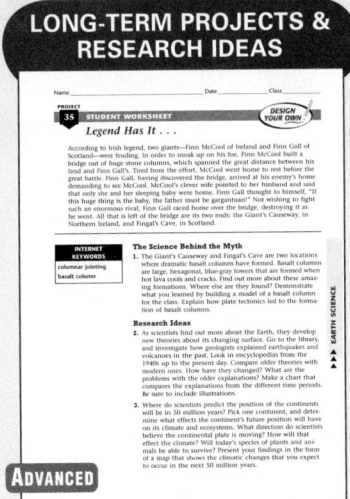

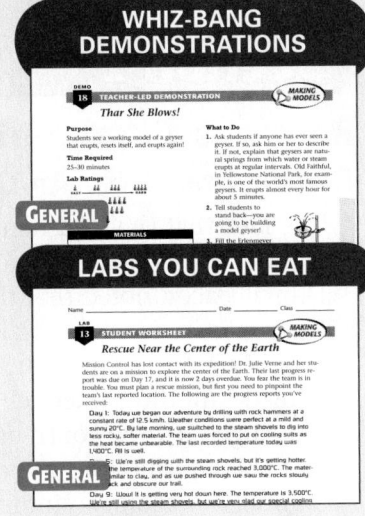

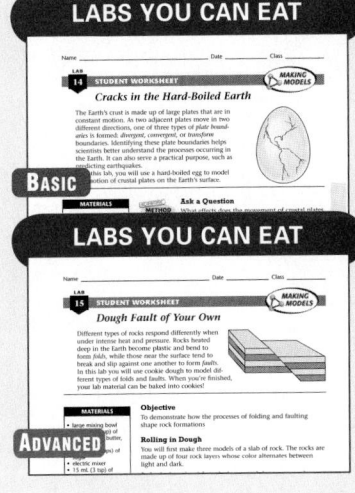

Review and Assessments

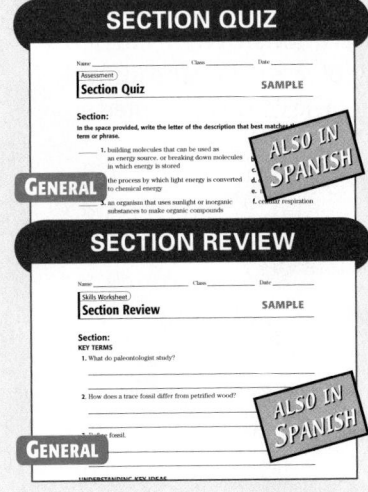

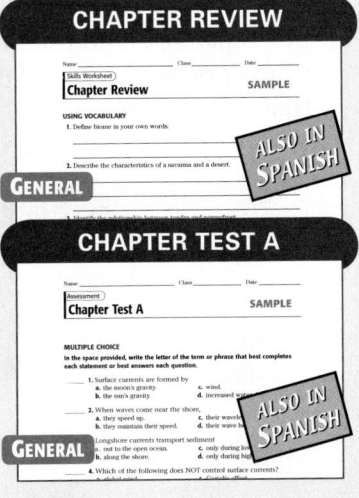

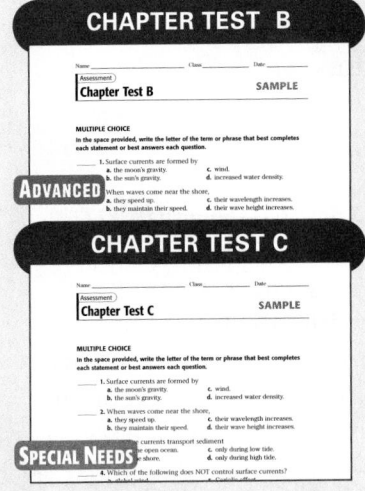

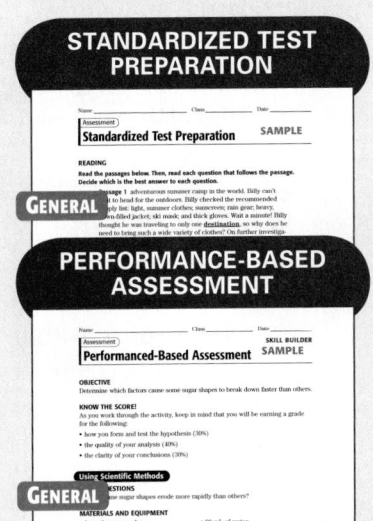

This Chapter Enrichment provides relevant and interesting information to expand and enhance your presentation of the chapter material.

Section 1

Inside the Earth

Continents and the Earth's Crust

- Continents are large, continuous landmasses composed of crust that is generally much older than the surrounding oceanic crust. The core or central, older, stabler part of a continent, called a *craton,* is generally composed of ancient, crystalline igneous and metamorphic rock. Cratons range from 3.9 billion to 200 million years old. Rocks of the North American craton are exposed more or less without interruption in the eastern two-thirds of Canada, along the U.S. margins of Lake Superior, and in most of Greenland.

Heat Within the Earth

- The Earth's internal heat contributes to the process of differentiation—the division of the Earth into layers that have distinct characteristics. This heat has three main sources: the decay of radioactive elements, which is a continuous process; the collapse of iron into the Earth's core during the process of differentiation 4.5 billion years ago; and leftover energy from the accretion and compression of particles that coalesced to form Earth 4.6 billion years ago.

Is That a Fact!

◆ Earth's magnetic poles have reversed more than 177 times in the last 85 million years. The most recent reversal occurred within the last 600,000 years. By using complex computer models, scientists are beginning to understand how this process happens, but they are unable to predict when the poles will reverse again or how life on Earth will be affected by this reversal.

Earth's Inner Core

- Research conducted in 1996 suggests that the solid inner core of the Earth spins faster than the rest of the planet. This 2,456 km wide sphere of hot iron moves at a speed that would allow it to lap Earth's surface once every 400 years. This information may give scientists clues about how the Earth formed.

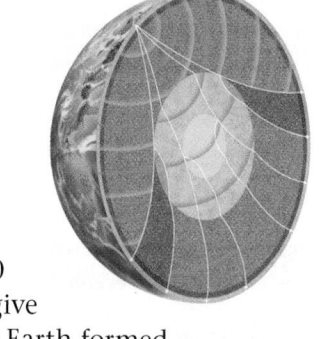

- The Earth's outer core is a hot, electrically conducting liquid that is thought to be continuously moved by convection. This layer's conductivity combines with the differential spin of the Earth's inner core to create powerful electric currents that, in turn, generate the Earth's magnetic field.

Section 2

Restless Continents

Continental Drift: An Old Idea

- The idea that the continents were once joined together was not a new idea in Alfred Wegener's time. In 1620, Francis Bacon noted that the continents seemed to fit together like a jigsaw puzzle, but no one could understand how they moved. In 1858, a French scientist named Antonio Snider-Pellegrini cited fossil evidence that suggested the continents had been joined. In 1910, an American geologist named Frank Taylor pointed out geologic similarities between South America and Africa. Wegener's studies in 1915 were the first exhaustive research on the topic and combined evidence from many disciplines. Neither Wegener nor Taylor could explain how the continents had separated, and their observations were dismissed. It was not until the discovery of sea-floor spreading that the continental drift hypothesis was accepted.

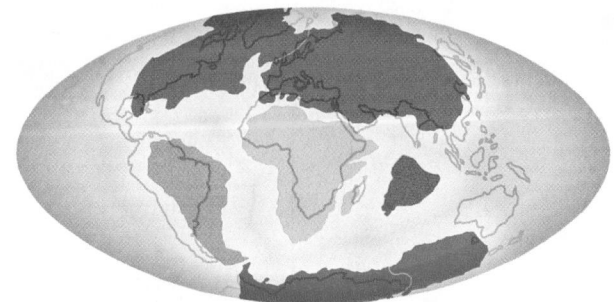

Testing the Continental Drift Hypothesis

- After sea-floor spreading was discovered in the 1960s, research groups tested Wegener's hypothesis using as many methods as possible:
  - The edges of continental slopes were mapped with sonar and have been shown to fit together even better than the coastlines do.
  - New radiometric dating methods showed that rocks in corresponding parts of Africa and South America formed at the same time.

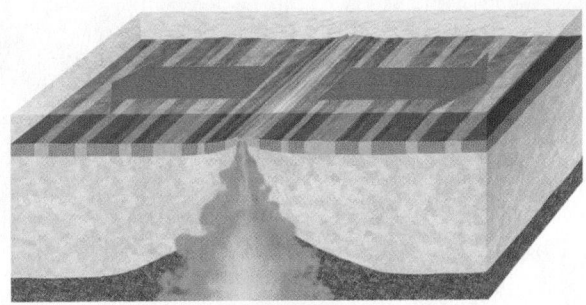

  - The dating of igneous rocks around mid-ocean ridges showed a symmetrical pattern, in which older rocks were located farther away from the rifts. Few rocks older than 180 million years were discovered on the ocean floor. This discovery indicates that the oceanic lithosphere is continuously recycled.
  - Scientists found that zones of magnetic reversals also followed a symmetrical pattern on either side of mid-ocean ridges. The pattern of reversals matched the pattern revealed by the ages of the rocks.
  - The horizontal magnetic reversals recorded in the ocean floor matched those recorded in vertical sequences of lava flows on continents.

Section 3

The Theory of Plate Tectonics

Trenches

- Where an oceanic plate subducts under another tectonic plate, a long, steep-sided trench forms on the sea floor. On average, subduction trenches are 2,000 to 4,000 m deeper than the rest of the ocean floor. Nevertheless, some animals, including species of sea cucumbers, sea anemones, and marine worms, are capable of living in the cold, pressurized depths of ocean trenches.

Is That a Fact!

- ◆ The Mariana Trench, which is 2,500 km long and 11,033 m below sea level at its deepest point, is the deepest known place on Earth.

Section 4

Deforming the Earth's Crust

Fault Versus Fold

- Tectonic activity exerts a tremendous amount of pressure on crustal rocks. Whether they bend or break depends on several factors:
  - **Type of Stress** If stress is applied gradually, rocks often fold; if stress is applied suddenly, rocks tend to fault.
  - **Composition of Rock** Brittle rocks, such as sandstone, tend to break; ductile rocks, such as shale, tend to fold.
  - **Temperature** As the temperature at the point of stress increases, rocks are more likely to fold rather than fault.

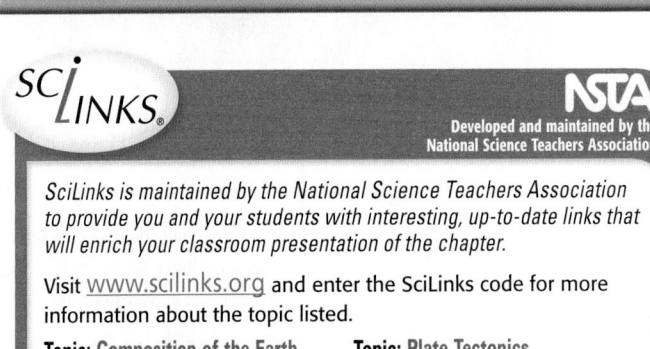

SciLinks is maintained by the National Science Teachers Association to provide you and your students with interesting, up-to-date links that will enrich your classroom presentation of the chapter.

Visit www.scilinks.org and enter the SciLinks code for more information about the topic listed.

Topic: Composition of the Earth
SciLinks code: HSM0329

Topic: Plate Tectonics
SciLinks code: HSM1171

Topic: Structure of the Earth
SciLinks code: HSM1468

Topic: Faults
SciLinks code: HSM0566

Topic: Tectonic Plates
SciLinks code: HSM1497

Topic: Mountain Building
SciLinks code: HSM0999

Overview

Tell students that this chapter will help them learn about the structure of the Earth and the forces that continually reshape the crust of our planet.

Assessing Prior Knowledge

Students should be familiar with the following topics:

- the principle of uniformitarianism
- the geologic time scale

Identifying Misconceptions

Students may think that the theory of plate tectonics was developed a long time ago. Stress that this key concept in geology was accepted in the mainstream of geologic thought less than 50 years ago. Parents and teachers may remember learning alternative theories in Earth science classes. Even today, scientists have still not fully identified the mechanisms of tectonic plate movement. Although the theory of plate tectonics was accepted in relatively recent times, it is still the best explanation for many different lines of geologic evidence and observations.

Plate Tectonics

The Big Idea

Plate tectonics accounts for important features of Earth's surface and major geologic events.

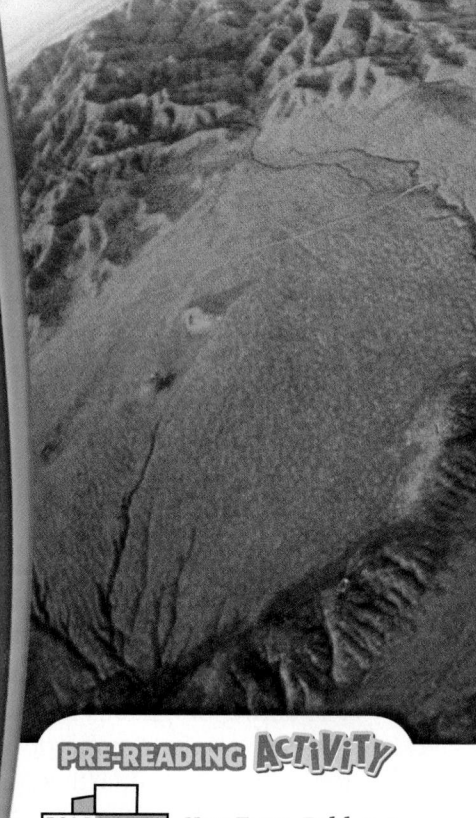

About the Photo

The San Andreas fault stretches across the California landscape like a giant wound. The fault, which is 1,000 km long, breaks the Earth's crust from Northern California to Mexico. Because the North American plate and Pacific plate are slipping past one another along the fault, many earthquakes happen.

PRE-READING ACTIVITY

FOLDNOTES **Key-Term Fold** Before you read the chapter, create the FoldNote entitled "Key-Term Fold" described in the **Study Skills** section of the Appendix. Write a key term from the chapter on each tab of the key-term fold. Under each tab, write the definition of the key term.

Standards Correlations

National Science Education Standards

The following codes indicate the National Science Education Standards that correlate to this chapter. The full text of the standards is at the front of the book.

Chapter Opener
SAI 1, 2; ES 1a, 2a

Section 1 Inside the Earth
UCP 2; SAI 1, 2; ST 2; ES 1a

Section 2 Restless Continents
UCP 2; HNS 1, 2, 3; ES 1b, 2a; SPSP 5; ST 2; SAI 1, 2

Section 3 The Theory of Plate Tectonics
UCP 2; HNS 2; ES 1b, 2a; SPSP 3, 4, 5

Section 4 Deforming the Earth's Crust
UCP 2; ES 1b, 2a; SAI 1, 2; *LabBook:* SAI 1, 2

Chapter Lab
SAI 1, 2

Chapter Review
UCP 2; SAI 1, 2; HNS 2; ES 1a, 1b, 2a; ST 2

Science in Action
UCP 2; ES 1b, 2a; HNS 1, 2, 3; ST 2; SAI 1, 2

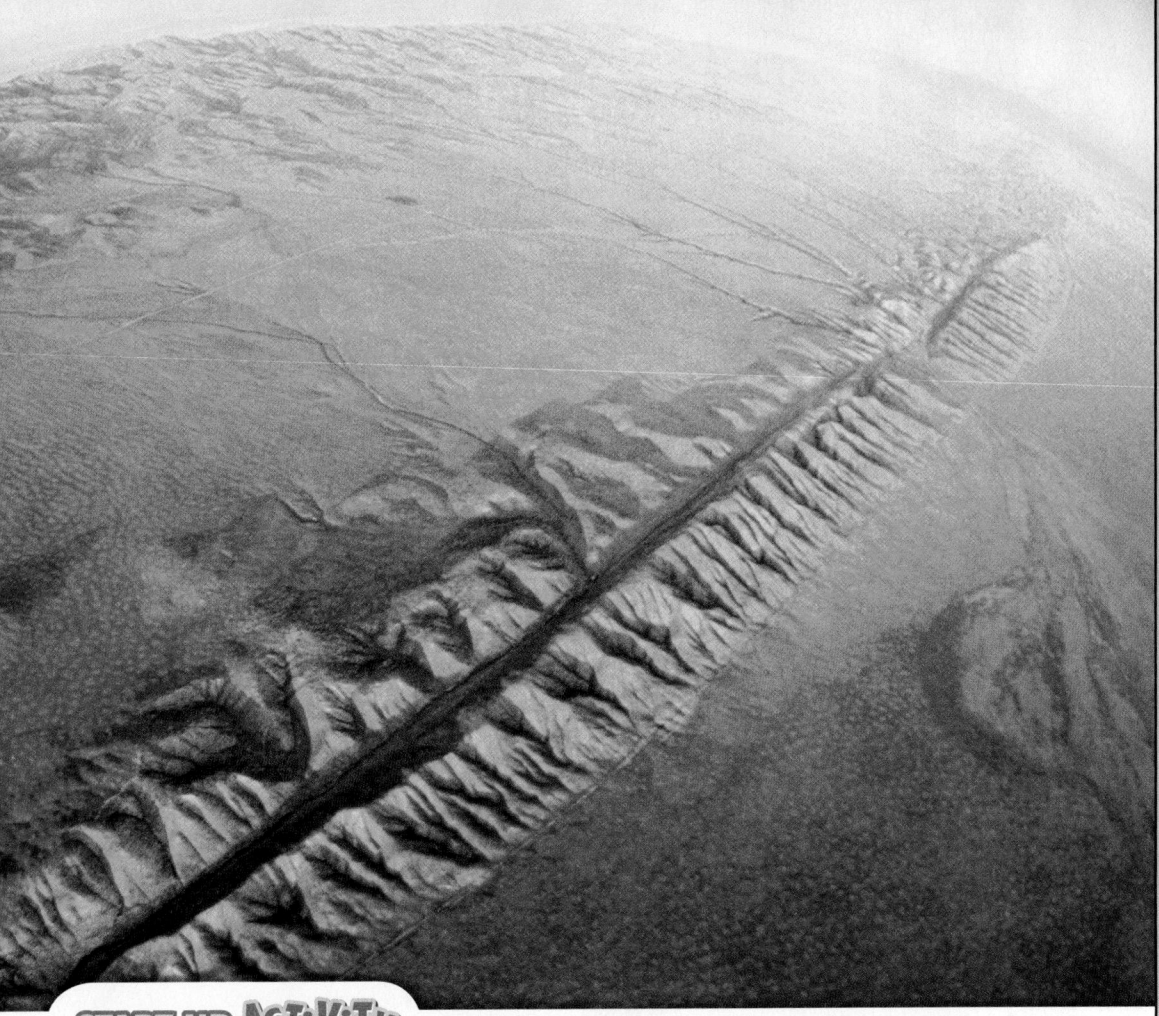

Answers

1. Sample answer: The stacks of paper buckle and fold over. Some of the paper in one stack slid under the paper in the other stack.

2. Sample answer: No, some pieces of paper slid under the opposite stack. Other pieces of paper slid into the other stack.

3. Sample answer: Continental collisions form high mountain ranges, such as the Himalayas.

START-UP ACTIVITY

Continental Collisions

As you can see, continents not only move but can also crash into each other. In this activity, you will model the collision of two continents.

Procedure

1. Obtain **two stacks of paper** that are each about 1 cm thick.

2. Place the two stacks of paper on a **flat surface,** such as a desk.

3. Very slowly, push the stacks of paper together so that they collide. Continue to push the stacks until the paper in one of the stacks folds over.

Analysis

1. What happens to the stacks of paper when they collide with each other?

2. Are all of the pieces of paper pushed upward? If not, what happens to the pieces that are not pushed upward?

3. What type of landform will most likely result from this continental collision?

This Really Happened!

It was a grueling climb to the top of Mount Everest. The temperature was well below freezing, and the blinding snow made it difficult to see. These harsh conditions and the extreme altitude are what make Mount Everest one of the most difficult mountains to climb. But these conditions did not stop a professional mountain climber by the name of Wally Berg. He was on a mission—a scientific mission that had been years in the planning.

Once at the top of the world's highest mountain, some 8,848 m high, Wally began drilling a hole in the rock. At this altitude the air is so thin that even easy tasks are difficult to accomplish. Wally brought bottles of oxygen with him to make his breathing easier.

Why did Wally drill a hole in Mount Everest? He needed the hole in order to secure a special device that receives and records signals from a network of satellites called the Global Positioning System (GPS).

GPS can pinpoint the exact location of these special receivers over long periods of time. In analyzing GPS data, scientists found out that Mount Everest not only is moving but also is growing taller every year. Over a year's time, the mountain moves northeast about 27 mm and grows from 3 to 5 mm taller!

Why is Mount Everest moving and growing? The answer is plate tectonics. Plate tectonics is also the reason why California has so many earthquakes and why volcanoes are found all around the rim of the Pacific Ocean. Get ready to learn much more about plate tectonics in this chapter.

Chapter Starter Transparency
Use this transparency to help students begin thinking about how tectonic forces have created tall mountains.

CHAPTER RESOURCES

Technology

 Transparencies
• Chapter Starter Transparency

READING SKILLS

 **Student Edition on CD-ROM**

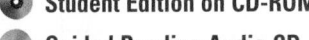 **Guided Reading Audio CD**
• English or Spanish

 Classroom Videos
• Brain Food Video Quiz

Workbooks

 Science Puzzlers, Twisters & Teasers
• Plate Tectonics GENERAL

Focus

Overview

This section describes the classification of the Earth according to composition (crust, mantle, and core) and according to physical structure (lithosphere, asthenosphere, mesosphere, outer core, and inner core). This section also describes tectonic plates. The section concludes with a discussion of how scientists study seismic waves to map the Earth's interior.

 Bellringer

Ask students, "If you journeyed to the center of the Earth, what do you think you would observe along the way?" Have students draw an illustration of their journey in their **science journal.**

Motivate

ACTIVITY ——————— GENERAL

Earth Models Have groups of students use materials of their choice to build a cutaway scale model of the Earth based on the dimensions shown in **Figure 3.** Encourage students to be creative. For example, they could use a chain of paperclips 64 clips long (34 clips for the core, 29 clips for the mantle, and 1 clip for the crust). **LS Kinesthetic/ Visual**

What You Will Learn

● Identify the layers of the Earth by their chemical composition.
● Identify the layers of the Earth by their physical properties.
● Describe a tectonic plate.
● Explain how scientists know about the structure of Earth's interior.

Vocabulary

crust   asthenosphere
mantle   mesosphere
core   tectonic plate
lithosphere

READING STRATEGY

Reading Organizer As you read this section, create an outline of the section. Use the headings from the section in your outline.

Inside the Earth

If you tried to dig to the center of the Earth, what do you think you would find? Would the Earth be solid or hollow? Would it be made of the same material throughout?

Actually, the Earth is made of several layers. Each layer is made of different materials that have different properties. Scientists think about physical layers in two ways—by their chemical composition and by their physical properties.

The Composition of the Earth

The Earth is divided into three layers—the crust, the mantle, and the core—based on the compounds that make up each layer. A *compound* is a substance composed of two or more elements. The less dense compounds make up the crust and mantle, and the densest compounds make up the core. The layers form because heavier elements are pulled toward the center of the Earth by gravity, and elements of lesser mass are found farther from the center.

The Crust

The outermost layer of the Earth is the **crust.** The crust is 5 to 100 km thick. It is the thinnest layer of the Earth.

As **Figure 1** shows, there are two types of crust—continental and oceanic. Both continental crust and oceanic crust are made mainly of the elements oxygen, silicon, and aluminum. However, the denser oceanic crust has almost twice as much iron, calcium, and magnesium, which form minerals that are denser than those in the continental crust.

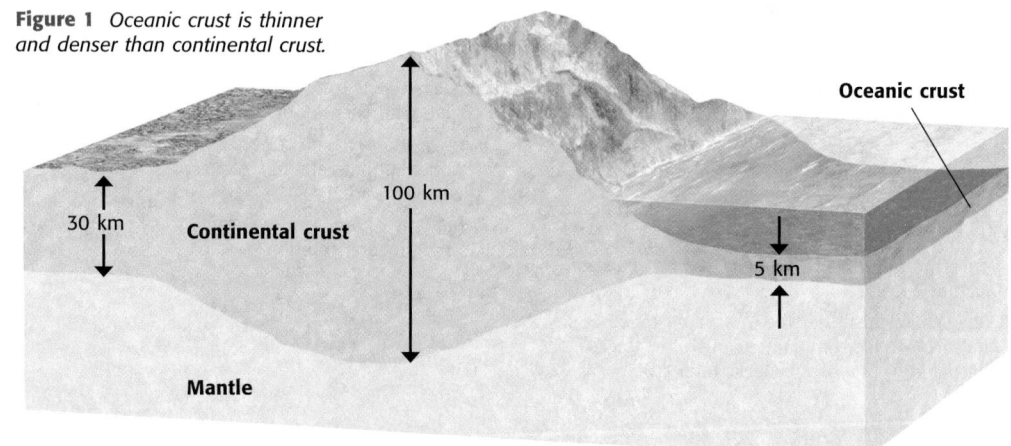
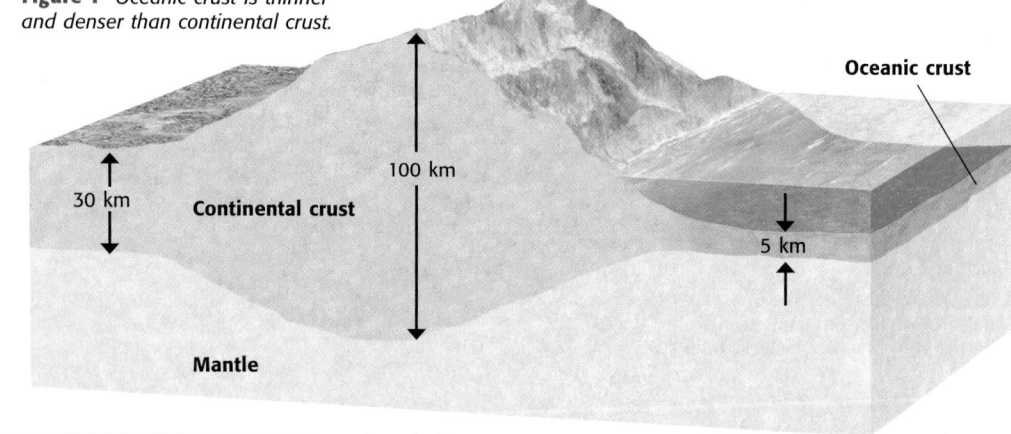

Figure 1 *Oceanic crust is thinner and denser than continental crust.*

Oceanic crust

100 km

30 km   **Continental crust**

5 km

Mantle

CHAPTER RESOURCES

Chapter Resource File

• **Lesson Plan**
• **Directed Reading A** BASIC
• **Directed Reading B** SPECIAL NEEDS

Technology

Transparencies
• Bellringer
• E17 The Composition of the Earth

Workbooks

Interactive Textbook Struggling Readers

Is That a Fact!

Two lines of evidence indicate that Earth's core is a mixture of iron and nickel. The core's density, which is similar to a mixture of iron and nickel, was determined by studying the way seismic waves travel through it. The Earth's magnetic field also suggests this composition.

The Mantle

The layer of the Earth between the crust and the core is the **mantle.** The mantle is much thicker than the crust and contains most of the Earth's mass.

No one has ever visited the mantle. The crust is too thick to drill through to reach the mantle. Scientists must draw conclusions about the composition and other physical properties of the mantle from observations made on the Earth's surface. In some places, mantle rock pushes to the surface, which allows scientists to study the rock directly.

As you can see in **Figure 2,** another place scientists look for clues about the mantle is the ocean floor. Magma from the mantle flows out of active volcanoes on the ocean floor. These underwater volcanoes have given scientists many clues about the composition of the mantle. Because the mantle has more magnesium and less aluminum and silicon than the crust does, the mantle is denser than the crust.

The Core

The layer of the Earth that extends from below the mantle to the center of the Earth is the **core.** Scientists think that the Earth's core is made mostly of iron and contains smaller amounts of nickel but almost no oxygen, silicon, aluminum, or magnesium. As shown in **Figure 3,** the core makes up roughly one-third of the Earth's mass.

✓ **Reading Check** Briefly describe the layers that make up the Earth. (*See the Appendix for answers to Reading Checks.*)

Figure 2 *Volcanic vents on the ocean floor, such as this vent off the coast of Hawaii, allow magma to rise up through the crust from the mantle.*

crust the thin and solid outermost layer of the Earth above the mantle

mantle the layer of rock between the Earth's crust and core

core the central part of the Earth below the mantle

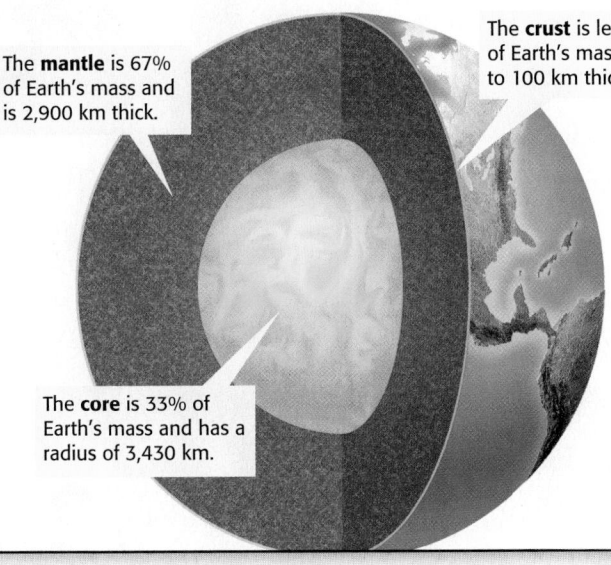

The **mantle** is 67% of Earth's mass and is 2,900 km thick.

The **crust** is less than 1% of Earth's mass and is 5 to 100 km thick.

The **core** is 33% of Earth's mass and has a radius of 3,430 km.

Figure 3 *The Earth is made up of three layers based on the composition of each layer.*

Teach

CONNECTION ACTIVITY
Math ——— GENERAL

Comparing the Mantle and Crust Tell students to assume that the average thickness for the crust is 50 km, and have them calculate how much thicker the mantle is than the crust. Invite volunteers to write their calculations on the board. (2,900 km ÷ 50 km = 58; The mantle is 58 times thicker than the crust.) You may want to have students compare thicknesses for all of Earth's compositional and physical layers. **LS Logical**

CONNECTION to
Physical Science — GENERAL

Mass, Volume, and Density Use **Figure 3** to discuss the relationship between mass, volume, and density. Point out that although the core is 33% of Earth's mass, the core is only 10% of Earth's volume. The Earth's core is composed mainly of iron, which is much denser than the mantle and crustal rocks that make up the rest of the Earth. Ask students to speculate why density increases with depth. **LS Logical**

MISCONCEPTION
///ALERT\\\

Measuring Earth's Layers Students may think that the crust, mantle, and core are all measured by their thickness. Explain that the core is a sphere, so it is measured by its diameter or radius. Some students may think that the crust is the same as the lithosphere. Explain that the crust is the outermost compositional layer of Earth. The lithosphere is the outermost structural layer of Earth and is made up of the crust and the upper part of the mantle.

Answers to Math Practice

150 km ÷ 6,380 km = 0.0235 =
    2.35%

2.35% × 1.00 m = 0.0235 m,
    or 2.35 cm

In the pie graph, the portions of the circle that represent each layer should accurately reflect the size of the layer. The bars in the bar graph should be similarly proportionate.

READING STRATEGY — GENERAL

Prediction Guide Before students read this page, ask them the following question: "If you could burrow to the center of the Earth, what would you expect to happen to the pressure, the temperature, and the physical state of matter?" (Each successive layer will become hotter and have higher pressure. The solidity of layers will depend on temperature, pressure, and chemical composition.) **LS Logical**

SUPPORT FOR

English Language Learners

Multiple Meanings The use of the word *plastic* in the description of the asthenosphere may be confusing. Ask, "What happens to a plastic spoon that has been heated a little bit?" (It becomes pliable, and its shape can be changed.) Then, ask students why the word *plastic* can be applied to the asthenosphere. (because it is made up of slowly flowing rock) Have students add the word plastic to their word webs. **LS Verbal/Logical**

Answer to Reading Check

The five physical layers of the Earth are the lithosphere, asthenosphere, mesosphere, outer core, and inner core.

MATH PRACTICE

Using Models
Imagine that you are building a model of the Earth that will have a radius of 1 m. You find out that the average radius of the Earth is 6,380 km and that the thickness of the lithosphere is about 150 km. What percentage of the Earth's radius is the lithosphere? How thick (in centimeters) would you make the lithosphere in your model?

CHAPTER RESOURCES

Technology

Transparencies
• E18 The Earth's Crust, Lithosphere, and Asthenosphere
• E19 The Earth's Mesosphere, Outer Core, and Inner Core

The Physical Structure of the Earth

Another way to look at the Earth is to examine the physical properties of its layers. The Earth is divided into five physical layers—the lithosphere, asthenosphere, mesosphere, outer core, and inner core. As shown in the figure below, each layer has its own set of physical properties.

✓ Reading Check What are the five physical layers of the Earth?

Lithosphere The outermost, rigid layer of the Earth is the **lithosphere.** The lithosphere is made of two parts—the crust and the rigid upper part of the mantle. The lithosphere is divided into pieces called *tectonic plates*.

Asthenosphere The **asthenosphere** is a plastic layer of the mantle on which pieces of the lithosphere move. The asthenosphere is made of solid rock that flows very slowly.

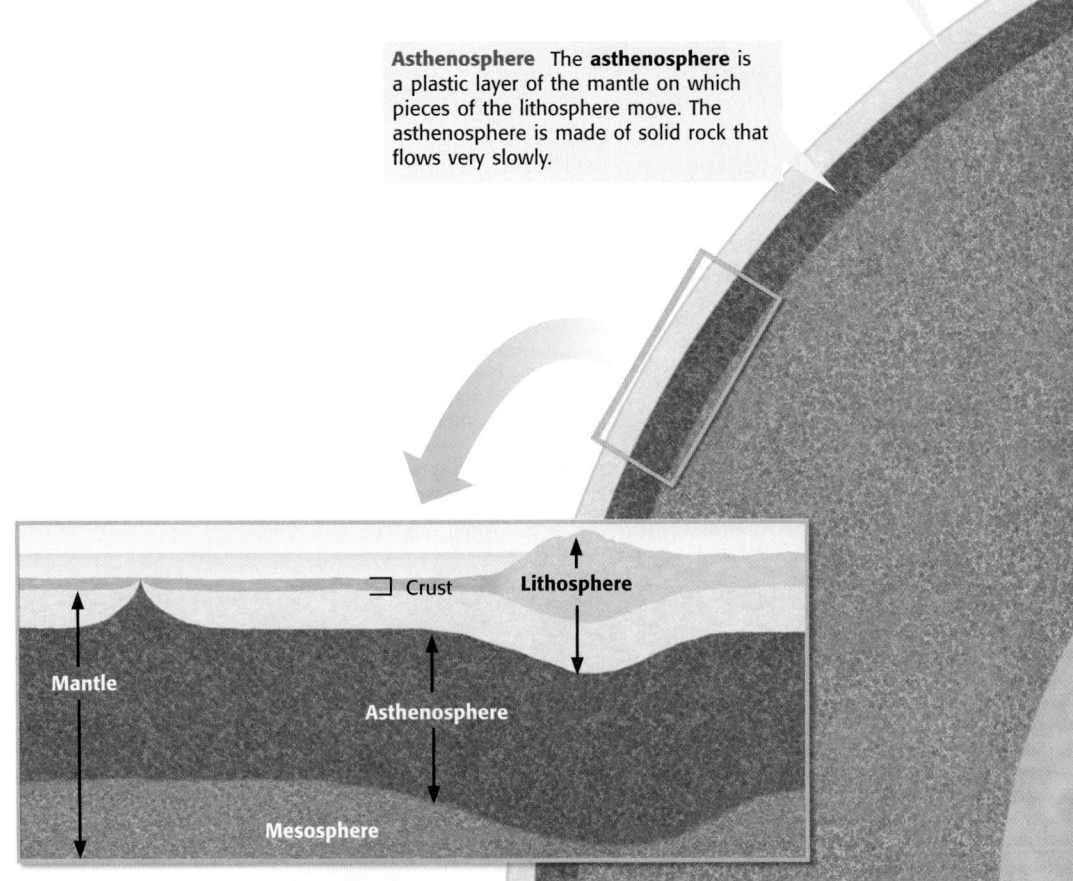

MISCONCEPTION ///ALERT\\\

Chemical and Physical Properties
Some students may not understand that the two systems of naming Earth's layers describe different properties. *Crust, mantle,* and *core* describe differences in chemical composition; *lithosphere, asthenosphere, mesosphere, outer core,* and *inner core* describe differences in the response of the material to stress caused by differences in temperature and pressure.

Mesosphere Beneath the asthenosphere is the strong, lower part of the mantle called the **mesosphere.** The mesosphere extends from the bottom of the asthenosphere to the Earth's core.

lithosphere the solid, outer layer of the Earth that consists of the crust and the rigid upper part of the mantle

asthenosphere the soft layer of the mantle on which the tectonic plates move

mesosphere the strong, lower part of the mantle between the asthenosphere and the outer core

Lithosphere
15–300 km

Asthenosphere
250 km

Mesosphere
2,550 km

Outer Core The Earth's core is divided into two parts—the outer core and the inner core. The outer core is the liquid layer of the Earth's core that lies beneath the mantle and surrounds the inner core.

Inner Core The inner core is the solid, dense center of our planet that extends from the bottom of the outer core to the center of the Earth, which is about 6,380 km beneath the surface.

Outer core
2,200 km

Inner core
1,230 km

INCLUSION Strategies

- **Learning Disabled**
- **Attention Deficit Disorder**
- **Visually Impaired**

Organize students into groups. Give each group modeling clay in three colors, a piece of cardboard, and self-stick notes. Ask each group to use the clay to create a model of the Earth's layers. After groups create their model, ask each group to label each layer with a self-stick note. Next, ask each group to write two facts about each layer on individual self-stick notes and apply them to the appropriate place on the model. Have groups share their model and facts with the class.

LS Kinesthetic/Logical   English Language Learners

Writing **Tectonic Essay** *Tectonic* comes from the Greek word *tektonikos*, which means "of a builder." Ask students to consider how this meaning is appropriate for tectonic plates. Ask students, "In what ways are tectonic plates responsible for building features on the Earth's surface?" Have students write a short essay that describes how the movement of tectonic plates slowly shapes the landscape around us. **LS** Verbal

BRAIN FOOD

The Deepest Hole The deepest hole ever drilled into the continental crust was in the Kola Peninsula, in Russia, in 1984. It was 12,226 m deep! Because the temperature of the crust increases with depth, it is impossible to drill much deeper into crust. Hot rock flows around the drill bit and fills the hole faster than the hole can be drilled. Ask students, "How deep is the hole compared to the height of Mount Everest? Did it extend to the mantle?" (12,226 m − 8,850 m = 3,376 m; no)

tectonic plate a block of lithosphere that consists of the crust and the rigid, outermost part of the mantle

Tectonic Plates

Pieces of the lithosphere that move around on top of the asthenosphere are called **tectonic plates**. But what exactly does a tectonic plate look like? How big are tectonic plates? How and why do they move around? To answer these questions, begin by thinking of the lithosphere as a giant jigsaw puzzle.

A Giant Jigsaw Puzzle

All of the tectonic plates have names, some of which you may already know. Some of the major tectonic plates are named on the map in **Figure 4.** Notice that each tectonic plate fits together with the tectonic plates that surround it. The lithosphere is like a jigsaw puzzle, and the tectonic plates are like the pieces of a jigsaw puzzle.

Notice that not all tectonic plates are the same. For example, compare the size of the South American plate with that of the Cocos plate. Tectonic plates differ in other ways, too. For example, the South American plate has an entire continent on it and has oceanic crust, but the Cocos plate has only oceanic crust. Some tectonic plates, such as the South American plate, include both continental and oceanic crust.

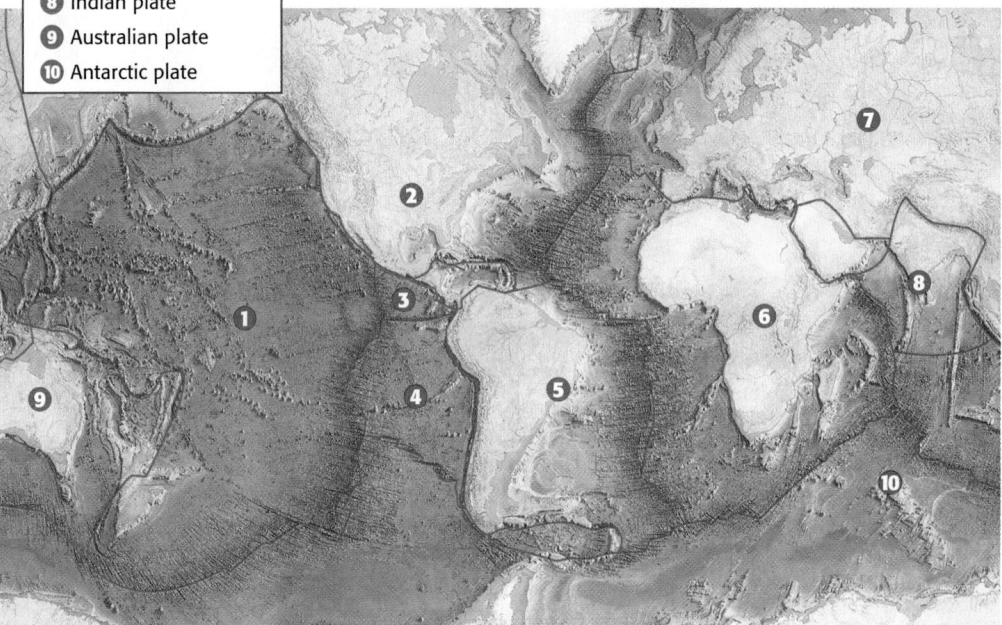

Major Tectonic Plates
1. Pacific plate
2. North American plate
3. Cocos plate
4. Nazca plate
5. South American plate
6. African plate
7. Eurasian plate
8. Indian plate
9. Australian plate
10. Antarctic plate

Figure 4 *Tectonic plates fit together like the pieces of a giant jigsaw puzzle.*

MISCONCEPTION
**/// ALERT **

Tectonic Plates Students may think that tectonic plates are always neatly divided along continental lines, but the lines are not so neat. For example, the North American plate includes the North American continent, Greenland, half of Iceland, and part of Eurasia. All six of the Earth's large continental plates contain a continent and a large section of oceanic crust. Some of the 10 other small tectonic plates contain only oceanic crust.

Figure 5 The South American Plate

This image shows what you might see if you could lift the South American plate out of its position between other tectonic plates.

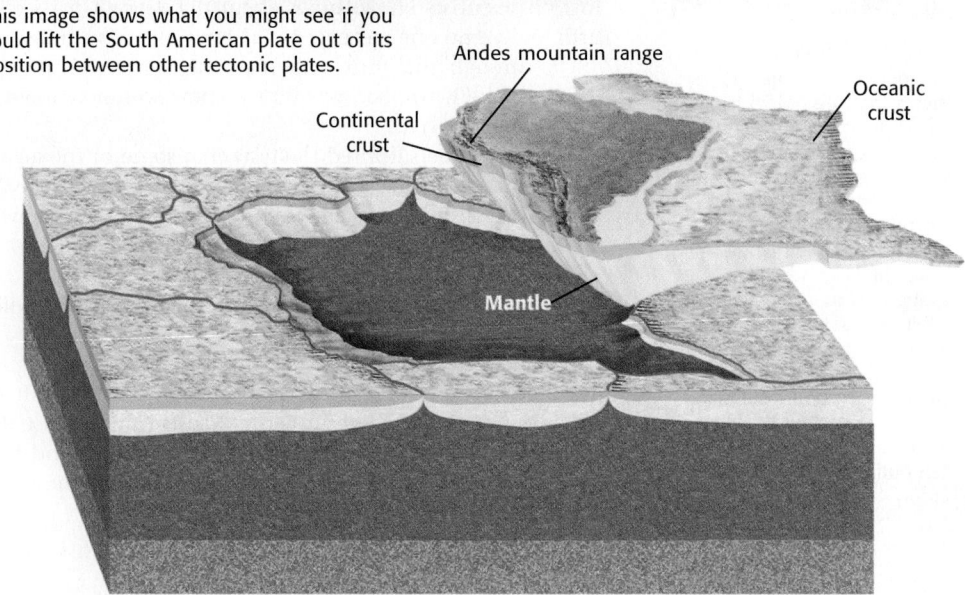

Andes mountain range

Continental crust

Oceanic crust

Mantle

A Tectonic Plate Close-Up

What would a tectonic plate look like if you could lift it out of its place? **Figure 5** shows what the South American plate might look like if you could. Notice that this tectonic plate not only consists of the upper part of the mantle but also consists of both oceanic crust and continental crust. The thickest part of the South American plate is the continental crust. The thinnest part of this plate is in the mid-Atlantic Ocean.

Like Ice Cubes in a Bowl of Punch

Think about ice cubes floating in a bowl of punch. If there are enough cubes, they will cover the surface of the punch and bump into one another. Parts of the ice cubes are below the surface of the punch and displace the punch. Large pieces of ice displace more punch than small pieces of ice. Tectonic plates "float" on the asthenosphere in a similar way. The plates cover the surface of the asthenosphere, and they touch one another and move around. The lithosphere displaces the asthenosphere. Thick tectonic plates, such as those made of continental crust, displace more asthenosphere than do thin plates, such as those made of oceanic lithosphere.

✔ **Reading Check** Why do tectonic plates made of continental lithosphere displace more asthenosphere than tectonic plates made of oceanic lithosphere do?

Quick Lab

Tectonic Ice Cubes

1. Take the bottom half of a clear, **2 L soda bottle** that has been cut in half. Make sure that the label has been removed.
2. Fill the bottle with **water** to about 1 cm below the top edge of the bottle.
3. Get **three pieces of irregularly shaped ice** that are small, medium, and large.
4. Float the ice in the water, and note how much of each piece is below the surface of the water.
5. Do all pieces of ice float mostly below the surface? Which piece is mostly below the surface? Why?

Close

Reteaching

Putting the Layers in Order
List Earth's physical layers on the board in random order. Have students arrange the list in the correct order. Then, have students help you write the compositional layers beside the physical layers (using brackets to indicate overlaps). Then, have students help you describe the characteristics of each layer.
 Logical

Quiz

Ask students whether each of the statements below is true or false. Have students correct false statements.

1. The inner core of the Earth is solid and made primarily of iron. (true)

2. The asthenosphere is the thinnest physical layer. (false; The lithosphere is the thinnest layer.)

Alternative Assessment

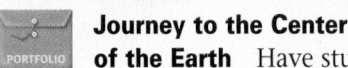 **Journey to the Center of the Earth** Have students write a story describing their "journey to the center of the Earth," or have them write a travel guide that describes the experience of traveling through Earth's different layers. Have them draw and color-code a model of Earth to include with their project. Emphasize that this model must show layers defined by chemical composition and by physical properties. Visual

Build a Seismograph
Seismographs are instruments that seismologists, scientists who study earthquakes, use to detect seismic waves. Research seismograph designs with an adult. For example, a simple seismograph can be built by using a weight suspended by a spring next to a ruler. With an adult, attempt to construct a home seismograph based on a design you have selected. Outline each of the steps used to build your seismograph, and present the written outline to your teacher.

ACTIVITY

Mapping the Earth's Interior

How do scientists know things about the deepest parts of the Earth, where no one has ever been? Scientists have never even drilled through the crust, which is only a thin skin on the surface of the Earth. So, how do we know so much about the mantle and the core?

Would you be surprised to know that some of the answers come from earthquakes? When an earthquake happens, vibrations called *seismic waves* are produced. Seismic waves travel at different speeds through the Earth. Their speed depends on the density and composition of material that they pass through. For example, a seismic wave traveling through a solid will go faster than a seismic wave traveling through a liquid.

When an earthquake happens, machines called *seismographs* measure the times at which seismic waves arrive at different distances from an earthquake. Seismologists can then use these distances and travel times to calculate the density and thickness of each physical layer of the Earth. **Figure 6** shows how seismic waves travel through the Earth.

Reading Check What are some properties of seismic waves?

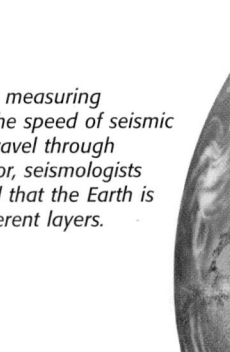

Figure 6 *By measuring changes in the speed of seismic waves that travel through Earth's interior, seismologists have learned that the Earth is made of different layers.*

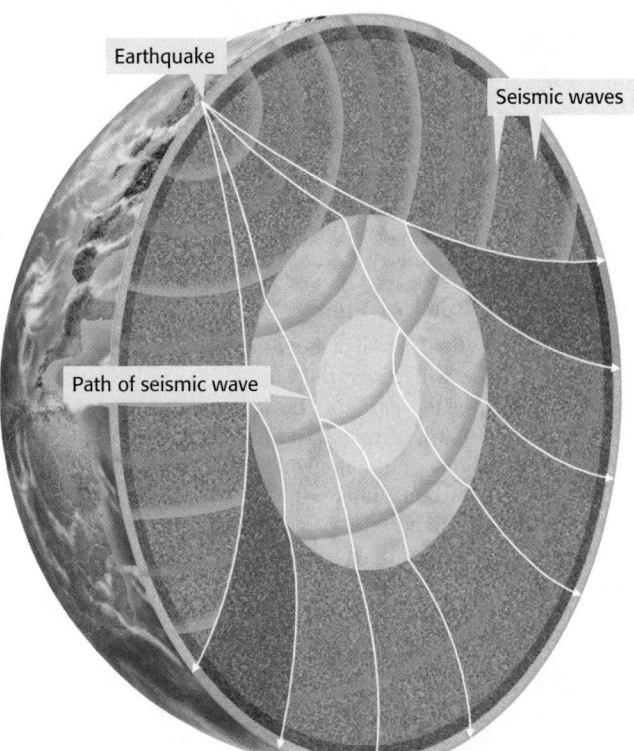

Earthquake

Seismic waves

Path of seismic wave

CHAPTER RESOURCES

Technology

Transparencies
• E21 Discoveries of the Earth's Interior

Answer to Reading Check
Answers may vary. A seismic wave traveling through a solid will go faster than a seismic wave traveling through a liquid.

Summary

- The Earth is made up of three layers—the crust, the mantle, and the core—based on chemical composition. Less dense compounds make up the crust and mantle. Denser compounds make up the core.

- The Earth is made up of five main physical layers: the lithosphere, the asthenosphere, the mesosphere, the outer core, and the inner core.

- Tectonic plates are large pieces of the lithosphere that move around on the Earth's surface.

- The crust in some tectonic plates is mainly continental. Other plates have only oceanic crust. Still other plates include both continental and oceanic crust.

- Thick tectonic plates, such as those in which the crust is mainly continental, displace more asthenosphere than do thin plates, such as those in which the crust is mainly oceanic.

- Knowledge about the layers of the Earth comes from the study of seismic waves caused by earthquakes.

Using Key Terms

For each pair of terms, explain how the meanings of the terms differ.

1. *crust* and *mantle*

2. *lithosphere* and *asthenosphere*

Understanding Key Ideas

3. The part of the Earth that is molten is the
   a. crust.
   b. mantle.
   c. outer core.
   d. inner core.

4. The part of the Earth on which the tectonic plates move is the
   a. lithosphere.
   b. asthenosphere.
   c. mesosphere.
   d. crust.

5. Identify the layers of the Earth by their chemical composition.

6. Identify the layers of the Earth by their physical properties.

7. Describe a tectonic plate.

8. Explain how scientists know about the structure of the Earth's interior.

Interpreting Graphics

9. According to the wave speeds shown in the table below, which two physical layers of the Earth are densest?

| Speed of Seismic Waves in Earth's Interior ||
Physical layer	Wave speed
Lithosphere	7 to 8 km/s
Asthenosphere	7 to 11 km/s
Mesosphere	11 to 13 km/s
Outer core	8 to 10 km/s
Inner core	11 to 12 km/s

Critical Thinking

10. **Making Comparisons** Explain the difference between the crust and the lithosphere.

11. **Analyzing Ideas** Why does a seismic wave travel faster through solid rock than through water?

For a variety of links related to this chapter, go to www.scilinks.org
Topic: Composition of the Earth; Structure of the Earth
SciLinks code: HSM0329; HSM1468

Answers to Section Review

1. Sample answer: The crust is the thin, outermost layer of the Earth. It is made mainly of less dense compounds and is less than 1% of the Earth's mass. The mantle is a thick layer beneath the crust. The mantle is made of dense compounds and is 67% of the Earth's mass.

2. Sample answer: The lithosphere is rigid and is divided into tectonic plates. The asthenosphere is a layer of soft mantle material that flows very slowly.

3. c

4. b

CHAPTER RESOURCES

Chapter Resource File

- Section Quiz **GENERAL**
- Section Review **GENERAL**
- Vocabulary and Section Summary **GENERAL**
- Reinforcement Worksheet **BASIC**
- Datasheet for Quick Lab

5. The crust is made mainly of the elements oxygen, silicon, and aluminum. The mantle has more magnesium and less aluminum and silicon than the crust has. The core is made mostly of iron.

6. The lithosphere is the outermost, rigid layer of the Earth. Beneath the lithosphere is the asthenosphere, a plastic layer of the mantle on which the lithosphere moves. The mesosphere is the strong, lower part of the mantle. The outer core is the liquid layer of the Earth's core that lies between the mantle and the inner core. The solid, dense center of our planet is the inner core.

7. A tectonic plate is a large piece of the Earth's lithosphere that moves slowly on top of the asthenosphere. Tectonic plates are composed of continental crust, oceanic crust, and both continental and oceanic crust.

8. Scientists can measure the speeds at which seismic waves travel through different parts of the Earth. This measurement helps them calculate the density and thickness of each layer the waves pass through.

9. According to the wave speeds in the table, the mesosphere and the inner core are the two densest physical layers. (In reality, the outer core and inner core are the two densest layers. Because the outer core is liquid, wave speed through the outer core is slower than it is in the mesosphere.)

10. The crust is the thin, outermost layer of the Earth that is compositionally different than the mantle. The lithosphere is a thick layer containing both the crust and upper mantle but which is rigid compared to the underlying asthenosphere.

11. Seismic waves travel through solid rock faster than they do through water because solid rock is denser than water.

Focus

Overview

This section explains the continental drift hypothesis and how the continents have moved to their present locations. Students will learn that support for this hypothesis came when mid-ocean ridges were discovered. They will also learn that sea-floor spreading was supported by the record of reversals of the Earth's magnetic field present in oceanic crust.

Bellringer

Ask students to explain why the following statement is true or false: "The North American continent is moving westward." (true; The plate that North America sits on is moving to the west.)

Motivate

ACTIVITY ──────── GENERAL

Reconstructing Pangaea Have students work in small groups to create a model of Pangaea. Provide each group with two world maps. Have the groups cut the continents out of one map and treat them as puzzle pieces by seeing how they best fit together. Refer to both the complete and the altered maps, and help students explain and demonstrate how each continent moved from its original position.

LS Visual — English Language Learners

What You Will Learn

- Describe Wegener's hypothesis of continental drift.
- Explain how sea-floor spreading provides a way for continents to move.
- Describe how new oceanic lithosphere forms at mid-ocean ridges.
- Explain how magnetic reversals provide evidence for sea-floor spreading.

Vocabulary

continental drift
sea-floor spreading

READING STRATEGY

Paired Summarizing Read this section silently. In pairs, take turns summarizing the material. Stop to discuss ideas that seem confusing.

Restless Continents

Have you ever looked at a map of the world and noticed how the coastlines of continents on opposite sides of the oceans appear to fit together like the pieces of a puzzle? Is it just coincidence that the coastlines fit together well? Is it possible that the continents were actually together sometime in the past?

Wegener's Continental Drift Hypothesis

One scientist who looked at the pieces of this puzzle was Alfred Wegener (VAY guh nuhr). In the early 1900s, he wrote about his hypothesis of *continental drift*. **Continental drift** is the hypothesis that states that the continents once formed a single landmass, broke up, and drifted to their present locations. This hypothesis seemed to explain a lot of puzzling observations, including the observation of how well continents fit together.

Continental drift also explained why fossils of the same plant and animal species are found on continents that are on different sides of the Atlantic Ocean. Many of these ancient species could not have crossed the Atlantic Ocean. As you can see in **Figure 1,** without continental drift, this pattern of fossils would be hard to explain. In addition to fossils, similar types of rock and evidence of the same ancient climatic conditions were found on several continents.

✓ **Reading Check** How did fossils provide evidence for Wegener's hypothesis of continental drift? (*See the Appendix for answers to Reading Checks.*)

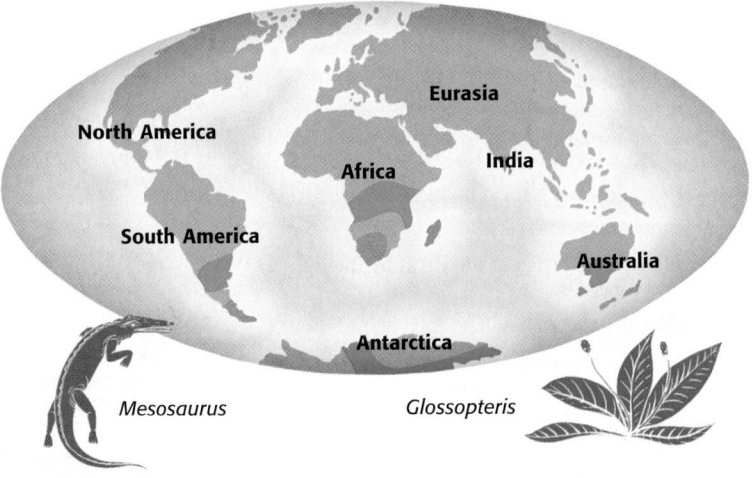

Figure 1 *Fossils of* Mesosaurus, *a small, aquatic reptile, and* Glossopteris, *an ancient plant species, have been found on several continents.*

CHAPTER RESOURCES

Chapter Resource File

 • Lesson Plan
• Directed Reading A **BASIC**
• Directed Reading B **SPECIAL NEEDS**

Technology

 Transparencies
• Bellringer
• E22 The Breakup of Pangaea
• **LINK TO LIFE SCIENCE** L26 Evolution of the Galápagos Finches

Workbooks

 Interactive Textbook Struggling Readers

Answer to Reading Check

Similar fossils were found on landmasses that are very far apart. The best explanation for this phenomenon is that the landmasses were once joined.

Figure 2 The Drifting Continents

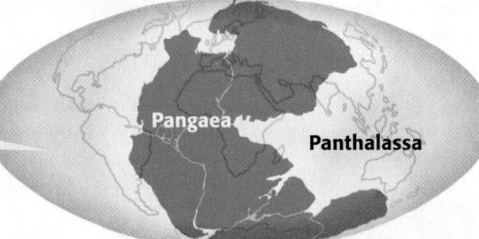

245 Million Years Ago
Pangaea existed when some of the earliest dinosaurs were roaming the Earth. The continent was surrounded by a sea called *Panthalassa*, which means "all sea."

180 Million Years Ago
Gradually, Pangaea broke into two big pieces. The northern piece is called *Laurasia*. The southern piece is called *Gondwana*.

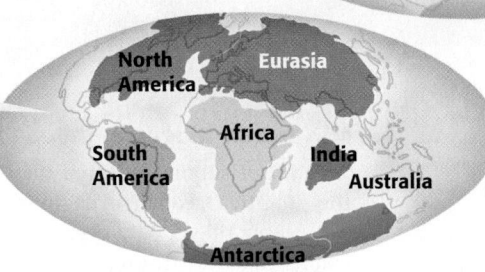

65 Million Years Ago
By the time the dinosaurs became extinct, Laurasia and Gondwana had split into smaller pieces.

The Breakup of Pangaea

Wegener made many observations before proposing his hypothesis of continental drift. He thought that all of the present continents were once joined in a single, huge continent. Wegener called this continent *Pangaea* (pan JEE uh), which is Greek for "all earth." We now know from the hypothesis of plate tectonics that Pangaea existed about 245 million years ago. We also know that Pangaea further split into two huge continents—Laurasia and Gondwana—about 180 million years ago. As shown in **Figure 2,** these two continents split again and formed the continents we know today.

Sea-Floor Spreading

When Wegener put forth his hypothesis of continental drift, many scientists would not accept his hypothesis. From the calculated strength of the rocks, it did not seem possible for the crust to move in this way. During Wegener's life, no one knew the answer. It wasn't until many years later that evidence provided some clues to the forces that moved the continents.

continental drift the hypothesis that states that the continents once formed a single landmass, broke up, and drifted to their present locations

MISCONCEPTION ///ALERT\\\

Supercontinents Past and Future
About 500 million years before Pangaea began to form, another supercontinent dominated the globe—Rodinia. Some scientists speculate that the formation of supercontinents occurs as a cycle of accretion and breakup.

Reteaching — **BASIC**

Evidence for Continental Drift

Organize the class into groups of three. Ask each group to choose one of the following lines of evidence that support the continental drift hypothesis: fossil similarities, landform similarities, and sea-floor spreading. Have each group work for 20 min to gather evidence for the continental drift hypothesis, and then ask groups to share their findings with the class. **LS** Logical **Co-op Learning**

Quiz — **GENERAL**

1. What material creates new lithosphere at a mid-ocean ridge? (solidified magma)

2. What was Pangaea? (the large landmass that later broke up to form two supercontinents and then fragmented further to form the six continents that exist today)

Alternative Assessment — **GENERAL**

Writing **Sea-Floor Spreading**
Have students write a paragraph explaining how sea-floor spreading causes continents to move apart. Students should also include a diagram of this process. **LS** Logical/Visual

---

Figure 3 **Sea-Floor Spreading**

Sea-floor spreading creates new oceanic lithosphere at mid-ocean ridges.

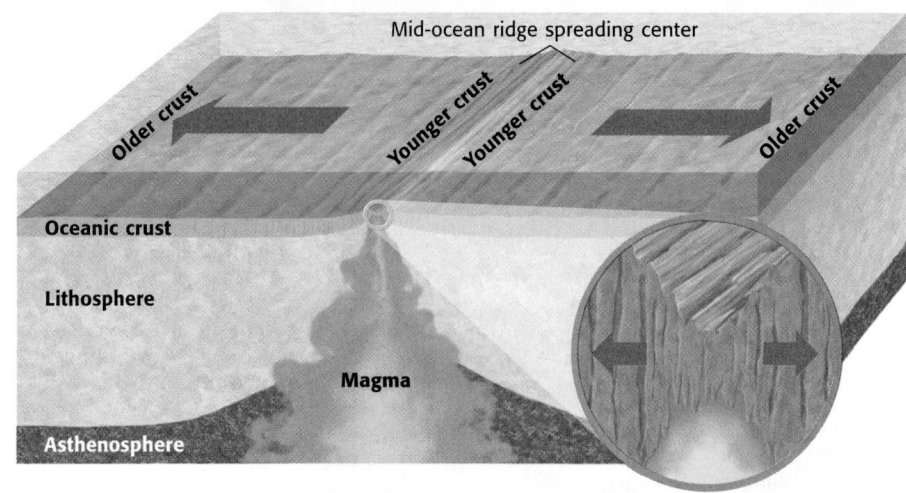

sea-floor spreading the process by which new oceanic lithosphere forms as magma rises toward the surface and solidifies

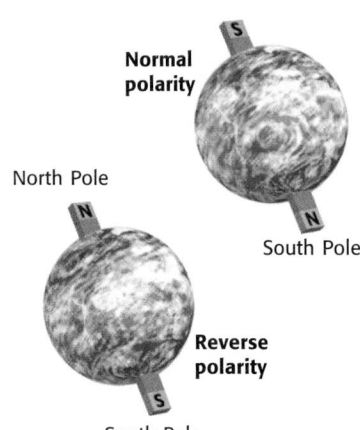

Figure 4 *The polarity of Earth's magnetic field changes over time.*

Mid-Ocean Ridges and Sea-Floor Spreading

A chain of submerged mountains runs through the center of the Atlantic Ocean. The chain is part of a worldwide system of mid-ocean ridges. Mid-ocean ridges are underwater mountain chains that run through Earth's ocean basins.

Mid-ocean ridges are places where sea-floor spreading takes place. **Sea-floor spreading** is the process by which new oceanic lithosphere forms as magma rises toward the surface and solidifies. As the tectonic plates move away from each other, the sea floor spreads apart and magma fills in the gap. As this new crust forms, the older crust gets pushed away from the mid-ocean ridge. As **Figure 3** shows, the older crust is farther away from the mid-ocean ridge than the younger crust is.

Evidence for Sea-Floor Spreading: Magnetic Reversals

Some of the most important evidence of sea-floor spreading comes from magnetic reversals recorded in the ocean floor. Throughout Earth's history, the north and south magnetic poles have changed places many times. When the poles change places, the polarity of Earth's magnetic poles changes, as shown in **Figure 4**. When Earth's magnetic poles change places, this change is called a *magnetic reversal*.

CONNECTION to Physical Science — **GENERAL**

Sonar Researchers used sonar to discover that the ocean floor is not flat. In the 1950s, scientists broadcast sound waves toward the sea floor and measured how long the waves took to return. The echoes revealed valleys and mountains. Scientists were amazed to find a chain of undersea mountains snaking thousands of kilometers around the globe— the mid-ocean ridges.

Homework — **GENERAL**

Mid-Ocean Ridges Have students research and answer the following questions about **Figure 3:**

• Why does molten rock from the mantle come to the surface at the ridges?

• Why does the ocean floor spread apart at the ridges?

• Why is rock formed at the ridges called *new rock*?

Emphasize that mid-ocean ridges are not always in the center of an ocean. **LS** Verbal

Magnetic Reversals and Sea-Floor Spreading

The molten rock at the mid-ocean ridges contains tiny grains of magnetic minerals. These mineral grains contain iron and are like compasses. They align with the magnetic field of the Earth. When the molten rock cools, the record of these tiny compasses remains in the rock. This record is then carried slowly away from the spreading center of the ridge as sea-floor spreading occurs.

As you can see in **Figure 5,** when the Earth's magnetic field reverses, the magnetic mineral grains align in the opposite direction. The new rock records the direction of the Earth's magnetic field. As the sea floor spreads away from a mid-ocean ridge, it carries with it a record of magnetic reversals. This record of magnetic reversals was the final proof that sea-floor spreading does occur.

✓ Reading Check How is a record of magnetic reversals recorded in molten rock at mid-ocean ridges?

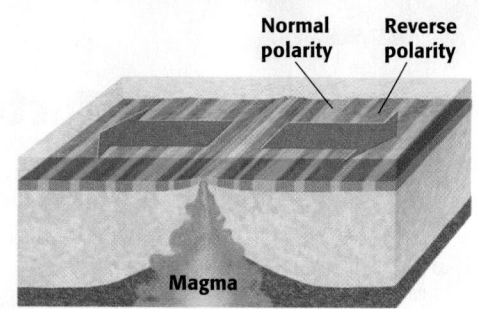

Normal polarity   Reverse polarity

Magma

Figure 5 *Magnetic reversals in oceanic crust are shown as bands of light blue and dark blue oceanic crust. Light blue bands indicate normal polarity, and dark blue bands indicate reverse polarity.*

SECTION Review

Summary

- Wegener hypothesized that continents drift apart from one another and have done so in the past.

- The process by which new oceanic lithosphere forms at mid-ocean ridges is called sea-floor spreading.

- As tectonic plates separate, the sea floor spreads apart and magma fills in the gap.

- Magnetic reversals are recorded over time in oceanic crust.

Using Key Terms

1. In your own words, write a definition for each of the following terms: *continental drift* and *sea-floor spreading*.

Understanding Key Ideas

2. At mid-ocean ridges,
   a. the crust is older.
   b. sea-floor spreading occurs.
   c. oceanic lithosphere is destroyed.
   d. tectonic plates are colliding.

3. Explain how oceanic lithosphere forms at mid-ocean ridges.

4. What is magnetic reversal?

Math Skills

5. If a piece of sea floor has moved 50 km in 5 million years, what is the yearly rate of sea-floor motion?

Critical Thinking

6. **Identifying Relationships** Explain how magnetic reversals provide evidence for sea-floor spreading.

7. **Applying Concepts** Why do bands indicating magnetic reversals appear to be of similar width on both sides of a mid-ocean ridge?

8. **Applying Concepts** Why do you think that old rocks are rare on the ocean floor?

For a variety of links related to this chapter, go to www.scilinks.org

Topic: Tectonic Plates
SciLinks code: HSM1497

Answers to Section Review

1. Sample answer: Continental drift is the hypothesis developed by Alfred Wegener to explain why the continents are in their present locations. Sea-floor spreading is a process in which magma rises to the surface at a mid-ocean ridge, solidifies, and forms new oceanic lithosphere.

2. b

3. Magma rises to the surface at a mid-ocean ridge and solidifies to form new oceanic lithosphere.

4. Magnetic reversal is the change in the polarity of Earth's magnetic field.

5. *rate = time ÷ distance;*
   50 km ÷ 5,000,000 y =
   .00001 km/y = 10 mm/y

6. As oceanic crust spreads away from a mid-ocean ridge, the crust carries a sequence of bands of rock that shows magnetic reversals. The similar sequence of magnetic reversals on both sides of the ridge, even at a large distance from the ridge, indicates that the sea floor is spreading away from a center at which new oceanic lithosphere is forming.

7. The rate of sea-floor spreading on opposite sides of a mid-ocean ridge occurs at a similar rate, so bands indicating magnetic reversals will have a similar width.

8. Answers may vary. Students may suspect that older rocks re-enter the rock cycle at plate boundaries.

Answer to Reading Check

The molten rock at mid-ocean ridges contains tiny grains of magnetic minerals. The minerals align with the Earth's magnetic field before the rock cools and hardens. When the Earth' magnetic field reverses, the orientation of the mineral grains in new rocks will match the new direction of Earth's magnetic field.

CHAPTER RESOURCES

Chapter Resource File

- Section Quiz **GENERAL**
- Section Review **GENERAL**
- Vocabulary and Section Summary **GENERAL**

Technology

Transparencies
- E23 Sea-Floor Spreading

Overview

This section discusses the theory of plate tectonics. Students will learn about possible causes of some plate movements. Students will also learn about types of plate boundaries.

 Bellringer

Have students calculate the number of years that New York and the northwest coast of Africa took to reach their current locations, 6,760 km apart, if the sea floor is spreading at an average of 4 cm per year.
6,760 km = 676,000,000 cm ÷ 4 cm = 169,000,000 y. Point out that this number is fairly close to the estimate of when the breakup of Pangaea began 180 million years ago.)

Motivate

Discussion ———— GENERAL

A Preposterous Theory Write the word "preposterous" on the board. Then, discuss its meaning. Students may not realize how controversial and revolutionary the theory of continental drift was. Discuss why the idea that the enormous landmasses could "slide" across the asthenosphere seemed preposterous to some people. **LS Verbal**

What You Will Learn

● Describe the three types of tectonic plate boundaries.
● Describe the three forces thought to move tectonic plates.
● Explain how scientists measure the rate at which tectonic plates move.

Vocabulary
plate tectonics
convergent boundary
divergent boundary
transform boundary

READING STRATEGY

Brainstorming The key idea of this section is plate tectonics. Brainstorm words and phrases related to plate tectonics.

The Theory of Plate Tectonics

It takes an incredible amount of force to move a tectonic plate! But where does this force come from?

As scientists' understanding of mid-ocean ridges and magnetic reversals grew, scientists formed a theory to explain how tectonic plates move. **Plate tectonics** is the theory that the Earth's lithosphere is divided into tectonic plates that move around on top of the asthenosphere. In this section, you will learn what causes tectonic plates to move. But first you will learn about the different types of tectonic plate boundaries.

Tectonic Plate Boundaries

A boundary is a place where tectonic plates touch. All tectonic plates share boundaries with other tectonic plates. These boundaries are divided into three types: convergent, divergent, and transform. The type of boundary depends on how the tectonic plates move relative to one another. Tectonic plates can collide, separate, or slide past each other. Earthquakes can occur at all three types of plate boundaries. The figure below shows examples of tectonic plate boundaries.

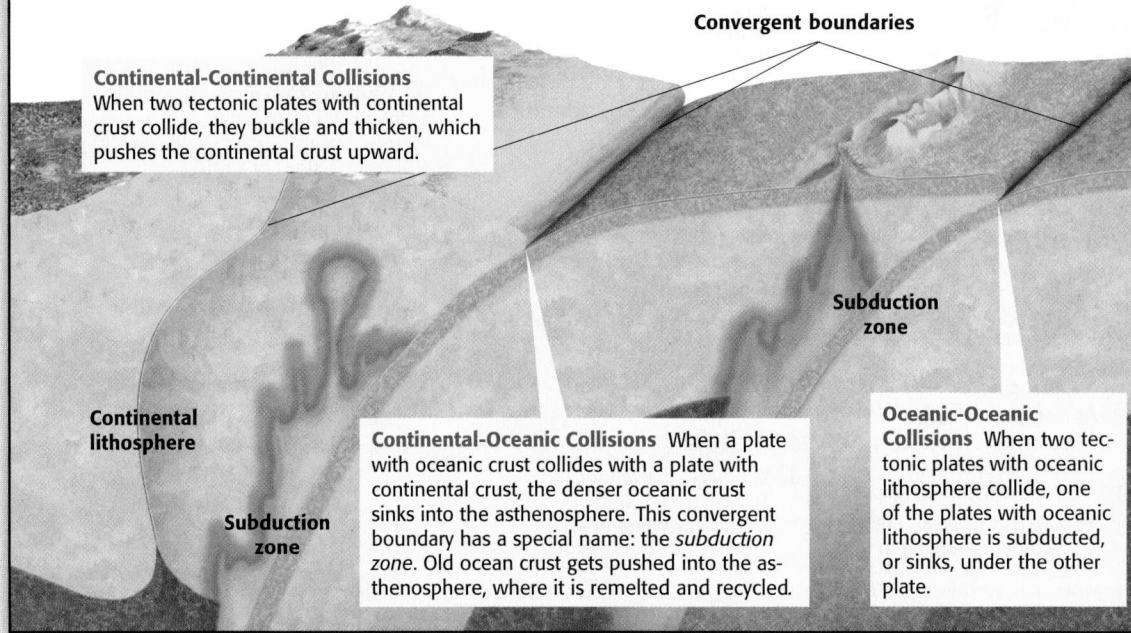

Convergent boundaries

Continental-Continental Collisions
When two tectonic plates with continental crust collide, they buckle and thicken, which pushes the continental crust upward.

Subduction zone

Continental lithosphere

Subduction zone

Continental-Oceanic Collisions When a plate with oceanic crust collides with a plate with continental crust, the denser oceanic crust sinks into the asthenosphere. This convergent boundary has a special name: the *subduction zone*. Old ocean crust gets pushed into the asthenosphere, where it is remelted and recycled.

Oceanic-Oceanic Collisions When two tectonic plates with oceanic lithosphere collide, one of the plates with oceanic lithosphere is subducted, or sinks, under the other plate.

CHAPTER RESOURCES

Chapter Resource File

📁 • Lesson Plan
• Directed Reading A **BASIC**, B **SPECIAL NEEDS**

Technology

💾 **Transparencies**
• Bellringer
• E25 & E26 Tectonic Plate Boundaries: A and B

Workbooks

📓 **Interactive Textbook** Struggling Readers

📓 **Math Skills for Science**
• A Shortcut for Multiplying Large Numbers **GENERAL**

CONNECTION to Physical Science — **GENERAL**

Temperature and Density Point out how the movement of tectonic plates is driven by differences in temperature and density. In slab pull and ridge push, gravity pulls the oceanic plate downward because the oceanic plate is denser than the continental lithosphere. In convection, hot material rises because it is less dense than cooler material, which sinks.

Convergent Boundaries

When two tectonic plates collide, the boundary between them is a **convergent boundary.** What happens at a convergent boundary depends on the kind of crust at the leading edge of each tectonic plate. The three types of convergent boundaries are continental-continental boundaries, continental-oceanic boundaries, and oceanic-oceanic boundaries.

Divergent Boundaries

When two tectonic plates separate, the boundary between them is called a **divergent boundary.** New sea floor forms at divergent boundaries. Mid-ocean ridges are the most common type of divergent boundary.

Transform Boundaries

When two tectonic plates slide past each other horizontally, the boundary between them is a **transform boundary.** The San Andreas Fault in California is a good example of a transform boundary. This fault marks the place where the Pacific and North American plates are sliding past each other.

✔️ **Reading Check** Define the term *transform boundary.* (*See the Appendix for answers to Reading Checks.*)

plate tectonics the theory that explains how large pieces of the Earth's outermost layer, called *tectonic plates,* move and change shape

convergent boundary the boundary formed by the collision of two lithospheric plates

divergent boundary the boundary between two tectonic plates that are moving away from each other

transform boundary the boundary between tectonic plates that are sliding past each other horizontally

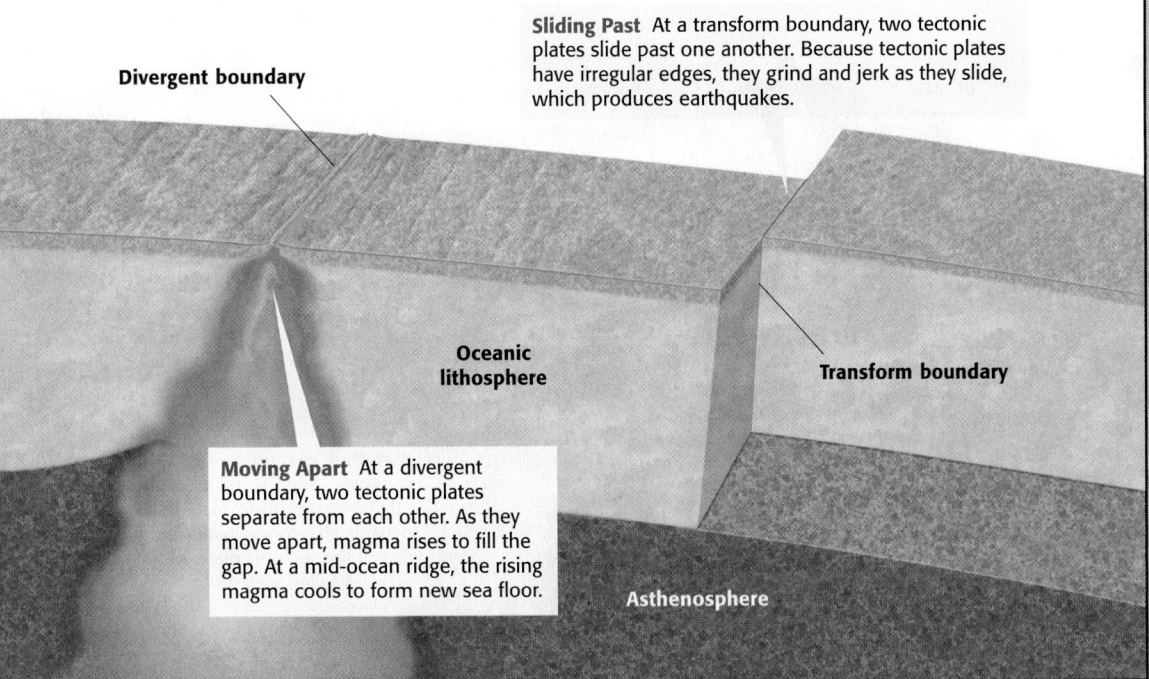

Divergent boundary

Sliding Past At a transform boundary, two tectonic plates slide past one another. Because tectonic plates have irregular edges, they grind and jerk as they slide, which produces earthquakes.

Oceanic lithosphere

Transform boundary

Moving Apart At a divergent boundary, two tectonic plates separate from each other. As they move apart, magma rises to fill the gap. At a mid-ocean ridge, the rising magma cools to form new sea floor.

Asthenosphere

SUPPORT FOR

English Language Learners
Synonyms First, check student understanding of the word *boundary.* Then, remind students that a synonym is a different word with the same meaning. Have pairs write synonyms for *boundary* in one minute. Review the lists of synonyms, and have students correct answers, if necessary. Repeat with *divergent, convergent,* and *transform.* **LS Verbal**

Answer to Reading Check

A transform boundary forms when two tectonic plates slide past each other horizontally.

Teach

 ——————— GENERAL

Geologic Features at Tectonic Plate Boundaries Ask students to form hypotheses about what kinds of geologic features exist at different types of plate boundaries. Then, have them compare a topographic world map with a world map of tectonic plates. Help students conduct library and Internet research to find out if their hypotheses were correct. **LS Logical/Visual**

MISCONCEPTION ALERT

Laws and Theories Students may think that if a theory is accepted by enough people for a long enough period of time, the theory will become a scientific law. Emphasize that scientific laws and theories are both correct and useful but that they serve different functions. A scientific law is a concise statement of fact that is accepted as true and universal. Theories are statements that are products of many scientific observations and may encompass numerous hypotheses or laws. Like a scientific law, a theory is accepted as true, but theories are much more complex than laws. A scientific law can be compared to an observation of a rubber ball. When dropped under constant conditions, the ball will always bounce as predicted. Bouncing is the only action the ball performs. On the other hand, a theory can be compared to a car. A car has many components that perform different tasks and work in unison. A part of the car may be improved, but the general function of the car is unchanged. **LS Logical**

Reteaching — BASIC

Boundary Review On the board, write the names of the five types of boundaries. Then, have student volunteers draw each boundary on the board. As a class, discuss the landforms that result from each type of boundary. **LS** Verbal

Quiz — GENERAL

1. Why are there several categories of convergent plate boundaries? (Continental and oceanic plates behave differently when they are pushed together because their composition and density differs.)

2. Explain the process of subduction. (A denser oceanic plate is forced beneath a less dense oceanic or continental plate at a convergent boundary. Gravity pulls the denser oceanic plate into the hot asthenosphere, which causes melting.)

Alternative Assessment — GENERAL

Modeling Plate Boundaries
Challenge students to model plate movement at each type of tectonic boundary. Have them work in pairs with materials they have chosen. As students demonstrate plate movements, they should be prepared to explain the composition of each plate and the differences between the forces at work. **LS** Kinesthetic/Logical

English Language Learners

Possible Causes of Tectonic Plate Motion

You have learned that plate tectonics is the theory that the lithosphere is divided into tectonic plates that move around on top of the asthenosphere. What causes the motion of tectonic plates? Remember that the solid rock of the asthenosphere flows very slowly. This movement occurs because of changes in density within the asthenosphere. These density changes are caused by the outward flow of thermal energy from deep within the Earth. When rock is heated, it expands, becomes less dense, and tends to rise to the surface of the Earth. As the rock gets near the surface, the rock cools, becomes more dense, and tends to sink. **Figure 1** shows three possible causes of tectonic plate motion.

✓ Reading Check What causes changes in density in the asthenosphere?

Figure 1 Three Possible Driving Forces of Plate Tectonics

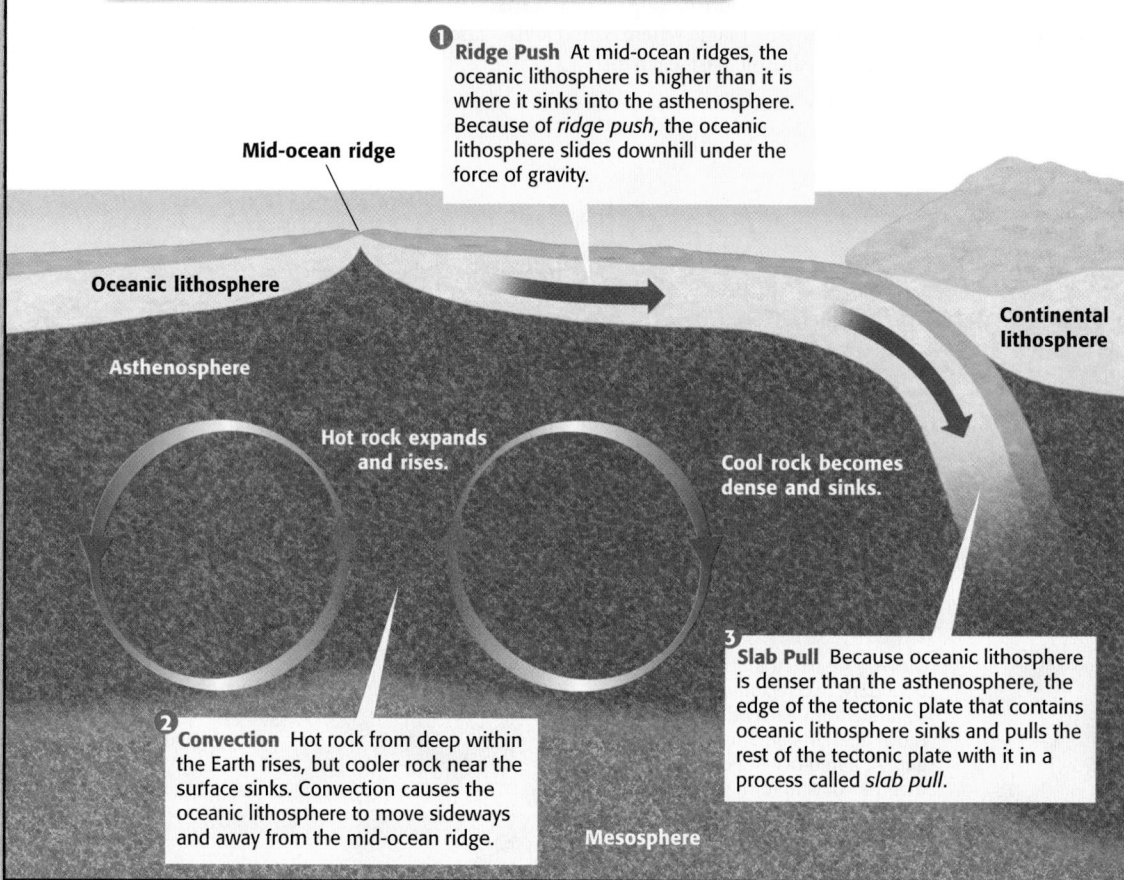

1 Ridge Push At mid-ocean ridges, the oceanic lithosphere is higher than it is where it sinks into the asthenosphere. Because of *ridge push*, the oceanic lithosphere slides downhill under the force of gravity.

Mid-ocean ridge

Oceanic lithosphere

Continental lithosphere

Asthenosphere

Hot rock expands and rises.

Cool rock becomes dense and sinks.

2 Convection Hot rock from deep within the Earth rises, but cooler rock near the surface sinks. Convection causes the oceanic lithosphere to move sideways and away from the mid-ocean ridge.

3 Slab Pull Because oceanic lithosphere is denser than the asthenosphere, the edge of the tectonic plate that contains oceanic lithosphere sinks and pulls the rest of the tectonic plate with it in a process called *slab pull*.

Mesosphere

Answer to Reading Check
The circulation of thermal energy causes changes in density in the asthenosphere. As rock is heated, it expands, becomes less dense, and rises. As rock cools, it contracts, becomes denser, and sinks.

Homework — ADVANCED

Writing **Controversial Theories** Alfred Wegener wrote, "If it turns out that sense and meaning are now becoming evident in the whole history of the Earth's development, why should we hesitate to toss the old views overboard?" Ask students to think about why the acceptance of new ideas in science is a slow process. Ask students to explain why continental drift and other controversial theories took a long time to be accepted. **LS** Logical

Tracking Tectonic Plate Motion

How fast do tectonic plates move? The answer to this question depends on many factors, such as the type and shape of the tectonic plate and the way that the tectonic plate interacts with the tectonic plates that surround it. Tectonic plate movements are so slow and gradual that you can't see or feel them—the movement is measured in centimeters per year.

The Global Positioning System

Scientists use a system of satellites called the *global positioning system* (GPS), shown in **Figure 2**, to measure the rate of tectonic plate movement. Radio signals are continuously beamed from satellites to GPS ground stations, which record the exact distance between the satellites and the ground station. Over time, these distances change slightly. By recording the time it takes for the GPS ground stations to move a given distance, scientists can measure the speed at which each tectonic plate moves.

GPS satellite

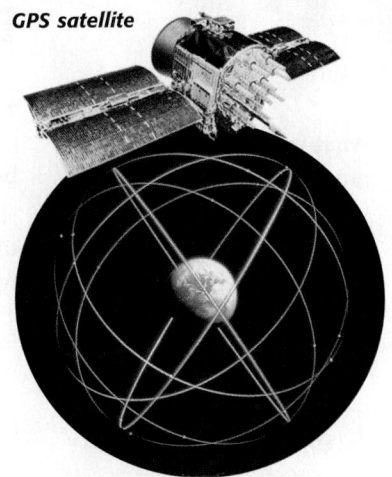

Figure 2 *The image above shows the orbits of the GPS satellites.*

Using Key Terms

1. In your own words, write a definition for the term *plate tectonics*.

Understanding Key Ideas

2. The speed a tectonic plate moves per year is best measured in
   a. kilometers per year.
   b. centimeters per year.
   c. meters per year.
   d. millimeters per year.

3. Briefly describe three possible driving forces of tectonic plate movement.

4. Explain how scientists use GPS to measure the rate of tectonic plate movement.

Math Skills

5. If an orbiting satellite has a diameter of 60 cm, what is the total surface area of the satellite? (Hint: *surface area* $= 4\pi r^2$)

Critical Thinking

6. **Identifying Relationships** When convection takes place in the mantle, why does cool rock material sink and warm rock material rise?

7. **Analyzing Processes** Why does oceanic crust sink beneath continental crust at convergent boundaries?

For a variety of links related to this chapter, go to www.scilinks.org

Topic: Plate Tectonics
SciLinks code: HSM1171

Developed and maintained by the National Science Teachers Association

Answers to Section Review

1. Sample answer: Plate tectonics is the theory that the lithosphere is divided into tectonic plates that move slowly across the asthenosphere.

2. b

3. Three possible driving forces of tectonic plate movement are ridge push, slab pull, and convection. Ridge push occurs when an oceanic plate slides down the boundary between the lithosphere and asthenosphere because of gravity. Slab pull occurs when the sinking edge of an oceanic plate pulls the rest of the plate down with it into the subduction zone. Convection occurs when hot mantle material in the asthenosphere convects and causes the tectonic plate to move sideways.

4. In the GPS process, radio signals are beamed from satellites to ground stations. The distance between the satellites and a ground station is recorded. Over time, these distances change slightly. Scientists can measure the rate at which tectonic plates move by recording the time it takes for ground stations to move a given distance.

5. $(4 \times 3.1416 \times 30\,cm^2) = 11{,}310\ cm^2$

6. During the convection process in the mantle, cooler material sinks because it is denser than warmer material.

7. Oceanic crust sinks beneath continental crust at convergent boundaries because oceanic crust is denser than continental crust.

Focus

Overview

This section explores effects of tectonic forces on the Earth's crust. Students will learn how stress on rock causes it to fold or fault in various ways. The section also discusses how different types of mountains form from the action of tectonic forces and volcanic activity.

 Bellringer

Display photographs of each type of mountain discussed in this section. Have students write a description of each example and suggest how each might have formed.

Motivate

Demonstration — GENERAL

Modeling Deformation Display two thin strips of modeling clay, one frozen and one at room temperature. Have a volunteer demonstrate what happens when the warm clay is bent. (It folds.)

Ask students to predict what will happen to the frozen clay when a force is applied to it. Provide protective gloves, and have a second volunteer attempt to bend the frozen clay. (It should break.) **LS Kinesthetic/Visual**

What You Will Learn

- Describe two types of stress that deform rocks.
- Describe three major types of folds.
- Explain the differences between the three major types of faults.
- Identify the most common types of mountains.
- Explain the difference between uplift and subsidence.

Vocabulary

compression	fault
tension	uplift
folding	subsidence

READING STRATEGY

Discussion Read this section silently. Write down questions that you have about this section. Discuss your questions in a small group.

Deforming the Earth's Crust

Have you ever tried to bend something, only to have it break? Take long, uncooked pieces of spaghetti, and bend them very slowly but only a little. Now, bend them again, but this time, bend them much farther and faster. What happened?

How can a material bend at one time and break at another time? The answer is that the stress you put on the material was different each time. *Stress* is the amount of force per unit area on a given material. The same principle applies to the rocks in the Earth's crust. Different things happen to rock when different types of stress are applied.

Deformation

The process by which the shape of a rock changes because of stress is called *deformation*. In the example above, the spaghetti deformed in two different ways—by bending and by breaking. **Figure 1** illustrates this concept. The same thing happens in rock layers. Rock layers bend when stress is placed on them. But when enough stress is placed on rocks, they can reach their elastic limit and break.

Compression and Tension

The type of stress that occurs when an object is squeezed, such as when two tectonic plates collide, is called **compression.** When compression occurs at a convergent boundary, large mountain ranges can form.

Another form of stress is *tension*. **Tension** is stress that occurs when forces act to stretch an object. As you might guess, tension occurs at divergent plate boundaries, such as mid-ocean ridges, when two tectonic plates pull away from each other.

✓ **Reading Check** How do the forces of plate tectonics cause rock to deform? (*See the Appendix for answers to Reading Checks.*)

Figure 1 *When a small amount of stress is placed on uncooked spaghetti, the spaghetti bends. Additional stress causes the spaghetti to break.*

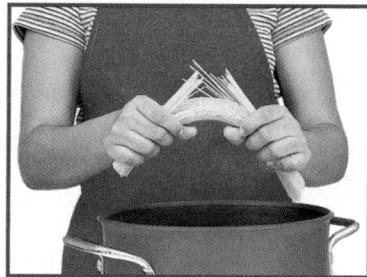

CHAPTER RESOURCES

Chapter Resource File

 • **Lesson Plan**
 • **Directed Reading A** BASIC
 • **Directed Reading B** SPECIAL NEEDS

Technology

 Transparencies
 • Bellringer

Workbooks

 Interactive Textbook Struggling Readers

Answer to Reading Check

Compression can cause rocks to be pushed into mountain ranges as tectonic plates collide at convergent boundaries. Tension can pull rocks apart as tectonic plates separate at divergent boundaries.

Figure 2 Folding: When Rock Layers Bend Because of Stress

Unstressed

Horizontal stress

Vertical stress

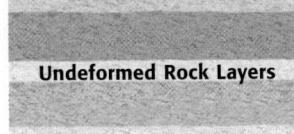

Undeformed Rock Layers

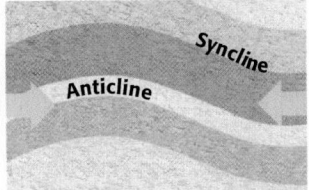

Syncline

Anticline

Monocline

Folding

The bending of rock layers because of stress in the Earth's crust is called **folding.** Scientists assume that all rock layers started as horizontal layers. So, when scientists see a fold, they know that deformation has taken place.

Types of Folds

Depending on how the rock layers deform, different types of folds are made. **Figure 2** shows the two most common types of folds—*anticlines*, or upward-arching folds, and *synclines,* downward, troughlike folds. Another type of fold is a *monocline*. In a monocline, rock layers are folded so that both ends of the fold are horizontal. Imagine taking a stack of paper and laying it on a table. Think of the sheets of paper as different rock layers. Now put a book under one end of the stack. You can see that both ends of the sheets are horizontal, but all of the sheets are bent in the middle.

Folds can be large or small. The largest folds are measured in kilometers. Other folds are also obvious but are much smaller. These small folds can be measured in centimeters. **Figure 3** shows examples of large and small folds.

compression stress that occurs when forces act to squeeze an object

tension stress that occurs when forces act to stretch an object

folding the bending of rock layers due to stress

Figure 3 *The large photo shows mountain-sized folds in the Rocky Mountains. The small photo shows a rock that has folds smaller than a penknife.*

Section 4 • Deforming the Earth's Crust **395**

Hanging Walls Versus Footwalls
Have students refer to **Figure 4** while you give the following explanation of hanging walls and footwalls: "When a fault occurs at an angle, the hanging wall is the block above the fault surface and the footwall is the block beneath the fault surface." Have students identify the hanging walls and footwalls in **Figure 5.** Have students do hand motions as they explain so that they can feel compression and tension. **LS Visual/Kinesthetic**

Discussion ─── **GENERAL**

Forces that Cause Faults Have students look at **Figure 5,** and point out that in a normal fault the hanging wall moves downward. Ask students to describe the tectonic force that causes this type of fault movement. (tension or stretching from plate movements pulling rocks apart) Have a student volunteer to use **Figure 5** to discuss the forces that cause reverse faults. (When plate movements squeeze rocks, compression forces the hanging wall up over the footwall.) **LS Visual/Logical**   English Language Learners

Fault

Footwall   **Hanging wall**

Figure 4 *The position of a fault block determines whether it is a hanging wall or a footwall.*

fault a break in a body of rock along which one block slides relative to another

Faulting

Some rock layers break when stress is applied to them. The surface along which rocks break and slide past each other is called a **fault.** The blocks of crust on each side of the fault are called *fault blocks.*

When a fault is not vertical, understanding the difference between its two sides—the *hanging wall* and the *footwall*—is useful. **Figure 4** shows the difference between a hanging wall and a footwall. Two main types of faults can form. The type of fault that forms depends on how the hanging wall and footwall move in relationship to each other.

Normal Faults

A *normal fault* is shown in **Figure 5.** When a normal fault moves, it causes the hanging wall to move down relative to the footwall. Normal faults usually occur when tectonic forces cause tension that pulls rocks apart.

Reverse Faults

A *reverse fault* is shown in **Figure 5.** When a reverse fault moves, it causes the hanging wall to move up relative to the footwall. This movement is the reverse of a normal fault. Reverse faults usually happen when tectonic forces cause compression that pushes rocks together.

✓ Reading Check How does the hanging wall in a normal fault move in relation to a reverse fault?

Figure 5   Normal and Reverse Faults

Normal Fault When rocks are pulled apart because of tension, normal faults often form.

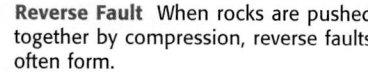

Reverse Fault When rocks are pushed together by compression, reverse faults often form.

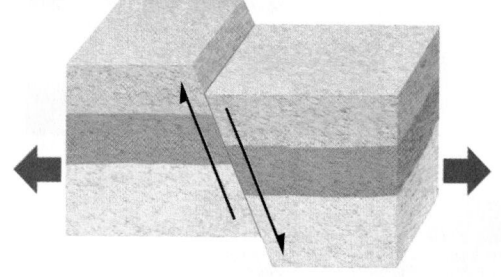

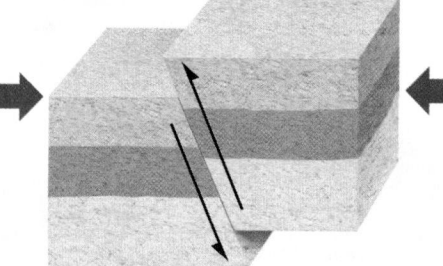

Answer to Reading Check
In a normal fault, the hanging wall moves down. In a reverse fault, the hanging wall moves up.

Is That a Fact!

Thrust faults are large-scale, low-angle reverse faults caused by the collision of tectonic plates. They are an example of what can happen when stress (compression) is applied to the crust. An important example of thrust faulting in the United States is the Idaho-Wyoming thrust belt. Large-scale folding can also result from compression.

Figure 6 *The photo at left is a normal fault. The photo at right is a reverse fault.*

Telling the Difference Between Faults

It's easy to tell the difference between a normal fault and a reverse fault in drawings with arrows. But what types of faults are shown in **Figure 6**? You can certainly see the faults, but which one is a normal fault, and which one is a reverse fault? In the top left photo in **Figure 6,** one side has obviously moved relative to the other side. You can tell this fault is a normal fault by looking at the order of sedimentary rock layers. If you compare the two dark layers near the surface, you can see that the hanging wall has moved down relative to the footwall.

Strike-Slip Faults

A third major type of fault is called a *strike-slip fault.* An illustration of a strike-slip fault is shown in **Figure 7.** *Strike-slip faults* form when opposing forces cause rock to break and move horizontally. If you were standing on one side of a strike-slip fault looking across the fault when it moved, the ground on the other side would appear to move to your left or right. The San Andreas Fault in California is a spectacular example of a strike-slip fault.

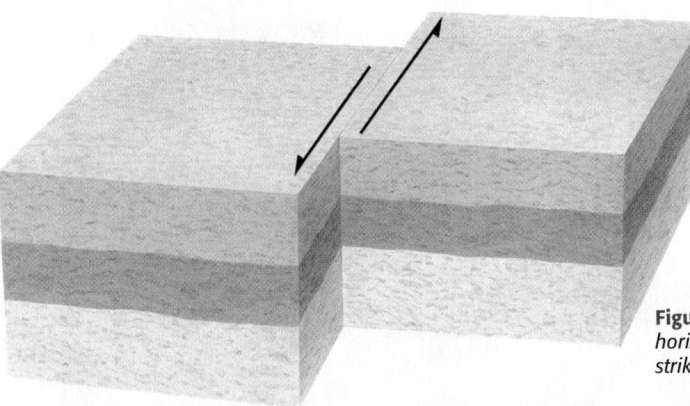

Figure 7 *When rocks are moved horizontally by opposing forces, strike-slip faults often form.*

BRAIN FOOD

The "Solid" Earth
Ask students to write a one-page paper that explains their thoughts about the following quote from *Planet Earth* by Jonathan Weiner: "What we have been pleased to call 'solid Earth' is not as solid as we thought. It is energetic, dynamic, and fundamentally restless."

LS Logical

CONNECTION to Astronomy ——— GENERAL

Extraterrestrial Mountains and Mountain Ranges Earth is not the only place with mountains. Astronomers give extraterrestrial mountains the name *mons,* and extraterrestrial mountain ranges are called either *montes* or *highlands.* Encourage students to find out more about the formation of mountains on Mercury, Venus, Mars, Earth's moon, or on one of the moons of Jupiter or Saturn. Have students compare the mountains they study with mountains on Earth.

LS Logical

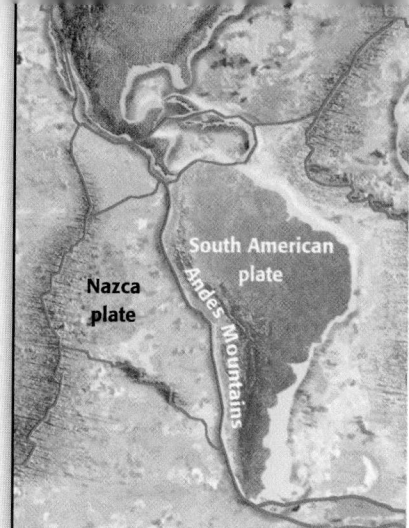

Figure 8 *The Andes Mountains formed on the edge of the South American plate where it converges with the Nazca plate.*

Figure 9 *The Appalachian Mountains were once as tall as the Himalaya Mountains but have been worn down by hundreds of millions of years of weathering and erosion.*

Plate Tectonics and Mountain Building

You have just learned about several ways the Earth's crust changes because of the forces of plate tectonics. When tectonic plates collide, land features that start as folds and faults can eventually become large mountain ranges. Mountains exist because tectonic plates are continually moving around and colliding with one another. As shown in **Figure 8,** the Andes Mountains formed above the subduction zone where two tectonic plates converge.

When tectonic plates undergo compression or tension, they can form mountains in several ways. Take a look at three of the most common types of mountains—folded mountains, fault-block mountains, and volcanic mountains.

Folded Mountains

The highest mountain ranges in the world are made up of folded mountains. These ranges form at convergent boundaries where continents have collided. *Folded mountains* form when rock layers are squeezed together and pushed upward. If you place a pile of paper on a table and push on opposite edges of the pile, you will see how folded mountains form.

An example of a folded mountain range that formed at a convergent boundary is shown in **Figure 9.** About 390 million years ago, the Appalachian Mountains formed when the landmasses that are now North America and Africa collided. Other examples of mountain ranges that consist of very large and complex folds are the Alps in central Europe, the Ural Mountains in Russia, and the Himalayas in Asia.

✓ **Reading Check** Explain how folded mountains form.

Answer to Reading Check
Folded mountains form when rock layers are squeezed together and pushed upward.

Is That a Fact!

The Sierra Nevada mountain range, in California, and the Teton Range, in Wyoming, are examples of fault-block mountains. The Appalachian Mountains, in eastern North America, are an example of folded mountains.

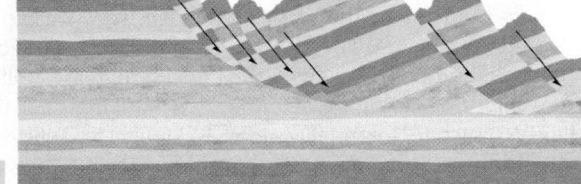

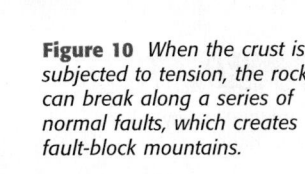

Figure 10 *When the crust is subjected to tension, the rock can break along a series of normal faults, which creates fault-block mountains.*

Fault-Block Mountains

When tectonic forces put enough tension on the Earth's crust, a large number of normal faults can result. *Fault-block mountains* form when this tension causes large blocks of the Earth's crust to drop down relative to other blocks. **Figure 10** shows one way that fault-block mountains form.

When sedimentary rock layers are tilted up by faulting, they can produce mountains that have sharp, jagged peaks. As shown in **Figure 11,** the Tetons in western Wyoming are a spectacular example of fault-block mountains.

Volcanic Mountains

Most of the world's major volcanic mountains are located at convergent boundaries where oceanic crust sinks into the asthenosphere at subduction zones. The rock that is melted in subduction zones forms magma, which rises to the Earth's surface and erupts to form *volcanic mountains*. Volcanic mountains can also form under the sea. Sometimes these mountains can rise above the ocean surface to become islands. The majority of tectonically active volcanic mountains on the Earth have formed around the tectonically active rim of the Pacific Ocean. The rim has become known as the *Ring of Fire*.

CONNECTION TO
Social Studies

WRITING SKILL **The Naming of the Appalachian Mountains** How did the Appalachian Mountains get their name? It is believed that the Appalachian Mountains were named by Spanish explorers in North America during the 16th century. It is thought that the name was taken from a Native American tribe called *Appalachee,* who lived in northern Florida. Research other geological features in the United States, including mountains and rivers, whose names are of Native American origin. Write the results of your research in a short essay.

Figure 11 *The Tetons formed as a result of tectonic forces that stretched the Earth's crust and caused it to break in a series of normal faults.*

ACTIVITY — GENERAL

Mountain-Building Gallery
Tell students to locate photographs of mountains in magazines, books, or on the Internet. Have them cut out, copy, or print these images and mount them on paper. Then, have them write the type of mountain, a description of how the mountains formed, and the location of the mountains relative to tectonic plates on a card and tape the card to the back of the photo. Number and post the photos around the room so that students can view the gallery and write their own guesses as to which type of mountain each is. Have students check their guesses against the cards. **LS** Visual/Logical

Cultural Awareness GENERAL

Mountain Cultures Although people living in mountainous regions are part of some of the world's most impoverished populations, they inhabit diverse ecosystems and have developed innovative technologies to live at high altitudes, where resources may be scarce. Encourage students to learn about the cultures living in the Andes, the Himalayas, or the Alps. Students should give a presentation about the culture they researched and hold a round-table discussion of the problems and opportunities people of these cultures face. The Mountain Institute in Washington, D.C., offers information about natural resource management issues in mountain environments. **LS** Interpersonal/Verbal

CONNECTION to Life Science — GENERAL

Adaptations for High-Altitude Living Point out that living at high altitudes places stress on organisms. Organisms that live at these elevations have adaptations that help them survive. For example, some animals that live on mountains produce more red blood cells. This makes the blood able to deliver more oxygen to body tissues. Have students find out about the adaptations of other organisms, including humans, that live in high-altitude environments. **LS** Logical

Is That a Fact!

When the Appalachian Mountains formed, they were probably very similar to the Himalayas. But the Appalachians are about 350 million years older than the Himalayas. The Appalachians have been worn down by weathering and erosion over hundreds of millions of years, forming the Atlantic coastal plain and the continental shelf along the Atlantic seaboard.

Reteaching ——————— BASIC
Review of Mountain Building
After students have read this section, invite volunteers to sketch examples of each type of mountain on the board. Ask other students to explain how each mountain type forms by referring to the diagram and by adding labels and arrows to show the direction of forces at work. **LS** Visual

English Language Learners

Quiz ————————— GENERAL
1. What three features form when rock layers bend? (anticlines, synclines, and monoclines)

2. Why are the Appalachian Mountains no longer located at the edge of the North American plate? (The Appalachians formed when North America and Africa collided. In time, the plates separated and so much new crust was created that the mountains were no longer at the plate boundary.)

Alternative Assessment ——— GENERAL
PORTFOLIO **Identifying the Forces That Create Mountains**
Have students choose a mountain range to research. Then, ask students to identify in writing the relationship between the mountain range and the forces that created it. **LS** Logical

INTERNET ACTIVITY
For another activity related to this chapter, go to **go.hrw.com** and type in the keyword **HZ5TECW.**

uplift the rising of regions of the Earth's crust to higher elevations

subsidence the sinking of regions of the Earth's crust to lower elevations

Uplift and Subsidence

Vertical movements in the crust are divided into two types—uplift and subsidence. The rising of regions of Earth's crust to higher elevations is called **uplift.** Rocks that are uplifted may or may not be highly deformed. The sinking of regions of Earth's crust to lower elevations is known as **subsidence** (suhb SIED'ns). Unlike some uplifted rocks, rocks that subside do not undergo much deformation.

Uplifting of Depressed Rocks

The formation of mountains is one type of uplift. Uplift can also occur when large areas of land rise without deforming. One way areas rise without deforming is a process known as *rebound.* When the crust rebounds, it slowly springs back to its previous elevation. Uplift often happens when a weight is removed from the crust.

Subsidence of Cooler Rocks

Rocks that are hot take up more space than cooler rocks. For example, the lithosphere is relatively hot at mid-ocean ridges. The farther the lithosphere is from the ridge, the cooler and denser the lithosphere becomes. Because the oceanic lithosphere now takes up less volume, the ocean floor subsides.

Tectonic Letdown

Subsidence can also occur when the lithosphere becomes stretched in rift zones. A *rift zone* is a set of deep cracks that forms between two tectonic plates that are pulling away from each other. As tectonic plates pull apart, stress between the plates causes a series of faults to form along the rift zone. As shown in **Figure 12,** the blocks of crust in the center of the rift zone subside.

Figure 12 *The East African Rift, from Ethiopia to Kenya, is part of a divergent boundary, but you can see how the crust has subsided relative to the blocks at the edge of the rift zone.*

Rift zone

Fault blocks

INCLUSION Strategies

• *Learning Disabled*
• *Behavior Control Issues*
Organize students into groups of four. Hand out a deck of cards that contain terms and concepts from this section. A different-colored set of cards should contain the definitions for the terms and explanations of the concepts. Ask each group to match the terms to the correct definition or explanation. Students can use their textbooks as a resource if necessary. Next, ask groups to separate terms/concepts and definitions/ explanations into two decks. A team of two students should choose from the term/concept deck and attempt to give the definition/explanation without looking at the card. The other two members can give clues if requested. Ask students to write down terms or concepts they have difficulty remembering in their **science journal.** **LS** Logical

Summary

- Compression and tension are two forces of plate tectonics that can cause rock to deform.
- Folding occurs when rock layers bend because of stress.
- Faulting occurs when rock layers break because of stress and then move on either side of the break.
- Mountains are classified as either folded, fault-block, or volcanic depending on how they form.

- Mountain building is caused by the movement of tectonic plates. Folded mountains and volcanic mountains form at convergent boundaries. Fault-block mountains form at divergent boundaries.
- Uplift and subsidence are the two types of vertical movement in the Earth's crust. Uplift occurs when regions of the crust rise to higher elevations. Subsidence occurs when regions of the crust sink to lower elevations.

Using Key Terms

For each pair of key terms, explain how the meanings of the terms differ.

1. *compression* and *tension*

2. *uplift* and *subsidence*

Understanding Key Ideas

3. The type of fault in which the hanging wall moves up relative to the footwall is called a
   a. strike-slip fault.
   b. fault-block fault.
   c. normal fault.
   d. reverse fault.

4. Describe three types of folds.

5. Describe three types of faults.

6. Identify the most common types of mountains.

7. What is rebound?

8. What are rift zones, and how do they form?

Critical Thinking

9. **Predicting Consequences** If a fault occurs in an area where rock layers have been folded, which type of fault is it likely to be? Why?

10. **Identifying Relationships** Would you expect to see a folded mountain range at a mid-ocean ridge? Explain your answer.

Interpreting Graphics

Use the diagram below to answer the questions that follow.

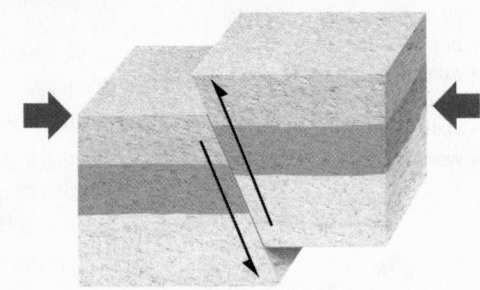

11. What type of fault is shown in the diagram?

12. At what kind of tectonic boundary would you most likely find this fault?

Developed and maintained by the National Science Teachers Association

For a variety of links related to this chapter, go to www.scilinks.org

Topic: Faults; Mountain Building
SciLinks code: HSM0566; HSM0999

Answers to Section Review

1. Sample answer: Compression is stress that occurs when forces act to squeeze an object. Tension is stress that occurs when forces act to stretch an object.

2. Sample answer: Uplift is the rising of Earth's crust to higher elevations. Subsidence is the sinking of Earth's crust to lower elevations.

3. d

4. The three types of folds include anticlines, which are upward-arching folds; synclines, which are downward-arching folds; and monoclines, in which rock layers are folded so that both ends of the fold are horizontal.

5. The three types of faults include normal faults, in which the hanging wall moves down relative to the footwall; reverse faults, in which the hanging wall moves up relative to the footwall; and strike-slip faults, in which opposing forces cause rock to break and move horizontally.

6. The most common types of mountains are folded mountains, fault-block mountains, and volcanic mountains.

7. Rebound is a process in which Earth's crust slowly springs back to its previous elevation.

8. Rift zones are a set of deep cracks in the Earth's crust that form when two tectonic plates pull away from each other. As tectonic plates pull apart, stress builds up between the plates. This stress causes strain in the Earth's crust, and a series of faults forms along the rift zone.

9. A reverse fault is likely to form because both reverse faults and folding occur in areas where compression takes place.

10. No, you would be more likely to see volcanic mountains or fault-block mountains where magma is rising along the mid-ocean ridge spreading center.

11. a reverse fault

12. a convergent boundary

Convection Connection

Teacher's Notes

Time Required

One 45-minute class period

Lab Ratings

EASY ———————————→ HARD

Teacher Prep 🧪
Student Set-Up 🧪🧪🧪
Concept Level 🧪🧪
Clean Up 🧪🧪

MATERIALS

The materials listed on the student page are enough for a group of 2 or 3 students.

Safety Caution

Remind students to review all safety cautions and icons before beginning this lab activity.

Preparation Notes

Because of the volume of water being used, you may wish to set up the blocks and hot plates ahead of time. Also, breezes and drafts may move the craft sticks, so eliminate or reduce as many of these variables as possible.

Convection Connection

Some scientists think that convection currents within the Earth's mantle cause tectonic plates to move. Because these convection currents cannot be observed directly, scientists use models to simulate the process. In this activity, you will make your own model to simulate tectonic plate movement.

OBJECTIVES

Model convection currents to simulate plate tectonic movement.

Draw conclusions about the role of convection in plate tectonics.

MATERIALS

- craft sticks (2)
- food coloring
- gloves, heat-resistant
- hot plates, small (2)
- pan, aluminum, rectangular
- pencil
- ruler, metric
- thermometers (3)
- water, cold
- wooden blocks

SAFETY

Ask a Question

1 How can I make a model of convection currents in the Earth's mantle?

Form a Hypothesis

2 Turn the question above into a statement in which you give your best guess about what factors will have the greatest effect on your convection model.

Test the Hypothesis

3 Place two hot plates side by side in the center of your lab table. Be sure that they are away from the edge of the table.

4 Place the pan on top of the hot plates. Slide the wooden blocks under the pan to support the ends. Make sure that the pan is level and secure.

5 Fill the pan with cold water. The water should be at least 4 cm deep. Turn on the hot plates, and put on your gloves.

6 After a minute or two, tiny bubbles will begin to rise in the water above the hot plates. Gently place two craft sticks on the water's surface.

7 Use the pencil to align the sticks parallel to the short ends of the pan. The sticks should be about 3 cm apart and near the center of the pan.

8 As soon as the sticks begin to move, place a drop of food coloring in the center of the pan. Observe what happens to the food coloring.

Holt Lab Generator CD-ROM

Search for any lab by topic, standard, difficulty level, or time. Edit any lab to fit your needs, or create your own labs. Use the Lab Materials QuickList software to customize your lab materials list.

Terry J. Rakes
Elmwood Jr. High
Rogers, Arkansas

CHAPTER RESOURCES

Chapter Resource File

- Datasheet for Chapter Lab
- Lab Notes and Answers

Technology

 Classroom Videos
- Lab Video

 LabBook
- Oh, the Pressure!

9 With the help of a partner, hold one thermometer bulb just under the water at the center of the pan. Hold the other two thermometers just under the water near the ends of the pan. Record the temperatures.

10 When you are finished, turn off the hot plates. After the water has cooled, carefully empty the water into a sink.

Analyze the Results

1 **Explaining Events** Based on your observations of the motion of the food coloring, how does the temperature of the water affect the direction in which the craft sticks move?

Draw Conclusions

2 **Drawing Conclusions** How does the motion of the craft sticks relate to the motion of the water?

3 **Applying Conclusions** How does this model relate to plate tectonics and the movement of the continents?

4 **Applying Conclusions** Based on your observations, what can you conclude about the role of convection in plate tectonics?

Applying Your Data

Suggest a substance other than water that might be used to model convection in the mantle. Consider using a substance that flows more slowly than water.

Analyze the Results

1. Based on the motion of the food coloring, the warmer water rises and the cooler water sinks. Therefore, as the water warms, the craft sticks should move in a direction away from the center of the pan.

Draw Conclusions

2. The hot water flowed outward from the center of the pan. This movement pushed the sticks away from each other and toward the edges of the pan.

3. Convection currents within Earth's mantle may move tectonic plates in the same way that the convecting water moved the craft sticks. The convection currents in this model were created by the hot plates warming the water. In the mantle, convection currents are caused by thermal energy from deep within Earth.

4. Answers may vary but should include a description of how convection may be at least partially responsible for the movement of tectonic plates.

Applying Your Data

Suggestions for improving the model will vary. Students may suggest increasing the size of the model or using model tectonic plates that have differing sizes and densities. Students may also suggest incorporating the processes of ridge push or slab pull into the model.

Assignment Guide

Section	Questions
1	1, 3, 6, 11, 12, 21–24
2	2, 13, 14
3	7, 16, 18, 19
4	4, 5, 8–10, 15, 20
1, 2, and 3	17

ANSWERS

Using Key Terms

1. Sample answer: Scientists divide the Earth into the crust, mantle, and core based on the chemical elements that make up each of these layers.
2. continental drift
3. asthenosphere
4. Tension
5. uplift

Understanding Key Ideas

6. b
7. c
8. b
9. d
10. a
11. c
12. Scientists can measure the differences in the speeds of seismic waves that travel through the Earth's interior to calculate the density and thickness of each of the Earth's physical layers.

USING KEY TERMS

1 Use the following terms in the same sentence: *crust, mantle,* and *core.*

Complete each of the following sentences by choosing the correct term from the word bank.

asthenosphere   uplift
tension   continental drift

2 The hypothesis that continents can drift apart and have done so in the past is known as ___.

3 The ___ is the soft layer of the mantle on which the tectonic plates move.

4 ___ is stress that occurs when forces act to stretch an object.

5 The rising of regions of the Earth's crust to higher elevations is called ___.

UNDERSTANDING KEY IDEAS

Multiple Choice

6 The strong, lower part of the mantle is a physical layer called the

a. lithosphere.
b. mesosphere.
c. asthenosphere.
d. outer core.

7 The type of tectonic plate boundary that forms from a collision between two tectonic plates is a

a. divergent plate boundary.
b. transform plate boundary.
c. convergent plate boundary.
d. normal plate boundary.

8 The bending of rock layers due to stress in the Earth's crust is known as

a. uplift.
b. folding.
c. faulting.
d. subsidence.

9 The type of fault in which the hanging wall moves up relative to the footwall is called a

a. strike-slip fault.
b. fault-block fault.
c. normal fault.
d. reverse fault.

10 The type of mountain that forms when rock layers are squeezed together and pushed upward is the

a. folded mountain.
b. fault-block mountain.
c. volcanic mountain.
d. strike-slip mountain.

11 Scientists' knowledge of the Earth's interior has come primarily from

a. studying magnetic reversals in oceanic crust.
b. using a system of satellites called the *global positioning system.*
c. studying seismic waves generated by earthquakes.
d. studying the pattern of fossils on different continents.

Short Answer

12 Explain how scientists use seismic waves to map the Earth's interior.

13 How do magnetic reversals provide evidence of sea-floor spreading?

13. As oceanic crust spreads away from a mid-ocean ridge, the crust carries bands that contain minerals that were aligned with Earth's magnetic field when the crust formed. The similar sequence of bands on both sides of a mid-ocean ridge, even at a large distance from the ridge, indicates that the sea floor is spreading away from a center point.

14 Explain how sea-floor spreading provides a way for continents to move.

15 Describe two types of stress that deform rock.

16 What is the global positioning system (GPS), and how does GPS allow scientists to measure the rate of motion of tectonic plates?

CRITICAL THINKING

17 **Concept Mapping** Use the following terms to create a concept map: *sea-floor spreading, convergent boundary, divergent boundary, subduction zone, transform boundary,* and *tectonic plates.*

18 **Applying Concepts** Why does oceanic lithosphere sink at subduction zones but not at mid-ocean ridges?

19 **Identifying Relationships** New tectonic material continually forms at divergent boundaries. Tectonic plate material is also continually destroyed in subduction zones at convergent boundaries. Do you think that the total amount of lithosphere formed on the Earth is about equal to the amount destroyed? Why?

20 **Applying Concepts** Folded mountains usually form at the edge of a tectonic plate. How can you explain folded mountain ranges located in the middle of a tectonic plate?

INTERPRETING GRAPHICS

Imagine that you could travel to the center of the Earth. Use the diagram below to answer the questions that follow.

Composition	Structure
Crust (50 km)	Lithosphere (150 km)
Mantle (2,900 km)	Asthenosphere (250 km)
	Mesosphere (2,550 km)
Core (3,430 km)	Outer core (2,200 km)
	Inner core (1,228 km)

21 How far beneath the Earth's surface would you have to go before you were no longer passing through rock that had the composition of granite?

22 How far beneath the Earth's surface would you have to go to find liquid material in the Earth's core?

23 At what depth would you find mantle material but still be within the lithosphere?

24 How far beneath the Earth's surface would you have to go to find solid iron and nickel in the Earth's core?

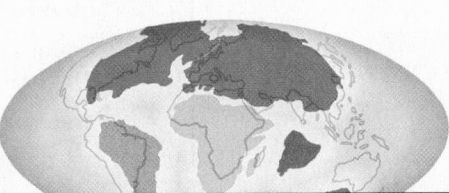

16. The global positioning system is a system of satellites that orbit the Earth. Radio signals are continuously beamed from these satellites to ground stations. The distance between satellites and ground stations is recorded. By recording the time it takes for ground stations to move a given distance, scientists can measure the rate at which tectonic plates move.

Critical Thinking

17. 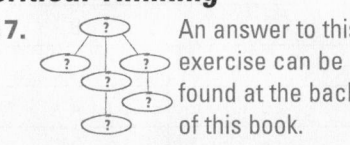 An answer to this exercise can be found at the back of this book.

18. Answers may vary. The lithosphere at a subduction zone is denser than at a mid-ocean ridge. Convection causes oceanic lithosphere to move away from the mid-ocean ridge. Oceanic lithosphere is also higher at a mid-ocean ridge, so oceanic lithosphere moves down toward the subduction zone because of gravity.

19. Answers may vary. The amount of crust formed is roughly equal to the amount of crust destroyed. If this were not true, the Earth would either be expanding or shrinking.

20. At the time they formed, the folded mountains must have been on the edge of a tectonic plate. New material was later added to the tectonic plate, causing the folded mountains to be located closer to the center of the continent.

Interpreting Graphics

21. 50 km

22. 150 km + 250 km + 2,550 km = 2,950 km

23. between 50 km and 150 km

24. 150 km + 250 km + 2,550 km + 2,200 km = 5,150 km

14. As new crust forms at mid-ocean ridges, plates on either side of the ridge move away from the ridge. Therefore, continents on those plates also move.

15. Compression and tension are two types of stress that deform rock. Compression squeezes rock at convergent plate boundaries; tension stretches rock at divergent plate boundaries.

Teacher's Notes

To provide practice under more realistic conditions, give students 20 minutes to answer all of the questions in this Standardized Test Preparation.

Answer Key

Question	Answer
1	B
2	C
3	A
4	D
5	C
6	C
7	D
8	C
9	D
10	B
11	A
12	*
13	*

*See Test Doctor.

Multiple Choice

1. **How do mid-ocean ridges support both the idea of continental drift and the theory of plate tectonics?**

   A. Oceanic lithosphere is destroyed at mid-ocean ridges.

   B. New crust forms at mid-ocean ridges.

   C. Tectonic plates collide at mid-ocean ridges.

   D. The crust at mid-ocean ridges is old oceanic lithosphere.

2. **Which of the following compositional layers makes up the greatest percentage of Earth's mass?**

   A. continental crust

   B. oceanic crust

   C. the mantle

   D. the core

3. **How does fossil evidence support Wegener's hypothesis of continental drift?**

   A. Similar fossils found on widely separated landmasses suggest that the continents were once a single landmass.

   B. Fossil evidence suggests that the continents were always in their current positions.

   C. No similarities exist between fossils on different continents.

   D. Plant and animal fossils show evidence of changes in Earth's polarity.

4. **Most of the world's folded mountains formed as a result of**

   A. oceanic-oceanic separation at mid-ocean ridges.

   B. continental-continental separation at rift zones.

   C. continental-oceanic collision at subduction zones.

   D. continental-continental collision at convergent boundaries.

5. **Which of the following geologic features is formed as a result of tension?**

   A. an anticline

   B. a syncline

   C. a normal fault

   D. a reverse fault

Use the diagram below to answer question 6.

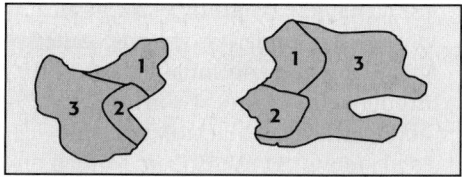

6. **Which of the following statements best explains the relative positions of the two landmasses above?**

   A. The landmasses slid away from each other at a transform boundary.

   B. Subduction occurred, causing the land between the two landmasses to sink.

   C. Sea-floor spreading pushed the two landmasses apart.

   D. An earthquake split the tectonic plate in two, separating the landmasses.

TEST DOCTOR

Question 1 A: Oceanic lithosphere is created at mid-ocean ridges, which occur at divergent plate boundaries. Lithosphere can be destroyed at convergent plate boundaries. B: Correct. C: Tectonic plates move apart from each other at mid-ocean ridges. D: Crust near a mid-ocean ridge is younger than crust that is far away from a mid-ocean ridge.

Question 2 A and B: Together, continental crust and oceanic crust make up less than 1% of Earth's mass. C: Correct. D: The core makes up approximately 33% of Earth's mass.

Question 3 A: Correct. B, C: Many fossils of the same plant and animal species are found on continents that are on different sides of the Atlantic Ocean. Many of these ancient species could not have crossed the Atlantic Ocean. D: Magnetic reversals, recorded in the rocks along the ocean floor, show evidence of changing polarity throughout Earth's history.

Use the illustration below to answer question 7.

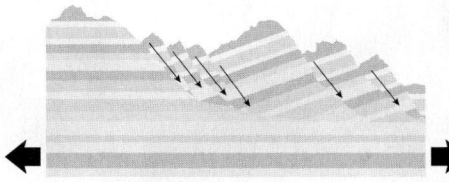

Mountain Formation

7. How were these mountains formed?

A. Rock layers were squeezed and folded by tectonic forces.

B. Volcanoes formed rock layers that then cooled and subsided.

C. Rocks pushed past each other at a transform boundary.

D. Tension caused some rock blocks to drop and tilt upward.

8. Sea-floor spreading occurs at which of the following types of tectonic plate boundaries?

A. transform

B. convergent

C. divergent

D. strike-slip

9. The process by which hot rock from deep within Earth rises and cooler rock near the surface sinks is called

A. ridge push.

B. slab pull.

C. subduction.

D. convection.

10. The sinking of Earth's crust to lower elevations is called

A. rebound.

B. subsidence.

C. uplift.

D. deformation.

11. Strike-slip faults generally form as a result of tectonic forces that cause

A. rock to break and move horizontally.

B. compression that pushes rock together.

C. tension that pulls rock apart.

D. rock layers to bend.

Open Response

12. The Blue Ridge Mountains form the eastern front of the Appalachian Mountains. Both the Appalachian Mountains and the Himalayas in Asia were formed by folding. However, the Himalayas are still growing, while the Appalachian Mountains are losing height and becoming more rounded. Why are these mountains changing in different ways?

13. The Cartersville fault is one section of a huge fault zone that extends from Pennsylvania to Alabama. The Cartersville fault formed when metamorphic rocks from Georgia's Piedmont region were pushed over sedimentary rock layers. This collision most likely occurred during the formation of Pangaea. What kind of fault is the Cartersville fault? Explain your answer.

Standardized Test Preparation

Question 8 A: Strike-slip motion occurs at transform boundaries. B: Subduction occurs at convergent boundaries. C: Correct. D: Strike-slip is not a type of plate boundary but a type of fault.

Question 9 A: Ridge push is the process by which oceanic lithosphere slides downhill under the force of gravity. B: Slab pull is the process in which the edge of a tectonic plate that contains oceanic lithosphere sinks and pulls the rest of the tectonic plate with it. C: Subduction is the process in which old ocean crust is pushed into the asthenosphere, where it melts. D: Correct.

Question 10 A: Rebound is the rising of Earth's lithosphere after a weight has been removed. B: Correct. C: Uplift is the rising of Earth's crust to higher elevations. D: Deformation is the process by which the shape of a rock changes because of stress.

Question 11 A: Correct. B: Reverse faults form when tectonic forces cause compression that pushes rock together. C: Normal faults form when tectonic forces cause tension that pulls rock apart. D: Folding occurs when tectonic forces cause rock layers to bend.

Question 12 Full-credit answers should include the following points:

• The Himalayas are still growing because they are at a convergent boundary that is still active.

• The Appalachian Mountains are no longer at an active convergent boundary, so their rock layers are no longer being pushed upward.

• The Appalachian Mountains are being worn down by weathering and erosion.

Question 13 Full-credit answers should include the following points:

• The Cartersville fault is a reverse fault.

• The two types of rock were pushed together, causing the metamorphic rock to form a hanging wall over the sedimentary-rock footwall.

Question 4 A: Volcanic mountains are formed by oceanic-oceanic separation at mid-ocean ridges. B: Volcanic mountains are formed by continental-continental separation at divergent boundaries. C: Volcanic mountains are formed by continental-oceanic collision at subduction zones. D: Correct.

Question 5 A, B, D: Compression is a factor in the formation of anticlines, synclines, and reverse faults. C: Correct.

Question 6 A: At a transform boundary, two plates slide past each other but remain in contact. B: At a subduction zone, one plate sinks below the other as the plates collide. However, the plates remain in contact. C: Correct. D: An earthquake can cause a split in the Earth called a fault, but land on one side stays in contact with land on the other.

Question 7 A: Folding causes rock layers to be pushed upward, but it does not cause faulting. B: Volcanic eruptions build cones that do not have the faulting shown in the figure above. C: As rocks slide past each other at a transform boundary, they can create earthquakes, not mountains. D: Correct.

Science, Technology, and Society

Background

In addition to GPS satellites, satellite laser ranging (SLR) satellites are used to track the motion of tectonic plates. The *LAGEOS II SLR* satellite (pictured at right) is 60 cm in diameter and weighs approximately 405 kg. Imbedded in the surface of the satellite are 426 three-dimensional prisms. These prisms reflect laser beams directly back to their source.

Scientific Discoveries

Background

Megaplumes are giant, rotating disks of hot water that drift horizontally through the ocean. Megaplumes form at mid-ocean ridges during underwater volcanic eruptions. During an eruption, a column of boiling seawater rises upward from the volcano and expands until it forms a disk. The disks of megaplumes can drift through the oceans for hundreds of kilometers over a period of months. The first megaplume was discovered in 1986 along the Juan de Fuca Ridge, which is located approximately 300 miles off the northwest coast of the United States. Since 1986, at least seven more megaplumes have been recorded along the ridge.

Science in Action

Science, Technology, and Society

Using Satellites to Track Plate Motion

When you think of laser beams firing, you may think of science fiction movies. However, scientists use laser beams to determine the rate and direction of motion of tectonic plates. From ground stations on Earth, laser beams are fired at several small satellites orbiting 5,900 km above Earth. From the satellites, the laser beams are reflected back to ground stations. Differences in the time it takes signals to be reflected from targets are measured over a period of time. From these differences, scientists can determine the rate and direction of plate motion.

Social Studies ACTIVITY

WRITING SKILL Research a society that lives at an active plate boundary. Find out how the people live with dangers such as volcanoes and earthquakes. Include your findings in a short report.

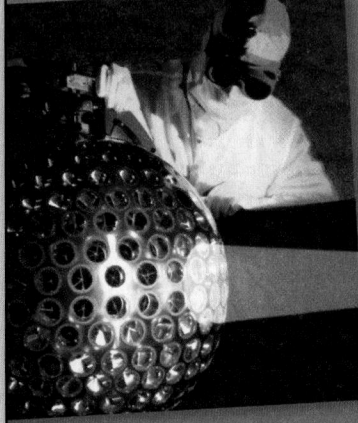

This scientist is using a laser to test one of the satellites that will be used to track plate motion.

Scientific Discoveries

Megaplumes

Eruptions of boiling water from the sea floor form giant, spiral disks that twist through the oceans. Do you think it's impossible? Oceanographers have discovered these disks at eight locations at mid-ocean ridges over the past 20 years. These disks, which may be tens of kilometers across, are called *megaplumes*. Megaplumes are like blenders. They mix hot water with cold water in the oceans. Megaplumes can rise hundreds of meters from the ocean floor to the upper layers of the ocean. They carry gases and minerals and provide extra energy and food to animals in the upper layers of the ocean.

Language Arts ACTIVITY

WRITING SKILL Did you ever wonder about the origin of the name *Himalaya*? Research the origin of the name *Himalaya*, and write a short report about what you find.

Answers to Social Studies Activity

Have students give a short report on the society they researched. Before each report, have students find the geographical location of that society on a tectonic map of the world.

Answers to Language Arts Activity

Students should include in their report that the name *Himalaya* comes from the Sanskrit word *hima*, which means "snow," and *alaya*, which means "abode." Therefore, the word *Himalaya* means "the abode of snow."

People in Science

Alfred Wegener

Continental Drift Alfred Wegener's greatest contribution to science was the hypothesis of continental drift. This hypothesis states that continents drift apart from one another and have done so in the past. To support his hypothesis, Wegener used geologic, fossil, and glacial evidence gathered on both sides of the Atlantic Ocean. For example, Wegener recognized similarities between rock layers in North America and Europe and between rock layers in South America and Africa. He believed that these similarities could be explained only if these geologic features were once part of the same continent.

Although continental drift explained many of his observations, Wegener could not find scientific evidence to develop a complete explanation of how continents move. Most scientists were skeptical of Wegener's hypothesis and dismissed it as foolishness. It was not until the 1950s and 1960s that the discoveries of magnetic reversals and sea-floor spreading provided evidence of continental drift.

Math

The distance between South America and Africa is 7,200 km. As new crust is created at the mid-ocean ridge, South America and Africa are moving away from each other at a rate of about 3.5 cm per year. How many millions of years ago were South America and Africa joined?

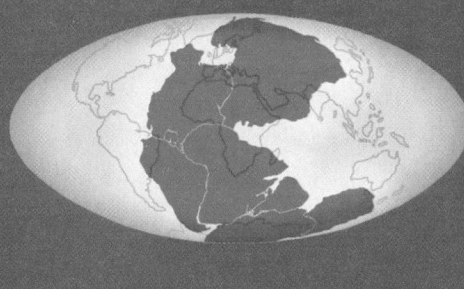

go.hrw.com
To learn more about these Science in Action topics, visit **go.hrw.com** and type in the keyword **HZ5TECF.**

Current Science
Check out Current Science® articles related to this chapter by visiting **go.hrw.com. Just type in the keyword HZ5CS07.**

Answers to Math Activity
7,200 km = 720,000,000 cm;
720,000,000 cm ÷ 3.5 cm/y =
206,000,000 years ago

Compression guide:
To shorten instruction because of time limitations, omit the Chapter Lab.

OBJECTIVES	LABS, DEMONSTRATIONS, AND ACTIVITIES	TECHNOLOGY RESOURCES
PACING • 90 min pp. 410–417 **Chapter Opener**	**SE** Start-up Activity, p. 411 ◆ GENERAL	**OSP** Parent Letter ■ **CD** Student Edition on CD-ROM **CD** Guided Reading Audio CD ■ **TR** Chapter Starter Transparency* **VID** Brain Food Video Quiz
Section 1 What Are Earthquakes? • Explain where earthquakes take place. • Explain what causes earthquakes. • Identify three different types of faults that occur at plate boundaries. • Describe how energy from earthquakes travels through the Earth.	**TE** Demonstration Faults and Earthquakes, p. 413 ◆ BASIC **SE** Quick Lab Modeling Seismic Waves, p. 416 GENERAL **CRF** Datasheet for Quick Lab* **SE** Science in Action Math, Social Studies, and Language Arts Activities, pp. 434–435 GENERAL	**OSP** Lesson Plans (also in print) **TR** Bellringer Transparency* **TR** E27 Elastic Rebound* **TR** LINK TO PHYSICAL SCIENCE P82 Comparing Longitudinal and Transverse Waves* **TR** E28 Primary Waves; Secondary Waves; Surface Waves* **CRF** SciLinks Activity* GENERAL
PACING • 45 min pp. 418–421 **Section 2 Earthquake Measurement** • Explain how earthquakes are detected. • Describe how to locate an earthquake's epicenter. • Explain how the strength of an earthquake is measured. • Explain how the intensity of an earthquake is measured.	**TE** Activity Exploring a Seismic Network, p. 418 GENERAL **SE** Skills Practice Lab Earthquake Waves, p. 726 GENERAL **CRF** Datasheet for LabBook* **LB** Long-Term Projects & Research Ideas A Whole Lotta Shakin'* ADVANCED	**OSP** Lesson Plans (also in print) **TR** Bellringer Transparency* **TR** E29 Finding an Earthquake's Epicenter*
PACING • 90 min pp. 422–427 **Section 3 Earthquakes and Society** • Explain how earthquake-hazard level is determined. • Compare methods of earthquake forecasting. • Describe five ways to safeguard buildings against earthquakes. • Outline earthquake safety procedures.	**TE** Connection Activity Art, p. 422 GENERAL **TE** Connection Activity Math, p. 423 GENERAL **TE** Activity Tools of the Trade, p. 424 ADVANCED **TE** Demonstration Flexible Buildings, p. 425 BASIC **TE** Connection Activity Real Life, p. 425 GENERAL **SE** Connection to Physics Earthquake Proof Buildings, p. 426 GENERAL **SE** School-to-Home Activity Disaster Planning, p. 427 GENERAL **SE** Inquiry Lab Quake Challenge, p. 428 ◆ GENERAL **CRF** Datasheet for Chapter Lab* **LB** Whiz-Bang Demonstrations When Buildings Boogie* ◆ GENERAL	**OSP** Lesson Plans (also in print) **TR** Bellringer Transparency* **SE** Internet Activity, p. 423 GENERAL **VID** Lab Videos for Earth Science

PACING • 90 min

CHAPTER REVIEW, ASSESSMENT, AND STANDARDIZED TEST PREPARATION

CRF Vocabulary Activity* GENERAL
SE Chapter Review, pp. 430–431 GENERAL
CRF Chapter Review* ■ GENERAL
CRF Chapter Tests A* ■ GENERAL, B* ADVANCED, C* SPECIAL NEEDS
SE Standardized Test Preparation, pp. 432–433 GENERAL
CRF Standardized Test Preparation* GENERAL
CRF Performance-Based Assessment* GENERAL
OSP Test Generator, Test Item Listing

Online and Technology Resources

 Holt Online Learning

Visit **go.hrw.com** for access to Holt Online Learning, or enter the keyword **HS7 Home** for a variety of free online resources.

 **One-Stop Planner® CD-ROM**

This CD-ROM package includes:
• Lab Materials QuickList Software
• Holt Calendar Planner
• Customizable Lesson Plans
• Printable Worksheets
• ExamView® Test Generator
• Interactive Teacher's Edition
• Holt PuzzlePro®
• Holt PowerPoint® Resources

SKILLS DEVELOPMENT RESOURCES	SECTION REVIEW AND ASSESSMENT	CORRELATIONS
SE Pre-Reading Activity, p. 410 `GENERAL` **OSP** Science Puzzlers, Twisters & Teasers `GENERAL`		**National Science Education Standards** SAI 1, 2
CRF Directed Reading A* ■ `BASIC`, B* `SPECIAL NEEDS` **WB** Workbook* `Struggling Readers` **CRF** Vocabulary and Section Summary* ■ `GENERAL` **SE** Reading Strategy Paired Summarizing, p. 412 `GENERAL` **TE** Support for English Language Learners, p. 413 **TE** Inclusion Strategies, p. 416	**SE** Reading Checks, pp. 413, 415, 417 `GENERAL` **TE** Homework, p. 413 `ADVANCED` **TE** Homework, p. 414 `GENERAL` **TE** Reteaching, p. 416 `BASIC` **TE** Quiz, p. 416 `GENERAL` **TE** Alternative Assessment, p. 416 `GENERAL` **SE** Section Review,* p. 417 ■ `GENERAL` **CRF** Section Quiz* `GENERAL`	UCP 2; SAI 1, 2; SPSP 3, 4; ES 1b
CRF Directed Reading A* ■ `BASIC`, B* `SPECIAL NEEDS` **WB** Workbook* `Struggling Readers` **CRF** Vocabulary and Section Summary* ■ `GENERAL` **SE** Reading Strategy Reading Organizer, p. 418 `GENERAL` **TE** Support for English Language Learners, p. 419 **SE** Connection to Social Studies New Madrid Earthquakes, p. 420 `GENERAL` **CRF** Reinforcement Worksheet Complete a Seismic Story* `BASIC` **MS** Math Skills for Science Earthquake Power!* `GENERAL`	**SE** Reading Checks, pp. 418, 420 `GENERAL` **TE** Reteaching, p. 420 `BASIC` **TE** Quiz, p. 420 `GENERAL` **TE** Alternative Assessment, p. 420 `GENERAL` **SE** Section Review,* p. 421 ■ `GENERAL` **CRF** Section Quiz* ■ `GENERAL`	UCP 3; SAI 1, 2; ST 2; SPSP 3, 4; HNS 1, 3; *LabBook:* SAI 1, 2
CRF Directed Reading A* ■ `BASIC`, B* `SPECIAL NEEDS` **WB** Workbook* `Struggling Readers` **CRF** Vocabulary and Section Summary* ■ `GENERAL` **SE** Reading Strategy Discussion, p. 422 `GENERAL` **TE** Reading Strategy Prediction Guide, p. 423 `GENERAL` **TE** Support for English Language Learners, p. 423 **TE** Inclusion Strategies, p. 426 ◆ **MS** Math Skills for Science Dividing Whole Numbers with Long Division* `GENERAL` **CRF** Critical Thinking Nearthlings Unite!* `ADVANCED`	**SE** Reading Checks, pp. 423, 424, 426 `GENERAL` **TE** Homework, p. 424 `GENERAL` **TE** Reteaching, p. 426 `BASIC` **TE** Quiz, p. 426 `GENERAL` **TE** Alternative Assessment, p. 426 `GENERAL` **SE** Section Review,* p. 427 ■ `GENERAL` **CRF** Section Quiz* ■ `GENERAL`	UCP 2, 3; SAI 1; ST 2; SPSP 1, 3, 4, 5; ES 1b; HNS 2 *Chapter Lab:* SAI 1, 2

www.scilinks.org

Maintained by the **National Science Teachers Association.** See Chapter Enrichment pages that follow for a complete list of topics.

Check out *Current Science* articles and activities by visiting the HRW Web site at **go.hrw.com.** Just type in the keyword **HZ5CS08T.**

Classroom Videos

- **Lab Videos** demonstrate the chapter lab.
- **Brain Food Video Quizzes** help students review the chapter material.

Classroom CD-ROMs

- **Guided Reading Audio CD** (Also in Spanish)
- **Interactive Explorations**
- **Virtual Investigations**
- **Visual Concepts**
- **Science Tutor**

Holt Lab Generator CD-ROM

Search for any lab by topic, standard, difficulty level, or time. Edit any lab to fit your needs, or create your own labs. Use the Lab Materials QuickList software to customize your lab materials list.

Visual Resources

CHAPTER STARTER TRANSPARENCY

BELLRINGER TRANSPARENCIES

TEACHING TRANSPARENCIES

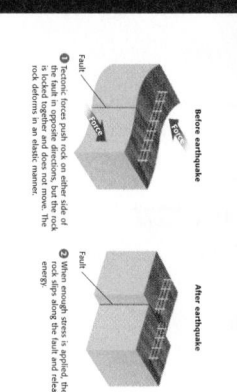

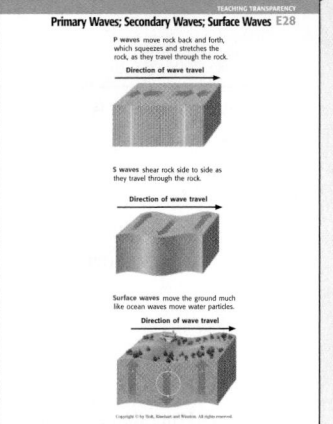

TEACHING TRANSPARENCIES

CONCEPT MAPPING TRANSPARENCY

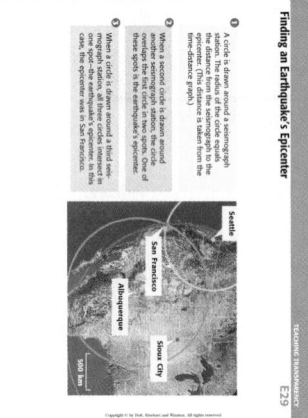

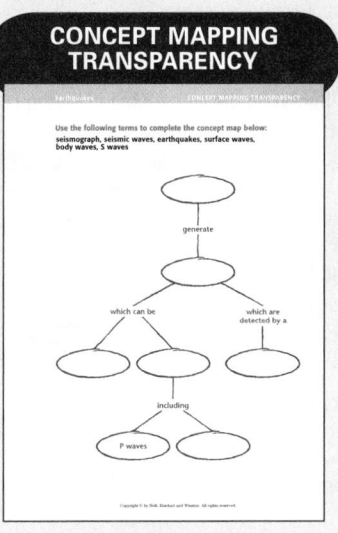

Planning Resources

LESSON PLANS

PARENT LETTER

TEST ITEM LISTING

One-Stop Planner® CD-ROM

This CD-ROM includes all of the resources shown here and the following time-saving tools:

- *Lab Materials QuickList Software*
- *Customizable lesson plans*
- *Holt Calendar Planner*
- *The powerful ExamView® Test Generator*

Meeting Individual Needs

DIRECTED READING A
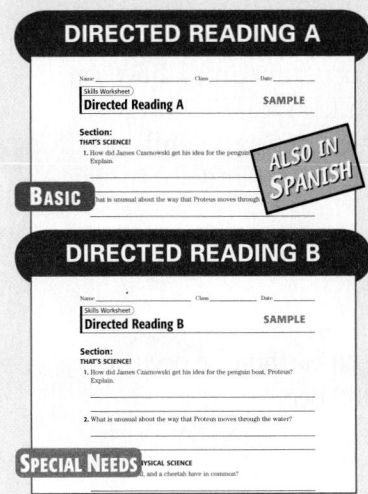
BASIC — ALSO IN SPANISH

DIRECTED READING B
SPECIAL NEEDS

VOCABULARY ACTIVITY
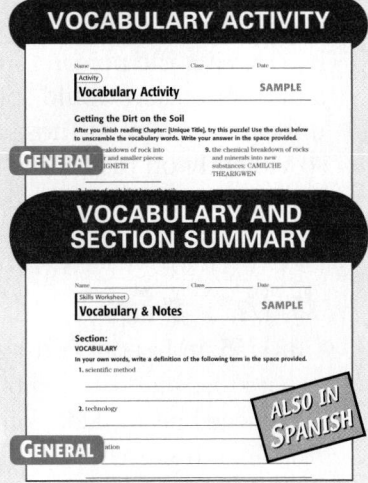
GENERAL

VOCABULARY AND SECTION SUMMARY
GENERAL — ALSO IN SPANISH

REINFORCEMENT
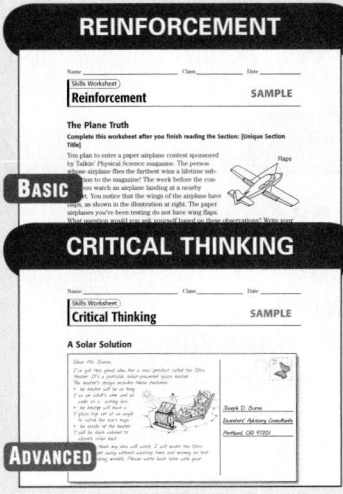
BASIC

CRITICAL THINKING
ADVANCED

SCILINKS ACTIVITY

GENERAL

SCIENCE PUZZLERS, TWISTERS & TEASERS
GENERAL

Labs and Activities

LONG-TERM PROJECTS & RESEARCH IDEAS
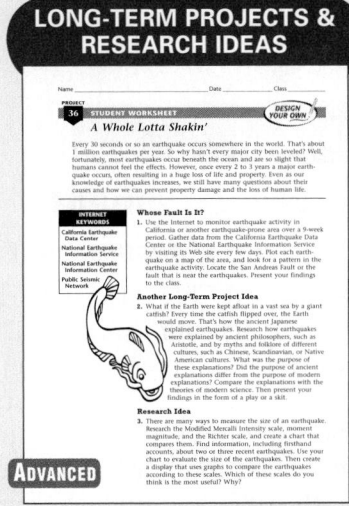
ADVANCED

WHIZ-BANG DEMONSTRATIONS
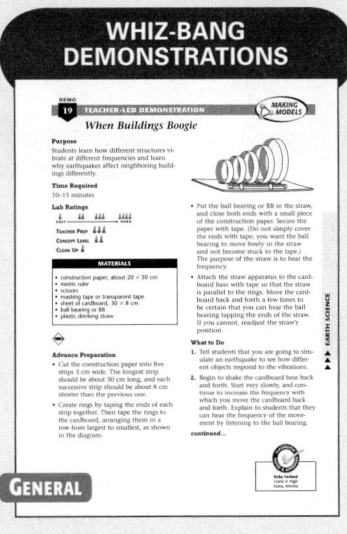
GENERAL

DATASHEETS FOR QUICK LABS

DATASHEETS FOR CHAPTER LABS

DATASHEETS FOR LABBOOK

Review and Assessments

SECTION QUIZ
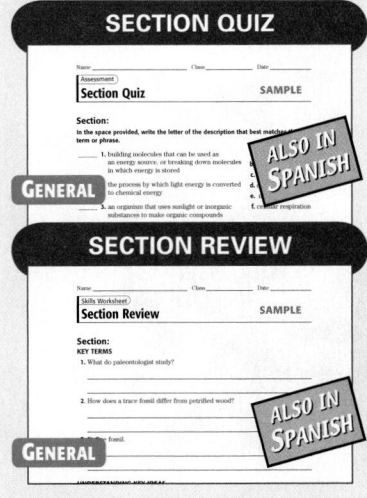
GENERAL — ALSO IN SPANISH

SECTION REVIEW
GENERAL — ALSO IN SPANISH

CHAPTER REVIEW
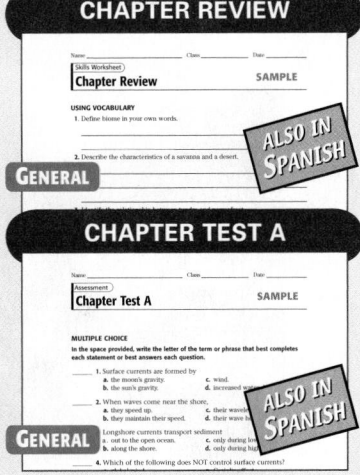
GENERAL — ALSO IN SPANISH

CHAPTER TEST A
GENERAL — ALSO IN SPANISH

CHAPTER TEST B
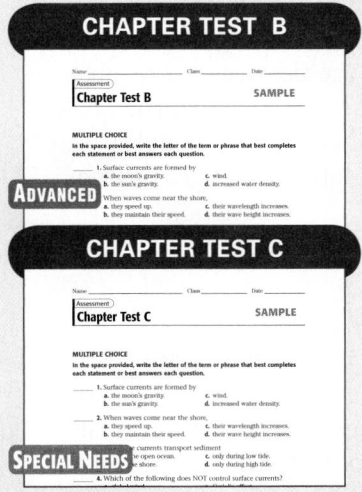
ADVANCED

CHAPTER TEST C
SPECIAL NEEDS

STANDARDIZED TEST PREPARATION
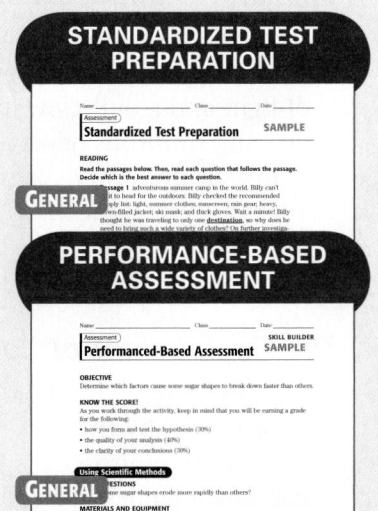
GENERAL

PERFORMANCE-BASED ASSESSMENT
GENERAL

This Chapter Enrichment provides relevant and interesting information to expand and enhance your presentation of the chapter material.

Section 1

What Are Earthquakes?

Earthquake Origins

- Earthquakes originate at different depths. Shallow earthquakes are those that originate within about 60 km of Earth's surface. Intermediate-depth earthquakes originate between depths of about 60 km and 300 km. Deep earthquakes originate below 300 km.

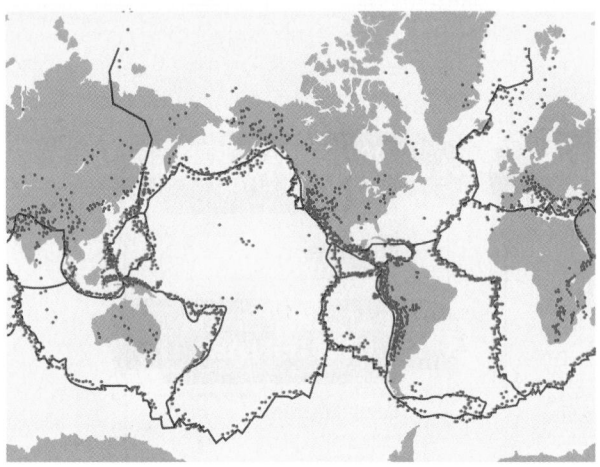

- Tectonic activity is not the only source of earthquakes. Earthquakes can also be caused by volcanic eruptions and by the impacts of cosmic bodies. These earthquakes, however, are less common than those occurring along faults.

The New Madrid Earthquakes

- Eyewitnesses to the 1811–1812 earthquakes in New Madrid, Missouri, reported seeing bright flashes of light and a dull glow in the sky over a wide area. Reeking sulfurous odors also accompanied the quakes. Many survivors were convinced that the quakes were a heavenly sign meant to frighten the local citizens back to church. As a result, church attendance in the area rose between 1811 and 1812!

The Punishment of Loki

- In Scandinavian mythology, earthquakes are believed to be caused by the clever prankster Loki. The gods decided to punish Loki when they discovered that he had killed Balder, the god of light and joy. Loki was chained in a deep cave, and a huge, poisonous snake was hung above him. As the poison from the snake's fangs dripped down, Loki's sister tried to protect him by catching the poison in a cup. Sometimes, however, a drop of poison would splash Loki, causing him unbearable pain. At those times, he would pull so violently on his chains that the ground above would tremble.

Is That a Fact!

- ◆ In 1755, in Lisbon, Portugal, an earthquake occurred that killed an estimated 60,000 people. Because it happened near midday on a religious holiday, many fatalities occurred when churches collapsed on churchgoers. This tragedy resulted in an analytic and systematic approach to studying earthquakes, the basis of seismology.

Section 2

Earthquake Measurement

Chinese Earthquake Measurement

- A Chinese man named Chang Heng designed the first known "earthquake detector" around 132 CE. Heng's earthquake detector was a bronze urn decorated with six dragons' heads. Each head held a bronze ball in its mouth. A pendulum was suspended inside the urn. During a tremor, the pendulum would strike the urn, causing one of the balls to drop into the mouth of a bronze toad below. The ball would make a loud noise, signaling the occurrence of an earthquake. By noting which ball fell, people could supposedly determine the direction of the earthquake's epicenter.

Magnitude Versus Intensity

- Earthquakes can be measured by magnitude or intensity. An earthquake's magnitude is a quantitative measurement of its strength. The Richter scale, and other, more modern scales, are used to measure magnitude. Intensity is a qualitative measurement of an earthquake's effect in a particular area. The Modified Mercalli Intensity Scale is used to assess shaking. This scale incorporates observations of the earthquake's effects at a particular location. Although an earthquake may have different intensities at different locations, it has only one magnitude.

Is That a Fact!

- ◆ The strongest earthquake recorded since the invention of seismographs occurred in Chile in 1960. It measured 9.5 on the Richter scale. This magnitude is equivalent to detonating more than 1 billion tons of TNT!

Section 3

Earthquakes and Society

Magnetometers

- Magnetometers are devices that measure changes in the Earth's magnetic field. Some theories suggest that changes in the Earth's magnetic field might be indicative of an upcoming earthquake, although such theories are controversial.

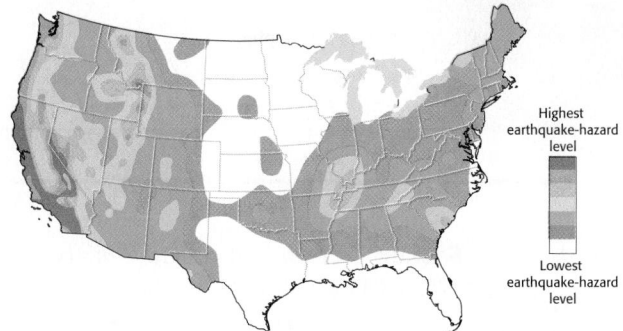

Highest earthquake-hazard level

Lowest earthquake-hazard level

Aftershocks

- Aftershocks occur in sequences that take place within a particular time frame. They are most numerous after an earthquake and decrease with time. The largest aftershocks often occur within hours of an earthquake. These aftershocks can be the same size or smaller than the earthquake they follow. However, seismologists have found that the number of aftershocks decreases, but their magnitude does not necessarily decrease. Therefore, large aftershocks can occur months after an earthquake. Aftershocks may also produce their own subsequences, with an aftershock generating other aftershocks.

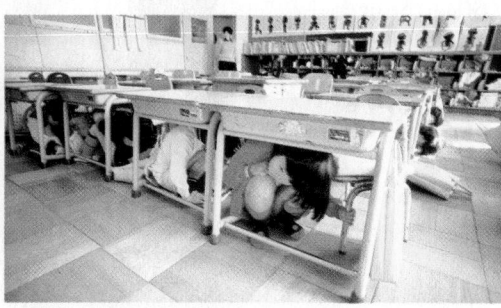

Survival of Structures

- The ability of a structure to withstand a quake depends on a variety of factors, including the composition of the ground on which the structure stands. Structures built on waterlogged or unconsolidated sediment, such as sand, are more likely to suffer intense damage than structures built on bedrock.

Is That a Fact!

- ◆ Sand boils are common during earthquakes that occur in areas with unconsolidated sediments. Loose, sandy sediments behave as fluids do as the ground moves. This condition can create a miniature "geyser" that spews buried debris from beneath the Earth's surface.

- ◆ One of the best structures for resisting damage from earthquakes is a wood-framed building. Wood-framed buildings are not very rigid and can therefore flex quite a bit without collapsing.

SciLINKS

NSTA
Developed and maintained by the
National Science Teachers Association

SciLinks is maintained by the National Science Teachers Association to provide you and your students with interesting, up-to-date links that will enrich your classroom presentation of the chapter.

Visit www.scilinks.org and enter the SciLinks code for more information about the topic listed.

Topic: What Is an Earthquake?
SciLinks code: HSM1658

Topic: Earthquakes and Society
SciLinks code: HSM0455

Topic: Earthquake Measurement
SciLinks code: HSM0452

Overview

Tell students that this chapter will help them learn about earthquakes. The chapter is an introduction to the geophysical concepts that seismologists use in the study of earthquakes.

Assessing Prior Knowledge

Students should be familiar with the following topics:

- plate tectonics
- faults

Identifying Misconceptions

Students often assume that earthquakes are relatively rare phenomena. Point out that thousands of small earthquakes happen every day. Also, students may assume that earthquakes occur only near plate boundaries, in areas such as southern California. Point out that earthquakes can happen far from plate boundaries, for example, in places such as Charleston, South Carolina. Finally, students may think that the loss of life that occurs during an earthquake is a direct result of Earth movement. Point out that the majority of deaths are caused by the collapse of buildings and the disease and famine that may result from the disruption of infrastructure.

Earthquakes

The Big Idea Earthquakes result from sudden motions along breaks in Earth's crust and can affect landforms and societies.

About the Photo

On January 17, 1995, an earthquake of magnitude 7.0 shook the area in and around Kobe, Japan. Though the earthquake lasted for less than a minute, more than 5,000 people lost their lives and another 300,000 people were left homeless. More than 200,000 buildings were damaged or destroyed. Large sections of the elevated Hanshin Expressway, shown in the photo, toppled when the columns supporting the expressway failed. The expressway passed over ground that was soft and wet, where the shaking was stronger and longer lasting.

PRE-READING ACTIVITY

Graphic Organizer

Spider Map Before you read the chapter, create the graphic organizer entitled "Spider Map" described in the **Study Skills** section of the Appendix. Label the circle "Earthquakes." Create a leg for each of the sections in this chapter. As you read the chapter, fill in the map with details about the material presented in each section of the chapter.

Standards Correlations

National Science Education Standards

The following codes indicate the National Science Education Standards that correlate to this chapter. The full text of the standards is at the front of the book.

Chapter Opener
SAI 1, 2

Section 1 What Are Earthquakes?
UCP 2; SAI 1, 2; SPSP 3, 4; ES 1b

Section 2 Earthquake Measurement
UCP 3; HNS 1, 3; SPSP 3,4; ST 2; SAI 1, 2; *LabBook*: SAI 1, SAI 2

Section 3 Earthquakes and Society
UCP 2, 3; SAI 1; ST 2; SPSP 1, 3, 4, 5; ES 1b; HNS 2

Chapter Lab
SAI 1, 2

Chapter Review
UCP 2, 3; ES 1b; ST 2; SPSP 1, 3, 4; HNS 2; SAI 1, 2

Science in Action
UCP 2; ES 1b; ST 2; SPSP 3, 5; HNS 1, 2, 3: SAI 1, 2

START-UP ACTIVITY
MATERIALS

FOR EACH GROUP
- clothes hanger, plastic
- clothes hanger, wire
- goggles, safety
- paper (1 per student)
- protractor (1 per student)
- stick, wooden, small

Safety Caution: Remind students to review all safety cautions and icons before beginning this lab activity.

Teacher's Note: Assist students who have difficulty using the protractors. You may want to provide them with paper on which the angles have already been drawn.

Answers

1. Answers may vary depending on the materials used and on the strength of the materials. The wooden stick would most likely break at greater angles, the wire hanger would bend, and the plastic hanger would bend but return to its original shape.

2. Answers may vary. Desirable building materials would behave in the same way as the materials that did not break or bend permanently.

START-UP ACTIVITY

Bend, Break, or Shake

In this activity, you will test different materials in a model earthquake setting.

Procedure

1. Gather a **small wooden stick,** a **wire clothes hanger,** and a **plastic clothes hanger.**

2. Draw a straight line on a **sheet of paper.** Use a **protractor** to measure and draw the following angles from the line: 20°, 45°, and 90°.

3. Put on your **safety goggles.** Using the angles that you drew as a guide, try bending each item 20° and then releasing it. What happens? Does it break? If it bends, does it return to its original shape?

4. Repeat step 3, but bend each item 45°. Repeat the test again, but bend each item 90°.

Analysis

1. How do the different materials' responses to bending compare?

2. Where earthquakes happen, engineers use building materials that are flexible but that do not break or stay bent. Which materials from this experiment would you want building materials to behave like? Explain your answer.

CHAPTER RESOURCES

Technology

Transparencies
- Chapter Starter Transparency

READING SKILLS

Student Edition on CD-ROM

Guided Reading Audio CD
- English or Spanish

Classroom Videos
- Brain Food Video Quiz

Workbooks

Science Puzzlers, Twisters & Teasers
- Earthquakes **GENERAL**

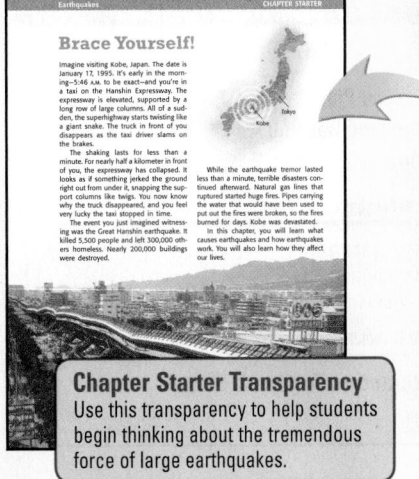

Chapter Starter Transparency
Use this transparency to help students begin thinking about the tremendous force of large earthquakes.

Focus

Overview

This section discusses the seismic events known as earthquakes. Students learn where earthquakes most commonly occur and what causes them. The section also covers different kinds of faults and discusses how earthquakes travel as waves of energy through the Earth.

Bellringer

Ask students to write a few sentences describing what they think an earthquake is. Ask students to review what they wrote after completing this section.

Motivate

Discussion ——— GENERAL

Seismic Definitions Explain to students that *seismos* is a Greek word that means "to shake." Have students make a list of all the words that contain the root *seis-*. (These include *seismology, seismologist, seismic, seismograph, Seismosaurus,* and *seismogram.*) Have students copy the words onto a sheet of paper and consult a dictionary to divide each word into its proper parts. Then, have students define each word part and write a definition of each complete term using the meanings of its parts. **LS Logical**

English Language Learners

What You Will Learn

● Explain where earthquakes take place.
● Explain what causes earthquakes.
● Identify three different types of faults that occur at plate boundaries.
● Describe how energy from earthquakes travels through the Earth.

Vocabulary

seismology   P waves
deformation   S waves
elastic rebound
seismic waves

READING STRATEGY

Paired Summarizing Read this section silently. In pairs, take turns summarizing the material. Stop to discuss ideas that seem confusing.

What Are Earthquakes?

Have you ever felt the earth move under your feet? Many people have. Every day, somewhere within this planet, an earthquake is happening.

The word *earthquake* defines itself fairly well. But there is more to earthquakes than just the shaking of the ground. An entire branch of Earth science, called **seismology** (siez MAHL uh jee), is devoted to studying earthquakes. Earthquakes are complex, and they present many questions for *seismologists,* the scientists who study earthquakes.

Where Do Earthquakes Occur?

Most earthquakes take place near the edges of tectonic plates. *Tectonic plates* are giant pieces of Earth's thin, outermost layer. Tectonic plates move around on top of a layer of plastic rock. **Figure 1** shows the Earth's tectonic plates and the locations of recent major earthquakes.

Tectonic plates move in different directions and at different speeds. Two plates can push toward or pull away from each other. They can also slip slowly past each other. As a result of these movements, numerous features called faults exist in the Earth's crust. A *fault* is a break in the Earth's crust along which blocks of the crust slide relative to one another. Earthquakes occur along faults because of this sliding.

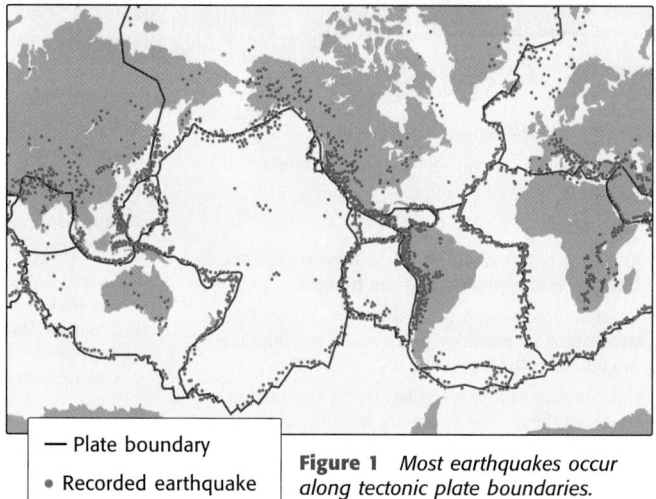

— Plate boundary
• Recorded earthquake

Figure 1 *Most earthquakes occur along tectonic plate boundaries.*

CHAPTER RESOURCES

Chapter Resource File

 • Lesson Plan
• Directed Reading A **BASIC**
• Directed Reading B **SPECIAL NEEDS**

Technology

 Transparencies
• Bellringer
• E27 Elastic Rebound

Workbooks

 Interactive Textbook Struggling Readers

MISCONCEPTION ////ALERT\\\\

Earthquake Frequency Earthquakes are not a rare phenomenon. In fact, more than 3 million earthquakes with Richter magnitudes of 1 or more happen each year—about one every 10 seconds! Most earthquakes are too weak to be felt by humans. The Ring of Fire, a volcanic zone that lies along the plate boundaries surrounding the Pacific Ocean, is the world's largest and most active earthquake zone.

What Causes Earthquakes?

As tectonic plates push, pull, or slip past each other, stress increases along faults near the plates' edges. In response to this stress, rock in the plates deforms. **Deformation** is the change in the shape of rock in response to stress. Rock along a fault deforms in mainly two ways. It deforms in a plastic manner, like a piece of molded clay, or in an elastic manner, like a rubber band. *Plastic deformation,* which is shown in **Figure 2,** does not lead to earthquakes.

Elastic deformation, however, does lead to earthquakes. Rock can stretch farther without breaking than steel can, but rock will break at some point. Think of elastically deformed rock as a stretched rubber band. You can stretch a rubber band only so far before it breaks. When the rubber band breaks, it releases energy. Then, the broken pieces return to their unstretched shape.

Elastic Rebound

The sudden return of elastically deformed rock to its original shape is called **elastic rebound.** Elastic rebound is like the return of the broken rubber-band pieces to their unstretched shape. Elastic rebound occurs when more stress is applied to rock than the rock can withstand. During elastic rebound, energy is released. Some of this energy travels as seismic waves. These seismic waves cause an earthquake, as shown in **Figure 3.**

✓ **Reading Check** How does elastic rebound relate to earthquakes? (*See the Appendix for answers to Reading Checks.*)

Figure 2 *This road cut is adjacent to the San Andreas Fault in southern California. The rocks in the cut have undergone deformation because of the continuous motion of the fault.*

seismology the study of earthquakes

deformation the bending, tilting, and breaking of the Earth's crust; the change in the shape of rock in response to stress

elastic rebound the sudden return of elastically deformed rock to its undeformed shape

Figure 3 | Elastic Rebound and Earthquakes

Before earthquake

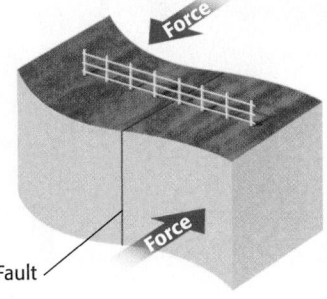

Fault

❶ Tectonic forces push rock on either side of the fault in opposite directions, but the rock is locked together and does not move. The rock deforms in an elastic manner.

After earthquake

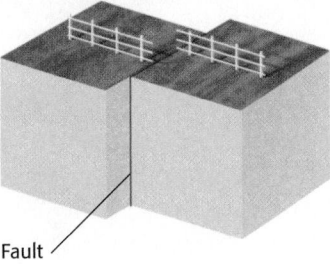

Fault

❷ When enough stress is applied, the rock slips along the fault and releases energy.

Homework —— **ADVANCED**

Mapping Have students create an earthquake map using data from Internet sites that contain a log of the time and location of earthquakes around the world. This activity will help students understand that earthquakes occur every day, mainly near tectonic plate boundaries. This activity can become an ongoing investigation in which students keep records of earthquakes during the school year. **LS Visual**

Demonstration —— BASIC

Faults and Earthquakes Use two smooth wooden blocks to demonstrate how blocks of crust move along a fault. Glue coarse sandpaper onto one side of each block. Firmly slide the sandpaper-covered sides against each other until there is a sudden movement. Explain that this model shows how rock slides along a fault during elastic rebound. As the rock slides, it releases energy that travels as waves. **LS Visual**   English Language Learners

Cultural Awareness GENERAL

Earthquake Mythology Many different cultures have myths about earthquakes. According to Japanese mythology, earthquakes are caused by the *namazu,* a giant catfish that lives in mud beneath the Earth. *Kamisha,* a brave warrior, protects Japan from earthquakes by using divine powers to trap the *namazu* under an enormous rock. Earthquakes occur when *Kamisha* lets his guard down and allows the *namazu* to thrash about. Encourage students to research other cultural myths about earthquakes and to share their research with the class. Students can also write their own legend about the origin of earthquakes. **LS Verbal**

Answer to Reading Check
During elastic rebound, rock releases energy. Some of this energy travels as seismic waves that cause earthquakes.

Faults and Tectonics Each circle in the figure is a magnified view of a fault at the edge of a tectonic plate. In fact, large systems of multiple faults define the boundaries between plates. The sliding of crust along these faults and the overall movement of crust along plate boundaries are similar. For example, the block of crust to the right of the reverse fault moves down relative to the block to the left of the fault. Similarly, the plate to the right of the convergent plate boundary moves down relative to the plate to the left of the boundary. **LS** Visual/Logical

Homework —— GENERAL

Illustrating Faults
PORTFOLIO
  Ask students to draw the three types of faults illustrated on these pages. Students should label each fault and state the type of plate motion that creates each fault. Encourage students to locate an example of each type of tectonic plate boundary on a map. (An example of a transform plate boundary is the San Andreas Fault in California; an example of a convergent plate boundary is off the west coast of South America; an example of a divergent plate boundary is the Mid-Atlantic Ridge, on the bottom of the Atlantic Ocean.) **LS** Visual   English Language Learners

Faults at Tectonic Plate Boundaries

A specific type of plate motion takes place at different tectonic plate boundaries. Each type of motion creates a particular kind of fault that can produce earthquakes. Examine **Table 1** and the diagram below to learn more about plate motion.

Table 1 Plate Motion and Fault Types

Plate motion	Major fault type
Transform	strike-slip fault
Convergent	reverse fault
Divergent	normal fault

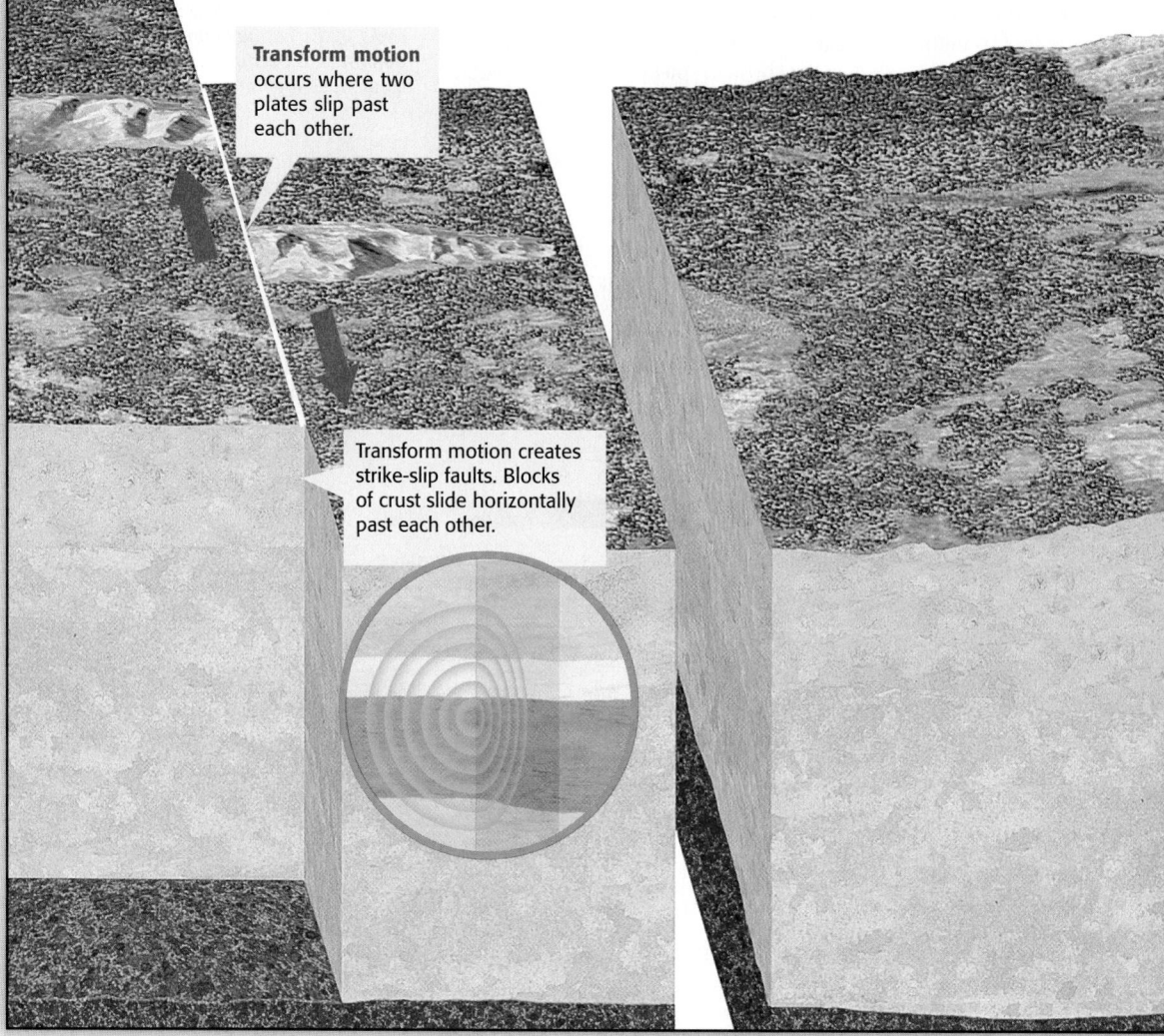

Transform motion occurs where two plates slip past each other.

Transform motion creates strike-slip faults. Blocks of crust slide horizontally past each other.

MISCONCEPTION
///ALERT

Aftershocks A general misconception is that aftershocks do not present the same level of danger as the earthquake, or mainshock, that they follow. Seismological evidence has proven that the opposite can be true. Aftershocks can be powerful earthquakes. An aftershock of magnitude 6.5 followed 3 hours after the 1992 magnitude 7.3 Landers earthquake! Aftershocks can be as damaging as, or even more damaging than, a mainshock. The reasons are that building damage is cumulative and aftershocks vary in location and in the pattern of radiation from the mainshock.

Earthquake Zones

Earthquakes can happen both near Earth's surface or far below it. Most earthquakes happen in the earthquake zones along tectonic plate boundaries. Earthquake zones are places where a large number of faults are located. The San Andreas Fault Zone in California is an example of an earthquake zone. But not all faults are located at tectonic plate boundaries. Sometimes, earthquakes happen along faults in the middle of tectonic plates.

Reading Check Where are earthquake zones located?

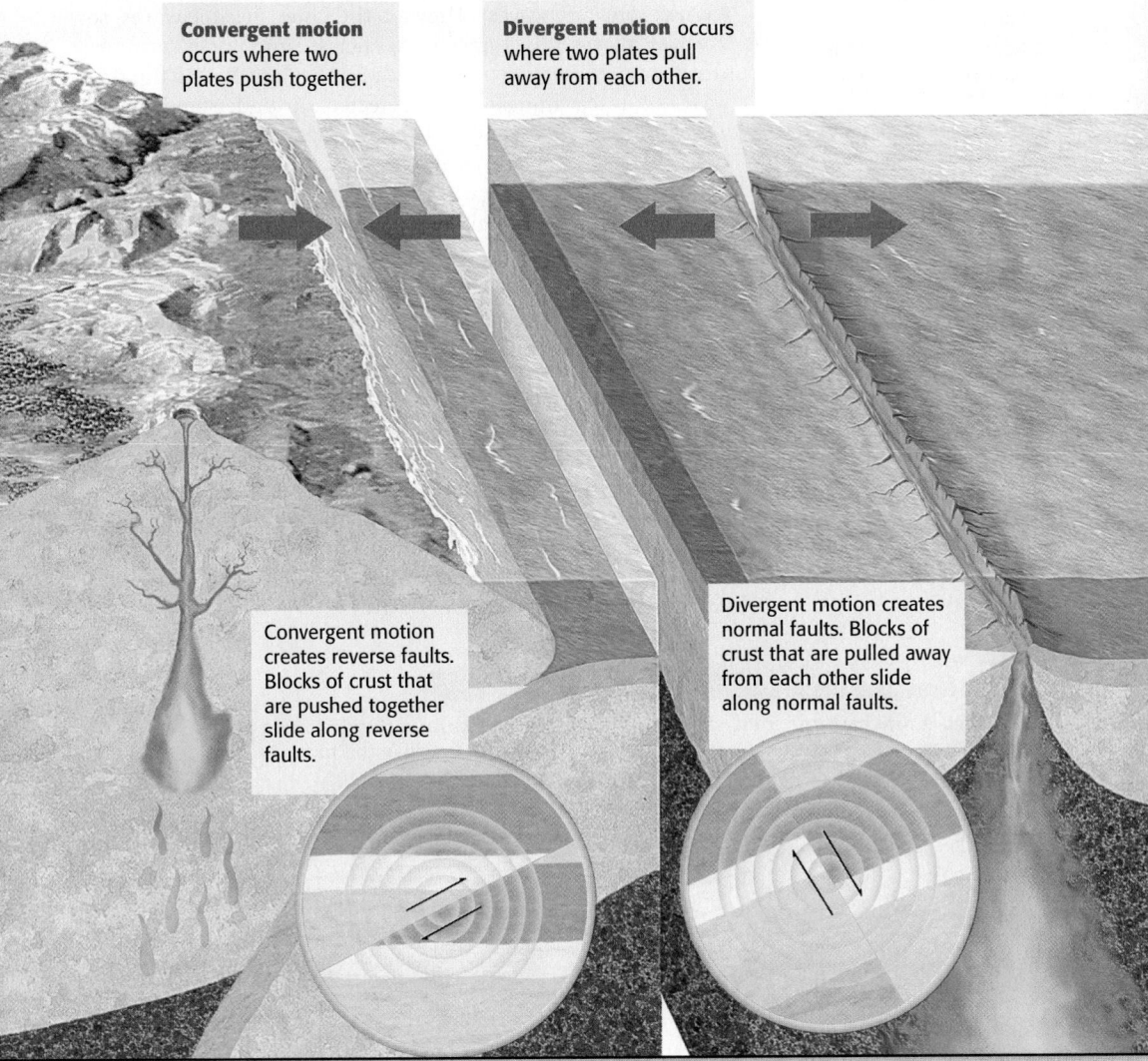

Convergent motion occurs where two plates push together.

Divergent motion occurs where two plates pull away from each other.

Convergent motion creates reverse faults. Blocks of crust that are pushed together slide along reverse faults.

Divergent motion creates normal faults. Blocks of crust that are pulled away from each other slide along normal faults.

Answer to Reading Check

Earthquake zones are usually located along tectonic plate boundaries.

Close

Reteaching — BASIC

P and S Waves Tell students that the *P* in P waves and the *S* in S waves each stand for two descriptive words. The letters describe how each type of wave affects rock—P stands for *pressure,* and S stands for *shear.* P also stands for *primary,* and S stands for *secondary.* This scheme describes the arrival times of each type of wave— P waves always arrive first, and S waves always arrive second. **[LS]** Logical

Quiz — GENERAL

1. What is a fault? (A fault is a break in the Earth's crust along which blocks of the crust slide relative to one another.)

2. How does rock that is along a fault deform in response to a decrease in stress? (Rock deforms in an elastic manner, as a rubber band does, by snapping back to its original shape.)

Alternative Assessment — GENERAL

Concept Mapping Have students create a concept map explaining the relationship between tectonic plate motion and fault types. **[LS]** Visual

Quick Lab

Modeling Seismic Waves

1. Stretch a **spring toy** lengthwise on a **table.**

2. Hold one end of the spring while a partner holds the other end. Push your end toward your partner's end, and observe what happens.

3. Repeat step 2, but this time shake the spring from side to side.

4. Which type of seismic wave is represented in step 2? in step 3?

seismic wave a wave of energy that travels through the Earth, away from an earthquake in all directions

P wave a seismic wave that causes particles of rock to move in a back-and-forth direction

S wave a seismic wave that causes particles of rock to move in a side-to-side direction

How Do Earthquake Waves Travel?

Waves of energy that travel through the Earth are called **seismic waves.** Seismic waves that travel through the Earth's interior are called *body waves.* There are two types of body waves: P waves and S waves. Seismic waves that travel along the Earth's surface are called *surface waves.* Each type of seismic wave travels through Earth's layers in a different way and at a different speed. Also, the speed of a seismic wave depends on the kind of material the wave travels through.

P Waves

Waves that travel through solids, liquids, and gases are called **P waves** (pressure waves). They are the fastest seismic waves, so P waves always travel ahead of other seismic waves. P waves are also called *primary waves,* because they are always the first waves of an earthquake to be detected. To understand how P waves affect rock, imagine a cube of gelatin sitting on a plate. Like most solids, gelatin is an elastic material. It wiggles if you tap it. Tapping the cube of gelatin changes the pressure inside the cube, which momentarily deforms the cube. The gelatin then reacts by springing back to its original shape. This process is how P waves affect rock, as shown in **Figure 4.**

S Waves

Rock can also be deformed from side to side. After being deformed from side to side, the rock springs back to its original position and S waves are created. **S waves,** or shear waves, are the second-fastest seismic waves. S waves shear rock side to side, as shown in **Figure 4,** which means they stretch the rock sideways. Unlike P waves, S waves cannot travel through parts of the Earth that are completely liquid. Also, S waves are slower than P waves and always arrive later. Thus, another name for S waves is *secondary waves.*

Figure 4 **Body Waves**

P waves move rock back and forth, which squeezes and stretches the rock, as they travel through the rock.

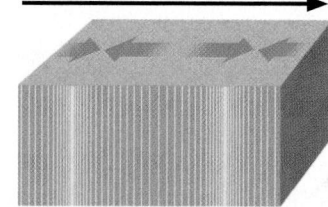

Direction of wave travel

S waves shear rock side to side as they travel through the rock.

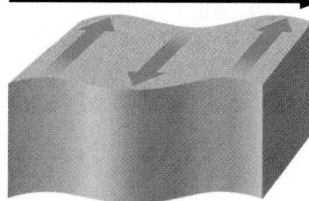

Direction of wave travel

 INCLUSION Strategies

• *Hearing Impaired*
• *Attention Deficit Disorder*
• *Learning Disabled*

Student groups will model pressure, shear, and surface waves. Organize students into groups of six or seven students. Move the furniture back to classroom walls. Have each group stand side by side and hold hands. Tell students that each group will have

15 seconds to gently model a P wave. Ask groups to plan their approach first, and then time them as they model a P wave. Repeat for an S wave and for a surface wave. Finally, assign three groups each one of the three waves, and have them model an earthquake. Allow them 30 seconds to complete their demonstration. **[LS]** Interpersonal/Kinesthetic

English Language Learners

Surface Waves

Surface waves move along the Earth's surface and produce motion mostly in the upper few kilometers of Earth's crust. There are two types of surface waves. One type of surface wave produces motion up, down, and around, as shown in **Figure 5.** The other type produces back-and-forth motion like the motion produced by S waves. Surface waves are different from body waves in that surface waves travel more slowly and are more destructive.

✓**Reading Check** Explain the differences between surface waves and body waves.

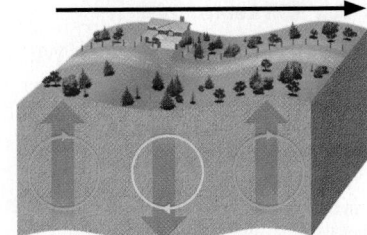

Figure 5 **Surface Waves**

Surface waves move the ground much like ocean waves move water particles.

Direction of wave travel

SECTION Review

Summary

- Earthquakes occur mainly near the edges of tectonic plates.
- Elastic rebound is the direct cause of earthquakes.
- Three major types of faults occur at tectonic plate boundaries: normal faults, reverse faults, and strike-slip faults.
- Earthquake energy travels as body waves through the Earth's interior or as surface waves along the surface of the Earth.

Using Key Terms

Complete each of the following sentences by choosing the correct term from the word bank.

Deformation	P waves
Elastic rebound	S waves

1. _____ is the change in shape of rock due to stress.

2. _____ always travel ahead of other waves.

Understanding Key Ideas

3. Seismic waves that shear rock side to side are called
   a. surface waves.
   b. S waves.
   c. P waves.
   d. Both (b) and (c)

4. Where do earthquakes occur?

5. What is the direct cause of earthquakes?

6. Describe the three types of plate motion and the faults that are characteristic of each type of motion.

7. What is an earthquake zone?

Math Skills

8. A seismic wave is traveling through the Earth at an average rate of speed of 8 km/s. How long will it take the wave to travel 480 km?

Critical Thinking

9. **Applying Concepts** Given what you know about elastic rebound, why do you think some earthquakes are stronger than others?

10. **Identifying Relationships** Why are surface waves more destructive to buildings than P waves or S waves are?

11. **Identifying Relationships** Why do you think the majority of earthquake zones are located at tectonic plate boundaries?

SCI LINKS®

NSTA
Developed and maintained by the
National Science Teachers Association

For a variety of links related to this chapter, go to www.scilinks.org

Topic: What Is an Earthquake?
SciLinks code: HSM1658

CONNECTION to Physical Science—ADVANCED

Seismic Waves Use the teaching transparency "Comparing Transverse and Longitudinal Waves" to discuss the differences between P waves (longitudinal) and S waves (transverse). P waves travel faster than S waves. P waves travel through solids, liquids, and gases; S waves cannot travel through materials that are completely liquid. P waves move rock back and forth between a squeezed and stretched position, and S waves shear rock back and forth.

CHAPTER RESOURCES

Chapter Resource File

- Section Quiz **GENERAL**
- Section Review **GENERAL**
- Vocabulary and Section Summary **GENERAL**
- SciLinks Activity **GENERAL**
- Datasheet for Quick Lab

Technology

Transparencies
- **LINK TO PHYSICAL SCIENCE** P82 Comparing Longitudinal and Transverse Waves
- E28 Primary Waves; Secondary Waves; Surface Waves

Focus

Overview

In this section, students learn how seismographs are used to detect and locate earthquakes. This section explains the difference between an earthquake's focus and epicenter. Students will also learn how the Richter scale is used to measure the magnitude of earthquakes.

 Bellringer

Ask students to create a qualitative scale for gauging earthquake intensity. Students should use brief phrases to describe the effects of very minor to extreme earthquakes. Discuss the advantages and disadvantages of their finished scale.

Motivate

ACTIVITY ——————— GENERAL

Exploring a Seismic Network

Have students locate a map on the Internet that shows worldwide seismic stations. Students should select an earthquake of magnitude 5.5 or greater that has been recorded at one of these stations during the past month. Have students find press releases that relate to the earthquake they have selected and then write a short report on the quake. **LS** Visual/Logical

What You Will Learn

● Explain how earthquakes are detected.
● Describe how to locate an earthquake's epicenter.
● Explain how the strength of an earthquake is measured.
● Explain how the intensity of an earthquake is measured.

Vocabulary

seismograph   epicenter
seismogram   focus

READING STRATEGY

Reading Organizer As you read this section, create an outline of the section. Use the headings from the section in your outline.

seismograph an instrument that records vibrations in the ground and determines the location and strength of an earthquake

seismogram a tracing of earthquake motion that is created by a seismograph

epicenter the point on Earth's surface directly above an earthquake's starting point, or focus

focus the point along a fault at which the first motion of an earthquake occurs

Earthquake Measurement

Imagine walls shaking, windows rattling, and glassware and dishes clinking and clanking. After only seconds, the vibrating stops and the sounds die away.

Within minutes, news reports give information about the strength, the time, and the location of the earthquake. You are amazed at how scientists could have learned this information so quickly.

Locating Earthquakes

How do seismologists know when and where earthquakes begin? They depend on earthquake-sensing instruments called seismographs. **Seismographs** are instruments located at or near the surface of the Earth that record seismic waves. When the waves reach a seismograph, the seismograph creates a seismogram. A **seismogram** is a tracing of earthquake motion and is created by a seismograph.

Determining Time and Location of Earthquakes

Seismologists use seismograms to calculate when an earthquake began. Seismologists find an earthquake's start time by comparing seismograms and noting the differences in arrival times of P waves and S waves. Seismologists also use seismograms to find an earthquake's epicenter. An **epicenter** is the point on the Earth's surface directly above an earthquake's starting point. A **focus** is the point inside the Earth where an earthquake begins. **Figure 1** shows the location of an earthquake's epicenter and its focus.

Reading Check How do seismologists determine an earthquake's start time? (*See the Appendix for answers to Reading Checks.*)

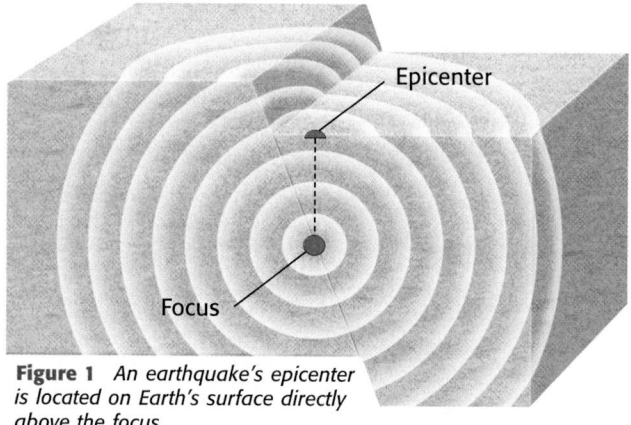

Figure 1 An earthquake's epicenter is located on Earth's surface directly above the focus.

CHAPTER RESOURCES

Chapter Resource File

● **Lesson Plan**
● **Directed Reading A** BASIC
● **Directed Reading B** SPECIAL NEEDS

Technology

Transparencies
● Bellringer
● E29 Finding an Earthquake's Epicenter

Workbooks

Interactive Textbook Struggling Readers

Answer to Reading Check

Seismologists determine an earthquake's start time by comparing seismograms and noting differences in arrival times of P waves and S waves.

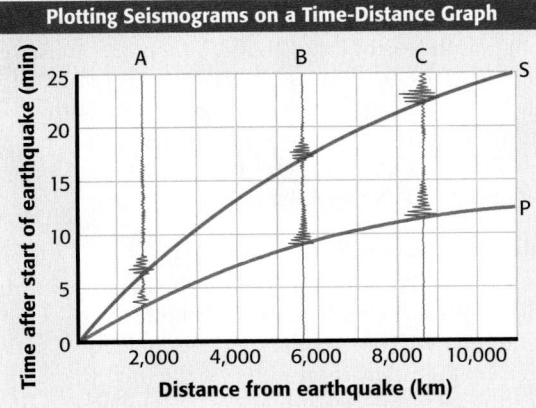

Plotting Seismograms on a Time-Distance Graph

Time after start of earthquake (min) / *Distance from earthquake (km)*

Figure 2 *After identifying P and S waves, seismologists can use the time difference to determine an earthquake's start time and the distance from the epicenter to each station. The vertical axis tells how much time passed between the start of the earthquake and the arrival of seismic waves at a station. The horizontal axis tells the distance between a station and the earthquake's epicenter.*

The S-P Time Method

Perhaps the simplest method by which seismologists find an earthquake's epicenter is the *S-P time method*. The first step in this method is to collect several seismograms of the same earthquake from different locations. Then, the seismograms are placed on a time-distance graph. The seismogram tracing of the first P wave is lined up with the P-wave time-distance curve, and the tracing of the first S wave is lined up with the S-wave curve, as shown in **Figure 2**. The distance of each station from the earthquake can be found by reading the horizontal axis. After finding out the distances, a seismologist can locate an earthquake's epicenter, as shown in **Figure 3**.

| **Figure 3** | **Finding an Earthquake's Epicenter** |

❶ A circle is drawn around a seismograph station. The radius of the circle equals the distance from the seismograph to the epicenter. (This distance is taken from the time-distance graph.)

❷ When a second circle is drawn around another seismograph station, the circle overlaps the first circle in two spots. One of these spots is the earthquake's epicenter.

❸ When a circle is drawn around a third seismograph station, all three circles intersect in one spot—the earthquake's epicenter. In this case, the epicenter was in San Francisco.

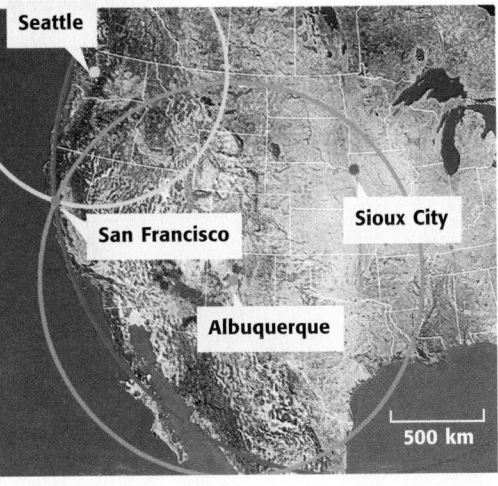

Seattle
San Francisco
Sioux City
Albuquerque
500 km

Reteaching — **BASIC**

Defining Terms Have students help you come up with definitions for the following terms: *seismograph, seismogram, epicenter, focus, S-P time method, Richter magnitude scale,* and *Modified Mercalli Intensity Scale.*

LS Logical

English Language Learners

Quiz — **GENERAL**

1. How is an earthquake's epicenter related to its focus? (The epicenter is the point on the Earth's surface directly above the focus, which is where the earthquake originates.)

2. As seismic waves travel farther, what happens to the difference in arrival times of P waves and S waves? (It increases.)

Alternative Assessment — **GENERAL**

Recent Earthquakes
Have students identify 10 recent earthquakes with a magnitude greater than 5.0 on the Richter scale. Students can compile their findings in a table that includes the epicenter and the magnitude of the quake, the damage it caused, and any other interesting information about the quake. Challenge students to find trends in the data.

LS Logical

CONNECTION TO Social Studies

WRITING SKILL New Madrid Earthquakes

During the winter of 1811–1812, three of the most powerful earthquakes in U.S. history were centered near New Madrid, Missouri, thousands of miles from the nearest tectonic plate boundary. Research the New Madrid earthquakes, and summarize your findings in a one-page essay.

Measuring Earthquake Strength and Intensity

"How strong was the earthquake?" is a common question asked of seismologists. This question is not easy to answer. But it is an important question for anyone living near an earthquake zone. Fortunately, seismograms can be used not only to determine an earthquake's epicenter and its start time but also to find out an earthquake's strength.

The Richter Magnitude Scale

Throughout much of the 20th century, seismologists used the *Richter magnitude scale*, commonly called the Richter scale, to measure the strength of earthquakes. Seismologist Charles Richter created the scale in the 1930s. Richter wanted to compare earthquakes by measuring ground motion recorded by seismograms at seismograph stations.

Earthquake Ground Motion

A measure of the strength of an earthquake is called *magnitude*. The Richter scale measures the ground motion from an earthquake and adjusts for distance to find its strength. Each time the magnitude increases by one unit, the measured ground motion becomes 10 times larger. For example, an earthquake with a magnitude of 5.0 on the Richter scale will produce 10 times as much ground motion as an earthquake with a magnitude of 4.0. Furthermore, an earthquake with a magnitude of 6.0 will produce 100 times as much ground motion (10 × 10) as an earthquake with a magnitude of 4.0. **Table 1** shows the differences in the estimated effects of earthquakes with each increase of one unit of magnitude.

✓ **Reading Check** How are magnitude and ground motion related in the Richter scale?

Table 1 Effects of Different-Sized Earthquakes	
Magnitude	**Estimated effects**
2.0	can be detected only by seismograph
3.0	can be felt at epicenter
4.0	can be felt by most people in the area
5.0	causes damage at epicenter
6.0	can cause widespread damage
7.0	can cause great, widespread damage

Answer to Reading Check

Each time the magnitude increases by 1 unit, the amount of ground motion increases by 10 times.

Answer to Social Studies Activity

Have students present their one-page summary to the class. Encourage students to use visual aids, such as maps of the earthquake area, in their presentations. A variety of books have been written on the New Madrid earthquakes, and accounts are also available on the Internet.

Modified Mercalli Intensity Scale

A measure of the degree to which an earthquake is felt by people and the amount of damage caused by the earthquake, if any, is called *intensity*. Currently, seismologists in the United States use the Modified Mercalli Intensity Scale to measure earthquake intensity. This scale is a numerical scale that uses Roman numerals from I to XII to describe increasing earthquake intensity levels. An intensity level of I describes an earthquake that is not felt by most people. An intensity level of XII indicates total damage of an area. **Figure 4** shows the type of damage caused by an earthquake that has a Modified Mercalli intensity level of XI.

Because the effects of an earthquake vary from place to place, any earthquake will have more than one intensity value. Intensity values are usually higher near an earthquake's epicenter.

Figure 4 *Intensity values for the 1906 San Francisco earthquake varied from place to place. The maximum intensity level was XI.*

SECTION Review

Summary

- Seismologists detect seismic waves and record them as seismograms.
- The S-P time method is the simplest method to use to find an earthquake's epicenter.
- Seismologists use the Richter scale to measure an earthquake's strength.
- Seismologists use the Modified Mercalli Intensity Scale to measure an earthquake's intensity.

Using Key Terms

1. In your own words, write a definition for each of the following terms: *epicenter* and *focus*.

Understanding Key Ideas

2. What is the difference between a seismograph and a seismogram?

3. Explain how earthquakes are detected.

4. Briefly explain the steps of the S-P time method for locating an earthquake's epicenter.

5. Why might an earthquake have more than one intensity value?

Math Skills

6. How much more ground motion is produced by an earthquake of magnitude 7.0 than by an earthquake of magnitude 4.0?

Critical Thinking

7. **Making Inferences** Why is a 6.0 magnitude earthquake so much more destructive than a 5.0 magnitude earthquake?

8. **Identifying Bias** Which do you think is the more important measure of earthquakes, strength or intensity? Explain.

9. **Making Inferences** Do you think an earthquake of moderate magnitude can produce high Modified Mercalli intensity values?

For a variety of links related to this chapter, go to www.scilinks.org

Topic: Earthquake Measurement
SciLinks code: HSM0452

CHAPTER RESOURCES

Chapter Resource File

- Section Quiz **GENERAL**
- Section Review **GENERAL**
- Vocabulary and Section Summary **GENERAL**
- Reinforcement Worksheet **BASIC**

Workbooks

Math Skills for Science
- Earthquake Power! **GENERAL**

Overview

In this section, students learn how earthquake hazard is determined. The section explores the methods seismologists use to make forecasts about earthquakes. Students learn about the technologies used to reinforce buildings against earthquakes. The section concludes with a discussion of earthquake safety procedures.

 Bellringer

If any of your students have experienced an earthquake, have them write a short paragraph describing how they felt and what they did to protect themselves during the earthquake. Have students who have not experienced an earthquake write a paragraph describing what they think they would do during a moderate earthquake.

Motivate

Discussion ——— GENERAL

Hazard Levels Have students examine **Figure 1**. Challenge them to explain why the West Coast has such high levels of earthquake hazard. If they need a hint, have them look again at **Figure 1** in Section 1. (There is a tectonic plate boundary along the western coast of the United States.) **LS** Logical/Visual

---

SECTION

3

What You Will Learn

- Explain how earthquake-hazard level is determined.
- Compare methods of earthquake forecasting.
- Describe five ways to safeguard buildings against earthquakes.
- Outline earthquake safety procedures.

Vocabulary
gap hypothesis
seismic gap

READING STRATEGY

Discussion Read this section silently. Write down questions that you have about this section. Discuss your questions in a small group.

Earthquakes and Society

Imagine that you are in class and the ground begins to shake beneath your feet. What do you do?

Seismologists are not able to predict the exact time when and place where an earthquake will occur. They can, at best, make forecasts based on the frequency with which earthquakes take place. Therefore, seismologists are always looking for better ways to forecast when and where earthquakes will happen. In the meantime, it is important for people in earthquake zones to be prepared before an earthquake strikes.

Earthquake Hazard

Earthquake hazard is a measurement of how likely an area is to have damaging earthquakes in the future. An area's earthquake-hazard level is determined by past and present seismic activity. The map in **Figure 1** shows that some areas of the United States have a higher earthquake-hazard level than others do. This variation is caused by differences in seismic activity. The greater the seismic activity, the higher the earthquake-hazard level. The West Coast, for example, has a very high earthquake-hazard level because it has a lot of seismic activity.

Look at the map. What earthquake-hazard level or levels are shown in the area in which you live? How do the hazard levels of nearby areas compare with your area's hazard level?

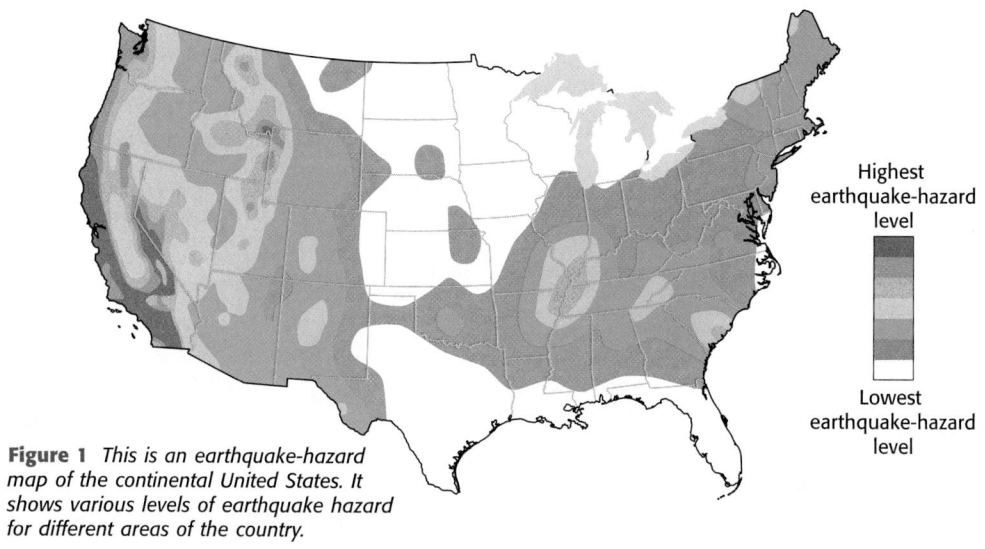

Highest
earthquake-hazard
level

Lowest
earthquake-hazard
level

Figure 1 *This is an earthquake-hazard map of the continental United States. It shows various levels of earthquake hazard for different areas of the country.*

CHAPTER RESOURCES

Chapter Resource File

- **Lesson Plan**
- **Directed Reading A** (BASIC)
- **Directed Reading B** (SPECIAL NEEDS)

Technology

Transparencies
- Bellringer

Workbooks

Interactive Textbook Struggling Readers

CONNECTION ACTIVITY
Art ——— GENERAL

The Protection of Art Treasures Have students find out what has been done to protect sculptures from earthquake damage at the J. Paul Getty Museum in Pacific Palisades, California, or at another museum in an earthquake-prone area. **LS** Logical

---

Table 1 Worldwide Earthquake Frequency (Based on Observations Since 1900)

Descriptor	Magnitude	Average number annually
Great	8.0 and higher	1
Major	7.0–7.9	18
Strong	6.0–6.9	120
Moderate	5.0–5.9	800
Light	4.0–4.9	about 6,200
Minor	3.0–3.9	about 49,000
Very minor	2.0–2.9	about 365,000

Earthquake Forecasting

Forecasting when and where earthquakes will occur and their strength is difficult. By looking carefully at areas of seismic activity, seismologists have discovered some patterns in earthquakes that allow them to make some general predictions.

Strength and Frequency

Earthquakes vary in strength. And you can probably guess that earthquakes don't occur on a set schedule. But what you may not know is that the strength of earthquakes is related to how often they occur. **Table 1** provides more detail about this relationship worldwide.

The relationship between earthquake strength and frequency is also at work on a local scale. For example, each year approximately 1.6 earthquakes with a magnitude of 4.0 on the Richter scale occur in the Puget Sound area of Washington State. Over this same time period, approximately 10 times as many earthquakes with a magnitude of 3.0 occur in this area. Scientists use these statistics to make forecasts about the strength, location, and frequency of future earthquakes.

Reading Check What is the relationship between the strength of earthquakes and earthquake frequency? (*See the Appendix for answers to Reading Checks.*)

The Gap Hypothesis

Another method of forecasting an earthquake's strength, location, and frequency is based on the gap hypothesis. The **gap hypothesis** is a hypothesis that states that sections of active faults that have had relatively few earthquakes are likely to be the sites of strong earthquakes in the future. The areas along a fault where relatively few earthquakes have occurred are called **seismic gaps.**

INTERNET ACTIVITY

For another activity related to this chapter, go to **go.hrw.com** and type in the keyword **HZ5EQKW.**

gap hypothesis a hypothesis that is based on the idea that a major earthquake is more likely to occur along the part of an active fault where no earthquakes have occurred for a certain period of time

seismic gap an area along a fault where relatively few earthquakes have occurred recently but where strong earthquakes have occurred in the past

Tools of the Trade Have interested students research the various types of instruments used to detect seismic activity, including tiltmeters, gravimeters, strainmeters, magnetometers, and laser range finders. Students' findings should include illustrations and detailed descriptions of how the instruments work.
LS Logical/Visual

Debate ———— **GENERAL**

Nuclear Waste Disposal?
Scientists must consider the geologic stability of potential sites for nuclear waste facilities. Have students research and debate the issue of nuclear waste disposal. Have them consider that there are few viable options for the disposal of the world's nuclear waste. Remind them that no one can be sure that an area will be stable over the thousands of years it takes for nuclear waste to decay. **LS** Interpersonal

Homework ———— **GENERAL**

Presentation Have students create a poster to promote earthquake safety. Posters should focus on one of the following: how to prepare for an earthquake, what to do during an earthquake, or what to do after an earthquake. Students can create a display to educate the school about earthquake safety. **LS** Visual

---

Figure 2 **A Seismic Gap on the San Andreas Fault**

This diagram shows a cross section of the San Andreas Fault. Note how the seismic gap was filled by the 1989 Loma Prieta earthquake and its aftershocks. *Aftershocks* are weaker earthquakes that follow a stronger earthquake.

● Earthquakes prior to 1989 earthquake

● 1989 earthquake and aftershocks

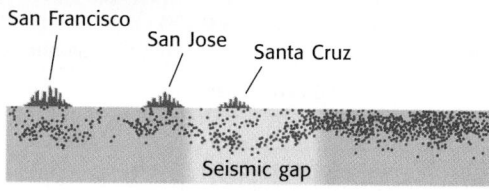

Before 1989 earthquake

Filled seismic gap

After 1989 earthquake

Using the Gap Hypothesis

Not all seismologists believe the gap hypothesis is an accurate method of forecasting earthquakes. But some seismologists think the gap hypothesis helped forecast the approximate location and strength of the 1989 Loma Prieta earthquake in the San Francisco Bay area. The seismic gap that they identified is illustrated in **Figure 2.** In 1988, these seismologists predicted that over the next 30 years there was a 30% chance that an earthquake with a magnitude of at least 6.5 would fill this seismic gap. Were they correct? The Loma Prieta earthquake, which filled in the seismic gap in 1989, measured 6.9 on the Richter scale. Their prediction was very close, considering how complicated the forecasting of earthquakes is.

Figure 3 *During the January 17, 1995, earthquake, the fronts of entire buildings collapsed into the streets of Kobe, Japan.*

Earthquakes and Buildings

Figure 3 shows what can happen to buildings during an earthquake. These buildings were not designed or constructed to withstand the forces of an earthquake.

Today, older structures in seismically active places, such as California, are being made more earthquake resistant. The process of making older structures more earthquake resistant is called *retrofitting*. A common way to retrofit an older home is to securely fasten it to its foundation. Steel can be used to strengthen structures made of brick.

✓ Reading Check Explain the meaning of the term *retrofitting*.

WEIRD SCIENCE

Engineers have devised giant shock absorbers for buildings. The shock absorbers contain a ferrofluid solution that becomes rigid in a magnetic field. When an earthquake occurs, a computer controls electromagnets in the shock absorbers to damp the vibrations!

Answer to Reading Check
Retrofitting is the process of making older structures more earthquake resistant.

Earthquake-Resistant Buildings

A lot has been learned from building failure during earthquakes. Armed with this knowledge, architects and engineers use the newest technology to design and construct buildings and bridges to better withstand earthquakes. Carefully study **Figure 4** to learn more about this modern technology.

| Figure 4 | Earthquake-Resistant Building Technology |

The **mass damper** is a weight placed in the roof of a building. Motion sensors detect building movement during an earthquake and send messages to a computer. The computer then signals controls in the roof to shift the mass damper to counteract the building's movement.

The **active tendon system** works much like the mass damper system in the roof. Sensors notify a computer that the building is moving. Then, the computer activates devices to shift a large weight to counteract the movement.

Base isolators act as shock absorbers during an earthquake. They are made of layers of rubber and steel wrapped around a lead core. Base isolators absorb seismic waves, preventing them from traveling through the building.

Steel **cross braces** are placed between floors. These braces counteract pressure that pushes and pulls at the side of a building during an earthquake.

Flexible pipes help prevent waterlines and gas lines from breaking. Engineers design the pipes with flexible joints so that the pipes are able to twist and bend without breaking during an earthquake.

Reteaching ——— **BASIC**

Earthquake Hazards Ask students to write a description of the hazards they might face if an earthquake occurred when they were in each of the following situations:

- asleep in bed (collapsing building)
- at the beach (tsunamis)
- snow skiing (avalanche)

LS Logical

Quiz ——————— **GENERAL**

1. What is the gap hypothesis? (The gap hypothesis states that sections of active faults that have had relatively few earthquakes are likely to be the sites of strong earthquakes in the future.)

2. Why should you lie under a table or desk during an earthquake? (The table or desk might prevent falling objects from hitting you and causing injury.)

3. What are aftershocks? (They are generally weaker quakes that follow stronger earthquakes.)

Alternative Assessment ——— **GENERAL**

Earthquake Safety Guidelines Have students work together to create a pamphlet that instructs the general public what to do when an earthquake occurs.

LS Visual

Answer to Reading Check

You should crouch or lie face down under a table or desk.

CONNECTION TO
Physics

WRITING SKILL **Earthquake Proof Buildings** During earthquakes, buildings often sway from side to side when the ground beneath them moves. This swaying can cause structural damage to buildings. Scientists and engineers are developing computer-controlled systems that counteract the swaying of buildings during earthquakes. Research a computer-controlled system that uses mass dampers or active tendons to reduce damage to buildings. Summarize your research in a short essay.

Are You Prepared for an Earthquake?

If you live in an area where earthquakes are common, there are many things you can do to protect yourself and your property from earthquakes. Plan ahead so that you will know what to do before, during, and after an earthquake. Stick to your plan as closely as possible.

Before the Shaking Starts

The first thing you should do is safeguard your home against earthquakes. You can do so by putting heavier objects on lower shelves so that they do not fall during the earthquake. You can also talk to a parent about having your home strengthened. Next, you should find safe places within each room of your home and outside of your home. Then, make a plan with others (your family, neighbors, or friends) to meet in a safe place after the earthquake is over. This plan ensures that you will all know who is safe. During the earthquake, waterlines, power lines, and roadways may be damaged. So, you should store water, nonperishable food, a fire extinguisher, a flashlight with batteries, a portable radio, medicines, and a first-aid kit in a place you can access after the earthquake.

When the Shaking Starts

The best thing to do if you are indoors when an earthquake begins is to crouch or lie face down under a table or desk in the center of a room, as shown in **Figure 5.** If you are outside, lie face down away from buildings, power lines, and trees and cover your head with your hands. If you are in a car on an open road, you should stop the car and remain inside.

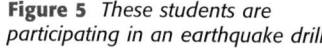 **Reading Check** Explain what you would do if you were in class and an earthquake began to shake the ground.

Figure 5 These students are participating in an earthquake drill.

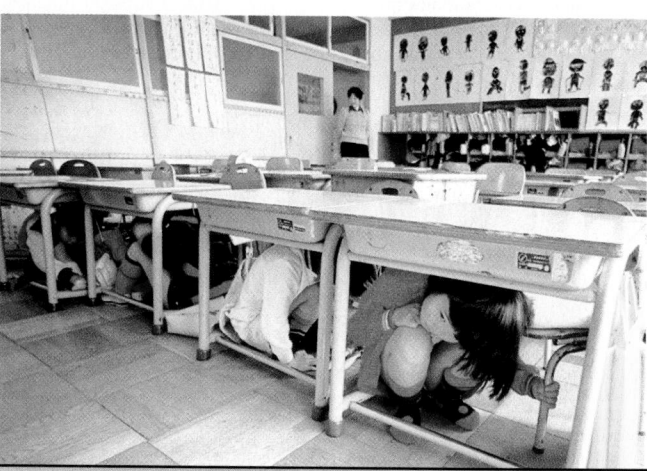

 INCLUSION *Strategies*

- **Developmentally Delayed**
- **Attention Deficit Disorder**
- **Behavior Control Issues**

Have students create models of transform, divergent, and convergent tectonic plate motion. A large world map with areas marked that illustrate different tectonic plate motion should be visible in the classroom. Organize students into groups of four. Hand out six plastic foam blocks (edges should meet on an angle) and magic markers. Ask students to use the

blocks to model transform, divergent, and convergent tectonic plate motion. Students should use the magic marker to put arrows signifying what direction the plates are moving and to label the model with a "T" for transform, "D" for divergent, and "C" for convergent. Next, ask students to look at the map and review where these types of tectonic plate motion occur, and the landforms that are associated with them. **LS** Visual/Logical

English Language Learners

After the Shaking Stops

Being in an earthquake is a startling and often frightening experience for most people. After being in an earthquake, you should not be surprised to find yourself and others puzzled about what took place. You should try to calm down and get your bearings as quickly as possible. Then, remove yourself from immediate danger, such as downed power lines, broken glass, and fire hazards. Always stay out of damaged buildings, and return home only when you are told that it is safe to do so by someone in authority. Be aware that there may be aftershocks, which may cause more damage to structures. Recall your earthquake plan, and follow it.

SCHOOL to HOME

Disaster Planning

With an adult, create a plan that will protect your family in the event of a natural disaster, such as an earthquake. The plan should include steps to take before, during, and after a disaster. Present your disaster plan in the form of an oral report to your class.

ACTIVITY

SECTION Review

Summary

● Earthquake hazard is a measure of how likely an area is to have earthquakes in the future.

● Seismologists use their knowledge of the relationship between earthquake strength and frequency and of the gap hypothesis to forecast earthquakes.

● Homes and buildings and bridges can be strengthened to decrease earthquake damage.

● People who live in earthquake zones should safeguard their home against earthquakes.

Using Key Terms

1. In your own words, write a definition for each of the following terms: *gap hypothesis* and *seismic gap.*

Understanding Key Ideas

2. A weight that is placed on a building to make the building earthquake resistant is called a(n)
   a. active tendon system.
   b. cross brace.
   c. mass damper.
   d. base isolator.

3. How is an area's earthquake-hazard level determined?

4. Compare the strength and frequency method with the gap hypothesis method for predicting earthquakes.

5. What is a common way of making homes more earthquake resistant?

6. Describe four pieces of technology that are designed to make buildings earthquake resistant.

7. Name five items that you should store in case of an earthquake.

Math Skills

8. Of the approximately 420,000 earthquakes recorded each year, about 140 have a magnitude greater than 6.0. What percentage of total earthquakes have a magnitude greater than 6.0?

Critical Thinking

9. **Evaluating Hypotheses** Seismologists predict that there is a 20% chance that an earthquake of magnitude 7.0 or greater will fill a seismic gap during the next 50 years. Is the hypothesis incorrect if the earthquake does not happen? Explain your answer.

10. **Applying Concepts** Why is a large earthquake often followed by numerous aftershocks?

SCILINKS

Developed and maintained by the National Science Teachers Association

For a variety of links related to this chapter, go to www.scilinks.org

Topic: Earthquakes and Society
SciLinks code: HSM0455

Answers to Section Review

1. Sample answer: According to the gap hypothesis, strong earthquakes are likely to occur along sections of active faults that have had relatively few earthquakes. A seismic gap is an area along an active fault where relatively few earthquakes have occurred.

2. c

3. The earthquake hazard level of a particular area is determined by the amount of past and present seismic activity that has occurred in the area.

CHAPTER RESOURCES

Chapter Resource File

- Section Quiz GENERAL
- Section Review GENERAL
- Vocabulary and Section Summary GENERAL
- Critical Thinking ADVANCED

Workbooks

Math Skills for Science
- Dividing Whole Numbers with Long Division GENERAL

4. Sample answer: According to the strength and frequency method, earthquake strength is related to how often earthquakes occur. The gap hypothesis predicts an earthquake's strength and location by finding out the parts of an active fault where no earthquakes have recently occurred.

5. Sample answer: A common way of making a home more earthquake resistant is to securely fasten it to its foundation.

6. Answers may vary. Sample answer: Flexible pipes that are able to twist and bend during earthquakes prevent water and gas lines from breaking. A base isolator made of rubber and steel wrapped around lead absorbs seismic waves. A mass damper placed in the roof of a building counteracts the movement of the building during an earthquake. Cross braces placed between floors in a building counteract pressure that pushes and pulls at the side of a building.

7. Answers may vary. Sample answer: nonperishable food, a flashlight, a portable radio, a fire extinguisher, and a first-aid kit

8. $140 \div 420,000 \times 100 = .03\%$

9. The hypothesis is not incorrect because there was only a 20% probability an earthquake would fill the seismic gap.

10. Aftershocks follow a large earthquake because the earthquake causes elastically deformed rock along other nearby faults to break.

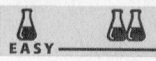

Quake Challenge

Teacher's Notes

Time Required

One 45-minute class period

Lab Ratings

EASY ————————————→ HARD

Teacher Prep 🧪🧪
Student Set-Up 🧪
Concept Level 🧪🧪
Clean Up 🧪🧪

MATERIALS

The materials listed on the student page are enough for 2 students.

Safety Caution

Remind students to review all safety cautions and icons before beginning this lab activity.

Preparation Notes

Make the gelatin 24 hours in advance. When making the gelatin, experiment with the ratio of water to gelatin. The more water you use, the more "wiggly" your gelatin will be. Cut the gelatin squares ahead of time, and place each square on a piece of wax paper. For steps 8 and 9, you will need to create a gelatin square large enough to place all the student structures on. This allows each group's structure to be evaluated on its own merit.

OBJECTIVES

Build a model of a structure that can withstand a simulated earthquake.

Evaluate ways in which you can strengthen your model.

MATERIALS

- gelatin, square, approximately 8 × 8 cm
- marshmallows (10)
- paper plate
- toothpicks (10)

SAFETY

Quake Challenge

In many parts of the world, people must have earthquakes in mind when they construct buildings. Each building must be designed so that the structure is protected during an earthquake. Architects have greatly improved the design of buildings since 1906, when an earthquake and the fires it caused destroyed much of San Francisco. In this activity, you will use marshmallows and toothpicks to build a structure that can withstand a simulated earthquake. In the process, you will discover some of the ways a building can be built to withstand an earthquake.

Ask a Question

1 What features help a building withstand an earthquake? How can I use this information to build my structure?

Form a Hypothesis

2 Brainstorm with a classmate to design a structure that will resist the simulated earthquake. Write two or three sentences to describe your design. Explain why you think your design will be able to withstand a simulated earthquake.

Test the Hypothesis

3 Follow your design to build a structure using the toothpicks and marshmallows.

4 Set your structure on a square of gelatin, and place the gelatin on a paper plate.

5 Shake the square of gelatin to test whether your building will remain standing during a quake. Do not pick up the gelatin.

6 If your first design does not work well, change it until you find a design that does. Try to determine why your building is falling so that you can improve your design each time.

7 Sketch your final design.

Holt Lab Generator CD-ROM

Search for any lab by topic, standard, difficulty level, or time. Edit any lab to fit your needs, or create your own labs. Use the Lab Materials QuickList software to customize your lab materials list.

Helen Schiller
Northwood Middle School
Taylors, South Carolina

CHAPTER RESOURCES

Chapter Resource File

 • Datasheet for Chapter Lab
• Lab Notes and Answers

Technology

 Classroom Videos
• Lab Video

 LabBook
• Earthquake Waves

⑧ After you have tested your final design, place your structure on the gelatin square on your teacher's desk.

⑨ When every group has added a structure to the teacher's gelatin, your teacher will simulate an earthquake by shaking the gelatin. Watch to see which buildings withstand the most severe quake.

Analyze the Results

❶ Explaining Events Which buildings were still standing after the final earthquake? What features made them more stable?

❷ Analyzing Results How would you change your design in order to make your structure more stable?

Draw Conclusions

❸ Evaluating Models This was a simple model of a real-life problem for architects. Based on this activity, what advice would you give to architects who design buildings in earthquake zones?

❹ Evaluating Models What are some limitations of your earthquake model?

❺ Making Predictions How could your research have an impact on society?

Analyze the Results

1. Answers may vary. Sample answer: Structures that had a wide base generally withstood the earthquake. Structures that used triangles in the design also were successful.

2. Answers may vary. Sample answer: By experimenting with different design shapes, such as cubes or triangles, we could find the most stable structure.

Draw Conclusions

3. Buildings designed in earthquake zones should have wide and flexible foundations. The buildings should also be reinforced to prevent collapse.

4. Answers may vary. Accept all reasonable answers. Sample answer: Rocks and gelatin have very different physical properties, such as hardness and density. Seismic waves may have different effects on rock than shaking does on gelatin.

5. Answers may vary. Accept all reasonable answers. Sample answer: By changing the design of our marshmallow-and-toothpick building, we can come up with better designs for buildings.

Chapter Review

Assignment Guide

SECTION	QUESTIONS
1	1, 5–7, 14, 18, 20
2	2, 3, 11, 12, 21–23
3	4, 8–10, 13, 15, 17, 19
1 and 2	16

ANSWERS

Using Key Terms

1. Sample answer: A seismic wave is released when elastically deformed rock along a fault slips. A P wave is the fastest seismic wave and can move through all parts of the Earth. An S wave moves rock from side to side as the wave travels through the Earth.

2. Sample answer: A seismograph is an instrument that is used to record seismic waves. A seismogram is the tracing of earthquake motion created by a seismograph.

3. Sample answer: A focus is the point along a fault where an earthquake starts. An epicenter is the point on Earth's surface above the focus.

4. Sample answer: The gap hypothesis states that strong earthquakes are likely to occur along sections of active faults that have had relatively few earthquakes. Seismic gaps are areas along active faults where relatively few earthquakes have occurred.

USING KEY TERMS

1. Use each of the following terms in a separate sentence: *seismic wave*, *P wave*, and *S wave*.

For each pair of terms, explain how the meanings of the terms differ.

2. *seismograph* and *seismogram*

3. *epicenter* and *focus*

4. *gap hypothesis* and *seismic gap*

UNDERSTANDING KEY IDEAS

Multiple Choice

5. When rock is ___, energy builds up in it. Seismic waves occur as this energy is ___.
   a. plastically deformed, increased
   b. elastically deformed, released
   c. plastically deformed, released
   d. elastically deformed, increased

6. Reverse faults are created
   a. by divergent plate motion.
   b. by convergent plate motion.
   c. by transform plate motion.
   d. All of the above

7. The last seismic waves to arrive are
   a. P waves.
   b. body waves.
   c. S waves.
   d. surface waves.

8. If an earthquake begins while you are in a building, the safest thing for you to do is
   a. to run out into an open space.
   b. to get under the strongest table, chair, or other piece of furniture.
   c. to call home.
   d. to crouch near a wall.

9. How many major earthquakes (magnitude 7.0 to 7.9) happen on average in the world each year?
   a. 1
   b. 18
   c. 120
   d. 800

10. ___ counteract pressure that pushes and pulls at the side of a building during an earthquake.
    a. Base isolators
    b. Mass dampers
    c. Active tendon systems
    d. Cross braces

Short Answer

11. Can the S-P time method be used with one seismograph station to locate the epicenter of an earthquake? Explain your answer.

12. Explain how the Richter scale and the Modified Mercalli Intensity Scale are different.

13. What is the relationship between the strength of earthquakes and earthquake frequency?

Understanding Key Ideas

5. b
6. b
7. d
8. b
9. b
10. d

11. No, a minimum of three seismograph stations are needed to find an earthquake's epicenter using the S-P time method.

12. The Richter magnitude scale measures the ground motion from an earthquake and adjusts for distance to find earthquake strength. The Modified Mercalli Intensity Scale measures the degree to which an earthquake is felt by people and the amount of damage caused by an earthquake.

13. With each step down in earthquake strength or magnitude, the number of earthquakes per year is greater.

14 Explain the way that different seismic waves affect rock as they travel through it.

15 Describe some steps you can take to protect yourself and your property from earthquakes.

CRITICAL THINKING

16 **Concept Mapping** Use the following terms to create a concept map: *focus, epicenter, earthquake start time, seismic waves, P waves,* and *S waves.*

17 **Identifying Relationships** Would a strong or light earthquake be more likely to happen along a major fault where there have not been many recent earthquakes? Explain. (Hint: Think about the average number of earthquakes of different magnitudes that occur annually.)

18 **Applying Concepts** Japan is located near a point where three tectonic plates converge. What would you imagine the earthquake-hazard level in Japan to be? Explain why.

19 **Applying Concepts** You learned that if you are in a car during an earthquake and are out in the open, it is best to stay in the car. Can you think of any situation in which you might want to leave a car during an earthquake?

20 **Identifying Relationships** You use gelatin to simulate rock in an experiment in which you are investigating the way different seismic waves affect rock. In what ways is your gelatin model limited?

INTERPRETING GRAPHICS

The graph below illustrates the relationship between earthquake magnitude and the height of tracings on a seismogram. Charles Richter initially formed his magnitude scale by comparing the heights of seismogram readings for different earthquakes. Use the graph below to answer the questions that follow.

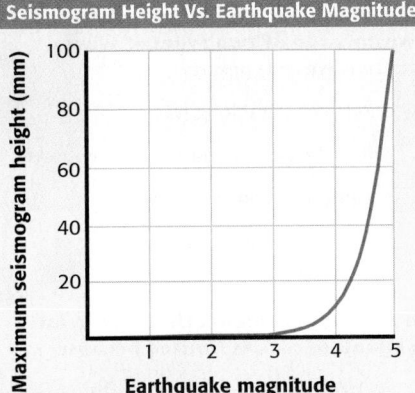

21 According to the graph, what would the magnitude of an earthquake be if its maximum seismogram height is 10 mm?

22 According to the graph, what is the difference in maximum seismogram height (in mm) between an earthquake of magnitude 4.0 and an earthquake of magnitude 5.0?

23 Look at the shape of the curve on the graph. What does this tell you about the relationship between seismogram heights and earthquake magnitudes? Explain.

14. P waves move rock back and forth, squeezing and stretching the rock. S waves stretch rock sideways as well as back and forth. Surface waves move rock up, down, and around, or in a back-and-forth motion.

15. Answers may vary. Sample answer: You should protect yourself and your property against earthquakes by creating an earthquake kit of items you may need after a strong, damaging earthquake. You should put heavy items closer to the floor so that they do not fall during earthquakes. You should find safe places within each room of your home or outdoors in the event there is an earthquake.

Critical Thinking

16. An answer to this exercise can be found at the end of this book.

17. Answers may vary. Sample answer: Based on the average number of earthquakes of different magnitudes that happen annually, a light earthquake would be more likely to happen along a major fault where there have not been many major earthquakes.

18. Because most earthquakes occur at tectonic plate boundaries, the earthquake-hazard level in Japan would be high.

19. Answers may vary. Sample answer: You might want to leave your car if it was stranded on or beneath a highway overpass.

20. A gelatin model is limited because it does not have the same properties as rock, such as density and hardness.

Interpreting Graphics

21. 4

22. 100 mm − 10 mm = 90 mm

23. Students should recognize that seismogram heights increase at a greater rate with each increase in earthquake magnitude. The relationship is logarithmic, not linear.

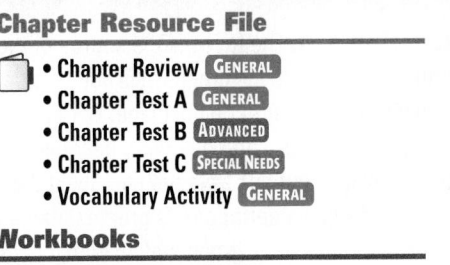

CHAPTER RESOURCES

Chapter Resource File

- Chapter Review **GENERAL**
- Chapter Test A **GENERAL**
- Chapter Test B **ADVANCED**
- Chapter Test C **SPECIAL NEEDS**
- Vocabulary Activity **GENERAL**

Workbooks

Study Guide
- Study Guide is also available in Spanish.

Teacher's Notes

To provide practice under more realistic conditions, give students 20 minutes to answer all of the questions in this Standardized Test Preparation.

Answer Key

Question	Answer
1	C
2	D
3	B
4	C
5	C
6	C
7	C
8	A
9	B
10	A
11	D
12	*
13	*

*See Test Doctor.

Multiple Choice

1. **The greatest earthquake damage happens at the**

   A. focus.

   B. boundary between tectonic plates.

   C. epicenter.

   D. seismograph station.

2. **An earthquake typically involves the transmission of two types of waves. The two wave types are**

   A. short waves and long waves.

   B. primary waves and complementary waves.

   C. ocean waves and land waves.

   D. body waves and surface waves.

3. **An earthquake model that uses gelatin to simulate rock is limited because**

   A. rock does not shake during earthquakes.

   B. gelatin has a different density than rock.

   C. you cannot eat rock.

   D. gelatin has a different color than rock.

4. **Earthquake waves that cause the ground to move up and down, much like ocean waves move water particles, are known as**

   A. S waves.

   B. body waves.

   C. surface waves.

   D. P waves.

5. **What happens when two tectonic plates push against each other?**

   A. Potential energy is released.

   B. Kinetic energy is released.

   C. Potential energy builds up.

   D. Nothing happens.

6. **The table below summarizes the frequency of several earthquake types throughout the world. Based on the data given in the table, how many earthquakes in the range 4.0–4.9 probably happen each year?**

Worldwide Earthquake Frequency		
Description	Magnitude	Yearly average
Great	8.0+	1
Major	7.0–7.9	18
Strong	6.0–6.9	120
Moderate	5.0–5.9	800

   A. approximately 900

   B. approximately 1100

   C. several thousand

   D. several million

7. **As part of an earthquake-modeling lab experiment, Dale must determine the density of a sample of sand. Density is determined by dividing the mass of the sample by its volume. Which pieces of laboratory equipment would be the best choice for making the necessary measurements?**

   A. beaker, graduated cylinder

   B. petri dish, balance

   C. balance, graduated cylinder

   D. graduated cylinder, stopwatch

➕ TEST DOCTOR

Question 1 A: The focus is the source of the earthquake, beneath the ground. It is not the location of an earthquake's greatest damage. B: Most earthquakes occur at the boundary between tectonic plates, but this says nothing about the location of a given earthquake's greatest damage. C: Correct. D: A seismograph station would not be the location of the earthquake's greatest damage, unless it happened to be at the epicenter.

Question 2 A: Length is not a classification of earthquake waves. B: No earthquake waves are called "complementary." C: Ocean waves have nothing to do with earthquakes. D: Correct.

Question 3 A: Rocks do shake during earthquakes. B: Correct. C: This statement is not relevant. D: This statement is not relevant.

8. **Which of the following is least likely to be a limitation in the modeling and predicting of earthquakes?**

   A. Seismologists need to have data on the recent seismic activity of an area.

   B. Seismologists need to have detailed and accurate fault stress data for every meter of the fault line.

   C. Seismologists need to know the exact amount of potential energy a fault can store before causing an earthquake.

   D. Seismologists need to know the locations of all the existing faults in the world.

9. **Herbert is drawing a diagram of an earthquake as part of a field investigation. What label should Herbert apply to the point inside Earth where the earthquake begins?**

   A. epicenter

   B. focus

   C. ground zero

   D. plate boundary

10. **What is one way society benefits from earthquake research?**

    A. We are better able to predict when an earthquake will happen.

    B. We can now cause earthquakes to happen.

    C. We can now be certain of exactly when an earthquake will happen.

    D. We can now prevent earthquakes from happening as often.

Use the graph below to answer question 11.

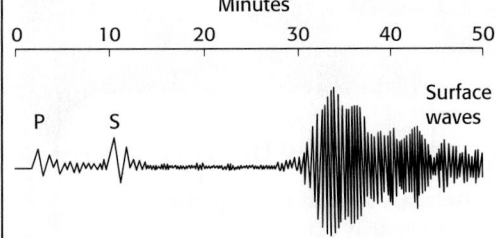

11. **Marcus made the graph above as part of a field investigation at the Kentucky Geological Institute. It shows the ground movement that occurred during a recent earthquake in western Kentucky. Which wave type caused the largest ground movements?**

    A. P waves

    B. S waves

    C. body waves

    D. surface waves

Open Response

12. **The series of major earthquakes that struck New Madrid, Missouri, in the winter of 1811–12 were so violent that Reelfoot Lake, which extends into Kentucky, was formed. Was New Madrid the earthquake's focus or its epicenter? Why?**

13. **On September 5, 2005, a small earthquake struck central Kentucky, just north of Sharpsburg. How is energy converted during an earthquake?**

Standardized Test Preparation

Question 8 A: Correct. B: It is impossible to have fault stress data for every meter of a fault because many faults have not been mapped thoroughly. C: Faults vary in the amount of potential energy that can build along their lengths because the type of rock along the fault changes, as do the direction and magnitude of the force of motion. D: Not every fault in the world has been located, and the interactions of all faults are not known.

Question 9 A: The epicenter is the point on the surface directly above the earthquake. B: Correct. C: Ground zero is not applied by scientists to earthquakes. D: Plate boundaries experience earthquakes but do not name the origin of an earthquake.

Question 10 A: Correct. B: People cannot cause an earthquake. C: At this time, scientists cannot consistently predict earthquakes. D: No one can prevent an earthquake.

Question 11 A, B, C: All these are waves that travel through Earth's interior. They do not cause as much ground movement as surface waves. D: Correct.

Question 12 Full credit answers should include the following points:

- The focus is the point inside Earth where the earthquake originated; it is not on Earth's surface.

- The epicenter is located at the point on Earth's surface directly above the earthquake's focus.

- New Madrid was the earthquake's epicenter.

Question 13 Full credit answers should include the following points:

- During an earthquake, stationary fault blocks suddenly move past one another.

- The stationary fault blocks have potential energy before they move.

- The movement of the fault blocks converts potential energy into kinetic energy.

Question 4 A: S waves move rock from side to side. B: Body waves move through Earth's interior. C: Correct. D: P waves move rock back and forth.

Question 5 A: As tectonic plates push against each other, they build up potential energy. Potential energy is released as kinetic energy when the plates move past each other. B: Kinetic energy is released when the plates move past each other. When tectonic plates are pushing against each other, but not moving, they have potential energy. C: Correct. D: When tectonic plates are pushing against each other, but not moving, they have potential energy.

Question 6 A, B, D: According to the table, earthquake frequency increases as earthquake magnitude decreases at an approximate rate of 7 times the yearly average of the next higher magnitude. Neither 900, 1100, nor several million are 7 times the yearly average of moderate earthquakes. C: Correct.

Question 7 A, D: Neither piece of equipment can measure the mass of the sample. B: Neither piece of equipment can measure the volume of the sample. C: Correct.

Weird Science

Background

There have been many studies on the different types of animal responses to the geophysical environment. Most of these studies indicate that the behavior of living organisms is affected by electromagnetic fields. Studies have been performed on how migrating birds find their way and how fish navigate. Fish such as catfish and sharks use electroreceptors to detect objects around them and to communicate. Even earthworms respond to changes in Earth's magnetic field.

Science, Technology, and Society

Background

During the summer of 2002, a pilot hole 2 km in depth was drilled at the SAFOD site. When drilling concluded, seismometers were placed in the drill hole to locate the microearthquakes that will be targeted with SAFOD.

Science in Action

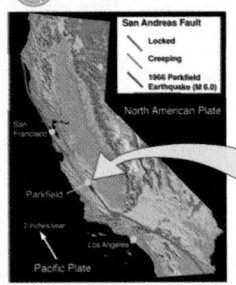 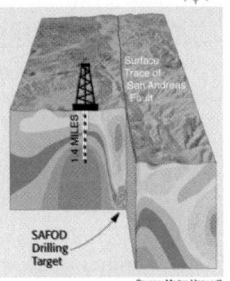

SAFOD PILOT HOLE

Weird Science

Can Animals Predict Earthquakes?

Is it possible that animals close to the epicenter of an earthquake are able to sense changes in their environment? And should we be paying attention to such animal behavior? As long ago as the 1700s, unusual animal activity prior to earthquakes has been recorded. Examples include domestic cattle seeking higher ground and zoo animals refusing to enter their shelters at night. Other animals, such as lizards, snakes, and small mammals, evacuate their underground burrows, and wild birds leave their usual habitats. These events occur days, hours, or even minutes before an earthquake.

Language Arts ACTIVITY

WRITING SKILL Create an illustrated field guide of animal activity to show how animal activity can predict earthquakes. Each illustration must have a paragraph that describes the activity of a specific animal.

Science, Technology, and Society

San Andreas Fault Observatory at Depth (SAFOD)

Seismologists are creating an underground observatory in Parkfield, California, to study earthquakes along the San Andreas Fault. The observatory will be named the San Andreas Fault Observatory at Depth (SAFOD). A deep hole will be drilled directly into the fault zone near a point where earthquakes of magnitude 6.0 have been recorded. Instruments will be placed at the bottom of the hole, 3 to 4 km beneath Earth's surface. These instruments will make seismological measurements of earthquakes and measure the deformation of rock.

Social Studies ACTIVITY

Research the great San Francisco earthquake of 1906. Find images of the earthquake on the Internet and download them, or cut them out of old magazines. Create a photo collage of the earthquake that shows San Francisco before and after the earthquake.

Answer to Language Arts Activity

Have students bring their field guides to class. In the classroom, have students play the role of scientists who are discussing how animal behavior might be used to forecast earthquakes. Students should use facts taken from their field guides to discuss animal behavior that might be useful in earthquake forecasting.

Answer to Social Studies Activity

Have students bring their montages to class. Create a classroom exhibit using the student montages. Use the exhibit to stimulate a discussion about the type of damage that can be caused by a major earthquake, such as the earthquake that struck San Francisco in 1906.

Hiroo Kanamori

Seismologist Hiroo Kanamori is a seismologist at the California Institute of Technology in Pasadena, California. Dr. Kanamori studies how earthquakes occur and tries to reduce their impact on our society. He also analyzes what the effects of earthquakes on oceans are and how earthquakes create giant ocean waves called *tsunamis* (tsoo NAH meez). Tsunamis are very destructive to life and property when they reach land. Kanamori has discovered that even some weak earthquakes can cause powerful tsunamis. He calls these events *tsunami earthquakes,* and he has learned to predict when tsunamis will form. In short, when tectonic plates grind together slowly, special waves called *long-period seismic waves* are created. When Kanamori sees a long-period wave recorded on a seismogram, he knows a tsunami will form. Because long-period waves travel faster than tsunamis, they arrive at recording stations earlier. When an earthquake station records an earthquake, information about that earthquake is provided to a tsunami warning center. The center determines if the earthquake may cause a tsunami and, if so, issues a tsunami warning to areas that may be affected.

Careers

Background

In 1996, Dr. Kanamori received the Bucher Medal for his outstanding achievements in seismology. He and his colleague Tom Hanks bridged the gap between seismology and physics by developing an earthquake scale called the "moment magnitude scale." It rates earthquakes by the minimum energy released and is consistent with the Richter scale.

Math ACTIVITY

An undersea earthquake causes a tsunami to form. The tsunami travels across the open ocean at 800 km/h. How long will the tsunami take to travel from the point where it formed to a coastline 3,600 km away?

go.hrw.com

To learn more about these Science in Action topics, visit go.hrw.com and type in the keyword **HZ5EQKF.**

Current Science

Check out Current Science® articles related to this chapter by visiting go.hrw.com. Just type in the keyword **HZ5CS08.**

Answer to Math Activity

The speed of the tsunami in the open ocean is 800 km/h. It will take the tsunami 4.5 h to travel the 3,600 km distance to the coastline (3,600 km ÷ 800 km/h = 4.5 h).

Volcanoes
Chapter Planning Guide

Compression guide:
To shorten instruction because of time limitations, omit the Chapter Lab.

OBJECTIVES	LABS, DEMONSTRATIONS, AND ACTIVITIES	TECHNOLOGY RESOURCES
PACING • 90 min pp. 436–443 **Chapter Opener**	SE **Start-up Activity,** p. 437 ◆ GENERAL	OSP **Parent Letter** ■ CD **Student Edition on CD-ROM** CD **Guided Reading Audio CD** ■ TR **Chapter Starter Transparency*** VID **Brain Food Video Quiz**
Section 1 Volcanic Eruptions • Distinguish between nonexplosive and explosive volcanic eruptions. • Identify the features of a volcano. • Explain how the composition of magma affects the type of volcanic eruption that will occur. • Describe four types of lava and four types of pyroclastic material.	TE **Activity** Volcano Pen Pals, p. 438 GENERAL SE **Connection to Social Studies** Fertile Farmlands, p. 441 GENERAL TE **Group Activity** Describing Viscosity, p. 441 GENERAL SE **Quick Lab** Modeling an Explosive Eruption, p. 442 GENERAL CRF **Datasheet for Quick Lab***	OSP **Lesson Plans** (also in print) TR **Bellringer Transparency*** TR *LINK TO PHYSICAL SCIENCE* P5 Models of a Solid, a Liquid, and a Gas* TR E30 Four Types of Lava*
PACING • 45 min pp. 444–447 **Section 2 Effects of Volcanic Eruptions** • Explain how volcanic eruptions can affect climate. • Compare the three types of volcanoes. • Compare craters, calderas, and lava plateaus.	TE **Connection Activity** History, p. 445 GENERAL TE **Activity** Classifying Volcanoes, p. 445 BASIC TE **Activity** Book Report, p. 445 ADVANCED TE **Connection Activity** Astronomy, p. 446 ADVANCED SE **Skills Practice Lab** Some Go "Pop," Some Do Not, p. 728 GENERAL CRF **Datasheet for LabBook*** LB **Whiz-Bang Demonstrations** How's Your Lava Life?* ◆ GENERAL	OSP **Lesson Plans** (also in print) TR **Bellringer Transparency*** TR E31 Three Types of Volcanoes* TR E32 The Formation of a Caldera*
PACING • 90 min pp. 448–453 **Section 3 Causes of Volcanic Eruptions** • Describe the formation and movement of magma. • Explain the relationship between volcanoes and plate tectonics. • Summarize the methods scientists use to predict volcanic eruptions.	SE **Quick Lab** Reaction to Stress, p. 449 ◆ GENERAL TE **Connection Activity** Math, p. 450 GENERAL SE **School-to-Home Activity** Tectonic Models, p. 451 GENERAL TE **Group Activity** Preparing for an Eruption, p. 451 ADVANCED SE **Skills Practice Lab** Volcano Verdict, p. 454 ◆ GENERAL LB **Labs You Can Eat** Hot Spots* ◆ GENERAL LB **Whiz-Bang Demonstrations** What Makes a Vent Event?* ◆ GENERAL LB **Long-Term Projects & Research Ideas** A City Lost and Found* ADVANCED SE **Science In Action** Math, Social Studies, and Language Arts Activities, pp. 460–461 GENERAL CD **Interactive Explorations CD-Rom,** What's the Matter? GENERAL	OSP **Lesson Plans** (also in print) TR **Bellringer Transparency*** TR E33 The Location of Major Volcanoes* TR E34 How Magma Forms at a Divergent Boundary* TR E35 How Magma Forms at a Convergent Boundary* SE **Internet Activity,** p. 453 GENERAL CRF **SciLinks Activity*** GENERAL VID **Lab Videos for Earth Science**

PACING • 90 min

CHAPTER REVIEW, ASSESSMENT, AND STANDARDIZED TEST PREPARATION

CRF **Vocabulary Activity*** GENERAL
SE **Chapter Review,** pp. 456–457 GENERAL
CRF **Chapter Review*** ■ GENERAL
CRF **Chapter Tests A*** ■ GENERAL, **B*** ADVANCED, **C*** SPECIAL NEEDS
SE **Standardized Test Preparation,** pp. 458–459 GENERAL
CRF **Standardized Test Preparation*** GENERAL
CRF **Performance-Based Assessment*** GENERAL
OSP **Test Generator, Test Item Listing**

Online and Technology Resources

 Holt Online Learning

Visit **go.hrw.com** for access to Holt Online Learning, or enter the keyword **HS7 Home** for a variety of free online resources.

  **One-Stop Planner® CD-ROM**

This CD-ROM package includes:
• Lab Materials QuickList Software
• Holt Calendar Planner
• Customizable Lesson Plans
• Printable Worksheets
• ExamView® Test Generator
• Interactive Teacher's Edition
• Holt PuzzlePro®
• Holt PowerPoint® Resources

SKILLS DEVELOPMENT RESOURCES	SECTION REVIEW AND ASSESSMENT	CORRELATIONS
SE Pre-Reading Activity, p. 436 GENERAL OSP Science Puzzlers, Twisters & Teasers GENERAL		National Science Education Standards SAI 1; ST 1; SPSP 3, 4
CRF Directed Reading A* ■ BASIC, B* SPECIAL NEEDS WB Workbook* Struggling Readers CRF Vocabulary and Section Summary* ■ GENERAL SE Reading Strategy Reading Organizer, p. 438 GENERAL TE Support for English Language Learners, p. 439 TE Inclusion Strategies, p. 441	SE Reading Checks, pp. 439, 440, 442 GENERAL TE Reteaching, p. 442 BASIC TE Quiz, p. 442 GENERAL TE Alternative Assessment, p. 442 BASIC SE Section Review,* p. 443 ■ GENERAL TE Homework, p. 443 GENERAL CRF Section Quiz* ■ GENERAL	SAI 1; HNS 2; ES 1c
CRF Directed Reading A* ■ BASIC, B* SPECIAL NEEDS WB Workbook* Struggling Readers CRF Vocabulary and Section Summary* ■ GENERAL SE Reading Strategy Paired Summarizing, p. 444 GENERAL TE Support for English Language Learners, p. 445 CRF Reinforcement Worksheet A Variety of Volcanoes* BASIC	SE Reading Checks, pp. 444, 446 GENERAL TE Reteaching, p. 446 BASIC TE Quiz, p. 446 GENERAL TE Alternative Assessment, p. 446 GENERAL SE Section Review,* p. 447 ■ GENERAL CRF Section Quiz* ■ GENERAL	ST 2; SPSP 3, 4; ES 1c; *LabBook:* SAI 1
CRF Directed Reading A* ■ BASIC, B* SPECIAL NEEDS WB Workbook* Struggling Readers CRF Vocabulary and Section Summary* ■ GENERAL SE Reading Strategy Reading Organizer, p. 448 GENERAL SE Math Practice How Hot is Hot?, p. 450 GENERAL TE Support for English Language Learners, p. 450 TE Inclusion Strategies, p. 451 MS Math Skills for Science Using Temperature Scales* GENERAL CRF Reinforcement Worksheet Tectonic Plate Movement* BASIC CRF Critical Thinking Eruption Disruption* ADVANCED	SE Reading Checks, pp. 449, 451, 452 GENERAL TE Reteaching, p. 452 BASIC TE Quiz, p. 452 GENERAL TE Alternative Assessment, p. 452 ADVANCED TE Homework, p. 452 GENERAL SE Section Review,* p. 453 ■ GENERAL CRF Section Quiz* ■ GENERAL	UCP 3; SAI 1; ST 2; ES 1b, 1c; *Chapter Lab:* SAI 1, ST2

SCI LINKS.
NSTA
www.scilinks.org

Maintained by the **National Science Teachers Association.** See Chapter Enrichment pages that follow for a complete list of topics.

Check out *Current Science* articles and activities by visiting the HRW Web site at **go.hrw.com.** Just type in the keyword **HZ5CS09T.**

 Classroom Videos

• **Lab Videos** demonstrate the chapter lab.
• **Brain Food Video Quizzes** help students review the chapter material.

Classroom CD-ROMs

• **Guided Reading Audio CD** (Also in Spanish)
• **Interactive Explorations**
• **Virtual Investigations**
• **Visual Concepts**
• **Science Tutor**

 Holt Lab Generator CD-ROM

Search for any lab by topic, standard, difficulty level, or time. Edit any lab to fit your needs, or create your own labs. Use the Lab Materials QuickList software to customize your lab materials list.

Visual Resources

CHAPTER STARTER TRANSPARENCY

BELLRINGER TRANSPARENCIES

TEACHING TRANSPARENCIES

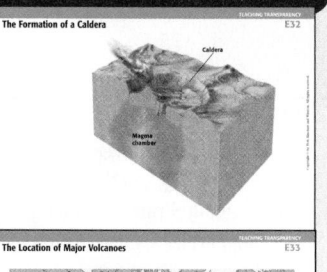

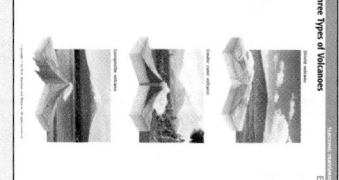

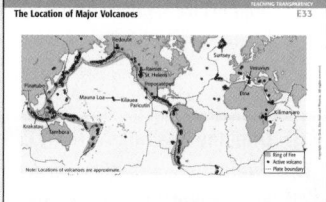

TEACHING TRANSPARENCIES

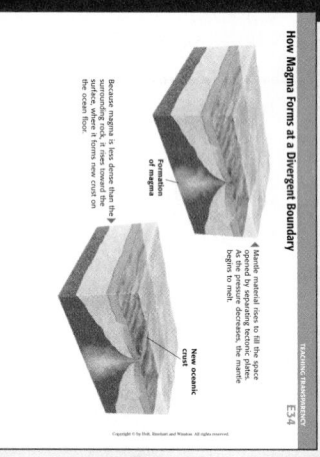

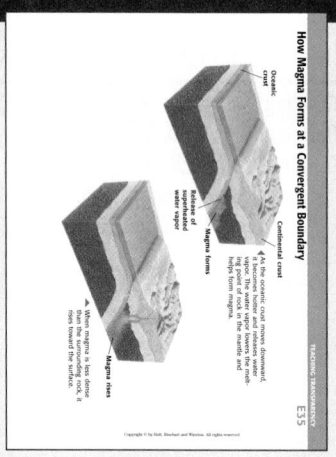

CONCEPT MAPPING TRANSPARENCY

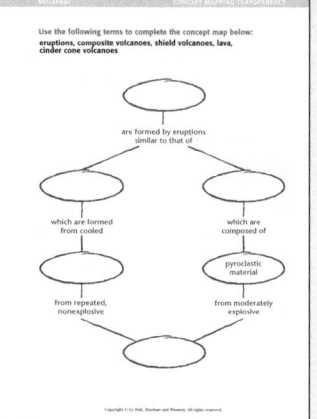

Planning Resources

LESSON PLANS

PARENT LETTER

ALSO IN SPANISH

TEST ITEM LISTING

One-Stop
Planner® CD-ROM

This CD-ROM includes all of the resources shown here and the following time-saving tools:

- *Lab Materials QuickList Software*
- *Customizable lesson plans*
- *Holt Calendar Planner*
- *The powerful ExamView® Test Generator*

Meeting Individual Needs

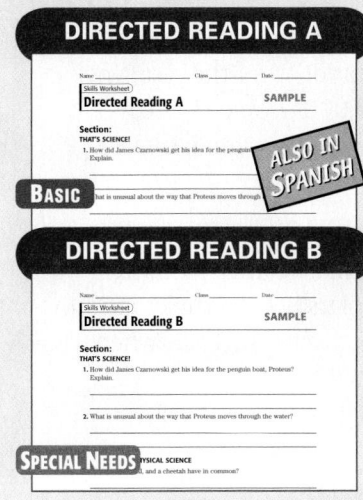

DIRECTED READING A

BASIC — ALSO IN SPANISH

DIRECTED READING B

SPECIAL NEEDS

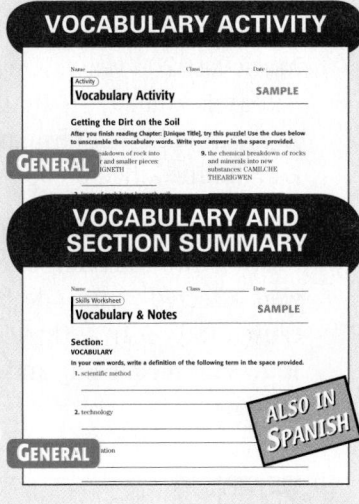

VOCABULARY ACTIVITY

GENERAL

VOCABULARY AND SECTION SUMMARY

GENERAL — ALSO IN SPANISH

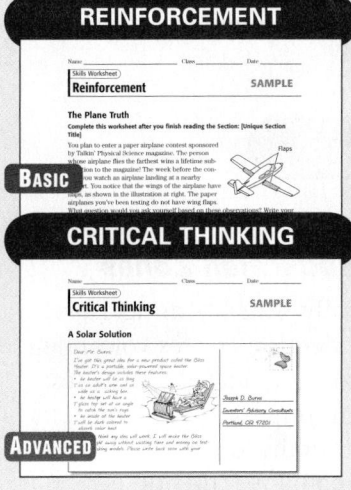

REINFORCEMENT

BASIC

CRITICAL THINKING

ADVANCED

SCILINKS ACTIVITY

GENERAL

SCIENCE PUZZLERS, TWISTERS & TEASERS

GENERAL

Labs and Activities

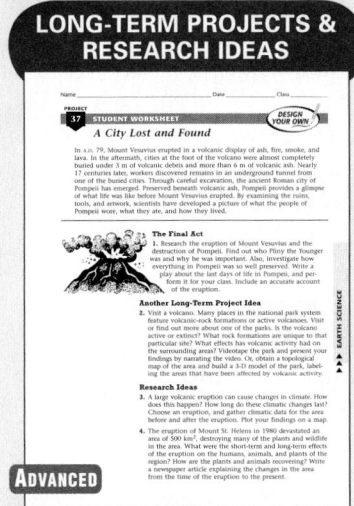

LONG-TERM PROJECTS & RESEARCH IDEAS

ADVANCED

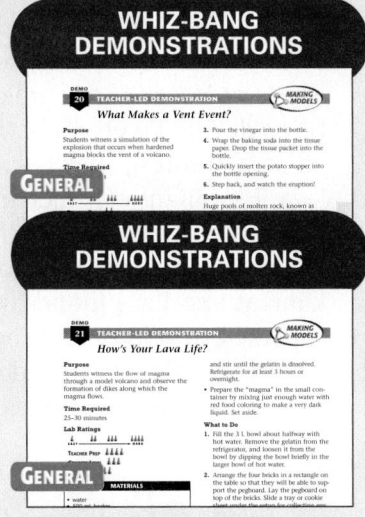

WHIZ-BANG DEMONSTRATIONS

GENERAL

WHIZ-BANG DEMONSTRATIONS

GENERAL

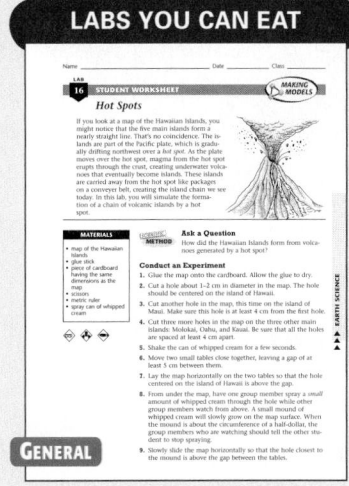

LABS YOU CAN EAT

GENERAL

DATASHEETS FOR QUICK LABS

DATASHEETS FOR CHAPTER LABS

DATASHEETS FOR LABBOOK

Review and Assessments

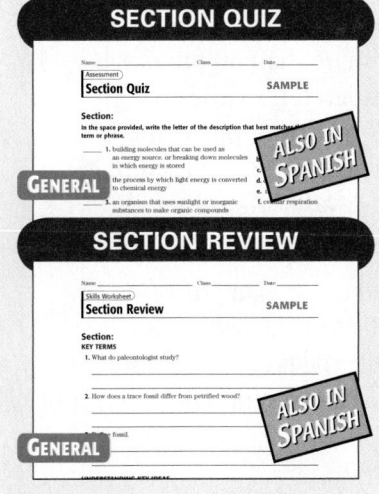

SECTION QUIZ

GENERAL — ALSO IN SPANISH

SECTION REVIEW

GENERAL — ALSO IN SPANISH

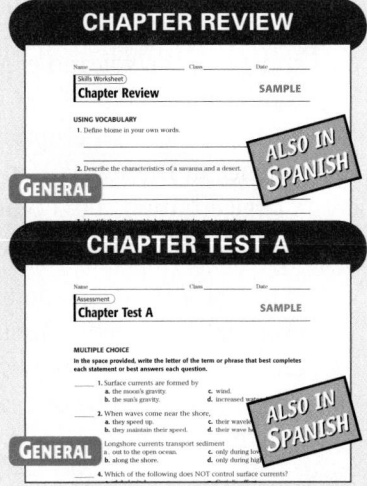

CHAPTER REVIEW

GENERAL — ALSO IN SPANISH

CHAPTER TEST A

GENERAL — ALSO IN SPANISH

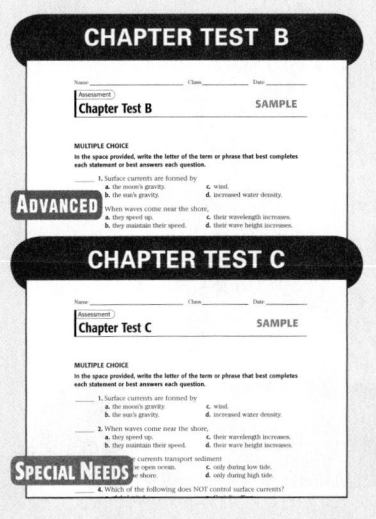

CHAPTER TEST B

ADVANCED

CHAPTER TEST C

SPECIAL NEEDS

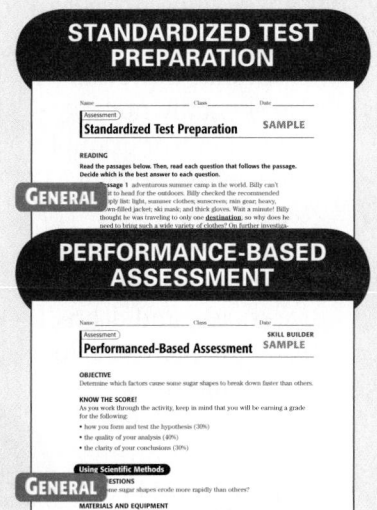

STANDARDIZED TEST PREPARATION

GENERAL

PERFORMANCE-BASED ASSESSMENT

GENERAL

This Chapter Enrichment provides relevant and interesting information to expand and enhance your presentation of the chapter material.

Section 1

Volcanic Eruptions

Mineral Formation in Subduction Zones

- The formation of commercially valuable minerals is common in areas where subduction creates volcanoes. As magma that is formed from subducted crust rises, the magma heats the surrounding rocks, which causes the fluids the rocks contain to circulate around and above the magma body. The hot fluids react with the magma and surrounding rocks and dissolve some metals (including iron, lead, silver, and gold). As the water-rich fluid rises through Earth's crust, mineral precipitation occurs at points where the fluid cools. This process can form rich mineral veins.

The Origin of Volcanic Terms

- Many terms for nonexplosive eruptions are Hawaiian. For example, lava that blows into fine, spiky strands are called *Pele's hair,* for the Hawaiian goddess of volcanoes. *Limu o Pele,* which means "Pele's seaweed," is the term for delicate, translucent sheets of spatter filled with tiny glass bubbles.

- The terms for explosive eruptions, however, are generally not Hawaiian. For example, *nuée ardente,* a French term that means "burning cloud," is a hot mass of volcanic gases, ash, and debris that is expelled explosively and then travels at tremendous speeds down a mountainside.

Is That a Fact!

- The Tambora eruption in Indonesia was the largest in the last 200 years. The eruption and the resulting tsunamis killed more than 10,000 people. Ash covered so much land that farmland was devastated; disease and famine killed 80,000 more people.

- During the Tambora eruption, so much ash was thrown into the atmosphere that weather patterns were affected worldwide. Scholars believe the eruption caused the "Year Without a Summer" in 1816, when snow fell in New England in July.

Section 2

Effects of Volcanic Eruptions

Islands of Survival

- Nonexplosive volcanoes, such as Kilauea, on the island of Hawaii, may produce many different lava flows during an eruption. If these flows surround an area of forest, they create an island in a sea of lava. Hawaiians call such areas *kipukas,* which means "islands of survival." Over the last 20 years, biologists have studied populations of animals isolated in kipukas and have found interesting evidence to support evolution. Fruit flies called picture-wing drosophila have exhibited changes that ultimately could produce new species.

Is That a Fact!

- In the Caribbean, a submarine volcano named Kick'em Jenny is gaining a very bad reputation. As one sailboat captain said, "Kick'em Jenny . . . has a reputation of kicking up a nasty sea." Between 1986 and 1996, the volcano grew more than 50 m; its top is now only 200 m below sea level. It's close enough to the surface that eruptions can cause waves and turbulence in the sea. Volcanologists are concerned that a large eruption could cause devastating tsunamis throughout the Caribbean.

- When lava flows in a defined channel, a crust eventually forms on the surface of the lava. If the crust remains stationary while the lava below is still flowing, a lava tube or a lava cave several kilometers long may form.

Section 3

Causes of Volcanic Eruptions

Merapi, "Mountain of Fire"

- There are more active volcanoes in Indonesia than anywhere on Earth—130! One of the most dangerous volcanoes is called Merapi, or "Mountain of Fire," on the island of Java. Since 1548, Merapi has erupted violently 68 times. In 1998, it became active again, and people began to evacuate the area. Scientists are worried about the city of Yogyakarta, which is 70 km north of the volcano and is home to about 500,000 people. A large eruption could destroy the city.

Predicting the Mount Pinatubo Eruptions

- Perhaps the most successful prediction of a volcanic eruption was on Mount Pinatubo, in the Philippines. When Pinatubo became active in March and April 1991, scientists rushed to the area and quickly established monitoring systems. Scientists from the Philippines and the United States distributed a five-level alert system to civil defense and local officials. Evacuations began when an eruption appeared imminent (level 4 alert); more than 250,000 people evacuated the area. The eruption caused enormous losses of land, housing, and crops, but because of the preparations and warnings, only 300 people died during the eruption. Lahars killed an additional 500 people.

- Most volcanic eruptions are not as predictable as those of Mount Pinatubo. For example, the monitoring methods used at Pinatubo have been much less successful on Montserrat, in the Caribbean.

Predicting the Eruption of Mount St. Helens

- Earthquake tremors are often a sign that a volcano is about to erupt. In the months before the eruption of Mount St. Helens, small earthquakes, which grew in number and intensity, shook the area.

On March 27, 1980, the volcano began venting steam and ash. Geologists had set up seismometers to record the frequency, location, and magnitude of the quakes. Electronic surveying equipment employed laser beams to measure ground swelling as the lava dome rose. Tiltmeters measured changes in the mountain's slope. Stream gauges recorded water temperatures, pH levels, and amounts of dissolved minerals in the waters around the volcano. Gas sensors on the ground and in aircraft monitored hydrogen, carbon dioxide, and sulfur dioxide levels that might signal the movement of magma toward the surface. Mount St. Helens continues to be a major site for volcano research, long after the major eruption that occured on May 18, 1980.

Is That a Fact!

- The youngest Hawaiian "island," Loihi, is 3,500 m above the ocean floor. But it must grow almost 1 km before coming out of the ocean, which, scientists say, could take more than 20,000 years.

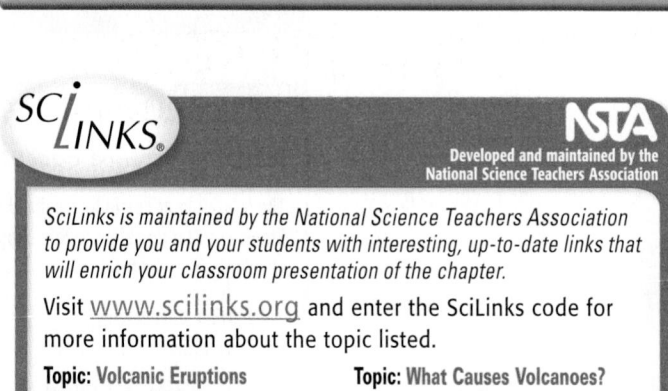

SCiLINKS

NSTA
Developed and maintained by the
National Science Teachers Association

SciLinks is maintained by the National Science Teachers Association to provide you and your students with interesting, up-to-date links that will enrich your classroom presentation of the chapter.

Visit www.scilinks.org and enter the SciLinks code for more information about the topic listed.

Topic: Volcanic Eruptions
SciLinks code: HSM1616

Topic: What Causes Volcanoes?
SciLinks code: HSM1654

Topic: Volcanic Effects
SciLinks code: HSM1615

Overview

This chapter discusses volcanoes, the effects of eruptions, and how eruptions are predicted. About 500 million people live near active volcanoes. Volcanoes are carefully studied so that eruptions may be predicted.

Assessing Prior Knowledge

Students should be familiar with the following topics:

• the rock cycle
• plate tectonics
• changes of state

Identifying Misconceptions

Students may think that all volcanic eruptions are explosive and destructive. Point out that the majority of volcanic activity is nonexplosive. Also, reinforce the idea that volcanic activity plays a major role in forming the Earth's crust and in creating fertile land. Students may also think that volcanoes are uncommon and that volcanic activity is rare. Point out that the Earth has more than 1,300 active volcanoes and that at any moment, between 1 and 20 volcanoes are erupting on land. Many more volcanoes are erupting on the ocean floor. Volcano World is a Website that has updates on volcanoes that are currently erupting.

16
Volcanoes

The Big Idea
Volcanoes are locations where molten rock reaches Earth's surface, and volcanoes can affect landforms and societies.

About the Photo

When you think of a volcanic eruption, you probably think of a cone-shaped mountain exploding and sending huge clouds of ash into the air. Some volcanic eruptions do just that! Most volcanic eruptions, such as the one shown here, which is flowing over a road in Hawaii, are slow and quiet. Volcanic eruptions happen throughout the world, and they play a major role in shaping the Earth's surface.

PRE-READING ACTIVITY

FOLDNOTES **Layered Book** Before you read the chapter, create the FoldNote entitled "Layered Book" described in the **Study Skills** section of the Appendix. Label the tabs of the layered book with "Volcanic eruptions," "Effects of eruptions," and "Causes of eruptions." As you read the chapter, write information you learn about each category under the appropriate tab.

Standards Correlations

National Science Education Standards

The following codes indicate the National Science Education Standards that correlate to this chapter. The full text of the standards is at the front of the book.

Chapter Opener
SAI 1; ST 1; SPSP 3, 4

Section 1 Volcanic Eruptions
SAI 1; HNS 2; ES 1c

Section 2 Effects of Volcanic Eruptions
ST 2; SPSP 3, 4; ES 1c; *LabBook:* SAI 1

Section 3 Causes of Volcanic Eruptions
UCP 3; SAI 1; ST 2; ES 1b, 1c

Chapter Lab
SAI 1; ST 2

Chapter Review
ES 1b, 1c

Science In Action
SPSP 3, SPSP 5; HNS 1, 2

FOR EACH GROUP
- baking soda, 10 mL
- bathroom tissue
- beaker or measuring cup, 200 mL
- clay, modeling
- dish soap, liquid
- funnel
- plate or pan, large
- stirring rod
- stopwatch
- vinegar, 50 mL

Safety Caution: Students should wear safety goggles and aprons during this activity.

Answers

1. Sample answer: The reaction between vinegar and baking soda produced CO_2 gas. The formation of gas bubbles caused the "magma" to increase in volume. Then, the "magma" erupted from the model volcano.

2. Answers may vary.

3. If the size of the funnel opening is smaller, the eruption may happen more quickly. If the amount of baking soda and vinegar is increased, the eruption will also happen more quickly.

START-UP ACTIVITY

Anticipation

In this activity, you will build a simple model of a volcano and you will try to predict an eruption.

Procedure

1. Place **10 mL of baking soda** on a **sheet of tissue.** Fold the corners of the tissue over the baking soda, and place the tissue packet in a **large pan.**

2. Put **modeling clay** around the top edge of a **funnel.** Press that end of the funnel over the tissue packet to make a tight seal.

3. After you put on **safety goggles,** add **50 mL of vinegar** and **several drops of liquid dish soap** to a **200 mL beaker** and stir.

4. Predict how long it will take the volcano to erupt after the liquid is poured into the funnel. Then, carefully pour the liquid into the funnel, and use a **stopwatch** to measure how long the volcano takes to begin erupting.

Analysis

1. Based on your observations, explain what happened to cause the eruption.

2. How accurate was your prediction? By how many seconds did the class predictions vary?

3. How do the size of the funnel opening and the amount of baking soda and vinegar affect the amount of time that the volcano takes to erupt?

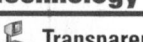
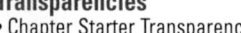

This Really Happened!

Auguste Ciparis was a condemned man. He was sentenced to be executed for murder in the town of St. Pierre, on Martinique, a small volcanic island in the Caribbean Sea. On the morning of May 8, 1902, Ciparis sat in jail waiting for his breakfast. As he waited, disaster struck the town—a disaster that killed thousands of people.

That morning, one of the island's volcanoes, Mount Pelée, erupted in a series of explosions. The eruption sent a fiery cloud of volcanic debris, superheated steam, and toxic gases through

Chapter Starter Transparency
Use this transparency to help students begin thinking about the effects of volcanic eruptions on human societies.

CHAPTER RESOURCES

Technology

Transparencies
- Chapter Starter Transparency

READING SKILLS

Student Edition on CD-ROM

Guided Reading Audio CD
- English or Spanish

Classroom Videos
- Brain Food Video Quiz

Workbooks

Science Puzzlers, Twisters & Teasers
- Volcanoes GENERAL

Focus

Overview

In this section, students will learn how the composition of magma affects volcanic eruptions. Students will also learn to identify the internal structure of a volcano and the types of lava and pyroclastic material released during an eruption.

🔊 Bellringer

Have students create in their **science journal** a labeled drawing that illustrates what happens when a volcano erupts. Then, have students describe the photographs shown on this page and the next. Ask them to think about why the characteristics of volcanic eruptions vary.

Motivate

ACTIVITY ———— GENERAL

Volcano Pen Pals Have students write a letter to a friend from a fictional survivor of a volcanic eruption. Have students describe the volcano hours before the eruption, during the eruption, and after the eruption. Students can then exchange letters and read the letters to the class. **LS** Verbal

What You Will Learn

● Distinguish between nonexplosive and explosive volcanic eruptions.
● Identify the features of a volcano.
● Explain how the composition of magma affects the type of volcanic eruption that will occur.
● Describe four types of lava and four types of pyroclastic material.

Vocabulary

volcano   vent
magma chamber

READING STRATEGY

Reading Organizer As you read this section, make a table comparing types of lava and pyroclastic material.

volcano a vent or fissure in the Earth's surface through which magma and gases are expelled

Sometimes, nonexplosive eruptions can spray lava into the air. Lava fountains, such as this one, pulse with the pressure of escaping gases.

Volcanic Eruptions

Think about the force released when the first atomic bomb exploded during World War II. Now imagine an explosion 10,000 times stronger, and you will get an idea of how powerful a volcanic eruption can be.

The explosive pressure of a volcanic eruption can turn an entire mountain into a billowing cloud of ash and rock in a matter of seconds. But eruptions are also creative forces—they help form fertile farmland. They also create some of the largest mountains on Earth. During an eruption, molten rock, or *magma,* is forced to the Earth's surface. Magma that flows onto the Earth's surface is called *lava.* **Volcanoes** are areas of Earth's surface through which magma and volcanic gases pass.

Nonexplosive Eruptions

At this moment, volcanic eruptions are occurring around the world—on the ocean floor and on land. Nonexplosive eruptions are the most common type of eruption. These eruptions produce relatively calm flows of lava, such as those shown in **Figure 1.** Nonexplosive eruptions can release huge amounts of lava. Vast areas of the Earth's surface, including much of the sea floor and the Northwest region of the United States, are covered with lava from nonexplosive eruptions.

Figure 1 Examples of Nonexplosive Eruptions

▲ The speed of a lava flow can range from a slow creep to as fast as 60 km/h.

CHAPTER RESOURCES

Chapter Resource File

• **Lesson Plan**
• **Directed Reading A** BASIC
• **Directed Reading B** SPECIAL NEEDS

Technology

• **Transparencies**
• Bellringer

Workbooks

Interactive Textbook Struggling Readers

MISCONCEPTION ///ALERT\\\

Nonexplosive Eruptions Although explosive volcanoes get the most attention, nonexplosive eruptions play a much more significant role in shaping our world. For instance, much of the ocean floor is basaltic pillow lava, and nonexplosive volcanoes formed many of the islands in the Pacific Ocean.

Explosive Eruptions

Explosive eruptions, such as the one shown in **Figure 2,** are much rarer than nonexplosive eruptions. However, the effects of explosive eruptions can be incredibly destructive. During an explosive eruption, clouds of hot debris, ash, and gas rapidly shoot out from a volcano. Instead of producing lava flows, explosive eruptions cause molten rock to be blown into tiny particles that harden in the air. The dust-sized particles, called *ash,* can reach the upper atmosphere and can circle the Earth for years. Larger pieces of debris fall closer to the volcano. An explosive eruption can also blast millions of tons of lava and rock from a volcano. In a matter of seconds, an explosive eruption can demolish an entire mountainside, as shown in **Figure 3.**

 **Reading Check** List two differences between explosive and nonexplosive eruptions. (*See the Appendix for answers to Reading Checks.*)

Figure 2 *In what resembles a nuclear explosion, volcanic ash rockets skyward during the 1990 eruption of Mount Redoubt in Alaska.*

Figure 3 *Within seconds, the 1980 eruption of Mount St. Helens in Washington State caused the side of the mountain to collapse. The blast scorched and flattened 600 km² of forest.*

Cultural Awareness GENERAL

Volcano Legends The Klickitats of the Pacific Northwest had two names for Mount St. Helens. The first name was *Loo-Wit,* which referred to a lovely maiden who changed into a beautiful, white mountain. The other name was *Tah-one-lat-clah,* which means "fire mountain" and indicates the tribe's

knowledge that the volcano was prone to eruptions. Ask students why they think the Klickitats had two very different names for Mount St. Helens. Have students research other American Indian names and legends for volcanic peaks in North America.

CONNECTION to
Physical Science—ADVANCED

States of Matter Use the teaching transparency entitled "Models of a Solid, a Liquid, and a Gas" to discuss changes of state in magma. When water or carbon dioxide is a part of the crystal structure of minerals in a rock, these compounds are in the solid state. When rock melts to form magma, the water or carbon dioxide is released into the molten liquid. In other words, the water or carbon dioxide is dissolved in the magma. When temperature and pressure conditions are right, water and carbon dioxide in the magma solution *exsolve,* or vaporize, changing from liquid to gas. The exsolution of gases forms bubbles that greatly increase the volume of the magma. When the magma erupts on the surface, it cools and solidifies, changing from a liquid to a solid. The gases escape into the air, but they leave distinctive round holes called *vesicles.* **LS** Visual

Answer to Reading Check

Because silica-rich magma has a high viscosity, it tends to trap gases and plug volcanic vents. This causes pressure to build up and can result in an explosive eruption.

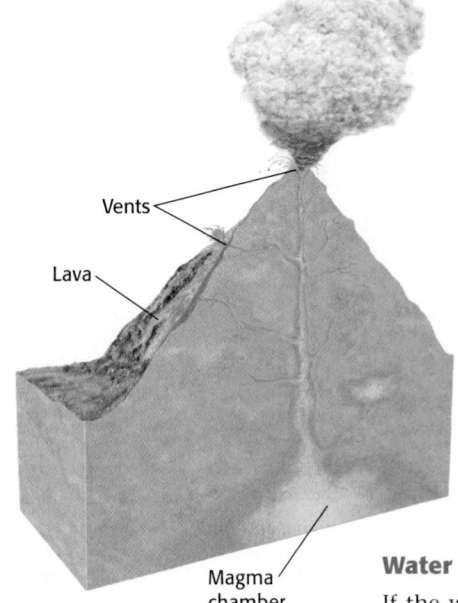

Vents

Lava

Magma chamber

Figure 4 *Volcanoes form when lava is released from vents.*

magma chamber the body of molten rock that feeds a volcano

vent an opening at the surface of the Earth through which volcanic material passes

What Is Inside a Volcano?

If you could look inside an erupting volcano, you would see the features shown in **Figure 4.** A **magma chamber** is a body of molten rock deep underground that feeds a volcano. Magma rises from the magma chamber through cracks in the Earth's crust to openings called **vents.** Magma is released from the vents during an eruption.

What Makes Up Magma?

By comparing the composition of magma from different eruptions, scientists have made an important discovery. The composition of the magma affects how explosive a volcanic eruption is. The key to whether an eruption will be explosive lies in the silica, water, and gas content of the magma.

Water and Magma Are an Explosive Combination

If the water content of magma is high, an explosive eruption is more likely. Because magma is underground, it is under intense pressure and water stays dissolved in the magma. If the magma quickly moves to the surface, the pressure suddenly decreases and the water and other compounds, such as carbon dioxide, become gases. As the gases expand rapidly, an explosion can result. This process is similar to what happens when you shake a can of soda and open it. When a can of soda is shaken, the CO_2 dissolved in the soda is released and pressure builds up. When the can is opened, the soda shoots out, just as lava shoots out of a volcano during an explosive eruption. In fact, some lava is so frothy with gas when it reaches the surface that its solid form, called *pumice,* can float in water!

Silica-Rich Magma Traps Explosive Gases

Magma that has a high silica content also tends to cause explosive eruptions. Silica-rich magma has a stiff consistency. It flows slowly and tends to harden in a volcano's vents. As a result, it plugs the vent. As more magma pushes up from below, pressure increases. If enough pressure builds up, an explosive eruption takes place. Stiff magma also prevents water vapor and other gases from easily escaping. Gas bubbles trapped in magma can expand until they explode. When they explode, the magma shatters and ash and pumice are blasted from the vent. Magma that contains less silica has a more fluid, runnier consistency. Because gases escape this type of magma more easily, explosive eruptions are less likely to occur.

✓ Reading Check How do silica levels affect an eruption?

WEIRD SCIENCE

Lava cools very slowly not only because it is very hot to start with but also because it is a good insulator. When a lava flow in Mexico in 1952 stopped, the flow was 10 m thick. Four years later, in 1956, the lava still steamed when it rained.

What Erupts from a Volcano?

Magma erupts as either lava or pyroclastic (PIE roh KLAS tik) material. *Lava* is liquid magma that flows from a volcanic vent. *Pyroclastic material* forms when magma is blasted into the air and hardens. Nonexplosive eruptions produce mostly lava. Explosive eruptions produce mostly pyroclastic material. Over many years—or even during the same eruption—a volcano's eruptions may alternate between lava and pyroclastic eruptions.

Types of Lava

The viscosity of lava, or how lava flows, varies greatly. To understand viscosity, remember that a milkshake has high viscosity and a glass of milk has low viscosity. Lava that has high viscosity is stiff. Lava that has low viscosity is more fluid. The viscosity of lava affects the surface of a lava flow in different ways, as shown in **Figure 5**. *Blocky lava* and *pahoehoe* (puh HOY HOY) have a high viscosity and flow slowly. Other types of lava flows, such as *aa* (AH AH) and *pillow lava,* have lower viscosities and flow more quickly.

CONNECTION TO Social Studies

Fertile Farmlands Volcanic ash helps create some of the most fertile farmland in the world. Use a world map and reference materials to find the location of volcanoes that have helped create farmland in Italy, Africa, South America, and the United States. Make an illustrated map on a piece of poster board to share your findings. **ACTIVITY**

Figure 5 Four Types of Lava

◀ **Aa** lava pours out quickly and forms a brittle crust. The crust is torn into jagged pieces as molten lava continues to flow underneath.

Pahoehoe lava flows slowly, ▶ like wax dripping from a candle. Its glassy surface has rounded wrinkles.

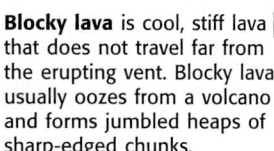

◀ **Pillow lava** forms when lava erupts underwater. As you can see here, this lava forms rounded lumps that are the shape of pillows.

Blocky lava is cool, stiff lava ▶ that does not travel far from the erupting vent. Blocky lava usually oozes from a volcano and forms jumbled heaps of sharp-edged chunks.

MISCONCEPTION ALERT

The Force of Water Students may think that it seems illogical that water makes magma more likely to explode. Explain that magma contains water and that the water is dissolved in the magma. When the water changes from a liquid to a gas, the volume of the magma increases dramatically. This change causes a pressure increase that can generate a large explosive force. Discuss with students what would happen if water is boiled in a pot with a tight lid. Then, have students think of other examples in which water can have an explosive force, such as in a car's radiator or in popcorn.

Volcano Field Guide Have students make an illustrated field guide to volcanic eruptions and types of lava. Students can add to the field guides as they read other sections in this chapter.

LS Visual

Quiz ———————— GENERAL

1. Describe the lava flow from a nonexplosive eruption. (a calm stream of magma that flows out of a vent onto Earth's surface)

2. Describe an explosive eruption. (Ash, hot debris, gases, and chunks of rock spew from a volcano.)

3. Define *blocky lava*, *pahoehoe*, and *aa*. (Blocky lava is cool, stiff lava that doesn't travel far from the erupting vent. Pahoehoe is lava that flows slowly and forms a wrinkled surface. Aa is lava that flows more quickly than pahoehoe and that forms a brittle, jagged crust.)

Alternative Assessment ———— BASIC

Making Lava Provide students with cornstarch, salt, and water to make a paste. Then, have students experiment with the ingredients to create representations of the types of lava discussed in this section. Have students work independently to describe the eruptions that would produce each lava type.

LS Kinesthetic

Figure 6 Four Types of Pyroclastic Material

◄ **Volcanic bombs** are large blobs of magma that harden in the air. The shape of this bomb was caused by the magma spinning through the air as it cooled.

◄ **Lapilli**, which means "little stones" in Italian, are pebblelike bits of magma that hardened before they hit the ground.

◄ **Volcanic ash** forms when the gases in stiff magma expand rapidly and the walls of the gas bubbles explode into tiny, glasslike slivers. Ash makes up most of the pyroclastic material in an eruption.

▼ **Volcanic blocks**, the largest pieces of pyroclastic material, are pieces of solid rock erupted from a volcano.

Types of Pyroclastic Material

Pyroclastic material forms when magma explodes from a volcano and solidifies in the air. This material also forms when powerful eruptions shatter existing rock. The size of pyroclastic material ranges from boulders that are the size of houses to tiny particles that can remain suspended in the atmosphere for years. **Figure 6** shows four types of pyroclastic material: volcanic bombs, volcanic blocks, lapilli (lah PIL IE), and volcanic ash.

✓ Reading Check Describe four types of pyroclastic material.

Modeling an Explosive Eruption

1. Inflate a **large balloon**, and place it in a **cardboard box.**

2. Spread a **sheet** on the floor. Place the box in the middle of the sheet. Mound a thin layer of **sand** over the balloon to make a volcano that is taller than the edges of the box.

3. Lightly mist the volcano with **water**. Sprinkle **tempera paint** on the volcano until the volcano is completely covered.

4. Place **small objects** such as **raisins** randomly on the volcano. Draw a sketch of the volcano.

5. Put on your **safety goggles**. Pop the balloon with a **pin**.

6. Use a **metric ruler** to calculate the average distance that 10 grains of sand and 10 raisins traveled.

7. How did the relative weight of each type of material affect the average distance that the material traveled?

8. Draw a sketch of the exploded volcano.

Answers to Quick Lab

7. Sample answer: Lighter materials such as sand traveled farther than heavier materials such as raisins.

8. Sketches may vary.

Teacher's Notes: This activity will work best if students use a very large balloon and if they cover the top of the balloon with a minimal amount of sand. Placing a few tablespoons of talcum powder inside the balloon will create a more dramatic effect when the balloon is popped. This activity models caldera formation as well. Students who have asthma or allergies to airborne particles should wear a filter mask for this activity.

Answer to Reading Check

Volcanic bombs are large blobs of magma that harden in the air. Lapilli are small pieces of magma that harden in the air. Volcanic blocks are pieces of solid rock erupted from a volcano. Ash forms when gases in stiff magma expand rapidly and the walls of the gas bubbles shatter into tiny glasslike slivers.

Pyroclastic Flows

One particularly dangerous type of volcanic flow is called a *pyroclastic flow*. Pyroclastic flows are produced when enormous amounts of hot ash, dust, and gases are ejected from a volcano. This glowing cloud of pyroclastic material can race downhill at speeds of more than 200 km/h—faster than most hurricane-force winds! The temperature at the center of a pyroclastic flow can exceed 700°C. A pyroclastic flow from the eruption of Mount Pinatubo is shown in **Figure 7**. Fortunately, scientists were able to predict the eruption and a quarter of a million people were evacuated before the eruption.

Figure 7 *The 1991 eruption of Mount Pinatubo in the Philippines released terrifying pyroclastic flows.*

SECTION Review

Summary

- Volcanoes erupt both explosively and nonexplosively.
- Magma that has a high level of water, CO_2, or silica tends to erupt explosively.
- Lava can be classified by its viscosity and by the surface texture of lava flows.
- Pyroclastic material, such as ash and volcanic bombs, forms when magma solidifies as it travels through the air.

Using Key Terms

1. In your own words, write a definition for each of the following terms: *volcano, magma chamber,* and *vent.*

Understanding Key Ideas

2. Which of the following factors influences whether a volcano erupts explosively?
   a. the concentration of volcanic bombs in the magma
   b. the concentration of phosphorus in the magma
   c. the concentration of aa in the magma
   d. the concentration of water in the magma

3. How are lava and pyroclastic material classified? Describe four types of lava.

4. Which produces more pyroclastic material: an explosive eruption or a nonexplosive eruption?

5. Explain how the presence of silica and water in magma increases the chances of an explosive eruption.

6. What is a pyroclastic flow?

Math Skills

7. A sample of magma is 64% silica. Express this percentage as a simplified fraction.

Critical Thinking

8. **Analyzing Ideas** How is an explosive eruption similar to opening a can of soda that has been shaken? Be sure to describe the role of carbon dioxide.

9. **Making Inferences** Predict the silica content of aa, pillow lava, and blocky lava.

10. **Making Inferences** Explain why the names of many types of lava are Hawaiian but the names of many types of pyroclastic material are Italian and Indonesian.

SCLINKS. **NSTA**
Developed and maintained by the National Science Teachers Association

For a variety of links related to this chapter, go to www.scilinks.org

Topic: Volcanic Eruptions
SciLinks code: HSM1616

Homework —— GENERAL

Writing **Deadly Mudflows** *Lahar* is an Indonesian term for a particularly deadly kind of volcanic mudflow. A lahar is a flow of water-saturated volcanic debris that races down the slope of a volcano with the consistency of wet cement. Volcanic debris can be saturated by the melting of ice or snow during an eruption, or by rain afterwards. When Nevado del Ruiz erupted in Colombia, its lahar killed more than 25,000 people. Have students research lahars from two eruptions. **LS Intrapersonal**

CHAPTER RESOURCES

Chapter Resource File

- **Section Quiz** GENERAL
- **Section Review** GENERAL
- **Vocabulary and Section Summary** GENERAL
- **Datasheet for Quick Lab**

Answers to Section Review

1. Sample answer: A volcano is a vent or fissure through which magma and gasses are expelled. A magma chamber is the body of molten rock that feeds a volcano. A vent is an opening through which lava or pyroclastic material passes.

2. d

3. Lava is classified by its surface texture. The way that lava flows may also be used to help classify it. Pyroclastic material is classified by size and how it forms. Four types of lava are aa, pahoehoe, blocky lava, and pillow lava. Aa flows quickly and has a jagged crust. Pahoehoe flows slowly and has a wrinkled surface. Pillow lava erupts underwater and forms rounded lumps. Blocky lava is cool, stiff lava that does not travel far from the erupting vent.

4. an explosive eruption

5. The presence of water increases the chance of an explosive eruption because as the magma body moves toward the surface, the water changes to a gas and expands rapidly. This rapid expansion causes an explosion. Silica-rich magma tends to trap volcanic gases and plug vents because of its high viscosity. The resulting pressure increase can cause an explosive eruption.

6. A pyroclastic flow is a cloud of very hot ash, dust, and gases that flows from a volcano.

7. $64/100 = 32/50 = 16/25$

8. Magma and soda have carbon dioxide dissolved in them. When the pressure on the magma and the soda is reduced, the carbon dioxide becomes a gas and expands rapidly.

9. Because aa and pillow lava have low viscosity, they must have a low silica content. Because blocky lava has a high viscosity, it must have a high silica content.

10. Students should conclude that Indonesian and Italian volcanoes are more likely to erupt explosively than Hawaiian volcanoes.

Focus

Overview

This section explores the effects of volcanic eruptions on Earth. Students will learn to identify different types of volcanoes and physical features created by volcanic activity, such as craters and calderas.

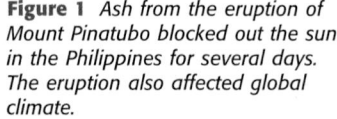 Bellringer

Write the following terms on the board:

composite volcano, shield volcano, cinder cone volcano, volcanic crater, caldera

Group students in teams of three, and have the groups look through the section to come up with a definition for each of the terms. Have them record their definitions and revise the definitions after they read the section.

Motivate

Discussion ——— GENERAL

Student Impressions of Eruptions Have students discuss the most exciting images they've seen in movies and television programs featuring volcanoes. Have them describe what they think about volcanic eruptions in their **science journal** so that they can revisit these impressions after reading this section. **LS Verbal**

What You Will Learn

- Explain how volcanic eruptions can affect climate.
- Compare the three types of volcanoes.
- Compare craters, calderas, and lava plateaus.

Vocabulary

crater
caldera
lava plateau

READING STRATEGY

Paired Summarizing Read this section silently. In pairs, take turns summarizing the material. Stop to discuss ideas that seem confusing.

Figure 1 *Ash from the eruption of Mount Pinatubo blocked out the sun in the Philippines for several days. The eruption also affected global climate.*

Effects of Volcanic Eruptions

In 1816, Chauncey Jerome, a resident of Connecticut, wrote that the clothes his wife had laid out to dry the day before had frozen during the night. This event would not have been unusual except that the date was June 10!

At that time, residents of New England did not know that the explosion of a volcanic island on the other side of the world had severely changed the global climate and was causing "The Year Without a Summer."

Volcanic Eruptions and Climate Change

The explosion of Mount Tambora in 1815 blanketed most of Indonesia in darkness for three days. It is estimated that 12,000 people died directly from the explosion and 80,000 people died from the resulting hunger and disease. The global effects of the eruption were not felt until the next year, however.

During large-scale eruptions, enormous amounts of volcanic ash and gases are ejected into the upper atmosphere. As volcanic ash and gases spread throughout the atmosphere, they can block enough sunlight to cause global temperatures to drop. The Tambora eruption affected the global climate enough to cause food shortages in North America and Europe. More recently, the eruption of Mount Pinatubo, shown in **Figure 1,** caused average global temperatures to drop by as much as 0.5°C. Although this may seem insignificant, such a shift can disrupt climates all over the world.

✓ Reading Check How does a volcanic eruption affect climate? *(See the Appendix for answers to Reading Checks.)*

CHAPTER RESOURCES

Chapter Resource File

- **Lesson Plan**
- **Directed Reading A** BASIC
- **Directed Reading B** SPECIAL NEEDS

Technology

Transparencies
- Bellringer
- E31 Three Types of Volcanoes

Workbooks

Interactive Textbook Struggling Readers

Answer to Reading Check

Eruptions release large quantities of ash and gases, which can block sunlight and cause global temperatures to drop.

Different Types of Volcanoes

Volcanic eruptions can cause profound changes in climate. But the changes to Earth's surface caused by eruptions are probably more familiar. Perhaps the best known of all volcanic landforms are the volcanoes themselves. The three basic types of volcanoes are illustrated in **Figure 2.**

Shield Volcanoes

Shield volcanoes are built of layers of lava released from repeated nonexplosive eruptions. Because the lava is very runny, it spreads out over a wide area. Over time, the layers of lava create a volcano that has gently sloping sides. Although their sides are not very steep, shield volcanoes can be enormous. Hawaii's Mauna Kea, the shield volcano shown here, is the tallest mountain on Earth. Measured from its base on the sea floor, Mauna Kea is taller than Mount Everest.

Cinder Cone Volcanoes

Cinder cone volcanoes are made of pyroclastic material usually produced from moderately explosive eruptions. The pyroclastic material forms steep slopes, as shown in this photo of the Mexican volcano Paricutín. Cinder cones are small and usually erupt for only a short time. Paricutín appeared in a cornfield in 1943 and erupted for only nine years before stopping at a height of 400 m. Cinder cones often occur in clusters, commonly on the sides of other volcanoes. They usually erode quickly because the pyroclastic material is not cemented together.

Composite Volcanoes

Composite volcanoes, sometimes called *stratovolcanoes,* are one of the most common types of volcanoes. They form from explosive eruptions of pyroclastic material followed by quieter flows of lava. The combination of both types of eruptions forms alternating layers of pyroclastic material and lava. Composite volcanoes, such as Japan's Mount Fuji (shown here), have broad bases and sides that get steeper toward the top. Composite volcanoes in the western region of the United States include Mount Hood, Mount Rainier, Mount Shasta, and Mount St. Helens.

Figure 2 **Three Types of Volcanoes**

Shield volcano

Cinder cone volcano

Composite volcano

Teach

ACTIVITY ———— BASIC

Writing **Classifying Volcanoes** Have students write descriptive phrases about the three types of volcanoes in their **science journal.** Have them draw a cross section of each type of volcano beside the appropriate entry. Students should find an example of each volcano type and write three paragraphs about each type. The paragraphs should describe how the volcano fits its category, detail its last eruption, and explain how the volcano's shape is related to the way the volcano erupted. **LS Visual** **English Language Learners**

ACTIVITY ———— ADVANCED

Book Report In 1943, Dominic Pulido, a farmer in central Mexico, was working in his cornfield when the ground began to tremble and a noise like thunder filled the air. Pulido discovered a fissure in the field about 0.5 m wide. The ground began to swell and formed a mound 2.5 m high! A volcano named Paricutín was being born. In 1 year, the cinder cone volcano grew to 334 m high! Encourage students to read *Hill of Fire,* by Thomas Page Lewis, and to write a book report about it. **LS Intrapersonal**

CONNECTION ACTIVITY
History ———— GENERAL

The Battle of Iwo Jima One of World War II's fiercest battles was fought on the volcanic island of Iwo Jima. More than 6,000 Allied soldiers and 20,000 Japanese soldiers died fighting for an island that is about 8 km long and 4 km wide. Have students research the battle of Iwo Jima and prepare a map to show why this volcanic island was difficult to capture. **LS Visual**

SUPPORT FOR

English Language Learners
Model Volcanoes Place students from the same geographic area in groups. Have them research a type of volcano found in or near their area(s) and create a model of it with clay. Have groups present their models to the class and orally explain the features of their volcanoes. Evaluate presentations for accuracy and pronunciation. Say any mispronounced words, and have students repeat. **LS Visual/Verbal**

Section Quizzes Have students write five quiz questions based on the section. Students should exchange questions and then grade each other's work. Collect the quizzes, and use the best questions in an open-book quiz.

Quiz — **GENERAL**

1. Describe the shapes of shield, cinder cone, and composite volcanoes. (shield volcano: broad with gentle, shallow slopes; cinder cone volcano: generally smaller and steeper with more angled sides; composite volcano: high, covers less area than shield volcanoes, and has sides that are steeper near the peak)

2. What is a lava plateau? (It is a wide, flat landform that is formed from repeated nonexplosive eruptions of lava that spread over a large area.)

Alternative Assessment — **GENERAL**

Volcano Poster Have students draw a poster of each type of volcano. Students must label and write a caption for all of the volcano's parts. Students should also create a cartoon-panel illustration of how craters and calderas form. **LS Visual**

Answer to Reading Check

Calderas form when a magma chamber partially empties and the roof overlying the chamber collapses.

Figure 3 A crater, such as this one in Kamchatka, Russia, forms around the central vent of a volcano.

crater a funnel-shaped pit near the top of the central vent of a volcano

caldera a large, semicircular depression that forms when the magma chamber below a volcano partially empties and causes the ground above to sink

Other Types of Volcanic Landforms

In addition to volcanoes, other landforms are produced by volcanic activity. These landforms include craters, calderas, and lava plateaus. Read on to learn more about these landforms.

Craters

Around the central vent at the top of many volcanoes is a funnel-shaped pit called a **crater.** An example of a crater is shown in **Figure 3.** During less explosive eruptions, lava flows and pyroclastic material can pile up around the vent creating a cone with a central crater. As the eruption stops, the lava that is left in the crater often drains back underground. The vent may then collapse to form a larger crater. If the lava hardens in the crater, the next eruption may blast it away. In this way, a crater becomes larger and deeper.

Calderas

Calderas can appear similar to craters, but they are many times larger. A **caldera** is a large, semicircular depression that forms when the chamber that supplies magma to a volcano partially empties and the chamber's roof collapses. As a result, the ground above the magma chamber sinks, as shown in **Figure 4.** Much of Yellowstone Park is made up of three large calderas that formed when volcanoes collapsed between 1.9 million and 0.6 million years ago. Today, hot springs, such as Old Faithful, are heated by the thermal energy left over from those events.

Reading Check How do calderas form?

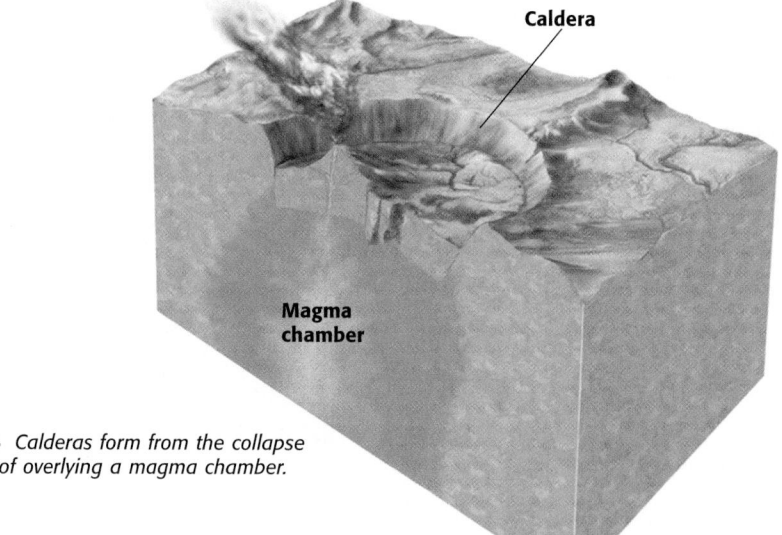

Caldera

Magma chamber

Figure 4 Calderas form from the collapse of the roof overlying a magma chamber.

CONNECTION ACTiViTy
Astronomy — **ADVANCED**

Lunar Maria Early astronomers thought that the dark patches on the moon were lunar seas. Thus, the areas were called *maria,* which is Latin for "seas." Today, we know that the dark patches are basins filled with basaltic lava that erupted after the moon's formation. Most of the lunar maria are on the side of the moon that faces Earth. Scientists think that after the moon's formation, the tidal attraction of Earth caused volcanic eruptions on the side of the moon that faces Earth. Like the jelly that comes out of a donut when it is squeezed, lava was pushed out of the moon by the Earth's gravitational force deforming the moon's suface more on the side closer to Earth. Have students research volcanism on another planet or moon in our solar system and report their findings to the class. **LS Logical**

Lava Plateaus

The most massive outpourings of lava do not come from individual volcanoes. Most of the lava on Earth's surface erupted from long cracks, or *rifts,* in the crust. In this type of eruption, runny lava can pour out for millions of years and spread over huge areas. A landform that results from repeated eruptions of lava spread over a large area is called a **lava plateau.** The Columbia River Plateau, part of which is shown in **Figure 5,** is a lava plateau that formed between 17 million and 14 million years ago in the northwestern region of the United States. In some places, the Columbia River Plateau is 3 km thick.

Figure 5 *The Columbia River Plateau formed from a massive outpouring of lava that began 17 million years ago.*

lava plateau a wide, flat landform that results from repeated nonexplosive eruptions of lava that spread over a large area

---

SECTION Review

Summary

- The large volumes of gas and ash released from volcanic eruptions can affect climate.
- Shield volcanoes result from many eruptions of relatively runny lava.
- Cinder cone volcanoes result from mildly explosive eruptions of pyroclastic material.
- Composite volcanoes result from alternating explosive and nonexplosive eruptions.
- Craters, calderas, and lava plateaus are volcanic landforms.

Using Key Terms

Complete each of the following sentences by choosing the correct term from the word bank.

caldera   crater

1. A ___ is a funnel-shaped hole around the central vent.

2. A ___ results when a magma chamber partially empties.

Understanding Key Ideas

3. Which type of volcano results from alternating explosive and nonexplosive eruptions?
   a. composite volcano
   b. cinder cone volcano
   c. rift-zone volcano
   d. shield volcano

4. Why do cinder cone volcanoes have narrower bases and steeper sides than shield volcanoes do?

5. Why does a volcano's crater tend to get larger over time?

Math Skills

6. The fastest lava flow recorded was 60 km/h. A horse can gallop as fast as 48 mi/h. Could a galloping horse outrun the fastest lava flow? (Hint: 1 km = 0.621 mi)

Critical Thinking

7. **Making Inferences** Why did it take a year for the effects of the Tambora eruption to be experienced in New England?

For a variety of links related to this chapter, go to www.scilinks.org

Topic: Volcanic Effects
SciLinks code: HSM1615

SCIENTISTS AT ODDS

Did Volcanism Play a Role in Dinosaur Extinctions? Most scientists think that the dinosaurs became extinct 65 million years ago when a large asteroid struck Earth. However, some scientists think that climatic changes caused by a period of catastrophic volcanism that occurred before and after the impact may have been a factor in the extinctions. Encourage students to find out more about these scientific hypotheses.

CHAPTER RESOURCES

Chapter Resource File

- **Section Quiz** GENERAL
- **Section Review** GENERAL
- **Vocabulary and Section Summary** GENERAL
- **Reinforcement Worksheet** BASIC

Technology

Transparencies
- E32 The Formation of a Caldera

Focus

Overview

In this section, students will learn how magma forms and how pressure affects the temperature at which rocks melt. The section draws a connection between volcanic activity and tectonic movement and concludes with a discussion of the challenges involved in predicting eruptions.

 Bellringer

Ask students to imagine that they live on a volcanic island. Have them list in their **science journal** the signals that would tell them the volcano was about to erupt.

Motivate

Discussion ——— GENERAL

Volcano Safety Have students brainstorm measures a community could take to protect citizens from a volcanic eruption and then write their ideas in their **science journal.** Have them compare their suggestions with the information they learn in the chapter. **LS** Logical

What You Will Learn

- Describe the formation and movement of magma.
- Explain the relationship between volcanoes and plate tectonics.
- Summarize the methods scientists use to predict volcanic eruptions.

Vocabulary

rift zone
hot spot

READING STRATEGY

Reading Organizer As you read this section, make a flowchart of the steps of magma formation in different tectonic environments.

Causes of Volcanic Eruptions

More than 2,000 years ago, Pompeii was a busy Roman city near the sleeping volcano Mount Vesuvius. People did not see Vesuvius as much of a threat. Everything changed when Vesuvius suddenly erupted and buried the city in a deadly blanket of ash that was almost 20 ft thick!

Today, even more people are living on and near active volcanoes. Scientists closely monitor volcanoes to avoid this type of disaster. They study the gases coming from active volcanoes and look for slight changes in the volcano's shape that could indicate that an eruption is near. Scientists know much more about the causes of eruptions than the ancient Pompeiians did, but there is much more to be discovered.

The Formation of Magma

Understanding how magma forms helps explain why volcanoes erupt. Magma forms in the deeper regions of the Earth's crust and in the uppermost layers of the mantle where the temperature and pressure are very high. Changes in pressure and temperature cause magma to form.

Pressure and Temperature

Part of the upper mantle is made of very hot, puttylike rock that flows slowly. The rock of the mantle is hot enough to melt at Earth's surface, but it remains a puttylike solid because of pressure. This pressure is caused by the weight of the rock above the mantle. In other words, the rock above the mantle presses the atoms of the mantle so close together that the rock cannot melt. As **Figure 1** shows, rock melts when its temperature increases or when the pressure on the rock decreases.

Figure 1 The curved line indicates the melting point of a rock. As pressure decreases and temperature increases, the rock begins to melt.

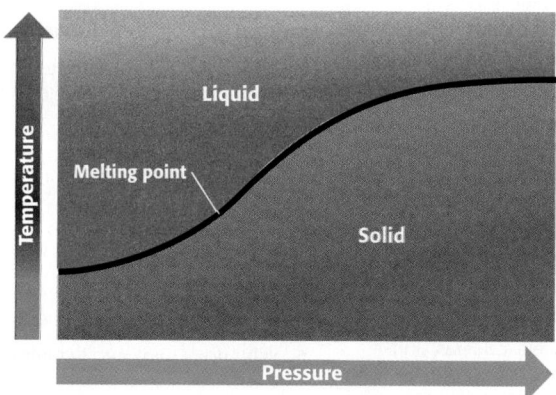

CHAPTER RESOURCES

Chapter Resource File

- **Lesson Plan**
- **Directed Reading A** BASIC
- **Directed Reading B** SPECIAL NEEDS

Technology

Transparencies
- Bellringer
- E33 The Location of Major Volcanoes

Workbooks

Interactive Textbook Struggling Readers

Magma Formation in the Mantle

Because the temperature of the mantle is fairly constant, a decrease in pressure is the most common cause of magma formation. Magma often forms at the boundary between separating tectonic plates, where pressure is decreased. Once formed, the magma is less dense than the surrounding rock, so the magma slowly rises toward the surface like an air bubble in a jar of honey.

Where Volcanoes Form

The locations of volcanoes give clues about how volcanoes form. The map in **Figure 2** shows the location of some of the world's major active volcanoes. The map also shows the boundaries between tectonic plates. A large number of volcanoes lie directly on tectonic plate boundaries. In fact, the plate boundaries surrounding the Pacific Ocean have so many volcanoes that the area is called the *Ring of Fire*.

Tectonic plate boundaries are areas where tectonic plates either collide, separate, or slide past one another. At these boundaries, it is possible for magma to form and travel to the surface. About 80% of active volcanoes on land form where plates collide, and about 15% form where plates separate. The remaining few occur far from tectonic plate boundaries.

✓ Reading Check Why are most volcanoes on plate boundaries?
(See the Appendix for answers to Reading Checks.)

Reaction to Stress

1. Make a pliable "rock" by pouring **60 mL of water** into a **plastic cup** and adding **150 mL of cornstarch,** 15 mL at a time. Stir well each time.

2. Pour half of the cornstarch mixture into a **clear bowl.** Carefully observe how the "rock" flows. Be patient—this process is slow!

3. Scrape the rest of the "rock" out of the cup with a **spoon.** Observe the behavior of the "rock" as you scrape.

4. What happened to the "rock" when you let it flow by itself? What happened when you put stress on the "rock"?

5. How is this pliable "rock" similar to the rock of the upper part of the mantle?

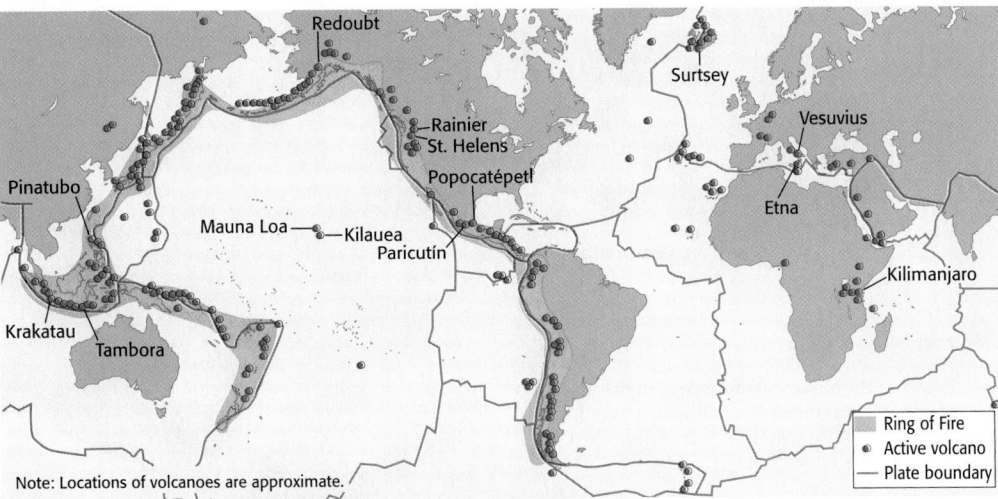

Figure 2 *Tectonic plate boundaries are likely places for volcanoes to form. The Ring of Fire contains nearly 75% of the world's active volcanoes on land.*

BRAIN FOOD

Rates of Cooling Affect Crystal Size

Igneous rocks form when magma cools and solidifies either at or beneath Earth's surface. Magma that solidifies deep underground usually cools much more slowly than magma that solidifies closer to the surface. The difference in the rate of cooling affects the texture of the igneous rock that forms. Rocks that form from magma that cools slowly contain larger crystals than rocks that form from magma that cools quickly. Ask students how scientists could use information about crystal size to study an igneous outcrop. (By studying mineral type and crystal size, scientists can determine the origin of igneous rock.)

English Language Learners

Activate Vocabulary

Before students read this section, remind them that they already have learned several of the words here in the chapter on plate tectonics (such words as *mantle* and *divergent boundary*). Tell them to check the Glossary or return to their notes to be reminded of the definitions. **LS** Verbal

Using the Figure — GENERAL

Plate Tectonics Have students study **Figure 4,** in which a continental plate and an oceanic plate converge.

- Ask students which plate is more dense. (oceanic)

- Explain that when an oceanic plate sinks, or *subducts,* beneath another tectonic plate, the scraping, pushing, and jostling may cause earthquakes and tsunamis.

- Ask students what kind of tectonic plate contains more water. (oceanic)

- Have students explain how water content in mantle rock affects magma formation. (Water lowers the melting point of the rock, which makes the rock more likely to melt.)

- Have students explain how magma forms when these two tectonic plates converge. (The subducted oceanic plate moves downward, and the water from the subducted plate causes the overlying material to melt and form magma.)

- Ask students if they think that explosive eruptions tend to occur near convergent or divergent boundaries. (They tend to occur near convergent boundaries because the water content of the magma is higher near convergent boundaries.)

LS Logical/Visual

How Hot Is Hot?

Inside the Earth, magma can reach a burning-hot 1,400°C! You may be more familiar with Fahrenheit temperatures, so convert 1,400°C to degrees Fahrenheit by using the formula below.

°F = (°C ÷ 5 × 9) + 32

What is the temperature in degrees Fahrenheit?

rift zone an area of deep cracks that forms between two tectonic plates that are pulling away from each other

When Tectonic Plates Separate

At a *divergent boundary,* tectonic plates move away from each other. As tectonic plates separate, a set of deep cracks called a **rift zone** forms between the plates. Mantle rock then rises to fill in the gap. When mantle rock gets closer to the surface, the pressure decreases. The pressure decrease causes the mantle rock to melt and form magma. Because magma is less dense than the surrounding rock, it rises through the rifts. When the magma reaches the surface, it spills out and hardens, creating new crust, as shown in **Figure 3.**

Mid-Ocean Ridges Form at Divergent Boundaries

Lava that flows from undersea rift zones produces volcanoes and mountain chains called *mid-ocean ridges.* Just as a baseball has stitches, the Earth is circled with mid-ocean ridges. At these ridges, lava flows out and creates new crust. Most volcanic activity on Earth occurs at mid-ocean ridges. While most mid-ocean ridges are underwater, Iceland, with its volcanoes and hot springs, was created by lava from the Mid-Atlantic Ridge. In 1963, enough lava poured out of the Mid-Atlantic Ridge near Iceland to form a new island called *Surtsey.* Scientists watched this new island being born!

Figure 3 How Magma Forms at a Divergent Boundary

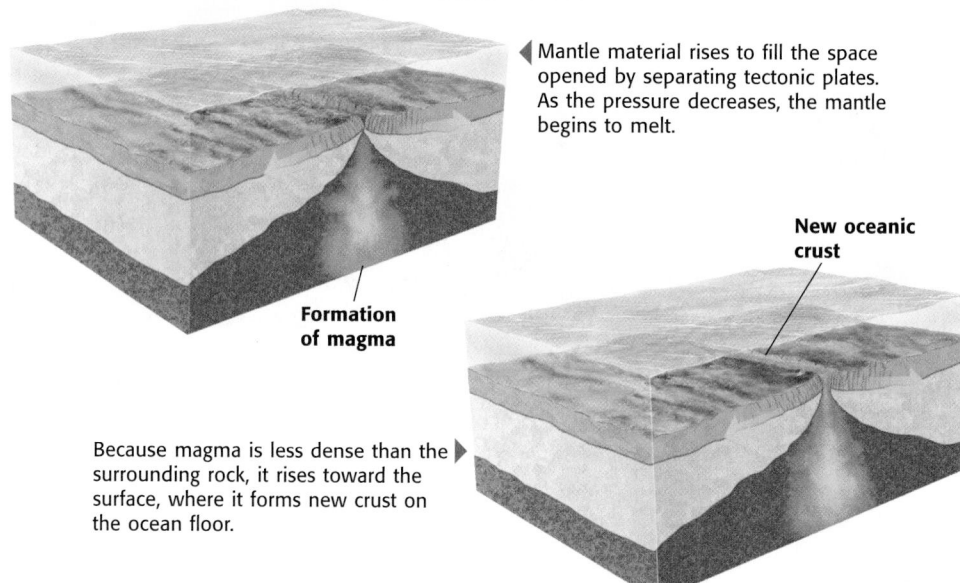

Mantle material rises to fill the space opened by separating tectonic plates. As the pressure decreases, the mantle begins to melt.

New oceanic crust

Formation of magma

Because magma is less dense than the surrounding rock, it rises toward the surface, where it forms new crust on the ocean floor.

CONNECTION ACTIVITY
Math — GENERAL

Kilauea Kilauea, in Hawaii, is one of the most studied volcanoes in the world. It has been erupting regularly since 1983. Every day, enough lava to pave a two-lane road 32 km long pours from the volcano. Have students calculate how long this lava "road" would be if the volcano erupted at that rate for 40 years.

(365 days/y × 32 km/day = 11,680 km/y; 11,680 km/y × 40 y = 467,200 km, more than 10 times the Earth's circumference) **LS** Logical

Answer to Math Practice

9/5 × 1,400°C + 32 = 2,552°F

Figure 4 | **How Magma Forms at a Convergent Boundary**

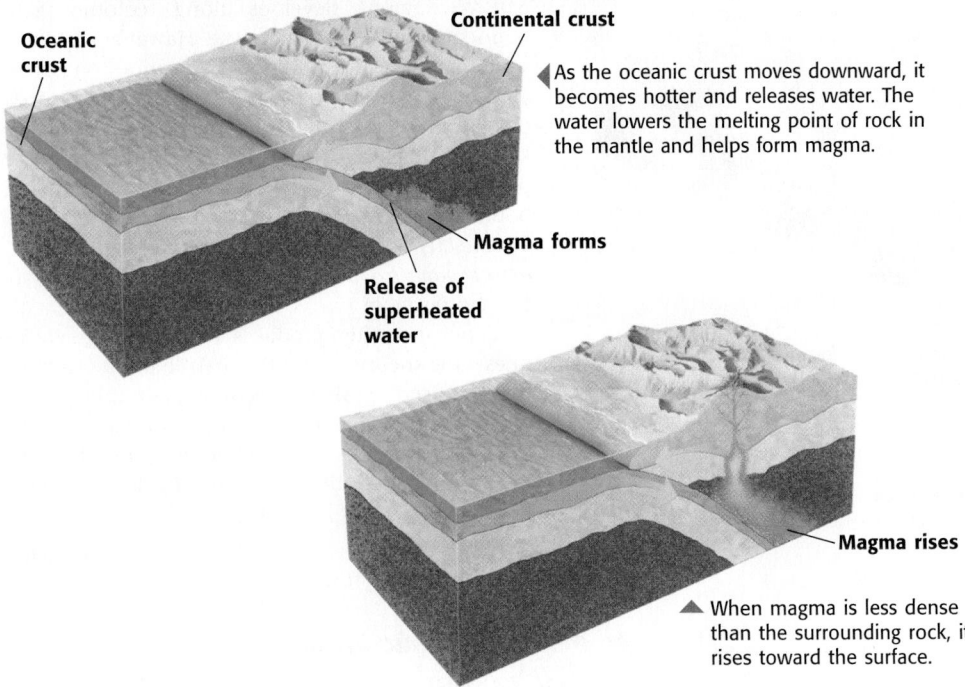

Oceanic crust

Continental crust

As the oceanic crust moves downward, it becomes hotter and releases water. The water lowers the melting point of rock in the mantle and helps form magma.

Magma forms

Release of superheated water

Magma rises

▲ When magma is less dense than the surrounding rock, it rises toward the surface.

When Tectonic Plates Collide

If you slide two pieces of notebook paper into one another on a flat desktop, the papers will either buckle upward or one piece of paper will move under the other. This is similar to what happens at a convergent boundary. A *convergent boundary* is a place where tectonic plates collide. When an oceanic plate collides with a continental plate, the oceanic plate usually slides underneath the continental plate. The process of *subduction,* the movement of one tectonic plate underneath another, is shown in **Figure 4.** Oceanic crust is subducted because it is denser and thinner than continental crust.

Subduction Produces Magma

As the descending oceanic crust scrapes past the continental crust, the temperature and pressure increase. The combination of increased heat and pressure causes the water contained in the oceanic crust to be released. The water then mixes with the mantle rock, which lowers the rock's melting point, causing it to melt. This body of magma can rise to form a volcano.

> **✓ Reading Check** How does subduction produce magma?

SCHOOL to HOME

Tectonic Models

Create models of convergent and divergent boundaries by using materials of your choice. Have your teacher approve your list before you start building your model at home with an adult. In class, use your model to explain how each type of boundary leads to the formation of magma.

INCLUSION Strategies

- *Learning Disabled*
- *Gifted and Talented*
- *Attention Deficit Disorder*

Organize students into small teams to play a volcano quiz game. Each team should choose a category that relates to a heading in the section and write five questions and answers for the category on separate index cards. The difficulty

and point value of the questions should increase incrementally. Review each team's questions and answers before you start the game. If a team cannot answer a question, the team should work with another team to answer the question. If teams cooperate, they should share the points. **LS** Interpersonal

---

Group ACTiViTY — ADVANCED

Preparing for an Eruption More than 30 earthquakes per year are caused by the movement of magma beneath Mount Rainier, in Washington State. Mount Rainier is the most seismically active volcano in the Cascade Range after Mount St. Helens. Because the area around Mount Rainier is heavily populated, an eruption would endanger thousands of people and destroy property worth millions of dollars. Many groups of people are studying Mount Rainier and are preparing for a possible eruption. Divide the class into groups, and give the following assignments:

- **Research Group** Members investigate the volcano's history to determine why the volcano has been ranked as a "decade volcano."

- **Early-Warning Group** Members research how the volcano's activity is being monitored with scientific equipment and other methods.

- **Washington State Emergency Management Agency (WaSEMA) Group** Members find out how this state organization plans to help people in case of an eruption.

- **Schools, Police, and Fire Group** Members investigate how local agencies would design a plan for warning people of an eruption and a plan for coping with the aftermath of an eruption.

After the groups do research, have them make presentations using posters, models, maps, and graphs. **LS** Interpersonal Co-op Learning

Answer to Reading Check

When a tectonic plate subducts, it becomes hotter and releases water. The water lowers the melting point of the rock above the plate, causing magma to form.

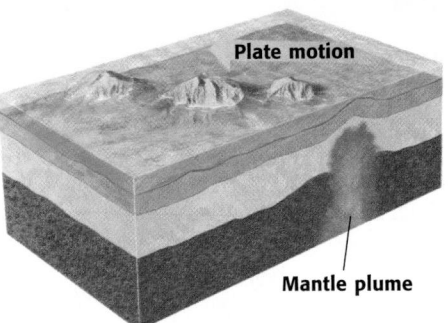

Figure 5 *According to one theory, a string of volcanic islands forms as a tectonic plate passes over a mantle plume.*

hot spot a volcanically active area of Earth's surface far from a tectonic plate boundary

Figure 6 *As if being this close to an active volcano is not dangerous enough, the gases being collected are extremely poisonous.*

Hot Spots

Not all magma develops along tectonic plate boundaries. For example, the Hawaiian Islands, some of the most well-known volcanoes on Earth, are nowhere near a plate boundary. The volcanoes of Hawaii and several other places on Earth are known as *hot spots*. **Hot spots** are volcanically active places on the Earth's surface that are far from plate boundaries. Some scientists think that hot spots are directly above columns of rising magma, called *mantle plumes*. Other scientists think that hot spots are the result of cracks in the Earth's crust.

A hot spot often produces a long chain of volcanoes. One theory is that the mantle plume stays in the same spot while the tectonic plate moves over it, as shown in **Figure 5.** Another theory argues that hot-spot volcanoes occur in long chains because they form along the cracks in the Earth's crust. Both theories may be correct.

✓ **Reading Check** Describe two theories that explain the existence of hot spots.

Predicting Volcanic Eruptions

You now understand some of the processes that produce volcanoes, but how do scientists predict when a volcano is going to erupt? Volcanoes are classified in three categories. *Extinct volcanoes* have not erupted in recorded history and probably never will erupt again. *Dormant volcanoes* are currently not erupting, but the record of past eruptions suggests that they may erupt again. *Active volcanoes* are currently erupting or show signs of erupting in the near future. Scientists study active and dormant volcanoes for signs of a future eruption.

Measuring Small Quakes and Volcanic Gases

Most active volcanoes produce small earthquakes as the magma within them moves upward and causes the surrounding rock to shift. Just before an eruption, the number and intensity of the earthquakes increase and the occurrence of quakes may be continuous. Monitoring these quakes is one of the best ways to predict an eruption.

As **Figure 6** shows, scientists also study the volume and composition of volcanic gases. The ratio of certain gases, especially that of sulfur dioxide, SO_2, to carbon dioxide, CO_2, may be important in predicting eruptions. Changes in this ratio may indicate changes in the magma chamber below.

Measuring Slope and Temperature

As magma moves upward prior to an eruption, it can cause the Earth's surface to swell. The side of a volcano may even bulge as the magma moves upward. An instrument called a *tiltmeter* helps scientists detect small changes in the angle of a volcano's slope. Scientists also use satellite technology such as the Global Positioning System (GPS) to detect the changes in a volcano's slope that may signal an eruption.

One of the newest methods for predicting volcanic eruptions includes using satellite images. Infrared satellite images record changes in the surface temperature and gas emissions of a volcano over time. If the site is getting hotter, the magma below is probably rising!

INTERNET ACTIVITY

For another activity related to this chapter, go to **go.hrw.com** and type in the keyword **HZ5VOLW**.

SECTION Review

Summary

- Temperature and pressure influence magma formation.
- Most volcanoes form at tectonic boundaries.
- As tectonic plates separate, magma rises to fill the cracks, or rifts, that develop.
- As oceanic and continental plates collide, the oceanic plate tends to subduct and cause the formation of magma.
- To predict eruptions, scientists study the frequency and type of earthquakes associated with the volcano as well as changes in slope, changes in the gases released, and changes in the volcano's surface temperature.

Using Key Terms

1. Use each of the following terms in a separate sentence: *hot spot* and *rift zone*.

Understanding Key Ideas

2. If the temperature of a rock remains constant but the pressure on the rock decreases, what tends to happen?
   a. The temperature increases.
   b. The rock becomes liquid.
   c. The rock becomes solid.
   d. The rock subducts.

3. Which of the following words is a synonym for *dormant*?
   a. predictable
   b. active
   c. dead
   d. sleeping

4. What is the Ring of Fire?

5. Explain how convergent and divergent plate boundaries cause magma formation.

6. Describe four methods that scientists use to predict volcanic eruptions.

7. Why does a oceanic plate tend to subduct when it collides with a continental plate?

Math Skills

8. If a tectonic plate moves at a rate of 2 km every 1 million years, how long would it take a hot spot to form a chain of volcanoes 100 km long?

Critical Thinking

9. **Making Inferences** New crust is constantly being created at mid-ocean ridges. So, why is the oldest oceanic crust only about 150 million years old?

10. **Identifying Relationships** If you are studying a volcanic deposit, would the youngest layers be more likely to be found on the top or on the bottom? Explain your answer.

SCiLINKS®

NSTA
Developed and maintained by the National Science Teachers Association

For a variety of links related to this chapter, go to www.scilinks.org

Topic: What Causes Volcanoes?
SciLinks code: HSM1654

Answers to Section Review

1. Sample answer: A hot spot may form above a mantle plume. A rift zone is a series of cracks that form along a divergent plate boundary.

2. b

3. d

4. The Ring of Fire is a group of volcanoes that are located on convergent plate boundaries in the Pacific Ocean.

5. At convergent boundaries a plate is subducted. The subducted plate is heated and releases water. The water causes the melting point of the rock to decrease, forming magma. At divergent boundaries, mantle rock rises to fill the gap created by separating tectonic plates. As the rock rises, pressure decreases and the rock melts, forming magma.

6. Scientists monitor seismic activity associated with the volcano. If seismic activity increases, magma might be moving in the magma chamber. Scientists study the composition and volume of gases released from the volcano. If the composition of gases changes, an eruption may be imminent. Scientists also study the slope and temperature of volcanoes. If the slope or surface temperature change, an eruption might be imminent.

7. Oceanic plates tend to subduct because they are denser than continental plates.

8. 100 km ÷ 2 km/million years = 50 million years

9. New crust is constantly being created, but it is also being subducted at convergent boundaries.

10. The youngest layers would most likely be at the top because they were deposited over the older layers.

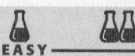

Volcano Verdict

Teacher's Notes

Time Required
One 45-minute class period

Lab Ratings

EASY ————————————→ HARD

Teacher Prep 🧪🧪
Student Set-Up 🧪🧪🧪
Concept Level 🧪🧪
Clean Up 🧪🧪

MATERIALS

The materials listed on the student page are sufficient for a pair of students.

Safety Caution
Remind students to review all safety cautions and icons before beginning this activity.

Preparation Notes
You may want to combine this activity with an activity involving a tiltmeter. Emphasize to students that a gas-emissions tester is just one tool used by volcanologists. These scientists must compare the data gathered through many tests before drawing any conclusions.

In this experiment, 10 mL of bromothymol blue may be substituted for limewater. Bromothymol blue changes from blue to yellow-green when carbon dioxide is present.

Skills Practice Lab

OBJECTIVES

Build a working apparatus to test carbon dioxide levels.

Test the levels of carbon dioxide emitted from a model volcano.

MATERIALS

- baking soda, 15 mL
- bottle, drinking, 16 oz
- box or stand for plastic cup
- clay, modeling
- coin
- cup, clear plastic, 9 oz
- graduated cylinder
- limewater, 1 L
- straw, drinking, flexible
- tissue, bathroom (2 sheets)
- vinegar, white, 140 mL
- water, 100 mL

SAFETY

Volcano Verdict

You will need to pair up with a partner for this exploration. You and your partner will act as geologists who work in a city located near a volcano. City officials are counting on you to predict when the volcano will erupt next. You and your partner have decided to use limewater as a gas-emissions tester. You will use this tester to measure the levels of carbon dioxide emitted from a simulated volcano. The more active the volcano is, the more carbon dioxide it releases.

Procedure

1. Put on your safety goggles, and carefully pour limewater into the plastic cup until the cup is three-fourths full. You have just made your gas-emissions tester.

2. Now, build a model volcano. Begin by pouring 50 mL of water and 70 mL of vinegar into the drink bottle.

3. Form a plug of clay around the short end of the straw, as shown at left. The clay plug must be large enough to cover the opening of the bottle. Be careful not to get the clay wet.

4. Sprinkle 5 mL of baking soda along the center of a single section of bathroom tissue. Then, roll the tissue, and twist the ends so that the baking soda can't fall out.

💿 **Holt Lab Generator CD-ROM**

Search for any lab by topic, standard, difficulty level, or time. Edit any lab to fit your needs, or create your own labs. Use the Lab Materials QuickList software to customize your lab materials list.

Gordon Zibelman
Drexel Hill Middle School
Drexel Hill, Pennsylvania

CHAPTER RESOURCES

Chapter Resource File

 • Datasheet for Chapter Lab
   • Lab Notes and Answers

Technology

 Classroom Videos
   • Lab Video

 LabBook

• Some Go "Pop," Some Do Not

5 Drop the tissue into the drink bottle, and immediately put the short end of the straw inside the bottle to make a seal with the clay.

6 Put the other end of the straw into the lime-water, as shown at right.

7 You have just taken your first measurement of gas levels from the volcano. Record your observations.

8 Imagine that it is several days later and you need to test the volcano again to collect more data. Before you continue, toss a coin. If it lands heads up, go to step 9. If it lands tails up, go to step 10. Write down the step that you follow.

9 Repeat steps 1–7. This time, add 2 mL of baking soda to the vinegar and water. (Note: You must use fresh water, vinegar, and limewater.) Write down your observations. Go to step 11.

10 Repeat steps 1–7. This time, add 8 mL of baking soda to the vinegar and water. (Note: You must use fresh water, vinegar, and limewater.) Write down your observations. Go to step 11.

11 Return to step 8 once. Then, answer the questions below.

Analyze the Results

1 **Explaining Events** How do you explain the difference in the appearance of the limewater from one trial to the next?

2 **Recognizing Patterns** What does the data that you collected indicate about the activity in the volcano?

Draw Conclusions

3 **Evaluating Results** Based on your results, do you think it would be necessary to evacuate the city?

4 **Applying Conclusions** How would a geologist use a gas-emissions tester to predict volcanic eruptions?

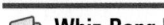
MISCONCEPTION ALERT

Predicting Volcanic Eruptions
Scientists base their predictions of eruptions on several different kinds of evidence. If many types of evidence indicate that an eruption is imminent, they will recommend evacuation. They are much less likely to recommend evacuation if only one kind of evidence suggests that an eruption is imminent.

Chapter Review

Assignment Guide

SECTION	QUESTIONS
1	2, 3, 6, 7, 13, 17, 18,
2	1, 5, 10, 15, 16
3	8, 9, 11, 12, 14, 19, 20
1 and 3	4

ANSWERS

Using Key Terms

1. Sample answer: A caldera forms when the roof of a magma chamber collapses. A crater forms when the material above the main vent of a volcano is blasted out.

2. Sample answer: Magma is hot, liquid rock material beneath Earth's surface. Lava is magma that flows onto Earth's surface.

3. Sample answer: Lava is liquid magma that flows out of a volcanic vent onto the ground. Pyroclastic material is mostly ash and solid rock that is blasted into the air during an explosive volcanic eruption.

4. Sample answer: A vent is a spot in Earth's surface through which lava or pyroclastic material passes. A rift is a long crack in Earth's crust.

5. Sample answer: A cinder cone volcano forms when pyroclastic material erupts and piles up around a volcanic vent. A shield volcano forms when lava spreads out over large areas.

USING KEY TERMS

For each pair of terms, explain how the meanings of the terms differ.

1. *caldera* and *crater*

2. *lava* and *magma*

3. *lava* and *pyroclastic material*

4. *vent* and *rift*

5. *cinder cone volcano* and *shield volcano*

UNDERSTANDING KEY IDEAS

Multiple Choice

6. The type of magma that tends to cause explosive eruptions has a
   a. high silica content and high viscosity.
   b. high silica content and low viscosity.
   c. low silica content and low viscosity.
   d. low silica content and high viscosity.

7. Lava that flows slowly to form a glassy surface with rounded wrinkles is called
   a. aa lava.
   b. pahoehoe lava.
   c. pillow lava.
   d. blocky lava.

8. Magma forms within the mantle most often as a result of
   a. high temperature and high pressure.
   b. high temperature and low pressure.
   c. low temperature and high pressure.
   d. low temperature and low pressure.

9. What causes an increase in the number and intensity of small earthquakes before an eruption?
   a. the movement of magma
   b. the formation of pyroclastic material
   c. the hardening of magma
   d. the movement of tectonic plates

10. If volcanic dust and ash remain in the atmosphere for months or years, what do you predict will happen?
    a. Solar reflection will decrease, and temperatures will increase.
    b. Solar reflection will increase, and temperatures will increase.
    c. Solar reflection will decrease, and temperatures will decrease.
    d. Solar reflection will increase, and temperatures will decrease.

11. At divergent plate boundaries,
    a. heat from Earth's core causes mantle plumes.
    b. oceanic plates sink, which causes magma to form.
    c. tectonic plates move apart.
    d. hot spots cause volcanoes.

12. A theory that helps explain the causes of both earthquakes and volcanoes is the theory of
    a. pyroclastics.
    b. plate tectonics.
    c. climatic fluctuation.
    d. mantle plumes.

Understanding Key Ideas

6. a
7. b
8. b
9. a
10. d
11. c
12. b

Short Answer

13 How does the presence of water in magma affect a volcanic eruption?

14 Describe four clues that scientists use to predict eruptions.

15 Identify the characteristics of the three types of volcanoes.

16 Describe the positive effects of volcanic eruptions.

CRITICAL THINKING

17 **Concept Mapping** Use the following terms to create a concept map: *volcanic bombs, aa, pyroclastic material, pahoehoe, lapilli, lava,* and *volcano.*

18 **Identifying Relationships** You are exploring a volcano that has been dormant for some time. You begin to keep notes on the types of volcanic debris that you see as you walk. Your first notes describe volcanic ash. Later, your notes describe lapilli. In what direction are you most likely traveling—toward the crater or away from the crater? Explain your answer.

19 **Making Inferences** Loihi is a submarine Hawaiian volcano that might grow to form a new island. The Hawaiian Islands are located on the Pacific plate, which is moving northwest. Considering how this island chain may have formed, where do you think the new volcanic island will be located? Explain your answer.

20 **Evaluating Hypotheses** What evidence could confirm the existence of mantle plumes?

INTERPRETING GRAPHICS

The graph below illustrates the average change in temperature above or below normal for a community over several years. Use the graph below to answer the questions that follow.

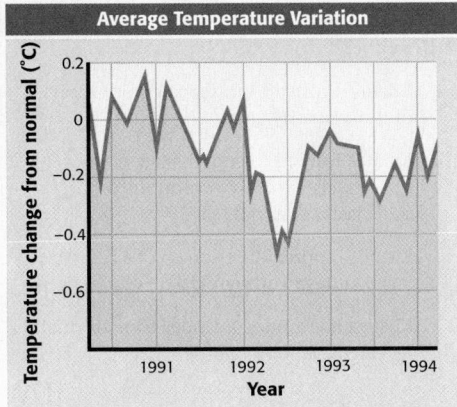

Average Temperature Variation

21 If the variation in temperature over the years was influenced by a major volcanic eruption, when did the eruption most likely take place? Explain.

22 If the temperature were measured only once each year (at the beginning of the year), how would your interpretation be different?

15. Cinder cones are made from eruptions of pyroclastic materials. They are small and have steep sides. Shield volcanoes are made of lava that spreads over large distances before it solidifies, making very large, gently sloped volcanoes. Composite volcanoes are made of both lava and pyroclastic material. Composite volcanoes have large, gently sloping bases and steep sides.

16. Sample answer: Volcanoes form new crust and help create fertile soil.

Critical Thinking

17. 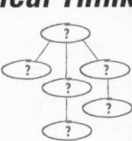 An answer to this exercise can be found at the end of this book.

18. You would be traveling toward the volcano because the larger the pyroclastic material is, the closer it will be to the vent. It takes more energy to move larger particles than it does to move smaller particles.

19. The new island will be located southeast of Hawaii because the Pacific plate is moving toward the northwest.

20. Answers may vary. Students may suggest studying the composition and temperature of rock in the area where a mantle plume is thought to be.

Interpreting Graphics

21. The eruption probably happened in 1992 because that year had the lowest below-normal temperature. The volcanic ash that erupted into the atmosphere blocked the sunlight and lowered the temperature.

22. If the temperature were measured once a year, the graph would indicate that 1991 had the lowest temperature. This would indicate that the eruptions happened in 1991 instead of 1992.

---

13. The presence of water in magma tends to cause explosive eruptions.

14. Earthquakes may indicate the movement of magma. Changes in the composition of volcanic gases may indicate changes in the magma chamber that may precede an eruption. Changes in the slope of a volcano may indicate that magma is rising. Finally, satellite data can reveal changes in surface temperature that may indicate that magma is rising.

CHAPTER RESOURCES

Chapter Resource File

- **Chapter Review** GENERAL
- **Chapter Test A** GENERAL
- **Chapter Test B** ADVANCED
- **Chapter Test C** SPECIAL NEEDS
- **Vocabulary Activity** GENERAL

Workbooks

Study Guide
- Study Guide is also available in Spanish.

Teacher's Notes

To provide practice under more realistic conditions, give students 20 minutes to answer all of the questions in this Standardized Test Preparation.

Answer Key

Question	Answer
1	D
2	A
3	A
4	C
5	D
6	B
7	B
8	C
9	C
10	D
11	*
12	*

*See Test Doctor.

Multiple Choice

1. **A benefit to society of volcano research is that it allows scientists**

   A. to measure volcanic gases.

   B. to measure temperature changes.

   C. to prevent volcanoes from erupting.

   D. to better predict when eruptions will occur.

2. **One of the active volcanoes on the island of Hawaii is named Kilauea. If Kilauea is a shield volcano, which of the following would be a reasonable inference?**

   A. Kilauea formed from repeated eruptions of low viscosity lava.

   B. Kilauea formed from repeated moderately explosive eruptions of pyroclastic material.

   C. Kilauea is primarily made up of alternating layers of lava and pyroclastic material.

   D. Kilauea has formed a cinder cone through repeated eruptions of high viscosity lava.

3. **Which of the following is a likely result of large amounts of volcanic ash in the atmosphere?**

   A. The average global temperature will decrease.

   B. The average duration of a day will become shorter.

   C. Ocean tide levels will be affected.

   D. Only the area near the volcano will be affected.

4. **When magma builds up beneath a volcano, a large amount of pressure is created. What form does this pressure take?**

   A. kinetic energy

   B. chemical energy

   C. potential energy

   D. explosive energy

Use the table below to answer question 5.

Magma Viscosity	
Magma type	Viscosity
Felsic	High
Intermediate	Intermediate
Mafic	Low
Ultramafic	Very low

5. **According to the data collected above, which type of magma is least likely to cause an explosive eruption?**

   A. felsic magma

   B. intermediate magma

   C. mafic

   D. ultramafic

6. **If a volcanic eruption covered farmland with several meters of ash, which of the following could be said about the ash?**

   A. It would be an effective fertilizer, causing record crop yields.

   B. It would smother the crops and possibly lead to food shortages.

   C. It would be a nuisance, but it could be easily removed.

   D. Farmers would mix it with water and use it as a substitute for concrete.

 **TEST DOCTOR**

Question 1 A: This statement is true, but it is not a benefit to society. B: This statement is true, but it is not a benefit to society. C: No one can prevent a volcanic eruption. D: Correct.

Question 2 A: Correct. B: Moderately explosive eruptions of pyroclastic material are characteristic of a cinder cone volcano, not of a shield volcano. C: Alternating layers of lava and pyroclastic material are characteristic of composite volcanoes, not of shield volcanoes. D: Kilauea is a shield volcano, not a cinder cone volcano. Shield volcanoes form from repeated non-explosive eruptions of low viscosity lava.

Question 3 A: Correct. B: The duration of a day on Earth depends on Earth's position in relation to the sun; the duration of a day is unaffected by volcanic eruptions. C: Ocean tide levels depend on Earth's position relative to the moon and the sun; tide levels are unaffected by volcanic eruptions. D: The effect of volcanic explosions is not localized; large volcanic eruptions have affected the weather worldwide.

Question 4 A: Because the magma is only exerting pressure on the surrounding rock but is not moving, the magma does not have kinetic

7. In which of the following situations would there be the greatest amount of kinetic energy?

    A. just prior to eruption, when great pressure has built up inside a volcano

    B. during an explosive eruption in which pyroclastic material is blown high into the atmosphere

    C. just after an explosive eruption, when most of the debris has settled back to the ground

    D. long after a shield volcano has moved from a hot spot

8. Which of the following situations represents the greatest amount of potential energy?

    A. A large boulder is blown into the air by an explosive eruption.

    B. Low viscosity lava flows quickly downhill.

    C. A huge boulder is perched atop a cliff and is on the verge of falling 1000 m to the ground below.

    D. A tree that was blown over by a powerful eruption lies flat on the ground.

9. What percentage of active volcanoes on land formed where tectonic plates separate?

    A. 80%

    B. 75%

    C. 15%

    D. 5%

Use the illustration below to answer question 10.

10. What is the term for the area to which the arrow is pointing?

    A. lava

    B. crater

    C. caldera

    D. magma chamber

Open Response

11. Unlike the west coast of North America, Kentucky's position closer to the center of the continental plate makes it free from volcanoes. Yet its climate can still be affected by volcanoes. How?

12. At what point does a volcanic system reach equilibrium?

---

volcano has potential energy, not kinetic energy. B: Correct. C: After the eruption, the debris that has settled to the ground does not have kinetic energy because it is not moving. D: Shield volcanoes do not normally have explosive eruptions; so there may not be a large amount of energy to begin with.

Question 8 A: The boulder has kinetic energy as it moves through the air. B: As the lava moves downhill, it has kinetic energy. C: Correct. D: The tree lying on the ground has only a small amount of potential energy, because the tree has nowhere to fall. The tree does not have as much potential energy as the boulder in C.

Question 9 A: This is the percentage of active land volcanoes that formed where tectonic plates collide. B: This is the percentage of active land volcanoes on the Ring of Fire (the tectonic plate boundaries that surround the Pacific Ocean). C: Correct. D: This is the percentage of active land volcanoes that formed away from tectonic plate boundaries.

Question 10 A: Lava is molten rock that flows from a volcanic vent. B: Craters are funnel-shaped pits that form around the central vent at the top of many volcanoes. C: A caldera is a large, circular depression that forms when the magma chamber partially empties. This causes the ground above the magma chamber to sink. D: Correct.

Question 11 Full-credit answers should include the following points:

- Erupting volcanoes can throw volcanic ash and gases high into the upper atmosphere.

- Winds can move ash and gases around the globe.

- When much volcanic ash is hurled into the atmosphere, the ash blocks sunlight and briefly lowers the global temperature.

Question 12 Full-credit answers should explain that a volcanic system is in equilibrium when the upward force of magma equals the downward force of rock above the magma.

---

energy. B: The pressure of the magma on the rock in the volcano is not a form of chemical energy. C: Correct. D: There is no form of energy called "explosive energy."

Question 5 A: Felsic magma has the highest viscosity and therefore is more likely to cause an explosive eruption. B: Intermediate magma has intermediate viscosity and therefore is more likely to cause a mildly explosive eruption. C: While mafic magma has a low viscosity and is therefore not likely to cause an explosive eruption, its viscosity is not the lowest of those listed in the table. D: Correct.

Question 6 A: Volcanic ash does contain nutrients necessary for plant growth, but several meters of ash would cover the plants and prevent them from getting sunlight, which would cause the plants to die. B: Correct. C: Several meters of ash spread over an area of at least several miles is a large volume of ash. Such a large volume would be very difficult to remove. D: The ash could contain substances that act like cement when combined with water, but it is unlikely that the farmers in the area would be interested in that property of the ash.

Question 7 A: Before the eruption, the magma within the volcano is not moving. Therefore, the

Science in Action

Weird Science

Background

According to native Hawaiian mythology, Pele lives in the active crater of Kilauea. If Pele is angered, she stamps her feet, causing earthquakes and lava flows. Hawaiian myth states that she appears as an old woman just before an eruption. To prevent eruptions, villagers sometimes made sacrifices to appease her. Typically they sacrificed a pig, but if no pigs were available, a thick skinned fish called *Humu-humu-nuku-nuku-a-puaa* (which grunts like a pig) would suffice. Have students research myths about volcanoes and share their findings with the class.

Science, Technology, and Society

Background

The villagers in Heimaey lost about a third of their village to the Eldfell eruption but succeeded in protecting their harbor. If the eruption had flowed its course, lava would have filled in the harbor of one of Iceland's most profitable fishing communities. After the eruption was over, villagers constructed a geothermal power plant to take advantage of the thermal energy of the lava flow.

Science in Action

Weird Science

Pele's Hair

It is hard to believe that the fragile specimen shown below is a volcanic rock. This strange type of lava, called *Pele's hair*, forms when volcanic gases spray molten rock high into the air. When conditions are right, the lava can harden into strands of volcanic glass as thin as a human hair. This type of lava is named after Pele, the Hawaiian goddess of volcanoes. Several other types of lava are named in Pele's honor. Pele's tears are tear-shaped globs of volcanic glass often found at the end of strands of Pele's hair. Pele's diamonds are green, gemlike stones found in hardened lava flows.

Science, Technology, and Society

Fighting Lava with Fire Hoses

What would you do if a 60 ft wall of lava was advancing toward your home? Most people would head for safety. But when an eruption threatened to engulf the Icelandic fishing village of Heimaey in 1973, some villagers held their ground and fought back. Working 14-hour days in conditions so hot that their boots would catch on fire, villagers used fire-hoses to spray sea water on the lava flow. For several weeks, the lava advanced toward the town, and it seemed as if there was no hope. But the water eventually cooled the lava fast enough to divert the flow and save the village. It took 5 months and about 1.5 billion gallons of water to fight the lava flow. When the eruption stopped, villagers found that the island had grown by 20%!

Language Arts ACTIVITY

Volcanic terms come from many languages. Research some volcanic terms on the Internet, and create an illustrated volcanic glossary to share with your class.

Social Studies ACTIVITY

WRITING SKILL To try to protect the city of Hilo, Hawaii, from an eruption in 1935, planes dropped bombs on the lava. Find out if this mission was successful, and write a report about other attempts to stop lava flows.

Answer to Language Arts Activity

Sample terms: *Limu o Pele* is a Hawaiian term that means "Pele's seaweed" and that refers to delicate, translucent sheets of splatter filled with tiny gas bubbles. *Nuée ardente* is a French term that means "burning cloud" and that refers to a hot mass of volcanic gases, ash, and debris that is expelled explosively and then travels at tremendous speeds down a mountainside. *Lahar* is an Indonesian term for a particularly deadly kind of volcanic mudflow.

Answer to Social Studies Activity

B-3 and B-4 bombers tried to stop the flow of lava into the city of Hilo. The mission was unsuccessful. Ground-based explosives have been more successful. In 1996, the Italian army detonated 15,000 pounds of explosives to stop a lava flow. They also built earthen walls to dam the lava.

Careers

Tina Neal

Volcanologist Would you like to study volcanoes for a living? Tina Neal is a volcanologist at the Alaska Volcano Observatory in Anchorage, Alaska. Her job is to monitor and study some of Alaska's 41 active volcanoes. Much of her work focuses on studying volcanoes in order to protect the public. According to Neal, being near a volcano when it is erupting is a wonderful adventure for the senses. "Sometimes you can get so close to an erupting volcano that you can feel the heat, hear the activity, and smell the lava. It's amazing! In Alaska, erupting volcanoes are too dangerous to get very close to, but they create a stunning visual display even from a distance."

Neal also enjoys the science of volcanoes. "It's fascinating to be near an active volcano and become aware of all the chemical and physical processes taking place. When I'm watching a volcano, I think about everything we understand and don't understand about what is happening. It's mind-boggling!" Neal says that if you are interested in becoming a volcanologist, it is important to be well rounded as a scientist. So, you would have to study math, geology, chemistry, and physics. Having a good understanding of computer tools is also important because volcanologists use computers to manage a lot of data and to create models. Neal also suggests learning a second language, such as Spanish. In her spare time, Neal is learning Russian so that she can better communicate with research partners in Kamchatka, Siberia.

Math ACTiViTY

The 1912 eruption of Mt. Katmai in Alaska could be heard 5,620 km away in Atlanta, Georgia. If the average speed of sound in the atmosphere is 342 m/s, how many hours after the eruption did the citizens of Atlanta hear the explosion?

go.hrw.com

To learn more about these Science in Action topics, visit go.hrw.com and type in the keyword **HZ5VOLF**.

Current Science

Check out Current Science® articles related to this chapter by visiting go.hrw.com. Just type in the keyword **HZ5CS09**.

Careers

Background

Tina Neal always wanted to be an astronaut. She heard space programs needed medical doctors, so she decided to follow a pre-med track in college. But then she went to a fascinating lecture on the geology of Mars. Soon, she had enrolled in her first geology course and discovered that volcanoes are a common link among the planets. When Neal got a chance to see Mt. St. Helen's erupt, that was it. She was hooked on the field of volcanology—and the idea of staying on Earth!

Tina Neal received a degree in Geology from Brown University and an M.S. in Geology from Arizona State University. She has done additional graduate studies in Geology at the University of California at Santa Barbara.

She now works for the United States Geological Survey (USGS) as a physical volcanologist specializing in the study of young, active volcanoes.

Answer to Math Activity

342 m/s × 60 s/min × 60 min/h = 1,231,200 m/h

1,231,200 m/h ÷ 1,000 m/km = 1,231 km/h

5,620 km ÷ 1,231 km/h = 4.6 h

Homework — ADVANCED

USAID Between 1999 and 2000, Neal served a two-year detail with the United States Agency for International Development (USAID) in Washington, D.C. Through USAID, Neal worked with the Office of U.S. Foreign Disaster Assistance to help other nations prevent or cope with natural disasters. In this role, Neal visited Nepal, Colombia, Ecuador, Kazakhstan, and other countries. Have students find out more about how USAID employs Earth scientists in international programs.

Big Idea:
Structure and
Transformation of Matter

A basic understanding of matter is essential to the development of more complex ideas in science. In this unit, students will learn about physical and chemical changes in matter and begin to relate these changes to atoms and molecules. The use of models will help students learn about the structure of matter; however, students must be aware of the limitations of models. Since all matter essentially consists of the same components, looking for patterns in the properties of various substances is a critical step in studying matter.

In this unit, students will look at structure and transformations of matter by studying atoms and molecules. **Properties of Matter** introduces the physical and chemical properties of matter and shows how substances differ from one another. Next, **States of Matter** describes the structure and properties of the different states of matter. **Elements, Compounds and Mixtures** describes how matter is classified based on its structure. In **Introduction to Atoms** students study the internal components of atoms. And in **The Periodic Table** atoms and their categorization based on patterns of internal structure are described.

UNIT 5

TIMELINE

Matter and Atoms

In this unit, you will explore a basic question that people have been pondering for centuries: What is the nature of matter? You will learn how to define the word *matter* and the ways to describe matter and the changes it goes through. You will also learn about the different states of matter and how to classify different arrangements of matter as elements, compounds, or mixtures. This timeline shows some of the events and discoveries that have occurred throughout history as scientists have sought to understand the nature of matter.

1661

Robert Boyle, a chemist in England, determines that elements are substances that cannot be broken down into anything simpler by chemical processes.

1712

Thomas Newcomen invents the first practical steam engine.

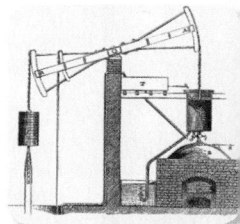

1937

The *Hindenburg* explodes while docking in Lakehurst, New Jersey. To make it lighter than air, the airship was filled with flammable hydrogen gas.

1971

The first commercially available "pocket" calculator is introduced. It has a mass of nearly 1 kg and a price of about $400, hardly the kind of pocket calculator that exists today.

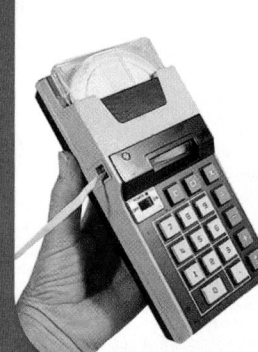

1766

English chemist Henry Cavendish discovers and describes the properties of a highly flammable substance now known as hydrogen gas.

1800

Current from an electric battery is used to separate water into the elements hydrogen and oxygen for the first time.

1920

American women win the right to vote with the ratification of the 19th Amendment to the Constitution.

1950

Silly Putty® is sold in a toy store for the first time. The soft, gooey substance quickly becomes popular because of its strange properties, including the ability to "pick up" the print from a newspaper page.

1957

The space age begins when the Soviet Union launches *Sputnik I*, the first artificial satellite to circle the Earth.

1989

An oil tanker strikes a reef in Prince William Sound, Alaska, and spills nearly 11 million gallons of oil. The floating oil injures or kills thousands of marine mammals and seabirds and damages the Alaskan coastline.

2000

The World's Fair, an international exhibition featuring exhibits and participants from around the world, is held in Hanover, Germany. The theme is "Humankind, Nature, and Technology."

2003

Sally Ride, the first American woman in space, is inducted into the Astronaut Hall of Fame.

Group ACTIViTY
Structure and Transformation of Matter

MATERIALS

drawings or pictures of substances, elements, compounds, and mixtures, one per group and one for class demonstration

Teacher's Note: For these diagrams, make simple circle drawings. Pure elements should be identical circles, compounds should be several identical clusters of circles connected together (similar to those used in figure 4, p. 606), and mixtures should have a mix of non-identical clusters and circles (similar to those used in figure 6, p. 638) Use different colors and structures in the diagrams passed out to groups to represent different substances than the examples.

Identifying Substances Show students a diagram each of an element, compound, and mixture. Describe the properties of the substance shown to the class. Divide the class into groups of four or five students each. Give each group a diagram of an element, compound, or mixture. Ask students to identify what type of substance is shown in their diagram or drawing. Ask students to explain what characteristic(s) lead them to their conclusion.

The Properties of Matter
Chapter Planning Guide

Compression guide:
To shorten instruction because of time limitations, omit the Chapter Lab.

OBJECTIVES	LABS, DEMONSTRATIONS, AND ACTIVITIES	TECHNOLOGY RESOURCES
PACING • 90 min pp. 464–471 **Chapter Opener**	SE **Start-up Activity,** p. 465 GENERAL	OSP **Parent Letter** CD **Student Edition on CD-ROM** CD **Guided Reading Audio CD** TR **Chapter Starter Transparency*** VID **Brain Food Video Quiz**
Section 1 What Is Matter? • Describe the two properties of all matter. • Identify the units used to measure volume and mass. • Compare mass and weight. • Explain the relationship between mass and inertia.	TE **Connection Activity** Music, p. 466 GENERAL TE **Demonstration** Explaining Volume, p. 466 GENERAL SE **Quick Lab** Space Case, p. 467 GENERAL CRF **Datasheet for Quick Lab*** TE **Group Activity,** p. 467 GENERAL TE **Connection Activity** Math, p. 468 GENERAL TE **Demonstration** Relating Matter, Mass, and Volume, p. 468 GENERAL SE **Skills Practice Lab** Volumania!, p. 730 GENERAL CRF **Datasheet for LabBook***	OSP **Lesson Plans** (also in print) TR **Bellringer Transparency*** TR **P3 Differences Between Mass and Weight*** TR *LINK TO LIFE SCIENCE* L6 Math Focus: Surface Area-to-Volume Ratio* CRF **SciLinks Activity*** GENERAL
PACING • 45 min pp. 472–477 **Section 2 Physical Properties** • Identify six examples of physical properties of matter. • Describe how density is used to identify substances. • List six examples of physical changes. • Explain what happens to matter during a physical change.	TE **Demonstration** An Accurate Description, p. 472 GENERAL TE **Connection Activity** Math, p. 474 GENERAL SE **School-to-Home Activity** Twenty Questions, p. 475 GENERAL TE **Activity** Densities of Vinegar and Oil, p. 475 BASIC SE **Skills Practice Lab** Determining Density, p. 732 GENERAL SE **Skills Practice Lab** Layering Liquids, p. 733 GENERAL LB **Inquiry Lab** Whatever Floats Your Boat* ADVANCED SE **Science in Action** Math, Social Studies, and Language Arts Activities, pp. 490–491 GENERAL	OSP **Lesson Plans** (also in print) TR **Bellringer Transparency***
PACING • 90 min pp. 478–483 **Section 3 Chemical Properties** • Describe two examples of chemical properties. • Explain what happens during a chemical change. • Distinguish between physical and chemical changes.	TE **Demonstration** Physical and Chemical Changes, p. 478 ♦ GENERAL TE **Connection Activity** Life Science, p. 479 GENERAL SE **Quick Lab** Changing Change, p. 480 GENERAL TE **Activity** Expense of Desalination, p. 481 ADVANCED TE **Activity** Observing a Chemical Change, p. 481 ♦ GENERAL SE **Quick Lab** Physical or Chemical Change?, p. 482 ♦ GENERAL SE **Skills Practice Lab** White Before Your Eyes, p. 484 GENERAL LB **Whiz-Bang Demonstrations** Curious Cubes* BASIC LB **Whiz-Bang Demonstrations** The Dancing Toothpicks* GENERAL LB **Whiz-Bang Demonstrations** Does 2 + 2 = 4?* GENERAL LB **Long-Term Projects and Research Ideas** And We Have Thales to Thank* ADVANCED	OSP **Lesson Plans** (also in print) TR **Bellringer Transparency*** TR **P4 Examples of Chemical Changes*** SE **Internet Activity,** p. 481 GENERAL VID **Lab Videos for Physical Science**

PACING • 90 min

CHAPTER REVIEW, ASSESSMENT, AND STANDARDIZED TEST PREPARATION

CRF **Vocabulary Activity*** GENERAL
SE **Chapter Review,** pp. 486–487 GENERAL
CRF **Chapter Review*** GENERAL
CRF **Chapter Tests A*** GENERAL, **B*** ADVANCED, **C*** SPECIAL NEEDS
SE **Standardized Test Preparation,** pp. 488–489 GENERAL
CRF **Standardized Test Preparation*** GENERAL
CRF **Performance-Based Assessment*** GENERAL
OSP **Test Generator, Test Item Listing**

Online and Technology Resources

 Holt Online Learning

Visit **go.hrw.com** for access to Holt Online Learning, or enter the keyword **HS7 Home** for a variety of free online resources.

 One-Stop Planner® CD-ROM

This CD-ROM package includes:
• Lab Materials QuickList Software
• Holt Calendar Planner
• Customizable Lesson Plans
• Printable Worksheets
• ExamView® Test Generator
• Interactive Teacher's Edition
• Holt PuzzlePro®
• Holt PowerPoint® Resources

SKILLS DEVELOPMENT RESOURCES	SECTION REVIEW AND ASSESSMENT	CORRELATIONS
SE Pre-Reading Activity, p. 464 `GENERAL` **OSP** Science Puzzlers, Twisters & Teasers `GENERAL`		**National Science Education Standards** SAI 2; PS 1a
CRF Directed Reading A* ■ `BASIC`, B* `SPECIAL NEEDS` **WB** Workbook* Struggling Readers **CRF** Vocabulary and Section Summary* `GENERAL` **SE** Reading Strategy Prediction Guide, p. 466 `GENERAL` **SE** Math Focus Volume of a Rectangular Solid, p. 468 `GENERAL` **TE** Inclusion Strategies, p. 469 **TE** Support for English Language Learners, p. 469 **SE** Math Focus Converting Mass to Weight, p. 470 `GENERAL` **MS** Math Skills for Science The Unit Factor and Dimensional Analysis* `GENERAL` **SS** Science Skills Measuring `GENERAL`	**SE** Reading Checks, pp. 467, 468, 470 `GENERAL` **TE** Reteaching, p. 470 `BASIC` **TE** Quiz, p. 470 `GENERAL` **TE** Alternative Assessment, p. 470 `GENERAL` **SE** Section Review, p. 471 `GENERAL` **CRF** Section Quiz* ■ `GENERAL`	ST 1, 2; SPSP 1, 5; PS 1a, 1c; *LabBook:* PS 1a
CRF Directed Reading A* ■ `BASIC`, B* `SPECIAL NEEDS` **WB** Workbook* Struggling Readers **CRF** Vocabulary and Section Summary* `GENERAL` **SE** Reading Strategy Mnemonics, p. 472 `GENERAL` **TE** Support for English Language Learners, p. 473 **SE** Math Focus Calculating Density, p. 475 `GENERAL` **TE** Inclusion Strategies, p. 476 ♦ **MS** Math Skills for Science Density* `GENERAL` **CRF** Reinforcement Worksheet A Matter of Density* `BASIC`	**SE** Reading Checks, pp. 472, 474, 476 `GENERAL` **TE** Homework, p. 473 `GENERAL` **TE** Reteaching, p. 476 `BASIC` **TE** Quiz, p. 476 `GENERAL` **TE** Alternative Assessment, p. 476 `GENERAL` **SE** Section Review, p. 477 `GENERAL` **CRF** Section Quiz* ■ `GENERAL`	PS 1a, 1b; *LabBook:* PS 1a
CRF Directed Reading A* `BASIC`, B* `SPECIAL NEEDS` **WB** Workbook* Struggling Readers **CRF** Vocabulary & Section Summary* `GENERAL` **SE** Reading Strategy Reading Organizer, p. 478 `GENERAL` **TE** Reading Strategy Prediction Guide, p. 479 `GENERAL` **TE** Support for English Language Learners, p. 481 **CRF** Critical Thinking As a Matter of Fact!* `ADVANCED`	**SE** Reading Checks, pp. 478, 480 `GENERAL` **TE** Reteaching, p. 482 `BASIC` **TE** Quiz, p. 482 `GENERAL` **TE** Alternative Assessment, p. 482 `GENERAL` **SE** Section Review, p. 483 `GENERAL` **CRF** Section Quiz* ■ `GENERAL`	PS 1a; *Chapter Lab:* PS 1a

SCILINKS.
NSTA
www.scilinks.org
Maintained by the **National Science Teachers Association.** See Chapter Enrichment pages that follow for a complete list of topics.

Current Science®
Check out *Current Science* articles and activities by visiting the HRW Web site at **go.hrw.com.** Just type in the keyword **HP5CS02T.**

 Classroom Videos
• **Lab Videos** demonstrate the chapter lab.
• **Brain Food Video Quizzes** help students review the chapter material.

Classroom CD-ROMs
• **Guided Reading Audio CD** (Also in Spanish)
• **Interactive Explorations**
• **Virtual Investigations**
• **Visual Concepts**
• **Science Tutor**

 Holt Lab Generator CD-ROM
Search for any lab by topic, standard, difficulty level, or time. Edit any lab to fit your needs, or create your own labs. Use the Lab Materials QuickList software to customize your lab materials list.

Visual Resources

CHAPTER STARTER TRANSPARENCY

BELLRINGER TRANSPARENCIES

TEACHING TRANSPARENCIES

TEACHING TRANSPARENCIES

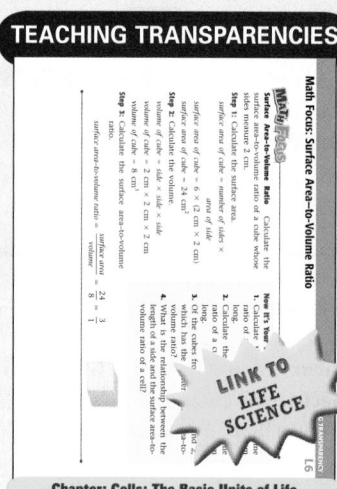

Chapter: Cells: The Basic Units of Life

CONCEPT MAPPING TRANSPARENCY

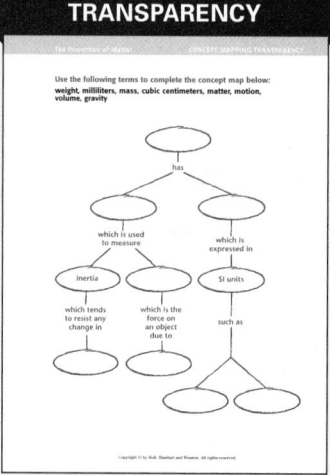

Planning Resources

LESSON PLANS

PARENT LETTER

TEST ITEM LISTING

One-Stop Planner® CD-ROM

This CD-ROM includes all of the resources shown here and the following time-saving tools:

- *Lab Materials QuickList Software*
- *Customizable lesson plans*
- *Holt Calendar Planner*
- *The powerful ExamView® Test Generator*

Meeting Individual Needs

DIRECTED READING A
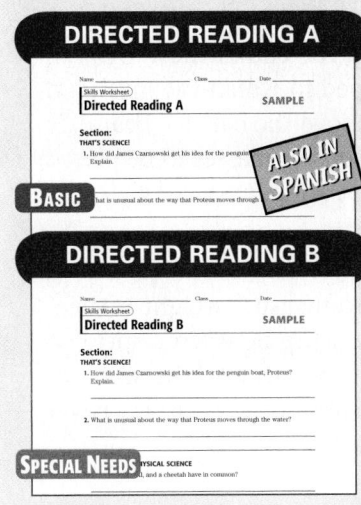
BASIC — ALSO IN SPANISH

DIRECTED READING B
SPECIAL NEEDS

VOCABULARY ACTIVITY
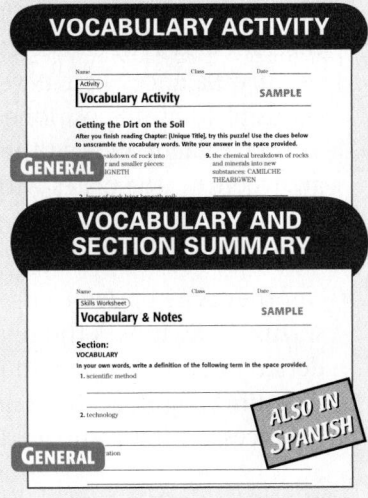
GENERAL

VOCABULARY AND SECTION SUMMARY
GENERAL — ALSO IN SPANISH

REINFORCEMENT
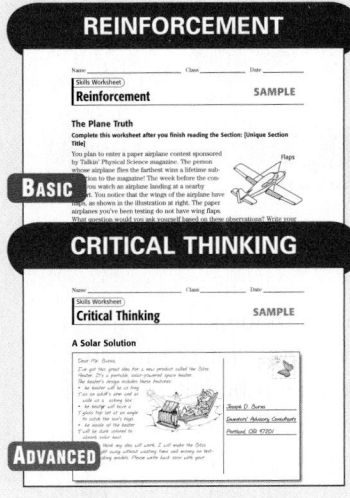
BASIC

CRITICAL THINKING
ADVANCED

SCILINKS ACTIVITY

GENERAL

SCIENCE PUZZLERS, TWISTERS & TEASERS
GENERAL

Labs and Activities

LONG-TERM PROJECTS & RESEARCH IDEAS
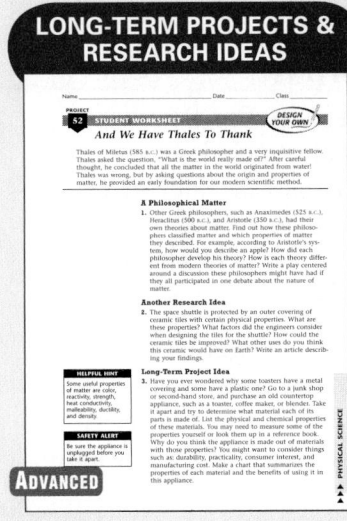
ADVANCED

WHIZ-BANG DEMONSTRATIONS
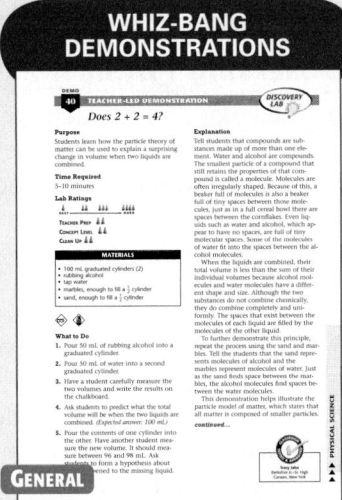
GENERAL

INQUIRY LABS
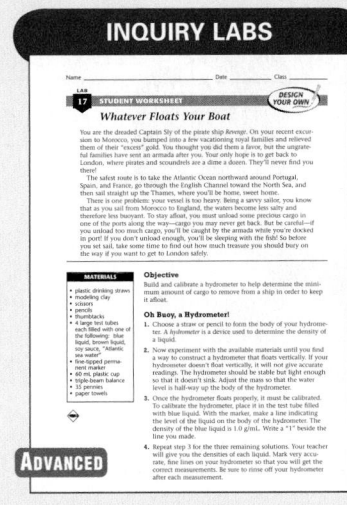
ADVANCED

DATASHEETS FOR QUICK LABS

DATASHEETS FOR CHAPTER LABS

DATASHEETS FOR LABBOOK

Review and Assessments

SECTION QUIZ

GENERAL — ALSO IN SPANISH

SECTION REVIEW
GENERAL — ALSO IN SPANISH

CHAPTER REVIEW
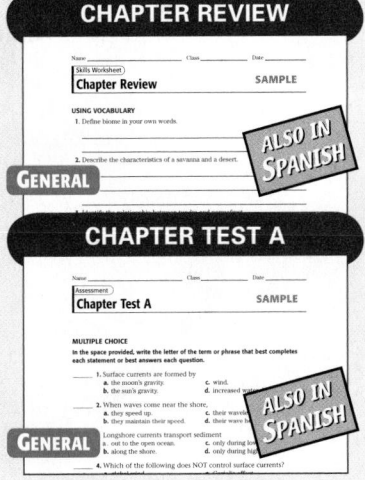
GENERAL — ALSO IN SPANISH

CHAPTER TEST A
GENERAL — ALSO IN SPANISH

CHAPTER TEST B
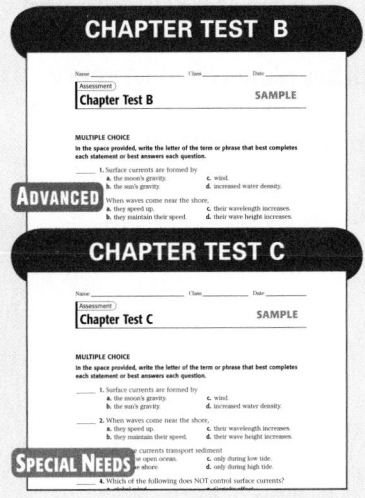
ADVANCED

CHAPTER TEST C
SPECIAL NEEDS

STANDARDIZED TEST PREPARATION
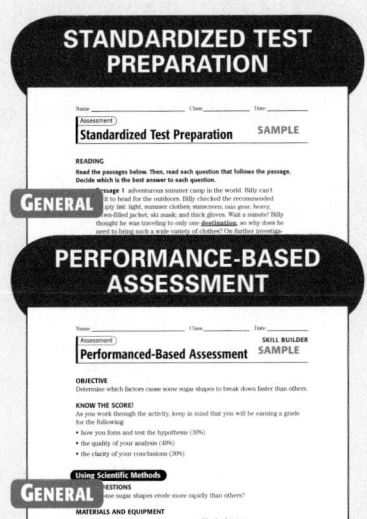
GENERAL

PERFORMANCE-BASED ASSESSMENT
GENERAL

This Chapter Enrichment provides relevant and interesting information to expand and enhance your presentation of the chapter material.

Section 1

What Is Matter?

Measuring Volume

- Body measurements probably provided the basis for many early measurements. The Babylonian liquid measure, the ka, was the volume of a cube with sides of the length of one hand (between 99 and 102 mm). Three hundred ka equaled 3,000 gin or 1 gur. The gur was equal to a volume of approximately 50 L. The basic Roman unit of volume was the sextarius. It had several subdivisions and multiples. The largest multiple, the amphora, was equal to 48 sextarii. The amphora was equal to 25.5 L.

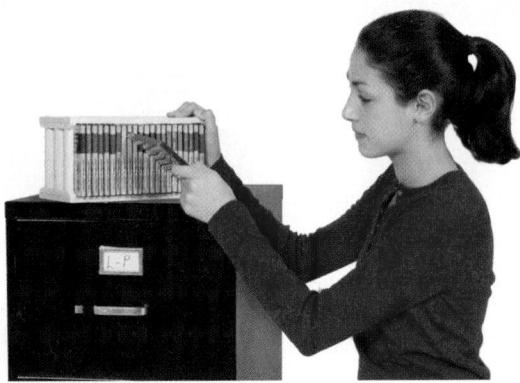

Weight on Other Planets

- The weight of a person on any given planet depends on the attraction between the person and the planet. The more massive the planet is, the greater the gravitational force on the person and the greater the person's weight is. A person who weighs 445 N on Earth would have different weights on other planets. On Mercury, the person would weigh about 164.6 N, on Venus 400.3 N, on Mars 169 N, on Jupiter 1,169.8 N, on Saturn 502.6 N, on Uranus 351.4 N, on Neptune 498.2 N, and on Pluto about 22.2 N.

Is That a Fact!

- ◆ A balance is a freely suspended beam that is balanced by known and unknown masses. Balances have been used for almost 3,000 years.

Knife-Edge Balances

- The modern knife-edge balance was developed during the 16th and 17th centuries. At the end of the 17th century, balances were developed in which the mass and goods plates were positioned above the balance beam. This placement allowed the goods or masses to be placed anywhere on the plates without affecting accuracy.

Spring Scales

- Another type of device used to measure weight is the spring scale. It uses the relationship between a spring's deflection and the weight of the object on the scale to measure weight. Spring scales are not as accurate as balances, which compare a pair of masses.

Section 2

Physical Properties

Observing Physical Properties

- The color and the density of a substance are physical properties. Physical properties also include the temperatures at which a substance changes state at a given pressure. For example, chlorine is a greenish yellow gas with a density of 0.00321 g/cm^3. It can be changed to a liquid by cooling it to $-34.6°C$.

- By comparing the density of King Hieron II's crown with that of a bar of pure gold, the Greek inventor and mathematician Archimedes was able to prove that the crown was not made of pure gold and that a goldsmith had cheated the king.

Physical Changes

- When matter undergoes a physical change, no new substance is formed. The appearance of the matter may change drastically, but most of the identifying properties remain unchanged. Remind students that changes of state, such as those that occur with water, are also physical changes.

- Physical changes are reversible. When sugar dissolves in water, a physical change occurs. This physical change can be reversed by evaporating the water so that the sugar remains chemically unchanged.

Dealing with Density

- Density is often a difficult concept for some middle school students to grasp. Discuss with students the principles that the world is made up of a variety of matter and that all matter has mass and volume.

- Not all matter is the same. Ask students which they would rather carry around all day, a backpack full of feathers or a backpack full of sand. Ask them to explain why. Lead them to the idea that even though the backpack is fixed in size (volume), there is more mass in it when it is full of sand because sand is denser than feathers.

Section 3

Chemical Properties

Observing Chemical Properties

- Chemical properties are related to the specific elements that make up substances. Flammability is a chemical property that describes whether substances will react in the presence of oxygen and burn when exposed to a flame.

- The ability of the element chlorine to react explosively with the element sodium to form sodium chloride (table salt) is a chemical property. When chlorine reacts with sodium, a new substance is formed.

Is That a Fact!

- Before the early 1960s noble gases were thought to be chemically unreactive. But in 1962, Dr. Neil Bartlett, a chemist at the University of British Columbia, was the first scientist to form a new compound by combining platinum, fluorine, and the noble gas xenon. In 2002, chemists at Ohio State University and the University of Virginia created new compounds consisting of uranium bonded to atoms of the noble gases argon, krypton, and xenon.

NSTA
Developed and maintained by the
National Science Teachers Association

SciLinks is maintained by the National Science Teachers Association to provide you and your students with interesting, up-to-date links that will enrich your classroom presentation of the chapter.

Visit www.scilinks.org and enter the SciLinks code for more information about the topic listed.

Topic: What Is Matter?
SciLinks code: HSM1662

Topic: Chemical Changes
SciLinks code: HSM0266

Topic: Describing Matter
SciLinks code: HSM0391

Topic: Building a Better Body
SciLinks code: HSM0196

Topic: Physical Changes
SciLinks code: HSM1142

Overview

In this chapter, students will learn what matter is and how it can be described. They will also learn that different types of matter have unique physical and chemical properties. The physical and chemical changes that matter can undergo are also presented.

Assessing Prior Knowledge

Students should be familiar with the following topics:
• SI units of measurement
• scientific methods

Identifying Misconceptions

Some students may believe that matter is something that they must be able to see and touch. Tell students that invisible gases are also forms of matter that have physical and chemical properties just as solids and liquids do. Invisible gases occupy space, have mass, and undergo physical and chemical changes. Tell students that because the particles of a gas are spaced far apart, the density of the gas is very low. Remind students that even though we cannot usually see gases in the atmosphere, we are able to feel wind and see its effects.

The Properties of Matter

The Big Idea

Matter is described by its properties and may undergo changes.

About the Photo

This giant ice dragon began as a 1,700 kg block of ice! Making the blocks of ice takes six weeks. Then, the ice blocks are stored at −30°C until the sculpting begins. The artist has to work at −10°C to keep the ice from melting. An ice sculptor has to be familiar with the many properties of water, including its melting point.

PRE-READING ACTIVITY

FOLDNOTES **Booklet** Before you read the chapter, create the FoldNote entitled "Booklet" described in the **Study Skills** section of the Appendix. Label each page of the booklet with a main idea from the chapter. As you read the chapter, write what you learn about each main idea on the appropriate page of the booklet.

Standards Correlations

National Science Education Standards

The following codes indicate the National Science Education Standards that correlate to this chapter. The full text of the standards is at the front of the book.

Chapter Opener
SAI 2; PS 1a

Section 1 What Is Matter?
ST 1, 2; SPSP 1, 5; PS 1a, 1c; *LabBook:* PS 1a

Section 2 Physical Properties
PS 1a, 1b; *LabBook:* PS 1a

Section 3 Chemical Properties
PS 1a

Chapter Lab
PS 1a

Chapter Review
PS 1a

Science in Action
ST 1; SPSP 1, 2, 4

START-UP ACTIVITY

MATERIALS

FOR EACH GROUP
Anything that fits in the sack can be used for the object. Objects with interesting shapes, odors, and textures are preferable. Some objects to consider are a rubber ball, a jack, a pink school eraser, a piece of chalk, an orange, and a potato. Almost anything that is not sharp, corrosive, or prone to spoilage will work. Giving each group a different object will add to the mystery.

Answers

4. Students may or may not be able to identify the object, but their observations should demonstrate an attempt to identify various properties of the object, such as mass, shape, odor, and sound when shaken.

START-UP ACTIVITY

Sack Secrets

In this activity, you will test your skills in determining an object's identity based on the object's properties.

Procedure

1. You and two or three of your classmates will receive a **sealed paper sack** containing a **mystery object.** Do not open the sack!

2. For five minutes, make as many observations about the object as you can without opening the sack. You may touch, smell, shake, or listen to the object through the sack. Record your observations.

Analysis

1. At the end of five minutes, discuss your findings with your partners.

2. List the object's properties that you can identify. Make another list of properties that you cannot identify. Make a conclusion about the object's identity.

3. Share your observations, your list of properties, and your conclusion with the class. Then, open the sack.

4. Did you properly identify the object? If so, how? If not, why not? Record your answers.

Chapter Starter Transparency
Use this transparency to help students begin thinking about the many unique properties of matter.

CHAPTER RESOURCES

Technology

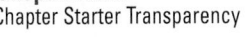 **Transparencies**
• Chapter Starter Transparency   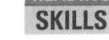 READING SKILLS

 **Student Edition on CD-ROM**

Guided Reading Audio CD
• English or Spanish

Classroom Videos
• Brain Food Video Quiz

Workbooks

 Science Puzzlers, Twisters & Teasers
• The Properties of Matter GENERAL

Focus

Overview

This section explains that matter is anything that has volume and mass. Students will explore how the volumes of solids, liquids, and gases are measured. Students learn the difference between mass and weight and learn how both are measured. Finally, students learn about inertia.

 Bellringer

Ask students to write what they think some of the ingredients or components are for the following items: a loaf of bread, a text-book, and a bicycle. Discuss the reason for the variety of answers students come up with.

Motivate

Demonstration —— GENERAL

Explaining Volume Display common objects such as a rock, a paper clip, a book, a pencil, and a large cardboard box. Point out that the objects are alike because they all take up space. Discuss with students which objects are largest and smallest, and discuss what those terms mean. Then, discuss the connection between "taking up space" and volume. Point out that the amount of space something takes up is its volume.

LS Visual/Logical   English Language Learners

What You Will Learn

- Describe the two properties of all matter.
- Identify the units used to measure volume and mass.
- Compare mass and weight.
- Explain the relationship between mass and inertia.

Vocabulary

matter   mass
volume   weight
meniscus   inertia

READING STRATEGY

Prediction Guide Before reading this section, write the title of each heading in this section. Next, under each heading, write what you think you will learn.

---

matter anything that has mass and takes up space

volume a measure of the size of a body or region in three-dimensional space

---

What Is Matter?

What do you have in common with a toaster, a steaming bowl of soup, or a bright neon sign?

You are probably thinking that this is a trick question. It is hard to imagine that a person has anything in common with a kitchen appliance, hot soup, or a glowing neon sign.

Matter

From a scientific point of view, you have at least one characteristic in common with these things. You, the toaster, the bowl, the soup, the steam, the glass tubing of a neon sign, and the glowing gas are made of matter. But exactly what is matter? **Matter** is anything that has mass and takes up space. It's that simple! Everything in the universe that you can see is made up of some type of matter.

Matter and Volume

All matter takes up space. The amount of space taken up, or occupied, by an object is known as the object's **volume.** Your fingernails, the Statue of Liberty, the continent of Africa, and a cloud have volume. And because these things have volume, they cannot share the same space at the same time. Even the tiniest speck of dust takes up space. Another speck of dust cannot fit into that space without somehow bumping the first speck out of the way. **Figure 1** shows an example of how one object cannot share with another object the same space at the same time. Try the Quick Lab on the next page to see for yourself that matter takes up space.

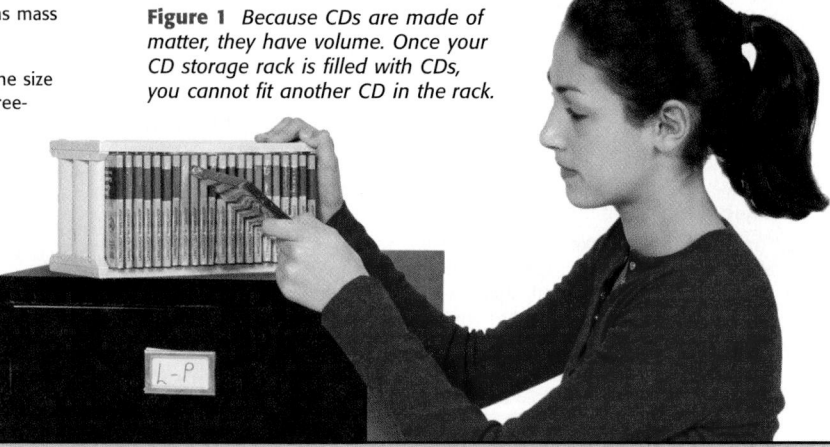

Figure 1 *Because CDs are made of matter, they have volume. Once your CD storage rack is filled with CDs, you cannot fit another CD in the rack.*

CHAPTER RESOURCES

Chapter Resource File

- **Lesson Plan**
- **Directed Reading A** BASIC
- **Directed Reading B** SPECIAL NEEDS

Technology

Transparencies
- Bellringer
- P3 Differences Between Mass and Weight
- **LINK TO LIFE SCIENCE** L6 Math Focus: Surface Area-to-Volume Ratio

Workbooks

Interactive Textbook Struggling Readers

CONNECTION ACTiViTY
Music —————— GENERAL

Water Music Provide students with several identical glass containers. Tell students to add a different amount of water to each container, and then lightly strike each container with a pen to hear the pitch of the sound it makes. Have students measure the volume of water in each container, and ask them to determine the relationship they see between pitch and the volume of water. English Language Learners
LS Auditory/Visual

Space Case

1. Crumple a **piece of paper.** Fit it tightly in the bottom of a **clear plastic cup** so that it won't fall out.

2. Turn the cup upside down. Lower the cup straight down into a **bucket** half-filled with **water.** Be sure that the cup is completely underwater.

3. Lift the cup straight out of the water. Turn the cup upright, and observe the paper. Record your observations.

4. Use the point of a **pencil** to punch a small hole in the bottom of the cup. Repeat steps 2 and 3.

5. How do the results show that air has volume? Explain your answer.

Liquid Volume

Lake Erie, the smallest of the Great Lakes, has a volume of approximately 483 trillion (that's 483,000,000,000,000) liters of water. Can you imagine that much water? Think of a 2-liter bottle of soda. The water in Lake Erie could fill more than 241 trillion 2-liter soda bottles. That's a lot of water! On a smaller scale, a can of soda has a volume of only 355 milliliters, which is about one-third of a liter. You can check the volume of the soda by using a large measuring cup from your kitchen.

Liters (L) and milliliters (mL) are the units used most often to express the volume of liquids. The volume of any amount of liquid, from one raindrop to a can of soda to an entire ocean, can be expressed in these units.

✓Reading Check What are two units used to measure volume? (*See the Appendix for answers to Reading Checks.*)

Measuring the Volume of Liquids

In your science class, you'll probably use a graduated cylinder instead of a measuring cup to measure the volume of liquids. Graduated cylinders are used to measure the liquid volume when accuracy is important. The surface of a liquid in any container, including a measuring cup or a large beaker, is curved. The curve at the surface of a liquid is called a **meniscus** (muh NIS kuhs). To measure the volume of most liquids, such as water, you must look at the bottom of the meniscus, as shown in **Figure 2.** Note that you may not be able to see a meniscus in a large beaker. The meniscus looks flat because the liquid is in a wide container.

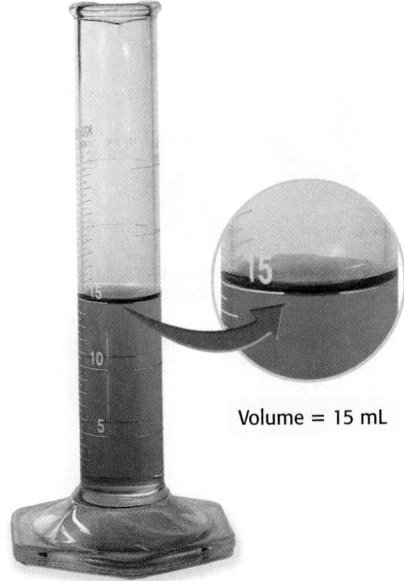

Volume = 15 mL

Figure 2 *To measure volume correctly, read the scale of the lowest part of the meniscus (as shown) at eye level.*

meniscus the curve at a liquid's surface by which one measures the volume of the liquid

Scientists at Odds

Determining Official Standards The official standard kilogram is a cylinder made of platinum-iridium alloy. The mass of the cylinder is supposed to equal the mass of 1 dL^3 of pure water at 4°C. Some scientists believe that this cylinder is imprecise and needs to be changed. In fact, the kilogram is the only SI unit that is based on a single physical standard and that can be destroyed or altered. Some scientists now suggest redefining the kilogram as the mass of an exact number of atoms of a particular element.

Answer to Reading Check

liters (L) and milliliters (mL)

A "Refreshing" Statistic In 1997, Americans consumed an average of 204 L of soft drinks per person. How many cans of soft drinks would that be? Assume that a can holds 355 mL and remember that 1 L = 1,000 mL. (more than 574 cans)

The total volume of soft drinks consumed by Americans in 1997 was approximately 53 billion liters. How many cans of soft drinks would that be? (more than 149 billion cans) **LS Logical**

Answers to Math Focus

1. 1,800 cm³

2. 95,000 cm³, or 0.095 m³

3. 176.08 cm³

Demonstration ——— GENERAL

Relating Matter, Mass, and Volume Display a variety of classroom objects, such as pencils, books, and notebook paper. Ask students which objects contain the largest amount of matter and thus have the greatest mass. Then, ask which objects contain the smallest amount of matter and thus have the smallest mass. Ask them if the objects that have the greatest volume always have the most mass. **English Language Learners** **LS Visual/Logical**

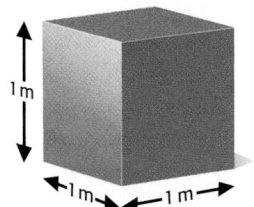

Figure 3 A cubic meter (1 m³) is a cube that has a length, width, and height of 1 m.

Figure 4 The 12-sided object displaced 15 mL of water. Because 1 mL = 1 cm³, the volume of the object is 15 cm³.

Volume of a Regularly Shaped Solid Object

The volume of any solid object is expressed in cubic units. The word *cubic* means "having three dimensions." In science, cubic meters (m³) and cubic centimeters (cm³) are the units most often used to express the volume of solid things. The 3 in these unit symbols shows that three quantities, or dimensions, were multiplied to get the final result. You can see the three dimensions of a cubic meter in **Figure 3.** There are formulas to find the volume of regularly shaped objects. For example, to find the volume of a cube or a rectangular object, multiply the length, width, and height of the object, as shown in the following equation:

$$volume = length \times width \times height$$

Volume of an Irregularly Shaped Solid Object

How do you find the volume of a solid that does not have a regular shape? For example, to find the volume of a 12-sided object, you cannot use the equation given above. But you can measure the volume of a solid object by measuring the volume of water that the object displaces. In **Figure 4,** when a 12-sided object is added to the water in a graduated cylinder, the water level rises. The volume of water displaced by the object is equal to its volume. Because 1 mL is equal to 1 cm³, you can express the volume of the water displaced by the object in cubic centimeters. Although volumes of liquids can be expressed in cubic units, volumes of solids should not be expressed in liters or milliliters.

✔ **Reading Check** Explain how you would measure the volume of an apple.

MATH FOCUS

Volume of a Rectangular Solid What is the volume of a box that has a length of 5 cm, a width of 1 cm, and a height of 2 cm?

Step 1: Write the equation for volume.

$$volume = length \times width \times height$$

Step 2: Replace the variables with the measurements given to you, and solve.

$$volume = 5 \text{ cm} \times 1 \text{ cm} \times 2 \text{ cm} = 10 \text{ cm}^3$$

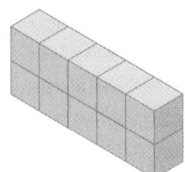

Now It's Your Turn

1. A book has a length of 25 cm, a width of 18 cm, and a height of 4 cm. What is its volume?

2. What is the volume of a suitcase that has a length of 95 cm, a width of 50 cm, and a height of 20 cm?

3. A CD case is 14.2 cm long, 12.4 cm wide, and 1 cm deep. What is its volume?

WEIRD SCIENCE

Mauna Loa, in Hawaii, is the world's most active volcano. The volume of lava that has flowed from the volcano is enough to pave a four-lane highway that reaches around the world 30 times.

Answer to Reading Check

You could measure the volume of an apple by submerging it in a container of water and measuring the volume of the water that the apple displaces.

Matter and Mass

Another characteristic of all matter is mass. **Mass** is the amount of matter in an object. For example, you and a peanut are made of matter. But you are made of more matter than a peanut is, so you have more mass. The mass of an object is the same no matter where in the universe the object is located. The only way to change the mass of an object is to change the amount of matter that makes up the object.

The Difference Between Mass and Weight

The terms *mass* and *weight* are often used as though they mean the same thing, but they don't. **Weight** is a measure of the gravitational (GRAV i TAY shuh nuhl) force exerted on an object. Gravitational force keeps objects on Earth from floating into space. The gravitational force between an object and the Earth depends partly on the object's mass. The more mass an object has, the greater the gravitational force on the object and the greater the object's weight. But an object's weight can change depending on its location in the universe. An object would weigh less on the moon than it does on Earth because the moon has less gravitational force than Earth does. **Figure 5** explains the differences between mass and weight.

mass a measure of the amount of matter in an object

weight a measure of the gravitational force exerted on an object; its value can change with the location of the object in the universe

Figure 5	Differences Between Mass and Weight

Mass	Weight
• Mass is a measure of the amount of matter in an object.	• Weight is a measure of the gravitational force on an object.
• Mass is always constant for an object no matter where the object is located in the universe.	• Weight varies depending on where the object is in relation to the Earth (or any large body in the universe).
• Mass is measured by using a balance (shown below).	• Weight is measured by using a spring scale (shown at right).
• Mass is expressed in kilograms (kg), grams (g), and milligrams (mg).	• Weight is expressed in newtons (N).

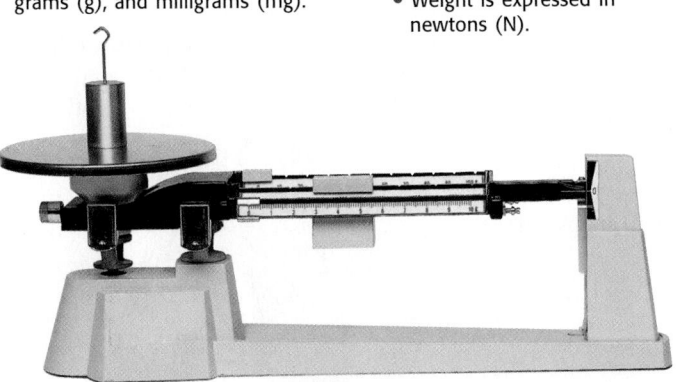

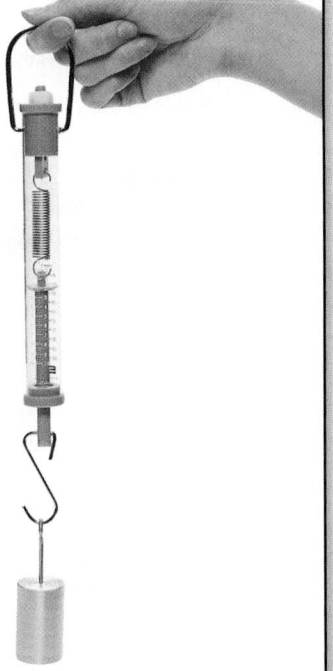

Close

Reteaching — BASIC

Provide students with graduated cylinders, spring scales, and triple-beam balances. Have students take turns explaining step-by-step how to measure the volume and the mass of a given substance. Help them observe the difference between mass and weight using a spring scale. **LS** Logical

Quiz — GENERAL

Ask students whether these questions are true or false.

1. The volume of a marble can be measured with a graduated cylinder. (true)

2. Volumes of solids can be expressed in liters or milliliters. (false)

3. Weight and mass are the same thing. (false)

Alternative Assessment — GENERAL

An Alternate Universe
Have students write a short science-fiction story about a universe in which matter does not behave in the ways described in this section. Ask them to consider what life would be like in this kind of universe. Some examples are a universe where gravity does not exist; a universe where objects repel rather than attract one another; and a universe where inertia becomes greater as mass decreases. **LS** Visual

Figure 6 *The brick and the sponge take up the same amount of space. But the brick has more matter in it, so its mass—and thus its weight—is greater.*

inertia the tendency of an object to resist being moved or, if the object is moving, to resist a change in speed or direction until an outside force acts on the object

Measuring Mass and Weight

The brick and the sponge in **Figure 6** have the same volume. But because the brick has more mass, a greater gravitational force is exerted on the brick than on the sponge. As a result, the brick weighs more than the sponge.

The SI unit of mass is the kilogram (kg), but mass is often expressed in grams (g) and milligrams (mg), too. These units can be used to express the mass of any object in the universe.

Weight is a measure of gravitational force and is expressed in the SI unit of force, the *newton* (N). One newton is about equal to the weight of an object that has a mass of 100 g on Earth. So, if you know the mass of an object, you can calculate the object's weight on Earth. Weight is a good estimate of the mass of an object because, on Earth, gravity doesn't change.

✓ Reading Check What units are often used to measure mass?

Inertia

Imagine kicking a soccer ball that has the mass of a bowling ball. It would be not only painful but also very difficult to get the ball moving in the first place! The reason is inertia (in UHR shuh). **Inertia** is the tendency of an object to resist a change in motion. So, an object at rest will remain at rest until something causes the object to move. Also, a moving object will keep moving at the same speed and in the same direction unless something acts on the object to change its speed or direction.

MATH FOCUS

Converting Mass to Weight A student has a mass of 45,000 g. How much does this student weigh in newtons?

Step 1: Write the information given to you.

45,000 g

Step 2: Write the conversion factor to change grams into newtons.

1 N = 100 g

Step 3: Write the equation so that grams will cancel.

$$45,000 \text{ g} \times \frac{1 \text{ N}}{100 \text{ g}} = 450 \text{ N}$$

Now It's Your Turn

1. What is the weight of a car that has a mass of 1,362,000 g?

2. Your pair of boots has a mass of 850 g. If each boot has exactly the same mass, what is the weight of each boot?

Answers to Math Focus
1. 13,620 N
2. 4.25 N

Answer to Reading Check
kilograms (kg), grams (g), and milligrams (mg)

Mass: The Measure of Inertia

Mass is a measure of inertia. An object that has a large mass is harder to get moving and harder to stop than an object that has less mass. The reason is that the object with the large mass has greater inertia. For example, imagine that you are going to push a grocery cart that has only one potato in it. Pushing the cart is easy because the mass and inertia are small. But suppose the grocery cart is stacked with potatoes, as in **Figure 7.** Now the total mass—and the inertia—of the cart full of potatoes is much greater. It will be harder to get the cart moving. And once the cart is moving, stopping the cart will be harder.

Figure 7 *Because of inertia, moving a cart full of potatoes is more difficult than moving a cart that is empty.*

SECTION Review

Summary

- Two properties of matter are volume and mass.
- Volume is the amount of space taken up by an object.
- The SI unit of volume is the liter (L).
- Mass is the amount of matter in an object.
- The SI unit of mass is the kilogram (kg).
- Weight is a measure of the gravitational force on an object, usually in relation to the Earth.
- Inertia is the tendency of an object to resist being moved or, if the object is moving, to resist a change in speed or direction. The more massive an object is, the greater its inertia.

Using Key Terms

1. Use the following terms in the same sentence: *volume* and *meniscus.*

2. In your own words, write a definition for each of the following terms: *mass, weight,* and *inertia.*

Understanding Key Ideas

3. Which of the following is matter?
   a. dust
   b. the moon
   c. strand of hair
   d. All of the above

4. A graduated cylinder is used to measure
   a. volume.
   b. weight.
   c. mass.
   d. inertia.

5. The volume of a solid is measured in
   a. liters.
   b. grams.
   c. cubic centimeters.
   d. All of the above

6. Mass is measured in
   a. liters.
   b. centimeters.
   c. newtons.
   d. kilograms.

7. Explain the relationship between mass and inertia.

Math Skills

8. A nugget of gold is placed in a graduated cylinder that contains 80 mL of water. The water level rises to 225 mL after the nugget is added to the cylinder. What is the volume of the gold nugget?

9. One newton equals about 100 g on Earth. How many newtons would a football weigh if it had a mass of 400 g?

Critical Thinking

10. **Identifying Relationships** Do objects with large masses always have large weights? Explain.

11. **Applying Concepts** Would an elephant weigh more or less on the moon than it would weigh on Earth? Explain your answer.

SCILINKS®

NSTA
Developed and maintained by the
National Science Teachers Association

For a variety of links related to this chapter, go to www.scilinks.org

Topic: What Is Matter?
SciLinks code: HSM1662

CHAPTER RESOURCES

Chapter Resource File

- Section Quiz **GENERAL**
- Section Review **GENERAL**
- Vocabulary and Section Summary **GENERAL**
- SciLinks Activity **GENERAL**
- Datasheet for Quick Lab

Focus

Overview

This section introduces students to the physical properties of matter. It also explains how density is used to identify different substances. The section concludes with an explanation of what happens to matter during physical changes.

 Bellringer

Have your students write an answer to the following question, "If you were asked to describe an orange to someone who had never seen an orange, what would you tell the person?" Then, have volunteers present their answers to the class.

Motivate

Demonstration — GENERAL

An Accurate Description Display several objects that have differences in color, odor, texture, size, shape, and state. Allow students to examine the objects. Then, ask them to describe each object in terms of its color, odor, texture, size, shape, and state. Ask students why it is important to use a variety of properties when describing objects.
LS Visual/Kinesthetic

What You Will Learn

● Identify six examples of physical properties of matter.
● Describe how density is used to identify substances.
● List six examples of physical changes.
● Explain what happens to matter during a physical change.

Vocabulary

physical property
density
physical change

READING STRATEGY

Mnemonics As you read this section, create a mnemonic device to help you remember examples of physical properties.

Physical Properties

Have you ever played the game 20 Questions? The goal of this game is to figure out what object another person is thinking of by asking 20 yes/no questions or less.

If you can't figure out the object's identity after asking 20 questions, you may not be asking the right kinds of questions. What kinds of questions should you ask? You may want to ask questions about the physical properties of the object. Knowing the properties of an object can help you find out what it is.

Physical Properties

The questions in **Figure 1** help someone gather information about color, odor, mass, and volume. Each piece of information is a physical property of matter. A **physical property** of matter can be observed or measured without changing the matter's identity. For example, you don't have to change an apple's identity to see its color or to measure its volume.

Other physical properties, such as magnetism, the ability to conduct electric current, strength, and flexibility, can help someone identify how to use a substance. For example, think of a scooter with an electric motor. The magnetism produced by the motor is used to convert energy stored in a battery into energy that will turn the wheels.

Reading Check List four physical properties. (*See the Appendix for answers to Reading Checks.*)

Figure 1 *Asking questions about the physical properties of an object can help you identify it.*

Could I hold it in my hand? **Yes.**
Does it have an odor? **Yes.**
Is it safe to eat? **Yes.**
Is it orange? **No.**
Is it yellow? **No.**
Is it red? **Yes.**
Is it an apple? **Yes!**

CHAPTER RESOURCES

Chapter Resource File
- Lesson Plan
- Directed Reading A **BASIC**
- Directed Reading B **SPECIAL NEEDS**

Technology
Transparencies
- Bellringer

Workbooks
Interactive Textbook **Struggling Readers**

Answer to Reading Check

Some physical properties are color, shape, odor, weight, volume, texture, state, and density.

Figure 2 Examples of Physical Properties

Thermal conductivity (KAHN duhk TIV uh tee) is the rate at which a substance transfers heat. Plastic foam is a poor conductor.

State is the physical form in which a substance exists, such as a solid, liquid, or gas. Ice is water in the solid state.

Density is the mass per unit volume of a substance. Lead is very dense, so it makes a good sinker for a fishing line.

Solubility (SAHL yoo BIL uh tee) is the ability of a substance to dissolve in another substance. Flavored drink mix dissolves in water.

Ductility (duhk TIL uh tee) is the ability of a substance to be pulled into a wire. Copper is often used to make wiring because it is ductile.

Malleability (MAL ee uh BIL uh tee) is the ability of a substance to be rolled or pounded into thin sheets. Aluminum can be rolled into sheets to make foil.

Identifying Matter

You use physical properties every day. For example, physical properties help you determine if your socks are clean (odor), if your books will fit into your backpack (volume), or if your shirt matches your pants (color). **Figure 2** gives more examples of physical properties.

Density

Density is a physical property that describes the relationship between mass and volume. **Density** is the amount of matter in a given space, or volume. A golf ball and a table-tennis ball, such as those in **Figure 3**, have similar volumes. But a golf ball has more mass than a table-tennis ball does. So, the golf ball has a greater density.

physical property a characteristic of a substance that does not involve a chemical change, such as density, color, or hardness

density the ratio of the mass of a substance to the volume of the substance

mass = 46 g

mass = 2 g

Figure 3 *A golf ball is denser than a table-tennis ball because the golf ball contains more matter in a similar volume.*

CONNECTION ACTIVITY
Math ─────── GENERAL

Density Calculations Ask students to use the equation for density to solve the following problems.

1. A block of pine wood has a mass of 120 g and a volume of 300 cm³. What is the density of the wood? (0.4 g/cm³) Will this block of pine float in a pool of water? Why or why not? (It will float because it is less dense than water.)

2. A sample of metal has a mass of 3,623 g and a volume of 508 cm³. What metal is it? (zinc)

LS Logical

MISCONCEPTION
**/// ALERT **

Changes in Density
Students may think that the density of a substance remains constant as temperature and pressure change. Remind students that densities such as those listed in the table on the following page are valid only at the given temperature and pressure. As the temperature and pressure conditions change, the density will also change.

Figure 4 *This graduated cylinder contains six liquids. From top to bottom, they are corn oil, water, shampoo, dish detergent, antifreeze, and maple syrup.*

Liquid Layers

What do you think causes the liquid in **Figure 4** to look the way it does? Is it trick photography? No, it is differences in density! There are six liquids in the graduated cylinder. Each liquid has a different density. If the liquids are carefully poured into the cylinder, they can form six layers because of the differences in density. The densest layer is on the bottom. The least dense layer is on top. The order of the layers shows the order of increasing density. Yellow is the least dense, followed by the colorless layer, red, blue, green, and brown (the densest).

Density of Solids

Which would you rather carry around all day: a kilogram of lead or a kilogram of feathers? At first, you might say feathers. But both the feathers and the lead have the same mass, just as the cotton balls and the tomatoes have the same mass, as shown in **Figure 5.** So, the lead would be less awkward to carry around than the feathers would. The feathers are much less dense than the lead. So, it takes a lot of feathers to equal the same mass of lead.

Knowing the density of a substance can also tell you if the substance will float or sink in water. If the density of an object is less than the density of water, the object will float. Likewise, a solid object whose density is greater than the density of water will sink when the object is placed in water.

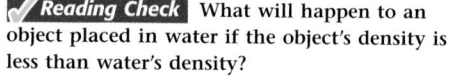
Reading Check What will happen to an object placed in water if the object's density is less than water's density?

Figure 5 *The cotton balls and the tomatoes have the same mass. But cotton is much less dense than the tomatoes.*

Answer to Reading Check
If the object's density is less than the water's density, the object will float.

WEIRD SCIENCE

There was a period of time in history when a person who was suspected of being a witch was tossed into a lake. It was believed that a witch would float, while a person who was not a witch would sink.

Solving for Density

To find an object's density (D), first measure its mass (m) and volume (V). Then, use the equation below.

$$D = \frac{m}{V}$$

Units for density consist of a mass unit divided by a volume unit. Some units for density are g/cm^3, g/mL, kg/m^3, and kg/L. Remember that the volume of a solid is often given in cubic centimeters or cubic meters. So, the density of a solid should be given in units of g/cm^3 or kg/m^3.

Using Density to Identify Substances

Density is a useful physical property for identifying substances. Each substance has a density that differs from the densities of other substances. And the density of a substance is always the same at a given temperature and pressure. Look at **Table 1** to compare the densities of several common substances.

Table 1 Densities of Common Substances*			
Substance	**Density* (g/cm^3)**	**Substance**	**Density* (g/cm^3)**
Helium (gas)	0.0001663	Zinc (solid)	7.13
Oxygen (gas)	0.001331	Silver (solid)	10.50
Water (liquid)	1.00	Lead (solid)	11.35
Pyrite (solid)	5.02	Mercury (liquid)	13.55

*at 20°C and 1.0 atm

Calculating Density What is the density of an object whose mass is 25 g and whose volume is 10 cm^3?

Step 1: Write the equation for density.

$$D = \frac{m}{V}$$

Step 2: Replace m and V with the measurements given in the problem, and solve.

$$D = \frac{25\ g}{10\ cm^3} = 2.5\ g/cm^3$$

The equation for density can also be re-arranged to find mass and volume, as shown.

$m = D \times V$ (Rearrange by multiplying by V.)

$V = \frac{m}{D}$ (Rearrange by dividing by D.)

Now It's Your Turn

1. Find the density of a substance that has a mass of 45 kg and a volume of 43 m^3. (Hint: Make sure your answer's units are units of density.)
2. Suppose you have a lead ball whose mass is 454 g. What is the ball's volume? (Hint: Use **Table 1** above.)
3. What is the mass of a 15 mL sample of mercury?

Close

Figure 6 Examples of Physical Changes

Changing from a solid to a liquid is a physical change. All changes of state are physical changes.

This aluminum can has gone through the physical change of being crushed. The properties of the can are the same.

Reteaching — BASIC

Divide students into groups. Give each group a banana, a lump of clay, and a sheet of paper. Ask groups to brainstorm ways to change the physical properties of each object. Have students demonstrate the changes within their group. Emphasize that each object remains the same substance after a physical change.
LS Logical

Quiz — GENERAL

1. List three physical properties of water. (colorless; liquid at room temperature; density of 1.00 g/mL; odorless; melting point of 0°C; boiling point of 100°C; can dissolve table salt and sugar)

2. You have two objects, both about the size of an orange. Object A has a mass of 1,487 g, and object B has a mass of 878 g. Which object has the greater density? Explain. (object A; Both objects have the same volume, so the object with more mass has the greater density.)

Alternative Assessment — GENERAL

Sugar Cube Activity Give each student a sugar cube to examine. Have them write the physical properties they observe. Then, have them write three things they could do to the sugar cube to cause it to undergo a physical change. **LS** Visual

Physical Changes Do Not Form New Substances

physical change a change of matter from one form to another without a change in chemical properties

A **physical change** is a change that affects one or more physical properties of a substance. Imagine that a piece of silver is pounded and molded into a heart-shaped pendant. This change is a physical one because only the shape of the silver has changed. The piece of silver is still silver. Its properties are the same. **Figure 6** shows more examples of physical changes.

✔ **Reading Check** What is a physical change?

Examples of Physical Changes

Freezing water to make ice cubes and sanding a piece of wood are examples of physical changes. These changes do not change the identities of the substances. Ice is still water. And sawdust is still wood. Another interesting physical change takes place when certain substances dissolve in other substances. For example, when you dissolve sugar in water, the sugar seems to disappear. But if you heat the mixture, the water evaporates. Then, you will see that the sugar is still there. The sugar went through a physical change when it dissolved.

CONNECTION TO Geology

WRITING SKILL **Erosion** Erosion of soil is a physical change. Soil erodes when wind and water move soil from one place to another. Research the history of the Grand Canyon. Write a one-page report about how erosion formed the Grand Canyon.

INCLUSION Strategies

- *Visually Impaired*
- *Developmentally Delayed*
- *Hearing Impaired*

Divide the class into four teams. Give each team one of the sets of items listed below. Within each team, try to keep the four items similar in size.

Team 1: potato, softball, ball of crumpled aluminum foil, and ball of string

Team 2: softball, styrofoam ball, grapefruit, and croquet or bocce ball

Team 3: brick, box, sponge, and piece of 2 × 4 wood board

Team 4: ping-pong ball, fishing weight, piece of charcoal, and small balloon with air in it

Ask teams to arrange the items in their set in order of density, from most dense to least dense. Then, have each team demonstrate their arrangement to the class and explain why they chose the order they did. **LS** Kinesthetic/Interpersonal

Matter and Physical Changes

Physical changes do not change the identity of the matter involved. A stick of butter can be melted and poured over a bowl of popcorn, as shown in **Figure 7.** Although the shape of the butter has changed, the butter is still butter, so a physical change has occurred. In the same way, if you make a figure from a lump of clay, you change the clay's shape and cause a physical change. But the identity of the clay does not change. The properties of the figure are the same as those of the lump of clay.

Figure 7 Melting butter for popcorn involves a physical change.

SECTION Review

Summary

- Physical properties of matter can be observed without changing the identity of the matter.
- Examples of physical properties are conductivity, state, malleability, ductility, solubility, and density.
- Density is the amount of matter in a given space.
- Density is used to identify substances because the density of a substance is always the same at a given pressure and temperature.
- When a substance undergoes a physical change, its identity stays the same.
- Examples of physical changes are freezing, cutting, bending, dissolving, and melting.

Using Key Terms

1. Use each of the following terms in a separate sentence: *physical property* and *physical change.*

Understanding Key Ideas

2. The units of density for a rectangular piece of wood are
   a. grams per milliliter.
   b. cubic centimeters.
   c. kilograms per liter.
   d. grams per cubic centimeter.

3. Explain why a golf ball is heavier than a table-tennis ball even though the balls are the same size.

4. Describe what happens to a substance when it goes through a physical change.

5. Identify six examples of physical properties.

6. List six physical changes that matter can go through.

Math Skills

7. What is the density of an object that has a mass of 350 g and a volume of 95 cm^3? Would this object float in water? Explain.

8. The density of an object is 5 g/cm^3, and the volume of the object is 10 cm^3. What is the mass of the object?

Critical Thinking

9. **Applying Concepts** How can you determine that a coin is not pure silver if you know the mass and volume of the coin?

10. **Identifying Relationships** What physical property do the following substances have in common: water, oil, mercury, and alcohol?

11. **Analyzing Processes** Explain how you would find the density of an unknown liquid if you have all of the laboratory equipment that you need.

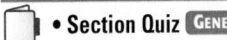

Developed and maintained by the National Science Teachers Association

For a variety of links related to this chapter, go to www.scilinks.org

Topic: Describing Matter; Physical Changes
SciLinks code: HSM0391; HSM1142

Answer to Reading Check

A physical change is a change that occurs to a substance or object and that does not change the identity of the substance.

Focus

Overview

In this section, students will learn about the chemical properties of matter and how chemical properties differ from physical properties. They will also learn that when chemical changes occur to matter, new substances are formed.

 **Bellringer**

Have students look at the picture of the car in **Figure 1.** Then, have them describe where they have seen other examples of rusting. Have volunteers share their descriptions aloud with the class.

Motivate

Demonstration — GENERAL

Physical and Chemical Changes

Show students a match, a candle, and a stick. Ask them what physical changes can be made to each item. Light the match, and melt some of the candle wax. Ask students if the melting wax is a physical or chemical change. Light the candle wick, and point out that the candle wax and the wick are burning and undergoing a chemical change. The wax and the wick do not remain the same substances they were before they were burned.

LS Visual/Logical

What You Will Learn

● Describe two examples of chemical properties.
● Explain what happens during a chemical change.
● Distinguish between physical and chemical changes.

Vocabulary
chemical property
chemical change

READING STRATEGY

Reading Organizer As you read this section, create an outline of the section. Use the headings from the section in your outline.

Chemical Properties

How would you describe a piece of wood before and after it is burned? Has it changed color? Does it have the same texture? The original piece of wood changed, and physical properties alone can't describe what happened to it.

Chemical Properties

Physical properties are not the only properties that describe matter. **Chemical properties** describe matter based on its ability to change into new matter that has different properties. For example, when wood is burned, ash and smoke are created. These new substances have very different properties than the original piece of wood had. Wood has the chemical property of flammability. *Flammability* is the ability of a substance to burn. Ash and smoke cannot burn, so they have the chemical property of nonflammability.

Another chemical property is reactivity. *Reactivity* is the ability of two or more substances to combine and form one or more new substances. The photo of the old car in **Figure 1** illustrates reactivity and nonreactivity.

✓ **Reading Check** What does the term *reactivity* mean? (*See the Appendix for answers to Reading Checks.*)

| Figure 1 | Reactivity with Oxygen |

The iron used in this old car has the chemical property of **reactivity with oxygen**. When iron is exposed to oxygen, it rusts.

The bumper on this car still looks new because it is coated with chromium. Chromium has the chemical property of **nonreactivity with oxygen**.

CHAPTER RESOURCES

Chapter Resource File

- **Lesson Plan**
- **Directed Reading A** BASIC
- **Directed Reading B** SPECIAL NEEDS

Technology

Transparencies
- Bellringer
- P4 Examples of Chemical Changes

Workbooks

Interactive Textbook Struggling Readers

Answer to Reading Check

Reactivity describes the ability of two or more substances to combine and form one or more new substances.

Figure 2 Physical Versus Chemical Properties

Physical property	Chemical property

Shape Bending an iron nail will change its shape.	**Reactivity with Oxygen** An iron nail can react with oxygen in the air to form iron oxide, or rust.
State Rubbing alcohol is a clear liquid at room temperature.	**Flammability** Rubbing alcohol is able to burn easily.

Comparing Physical and Chemical Properties

How do you tell a physical property from a chemical property? You can observe physical properties without changing the identity of the substance. For example, you can find the density and hardness of wood without changing anything about the wood.

Chemical properties, however, aren't as easy to observe. For example, you can see that wood is flammable only while it is burning. And you can observe that gold is nonflammable only when it won't burn. But a substance always has chemical properties. A piece of wood is flammable even when it's not burning. **Figure 2** shows examples of physical and chemical properties.

Characteristic Properties

The properties that are most useful in identifying a substance are *characteristic properties*. These properties are always the same no matter what size the sample is. Characteristic properties can be physical properties, such as density and solubility, as well as chemical properties, such as flammability and reactivity. Scientists rely on characteristic properties to identify and classify substances.

CONNECTION TO Social Studies

WRITING SKILL **The Right Stuff** When choosing materials to use in manufacturing, you must make sure their properties are suitable for their uses. For example, false teeth can be made from acrylic plastic, porcelain, or gold. According to legend, George Washington wore false teeth made of wood. Do research and find what Washington's false teeth were really made of. In your **science journal,** write a paragraph about what you have learned. Include information about the advantages of the materials used in modern false teeth.

chemical property a property of matter that describes a substance's ability to participate in chemical reactions

CONNECTION to Real World——— GENERAL

Rustproofing Rustproofing is one way to help protect cars from rust. The process involves treating the car's underside and panels—such as the doors, the trunk, and the hood—with sealants. The sealants penetrate all the seams, cracks, and holes to keep out air and moisture, which can increase the rate at which rust forms.

Is That a Fact!

Galvanized steel is steel that is coated with zinc to prevent rusting. It is used in buckets and nails. And steel plated with tin was used in food cans and containers. Today, aluminum cans have replaced most steel cans.

MATERIALS

FOR EACH GROUP
- paper towel
- pennies, shiny (2 or 3)
- pie plate
- vinegar

Safety Caution: Have students wear goggles, gloves, and an apron for this activity.

Answer

5. The shiny copper surface became coated with a dull, green substance. The color change and change in the appearance of the coin indicated that a chemical change took place.

Changing Change

1. Place a folded **paper towel** in a small **pie plate.**
2. Pour **vinegar** into the pie plate until the entire paper towel is damp.
3. Place three shiny **pennies** on top of the paper towel.
4. Put the pie plate in a safe place. Wait 24 hours.
5. Describe and explain the change that took place.

Chemical Changes and New Substances

A **chemical change** happens when one or more substances are changed into new substances that have new and different properties. Chemical changes and chemical properties are not the same. Chemical properties of a substance describe which chemical changes will occur and which chemical changes will not occur. But chemical changes are the process by which substances actually change into new substances. You can learn about the chemical properties of a substance by looking at the chemical changes that take place.

You see chemical changes more often than you may think. For example, a chemical reaction happens every time a battery is used. Chemicals failing to react results in a dead battery. Chemical changes also take place within your body when the food you eat is digested. **Figure 3** describes other examples of chemical changes.

✓ **Reading Check** How does a chemical change differ from a chemical property?

Figure 3 Examples of Chemical Changes

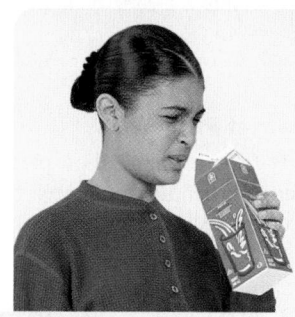

Soured milk smells bad because bacteria have formed new substances in the milk.

Effervescent tablets bubble when the citric acid and baking soda in them react in water.

The **hot gas** formed when hydrogen and oxygen join to make water helps blast the space shuttle into orbit.

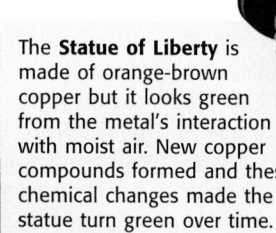

The **Statue of Liberty** is made of orange-brown copper but it looks green from the metal's interaction with moist air. New copper compounds formed and these chemical changes made the statue turn green over time.

Answer to Reading Check

Chemical changes occur when one or more substances are changed into entirely new substances with different properties. A chemical property of a substance determines whether a chemical change will occur.

Figure 4 *Each of the original ingredients has different physical and chemical properties than the final product, the cake, does!*

What Happens During a Chemical Change?

A fun way to see what happens during chemical changes is to bake a cake. You combine eggs, flour, sugar, and other ingredients, as shown in **Figure 4.** When you bake the batter, you end up with something completely different. The heat of the oven and the interaction of the ingredients cause a chemical change. The result is a cake that has properties that differ from the properties of the ingredients.

Signs of Chemical Changes

Look back at **Figure 3.** In each picture, at least one sign indicates a chemical change. Other signs that indicate a chemical change include a change in color or odor, production of heat, fizzing and foaming, and sound or light being given off.

In the cake example, you would smell the cake as it baked. You would also see the batter rise and begin to brown. When you cut the finished cake, you would see the air pockets made by gas bubbles that formed in the batter. These signs show that chemical changes have happened.

Matter and Chemical Changes

Chemical changes change the identity of the matter involved. So, most of the chemical changes that occur in your daily life, such as a cake baking, would be hard to reverse. Imagine trying to unbake a cake. However, some chemical changes can be reversed by more chemical changes. For example, the water formed in the space shuttle's rockets could be split into hydrogen and oxygen by using an electric current.

chemical change a change that occurs when one or more substances change into entirely new substances with different properties

INTERNET ACTIVITY

For another activity related to this chapter, go to **go.hrw.com** and type in keyword **HP5MATW.**

Close

Reteaching — BASIC

Chemical Changes Show students the following items: a raw egg that you have cracked open and placed in a beaker, a sheet of paper, and an iron nail. Ask students to think of ways that chemical changes could occur to each item. Have them write down the changes that they think of, along with a description of how the item is different after the change occurred. **LS** Logical

Quiz — GENERAL

1. Give an example of a chemical change that occurs during the preparation of a meal. (Sample answer: burning of gas in an oven or a stove burner)

2. List three clues that a chemical change might be taking place. (Possible answers include color change; bubbling and fizzing or foaming.)

Alternative Assessment — GENERAL

Another Sugar Cube Activity
Give each student a sugar cube. Have them write two things they could do to the sugar cube to cause it to undergo a chemical change, and have them write the chemical properties these changes represent. Students may use their book to find examples. **LS** Visual

Figure 5 Physical and Chemical Changes

Change in Texture Grinding baking soda into a fine, powdery substance is a physical change.

Reactivity with Vinegar Gas bubbles are produced when vinegar is poured into baking soda.

CONNECTION TO Environmental Science

Acid Rain When fossil fuels are burned, a chemical change takes place. Sulfur from fossil fuels and oxygen from the air combine to produce sulfur dioxide, a gas. When sulfur dioxide enters the atmosphere, it undergoes another chemical change by interacting with water and oxygen. Research this chemical reaction. Make a poster describing the reaction and showing how the final product affects the environment. **ACTiViTY**

Physical Versus Chemical Changes

The most important question to ask when trying to decide if a physical or chemical change has happened is, Did the composition change? The *composition* of an object is the type of matter that makes up the object and the way that the matter is arranged in the object. **Figure 5** shows both a physical and a chemical change.

A Change in Composition

Physical changes do not change the composition of a substance. For example, water is made of two hydrogen atoms and one oxygen atom. Whether water is a solid, liquid, or gas, its composition is the same. But chemical changes do alter the composition of a substance. For example, through a process called *electrolysis*, water is broken down into hydrogen and oxygen gases. The composition of water has changed, so you know that a chemical change has taken place.

Physical or Chemical Change?

1. Watch as your teacher places a burning **wooden stick** into a **test tube.** Record your observations.

2. Place a mixture of **powdered sulfur** and **iron filings** on a **sheet of paper.** Place a **bar magnet** underneath the paper, and try to separate the iron from the sulfur.

3. Drop an **effervescent tablet** into a **beaker of water.** Record your observations.

4. Identify whether each change is a physical change or a chemical change. Explain your answers.

MATERIALS

FOR EACH GROUP
- effervescent tablet
- magnet, bar
- paper, sheet of plain white
- sulfur and iron filings, mixture of powdered
- water, beaker of

Safety Caution: Remind students to wash their hands before leaving the laboratory.

Answer

4. The burning wooden stick is undergoing a chemical change because the wood is being changed into a new substance with different properties. Separating the iron filings and the powdered sulfur is a physical change because the components of the mixture did not change into new substances. The effervescent tablet undergoes a chemical change when it is dropped in the water because it forms a new substance with different properties.

Reversing Changes

Can physical and chemical changes be reversed? Many physical changes are easily reversed. They do not change the composition of a substance. For example, if an ice cube melts, you could freeze the liquid water to make another ice cube. But composition does change in a chemical change. So, most chemical changes are not easily reversed. Look at **Figure 6.** The chemical changes that happen when a firework explodes would be almost impossible to reverse, even if you collected all of the materials made in the chemical changes.

Figure 6 *This display of fireworks represents many chemical changes happening at the same time.*

Another example is the flammability of firewood to form ash, smoke, and heat energy. Flammability tells you whether or not a substance will burn.

SECTION Review

Summary

- Chemical properties describe a substance based on its ability to change into a new substance that has different properties.
- Chemical properties can be observed only when a chemical change might happen.
- Examples of chemical properties are flammability and reactivity.
- New substances form as a result of a chemical change.
- Unlike a chemical change, a physical change does not alter the identity of a substance.

Using Key Terms

1. In your own words, write a definition for each of the following terms: *chemical property* and *chemical change.*

Understanding Key Ideas

2. Rusting is an example of a
   a. physical property.
   b. physical change.
   c. chemical property.
   d. chemical change.

3. Which of the following is a characteristic property?
   a. density
   b. chemical reactivity
   c. solubility in water
   d. All of the above

4. Write two examples of chemical properties and explain what they are.

5. The Statue of Liberty was originally a copper color. After being exposed to the air, she turned a greenish color. What kind of change happened? Explain your answer.

6. Explain how to tell the difference between a physical and a chemical property.

Math Skills

7. The temperature of an acid solution is 25°C. A strip of magnesium is added, and the temperature rises 2°C each minute for the first 3 min. After another 5 min, the temperature has risen two more degrees. What is the final temperature?

Critical Thinking

8. **Making Comparisons** Describe the difference between physical and chemical changes in terms of what happens to the matter involved in each kind of change.

9. **Applying Concepts** Identify two physical properties and two chemical properties of a bag of microwave popcorn before popping and after.

For a variety of links related to this chapter, go to www.scilinks.org

Topic: Chemical Changes
SciLinks code: HSM0266

Answers to Section Review

1. Sample answer: A chemical property determines whether or not a substance will react with another substance. A chemical change is a change to a substance that causes it to form a new substance or substances with different properties.

2. d

3. d

4. One example of a chemical property is the reactivity of iron with oxygen to form rust. Reactivity tells you whether or not a substance will react with another substance and form new products with new properties.

5. Sample answer: A chemical change occurred. The copper in the Statue of Liberty combined with oxygen in the air and formed new copper compounds with different properties.

6. Sample answer: A physical property can be observed or determined without changing the identity of the substance, but a chemical property can be observed only while the chemical change is occurring.

7. The final temperature is 33°C.

8. Sample answer: When matter undergoes a physical change, its shape or form changes, but its identity remains the same. When matter undergoes a chemical change, its identity and properties change.

9. Sample answer: Physical properties of a bag of uncooked popcorn include an almost flat bag and a bag that is cool to the touch. Chemical properties of a bag of uncooked popcorn include a flammable bag and popcorn kernels that pop and change into fluffy popcorn when heated. Physical properties of a cooked bag of popcorn include a bag that is hot, and has increased in volume. Chemical properties of the bag of cooked popcorn include inability of popcorn to change back into uncooked kernels and flammability of the fluffy popcorn.

CHAPTER RESOURCES

Chapter Resource File

- **Section Quiz** GENERAL
- **Section Review** GENERAL
- **Vocabulary and Section Summary** GENERAL
- **Datasheet for Quick Lab**
- **Critical Thinking** ADVANCED

White Before Your Eyes

Teacher's Notes

Time Required
One or two 45-minute class periods

Lab Ratings

EASY ———————————→ HARD

Teacher Prep
Student Set-Up
Concept Level
Clean Up

MATERIALS
Use an iodine solution that contains no more than 1.0% iodine in water. You may wish to use a 24-well spot plate or test tubes. A small test tube taped to the bottle makes a great holder for a dropper or pipette and decreases the chance of contamination. A drinking straw cut in half at an angle works well as a spatula; the pointed end is a great scoop, and its large size makes it easy to handle.

Safety Caution
When iodine is being used, be certain that a functioning eyewash is available. Caution students that iodine can stain skin and clothes. Students should wash their face and hands when finished. Clean up any spills immediately to avoid slips and falls.

Skills Practice Lab

White Before Your Eyes

You have learned how to describe matter based on its physical and chemical properties. You have also learned some signs that can help you determine whether a change in matter is a physical change or a chemical change. In this lab, you'll use what you have learned to describe four substances based on their properties and the changes that they undergo.

OBJECTIVES

Describe the physical properties of four substances.

Identify physical and chemical changes.

Classify four substances by their chemical properties.

MATERIALS

- baking powder
- baking soda
- carton, egg, plastic-foam
- cornstarch
- eyedroppers (3)
- iodine solution
- spatulas (4)
- stirring rod
- sugar
- vinegar
- water

SAFETY

Procedure

1. Copy Table 1 and Table 2 shown on the next page. Be sure to leave plenty of room in each box to write down your observations.

2. Using a spatula, place a small amount of baking powder into three cups of your egg carton. Use just enough baking powder to cover the bottom of each cup. Record your observations about the baking powder's appearance, such as color and texture, in the "Unmixed" column of Table 1.

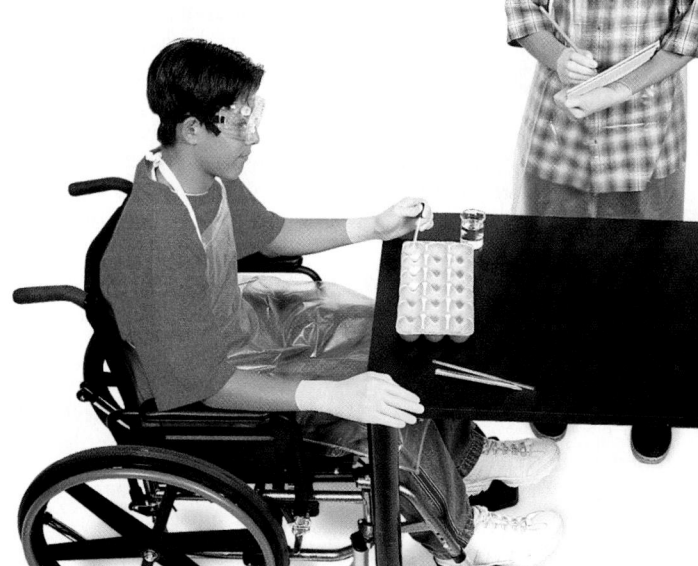

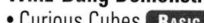

Analyze the Results
1. All four substances are white solids, and are granular or powdery.
2. See the table at the bottom of the page.

③ Use an eyedropper to add 60 drops of water to the baking powder in the first cup. Stir with the stirring rod. Record your observations in Table 1 in the column labeled "Mixed with water." Clean your stirring rod.

④ Use a clean dropper to add 20 drops of vinegar to the second cup of baking powder. Stir. Record your observations in Table 1 in the column labeled "Mixed with vinegar." Clean your stirring rod.

⑤ Use a clean dropper to add five drops of iodine solution to the third cup of baking powder. Stir. Record your observations in Table 1 in the column labeled "Mixed with iodine solution." Clean your stirring rod. **Caution:** Be careful when using iodine. Iodine will stain your skin and clothes.

⑥ Repeat steps 2–5 for each of the other substances (baking soda, cornstarch, and sugar). Use a clean spatula for each substance.

Analyze the Results

① **Examining Data** What physical properties do all four substances share?

② **Analyzing Data** In Table 2, write the type of change—physical or chemical—that you observed for each substance. State the property that the change demonstrates.

Draw Conclusions

③ **Evaluating Results** Classify the four substances by the chemical property of reactivity. For example, which substances are reactive with vinegar (acid)?

Table 1 Observations

Substance	Unmixed	Mixed with water	Mixed with vinegar	Mixed with iodine solution
Baking powder				
Baking soda				
Cornstarch				
Sugar				

DO NOT WRITE IN BOOK

Table 2 Changes and Properties

Substance	Mixed with water		Mixed with vinegar		Mixed with iodine solution	
	Change	Property	Change	Property	Change	Property
Baking powder						
Baking soda						
Cornstarch						
Sugar						

DO NOT WRITE IN BOOK

Lab Notes

Remind students that vinegar is an acid and that they should use caution when handling it. Although **Table 2** shows that baking powder reacts with water, baking powder is not reactive with water. Baking powder can contain baking soda (a base), a weak acid, and a starch. The baking soda and the weak acid in baking powder will react with each other when the baking powder is dissolved in water. This reaction produces the bubbles that students observe in this experiment.

Disposal Information

Dispose of any unreacted iodine solution by combining all student solutions. Decolorize if necessary by adding 1.0 M $Na_2S_2O_3$ while stirring until the dark color disappears. Dilute the mixture with at least 10 times its volume of water before discarding. If local wastewater regulations permit, the diluted solution may be poured down the drain.

2.

Substance	Mixed with water		Mixed (vinegar)		Mixed (iodine solution)	
	Change	Property	Change	Property	Change	Property
Baking powder	chemical	reactivity with water	chemical	reactivity with acid	physical	solubility
Baking soda	physical	solubility	chemical	reactivity with acid	physical	solubility
Cornstarch	physical	solubility	physical	solubility	chemical	reactivity with iodine
Sugar	physical	solubility	physical	solubility	physical	solubility

Holt Lab Generator CD-ROM

Search for any lab by topic, standard, difficulty level, or time. Edit any lab to fit your needs, or create your own labs. Use the Lab Materials QuickList software to customize your lab materials list.

CLASSROOM TESTED & APPROVED

Joseph Price
H. M. Browne
Junior High
Washington, D.C.

Assignment Guide

SECTION	QUESTIONS
1	2–3, 6–9, 12, 15, 17, 20–21
2	11, 13, 16, 22, 24
3	5, 19, 25
1 and 2	4
2 and 3	1, 10, 14, 23
1, 2, and 3	18

ANSWERS

Using Key Terms

1. Sample answers: Physical properties of a substance include color, shape, and density. Flammability is a chemical property of matter. Sugar dissolving in water is an example of a physical change. When a piece of iron metal rusts it is undergoing a chemical change.

2. Sample answer: Mass is the amount of matter in an object and is always constant. Weight is a measure of the gravitational force, and weight will change, depending on the object's distance from the Earth or other celestial bodies.

3. Sample answer: Mass is a measure of inertia. The more mass an object has, the more inertia it has.

4. Sample answer: Volume is the amount of space occupied by an object, and density is the amount of mass in a given volume.

USING KEY TERMS

1 Use each of the following terms in a separate sentence: *physical property, chemical property, physical change,* and *chemical change.*

For each pair of terms, explain how the meanings of the terms differ.

2 *mass* and *weight*

3 *inertia* and *mass*

4 *volume* and *density*

UNDERSTANDING KEY IDEAS

Multiple Choice

5 Which of the following properties is NOT a chemical property?
a. reactivity with oxygen
b. malleability
c. flammability
d. reactivity with acid

6 The volume of a liquid can be expressed in all of the following units EXCEPT
a. grams.
b. liters.
c. milliliters.
d. cubic centimeters.

7 The SI unit for the mass of a substance is the
a. gram.
b. liter.
c. milliliter.
d. kilogram.

8 The best way to measure the volume of an irregularly shaped solid is to
a. use a ruler to measure the length of each side of the object.
b. weigh the solid on a balance.
c. use the water displacement method.
d. use a spring scale.

9 Which of the following statements about weight is true?
a. Weight is a measure of the gravitational force on an object.
b. Weight varies depending on where the object is located in relation to the Earth.
c. Weight is measured by using a spring scale.
d. All of the above

10 Which of the following statements does NOT describe a physical property of a piece of chalk?
a. Chalk is a solid.
b. Chalk can be broken into pieces.
c. Chalk is white.
d. Chalk will bubble in vinegar.

11 Which of the following statements about density is true?
a. Density is expressed in grams.
b. Density is mass per unit volume.
c. Density is expressed in milliliters.
d. Density is a chemical property.

Short Answer

12 In one or two sentences, explain how the process of measuring the volume of a liquid differs from the process of measuring the volume of a solid.

Understanding Key Ideas

5. b
6. a
7. d
8. c
9. d
10. d
11. b

12. Sample answer: The volume of a liquid can be measured by pouring it into a graduated cylinder and reading the scale at the bottom of the meniscus. The volume of a rectangular solid can be determined by multiplying the object's length, width, and height. The volume of an irregular solid can be measured by measuring water displacement.

13 What is the formula for calculating density?

14 List three characteristic properties of matter.

Math Skills

15 What is the volume of a book that has a width of 10 cm, a length that is 2 times the width, and a height that is half the width? Remember to express your answer in cubic units.

16 A jar contains 30 mL of glycerin (whose mass is 37.8 g) and 60 mL of corn syrup (whose mass is 82.8 g). Which liquid is on top? Show your work, and explain your answer.

CRITICAL THINKING

17 **Concept Mapping** Use the following terms to create a concept map: *matter, mass, inertia, volume, milliliters, cubic centimeters, weight,* and *gravity.*

18 **Applying Concepts** Develop a set of questions that would be useful when identifying an unknown substance. The substance may be a liquid, a gas, or a solid.

19 **Analyzing Processes** You are making breakfast for your friend Filbert. When you take the scrambled eggs to the table, he asks, "Would you please poach these eggs instead?" What scientific reason do you give Filbert for not changing his eggs?

20 **Identifying Relationships** You look out your bedroom window and see your new neighbor moving in. Your neighbor bends over to pick up a small cardboard box, but he cannot lift it. What can you conclude about the item(s) in the box? Use the terms *mass* and *inertia* to explain how you came to your conclusion.

21 **Analyzing Ideas** You may sometimes hear on the radio or on TV that astronauts are weightless in space. Explain why this statement is not true.

INTERPRETING GRAPHICS

Use the photograph below to answer the questions that follow.

22 List three physical properties of this aluminum can.

23 When this can was crushed, did it undergo a physical change or a chemical change?

24 How does the density of the metal in the crushed can compare with the density of the metal before the can was crushed?

25 Can you tell what the chemical properties of the can are by looking at the picture? Explain your answer.

Critical Thinking

17. 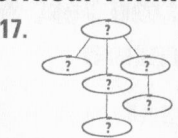 An answer to this exercise can be found at the end of this book.

18. Answers may vary. Questions may include the following topics: size, shape, color, weight, density, state, and odor.

19. Sample answer: Cooking eggs involves a chemical change. I cannot change the cooked eggs back to raw eggs in order to poach them.

20. Sample answer: If my neighbor has trouble lifting a small box, I would conclude that the box's inertia is large. The box resists my neighbor's attempt to move it. A large inertia means that the mass of the contents of the box is large.

21. Sample answer: An astronaut weighs less in space than on Earth because of the astronaut's increased distance from Earth. But, an astronaut is not weightless because there are still gravitational forces between the astronaut and all other objects in the universe.

Interpreting Graphics

22. Sample answer: crushed shape, somewhat shiny, and metallic

23. a physical change

24. The density before and after the change is the same because density is a characteristic property of matter.

25. No, chemical properties cannot be determined simply by looking at a substance. Chemical properties can only be observed when a chemical change might occur.

13. *density = mass/volume*

14. Characteristic properties include density, solubility, reactivity with acid, melting point, and boiling point.

15. *volume = length × width × height =* 20 cm × 10 cm × 5 cm = 1,000 cm³

16. Density of glycerin = 37.8 g/30 mL = 1.26 g/mL. Density of corn syrup = 82.8 g/60 mL = 1.38 g/mL. The glycerin will be on top because it is less dense than corn syrup.

CHAPTER RESOURCES

Chapter Resource File

- Chapter Review **GENERAL**
- Chapter Test A **GENERAL**
- Chapter Test B **ADVANCED**
- Chapter Test C **SPECIAL NEEDS**
- Vocabulary Activity **GENERAL**

Workbooks

Study Guide
- Study Guide is also available in Spanish.

Standardized Test Preparation

Standardized Test Preparation

Teacher's Notes

To provide practice under more realistic conditions, give students 20 minutes to answer all of the questions in this Standardized Test Preparation.

Answer Key

Question	Answer
1	D
2	C
3	B
4	A
5	A
6	D
7	B
8	A
9	D
10	D
11	*
12	*

*See Test Doctor.

Multiple Choice

Use the chart below to answer questions 1 and 2.

Substance	State*	Density* (g/cm³)	Color
Helium	Gas	0.0001663	Colorless
Iron pyrite	Solid	5.02	Metallic Yellow
Mercury	Liquid	13.55	Metallic Gray
Oxygen	Gas	0.001331	Colorless
Gold	Solid	19.32	Metallic Yellow
Water	Liquid	1.00	Colorless

* at 20° C and 1.0 atm

1. **Look at the chart above. Which is true of mercury?**

   A. It is the densest substance listed.

   B. Its density is less than the density of water.

   C. It is a solid at 20°C and 1.0 atm.

   D. It is the densest liquid listed in the chart.

2. **A substance has a mass of 10 g and a volume of 10 cm³. Based on the chart above, what is the substance?**

   A. mercury

   B. oxygen

   C. water

   D. helium

3. **When oxygen in the air reacts with iron, iron oxide forms. Which statement is correct?**

   A. This is a physical change.

   B. This is a chemical change.

   C. Iron and iron oxide have the same properties.

   D. Oxygen and iron have similar properties.

4. **Which of the following statements regarding chemical properties is true?**

   A. They can be observed when the identity of a substance changes.

   B. They can always be observed without changing the identity of a substance.

   C. They are easier to observe than physical properties.

   D. They are the properties that are most useful in identifying a substance.

5. **A chemical change takes place during a laboratory investigation of the properties of magnesium. Which of the following might have been observed?**

   A. Magnesium burns in the presence of oxygen.

   B. Magnesium melts at 649°C.

   C. Magnesium becomes malleable when heated.

   D. Magnesium conducts an electric current.

6. **Which is a chemical change?**

   A. Clear water turns red after a dye is added.

   B. Ice melts.

   C. Salt dissolves in water.

   D. Milk sours.

7. **Which physical property could be used to classify oxygen, propane, and hydrogen as being similar to one another?**

   A. flammability

   B. state

   C. reactivity

   D. malleability

 TEST DOCTOR

Question 1 A: Gold is the densest substance listed. B: Mercury has a higher density than water. C: Mercury is a liquid at normal room temperature. D: Correct.

Question 2 A, B, D: 10 g/10 cm³ = 1 g/cm³. C: Correct.

Question 3 A: When iron and oxygen react, they combine chemically. The formation of iron oxide is an example of a chemical change, not a physical change. B: Correct. C: Elements and compounds have characteristic properties. Some of their

properties may be similar, but the substances will never share all of the same properties. Compounds do not have the same set of characteristic properties as the elements that compose them. D: Oxygen and iron are different elements, and because iron is a metal and oxygen is a nonmetal, these two elements do not have similar properties.

Question 4 A: Correct. B: Chemical properties can be observed when a substance reacts with another substance and changes identity. Physical properties can always be observed without changing the identity of a substance. C: Chemical properties cannot always be observed when a substance

Use the diagram below to answer questions 8 and 9.

Before   **After**

8. An irregular object's volume is determined by displacement of water, as shown above. What is the volume of the object?

  A. 15 mL

  B. 40 mL

  C. 55 mL

  D. 95 mL

9. A lab assistant finds the mass of the submerged object shown above to be 13.07 g. What can you conclude about the measurement?

  A. The measurement cannot be used to determine density without also knowing the force of gravity.

  B. The measurement is accurate because the resulting density is 0.87 g/mL, a common density of irregular objects.

  C. The measurement can be used to determine density because the object is not completely submerged in the water.

  D. The measurement is likely inaccurate because the resulting density, 0.87 g/mL, is less than that of water, 1.0 g/mL, which means it would float.

10. Max drops one effervescent tablet into a beaker of water and places a second tablet on the lab table. He observes bubbles of gas form on the surface of the tablet. The bubbles rise and break on the surface of the water. After several minutes, no more bubbles form and no tablet is visible in the water. The tablet on the lab table is unchanged. What conclusion should Max draw from his observations?

  A. The solid tablet changes directly into a gas through a physical change.

  B. The tablet breaks down when exposed to light and forms a gas through a chemical change.

  C. The tablet causes dissolved gases in the water to be released through a physical change.

  D. The tablet interacts with water to form a gas through a chemical change.

Open Response

11. Two ball-shaped objects are made of white plastic. Both balls have the same diameter and are completely solid. One ball has twice the mass of the other. What can you conclude about the material of each ball?

12. What chemical properties would be important to consider when choosing a material to make a safe baking dish?

Question 9 A: The force of gravity need only be taken into consideration with measurements of weight. Mass measurements are independent of gravity. B: Whether or not the density is common does not confirm the accuracy of this measurement. Its density does not match the visual information, which is that it sinks in water and thus should have a density greater than 1 g/mL. C: The object is in fact completely submerged, so a density calculation would take into account its full mass. D: Correct.

Question 10 A: The unchanged tablet on the lab table is evidence that the tablet did not change directly into a gas through a physical change. B: The unchanged tablet on the lab table is evidence that the tablet did not break down in the presence of light to form a gas through a chemical change. C: The disappearance of the tablet, combined with the formation of a gas, is evidence of a chemical change. D: Correct.

Question 11 Full-credit answers should include the following points:

  • If the two plastic balls have the same volume but one has twice the mass of the other, then the plastics that form them must have different densities.

  • If they have different densities, then they are different materials.

Question 12 Full-credit answers should include the following points:

  • Because the object will be regularly used at very high temperatures, it is important that it not burn.

  • Because the object must be washed between uses, it should not react with water.

  • Because the object will hold food products, it should not be very reactive.

changes identity; they are more difficult to observe than physical properties. D: Physical properties can be just as useful in identifying a substance.

Question 5 A: Correct. B: Melting is a physical change. C, D: Malleability and conductivity are both physical properties.

Question 6 A: Because the red food color does not alter the identity of the water, this is an example of a physical change. B: Changes of state are physical changes because the identity of the substance (water) does not change. C: Because the identities of the two substances (water and salt) do not change, dissolving is an example of a physical change. D: Correct.

Question 7 A: Flammability is a chemical property. B: Correct. C: Reactivity is a chemical property. D: Malleability is a physical property, but all of the substances are gases, so their malleability is not an observable property.

Question 8 A: Correct. B: This is the volume of water before the object is submerged. C: This is the volume of water after the object is submerged, so it includes both the volume of the object and the volume of the original water. D: This is the volume that results when you add rather than subtract the before and after volumes.

Scientific Debate

ACTIVITY ———— GENERAL

Tell students to imagine that the local landfill is becoming full at a faster rate than community leaders originally thought it would be filled. Have students develop a presentation or brochure that they could use to convince people in their community to recycle paper and plastic bags as one way to reduce the amount of waste that is put into the landfill. **LS Interpersonal**

Science, Technology, and Society

Discussion ———— GENERAL

Tell students that the nitrogen implanted in the surface of the titanium bones is actually nitrogen ions that have been blasted into the surface of the titanium by a particle accelerator. The ions bond to the titanium atoms, and the surface becomes harder and smoother. The nitrogen-titanium bond also attracts and holds a thin film of joint fluid that lubricates moving parts of the joint and increases the durability of the bone replacement. Surgeons and scientists are also making replacement bones that use a titanium-cobalt alloy or a cobalt-chrome alloy and a plastic socket.

Science in Action

Scientific Debate

Paper or Plastic?

What do you choose at the grocery store: paper or plastic bags? Plastic bags are waterproof and take up less space. You can use them to line waste cans and to pack lunches. Some places will recycle plastic bags. But making 1 ton of plastic bags uses 11 barrels of oil, which can't be replaced, and produces polluting chemicals. On the other hand, making 1 ton of paper bags destroys 13 to 17 trees, which take years to replace. Paper bags, too, can be reused for lining waste cans and wrapping packages. Recycling paper pollutes less than recycling plastic does. What is the answer? Maybe we should reuse both!

Language Arts ACTIVITY

WRITING SKILL There are advantages and disadvantages of each kind of bag. Write a one-page essay defending your position on this subject. Support your opinion with facts.

Science, Technology, and Society

Building a Better Body

Have you ever broken a bone? If so, you probably wore a cast while the bone healed. But what happens if the bone is too damaged to heal? Sometimes, a false bone made from titanium can replace the damaged bone. Titanium appears to be a great bone-replacement material. It is a lightweight but strong metal. It can attach to existing bone and resists chemical changes. But, friction can wear away titanium bones. Research has found that implanting a form of nitrogen on the titanium makes the metal last longer.

Social Studies ACTIVITY

Do some research on the history of bone-replacement therapy. Make a poster that shows a timeline of events leading up to current technology.

Answer to Language Arts Activity

Students' essays should include strong supporting material for their viewpoint. Some aspects of this debate that would be important to consider in support of their viewpoint include environmental, economic, and practical use issues.

Answers to Social Studies Activity

Students' posters should include information on the history of prosthetics, which dates back to about 500 BCE. References to current technological advancements should include information about other materials being used in bone and joint replacement.

Mimi So

Gemologist and Jewelry Designer A typical day for gemologist and jewelry designer Mimi So involves deciding what materials to work with. When she chooses a gemstone for a piece of jewelry, she must consider the size, hardness, color, grade, and cut of the stone. When choosing a metal to use as a setting for a stone, she must look at the hardness, melting point, color, and malleability of the metal. She needs to choose a metal that not only looks good with a particular stone but also has physical properties that will work with that stone. For example, Mimi So says emeralds are soft and fragile. A platinum setting would be too hard and could damage the emerald. So, emeralds are usually set in a softer metal, such as 18-karat gold.

The chemical properties of stones must also be considered. Heating can burn or discolor some gemstones. Mimi So says, "If you are using pearls in a design that requires heating the metal, the pearl is not a stone, so you cannot heat the pearl, because it would destroy the pearl."

Math ACTIVITY

Pure gold is 24-karat (24K). Gold that contains 18 parts gold and 6 parts other metals is 18-karat gold. The percentage of gold in 18K gold is found by dividing the amount of gold by the total amount of the material and then multiplying by 100%. For example, (18 parts gold)/(24 parts total) equals $0.75 \times 100\% = 75\%$ gold. Find the percentage of gold in 10K and 14K gold.

go.hrw.com

To learn more about these Science in Action topics, visit go.hrw.com and type in the keyword **HP5MATF**.

Current Science

Check out Current Science® articles related to this chapter by visiting go.hrw.com. Just type in the keyword **HP5CS02**.

Careers

Background

At a young age, Mimi So helped out in her parent's jewelry store by greeting customers and arranging displays. She eventually went to school and earned a Bachelor of Fine Arts degree in design, and her Gemologist Certification. Though certification is not required in jewelry making, she says, "It is important to have a better knowledge of stones and a technical point of view to understand certain processes for working with diamonds." However, she adds that some people go to gemology school to get the technical background and come to find that they are disappointed with their real-world jobs. Mimi So advises young people to explore gemology before going to school. "I think it's really important that if they are interested in this industry or they're not certain, that they go out there and get a part-time job or a weekend job so that they can truly find out which area that they would actually enjoy doing."

Answers to Math Activity

The percentage of gold in 10K gold is 41.67%.
The percentage of gold in 14K gold is 58.33%.

Compression guide:
To shorten instruction because of time limitations, omit Section 2.

OBJECTIVES	LABS, DEMONSTRATIONS, AND ACTIVITIES	TECHNOLOGY RESOURCES
PACING • 90 min pp. 492–497 **Chapter Opener**	**SE Start-up Activity,** p. 493 `GENERAL`	**OSP Parent Letter** ■ **CD Student Edition on CD-ROM** **CD Guided Reading Audio CD** ■ **TR Chapter Starter Transparency*** **VID Brain Food Video Quiz**
Section 1 Three States of Matter • Describe the properties shared by particles of all matter. • Describe three states of matter. • Explain the differences between the states of matter.	**TE Demonstration** Particles in the Air, p. 494 ◆ `GENERAL` **SE Connection to Physics** Is Glass a Liquid?, p. 495 `GENERAL` **SE Skills Practice Lab** Full of Hot Air!, p. 734 `GENERAL` **CRF Datasheet for LabBook*** **LB Whiz-Bang Demonstrations** Demonstration with a CRUNCH! `BASIC`	**OSP Lesson Plans** (also in print) **TR Bellringer Transparency*** **TR P5 Models of a Solid, a Liquid, and a Gas*** **CRF SciLinks Activity*** `GENERAL`
PACING • 45 min pp. 498–501 **Section 2 Behavior of Gases** • Describe three factors that affect how gases behave. • Predict how a change in pressure or temperature will affect the volume of a gas.	**TE Demonstration** A Mini-explosion, p. 498 ◆ `BASIC` **TE Activity** Changes in Gas Volume, p. 499 `GENERAL` **SE Science in Action** Math, Social Studies, and Language Arts Activities, pp. 86–87 `GENERAL`	**OSP Lesson Plans** (also in print) **TR Bellringer Transparency*** **TR P6 Boyle's Law; Charles's Law*** **SE Internet Activity,** p. 499 `GENERAL`
PACING • 90 min pp. 502–507 **Section 3 Changes of State** • Describe how energy is involved in changes of state. • Describe what happens during melting and freezing. • Compare evaporation and condensation. • Explain what happens during sublimation. • Identify the two changes that can happen when a substance loses or gains energy.	**TE Demonstration** Do Solids Move?, p. 502 ◆ `GENERAL` **SE Connection to Language Arts** Cooking at High Altitudes, p. 505 `GENERAL` **SE Quick Lab** Boiling Water is Cool, p. 506 `GENERAL` **CRF Datasheet for Quick Lab*** **SE Skills Practice Lab** A Hot and Cool Lab, p. 508 `GENERAL` **CRF Datasheet for Chapter Lab*** **SE Skills Practice Lab** Can Crusher, p. 735 `GENERAL` **CRF Datasheet for LabBook*** **LB Labs You Can Eat** How Cold Is Ice-Cream Cold?* `GENERAL` **LB Long-Term Projects & Research Ideas** Episode IV: Sam and His Elephants Get That Sinking Feeling* `ADVANCED` **LB Calculator-Based Lab** Keeping Things Cool `ADVANCED`	**OSP Lesson Plans** (also in print) **TR Bellringer Transparency*** **TR P7 Changing the State of Water*** **VID Lab Videos for Physical Science** **TR** *LINK TO EARTH SCIENCE* E39 The Water Cycle

PACING • 90 min

CHAPTER REVIEW, ASSESSMENT, AND STANDARDIZED TEST PREPARATION

CRF Vocabulary Activity* `GENERAL`
SE Chapter Review, pp. 510–511 `GENERAL`
CRF Chapter Review* ■ `GENERAL`
CRF Chapter Tests A* ■ `GENERAL`, **B*** `ADVANCED`, **C*** `SPECIAL NEEDS`
SE Standardized Test Preparation, pp. 512–513 `GENERAL`
CRF Standardized Test Preparation* `GENERAL`
CRF Performance-Based Assessment* `GENERAL`
OSP Test Generator, Test Item Listing

Online and Technology Resources

  Holt Online Learning

Visit **go.hrw.com** for access to Holt Online Learning, or enter the keyword **HS7 Home** for a variety of free online resources.

 **One-Stop Planner® CD-ROM**

This CD-ROM package includes:
• Lab Materials QuickList Software
• Holt Calendar Planner
• Customizable Lesson Plans
• Printable Worksheets
• ExamView® Test Generator
• Interactive Teacher's Edition
• Holt PuzzlePro®
• Holt PowerPoint® Resources

SKILLS DEVELOPMENT RESOURCES	SECTION REVIEW AND ASSESSMENT	CORRELATIONS
SE Pre-Reading Activity, p. 492 `GENERAL` **OSP** Science Puzzlers, Twisters & Teasers* `GENERAL`		**National Science Education Standards** UCP 2, 3; SAI 1; PS 1a, 3a
CRF Directed Reading A* ■ `BASIC`, B* `SPECIAL NEEDS` **WB** Workbook* `Struggling Readers` **CRF** Vocabulary and Section Summary* ■ `GENERAL` **SE** Reading Strategy Paired Summarizing, p. 494 `GENERAL` **TE** Inclusion Strategies, p. 494 **TE** Support for English Language Learners, p. 495	**SE** Reading Checks, pp. 495, 496 `GENERAL` **TE** Reteaching, p. 496 `BASIC` **TE** Quiz, p. 496 `GENERAL` **TE** Alternative Assessment, p. 496 `BASIC` **SE** Section Review,* p. 497 ■ `GENERAL` **CRF** Section Quiz* ■ `GENERAL`	UCP 1, 2; PS 1a; *LabBook:* UCP 2, 3; SAI 1, 2; PS 1a
CRF Directed Reading A* ■ `BASIC`, B* `SPECIAL NEEDS` **WB** Workbook* `Struggling Readers` **CRF** Vocabulary and Section Summary* ■ `GENERAL` **SE** Reading Strategy Reading Organizer, p. 498 `GENERAL` **TE** Reading Strategy Prediction Guide, p. 499 `GENERAL` **TE** Support for English Language Learners, p. 499 **CRF** Reinforcement Worksheet Make a Statement* `BASIC` **MS** Math Skills for Science Checking Division with Multiplication* `GENERAL`	**SE** Reading Checks, pp. 499, 500 `GENERAL` **TE** Reteaching, p. 500 `BASIC` **TE** Quiz, p. 500 `GENERAL` **TE** Alternative Assessment, p. 500 `GENERAL` **TE** Homework, p. 500 `ADVANCED` **SE** Section Review,* p. 501 ■ `GENERAL` **CRF** Section Quiz* ■ `GENERAL`	UCP 1, 2, 3; PS 1a
CRF Directed Reading A* ■ `BASIC`, B* `SPECIAL NEEDS` **WB** Workbook* `Struggling Readers` **CRF** Vocabulary and Section Summary* ■ `GENERAL` **SE** Reading Strategy Mnemonics, p. 502 `GENERAL` **TE** Support for English Language Learners, p. 503 **TE** Reading Strategy Prediction Guide, p. 504 `GENERAL` **CRF** Critical Thinking What a State!* `ADVANCED`	**SE** Reading Checks, pp. 502, 504, 506 `GENERAL` **TE** Homework, p. 504 `GENERAL` **TE** Homework, p. 505 `GENERAL` **TE** Reteaching, p. 506 `BASIC` **TE** Quiz, p. 506 `GENERAL` **TE** Alternative Assessment, p. 506 `GENERAL` **SE** Section Review,* p. 507 ■ `GENERAL` **CRF** Section Quiz* ■ `GENERAL`	UCP 3; SAI 1; PS 1a, 3a; *Chapter Lab:* UCP 2, 3; SAI 1, 2; PS 1a, 3a; LabBook: SAI 1

www.scilinks.org
Maintained by the **National Science Teachers Association.** See Chapter Enrichment pages that follow for a complete list of topics.

Current Science®

Check out *Current Science* articles and activities by visiting the HRW Web site at **go.hrw.com.** Just type in the keyword **HP5CS03T.**

 Classroom Videos
- **Lab Videos** demonstrate the chapter lab.
- **Brain Food Video Quizzes** help students review the chapter material.

 Classroom CD-ROMs
- **Guided Reading Audio CD** (Also in Spanish)
- **Interactive Explorations**
- **Virtual Investigations**
- **Visual Concepts**
- **Science Tutor**

 Holt Lab Generator CD-ROM

Search for any lab by topic, standard, difficulty level, or time. Edit any lab to fit your needs, or create your own labs. Use the Lab Materials QuickList software to customize your lab materials list.

Visual Resources

CHAPTER STARTER TRANSPARENCY

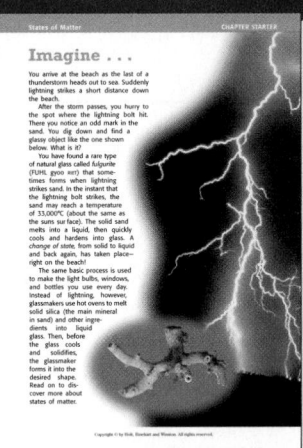

Imagine . . .

You arrive at the beach as the last of a thunderstorm heads out to sea. Suddenly lightning strikes a short distance down the beach.

After the storm passes, you hurry to the spot where the lightning bolt hit. There you notice an odd mark in the sand. You dig down and find a glassy object like the one shown below. What is it?

You have found a rare type of natural glass called fulgurite (FUHL gyoo ryt) that sometimes forms when lightning strikes sand. In the instant that the lightning bolt strikes, the sand may reach a temperature of 33,000°C (about the same as the suns surface). The solid sand melts into a liquid, then quickly cools and hardens into glass. A change of state, from solid to liquid and back again, has taken place—right on the beach!

The same basic process is used to make the light bulbs, windows, and bottles you use every day. Instead of lightning, however, glassmakers use hot ovens to melt solid silica (the main mineral in sand) and other ingredients into liquid glass. Then, before the glass cools and solidifies, the glassmaker forms it into the desired shape. Read on to discover more about states of matter.

BELLRINGER TRANSPARENCIES

Section: Three States of Matter
In the kitchen, you might find three different forms of water. What are these three forms of water, and where exactly in the kitchen would you find them? Further, how do you use water in each of these forms?

Record your answers in your **science journal**.

Section: Behavior of Gases
What gas is used to fill balloons that will float in the air? How does a hot-air balloon float if it is filled only with air and not helium?

Record your answers in your **science journal**.

TEACHING TRANSPARENCIES

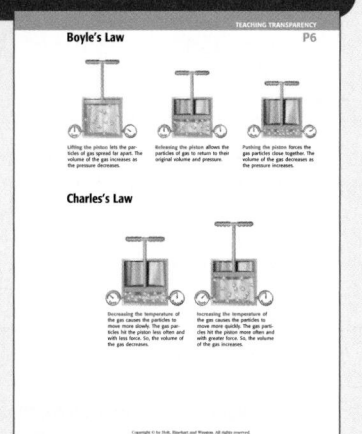

Models of a Solid, a Liquid, and a Gas

Boyle's Law

Charles's Law

TEACHING TRANSPARENCIES

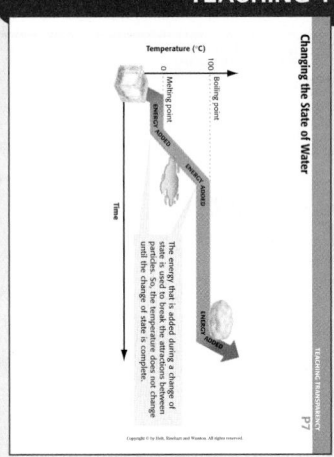

Changing the State of Water

The Water Cycle

LINK TO EARTH SCIENCE

Chapter: Understanding Weather

CONCEPT MAPPING TRANSPARENCY

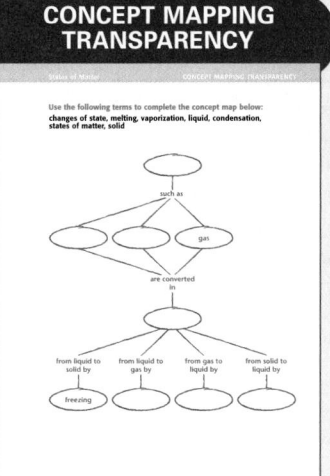

Use the following terms to complete the concept map below: **changes of state, melting, vaporization, liquid, condensation, states of matter, solid**

Planning Resources

LESSON PLANS

Lesson Plan   SAMPLE

Section: Waves

Pacing
Regular Schedule: with lab(s)2 days   without lab(s)2 days
Block Schedule: with lab(s)1 1/2 days without lab(s)1 day

Objectives
1. Relate the seven properties of life to a living organism.
2. Describe seven themes that can help you to organize what you learn about biology.
3. Identify the tiny structures that make up all living organisms.
4. Differentiate between reproduction and heredity and between metabolism and homeostasis.

National Science Education Standards Covered
LSInter6:Cells have particular structures that underlie their functions.
LSMat1:Most cell functions involve chemical reactions.
LSBeh1:Cells store and use information to guide their functions.
UCP1:Cell functions are regulated.
SI1: Cells can differentiate and form complete multicellular organisms.
PS1: Species evolve over time.
ESS1: The great diversity of organisms is the result of more than 3.5 billion years of evolution.
ESS2: Natural selection and its evolutionary consequences provide a scientific explanation for the fossil record of ancient life forms as well as for the striking molecular similarities observed among the diverse species of living organisms.
ST1: The millions of different species of plants, animals, and microorganisms that live on Earth today are related by descent from common ancestors.
ST2: The energy for life primarily comes from the sun.
SPSP1: The complexity and organization of organisms accommodates the need for obtaining, transforming, transporting, releasing, and eliminating the matter and energy used to sustain the organism.
SPSP6: As matter and energy flows through different levels of organization of living systems—cells, organs, communities—and between living systems and the physical environment, the recombined matter and energy used in different ways.
HNS1: Organisms have behavioral responses to internal and external stimuli.

PARENT LETTER

Dear Parent,   SAMPLE

Your son's or daughter's science class will soon begin exploring the chapter entitled "The World of Physical Science." In this chapter, students will learn about how the scientific method applies to the world of physical science and the role of physical science in the world. By the end of the chapter, students should demonstrate a clear understanding of the chapter's main ideas and be able to discuss the following topics:

1. physical science as the study of energy and matter (Section 1)
2. the role of physical science in the world around them (Section 1)
3. careers that rely on physical science (Section 1)
4. the steps used in the scientific method (Section 2)
5. examples of technology (Section 2)
6. how the scientific method is used to answer questions and solve problems (Section 2)
7. how our knowledge of science changes over time (Section 2)
8. how models represent real objects or systems (Section 3)
9. examples of different ways models are used in science (Section 3)
10. the importance of the International System of Units (Section 4)
11. the appropriate units to use for particular measurements (Section 4)
12. how area and density are derived quantities (Section 4)

Questions to Ask Along the Way
You can help your son or daughter learn about these topics by asking interesting questions such as the following:
• What are some surprising careers that use physical science?
• What is a characteristic of a good hypothesis?
• When is it a good idea to use a model?
• Why do Americans measure things in terms of inches and yards and meters?

ALSO IN SPANISH

TEST ITEM LISTING

TEST ITEM LISTING
The World of Science   SAMPLE

MULTIPLE CHOICE
1. A limitation of models is that
   a. they are large enough to see.
   b. they do not act exactly like the things that they model.
   c. they are smaller than the things that they model.
   d. they model unfamiliar things.
   Answer: B   Difficulty: 1   Section: 3   Objective: 2
2. The length 10 m is equal to
   a. 100 cm.   c. 10,000 mm.
   b. 1,000 cm.   d. Both (b) and (c)
   Answer: B   Difficulty: 1   Section: 3   Objective: 2
3. To be valid, a hypothesis must be
   a. testable.   c. made into a law.
   b. supported by evidence.   d. Both (a) and (b)
   Answer: D   Difficulty: 1   Section: 3   Objective: 2: 1
4. The statement "Sheila has a stain on her shirt" is an example of a(n)
   a. law.   c. observation.
   b. hypothesis.   d. prediction.
   Answer: B   Difficulty: 1   Section: 3   Objective: 2
5. A hypothesis is often developed out of
   a. observations.   c. laws.
   b. experiments.   d. Both (a) and (b)
   Answer: D   Difficulty: 1   Section: 3   Objective: 2
6. How many milliliters are in 3.5 kL?
   a. 3,500 mL   c. 3,500, 000 mL
   b. 0.0035 mL   d. 35,000 mL
   Answer: B   Difficulty: 1   Section: 3   Objective: 2
7. A map of Seattle is an example of a
   a. law.   c. model.
   b. theory.   d. unit.
   Answer: B   Difficulty: 1   Section: 3   Objective: 2
8. A lab has the safety icons shown below. These icons mean that you should wear
   a. only safety goggles.   c. safety goggles and a lab apron.
   b. safety goggles and a lab apron. d. safety goggles, a lab apron, and gloves.
   Answer: B   Difficulty: 1   Section: 3   Objective: 2
9. The law of conservation of mass says the lot of mass before a chemical change is
   a. more than the total mass after the change.
   b. less than the total mass after the change.
   c. the same as the total mass after the change.
   d. not the same as the total mass after the change.
   Answer: B   Difficulty: 1   Section: 3   Objective: 2
10. In which of the following areas might you find a geochemist at work?
    a. studying the chemistry of rocks   c. studying the atmosphere
    b. studying forestry   d. studying the atmosphere
    Answer: B   Difficulty: 1   Section: 3   Objective: 2

One-Stop Planner® CD-ROM

This CD-ROM includes all of the resources shown here and the following time-saving tools:

• *Lab Materials QuickList Software*
• *Customizable lesson plans*
• *Holt Calendar Planner*
• *The powerful ExamView® Test Generator*

Meeting Individual Needs

DIRECTED READING A
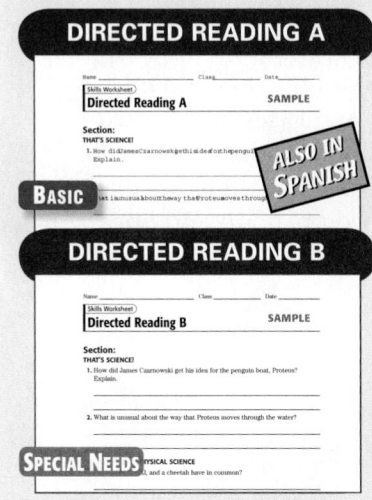

BASIC · **ALSO IN SPANISH**

DIRECTED READING B
SPECIAL NEEDS

VOCABULARY ACTIVITY
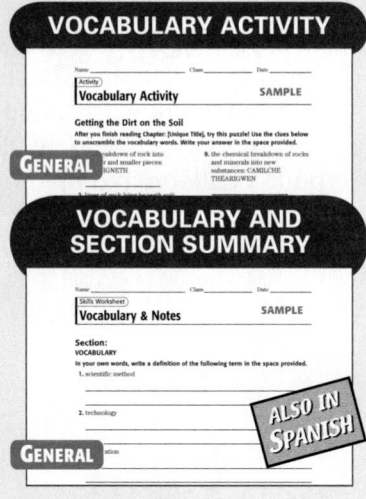

GENERAL

VOCABULARY AND SECTION SUMMARY
GENERAL · **ALSO IN SPANISH**

REINFORCEMENT
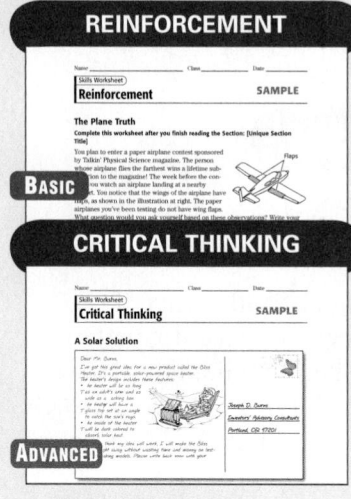

BASIC

CRITICAL THINKING
ADVANCED

SCILINKS ACTIVITY

GENERAL

SCIENCE PUZZLERS, TWISTERS & TEASERS
GENERAL

Labs and Activities

LONG-TERM PROJECTS & RESEARCH IDEAS
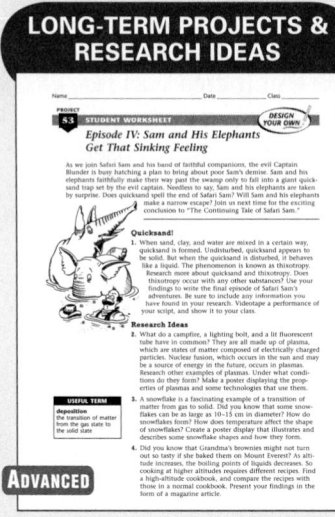

ADVANCED

WHIZ-BANG DEMONSTRATIONS
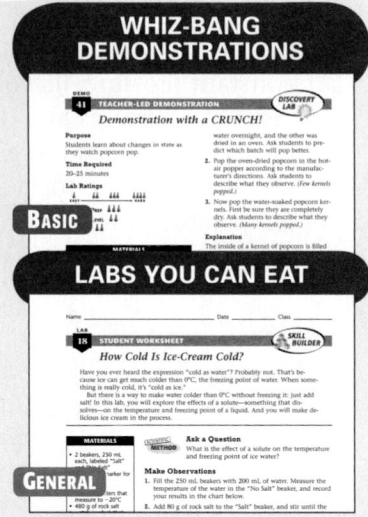

BASIC

LABS YOU CAN EAT
GENERAL

CALCULATOR-BASED LABS
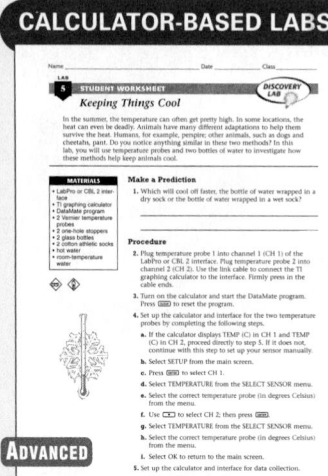

ADVANCED

DATASHEETS FOR QUICK LABS

DATASHEETS FOR CHAPTER LABS

DATASHEETS FOR LABBOOK

Review and Assessments

SECTION QUIZ

GENERAL · **ALSO IN SPANISH**

SECTION REVIEW
GENERAL · **ALSO IN SPANISH**

CHAPTER REVIEW
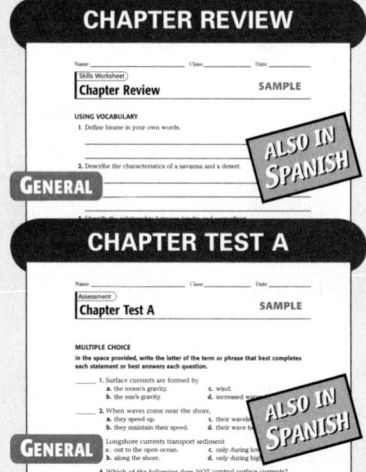

GENERAL · **ALSO IN SPANISH**

CHAPTER TEST A
GENERAL · **ALSO IN SPANISH**

CHAPTER TEST B
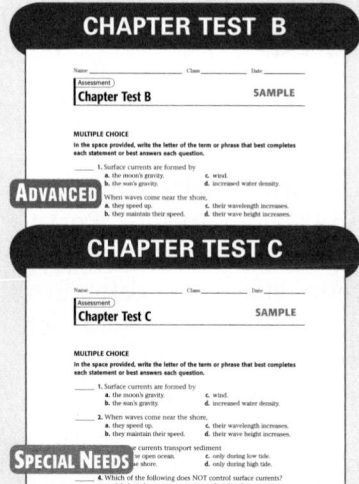

ADVANCED

CHAPTER TEST C
SPECIAL NEEDS

STANDARDIZED TEST PREPARATION
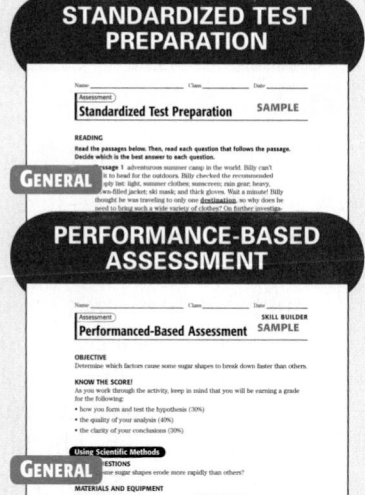

GENERAL

PERFORMANCE-BASED ASSESSMENT
GENERAL

This Chapter Enrichment provides relevant and interesting information to expand and enhance your presentation of the chapter material.

Section 1

Three States of Matter

Solids

- In solids, particles vibrate about fixed points. If the particles are arranged in a regular, repeating pattern, the solid is defined as a crystalline solid. If a crystalline solid is melted and cooled down quickly, it usually forms an amorphous solid. Amorphous solid particles are not arranged in regular, repeating patterns.

Liquids

- The properties of liquids are caused by *cohesion,* the attraction between atoms and molecules of the liquid, and *adhesion,* the attraction between atoms and molecules of the liquid and other atoms and molecules. Because the surface of a liquid has no liquid particles above it, the particles at the surface cohere to the liquid below, and the surface exhibits surface tension.

Gases

- The defining property of gases is the ability to expand indefinitely. Gases are extremely compressible. Gases are also miscible with other gases in all proportions.

Section 2

Behavior of Gases

Robert Boyle and Boyle's Law

- Robert Boyle (1627–1691) was born in Ireland and educated at Eton, Geneva, and Oxford. In 1662, Boyle was experimenting with mercury in a closed, J-shaped tube. He discovered the inverse relationship between the volume of a confined gas and its pressure. Through experimentation, Boyle discovered that if the volume of a gas at a constant temperature is doubled, the pressure is reduced by half. And for any decrease in volume, there is a proportional increase in pressure.

Jacques Charles and Charles's Law

- Jacques Alexander Charles (1746–1823) was a professor of physics at the University of Paris and a friend of Benjamin Franklin. Charles was an avid balloonist. From his work with balloons and gases, he realized that hydrogen would be ideal for balloon flight. He built a balloon and used hydrogen to fill it. He made several flights with his hydrogen balloon and once flew to a height of over 1.7 km.

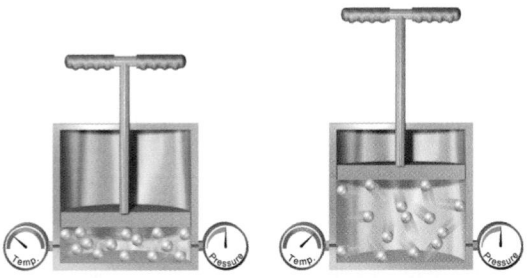

- Charles's law states that if an ideal gas is held at a constant pressure, its volume will increase as temperature increases and decrease as temperature decreases. Charles's research with gases was used by Lord Kelvin to formulate the absolute, or Kelvin, temperature scale.

Is That a Fact!

◆ The sun, fire, and lightning are examples of a fourth state of matter called plasma.

Section 3

Changes of State

Change of State

- For a solid substance to melt, it must gain sufficient energy to overcome intermolecular attraction. As a substance such as ice absorbs energy, the individual molecules of the ice vibrate faster and

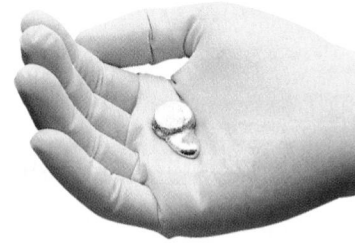

faster, weakening the forces that hold the molecules together. This weakening allows the molecules to begin sliding past one another. If sufficient energy is added, the liquid begins to boil.

Temperature

- Temperature is a measure of the average speed of a substance's particles. Temperature differences indicate in which direction thermal energy will move.

Fahrenheit Scale

- Gabriel Daniel Fahrenheit (1686–1736), a German physicist, developed the Fahrenheit temperature scale.

- Fahrenheit's zero point was the freezing temperature of icy brine water. Fahrenheit chose icy brine water because in the late 1600s, it had the lowest known temperature. Pure water froze at 32° on Fahrenheit's scale. The scale has 180 divisions between the freezing point and boiling point of pure water.

Celsius Scale

- Swedish astronomer Anders Celsius (1704–1744) developed his thermometer so scientists could have a common scale and standard by which to compare experiments. The Celsius scale, also known as the centigrade scale, has 100 divisions between the freezing and boiling points of pure water at 1 atm. Celsius originally assigned the freezing point of water as 100° and the boiling point as 0°. This scale was later changed to the scale we use today.

William Thomson, Lord Kelvin

- William Thomson, Lord Kelvin (1824–1907), was born in Ireland. Thomson was considered a child prodigy—he began his studies at the University of Glasgow when he was only 11 years old. Thomson had many interests (for instance, he investigated the age of Earth), but he is probably best known for his work with absolute temperature.

Kelvin Scale

- The Kelvin scale's divisions are based on the centigrade scale, but the scale does not have any negative numbers. Pure water boils at 373 K and freezes at 273 K.

Is That a Fact!

- ◆ There is no apparent limit to how hot a substance can become, but there is a limit to how cold something can become. Lord Kelvin stated that temperature is related to volume and energy and that at absolute zero, a substance's volume and energy would achieve their lowest values.

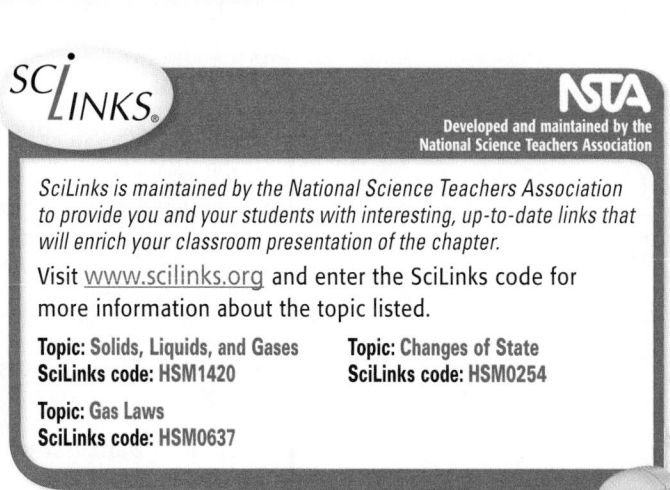

SCiLINKS

NSTA
Developed and maintained by the
National Science Teachers Association

SciLinks is maintained by the National Science Teachers Association to provide you and your students with interesting, up-to-date links that will enrich your classroom presentation of the chapter.

Visit www.scilinks.org and enter the SciLinks code for more information about the topic listed.

Topic: Solids, Liquids, and Gases
SciLinks code: HSM1420

Topic: Changes of State
SciLinks code: HSM0254

Topic: Gas Laws
SciLinks code: HSM0637

Overview

This chapter introduces students to three common states of matter and the characteristics of each state. Students will also learn how gases behave when they are subjected to changes in temperature and pressure. Finally, students will learn how matter changes from one state to another.

Assessing Prior Knowledge

Students should be familiar with the following topics:

- physical properties of matter
- physical changes in matter

Identifying Misconceptions

Some students may assume that because gases lack some of the physical properties of solids and liquids, gases do not have mass. Remind students that gases consist of molecules or atoms, just as solids and liquids do, but the particles of a gas are spaced very far apart relative to their size. Because most of the volume occupied by a gas is empty space, gases have a much lower density than that of liquids or solids.

18
States of Matter

The Big Idea Matter exists in various physical states, which are determined by the movement of the matter's particles.

About the Photo

This beautiful glass creation by artist Dale Chihuly is entitled "Mille Fiori" (A Thousand Flowers). The pieces that form the sculpture were not always solid and unchanging. Each individual piece started as a blob of melted glass on the end of a hollow pipe. The artist worked with his assistants to quickly form each shape before the molten glass cooled and became a solid again.

PRE-READING ACTIVITY

FOLDNOTES **Three-Panel Flip Chart**
Before you read the chapter, create the FoldNote entitled "Three-Panel Flip Chart" described in the **Study Skills** section of the Appendix. Label the flaps of the three-panel flip chart with "Solid," "Liquid," and "Gas." As you read the chapter, write information you learn about each category under the appropriate flap.

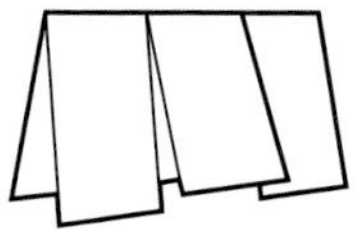

Standards Correlations

National Science Education Standards

The following codes indicate the National Science Education Standards that correlate to this chapter. The full text of the standards is at the front of the book.

Chapter Opener
UCP 2, 3; SAI 1; PS 1a, 3a

Section 1 Three States of Matter
UCP 1, 2; PS 1a; *LabBook:* UCP 2, 3; SAI 1, 2; PS 1a

Section 2 Behavior of Gases
UCP 1, 2, 3; PS 1a

Section 3 Changes of State
UCP 3; SAI 1; PS 1a, 3a; *LabBook:* SAI 1

Chapter Lab
UCP 2, 3; SAI 1, 2; PS 1a, 3a

Chapter Review
UCP 1, 2, 3; SAI 1, 2; PS 1a, 3a

Science in Action
SAI 1, 2; SPSP 5

START-UP ACTIVITY

MATERIALS

FOR EACH GROUP
- cotton swab
- cup, plastic small
- rubbing alcohol

Safety Caution: Remind students to review all safety cautions and icons before beginning this activity. Students should wear safety goggles and aprons during this activity.

Teacher's Notes: Only a small amount of alcohol is needed for this activity. Demonstrate how little alcohol is needed by pouring an amount sufficient for this activity into your cup.

Answers

1. The alcohol disappeared by evaporating.

2. Students should feel a cooling sensation. As the alcohol evaporates, it absorbs energy from the student's hand.

START-UP ACTIVITY

Vanishing Act

In this activity, you will use isopropyl alcohol (rubbing alcohol) to investigate a change of state.

Procedure

1. Pour **rubbing alcohol** into a **small plastic cup** until the alcohol just covers the bottom of the cup.

2. Moisten the tip of a **cotton swab** by dipping it into the alcohol in the cup.

3. Rub the cotton swab on the palm of your hand. Make sure there are no cuts or abrasions on your hands.

4. Record your observations.

5. Wash your hands thoroughly.

Analysis

1. Explain what happened to the alcohol after you rubbed the swab on your hand.

2. Did you feel a sensation of hot or cold? If so, how do you explain what you observed?

3. Record your answers.

Chapter Starter Transparency
Use this transparency to help students begin thinking about the states of matter and how matter changes state.

CHAPTER RESOURCES

Technology

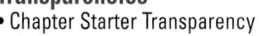
Transparencies
- Chapter Starter Transparency

READING SKILLS

Student Edition on CD-ROM

Guided Reading Audio CD
- English or Spanish

Classroom Videos
- Brain Food Video Quiz

Workbooks

Science Puzzlers, Twisters & Teasers
- States of Matter GENERAL

Focus

Overview

This section introduces three states of matter, and students explore the similarities and differences between these states.

 Bellringer

Have students answer the following question: "In the kitchen, you might find three different forms of water. What are these three forms of water, and where exactly in the kitchen would you find them?"

Motivate

Demonstration — GENERAL

Particles in the Air From one corner of the room or from the very front, spray room deodorizer into the air. Ask students to raise their hand when they smell the deodorizer. Discuss a possible model that would explain why different students smelled the deodorizer at different times.

LS Intrapersonal

English Language Learners

What You Will Learn

● Describe the properties shared by particles of all matter.
● Describe three states of matter.
● Explain the differences between the states of matter.

Vocabulary

states of matter
solid
liquid
surface tension
viscosity
gas

READING STRATEGY

Paired Summarizing Read this section silently. In pairs, take turns summarizing the material. Stop to discuss ideas that seem confusing.

Three States of Matter

You've just walked home on one of the coldest days of the year. A fire is blazing in the fireplace. And there is a pot of water on the stove to make hot chocolate.

The water begins to bubble. Steam rises from the pot. You make your hot chocolate, but it is too hot to drink. You don't want to wait for it to cool down. So, you add an ice cube. You watch the ice melt in the hot liquid until the drink is at just the right temperature. Then, you enjoy your hot drink while warming yourself by the fire.

The scene described above has examples of the three most familiar states of matter: solid, liquid, and gas. The **states of matter** are the physical forms in which a substance can exist. For example, water commonly exists in three states of matter: solid (ice), liquid (water), and gas (steam).

Particles of Matter

Matter is made up of tiny particles called *atoms* and *molecules* (MAHL i kyoolz). These particles are too small to see without a very powerful microscope. Atoms and molecules are always in motion and are always bumping into one another. The particles interact with each other, and the way they interact with each other helps determine the state of the matter. **Figure 1** describes three states of matter—solid, liquid, and gas—in terms of the speed and attraction of the particles.

Figure 1 Models of a Solid, a Liquid, and a Gas

Particles of a solid do not move fast enough to overcome the strong attraction between them. So, they are close together and vibrate in place.

Particles of a liquid move fast enough to overcome some of the attraction between them. The particles are close together but can slide past one another.

Particles of a gas move fast enough to overcome almost all of the attraction between them. The particles are far apart and move independently of one another.

INCLUSION Strategies

• *Learning Disabled*   • *Developmentally Delayed*
• *Hearing Impaired*

Many students are more likely to remember a concept if they have tactile involvement. Give each student two pieces of drawing paper along with markers. Ask them to each create a full-page drawing of the particles in an amorphous solid.   English Language Learners
LS Kinesthetic

Solids

Imagine dropping a marble into a bottle. Would anything happen to the shape or size of the marble? Would the shape or size of the marble change if you put it in a larger bottle?

Solids Have Definite Shape and Volume

Even in a bottle, a marble keeps its original shape and volume. The marble's shape and volume stay the same no matter what size bottle you drop it into because the marble is a solid. A **solid** is the state of matter that has a definite shape and volume.

The particles of a substance in a solid state are very close together. The attraction between them is stronger than the attraction between the particles of the same substance in the liquid or gaseous state. The particles in a solid move, but they do not move fast enough to overcome the attraction between them. Each particle vibrates in place. Therefore, each particle is locked in place by the particles around it.

There Are Two Kinds of Solids

There are two kinds of solids—*crystalline* (KRIS tuhl in) and *amorphous* (uh MAWR fuhs). Crystalline solids have a very orderly, three-dimensional arrangement of particles. The particles of crystalline solids are in a repeating pattern of rows. Iron, diamond, and ice are examples of crystalline solids.

Amorphous solids are made of particles that do not have a special arrangement. So, each particle is in one place, but the particles are not arranged in a pattern. Examples of amorphous solids are glass, rubber, and wax. **Figure 2** shows a photo of quartz (a crystalline solid) and glass (an amorphous solid).

Reading Check How are the particles in a crystalline solid arranged? (*See the Appendix for answers to Reading Checks.*)

states of matter the physical forms of matter, which include solid, liquid, and gas

solid the state of matter in which the volume and shape of a substance are fixed

CONNECTION TO Physics

Is Glass a Liquid? At one time, there was a theory that glass was a liquid. This theory came about because of the observation that ancient windowpanes were often thicker at the bottom than at the top. People thought that the glass had flowed to the bottom of the pane, so glass must be a liquid. Research this theory. Present your research to your class in an oral presentation. **ACTIVITY**

Figure 2   Crystalline and Amorphous Solids

The particles of crystalline solids, such as this quartz crystal, have an orderly three-dimensional pattern.

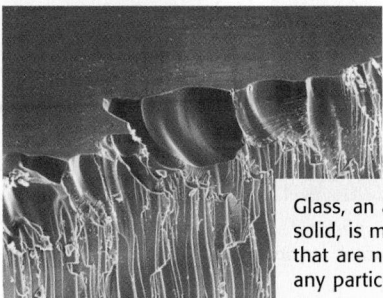

Glass, an amorphous solid, is made of particles that are not arranged in any particular pattern.

Discussion ——— GENERAL

Visualizing Particles The images in this chapter depict particles in matter as gray spheres. Although these particles can be atoms or molecules, the general term *particle* is frequently used to help students better grasp the concepts of particle arrangement and behavior in each of the states of matter. Discuss with students the movement of particles (atoms and molecules) in each of the states of matter. Have them predict what might happen to the particles if the temperature or pressure on the matter in the jar is changed. **LS** Visual/Logical

MISCONCEPTION /// ALERT \\\

Particles in Solids A common misconception is that crystalline solids hold their shape, but amorphous solids do not. It is true that the particles in an amorphous solid are not arranged in a definite pattern, but each particle remains in position relative to surrounding particles.

Answer to Reading Check

The particles in a crystalline solid are arranged in a repeating pattern of rows that forms an orderly, three-dimensional arrangement.

SUPPORT FOR

English Language Learners

Scientific Vocabulary Students may have some difficulty with the specialized use of vocabulary in this section. As they read each page, have them note any words they do not understand. When they have finished reading, ask them to return to the beginning and work with a partner to see how many words they can define. Students should write the terms and their definitions in their science journals. If after the second reading some terms remain undefined, allow students to use a dictionary to learn their meanings. Remind them to add those terms and definitions to their science journals. Check journals for accuracy and spelling, and have students make corrections as necessary. (challenging terms or parts of terms may include: *bubble, steam, states, substance, motion, interact, determine, vibrate, three-dimensional, arrangement, spherical, flow, break away*) **LS** Visual/Interpersonal

Reteaching — BASIC

Solid, Liquid, or Gas? Provide students with a hand lens and samples of salt, flour, margarine or butter, cooking oil, a helium-filled balloon, and a rubber band. Give them time to look at and compare all the samples, and then have them classify each sample according to state. Also, encourage them to investigate and describe the visual differences between an amorphous solid and a crystalline solid.
LS Kinesthetic/Visual

Quiz — GENERAL

Have students answer the following questions:

1. The particles of a _____ are very far apart and move independently of one another. (gas)

2. A liquid's resistance to flow is called _____. (viscosity)

3. The shape and volume of matter in the _____ state do not change. (solid)

Alternative Assessment — BASIC

Graphic Organizer Have students create a graphic organizer in which they describe the properties and characteristics of the three states of matter discussed in this section. Have them include two examples of matter for each state. **LS** Visual/Logical

Figure 3 *Although their shapes are different, the beaker and the graduated cylinder each contain 350 mL of juice.*

liquid the state of matter that has a definite volume but not a definite shape

surface tension the force that acts on the surface of a liquid and that tends to minimize the area of the surface

viscosity the resistance of a gas or liquid to flow

gas a form of matter that does not have a definite volume or shape

Figure 4 *Water forms spherical drops as a result of surface tension.*

Liquids

What do you think would change about orange juice if you poured the juice from a can into a glass? Would the volume of juice be different? Would the taste of the juice change?

Liquids Change Shape but Not Volume

The only thing that would change when the juice is poured into the glass is the shape of the juice. The shape changes because juice is a liquid. **Liquid** is the state of matter that has a definite volume but takes the shape of its container. The particles in liquids move fast enough to overcome some of the attractions between them. The particles slide past each other until the liquid takes the shape of its container.

Although liquids change shape, they do not easily change volume. A can of juice contains a certain volume of liquid. That volume stays the same if you pour the juice into a large container or a small one. **Figure 3** shows the same volume of liquid in two different containers.

Liquids Have Unique Characteristics

A special property of liquids is surface tension. **Surface tension** is a force that acts on the particles at the surface of a liquid. Surface tension causes some liquids to form spherical drops, like the beads of water shown in **Figure 4**. Different liquids have different surface tensions. For example, gasoline has a very low surface tension and forms flat drops.

Another important property of liquids is viscosity. **Viscosity** is a liquid's resistance to flow. Usually, the stronger the attractions between the molecules of a liquid, the more viscous the liquid is. For example, honey flows more slowly than water. So, honey has a higher viscosity than water.

Reading Check What is viscosity?

Is That a Fact!

A *gel* is a liquid that has tiny particles of a solid suspended in it. Gels are best known for their elasticity, or ability to bounce. In a gel, the solid particles remain suspended, unaffected by gravity. These suspended solids give gels their limited firmness. Examples of gels are flavored gelatin and some kinds of toothpaste.

Answer to Reading Check
Viscosity is a liquid's resistance to flow.

Gases

Would you believe that one small tank of helium can fill almost 700 balloons? How is this possible? After all, the volume of a tank is equal to the volume of only about five filled balloons. The answer has to do with helium's state of matter.

Gases Change in Both Shape and Volume

Helium is a gas. **Gas** is the state of matter that has no definite shape or volume. The particles of a gas move quickly. So, they can break away completely from one another. There is less attraction between particles of a gas than between particles of the same substance in the solid or liquid state.

The amount of empty space between gas particles can change. Look at **Figure 5.** The particles of helium in the balloons are farther apart than the particles of helium in the tank. The particles spread out as helium fills the balloon. So, the amount of empty space between the gas particles increases.

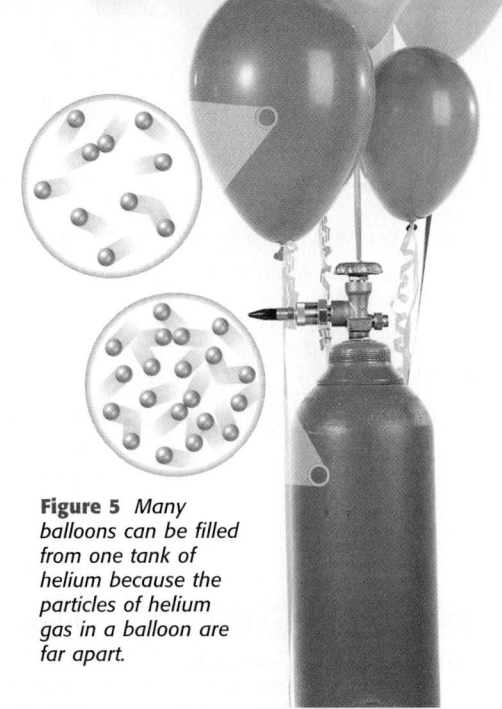

Figure 5 Many balloons can be filled from one tank of helium because the particles of helium gas in a balloon are far apart.

SECTION Review

Summary

- The three most familiar states of matter are solid, liquid, and gas.
- All matter is made of tiny particles called atoms and molecules that attract each other and move constantly.
- A solid has a definite shape and volume.
- A liquid has a definite volume but not a definite shape.
- A gas does not have a definite shape or volume.

Using Key Terms

1. Use each of the following terms in a separate sentence: *viscosity* and *surface tension.*

Understanding Key Ideas

2. One property that all particles of matter have in common is they
   a. never move in solids.
   b. only move in gases.
   c. move constantly.
   d. None of the above

3. Describe solids, liquids, and gases in terms of shape and volume.

Critical Thinking

4. **Applying Concepts** Classify each substance according to its state of matter: apple juice, bread, a textbook, and steam.

5. **Identifying Relationships** The volume of a gas can change, but the volume of a solid cannot. Explain why this is true.

Interpreting Graphics

Use the image below to answer the questions that follow.

6. Identify the state of matter shown in the jar.

7. Discuss how the particles in the jar are attracted to each other.

Developed and maintained by the National Science Teachers Association

For a variety of links related to this chapter, go to www.scilinks.org

Topic: Solids, Liquids, and Gases
SciLinks code: HSM1420

Focus

Overview

In this section, students will learn how gases behave when subjected to changes in temperature and pressure. They will also learn about two important gas laws.

🔊 Bellringer

Ask students what gas is used in a balloon to make it float in the air. Then, ask students if they have ever seen a hot-air balloon floating in the sky. Ask them to write an explanation of why they think the balloon can fly with only air in it and not helium.

Motivate

Demonstration —— BASIC

A Mini-explosion Place two teaspoons of baking soda and two tablespoons of vinegar into a small container with a snap-on lid. Quickly snap the lid on. Shake the container once, and then leave it on the desk. The lid should pop off within seconds. Repeat the demonstration using a larger container, but use the same amount of reactants. Discuss what happened and why the lid on the larger container took longer to pop off.

LS Visual/Logical

What You Will Learn

● Describe three factors that affect how gases behave.
● Predict how a change in pressure or temperature will affect the volume of a gas.

Vocabulary

temperature
volume
pressure
Boyle's Law
Charles's Law

READING STRATEGY

Reading Organizer As you read this section, make a table comparing the effects of temperature, volume, and pressure on gases.

temperature a measure of how hot (or cold) something is; specifically, a measure of the movement of particles.

Figure 1 *To properly inflate a helium balloon, you must consider the temperature outside of the balloon.*

Behavior of Gases

Suppose you are watching a parade that you have been looking forward to for weeks. You may be fascinated by the giant balloons floating high overhead.

You may wonder how the balloons were arranged for the parade. How much helium was needed to fill all of the balloons? What role does the weather play in getting the balloons to float?

Describing Gas Behavior

Helium is a gas. Gases behave differently from solids or liquids. Unlike the particles that make up solids and liquids, gas particles have a large amount of empty space between them. The space that gas particles occupy is the gas's volume, which can change because of temperature and pressure.

Temperature

How much helium is needed to fill a parade balloon, like the one in **Figure 1?** The answer depends on the outdoor temperature. **Temperature** is a measure of how fast the particles in an object are moving. The faster the particles are moving, the more energy they have. So, on a hot day, the particles of gas are moving faster and hitting the inside walls of the balloon harder. Thus, the gas is expanding and pushing on the walls of the balloon with greater force. If the gas expands too much, the balloon will explode. But, what will happen if the weather is cool on the day of the parade? The particles of gas in the balloon will have less energy. And, the particles of gas will not push as hard on the walls of the balloon. So, more gas must be used to fill the balloons.

CHAPTER RESOURCES

Chapter Resource File

 • Lesson Plan
• Directed Reading A **BASIC**
• Directed Reading B **SPECIAL NEEDS**

Technology

 Transparencies
• Bellringer
• P6 Boyle's Law; Charles's Law

Workbooks

 Interactive Textbook Struggling Readers

SCIENTISTS AT ODDS

Early Scientific Beliefs Many early scientists believed that all matter was made of four elements: earth, air, fire, and water. In 1661, Robert Boyle wrote a book called the *Sceptical Chymist* in which he disagreed with this belief. Boyle proposed that matter was made of primitive and simple bodies called *corpuscles*. He believed that corpuscles had different shapes and sizes that mixed together to give elements their unique properties.

Volume

Volume is the amount of space that an object takes up. But because the particles of a gas spread out, the volume of any gas depends on the container that the gas is in. For example, have you seen inflated balloons that were twisted into different shapes? Shaping the balloons was possible because particles of gas can be compressed, or squeezed together, into a smaller volume. But, if you tried to shape a balloon filled with water, the balloon would probably explode. It would explode because particles of liquids can't be compressed as much as particles of gases.

Pressure

The amount of force exerted on a given area of surface is called **pressure.** You can think of pressure as the number of times the particles of a gas hit the inside of their container.

The balls in **Figure 2** are the same size, which means they can hold the same volume of air, which is a gas. Notice, however, that there are more particles of gas in the basketball than in the beach ball. So, more particles hit the inside surface of the basketball than hit the inside surface of the beach ball. When more particles hit the inside surface of the basketball, the force on the inside surface of the ball increases. This increased force leads to greater pressure, which makes the basketball feel harder than the beach ball.

✓ Reading Check Why is the pressure greater in a basketball than in a beach ball? (*See the Appendix for answers to Reading Checks.*)

volume a measure of the size of a body or region in three-dimensional space

pressure the amount of force exerted per unit area of a surface

INTERNET ACTIVITY

For another activity related to this chapter, go to **go.hrw.com** and type in the keyword **HP5STAW**.

Figure 2 · Gas and Pressure

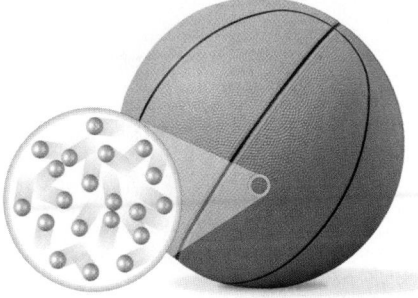 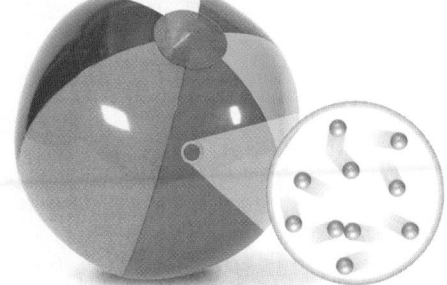

High pressure   **Low pressure**

The basketball has a higher pressure because there are more particles of gas in it, and they are closer together. The particles collide with the inside of the ball at a faster rate.

The beach ball has a lower pressure because there are fewer particles of gas, and they are farther apart. The particles in the beach ball collide with the inside of the ball at a slower rate.

SUPPORT FOR

English Language Learners

Graphics Creating visual aids showing the effects of temperature and pressure on gases may help students understand the concepts. After students read the section, draw four circles on the board. Label the first circle high temperature. Ask a volunteer to come to the board and draw what gas particles would look like under these conditions. Do the same for low temperature, high pressure, and low pressure in the other circles. Students may copy the circles into their science journals. **LS Visual**

Answer to Reading Check

There are more particles of gas in the basketball than there are in the beach ball. More particles hit the inside surface of the basketball, which causes increased force.

READING STRATEGY —— GENERAL

Prediction Guide Before students read this page, ask: "Assuming that a beach ball is the same size and volume as a basketball, which do you think contains more particles of air? Explain your answer."

Have students evaluate their answers after they read about pressure. **LS Visual/Logical**

ACTIVITY —— GENERAL

Changes in Gas Volume Have students perform the following activity during class or at home. If the activity is performed at home, students can report their results in class the next day. Give students one balloon each, and instruct them to blow up the balloon and tie it closed. Then, have them use a measuring tape to measure the circumference around the widest part of the balloon and record their measurement. Instruct students to then place the balloon in a sunny window for 20 min. Have them measure the circumference again and note any change in measurement. Then, have them place the balloon in a freezer for 20 min. Instruct students to quickly measure the balloon again and note any change. Discuss the changes in circumference, and ask students why they think the circumference of the balloon increased or decreased. Refer back to the results of this activity in your discussion of the gas laws. **LS Kinesthetic/Logical**

Reteaching — **BASIC**

Gas Behavior Have students make a table on paper with three columns labeled temperature, volume, and pressure. Then, have them make four rows and label two of them Boyle's law and the other two Charles's law. Have students review the gas laws and then fill in the spaces in the table using the words constant, increases, and decreases, based on what they have learned about gas behavior. **LS** Visual/Logical

Quiz — **GENERAL**

Ask students whether each of the following statements is true or false.

1. Changing the temperature of a gas has no effect on the volume of the gas. (false)

2. Pressure in a gas-filled container is caused by gas particles hitting the walls of the container. (true)

Alternative Assessment — **GENERAL**

Concept Mapping Have students work in pairs to create a concept map that shows how Boyle's law, Charles's law, temperature, pressure, and volume are related. Have them provide an example from everyday life that illustrates each relationship. Post the concept maps in the classroom so students can share their ideas with their classmates. **LS** Interpersonal/Verbal

Gas Behavior Laws

Scientists found that the temperature, pressure, and volume of a gas are linked. Changing one of the factors changes the other two factors. The relationships between temperature, pressure, and volume are described by gas laws.

Boyle's Law

Imagine that a diver 10 m below the surface of a lake blows a bubble of air. When the bubble reaches the surface, the bubble's volume has doubled. The difference in pressure between the surface and 10 m below the surface caused this change.

The relationship between the volume and pressure of a gas was first described by Robert Boyle, a 17th-century Irish chemist. The relationship is now known as Boyle's law. **Boyle's law** states that for a fixed amount of gas at a constant temperature, the volume of the gas is inversely related to the pressure. So, as the pressure of a gas increases, the volume decreases by the same amount, as shown in **Figure 3**.

Charles's Law

If you blow air into a balloon and leave it in the hot sun, the balloon might pop. **Charles's law** states that for a fixed amount of gas at a constant pressure, the volume of the gas changes in the same way that the temperature of the gas changes. So, if the temperature increases, the volume of gas also increases by the same amount. Charles's law is shown by the model in **Figure 4**.

 Reading Check State Charles's law in your own words.

Boyle's law the law that states that the volume of a gas is inversely proportional to the pressure of a gas when temperature is constant

Charles's law the law that states that the volume of a gas is directly proportional to the temperature of a gas when pressure is constant

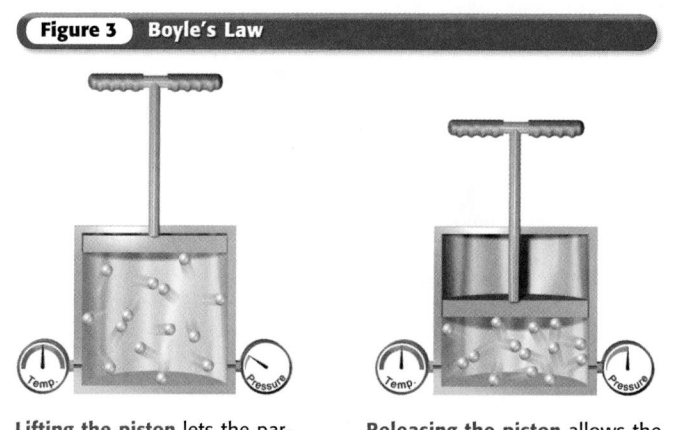

Figure 3 Boyle's Law

Lifting the piston lets the particles of gas spread far apart. The volume of the gas increases as the pressure decreases.

Releasing the piston allows the particles of gas to return to their original volume and pressure.

Pushing the piston forces the gas particles close together. The volume of the gas decreases as the pressure increases.

Homework — **ADVANCED**

 Writing **What Are Plasmas?** There is a fourth state of matter called *plasma* that makes up about 99% of the known matter in the universe. Have students write a research paper discussing the properties of plasma and where plasma is found. Also, have them include information about plasma and controlled nuclear fusion as a source of energy for people to use. **LS** Logical

Answer to Reading Check

Charles's law states that the volume of a gas in a closed container changes as the temperature of the gas changes. If the temperature increases, the volume increases. If the temperature decreases, the volume decreases.

Figure 4 Charles's Law

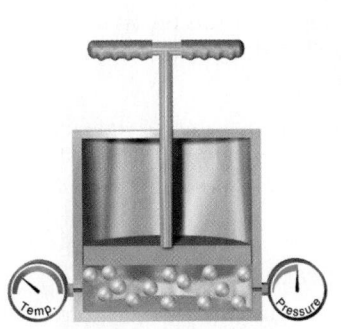
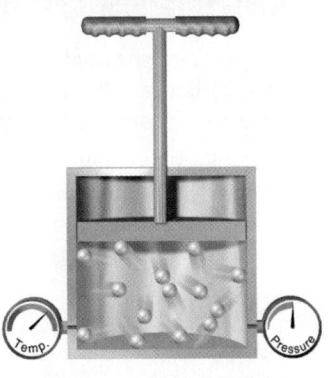

Decreasing the temperature of the gas causes the particles to move more slowly. The gas particles hit the piston less often and with less force. So, the volume of the gas decreases.

Increasing the temperature of the gas causes the particles to move more quickly. The gas particles hit the piston more often and with greater force. So, the volume of the gas increases.

SECTION Review

Summary

- Temperature measures how fast the particles in an object are moving.
- Gas pressure increases as the number of collisions of gas particles increases.
- Boyle's law states that if the temperature doesn't change, the volume of a gas increases as the pressure decreases.
- Charles's law states that if the pressure doesn't change, the volume of a gas increases as the temperature increases.

Using Key Terms

1. Use each of the following terms in the same sentence: *temperature, pressure, volume,* and *Charles's law.*

Understanding Key Ideas

2. Boyle's law describes the relationship between
   a. volume and pressure.
   b. temperature and pressure.
   c. temperature and volume.
   d. All of the above

3. What are the effects of a warm temperature on gas particles?

Math Skills

4. You have 3 L of gas at a certain temperature and pressure. What would the volume of the gas be if the temperature doubled and the pressure stayed the same?

Critical Thinking

5. **Applying Concepts** What happens to the volume of a balloon that is taken outside on a cold winter day? Explain.

6. **Making Inferences** When scientists record a gas's volume, they also record its temperature and pressure. Why?

7. **Analyzing Ideas** What happens to the pressure of a gas if the volume of gas is tripled at a constant temperature?

 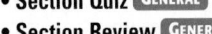

For a variety of links related to this chapter, go to www.scilinks.org

Topic: Gas Laws
SciLinks code: HSM0637

Is That a Fact!

Scuba is an acronym for *self-*contained *underwater* *breathing* *apparatus.* Credit for the invention of scuba in 1943 is usually given to Jacques-Yves Cousteau and Emile Gagnan.

CHAPTER RESOURCES

Chapter Resource File
- Section Quiz GENERAL
- Section Review GENERAL
- Vocabulary and Section Summary GENERAL
- Reinforcement Worksheet BASIC

Workbooks

Math Skills for Science
- Checking Division with Multiplication GENERAL

Answers to Section Review

1. Sample answer: Charles's law states that when the temperature of a gas under constant pressure is decreased, the volume of the gas decreases.

2. a

3. Sample answer: When gas particles become warmer, they move more rapidly and hit the sides of their container more often and with greater force, thus increasing the volume of the gas.

4. The volume of the gas would also double to 6 L.

5. Sample answer: The volume of the balloon will decrease. When the air particles inside the balloon become cooler, they slow down and do not hit the inside of the balloon as often, so the balloon's volume decreases.

6. Sample answer: The volume, pressure, and temperature of a gas are all related. The volume of a gas can be changed by changing the temperature and the pressure.

7. Sample answer: Boyle's law states that the volume of a gas is inversely proportional to its pressure. If the volume is tripled, the pressure of the gas would drop to one-third of the original value.

Focus

Overview

This section examines how matter changes from state to state. Changes in state are explained in terms of matter gaining or losing energy.

 Bellringer

Have students write a description of what must be done to liquid water to change it to ice or to change it to steam. Then, have students use these explanations to predict what must happen, in general, to cause matter to change state.

Motivate

Demonstration — GENERAL

Do Solids Move? Ask four students to stand close together to form a square. Wrap masking tape around the students several times. Tell the class that the four students represent the particles in a solid. Have the students demonstrate that they can still move a bit without breaking the tape, just as particles in a solid move a bit but generally stay close together. Then, have the four students move around more and more until they break the tape. Discuss with the class that when particles in a solid move faster, they move apart, and the solid changes to the liquid state. **LS** Visual/Interpersonal

What You Will Learn

● Describe how energy is involved in changes of state.
● Describe what happens during melting and freezing.
● Compare evaporation and condensation.
● Explain what happens during sublimation.
● Identify the two changes that can happen when a substance loses or gains energy.

Vocabulary

change of   boiling
  state   condensation
melting   sublimation
evaporation

READING STRATEGY

Mnemonics As you read this section, create a mnemonic device to help you remember the five changes of state.

change of state the change of a substance from one physical state to another

Changes of State

It can be tricky to eat a frozen juice bar outside on a hot day. In just minutes, the juice bar will start to melt. Soon the solid juice bar becomes a liquid mess.

As the juice bar melts, it goes through a change of state. In this section, you will learn about the four changes of state shown in **Figure 1** as well as a fifth change of state called *sublimation* (SUHB luh MAY shuhn).

Energy and Changes of State

A **change of state** is the change of a substance from one physical form to another. All changes of state are physical changes. In a physical change, the identity of a substance does not change. In **Figure 1,** the ice, liquid water, and steam are all the same substance—water.

The particles of a substance move differently depending on the state of the substance. The particles also have different amounts of energy when the substance is in different states. For example, particles in liquid water have more energy than particles in ice. But particles of steam have more energy than particles in liquid water. So, to change a substance from one state to another, you must add or remove energy.

✔ **Reading Check** What is a change of state? (*See the Appendix for answers to Reading Checks.*)

Figure 1 **Changes of State**

The terms in the arrows are changes of state. Water commonly goes through the changes of state shown here.

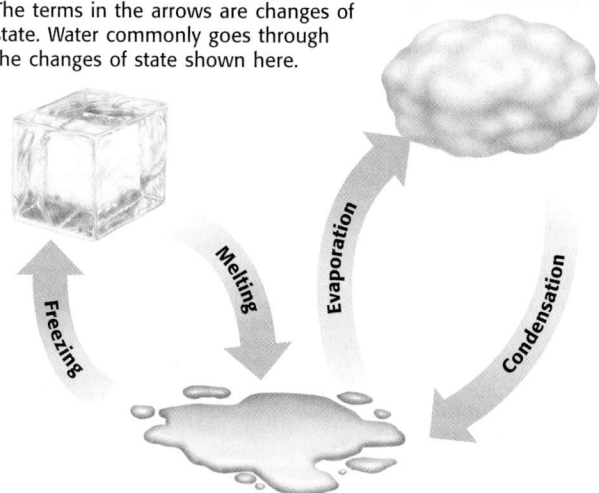

Freezing · Melting · Evaporation · Condensation

Answer to Reading Check

A change of state is the change of a substance from one physical form to another.

Melting: Solid to Liquid

One change of state that happens when you add energy to a substance is melting. **Melting** is the change of state from a solid to a liquid. This change of state is what happens when ice melts. Adding energy to a solid increases the temperature of the solid. As the temperature increases, the particles of the solid move faster. When a certain temperature is reached, the solid will melt. The temperature at which a substance changes from a solid to a liquid is the *melting point* of the substance. Melting point is a physical property. Different substances have different melting points. For example, gallium melts at about 30°C. Because your normal body temperature is about 37°C, gallium will melt in your hand! This is shown in **Figure 2.** Table salt, however, has a melting point of 801°C, so it will not melt in your hand.

Adding Energy

For a solid to melt, particles must overcome some of their attractions to each other. When a solid is at its melting point, any energy added to it is used to overcome the attractions that hold the particles in place. Melting is an *endothermic* (EN doh THUHR mik) change because energy is gained by the substance as it changes state.

Freezing: Liquid to Solid

The change of state from a liquid to a solid is called *freezing*. The temperature at which a liquid changes into a solid is the liquid's *freezing point*. Freezing is the reverse process of melting. Thus, freezing and melting occur at the same temperature, as shown in **Figure 3.**

Removing Energy

For a liquid to freeze, the attractions between the particles must overcome the motion of the particles. Imagine that a liquid is at its freezing point. Removing energy will cause the particles to begin locking into place. Freezing is an *exothermic* (EK so THUHR mik) change because energy is removed from the substance as it changes state.

Figure 2 *Even though gallium is a metal, it would not be very useful as jewelry!*

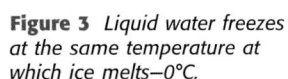

melting the change of state in which a solid becomes a liquid by adding energy

Figure 3 *Liquid water freezes at the same temperature at which ice melts—0°C.*

If energy is added at 0°C, the ice will melt.

If energy is removed at 0°C, the liquid water will freeze.

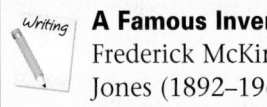

Prediction Guide Before students read this page, ask them if they agree with the following three statements:

• Evaporation can occur at any temperature. (true)

• Boiling occurs only at the surface of a liquid. (false)

• Evaporation is simply a liquid changing to a gas. (true)

LS Logical

Homework —— GENERAL

Dressing for the Weather
Traditional clothing varies from culture to culture. People who live in warm climates wear lightweight and loose-fitting clothes that allow air to circulate near the body. This air circulation allows perspiration to evaporate, which cools the body. Examples of cultures that wear such lightweight clothing are those of the Middle East and northern Africa. Ask students to research other examples of how people dress to fit the climate where they live. Have them make posters showing the examples they found.

LS Logical/
Intrapersonal

English Language Learners

Evaporation: Liquid to Gas

One way to experience evaporation is to iron a shirt using a steam iron. You will notice steam coming up from the iron as the wrinkles disappear. This steam forms when the liquid water in the iron becomes hot and changes to gas.

Boiling and Evaporation

Evaporation (ee VAP uh RAY shuhn) is the change of a substance from a liquid to a gas. Evaporation can occur at the surface of a liquid that is below its boiling point. For example, when you sweat, your body is cooled through evaporation. Your sweat is mostly water. Water absorbs energy from your skin as the water evaporates. You feel cooler because your body transfers energy to the water. Evaporation also explains why water in a glass on a table disappears after several days.

Figure 4 explains the difference between boiling and evaporation. **Boiling** is the change of a liquid to a vapor, or gas, throughout the liquid. Boiling occurs when the pressure inside the bubbles, which is called *vapor pressure*, equals the outside pressure on the bubbles, or atmospheric pressure. The temperature at which a liquid boils is called its *boiling point*. No matter how much of a substance is present, neither the boiling point nor the melting point of a substance change. For example, 5 mL and 5 L of water both boil at 100°C.

✓ Reading Check What is evaporation?

evaporation the change of a substance from a liquid to a gas

boiling the conversion of a liquid to a vapor when the vapor pressure of the liquid equals the atmospheric pressure

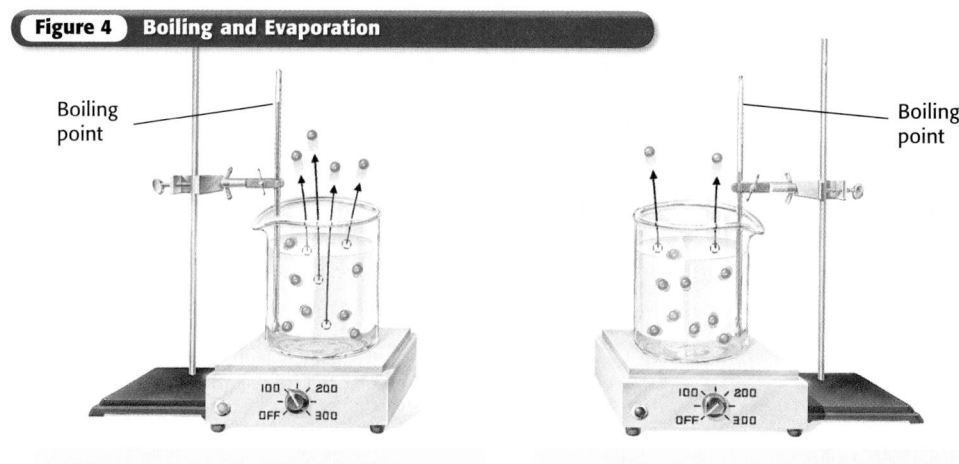

Figure 4 **Boiling and Evaporation**

Boiling point

Boiling point

Boiling occurs in a liquid at its boiling point. As energy is added to the liquid, particles throughout the liquid move faster. When they move fast enough to break away from other particles, they evaporate and become a gas.

Evaporation can also occur in a liquid below its boiling point. Some particles at the surface of the liquid move fast enough to break away from the particles around them and become a gas.

Science BI∞opers

To Sweat or Not to Sweat Most people do not want to get too sweaty, so they wear an antiperspirant. In addition to covering unpleasant odors, antiperspirants contain compounds that clog pores in the skin. So, sweat cannot be excreted by the body. However, sweat is the body's natural air conditioner. When sweat evaporates, it cools the skin. So when you wear antiperspirant, you may cause your body to cool less efficiently.

Answer to Reading Check
Evaporation is the change of a substance from a liquid to a gas.

Effects of Pressure on Boiling Point

Earlier, you learned that water boils at 100°C. In fact, water boils at 100°C only at sea level, because of atmospheric pressure. Atmospheric pressure is caused by the weight of the gases that make up the atmosphere.

Atmospheric pressure varies depending on where you are in relation to sea level. Atmospheric pressure is lower at higher elevations. The higher you go above sea level, the fewer air particles there are above you. So, the atmospheric pressure is lower. Imagine boiling water at the top of a mountain. The boiling point would be lower than 100°C. For example, Denver, Colorado, is 1.6 km above sea level. In Denver, water boils at about 95°C.

Condensation: Gas to Liquid

Look at the dragonfly in **Figure 5.** Notice the beads of water that have formed on the wings. They form because of condensation of gaseous water in the air. **Condensation** is the change of state from a gas to a liquid. Condensation and evaporation are the reverse of each other. The *condensation point* of a substance is the temperature at which the gas becomes a liquid. And the condensation point is the same temperature as the boiling point at a given pressure.

For a gas to become a liquid, large numbers of particles must clump together. Particles clump together when the attraction between them overcomes their motion. For this to happen, energy must be removed from the gas to slow the movement of the particles. Because energy is removed, condensation is an exothermic change.

CONNECTION TO Language Arts

WRITING SKILL **Cooking at High Altitudes** Many times, cake mixes and other prepared foods will have special instructions for baking and cooking at high altitudes. Even poaching an egg at a high altitude requires a different amount of cooking time. Imagine that you got a letter from a cousin in Denver. He is upset that a cake he made turned out poorly, even though he followed the recipe. Do research on cooking at high altitudes. Write a letter to your cousin explaining why he may have had problems baking the cake.

condensation the change of state from a gas to a liquid

Figure 5 *Beads of water form when water vapor in the air contacts a cool surface, such as the wings of this dragonfly.*

Teach, *continued*

Homework ——— GENERAL

Does the Temperature Change?
Pose the following situation to students:

A scientist and her assistant have an unmarked thermometer on which they want to mark the temperatures of 0°C and 100°C. They heat a beaker of water and take several cubes of ice out of the freezer. Just as they are about to mark the thermometer, the phone rings. The scientist spends 15 minutes on the phone. When she is finished, she again places the thermometer on the ice to mark 0°C. The scientist's assistant stops her and says that after 15 minutes, the ice has begun to melt and must be warmer than 0°C. Also, since the water has been boiling for 15 minutes, it must be hotter than 100°C. Write an explanation of why the assistant's assumptions are not correct. **LS** Logical

Is That a Fact!

Helium, an unreactive gas, has one of the lowest boiling points. Helium boils at 4.2 K, a little above absolute zero.

WEIRD SCIENCE

Ice and snow sometimes sublime directly to water vapor. If the air is dry after a snowstorm, a thin layer of ice on a driveway or street may simply disappear in a matter of hours, even though the temperature never rises above freezing.

Close

Reteaching — BASIC

The Phases of Water Use "The Water Cycle" teaching transparency to help students understand the changes of state that water undergoes as it cycles through the environment. Have students explain in their own words how changing the state of water **(Figure 7)** relates to the water cycle. **LS** Visual/Logical

Quiz — GENERAL

Have students answer the following questions:

1. What are two changes of state that are endothermic?
(melting and evaporation)

2. Do the particles of a substance move faster or slower as the substance is heated?
(faster)

3. When water evaporates, has a chemical change or a physical change occurred?
(physical)

Alternative Assessment — GENERAL

Picturing Changes of State
Draw a sequence of state changes. For example, a solid is melting, or a gas is condensing. Ask students how the next drawing will look. After completing the drawings, ask the students to create a concept map showing changes of state and separating endothermic and exothermic changes. **LS** Visual/Logical

Figure 6 *Dry ice changes directly from a solid to a gas. This change of state is called* sublimation.

sublimation the process in which a solid changes directly into a gas

Sublimation: Solid to Gas

The solid in **Figure 6** is dry ice. Dry ice is carbon dioxide in a solid state. It is called *dry ice* because instead of melting into a liquid, it goes through sublimation. **Sublimation** is the change of state in which a solid changes directly into a gas. Dry ice is much colder than ice made from water.

For a solid to change directly into a gas, the particles of the substance must move from being very tightly packed to being spread far apart. So, the attractions between the particles must be completely overcome. The substance must gain energy for the particles to overcome their attractions. Thus, sublimation is an endothermic change because energy is gained by the substance as it changes state.

Change of Temperature Vs. Change of State

When most substances lose or gain energy, one of two things happens to the substance: its temperature changes or its state changes. The temperature of a substance is related to the speed of the substance's particles. So, when the temperature of a substance changes, the speed of the particles also changes. But the temperature of a substance does not change until the change of state is complete. For example, the temperature of boiling water stays at 100°C until it has all evaporated. In **Figure 7,** you can see what happens to ice as energy is added to the ice.

Reading Check What happens to the temperature of a substance as it changes state?

Quick Lab

Boiling Water Is Cool
1. Remove the cap from a **syringe.**
2. Place the tip of the syringe in the **warm water** that is provided by your teacher. Pull the plunger out until you have 10 mL of water in the syringe.
3. Tighten the cap on the syringe.
4. Hold the syringe, and slowly pull the plunger out.
5. Observe any changes you see in the water. Record your observations.
6. Why are you not burned by the water in the syringe?

MATERIALS

FOR EACH STUDENT
• syringe
• warm water

Safety Caution: Remind students to review all safety cautions and icons before beginning this activity. Students should wear safety goggles and aprons during this activity.

Because the temperature of the water required depends on the size of the syringes used, determine the necessary temperature based on the syringes.

Answers

5. Bubbles form in the water as the plunger is pulled out.

6. The boiling water is not 100°C. The lower pressure causes the water to boil at a much lower temperature.

Figure 7 | Changing the State of Water

The energy that is added during a change of state is used to break the attractions between particles. So, the temperature does not change until the change of state is complete.

SECTION Review

Summary

- A change of state is the conversion of a substance from one physical form to another.

- Energy is added during endothermic changes. Energy is removed during exothermic changes.

- The freezing point and the melting point of a substance are the same temperature.

- Both boiling and evaporation result in a liquid changing to a gas.

- Condensation is the change of a gas to a liquid. It is the reverse of evaporation.

- Sublimation changes a solid directly to a gas.

- The temperature of a substance does not change during a change of state.

Using Key Terms

For each pair of terms, explain how the meanings of the terms differ.

1. *melting* and *freezing*

2. *condensation* and *evaporation*

Understanding Key Ideas

3. The change from a solid directly to a gas is called
   a. evaporation.
   b. boiling.
   c. melting.
   d. sublimation.

4. Describe how the motion and arrangement of particles in a substance change as the substance freezes.

5. Explain what happens to the temperature of an ice cube as it melts.

6. How are evaporation and boiling different? How are they similar?

Math Skills

7. The volume of a substance in the gaseous state is about 1,000 times the volume of the same substance in the liquid state. How much space would 18 mL of water take up if it evaporated?

Critical Thinking

8. **Evaluating Data** The temperature of water in a beaker is 25°C. After adding a piece of magnesium to the water, the temperature increases to 28°C. Is this an exothermic or endothermic reaction? Explain your answer.

9. **Applying Concepts** Solid crystals of iodine were placed in a flask. The top of the flask was covered with aluminum foil. The flask was gently heated. Soon, the flask was filled with a reddish gas. What change of state took place? Explain your answer.

10. **Predicting Consequences** Would using dry ice in your holiday punch cause it to become watery after several hours? Why or why not?

SCI LINKS®

NSTA
Developed and maintained by the
National Science Teachers Association

For a variety of links related to this chapter, go to www.scilinks.org

Topic: Changes of State
SciLinks code: HSM0254

Answer to Reading Check

As a substance changes state, its temperature remains constant until the change of state is complete.

Skills Practice Lab

A Hot and Cool Lab

Teacher's Notes

Time Required

One or two 45-minute class periods

Lab Ratings

EASY ——————→ HARD

Teacher Prep 🧪🧪🧪
Student Set-Up 🧪🧪
Concept Level 🧪🧪🧪
Clean Up 🧪🧪

MATERIALS

The materials listed are for a group of 3–4 students.

Safety Caution

Remind students to review all safety cautions and icons before beginning this lab activity.

Preparation Notes

To construct the wire-loop stirring device, make a small loop at one end of a 25 cm piece of copper wire. The loop should easily fit into the graduated cylinder with the thermometer in place. Angle the loop so that it is perpendicular to the rest of the wire. Make a handle that extends in the opposite direction of the loop, at the other end of the wire. Place the loop around the thermometer, and use the handle to move the device up and down.

Skills Practice Lab

OBJECTIVES

Measure and record time and temperature accurately.

Graph the temperature change of water as it changes state.

Analyze and interpret graphs of changes of state.

MATERIALS

- beaker, 250 or 400 mL
- coffee can, large
- gloves, heat-resistant
- graduated cylinder, 100 mL
- graph paper
- hot plate
- ice, crushed
- rock salt
- stopwatch
- thermometer
- water
- wire-loop stirring device

SAFETY

A Hot and Cool Lab

When you add energy to a substance through heating, does the substance's temperature always go up? When you remove energy from a substance through cooling, does the substance's temperature always go down? In this lab you'll investigate these important questions with a very common substance—water.

Procedure

1 Fill the beaker about one-third to one-half full with water.

2 Put on heat-resistant gloves. Turn on the hot plate, and put the beaker on it. Put the thermometer in the beaker. **Caution:** Be careful not to touch the hot plate.

3 Make a copy of Table I. Record the temperature of the water every 30 seconds. Continue doing this until about one-fourth of the water boils away. Note the first temperature reading at which the water is steadily boiling.

Table 1								
Time (s)	30	60	90	120	150	180	210	etc.
Temperature (°C)	DO NOT WRITE IN BOOK							

4 Turn off the hot plate.

5 While the beaker is cooling, make a graph of temperature (y-axis) versus time (x-axis). Draw an arrow pointing to the first temperature at which the water was steadily boiling.

Holt Lab Generator CD-ROM

Search for any lab by topic, standard, difficulty level, or time. Edit any lab to fit your needs, or create your own labs. Use the Lab Materials QuickList software to customize your lab materials list.

C. John Graves
Monforton Middle School
Bozeman, Montana

CHAPTER RESOURCES

Chapter Resource File

- Datasheet for Chapter Lab
- Lab Notes and Answers

Technology

Classroom Videos
- Lab Video

LabBook

- Full of Hot Air!
- Can Crusher

6 After you finish the graph, use heat-resistant gloves to pick up the beaker. Pour the warm water out, and rinse the warm beaker with cool water.
Caution: Even after cooling, the beaker is still too warm to handle without gloves.

7 Put approximately 20 mL of water in the graduated cylinder.

8 Put the graduated cylinder in the coffee can, and fill in around the graduated cylinder with crushed ice. Pour rock salt on the ice around the graduated cylinder. Place the thermometer and the wire-loop stirring device in the graduated cylinder.

9 As the ice melts and mixes with the rock salt, the level of ice will decrease. Add ice and rock salt to the can as needed.

10 Make another copy of Table I. Record the temperature of the water in the graduated cylinder every 30 seconds. Stir the water with the stirring device.
Caution: Do not stir with the thermometer.

11 Once the water begins to freeze, stop stirring. Do not try to pull the thermometer out of the solid ice in the cylinder.

12 Note the temperature when you first notice ice crystals forming in the water. Continue taking readings until the water in the graduated cylinder is completely frozen.

13 Make a graph of temperature (*y*-axis) versus time (*x*-axis). Draw an arrow to the temperature reading at which the first ice crystals form in the water in the graduated cylinder.

Analyze the Results

1 **Describing Events** What happens to the temperature of boiling water when you continue to add energy through heating?

2 **Describing Events** What happens to the temperature of freezing water when you continue to remove energy through cooling?

3 **Analyzing Data** What does the slope of each graph represent?

4 **Analyzing Results** How does the slope of the graph that shows water boiling compare with the slope of the graph before the water starts to boil? Why is the slope different for the two periods?

5 **Analyzing Results** How does the slope of the graph showing water freezing compare with the slope of the graph before the water starts to freeze? Why is the slope different for the two periods?

Draw Conclusions

6 **Evaluating Data** The particles that make up solids, liquids, and gases are in constant motion. Adding or removing energy causes changes in the movement of these particles. Using this idea, explain why the temperature graphs of the two experiments look the way they do.

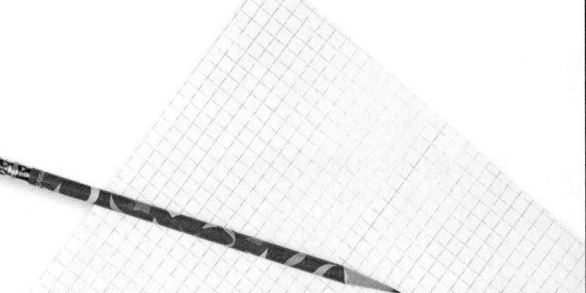

Analyze the Results

1. The temperature remains constant.

2. When energy is removed, the temperature stops falling, and the liquid turns to solid. At this point, the particles have less energy, but the temperature of the water stays the same.

3. The slope of each graph represents the rate of temperature change.

4. Sample answer: The slope is less steep (line should be horizontal) when the water starts to boil. The slope is different because the energy added to the water through heating is making steam rather than increasing the temperature.

5. Sample answer: The slope is less steep (the line should be horizontal) when the water starts to freeze. The slope is different because the removal of energy from the water is allowing crystal structures (ice) to form rather than decreasing the temperature.

Draw Conclusions

6. Sample answer: When the particles speed up enough, water can become gas (steam), which has more energy at the same temperature. Even though energy is being added the whole time, the temperature stops rising when the liquid starts changing into a gas. When the particles slow down enough, the water can become solid ice, which has less energy at the same temperature. Even though energy is being removed the whole time, the temperature stops falling when the liquid starts changing to a solid. The fact that the temperature stops rising or falling explains the parts of the graphs that level off.

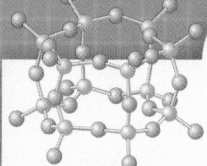

Assignment Guide

Section	Questions
1	1, 5, 12–14
2	2, 6, 11
3	3, 4, 7–10, 15–23
1 and 3	16

ANSWERS

Using Key Terms

1. Solid is the state of matter in which the substance has a definite shape and volume. Liquid is the state in which the substance takes the shape of its container but has a definite volume.

2. Boyle's law states that when the pressure of a gas increases at a constant temperature, its volume decreases. Charles's law states that when the temperature of a gas increases at a constant pressure, its volume increases.

3. Evaporation is the change of a liquid to a gas at the surface of a liquid. Boiling is the change of a liquid to a gas throughout a liquid.

4. Condensation is the change of a gas to a liquid. Sublimation is the change of a substance from a solid to a gas without becoming a liquid.

Understanding Key Ideas

5. b

6. b

7. b

8. a

9. b

10. c

11. a

12. d

13. Sample answer: The particles of liquid water can move past one another and take the shape of a container. Particles in an ice cube are locked in place and cannot move past one another. An ice cube holds its shape no matter what container you put it in.

14. gases, liquids, solids

USING KEY TERMS

For each pair of terms, explain how the meanings of the terms differ.

1. *solid* and *liquid*

2. *Boyle's law* and *Charles's law*

3. *evaporation* and *boiling*

4. *condensation* and *sublimation*

UNDERSTANDING KEY IDEAS

Multiple Choice

5. Which of the following statements best describes the particles of a liquid?
   a. The particles are far apart and moving fast.
   b. The particles are close together but moving past each other.
   c. The particles are far apart and moving slowly.
   d. The particles are closely packed and vibrating in place.

6. Which of the following statements describes what happens as the temperature of a gas in a balloon increases?
   a. The speed of the particles decreases.
   b. The volume of the gas increases, and the speed of the particles increases.
   c. The volume of the gas decreases.
   d. The pressure of the gas decreases.

7. Boiling points and freezing points are examples of
   a. chemical properties.   c. energy.
   b. physical properties.   d. matter.

8. Dew collecting on a spider web in the early morning is an example of
   a. condensation.   c. sublimation.
   b. evaporation.   d. melting.

9. During which change of state do atoms or molecules become more ordered?
   a. boiling   c. melting
   b. condensation   d. sublimation

10. Which of the following changes of state is exothermic?
    a. evaporation   c. freezing
    b. melting   d. All of the above

11. What happens to the volume of a gas inside a cylinder if the temperature does not change but the pressure is reduced?
    a. The volume of the gas increases.
    b. The volume of the gas stays the same.
    c. The volume of the gas decreases.
    d. There is not enough information to determine the answer.

12. The atoms and molecules in matter
    a. are attracted to one another.
    b. are constantly moving.
    c. move faster at higher temperatures.
    d. All of the above

Short Answer

13. Explain why liquid water takes the shape of its container but an ice cube does not.

14. Rank solids, liquids, and gases in order of particle speed from the highest speed to the lowest speed.

Math Skills

15 Kate placed 100 mL of water in five different pans, placed the pans on a windowsill for a week, and measured how much water evaporated from each pan. Draw a graph of her data, which is shown below. Place surface area on the *x*-axis and volume evaporated on the *y*-axis. Is the graph linear or non-linear? What does this information tell you?

Pan number	1	2	3	4	5
Surface area (cm²)	44	82	20	30	65
Volume evaporated (mL)	42	79	19	29	62

CRITICAL THINKING

16 Concept Mapping Use the following terms to create a concept map: *states of matter, solid, liquid, gas, changes of state, freezing, evaporation, condensation,* and *melting.*

17 Analyzing Ideas In the photo below, water is being split to form two new substances, hydrogen and oxygen. Is this a change of state? Explain your answer.

18 Applying Concepts After taking a shower, you notice that small droplets of water cover the mirror. Explain how this happens. Be sure to describe where the water comes from and the changes it goes through.

19 Analyzing Methods To protect their crops during freezing temperatures, orange growers spray water onto the trees and allow it to freeze. In terms of energy lost and energy gained, explain why this practice protects the oranges from damage.

20 Making Inferences At sea level, water boils at 100°C, while methane boils at –161°C. Which of these substances has a stronger force of attraction between its particles? Explain your reasoning.

INTERPRETING GRAPHICS

Use the graph below to answer the questions that follow.

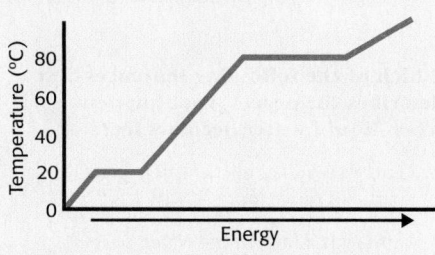

21 What is the boiling point of the substance? What is the melting point?

22 Which state is present at 30°C?

23 How will the substance change if energy is added to the liquid at 20°C?

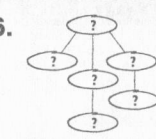

Critical Thinking

16. An answer to this exercise can be found at the end of this book.

17. The splitting of water into hydrogen and oxygen is not a change of state because the substance (water) does not keep its identity during the change. The water is changed into two new substances, hydrogen and oxygen.

18. Sample answer: As you take a shower, some of the liquid water evaporates and becomes a gas. When the gaseous water touches the mirror, the water releases energy to the mirror and condenses into drops of liquid water.

19. Sample answer: Freezing is an exothermic change. As the water freezes, it releases energy. The oranges absorb some of this energy and warm up. (The ice also helps to insulate the oranges from the cold air.)

20. Sample answer: Water has a stronger force of attraction between its particles; A higher temperature, and therefore more energy, is required to separate the water particles from one another than is needed to separate the methane particles from one another.

Interpreting Graphics

21. 80°C; 20°C

22. liquid

23. The temperature of the liquid will rise.

15.

Volume evaporated (mL) / Surface area (cm²)

The graph is linear. Both variables (surface area and volume evaporated) increase together.

CHAPTER RESOURCES

Chapter Resource File

- **Chapter Review** GENERAL
- **Chapter Test A** GENERAL
- **Chapter Test B** ADVANCED
- **Chapter Test C** SPECIAL NEEDS
- **Vocabulary Activity** GENERAL

Workbooks

Study Guide
- Study Guide is also available in Spanish.

Teacher's Notes

To provide practice under more realistic conditions, give students 20 minutes to answer all of the questions in this Standardized Test Preparation.

Answer Key

Question	Answer
1	D
2	C
3	C
4	C
5	A
6	B
7	D
8	C
9	A
10	*
11	*

*See Test Doctor.

Multiple Choice

Use the diagram below to answer question 1.

Substance	Temperature (°C)
Ice	−2
Iced water	0
Water	27
Boiling Water	100

1. **The table above shows data from a laboratory experiment in which Andrew measured the temperatures of water in various states. Which of the following would be a correct conclusion from this experiment?**

   A. The particles in ice water have less energy than the particles in ice.

   B. The particles in ice have more energy than the particles in water.

   C. The particles in iced water have more energy than the particles in boiling water.

   D. The particles in boiling water have more energy than the particles in iced water.

2. **Which of the following sentences best describes the process that happens when liquid water becomes ice?**

   A. Energy is added to the water, so its particles move more slowly.

   B. Energy is added to the water, so its particles move more quickly.

   C. Energy is removed from the water, so its particles lock into place.

   D. Energy is removed from the water, so its particles move apart.

3. **Which of the following could describe oxygen at room temperature?**

   A. It has a constant volume and a definite shape.

   B. It has a constant volume but takes the shape of its container.

   C. Its particles move fast enough to overcome the attraction between them.

   D. Its particles have a very orderly, three-dimensional arrangement.

4. **Kevin compared the viscosities of several substances. Substances A, B, and C flowed at different rates, but substance D did not flow at all. Which of the following is a valid conclusion?**

   A. Substance D must be at its melting point.

   B. Substance D is in the same state of matter as the other substances.

   C. Substance D is neither a liquid nor a gas.

   D. Substance D's particles have little attraction for one another.

5. **In a laboratory experiment, Joel observed water as it vaporized, froze, melted, and condensed. Which of the following is a valid conclusion?**

   A. He observed four different changes of state.

   B. Each of these processes happened at different temperatures.

   C. All of the changes required energy to be absorbed.

   D. All of the changes required energy to be released.

 TEST DOCTOR

Question 1 A: The particles in iced water are at a higher temperature and therefore have more energy than the particles in solid ice. B: The particles in ice are at a lower temperature and therefore have less energy than the particles in water. C: The particles in iced water are at a lower temperature and therefore have less energy than the particles in boiling water. D: Correct.

Question 2 A, B, D: Freezing is a change of state in which energy is removed from a liquid. As

water molecules lose energy at the freezing point, they lock into place and form ice. C: Correct.

Question 3 A: Oxygen is a gas at room temperature. Solid is the state in which matter has both a definite shape and a definite volume. B: Oxygen is a gas. Liquid is the state in which matter has a definite volume but takes the shape of its container. C: Correct. D: Oxygen is a gas. Crystalline solids have a very orderly, three-dimensional arrangement of particles.

Question 4 A: Substance D must be solid because it does not flow. Although Substance D could be a solid at its melting point, it does not have to be at its melting point. B: Substances A, B, and C must be

Use the picture below to answer question 6.

6. **A cup filled to the rim with water was left at room temperature overnight. The figure above shows how much water was left the next morning. Which of the following is a reasonable hypothesis for what happened to the water?**

   A. The water at the surface lost enough energy to evaporate.

   B. The water at the surface gained enough energy to evaporate.

   C. The water at the surface lost enough energy to condense.

   D. The water at the surface gained enough energy to sublimate.

7. **A sealed, inflated beach ball was placed in a freezer overnight. The next day, the ball was still sealed but had shrunk. Analyze the following hypotheses to determine which is the best.**

   A. The pressure inside the ball increased, so the gas particles moved faster.

   B. The gas inside the ball escaped, which caused the ball to shrink.

   C. The temperature of the gas increased, which pushed gas out of the ball.

   D. The temperature of the gas decreased, so the particles of gas moved closer together.

8. **In a laboratory investigation on changes of state, Rebecca observes that the melting point of water is 0°C and that the freezing point of water is 0°C. What can Rebecca conclude from these observations?**

   A. Both melting and freezing are exothermic reactions.

   B. Water boils at 0°C at normal atmospheric pressure.

   C. Melting and freezing can occur at the same temperature.

   D. She made an error in her measurements.

9. **An ad for a brand of dry ice claims that it keeps food cold without getting it wet. Which of the following is a good explanation for this claim?**

   A. Dry ice undergoes sublimation.

   B. Dry ice is not frozen.

   C. Dry ice is colder than regular ice.

   D. Dry ice keeps food from freezing.

Open Response

10. **Describe how the physical properties of solids, liquids, and gases affect how each state of matter behaves when placed into a new container.**

11. **Keisha fills a balloon with helium while inside a heated building. She then takes the balloon outside on a cold winter day. The air pressure is the same inside and outside. Predict what will happen to the balloon and explain your answer.**

liquids or gases because they flow. Substance D is probably a solid because it does not flow. C: Correct. D: Substance D is a solid, so its particles would have a very strong attraction to one another.

Question 5 A: Correct. B: The boiling point of water is 100°C, which means that both vaporization and condensation occur at this temperature. The freezing point of water is 0°C, which means that both freezing and melting take place at this temperature. C, D: Because there are two pairs of opposing changes of state, energy must be absorbed during only two of the changes (vaporization and melting) and energy must be released during the other two changes (condensation and freezing).

Question 6 A: To evaporate, water at the surface needs to gain energy, not lose energy. B: Correct. C: Condensation is the change of state from gas to liquid, not the change of state that occurred overnight was a change of state from a liquid to a gas. D: Sublimation is the change of state from a solid to a gas. The change of state that occurred overnight was a change of state from a liquid to a gas.

Question 7 A: An increase in either the pressure inside the ball or in the speed of the particles would likely cause the volume of the ball to increase. B: Although a loss of gas could cause the

ball to shrink, the ball was still sealed, so this is an unlikely hypothesis. C: An increase in temperature might cause gas to leave the ball. However, the ball was still sealed, so gas could not escape. In addition, when the ball was placed in a freezer, the temperature of the gas would decrease, not increase. D: Correct.

Question 8 A: Melting is an endothermic change because the particles in the substance gain energy. B: More than one change of state can occur at the same temperature, but that does not mean that all changes of state occur at the same temperature. C: Correct. D: Rebecca's observation does not suggest that she made an error in her measurements. The two changes occur at the same temperature, depending on whether the particles are gaining or losing energy.

Question 9 A: Correct. B: Dry ice is frozen carbon dioxide. Because it is solid, it must be a frozen form of some substance. C: Dry ice is colder than water ice, but that does not explain how it could keep food cold without getting it wet. D: Because dry ice is colder than water ice, it would be more likely to cause food to freeze.

Question 10 Full-credit answers should include the following points:

• Solids have definite shape and volume. A solid in a new container will retain its original shape and volume.

• Liquids have definite volume but can change shape. Liquid takes the shape of a new container but its volume will not change.

• Gases can change shape and volume. Gas in a new container will take the shape of the container and expand or contract in volume.

Question 11 Full-credit answers should include the following points:

• The balloon's volume will decrease.

• According to Charles's law, the volume of a gas will decrease as the temperature decreases.

• The helium inside the balloon behaves according to Charles's law because it remains at the same pressure.

Science in Action

Science, Technology, and Society

Discussion — GENERAL

Lead students in a discussion about using heliox for deep-sea diving. Ask students why conducting heat is a disadvantage to divers. (The water is very cold at greater depths, and using heliox could lead to hypothermia.) Ask students to think of ways to overcome this disadvantage. (Answers may vary. Sample answer: Divers could wear heated wet suits to prevent hypothermia.)
LS Verbal

Scientific Discoveries

Background

If enough energy is added to a gas, the gas particles will break apart. This process creates a plasma, the state of matter that is a blend of electrons and positively charged ions. Plasma occurs on Earth in the outer atmosphere, called the *ionosphere*, and in auroras, flames, and lightning. Plasma also forms in neon and fluorescent light bulbs and in plasma screens when energy from an electric current is passed through a gas in the device. The electric current excites the gas particles and creates a plasma.

Science, Technology, and Society

Deep-sea Diving with Helium

Divers who breathe air while deep in the ocean run the risk of suffering from nitrogen narcosis. Nitrogen narcosis produces an alcohol-like effect, which can cause a diver to become disoriented and to use poor judgment. This toxic effect can lead to dangerous behavior. To avoid nitrogen narcosis, divers who work at depths of more than 60 m breathe heliox. *Heliox* is a mixture of helium and oxygen, instead of air. The main disadvantage of heliox is that helium conducts heat about six times faster than nitrogen does, so a diver using heliox will feel cold sooner than a diver who is breathing air.

Math ACTIVITY

There are 2.54 centimeters in one inch. How many feet deep could a diver go before he or she started experiencing nitrogen narcosis?

Scientific Discoveries

The Fourth State of Matter

If you heat water, it will eventually turn into a gas. But what would happen if you kept on heating the gas? Scientists only had to look to the sun for the answer. The sun, like other stars, is made of the fourth state of matter—plasma. Plasma is a superheated gas. Once a gas's temperature rises above 10,000°C to 20,000°C, its particles start to break apart and it becomes plasma. Unlike gas, plasma can create, and be affected by, electrical and magnetic fields. More than 99% of the known universe is made of plasma! Even Earth has some naturally occurring plasma. Plasma can be found in auroras, flames, and lightning.

Social Studies ACTIVITY

Research plasma. Find out how plasma is used in today's technology, such as plasma TVs. How will this new technology affect you and society in general? Describe your findings in a poster.

Answer to Math Activity

Divers can reach depths up to 60 m before experiencing nitrogen narcosis.

60 m × 100 cm/m = 6,000 cm

6000 cm ÷ 2.54 cm/inch = 2,362 inches

2,362 inches ÷ 12 inches/foot = 197 feet

Answer to Social Studies Activity

Answers may vary. Accept any reasonable answer. Students may choose to create a poster about current technology and how they think it will change. They might also describe using fusion energy to replace gasoline and how that would affect society.

Andy Goldsworthy

Nature Artist Most of the art that Andy Goldsworthy creates will melt, decay, evaporate, or just blow away. He uses leaves, water, sticks, rocks, ice, and snow to create art. Goldsworthy observes how nature works and how it changes over time, and uses what he learns to create his art. For example, on cold, sunny mornings, Goldsworthy makes frost shadows. He stands with his back to the sun, which creates a shadow on the ground. The rising sun warms the ground and melts the frost around his shadow. When he steps away, he can see the shape of his body in the frost that is left on the ground.

In his art, Goldsworthy sometimes shows water in the process of changing states. For example, he made huge snowballs filled with branches, pebbles, and flowers. He then stored these snowballs in a freezer until summer, when they were displayed in a museum. As they melted, the snowballs slowly revealed their contents. Goldsworthy says his art reflects nature, because nature is constantly changing. Fortunately, he takes pictures of his art so we can enjoy it even after it disappears!

Language Arts ACTiViTY

Research Andy Goldsworthy's art. Write a one-page review of one of his creations. Be sure to include what you like or don't like about the art.

go.hrw.com

To learn more about these Science in Action topics, visit go.hrw.com and type in the keyword **HP5STAF.**

Current Science

Check out Current Science® articles related to this chapter by visiting go.hrw.com. Just type in the keyword **HP5CS03.**

People Science

Background

Goldsworthy also uses the process of evaporation in his art. He has experimented with the effects of evaporation on clay. As the water in clay evaporates, the clay dries and cracks. Thinner clay dries faster than thicker clay. Goldsworthy discovered that by creating patterns with thicker clay, he could guide where the cracks formed. Goldsworthy has covered many large rocks with clay, which dries, cracks, and falls off in large chunks. Goldsworthy has also covered walls with clay, including a wall in a San Francisco museum. The clay dried and cracked but did not fall off, even through several earthquakes!

ACTiViTY ——— GENERAL

Art in Changing States Have students create their own art to display changing states of matter. They might mimic some of Goldsworthy's art, such as frost shadows or clay-covered rocks. They might create their own way to illustrate matter changing from one state to another. Take photos of students' artwork, and display the photos with a caption explaining how the students created the art and what state of matter it represents. **LS Kinesthetic**

Answer to Language Arts Activity
Answers may vary. Accept any reasonable answer.

Elements, Compounds, and Mixtures
Chapter Planning Guide

Compression guide:
To shorten instruction because of time limitations, omit the Chapter Lab.

OBJECTIVES	LABS, DEMONSTRATIONS, AND ACTIVITIES	TECHNOLOGY RESOURCES
PACING • 90 min pp. 516–521 **Chapter Opener**	**SE Start-up Activity,** p. 517 GENERAL	**OSP Parent Letter** ■ **CD Student Edition on CD-ROM** **CD Guided Reading Audio CD** ■ **TR Chapter Starter Transparency*** **VID Brain Food Video Quiz**
Section 1 Elements • Describe pure substances. • Describe the characteristics of elements, and give examples. • Explain how elements can be identified. • Classify elements according to their properties.	**TE Demonstration** Properties of Aluminum, p. 518 GENERAL **SE Quick Lab** Separating Elements, p. 519 GENERAL **CRF Datasheet for Quick Lab*** **TE Connection Activity** Math, p. 519 GENERAL **LB Labs You Can Eat** An Iron-ic Cereal Experience* BASIC **SE Science in Action** Math, Social Studies, and Language Arts Activities, pp. 540–541 GENERAL	**OSP Lesson Plans** (also in print) **TR Bellringer Transparency*** **TR P8 The Three Major Categories of Elements*** **CD Interactive Explorations CD-ROM** What's the Matter? GENERAL
PACING • 90 min pp. 522–525 **Section 2 Compounds** • Explain how elements make up compounds. • Describe the properties of compounds. • Explain how a compound can be broken down into its elements. • Give examples of common compounds.	**TE Demonstration** Forming Magnesium Oxide, p. 522 GENERAL **SE Quick Lab** Compound Confusion, p. 523 GENERAL **CRF Datasheet for Quick Lab*** **SE Connection to Physics** Electrolysis, p. 524 GENERAL **SE Skills Practice Lab** Flame Tests, p. 534 GENERAL **CRF Datasheet for Chapter Lab***	**OSP Lesson Plans** (also in print) **TR Bellringer Transparency*** **SE Internet Activity,** p. 524 GENERAL **VID Lab Videos for Physical Science**
PACING • 45 min pp. 526–533 **Section 3 Mixtures** • Describe three properties of mixtures. • Describe four methods of separating the parts of a mixture. • Analyze a solution in terms of its solute and solvent. • Explain how concentration affects a solution. • Describe the particles in a suspension. • Explain how a colloid differs from a solution and a suspension.	**TE Activity** Separating Mixtures, p. 527 ◆ GENERAL **TE Demonstration** Filtering a Mixture, p. 527 ◆ GENERAL **TE Connection Activity** Earth Science, p. 528 GENERAL **SE Connection to Language Arts** Alloys, p. 529 GENERAL **TE Connection Activity** Math, p. 529 GENERAL **TE Activity** Comparing Solutions, p. 530 ◆ GENERAL **TE Connection Activity** Math, p. 530 GENERAL **TE Connection Activity** Earth Science, p. 530 GENERAL **SE School-to-Home Activity** Suspensions, p. 532 GENERAL **SE Skills Practice Lab** A Sugar Cube Race!, p. 736 GENERAL **SE Skills Practice Lab** Making Butter, p. 737 GENERAL **SE Model-Making Lab** Unpolluting Water, p. 738 GENERAL **CRF Datasheet for LabBook*** **LB Inquiry Labs** Separation Anxiety* GENERAL **LB Whiz-Bang Demonstrations** Dense Suspense* BASIC **LB EcoLabs & Field Activities** Ozone News Zone* BASIC **LB Long-Term Projects & Research Ideas** A Coincidence?* ADVANCED	**OSP Lesson Plans** (also in print) **TR Bellringer Transparency*** **TR LINK TO EARTH SCIENCE** E31 Three Types of Volcanoes*** **TR P9 Separation of a Mixture*** **TR P10 Solubility Graph*** **CRF SciLinks Activity*** GENERAL

PACING • 90 min

CHAPTER REVIEW, ASSESSMENT, AND STANDARDIZED TEST PREPARATION

CRF Vocabulary Activity* GENERAL
SE Chapter Review, pp. 536–537 GENERAL
CRF Chapter Review* ■ GENERAL
CRF Chapter Tests A* ■ GENERAL, **B*** ADVANCED, **C*** SPECIAL NEEDS
SE Standardized Test Preparation, pp. 538–539 GENERAL
CRF Standardized Test Preparation* GENERAL
CRF Performance-Based Assessment* GENERAL
OSP Test Generator, Test Item Listing

Online and Technology Resources

Holt Online Learning

Visit go.hrw.com for access to Holt Online Learning, or enter the keyword **HS7 Home** for a variety of free online resources.

One-Stop Planner® CD-ROM

This CD-ROM package includes:
• Lab Materials QuickList Software
• Holt Calendar Planner
• Customizable Lesson Plans
• Printable Worksheets
• ExamView® Test Generator
• Interactive Teacher's Edition
• Holt PuzzlePro®
• Holt PowerPoint® Resources

SKILLS DEVELOPMENT RESOURCES | SECTION REVIEW AND ASSESSMENT | CORRELATIONS

SKILLS DEVELOPMENT RESOURCES	SECTION REVIEW AND ASSESSMENT	CORRELATIONS
SE Pre-Reading Activity, p. 516 GENERAL **OSP** Science Puzzlers, Twisters & Teasers* GENERAL		**National Science Education Standards** PS 1a; SAI 1, 2; UCP 1, 2, 3
CRF Directed Reading A* ■ BASIC, B* SPECIAL NEEDS **WB** Workbook* Struggling Readers **CRF** Vocabulary and Section Summary* ■ GENERAL **SE** Reading Strategy Reading Organizer, p. 518 GENERAL **TE** Support for English Language Learners, p. 519 **MS** Math Skills for Science Percentages, Fractions, and Decimals* GENERAL **SS** Science Skills Introduction to Graphs* GENERAL	**SE** Reading Checks, pp. 518, 520 GENERAL **TE** Reteaching, p. 520 BASIC **TE** Quiz, p. 520 GENERAL **TE** Alternative Assessment, p. 520 GENERAL **SE** Section Review,* p. 521 GENERAL **CRF** Section Quiz* ■ GENERAL	PS 1a, 1c; SAI 1; UCP 1, 2
CRF Directed Reading A* ■ BASIC, B* SPECIAL NEEDS **WB** Workbook* Struggling Readers **CRF** Vocabulary and Section Summary* ■ GENERAL **SE** Reading Strategy Prediction Guide, p. 522 GENERAL **TE** Inclusion Strategies, p. 523 **TE** Support for English Language Learners, p. 523	**SE** Reading Checks, pp. 523, 524 GENERAL **TE** Reteaching, p. 524 BASIC **TE** Quiz, p. 524 GENERAL **TE** Alternative Assessment, p. 524 GENERAL **SE** Section Review,* p. 525 ■ GENERAL **CRF** Section Quiz* ■ GENERAL	UCP 1, 2; SAI 2; SPSP 5; PS 1a, 1c; *Chapter Lab:* UCP 1, 2; SPSP 5
CRF Directed Reading A* ■ BASIC, B* SPECIAL NEEDS **WB** Workbook* Struggling Readers **CRF** Vocabulary and Section Summary* ■ GENERAL **SE** Reading Strategy Reading Organizer, p. 526 GENERAL **TE** Support for English Language Learners, p. 528 **TE** Reading Strategy Prediction Guide, p. 529 GENERAL **SE** Math Focus Calculating Concentration, p. 530 GENERAL **TE** Inclusion Strategies, p. 531 **MS** Math Skills for Science Parts of 100: Calculating Percentages GENERAL **MS** Math Skills for Science Using Proportions and Cross-Multiplication GENERAL **CRF** Reinforcement Worksheet It's All Mixed Up* BASIC **CRF** Critical Thinking Jet Smart* ADVANCED	**SE** Reading Checks, pp. 526, 529, 531, 532 GENERAL **TE** Reteaching, p. 532 BASIC **TE** Quiz, p. 532 GENERAL **TE** Alternative Assessment, p. 532 GENERAL **SE** Section Review,* p. 533 ■ GENERAL **CRF** Section Quiz* ■ GENERAL	UCP 1, 2; SAI 1, 2; SPSP 3; *LabBook:* UCP 1, 2; SAI 1, 2; ST 2; SPSP 5

www.scilinks.org
Maintained by the **National Science Teachers Association.** See Chapter Enrichment pages that follow for a complete list of topics.

Check out *Current Science* articles and activities by visiting the HRW Web site at **go.hrw.com.** Just type in the keyword **HP5CS04T.**

Classroom Videos
• **Lab Videos** demonstrate the chapter lab.
• **Brain Food Video Quizzes** help students review the chapter material.

Classroom CD-ROMs
• **Guided Reading Audio CD** (Also in Spanish)
• **Interactive Explorations**
• **Virtual Investigations**
• **Visual Concepts**
• **Science Tutor**

Holt Lab Generator CD-ROM
Search for any lab by topic, standard, difficulty level, or time. Edit any lab to fit your needs, or create your own labs. Use the Lab Materials QuickList software to customize your lab materials list.

Visual Resources

CHAPTER STARTER TRANSPARENCY

Elements, Compounds, and Mixtures   CHAPTER STARTER

This Really Happened!

In the early morning hours of April 15, 1912, the *Titanic*, the largest ship ever to set sail, sank on its first voyage. The *Titanic* was considered to be unsinkable, yet more than 1,500 of its passengers and crew were killed after it hit an iceberg and sank.

How could an iceberg, which is made of ice, destroy the 2.5 cm thick steel plates that made up the *Titanic*'s hull? Analysis of a recovered piece of the *Titanic*'s hull showed that the steel contained large amounts of the element sulfur, which is a normal component of steel. However, in this case, the steel contained much more sulfur than is the

standard for steel made today. The excess sulfur may have caused the steel to be brittle, much like glass. Scientists suspect that this brittle steel may have cracked on impact with the iceberg, allowing water to enter the hull.

Could something as simple as using less sulfur in the *Titanic*'s steel have prevented the ship from sinking? We may never know. What is known, however, is that the composition of compounds and mixtures is very important in preventing future disasters. In this chapter, you will learn about elements and how they are assembled into compounds and mixtures with some very different properties.

This piece of steel hull from the Titanic (at left) was recovered from the wreck.

BELLRINGER TRANSPARENCIES

Elements, Compounds, and Mixtures   BELLRINGER TRANSPARENCY

Section: Elements
What do gold, iron, and aluminum have in common? What do oxygen, neon, and sulfur have in common? How is silicon different from aluminum or oxygen?

Record your responses in your **science journal.**

Section: Compounds
The word *compound* refers to something that consists of two or more parts. How might you make a compound using elements? How many compounds can you think of that you use every day?

Record your answers in your **science journal.**

TEACHING TRANSPARENCIES

The Three Major Categories of Elements

P8

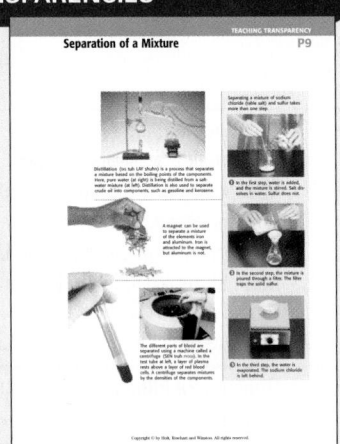

Separation of a Mixture   P9

TEACHING TRANSPARENCIES

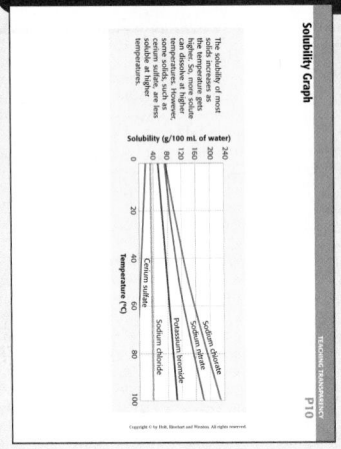

Solubility Graph

P10

Three Types of Volcanoes   E31

LINK TO EARTH SCIENCE

Chapter: Volcanoes

CONCEPT MAPPING TRANSPARENCY

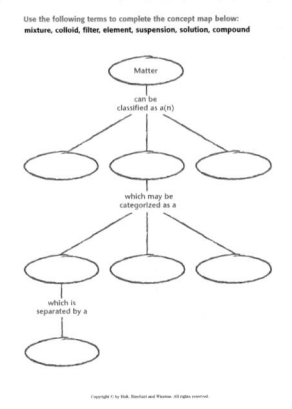

ELEMENTS, COMPOUNDS, AND MIXTURES   CONCEPT MAPPING TRANSPARENCY

Use the following terms to complete the concept map below: **mixture, colloid, filter, element, suspension, solution, compound**

Planning Resources

LESSON PLANS

Lesson Plan   SAMPLE

Section: Waves

Pacing
Regular Schedule: with labs2 days   without labs2 days
Block Schedule: with labs1 1/2 days   without labs1 day

Objectives
1. Relate the seven properties of life to a living organism.
2. Describe seven themes that can help you to organize what you learn about biology.
3. Identify the tiny structures that make up all living organisms.
4. Differentiate between reproduction and heredity and between metabolism and homeostasis.

National Science Education Standards Covered
LSInter6:Cells have particular structures that underlie their functions.
LSMat1:Most cell functions involve chemical reactions.
LSBeh1:Cells move and use information to guide their functions.
UCP1:Cell functions are regulated.
SI1: Cells can differentiate and form complete multicellular organisms.
PS1: Species evolve over time.
ESS1: The great diversity of organisms is the result of more than 3.5 billion years of evolution.
ESS2: Natural selection and its evolutionary consequences provide a scientific explanation for the fossil record of ancient life forms as well as for the striking molecular similarities observed among the diverse species of living organisms.
ST1: The millions of different species of plants, animals, and microorganisms that live on Earth today are related by descent from common ancestors.
ST2: The energy for life primarily comes from the sun.
SPSP1: The complexity and organization of organisms accommodates the need for obtaining, transforming, transporting, releasing, and eliminating the matter and energy used to sustain the organism.
SPSP6: As matter and energy flow through different levels of organization of living systems—cells, organs, communities—and between living systems and the physical environment, chemicals are recombined in different ways.
HNS1: Organisms have behavioral responses to internal changes and to external stimuli.

PARENT LETTER

SAMPLE

Dear Parent,

Your son's or daughter's science class will soon begin exploring the chapter entitled "The World of Physical Science." In this chapter, students will learn about how the scientific method applies to the world of physical science and the role of physical science in the world. By the end of the chapter, students should demonstrate a clear understanding of the chapter's main ideas and be able to discuss the following topics:

1. physical science in the study of energy and matter (Section 1)
2. the role of physical science in the world around them (Section 1)
3. careers that rely on physical science (Section 1)
4. the steps used in the scientific method (Section 2)
5. examples of technology (Section 2)
6. how the scientific method is used to answer questions and solve problems (Section 2)
7. how our knowledge of science changes over time (Section 2)
8. how models represent real objects or systems (Section 3)
9. the importance of the International System of Units (Section 4)
10. the appropriate units to use for particular measurements (Section 4)
11. how area and density are derived quantities (Section 4)

Questions to Ask Along the Way

You can help your son or daughter learn about these topics by asking interesting questions such as the following:

• What are some surprising careers that one physical science?
• What is a characteristic of a good hypothesis?
• When is it a good idea to use a model?
• Why do Americans measure things in terms of inches and yards and meters?

ALSO IN SPANISH

TEST ITEM LISTING

TEST ITEM LISTING
The World of Science   SAMPLE

MULTIPLE CHOICE

1. A limitation of models is that
   a. they are large enough to see.
   b. they do not act exactly like the things that they model.
   c. they are smaller than the things that they model.
   d. they model unfamiliar things.
   Answer: B   Difficulty: 1   Section: 3   Objective: 2

2. The length 10 is be equal to
   a. 100 cm.   c. 10,000 mm.
   b. 1,000 cm.   d. Both (b) and (c)
   Answer: B   Difficulty: 1   Section: 3   Objective: 2

3. To be valid, a hypothesis must be
   a. testable.   c. made into a law.
   b. supported by evidence.   d. Both (a) and (b)
   Answer: B   Difficulty: 1   Section: 2   Objective: 2 1

4. The statement "Sheila has a stain on her shirt" is an example of a(n)
   a. law.   c. observation.
   b. hypothesis.   d. prediction.
   Answer: B   Difficulty: 1   Section: 2   Objective: 2

5. A hypothesis is often developed out of
   a. observations.   c. laws.
   b. experiments.   d. Both (a) and (b)
   Answer: B   Difficulty: 1   Section: 2   Objective: 2

6. How many milliliters are in 3.5 kL?
   a. 3,500 mL   c. 3,500, 000 mL
   b. 0.0035 mL   d. 35,000 mL
   Answer: B   Difficulty: 1   Section: 3   Objective: 2

7. A map of Seattle is an example of a
   a. law.   c. model.
   b. theory.   d. unit.
   Answer: B   Difficulty: 1   Section: 3   Objective: 2

8. A lab has the safety icons shown below. These icons mean that you should wear
   a. only safety goggles.   c. safety goggles and a lab apron.
   b. only a lab apron.   d. safety goggles, a lab apron, and gloves.
   Answer: B   Difficulty: 1   Section: 3   Objective: 3

9. The law of conservation of mass says the the total mass before a chemical change is
   a. more than the total mass after the change.
   b. less than the total mass after the change.
   c. the same as the total mass after the change.
   d. zero once the are the total mass after the change.
   Answer: B   Difficulty: 1   Section: 3   Objective: 2

10. In which of the following areas might you find a geochemist at work?
    a. studying the chemistry of rocks   c. studying fishes
    b. studying forestry   d. studying the atmosphere
    Answer: B   Difficulty: 1   Section: 3

One-Stop Planner® CD-ROM

This CD-ROM includes all of the resources shown here and the following time-saving tools:

• **Lab Materials QuickList Software**
• **Customizable lesson plans**
• **Holt Calendar Planner**
• **The powerful ExamView® Test Generator**

Meeting Individual Needs

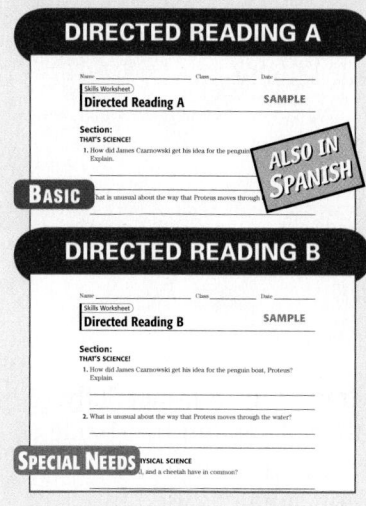

DIRECTED READING A

Skills Worksheet
Directed Reading A SAMPLE
Section: THAT'S SCIENCE!
1. How did James Czarnowski get his idea for the penguin...
Explain.

ALSO IN SPANISH

BASIC

DIRECTED READING B

Skills Worksheet
Directed Reading B SAMPLE
Section: THAT'S SCIENCE!
1. How did James Czarnowski get his idea for the penguin boat, Proteus? Explain.

2. What is unusual about the way that Proteus moves through the water?

SPECIAL NEEDS

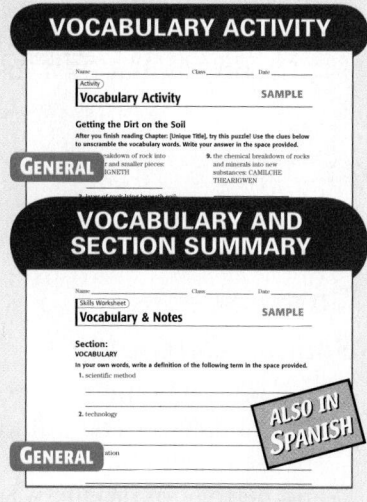

VOCABULARY ACTIVITY

Activity
Vocabulary Activity SAMPLE
Getting the Dirt on the Soil
After you finish reading Chapter: [Unique Title], try this puzzle! Use the clues below to unscramble the vocabulary words. Write your answer in the space provided.

GENERAL

VOCABULARY AND SECTION SUMMARY

Skills Worksheet
Vocabulary & Notes SAMPLE
Section: VOCABULARY
In your own words, write a definition of the following term in the space provided.
1. scientific method

2. technology

ALSO IN SPANISH

GENERAL

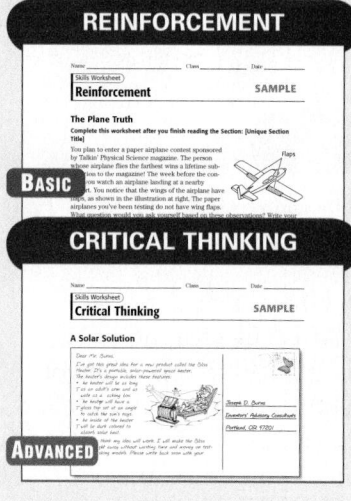

REINFORCEMENT

Skills Worksheet
Reinforcement SAMPLE
The Plane Truth
Complete this worksheet after you finish reading the Section: [Unique Section Title]

BASIC

CRITICAL THINKING

Skills Worksheet
Critical Thinking SAMPLE
A Solar Solution

ADVANCED

SCILINKS ACTIVITY

SciLinks Activity SAMPLE
MARINE ECOSYSTEMS
Go to www.scilinks.org. To find links related to marine ecosystems, type in the keyword...

GENERAL

SCIENCE PUZZLERS, TWISTERS & TEASERS

CHAPTER
SCIENCE PUZZLERS, TWISTERS & TEASERS
Elements, Compounds, and Mixtures
I Am Not a Metalloid
1. Professor Medeski, the mad scientist, wants to create an army of metalloids to take over the world.

GENERAL

Labs and Activities

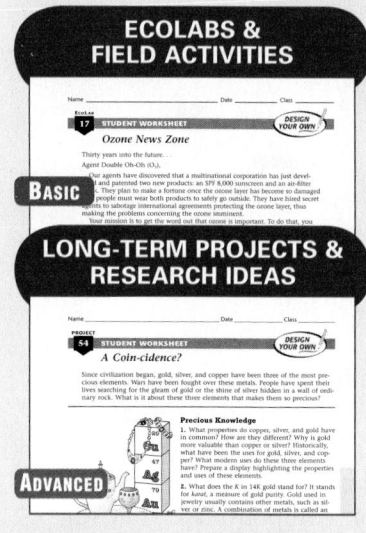

ECOLABS & FIELD ACTIVITIES

EcoLab
17 **STUDENT WORKSHEET** DESIGN YOUR OWN
Ozone News Zone
Thirty years into the future......
Agent Double Oh-Oh (O₃),

BASIC

LONG-TERM PROJECTS & RESEARCH IDEAS

PROJECT
54 **STUDENT WORKSHEET** DESIGN YOUR OWN
A Coin-cidence?
Since civilization began, gold, silver, and copper have been three of the most precious elements.

Precious Knowledge

ADVANCED

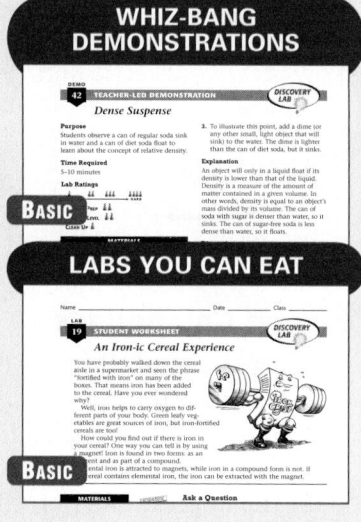

WHIZ-BANG DEMONSTRATIONS

DEMO
42 **TEACHER-LED DEMONSTRATION** DISCOVERY LAB
Dense Suspense
Purpose
Students observe a can of regular soda sink in water and a can of diet soda float to learn about the concept of relative density.
Time Required
5–10 minutes
Lab Ratings

BASIC

LABS YOU CAN EAT

LAB
19 **STUDENT WORKSHEET** DISCOVERY LAB
An Iron-ic Cereal Experience

BASIC

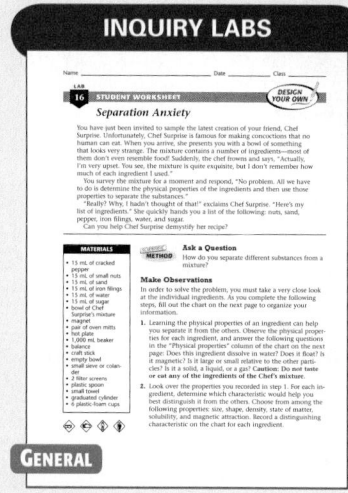

INQUIRY LABS

LAB
16 **STUDENT WORKSHEET** DESIGN YOUR OWN
Separation Anxiety

MATERIALS
Ask a Question

GENERAL

DATASHEETS FOR QUICK LABS

TEACHER RESOURCE PAGE
Quick Lab **DATASHEET FOR QUICK LAB**
Reaction to Stress SAMPLE
Background

DATASHEETS FOR CHAPTER LABS

TEACHER RESOURCE PAGE
Skills Practice Lab **DATASHEET FOR CHAPTER LAB**
Using Scientific Methods SAMPLE
Teacher's Notes
TIME REQUIRED
One 45-minute class period.

DATASHEETS FOR LABBOOK

TEACHER RESOURCE PAGE
Skills Practice Lab **DATASHEET FOR LABBOOK LAB**
Does It All Add Up? SAMPLE
Teacher's Notes
TIME REQUIRED
One 45-minute class period.

Review and Assessments

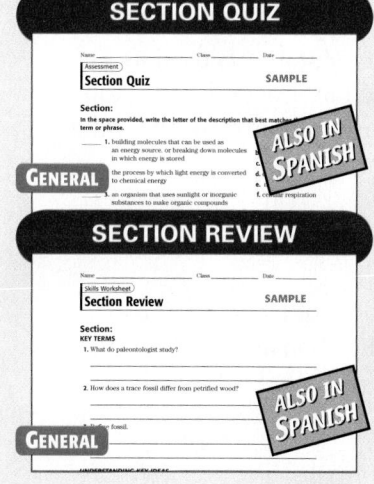

SECTION QUIZ

Assessment
Section Quiz SAMPLE
Section:
In the space provided, write the letter of the description that best matches the term or phrase.

ALSO IN SPANISH

GENERAL

SECTION REVIEW

Skills Worksheet
Section Review SAMPLE
Section: KEY TERMS
1. What do paleontologists study?

2. How does a trace fossil differ from petrified wood?

ALSO IN SPANISH

GENERAL

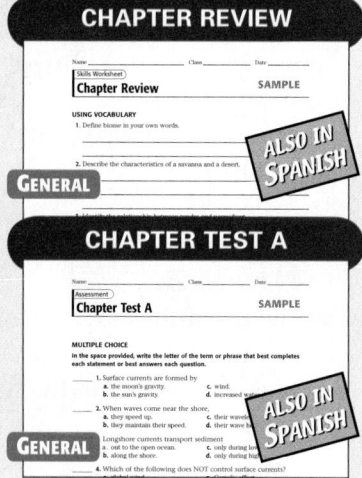

CHAPTER REVIEW

Skills Worksheet
Chapter Review SAMPLE
USING VOCABULARY
1. Define biome in your own words.

2. Describe the characteristics of a savanna and a desert.

ALSO IN SPANISH

GENERAL

CHAPTER TEST A

Assessment
Chapter Test A SAMPLE
MULTIPLE CHOICE
In the space provided, write the letter of the term or phrase that best completes each statement or best answers each question.
1. Surface currents are formed by
   a. the moon's gravity.   c. wind.
   b. the sun's gravity.   d. increased water...

ALSO IN SPANISH

GENERAL

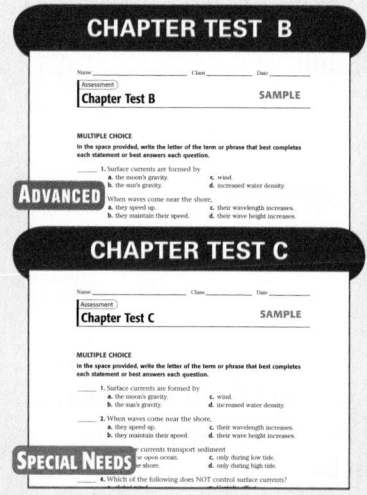

CHAPTER TEST B

Assessment
Chapter Test B SAMPLE
MULTIPLE CHOICE
In the space provided, write the letter of the term or phrase that best completes each statement or best answers each question.
1. Surface currents are formed by
   a. the moon's gravity.   c. wind.
   b. the sun's gravity.   d. increased water density.
2. When waves come near the shore,
   a. they speed up.   c. their wavelength increases.
   b. they maintain their speed. d. their wave height increases.

ADVANCED

CHAPTER TEST C

Assessment
Chapter Test C SAMPLE
MULTIPLE CHOICE
In the space provided, write the letter of the term or phrase that best completes each statement or best answers each question.
1. Surface currents are formed by
   a. the moon's gravity.   c. wind.
   b. the sun's gravity.   d. increased water density.
2. When waves come near the shore,
   a. they speed up.   c. their wavelength increases.
   b. they maintain their speed. d. their wave height increases.

SPECIAL NEEDS

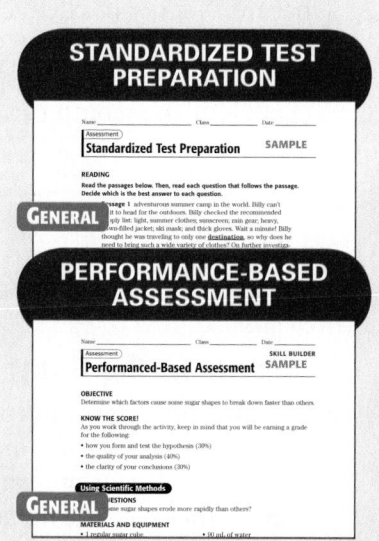

STANDARDIZED TEST PREPARATION

Assessment
Standardized Test Preparation SAMPLE
READING
Read the passages below. Then, read each question that follows the passage. Decide which is the best answer to each question.

GENERAL

PERFORMANCE-BASED ASSESSMENT

Assessment
Performanced-Based Assessment SKILL BUILDER
SAMPLE
OBJECTIVE
Determine which factors cause some sugar shapes to break down faster than others.
KNOW THE SCORE!
As you work through the activity, keep in mind that you will be earning a grade for the following:
• how you form and test the hypothesis (30%)
• the quality of your analysis (40%)
• the clarity of your conclusions (30%)

GENERAL

This Chapter Enrichment provides relevant and interesting information to expand and enhance your presentation of the chapter material.

Section 1

Elements

Electrolysis

● Sir Humphry Davy (1778–1829) was a professor at England's Royal Institution. After the creation of the voltaic pile in 1800, Davy built a battery made of voltaic cells and applied the electric current to potash and to soda. The compounds decomposed to form two previously unknown elements—potassium and sodium. He later used electrolysis to isolate the elements magnesium, calcium, strontium, barium, boron, and silicon.

Gold—A Metal

● Gold is often found in its elemental state because it is not a chemically reactive element. The ancient Egyptians hammered gold into sheets so thin that it took 367,000 leaves to make a pile 2.5 cm high. Gold is often used with other metals in jewelry because it can be reshaped easily.

Sulfur—A Nonmetal

● Sulfur is found both uncombined and combined in nature. A series of chemical reactions causes uncombined sulfur to form and fall onto the slopes of volcanoes in a volcanic eruption. Sulfur is also found in crystals at the mouth of volcanic vents.

Elements in the Body

● Sodium and potassium compounds in blood, muscle tissue, and nerve tissue are vital to the human body. These are only two of many elements present in compounds that keep the human body functioning properly.

Is That a Fact!

◆ Jupiter's moon Io appears yellow because of large deposits of sulfur from volcanic activity.

Section 2

Compounds

Sodium Compounds

● Sodium compounds are very important commercially. For example, several million tons of sodium hydroxide are used each year to make paper, other chemicals, and petroleum products. Sodium sulfate is used in the manufacture of paper, glass, and detergents, and sodium silicate is used in the manufacture of soaps and detergents.

Silicon Compounds

● In nature, most silicon is combined with oxygen to form silicon dioxide. Silicon dioxide makes up sand, flint, quartz, and opal. Silicon is also found combined with metals such as iron and aluminum. One reason for the large number of silicon compounds is that silicon forms long chains of atoms, often in the form of silicates (compounds of silicon, oxygen, and a metal).

● When silicon dioxide contains small amounts of manganese or iron, it forms a type of quartz called amethyst, which is purple in color and is used as a gemstone. Many silicates, such as emerald, jade, aquamarine, garnet, opal, onyx, and moonstone, are valued as gemstones.

Is That a Fact!

◆ The greenish color of the Statue of Liberty is caused by the compound copper(II) carbonate, which formed when the copper in the statue reacted with carbon dioxide and water.

Carbon Compounds

● In 1945, Dorothy Hodgkin used X-ray diffraction to determine the structure of penicillin. Once its structure was known, penicillin could be synthesized and mass-produced. Hodgkin went on to determine the structures of insulin and vitamin B_{12}.

● The science of carbon compounds, organic chemistry, has produced plastics, fuels, medicines, fibers, and armor. Carbon compounds are everywhere, and our lives would be vastly different without plastic containers, gasoline, penicillin, nylon, and Teflon®, all of which are made from carbon compounds.

Section 3

Mixtures

Describing Solution Concentrations

● Students are shown three methods of describing how much solute is dissolved in a solvent. The most general method uses the terms *concentrated* and *dilute*. Describing a solution in terms of its saturation is more specific because it relates the amount of solute to a specific number value. Calculating the *concentration* is the most specific method because it gives a number value for the solution.

Supersaturated Solutions

● A solution that contains more dissolved solute than is normally possible is *supersaturated*. Supersaturated solutions will become saturated solutions when some of the solute comes out of the solution. This can occur if more solute is added or if the solution is shaken. To make a supersaturated solution, make a saturated solution at a higher temperature; then, allow it to cool undisturbed. Several kinds of reusable hand warmers make use of supersaturated solutions.

Colloids

● Colloids resist separation for several reasons. The small particle size makes gravitational force less effective in causing their separation. Another factor is the constant, random motion of the colloid particles, called *Brownian motion*. Third, in any colloid, all the particles have the same charge and will repel each other.

Colloids You Know

● Gels are colloids in which solid particles are spread out in a liquid. Aerosols are colloids made with solid or liquid particles that are suspended in a gas. Emulsions are colloids made of two liquids. Smog is a colloid of dust and other solid particles in the air.

SciLINKS®

NSTA

Developed and maintained by the National Science Teachers Association

SciLinks is maintained by the National Science Teachers Association to provide you and your students with interesting, up-to-date links that will enrich your classroom presentation of the chapter.

Visit www.scilinks.org and enter the SciLinks code for more information about the topic listed.

Topic: Elements
SciLinks code: HSM0496

Topic: Mixtures
SciLinks code: HSM0974

Topic: Compounds
SciLinks code: HSM0332

Overview

Tell students that this chapter will help them learn about elements, compounds, and mixtures. Students will learn the properties of each classification of matter.

Assessing Prior Knowledge

Students should be familiar with the following topics:

• states of matter

• SI units of measurement

Identifying Misconceptions

As students learn the material in this chapter, some of them may be confused about the term *molecule*. The text states that a particle of a compound is a molecule. However, students should understand that it is not true that a molecule can be only a particle of a compound. For example, oxygen gas is not a compound because it is not made of atoms of two or more elements. But a particle of oxygen gas (O_2) is still a molecule—it is a molecule of an element.

19

Elements, Compounds, and Mixtures

The Big Idea

Matter can be classified into elements, compounds, and mixtures.

About the Photo

Within these liquid-filled glass lamps, colored globs slowly rise and fall. But what are these liquids, and what keeps them from mixing together? The liquid inside these lamps is a mixture. This mixture is composed of four compounds, which include mineral oil, wax, water, and alcohol. The water and alcohol mix, but they remain separated from the globs of wax and oil.

PRE-READING ACTIVITY

FOLDNOTES **Key-Term Fold** Before you read the chapter, create the FoldNote entitled "Key-Term Fold" described in the **Study Skills** section of the Appendix. Write a key term from the chapter on each tab of the key-term fold. Under each tab, write the definition of the key term.

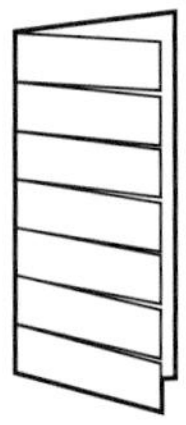

Standards Correlations

National Science Education Standards

The following codes indicate the National Science Education Standards that correlate to this chapter. The full text of the standards is at the front of the book.

Chapter Opener
UCP 1, 2, 3; SAI 1, 2; PS 1a

Section 1 Elements
UCP 1, 2; SAI 1; PS 1a, 1c

Section 2 Compounds
UCP 1, 2; SAI 2; SPSP 5; PS 1a, 1c

Section 3 Mixtures
UCP 1, 2; SAI 1, 2; SPSP 3; *LabBook:* UCP 1, 2; SAI 1, 2; ST 2; SPSP 5

Chapter Lab
UCP 1, 2; SPSP 5

Chapter Review
SAI 1; PS 1a, 1c

Science in Action
ST 1, 2; SPSP 5

START-UP ACTIVITY
MATERIALS

FOR EACH GROUP
- cup or beaker, clear plastic
- marker, water-soluble, black, felt-tip (not permanent marker)
- pencil
- strip of paper from a coffee filter or filter paper, 3 cm x 15 cm
- tape
- water

Teacher's Notes: The size of the strips can be adjusted to better fit the cups that students will be using. You might want students to wear lab aprons during this activity. This activity works best if students are given a variety of brands of markers. Brands that are known to work include Mr. Sketch®, Vis-à-Vis®, Crayola Washable®, and Flair®. Test the markers for suitability. This procedure (called *chromatography*) can be used to identify a sample: Students can determine the type of marker you used by comparing the pattern of colors on your paper with the pattern on theirs.

Answers

1. The ink in the dot separated into several colors and moved up the paper.

2. Answers may vary. If several varieties of markers are used, differences in the order and colors of ink can be seen.

4. The process involved is a physical change. The colors of ink are separated without changing their chemical makeup.

START-UP ACTIVITY

Mystery Mixture

In this activity, you will separate the different dyes found in an ink mixture.

Procedure

1. Place a **pencil** on top of a **clear plastic cup.** Tear a strip of paper (3 cm × 15 cm) from a **coffee filter.** Wrap one end of the strip around a pencil so that the other end will touch the bottom of the plastic cup. Use **tape** to attach the paper to the pencil.

2. Take the paper out of the cup. Using a **water-soluble black marker,** make a small dot in the center of the strip about 2 cm from the bottom.

3. Pour **water** in the cup to a depth of 1 cm. Lower the paper into the cup. Keep the dot above water.

4. Remove the paper when the water is 1 cm from the top. Record your observations.

Analysis

1. What happened as the paper soaked up the water?

2. Which colors make up the marker's black ink?

3. Compare your results with those of your classmates. Record your observations.

4. Is the process used to make the ink separate a physical or a chemical change? Explain.

This Really Happened!

In the early morning hours of April 15, 1912, the *Titanic*, the largest ship ever to set sail, sank on its first voyage. The *Titanic* was considered to be unsinkable, yet more than 1,500 of its passengers and crew were killed after it hit an iceberg and sank.

How could an iceberg, which is made of ice, destroy the 2.5 cm thick steel plates that made up the *Titanic*'s hull? Analysis of a recovered piece of the *Titanic*'s hull showed that the steel contained large amounts of the element sulfur, which is a normal component of steel. However, in this case, the steel contained much more sulfur than is the

standard for steel made today. The excess sulfur may have caused the steel to be brittle, much like glass. Scientists suspect that this brittle steel may have cracked on impact with the iceberg, allowing water to enter the hull.

Could something as simple as using less sulfur in the *Titanic*'s steel have prevented the ship from sinking? We may never know. What is known, however, is that the composition of compounds and mixtures is very important in preventing future disasters. In this chapter, you will learn about elements and how they are assembled into compounds and mixtures with some very different properties.

This piece of steel hull from the Titanic (at left) was recovered from the wreck.

Chapter Starter Transparency
Use this transparency to help students begin thinking about elements, compounds, and mixtures.

CHAPTER RESOURCES

Technology

Transparencies
- Chapter Starter Transparency

READING SKILLS

Student Edition on CD-ROM

Guided Reading Audio CD
- English or Spanish

Classroom Videos
- Brain Food Video Quiz

Workbooks

Science Puzzlers, Twisters & Teasers
- Elements, Compounds, and Mixtures **GENERAL**

SECTION
1

Focus

Overview

This section explains the characteristics of elements and gives examples of these characteristics. It also explains how to identify and classify elements as metals, nonmetals, and metalloids based on their properties.

📀 Bellringer

Have students use **Figure 4** to help them answer the following question: "What do gold, iron, and aluminum have in common? What do oxygen, neon, and sulfur have in common? How is silicon different from aluminum or oxygen?"

Motivate

Demonstration — GENERAL

Properties of Aluminum Hold up a large piece of heavy-duty aluminum foil, and ask students to identify it. Fold the foil into a strip. Demonstrate that it will conduct electric current by touching both electrodes of a conductivity apparatus to the strip. (Do not touch the metal strip while it is attached to the apparatus.) Next, bunch the foil into a ball, and then flatten it by pounding it with a hammer. Ask students to list as many properties of aluminum as they can.
LS Visual

What You Will Learn

● Describe pure substances.
● Describe the characteristics of elements, and give examples.
● Explain how elements can be identified.
● Classify elements according to their properties.

Vocabulary

element   nonmetal
pure substance   metalloid
metal

READING STRATEGY

Reading Organizer As you read this section, make a concept map by using the terms above.

Elements

Imagine that you work for the Break-It-Down Company. Your job is to break down materials into simpler substances.

You haven't had any trouble breaking down materials so far. But one rainy Monday morning, you get a material that seems very hard to break down. First, you try physical changes, such as crushing and melting. But these do not change the material into something simpler. Next, you try some chemical changes, such as passing an electric current through the material. These do not change it either. What's going on?

Elements, the Simplest Substances

You couldn't break down the material described above because it is an element. An **element** is a pure substance that cannot be separated into simpler substances by physical or chemical means. In this section, you'll learn about elements and the properties that help you classify them.

Only One Type of Particle

Elements are pure substances. A **pure substance** is a substance in which there is only one type of particle. So, each element contains only one type of particle. These particles, called *atoms*, are much too small for us to see. For example, every atom in a 5 g nugget of the element gold is like every other atom of gold. The particles of a pure substance are alike no matter where they are found, as shown in **Figure 1**.

✔ **Reading Check** Explain why an element is a pure substance. (*See the Appendix for answers to Reading Checks.*)

Figure 1 *A meteorite might travel more than 400 million kilometers to reach Earth. But the particles of iron in a meteorite, a steel spoon, and even steel braces are alike.*

CHAPTER RESOURCES

Chapter Resource File

 • **Lesson Plan**
• **Directed Reading A** BASIC, **B** SPECIAL NEEDS

Technology

 Transparencies
• Bellringer

Workbooks

 Interactive Textbook Struggling Readers

 Math Skills for Science
• Percentages, Fractions, and Decimals GENERAL

Science Skills
• Introduction to Graphs GENERAL

BRAIN FOOD

Naming Particles Correctly Three particle names are used when discussing pure substances. The term *atom* is used for most elements. The term *molecule* is used for diatomic elements. *Molecule* is also used for covalent compounds. The term *formula unit* is used for ionic compounds, although the term *molecule* is also widely used and accepted.

Properties of Elements

Each element can be identified by its unique set of properties. For example, each element has its own *characteristic properties*. These properties do not depend on the amount of the element present. Characteristic properties include some physical properties, such as boiling point, melting point, and density. Chemical properties, such as reactivity with acid, are also characteristic properties.

An element may share a property with another element, but other properties can help you tell the elements apart. For example, the elements helium and krypton are both unreactive gases. However, the densities (mass per unit volume) of these elements are different. Helium is less dense than air. A helium-filled balloon will float up if it is released. Krypton is denser than air. A krypton-filled balloon will sink to the ground if it is released.

Identifying Elements by Their Properties

Look at the elements shown in **Figure 2.** These three elements have some similar properties. But each element can be identified by its unique set of properties.

Notice that the physical properties shown in **Figure 2** include melting point and density. Other physical properties, such as color, hardness, and texture, could be added to the list. Chemical properties might also be useful. For example, some elements, such as hydrogen and carbon, are flammable. Other elements, such as sodium, react with oxygen at room temperature. Still other elements, including zinc, are reactive with acid.

Quick Lab

Separating Elements

1. Examine a sample of nails provided by your teacher.
2. Your sample has **aluminum nails** and **iron nails.** Try to separate the two kinds of nails. Group similar nails into piles.
3. Pass a **bar magnet** over each pile of nails. Record your results.
4. Were you successful in completely separating the two types of nails? Explain.
5. Based on your observations, explain how the properties of aluminum and iron could be used to separate cans in a recycling plant.

Figure 2 The Unique Properties of Elements

Cobalt	Iron	Nickel
		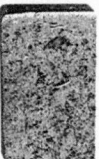

Cobalt
- Melting point: 1,495°C
- Density: 8.9 g/cm³
- Conducts electric current and heat energy
- Unreactive with oxygen in the air

Iron
- Melting point: 1,535°C
- Density: 7.9 g/cm³
- Conducts electric current and heat energy
- Combines slowly with oxygen in the air to form rust

Nickel
- Melting point: 1,455°C
- Density: 8.9 g/cm³
- Conducts electric current and heat energy
- Unreactive with oxygen in the air

Teach

SUPPORT FOR

English Language Learners

Characteristic Properties
Students may need the diagram of the unique properties of elements broken into meaningful portions in order to grasp the information presented. First, ask for volunteers to define *melting point, density, conducts electric current,* and *unreactive with oxygen.* Write terms and student definitions on the board for reference. Then, discuss the following questions with students:

- Can you tell these elements apart based on whether they conduct electric current? (No, all three elements conduct electric current.)
- Can you tell these elements apart based on melting point? (Yes, they all have different melting points.)

Remind students that it is the *set* of properties of an element, not any single property, that identifies an element. **LS** Auditory/Visual

CONNECTION ACTIVITY
Math ———— GENERAL

Our Elemental Makeup The percentages by mass of the elements composing the compounds that make up the human body are oxygen, 64.6%; carbon, 18.0%; hydrogen, 10.0%; nitrogen, 3.1%; calcium, 1.9%; phosphorus, 1.1%; other elements, 1.3%.

Have students prepare a pie chart or bar graph to illustrate this information. **LS** Visual/Logical

Answer to Reading Check

An element is a pure substance because it contains only one type of particle.

Quick Lab

MATERIALS

FOR EACH GROUP
- magnet, bar
- nails, mixed sample, some iron and some aluminum

Safety Caution: Remind students to wear safety goggles and to handle sharp objects carefully.

Answers

4. The iron nails are attracted to the magnet, but the aluminum nails are not.
5. Sample answer: A magnet can be used to separate materials that are magnetic and nonmagnetic. In an aluminum recycling plant, nonaluminum materials like iron can be separated by using a magnet.

Different Types of Elements
Show students samples of elements, such as aluminum, iron, sulfur, iodine, and silicon, in closed plastic containers. Ask students to write a description of the properties of the elements. Then, ask them to classify the elements as metals, nonmetals, or metalloids. **LS** Verbal/Logical

Quiz — GENERAL

Ask students to identify the group or groups of elements that have each of the following properties:

1. good conductors of electric current (metals, some metalloids)

2. brittle and nonmalleable (nonmetals)

3. shiny (metals, some metalloids)

4. poor conductors of thermal energy (nonmetals, some metalloids)

Alternative Assessment — GENERAL

Concept Mapping Have students make a concept map that compares the properties of metals, nonmetals, and metalloids.
LS Visual/Logical   English Language Learners

Figure 3 *Even though these dogs are different breeds, they have enough in common to be classified as terriers.*

metal an element that is shiny and that conducts heat and electricity well

nonmetal an element that conducts heat and electricity poorly

metalloid an element that has properties of both metals and nonmetals

Classifying Elements by Their Properties

Think about how many different breeds of dogs there are. Now, think about how you tell one breed from another. Most often, you can tell just by their appearance, or the physical properties, of the dogs. **Figure 3** shows several breeds of terriers. Many terriers are fairly small in size and have short hair. Not all terriers are alike, but they share enough properties to be classified in the same group.

Categories of Elements

Elements are also grouped into categories by the properties they share. There are three major categories of elements: metals, nonmetals, and metalloids. The elements iron, nickel, and cobalt are all metals. Not all metals are exactly alike, but they do have some properties in common. **Metals** are shiny, and they conduct heat energy and electric current. **Nonmetals** make up the second category of elements. They do not conduct heat or electric current, and solid nonmetals are dull in appearance. **Metalloids,** which have properties of both metals and nonmetals, make up the last category.

✓ *Reading Check* What are three characteristics of metals?

Categories Are Similar

Imagine being in a music store. The CDs are categorized by type of music. If you like rock-and-roll, you would go to the rock-and-roll section. You might not know every CD, but you know that a CD has the characteristics of rock-and-roll for it to be in this section.

By knowing the category to which an unfamiliar element belongs, you can predict some of its properties. **Figure 4** shows examples of each category and describes the properties that identify elements in each category.

CONNECTION to Real Life — GENERAL

Lead Poisoning For hundreds of years, lead and lead compounds have been used in and around homes. But lead, although common, is toxic to humans (especially to children). It disrupts enzymes that are important to the function of brain cells.
LS Intrapersonal

Answer to Reading Check
Metals are shiny, conduct heat energy, and conduct electric current.

Figure 4 The Three Major Categories of Elements

Metals

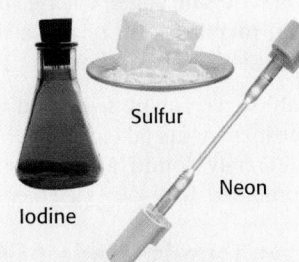

Lead

Tin

Copper

Metals are elements that are shiny and are good conductors of heat and electric current. They are *malleable.* (They can be hammered into thin sheets.) They are also *ductile.* (They can be drawn into thin wires.)

Nonmetals

Sulfur

Iodine

Neon

Nonmetals are elements that are dull (not shiny) and that are poor conductors of heat and electric current. Solids tend to be brittle and unmalleable. Few familiar objects are made of only nonmetals.

Metalloids

Boron

Silicon

Antimony

Metalloids are also called semiconductors. They have properties of both metals and nonmetals. Some metalloids are shiny. Some are dull. Metalloids are somewhat malleable and ductile. Some metalloids conduct heat and electric current as well.

SECTION Review

Summary

- A substance in which all of the particles are alike is a pure substance.
- An element is a pure substance that cannot be broken down into anything simpler by physical or chemical means.
- Each element has a unique set of physical and chemical properties.
- Elements are classified as metals, nonmetals, or metalloids, based on their properties.

Using Key Terms

1. Use the following terms in the same sentence: *element* and *pure substance.*

Understanding Key Ideas

2. A metalloid
   a. may conduct electric current.
   b. can be ductile.
   c. is also called a semiconductor.
   d. All of the above

3. What is a pure substance?

Math Skills

4. There are eight elements that make up 98.5% of the Earth's crust: 46.6% oxygen, 8.1% aluminum, 5.0% iron, 3.6% calcium, 2.8% sodium, 2.6% potassium, and 2.1% magnesium. The rest is silicon. What percentage of the Earth's crust is silicon?

Critical Thinking

5. **Applying Concepts** From which category of elements would you choose to make a container that wouldn't shatter if dropped? Explain your answer.

6. **Making Comparisons** Compare the properties of metals, nonmetals, and metalloids.

7. **Evaluating Assumptions** Your friend tells you that a shiny element has to be a metal. Do you agree? Explain.

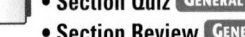

Developed and maintained by the
National Science Teachers Association

For a variety of links related to this chapter, go to www.scilinks.org

Topic: Elements
SciLinks code: HSM0496

Is That a Fact!

People in ancient times are thought to have used iron from meteorites before they learned to mine and process iron ore from the earth. A dagger found in the tomb of the Egyptian pharaoh Tutankhamen is thought to have been made from an iron meteorite.

Focus

Overview

This section describes the properties of compounds and explains the differences between compounds and elements. Students also learn about the properties and importance of common compounds.

🎧 Bellringer

Point out to students that the word *compound* refers to something that consists of two or more parts. Ask students to write in their **science journal** how they might make a compound using elements. Have them list any compounds they know about.

Motivate

Demonstration — GENERAL

Forming Magnesium Oxide The reaction between magnesium and oxygen in **Figure 1** is easily demonstrated for your students. The light produced in the chemical change is VERY bright. Looking directly at the flame may cause damage to the retina. Inform students of this, and remind them to look away as the magnesium begins to burn. In a darkened classroom, this demonstration is even more dramatic. This reaction was used in old flashbulbs. **LS** Visual/Kinesthetic

What You Will Learn

- Explain how elements make up compounds.
- Describe the properties of compounds.
- Explain how a compound can be broken down into its elements.
- Give examples of common compounds.

Vocabulary
compound

READING STRATEGY

Prediction Guide Before reading this section, write the title of each heading in this section. Next, under each heading, write what you think you will learn.

Figure 1 *As magnesium burns, it reacts with oxygen and forms the compound magnesium oxide.*

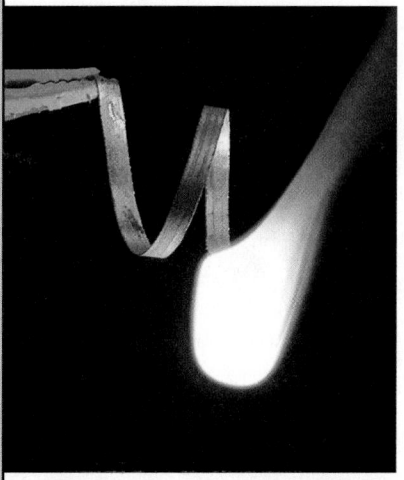

Compounds

What do salt, sugar, baking soda, and water have in common? You might use all of these to bake bread. Is there anything else similar about them?

Salt, sugar, baking soda, and water are all compounds. Because most elements take part in chemical changes fairly easily, they are rarely found alone in nature. Instead, they are found combined with other elements as compounds.

Compounds: Made of Elements

A **compound** is a pure substance composed of two or more elements that are chemically combined. Elements combine by reacting, or undergoing a chemical change, with one another. A particle of a compound is a molecule. Molecules of compounds are formed when atoms of two or more elements join together.

In **Figure 1**, you see magnesium reacting with oxygen. A compound called *magnesium oxide* is forming. The compound is a new pure substance. It is different from the elements that make it up. Most of the substances that you see every day are compounds. **Table 1** lists some familiar examples.

The Ratio of Elements in a Compound

Elements do not randomly join to form compounds. Elements join in a specific ratio according to their masses to form a compound. For example, the ratio of the mass of hydrogen to the mass of oxygen in water is 1 to 8. This mass ratio can be written as 1:8. This ratio is always the same. Every sample of water has a 1:8 mass ratio of hydrogen to oxygen. What happens if a sample of a compound has a different mass ratio of hydrogen to oxygen? The compound cannot be water.

Table 1 Familiar Compounds	
Compound	**Elements combined**
Table salt	sodium and chlorine
Water	hydrogen and oxygen
Vinegar	hydrogen, carbon, and oxygen
Carbon dioxide	carbon and oxygen
Baking soda	sodium, hydrogen, carbon, and oxygen

Answer to Reading Check

Three physical properties used to identify compounds are melting point, density, and color.

Quick Lab

Compound Confusion

1. Measure **4 g of compound A,** and place it in a **clear plastic cup.**

2. Measure **4 g of compound B,** and place it in a **second clear plastic cup.**

3. Observe the color and texture of each compound. Record your observations.

4. Add **5 mL of vinegar** to each cup. Record your observations.

5. Baking soda reacts with vinegar. Powdered sugar does not react with vinegar. Which compound is baking soda, and which compound is powdered sugar? Explain your answer.

Properties of Compounds

As an element does, each compound has its own physical properties. Physical properties include melting point, density, and color. Compounds can also be identified by their different chemical properties. Some compounds react with acid. For example, calcium carbonate, found in chalk, reacts with acid. Other compounds, such as hydrogen peroxide, react when exposed to light.

compound a substance made up of atoms of two or more different elements joined by chemical bonds

✓ **Reading Check** What are three physical properties used to identify compounds? (*See the Appendix for answers to Reading Checks.*)

Properties: Compounds Versus Elements

A compound has properties that differ from those of the elements that form it. Look at **Figure 2.** Sodium chloride, or table salt, is made of two very dangerous elements—sodium and chlorine. Sodium reacts violently with water. Chlorine is a poisonous gas. But when combined, these elements form a harmless compound with unique properties. Sodium chloride is safe to eat. It also dissolves (without exploding!) in water.

| **Figure 2** | **Forming Sodium Chloride** |

Sodium is a soft, silvery white metal that reacts violently with water.

Chlorine is a poisonous, greenish yellow gas.

Sodium chloride, or table salt, is a white solid. It dissolves easily in water and is safe to eat.

Quick Lab

MATERIALS

FOR EACH STUDENT
- baking soda
- cups, clear plastic (2)
- sugar, powdered
- teaspoon
- vinegar

Safety Caution: Caution students to wear an apron, safety goggles, and gloves while doing this activity.

Label the unknown compounds "A" and "B." The two unknown substances are baking soda and powdered sugar. The materials can be disposed of in a sink with running water.

Answer

5. One compound (baking soda) reacts with vinegar by bubbling; the other (powdered sugar) does not react.

Reteaching — BASIC

Comparing Words to Compounds Write the alphabet on the board, and get a large dictionary. Discuss with students the millions of words and other combinations of letters the alphabet can make. Then, discuss how elements, like letters, can combine in many different ways to form millions of compounds. Point out that of the more than 4 million compounds that exist, carbon is found in 94% of them.

LS Visual/Logical

English Language Learners

Quiz — GENERAL

1. Compounds cannot be broken down by any means. (false)

2. Compounds can be broken down only by chemical changes. (true)

3. Heating can break down some compounds. (true)

Alternative Assessment — GENERAL

Research Have each student pick a compound and conduct research to find out more about the compound. (You may want to post a list of interesting compounds.) Then, have students create a poster or other presentation about their compound. The presentation should contain written information as well as pictures or other visual aids. Display the posters in the classroom.

LS Visual/Kinesthetic

English Language Learners

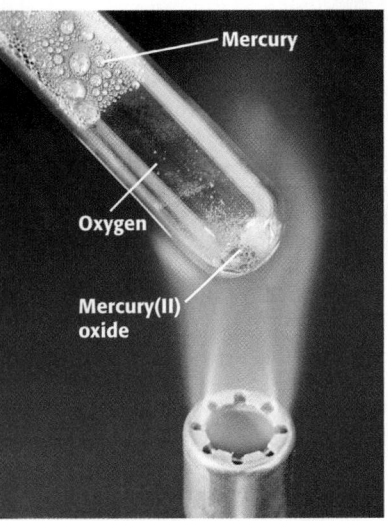

Mercury

Oxygen

Mercury(II) oxide

Figure 3 *Heating mercury(II) oxide causes a chemical change that separates it into the elements mercury and oxygen.*

INTERNET ACTIVITY

For another activity related to this chapter, go to **go.hrw.com** and type in the keyword **HP5MIXW.**

Answer to Reading Check

Compounds can be broken down into elements or simpler compounds.

Breaking Down Compounds

Some compounds can be broken down into their elements by chemical changes. Other compounds break down to form simpler compounds instead of elements. These simpler compounds can then be broken down into elements through more chemical changes. For example, carbonic acid is a compound that helps give carbonated beverages their "fizz." When you open a carbonated beverage, carbonic acid breaks down into carbon dioxide and water. Carbon dioxide and water can then be broken down into the elements carbon, oxygen, and hydrogen through chemical changes.

✓ **Reading Check** Compounds can be broken down into what two types of substances?

Methods of Breaking Down Compounds

The only way to break down a compound is through a chemical change. Sometimes, energy is needed for a chemical change to happen. Two ways to add energy to break down a compound are to apply heat and to apply an electric current. For example, heating the compound mercury(II) oxide breaks it down into the elements mercury and oxygen, as shown in **Figure 3**.

Compounds in Your World

You are surrounded by compounds. Compounds make up the food you eat, the school supplies you use, and the clothes you wear—even you!

Compounds in Industry

The compounds found in nature are not usually the raw materials needed by industry. Often, these compounds must be broken down to provide elements or other compounds that can be used as raw material. For example, aluminum is used in cans and airplanes. But aluminum is not found alone in nature. Aluminum is produced by breaking down the compound aluminum oxide. Ammonia is another important compound used in industry. It is used to make fertilizers. Ammonia is made by combining the elements nitrogen and hydrogen.

CONNECTION TO Physics

Electrolysis The process of using electric current to break down compounds is known as *electrolysis*. For example, electrolysis can be used to separate water into hydrogen and oxygen. Research ways that electrolysis is used in industry. Make a poster of what you learn, and present a report to your class.

ACTIVITY

BRAIN FOOD

History of Salt In ancient times, salt was a precious commodity. It was even traded for an equal weight of gold. Soldiers in ancient Rome were paid a *salarium*, a special ration of salt. This term eventually evolved into the English word *salary*.

Compounds in Nature

Proteins are compounds found in all living things. The element nitrogen is one of the elements needed to make proteins. **Figure 4** shows how some plants get the nitrogen they need. Other plants use nitrogen compounds that are in the soil. Animals get the nitrogen they need by eating plants or by eating animals that have eaten plants. The proteins in the food are broken down as an animal digests the food. The simpler compounds that form are used by the animal's cells to make new proteins.

Another compound that plays an important role in life is carbon dioxide. You exhale carbon dioxide that was made in your body. Plants take in carbon dioxide, which is used in photosynthesis. Plants use photosynthesis to make compounds called carbohydrates. These carbohydrates can then be broken down for energy through other chemical changes by plants or animals.

Figure 4 *The bumps on the roots of this pea plant are home to bacteria that form compounds from nitrogen in the air. The pea plant makes proteins from these compounds.*

Answers to Section Review

1. A compound is something that is made of atoms of two or more elements that are joined by chemical bonds.
2. d
3. A chemical change is needed to break down a compound.
4. 100% − 41.86% − 6.98% = 51.16% oxygen
5. When elements combine to form a compound, the compound's properties are different from the properties of the individual elements.
6. Sample answer: The jar does not contain a compound. The jar has carbon and oxygen, but the two elements are not joined by chemical bonds.

SECTION Review

Summary

- A compound is a pure substance composed of two or more elements.
- The elements that form a compound always combine in a specific ratio according to their masses.
- Each compound has a unique set of physical and chemical properties that differ from those of the elements that make up the compound.
- Compounds can be broken down into simpler substances only by chemical changes.

Using Key Terms

1. In your own words, write a definition for the term *compound*.

Understanding Key Ideas

2. The elements in a compound
   a. join in a specific ratio according to their masses.
   b. combine by reacting with one another.
   c. can be separated by chemical changes.
   d. All of the above

3. What type of change is needed to break down a compound?

Math Skills

4. Table sugar is a compound made of carbon, hydrogen, and oxygen. If sugar contains 41.86% carbon and 6.98% hydrogen, what percentage of sugar is oxygen?

Critical Thinking

5. **Applying Concepts** Iron is a solid, gray metal. Oxygen is a colorless gas. When they chemically combine, rust is made. Rust has a reddish brown color. Why is rust different from the iron and oxygen that it is made of?

6. **Analyzing Ideas** A jar contains samples of the elements carbon and oxygen. Does the jar contain a compound? Explain your answer.

SciLINKS

NSTA
Developed and maintained by the
National Science Teachers Association

For a variety of links related to this chapter, go to www.scilinks.org

Topic: Compounds
SciLinks code: HSM0332

Is That a Fact!

Some metals can have more than one charge when they form compounds. To identify the charge of a particular compound, a Roman numeral is used in the name. Thus, the mercury in mercury(II) oxide has a 2+ charge.

CHAPTER RESOURCES

Chapter Resource File

- Section Quiz GENERAL
- Section Review GENERAL
- Vocabulary and Section Summary GENERAL
- Datasheet for Quick Lab

Focus

Overview

This section explains the properties of mixtures. Students learn how mixtures can be separated. The concepts of solutes, concentration, and solvents are covered. Finally, students compare solutions, suspensions, and colloids.

Bellringer

Have students write an answer to the following question: "When you add sugar to coffee, tea, iced tea, or lemonade, the sugar disappears. What do you think happens to the sugar?"

Motivate

Discussion —— GENERAL

A Mixture You Can Eat Discuss with students the idea that pizza is a mixture. Ask students to write a recipe for their favorite pizza. Have volunteers write their pizza recipes on the board. Have the class compare recipes and discuss how they vary.

LS Interpersonal/Verbal

What You Will Learn

● Describe three properties of mixtures.
● Describe four methods of separating the parts of a mixture.
● Analyze a solution in terms of its solute and solvent.
● Explain how concentration affects a solution.
● Describe the particles in a suspension.
● Explain how a colloid differs from a solution and a suspension.

Vocabulary

mixture	concentration
solution	solubility
solute	suspension
solvent	colloid

READING STRATEGY

Reading Organizer As you read this section, create an outline of the section. Use the headings from the section in your outline.

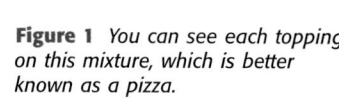

mixture a combination of two or more substances that are not chemically combined

Figure 1 You can see each topping on this mixture, which is better known as a pizza.

Mixtures

Imagine that you roll out some dough, add tomato sauce, and sprinkle some cheese on top. Then, you add green peppers, mushrooms, olives, and pepperoni! What have you just made?

A pizza, of course! But that's not all. You have also created a mixture—and a delicious one at that! In this section, you will learn about mixtures and their properties.

Properties of Mixtures

All mixtures—even pizza—share certain properties. A **mixture** is a combination of two or more substances that are not chemically combined. When two or more materials are put together, they form a mixture if they do not react to form a compound. For example, cheese and tomato sauce do not react when they are used to make a pizza. So, a pizza is a mixture.

No Chemical Changes in a Mixture

No chemical change happens when a mixture is made. So, each substance in a mixture has the same chemical makeup it had before the mixture formed. That is, each substance in a mixture keeps its identity. In some mixtures, such as the pizza in **Figure 1,** you can see each of the components. In other mixtures, such as salt water, you cannot see all the components.

✓ **Reading Check** Why do substances in a mixture keep their identities? (*See the Appendix for answers to Reading Checks.*)

Separating Mixtures Through Physical Methods

You don't like mushrooms on your pizza? Just pick them off. This change is a physical change of the mixture. The identities of the substances do not change. But not all mixtures are as easy to separate as a pizza. You cannot just pick salt out of a saltwater mixture. One way to separate the salt from the water is to heat the mixture until the water evaporates. The salt is left behind. Other ways to separate mixtures are shown in **Figure 2.**

CHAPTER RESOURCES

Chapter Resource File

• Lesson Plan
• Directed Reading A **BASIC**
• Directed Reading B **SPECIAL NEEDS**

Technology

Transparencies
• Bellringer
• P9 Separation of a Mixture

Workbooks

Interactive Textbook Struggling Readers

Answer to Reading Check

Substances in a mixture keep their identities because no chemical change takes place when a mixture is made.

Figure 2 Common Ways to Separate Mixtures

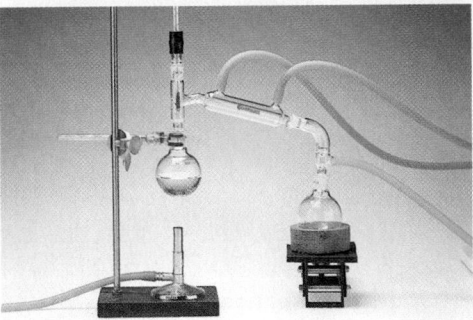

Distillation (DIS tuh LAY shuhn) is a process that separates a mixture based on the boiling points of the components. Here, pure water (at right) is being distilled from a salt-water mixture (at left). Distillation is also used to separate crude oil into components, such as gasoline and kerosene.

A **magnet** can be used to separate a mixture of the elements iron and aluminum. Iron is attracted to the magnet, but aluminum is not.

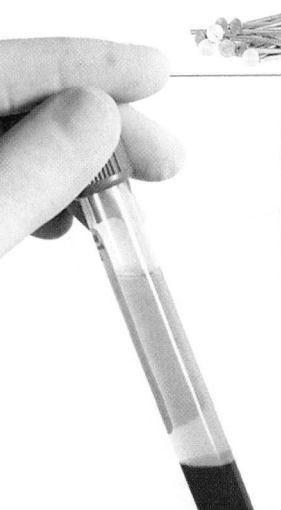
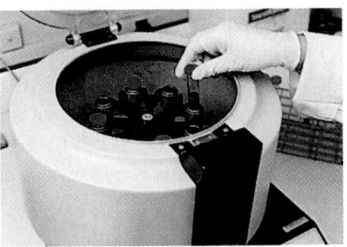

The different parts of blood are separated using a machine called a **centrifuge** (SEN truh FYOOJ). In the test tube at left, a layer of plasma rests above a layer of red blood cells. A centrifuge separates mixtures by the densities of the components.

Separating a mixture of sodium chloride (table salt) and sulfur takes more than one step.

❶ In the first step, water is added, and the mixture is stirred. Salt dissolves in water. Sulfur does not.

❷ In the second step, the mixture is poured through a filter. The filter traps the solid sulfur.

❸ In the third step, the water is evaporated. The sodium chloride is left behind.

BRAIN FOOD

Harvest of Cranberries The property of density can be used to separate a mixture of ripe and unripe cranberries. Ripe cranberries float in water, but unripe cranberries sink. During harvesting, cranberry bogs are flooded, and the floating cranberries are skimmed from the water.

Is That a Fact!

The Liberty Bell is a mixture of 70% copper, 25% tin, and small amounts of lead, zinc, arsenic, gold, and silver.

Research Have students research what happens when a major volcanic eruption sends particulate matter into the atmosphere. They could start with the 1991 eruption of Mount Pinatubo, in the Philippines. Use teaching transparency "Three Types of Volcanoes" to help students begin their project.
LS Visual/Logical

English Language Learners

SUPPORT FOR

English Language Learners

Mixtures and Solutions

Students will need more practice distinguishing mixtures and solutions. Show them the following five mixtures. Ask volunteers to identify which ones are solutions and give the reasons why they think so.

• Sugar and sand (no, grains can be physically separated)

• Diet Soda (yes, gas is dissolved in liquid)

• Air (yes, gases are dissolved in other gases)

• Water and oil (no, the liquids can be physically separated.)

• Chocolate chip cookie (no, the chips can be physically separated from the cookie).

Encourage questions and discussion for each example. Provide explanations if necessary. **LS** Visual/Logical

Table 1 Mixtures and Compounds	
Mixtures	**Compounds**
Made of elements, compounds, or both	Made of elements
No change in original properties of components	Change in original properties of components
Separated by physical means	Separated by chemical means
Formed using any ratio of components	Formed using a set ratio of components

Figure 3 *These paperweights are made of granite. They are different colors because the granite used in each has different ratios of minerals.*

solution a homogeneous mixture of two or more substances uniformly dispersed throughout a single phase

solute in a solution, the substance that dissolves in the solvent

solvent in a solution, the substance in which the solute dissolves

The Ratio of Components in a Mixture

A compound is made of elements in a specific mass ratio. However, the components of a mixture do not need to be mixed in a definite ratio. For example, granite is a mixture made of three minerals: feldspar, mica, and quartz. Feldspar is pink in color. Mica is black. Quartz is colorless. Look at the egg-shaped paperweights in **Figure 3.** The pink one is made from granite that has more feldspar than mica or quartz. That is why it is pink. The black one is made from granite that has more mica than the other minerals. The gray one is made from granite that has more quartz than the other minerals. Even though the proportions of the minerals change, this combination of minerals is always a mixture called *granite.* **Table 1** above summarizes the differences between mixtures and compounds.

Solutions

A **solution** is a mixture that appears to be a single substance. A solution is composed of particles of two or more substances that are distributed evenly among each other. Solutions have the same appearance and properties throughout the mixture.

The process in which particles of substances separate and spread evenly throughout a mixture is known as *dissolving*. In solutions, the **solute** is the substance that is dissolved. The **solvent** is the substance in which the solute is dissolved. A solute must be *soluble,* or able to dissolve, in the solvent. A substance that is *insoluble,* or unable to dissolve, forms a mixture that is not a solution.

Salt water is a solution. Salt is soluble in water, meaning that salt dissolves in water. So, salt is the solute, and water is the solvent. When two liquids or two gases form a solution, the substance that is present in the largest amount is the solvent.

SCIENCE HUMOR

Q: What did the compound say to the solution?

A: "You're all mixed up!"

Table 2 Examples of Different States in Solutions

States	Examples
Gas in gas	dry air (oxygen in nitrogen)
Gas in liquid	soft drinks (carbon dioxide in water)
Liquid in liquid	antifreeze (alcohol in water)
Solid in liquid	salt water (salt in water)
Solid in solid	brass (zinc in copper)

Examples of Solutions

You may think that all solutions are liquids. And in fact, tap water, soft drinks, gasoline, and many cleaning supplies are liquid solutions. However, solutions may also be gases, such as air. Solutions may even be solids, such as steel. *Alloys* are solid solutions of metals or nonmetals dissolved in metals. Brass is an alloy of the metal zinc dissolved in copper. Steel is an alloy made of the nonmetal carbon and other elements dissolved in iron. **Table 2** lists more examples of solutions.

✔ *Reading Check* What is an alloy?

Particles in Solutions

The particles in solutions are so small that they never settle out. They also cannot be removed by filtering. In fact, the particles are so small that they don't even scatter light. Both of the jars in **Figure 4** contain mixtures. The mixture in the jar on the left is a solution of table salt in water. The jar on the right holds a mixture—but not a solution—of gelatin in water.

CONNECTION TO Language Arts

WRITING SKILL **Alloys** Research an alloy. Find out what the alloy is made of and the amount of each substance in the alloy. Also, identify different ways that the alloy is used. Then, write a song or poem about the alloy to recite in class.

Figure 4 *Both of these jars contain mixtures. The mixture in the jar on the left, however, is a solution. The particles in solutions are so small that they don't scatter light. Therefore, you can't see the path of light through the solution.*

Answer to Reading Check
An alloy is a solid solution of metal or nonmetal dissolved in another metal.

Comparing Solutions Supply each pair of students with food coloring, water, and clear plastic cups.

Safety Caution: Caution students to wear an apron while doing this activity.

Have students work in pairs. One member of each pair makes a concentrated solution of food coloring and water. The other partner makes a dilute solution of the same.

Place all the cups containing concentrated solutions in front of a white sheet of paper so that students can compare the solutions' colors. Do the same thing with all the dilute solutions. Mention that not all of the concentrated solutions have the same color, nor do all the dilute solutions. This activity will reinforce that the terms *concentrated* and *dilute* are relative and do not specify amounts. **LS** Visual

CONNECTION ACTIVITY
Math ——————— GENERAL

Extending the Math Focus: Ask students the following question: "Suppose you have 45 g of sodium chloride (salt) dissolved in 150 mL of water, and you need 250 mL more of the same solution. How much sodium chloride do you need to make the additional solution?" (75 g)

Then, ask them, "What is the concentration of the solution?" (0.3 g/mL) **LS** Logical

Figure 5 *The dilute solution (left) contains less solute than the concentrated solution (right).*

concentration the amount of a particular substance in a given quantity of a mixture, solution, or ore

solubility the ability of one substance to dissolve in another at a given temperature and pressure

Concentration of Solutions

A measure of the amount of solute dissolved in a solvent is **concentration.** Concentration can be expressed in grams of solute per milliliter of solvent (g/mL).

Concentrated or Dilute?

Solutions can be described as being concentrated or dilute. In **Figure 5,** both solutions have the same amount of solvent. However, the solution on the left contains less solute than the solution on the right. The solution on the left is dilute. The solution on the right is concentrated. Keep in mind that the terms *dilute* and *concentrated* do not tell you the amount of solute that is dissolved.

Solubility

If you add too much sugar to a glass of lemonade, not all of the sugar can dissolve. Some of it sinks to the bottom. To find the maximum amount of sugar that can dissolve, you would need to know the solubility of sugar. The **solubility** of a solute is the ability of the solute to dissolve in a solvent at a certain temperature. **Figure 6** shows how the solubility of several different solid substances changes with temperature.

 **MATH FOCUS** ——————————————————

Calculating Concentration What is the concentration of a solution that has 35 g of salt dissolved in 175 mL of water?

Step 1: One equation for finding concentration is the following:

$$concentration = \frac{grams\ of\ solute}{milliliters\ of\ solvent}$$

Step 2: Replace grams of solute and milliliters of solvent with the values given, and solve.

$$\frac{35\ g\ salt}{175\ mL\ water} = 0.2\ g/mL$$

Now It's Your Turn

1. What is the concentration of solution A if it has 55 g of sugar dissolved in 500 mL of water?
2. What is the concentration of solution B if it has 36 g of sugar dissolved in 144 mL of water?
3. Which solution is more concentrated?

Answers to Math Focus

1. Solution A: 55 g/500 mL = 0.11 g/mL
2. Solution B: 36 g/144 mL = 0.25 g/mL
3. Solution B is more concentrated.

CONNECTION ACTIVITY
Earth Science ——————— GENERAL

Cave Formation Many caves, such as Carlsbad Caverns in New Mexico and Mammoth Cave in Kentucky, were formed by calcium carbonate alternately dissolving in water and being deposited when water evaporated. Have students find out how these caves formed and make a model or a poster or write a report. **LS** Visual

English Language Learners

Figure 6   Solubility of Different Solids In Water

The solubility of most solids increases as the temperature gets higher. So, more solute can dissolve at higher temperatures. However, some solids, such as cerium sulfate, are less soluble at higher temperatures.

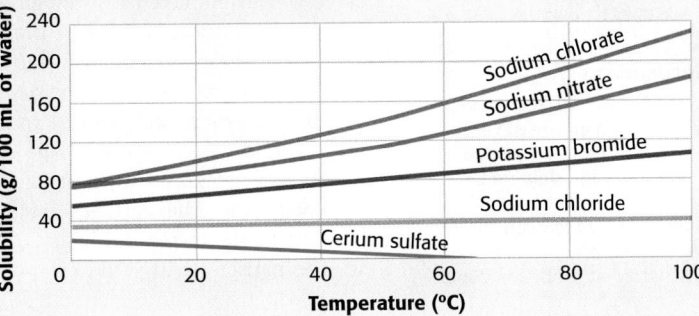

Sodium chlorate
Sodium nitrate
Potassium bromide
Sodium chloride
Cerium sulfate

Dissolving Gases in Liquids

Most solids are more soluble in liquids at higher temperatures. But gases become less soluble in liquids as the temperature is raised. A soft drink goes flat faster when warm. The gas that is dissolved in the soft drink cannot stay dissolved when the temperature increases. So, the gas escapes, and the soft drink becomes "flat."

Reading Check   How does the solubility of gases change with temperature?

Dissolving Solids Faster in Liquids

Several things affect how fast a solid will dissolve. Look at **Figure 7** to see three ways to make a solute dissolve faster. You can see why you will enjoy a glass of lemonade sooner if you stir granulated sugar into the lemonade before adding ice!

Figure 7   How to Dissolve Solids Faster

Mixing by stirring or shaking causes the solute particles to separate from one another and spread out more quickly among the solvent particles.

Heating causes particles to move more quickly. The solvent particles can separate the solute particles and spread them out more quickly.

Crushing the solute increases the amount of contact it has with the solvent. The particles of the crushed solute mix with the solvent more quickly.

CONNECTION to Life Science — GENERAL

Fish Need Oxygen, Too! Because less gas dissolves in a liquid if the temperature is raised, fish can suffocate when aquarium water becomes too warm—there may not be enough oxygen dissolved in the water.

Answer to Reading Check

As temperature increases, the solubility of a gas decreases.

CHAPTER RESOURCES

Technology

 Transparencies
• P10 Solubility Graph

Differences In Solubility   Ask students to use the graph in **Figure 6** to compare the solubility of the different solids at different temperatures. Then, ask, "Which solid's solubility decreases as temperature increases?" (cerium sulfate)

Point out to students that some elements and compounds, such as iodine and calcium carbonate, are not soluble (or are only slightly soluble) in water. Iodine is, however, soluble in alcohol, forming a solution called tincture of iodine. **LS** Visual/Logical

 **INCLUSION Strategies**

• *Attention Deficit Disorder*
• *Learning Disabled*

Help students understand the relationship between elements, compounds, and mixtures. Divide the class into teams of three. Have one student wear each of these signs: "element," "compound," "mixture." Ask one team to demonstrate an "oral chart" by having the team members put on their signs and announce the following facts that have to do with their "identity": sodium is an element (announced by "element"); sodium chloride —or salt—is a compound (announced by "compound"); salt on potatoes is a mixture (announced by "mixture"). Assign each team one of the following mixtures: ice pop, root beer float, cotton candy, toothpaste with fluoride, swimming pool water, air pollution, fortified cereal, oil and gas mixture in motorboat fuel, or handful of old coins. Then, ask each team to isolate a compound and an element and then to present a set of facts. **LS** Interpersonal

Reteaching — BASIC

Immiscible Substances Show students a bottle of an oil-and-vinegar salad dressing that has been shaken. Read the ingredients label aloud. Allow the bottle to sit undisturbed so that the ingredients separate. Discuss how the ingredients in the dressing retain their identities and how they could be mixed in any proportions. **LS** Visual/Kinesthetic

Quiz — GENERAL

1. Which of the following is not a solution: air in a scuba tank, muddy water, a soft drink, or salt water? (muddy water)

2. When solid iodine is dissolved in alcohol, which is the solute, and which is the solvent? (Iodine is the solute, and alcohol is the solvent.)

Alternative Assessment — GENERAL

Concept Mapping
Have students describe three ways to increase the speed at which a solid will dissolve in a liquid. (mixing or stirring, heating the solvent, or crushing the solute) Then, ask them to name some home appliances that are used to speed the solution process. (mixer, food processor, stove, microwave oven) Have students create a concept map to display their answers. **LS** Visual/Intrapersonal

School to Home

Suspensions
Many household items, such as paints, salad dressings, and medicines, are suspensions. With an adult, find several items that have directions that tell you to shake the bottle before use. Discuss what problems could arise if you do not shake the container before use.

suspension a mixture in which particles of a material are more or less evenly dispersed throughout a liquid or gas

colloid a mixture consisting of tiny particles that are intermediate in size between those in solutions and those in suspensions and that are suspended in a liquid, solid, or gas

Suspensions

Have you ever shaken a snow globe? If so, you have seen the solid snow particles mix with the water, as shown in **Figure 8.** When you stop shaking the globe, the snow settles to the bottom. This mixture is called a suspension. A **suspension** is a mixture in which particles of a material are dispersed throughout a liquid or gas but are large enough that they settle out.

The particles in a suspension are large enough to scatter or block light. The particles are also too large to stay mixed without being stirred or shaken. If a suspension is allowed to sit, the particles will settle out, as they do in a snow globe.

A suspension can be separated by passing it through a filter. So, the liquid or gas passes through the filter, but the solid particles are large enough to be trapped by the filter.

✓ Reading Check How can the particles of a suspension be separated?

Colloids

Some mixtures have properties between those of solutions and suspensions. These mixtures are known as colloids (KAHL OYDZ). A **colloid** is a mixture in which the particles are dispersed throughout but are not heavy enough to settle out. The particles in a colloid are relatively small and are fairly well mixed. You might be surprised at the number of colloids you see each day. Milk, mayonnaise, and stick deodorant—even the gelatin and whipped cream in **Figure 8**—are colloids.

The particles in a colloid are much smaller than the particles in a suspension. However, the particles are large enough to scatter light. A colloid cannot be separated by filtration. The particles are small enough to pass through a filter.

Figure 8 Properties of Suspensions and Colloids

Suspension This snow globe contains solid particles that will mix with the clear liquid when you shake it up. But the particles will soon fall to the bottom when the globe is at rest.

Colloid This dessert includes two tasty examples of colloids—fruity gelatin and whipped cream.

Answer to Reading Check

The particles of a suspension can be separated by passing the suspension through a filter.

SECTION Review

Summary

- A mixture is a combination of two or more substances, each of which keeps its own characteristics.
- Mixtures can be separated by physical means, such as filtration and evaporation.
- A solution is a mixture that appears to be a single substance but is composed of a solute dissolved in a solvent.
- Concentration is a measure of the amount of solute dissolved in a solvent.

- The solubility of a solute is the ability of the solute to dissolve in a solvent at a certain temperature.
- Suspensions are mixtures that contain particles large enough to settle out or be filtered and to block or scatter light.
- Colloids are mixtures that contain particles that are too small to settle out or be filtered but are large enough to scatter light.

Using Key Terms

The statements below are false. For each statement, replace the underlined term to make a true statement.

1. The <u>solvent</u> is the substance that is dissolved.

2. A <u>suspension</u> is composed of substances that are spread evenly among each other.

3. A measure of the amount of solute dissolved in a solvent is <u>solubility</u>.

4. A <u>colloid</u> contains particles that will settle out of the mixture if left sitting.

Understanding Key Ideas

5. A mixture
   a. has substances in it that are chemically combined.
   b. can always be separated using filtration.
   c. contains substances that are not mixed in a definite ratio.
   d. All of the above

6. List three ways to dissolve a solid faster.

Critical Thinking

7. **Making Comparisons** How do solutions, suspensions, and colloids differ?

8. **Applying Concepts** Suggest a procedure to separate iron filings from sawdust. Explain why this procedure works.

9. **Analyzing Ideas** Identify the solute and solvent in a solution made of 15 mL of oxygen and 5 mL of helium.

Interpreting Graphics

Use the graph below to answer the questions that follow.

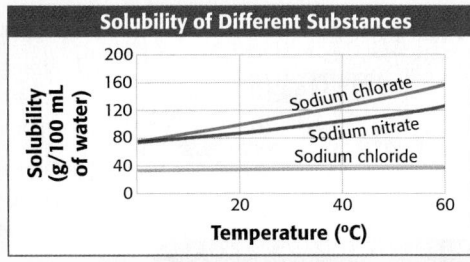

Solubility of Different Substances

10. At what temperature is 120 g of sodium nitrate soluble in 100 mL of water?

11. At 60°C, how much more sodium chlorate than sodium chloride will dissolve in 100 mL of water?

For a variety of links related to this chapter, go to www.scilinks.org

Topic: Mixtures
SciLinks code: HSM0974

Answers to Section Review

1. solute
2. solution
3. concentration
4. suspension
5. c
6. Three ways to dissolve a solid faster are crushing the solid, stirring the solid and liquid, and heating the solid and liquid.
7. A solution appears to be a single substance and contains particles evenly distributed among each other. The particles in a solution are very small and can't be filtered out. A clear solution will not scatter light. A suspension has larger particles that are dispersed but will settle out. The particles in a suspension can be filtered out and are large enough to block or scatter light. Particles in a colloid are smaller than the particles in a suspension but are still large enough to scatter light.
8. Sample answer: I would use a magnet to separate the iron from the sawdust. The magnet will attract the iron but will not attract the sawdust.
9. The solute is helium, and the solvent is oxygen.
10. about 60°C
11. About 120 g more of sodium chlorate will dissolve.

Q: What did the chemist say to the suspension?

A: "Settle down!"

CHAPTER RESOURCES

Chapter Resource File

- Section Quiz GENERAL
- Section Review GENERAL
- Vocabulary and Section Summary GENERAL
- Reinforcement Worksheet BASIC
- Critical Thinking ADVANCED
- SciLinks Activity GENERAL

Flame Tests

Teacher's Notes

Time Required

One or two 45-minute class periods

Lab Ratings

EASY —————————→ HARD

Teacher Prep ☒☒☒
Student Set-Up ☒☒
Concept Level ☒☒☒☒
Clean Up ☒☒☒

MATERIALS

The materials listed are for each group of 2–3 students. The unknown solution should be clear. Use only dilute hydrochloric acid—concentrations lower than 1.0 M. When diluting an acid, always add the acid to the water.

Preparation Notes

Prepare solutions of KCl, CaCl₂, and NaCl in a concentration of 10 g/500 mL of solution. Make enough of one of the solutions to serve as the "unknown." You will need 5 to 10 mL of each solution per group. Make the wire holder with Nichrome® wire or paper clips and ice-cream sticks or corks. Bend one end of the wire into a small loop like a bubble wand. Tape the other end of the wire to the stick, or insert it into the cork. If necessary, vinegar can be substituted for the dilute hydrochloric acid in this experiment.

Using Scientific Methods
Skills Practice Lab

Flame Tests

OBJECTIVES

Observe flame colors emitted by various compounds.

Determine the composition of an unknown compound.

MATERIALS

- Bunsen burner
- chloride test solutions (4)
- hydrochloric acid, dilute, in a small beaker
- spark igniter
- tape, masking
- test tubes, small (4)
- test-tube rack
- water, distilled, in a small beaker
- wire and holder

SAFETY

Flame Tests

Fireworks produce fantastic combinations of color when they are ignited. The different colors are the results of burning different compounds. Imagine that you are the head chemist for a fireworks company. The label has fallen off one box, and you must identify the unknown compound inside so that the fireworks may be used in the correct fireworks display. To identify the compound, you will use your knowledge that every compound has a unique set of properties.

Ask a Question

1 How can you identify an unknown compound by heating it in a flame?

Form a Hypothesis

2 Write a hypothesis that is a possible answer to the question above. Explain your reasoning.

Test the Hypothesis

3 Arrange the test tubes in the test-tube rack. Use masking tape to label each tube with one of the following names: calcium chloride, potassium chloride, sodium chloride, and unknown.

4 Copy the table below. Then, ask your teacher for your portions of the solutions. **Caution:** Be very careful in handling all chemicals. Tell your teacher immediately if you spill a chemical.

Test Results	
Compound	**Color of flame**
Calcium chloride	
Potassium chloride	DO NOT WRITE
Sodium chloride	IN BOOK
Unknown	

Safety Caution

Students should touch only the wooden handle of the wire holder device because the wire will become hot and could cause burns. Students should be careful with the dilute hydrochloric acid. If contact occurs, they should flush their skin immediately with water. Long hair and loose clothing should be restricted around an open flame. In case of an acid spill, first dilute the spill with water. Then, mop up the spill with wet cloths or a wet mop while wearing disposable plastic gloves.

CHAPTER RESOURCES

Chapter Resource File

- • Datasheet for Chapter Lab
- • Lab Notes and Answers

Technology

 Classroom Videos
- • Lab Video

- • A Sugar Cube Race!
- • Making Butter
- • Unpolluting Water

5 Light the burner. Clean the wire by dipping it into the dilute hydrochloric acid and then into distilled water. Holding the wooden handle, heat the wire in the blue flame of the burner until the wire is glowing and it no longer colors the flame. **Caution:** Use extreme care around an open flame.

6 Dip the clean wire into the first test solution. Hold the wire at the tip of the inner cone of the burner flame. Record in the table the color given to the flame.

7 Clean the wire by repeating step 5. Then, repeat steps 5 and 6 for the other solutions.

8 Follow your teacher's instructions for cleanup and disposal.

Analyze the Results

1 Identifying Patterns Is the flame color a test for the metal or for the chloride in each compound? Explain your answer.

2 Analyzing Data What is the identity of your unknown solution? How do you know?

Draw Conclusions

3 Evaluating Methods Why is it necessary to carefully clean the wire before testing each solution?

4 Making Predictions Would you expect the compound sodium fluoride to produce the same color as sodium chloride in a flame test? Why or why not?

5 Interpreting Information Each of the compounds you tested is made from chlorine, which is a poisonous gas at room temperature. Why is it safe to use these compounds without a gas mask?

Analyze the Results

1. The flame test is a test for the metal in each compound. Because each compound contains chloride, the color difference must be due to the different metals. Any color contribution from the chloride would be the same in each trial.

2. Answers will depend on the teacher's choice for the unknown compound. Students will know its identity because it will produce the same color flame as one of the other three test solutions.

Draw Conclusions

3. The wire must be cleaned so that the color observed is from the solution being tested, not from a mixture of two solutions.

4. yes; The sodium fluoride compound would likely burn the same color as the sodium chloride compound because the flame test is a test for the metal in a compound, and both compounds contain sodium.

5. Compounds have chemical and physical properties that are different from those of the elements the compounds are formed from.

Disposal Information

Hydrochloric Acid: Titrate with 0.1 M NaOH as required until the pH is between 6 and 8, and pour the liquid down the drain.

Calcium Chloride Solution: Adjust the pH of the waste liquid with 1.0 M acid or base until the pH is between 5 and 9. Pour the neutralized liquid down the drain.

Potassium Chloride and Sodium Chloride Solutions: These can be washed down the sink with plenty of water, provided your school drains are connected to a sanitary sewer system with a treatment plant.

Chapter Review

 Chapter Review

Assignment Guide

Section	Questions
1	4, 5, 9, 14, 15, 19
2	1, 11, 13, 15, 19, 21
3	2, 3, 6-8, 10, 12, 16–20, 22–26

ANSWERS

Using Key Terms

1. compound
2. solubility
3. suspension
4. element
5. nonmetal
6. solute

Understanding Key Ideas

7. c
8. b
9. c
10. b
11. c
12. a

USING KEY TERMS

Complete each of the following sentences by choosing the correct term from the word bank.

compound	element
suspension	solubility
solution	metal
nonmetal	solute

1 A(n) ___ has a definite ratio of components.

2 The ability of one substance to dissolve in another substance is the ___ of the solute.

3 A(n) ___ can be separated by filtration.

4 A(n) ___ is a pure substance that cannot be broken down into simpler substances by chemical means.

5 A(n) ___ is an element that is brittle and dull.

6 The ___ is the substance that dissolves to form a solution.

UNDERSTANDING KEY IDEAS

Multiple Choice

7 Which of the following increases the solubility of a gas in a liquid?

a. increasing the temperature of the liquid
b. increasing the amount of gas in the liquid
c. decreasing the temperature of the liquid
d. decreasing the amount of liquid

8 Which of the following best describes chicken noodle soup?

a. element
b. mixture
c. compound
d. solution

9 Which of the following statements describes elements?

a. All of the particles in the same element are different.
b. Elements can be broken down into simpler substances.
c. Elements have unique sets of properties.
d. Elements cannot be joined together in chemical reactions.

10 A solution that contains a large amount of solute is best described as

a. insoluble.
b. concentrated.
c. dilute.
d. weak.

11 Which of the following substances can be separated into simpler substances only by chemical means?

a. sodium
b. salt water
c. water
d. gold

12 Which of the following would not increase the rate at which a solid dissolves?

a. decreasing the temperature
b. crushing the solid
c. stirring
d. increasing the temperature

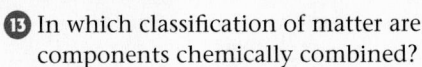

13 In which classification of matter are components chemically combined?

a. a solution   c. a compound

b. a colloid   d. a suspension

14 An element that conducts thermal energy well and is easily shaped is a

a. metal.

b. metalloid.

c. nonmetal.

d. None of the above

Short Answer

15 What is the difference between an element and a compound?

16 When nail polish is dissolved in acetone, which substance is the solute, and which is the solvent?

Math Skills

17 What is the concentration of a solution prepared by mixing 50 g of salt with 200 mL of water?

18 How many grams of sugar must be dissolved in 150 mL of water to make a solution that has a concentration of 0.6 g/mL?

CRITICAL THINKING

19 Concept Mapping Use the following terms to create a concept map: *matter, element, compound, mixture, solution, suspension,* and *colloid.*

20 Forming Hypotheses To keep the "fizz" in carbonated beverages after they have been opened, should you store them in a refrigerator or in a cabinet? Explain.

21 Making Inferences
A light green powder is heated in a test tube. A gas is given off, and the solid becomes black. In which classification of matter does the green powder belong? Explain your reasoning.

22 Predicting Consequences Why is it desirable to know the exact concentration of solutions rather than whether they are concentrated or dilute?

23 Applying Concepts Describe a procedure to separate a mixture of salt, finely ground pepper, and pebbles.

INTERPRETING GRAPHICS

Dr. Sol Vent did an experiment to find the solubility of a compound. The data below were collected using 100 mL of water. Use the table below to answer the questions that follow.

Temperature (°C)	10	25	40	60	95
Dissolved solute (g)	150	70	34	25	15

24 Use a computer or graph paper to construct a graph of Dr. Vent's results. Examine the graph. To increase the solubility, would you increase or decrease the temperature? Explain.

25 If 200 mL of water were used instead of 100 mL, how many grams of the compound would dissolve at 40°C?

26 Based on the solubility of this compound, is this compound a solid, liquid, or gas? Explain your answer.

Critical Thinking

19. 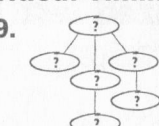 An answer to this exercise can be found at the end of this book.

20. Carbonated beverages should be stored in a refrigerator. Gases are more soluble at lower temperatures, so more gas will stay dissolved in the beverage if it is kept cold.

21. The powder is a compound. The change in color and the formation of a gas imply that a chemical change took place. Compounds can be broken down by chemical changes.

22. The exact concentration tells you exactly how much solute is dissolved in the solvent. *Concentrated* and *dilute* are descriptive terms that do not tell you the amount of solute.

23. Sample answer: Pass the mixture through a screen that allows the salt and pepper to pass through but traps the pebbles. Mix the salt and pepper with water to dissolve the salt. Filter the mixture to trap the pepper. Evaporate the water to recover the salt.

Interpreting Graphics

24. (Teacher's Note: The graph should have "dissolved solute" on the **y**-axis and "temperature" on the **x**-axis. The curve will decrease from left to right.) You should decrease the temperature to increase the solubility. As the temperature decreases, more solute can dissolve.

25. 68 g

26. Because the solubility increases as the temperature decreases, the solute is most likely a gas.

13. c

14. a

15. Elements cannot be separated into simpler substances, but compounds can be separated by chemical means.

16. Nail polish is the solute, and acetone is the solvent.

17. 50 g/200 mL = 0.25 g/mL

18. 150 mL × 0.6 g/mL = 90 g

Standardized Test Preparation

Teacher's Notes

To provide practice under more realistic conditions, give students 20 minutes to answer all of the questions in this Standardized Test Preparation.

Answer Key

Question	Answer
1	B
2	A
3	D
4	C
5	D
6	C
7	A
8	D
9	C
10	*
11	*

*See Test Doctor.

Multiple Choice

Use the pie charts below to answer question 1.

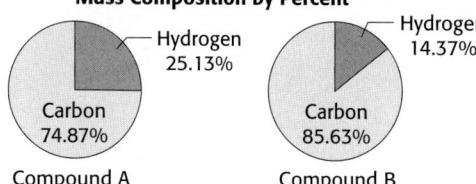

Mass Composition by Percent

Compound A: Hydrogen 25.13%, Carbon 74.87%
Compound B: Hydrogen 14.37%, Carbon 85.63%

1. **Based on the information given in the pie charts, which of the following statements is true?**

   A. Compound A and compound B are the same compound.

   B. Hydrogen and carbon combine in specific but different ratios in forming compounds A and B.

   C. Although the mass compositions of compounds A and B have different percentages, the two compounds have the same mass ratio of carbon to hydrogen.

   D. The compounds hydrogen and carbon combine to form both compound A and compound B.

2. **Imagine that you were asked to classify four samples of equal and known volume, each of which is made up of a single element. Which factor would be most useful for identifying them?**

   A. mass

   B. shape

   C. hardness

   D. original source

Use the table below to answer question 3.

Property	Substance A	Substance B	Substance C
appearance	shiny yellow solid	powdery yellow solid	shiny gray solid
conductivity	good conductor	poor conductor	conductor
malleability	malleable	not malleable	brittle, not malleable

3. **Which of the following statements is most accurate?**

   A. Substances A and C are metals.

   B. Substance B is a metalloid.

   C. Substances B and C are nonmetals.

   D. Substance C is a metalloid.

4. **If two poisonous elements are combined chemically, which of the following will be true of the resulting compound?**

   A. The compound will be more poisonous than the original elements.

   B. The compound will be as poisonous as the original elements.

   C. The compound may or may not be poisonous.

   D. The compound will not be poisonous.

5. **Which of the following processes could separate the components of a compound?**

   A. dissolving then filtering

   B. distilling at the boiling points of the compound's components

   C. using a magnet to attract the compound's metallic components

   D. applying an electric current

 TEST DOCTOR

Question 1 A: Elements always combine in a specific mass ratio to form a compound. The charts show that the mass ratios of the elements in the two compounds are different; therefore, they cannot be the same compound. B: Correct. C: The mass ratio of hydrogen to carbon in compound A is about 1:4, and the mass ratio of hydrogen to carbon in compound B is about 1:5; so their mass ratios are not the same. D: Hydrogen and carbon are elements, not compounds.

Question 2 A: Correct. B: It is possible for identical substances to have different shapes. Likewise, two different substances could have the same shape. C: Different substances may have similar hardnesses. D: The original source of the sample does not indicate the identity of the substance. More than one kind of substance can be found in a single place.

Question 3 A: Substance C is brittle and not malleable; so it is not a metal. B: The properties of substance B are the properties of nonmetals. Substance B is a nonmetal. C: Substance C has some properties of nonmetals and some properties of metals. Substance C is a metalloid. D: Correct.

Use the diagram below to answer question 6.

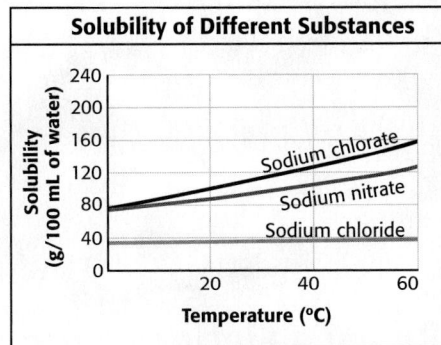

Solubility of Different Substances

6. **Which of the following values is the amount of sodium nitrate that can be dissolved in 100 mL of water at 40°C?**

A. 0 g

B. 40 g

C. 100 g

D. 130 g

7. **Two different atoms are chemically combined to form a new substance. What kind of substance formed?**

A. a compound

B. an element

C. a mixture

D. a solute

8. **Which chemical change may be used to break down a compound?**

A. boiling

B. freezing

C. distillation

D. combustion

9. **You are given two jars, each containing an unknown substance. You are asked to determine whether the substances are different or the same. How should you complete this task?**

A. Compare appearances. If the substances look the same, then they are the same.

B. Compare only physical properties. If the substances have the same density or melting point, then they are the same.

C. Compare physical and chemical properties. If the substances perform the same in a variety of tests, then they are the same.

D. Compare physical states. If the substances are in the same state, then they are the same.

Open Response

10. **Both vinegar and table sugar are composed of carbon, hydrogen, and oxygen atoms. Compare the properties of these two combinations of elements and explain why the same elements can produce different substances.**

11. **Valerie placed 1.0 g of salt into one beaker, 1.0 g of soil into a second beaker, and 1.0 g of sugar into a third beaker. She then added 200 mL of water to each beaker and stirred the contents for 3 minutes. How many solutions did Valerie make? Identify the solvent and solute of each of the solutions.**

Standardized Test Preparation

Question 8 A, B, C: Boiling, freezing, and distillation are physical changes. D: Correct.

Question 9 A: Different substances can look alike. For example, water and ethyl alcohol are identical in appearance but are very different substances. B: The properties of different substances sometimes look the same. C: Correct. D: Many different substances are in the same state at a given temperature and pressure. Comparing melting points would be more helpful, but would also not be conclusive.

Question 10 Full-credit answers should include the following points:

• Vinegar and table sugar are compounds.

• Vinegar is a clear liquid that tastes sour.

• Table sugar is a white solid that tastes sweet. (Some students may correctly state that sugar is crystalline.)

• The same elements can produce different substances because the elements can combine in different ratios.

Question 11 Full-credit answers should point out that Valerie made two solutions:

• In the first solution, water was the solvent and salt was the solute.

• In the second solution, water was the solvent and sugar was the solute.

Question 4 A, B: A compound does not necessarily take on the properties of the elements from which it is composed. C: Correct. D: A compound may have properties similar to its elements, but there is no requirement that it do so.

Question 5 A, B, C: A compound can only be separated into its components through chemical reactions. Dissolving, filtering, and distilling are examples of physical changes. Using a magnet is an example of using a substance's physical properties to cause a physical change. D: Correct.

Question 6 A: Students might have chosen this answer if they mistakenly looked for 40 on the *y*-axis. B: This value is the amount of sodium chloride that can dissolve at 40°C. C: Correct. D: This value is the amount of sodium chlorate that can dissolve at 40°C.

Question 7 A: Correct. B: An element is a pure substance that cannot be broken into simpler substances by physical or chemical means. C: A mixture is a physical combination of two or more substances. D: A solute is the part of a solution that dissolved in the solvent.

Science, Technology, and Society

Teaching Strategy—GENERAL

Bring in several items of clothing made of different types of materials. Show students how to read the information on the garment labels, which includes the types of materials used and laundering information. Conduct a discussion about what correlation they see between different types of fibers and different laundering methods.

Science Fiction

"The Strange Case of Dr. Jekyll and Mr. Hyde"

by Robert Louis Stevenson

When Dr. Jekyll mixes his "salts" and drinks his chemical mixture, he changes his life—and Edward Hyde's—completely.

Teaching Strategy—GENERAL

Reading Level This novelette is challenging for middle school readers. It may be helpful for you to review the story in advance and review some of the unfamiliar words and phrases with students ahead of time.

Science in Action

Science, Technology, and Society

Dry Cleaning: How Stains Are Dissolved
Sometimes, just water and detergent won't remove stains. For example, have you gotten ink on your favorite sweater? Or have you spilled something greasy on your shirt? In that case, your clothes will probably have to be dry-cleaned. In spite of its name, dry cleaning does involve liquids. First, the kind of stain on your clothing must be determined. If the stain will dissolve in water, a stain remover for that particular stain is applied. Then, the stain is removed with a steam gun. But some stains, such as grease or oil, won't dissolve in water. This kind of stain is treated with a liquid solvent. The clothing is then cleaned in a dry-cleaning machine.

Language Arts ACTIVITY

WRITING SKILL Imagine that you are a stained article of clothing. Write a five-paragraph short story describing how you became stained and how the stain was removed by the dry-cleaning process. You may have to research the dry-cleaning process before writing your story.

Science Fiction

"The Strange Case of Dr. Jekyll and Mr. Hyde" by Robert Louis Stevenson
Although Dr. Henry Jekyll was wild as a young man, he has become a respected doctor and scientist. Dr. Jekyll wants to understand the nature of human identity. His theory is that if he can separate his personality into "good" and "evil" parts, he can get rid of his evil side. Then, he can lead a happy, useful life.

Into Dr. Jekyll's life comes the mysterious Mr. Hyde, a man of action and anger. He sparks fear in the hearts of people he meets. Who is he? And what does he have to do with the deaths of two people? To find out more, read Stevenson's "The Strange Case of Dr. Jekyll and Mr. Hyde" in the *Holt Anthology of Science Fiction.*

Social Studies ACTIVITY

"The Strange Case of Dr. Jekyll and Mr. Hyde" was published in 1886. The story takes place in London, England. What was London like in the 1870s and 1880s? Use the library or the Internet to find information about London and its people at that time. Make a chart that compares London in the 1870s with your hometown today.

Answer to Language Arts Activity

Students' stories should include information about the cleaning substances and equipment used by the dry-cleaning industry. The types of stains that are most effectively cleaned by the dry-cleaning process are those that are not water based, such as grease and nail polish.

Answer to Social Studies Activity

Students' charts should include information about population, demographics, industry, government, and social life. During the 19th century, London grew very rapidly and became highly industrialized. Great Britain as a whole became a strong trading nation and almost one-third of the world was ruled by the British Empire at the time.

Careers

Aundra Nix

Metallurgist Aundra Nix is a chief metallurgist for a copper mine in Sahuarita, Arizona, where she supervises laboratories and other engineers. "To be able to look at rock in the ground and follow it through a process of drilling, blasting, hauling, crushing, grinding, and finally mineral separation—where you can hold a mineral that is one-third copper in your hand—is exciting."

Although she is a supervisor, Nix enjoys the flexible nature of her job. "My work environment includes office and computer work, plant work, and outdoor work. In this field you can 'get your hands into it,' which I always prefer," says Nix. "I did not want a career where it may be years before you see the results of your work." Aundra Nix enjoyed math and science, "so engineering seemed to be a natural area to study," she says. Nix's advice to students planning their own career is to learn all they can in science and technology, because that is the future.

Math ACTIVITY

A large copper-mining company employed about 2,300 people at three locations in New Mexico. Because of an increase in demand for copper, 570 of these workers were hired over a period of a year. Of the 570 new workers, 115 were hired within a three-week period. What percentage of the total work force do the newly hired employees represent? Of the new workers who were hired, what percentage was hired during the three-week hiring period?

go.hrw.com
To learn more about these Science in Action topics, visit go.hrw.com and type in the keyword HP5MIXF.

Current Science
Check out Current Science® articles related to this chapter by visiting go.hrw.com. Just type in the keyword HP5CS04.

Careers

Background

Aundra Nix received a bachelor of science degree in mining and mineral engineering from Virginia Polytechnic Institute and State University in 1989. To enhance her technical skills, in 2001 she obtained a master of science degree in computer information systems from the University of Phoenix. "I am still working in the field I studied and graduated from in 1989," she says.

Nix's biggest concern is the decline of the mining industry. "Most of mining is moving to other countries," she says, "and as a result the future of U.S. mining is grim. Our industry is in poor economic condition and is likely to remain so for a long time." Nix's company was purchased by a Mexican competitor in 1999.

Nix's hobbies include golf, cycling, hiking and fishing—and other activities like cooking and reading. "Females in male-dominated industries aren't necessarily all 'tomboys'!" she jokes.

Answer to Math Activity
The newly hired employees represent 25% of the total work force. This answer is calculated by dividing 570 by 2,300 and multiplying the result by 100. The percentage of employees that were hired during the three-week hiring period is 20.2%. This answer is calculated by dividing 115 by 570 and multiplying the result by 100.

Introduction to Atoms
Chapter Planning Guide

Compression guide: To shorten instruction because of time limitations, omit the Chapter Lab.

OBJECTIVES	LABS, DEMONSTRATIONS, AND ACTIVITIES	TECHNOLOGY RESOURCES
PACING • 90 min pp. 542–549 **Chapter Opener**	SE **Start-up Activity**, p. 543 GENERAL	OSP **Parent Letter** ■ CD **Student Edition on CD-ROM** CD **Guided Reading Audio CD** ■ TR **Chapter Starter Transparency*** VID **Brain Food Video Quiz**
Section 1 Development of the Atomic Theory • Describe some of the experiments that led to the current atomic theory. • Compare the different models of the atom. • Explain how the atomic theory has changed as scientists have discovered new information about the atom.	TE **Activity** Photographic Dots, p. 544 GENERAL TE **Activity** Scientist Flashcards, p. 545 BASIC TE **Connection Activity** Math, p. 546 GENERAL TE **Connection Activity** Literature, p. 547 GENERAL LB **Whiz-Bang Demonstrations** As a Matter of Space* BASIC	OSP **Lesson Plans** (also in print) TR **Bellringer Transparency*** TR **P45 Thomson's Cathode-Ray Tube Experiment*** TR **P46 Rutherford's Gold-Foil Experiment***
PACING • 90 min pp. 550–557 **Section 2 The Atom** • Describe the size of the atom. • Name the parts of an atom. • Describe the relationship between numbers of protons and neutrons and atomic number. • State how isotopes differ. • Calculate atomic masses. • Describe the forces within an atom.	TE **Connection Activity** Real World, p. 551 GENERAL SE **School-to-Home Activity** Atomic Diagrams, p. 554 GENERAL TE **Connection Activity** Life Science, p. 554 GENERAL TE **Activity** Reconstructing Atoms, p. 554 GENERAL TE **Connection Activity** Math, p. 555 GENERAL SE **Model-Making Lab** Made to Order, p. 558 GENERAL CRF **Datasheet for Chapter Lab*** LB **Whiz-Bang Demonstrations** Candy Lights* GENERAL LB **Long-Term Projects & Research Ideas** How Low Can They Go? ADVANCED SE **Science in Action** Math, Social Studies, and Language Arts Activities, pp. 564–565 GENERAL	OSP **Lesson Plans** (also in print) TR **Bellringer Transparency*** TR **P47 Parts of an Atom*** TR **P48 Forces in the Atom*** TR **LINK TO EARTH SCIENCE** E87 Fusion of Hydrogen in the Sun* SE **Internet Activity**, p. 553 GENERAL CRF **SciLinks Activity*** GENERAL VID **Lab Videos for Physical Science**

PACING • 90 min

CHAPTER REVIEW, ASSESSMENT, AND STANDARDIZED TEST PREPARATION

CRF **Vocabulary Activity*** GENERAL
SE **Chapter Review**, pp. 560–561 GENERAL
CRF **Chapter Review*** ■ GENERAL
CRF **Chapter Tests A*** ■ GENERAL, **B*** ADVANCED, **C*** SPECIAL NEEDS
SE **Standardized Test Preparation**, pp. 562–563 GENERAL
CRF **Standardized Test Preparation*** GENERAL
CRF **Performance-Based Assessment*** GENERAL
OSP **Test Generator, Test Item Listing**

Online and Technology Resources

 Holt Online Learning

Visit **go.hrw.com** for access to Holt Online Learning, or enter the keyword **HS7 Home** for a variety of free online resources.

 **One-Stop Planner® CD-ROM**

This CD-ROM package includes:
• Lab Materials QuickList Software
• Holt Calendar Planner
• Customizable Lesson Plans
• Printable Worksheets

• ExamView® Test Generator
• Interactive Teacher's Edition
• Holt PuzzlePro®
• Holt PowerPoint® Resources

SKILLS DEVELOPMENT RESOURCES	SECTION REVIEW AND ASSESSMENT	CORRELATIONS
SE Pre-Reading Activity, p. 542 `GENERAL` **OSP** Science Puzzlers, Twisters & Teasers `GENERAL`		**National Science Education Standards** SAI 1, 2
CRF Directed Reading A* ■ `BASIC`, B* `SPECIAL NEEDS` **WB** Workbook* Struggling Readers **CRF** Vocabulary and Section Summary* ■ `GENERAL` **SE** Reading Strategy Reading Organizer, p. 544 `GENERAL` **TE** Support for English Language Learners, p. 545 **SE** Connection to Language Arts Solving Mysteries, p. 547 `GENERAL` **TE** Inclusion Strategies, p. 547 **CRF** Reinforcement Worksheet Atomic Timeline* `BASIC` **MS** Math Skills for Science Using Proportions and Cross-Multiplication* `GENERAL`	**SE** Reading Checks, pp. 545, 547, 548 `GENERAL` **TE** Homework, p. 547 `GENERAL` **TE** Reteaching, p. 548 `BASIC` **TE** Quiz, p. 548 `GENERAL` **TE** Alternative Assessment, p. 548 `GENERAL` **SE** Section Review,* p. 549 ■ `GENERAL` **CRF** Section Quiz* ■ `GENERAL`	UCP 2; SAI 2; HNS 1, 2, 3
CRF Directed Reading A* ■ `BASIC`, B* `SPECIAL NEEDS` **WB** Workbook* Struggling Readers **CRF** Vocabulary and Section Summary* ■ `GENERAL` **SE** Reading Strategy Reading Organizer, p. 550 `GENERAL` **TE** Reading Strategy Atomic Diagrams, p. 551 `GENERAL` **SE** Connection to Astronomy Hydrogen, p. 552 `GENERAL` **TE** Inclusion Strategies, p. 553 **TE** Support for English Language Learners, p. 553 **SE** Math Focus Atomic Mass, p. 555 `GENERAL` **MS** Math Skills for Science Arithmetic with Decimals* `GENERAL` **CRF** Critical Thinking Incredible Shrinking Scientist!* `ADVANCED`	**SE** Reading Checks, pp. 551, 552, 554, 556 `GENERAL` **TE** Reteaching, p. 556 `BASIC` **TE** Quiz, p. 556 `GENERAL` **TE** Alternative Assessment, p. 556 `GENERAL` **SE** Section Review,* p. 557 ■ `GENERAL` **CRF** Section Quiz* ■ `GENERAL`	PS 1c *Chapter Lab* SAI 1

www.scilinks.org
Maintained by the **National Science Teachers Association.** See Chapter Enrichment pages that follow for a complete list of topics.

Check out **Current Science** articles and activities by visiting the HRW Web site at **go.hrw.com.** Just type in the keyword **HP5CS11T.**

 **Classroom Videos**

- **Lab Videos** demonstrate the chapter lab.
- **Brain Food Video Quizzes** help students review the chapter material.

Classroom CD-ROMs

- **Guided Reading Audio CD** (Also in Spanish)
- **Interactive Explorations**
- **Virtual Investigations**
- **Visual Concepts**
- **Science Tutor**

 **Holt Lab Generator CD-ROM**

Search for any lab by topic, standard, difficulty level, or time. Edit any lab to fit your needs, or create your own labs. Use the Lab Materials QuickList software to customize your lab materials list.

Visual Resources

CHAPTER STARTER TRANSPARENCY

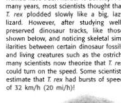

Would You Believe . . . ?

Tiny atoms have something in common with huge dinosaurs. In both cases, scientists have had to try to understand something they could not observe firsthand!

No one has ever seen a living dinosaur, but scientists have determined the appearance of *Tyrannosaurus rex* by studying fossilized skeletons. Scientists theorize that these now-extinct creatures had big hind legs, small front legs, a long, whip-like tail, and a mouth full of dagger-shaped teeth.

However, theories of how *T. rex* walked have been harder to develop. For many years, most scientists thought that *T. rex* plodded slowly like a big, lazy lizard. However, after studying well-preserved dinosaur tracks, like those shown below, and noticing skeletal similarities between certain dinosaur fossils and living creatures such as the ostrich, many scientists now theorize that *T. rex* could turn on the speed. Some scientists estimate that *T. rex* had bursts of speed of 32 km/h (20 mi/h)!

Theories about *T. rex* and other dinosaurs have changed gradually based on indirect evidence, such as dinosaur tracks. Likewise, our theory of the atom has changed as scientists have uncovered more evidence about the atom, even though they were unable to see an atom directly. In this chapter, you'll learn about the development of the atomic theory and our current understanding of atomic structure.

BELLRINGER TRANSPARENCIES

Section: Development of the Atomic Theory

The following is a quote by Democritus (c. 460–c. 370 BCE). Paraphrase this quote in your own words in your **science journal.**

"Color exists by convention, sweet by convention, bitter by convention; in reality nothing exists but atoms and the void."

What do you know about Democritus? And why are his thoughts important?

Section: The Atom

Answer the following question:

An *atom* is the smallest particle into which an element can be divided and still be that element. Now that scientists have learned that an atom is made up of even smaller particles, is this definition still accurate?

Explain your answer in your **science journal.**

TEACHING TRANSPARENCIES

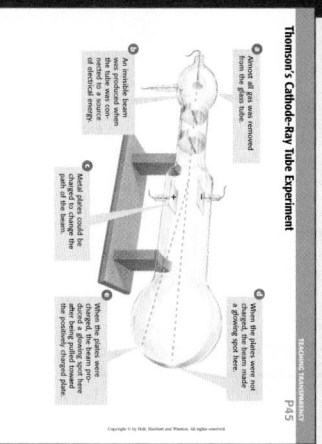

Thomson's Cathode-Ray Tube Experiment

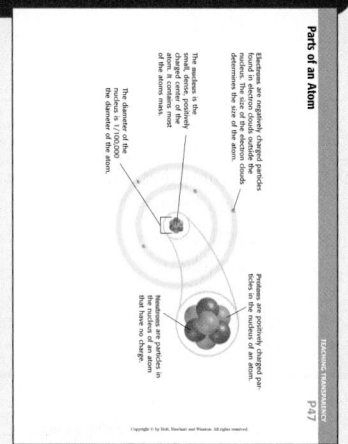

Parts of an Atom

TEACHING TRANSPARENCIES

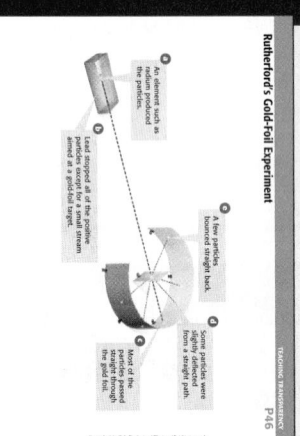

Rutherford's Gold-Foil Experiment

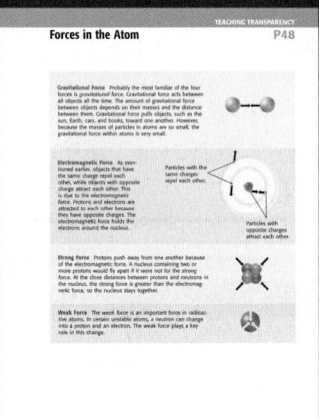

Forces in the Atom

Fusion of Hydrogen in the Sun

Chapter: Formation of the Solar System

CONCEPT MAPPING TRANSPARENCY

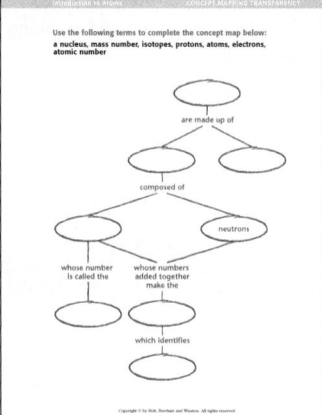

Use the following terms to complete the concept map below: **a nucleus, mass number, isotopes, protons, atoms, electrons, atomic number**

Planning Resources

LESSON PLANS

Lesson Plan   SAMPLE

Section: Waves

Pacing

Regular Schedule: with labs\x2 days   without labs\x2 days
Block Schedule: with labs\x1 1/2 days   without lab\x1 day

Objectives

1. Relate the seven properties of life to a living organism.
2. Describe seven themes that can help you to organize what you learn about biology.
3. Identify the tiny structures that make up all living organisms.
4. Differentiate between reproduction and heredity and between metabolism and homeostasis.

National Science Education Standards Covered

LSInter1:Cells have particular structures that underlie their functions.
LSMat1:Most cell functions involve chemical reactions.
LSBeh1:Cells store and use information to guide their functions.
UCP1:Cell functions are regulated.
SI1: Cells can differentiate and form complete multicellular organisms.
PS1: Species evolve over time.
ESS1: The great diversity of organisms is the result of more than 3.5 billion years of evolution.
ESS2: Natural selection and its evolutionary consequences provide a scientific explanation for the fossil record of ancient life forms as well as for the striking molecular similarities observed among the diverse species of living organisms.
ST1: The millions of different species of plants, animals, and microorganisms that live on Earth today are related by descent from common ancestors.
ST2: The energy for life primarily comes from the sun.
SPSP1: The complexity and organization of organisms accommodates the need for obtaining, transforming, transporting, releasing, and eliminating the matter and energy used to sustain the organism.
SPSP6: As matter and energy flows through different levels of organization of living systems—cells, organs, communities—and through living systems and the physical environment, chemical elements are recombined in different ways.
HNS1: Organisms have behavioral responses to internal changes and to external stimuli.

PARENT LETTER

SAMPLE

Dear Parent,

Your son's or daughter's science class will soon begin exploring the chapter entitled "The World of Physical Science." In this chapter, students will learn about how the scientific method applies to the world of physical science and the role of physical science in the world. By the end of the chapter, students should demonstrate a clear understanding of the chapter's main ideas and be able to discuss the following topics:

1. physical science is the study of energy and matter (Section 1)
2. the role of physical science and how it relates to other branches of science (Section 1)
3. careers that rely on physical science (Section 1)
4. the steps used in the scientific method (Section 2)
5. examples of technology (Section 2)
6. how the scientific method is used to answer questions and solve problems (Section 2)
7. how our knowledge of science changes over time (Section 2)
8. how models represent real objects or systems (Section 3)
9. examples of different ways models are used in science (Section 3)
10. the importance of the International System of Units (Section 4)
11. the appropriate units to use for particular measurements (Section 4)
12. area and density are derived quantities (Section 4)

Questions to Ask Along the Way

You can help your son or daughter learn about these topics by asking interesting questions such as the following:

• What are some surprising careers that use physical science?
• What is a characteristic of a good hypothesis?
• When is it a good idea to use a model?
• Why do Americans measure things in terms of inches and yards and miles and meters ?

ALSO IN SPANISH

TEST ITEM LISTING

TEST ITEM LISTING
The World of Science   SAMPLE

MULTIPLE CHOICE

1. A limitation of models is that
   a. they are large enough to see.
   b. they do not act exactly like the things that they model.
   c. they are smaller than things that they model.
   d. they model unfamiliar things.
   Answer: B   Difficulty: 1   Section: 3   Objective: 2

2. The length 10 m is equal to
   a. 100 cm.   c. 10,000 mm.
   b. 1,000 cm.   d. Both (b) and (c)
   Answer: B   Difficulty: 1   Section: 3   Objective: 1

3. To be valid, a hypothesis must be
   a. testable.   c. made into a law.
   b. supported by evidence.   d. Both (a) and (b)
   Answer: B   Difficulty: 1   Section: 2   Objective: 1

4. The statement "Sheila has a stain on her shirt" is an example of a(n)
   a. law.   c. observation.
   b. hypothesis.   d. prediction.
   Answer: B   Difficulty: 1   Section: 2   Objective: 2

5. A hypothesis is often developed out of
   a. observations.   c. laws.
   b. experiments.   d. Both (a) and (b)
   Answer: B   Difficulty: 1   Section: 2   Objective: 2

6. How many milliliters are in 3.5 kL?
   a. 3,500 mL   c. 3,500,000 mL
   b. 0.0035 mL   d. 35,000 mL
   Answer: B   Difficulty: 1   Section: 3   Objective: 2

7. A map of Seattle is an example of a
   a. law.   c. model.
   b. theory.   d. unit.
   Answer: B   Difficulty: 1   Section: 3   Objective: 2

8. A lab that has safety gions shown below. These icons mean that you should wear
   a. only safety goggles.   c. safety goggles and a lab apron.
   b. only a lab apron.   d. safety goggles, a lab apron, and gloves.
   Answer: B   Difficulty: 1   Section: 1   Objective: 1

9. The law of conservation of mass says the tol al mass before a chemical change is
   a. more than the total mass after the change.
   b. less than the total mass after the change.
   c. the same as the total mass after the change.
   d. not the same as the total mass after the change.
   Answer: B   Difficulty: 1   Section: 3   Objective: 2

10. In which of the following areas might you find a geochemist at work?
    a. studying the formation of rocks   c. studying fishes
    b. studying history   d. studying the atmosphere
    Answer: B   Difficulty: 1   Section: 3   Objective: 2

One-Stop Planner® CD-ROM

This CD-ROM includes all of the resources shown here and the following time-saving tools:

• *Lab Materials QuickList Software*
• *Customizable lesson plans*
• *Holt Calendar Planner*
• *The powerful ExamView® Test Generator*

Meeting Individual Needs

DIRECTED READING A
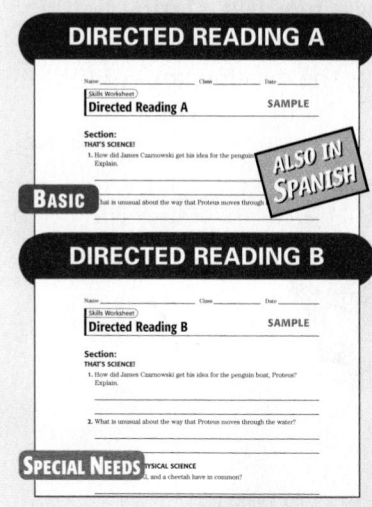

VOCABULARY ACTIVITY
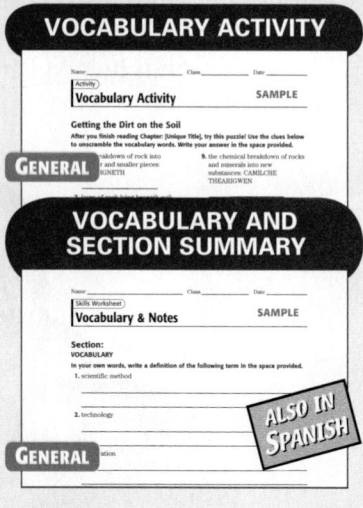

REINFORCEMENT
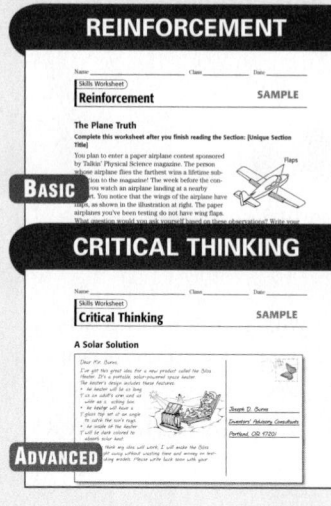

SCILINKS ACTIVITY

DIRECTED READING B

VOCABULARY AND SECTION SUMMARY

CRITICAL THINKING

SCIENCE PUZZLERS, TWISTERS & TEASERS

Labs and Activities

LONG-TERM PROJECTS & RESEARCH IDEAS
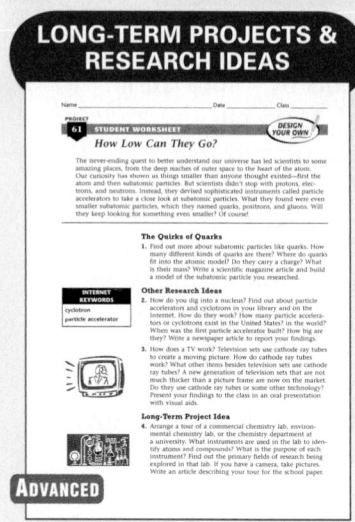

WHIZ-BANG DEMONSTRATIONS
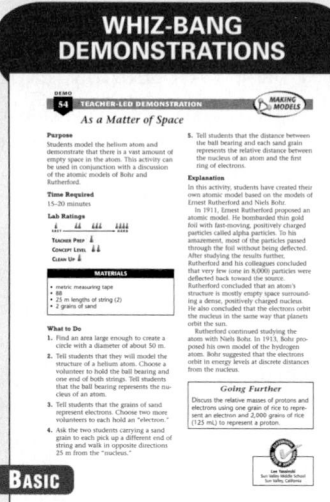

WHIZ-BANG DEMONSTRATIONS
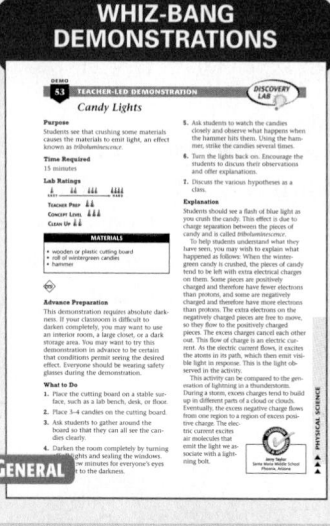

DATASHEETS FOR QUICK LABS

DATASHEETS FOR CHAPTER LABS

DATASHEETS FOR LABBOOK

Review and Assessments

SECTION QUIZ
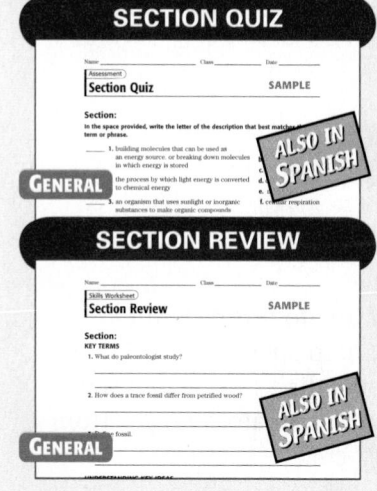

CHAPTER REVIEW
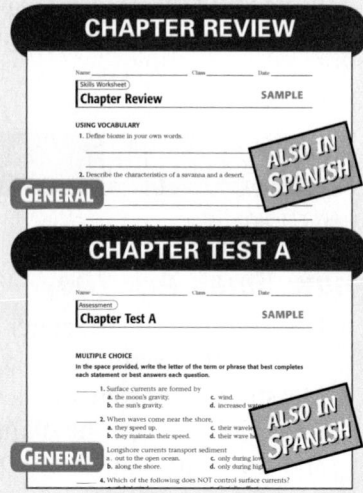

CHAPTER TEST B
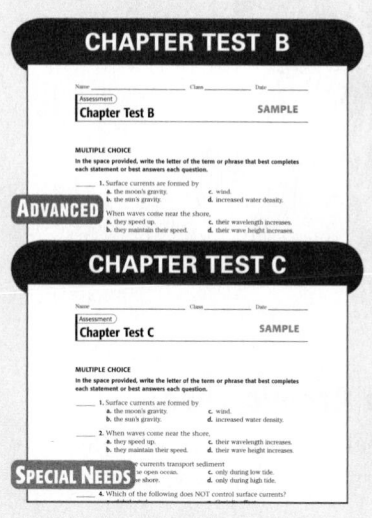

STANDARDIZED TEST PREPARATION
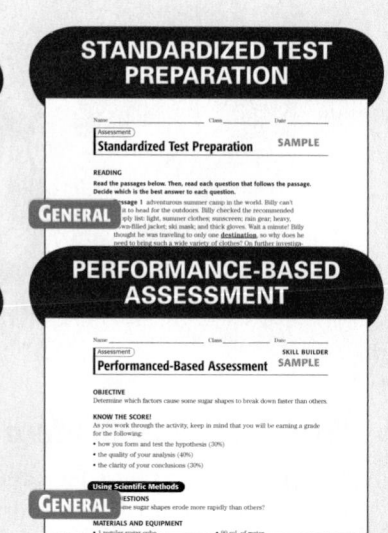

SECTION REVIEW

CHAPTER TEST A

CHAPTER TEST C

PERFORMANCE-BASED ASSESSMENT

This Chapter Enrichment provides relevant and interesting information to expand and enhance your presentation of the chapter material.

Section 1

Development of the Atomic Theory

Democritus

- Democritus (c. 460–c. 370 BCE) was a Greek philosopher and leading advocate of the theory that all phenomena in nature could be understood in terms of the movements of particles called atoms (from the Greek word *atomos*, meaning "indivisible").

- The views of Democritus sharply contrasted those of Aristotle and others, who held to the theory that all matter could be reduced to a combination of four elements: earth, water, air, and fire.

Is That a Fact!

- Democritus's ideas were not widely accepted because Aristotle, who was better known and respected, did not accept the idea of atoms. Only fragments of Democritus's writings survive, and most of our knowledge of his ideas comes from negative remarks about his theories in other people's writings.

From Greek to Modern Atomic Theory

- Democritus and other Greek philosophers laid the groundwork for the modern atomic theory, but it was not until the 16th and 17th centuries that interest in atoms and atomic structure was renewed. During that time, the work of Sir Isaac Newton, Robert Boyle, and Pierre Gassendi helped further the development of the atomic theory.

- In the 19th century, experiments by John Dalton, Amedeo Avogadro, James Clerk Maxwell, and Rudolf Clausius began to reveal the nature and structure of atoms.

- Sir Joseph John Thomson's discovery of electrons in 1897 and his later research on protons and gases indicated that atoms were not the smallest indivisible units of matter, as previously thought. Thomson showed that subatomic particles with either a negative or positive charge form at least part of the structure of an atom. Thomson won the Nobel Prize in physics in 1906.

- While Thomson was director of the Cavendish Laboratory at Cambridge University in Cambridge, England, one of his graduate students was Ernest Rutherford. Rutherford went on to win the Nobel Prize in chemistry in 1908 for his work on radioactivity.

Section 2

The Atom

How Small Are They?

- Determining the diameter of an atom is difficult because atoms are not small, hard spheres. Measurement often varies depending on the method used. On average, the diameter of an atom ranges from about 7×10^{-9} cm to 5×10^{-8} cm.

Isotopes

- While some isotopes are stable and can survive indefinitely, others are unstable. Unstable isotopes undergo radioactive decay toward a more stable form, often by becoming other elements.

- There are approximately 280 stable isotopes of the natural elements. A natural element is usually predominantly one stable isotope with smaller amounts of other stable and unstable isotopes.

- Radioactive isotopes can be natural or artificial. The naturally occurring radioisotopes have existed since Earth's formation.

- The first artificial radioisotopes were produced in 1934 by Frederic and Irene Joliot-Curie. Since then, more than 1,800 artificial radioisotopes have been produced by using a variety of nuclear bombardment techniques.

Quarks and Gluons

- Protons and neutrons are composed of smaller particles called *quarks*. The existence of quarks was suggested in 1963 by two physicists: Murray Gell-Mann and George Zweig.

- Hadrons are all particles that feel the strong force. They include baryons, quark triplets; antibaryons; and mesons, quark-antiquark pairs. Baryons include protons and neutrons.

- A gluon is believed to be a subatomic particle that "glues" quarks together with the strong nuclear force.

Is That a Fact!

- When gluons bind to each other, they are referred to as "glueballs."

- The term *quark* originated from a line in James Joyce's novel *Finnegan's Wake:* "Three quarks for Muster Mark."

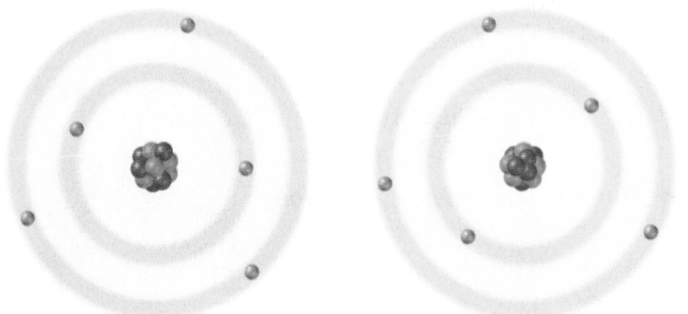

SciLINKS

Developed and maintained by the National Science Teachers Association

SciLinks is maintained by the National Science Teachers Association to provide you and your students with interesting, up-to-date links that will enrich your classroom presentation of the chapter.

Visit www.scilinks.org and enter the SciLinks code for more information about the topic listed.

Topic: Development of the Atomic Theory
SciLinks code: HSM0399

Topic: Current Atomic Theory
SciLinks code: HSM0371

Topic: Inside the Atom
SciLinks code: HSM0799

Topic: Isotopes
SciLinks code: HSM0820

Overview

This chapter discusses the development of the atomic theory over the years, from the prescientific ideas of Democritus through Dalton, Thomson, and Rutherford to modern "electron cloud" theory. Then, the parts of the atom, including the forces that hold an atom together, are described and discussed.

Assessing Prior Knowledge

Students should be familiar with the following topics:

- matter
- elements

Identifying Misconceptions

Students often believe that atoms possess macro properties such as hardness, color, shape, or stickiness. They may also believe that atoms contain no empty space and are static.

20

Introduction to Atoms

The Big Idea

Atoms are composed of small particles that determine the properties of the atom.

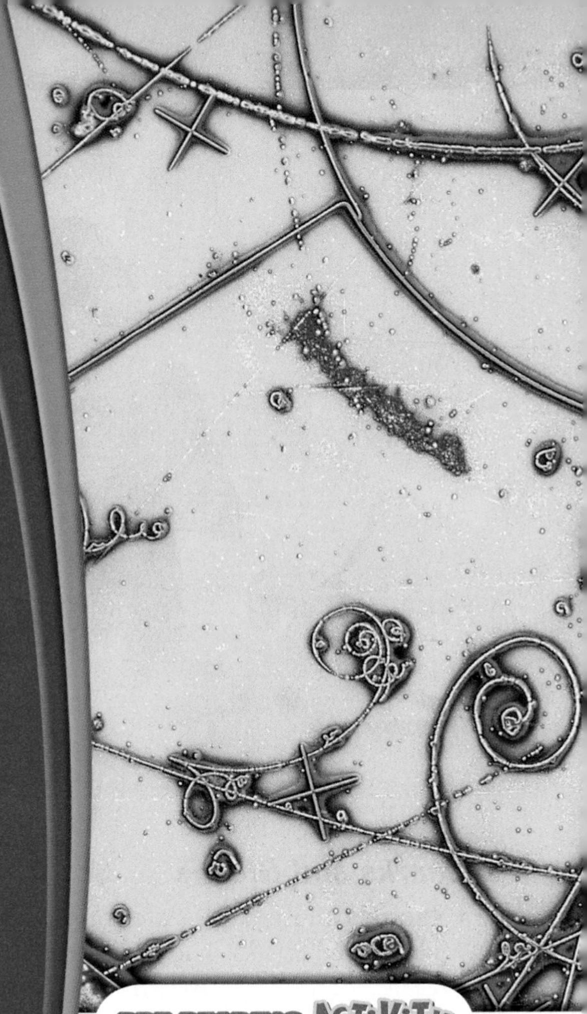

About the Photo

You have probably made bubbles with a plastic wand and a soapy liquid. Some scientists make bubbles by using a bubble chamber. A bubble chamber is filled with a pressurized liquid that forms bubbles when a charged particle moves through it. This photo shows the tracks made by charged particles moving through a bubble chamber. Bubble chambers help scientists learn about particles called *atoms,* which make up all objects.

PRE-READING ACTIVITY

Graphic Organizer

Chain-of-Events Chart Before you read the chapter, create the graphic organizer entitled "Chain-of-Events Chart" described in the **Study Skills** section of the Appendix. As you read the chapter, fill in the chart with details about each step in the historical development of ideas about atoms.

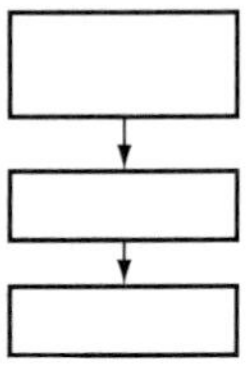

Standards Correlations

National Science Education Standards

The following codes indicate the National Science Education Standards that correlate to this chapter. The full text of the standards is at the front of the book.

Chapter Opener
SAI 1, 2

Section 1 Development of the Atomic Theory
UCP 2; SAI 2; HNS 1, 2, 3

Section 2 The Atom
PS 1c

Chapter Lab
SAI 2

Chapter Review
HNS 2, 3

Science in Action
HNS 1

FOR EACH GROUP
• book or block (4)
• cardboard, rectangular piece
• marble
• paper, plain, large piece
• unknown object

Teacher's Notes: The size of the cardboard should be large enough to prevent students from seeing the hidden object after you place it under the cardboard. Students will need to cover the cardboard completely with paper in order to mark the information they need to gather. Small pieces of wood cut into simple geometric shapes would work well as the objects used by each group.

Remind students to roll the marble gently as they try to establish where and what the object is.

Answer

1. Accept all reasonable answers. Students should make connections between the behavior of the marble and the nature of the hidden object.

2. Accept all reasonable answers.

START-UP ACTIVITY

Where Is It?

Scientists have been able to gather information about atoms without actually seeing them. In this activity, you will do something similar: you will form an idea about the location and size of a hidden object by rolling marbles at it.

Procedure

1. Place a **rectangular piece of cardboard** on **four books or blocks** so that each corner of the cardboard rests on a book or block.

2. Your teacher will place an **unknown object** under the cardboard. Be sure that you cannot see the object.

3. Place a **large piece of paper** on top of the cardboard.

4. Carefully roll a **marble** under the cardboard. Record on the paper the position where the marble enters and exits. Also, record the direction it travels.

5. Keep rolling the marble from different directions to collect data about the shape and location of the object. Write down all of your observations.

Analysis

1. Form a conclusion about the object's shape, size, and location. Record your conclusion.

2. Lift the cardboard, and look at the object. Compare your conclusions with the object's actual size, shape, and location.

Chapter Starter Transparency
Use this transparency to help students begin thinking about atoms.

CHAPTER RESOURCES

Technology

Transparencies
• Chapter Starter Transparency

Student Edition on CD-ROM

Guided Reading Audio CD
• English or Spanish

Classroom Videos
• Brain Food Video Quiz

Workbooks

Science Puzzlers, Twisters & Teasers
• Introduction to Atoms GENERAL

SECTION
1

Focus

Overview

Students will trace changes that have occurred in atomic theory as scientists have discovered more about atomic structure.

 **Bellringer**

Display the following quote by Democritus (c. 460–c. 370 BCE). Have students write what they think the statement means. Do not divulge the source.

> Color exists by convention, sweet by convention, bitter by convention; in reality nothing exists but atoms and the void.

Discuss Democritus and his statement with students.

Motivate

ACTIVITY ——— GENERAL

Photographic Dots Have students use a magnifying lens to examine photographs in a newspaper. Students should notice that the pictures are made up of tiny dots of ink. Explain that many objects that appear to be whole are actually made up of smaller parts. It was this idea that led early philosophers and scientists to theorize that matter is made up of tiny, indivisible parts. These tiny bits of matter became known as *atoms*. **LS** Visual   English Language Learners

What You Will Learn

● Describe some of the experiments that led to the current atomic theory.
● Compare the different models of the atom.
● Explain how the atomic theory has changed as scientists have discovered new information about the atom.

Vocabulary

atom   nucleus
electron   electron cloud

READING STRATEGY

Reading Organizer As you read this section, create an outline of the section. Use the headings from the section in your outline.

Figure 1 *Aluminum cans, like all matter, are made of atoms. Aluminum atoms can be seen here as an image from a scanning tunneling electron microscope.*

Development of the Atomic Theory

Have you ever watched a mystery movie and thought you knew who the criminal was? Have you ever changed your mind because of a new fact or clue?

The same thing happens in science! Sometimes an idea or model must be changed as new information is gathered. In this section, you will see how our ideas about atoms have changed over time. Your first stop is ancient Greece.

The Beginning of Atomic Theory

Imagine that you cut something in half. Then, you cut each half in half again, and so on. Could you keep cutting the pieces in half forever? Around 440 BCE, a Greek philosopher named Democritus (di MAHK ruh tuhs) thought that you would eventually end up with a particle that could not be cut. He called this particle an atom. The word *atom* is from the Greek word *atomos,* meaning "not able to be divided." Democritus said that all atoms are small, hard particles. He thought that atoms were made of a single material formed into different shapes and sizes.

From Aristotle to Modern Science

Aristotle (AR is TAHT'l), another Greek philosopher, disagreed with Democritus's ideas. He believed that you would never end up with a particle that could not be cut. He had such a strong influence on people's ideas that for a long time, most people thought he was right.

Democritus was right, though: Matter is made of particles, which we call atoms. An **atom** is the smallest particle into which an element can be divided and still be the same substance. **Figure 1** shows a picture of aluminum atoms taken with a scanning tunneling electron microscope (STM). Long before actually being able to scan atoms, scientists had ideas about them.

CHAPTER RESOURCES

Chapter Resource File

 • Lesson Plan
• Directed Reading A BASIC
• Directed Reading B SPECIAL NEEDS

Technology

 Transparencies
• Bellringer

Workbooks

Interactive Textbook Struggling Readers

Is That a Fact!

It would take 1.05×10^{17} gold atoms to cover the entire surface of a dollar bill. That's 105 quadrillion gold atoms!

Dalton's Atomic Theory Based on Experiments

By the late 1700s, scientists had learned that elements combine in certain proportions based on mass to form compounds. For example, hydrogen and oxygen always combine in the same proportion to form water. John Dalton, a British chemist and schoolteacher, wanted to know why. He experimented with different substances. His results suggested that elements combine in certain proportions because they are made of single atoms. Dalton, shown in **Figure 2,** published his atomic theory in 1803. His theory stated the following ideas:

- All substances are made of atoms. Atoms are small particles that cannot be created, divided, or destroyed.
- Atoms of the same element are exactly alike, and atoms of different elements are different.
- Atoms join with other atoms to make new substances.

✓ Reading Check Why did Dalton think that elements are made of single atoms? (*See the Appendix for answers to Reading Checks.*)

Not Quite Correct

Toward the end of the 1800s, scientists agreed that Dalton's theory explained much of what they saw. However, new information was found that did not fit some of Dalton's ideas. The atomic theory was then changed to describe the atom more correctly. As you read on, you will learn how Dalton's theory has changed, step by step, into the modern atomic theory.

atom the smallest unit of an element that maintains the properties of that element

Figure 2 *John Dalton developed his atomic theory from observations gathered from many experiments.*

Answer to Reading Check
Dalton thought that elements are made of single atoms because elements always combine in specific proportions to form compounds.

Is That a Fact!

Along with contributing to the atomic theory, John Dalton was also the first to describe colorblindness. Dalton himself was colorblind. The paper that contains his article describing the condition was published in 1794.

CONNECTION ACTIVITY
Math ——————— GENERAL

Counting Atoms The length of a dollar bill is 15.7 cm. The width is 6.65 cm. If it takes 500 million gold atoms laid end to end to measure the length of a dollar bill, how many gold atoms would it take to measure the width? (almost 212 million gold atoms) **LS** Logical

Homework ——————— GENERAL

Writing

Theories of Atomic Structure Thomson's model of the atom was the first of many models created to explain the atom's structure. Each model is revised or replaced as scientists learn more. Current models may be changed because of new discoveries. Have students write a paragraph explaining why making and using models of scientific discoveries is important. They should give at least two reasons. **LS** Logical

---

MISCONCEPTION ALERT

Charge Convention The terms *positive* and *negative* are arbitrary. The terms were first used by Benjamin Franklin to describe phenomena that he observed. The terms were quickly adopted by scientists.

Figure 3 Thomson's Cathode-Ray Tube Experiment

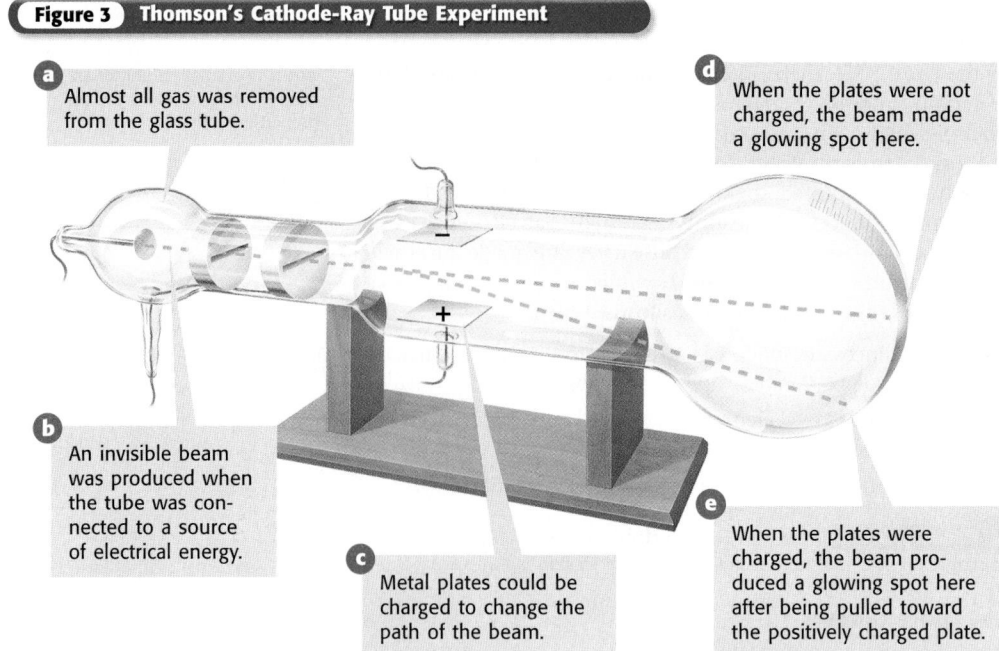

a Almost all gas was removed from the glass tube.

d When the plates were not charged, the beam made a glowing spot here.

b An invisible beam was produced when the tube was connected to a source of electrical energy.

c Metal plates could be charged to change the path of the beam.

e When the plates were charged, the beam produced a glowing spot here after being pulled toward the positively charged plate.

electron a subatomic particle that has a negative charge

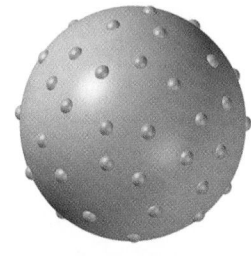

Figure 4 *Thomson proposed that electrons were located throughout an atom like plums in a pudding, as shown in this model.*

Thomson's Discovery of Electrons

In 1897, a British scientist named J. J. Thomson showed that there was a mistake in Dalton's theory. Thomson discovered that there are small particles *inside* the atom. This means that atoms can be divided into even smaller parts.

Thomson experimented with a cathode-ray tube like the one shown in **Figure 3.** He discovered that a positively charged plate (marked with a plus sign in the drawing) attracted the beam. Thomson concluded that the beam was made of particles that have negative electric charges. He also concluded that these negatively charged particles are present in every kind of atom. The negatively charged particles that Thomson discovered are now called **electrons.**

Like Plums in a Pudding

After learning that atoms contain electrons, Thomson proposed a new model of the atom. This model is shown in **Figure 4.** It is sometimes called the *plum-pudding model,* after a dessert that was popular in Thomson's day. Thomson thought that electrons were mixed throughout an atom, like plums in a pudding. Today, you might call Thomson's model the *chocolate chip ice-cream model.*

CHAPTER RESOURCES

Technology

 Transparencies
- P45 Thomson's Cathode-Ray Tube Experiment
- P46 Rutherford's Gold-Foil Experiment

Workbooks

 Math Skills for Science
- Using Proportions and Cross-Multiplication **GENERAL**

Is That a Fact!

Thales of Miletus, the earliest known Greek philosopher and scientist, is said to have been the first person to observe static electricity. He rubbed a piece of amber with a wool cloth and observed that lightweight objects were attracted to the amber.

Rutherford's Atomic "Shooting Gallery"

In 1909, a former student of Thomson's named Ernest Rutherford decided to test Thomson's theory. He designed an experiment to study the parts of the atom. He aimed a beam of small, positively charged particles at a thin sheet of gold foil. **Figure 5** shows Rutherford's experiment. Rutherford put a special coating behind the foil. The coating glowed when hit by the positively charged particles. Rutherford could then see where the particles went after hitting the gold.

Reading Check How could Rutherford tell where the positively charged particles went after hitting the gold foil?

Surprising Results

Rutherford started with Thomson's idea that atoms are soft "blobs" of matter. He expected the particles to pass right through the gold in a straight line. Most of the particles did just that. But to Rutherford's great surprise, some of the particles were deflected (turned to one side). Some even bounced straight back. Rutherford reportedly said,

"It was quite the most incredible event that has ever happened to me in my life. It was almost as if you fired a fifteen-inch shell into a piece of tissue paper and it came back and hit you."

Figure 5 Rutherford's Gold-Foil Experiment

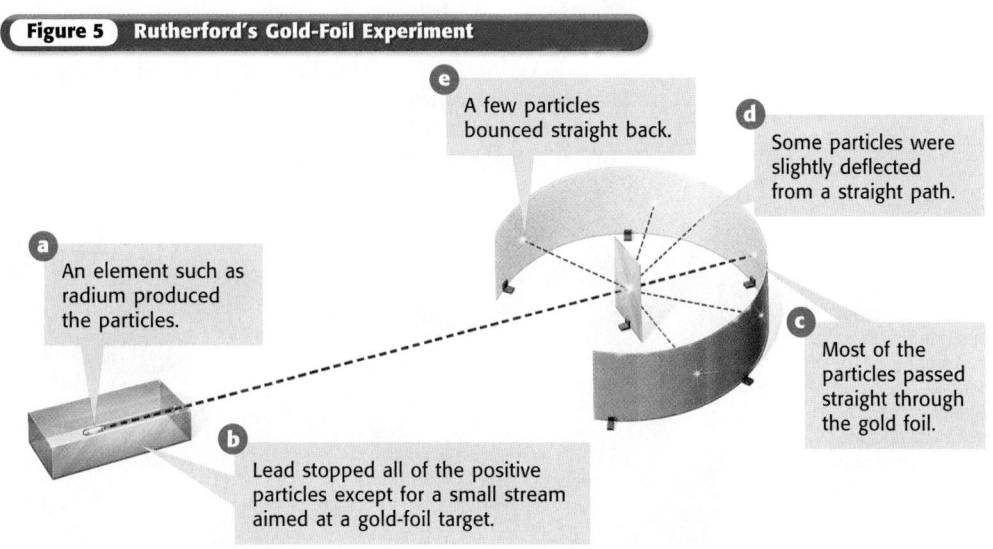

e A few particles bounced straight back.

d Some particles were slightly deflected from a straight path.

a An element such as radium produced the particles.

c Most of the particles passed straight through the gold foil.

b Lead stopped all of the positive particles except for a small stream aimed at a gold-foil target.

Table of Atomic Discoveries
Summarize the scientists covered in this section and their discoveries about the atom by constructing a table on the board. The first column should consist of the name of each scientist, and the second column should briefly state what the scientist discovered. Ask students to verbally elaborate on how each discovery was made. **LS** Visual

Quiz ——— GENERAL

1. What error did Thomson find in Dalton's atomic theory? (Thomson discovered that atoms are made of smaller parts.)

2. What is the name for Thomson's model of the atom? (the plum-pudding model)

3. What is the current model of the atom called? (the electron-cloud model)

Alternative Assessment ——— GENERAL

Role-Playing Randomly call on students to get up in front of the class and role-play a certain scientist or philosopher discussed in this section. Have them describe the experiment that was performed, what the individual was trying to find out, and what the individual discovered. **LS** Verbal

nucleus in physical science, an atom's central region, which is made up of protons and neutrons

electron cloud a region around the nucleus of an atom where electrons are likely to be found

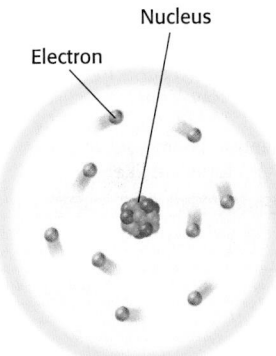

Figure 6 Rutherford's model of the atom had electrons surrounding the nucleus at a distance. (This model does not show the true scale of sizes and distances.)

Figure 7 The diameter of this pinhead is 100,000 times smaller than the diameter of the stadium. The pinhead represents the size of a nucleus, and the stadium represents the size of an atom.

Where Are the Electrons?

The plum-pudding model of the atom did not explain what Rutherford saw. Most of the tiny particles went straight through the gold foil, with a small number being deflected. He realized that in order to explain this, atoms must be considered mostly empty space, with a tiny part made of highly dense matter.

Far from the Nucleus

In 1911, Rutherford revised the atomic theory. He made a new model of the atom, as shown in **Figure 6.** Rutherford proposed that in the center of the atom is a tiny, extremely dense, positively charged part called the **nucleus** (NOO klee uhs). Because like charges repel, Rutherford reasoned that positively charged particles that passed close by the nucleus were pushed away by the positive charges in the nucleus. A particle that headed straight for a nucleus would be pushed almost straight back in the direction from which it came. From his results, Rutherford calculated that the diameter of the nucleus was 100,000 times smaller than the diameter of the gold atom. To get an idea of this kind of difference in size, look at **Figure 7.**

Reading Check How did Rutherford change Thomson's model of the atom?

Bohr's Electron Levels

In 1913, Niels Bohr, a Danish scientist who worked with Rutherford, studied the way that atoms react to light. Bohr's results led him to propose that electrons move around the nucleus in certain paths, or energy levels. In Bohr's model, there are no paths between the levels. But electrons can jump from a path in one level to a path in another level. Think of the levels as rungs on a ladder. You can stand on the rungs of a ladder but not *between* the rungs. Bohr's model was a valuable tool in predicting some atomic behavior, but the atomic theory still had room for improvement.

Answer to Reading Check

Rutherford changed Thomson's model of the atom by proposing that the nucleus is a tiny, dense, positively charged area surrounded by electrons.

The Modern Atomic Theory

Many 20th-century scientists added to our current understanding of the atom. An Austrian physicist named Erwin Schrödinger (SHROH ding uhr) and a German physicist named Werner Heisenberg (HIE zuhn berkh) did especially important work. They further explained the nature of electrons in the atom. For example, electrons do not travel in definite paths as Bohr suggested. In fact, the exact path of an electron cannot be predicted. According to the current theory, there are regions inside the atom where electrons are *likely* to be found. These regions are called **electron clouds.** The electron-cloud model of the atom is shown in **Figure 8.**

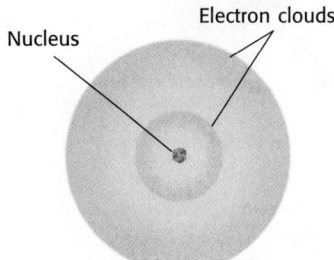

Figure 8 *In the current model of the atom, electrons surround the nucleus in electron clouds.*

SECTION Review

Summary

- Democritus thought that matter is composed of atoms.
- Dalton based his theory on observations of how elements combine.
- Thomson discovered electrons in atoms.
- Rutherford discovered that atoms are mostly empty space with a dense, positive nucleus.
- Bohr proposed that electrons are located in levels at certain distances from the nucleus.
- The electron-cloud model represents the current atomic theory.

Using Key Terms

1. In your own words, write a definition for the term *atom.*

The statements below are false. For each statement, replace the underlined term to make a true statement.

2. A <u>nucleus</u> is a particle with a negative electric charge.

3. The <u>electron</u> is where most of an atom's mass is located.

Understanding Key Ideas

4. Which of the following scientists discovered that atoms contain electrons?
   a. Dalton
   b. Thomson
   c. Rutherford
   d. Bohr

5. What did Dalton do in developing his theory that Democritus did not do?

6. What discovery demonstrated that atoms are mostly empty space?

7. What refinements did Bohr make to Rutherford's proposed atomic theory?

Critical Thinking

8. **Making Comparisons** Compare the location of electrons in Bohr's theory with the location of electrons in the current atomic theory.

9. **Analyzing Methods** How does the design of Rutherford's experiment show what he was trying to find out?

Interpreting Graphics

10. What about the atomic model shown below was shown to be incorrect?

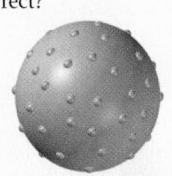

For a variety of links related to this chapter, go to www.scilinks.org
Topic: Development of the Atomic Theory; Current Atomic Theory
SciLinks code: HSM0399; HSM0371

Answers to Section Review

1. Sample answer: the smallest part of an element that has the properties of that element
2. electron
3. nucleus
4. b
5. He performed experiments and drew conclusions from them to develop his theory.
6. Rutherford's gold-foil experiment, in which Rutherford observed that most of the positively charged particles that he aimed at a piece of gold foil went straight through
7. Bohr suggested that electrons could move around the nucleus only in certain paths. They could jump from path to path, but not stay between the paths.
8. Bohr's theory held that electrons can travel only in certain paths around the nucleus. The current atomic theory is that electrons travel in regions where they are *likely* to be found.
9. Rutherford placed a surface behind the gold foil, which would glow where the positively charged particles hit it. This shows that he was trying to find out where the particles went after hitting the gold foil.
10. The model represents electrons as mixed throughout an atom. Rutherford showed this arrangement to be incorrect.

CHAPTER RESOURCES

Chapter Resource File

- Section Quiz **GENERAL**
- Section Review **GENERAL**
- Vocabulary and Section Summary **GENERAL**
- Reinforcement Worksheet **BASIC**

Focus

Overview

This section describes what is known about the particles inside an atom. Students will learn about the atomic number and mass number of an atom and about charge and isotopes. Finally, students will calculate the atomic mass of an element and determine the number of particles within an atom.

Bellringer

Tell students that an *atom* is the smallest particle into which an element can be divided and still be that element. Now that scientists have learned that an atom is made up of even smaller particles, is this definition still accurate? Explain your answer.

Motivate

Discussion ———— GENERAL

The Atomic Scale Students may have difficulty visualizing the very large and very small numbers that are used when atoms are discussed. Give each student a penny to hold and look at while the class discusses the large number of atoms in the penny and the extremely small size of each atom. **LS** Visual

What You Will Learn

● Describe the size of an atom.
● Name the parts of an atom.
● Describe the relationship between numbers of protons and neutrons and atomic number.
● State how isotopes differ.
● Calculate atomic masses.
● Describe the forces within an atom.

Vocabulary

proton	atomic number
atomic mass	isotope
unit	mass number
neutron	atomic mass

READING STRATEGY

Reading Organizer As you read this section, make a concept map by using the terms above.

The Atom

Even though atoms are very small, they are made up of even smaller things. You can learn a lot about the parts that make up an atom and what holds an atom together.

In this section, you'll learn about how atoms are alike and how they are different. But first you'll find out just how small an atom really is.

How Small Is an Atom?

Think about a penny. A penny contains about 2×10^{22} atoms (which can be written as 20,000,000,000,000,000,000,000 atoms) of copper and zinc. That's 20 thousand billion billion atoms—over 3,000,000,000,000 times more atoms than there are people on Earth! If there are that many atoms in a penny, each atom must be very small.

Scientists know that aluminum is made of average-sized atoms. An aluminum atom has a diameter of about 0.00000003 cm. That's three one-hundred-millionths of a centimeter. Take a look at **Figure 1.** Even things that are very thin, such as aluminum foil, are made up of very large numbers of atoms.

Figure 1 *This aluminum foil might seem thin to you. But it is about 50,000 atoms thick!*

CHAPTER RESOURCES

Chapter Resource File

● **Lesson Plan**
● **Directed Reading A** BASIC
● **Directed Reading B** SPECIAL NEEDS

Technology

Transparencies
● Bellringer
● P47 Parts of an Atom

Workbooks

Interactive Textbook Struggling Readers

Is That a Fact!

One molecule of water is composed of three atoms—two hydrogen atoms and one oxygen atom. One molecule of natural rubber is composed of approximately 295,000 atoms—175,000 carbon atoms and 120,000 hydrogen atoms.

 **Figure 2** **Parts of an Atom**

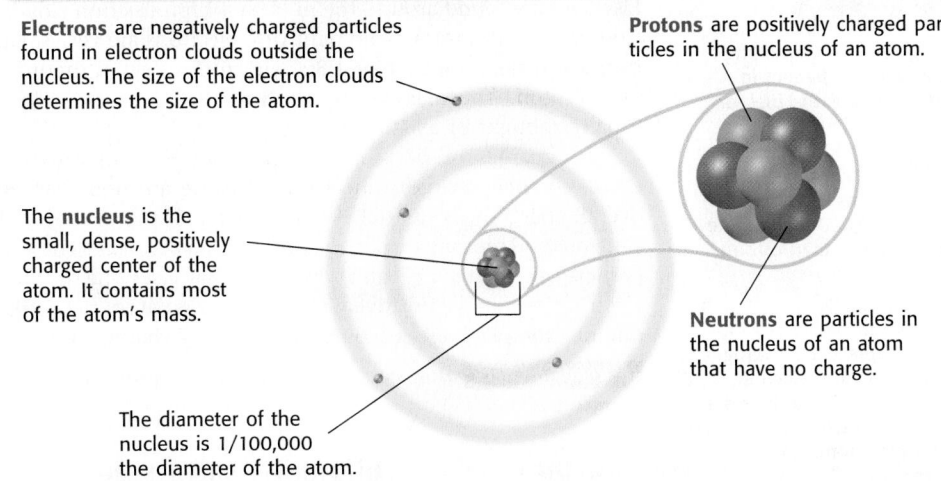

Electrons are negatively charged particles found in electron clouds outside the nucleus. The size of the electron clouds determines the size of the atom.

Protons are positively charged particles in the nucleus of an atom.

The **nucleus** is the small, dense, positively charged center of the atom. It contains most of the atom's mass.

Neutrons are particles in the nucleus of an atom that have no charge.

The diameter of the nucleus is 1/100,000 the diameter of the atom.

What Is an Atom Made Of?

As tiny as an atom is, it is made up of even smaller particles. These particles are protons, neutrons, and electrons, shown in the model in **Figure 2.** (The particles in the pictures are not shown in their correct proportions. If they were, the electrons would be too small to see.)

The Nucleus

Protons are positively charged particles in the nucleus. The mass of a proton is about 1.7×10^{-24} g. This number can also be written as 0.0000000000000000000000017 g. Because the masses of particles in atoms are so small, scientists made a new unit for them. The SI unit used to express the masses of particles in atoms is the **atomic mass unit** (amu). Each proton has a mass of about 1 amu.

    Neutrons are the particles of the nucleus that have no electrical charge. Neutrons are a little more massive than protons are. But the difference in mass is so small that the mass of a neutron can be thought of as 1 amu.

    Protons and neutrons are the most massive particles in an atom. But the volume of the nucleus is very small. So, the nucleus is very dense. If it were possible to have a nucleus the volume of a grape, that nucleus would have a mass greater than 9 million metric tons!

 **Reading Check** Name the two kinds of particles that can be found in the nucleus. (*See the Appendix for answers to Reading Checks.*)

proton a subatomic particle that has a positive charge and that is found in the nucleus of an atom

atomic mass unit a unit of mass that describes the mass of an atom or molecule

neutron a subatomic particle that has no charge and that is found in the nucleus of an atom

Is That a Fact!

Carbon-12 is used by scientists to determine an atomic mass unit (amu). The amu is exactly one-twelfth the mass of a carbon-12 atom. Because carbon-12 has six protons and six neutrons in its nucleus, the mass of a proton and the mass of a neutron are each considered to be 1 amu.

SCIENCE HUMOR

A neutron walks into a diner and orders a glass of orange juice at the lunch counter. When the waiter brings the juice, the neutron asks, "How much do I owe you?"

The waiter replies, "For you, no charge."

READING STRATEGY ——— GENERAL

Atomic Diagrams As students learn about the particles inside an atom, have them create and label diagrams of several different atoms in their **science journal.** Students can use **Figures 2–5** as guidelines. The diagrams should show the different particles, their locations, and other information, such as mass and charge.   **English Language Learners**
LS Visual/Logical

MISCONCEPTION ALERT

Atomic Size When students think of the smallest particle possible, they may picture a dust particle. As they read through this section, help them understand how small an atom is. Even one dust particle is made of millions of atoms!

CONNECTION **ACTIVITY**
Real World ——— GENERAL

Powers of 10 Attempting to comprehend the size and the components of atoms interests people other than chemists and physicists. Charles and Ray Eames were architects and designers who were fascinated with size and numbers. This interest led them to make the award-winning film *Powers of Ten* (1977). The film is available on video and is a fascinating exploration into the "small" of atoms and the "large" of the universe. **LS Visual**

Answer to Reading Check
Protons and neutrons can be found in the nucleus.

BRAIN FOOD

Quarks Scientists have learned that protons and neutrons are composed of even smaller particles called *quarks*. There are six kinds of quarks, which scientists have labeled "up," "down," "charm," "strange," "top," and "bottom." The labels are used to tell one type of quark from another; they don't really describe the quarks.

Answer to Reading Check

An atom becomes a positively charged ion when it loses an electron.

CONNECTION to Earth Science —— GENERAL

Fusion of Hydrogen in the Sun
In the sun (as well as other stars), hydrogen nuclei are fused in a nuclear reaction to form helium. This nuclear reaction gives off a tremendous amount of energy, which is given off in the form of electromagnetic radiation and is responsible for the light we see and heat we feel from the sun. Use the teaching transparency "Fusion of Hydrogen in the Sun."

CONNECTION TO Astronomy

Hydrogen Hydrogen is the most abundant element in the universe. It is the fuel for the sun and other stars. It is currently believed that there are roughly 2,000 times more hydrogen atoms than oxygen atoms and 10,000 times more hydrogen atoms than carbon atoms.

Make a model of a hydrogen atom using materials of your choice to represent a hydrogen atom's proton and electron. Present the model to the class, and explain in what ways your model resembles a hydrogen atom.

ACTIVITY

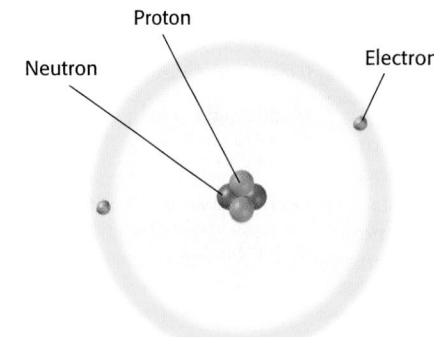

Figure 3 *A helium nucleus must have neutrons in it to keep the protons from moving apart.*

Outside the Nucleus

Electrons are the negatively charged particles in atoms. Electrons are found around the nucleus within electron clouds. Compared with protons and neutrons, electrons are very small in mass. It takes more than 1,800 electrons to equal the mass of 1 proton. The mass of an electron is so small that it is usually thought of as almost zero.

The charges of protons and electrons are opposite but equal, so their charges cancel out. Because an atom has no overall charge, it is neutral. What happens if the numbers of electrons and protons are not equal? The atom becomes a charged particle called an *ion* (IE ahn). An atom that loses one or more electrons becomes a positively-charged ion. An atom that gains one or more electrons becomes a negatively-charged ion.

✓ Reading Check How does an atom become a positively-charged ion?

How Do Atoms of Different Elements Differ?

There are more than 110 different elements. The atoms of each of these elements are different from the atoms of all other elements. What makes atoms different from each other? To find out, imagine that you could build an atom by putting together protons, neutrons, and electrons.

Starting Simply

It's easiest to start with the simplest atom. Protons and electrons are found in all atoms. The simplest atom is made of just one of each. It's so simple it doesn't even have a neutron. To "build" this atom, put just one proton in the center of the atom for the nucleus. Then, put one electron in the electron cloud. Congratulations! You have just made a hydrogen atom.

Now for Some Neutrons

Now, build an atom that has two protons. Both of the protons are positively charged, so they repel one another. You cannot form a nucleus with them unless you add some neutrons. For this atom, two neutrons will do. To have a neutral charge, your new atom will also need two electrons outside the nucleus. What you have is an atom of the element helium. A model of this atom is shown in **Figure 3.**

Building Bigger Atoms

You could build a carbon atom using 6 protons, 6 neutrons, and 6 electrons. You could build an oxygen atom using 8 protons, 9 neutrons, and 8 electrons. You could even build a gold atom with 79 protons, 118 neutrons, and 79 electrons! As you can see, an atom does not have to have equal numbers of protons and neutrons.

Protons and Atomic Number

How can you tell which elements these atoms represent? The key is the number of protons. The number of protons in the nucleus of an atom is the **atomic number** of that atom. All atoms of an element have the same atomic number. Every hydrogen atom has only one proton in its nucleus, so hydrogen has an atomic number of 1. Every carbon atom has six protons in its nucleus. So, carbon has an atomic number of 6.

Isotopes

An atom that has one proton, one electron, and one neutron is shown in **Figure 4.** The atomic number of this new atom is 1, so the atom is hydrogen. However, this hydrogen atom's nucleus has two particles. Therefore, this atom has a greater mass than the hydrogen atom you made.

The new atom is another isotope (IE suh TOHP) of hydrogen. **Isotopes** are atoms that have the same number of protons but have different numbers of neutrons. Atoms that are isotopes of each other are always the same element, because isotopes always have the same number of protons. They have different numbers of neutrons, however, which gives them different masses.

INTERNET ACTIVITY

For another activity related to this chapter, go to **go.hrw.com** and type in the keyword **HP5ATSW.**

atomic number the number of protons in the nucleus of an atom; the atomic number is the same for all atoms of an element

isotope an atom that has the same number of protons (or the same atomic number) as other atoms of the same element do but that has a different number of neutrons (and thus a different atomic mass)

| Figure 4 | Isotopes of Hydrogen |

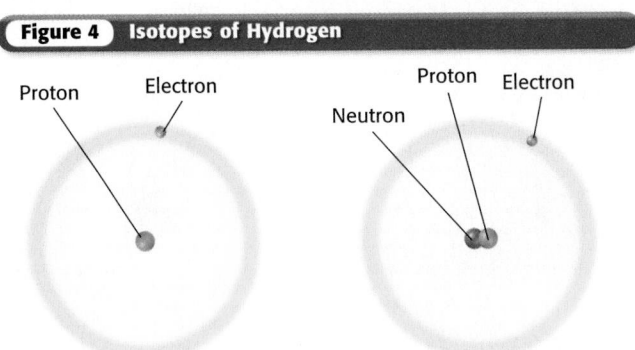

This isotope is a hydrogen atom that has one proton in its nucleus.

This isotope is a hydrogen atom that has one proton and one neutron in its nucleus.

CONNECTION to Paleontology — GENERAL

Carbon Dating The isotope carbon-14 is used in radiocarbon dating of animal and plant fossils. Uranium-238, uranium-235, and thorium-232 are isotopes that scientists use to tell the age of rocks and meteorites.

SCIENCE HUMOR

Have you heard the one about the chemist who was reading a book about helium? He couldn't put it down.

 CONNECTION ACTIVITY
Life Science —————— GENERAL

Uses of Isotopes Isotopes have many applications in the field of nuclear medicine. Cobalt-60 is used to treat cancerous tumors, and iodine-131 is used in the treatment of hyperthyroidism. Have students research the use of radioactive isotopes in the detection and treatment of disease. Students can present their results in posters, concept maps, or reports. **LS** Logical

Answer to Reading Check
Differences between isotopes are important when a certain isotope is radioactive.

ACTIVITY —————— GENERAL

MATERIALS

FOR EACH STUDENT
- colored dots (available at office-supply stores)
- construction paper
- markers

Reconstructing Atoms

1. Distribute dots, paper, and markers to students.

2. Have students study the atoms shown in **Figures 2–5.**

3. Instruct students to reconstruct each of the isotopes. Students should use a different-colored dot for the protons, neutrons, and electrons.

4. Remind students to notice that only the number of neutrons changes from isotope to isotope.
LS Visual

 SCHOOL to HOME

Atomic Diagrams

Explain what you have learned about isotopes to an adult. Together, draw diagrams of hydrogen-2, helium-3, and carbon-14. Show the correct number and location of each type of particle. For the electrons, simply write the total number of electrons in the electron cloud. Use colored pencils or markers to represent the protons, neutrons, and electrons.

 ACTIVITY

mass number the sum of the numbers of protons and neutrons in the nucleus of an atom

Properties of Isotopes

Each element has a limited number of isotopes that are found in nature. Some isotopes of an element have special properties because they are unstable. An unstable atom is an atom with a nucleus that will change over time. This type of isotope is *radioactive*. Radioactive atoms spontaneously fall apart after a certain amount of time. As they do, they give off smaller particles, as well as energy.

However, isotopes of an element share most of the same chemical and physical properties. For example, the most common oxygen isotope has 8 neutrons in the nucleus. Other isotopes of oxygen have 9 or 10 neutrons. All three isotopes are colorless, odorless gases at room temperature. Each isotope has the chemical property of combining with a substance as it burns. Different isotopes of an element even behave the same in chemical changes in your body.

✓ **Reading Check** In what cases are differences between isotopes important?

Telling Isotopes Apart

You can identify each isotope of an element by its mass number. The **mass number** is the sum of the protons and neutrons in an atom. Electrons are not included in an atom's mass number because their mass is so small that they have very little effect on the atom's total mass. Look at the boron isotope models shown in **Figure 5** to see how to calculate an atom's mass number.

Figure 5 Isotopes of Boron

Each of these boron isotopes has five protons. But because each has a different number of neutrons, each has a different mass number.

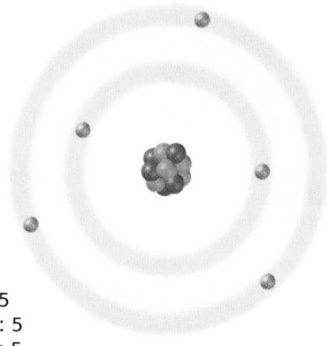
Protons: 5
Neutrons: 5
Electrons: 5
Mass number = protons + neutrons = 10

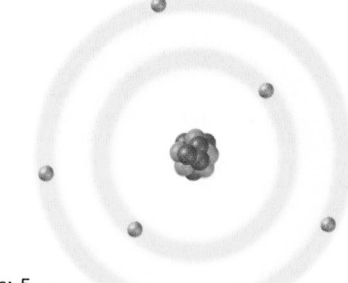
Protons: 5
Neutrons: 6
Electrons: 5
Mass number = protons + neutrons = 11

Is That a Fact!
There are at least 2,670 known isotopes. Tin has 38 isotopes, the most of any of the elements. The least stable isotope is lithium-5, which decays in 4.4×10^{-22} s.

Naming Isotopes

To identify a specific isotope of an element, write the name of the element followed by a hyphen and the mass number of the isotope. A hydrogen atom with one proton and no neutrons has a mass number of 1. Its name is hydrogen-1. Hydrogen-2 has one proton and one neutron. The carbon isotope with a mass number of 12 is called carbon-12. If you know that the atomic number for carbon is 6, you can calculate the number of neutrons in carbon-12 by subtracting the atomic number from the mass number. For carbon-12, the number of neutrons is 12 − 6, or 6.

$$
\begin{array}{r}
12 \text{ Mass number} \\
- \ 6 \text{ Number of protons (atomic number)} \\
\hline
6 \text{ Number of neutrons}
\end{array}
$$

Calculating the Mass of an Element

Most elements contain a mixture of two or more isotopes. For example, all copper is composed of copper-63 atoms and copper-65 atoms. The **atomic mass** of an element is the weighted average of the masses of all the naturally occurring isotopes of that element. A weighted average accounts for the percentages of each isotope that are present. Copper, including the copper in the Statue of Liberty, shown in **Figure 6,** is 69% copper-63 and 31% copper-65. The atomic mass of copper is 63.6 amu.

Figure 6 *The copper used to make the Statue of Liberty includes both copper-63 and copper-65. Copper's atomic mass is 63.6 amu.*

atomic mass the mass of an atom expressed in atomic mass units

Atomic Mass Chlorine-35 makes up 76% of all the chlorine in nature, and chlorine-37 makes up the other 24%. What is the atomic mass of chlorine?

Step 1: Multiply the mass number of each isotope by its percentage abundance in decimal form.

$$(35 \times 0.76) = 26.60$$
$$(37 \times 0.24) = 8.88$$

Step 2: Add these amounts together to find the atomic mass.

$$
\begin{array}{r}
(35 \times 0.76) = 26.60 \\
(37 \times 0.24) = + \ 8.88 \\
\hline
35.48 \text{ amu}
\end{array}
$$

Now It's Your Turn

1. Calculate the atomic mass of boron, which occurs naturally as 20% boron-10 and 80% boron-11.
2. Calculate the atomic mass of rubidium, which occurs naturally as 72% rubidium-85 and 28% rubidium-87.
3. Calculate the atomic mass of gallium, which occurs naturally as 60% gallium-69 and 40% gallium-71.
4. Calculate the atomic mass of silver, which occurs naturally as 52% silver-107 and 48% silver-109.
5. Calculate the atomic mass of silicon, which occurs naturally as 92% silicon-28, 5% silicon-29, and 3% silicon-30.

Descriptions of Atomic Structure Have students write a simple description of an atom for somebody who knows nothing about atoms. For example, students might explain atoms and atomic structure to a young child. Encourage students to use diagrams and examples in their descriptions. LS Verbal

Quiz ——————— GENERAL

1. What is an atom's mass number equal to? (the total number of protons and neutrons in that atom)

2. How is the atomic mass of an element calculated? (by taking a weighted average of the mass numbers of the isotopes of that element)

3. How do isotopes differ from one another? (in the number of neutrons that they have)

Alternative Assessment ——— GENERAL

Concept Mapping Have students use the following terms to create a concept map: *proton, atomic mass unit, neutron, atomic number, isotopes, mass number,* and *atomic mass.* LS Visual

Forces in Atoms

You have seen that atoms are made of smaller particles. But what are the *forces* (the pushes or pulls between objects) acting between these particles? Four basic forces are at work everywhere, even within the atom. These forces are gravitational force, electromagnetic force, strong force, and weak force. These forces work together to give an atom its structure and properties. Look at **Figure 7** to learn about each one.

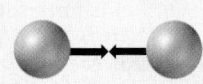 **Reading Check** What are the four basic forces at work everywhere in nature?

Figure 7   Forces in the Atom

Gravitational Force Probably the most familiar of the four forces is *gravitational force*. Gravitational force acts between all objects all the time. The amount of gravitational force between objects depends on their masses and the distance between them. Gravitational force pulls objects, such as the sun, Earth, cars, and books, toward one another. However, because the masses of particles in atoms are so small, the gravitational force within atoms is very small.

Electromagnetic Force As mentioned earlier, objects that have the same charge repel each other, while objects with opposite charge attract each other. This is due to the *electromagnetic force*. Protons and electrons are attracted to each other because they have opposite charges. The electromagnetic force holds the electrons around the nucleus.

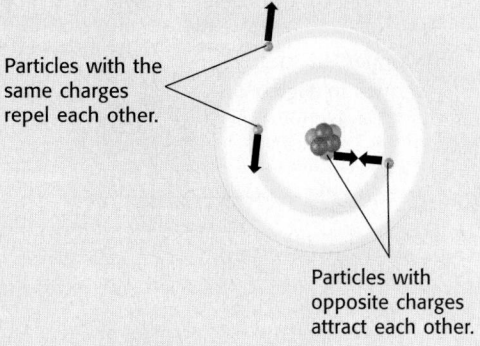

Particles with the same charges repel each other.

Particles with opposite charges attract each other.

Strong Force Protons push away from one another because of the electromagnetic force. A nucleus containing two or more protons would fly apart if it were not for the *strong force*. At the close distances between protons and neutrons in the nucleus, the strong force is greater than the electromagnetic force, so the nucleus stays together.

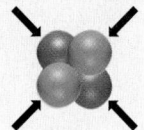

Weak Force The *weak force* is an important force in radioactive atoms. In certain unstable atoms, a neutron can change into a proton and an electron. The weak force plays a key role in this change.

Answer to Reading Check

The four basic forces are the gravitational force, electromagnetic force, strong force, and weak force.

SECTION
Review

Summary

- Atoms are extremely small. Ordinary-sized objects are made up of very large numbers of atoms.
- Atoms consist of a nucleus, which has protons and usually neutrons, and electrons, located in electron clouds around the nucleus.
- The number of protons in the nucleus of an atom is that atom's atomic number. All atoms of an element have the same atomic number.

- Different isotopes of an element have different numbers of neutrons in their nuclei. Isotopes of an element share most chemical and physical properties.
- The mass number of an atom is the sum of the atom's neutrons and protons.
- Atomic mass is a weighted average of the masses of natural isotopes of an element.
- The forces at work in an atom are gravitational force, electromagnetic force, strong force, and weak force.

Using Key Terms

1. Use the following terms in the same sentence: *proton*, *neutron*, and *isotope*.

Complete each of the following sentences by choosing the correct term from the word bank.

| atomic mass unit | atomic number |
| mass number | atomic mass |

2. An atom's ___ is equal to the number of protons in its nucleus.

3. An atom's ___ is equal to the weighted average of the masses of all the naturally occurring isotopes of that element.

Understanding Key Ideas

4. Which of the following particles has no electric charge?
   a. proton
   b. neutron
   c. electron
   d. ion

5. Name and describe the four forces that are at work within the nucleus of an atom.

Math Skills

6. The metal thallium occurs naturally as 30% thallium-203 and 70% thallium-205. Calculate the atomic mass of thallium.

Critical Thinking

7. **Analyzing Ideas** Why is gravitational force in the nucleus so small?

8. **Predicting Consequences** Could a nucleus of more than one proton but no neutrons exist? Explain.

Interpreting Graphics

9. Look at the two atomic models below. Do the two atoms represent different elements or different isotopes? Explain.

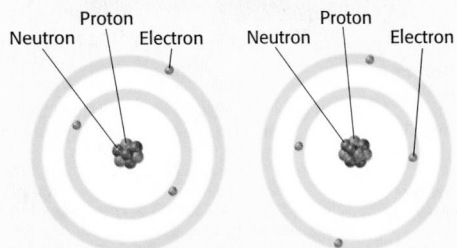

Proton   Proton
Neutron   Electron   Neutron   Electron

SCI LINKS.   NSTA
Developed and maintained by the
National Science Teachers Association

For a variety of links related to this chapter, go to www.scilinks.org

Topic: Inside the Atom; Isotopes
SciLinks code: HSM0799; HSM0820

Answers to Section Review

1. Sample answer: Different isotopes have the same number of protons but different numbers of neutrons.
2. atomic number
3. atomic mass
4. b
5. Gravitational force acts between objects based on their mass. Electromagnetic force attracts objects of opposite electric charge and repels objects of the same electric charge. The strong force holds the protons and neutrons of atomic nuclei together. The weak force plays a role in radioactive decay.
6. $(0.30 \times 203 \text{ amu}) + (0.70 \times 205 \text{ amu}) = 204.4 \text{ amu}$
7. Gravitational force in the nucleus is so small because the masses of nuclear particles are so small.
8. no; Without neutrons, two protons brought into close contact would repel each other.
9. The two atoms shown are different elements—they have different numbers of protons.

Made to Order

Teacher's Notes

Time Required

One 45-minute class period

Lab Ratings

EASY ——————————→ HARD

Teacher Prep
Student Set-Up
Concept Level
Clean Up

MATERIALS

The supplies listed are for a pair of students. Foam balls of any color are acceptable as long as there are two colors. Flexible pipe cleaners may be used instead of toothpicks.

Safety Caution

Remind students to review all safety cautions and icons before beginning this lab activity.

Preparation Notes

Before you begin this lab, review the concepts of isotopes, atomic number, and mass number.

To create colored balls, use colored markers or spray paint. Alternatively, you can label white balls "N" or "P."

Model-Making Lab

OBJECTIVES

Build models of nuclei of certain isotopes.

Use the periodic table to determine the composition of atomic nuclei.

MATERIALS

- periodic table
- plastic-foam balls, blue, 2–3 cm in diameter (6)
- plastic-foam balls, white, 2–3 cm in diameter (4)
- toothpicks (20)

SAFETY

Made to Order

Imagine that you are an employee at the Elements-4-U Company, which custom builds elements. Your job is to construct the atomic nucleus for each element ordered by your clients. You were hired for the position because of your knowledge about what a nucleus is made of and your understanding of how isotopes of an element differ from each other. Now, it's time to put that knowledge to work!

Procedure

1. Copy the table below onto another sheet of paper. Be sure to leave room to expand the table to include more elements.

2. Your first assignment is the nucleus of hydrogen-1. Pick up one proton (a white plastic-foam ball). Congratulations! You have built a hydrogen-1 nucleus, the simplest nucleus possible.

3. Count the number of protons and neutrons in the nucleus, and fill in rows 1 and 2 for this element in the table.

4. Use the information in rows 1 and 2 to determine the atomic number and mass number of the element. Record this information in the table.

Data Collection Table						
	Hydrogen-1	**Hydrogen-2**	**Helium-3**	**Helium-4**	**Beryllium-9**	**Beryllium-10**
Number of protons						
Number of neutrons						
Atomic number						
Mass number						

DO NOT WRITE IN BOOK

Holt Lab Generator CD-ROM

Search for any lab by topic, standard, difficulty level, or time. Edit any lab to fit your needs, or create your own labs. Use the Lab Materials QuickList software to customize your lab materials list.

Sharon L. Woolf
Langston Hughes
Middle School
Reston, Virginia

CHAPTER RESOURCES

Chapter Resource File
- Datasheet for Chapter Lab
- Lab Notes and Answers

Technology

Classroom Videos
- Lab Video

5. Draw a picture of your model.

6. Hydrogen-2 is an isotope of hydrogen that has one proton and one neutron. Using a strong-force connector, add a neutron to your hydrogen-1 nucleus. (Remember that in a nucleus, the protons and neutrons are held together by the strong force, which is represented in this activity by the toothpicks.) Repeat steps 3–5.

7. Helium-3 is an isotope of helium that has two protons and one neutron. Add one proton to your hydrogen-2 nucleus to create a helium-3 nucleus. Each particle should be connected to the other two particles so that they make a triangle, not a line. Protons and neutrons always form the smallest arrangement possible because the strong force pulls them together. Then, repeat steps 3–5.

8. For the next part of the lab, you will need to use information from the periodic table of the elements. Look at the illustration below. It shows the periodic table entry for carbon. You can find the atomic number of any element at the top of its entry on the periodic table. For example, the atomic number of carbon is 6.

Atomic number —— 6
C
Carbon

9. Use the information in the periodic table to build models of the following isotopes of elements: helium-4, lithium-7, beryllium-9, and beryllium-10. Remember to put the protons and neutrons as close together as possible—each particle should attach to at least two others. Repeat steps 3–5 for each isotope.

Analyze the Results

1. **Examining Data** What is the relationship between the number of protons and the atomic number?

2. **Analyzing Data** If you know the atomic number and the mass number of an isotope, how could you figure out the number of neutrons in its nucleus?

Draw Conclusions

3. **Applying Conclusions** Look up uranium on the periodic table. What is the atomic number of uranium? How many neutrons does the isotope uranium-235 have?

4. **Evaluating Models** Compare your model with the models of your classmates. How are the models similar? How are they different?

Applying Your Data

Combine your model with one that another student has made to create a single nucleus. Identify the element (and isotope) you have created.

Analyze the Results

1. The number of protons is the same as the atomic number.

2. The number of neutrons equals the mass number minus the atomic number.

Draw Conclusions

3. 92; 143 neutrons (235 − 92 = 143)

4. Sample answer: They differ in the way the protons and neutrons are connected to each other. They are the same in the number of protons and neutrons that each of the same isotope has, however.

Applying Your Data

If all of the protons and neutrons are used, the isotope created will be oxygen-20.

Chapter Review

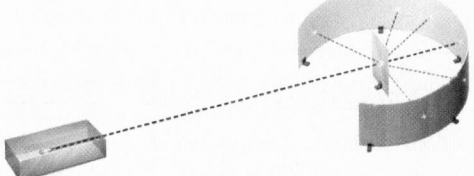

Chapter Review

Assignment Guide

SECTION	QUESTIONS
1	6, 8, 12, 17–18
2	1–5, 7, 9–11, 13–16, 19–21

ANSWERS

Using Key Terms

1. Protons
2. protons
3. Neutrons
4. mass number
5. atomic mass

Understanding Key Ideas

6. c
7. a
8. d
9. a
10. b
11. electromagnetic force
12. Sample answer: The plum-pudding model describes the atom as a lump of positively charged material with negatively charged particles throughout. The positively charged material is like the pudding, and electrons are like plums in the pudding.

USING KEY TERMS

The statements below are false. For each statement, replace the underlined term to make a true statement.

1. <u>Electrons</u> have a positive charge.

2. All atoms of the same element contain the same number of <u>neutrons</u>.

3. <u>Protons</u> have no electrical charge.

4. The <u>atomic number</u> of an element is the number of protons and neutrons in the nucleus.

5. The <u>mass number</u> is an average of the masses of all naturally occurring isotopes of an element.

UNDERSTANDING KEY IDEAS

Multiple Choice

6. The discovery of which particle proved that the atom is not indivisible?

    a. proton
    b. neutron
    c. electron
    d. nucleus

7. How many protons does an atom with an atomic number of 23 and a mass number of 51 have?

    a. 23
    b. 28
    c. 51
    d. 74

8. In Rutherford's gold-foil experiment, Rutherford concluded that the atom is mostly empty space with a small, massive, positively charged center because

    a. most of the particles passed straight through the foil.
    b. some particles were slightly deflected.
    c. a few particles bounced straight back.
    d. All of the above

9. Which of the following determines the identity of an element?

    a. atomic number
    b. mass number
    c. atomic mass
    d. overall charge

10. Isotopes exist because atoms of the same element can have different numbers of

    a. protons.
    b. neutrons.
    c. electrons.
    d. None of the above

Short Answer

11. What force holds electrons in atoms?

12. In two or three sentences, describe Thomson's plum-pudding model of the atom.

Math Skills

13 Calculate the atomic mass of gallium, which consists of 60% gallium-69 and 40% gallium-71.

14 Calculate the number of protons, neutrons, and electrons in an atom of zirconium-90 that has no overall charge and an atomic number of 40.

CRITICAL THINKING

15 Concept Mapping Use the following terms to create a concept map: *atom, nucleus, protons, neutrons, electrons, isotopes, atomic number,* and *mass number.*

16 Analyzing Processes Particle accelerators, such as the one below, are devices that speed up charged particles in order to smash them together. Scientists use these devices to make atoms. How can scientists determine whether the atoms formed are a new element or a new isotope of a known element?

17 Analyzing Ideas John Dalton made a number of statements about atoms that are now known to be incorrect. Why do you think his atomic theory is still found in science textbooks?

18 Analyzing Methods If scientists had tried to repeat Thomson's experiment and found that they could not, would Thomson's conclusion still have been valid? Explain your answer.

INTERPRETING GRAPHICS

Use the diagrams below to answer the questions that follow.

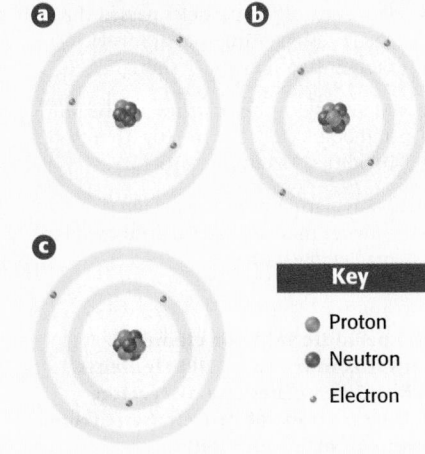

Key
● Proton
● Neutron
· Electron

19 Which diagrams represent isotopes of the same element?

20 What is the atomic number for A?

21 What is the mass number for B?

---

13. (0.60 × 69 amu) + (0.40 × 71 amu) = 69.8 amu

14. number of protons = atomic number = 40

number of neutrons = mass number − atomic number = 50

number of electrons = number of protons = 40

Critical Thinking

15. An answer to this exercise can be found at the back of this book.

16. Scientists must determine the atomic number, or the number of protons, in the newly formed nucleus. The nucleus is that of a new element only if the number of protons is different from all known elements.

17. Sample answer: Dalton's atomic theory was the first one based on experimental evidence. It helps show how a theory develops as new information is discovered.

18. No, the results of an experiment must be repeatable to be considered valid.

Interpreting Graphics

19. a and c

20. 3

21. 7

Teacher's Notes

To provide practice under more realistic conditions, give students 20 minutes to answer all of the questions in this Standardized Test Preparation.

Answer Key

Question	Answer
1	A
2	D
3	A
4	C
5	B
6	A
7	C
8	C
9	D
10	D
11	*
12	*

*See Test Doctor.

Multiple Choice

Use the diagram below to answer question 1.

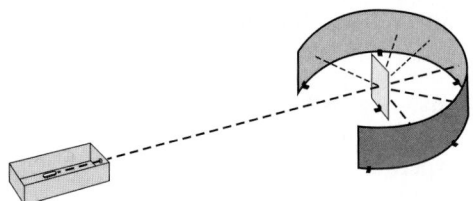

1. **In Rutherford's "shooting gallery" experiment, represented in the diagram above, what were the results?**

   A. Some particles were deflected, some passed through, and some bounced back, suggesting the existence of a nucleus.

   B. Only one of the particles passed through the foil, suggesting that atoms were denser than previously thought.

   C. Almost all of the particles hit the foil and bounced back, proving Thomson's hypothesis of atomic structure.

   D. Many particles were deflected, proving that electrons do not travel in predictable paths.

2. **The periodic table of elements contains more than 100 elements. What determines the difference between atoms of one element from atoms of other elements?**

   A. the number of electrons

   B. the number of isotopes

   C. the number of neutrons

   D. the number of protons

3. **The atoms of substance A contain 8 protons and 8 neutrons. The atoms of substance B contain 8 protons and 9 neutrons. The atoms of both substances combine with atoms of hydrogen to form water. What is the best way to classify substances A and B?**

   A. The atoms of substances A and B are isotopes.

   B. The atoms of substances A and B are radioactive.

   C. The atoms of substances A and B are atoms of different elements.

   D. The atoms of substances A and B have the same mass number.

4. **Which of the following pieces of equipment was used by J. J. Thomson to find electrons?**

   A. an electron microscope

   B. a magnifying lens

   C. a cathode-ray tube

   D. a telescope

5. **Which one of the following is true of a neutron?**

   A. A neutron has half the mass of a proton.

   B. A neutron is a little more massive than a proton.

   C. A neutron has the same mass as an electron.

   D. A neutron is a little more massive than an electron.

 TEST DOCTOR

Question 1 A: Correct. B: Most of the particles passed through the foil during Rutherford's experiment. C: Very few of the particles bounced back during Rutherford's experiment. D: Only some particles were deflected and their deflection did not prove anything about the movement of electrons.

Question 2 A: Although the number of electrons is equal to the number of protons in a neutral atom, the number of electrons can vary in ions of an atom. B: The number of isotopes that exist for an element is not unique to the different elements.

C: The number of neutrons in atoms of an element can vary. D: Correct.

Question 3 A: Correct. B: No information given indicates that either of the substances is radioactive. C: The atoms of the two substances have the same number of protons, so they are atoms of the same element. D: The atoms of substance B have one more neutron than the atoms of substance A, therefore the atoms in the substances have different mass numbers.

Question 4 A: Electron microscopes were developed many years after J.J. Thomson discovered the electron. B: A magnifying lens cannot be

6. How many electrons does an atom with an atomic number of 20 and a mass number of 42 have?

A. 20

B. 22

C. 42

D. 62

7. Oxygen has an atomic number of 8. Which of the following could form the nucleus of an isotope of oxygen?

A. 4 protons and 4 neutrons

B. 6 protons and 8 neutrons

C. 8 protons and 10 neutrons

D. 10 protons and 10 neutrons

8. All matter is made up of atoms. Which sentence correctly describes atoms?

A. All substances are made of the same atoms.

B. An atom is the smallest particle of a nucleus.

C. An atom is the smallest particle of an element.

D. An atom is a substance that has been cut in half.

9. What are the negatively charged particles inside an atom called?

A. protons

B. neutrons

C. nuclei

D. electrons

Use the diagram below to answer question 10.

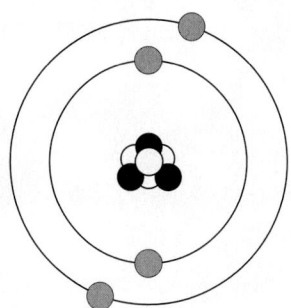

10. The black circles in the model above represent neutrons. What do the white circles represent?

A. electrons

B. isotopes

C. nuclei

D. protons

Open Response

11. Erwin Schrödinger and Werner Heisenberg expanded atomic theory in the 20th century. They accepted some of the work of earlier scientists, but added to atomic theory with new ideas about electrons. What were two of the main contributions of Schrödinger and Heisenberg to atomic theory? Current theory identifies regions where electrons are likely to be found. What are these regions called?

12. The atomic mass of an element and the mass number of an atom of that element often have similar values. However, atomic mass and mass number are not the same thing. Explain the difference.

Question 9 A: Protons are positively charged. B: Neutrons have no charge. C: Nuclei contain protons and neutrons, so nuclei are positively charged. D: Correct.

Question 10 A: Electrons are found in electron clouds outside of the nucleus. B: Isotopes are atoms that have the same number of protons but have a different number of neutrons. C: Nuclei are made of protons and neutrons and are the central parts of atoms. D: Correct. The white circles in the nucleus in the figure are protons.

Question 11 Full credit answers should include four of these points:

• Schrödinger and Heisenberg's theory included the idea that electrons do not travel in definite paths around the nucleus.

• They concluded that one cannot know exactly where electrons are in an atom. One can only predict where electrons are *likely* to be found.

• Current theory calls the regions where electrons are likely to be found *electron clouds*.

Question 12 Full credit answers should include the following points:

• The mass number of an atom is the sum of the protons and the neutrons.

• The atomic mass of an element is the weighted average of the masses of all the naturally occurring isotopes of that element.

---

used to view electrons. C: Correct. D: Telescopes are used to view images of distant objects.

Question 5 A: A neutron has a little more mass than a proton, not half the mass. B: Correct. C, D: A neutron is many times more massive than an electron. For students who have trouble with this question, review the relative masses of protons, neutrons and electrons.

Question 6 A: Correct. B: Twenty-two is the number of neutrons in the atom. The number of neutrons is found by subtracting the atomic number from the mass number. C: Forty-two is the mass number of the atom. D: Adding the atomic number

and the mass number yields 62, but this number is meaningless.

Question 7 A, B, and D: The atomic number of all isotopes of oxygen is 8. Therefore, the number of protons in an oxygen atom is always 8. C: Correct.

Question 8 A: Different substances are made of different atoms or different combinations of atoms. B: A nucleus is the center of an atom. Therefore, atoms are larger than nuclei. C: Correct. D: On the macroscopic level, one could not divide a substance in half to separate a single atom.

Science in Action

Scientific Discoveries

Background

The modern-day science of chemistry can be traced to the practice of alchemy, which was common in the 17th century and earlier. Alchemists devised experimental techniques and apparatus that remained valuable after alchemical theory had been discredited.

Weird Science

Discussion —————ADVANCED

Tell students that the United Nations has declared that no country can lay claim to the moon or the resources that exist there. However, the rule does not apply to private companies. Ask students: "Do you think private companies should be allowed to own mining rights on the moon? Explain."

Weird Science

Mining on the Moon?

Since the end of the Apollo moon missions in 1972, no one has set foot on the surface of the moon. But today, an isotope of helium known as *helium-3* is fueling new interest in returning to the moon. Some scientists speculate that helium-3 can be used as a safe and nonpolluting fuel for a new kind of power plant. Helium-3 is very rare on Earth, but a huge amount of the isotope exists on the surface of the moon. But how can helium-3 be brought to Earth? Some researchers imagine a robotic lunar mining operation that will harvest the helium-3 and transport it to Earth.

Language Arts ACTIVITY

WRITING SKILL Write a paragraph in which you rephrase the information above in your own words. Be sure to include what helium-3 is, where it can be found, and how it could be used.

Scientific Discoveries

Modern Alchemy

Hundreds of years ago, many people thought that if you treated lead with certain chemicals, it would turn into gold. People called *alchemists* often spent their whole lives trying to find a way to make gold from other metals, such as lead. We now know that the methods alchemists tried to change one element to another did not work. But in the 20th century, scientists learned that you really could change one element to another! In a nuclear reaction, small particles can be collided with atomic nuclei. This process makes the nuclei split apart to form two nuclei of different elements.

Math ACTIVITY

If you split apart an atom of lead (atomic number = 82) and one of the atoms left was gold (atomic number = 79), what would be the atomic number of the other atom that resulted from this change?

Answer to Math Activity
atomic number of other new atom = 82 − 79 = 3

Answer to Language Arts Activity
Accept all reasonable responses.

Careers

Melissa Franklin

Experimental Physicist In the course of a single day, you could find experimental physicist Melissa Franklin running a huge drill or showing her lab to a 10-year-old child. You could see her putting together a huge piece of electronic equipment or even telling a joke. Then you'd see her really get down to business—studying the smallest particles of matter in the universe.

"I am trying to understand the forces that describe how everything in the world moves—especially the smallest things," Franklin explains. Franklin and her team helped discover a particle called the top quark. (Quarks are the tiny particles that make up protons and neutrons.) "You can understand the ideas without having to be a math genius," Franklin says. "Anyone can have ideas," she says, "absolutely anyone." Franklin also has some advice for young people interested in physics. "Go and bug people at the local university. Just call up a physics person and say, 'Can I come visit you for a couple of hours?' Kids do that with me, and it's really fun."

Social Studies ACTiViTY

WRITING SKILL Find out about an experimental physicist who made an important discovery. Write a one-page report about how that discovery affected the ideas of other scientists.

To learn more about these Science in Action topics, visit go.hrw.com and type in the keyword HP5ATSF.

Current Science

Check out Current Science® articles related to this chapter by visiting go.hrw.com. Just type in the keyword HP5CS11.

The Periodic Table
Chapter Planning Guide

Compression guide:
To shorten instruction
because of time limitations,
omit the Chapter Lab.

OBJECTIVES	LABS, DEMONSTRATIONS, AND ACTIVITIES	TECHNOLOGY RESOURCES
PACING • 135 min pp. 566–575 **Chapter Opener**	SE **Start-up Activity,** p. 567 ◆ GENERAL	OSP **Parent Letter** ▪ CD **Student Edition on CD-ROM** CD **Guided Reading Audio CD** ▪ TR **Chapter Starter Transparency*** VID **Brain Food Video Quiz**
Section 1 Arranging the Elements • Describe how Mendeleev arranged elements in the first periodic table. • Explain how elements are arranged in the modern periodic table. • Compare metals, nonmetals, and metalloids based on their properties and on their location in the periodic table. • Describe the difference between a period and a group.	TE **Demonstration** Grouping, p. 568 GENERAL TE **Activity** Element Sampling, p. 569 ◆ GENERAL TE **Activity** Looking for Gaps, p. 571 ADVANCED SE **Quick Lab** Conduction Connection, p. 572 ◆ GENERAL CRF **Datasheet for Quick Lab*** TE **Activity** Element Game, p. 572 BASIC TE **Activity** Elements Everywhere, p. 573 GENERAL SE **School-to-Home Activity** Patterns of Symbols, p. 574 GENERAL SE **Model-Making Lab** Create a Periodic Table, p. 574 ◆ GENERAL CRF **Datasheet for Chapter Lab***	OSP **Lesson Plans** (also in print) TR **Bellringer Transparency*** TR P109 The Periodic Table of the Elements* CRF **SciLinks Activity*** GENERAL VID **Lab Videos for Physical Science** TE **Internet Activity,** p. 573 GENERAL
PACING • 45 min pp. 576–583 **Section 2 Grouping the Elements** • Explain why elements in a group often have similar properties. • Describe the properties of the elements in the groups of the periodic table.	TE **Connection Activity** Math, p. 579 GENERAL TE **Connection Activity** History, p. 580 ADVANCED SE **Connection to Biology** Water Treatment, p. 581 GENERAL LB **Whiz-Bang Demonstrations** Waiter, There's Carbon in My Sugar Bowl!* BASIC LB **Inquiry Labs** The Chemical Side of Light* GENERAL LB **Long-Term Projects & Research Ideas** It's Element-ary!* ADVANCED SE **Science in Action** Math, Social Studies, and Language Arts Activities, pp. 590–591 GENERAL	OSP **Lesson Plans** (also in print) TR **Bellringer Transparency*** TR **LINK TO LIFE SCIENCE** L79 The Skeleton* SE **Internet Activity,** p. 580 GENERAL CD **Interactive Explorations CD-ROM** Element of Surprise GENERAL

PACING • 90 min

CHAPTER REVIEW, ASSESSMENT, AND STANDARDIZED TEST PREPARATION

CRF **Vocabulary Activity*** GENERAL
SE **Chapter Review,** pp. 586–587 GENERAL
CRF **Chapter Review*** ▪ GENERAL
CRF **Chapter Tests A*** ▪ GENERAL, **B*** ADVANCED, **C*** SPECIAL NEEDS
SE **Standardized Test Preparation,** pp. 588–589 GENERAL
CRF **Standardized Test Preparation*** GENERAL
CRF **Performance-Based Assessment*** GENERAL
OSP **Test Generator, Test Item Listing**

Online and Technology Resources

Holt Online Learning

Visit **go.hrw.com** for access to Holt Online Learning, or enter the keyword **HS7 Home** for a variety of free online resources.

One-Stop Planner® CD-ROM

This CD-ROM package includes:
• Lab Materials QuickList Software
• Holt Calendar Planner
• Customizable Lesson Plans
• Printable Worksheets
• ExamView® Test Generator
• Interactive Teacher's Edition
• Holt PuzzlePro®
• Holt PowerPoint® Resources

SKILLS DEVELOPMENT RESOURCES	SECTION REVIEW AND ASSESSMENT	CORRELATIONS
SE Pre-Reading Activity, p. 566 `GENERAL` **OSP** Science Puzzlers, Twisters & Teasers `GENERAL`		**National Science Education Standards** UCP 1, 2; SAI 1; ST 2; SPSP 5; HNS 1, 3
CRF Directed Reading A* ■ `BASIC`, B* `SPECIAL NEEDS` **WB** Workbook* `Struggling Readers` **CRF** Vocabulary and Section Summary* ■ `GENERAL` **SE** Reading Strategy Mnemonics, p. 568 `GENERAL` **SE** Connection to Language Arts Hidden Help, p. 569 `GENERAL` **TE** Reading Strategy Discussion, p. 570 `GENERAL` **TE** Support for English Language Learners, p. 570 **TE** Inclusion Strategies, p. 571 **SE** Math Practice Percentages, p. 571 `GENERAL`	**SE** Reading Checks, pp. 568, 569, 572, 574 `GENERAL` **TE** Homework, p. 569 `GENERAL` **TE** Reteaching, p. 574 `BASIC` **TE** Quiz, p. 574 `GENERAL` **SE** Section Review,* p. 575 ■ `GENERAL` **TE** Alternative Assessment, p. 573 `GENERAL` **CRF** Section Quiz* ■ `GENERAL`	UCP 1; SAI 2; SPSP 5; HNS 1, 2, 3; PS 1b; *Chapter Lab:* UCP 1; SAI 1, 2
CRF Directed Reading A* ■ `BASIC`, B* `SPECIAL NEEDS` **WB** Workbook* `Struggling Readers` **CRF** Vocabulary and Section Summary* ■ `GENERAL` **SE** Reading Strategy Paired Summarizing, p. 576 `GENERAL` **TE** Inclusion Strategies, p. 576 **TE** Support for English Language Learners, p. 577 **SE** Connection to Environmental Science Recycling Aluminum, p. 579 `GENERAL` **MS** Math Skills for Science Checking Division with Multiplication* `GENERAL` **SS** Science Skills Finding Useful Sources* `GENERAL` **CRF** Reinforcement Worksheet Placing All Your Elements on the Table* `BASIC` **CRF** Critical Thinking Believe It or Not* `ADVANCED`	**SE** Reading Checks, pp. 577, 578, 579, 580, 582 `GENERAL` **TE** Homework, p. 581 `ADVANCED` **TE** Reteaching, p. 582 `BASIC` **TE** Quiz, p. 582 `GENERAL` **SE** Section Review,* p. 583 ■ `GENERAL` **TE** Alternative Assessment, p. 583 `GENERAL` **CRF** Section Quiz* ■ `GENERAL`	ST 2; PS 1b, 3e

SCILINKS.
NSTA
www.scilinks.org

Maintained by the **National Science Teachers Association.** See Chapter Enrichment pages that follow for a complete list of topics.

Current Science

Check out *Current Science* articles and activities by visiting the HRW Web site at **go.hrw.com.** Just type in the keyword **HP5CS12T.**

Classroom Videos

- **Lab Videos** demonstrate the chapter lab.
- **Brain Food Video Quizzes** help students review the chapter material.

Classroom CD-ROMs

- **Guided Reading Audio CD** (Also in Spanish)
- **Interactive Explorations**
- **Virtual Investigations**
- **Visual Concepts**
- **Science Tutor**

Holt Lab Generator CD-ROM

Search for any lab by topic, standard, difficulty level, or time. Edit any lab to fit your needs, or create your own labs. Use the Lab Materials QuickList software to customize your lab materials list.

Visual Resources

CHAPTER STARTER TRANSPARENCY

BELLRINGER TRANSPARENCIES

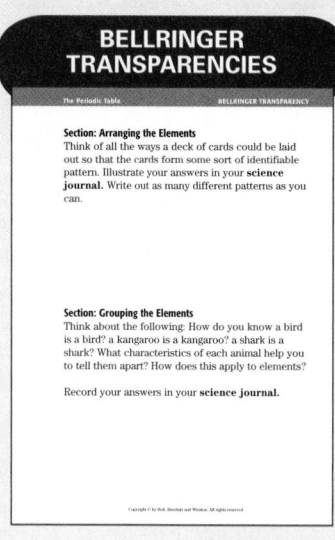

Section: Arranging the Elements
Think of all the ways a deck of cards could be laid out so that the cards form some sort of identifiable pattern. Illustrate your answers in your **science journal**. Write out as many different patterns as you can.

Section: Grouping the Elements
Think about the following: How do you know a bird is a bird? a kangaroo is a kangaroo? a shark is a shark? What characteristics of each animal help you to tell them apart? How does this apply to elements?

Record your answers in your **science journal**.

TEACHING TRANSPARENCIES

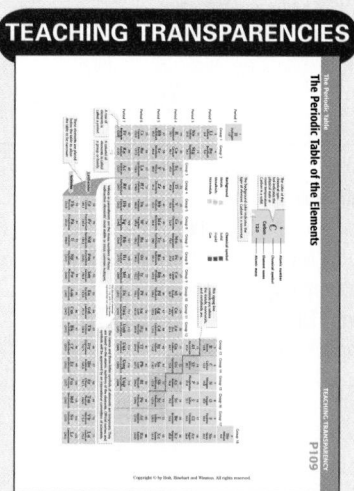

TEACHING TRANSPARENCIES

CONCEPT MAPPING TRANSPARENCY

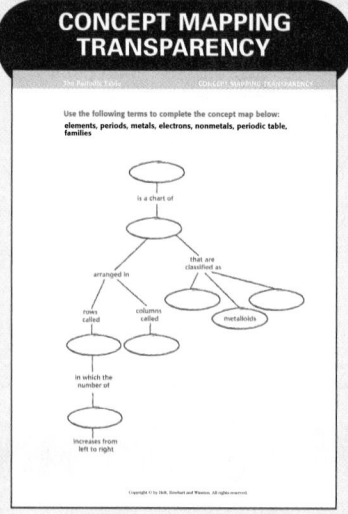

Planning Resources

LESSON PLANS

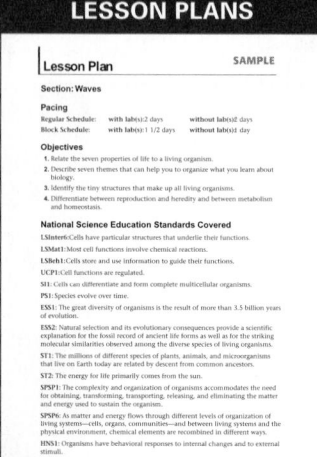

PARENT LETTER

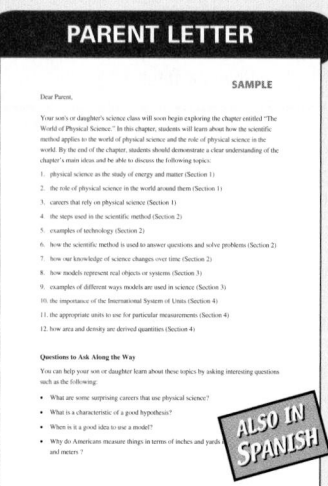

TEST ITEM LISTING

One-Stop Planner® CD-ROM

This CD-ROM includes all of the resources shown here and the following time-saving tools:

- *Lab Materials QuickList Software*
- *Customizable lesson plans*
- *Holt Calendar Planner*
- *The powerful ExamView® Test Generator*

Meeting Individual Needs

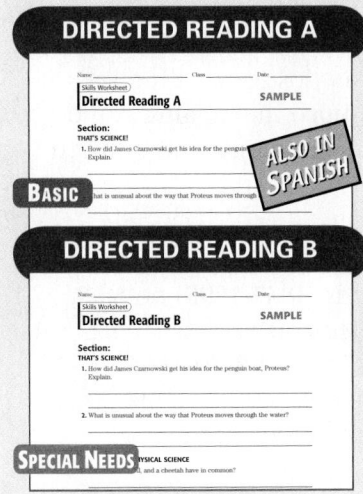

DIRECTED READING A

Skills Worksheet
Directed Reading A — SAMPLE

Section: THAT'S SCIENCE!
1. How did James Czarnowski get his idea for the penguin boat, Proteus? Explain.

BASIC — ALSO IN SPANISH

DIRECTED READING B

Skills Worksheet
Directed Reading B — SAMPLE

Section: THAT'S SCIENCE!
1. How did James Czarnowski get his idea for the penguin boat, Proteus? Explain.

2. What is unusual about the way that Proteus moves through the water?

SPECIAL NEEDS — PHYSICAL SCIENCE

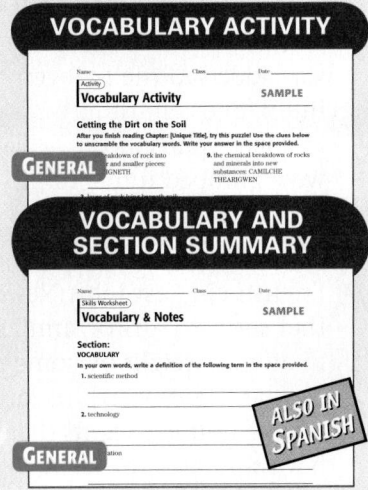

VOCABULARY ACTIVITY

Activity
Vocabulary Activity — SAMPLE

Getting the Dirt on the Soil
After you finish reading Chapter [ ], try this puzzle! Use the clues below to unscramble the vocabulary words. Write your answer in the space provided.

GENERAL

VOCABULARY AND SECTION SUMMARY

Skills Worksheet
Vocabulary & Notes — SAMPLE

Section: VOCABULARY
In your own words, write a definition of the following term in the space provided.
1. scientific method

2. technology

GENERAL — ALSO IN SPANISH

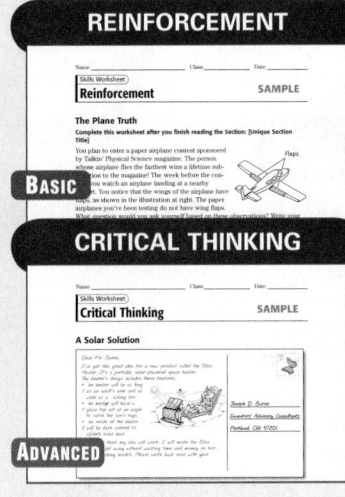

REINFORCEMENT

Skills Worksheet
Reinforcement — SAMPLE

The Plane Truth
Complete this worksheet after you finish reading the Section: [Unique Section Title]

BASIC

CRITICAL THINKING

Skills Worksheet
Critical Thinking — SAMPLE

Section:
A Solar Solution

ADVANCED

SCILINKS ACTIVITY

Activity
SciLinks Activity — SAMPLE

MARINE ECOSYSTEMS
Go to www.scilinks.org. To find links related to marine ecosystems, type in the keyword HL5400. Then, use the links to answer the questions about marine ecosystems.

GENERAL

SCIENCE PUZZLERS, TWISTERS & TEASERS

CHAPTER 12 — SCIENCE PUZZLERS, TWISTERS & TEASERS
The Periodic Table

Periodic Crime
1. This is an eyewitness account of a crime recently committed. Which element committed the crime?

Elements in the Round

GENERAL

Labs and Activities

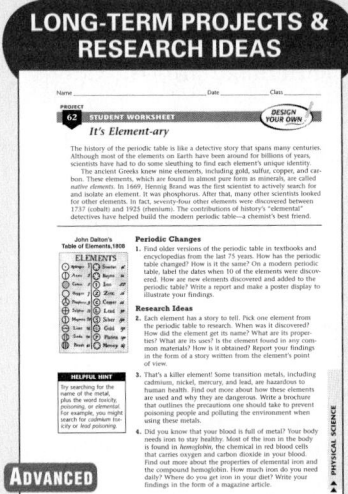

LONG-TERM PROJECTS & RESEARCH IDEAS

PROJECT 62 — STUDENT WORKSHEET — DESIGN YOUR OWN
It's Element-ary

Periodic Changes

Research Ideas

HELPFUL HINT

ADVANCED — PHYSICAL SCIENCE

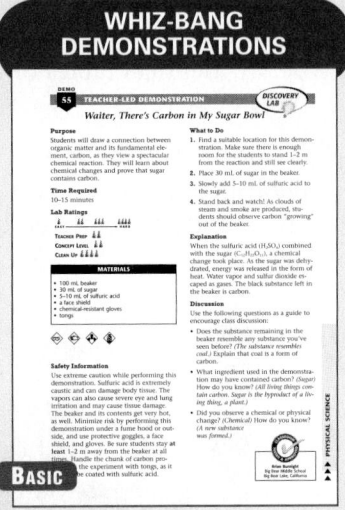

WHIZ-BANG DEMONSTRATIONS

DEMO 55 — TEACHER-LED DEMONSTRATION — DISCOVERY LAB
Waiter, There's Carbon in My Sugar Bowl

Purpose

Time Required
10–15 minutes

Lab Ratings

MATERIALS

Safety Information

BASIC — PHYSICAL SCIENCE

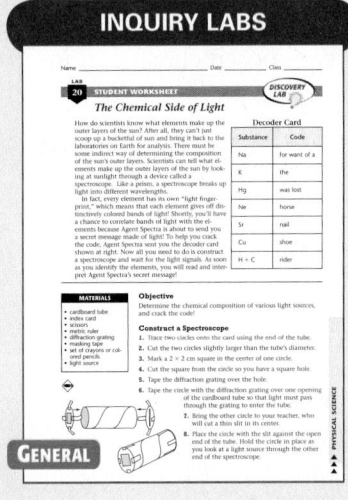

INQUIRY LABS

LAB 20 — STUDENT WORKSHEET — DISCOVERY LAB
The Chemical Side of Light

Decoder Card

Objective

Construct a Spectroscope

MATERIALS

GENERAL — PHYSICAL SCIENCE

DATASHEETS FOR QUICK LABS

TEACHER RESOURCE PAGE
Quick Lab — DATASHEET FOR QUICK LAB
Reaction to Stress — SAMPLE

Background

DATASHEETS FOR CHAPTER LABS

TEACHER RESOURCE PAGE
Skills Practice Lab — DATASHEET FOR CHAPTER LAB
Using Scientific Methods — SAMPLE

Teacher's Notes
TIME REQUIRED
One 45-minute class period.

DATASHEETS FOR LABBOOK

TEACHER RESOURCE PAGE
Skills Practice Lab — DATASHEET FOR LABBOOK LAB
Does It All Add Up? — SAMPLE

Teacher's Notes
TIME REQUIRED
One 45-minute class period.

Review and Assessments

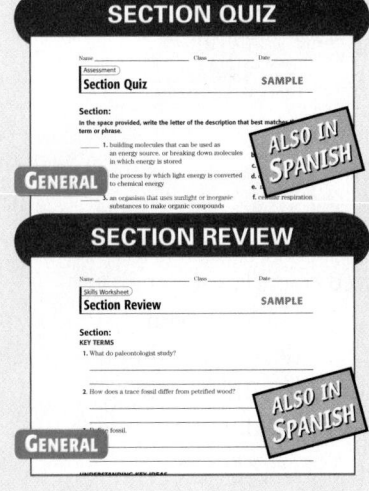

SECTION QUIZ

Assessment
Section Quiz — SAMPLE

Section:
In the space provided, write the letter of the description that best matches the term or phrase.

GENERAL — ALSO IN SPANISH

SECTION REVIEW

Skills Worksheet
Section Review — SAMPLE

Section: KEY TERMS
1. What do paleontologists study?

2. How does a trace fossil differ from petrified wood?

GENERAL — ALSO IN SPANISH

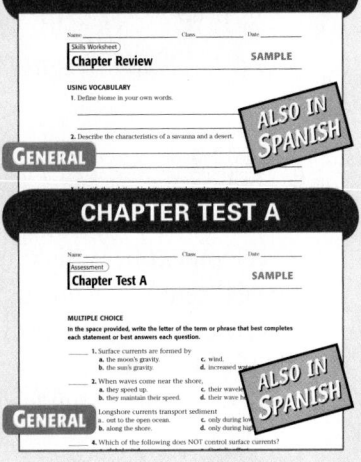

CHAPTER REVIEW

Skills Worksheet
Chapter Review — SAMPLE

USING VOCABULARY
1. Define biome in your own words.

2. Describe the characteristics of a savanna and a desert.

GENERAL — ALSO IN SPANISH

CHAPTER TEST A

Assessment
Chapter Test A — SAMPLE

MULTIPLE CHOICE
In the space provided, write the letter of the term or phrase that best completes each statement or best answers each question.
1. Surface currents are formed by
   a. the moon's gravity.   c. wind.
   b. the sun's gravity.   d. increased water density.
2. When waves come near the shore,
   a. they speed up.   c. their wavelength increases.
   b. they maintain their speed. d. their wave height increases.

GENERAL — ALSO IN SPANISH

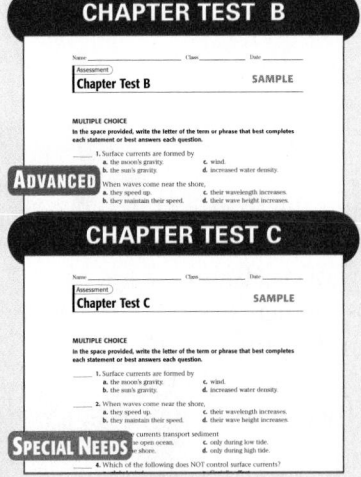

CHAPTER TEST B

Assessment
Chapter Test B — SAMPLE

MULTIPLE CHOICE
In the space provided, write the letter of the term or phrase that best completes each statement or best answers each question.
1. Surface currents are formed by
   a. the moon's gravity.   c. wind.
   b. the sun's gravity.   d. increased water density.
2. When waves come near the shore,
   a. they speed up.   c. their wavelength increases.
   b. they maintain their speed. d. their wave height increases.

ADVANCED

CHAPTER TEST C

Assessment
Chapter Test C — SAMPLE

MULTIPLE CHOICE
In the space provided, write the letter of the term or phrase that best completes each statement or best answers each question.
1. Surface currents are formed by
   a. the moon's gravity.   c. wind.
   b. the sun's gravity.   d. increased water density.
2. When waves come near the shore,
   a. they speed up.   c. their wavelength increases.
   b. they maintain their speed. d. their wave height increases.

SPECIAL NEEDS

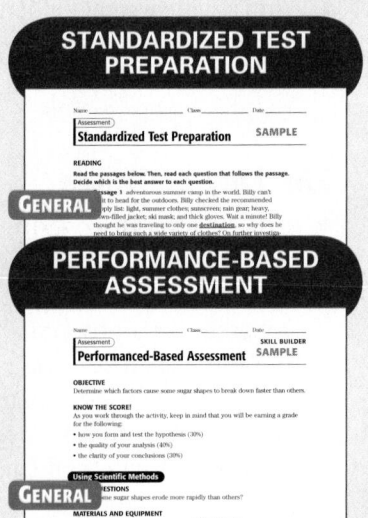

STANDARDIZED TEST PREPARATION

Assessment
Standardized Test Preparation — SAMPLE

READING
Read the passages below. Then, read each question that follows the passage. Decide which is the best answer to each question.

GENERAL

PERFORMANCE-BASED ASSESSMENT

Assessment
Performanced-Based Assessment — SKILL BUILDER — SAMPLE

OBJECTIVE

KNOW THE SCORE!

Using Scientific Methods

MATERIALS AND EQUIPMENT

GENERAL

This Chapter Enrichment provides relevant and interesting information to expand and enhance your presentation of the chapter material.

Section 1

Arranging the Elements

Before the Periodic Table

- Elements such as gold, silver, tin, copper, lead, and mercury have been known for thousands of years.

- The first modern discovery of an element was in 1669 when German alchemist Hennig Brand discovered phosphorus by precipitating it out of urine.

- Sixty-three elements had been discovered by 1869. As more elements were discovered, scientists recognized similarities and patterns in the properties of elements, and some scientists proposed classification schemes.

- In 1817, Johann Döbereiner (1780–1849) realized that calcium, strontium, and barium have similar properties and that the atomic weight of strontium is about halfway between those of the other two elements.

Is That a Fact!

◆ The first comprehensive arrangement of the elements showing the periodicity of chemical and physical properties was published in 1862 by French geologist A. E. Beguyer de Chancourtois. De Chancourtois positioned the elements on a cylinder in order of increasing atomic weight. When he arranged the elements so that there were 16 on the cylinder per turn, he noted that closely related elements lined up vertically.

The Law of Triads

- In 1829, after discovering the triad chlorine, bromine, and iodine and the triad lithium, sodium, and potassium, Döbereiner proposed his law of triads: In nature, there are triads of elements in which the middle element has an atomic weight that is the average of the atomic weights of the other two elements in the triad.

- Between 1829 and 1858, several scientists worked on the idea of triads. They discovered that the chemical relationship extended beyond groups of three. Fluorine was added to the halogen group; oxygen, sulfur, selenium, and tellurium were grouped into a family; and nitrogen, phosphorus, arsenic, antimony, and bismuth were grouped into a family.

The Law of Octaves

- English chemist John Newlands (1837–1898) noticed that several pairs of similar elements were separated in atomic weight by some multiple of 8. In 1864, Newlands proposed his law of octaves: Elements whose atomic weights differ by some multiple of 8 have similar properties.

The Father of the Periodic Table?

- Two chemists, a German named Lothar Meyer (1830–1895) and a Russian named Dmitri Mendeleev (1834–1907), produced—completely independently of each other—nearly identical tables of the elements at almost the same time.

- Unfortunately for Meyer, Mendeleev's table was published in 1869, a year before Meyer's table, and Mendeleev received credit for the first modern periodic table of the elements.

Is That a Fact!

◆ Mendeleev's (and Meyer's) table was a pioneering development because it allowed scientists to predict the existence of elements that had not yet been discovered. Most scientists were skeptical at first. But then gallium was discovered in 1875 and was found to closely match Mendeleev's predictions.

Section 2

Grouping the Elements

What Goes Where?

- Mendeleev's table showed that the elements could be grouped into periods, but it didn't explain why. As the modern periodic table took shape, scientists realized that the underlying order was based on atomic structure, namely, the number of protons in each atom.

- The known elements fall into three main categories, or classes: metals, metalloids (semiconductors), and nonmetals.

The Noble Gases

- One of the most important additions to the periodic table was the addition of the noble gases. English physicists John William Strutt, Lord Rayleigh (1842–1919), and William Ramsay (1852–1916) discovered argon in 1894.

- In 1895, Ramsay discovered that helium exists on Earth. Then, in 1898 Ramsay (and his assistant, Morris W. Travers) discovered three more noble gases—neon, krypton, and xenon.

- Radon was discovered by German scientist Friedrich Ernst Dorn (1848–1916) in 1900.

Is That a Fact!

◆ Argon makes up about 1% of Earth's atmosphere, but argon remained completely undetected until 1894 because it is unreactive under normal conditions.

The Modern Periodic Table

- In the early 1940s, Glenn Seaborg and his team worked on the Manhattan Project, the United States's secret effort to make the atomic bomb. Seaborg and his colleagues discovered the element plutonium in 1940.

- In the 1940s and 1950s, Seaborg's team synthesized and identified all transuranic elements that have atomic numbers 94 to 102. Seaborg also rearranged the periodic table by placing the actinide series below the lanthanide series. This change was the last major change to the modern periodic table.

Transuranic Elements

- Elements whose atomic numbers are greater than 92, known as *transuranic elements,* have been made in laboratories by bombarding heavy elements with neutrons or other subatomic particles. Plutonium (atomic number 94) occurs in small amounts in nature. Scientists continue to make heavier transuranic elements, so the periodic table continues to change.

- All transuranic elements are radioactive, and some exist for only short amounts of time before they decay into other, lighter elements.

SciLinks is maintained by the National Science Teachers Association to provide you and your students with interesting, up-to-date links that will enrich your classroom presentation of the chapter.

Visit www.scilinks.org and enter the SciLinks code for more information about the topic listed.

Topic: Periodic Table
SciLinks code: HSM1125

Topic: Metals
SciLinks code: HSM0947

Topic: Alkali Metals
SciLinks code: HSM0043

Topic: Halogens and Noble Gases
SciLinks code: HSM0711

Topic: Metalloids
SciLinks code: HSM0946

Topic: Nonmetals
SciLinks code: HSM1043

Overview

Tell students that this chapter will help them learn about the periodic table of the elements. The chapter describes some of the history of the development of the table and describes characteristics of each group of elements on the table.

Assessing Prior Knowledge

Students should be familiar with the following topics:

- chemical and physical properties
- atomic number

Identifying Misconceptions

As students learn the material in this chapter, some of them may be confused about how to tell whether an element is a metal, a metalloid, or a nonmetal. Remind students as they study the chapter that the zigzag line shown on most periodic tables is a helpful tool but that the elements are classified based on their properties.

21
The Periodic Table

The Big Idea
Elements are organized on the periodic table according to their properties.

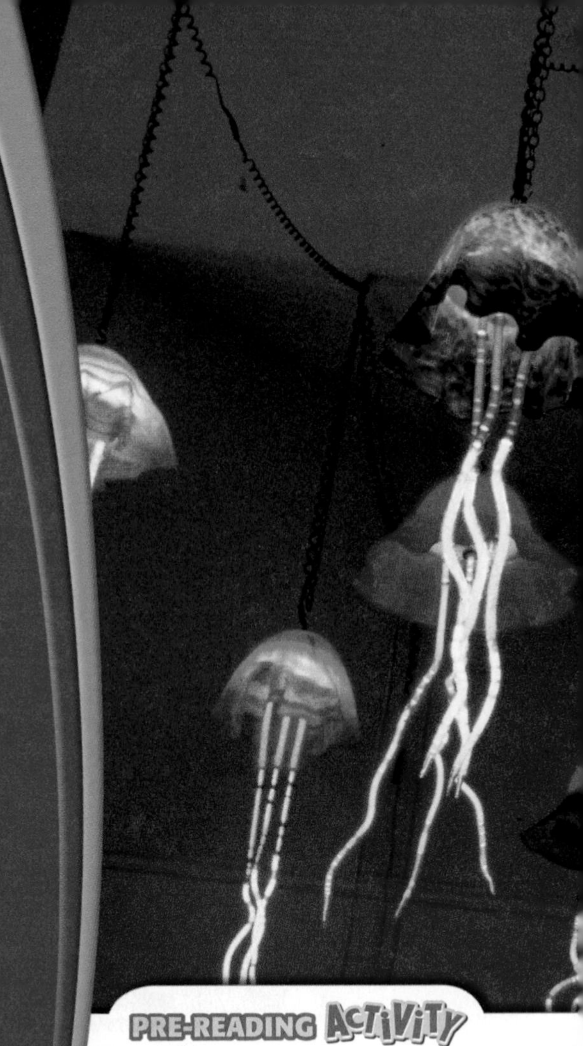

About the Photo

You already know or have heard about elements on the periodic table, such as oxygen, carbon, and neon. Neon gas was discovered in 1898. In 1902, a French engineer, chemist, and inventor named Georges Claude made the first neon lamp. In 1910, Claude made the first neon sign, and in 1923, he introduced neon signs to the United States. Now, artists such as Eric Ehlenberger use glass and neon to create interesting works of art, such as these neon jellyfish.

PRE-READING ACTIVITY

FOLDNOTES Three-Panel Flip Chart
Before you read the chapter, create the FoldNote entitled "Three-Panel Flip Chart" described in the **Study Skills** section of the Appendix. Label the flaps of the three-panel flip chart with "Metal," "Nonmetal," and "Metalloid." As you read the chapter, write information you learn about each category under the appropriate flap.

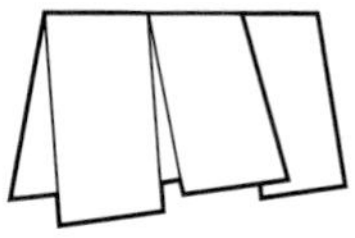

Standards Correlations

National Science Education Standards

The following codes indicate the National Science Education Standards that correlate to this chapter. The full text of the standards is at the front of the book.

Chapter Opener
UCP 1, 2; SAI 1; ST 2; SPSP 5; HNS 1, 3

Section 1 Arranging the Elements
UCP 1; SAI 2; SPSP 5; HNS 1, 2, 3; PS 1b

Section 2 Grouping the Elements
ST 2; PS 1b, 3e

Chapter Lab
UCP 1; SAI 1, 2

Chapter Review
PS 1b

Science in Action
UCP 5; HNS 1, 3

Teacher's Notes: To do this activity, you will need to make a seating chart before the class period. Possible organizational ideas for the arrangement include placing students by birth date, by height, or alphabetically by their first names. This activity can be repeated by using different patterns, including patterns that are periodic.

Answers

1. Students should be able to describe the new seating pattern and, using the information they collected, explain how they arrived at their result.

3. Some students may have difficulty determining the new seating pattern. Encourage other students to assist them in analyzing the data and finding the pattern.

START-UP ACTIVITY

Placement Pattern

In this activity, you will identify the pattern your teacher used to create a new classroom seating arrangement.

Procedure

1. Draw a seating chart for the new classroom arrangement that your teacher gave to you. Write the name of each of your classmates in the place on the chart that corresponds to his or her seat.

2. Write information about yourself, such as your name, date of birth, hair color, and height, in the space that represents you on the chart.

3. Gather the same information about the people near you, and write it in the spaces on the chart.

Analysis

1. From the information you gathered, identify a pattern that might explain the order of people in the chart. Collect more information if needed.

2. Test your pattern by gathering information from a person you did not talk to before.

3. If the new information does not support your pattern, reanalyze your data and collect more information to determine another pattern.

Chapter Starter Transparency
Use this transparency to help students begin thinking about classifying items based on shared properties.

CHAPTER RESOURCES

Technology

 **Transparencies**
• Chapter Starter Transparency

READING SKILLS

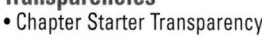 **Student Edition on CD-ROM**

 **Guided Reading Audio CD**
• English or Spanish

Classroom Videos
• Brain Food Video Quiz

Workbooks

 Science Puzzlers, Twisters & Teasers
• The Periodic Table GENERAL

Focus

Overview

This section gives a short history of the periodic table. Students learn about the modern periodic table and are shown how to interpret it, and they learn how characteristics of elements led to a logical way of grouping the elements.

Bellringer

Ask students to think of all of the ways a deck of cards could be laid out so that the cards form some sort of identifiable pattern. Have students write down as many patterns as they can.

Motivate

Demonstration — GENERAL

Grouping Ask three volunteers to stand at the front of the class. Put two of them together, and ask the third to step off to the side for a moment. Ask the class to list characteristics that the two students share. List student responses on the board.

Now, separate the two students, and ask the third student to stand next to one of the other students. Repeat the exercise. Compare the two lists of characteristics. Discuss with the class the similarities and differences in the lists. **LS** Visual/Logical

What You Will Learn

● Describe how Mendeleev arranged elements in the first periodic table.
● Explain how elements are arranged in the modern periodic table.
● Compare metals, nonmetals, and metalloids based on their properties and on their location in the periodic table.
● Describe the difference between a period and a group.

Vocabulary

periodic   period
periodic law   group

READING STRATEGY

Mnemonics As you read this section, create a mnemonic device to help you remember the difference between periods and groups.

Arranging the Elements

Suppose you went to the video store and all the videos were mixed together. How could you tell the comedies from the action movies? If the videos were not arranged in a pattern, you wouldn't know what kind of movie you had chosen!

Scientists in the early 1860s had a similar problem. At that time, scientists knew some of the properties of more than 60 elements. However, no one had organized the elements according to these properties. Organizing the elements according to their properties would help scientists understand how elements interact with each other.

Discovering a Pattern

Dmitri Mendeleev (duh MEE tree MEN duh LAY uhf), a Russian chemist, discovered a pattern to the elements in 1869. First, he wrote the names and properties of the elements on cards. Then, he arranged his cards, as shown in **Figure 1,** by different properties, such as density, appearance, and melting point. After much thought, he arranged the elements in order of increasing atomic mass. When he did so, a pattern appeared.

✓ *Reading Check* How had Mendeleev arranged elements when he noticed a pattern? (*See the Appendix for answers to Reading Checks.*)

Figure 1 *By playing "chemical solitaire" on long train rides, Mendeleev organized the elements according to their properties.*

CHAPTER RESOURCES

Chapter Resource File

  • Lesson Plan
• Directed Reading A **BASIC**
• Directed Reading B **SPECIAL NEEDS**

Technology

  Transparencies
• Bellringer

Workbooks

  Interactive Textbook Struggling Readers

Answer to Reading Check
Mendeleev had arranged elements based on increasing atomic mass.

Table 1 Properties of Germanium		
	Mendeleev's predictions (1869)	Actual properties
Atomic mass	70	72.6
Density*	5.5 g/cm³	5.3 g/cm³
Appearance	dark gray metal	gray metal
Melting point*	high melting point	937°C

* at room temperature and pressure

Periodic Properties of the Elements

Mendeleev saw that when the elements were arranged in order of increasing atomic mass, those that had similar properties occurred in a repeating pattern. That is, the pattern was periodic. **Periodic** means "happening at regular intervals." The days of the week are periodic. They repeat in the same order every 7 days. Similarly, Mendeleev found that the elements' properties followed a pattern that repeated every seven elements. His table became known as the *periodic table of the elements*.

Predicting Properties of Missing Elements

Figure 2 shows part of Mendeleev's first try at arranging the elements. The question marks show gaps in the pattern. Mendeleev predicted that elements yet to be found would fill these gaps. He used the pattern he found to predict their properties. **Table 1** compares his predictions for one missing element—germanium—with its actual properties. By 1886, all of the gaps had been filled. His predictions were right.

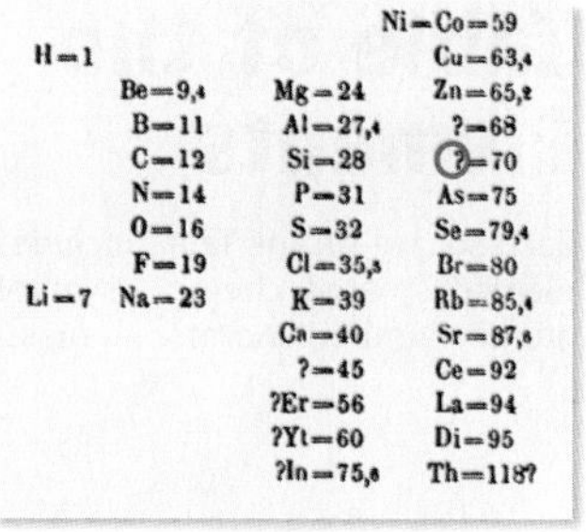

Changing the Arrangement

A few elements' properties did not fit the pattern in Mendeleev's table. Mendeleev thought that more-accurate atomic masses would fix these flaws in his table. But new atomic mass measurements showed that the masses he had used were correct. In 1914, Henry Moseley (MOHZ lee), a British scientist, determined the number of protons—the atomic number—in an atom. All elements fit the pattern in Mendeleev's periodic table when they were arranged by atomic number.

Look at the periodic table on the next two pages. All of the more than 30 elements discovered since 1914 follow the periodic law. The **periodic law** states that the repeating chemical and physical properties of elements change periodically with the elements' atomic numbers.

Reading Check What property is used to arrange elements in the periodic table?

		Ni—Co=59
H=1		Cu=63,₄
	Be=9,₄ Mg=24	Zn=65,₂
	B=11 Al=27,₄	?=68
	C=12 Si=28	?=70
	N=14 P=31	As=75
	O=16 S=32	Se=79,₄
	F=19 Cl=35,₅	Br=80
Li=7 Na=23	K=39	Rb=85,₄
	Ca=40	Sr=87,₆
	?=45	Ce=92
	?Er=56	La=94
	?Yt=60	Di=95
	?In=75,₆	Th=118?

Figure 2 *Mendeleev used question marks to mark some elements that he thought would be found later.*

periodic describes something that occurs or repeats at regular intervals

periodic law the law that states that the repeating chemical and physical properties of elements change periodically with the atomic numbers of the elements

Is That a Fact!

In the late 1800s, scientists began studying the color spectra that elements produced when heated. There are patterns within the spectra, and all of the patterns are different—no two elements have the same spectrum.

Homework ——— GENERAL

Reviewing Atoms Have students review information that they have learned about atoms by using the following terms to make a concept map: *atom, proton, neutron, electron, atomic number,* and *atomic mass*. **LS** Visual/Logical

Answer to Reading Check
atomic number

Discussion Help students recognize the layout pattern for the periodic table of the elements. Have them count across the table, group by group, to see that there are a total of 18 groups. Also, have students count the 7 periods. Discuss the triads that Döbereiner found (see the Chapter Enrichment pages at the beginning of this chapter), the expanded triads, and the noble gases. Emphasize that the lanthanides and actinides are parts of periods 6 and 7 and are not periods by themselves. **LS** Visual

SUPPORT FOR

English Language Learners

The Periodic Table Students may have difficulty reading such a complex table with so many symbols. Use the table in the book to help students as a class recognize the layout pattern for the periodic table of elements. Model counting across the table group by group. Ask students to count across and tell you how many groups there are. (18) Show that a row of elements is called a period, and have students count the seven periods. Point out that the last two rows, the lanthanides and actinides, are parts of periods 6 and 7 and are not periods by themselves. **LS** Visual/Logical

Periodic Table of the Elements

Each square on the table includes an element's name, chemical symbol, atomic number, and atomic mass.

The color of the chemical symbol indicates the physical state at room temperature. Carbon is a solid.

6
C
Carbon
12.0

— Atomic number
— Chemical symbol
— Element name
— Atomic mass

The background color indicates the type of element. Carbon is a nonmetal.

Background		Chemical symbol	
Metals	▢	Solid	■
Metalloids	▢	Liquid	■
Nonmetals	▢	Gas	■

Period 1	1 **H** Hydrogen 1.0

	Group 1	**Group 2**
Period 2	3 **Li** Lithium 6.9	4 **Be** Beryllium 9.0
Period 3	11 **Na** Sodium 23.0	12 **Mg** Magnesium 24.3

	Group 3	**Group 4**	**Group 5**	**Group 6**	**Group 7**	**Group 8**	**Group 9**
Period 4	21 **Sc** Scandium 45.0	22 **Ti** Titanium 47.9	23 **V** Vanadium 50.9	24 **Cr** Chromium 52.0	25 **Mn** Manganese 54.9	26 **Fe** Iron 55.8	27 **Co** Cobalt 58.9
Period 5	39 **Y** Yttrium 88.9	40 **Zr** Zirconium 91.2	41 **Nb** Niobium 92.9	42 **Mo** Molybdenum 95.9	43 **Tc** Technetium (98)	44 **Ru** Ruthenium 101.1	45 **Rh** Rhodium 102.9
Period 6	57 **La** Lanthanum 138.9	72 **Hf** Hafnium 178.5	73 **Ta** Tantalum 180.9	74 **W** Tungsten 183.8	75 **Re** Rhenium 186.2	76 **Os** Osmium 190.2	77 **Ir** Iridium 192.2
Period 7	89 **Ac** Actinium (227)	104 **Rf** Rutherfordium (261)	105 **Db** Dubnium (262)	106 **Sg** Seaborgium (266)	107 **Bh** Bohrium (264)	108 **Hs** Hassium (277)	109 **Mt** Meitnerium (268)

(Period 4 Group 1: 19 **K** Potassium 39.1; Group 2: 20 **Ca** Calcium 40.1)
(Period 5 Group 1: 37 **Rb** Rubidium 85.5; Group 2: 38 **Sr** Strontium 87.6)
(Period 6 Group 1: 55 **Cs** Cesium 132.9; Group 2: 56 **Ba** Barium 137.3)
(Period 7 Group 1: 87 **Fr** Francium (223); Group 2: 88 **Ra** Radium (226))

A row of elements is called a *period*.

A column of elements is called a *group* or *family*.

Values in parentheses are the mass numbers of those radioactive elements' most stable or most common isotopes.

Lanthanides	58 **Ce** Cerium 140.1	59 **Pr** Praseodymium 140.9	60 **Nd** Neodymium 144.2	61 **Pm** Promethium (145)	62 **Sm** Samarium 150.4

These elements are placed below the table to allow the table to be narrower.

Actinides	90 **Th** Thorium 232.0	91 **Pa** Protactinium 231.0	92 **U** Uranium 238.0	93 **Np** Neptunium (237)	94 **Pu** Plutonium (244)

CHAPTER RESOURCES

Technology

 Transparencies
• P109 The Periodic Table of the Elements

Topic: **Periodic Table**
Go To: **go.hrw.com**
Keyword: **HN0 PERIODIC**
Visit the HRW Web site for updates on the periodic table.

This zigzag line reminds you where the metals, nonmetals, and metalloids are.

Group 18

				Group 13	Group 14	Group 15	Group 16	Group 17	2 **He** Helium 4.0
				5 **B** Boron 10.8	6 **C** Carbon 12.0	7 **N** Nitrogen 14.0	8 **O** Oxygen 16.0	9 **F** Fluorine 19.0	10 **Ne** Neon 20.2

Group 10	Group 11	Group 12	13 **Al** Aluminum 27.0	14 **Si** Silicon 28.1	15 **P** Phosphorus 31.0	16 **S** Sulfur 32.1	17 **Cl** Chlorine 35.5	18 **Ar** Argon 39.9
28 **Ni** Nickel 58.7	29 **Cu** Copper 63.5	30 **Zn** Zinc 65.4	31 **Ga** Gallium 69.7	32 **Ge** Germanium 72.6	33 **As** Arsenic 74.9	34 **Se** Selenium 79.0	35 **Br** Bromine 79.9	36 **Kr** Krypton 83.8
46 **Pd** Palladium 106.4	47 **Ag** Silver 107.9	48 **Cd** Cadmium 112.4	49 **In** Indium 114.8	50 **Sn** Tin 118.7	51 **Sb** Antimony 121.8	52 **Te** Tellurium 127.6	53 **I** Iodine 126.9	54 **Xe** Xenon 131.3
78 **Pt** Platinum 195.1	79 **Au** Gold 197.0	80 **Hg** Mercury 200.6	81 **Tl** Thallium 204.4	82 **Pb** Lead 207.2	83 **Bi** Bismuth 209.0	84 **Po** Polonium (209)	85 **At** Astatine (210)	86 **Rn** Radon (222)
110 **Ds** Darmstadtium (281)	111 **Uuu** Unununium (272)	112 **Uub** Ununbium (285)	113 **Uut** Ununtrium (284)	114 **Uuq** Ununquadium (289)	115 **Uup** Ununpentium (288)			

The discovery of elements 113, 114, and 115 has been reported but not confirmed.

The names and three-letter symbols of elements are temporary. They are based on the atomic numbers of the elements. Official names and symbols will be approved by an international committee of scientists.

63 **Eu** Europium 152.0	64 **Gd** Gadolinium 157.2	65 **Tb** Terbium 158.9	66 **Dy** Dysprosium 162.5	67 **Ho** Holmium 164.9	68 **Er** Erbium 167.3	69 **Tm** Thulium 168.9	70 **Yb** Ytterbium 173.0	71 **Lu** Lutetium 175.0
95 **Am** Americium (243)	96 **Cm** Curium (247)	97 **Bk** Berkelium (247)	98 **Cf** Californium (251)	99 **Es** Einsteinium (252)	100 **Fm** Fermium (257)	101 **Md** Mendelevium (258)	102 **No** Nobelium (259)	103 **Lr** Lawrencium (262)

MATERIALS

FOR EACH STUDENT
- cup, plastic-foam
- graphite, mechanical pencil lead
- water, hot
- wire, copper, bare, 25 cm long

Safety Caution: Remind students to review all safety cautions and icons before beginning this lab activity.

Teacher's Notes: The wire should be approximately the same thickness and length as the pencil lead. Test the procedure; adjust the time if necessary.

Answer

4. The wire conducted thermal energy better than the pencil lead did. The wire is made of the metal copper; pencil lead is made of graphite, a form of the nonmetal carbon. Metals conduct thermal energy better than nonmetals do.

Answer to Reading Check

Most metals are solid at room temperature, ductile, malleable, and shiny. In addition, they are good conductors of electric current and thermal energy.

Conduction Connection

1. Fill a **plastic-foam cup** with **hot water**.
2. Stand a **piece of copper wire** and a **graphite lead** from a mechanical pencil in the water.
3. After 1 min, touch the top of each object. Record your observations.
4. Which material conducted thermal energy the best? Why?

The Periodic Table and Classes of Elements

At first glance, you might think studying the periodic table is like trying to explore a thick jungle without a guide—you can easily get lost! However, the table itself contains a lot of information that will help you along the way.

Elements are classified as metals, nonmetals, and metalloids, according to their properties. The number of electrons in the outer energy level of an atom is one characteristic that helps determine which category an element belongs in. The zigzag line on the periodic table can help you recognize which elements are metals, which are nonmetals, and which are metalloids.

Metals

Most elements are metals. Metals are found to the left of the zigzag line on the periodic table. Atoms of most metals have few electrons in their outer energy level. Most metals are solid at room temperature. Mercury, however, is a liquid at room temperature. Some additional information on properties shared by most metals is shown in **Figure 3.**

✓ **Reading Check** What are four properties shared by most metals?

Figure 3 **Properties of Metals**

Metals tend to be **shiny.** You can see a reflection in a mirror because light reflects off the shiny surface of a thin layer of silver behind the glass.

Most metals are **ductile,** which means that they can be drawn into thin wires. All metals are **good conductors of electric current.** The wires in the electrical devices in your home are made of copper.

Most metals are **malleable,** which means that they can be flattened with a hammer and will not shatter. Aluminum is flattened into sheets to make cans and foil.

Most metals are **good conductors of thermal energy.** This iron griddle conducts thermal energy from a stove top to cook your favorite foods.

Is That a Fact!

Mercury is the only metal that is liquid at room temperature. It was not thought to be a metal until it was frozen in 1759. The metal cesium is almost a liquid metal. It has a melting point of 28.4°C, so on a hot day, cesium metal would melt into a puddle.

ACTIVITY — BASIC

Element Game Make a memory game by using two sets of flip pages. Select 24 elements. Have students write descriptions of these elements on one set of flip pages and place images of items made from those elements on the second set of flip pages. The element's name and symbol should be on the back of each page. Have students try to guess the element from its description or its picture. Or have students match the pictures with the descriptions. **LS Visual**

English Language Learners

Figure 4 Properties of Nonmetals

Nonmetals are **not malleable or ductile.** In fact, solid non-metals, such as carbon in the graphite of the pencil lead, are brittle and will break or shatter when hit with a hammer.

Sulfur, like most non-metals, is **not shiny.**

Nonmetals are **poor conductors of thermal energy and electric current.** If the gap in a spark plug is too wide, the nonmetals nitrogen and oxygen in the air will stop the spark and a car's engine will not run.

Nonmetals

Nonmetals are found to the right of the zigzag line on the periodic table. Atoms of most nonmetals have an almost complete set of electrons in their outer level. Atoms of the elements in Group 18, the noble gases, have a complete set of electrons. More than half of the nonmetals are gases at room temperature. Many properties of nonmetals are the opposite of the properties of metals, as shown in **Figure 4.**

Metalloids

Metalloids, also called *semiconductors,* are the elements that border the zigzag line on the periodic table. Atoms of metalloids have about half of a complete set of electrons in their outer energy level. Metalloids have some properties of metals and some properties of nonmetals, as shown in **Figure 5.**

Percentages

Elements are classified as metals, nonmetals, and metalloids. Use the periodic table to determine the percentage of elements in each of the three categories.

Figure 5 Properties of Metalloids

Tellurium is **shiny,** but it is **brittle** and can easily be smashed into a powder.

Boron is almost as **hard** as diamond, but it is also **very brittle.** At high temperatures, it is a **good conductor of electric current.**

Is That a Fact!

Metalloids are also called *semiconductors* because they conduct electric current more easily than nonmetals do but less easily than metals do. The semiconductors silicon and germanium are extremely important in your everyday life. These elements are used to create microprocessors for computers.

SCIENTISTS AT ODDS

Naming New Elements Scientists who claim to have made a new element propose a name for it. Names are reviewed and suggested by a committee of the International Union of Pure and Applied Chemistry (IUPAC). This committee is made up of scientists who are competing with each other to make new elements, so the naming process is sometimes difficult. Eventually, the IUPAC designates one official name, and most scientists then refer to the new element by this official name.

CONNECTION to Real World — GENERAL

Wiring Homes built between 1965 and 1973 may contain aluminum wiring, which can be very dangerous. This type of wiring has conductors made of aluminum that may corrode at any connection. Corrosion causes increased electrical resistance, which may cause the wire to overheat and start a fire. By 1973, manufacturers had corrected the corrosion problem, so aluminum wiring used after 1973 is much safer. To be safe, people whose homes were wired between 1965 and 1973 should check the wiring and replace it if necessary.

Answers to Math Practice

79% metals, 5% metalloids, and 16% nonmetals

ACTIVITY — GENERAL

Elements Everywhere Have students check the ingredients of foods and other products in their homes and write down the ingredients that have familiar chemical names, such as *sodium fluoride.* In class, have students place self-adhesive notes containing product names on the corresponding elements on a wall-chart periodic table.
LS Visual

INTERNET ACTIVITY

Sequence Board — GENERAL

For an internet activity related to this chapter, have students go to **go.hrw.com** and type in the keyword **HP5PRTW.**

Patterns of Symbols

Divide a sheet of paper into four columns. Look at the elements whose atomic numbers are 1 to 20 on the periodic table. With a parent, find patterns that describe the relationship between the chemical symbols and names of elements. In each column, write all of the chemical symbols and names that follow a single pattern. At the top of each column, write a sentence describing the pattern.

period in chemistry, a horizontal row of elements in the periodic table

group a vertical column of elements in the periodic table; elements in a group share chemical properties

Decoding the Periodic Table

The periodic table may seem to be in code. In a way, it is. But the colors and symbols will help you decode the table.

Each Element Is Identified by a Chemical Symbol

Each square on the periodic table includes an element's name, chemical symbol, atomic number, and atomic mass. The names of the elements come from many sources. Some elements, such as mendelevium, are named after scientists. Others, such as californium, are named after places. Some element names vary by country. But the chemical symbols are the same worldwide. For most elements, the chemical symbol has one or two letters. The first letter is always capitalized. Any other letter is always lowercase. The newest elements have temporary three-letter symbols.

Rows Are Called *Periods*

Each horizontal row of elements (from left to right) on the periodic table is called a **period.** Look at Period 4 in **Figure 6.** The physical and chemical properties of elements in a row follow a repeating, or periodic, pattern as you move across the period. Properties such as conductivity and reactivity change gradually from left to right in each period.

Columns Are Called *Groups*

Each vertical column of elements (from top to bottom) on the periodic table is called a **group.** Elements in the same group often have similar chemical and physical properties. For this reason, a group is also called a *family.*

Reading Check Why is a group sometimes called a family?

Figure 6 *As you move from left to right across a row, the elements become less metallic.*

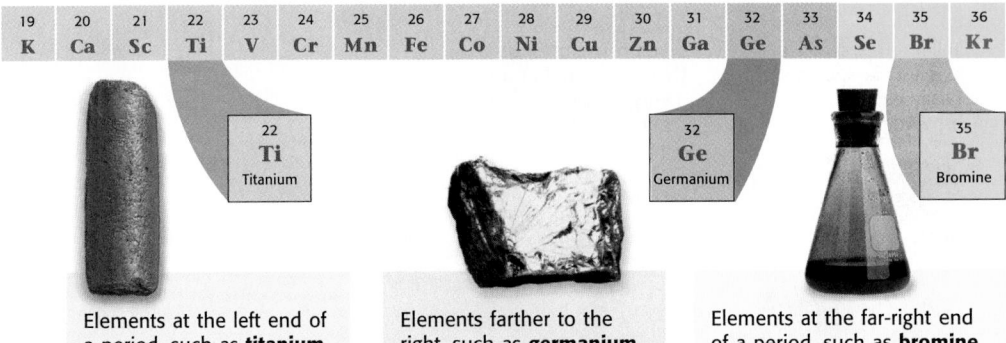

Elements at the left end of a period, such as **titanium,** are very metallic.

Elements farther to the right, such as **germanium,** are less metallic.

Elements at the far-right end of a period, such as **bromine,** are nonmetallic.

Summary

- Mendeleev developed the first periodic table by listing the elements in order of increasing atomic mass. He used his table to predict that elements with certain properties would be discovered later.

- Properties of elements repeat in a regular, or periodic, pattern.

- Moseley rearranged the elements in order of increasing atomic number.

- The periodic law states that the repeating chemical and physical properties of elements relate to and depend on elements' atomic numbers.

- Elements in the periodic table are classified as metals, nonmetals, and metalloids.

- Each element has a chemical symbol.

- A horizontal row of elements is called a *period*.

- Physical and chemical properties of elements change across each period.

- A vertical column of elements is called a *group* or *family*.

- Elements in a group usually have similar properties.

Using Key Terms

1. In your own words, write a definition for the term *periodic*.

Understanding Key Ideas

2. Which of the following elements should be the best conductor of electric current?
   a. germanium
   b. sulfur
   c. aluminum
   d. helium

3. Compare a period and a group on the periodic table.

4. What property did Mendeleev use to position the elements on the periodic table?

5. State the periodic law.

Critical Thinking

6. **Identifying Relationships** An atom that has 117 protons in its nucleus has not yet been made. Once this atom is made, to which group will element 117 belong? Explain your answer.

7. **Applying Concepts** Are the properties of sodium, Na, more like the properties of lithium, Li, or magnesium, Mg? Explain your answer.

Interpreting Graphics

8. The image below shows part of a periodic table. Compare the image below with the similar part of the periodic table in your book.

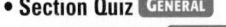

SCI LINKS

NSTA
Developed and maintained by the National Science Teachers Association

For a variety of links related to this chapter, go to www.scilinks.org

Topic: Periodic Table; Metals
SciLinks code: HSM1125; HSM0947

CHAPTER RESOURCES

Chapter Resource File

- Section Quiz GENERAL
- Section Review GENERAL
- Vocabulary and Section Summary GENERAL
- SciLinks Activity GENERAL
- Datasheet for Quick Lab

Answers to Section Review

1. Sample answer: *Periodic* means "happening in a regular repeating pattern."

2. c

3. A period in the periodic table is a horizontal row of elements. A group is a vertical column of elements.

4. atomic mass

5. The repeating chemical and physical properties of elements change periodically with the atomic numbers of the elements.

6. Group 17; Element 117 has 117 protons. So, it would fall under astatine in the periodic table.

7. lithium; Sodium and lithium are in the same group, so their properties should be more alike than the properties of sodium and magnesium are.

8. The periodic table has the same shape, atomic numbers, and chemical symbols. The names of the elements are in a different language (Japanese).

Focus

Overview

Students learn how properties of elements are used to group the elements in the periodic table. Students also study the relationship that elements have to each other and to the overall layout of elements within the table.

Bellringer

Ask students the following questions: "How do you know that a bird is a bird, that a kangaroo is a kangaroo, and that a shark is a shark?" "What characteristics of each animal help you to tell the animals apart?" and "How can such an analysis of characteristics be applied to elements?"

Motivate

Discussion ——— GENERAL

Universal Ingredients Hand out several kinds of cookies. Ask students to list the ingredients. (The goal is to list all of the things from which you can make cookies.) Show students the list of ingredients for the entire universe—the periodic table of the elements. Discuss with students how these elements combine to make all matter. You can also remind students that the basic ingredients of the atoms of the elements are protons, neutrons, and electrons. **LS** Visual

What You Will Learn

- Explain why elements in a group often have similar properties.
- Describe the properties of the elements in the groups of the periodic table.

Vocabulary

alkali metal
alkaline-earth metal
halogen
noble gas

READING STRATEGY

Paired Summarizing Read this section silently. In pairs, take turns summarizing the material. Stop to discuss ideas that seem confusing.

Although the element hydrogen appears above the alkali metals on the periodic table, it is not considered a member of Group 1. It will be described separately at the end of this section.

Grouping the Elements

You probably know a family with several members who look a lot alike. The elements in a family or group in the periodic table often—but not always—have similar properties.

The properties of the elements in a group are similar because the atoms of the elements have the same number of electrons in their outer energy level. Atoms will often take, give, or share electrons with other atoms in order to have a complete set of electrons in their outer energy level. Elements whose atoms undergo such processes are called *reactive* and can combine to form compounds.

Group 1: Alkali Metals

| 3 Li Lithium |
| 11 Na Sodium |
| 19 K Potassium |
| 37 Rb Rubidium |
| 55 Cs Cesium |
| 87 Fr Francium |

Group contains: metals
Electrons in the outer level: 1
Reactivity: very reactive
Other shared properties: softness; color of silver; shininess; low density

Alkali metals (AL kuh LIE MET uhlz) are elements in Group 1 of the periodic table. They share physical and chemical properties, as shown in **Figure 1.** Alkali metals are the most reactive metals because their atoms can easily give away the one outer-level electron. Pure alkali metals are often stored in oil. The oil keeps them from reacting with water and oxygen in the air. Alkali metals are so reactive that in nature they are found only combined with other elements. Compounds formed from alkali metals have many uses. For example, sodium chloride (table salt) is used to flavor your food. Potassium bromide is used in photography.

Figure 1 Properties of Alkali Metals

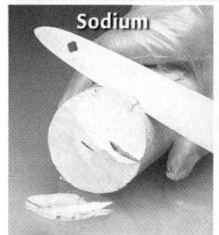 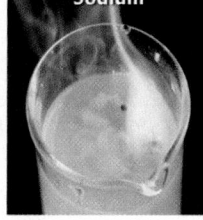 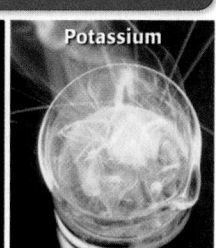

▲ Alkali metals are soft enough to be cut with a knife.

▲ Alkali metals react with water to form hydrogen gas.

CHAPTER RESOURCES

Chapter Resource File

- **Lesson Plan**
- **Directed Reading A** BASIC
- **Directed Reading B** SPECIAL NEEDS

Technology

Transparencies
- Bellringer
- *LINK TO LIFE SCIENCE* L79 The Skeleton

Workbooks

Interactive Textbook Struggling Readers

Group 2: Alkaline-Earth Metals

4 **Be** Beryllium	**Group contains:** metals **Electrons in the outer level:** 2 **Reactivity:** very reactive but less reactive than alkali metals **Other shared properties:** color of silver; higher densities than alkali metals
12 **Mg** Magnesium	
20 **Ca** Calcium	

Alkaline-earth metals (AL kuh LIEN UHRTH MET uhlz) are less reactive than alkali metals are. Atoms of alkaline-earth metals have two outer-level electrons. It is more difficult for atoms to give two electrons than to give one when joining with other atoms. Group 2 elements and their compounds have many uses. For example, magnesium can be mixed with other metals to make low-density materials used in airplanes. And compounds of calcium are found in cement, chalk, and even you, as shown in **Figure 2.**

Other elements shown in the left column:

38 **Sr** Strontium

56 **Ba** Barium

88 **Ra** Radium

Figure 2 *Calcium, an alkaline-earth metal, is an important part of a compound that keeps your bones and teeth healthy.*

Groups 3–12: Transition Metals

21 Sc	22 Ti	23 V	24 Cr	25 Mn	26 Fe	27 Co	28 Ni	29 Cu	30 Zn
39 Y	40 Zr	41 Nb	42 Mo	43 Tc	44 Ru	45 Rh	46 Pd	47 Ag	48 Cd
57 La	72 Hf	73 Ta	74 W	75 Re	76 Os	77 Ir	78 Pt	79 Au	80 Hg
89 Ac	104 Rf	105 Db	106 Sg	107 Bh	108 Hs	109 Mt	110 Ds	111 Uuu	112 Uub

Group contains: metals
Electrons in the outer level: 1 or 2
Reactivity: less reactive than alkaline-earth metals
Other shared properties: shininess; good conductors of thermal energy and electric current; higher densities and melting points than elements in Groups 1 and 2 (except for mercury)

Groups 3–12 do not have individual names. Instead, all of these groups are called *transition metals*. The atoms of transition metals do not give away their electrons as easily as atoms of the Group 1 and Group 2 metals do. So, transition metals are less reactive than alkali metals and alkaline-earth metals are.

 Reading Check Why are alkali metals more reactive than transition metals are? (*See the Appendix for answers to Reading Checks.*)

alkali metal one of the elements of Group 1 of the periodic table (lithium, sodium, potassium, rubidium, cesium, and francium)

alkaline-earth metal one of the elements of Group 2 of the periodic table (beryllium, magnesium, calcium, strontium, barium, and radium)

Answer to Reading Check

It is easier for atoms of alkali metals to lose their outer electron than for atoms of transition metals to lose their outer electrons. Therefore, alkali metals are more reactive than transition metals.

Answer to Reading Check

Yes, lanthanides and actinides are transition metals.

Figure 3 Properties of Transition Metals

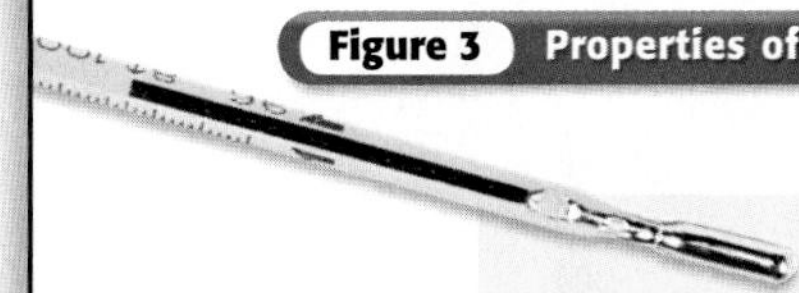

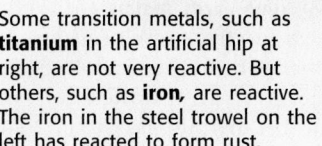

Mercury is used in thermometers. Unlike the other transition metals, mercury is liquid at room temperature.

Many transition metals—but not all—are silver colored! This **gold** ring proves it!

Some transition metals, such as **titanium** in the artificial hip at right, are not very reactive. But others, such as **iron**, are reactive. The iron in the steel trowel on the left has reacted to form rust.

Figure 4 *Do you see red? The color red appears on a computer monitor because of a compound formed from europium that coats the back of the screen.*

Properties of Transition Metals

The properties of the transition metals vary widely, as shown in **Figure 3**. But, because these elements are metals, they share the properties of metals. Transition metals tend to be shiny and to conduct thermal energy and electric current well.

Lanthanides and Actinides

Some transition metals from Periods 6 and 7 appear in two rows at the bottom of the periodic table to keep the table from being too wide. The elements in each row tend to have similar properties. Elements in the first row follow lanthanum and are called *lanthanides*. The lanthanides are shiny, reactive metals. Some of these elements are used to make steel. An important use of a compound of one lanthanide element is shown in **Figure 4**.

Elements in the second row follow actinium and are called *actinides*. All atoms of actinides are radioactive, or unstable. The atoms of a radioactive element can change into atoms of another element. Elements listed after plutonium, element 94, do not occur in nature. They are made in laboratories. Very small amounts of americium (AM uhr ISH ee uhm), element 95, are used in some smoke detectors.

Reading Check Are lanthanides and actinides transition metals?

| | 57 La Lanthanum |
| | 89 Ac Actinium |

	58	59	60	61	62	63	64	65	66	67	68	69	70	71
Lanthanides	Ce	Pr	Nd	Pm	Sm	Eu	Gd	Tb	Dy	Ho	Er	Tm	Yb	Lu
	90	91	92	93	94	95	96	97	98	99	100	101	102	103
Actinides	Th	Pa	U	Np	Pu	Am	Cm	Bk	Cf	Es	Fm	Md	No	Lr

Group 13: Boron Group

5 **B** Boron	**Group contains:** one metalloid and five metals **Electrons in the outer level:** 3 **Reactivity:** reactive **Other shared properties:** solids at room temperature
13 **Al** Aluminum	
31 **Ga** Gallium	
49 **In** Indium	
81 **Tl** Thallium	
113 **Uut** Ununtrium	

The most common element from Group 13 is aluminum. In fact, aluminum is the most abundant metal in Earth's crust. Until the 1880s, however, aluminum was considered a precious metal because the process used to make pure aluminum was very expensive. During the 1850s and 1860s, Emperor Napoleon III of France used aluminum dinnerware because aluminum was more valuable than gold.

Today, the process of making pure aluminum is easier and less expensive than it was in the 1800s. Aluminum is now an important metal used in making aircraft parts. Aluminum is also used to make lightweight automobile parts, foil, cans, and siding.

Like the other elements in the boron group, aluminum is reactive. Why can it be used in so many things? A thin layer of aluminum oxide quickly forms on aluminum's surface when aluminum reacts with oxygen in the air. This layer prevents further reaction of the aluminum.

Group 14: Carbon Group

6 **C** Carbon	**Group contains:** one nonmetal, two metalloids, and three metals **Electrons in the outer level:** 4 **Reactivity:** varies among the elements **Other shared properties:** solids at room temperature
14 **Si** Silicon	
32 **Ge** Germanium	
50 **Sn** Tin	
82 **Pb** Lead	
114 **Uuq** Ununquadium	

The nonmetal carbon can be found uncombined in nature, as shown in **Figure 5.** Carbon also forms a wide variety of compounds. Some of these compounds, such as proteins, fats, and carbohydrates, are necessary for living things on Earth.

The metalloids silicon and germanium, also in Group 14, are used to make computer chips. The metal tin is useful because it is not very reactive. For example, a tin can is really made of steel coated with tin. Because the tin is less reactive than the steel is, the tin keeps the iron in the steel from rusting.

Reading Check What metalloids from Group 14 are used to make computer chips?

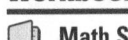

CONNECTION TO Environmental Science

WRITING SKILL **Recycling Aluminum**

Aluminum recycling is a very successful program. In your **science journal,** write a one-page report that describes how aluminum is processed from its ore. In your report, identify the ore and compare the energy needed to extract aluminum from the ore with the energy needed to process recycled aluminum.

Figure 5 *Diamond and soot have very different properties, yet both are natural forms of carbon.*

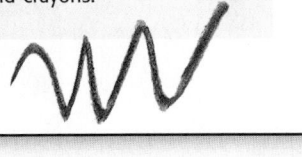

Diamond is the hardest material known. It is used as a jewel and on cutting tools, such as saws, drills, and files.

Soot is formed from burning oil, coal, and wood and is used as a pigment in paints and crayons.

CHAPTER RESOURCES

Workbooks

Math Skills for Science
• Checking Division with Multiplication **GENERAL**

CONNECTION ACTIVITY Math — GENERAL

Relative Masses The atomic masses of helium and carbon are approximately 4 and 12, respectively. Ask students the following questions: "How many helium atoms would together have about the same mass as one carbon atom? How many helium atoms would together have the mass of one silicon atom?" (Three helium atoms together have the same mass as one carbon atom, and seven helium atoms together have the same mass as one silicon atom.) **LS Logical**

CONNECTION to History — GENERAL

Canning Food preservation through canning was invented in 1809 by Frenchman Nicolas-François Appert (c. 1750–1841). Tin-plated cans were first used for canning in 1810 by English inventor Peter Durand. Commercial canning was brought to the United States in 1821 when it was introduced by the William Underwood Company in Boston. In 1874, the canning process was greatly improved when cans were first heated by high-pressure steam. The high pressure in this process kept cans from bursting during heating.

Using the Figure — GENERAL

Allotropes Many elements have several forms, called *allotropes*. For example, oxygen gas and ozone are allotropes of oxygen. Allotropes are usually stable at different temperatures and pressures. For example, diamond, graphite, and buckyballs are allotropes of carbon. Refer to **Figure 5.** **LS Visual**

Answer to Reading Check
silicon and germanium

Research ─────── GENERAL

Sulfuric Acid Ask students to find out more about sulfur and sulfuric acid. Sulfuric acid is widely used in the chemical industry. Have students find out how and why it is so widely used. Students may also investigate sulfur, sulfuric acid, smog, and acid rain.
LS Verbal/Logical

CONNECTION ACTIVITY
History ──────── ADVANCED

Sulfur Sulfur was used by prehistoric people as a pigment for cave drawings. It was also used in Egyptian ceremonies 4,000 years ago and in Chinese fireworks in about 500 BCE. Sulfur is even mentioned in Greek mythology. Have students write a report, make a poster, or prepare a presentation on the ways that sulfur was used before it was recognized as an element in 1777.
English Language Learners
LS Verbal

Answer to Reading Check

nitrogen and oxygen

Figure 6 *Simply striking a match on the side of this box causes chemicals on the match to react with phosphorus on the box and begin to burn.*

INTERNET ACTIVITY

For another activity related to this chapter, go to **go.hrw.com** and type in the keyword **HP5PRTW**.

Group 15: Nitrogen Group

| 7 **N** Nitrogen |
| 15 **P** Phosphorus |
| 33 **As** Arsenic |
| 51 **Sb** Antimony |
| 83 **Bi** Bismuth |
| 115 **Uup** Ununpentium |

Group contains: two nonmetals, two metalloids, and two metals
Electrons in the outer level: 5
Reactivity: varies among the elements
Other shared properties: solids at room temperature (except for nitrogen)

Nitrogen, which is a gas at room temperature, makes up about 80% of the air you breathe. Nitrogen removed from air can be reacted with hydrogen to make ammonia for fertilizers.

Although nitrogen is not very reactive, phosphorus is extremely reactive, as shown in **Figure 6.** In fact, in nature phosphorus is only found combined with other elements.

Group 16: Oxygen Group

| 8 **O** Oxygen |
| 16 **S** Sulfur |
| 34 **Se** Selenium |
| 52 **Te** Tellurium |
| 84 **Po** Polonium |

Group contains: three nonmetals, one metalloid, and one metal
Electrons in the outer level: 6
Reactivity: Reactive
Other shared properties: All but oxygen are solid at room temperature.

Oxygen makes up about 20% of air. Oxygen is necessary for substances to burn. Oxygen is also important to most living things, such as the diver in **Figure 7.** Sulfur is another commonly found member of Group 16. Sulfur can be found as a yellow solid in nature. It is used to make sulfuric acid, the most widely used compound in the chemical industry.

✓ **Reading Check** Which gases from Groups 15 and 16 make up most of the air you breathe?

Figure 7 *This diver is breathing a mixture that contains oxygen gas.*

CHAPTER RESOURCES

Workbooks

 Science Skills
• Finding Useful Sources GENERAL

Figure 8 Physical Properties of Some Halogens

Chlorine is a yellowish green gas.

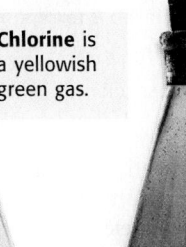

Bromine is a dark red liquid.

Iodine is a dark gray solid.

Group 17: Halogens

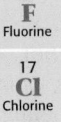

9 **F** Fluorine	
17 **Cl** Chlorine	
35 **Br** Bromine	
53 **I** Iodine	
85 **At** Astatine	

Group contains: nonmetals
Electrons in the outer level: 7
Reactivity: very reactive
Other shared properties: poor conductors of electric current; violent reactions with alkali metals to form salts; never in uncombined form in nature

Halogens (HAL oh juhnz) are very reactive nonmetals because their atoms need to gain only one electron to have a complete outer level. The atoms of halogens combine readily with other atoms, especially metals, to gain that missing electron. The reaction of a halogen with a metal makes a salt, such as sodium chloride. Both chlorine and iodine are used as disinfectants. Chlorine is used to treat water. Iodine mixed with alcohol is used in hospitals.

Although the chemical properties of the halogens are similar, the physical properties are quite different, as shown in **Figure 8.**

halogen one of the elements of Group 17 of the periodic table (fluorine, chlorine, bromine, iodine, and astatine); halogens combine with most metals to form salts

CONNECTION TO Biology

Water Treatment Chlorine has been used to treat drinking water since the early 20th century. Chlorinating water helps protect people from many diseases by killing the organisms in water that cause the diseases. But there is much more to water treatment than just adding chlorine. Research how a water treatment plant purifies water for your use. Construct a model of a treatment plant. Use labels to describe the role of each part of the plant in treating the water you use each day.

ACTIVITY

Cultural Awareness GENERAL

The Curies About a century ago, Marie Sklodowska Curie (1867–1934) made many contributions to the study of radioactivity and radioactive elements. In 1903, Marie, her husband, Pierre Curie (1859–1906), and French physicist Henri Becquerel (1852–1908) were awarded the Nobel Prize in physics for their contributions to understanding radioactivity. The Curies discovered the radioactive elements polonium and radium and isolated samples of these elements from tons of ore. For her discoveries of polonium and radium, Marie Curie was awarded the Nobel Prize in chemistry in 1911.

CONNECTION to Astronomy GENERAL

Element Factories Stars seem to be the factories that make the naturally occurring elements throughout the universe. Students can find information about and photographs of areas in the universe where new stars are born and areas where old stars have exploded. Have students research how elements may be generated or changed in these violent reactions. **LS Logical**

Homework ADVANCED

Salt Formers The word *halogen* comes from the Greek words meaning "salt former." Sodium chloride, or table salt, is composed of the halogen chlorine and the alkali metal sodium. Have students research halogens and their uses and then prepare a chart or a poster that shows what the students learned. **LS Visual/Logical**

Mendeleev, May I? To help students remember the properties of the groups, use chalk to draw a giant periodic table on the ground. Divide students into groups and play a game of Mother, may I? Give each group a command such as "Go to the group whose elements are unreactive." Students must decide where on the periodic table they should go and must ask you "Mendeleev, may we go to Group 18?" If they are correct, they should move to that area of the periodic table.

LS Kinesthetic/Interpersonal

Quiz ———————— GENERAL

1. Using the periodic table, determine which two groups include highly reactive metals. (on the left, Groups 1 and 2)

2. What are the actinides? What is one characteristic of all actinides? (the elements that follow actinium and that have atomic numbers 90–103; All actinides are radioactive.)

3. Of the gases oxygen, argon, chlorine, and neon, which two would be the most chemically reactive? (Oxygen and chlorine would be. Argon and neon are in Group 18, which consists of the noble gases, which are very unreactive.)

Answer to Reading Check

Atoms of noble gases have a full set of electrons in their outer level.

Figure 9 *In addition to neon, other noble gases can be used to make "neon" lights.*

noble gas one of the elements of Group 18 of the periodic table (helium, neon, argon, krypton, xenon, and radon); noble gases are unreactive

Figure 10 *Hydrogen reacts violently with oxygen. The hot water vapor that forms as a result of this reaction helps guide the space shuttle into orbit.*

Group 18: Noble Gases

2 He Helium	**Group contains:** nonmetals
10 Ne Neon	**Electrons in the outer level:** 8 (except helium, which has 2)
18 Ar Argon	**Reactivity:** unreactive
36 Kr Krypton	**Other shared properties:** colorless, odorless gases at room temperature
54 Xe Xenon	
86 Rn Radon	

Noble gases are unreactive nonmetals and are in Group 18 of the periodic table. The atoms of these elements have a full set of electrons in their outer level. So, they do not need to lose or gain any electrons. Under normal conditions, they do not react with other elements. Earth's atmosphere is almost 1% argon. But all the noble gases are found in small amounts.

The unreactivity of the noble gases makes them useful. For example, ordinary light bulbs last longer when they are filled with argon. Because argon is unreactive, it does not react with the metal filament in the light bulb even when the filament gets hot. A more reactive gas might react with the filament, causing the light to burn out. The low density of helium makes blimps and weather balloons float. Another popular use of noble gases is shown in **Figure 9.**

 Reading Check Why are noble gases unreactive?

Hydrogen

1 H Hydrogen	**Electrons in the outer level:** 1
	Reactivity: reactive
	Other properties: colorless, odorless gas at room temperature; low density; explosive reactions with oxygen

The properties of hydrogen do not match the properties of any single group, so hydrogen is set apart from the other elements in the table. Hydrogen is above Group 1 because atoms of the alkali metals also have only one electron in their outer level. Atoms of hydrogen can give away one electron when they join with other atoms. However, the physical properties of hydrogen are more like those of nonmetals than those of metals. So, hydrogen really is in a group of its own. Hydrogen is found in stars. In fact, it is the most abundant element in the universe. Its reactive nature makes it useful as a fuel in rockets, as shown in **Figure 10.**

MISCONCEPTION ALERT

Inert Gases Noble gases were originally called *inert gases* because it was thought that they would not react with any elements. However, scientists are able to use high temperatures and pressures to cause some of the elements in Group 18 to react. Thus, the term *inert* is incorrect, and the term *noble* is preferred.

SECTION Review

Summary

- Alkali metals (Group 1) are the most reactive metals. Atoms of the alkali metals have one electron in their outer level.

- Alkaline-earth metals (Group 2) are less reactive than the alkali metals are. Atoms of the alkaline-earth metals have two electrons in their outer level.

- Transition metals (Groups 3–12) include most of the well-known metals and the lanthanides and actinides.

- Groups 13–16 contain the metalloids and some metals and nonmetals.

- Halogens (Group 17) are very reactive non-metals. Atoms of the halogens have seven electrons in their outer level.

- Noble gases (Group 18) are unreactive nonmetals. Atoms of the noble gases have a full set of electrons in their outer level.

- Hydrogen is set off by itself in the periodic table. Its properties do not match the properties of any one group.

Using Key Terms

Complete each of the following sentences by choosing the correct term from the word bank.

noble gas	alkaline-earth metal
halogen	alkali metal

1. An atom of a(n) ___ has a full set of electrons in its outermost energy level.

2. An atom of a(n) ___ has one electron in its outermost energy level.

3. An atom of a(n) ___ tends to gain one electron when it combines with another atom.

4. An atom of a(n) ___ tends to lose two electrons when it combines with another atom.

Understanding Key Ideas

5. Which group contains elements whose atoms have six electrons in their outer level?
   - **a.** Group 2
   - **b.** Group 6
   - **c.** Group 16
   - **d.** Group 18

6. What are two properties of the alkali metals?

7. What causes the properties of elements in a group to be similar?

8. What are two properties of the halogens?

9. Why is hydrogen set apart from the other elements in the periodic table?

10. Which group contains elements whose atoms have three electrons in their outer level?

Interpreting Graphics

11. Look at the model of an atom below. Does the model represent a metal atom or a nonmetal atom? Explain your answer.

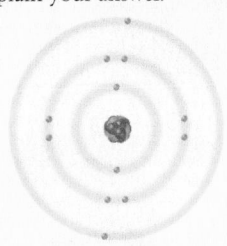

Critical Thinking

12. **Making Inferences** Why are neither the alkali metals nor the alkaline-earth metals found uncombined in nature?

13. **Making Comparisons** Compare the element hydrogen with the alkali metal sodium.

Developed and maintained by the National Science Teachers Association

For a variety of links related to this chapter, go to www.scilinks.org
Topic: Alkali Metals; Halogens and Noble Gases
SciLinks code: HSM0043; HSM0711

Alternative Assessment — GENERAL

Concept Mapping Have students prepare a concept map of the Periodic Table of the Elements, showing the groups as discussed in this chapter and the characteristics of each group or set of groups. Students do not have to show each individual element or each separate group. **LS Visual**

Answers to Section Review

1. noble gas

2. alkali metal

3. halogen

4. alkaline-earth metal

5. c

6. Answers may vary but could include that alkali metals have one electron in their outer level; are very reactive; are soft, silver colored, and shiny; and have a low density.

7. having the same number of electrons in the outer level of their atoms

8. Answers may vary but could include that halogens have seven electrons in their outer level, are very reactive, conduct electric current poorly, react violently with alkali metals to form salts, and are never found uncombined in nature.

9. The properties of hydrogen do not match the properties of any single group.

10. boron group (Group 13)

11. metal; The model shows two electrons in the outer level, so the atom represented is most likely a metal.

12. They are so reactive that they react with water or oxygen in the air.

13. Both hydrogen and sodium have one electron in their outer level. Atoms of both elements give away one electron when joining with other atoms. But hydrogen is a nonmetal and is a gas at room temperature, whereas sodium is a metal and is a solid at room temperature.

CHAPTER RESOURCES

Chapter Resource File

- Section Quiz **GENERAL**
- Section Review **GENERAL**
- Vocabulary and Section Summary **GENERAL**
- Reinforcement Worksheet **BASIC**
- Critical Thinking **ADVANCED**

Technology

- Interactive Explorations CD-ROM
  - Element of Surprise **GENERAL**

Create a Periodic Table

Teacher's Notes

Time Required
One to two 45-minute class periods

Lab Ratings

EASY —————————→ HARD

Teacher Prep 🧪🧪🧪
Student Set-Up 🧪
Concept Level 🧪🧪🧪
Clean Up 🧪

MATERIALS

For each group of 2–4 students, assemble a collection of 20 objects (5 sets of 4 objects). You should provide a bag containing 19 of these objects. A recommended collection of objects includes sets of coins (pennies, nickels, dimes, and quarters), sets of buttons that are similar but vary in diameter, and washers that vary in diameter. Other objects, such as nuts, bolts, and paper circles, will work and may be obtained easily. The difference in masses should be large enough for a beam balance to detect. Ideally, each set (one column on the table) should be of the same material and thickness and vary only in diameter.

Preparation Note
You may have students prepare the 20 squares of paper, but the lab will go faster if the squares are prepared ahead of time.

Model-Making Lab

OBJECTIVES

Classify objects based on their properties.

Identify patterns and trends in data.

MATERIALS

- bag of objects
- balance, metric
- meterstick
- paper, graphing (2 sheets)
- paper, 3 × 3 cm squares (20)

Create a Periodic Table

You probably have classification systems for many things in your life, such as your clothes, your books, and your CDs. One of the most important classification systems in science is the periodic table of the elements. In this lab, you will develop your own classification system for a collection of ordinary objects. You will analyze trends in your system and compare your system with the periodic table of the elements.

Procedure

1. Your teacher will give you a bag of objects. Your bag is missing one item. Examine the items carefully. Describe the missing object in as many ways as you can. Be sure to include the reasons why you think the missing object has the characteristics you describe.

2. Lay the paper squares out on your desk or table so that you have a grid of five rows of four squares each.

3. Arrange your objects on the grid in a logical order. (You must decide what order is logical!) You should end up with one blank square for the missing object.

4. Record a description of the basis for your arrangement.

 Holt Lab Generator CD-ROM

Search for any lab by topic, standard, difficulty level, or time. Edit any lab to fit your needs, or create your own labs. Use the Lab Materials QuickList software to customize your lab materials list.

Norman Holcomb
Marion Elementary School
Maria Stein, Ohio

CHAPTER RESOURCES

Chapter Resource File

 • Datasheet for Chapter Lab
• Lab Notes and Answers

Technology

 Classroom Videos
• Lab Video

5. Measure the mass (g) and diameter (mm) of each object, and record your results in the appropriate square. Each square (except the empty one) should have one object and two written measurements on it.

6. Examine your pattern again. Does the order in which your objects are arranged still make sense? Explain.

7. Rearrange the squares and their objects if necessary to improve your arrangement. Record a description of the basis for the new arrangement.

8. Working across the rows, number the squares 1 to 20. When you get to the end of a row, continue numbering in the first square of the next row.

9. Copy your grid. In each square, be sure to list the type of object and label all measurements with appropriate units.

Analyze the Results

1. **Constructing Graphs** Make a graph of mass (*y*-axis) versus object number (*x*-axis). Label each axis, and title the graph.

2. **Constructing Graphs** Now make a graph of diameter (*y*-axis) versus object number (*x*-axis).

Draw Conclusions

3. **Analyzing Graphs** Discuss each graph with your classmates. Try to identify any important features of the graph. For example, does the graph form a line or a curve? Is there anything unusual about the graph? What do these features tell you? Record your answers.

4. **Evaluating Models** How is your arrangement of objects similar to the periodic table of the elements found in this textbook? How is your arrangement different from that periodic table?

5. **Making Predictions** Look again at your prediction about the missing object. Do you think your prediction is still accurate? Try to improve your description by estimating the mass and diameter of the missing object. Record your estimates.

6. **Evaluating Methods** Mendeleev created a periodic table of elements and predicted characteristics of missing elements. How is your experiment similar to Mendeleev's work?

Analyze the Results

1. Graphs should be similar to sample graph A.

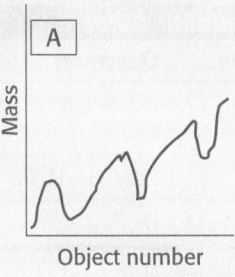

2. Graphs should be similar to sample graph B.

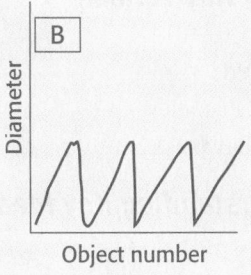

Draw Conclusions

3. Answers may vary. The primary feature is the repeating pattern of increases. This pattern in the first graph indicates the periodic nature of the mass of the items. This pattern in the second graph indicates the periodic nature of the diameter of the items.

4. Answers may vary. Similarities include repeating patterns (such as patterns of increasing mass) across the table. Differences may include no consistent family traits and no chemical properties associated with position in the table.

5. Answers may vary depending on the student's original prediction. Accept all reasonable answers. (You may wish to provide the students with the missing object so that they can further evaluate their prediction.)

6. This experiment is similar in that a pattern that helped identify characteristics of a missing object was identified.

Assignment Guide

Section	Questions
1	1–2, 5–8, 10–12, 15–16, 19–20
2	3–4, 9, 13–14, 18
1 and 2	17

ANSWERS

Using Key Terms

1. group
2. period
3. alkali metals
4. noble gases

Understanding Key Ideas

5. d
6. b
7. c
8. c
9. b
10. c

USING KEY TERMS

Complete each of the following sentences by choosing the correct term from the word bank.

group   period
alkali metals   halogens
alkaline-earth metals   noble gases

1 Elements in the same vertical column on the periodic table belong to the same ___.

2 Elements in the same horizontal row on the periodic table belong to the same ___.

3 The most reactive metals are ___.

4 Elements that are unreactive are called ___.

UNDERSTANDING KEY IDEAS

Multiple Choice

5 Mendeleev's periodic table was useful because it

  a. showed the elements arranged by atomic number.

  b. had no empty spaces.

  c. showed the atomic number of the elements.

  d. allowed for the prediction of the properties of missing elements.

6 Most nonmetals are

  a. shiny.

  b. poor conductors of electric current.

  c. flattened when hit with a hammer.

  d. solids at room temperature.

7 Which of the following items is NOT found on the periodic table?

  a. the atomic number of each element

  b. the name of each element

  c. the date that each element was discovered

  d. the atomic mass of each element

8 Which of the following statements about the periodic table is false?

  a. There are more metals than nonmetals on the periodic table.

  b. Atoms of elements in the same group have the same number of electrons in their outer level.

  c. The elements at the far left of the periodic table are nonmetals.

  d. Elements are arranged by increasing atomic number.

9 Which of the following statements about alkali metals is true?

  a. Alkali metals are generally found in their uncombined form.

  b. Alkali metals are Group 1 elements.

  c. Alkali metals should be stored underwater.

  d. Alkali metals are unreactive.

10 Which of the following statements about elements is true?

  a. Every element occurs naturally.

  b. All elements are found in their uncombined form in nature.

  c. Each element has a unique atomic number.

  d. All of the elements exist in approximately equal quantities.

Short Answer

11 How is Moseley's basis for arranging the elements different from Mendeleev's?

12 How is the periodic table like a calendar?

Math Skills

Examine the chart of the percentages of elements in the Earth's crust below. Then, answer the questions that follow.

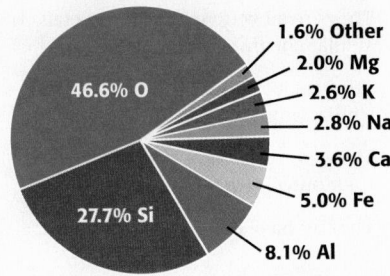

13 Excluding the "Other" category, what percentage of the Earth's crust are alkali metals?

14 Excluding the "Other" category, what percentage of the Earth's crust are alkaline-earth metals?

CRITICAL THINKING

15 Concept Mapping Use the following terms to create a concept map: *periodic table, elements, groups, periods, metals, nonmetals,* and *metalloids.*

16 Forming Hypotheses Why was Mendeleev unable to make any predictions about the noble gas elements?

17 Identifying Relationships When an element that has 115 protons in its nucleus is synthesized, will it be a metal, a nonmetal, or a metalloid? Explain your answer.

18 Applying Concepts Your classmate offers to give you a piece of sodium that he found on a hiking trip. What is your response? Explain.

19 Applying Concepts Identify each element described below.

a. This metal is very reactive, has properties similar to those of magnesium, and is in the same period as bromine.

b. This nonmetal is in the same group as lead.

INTERPRETING GRAPHICS

20 Study the diagram below to determine the pattern of the images. Predict the missing image, and draw it. Identify which properties are periodic and which properties are shared within a group.

   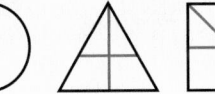 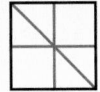

---

11. Moseley arranged elements by increasing atomic number. Mendeleev arranged elements by increasing atomic mass.

12. Both are periodic. The periodic table has repeating properties of elements. The calendar has repeating days and months.

13. 5.4% (sodium and potassium)

14. 5.6% (magnesium and calcium)

Critical Thinking

15. 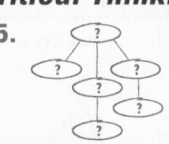 An answer to this exercise can be found at the end of this book.

16. Mendeleev could make predictions only about elements where there were clear gaps in his table. Because no noble gases were known at the time, there were no obvious gaps in the table and no way that he could have known that a whole column was missing.

17. metal; it will be located below the metal bismuth to the left of the zigzag

18. I would tell my classmate that he didn't find sodium. Sodium is very reactive and cannot be found uncombined in nature. Sodium would react with oxygen and water in the air to form compounds.

19. a. calcium

b. carbon

Interpreting Graphics

20.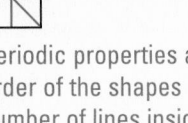

Periodic properties are the order of the shapes and the number of lines inside the shape. The properties shared in a group are the shape and the color of the lines inside the shape.

CHAPTER RESOURCES

Chapter Resource File

• Chapter Review GENERAL
• Chapter Test A GENERAL
• Chapter Test B ADVANCED
• Chapter Test C SPECIAL NEEDS
• Vocabulary Activity GENERAL

Workbooks

Study Guide
• Study Guide is also available in Spanish.

Standardized Test
Preparation

Teacher's Notes

To provide practice under more realistic conditions, give students 20 minutes to answer all of the questions in this Standardized Test Preparation.

Answer Key

Question	Answer
1	A
2	B
3	C
4	A
5	C
6	D
7	D
8	C
9	C
10	C
11	*
12	*

*See Test Doctor.

Multiple Choice

Use the diagram below to answer question 1.

Cobalt and Nickel Entries in Periodic Table

27	28
Co	**Ni**
Cobalt	Nickel
58.933	58.693

1. The diagram above is an enlargement of a section of the periodic table. What is the biggest difference between cobalt (Co) and nickel (Ni) as shown in the periodic table entries?

   A. Nickel has more protons.

   B. Cobalt has more electrons.

   C. Cobalt has a lower number of neutrons.

   D. Nickel has a higher value for atomic mass.

2. Approximately how many elements are in the periodic table?

   A. between 75 and 100

   B. between 100 and 125

   C. between 125 and 150

   D. more than 150

3. In what order are the regions arranged on the periodic table, reading left to right?

   A. inert gases, metals, nonmetals, metalloids

   B. metalloids, metals, nonmetals, inert gases

   C. metals, metalloids, nonmetals, inert gases

   D. nonmetals, inert gases, metals, metalloids

4. Fluorine, chlorine, bromine, iodine, and astatine make up Group 17, the halogens. Why are these elements grouped together?

   A. They are all very reactive nonmetals with similar chemical properties.

   B. They are all nonreactive gases with similar physical properties.

   C. Their atoms all have eight electrons in their outer energy levels.

   D. They all have the same atomic number.

5. Which of the following best describes the properties of metals?

   A. hard, brittle, and unconductive

   B. liquid, dark, and conductive

   C. shiny, malleable, and conductive

   D. soft, oily, and very reactive

6. Alberto has an element that is a shiny, brittle solid that conducts electricity. The element most likely belongs to which class of elements?

   A. halogens

   B. metals

   C. nonmetals

   D. metalloids

 TEST DOCTOR

Question 1 A: Correct. B: Cobalt has fewer electrons than nickel. C: One can infer from the atomic masses that cobalt generally has more neutrons than nickel. D: Nickel has a lower atomic mass.

Question 2 A, C, D: Approximately 114 elements are in the periodic table, of which 92 occur naturally. B: Correct.

Question 3 A, B, D: The periodic table begins with the metals, which comprise most of the elements. Next come the metalloids. The nonmetals are next, followed by the inert gases. C: Correct.

Question 4 A: Correct. B, C: The halogens are nonmetals whose atoms have seven electrons in their outer energy levels, which makes them very reactive. D: Each element in the periodic table has a unique atomic number.

Question 5 A, B, D: Metals tend to be shiny, malleable, and reactive, although as you move right on the periodic table, they become less reactive. Nonmetals tend to be hard, brittle, and nonconductive. C: Correct.

7. How are the elements in the periodic table arranged?

A. by their atomic mass

B. by their chemical symbol

C. by their chemical name

D. by their atomic number

Use the graph below to answer question 8.

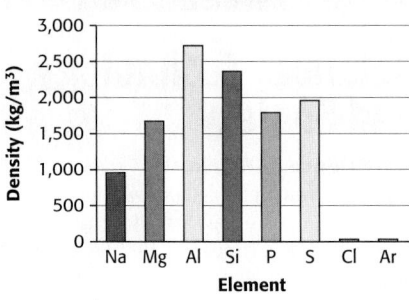

Density of Elements in the Second Period

8. The graph above shows the densities in kilograms per cubic meter (kg/m^3) of the elements in Period 2 of the periodic table. The densities of the elements of Period 3 follow this trend. Which of the following elements is most likely to have a lower density than calcium (Ca) has?

A. gallium (Ga)

B. germanium (Ge)

C. potassium (K)

D. selenium (Se)

9. Which of these statements about a group of elements is true?

A. The elements have a wide range of properties.

B. The elements have the same atomic number.

C. The elements have similar properties.

D. The elements have the same mass number.

10. According to its location on the periodic table, sodium can be described as

A. an alkaline-earth metal.

B. a transition metal.

C. an alkali metal.

D. a metalloid.

Open Response

11. The element hydrogen is usually placed at the top of Group 1 in the periodic table. However, hydrogen is not always considered to be a member of Group 1. Explain why hydrogen is placed in Group 1 and what properties set hydrogen apart from Group 1.

12. The elements in the periodic table can be classified into metals, nonmetals, and metalloids. Describe the properties of these classes, and explain where the elements that fall into these classes can be found on the periodic table.

Standardized Test Preparation

Question 10 A: Sodium is an alkali metal, located in Group 1 of the periodic table. Alkaline-earth metals are located in Group 2 of the periodic table. B: Transition metals are located in Groups 3–12. C: Correct. D: Metalloids are not located in one Group but border the zigzag line in the table.

Question 11 Full-credit answers should include the following points:

- The elements in Group 1 have one electron in their outermost energy level. Hydrogen also has one electron in its outermost level, so it is placed in Group 1.

- Hydrogen differs from the other elements in Group 1 because it is a nonmetal gas. The other elements in Group 1 are all solid metals.

Question 12 Full-credit answers should include the following points:

- Metals are shiny, malleable, ductile, and good conductors of thermal energy. Most metals have few electrons in their outermost energy levels, and are solid at room temperature.

- Metals are found to the left of the zigzag line in the periodic table.

- Nonmetals are not malleable or ductile, are dull (not shiny), and are poor conductors of thermal energy. Nonmetals have either a complete set of electrons in their outermost level or have an almost complete set of electrons. More than half of nonmetals are gases at room temperature.

- Nonmetals are found to the right of the zigzag line in the periodic table.

- Metalloids have some properties of metals and some properties of non-metals. Metalloids have about half of a complete set of electrons in their outermost energy level. Metalloids are solids at room temperature.

- Metalloids are the elements that border the zigzag line on the periodic table.

Question 6 A: Halogens are nonmetals that are not shiny and do not conduct electricity well. B: Metals are shiny and conduct electricity, but metals are malleable, not brittle. C: Nonmetals are not shiny and do not conduct electricity well. D: Correct.

Question 7 A, B, C: The elements in the modern periodic table are arranged according to their atomic numbers. Early versions of the periodic table were arranged by atomic mass. D: Correct.

Question 8 A, B, D: The graph shows that aluminum, silicon, and sulfur have higher densities than magnesium has. Magnesium is in the same group as calcium, aluminum is in the same group as gallium, silicon is in the same group as germanium, and sulfur is in the same group as selenium. Because the densities of the elements in Period 2 and Period 3 follow the same trend, students should conclude that gallium, germanium, and sulfur have higher densities than calcium has. C: Correct.

Question 9 A: Elements within a group have similar physical and chemical properties. B: Different elements do not have the same atomic number. C: Correct. D: Different elements do not have the same mass number.

Weird Science

Background

The hexagons and pentagons of Buckminster Fuller's geodesic domes provide great stability because they distribute stress evenly. The buckyball, C_{60}, is one member of a large family of carbon "cages" called *fullerenes*. Fullerenes that have fewer than 60 carbon atoms are called *buckybabies*. Buckytubes have more than 60 carbon atoms and are shaped like cylinders of spiraling honeycombs.

Scientists know that high temperatures are needed to form buckyballs, so they look for buckyballs in intensely heated sites, such as asteroid craters and lightning strikes. Buckyball molecules are found in greatest abundance in soot.

Science, Technology, and Society

Background

The colors in a fireworks display depend on the wavelengths of the light emitted by different chemicals. Light that has the shortest wavelength appears violet in color. Light that has the longest wavelength appears red. Refer to the chart at the bottom of the page for the colors produced by various elements. Charcoal gives the fireworks a sparkling, flaming tail.

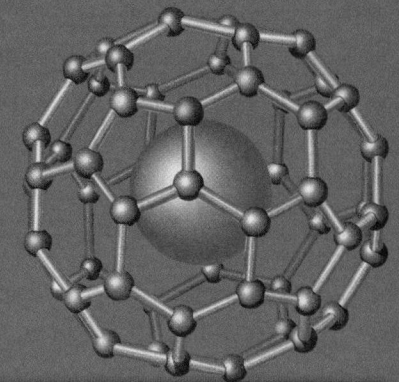

Weird Science

Buckyballs

In 1985, scientists found a completely new kind of molecule! This carbon molecule has 60 carbon atoms linked together in a shape similar to that of a soccer ball. This molecule is called a buckyball. Buckyballs have also been found in the soot from candle flames. And some scientists claim to have detected buckyballs in space. Chemists have been trying to identify the molecules' properties. One property is that a buckyball can act like a cage and hold smaller substances, such as individual atoms. Buckyballs are both slippery and strong. Scientists are exploring their use in tough plastics and cutting tools.

Language Arts ACTIVITY

WRITING SKILL Imagine that you are trapped within a buckyball. Write a one-page short story describing your experience. Describe the windows in your molecular prison.

Science, Technology, and Society

The Science of Fireworks

Explosive and dazzling, a fireworks display is both a science and an art. More than 1,000 years ago, the Chinese made black powder, or gunpowder. The powder was used to set off firecrackers and primitive missiles. The shells of fireworks contain several different chemicals. Black powder at the bottom of the shell launches the shell into the sky. A second layer of black powder ignites the rest of the chemicals and causes an explosion that lights up the sky! Colors can be created by mixing chemicals such as strontium (for red), magnesium (for white), or copper (for blue) with the gunpowder.

Math ACTIVITY

Fireworks can cost between $200 and $2,000 each. If a show uses 20 fireworks that cost $200 each, 12 fireworks that cost $500 each, and 10 fireworks that cost $1,200 each, what is the total cost for the fireworks?

Element	Color
Sodium	yellow
Barium	green
Copper	blue
Strontium	red
Lithium	bright red
Calcium	dark red
Magnesium	white

Answer to Language Arts Activity

The shapes of the windows are pentagons and hexagons. Each pentagon is surrounded by five hexagons.

Answer to Math Activity

Students should be aware that a fireworks display is costly. The cost of the display is $(20 \times \$200) + (12 \times \$500) + (10 \times \$1200) = \$22,000$.

Glenn T. Seaborg

Making Elements When you look at the periodic table, you can thank Dr. Glenn Theodore Seaborg and his colleagues for many of the actinide elements. While working at the University of California at Berkeley, Seaborg and his team added a number of elements to the periodic table. His work in identifying properties of plutonium led to his working on the top-secret Manhattan Project at the University of Chicago. He was outspoken about the beneficial uses of atomic energy and, at the same time, opposed the production and use of nuclear weapons.

Seaborg's revision of the layout of the periodic table—the actinide concept—is the most significant since Mendeleev's original design. For his scientific achievements, Dr. Seaborg was awarded the 1951 Nobel Prize in Chemistry jointly with his colleague, Dr. Edwin M. McMillan. Element 106, which Seaborg neither discovered nor created, was named seaborgium in his honor. This was the first time an element had been named after a living person.

Social Studies ACTIVITY

WRITING SKILL Write a newspaper editorial to express an opinion for or against the Manhattan Project. Be sure to include information to support your view.

go.hrw.com

To learn more about these Science in Action topics, visit **go.hrw.com** and type in the keyword **HP5PRTF**.

Current Science

Check out Current Science® articles related to this chapter by visiting **go.hrw.com**. Just type in the keyword **HP5CS12**.

Teaching Strategy—GENERAL

Show students that each element produces a certain color. Obtain samples of calcium chloride, strontium chloride, and sodium chloride. To prepare 0.5 M solutions, dissolve the following quantities in separate containers with enough water to make 100 mL of each solution: 5.5 g $CaCl_2$, 8.83 g $SrCl_2 \cdot H_2O$, and 2.9 g NaCl. Dip a different wooden splint in each solution, and use tongs to insert each splint into the flame of a portable burner to burn the chemical from the splint. Try not to ignite the splints. The splints can be dipped into the solutions again if necessary.

People in Science

Background

Seaborg was greatly influenced by his teachers, beginning with his high school science instructor, Dwight L. Reid. When Seaborg was a graduate student at the University of California, Berkeley, his instructors included several eminent scientists, such as Gilbert N. Lewis, Axel R. Olson, William F. Giauque, and J. Robert Oppenheimer. Dr. Seaborg was a strong proponent of education. He was committed to science education and to the creation of a scientifically literate society.

Answer to Social Studies Activity

The editorials written by students should convey a strong opinion either for or against the Manhattan Project and should incorporate information found through research to support that opinion. Students should not simply report the information that they find.

Big Idea:
Structure and
Transformation of Matter

A basic understanding of matter is important for understanding more complex ideas in science. In this unit, students will learn about physical and chemical changes in matter and begin to relate these changes to the smallest particles of matter—atoms and molecules. The use of models is an effective way to learn about the structure of matter, provided that students understand the limitations of models. Identifying patterns in the properties of matter is critical when comparing and explaining the differences in matter.

The chapters in this unit describe the ways that the structure of substances can be transformed in the formation of new substances. In **Chemical Bonding**, students will learn the structure of molecules and how that structure is responsible for the different kinds of chemical bonds that form. **Chemical Reactions** describes how molecules are able to transform from one substance into another by breaking and forming bonds. **Chemical Compounds** shows the classification of compounds based on the type of bonds present. The last chapter in this unit, **Atomic Energy**, describes the transformations which occur to the internal structure of atoms to form different kinds atoms.

UNIT
6

TIMELINE

Interactions of Matter

In this unit you will study the interactions through which matter can change its identity. You will learn how atoms bond with one another to form compounds and how atoms join in different combinations to form new substances through chemical reactions. You will also learn about the properties of several categories of compounds. Finally, you will learn how nuclear interactions can actually change the identity of an atom. This timeline includes some of the events leading to the current understanding of these interactions of matter.

1828
Urea, a compound found in urine, is produced in a laboratory. Until this time, chemists had believed that compounds created by living organisms could not be produced in the laboratory.

1858
German chemist Friedrich August Kekulé suggests that carbon forms four chemical bonds and can form long chains.

1942
The first nuclear chain reaction is carried out in a squash court under the football stadium at the University of Chicago.

1979
Public fear about nuclear power grows after an accident occurs at the Three Mile Island nuclear power station located in Pennsylvania.

1867

Swedish chemist Alfred Nobel develops dynamite. Dynamite's explosive power is a result of the decomposition reaction of nitroglycerin.

1898

The United States defeats Spain in the Spanish-American War.

1903

Marie Curie, Pierre Curie, and Henri Becquerel are awarded the Nobel Prize in physics for the discovery of radioactivity.

1964

Dr. Martin Luther King, Jr., American civil rights leader, is awarded the Nobel Peace Prize.

1969

The *Nimbus III* weather satellite is launched by the United States, representing the first civilian use of nuclear batteries.

1996

Evidence of organic compounds in a meteorite leads scientists to speculate that life may have existed on Mars more than 3.6 billion years ago.

2001

The first total solar eclipse of the millenium occurs on June 21.

2002

Hy-wire, the world's first drivable vehicle to combine a hydrogen fuel cell with by-wire technology, is introduced.

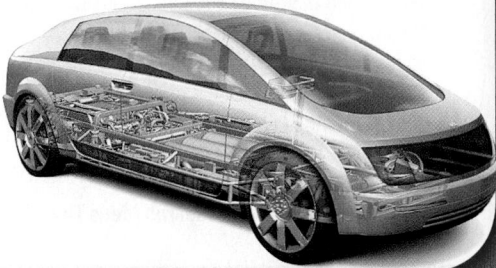

Group ACTIVITY

Structure and Transformation of Matter

MATERIALS

- ammonia, 50 ml
- beaker, 2, 500 ml each
- epsom salts, 70 gr [about 3 Tbls]
- water, 250 ml

Teacher's Note: Initially, students my need some guidance in describing substances in terms of their physical properties. Help students by asking questions about the physical state, color, and other physical properties of the substance.

A Simple Precipitate Demonstration Ask the students to describe the characteristics of the Epsom salts. Dissolve the salt in 250 ml of water. Allow students to observe the beaker. Ask the students to describe the characteristics of the liquid. Ask students to observe the ammonia and describe its characteristics. Carefully and slowly pour the ammonia into the solution prepared in step 2. Lead the students in a discussion about the transformation that occurred in the beaker when the ammonia was added. What happened? What are the properties of the substances in the beaker?

Chemical Bonding
Chapter Planning Guide

Compression guide:
To shorten instruction because of time limitations, omit the Chapter Lab.

OBJECTIVES	LABS, DEMONSTRATIONS, AND ACTIVITIES	TECHNOLOGY RESOURCES
PACING • 90 min pp. 594–599 **Chapter Opener**	**SE** Start-up Activity, p. 595 GENERAL	**OSP** Parent Letter ■ **CD** Student Edition on CD-ROM **CD** Guided Reading Audio CD ■ **TR** Chapter Starter Transparency* **VID** Brain Food Video Quiz
Section 1 Electrons and Chemical Bonding • Describe chemical bonding. • Identify the number of valence electrons in an atom. • Predict whether an atom is likely to form bonds.	**TE** Demonstration Breaking Bonds, p. 596 GENERAL **SE** Science in Action Math, Social Studies, and Language Arts Activities, pp. 616–617 GENERAL	**OSP** Lesson Plans (also in print) **TR** Bellringer Transparency* **TR** P50 Electron Arrangement in an Atom* **TR** P110 Determining the Number of Valence Electrons*
PACING • 45 min pp. 600–603 **Section 2 Ionic Bonds** • Explain how ionic bonds form. • Describe how positive ions form. • Describe how negative ions form. • Explain why ionic compounds are neutral.	**SE** School-to-Home Activity Studying Salt, p. 601 GENERAL	**OSP** Lesson Plans (also in print) **TR** Bellringer Transparency* **TR** P52 Forming Positive and Negative Ions* **CRF** SciLinks Activity* GENERAL
PACING • 90 min pp. 604–609 **Section 3 Covalent and Metallic Bonds** • Explain how covalent bonds form. • Describe molecules. • Explain how metallic bonds form. • Describe the properties of metals.	**TE** Activity Cereal-Dot Diagrams, p. 604 GENERAL **TE** Activity Hydrogen Bonds, p. 605 ADVANCED **TE** Making Models Gumdrop Models, p. 605 GENERAL **TE** Activity Drawing Diagrams, p. 606 GENERAL **SE** Connection to Biology Proteins, p. 607 GENERAL **TE** Connection Activity Art, p. 607 GENERAL **SE** Quick Lab Bending with Bonds, p. 608 GENERAL **CRF** Datasheet for Quick Lab* **SE** Model-Making Lab Covalent Marshmallows, p. 610 GENERAL **CRF** Datasheet for Chapter Lab* **LB** Long-Term Projects & Research Ideas The Wonders of Water* ADVANCED	**OSP** Lesson Plans (also in print) **TR** Bellringer Transparency* **TR** P53 Covalent Bond* **TR** P54 Covalent Bonds in a Water Molecule* **TR** *LINK TO LIFE SCIENCE* L19 The Making of a Protein A; L20 The Making of a Protein: B* **SE** Internet Activity, p. 606 GENERAL **VID** Lab Videos for Physical Science

PACING • 90 min

CHAPTER REVIEW, ASSESSMENT, AND STANDARDIZED TEST PREPARATION

CRF Vocabulary Activity* GENERAL
SE Chapter Review, pp. 612–613 GENERAL
CRF Chapter Review* ■ GENERAL
CRF Chapter Tests A* ■ GENERAL, B* ADVANCED, C* SPECIAL NEEDS
SE Standardized Test Preparation, pp. 614–615 GENERAL
CRF Standardized Test Preparation* GENERAL
CRF Performance-Based Assessment* GENERAL
OSP Test Generator, Test Item Listing

Online and Technology Resources

 Holt Online Learning

Visit **go.hrw.com** for access to Holt Online Learning, or enter the keyword **HS7 Home** for a variety of free online resources.

 One-Stop Planner® CD-ROM

This CD-ROM package includes:
• Lab Materials QuickList Software
• Holt Calendar Planner
• Customizable Lesson Plans
• Printable Worksheets

• ExamView® Test Generator
• Interactive Teacher's Edition
• Holt PuzzlePro®
• Holt PowerPoint® Resources

SKILLS DEVELOPMENT RESOURCES	SECTION REVIEW AND ASSESSMENT	CORRELATIONS
SE Pre-Reading Activity, p. 594 `GENERAL` **OSP** Science Puzzlers, Twisters & Teasers* `GENERAL`		**National Science Education Standards** SAI 1; PS 1b
CRF Directed Reading A* ■ `BASIC`, B* `SPECIAL NEEDS` **WB** Workbook* `Struggling Readers` **CRF** Vocabulary and Section Summary* ■ `GENERAL` **SE** Reading Strategy Discussion, p. 596 `GENERAL` **TE** Support for English Language Learners, p. 597 **SE** Connection to Social Studies History of a Noble Gas, p. 598 `GENERAL` **TE** Inclusion Strategies, p. 598	**SE** Reading Checks, pp. 597, 598 `GENERAL` **TE** Reteaching, p. 598 `BASIC` **TE** Quiz, p. 598 `GENERAL` **TE** Alternative Assessment, p. 598 `GENERAL` **SE** Section Review,* p. 599 ■ `GENERAL` **CRF** Section Quiz* ■ `GENERAL`	UCP 1, 2; PS 1b, 1c
CRF Directed Reading A* ■ `BASIC`, B* `SPECIAL NEEDS` **WB** Workbook* `Struggling Readers` **CRF** Vocabulary and Section Summary* ■ `GENERAL` **SE** Reading Strategy Paired Summarizing, p. 600 `GENERAL` **TE** Support for English Language Learners, p. 601 **SE** Math Practice Calculating Charge, p. 602 `GENERAL` **TE** Inclusion Strategies, p. 602 **MS** Math Skills for Science Comparing Integers on a Number Line* `GENERAL` **MS** Math Skills for Science Arithmetic with Positive and Negative Numbers* `GENERAL` **CRF** Reinforcement Worksheet Is It an Ion?* `BASIC`	**SE** Reading Checks, pp. 600, 602 `GENERAL` **TE** Reteaching, p. 602 `BASIC` **TE** Quiz, p. 602 `GENERAL` **TE** Alternative Assessment, p. 602 `GENERAL` **SE** Section Review,* p. 603 ■ `GENERAL` **CRF** Section Quiz* ■ `GENERAL`	UCP 1, 2, 3; PS 1b, 3a, 3e
CRF Directed Reading A* ■ `BASIC`, B* `SPECIAL NEEDS` **WB** Workbook* `Struggling Readers` **CRF** Vocabulary and Section Summary* ■ `GENERAL` **SE** Reading Strategy Reading Organizer, p. 604 `GENERAL` **TE** Support for English Language Learners, p. 607 **CRF** Reinforcement Worksheet Interview with an Electron* `BASIC` **CRF** Critical Thinking The Road to Knowledge* `ADVANCED`	**SE** Reading Checks, pp. 604, 606, 608 `GENERAL` **TE** Homework, p. 607 `GENERAL` **TE** Reteaching, p. 608 `BASIC` **TE** Quiz, p. 608 `GENERAL` **TE** Alternative Assessment, p. 608 `GENERAL` **SE** Section Review,* p. 609 ■ `GENERAL` **CRF** Section Quiz* ■ `GENERAL`	UCP 1, 2, 3; SAI 1; PS 1b; *Chapter Lab:* UCP 2

SCiLINKS.
NSTA
www.scilinks.org

Maintained by the **National Science Teachers Association.** See Chapter Enrichment pages that follow for a complete list of topics.

Check out *Current Science* articles and activities by visiting the HRW Web site at **go.hrw.com.** Just type in the keyword **HP5CS13T.**

 **Classroom Videos**

- **Lab Videos** demonstrate the chapter lab.
- **Brain Food Video Quizzes** help students review the chapter material.

 Classroom CD-ROMs

- **Guided Reading Audio CD** (Also in Spanish)
- **Interactive Explorations**
- **Virtual Investigations**
- **Visual Concepts**
- **Science Tutor**

Holt Lab Generator CD-ROM

Search for any lab by topic, standard, difficulty level, or time. Edit any lab to fit your needs, or create your own labs. Use the Lab Materials QuickList software to customize your lab materials list.

Visual Resources

CHAPTER STARTER TRANSPARENCY

Chemical Bonding — CHAPTER STARTER

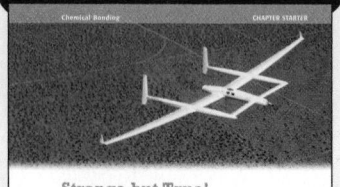

Strange but True!

In 1987, pilots Richard Rutan and Jeana Yeager flew the Voyager aircraft, shown above, around the world without refueling. The record-breaking trip lasted just over 9 days. In order to carry enough fuel for the trip, the plane had to be as lightweight as possible. Using fewer bolts than usual to attach parts would make the airplane lighter. But without the bolts, what would hold the parts together? The designers decided to use glue!

Not just any glue would do. They used superglue. When superglue is applied, it combines with water from the air to form chemical bonds. The result—the materials stick together as if they were one material. Superglue is so strong that the weight of a two-ton elephant cannot separate two metal plates glued together with just a few drops!

Along with household uses, superglue also has uses in industry and medicine. To make shoes stronger and lighter, manufacturers can replace some

of the stitching with superglue. And dentists can use superglue to hold a cracked tooth together.

Chemical bonding is responsible for the properties of materials. In this chapter, you will learn about the different types of bonds that hold atoms together and how those bonds affect the properties of the materials.

Superglue was discovered in the early 1950s by a scientist who was trying to develop a new plastic for the cockpit bubble of a jet plane.

BELLRINGER TRANSPARENCIES

Chemical Bonding — BELLRINGER TRANSPARENCY

Section: Electrons and Chemical Bonding
The following are some very common chemical formulas:

$C_6H_{12}O_6$
C_2H_5OH
$C_3H_8O_3$
$C_9H_8O_4$

Identify the elements in these compounds and predict whether the compounds are similar to each other and why.

Record your answers in your **science journal**.

Section: Ionic Bonds
Historically, salt has had many uses beyond just a spice you put in your soup. Salts are ionic compounds. Brainstorm some uses for salts, things that contain salts, or words and phrases containing the term *salt*. Where do you think salt comes from?

Write your answers in your **science journal**.

TEACHING TRANSPARENCIES

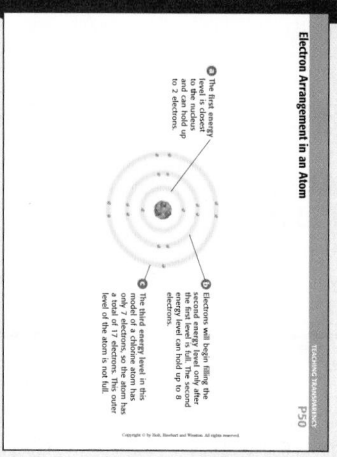

Electron Arrangement in an Atom — P50

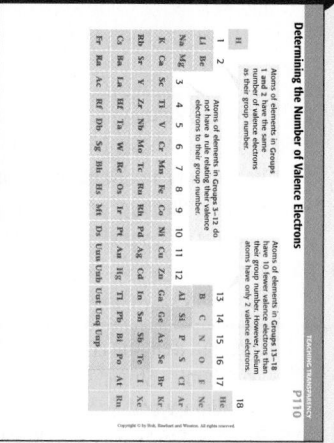

Determining the Number of Valence Electrons — P110

TEACHING TRANSPARENCIES

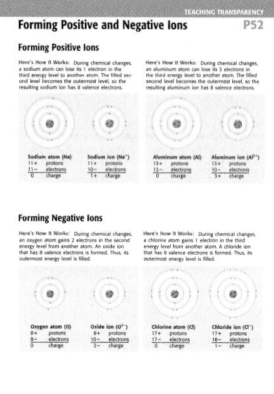

Forming Positive and Negative Ions — P52

Forming Positive Ions

Forming Negative Ions

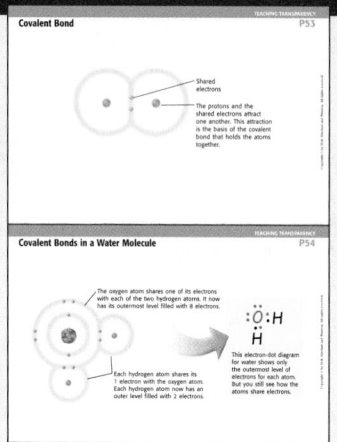

Covalent Bond — P53

Covalent Bonds in a Water Molecule — P54

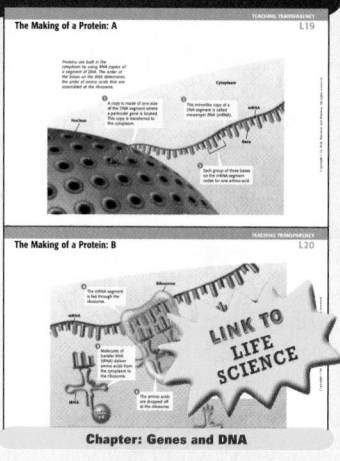

The Making of a Protein: A — L19

The Making of a Protein: B — L20

Chapter: Genes and DNA

CONCEPT MAPPING TRANSPARENCY

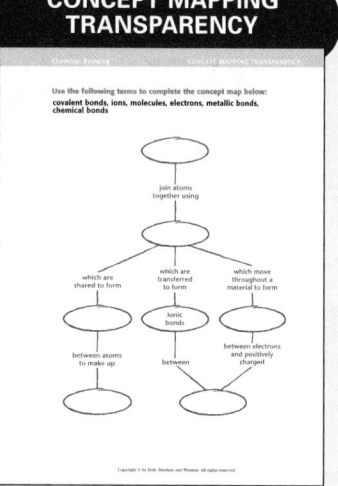

Use the following terms to complete the concept map below:
covalent bonds, ions, molecules, electrons, metallic bonds, chemical bonds

Planning Resources

LESSON PLANS

Lesson Plan — SAMPLE

Section: Waves

Pacing
Regular Schedule: with lab(s):2 days   without lab(s):1 days
Block Schedule: with lab(s): 1 1/2 days   without lab(s):1 day

Objectives
1. Relate the seven properties of life to a living organism.
2. Describe seven themes that can help you to organize what you learn about biology.
3. Identify the tiny structures that make up all living organisms.
4. Differentiate between reproduction and heredity and between metabolism and homeostasis.

National Science Education Standards Covered
LSInter6:Cells have particular structures that underlie their functions.
LSMat1:Most cell functions involve chemical reactions.
LSBeh1:Cells store and use information to guide their functions.
UCP1:Cell functions are regulated.
SI1: Cells can differentiate and form complete multicellular organisms.
PS1: Species evolve over time.
ESS1: The great diversity of organisms is the result of more than 3.5 billion years of evolution.
ESS2: Natural selection and its evolutionary consequences provide a scientific explanation for the fossil record of ancient life forms as well as for the striking molecular similarities observed among the diverse species of living organisms.
ST1: The millions of different species of plants, animals, and microorganisms that live on earth today are related by descent from common ancestors.
ST2: The energy for life primarily comes from the sun.
SPSP1: The complexity and organization of organisms accommodate the need for obtaining, transforming, transporting, releasing, and eliminating the matter and energy used to sustain the organisms.
SPSP6: As matter and energy flows through different levels of organization of living systems—cells, organs, communities—and between living systems and the physical environment, chemical elements are recombined in different ways.
HNS1: Organisms have behavioral responses to internal changes and to external stimuli.

PARENT LETTER

SAMPLE

Dear Parent,

Your son's or daughter's science class will soon begin exploring the chapter entitled "The World of Physical Science." In this chapter, students will learn about how the scientific method applies to the world of physical science and the role of physical science in the world. By the end of the chapter, students should demonstrate a clear understanding of the chapter's main ideas and be able to discuss the following topics:

1. physical science as the study of energy and matter (Section 1)
2. the role of physical science in the world around them (Section 1)
3. careers that rely on physical science (Section 1)
4. the steps used in the scientific method (Section 2)
5. examples of technology (Section 2)
6. how the scientific method is used to answer questions and solve problems (Section 2)
7. how our knowledge of science changes over time (Section 2)
8. how models represent real objects or systems (Section 3)
9. examples of different ways models are used in science (Section 3)
10. the importance of the International System of Units (Section 4)
11. the appropriate units to use for particular measurements (Section 4)
12. how area and density are derived quantities (Section 4)

Questions to Ask Along the Way

You can help your son or daughter learn about these topics by asking interesting questions such as the following:

• What are some surprising careers that use physical science?
• What is a characteristic of a good hypothesis?
• Where is it a good idea to use a model?
• Why do Americans measure things in terms of inches and yards and meters ?

ALSO IN SPANISH

TEST ITEM LISTING

TEST ITEM LISTING
The World of Science   SAMPLE

MULTIPLE CHOICE

1. A limitation of models is that
   a. they are large enough to see.
   b. they do not act exactly like the things that they model.
   c. they are smaller than the things that they model.
   d. they model unfamiliar things.
   Answer: B   Difficulty: 1   Section: 3   Objective: 2

2. The length 10 m is equal to
   a. 100 cm.   c. 10,000 mm.
   b. 1,000 cm.   d. Both (b) and (c)
   Answer: B   Difficulty: 1   Section: 3   Objective: 2

3. To be valid, a hypothesis must be
   a. testable.   c. made into a law.
   b. supported by evidence.   d. Both (a) and (b)
   Answer: D   Difficulty: 1   Section: 2   Objective: 2

4. The statement "Sheila has a stain on her shirt" is an example of a(n)
   a. law.   c. observation.
   b. hypothesis.   d. prediction.
   Answer: C   Difficulty: 1   Section: 2   Objective: 2

5. A hypothesis is often developed out of
   a. observations.   c. experiments.
   b. experiments.   d. Both (a) and (b)
   Answer: D   Difficulty: 1   Section: 2   Objective: 2

6. How many milliliters are in 3.5 kL?
   a. 3,500 mL   c. 3,500, 000 mL
   b. 0.0035 mL   d. 35,000 mL
   Answer: B   Difficulty: 1   Section: 3   Objective: 2

7. A map of beetle is an example of a
   a. law.   c. model.
   b. theory.   d. unit.
   Answer: C   Difficulty: 1   Section: 3   Objective: 2

8. A lab has the safety icons shown below. These icons mean that you should wear
   a. safety goggles.   c. safety goggles and a lab apron.
   b. only a lab apron. d. safety goggles, a lab apron, and gloves.
   Answer: B   Difficulty: 1   Section: 1   Objective: 2

9. The law of conservation of mass says the tot al mass before a chemical change is
   a. more than the total mass after the change.
   b. less than the total mass after the change.
   c. the same as the total mass after the change.
   d. not the same as the total mass after the change.
   Answer: B   Difficulty: 1   Section: 1   Objective: 2

10. In which of the following areas might you find a geochemist at work?
    a. studying the chemistry of rocks   c. studying fishes
    b. studying forestry   d. studying the atmosphere
    Answer: B   Difficulty: 1   Section: 1   Objective: 2

One-Stop Planner® CD-ROM

This CD-ROM includes all of the resources shown here and the following time-saving tools:

• Lab Materials QuickList Software
• Customizable lesson plans
• Holt Calendar Planner
• The powerful ExamView® Test Generator

Meeting Individual Needs

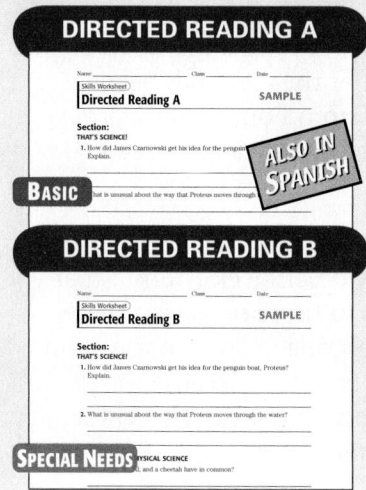

DIRECTED READING A

Skills Worksheet
Directed Reading A — SAMPLE

Section:
THAT'S SCIENCE!

1. How did James Czarnowski get his idea for the penguin boat, Proteus? Explain.

ALSO IN SPANISH

BASIC

DIRECTED READING B

Skills Worksheet
Directed Reading B — SAMPLE

Section:
THAT'S SCIENCE!

1. How did James Czarnowski get his idea for the penguin boat, Proteus? Explain.

2. What is unusual about the way that Proteus moves through the water?

SPECIAL NEEDS

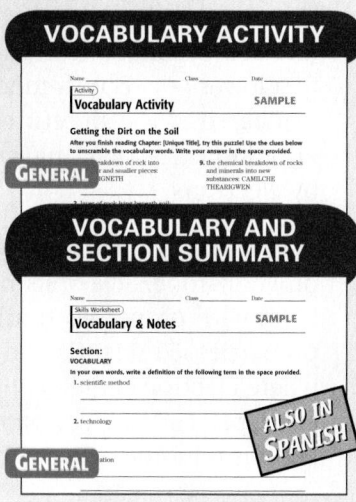

VOCABULARY ACTIVITY

Skills Worksheet
Vocabulary Activity — SAMPLE

Getting the Dirt on the Soil

Complete this reading Chapter: [Unique Title]. try this puzzle! Use the clues below to unscramble the vocabulary words. Write your answer in the space provided.

9. the chemical breakdown of rocks and minerals into new substances CAMELCHE THEAREGWEN

GENERAL

VOCABULARY AND SECTION SUMMARY

Skills Worksheet
Vocabulary & Notes — SAMPLE

Section:
VOCABULARY
In your own words, write a definition of the following term in the space provided.

1. scientific method

2. technology

ALSO IN SPANISH

GENERAL

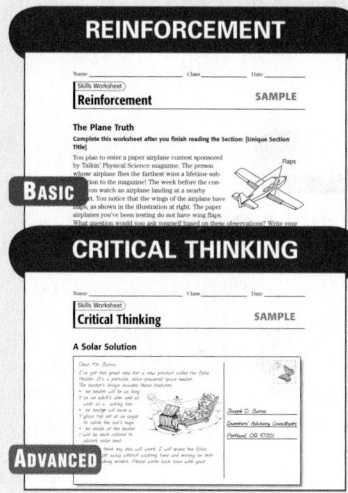

REINFORCEMENT

Skills Worksheet
Reinforcement — SAMPLE

The Plane Truth

Complete this worksheet after you finish reading the Section: [Unique Section Title]

You plan to enter a paper airplane contest sponsored by Talkin' Physical Science magazine. The person whose airplane flies the farthest wins a lifetime subscription to the magazine! The week before the contest you work on making an airplane landing at a nearby airport. You notice that the wings of the airplane have flaps, as shown in the illustration at right. The paper airplanes you've been testing do not have any flaps. What question would you ask yourself based on these observations? Write your...

BASIC

CRITICAL THINKING

Skills Worksheet
Critical Thinking — SAMPLE

A Solar Solution

Dear Mr. Burns,

[handwritten letter text]

Joseph D. Burns
Inventors' Advisory Consultants
Portland, OR 97201

ADVANCED

SCILINKS ACTIVITY

Activity
SciLinks Activity — SAMPLE

MARINE ECOSYSTEMS
Go to www.scilinks.com. To find links related to marine ecosystems, type in the keyword at right. Then, use the links to answer the questions.

percentage of the Earth's surface is covered by water?

GENERAL

SCIENCE PUZZLERS, TWISTERS & TEASERS

CHAPTER
13 — SCIENCE PUZZLERS, TWISTERS & TEASERS
Chemical Bonding

Dancing Elements

1. A number of elements from the periodic table have shown up at the spring dance, and they are looking for dance partners. Their chemical identities are hidden in the first two letters of their names. Whether two elements will make good dance partners depends on the number of valence electrons they have. Examine the situations below and answer the questions.

a. Nadine and Clark have sat at opposite ends of the table in science class since sixth grade. Clark thinks Nadine is cute, so he moves in closer. Will Nadine and Clark make good dance partners? Explain. If they could dance together, what type of bond would they form?

GENERAL

Labs and Activities

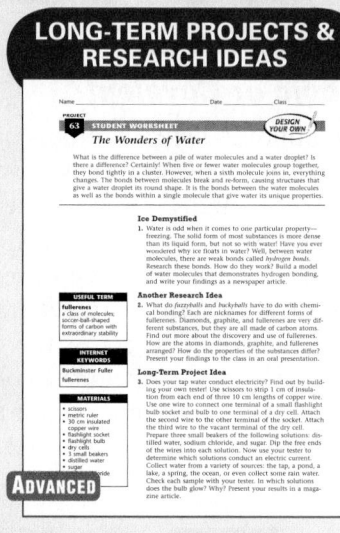

LONG-TERM PROJECTS & RESEARCH IDEAS

PROJECT
6.1 STUDENT WORKSHEET — DESIGN YOUR OWN
The Wonders of Water

What is the difference between a pile of water molecules and a water droplet? Is there a difference? Certainly! When five or fewer water molecules group together, they bond tightly in a cluster. However, when a sixth molecule joins in, everything changes. The bonds between molecules break and re-form, causing structures that give a water droplet its round shape. It is the bonds between the water molecules as well as the bonds within a single molecule that give water its unique properties.

Ice Demystified

1. Water is odd when it comes to one particular property—freezing. The solid form of most substances is more dense than its liquid form, but not so with water! Have you ever wondered why ice floats in water? Well, between water molecules, there are weak bonds called hydrogen bonds. Research these bonds. How do they work? Build a model of water molecules that demonstrates hydrogen bonding, and write your findings as a newspaper article.

USEFUL TERM
fullerenes
a class of molecules, soccer-ball-shaped forms of carbon with extraordinary stability

INTERNET KEYWORDS
Buckminster Fuller
fullerenes

MATERIALS
• scissors
• metric ruler
• 30 cm insulated copper wire
• flashlight socket
• flashlight bulb
• dry cells
• 3 small beakers
• distilled water
• sugar

Another Research Idea

2. What do fuzzyballs and buckyballs have to do with chemical bonding? Each are nicknames for different forms of fullerenes. Diamonds, graphite, and fullerenes are very different substances, but they are all made of carbon atoms. Find out more about the discovery and use of fullerenes. How are the atoms in diamonds, graphite, and fullerenes arranged? How do the properties of the substances differ? Present your findings to the class in an oral presentation.

Long-Term Project Idea

3. Does your tap water conduct electricity? Find out by building your own tester! Use scissors to strip 1 cm of insulation from each end of three 10 cm lengths of copper wire. Use one wire to connect one terminal of a small flashlight bulb socket and bulb to one terminal of a dry cell. Attach the second wire to the other terminal of the dry cell. Prepare three small beakers of the following solutions: distilled water, sodium chloride, and sugar. Dip the free ends of the wires into each solution. Now use your tester to determine which solutions conduct an electric current. Collect water from a variety of sources: the tap, a pond, a lake, a spring, the ocean, or even collect some rain water. Check each sample with your tester. In which solutions does the bulb glow? Why? Present your results in a magazine article.

ADVANCED

DATASHEETS FOR QUICK LABS

TEACHER RESOURCE PAGE
Quick Lab — DATASHEET FOR QUICK LAB
Reaction to Stress — SAMPLE

Background
The graph below illustrates changes that occur in the membrane potential of a neuron during an action potential. Use the graph to answer the following questions. Refer to Figure 3 as needed.

DATASHEETS FOR CHAPTER LABS

TEACHER RESOURCE PAGE
Skills Practice Lab — DATASHEET FOR CHAPTER LAB
Using Scientific Methods — SAMPLE

Teacher's Notes
TIME REQUIRED
One 45-minute class period.

DATASHEETS FOR LABBOOK

TEACHER RESOURCE PAGE
Skills Practice Lab — DATASHEET FOR LABBOOK LAB
Does It All Add Up? — SAMPLE

Teacher's Notes
TIME REQUIRED
One 45-minute class period.

Review and Assessments

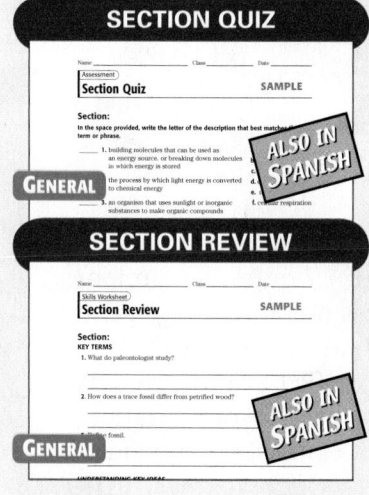

SECTION QUIZ

Assessment
Section Quiz — SAMPLE

Section:
In the space provided, write the letter of the description that best matches the term or phrase.

____ 1. building molecules that can be used as an energy source, or breaking down molecules in which energy is stored
____ 2. the process by which light energy is converted to chemical energy
____ 3. an organism that uses sunlight or inorganic substances to make organic compounds

ALSO IN SPANISH

GENERAL

SECTION REVIEW

Skills Worksheet
Section Review — SAMPLE

Section:
KEY TERMS
1. What do paleontologist study?

2. How does a trace fossil differ from petrified wood?

ALSO IN SPANISH

GENERAL

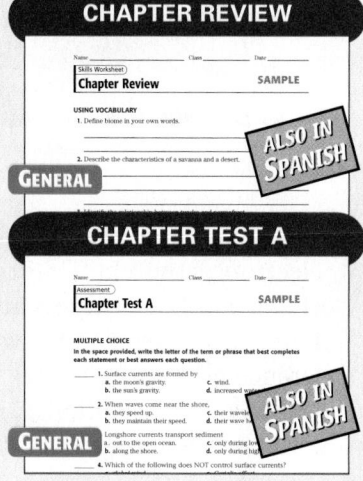

CHAPTER REVIEW

Skills Worksheet
Chapter Review — SAMPLE

USING VOCABULARY
1. Define biome in your own words.

2. Describe the characteristics of a savanna and a desert.

ALSO IN SPANISH

GENERAL

CHAPTER TEST A

Assessment
Chapter Test A — SAMPLE

MULTIPLE CHOICE
In the space provided, write the letter of the term or phrase that best completes each statement or best answers each question.

____ 1. Surface currents are formed by
a. the moon's gravity.   c. wind.
b. the sun's gravity.   d. increased water density.

____ 2. When waves come near the shore,
a. they speed up.   c. their wavelength increases.
b. they maintain their speed. d. their wave height increases.

Longshore currents transport sediment
a. out to the open ocean.
b. along the shore.

____ 3. Which of the following does NOT control surface currents?

ALSO IN SPANISH

GENERAL

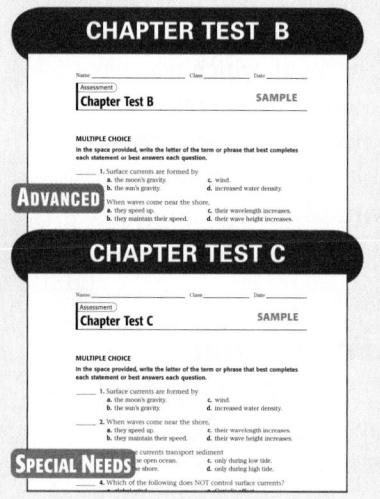

CHAPTER TEST B

Assessment
Chapter Test B — SAMPLE

MULTIPLE CHOICE
In the space provided, write the letter of the term or phrase that best completes each statement or best answers each question.

____ 1. Surface currents are formed by
a. the moon's gravity.   c. wind.
b. the sun's gravity.   d. increased water density.

____ 2. When waves come near the shore,
a. they speed up.   c. their wave height increases.
b. they maintain their speed. d. their wave height increases.

ADVANCED

CHAPTER TEST C

Assessment
Chapter Test C — SAMPLE

MULTIPLE CHOICE
In the space provided, write the letter of the term or phrase that best completes each statement or best answers each question.

____ 1. Surface currents are formed by
a. the moon's gravity.   c. wind.
b. the sun's gravity.   d. increased water density.

____ 2. When waves come near the shore,
a. they speed up.   c. their wave height increases.
b. they maintain their speed. d. their wave height increases.

currents transport sediment
a. the open ocean.   c. only during low tide.
b. the shore.   d. only during high tide.

____ 4. Which of the following does NOT control surface currents?

SPECIAL NEEDS

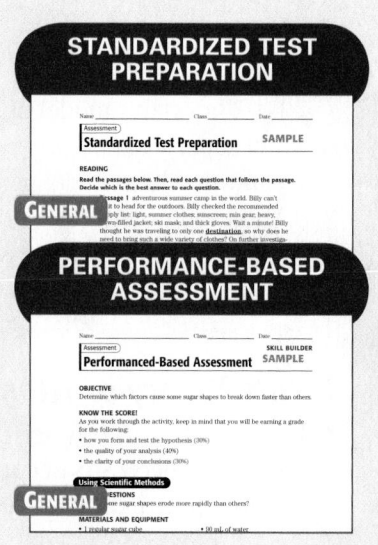

STANDARDIZED TEST PREPARATION

Assessment
Standardized Test Preparation — SAMPLE

READING
Read the passages below. Then, read each question that follows the passage. Decide which is the best answer to each question.

Passage 1 adventurous summer camp in the world. Billy can't wait to head for the outdoors. Billy checked the recommended supply list: light, summer clothes; sunscreen; rain gear; heavy, two-filled jacket; ski mask; and thick gloves. Wait a minute! Billy thought he was traveling to only one destination, so why does he need to bring such a variety of clothes? On further investigation...

GENERAL

PERFORMANCE-BASED ASSESSMENT

Assessment
Performanced-Based Assessment — SKILL BUILDER — SAMPLE

OBJECTIVE
Determine which factors cause some sugar shapes to break down faster than others

KNOW THE SCORE!
As you work through the activity, keep in mind that you will be earning a grade for the following:
• how you form and test the hypothesis (30%)
• the quality of your analysis (40%)
• the clarity of your conclusions (30%)

Using Scientific Methods
QUESTIONS

MATERIALS AND EQUIPMENT
• 1 regular sugar cube   • 90 mL of water

GENERAL

This Chapter Enrichment provides relevant and interesting information to expand and enhance your presentation of the chapter material.

Section 1

Electrons and Chemical Bonding
Discovery of the Electron

- Electrons are important in all types of chemical bonding. English physicist Joseph John Thomson (1856–1940) discovered the electron in 1897 when studying cathode rays. Cathode rays are invisible beams emitted from negative electrodes when electrical energy is passed through a vacuum tube.

- Thomson believed that cathode rays were composed of particles of matter that he called *corpuscles*. He also theorized that the corpuscles—later renamed electrons— were negatively charged and were identical, no matter what type of gas or metal carried the electrical energy.

Is That a Fact!
- J. J. Thomson's model of the atom, which was eventually superseded by other models, was dubbed the plum-pudding model because some people visualized Thomson's model as a positively charged sphere of "pudding" interspersed with negatively charged "plums," or electrons.

Bohr's Theory of Atomic Structure

- In 1913, Danish physicist Niels Bohr (1885–1962) theorized that electrons occupy energy levels, which are at certain specified distances from an atom's nucleus.

- Energy is absorbed when an electron moves from a lower energy level to a higher energy level. Energy is released when an electron moves from a higher level to a lower one. Bohr's model of the atom has been compared to the structure of an onion, with the layers of onion corresponding to the energy levels occupied by electrons.

- Bohr's idea of fixed energy levels was eventually proved wrong. Scientists now describe electrons as particles with properties similar to those of waves. These properties led scientists to describe regions in the atom where electrons are likely to be found because the exact path of an electron cannot be predicted. These regions are called *electron clouds*.

Section 2

Ionic Bonds
Ionic or Covalent?

- Bonding between atoms of different elements is rarely purely ionic or purely covalent. Bonding is usually somewhere between these two extremes, depending on how strongly the atoms of each element attract electrons. Electronegativity is a measure of an atom's ability to attract electrons. In general, the electronegativities of atoms increase across the rows of the periodic table and decrease down the columns. The degree to which a bond between atoms of two elements is ionic or covalent can be estimated by calculating the difference in the elements' electronegativities.

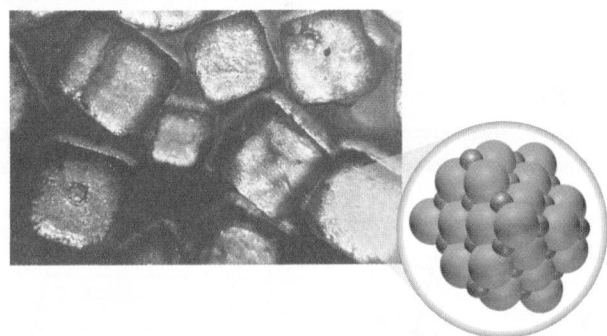

- In general, bonding between atoms with an electronegativity difference of 1.7 or less has an ionic character of 50% or less and is classified as covalent. Bonding between atoms with an electronegativity difference greater than 1.7 is classified as ionic. However, this rule has exceptions, and there are other ways to estimate the ionic or covalent character of a bond.

Section 3

Covalent and Metallic Bonds

G. N. Lewis and the Theory of the Electron Pair

- In the early 1900s, American chemist Gilbert Newton Lewis (1875–1946) noticed that elements with certain numbers of electrons are especially unreactive, and that other elements are highly reactive. Helium, which has 2 electrons, is inert, but hydrogen, which has 1 electron, is reactive. Lewis also noticed that the next nonreactive element on the periodic table, neon, has 8 more electrons than helium does.

- Lewis theorized that atoms have "layers" of electrons and that a specific number of electrons—8 electrons, for example—is required to fill the outermost layer. From this observation came Lewis's "octet rule." The octet rule states that ions or atoms with a filled outermost layer of 8 electrons are stable.

- Lewis published his theory in 1916. It was the first explanation of the covalent bond and went a long way toward explaining the mechanism of many chemical reactions.

- Electron-dot diagrams, often called *Lewis structures,* have helped several generations of chemistry students visualize molecular structures and bonding.

The Unique Bonding Properties of Carbon

- Carbon and carbon compounds are the basis of all living things. Carbon atoms have 4 valence electrons and can combine with other carbon atoms to form molecules with high molecular weight. These large molecules may take many forms, such as rings or long chains.

- Carbon rings can form when carbon atoms bond to other carbon atoms. The carbon compound benzene, C_6H_6, for example, is a hexagonal ring consisting of six carbon atoms bonded to each other with a hydrogen atom bonded to each carbon. The benzene ring is the parent compound of many substances, including aromatics, such as vanilla, perfumes, and mothballs.

- Long chains of repeating molecular units are known as *polymers*. The wide variety of plastics we use, with all of their different physical properties, are examples of polymers. These different properties are the result of the type of repeating unit and the way in which these units are bonded together.

Is That a Fact!

- ◆ To some people, the word *polymer* is synonymous with *plastic*. However, many polymers exist in nature. Cellulose, a polymer chain containing repeating units of the molecule glucose, is the chief constituent of plant cells. Wood is about 50% cellulose, and cotton is 90% cellulose.

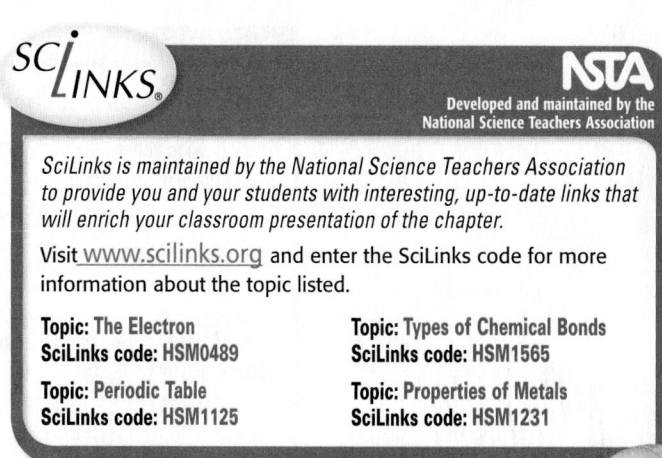

SciLinks is maintained by the National Science Teachers Association to provide you and your students with interesting, up-to-date links that will enrich your classroom presentation of the chapter.

Visit www.scilinks.org and enter the SciLinks code for more information about the topic listed.

Topic: The Electron
SciLinks code: HSM0489

Topic: Periodic Table
SciLinks code: HSM1125

Topic: Types of Chemical Bonds
SciLinks code: HSM1565

Topic: Properties of Metals
SciLinks code: HSM1231

Overview

Tell students that this chapter will help them learn about chemical bonding. The chapter describes how the valence electrons of atoms are involved in forming chemical bonds and describes the three kinds of chemical bonds—ionic, covalent, and metallic.

Assessing Prior Knowledge

Students should be familiar with the following topics:

- the periodic table
- the structure of the atom

Identifying Misconceptions

As students learn the material in this chapter, some of them may think that ionic compounds are made up of molecules of the compounds. Tell students that because ionic compounds form crystal lattices, chemists usually do not refer to molecules when discussing ionic compounds. Instead, chemists refer to the smallest ratio of ions in an ionic compound as a *formula unit*. For example, the chemical formulas of sodium chloride, NaCl, and calcium fluoride, CaF_2, represent one formula unit of each compound.

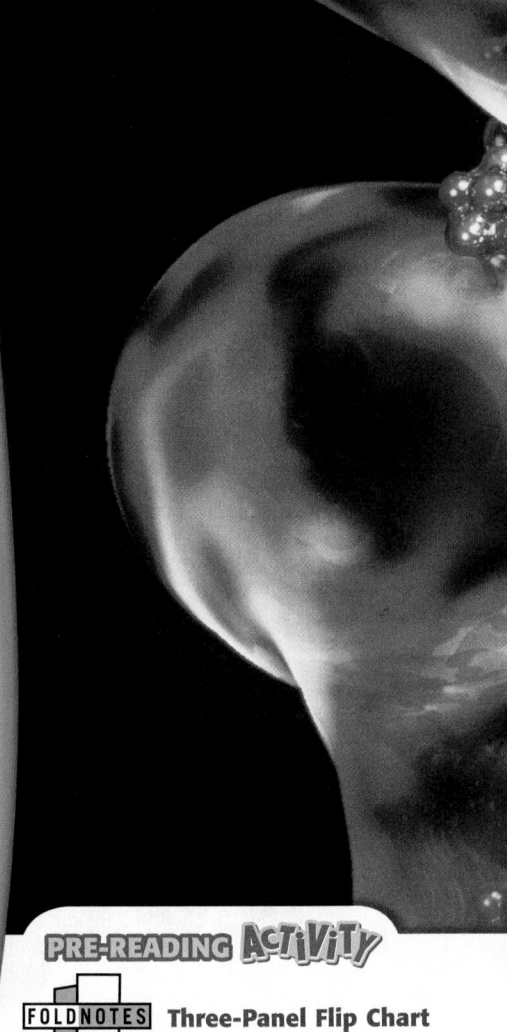

22
Chemical Bonding

The Big Idea
Atoms combine by forming ionic, covalent, and metallic bonds.

About the Photo

What looks like a fantastic "sculpture" is really a model of deoxyribonucleic acid (DNA). DNA is one of the most complex molecules in living things. In DNA, atoms are bonded together in two very long spiral strands. These strands join to form a double spiral. The DNA in living cells has all the coding for passing on the traits of that cell and that organism.

PRE-READING ACTIVITY

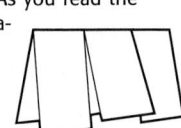

FOLDNOTES **Three-Panel Flip Chart**
Before you read the chapter, create the FoldNote entitled "Three-Panel Flip Chart" described in the **Study Skills** section of the Appendix. Label the flaps of the three-panel flip chart with "Ionic bond," "Covalent bond," and "Metallic bond." As you read the chapter, write information you learn about each category under the appropriate flap.

Standards Correlations

National Science Education Standards

The following codes indicate the National Science Education Standards that correlate to this chapter. The full text of the standards is at the front of the book.

Chapter Opener
SAI 1; PS 1b

Section 1 Electrons and Chemical Bonding
UCP 1, 2; PS 1b, 1c

Section 2 Ionic Bonds
UCP 1, 2, 3; PS 1b, 3a, 3e

Section 3 Covalent and Metallic Bonds
UCP 1, 2, 3; SAI 1; PS 1b

Chapter Lab
UCP 2

Chapter Review
PS 1b

Science in Action
ST 1; SPSP 3, 5; HNS 1

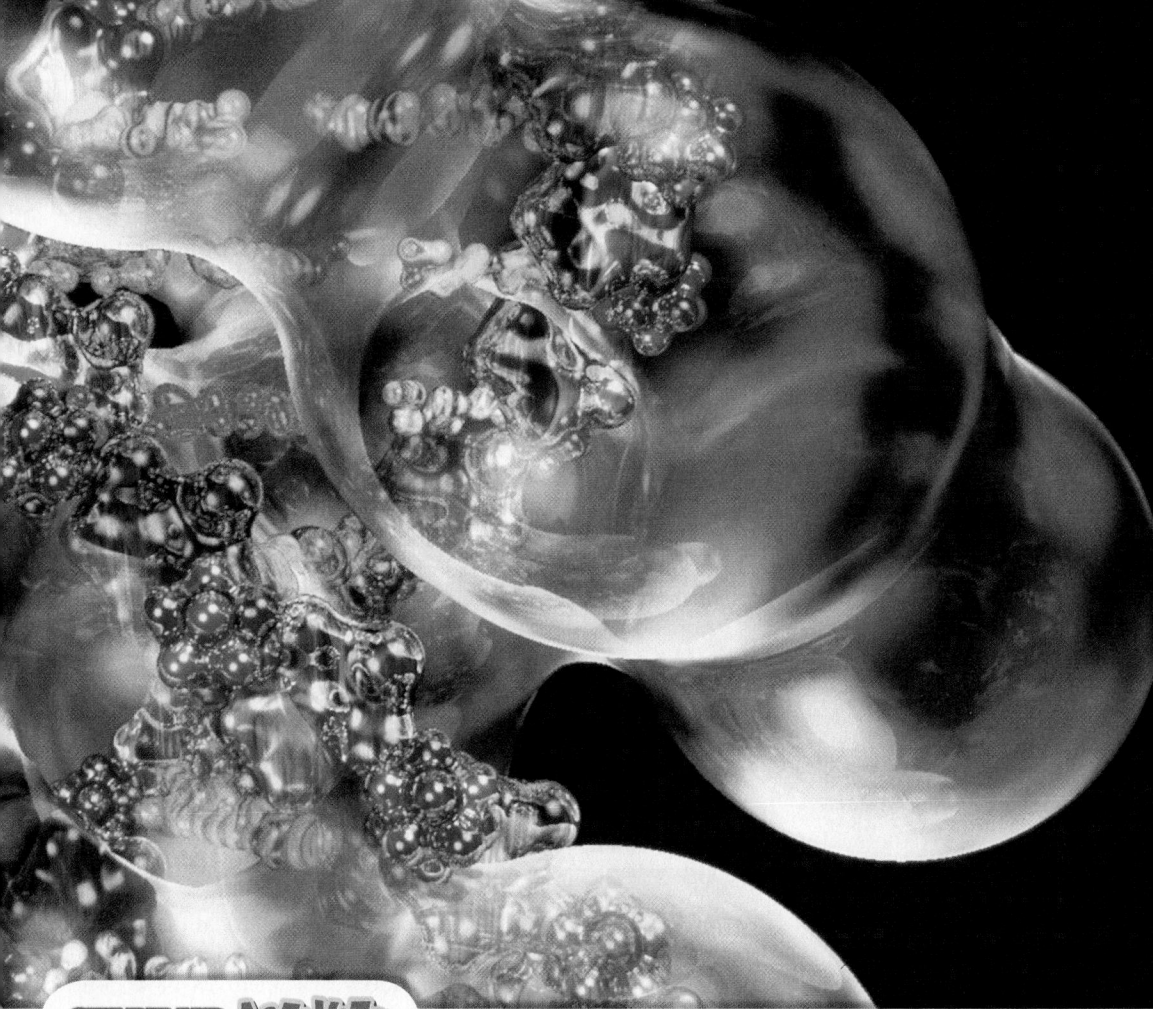

START-UP ACTIVITY

MATERIALS

FOR EACH STUDENT
- borax solution, 40 g/L (100 ml)
- cups, paper (2)
- glue, white (1 : 1 solution of glue and water)
- spoon, plastic (or craft stick, wooden)

Safety Caution: Caution students to wear safety goggles, gloves, and aprons during this lab activity. Caution students to keep their hands away from their eyes and face during this lab activity.

Ingestion of large amounts of borax can cause severe vomiting, diarrhea, and shock. Have the telephone number for your local poison control center available during this activity.

Be sure eyewash equipment is available and is working.

Caution students to wash their hands thoroughly when they are finished with this activity.

Use only nontoxic white glue.

Answers

1. The glue is a white liquid that flows easily. The new material is white and has properties that are more like those of a solid than like those of a liquid.

2. The properties of the material would be more like the properties of the glue. The material would flow more easily and would not hold its shape well.

START-UP ACTIVITY

From Glue to Goop

Particles of glue can bond to other particles and hold objects together. Different types of bonds create differences in the properties of substances. In this activity, you will see how the formation of bonds causes a change in the properties of white glue.

Procedure

1. Fill a **small paper cup** 1/4 full of **white glue.** Record the properties of the glue.

2. Fill a **second small paper cup** 1/4 full of **borax solution.**

3. Pour the borax solution into the cup of white glue, and stir well using a **plastic spoon** or a **wooden craft stick.**

4. When the material becomes too thick to stir, remove it from the cup and knead it with your fingers. Record the properties of the material.

Analysis

1. Compare the properties of the glue with those of the new material.

2. The properties of the material resulted from bonds between the borax and the glue. Predict the properties of the material if less borax is used.

Strange but True!

In 1987, pilots Richard Rutan and Jeana Yeager flew the *Voyager* aircraft, shown above, around the world without refueling. The record-breaking trip lasted just over 9 days. In order to carry enough fuel for the trip, the plane had to be as lightweight as possible. Using fewer bolts than usual to attach parts would make the airplane lighter. But without the bolts, what would hold the parts together? The designers decided to use glue!

Not just any glue would do. They used superglue. When superglue is applied, it combines with water from the air to form chemical bonds. The result—the materials stick together as if they were one material. Superglue is so strong

of the stitching with superglue. And dentists can use superglue to hold a cracked tooth together.

Chemical bonding is responsible for the properties of materials. In this chapter, you will learn about the different types of bonds that hold atoms together and how those bonds affect the properties of the materials.

Superglue was discovered in the early 1950s by a scientist who was trying to develop a new plastic for the cockpit bubble of a jet plane.

Chapter Starter Transparency
Use this transparency to help students begin thinking about chemical bonding.

CHAPTER RESOURCES

Technology

 **Transparencies**
- Chapter Starter Transparency

READING SKILLS

 Student Edition on CD-ROM

Guided Reading Audio CD
- English or Spanish

Classroom Videos
- Brain Food Video Quiz

Workbooks

 Science Puzzlers, Twisters & Teasers
- Chemical Bonding GENERAL

Focus

Overview

This section defines chemical bonding and describes the role of electrons in the formation of chemical bonds.

 Bellringer

Display the following chemical formulas but not their identities:

$C_6H_{12}O_6$ (glucose, a sugar)

C_2H_5OH (ethyl alcohol)

$C_6H_8O_6$ (vitamin C)

$C_6H_8O_7$ (citric acid)

Ask students to identify the elements in these compounds and to predict whether the compounds are similar to each other and why. Identify and discuss the compounds.

Motivate

Demonstration —— GENERAL

Breaking Bonds Heat sugar in a crucible with a Bunsen burner until a black goo remains. Ask students to identify the black goo. (carbon) Ask students to explain why the sugar turned into carbon. (Sugar is composed of carbon, hydrogen, and oxygen. The hydrogen and oxygen combine to form water. The thermal energy evaporates the water.) Explain that the energy broke the chemical bonds that were holding the atoms of the elements together.
LS Visual

What You Will Learn

● Describe chemical bonding.
● Identify the number of valence electrons in an atom.
● Predict whether an atom is likely to form bonds.

Vocabulary

chemical bonding
chemical bond
valence electron

READING STRATEGY

Discussion Read this section silently. Write down questions that you have about this section. Discuss your questions in a small group.

Electrons and Chemical Bonding

Have you ever stopped to consider that by using only the 26 letters of the alphabet, you make all of the words you use every day?

Although the number of letters is limited, combining the letters in different ways allows you to make a huge number of words. In the same way that words can be formed by combining letters, substances can be formed by combining atoms.

Combining Atoms Through Chemical Bonding

Look at **Figure 1.** Now, look around the room. Everything you see—desks, pencils, paper, and even your friends—is made of atoms of elements. All substances are made of atoms of one or more of the approximately 100 elements. For example, the atoms of carbon, hydrogen, and oxygen combine in different patterns to form sugar, alcohol, and citric acid. **Chemical bonding** is the joining of atoms to form new substances. The properties of these new substances are different from the properties of the original elements. An interaction that holds two atoms together is called a **chemical bond.** When chemical bonds form, electrons are shared, gained, or lost.

Discussing Bonding Using Theories and Models

We cannot see atoms and chemical bonds with the unaided eye. For more than 150 years, scientists have done many experiments that have led to a theory of chemical bonding. Remember that a theory is an explanation for some phenomenon that is based on observation, experimentation, and reasoning. The use of models helps people discuss the theory of how and why atoms form bonds.

Figure 1 *Everything you see in this photo is formed by combining atoms.*

SCIENTISTS AT ODDS

Noble Gas Compounds Before 1962, most scientists believed that noble gases could not form compounds with other elements. After all, no noble-gas compounds were known to exist. In that year, though, chemists first created a compound of xenon and fluorine called *xenon tetrafluoride*, XeF_4. Much to their surprise, these chemists found that xenon and fluorine reacted quite easily to form the compound. Under the right conditions, krypton and radon can also form compounds.

Figure 2 Electron Arrangement in an Atom

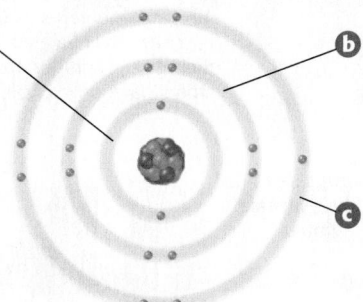

ⓐ The **first energy level** is closest to the nucleus and can hold up to 2 electrons.

ⓑ Electrons will begin filling the **second energy level** only after the first level is full. The second energy level can hold up to 8 electrons.

ⓒ The **third energy level** in this model of a chlorine atom has only 7 electrons, so the atom has a total of 17 electrons. This outer level of the atom is not full.

Electron Number and Organization

To understand how atoms form chemical bonds, you need to know about the electrons in an atom. The number of electrons in an atom can be determined from the atomic number of the element. The *atomic number* is the number of protons in an atom. But atoms have no charge. So, the atomic number also represents the number of electrons in the atom.

Electrons in an atom are organized in energy levels. **Figure 2** shows a model of the arrangement of electrons in a chlorine atom. This model and models like it are useful for counting electrons in energy levels of atoms. But, these models do not show the true structure of atoms.

Outer-Level Electrons and Bonding

Not all of the electrons in an atom make chemical bonds. Most atoms form bonds using only the electrons in the outermost energy level. An electron in the outermost energy level of an atom is a **valence electron** (VAY luhns ee LEK TRAHN). The models in **Figure 3** show the valence electrons for two atoms.

Reading Check Which electrons are used to form bonds?
(*See the Appendix for answers to Reading Checks.*)

chemical bonding the combining of atoms to form molecules or ionic compounds

chemical bond an interaction that holds atoms or ions together

valence electron an electron that is found in the outermost shell of an atom and that determines the atom's chemical properties

Figure 3 Counting Valence Electrons

Oxygen
Electron total: 8
First level: 2 electrons
Second level: 6 electrons

An oxygen atom has 6 valence electrons.

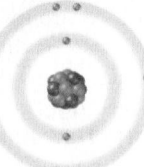

Sodium
Electron total: 11
First level: 2 electrons
Second level: 8 electrons
Third level: 1 electron

A sodium atom has 1 valence electron.

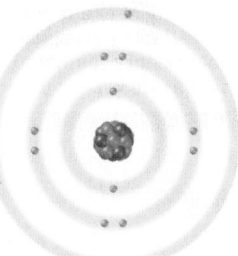

Is That a Fact!

An early theory of chemical bonding was developed by Swedish chemist Jöns Jacob Berzelius (1779–1848). Berzelius theorized that all elements had either a positive or a negative charge and that only positive and negative elements would bond with each other. His theory was widely accepted. In many ways, it is a fairly accurate explanation of ionic bonding. Berzelius's theory fell short, however, by implying that molecules containing more than one atom of the same element could not exist because those atoms would repel each other.

Using the Periodic Table Have students refer to **Figure 4** and answer the following questions:

1. How many valence electrons are there in an atom of radium? of lead? of iodine? of neon? of cesium? (2, 4, 7, 8, 1)

2. Which elements from question 1 would be likely to bond with other atoms? (radium, lead, iodine, cesium)

3. Which element from question 1 would be least likely to bond with other atoms? (neon)

LS Visual/Logical   English Language Learners

Quiz —— GENERAL

1. What is the joining of atoms to form new substances called? (chemical bonding)

2. Why do some atoms rarely bond? (They have a filled outermost energy level with 8 electrons, which makes them very nonreactive.)

Alternative Assessment —— GENERAL

Concept Mapping Have students create a concept map using the following terms: *chemical bonding, chemical bond,* and *valence electron.* Students should include examples of elements from the periodic table to clarify their concept map. **LS** Visual

---

Figure 4	Determining the Number of Valence Electrons

Atoms of elements in **Groups 1 and 2** have the same number of valence electrons as their group number.

Atoms of elements in **Groups 13–18** have 10 fewer valence electrons than their group number. However, helium atoms have only 2 valence electrons.

Atoms of elements in **Groups 3–12** do not have a rule relating their valence electrons to their group number.

CONNECTION TO Social Studies

WRITING SKILL **History of a Noble Gas** When Dmitri Mendeleev organized the first periodic table, he did not include the noble gases. The noble gases had not been discovered at that time. Research the history of the discovery of one of the noble gases. Write a paragraph in your **science journal** to summarize what you learned.

Valence Electrons and the Periodic Table

You can use a model to determine the number of valence electrons of an atom. But what would you do if you didn't have a model? You can use the periodic table to determine the number of valence electrons for atoms of some elements.

Elements are grouped based on similar properties. Within a group, or family, the atoms of each element have the same number of valence electrons. So, the group numbers can help you determine the number of valence electrons for some atoms, as shown in **Figure 4.**

To Bond or Not to Bond

Not all atoms bond in the same manner. In fact, some atoms rarely bond at all! The number of electrons in the outermost energy level of an atom determines whether an atom will form bonds.

Atoms of the noble gases (Group 18) do not usually form chemical bonds. Atoms of Group 18 elements (except helium) have 8 valence electrons. Having 8 valence electrons is a special condition. In fact, atoms that have 8 electrons in their outermost energy level do not usually form bonds. The outermost energy level of an atom is considered to be full if the energy level contains 8 electrons.

✓ Reading Check The atoms of which group in the periodic table rarely form chemical bonds?

INCLUSION Strategies

- *Behavior Control Issues*
- *Attention Deficit Disorder*
- *Gifted and Talented*

Friendly competition makes learning more fun for many students. Give students a chance to understand valence electrons by dividing the students into teams, randomly calling out different elements, and awarding points to the first team that holds up a card with the correct number of valence electrons.
LS Interpersonal

Answer to Reading Check

Atoms in Group 18 (the noble gases) rarely form chemical bonds.

Filling The Outermost Level

An atom that has fewer than 8 valence electrons is much more likely to form bonds than an atom that has 8 valence electrons is. Atoms bond by gaining, losing, or sharing electrons to have a filled outermost energy level. A filled outermost level contains 8 valence electrons. **Figure 5** describes how atoms can achieve a filled outermost energy level.

Is Two Electrons a Full Set?

Not all atoms need 8 valence electrons to have a filled outermost energy level. Helium atoms need only 2 valence electrons. The outermost energy level in a helium atom is the first energy level. The first energy level of any atom can hold only 2 electrons. So, the outermost energy level of a helium atom is full if the energy level has only 2 electrons. Atoms of hydrogen and lithium also form bonds by gaining, losing, or sharing electrons to achieve 2 electrons in the first energy level.

Figure 5 Filling Outermost Energy Levels

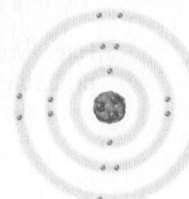

Sulfur
An atom of sulfur has 6 valence electrons. It can have 8 valence electrons by sharing 2 electrons with or gaining 2 electrons from other atoms.

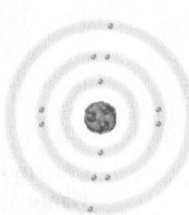

Magnesium
An atom of magnesium has 2 valence electrons. It can have a full outer level by losing 2 electrons. The second energy level becomes the outermost energy level and contains 8 electrons.

SECTION Review

Summary

- Chemical bonding is the joining of atoms to form new substances. A chemical bond is an interaction that holds two atoms together.

- A valence electron is an electron in the outermost energy level of an atom.

- Most atoms form bonds by gaining, losing, or sharing electrons until they have 8 valence electrons. Atoms of some elements need only 2 electrons to fill their outermost level.

Using Key Terms

1. Use the following terms in the same sentence: *chemical bond* and *valence electron*.

Understanding Key Ideas

2. Which of the following atoms do not usually form bonds?
   a. calcium   c. hydrogen
   b. neon   d. oxygen

3. Describe chemical bonding.

4. Explain how to use the valence electrons in an atom to predict if the atom will form bonds.

Critical Thinking

5. **Making Inferences** How can an atom that has 5 valence electrons achieve a full set of valence electrons?

6. **Applying Concepts** Identify the number of valence electrons in a barium atom.

Interpreting Graphics

7. Look at the model below. How many valence electrons are in a fluorine atom? Will fluorine atoms form bonds? Explain.

Fluorine

 SCiLINKS®

NSTA
Developed and maintained by the
National Science Teachers Association

For a variety of links related to this chapter, go to www.scilinks.org

Topic: The Electron; Periodic Table
SciLinks code: HSM0489; HSM1125

Focus

Overview

This section introduces ionic bonds and describes how ions are formed. Students will also learn about the properties of ionic compounds.

Bellringer

Salts are ionic compounds. Have students brainstorm uses for salts, things that contain salts, or words and phrases containing the term *salt*. (Sample answer: salt water, rubbing salt in a wound, salt on icy roads, salt in tears)

Motivate

Discussion ——— GENERAL

Penny Analogy Most convenience stores have a small container near the cash register with pennies in it. Discuss with students what purpose this container of pennies serves. (Many people leave a penny or two in it when they receive change. Others take a penny or two when they need to.) Discuss with students how this give-a-penny and take-a-penny strategy is similar to what atoms do when they form ionic bonds. **LS** Logical

What You Will Learn

● Explain how ionic bonds form.
● Describe how positive ions form.
● Describe how negative ions form.
● Explain why ionic compounds are neutral.

Vocabulary
ionic bond
ion
crystal lattice

READING STRATEGY

Paired Summarizing Read this section silently. In pairs, take turns summarizing the material. Stop to discuss ideas that seem confusing.

ionic bond a bond that forms when electrons are transferred from one atom to another, which results in a positive ion and a negative ion

ion a charged particle that forms when an atom or group of atoms gains or loses one or more electrons

Figure 1 *Calcium carbonate in this snail's shell contains ionic bonds.*

Ionic Bonds

Have you ever accidentally tasted sea water? If so, you probably didn't enjoy it. What makes sea water taste different from the water in your home?

Sea water tastes different because salt is dissolved in it. One of the salts in sea water is the same as the salt that you eat. The chemical bonds in salt are ionic (ie AHN ik) bonds.

Forming Ionic Bonds

An **ionic bond** is a bond that forms when electrons are transferred from one atom to another atom. During ionic bonding, one or more valence electrons are transferred from one atom to another. Like all chemical bonds, ionic bonds form so that the outermost energy levels of the atoms in the bonds are filled. **Figure 1** shows another substance that contains ionic bonds.

Charged Particles

An atom is neutral because the number of electrons in an atom equals the number of protons. So, the charges of the electrons and protons cancel each other. A transfer of electrons between atoms changes the number of electrons in each atom. But the number of protons stays the same in each atom. The negative charges and positive charges no longer cancel out, and the atoms become ions. **Ions** are charged particles that form when atoms gain or lose electrons. An atom normally cannot gain electrons without another atom nearby to lose electrons (or cannot lose electrons without a nearby atom to gain them). But it is easier to study the formation of ions one at a time.

Reading Check Why are atoms neutral? (*See the Appendix for answers to Reading Checks.*)

CHAPTER RESOURCES

Chapter Resource File

● **Lesson Plan**
● **Directed Reading A** BASIC
● **Directed Reading B** SPECIAL NEEDS

Technology

Transparencies
● Bellringer
● P52 Forming Positive and Negative Ions

Workbooks

Interactive Textbook Struggling Readers

Answer to Reading Check

Atoms are neutral because the number of protons in an atom always equals the number of electrons in the atom.

Figure 2 Forming Positive Ions

Here's How It Works: During chemical changes, a sodium atom can lose its 1 electron in the third energy level to another atom. The filled second level becomes the outermost level, so the resulting sodium ion has 8 valence electrons.

Here's How It Works: During chemical changes, an aluminum atom can lose its 3 electrons in the third energy level to another atom. The filled second level becomes the outermost level, so the resulting aluminum ion has 8 valence electrons.

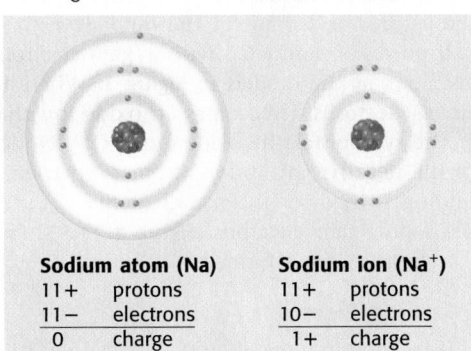

Sodium atom (Na)	Sodium ion (Na$^+$)
11+ protons	11+ protons
11− electrons	10− electrons
0 charge	1+ charge

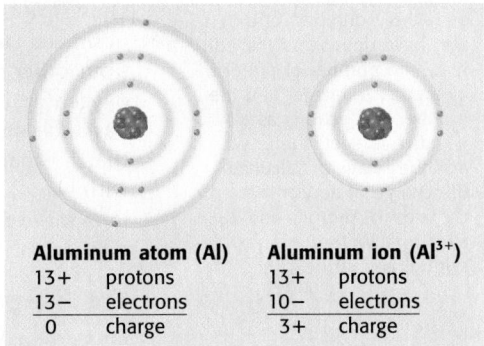

Aluminum atom (Al)	Aluminum ion (Al^{3+})
13+ protons	13+ protons
13− electrons	10− electrons
0 charge	3+ charge

Forming Positive Ions

Ionic bonds form during chemical changes when atoms pull electrons away from other atoms. The atoms that lose electrons form ions that have fewer electrons than protons. Because the positive charges outnumber the negative charges, these ions have a positive charge.

Metal Atoms and the Loss of Electrons

Atoms of most metals have few valence electrons. Metal atoms tend to lose these valence electrons and form positive ions. Look at the models in **Figure 2.** When a sodium atom loses its only valence electron to another atom, the sodium atom becomes a sodium ion. A sodium ion has 1 more proton than it has electrons. So, the sodium ion has a 1+ charge. The chemical symbol for this ion is written as Na$^+$. Notice that the charge is written to the upper right of the chemical symbol. **Figure 2** also shows a model for the formation of an aluminum ion.

The Energy Needed to Lose Electrons

Energy is needed to pull electrons away from atoms. Only a small amount of energy is needed to take electrons from metal atoms. In fact, the energy needed to remove electrons from atoms of elements in Groups 1 and 2 is so small that these elements react very easily. The energy needed to take electrons from metals comes from the formation of negative ions.

Studying Salt

Spread several grains of salt on a dark sheet of construction paper. Use a magnifying lens to examine the salt. Ask an adult at home to examine the salt. Discuss what you saw. Then, gently tap the salt with a small hammer. Examine the salt again. Describe your observations in your **science journal.**

Q: What do you call a bond that is fond of sarcasm?

A: an ironic bond

An ionic compound has properties different from those of the elements that form it. Table salt, or sodium chloride, is a good example. Elemental sodium is highly reactive—when it is placed in water, it bursts into flame! Elemental chlorine gas is toxic to humans. But when these two elements join, the resultant compound is nonreactive and harmless.

Close

Answer to Math Practice

(16+) + (18−) = 2−; S²⁻; sulfide ion

Reteaching ——— **BASIC**

Never Transfer Protons Ions form by transferring electrons, never by transferring protons. To reinforce this concept, draw models of a sodium atom and a chlorine atom on the board that show the atom's electrons. Then, draw an arrow to show how the valence electron from the sodium is transferred to the chlorine atom. **LS** Visual

Quiz ——— **GENERAL**

1. How does an atom develop a charge? (by gaining or losing electrons)

2. What is a crystal lattice? (the regular pattern in which a crystal is arranged)

Alternative Assessment ——— **GENERAL**

Ion Model Have students build models of atoms with "moveable" electrons. For example, a stack of quarters can represent the nucleus of an atom and pennies around the stack can represent the electrons. Have students use their models to demonstrate the formation of positive and negative ions. **LS** Kinesthetic

Answer to Reading Check

Atoms in Group 17 give off the most energy when forming negative ions.

Calculating Charge

Calculating the charge of an ion is the same as adding integers (positive or negative whole numbers and 0) that have opposite signs. You write the number of protons as a positive integer and the number of electrons as a negative integer. Then, you add the integers. Calculate the charge of an ion that contains 16 protons and 18 electrons. Write the ion's symbol and name.

Forming Negative Ions

Some atoms gain electrons from other atoms during chemical changes. The ions that form have more electrons than protons. So, these ions have a negative charge.

Nonmetal Atoms Gain Electrons

The outermost energy level of nonmetal atoms is almost full. Only a few electrons are needed to fill the outer level of a nonmetal atom. So, atoms of nonmetals tend to gain electrons from other atoms. Look at the models in **Figure 3.** When an oxygen atom gains 2 electrons, it becomes an oxide ion that has a 2− charge. The symbol for the oxide ion is O^{2-}. Notice that the name of the negative ion formed from oxygen ends with *-ide*. This ending is used for the names of the negative ions formed when atoms gain electrons. **Figure 3** also shows a model of how a chloride ion is formed.

The Energy of Gaining Electrons

Energy is given off by most nonmetal atoms when they gain electrons. The more easily an atom gains an electron, the more energy the atom releases. Atoms of Group 17 elements give off the most energy when they gain an electron. These elements are very reactive. An ionic bond will form between a metal and a nonmetal if the nonmetal releases more energy than is needed to take electrons from the metal.

✔ **Reading Check** Atoms of which group on the periodic table give off the most energy when forming negative ions?

Figure 3 **Forming Negative Ions**

Here's How It Works: During chemical changes, an oxygen atom gains 2 electrons in the second energy level from another atom. An oxide ion that has 8 valence electrons is formed. Thus, its outermost energy level is filled.

Here's How It Works: During chemical changes, a chlorine atom gains 1 electron in the third energy level from another atom. A chloride ion that has 8 valence electrons is formed. Thus, its outermost energy level is filled.

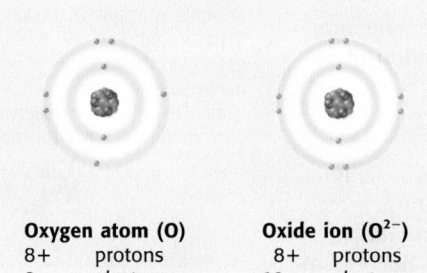

Oxygen atom (O)			Oxide ion (O^{2-})		
8+	protons		8+	protons	
8−	electrons		10−	electrons	
0	charge		2−	charge	

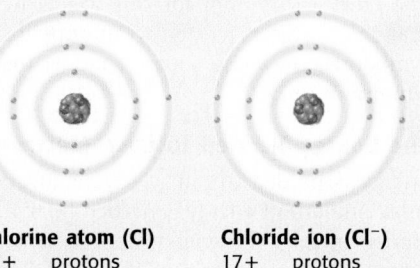

Chlorine atom (Cl)			Chloride ion (Cl^-)		
17+	protons		17+	protons	
17−	electrons		18−	electrons	
0	charge		1−	charge	

INCLUSION Strategies

- *Learning Disabled*   - *Developmentally Delayed*
- *Hearing Impaired*

Help students understand the concept of adding positive and negative charges. Ask six students to pair up. Have one student from each pair tape a minus sign to his or her shirt, and have the rest tape plus signs to their shirts. Explain that the group is neutral because the number of pluses is equal to the number of minuses. Then, ask one "negative" to sit down. Ask the partners to stand together. Explain that the group is no longer neutral because a "positive" has no partner. Tell students that this is what happens in atoms when an atom loses an electron—the atom is no longer neutral. Tell students that if the group in front of the room were an ion, it would be a positive ion because it has an extra, unmatched positive part. **English Language Learners**
LS Kinesthetic/Interpersonal

Ionic Compounds

When ionic bonds form, the number of electrons lost by the metal atoms equals the number gained by the nonmetal atoms. The ions that bond are charged, but the compound formed is neutral because the charges of the ions cancel each other. When ions bond, they form a repeating three-dimensional pattern called a **crystal lattice** (KRIS tuhl LAT is), like the one shown in **Figure 4**. The strong attraction between ions in a crystal lattice gives ionic compounds certain properties, which include brittleness, high melting points, and high boiling points.

crystal lattice the regular pattern in which a crystal is arranged

 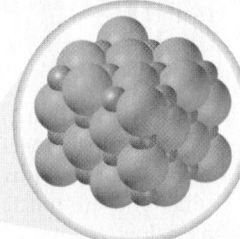

Figure 4 *This model of the crystal lattice of sodium chloride, or table salt, shows a three-dimensional view of the bonded ions. In the model, the sodium ions are pink and the chloride ions are green.*

SECTION Review

Summary

- An ionic bond is a bond that forms when electrons are transferred from one atom to another. During ionic bonding, the atoms become oppositely charged ions.
- Ionic bonding usually occurs between atoms of metals and atoms of nonmetals.
- Energy is needed to remove electrons from metal atoms. Energy is released when most nonmetal atoms gain electrons.

Using Key Terms

1. Use the following terms in the same sentence: *ion* and *ionic bond*.

2. In your own words, write a definition for the term *crystal lattice*.

Understanding Key Ideas

3. Which types of atoms usually become negative ions?
   a. metals
   b. nonmetals
   c. noble gases
   d. All of the above

4. How does an atom become a positive ion? a negative ion?

5. What are two properties of ionic compounds?

Math Skills

6. What is the charge of an ion that has 12 protons and 10 electrons? Write the ion's symbol.

Critical Thinking

7. **Applying Concepts** Which group of elements gains two valence electrons when the atoms form ionic bonds?

8. **Identifying Relationships** Explain why ionic compounds are neutral even though they are made up of charged particles.

9. **Making Comparisons** Compare the formation of positive ions with the formation of negative ions in terms of energy changes.

 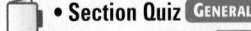

Answers to Section Review

1. Sample answer: A positive ion and a negative ion are needed to form an ionic bond.

2. Sample answer: A crystal lattice is a repeating pattern in which a crystal is arranged.

3. b

4. An atom becomes a positive ion by losing electrons. An atom becomes a negative ion by gaining electrons.

5. Sample answer: Ionic compounds are brittle and have high melting points.

6. The ion has a charge of 2+. The symbol is Mg^{2+}.

7. Elements in Group 16 gain two electrons when forming ionic bonds.

8. Ionic compounds are neutral because the number of electrons lost by the metal atoms is equal to the number of electrons gained by the nonmetal atoms. So, the charges on the ions cancel each other out.

9. Energy is needed to form positive ions, but energy is given off when negative ions are formed.

Focus

Overview

In this section, students will learn how covalent and metallic bonds are formed. Students will also learn how to draw electron-dot diagrams and will study the properties of metals.

 Bellringer

Give students one minute to brainstorm a list of things made of metal. Then, ask them to use their list to describe three properties of metals.

Motivate

ACTiViTY ———— **GENERAL**

Cereal-Dot Diagrams Use cereal pieces to represent electrons when making electron-dot diagrams. Have students write chemical symbols on index cards and place the correct number of cereal pieces around the symbol. Once students learn how to place the cereal pieces, have them make cereal-dot diagrams of water, H_2O, and ammonia, NH_3. Have students use cereal pieces of a different color for each atom to help them see where each electron originated. For example, a student may use green cereal pieces for oxygen electrons and red cereal pieces for the hydrogen electrons. **LS Kinesthetic**

What You Will Learn

● Explain how covalent bonds form.
● Describe molecules.
● Explain how metallic bonds form.
● Describe the properties of metals.

Vocabulary

covalent bond
molecule
metallic bond

READING STRATEGY

Reading Organizer As you read this section, create an outline of the section. Use the headings from the section in your outline.

covalent bond a bond formed when atoms share one or more pairs of electrons

Covalent and Metallic Bonds

Imagine bending a wooden coat hanger and a wire coat hanger. The wire one would bend easily, but the wooden one would break. Why do these things behave differently?

One reason is that the bonds between the atoms of each object are different. The atoms of the wooden hanger are held together by covalent bonds (KOH VAY luhnt BAHNDZ). But the atoms of the wire hanger are held together by metallic bonds. Read on to learn about the difference between these kinds of chemical bonds.

Covalent Bonds

Most things around you, such as water, sugar, oxygen, and wood, are held together by covalent bonds. Substances that have covalent bonds tend to have low melting and boiling points and are brittle in the solid state. For example, oxygen has a low boiling point, which is why it is a gas at room temperature. And wood is brittle, so it breaks when bent.

A **covalent bond** forms when atoms share one or more pairs of electrons. When two atoms of nonmetals bond, a large amount of energy is needed for either atom to lose an electron. So, two nonmetals don't transfer electrons to fill the outermost energy levels of their atoms. Instead, two nonmetal atoms bond by sharing electrons with each another, as shown in the model in **Figure 1.**

☑ Reading Check What is a covalent bond? (*See the Appendix for answers to Reading Checks.*)

Figure 1 *By sharing electrons in a covalent bond, each hydrogen atom (the smallest atom) has a full outermost energy level containing two electrons.*

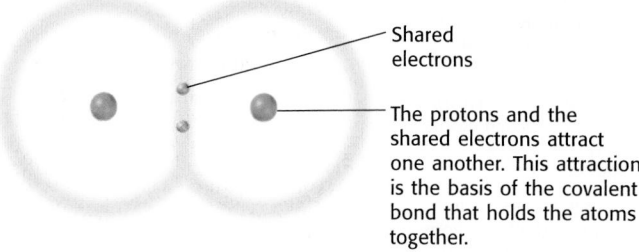

Shared electrons

The protons and the shared electrons attract one another. This attraction is the basis of the covalent bond that holds the atoms together.

CHAPTER RESOURCES

Chapter Resource File

 • Lesson Plan
• Directed Reading A **BASIC**
• Directed Reading B **SPECIAL NEEDS**

Technology

 Transparencies
• Bellringer
• P53 Covalent Bond
• P54 Covalent Bonds in a Water Molecule

Workbooks

 Interactive Textbook Struggling Readers

Answer to Reading Check

A covalent bond is a bond that forms when atoms share one or more pairs of electrons.

Figure 2 Covalent Bonds in a Water Molecule

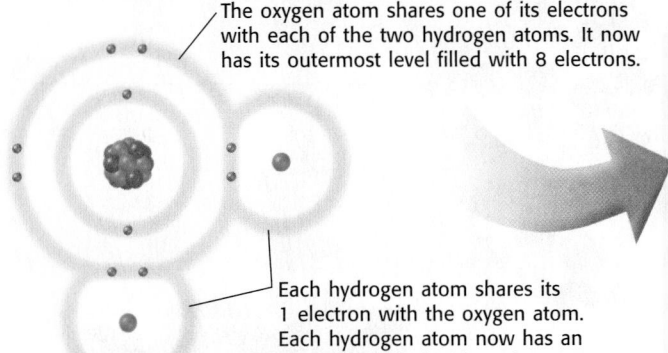

The oxygen atom shares one of its electrons with each of the two hydrogen atoms. It now has its outermost level filled with 8 electrons.

Each hydrogen atom shares its 1 electron with the oxygen atom. Each hydrogen atom now has an outer level filled with 2 electrons.

This electron-dot diagram for water shows only the outermost level of electrons for each atom. But you still see how the atoms share electrons.

Covalent Bonds and Molecules

Substances containing covalent bonds consist of individual particles called molecules (MAHL i KYOOLZ). A **molecule** usually consists of two or more atoms joined in a definite ratio. A hydrogen molecule is composed of two covalently bonded hydrogen atoms. However, most molecules are composed of atoms of two or more elements. The models in **Figure 2** show two ways to represent the covalent bonds in a water molecule.

One way to represent atoms and molecules is to use electron-dot diagrams. An electron-dot diagram is a model that shows only the valence electrons in an atom. Electron-dot diagrams can help you predict how atoms might bond. To draw an electron-dot diagram, write the symbol of the element and place one dot around the symbol for every valence electron in the atom, as shown in **Figure 3.** Place the first 4 dots alone on each side, and then pair up any remaining dots.

molecule the smallest unit of a substance that keeps all of the physical and chemical properties of that substance

Figure 3 Using Electron–Dot Diagrams

Carbon atoms have 4 valence electrons. A carbon atom needs 4 more electrons to have a filled outermost energy level.

Oxygen atoms have 6 valence electrons. An oxygen atom needs only 2 more electrons to have a filled outermost energy level.

Krypton atoms have 8 valence electrons. Krypton is nonreactive. Krypton atoms do not need any more electrons.

This diagram represents a hydrogen molecule. The dots between the letters represent a pair of shared electrons.

SCIENCE HUMOR

Q: What is the one thing that atoms in molecules do not have to teach their children?

A: how to share with others

MISCONCEPTION ALERT

Electron Sharing In certain covalent compounds, atoms may have fewer or more than 8 electrons in their outer energy level. In boron trifluoride, BF_3, the boron atom has only 6 electrons in its outer energy level. In sulfur hexafluoride, SF_6, sulfur has 12 electrons in its outer energy level. For the purposes of this chapter, students can assume that sharing electrons to have 8 electrons in the outermost energy level is the rule.

ACTIVITY ——— ADVANCED

Hydrogen Bonds In addition to the covalent bonds that link hydrogen atoms to an oxygen atom in a molecule of water, another type of bond is important in water. This bond, which is actually an intermolecular force, is called a *hydrogen bond*. Have students investigate hydrogen bonding and the properties they impart to water and other substances. Ask students to make a poster to illustrate what they learn. **LS** Visual

Making Models —— GENERAL

Gumdrop Models Demonstrate how to make three-dimensional models of hydrogen sulfide, H_2S, molecules using gumdrops and toothpicks. One color of gumdrop represents the sulfur atom, and another color represents the two hydrogen atoms. Use toothpicks to "bond" the hydrogen gumdrops to the sulfur gumdrop. Give students gumdrops and toothpicks, and have them make their own models of ammonia, NH_3, and methane, CH_4. English Language Learners **LS** Kinesthetic

Discussion —— GENERAL

Double and Triple Bonds Explain to students that atoms can form double or triple covalent bonds if they need more than one electron to complete their outermost energy level. An oxygen atom forms a double bond with another oxygen atom. Draw the electron-dot diagram for oxygen, O_2, on the chalkboard. Point out that each oxygen atom's outer energy level has 4 shared electrons (2 per bond) and 4 unshared electrons, so the outermost energy level has a total of 8 electrons. Ask students to make electron-dot diagrams for nitrogen, N_2, and carbon dioxide, CO_2. **LS** Logical

Discussion ───── BASIC

Valence Electrons Remind students that they can use the periodic table to find the number of valence electrons for atoms of elements in Groups 13–18. Subtracting 10 from any of these group numbers will determine the number of valence electrons in an atom of any element in the group. Display a periodic table, and have students determine the number of valence electrons for silicon (6) and iodine (7). **LS Visual/Logical**

ACTIVITY ───── GENERAL

Drawing Diagrams Follow these guidelines to construct electron-dot diagrams for chlorine gas, Cl_2, and ammonia, NH_3:

1. Add up the valence electrons for all of the atoms that make up the molecule.

2. Use one pair of electrons to indicate the bond(s) shared by atoms.

3. Arrange the remaining electrons to form a stable molecule. Each atom (except hydrogen) needs 8 electrons to fill its outermost energy level. **English Language Learners**
LS Visual

Answer to Reading Check

There are two atoms in a diatomic molecule.

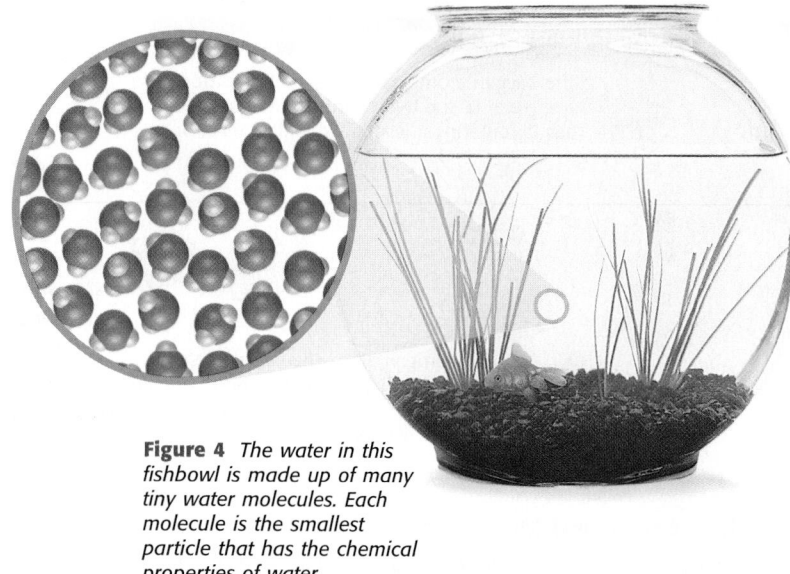

Figure 4 *The water in this fishbowl is made up of many tiny water molecules. Each molecule is the smallest particle that has the chemical properties of water.*

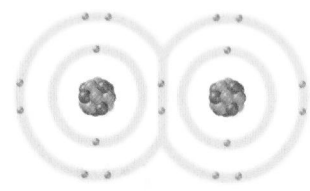

INTERNET ACTIVITY

For another activity related to this chapter, go to **go.hrw.com** and type in the keyword **HP5BNDW.**

Covalent Compounds and Molecules

An atom is the smallest particle into which an element can be divided and still be the same element. Likewise, a molecule is the smallest particle into which a covalently bonded compound can be divided and still be the same compound. Look at the three-dimensional models in **Figure 4.** They show how a sample of water is made up of many individual molecules of water. Imagine dividing water over and over. You would eventually end up with a single molecule of water. What would happen if you separated the hydrogen and oxygen atoms that make up a water molecule? Then, you would no longer have water.

The Simplest Molecules

Molecules are composed of at least two covalently bonded atoms. The simplest molecules are made up of two bonded atoms. Molecules made up of two atoms are called *diatomic molecules.* Elements that are found in nature as diatomic molecules are called *diatomic elements.* Hydrogen is a diatomic element. Oxygen, nitrogen, and the halogens fluorine, chlorine, bromine, and iodine are also diatomic elements. Look at **Figure 5.** The shared electrons are counted as valence electrons for each atom. So, both atoms of the molecule have filled outermost energy levels.

Figure 5 *Two covalently bonded fluorine atoms have filled outermost energy levels. The two electrons shared by the atoms are counted as valence electrons for each atom.*

✓ **Reading Check** How many atoms are in a diatomic molecule?

Is That a Fact!

Even though a molecule of water is bigger than the hydrogen and oxygen atoms it comprises, it is still an extremely tiny particle. There are about 2 million quadrillion (2 followed by 21 zeros) water molecules in a single drop of water!

MISCONCEPTION /// ALERT \\\

Arrangement of Water Molecules For clarity, the model of liquid water in **Figure 4** shows only one layer of molecules with spaces between them. Make sure students understand that, in reality, the molecules are always in contact with and sliding past molecules above and below the layer shown.

Hydrogen
Carbon
Oxygen

Figure 6 *A granola bar contains sucrose, or table sugar. A molecule of sucrose is composed of carbon atoms, hydrogen atoms, and oxygen atoms joined by covalent bonds.*

More-Complex Molecules

Diatomic molecules are the simplest molecules. They are also some of the most important molecules. You could not live without diatomic oxygen molecules. But other important molecules are much more complex. Soap, plastic bottles, and even proteins in your body are examples of complex molecules. Carbon atoms are the basis of many of these complex molecules. Each carbon atom needs to make four covalent bonds to have 8 valence electrons. These bonds can be with atoms of other elements or with other carbon atoms, as shown in the model in **Figure 6.**

Metallic Bonds

Look at the unusual metal sculptures shown in **Figure 7.** Some metal pieces have been flattened, while other metal pieces have been shaped into wires. How could the artist change the shape of the metal into all of these different forms without breaking the metal into pieces? Metal can be shaped because of the presence of a metallic bond, a special kind of chemical bond. A **metallic bond** is a bond formed by the attraction between positively charged metal ions and the electrons in the metal. Positively charged metal ions form when metal atoms lose electrons.

metallic bond a bond formed by the attraction between positively charged metal ions and the electrons around them

Figure 7 *The different shapes of metal in these sculptures are possible because of the bonds that hold the metal together.*

CONNECTION TO Biology

Proteins Proteins perform many functions throughout your body. A single protein can have thousands of covalently bonded atoms. Proteins are built from smaller molecules called *amino acids*. Make a poster showing how amino acids are joined to make proteins.

ACTIVITY

Homework ——— GENERAL

Writing **Plastics Around You** Tell students that plastics are a good example of materials made of covalently bonded molecules. Have students make a list of the plastic items they use during the day. Ask them to write a paragraph describing how their lives would be different without plastics. **LS** Verbal

CONNECTION to Life Science ——— GENERAL

Proteins Very large molecules that are made of many smaller, repeating units are called *polymers*. Many polymers are found in nature, including protein, cellulose, DNA, and rubber. Use the teaching transparencies entitled "Making of a Protein A and B" to show how proteins are made.

CONNECTION ACTIVITY Art ——— GENERAL

Metal Sculpting Copper is so malleable that it is not necessary to heat the metal in order to shape it. Give students some 18-gauge copper wire, and allow them to investigate its malleability by challenging them to create a small sculpture or piece of jewelry. **LS** Kinesthetic

MISCONCEPTION ///ALERT\\\

Covalent Versus Metallic Students may think that covalently bonded materials should have the same properties as metals because the electrons in both kinds of bonds can move around. Explain that the electrons involved in covalent bonding are confined to an area around the atoms but that the electrons in metallic bonds are not confined to the same area.

SUPPORT FOR

English Language Learners
Covalent and Metallic bonds Students may need reinforcement of the differences between covalent and metallic bonds. Diagram each type of bond on a transparency. When students have read the section, show the transparency. Ask them to write a brief description naming the bond each diagram represents and the reasons for their answer. Evaluate the descriptions on accuracy, reasoning, spelling, and grammar, and have students make corrections if necessary. **LS** Visual/Verbal/Logical

CHAPTER RESOURCES

Technology

Transparencies
• *LINK TO LIFE SCIENCE* L19 The Making of a Protein: A; L20 The Making of a Protein: B

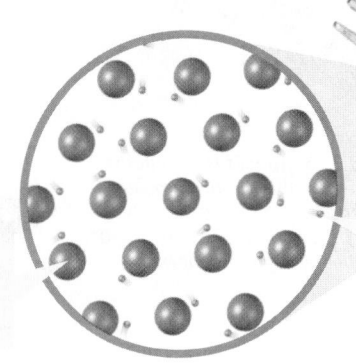

Figure 8 *Moving electrons are attracted to the metal ions, and the attraction forms metallic bonds.*

The positive metal ions are in fixed positions in the metal.

Negative electrons are free to move.

Close

Reteaching — BASIC

Malleability and Ductility To help students understand the difference between malleability and ductility, show students metal objects of different shapes. Ask students to identify whether malleability or ductility was more important to molding the metal into each shape. **LS Visual**

Quiz — GENERAL

1. What is the smallest particle of a covalently bonded compound? (a molecule)

2. List three common materials that contain covalent bonds (Sample answer: water, soap, and plastic bottles)

3. Why can metals conduct electric current? (Metals can conduct electric current because the electrons in metallic bonds are free to move around.)

Alternative Assessment — GENERAL

Bonding Charades Organize students in small groups. Have them develop a charade that depicts either covalent or metallic bonding. Students may want to use a few props, such as balls to represent electrons. Have each group present a charade. Then, have the remainder of the class determine the type of bond being portrayed. **LS Kinesthetic**

Answer to Reading Check

Ductility is the ability to be drawn into wires.

Bending with Bonds

1. Straighten out a **wire paper clip.** Record your observations.
2. Bend a **piece of chalk.** Record your observations.
3. Chalk is composed of calcium carbonate, a compound containing ionic bonds. What kind of bond is present in the paper clip?
4. Explain why you could change the shape of the paper clip but could not bend the chalk without breaking it.

Movement of Electrons Throughout a Metal

Bonding in metals is a result of the metal atoms being so close to one another that their outermost energy levels overlap. This overlapping allows valence electrons to move throughout the metal, as shown in **Figure 8.** You can think of a metal as being made up of positive metal ions that have enough valence electrons "swimming" around to keep the ions together. The electrons also cancel the positive charge of the ions. Metallic bonds extend throughout the metal in all directions.

Properties of Metals

Metallic bonding is what gives metals their particular properties. These properties include electrical conductivity, malleability, and ductility.

Conducting Electric Current

Metallic bonding allows metals to conduct electric current. For example, when you turn on a lamp, electrons move within the copper wire that connects the lamp to the outlet. The electrons that move are the valence electrons in the copper atoms. These electrons are free to move because the electrons are not connected to any one atom.

Reshaping Metals

Because the electrons swim freely around the metal ions, the atoms in metals can be rearranged. As a result, metals can be reshaped. The properties of *ductility* (the ability to be drawn into wires) and *malleability* (the ability to be hammered into sheets) describe a metal's ability to be reshaped. For example, copper is made into wires for use in electrical cords. Aluminum can be pounded into thin sheets and made into aluminum foil.

✓ Reading Check What is ductility?

MATERIALS

FOR EACH STUDENT
• chalk, piece
• paper clip, wire

Safety Caution: Remind students to review all safety cautions and icons before beginning this lab activity.

Answers

3. metallic bonds

4. The metallic bonds give the paper clip the ability to bend without breaking because the electrons move within the metal. The ionic bonds in the piece of chalk cause the chalk to be brittle.

Bending Without Breaking

When a piece of metal is bent, some of the metal ions are forced closer together. You might expect the metal to break because all of the metal ions are positively charged. Positively charged ions repel one another. However, positive ions in a metal are always surrounded by and attracted to the electrons in the metal—even if the metal ions move. The electrons constantly move around and between the metal ions. The moving electrons maintain the metallic bonds no matter how the shape of the metal changes. So, metal objects can be bent without being broken, as shown in **Figure 9.**

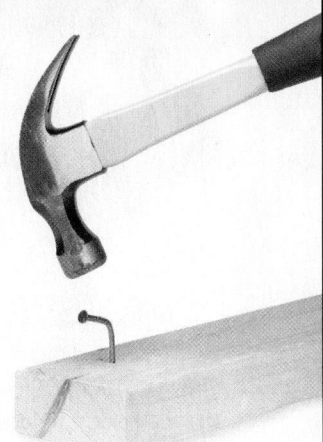

Figure 9 *Metal can be reshaped without breaking because metallic bonds occur in many directions.*

SECTION Review

Summary

- In covalent bonding, two atoms share electrons. A covalent bond forms when atoms share one or more pairs of electrons.

- Covalently bonded atoms form a particle called a *molecule.* A molecule is the smallest particle of a compound that has the chemical properties of the compound.

- In metallic bonding, the valence electrons move throughout the metal. A bond formed by the attraction between positive metal ions and the electrons in the metal is a metallic bond.

- Properties of metals include conductivity, ductility, and malleability.

Using Key Terms

1. Use each of the following terms in a separate sentence: *covalent bond* and *metallic bond.*

2. In your own words, write a definition for the term *molecule.*

Understanding Key Ideas

3. Between which of the following atoms is a covalent bond most likely to occur?
   a. calcium and lithium
   b. sodium and fluorine
   c. nitrogen and oxygen
   d. helium and argon

4. What happens to the electrons in covalent bonding?

5. How many dots does an electron-dot diagram of a sulfur atom have?

6. List three properties of metals that are a result of metallic bonds.

7. Describe how the valence electrons in a metal move.

8. Explain the difference between ductility and malleability. Give an example of when each property is useful.

Critical Thinking

9. **Identifying Relationships** How do the metallic bonds in a staple allow it to function properly?

10. **Applying Concepts** Draw an electron-dot diagram for ammonia (a nitrogen atom covalently bonded to three hydrogen atoms).

Interpreting Graphics

11. This electron-dot diagram is not complete. Which atom needs to form another bond? Explain.

For a variety of links related to this chapter, go to www.scilinks.org
Topic: Types of Chemical Bonds; Properties of Metals
SciLinks code: HSM1565; HSM1231

CHAPTER RESOURCES

Chapter Resource File

- Section Quiz `GENERAL`
- Section Review `GENERAL`
- Vocabulary and Section Summary `GENERAL`
- Reinforcement Worksheet `BASIC`
- Critical Thinking `ADVANCED`
- Datasheet for Quick Lab

Covalent Marshmallows

Teacher's Notes

Time Required

One 45-minute class period

Lab Ratings

EASY ——————→ HARD

Teacher Prep 🧪🧪
Student Set-Up 🧪
Concept Level 🧪🧪
Clean Up 🧪

MATERIALS

Materials listed are for one to two students. Colored marshmallows are available in some grocery stores. To create different colored marsh-mallows, "paint" the marshmallows lightly with diluted food coloring. To discourage students from eating the marshmallows, dust the marshmal-lows lightly with alum, a bitter spice that can be purchased at a grocery store. An alternative method of color-ing the marshmallows is to spray them lightly with hair spray, and sprinkle them with different colors of glitter. Be sure students do not eat the marshmallows.

Safety Caution

Remind students to review all safety cautions and icons before beginning this lab activity.

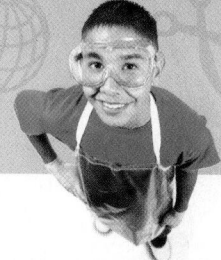

Model-Making Lab

Model-Making Lab

OBJECTIVES

Build a three-dimensional model of a water molecule.

Draw an electron-dot diagram of a water molecule.

MATERIALS

• marshmallows (two of one color, one of another color)
• toothpicks

SAFETY

Covalent Marshmallows

A hydrogen atom has 1 electron in its outermost energy level, but 2 electrons are required to fill its outermost level. An oxygen atom has 6 electrons in its outermost level, but 8 electrons are required to fill its outermost level. To fill their outermost energy levels, two atoms of hydrogen and one atom of oxygen can share electrons, as shown below. Such a sharing of electrons to fill the outermost level of atoms is called *covalent bonding*. When hydrogen and oxygen bond in this manner, a molecule of water is formed. In this lab, you will build a three-dimensional model of water to better understand the covalent bonds formed in a water molecule.

A Model of a Water Molecule

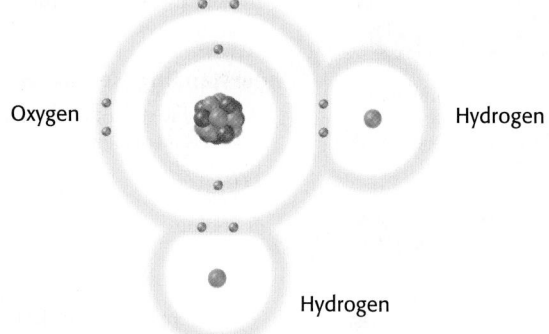

Procedure

1 Using the marshmallows and toothpicks, create a model of a water molecule. Use the diagram above for guidance in building your model.

2 Draw a sketch of your model. Be sure to label the hydrogen and oxygen atoms on your sketch.

3 Draw an electron-dot diagram of the water molecule.

Procedure Notes

To extend this activity, you may use addi-tional colors to create marshmallow models of various molecules. In addition, different-sized marshmallows can be used to repre-sent the relative sizes of atoms of different elements.

CHAPTER RESOURCES

Chapter Resource File
 • Datasheet for Chapter Lab
• Lab Notes and Answers

Technology

🔘 **Classroom Videos**
• Lab Video

Analyze the Results

1 **Classifying** What do the marshmallows represent? What do the toothpicks represent?

2 **Evaluating Models** Why are the marshmallows different colors?

3 **Analyzing Results** Compare your model with the diagram on the previous page. How might your model be improved to more accurately represent a water molecule?

Draw Conclusions

4 **Making Predictions** Hydrogen in nature can covalently bond to form hydrogen molecules, H₂. How could you use the marshmallows and toothpicks to model this bond?

5 **Applying Conclusions** Draw an electron-dot diagram of a hydrogen molecule.

6 **Drawing Conclusions** Which do you think would be more difficult to create—a model of an ionic bond or a model of a covalent bond? Explain your answer.

Applying Your Data

Create a model of a carbon dioxide molecule, which consists of two oxygen atoms and one carbon atom. The structure is similar to the structure of water, although the three atoms bond in a straight line instead of at angles. The bond between each oxygen atom and the carbon atom in a carbon dioxide molecule is a *double bond,* so use two connections. Do the double bonds in carbon dioxide appear stronger or weaker than the single bonds in water? Explain your answer.

Analyze the Results

1. The marshmallows represent atoms. The toothpicks represent the pairs of electrons that create the covalent bonds.

2. Marshmallows are different colors to represent atoms of different elements.

3. Accept all reasonable answers. Sample answer: I could use marshmallows of different sizes to show the difference in size between the atoms. Then, I could make sure the atoms form an angle and are not in a straight line.

Draw Conclusions

4. A hydrogen molecule could be modeled by using a toothpick to connect the two hydrogen marshmallows together.

5. An electron-dot diagram of the hydrogen molecule should look like the following: H : H.

6. Accept all reasonable answers. Sample answer: A model of an ionic bond would be more difficult to create because it involves the transfer of electrons. You would have to break off a little piece of one marshmallow and glue it to another marshmallow. But then there is no way to hold the marshmallows together.

Applying Your Data

The double bonds appear stronger than single bonds because there is more "attraction" (more toothpicks) holding atoms together. It is more difficult to separate two shared pairs of electrons (break two toothpicks) than to separate one shared pair of electrons (break one toothpick).

Rebecca Ferguson
North Ridge Middle School
North Richland Hills, Texas

Assignment Guide

SECTION	QUESTIONS
1	1, 5, 7
2	2, 6, 8, 10–11, 13, 15
3	3–4, 9, 12, 18–19, 21–23
2 and 3	14, 17, 20
1, 2, and 3	16

ANSWERS

Using Key Terms

1. chemical bond
2. ion
3. covalent bond
4. metallic bond
5. valence electron
6. crystal lattice

Understanding Key Ideas

7. b
8. c
9. c
10. a
11. b
12. Answers may include a low melting point, a low boiling point, and brittleness in the solid state. (Students should list at least two properties.)

USING KEY TERMS

Complete each of the following sentences by choosing the correct term from the word bank.

crystal lattice	ionic bond
molecule	chemical bond
chemical bonding	metallic bond
valence electron	ion
covalent bond	

1 An interaction that holds two atoms together is a(n) ___.

2 A charged particle that forms when an atom transfers electrons is a(n) ___.

3 A bond formed when atoms share electrons is a(n) ___.

4 Electrons free to move throughout a material are associated with a(n) ___.

5 An electron in the outermost energy level of an atom is a(n) ___.

6 Ionic compounds are bonded in a three-dimensional pattern called a(n) ___.

UNDERSTANDING KEY IDEAS

Multiple Choice

7 Which element has a full outermost energy level containing only two electrons?

- **a.** fluorine, F
- **b.** helium, He
- **c.** hydrogen, H
- **d.** oxygen, O

8 Which of the following describes what happens when an atom becomes an ion with a 2– charge?

- **a.** The atom gains 2 protons.
- **b.** The atom loses 2 protons.
- **c.** The atom gains 2 electrons.
- **d.** The atom loses 2 electrons.

9 The properties of ductility and malleability are associated with which type of bonds?

- **a.** ionic
- **c.** metallic
- **b.** covalent
- **d.** All of the above

10 What type of element tends to lose electrons when it forms bonds?

- **a.** metal
- **c.** nonmetal
- **b.** metalloid
- **d.** noble gas

11 Which pair of atoms can form an ionic bond?

- **a.** sodium, Na, and potassium, K
- **b.** potassium, K, and fluorine, F
- **c.** fluorine, F, and chlorine, Cl
- **d.** sodium, Na, and neon, Ne

Short Answer

12 List two properties of covalent compounds.

13 Explain why an iron ion is attracted to a sulfide ion but not to a zinc ion.

14 Compare the three types of bonds based on what happens to the valence electrons of the atoms.

13. Metal atoms tend to lose electrons and form positive ions. Both iron and zinc are metals, and both form ions that are positively charged. Ions with the same charge repel one another, so an iron ion is not attracted to a zinc ion. Nonmetal atoms tend to gain electrons and form negative ions. Sulfur is a nonmetal, so a sulfide ion is negatively charged. The positively charged iron ion is attracted to the sulfide ion.

14. Ionic bonds involve the transfer of valence electrons between atoms. Covalent bonds involve the sharing of valence electrons between atoms. Metallic bonds involve the movement of valence electrons between many atoms within a metal.

Math Skills

15 For each atom below, write the number of electrons it must gain or lose to have 8 valence electrons. Then, calculate the charge of the ion that would form.

a. calcium, Ca

b. phosphorus, P

c. bromine, Br

d. sulfur, S

CRITICAL THINKING

16 Concept Mapping Use the following terms to create a concept map: *chemical bonds, ionic bonds, covalent bonds, metallic bonds, molecule,* and *ions.*

17 Identifying Relationships Predict the type of bond each of the following pairs of atoms would form:

a. zinc, Zn, and zinc, Zn

b. oxygen, O, and nitrogen, N

c. phosphorus, P, and oxygen, O

d. magnesium, Mg, and chlorine, Cl

18 Applying Concepts Draw electron-dot diagrams for each of the following atoms, and state how many bonds it will have to make to fill its outer energy level.

a. sulfur, S

b. nitrogen, N

c. neon, Ne

d. iodine, I

e. silicon, Si

19 Predicting Consequences Using your knowledge of valence electrons, explain the main reason so many different molecules are made from carbon atoms.

20 Making Inferences Does the substance being hit in the photo below contain ionic or metallic bonds? Explain your answer.

INTERPRETING GRAPHICS

Use the picture of a wooden pencil below to answer the questions that follow.

21 In which part of the pencil are metallic bonds found?

22 List three materials in the pencil that are composed of molecules that have covalent bonds.

23 Identify two differences between the properties of the material that has metallic bonds and the materials that have covalent bonds.

15. a. lose 2 electrons; 2+

b. gain 3 electrons; 3–

c. gain 1 electron; 1–

d. gain 2 electrons; 2–

Critical Thinking

16. An answer to this exercise can be found at the end of this book.

17. a. metallic

b. covalent

c. covalent

d. ionic

18. a. 6 dots; 2 bonds

b. 5 dots; 3 bonds

c. 8 dots; no bonds

d. 7 dots; 1 bond

e. 4 dots; 4 bonds

19. Carbon atoms have 4 valence electrons. Each carbon atom must make 4 bonds to fill its outermost energy level with 8 electrons. Because each carbon atom can bond with up to 4 atoms (including other carbon atoms), carbon forms the basis of many different compounds.

20. It contains ionic bonds because the substance is breaking into smaller pieces as the hammer hits it. The substance is brittle, so the bonds are more likely to be ionic.

Interpreting Graphics

21. the metal band near the eraser

22. graphite, wood, and rubber (eraser)

23. Sample answer: The metallically bonded material is shiny, and the covalently bonded materials are not shiny. The metal can be bent without breaking, but the wood or graphite will break if bent.

CHAPTER RESOURCES

Chapter Resource File

- **Chapter Review** GENERAL
- **Chapter Test A** GENERAL
- **Chapter Test B** ADVANCED
- **Chapter Test C** SPECIAL NEEDS
- **Vocabulary Activity** GENERAL

Workbooks

Study Guide
- Study Guide is also available in Spanish.

Standardized Test Preparation

Teacher's Notes

To provide practice under more realistic conditions, give students 20 minutes to answer all of the questions in this Standardized Test Preparation.

Answer Key

Question	Answer
1	C
2	B
3	D
4	D
5	A
6	B
7	A
8	C
9	D
10	A
11	*
12	*

*See Test Doctor.

Multiple Choice

Use the figure below to answer question 1.

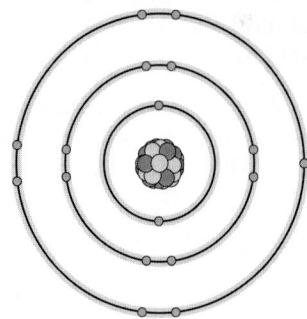

1. **What is the maximum number of electrons that can be held in the second energy level of an atom?**

   A. 2

   B. 7

   C. 8

   D. 9

2. **What happens when a nonmetal atom gains an electron from another atom? Energy is**

   A. given off by the atom losing the electron.

   B. given off by the atom gaining the electron.

   C. absorbed by the atom gaining the electron.

   D. transferred to the atom gaining the electron.

3. **An aluminum ion has 13 protons, 14 neutrons, and 10 electrons. What is the charge of an aluminum ion?**

   A. 10−

   B. 3−

   C. 1+

   D. 3+

4. **The atoms of elements in Group 17 of the periodic table are very reactive. Which of the following best describes the energy transfers that happen with the elements in this group?**

   A. The more easily an atom loses an electron, the less energy the atom releases.

   B. The more easily an atom gains an electron, the less energy the atom releases.

   C. The more easily an atom loses an electron, the more energy the atom releases.

   D. The more easily an atom gains an electron, the more energy the atom releases.

5. **Sodium chloride, or table salt, is formed when a chlorine atom takes an electron from a neighboring sodium atom. Which of the following describes the force that holds the resulting chlorine particle and the resulting sodium particle together?**

   A. an ionic bond

   B. a neutral bond

   C. a metallic bond

   D. a covalent bond

TEST DOCTOR

Question 1 A, B, and D: The second energy level of an atom can hold 8 electrons. The diagram has 8 electrons in its second energy level. C: Correct.

Question 2 A: Energy is given off by most non-metal atoms when they gain electrons. Energy is not given off by an atom that is losing electrons. Instead, energy is needed to remove electrons from atoms. B: Correct. C: The answer suggests that energy is gained by the atom gaining the electron, which is false. D: No energy is gained by the atom along with the electron.

Question 3 A: 13 protons provide a 13+ charge, 10 electrons provide a 10− charge, and neutrons have no charge. So, the net charge is 3+, not 10−. B: The net charge is 3+, not 3−. C: The net charge is 3+, not 1+. D: Correct.

Question 4 A: Atoms in Group 17 gain rather than lose electrons. B: This describes the wrong relationship between energy transfer and the reactivity of Group 17. C: Atoms in Group 17 gain rather than lose electrons, so this description is incorrect. D: Correct.

Use the diagram below to answer question 6.

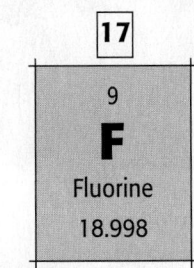

Periodic Table Listing for Fluorine

6. How many neutrons are in a typical fluorine atom?

A. 9

B. 10

C. 17

D. 19

7. What forms when atoms share one or more pairs of electrons?

A. covalent bond

B. ionic bond

C. valence electron

D. nonmetal ion

8. The ions that make up an ionic compound are bonded in a repeating three-dimensional pattern. What is this pattern called?

A. chloride lattice

B. covalent bond

C. crystal lattice

D. crystal pattern

9. What is a molecule?

A. the smallest particle of a substance that cannot be broken down any further by chemical bonding

B. a particle that forms when atoms gain or lose electrons

C. matter of particular or definite chemical composition

D. the smallest unit of a substance that keeps the physical and chemical properties of the substance

10. During a laboratory experiment, Juanita observes a model of two bonded atoms. She is told that the atoms are both nonmetals. She is looking at a model of

A. a covalent bond.

B. an acid.

C. an ionic bond.

D. a salt.

Open Response

11. Which of an atom's electrons are most likely to be involved in chemical bonding? Why?

12. Why don't the noble gases in Group 18 on the periodic table form chemical bonds?

B: A covalent bond forms when atoms share one or more pairs of electrons. C: Correct. D: The question describes a crystal lattice, not a crystal pattern.

Question 9 A: A molecule is a "particle," and it can be broken down in chemical reactions. B: Ions are atoms that gain or lose electrons. C: This is true but too general. It covers mixtures and solutions too. D: Correct.

Question 10 A: Correct. B: Using the information in the question, one cannot conclude that the model is an acid. C: A nonmetal and a metal can form an ionic bond. The question states that the atoms are nonmetals, so this answer is incorrect. D: Using the information in the passage, one cannot conclude that the model is a salt.

Question 11 Full-credit answers should include the following points:

• The electrons in an atom's outermost level of energy are attracted less strongly to protons in the nucleus of the atom than electrons in lower levels of energy are.

• The outermost electrons are most likely to be involved in chemical bonding.

• The outermost electrons are shared, lost, or gained most easily.

Question 12 Full-credit answers should include the following points:

• The number of electrons in the outermost energy level of an atom determines whether an atom will form bonds.

• Atoms of the noble gases (Group 18) do not usually form chemical bonds because all except helium have 8 valence electrons.

• When the outermost energy level of an atom has 8 valence electrons, it is considered full. Full atoms do not usually form bonds.

Question 5 A: Correct. B: Neutral bonds do not exist. C: Chlorine atoms and sodium atoms form ions when they gain and lose electrons respectively. Therefore, an ionic bond holds the particles (ions) together. Metallic bonds occur only between metal atoms. D: Covalent bonds involve sharing electrons.

Question 6 A: The correct answer is found by subtracting the atomic number of fluorine (9) from its rounded atomic mass (19). This answer is the atomic number of fluorine and is equal to the number of protons in a fluorine atom. B: Correct. C: This is the number of the group to which fluorine belongs. D: This is the rounded atomic mass of fluorine.

Question 7 A: Correct. B: A covalent bond forms when atoms share one or more pairs of electrons. An ionic bond forms when electrons pass from one atom to another, forming a positive ion and a negative ion. C: A valence electron is an electron in the outermost energy level of an atom. D: Two nonmetals do not transfer electrons because there is not enough energy for such a transfer.

Question 8 A: A crystal lattice is the three-dimensional pattern of ions bonded together in an ionic compound. An ionic bond formed with chlorine, such as sodium chloride, forms a crystal lattice, but it is not called a chloride lattice.

Science in Action

Science in Action

Science, Technology, and Society

Discussion ———— GENERAL

Lead a discussion comparing the use of superglue, stitches, and bandages to cover or close wounds. Ask students to name some advantages and disadvantages of using superglue to close wounds. (Sample answer: Bandages often fall off when they get wet, but superglue will stay on in water. Superglue bandages are more expensive than regular bandages.)

Weird Science

Background

A van der Waals force is a type of intermolecular force (a force between molecules). Van der Waals forces are attractions resulting from the uneven distribution of electrons and the creation of temporary dipoles. The positive end of a dipole on one molecule attracts the negative end of a dipole on another molecule, and the molecules are briefly held together. Van der Waals forces are compared to ionic bonds in the text because ionic bonds are also attractions between opposite charges. However, be sure your students understand that van der Waals forces are much weaker than ionic bonds.

Science, Technology, and Society

Superglue Bandages and Stitches

If you aren't careful when using superglue, you may accidentally learn that superglue quickly bonds skin together! This property of superglue led to the development of new kinds of superglue that can be used as alternatives for bandages and stitches. Using superglue to close wounds has several advantages over using bandages and stitches. For example, superglue bandages can cover cuts on parts of the body that are difficult to cover with regular bandages. And superglue stitches are less painful than regular stitches. Finally, wounds closed with superglue are easier to care for than wounds covered by bandages or closed with stitches.

Math ACTIVITY

A wound can be closed 3 times faster with glue than it can be with stitches. If it takes a doctor 27 min to close a wound by using stitches, how long would it take to close the same wound by using glue?

Weird Science

How Geckos Stick to Walls

Geckos are known for their ability to climb up smooth surfaces. Recently, scientists found the secret to the gecko's sticky talent. Geckos have millions of microscopic hairs on the bottom of their feet. Each hair splits into as many as 1,000 tinier hairs called *hairlets*. At the end of each hairlet is a small pad. As the gecko walks, each pad forms a van der Waals force with the surface on which the gecko is walking. A van der Waals force is an attraction similar to an ionic bond, but the van der Waals force is much weaker than an ionic bond and lasts for only an instant. But because there are so many pads on a gecko's foot, the van der Waals forces are strong enough to keep the gecko from falling.

Language Arts ACTIVITY

WRITING SKILL Imagine that you could stick to walls as well as a gecko can. Write a five-paragraph short story describing what you would do with your wall-climbing ability.

Answer to Math Activity
27 min ÷ 3 = 9 min

Answer to Language Arts Activity
Accept all reasonable responses. All stories should describe how students would use their wall-climbing ability. For example, students may discuss becoming a superhero and using their wall-climbing ability to fight crime.

Roberta Jordan

Analytical Chemist Have you ever looked at something and wondered what chemicals it contained? That's what analytical chemists do for a living. They use tests to find the chemical makeup of a sample. Roberta Jordan is an analytical chemist at the Idaho National Engineering and Environmental Laboratory in Idaho Falls, Idaho.

Jordan's work focuses on the study of radioactive waste generated by nuclear power plants and nuclear-powered submarines. Jordan works with engineers to develop safe ways to store the radioactive waste. She tells the engineers which chemicals need to be studied and which techniques to use to study those chemicals.

Jordan enjoys her job because she is always learning new techniques. "One of the things necessary to be a good chemist is you have to be creative. You have to be able to think above and beyond the normal ways of doing things to come up with new ideas, new experiments," she explains. Jordan believes that a person interested in a career in chemistry has many opportunities. "There are a lot of things out there that need to be discovered," says Jordan.

Social Studies ACTIVITY

Many elements in the periodic table were discovered by analytical chemists. Pick an element from the periodic table, and research its history. Make a poster about the discovery of that element.

go.hrw.com

To learn more about these Science in Action topics, visit go.hrw.com and type in the keyword HP5BNDF.

Current Science

Check out Current Science® articles related to this chapter by visiting go.hrw.com. Just type in the keyword HP5CS13.

Careers

Background

Originally, analytical chemists worked using tests in which they reacted the unknown substance with other substances. These methods often involved changing the original sample. But in the last 50 years, the field of instrumental analysis (in which instruments are used to analyze substances) has grown. Many of these instruments, such as infrared spectrophotometers and nuclear magnetic resonance spectrometers, are able to analyze a substance without changing it chemically.

Answer to Social Studies Activity

Encourage students to focus their research on the main group elements or the transition metals in periods 4–6. The discovery of these elements is better documented, and the elements often have interesting histories.

Accept all reasonable responses. All posters should include the name of the element researched, the name(s) of the person who discovered it, and the year it was discovered.

Compression guide:
To shorten instruction because of time limitations, omit the Chapter Lab.

OBJECTIVES	LABS, DEMONSTRATIONS, AND ACTIVITIES	TECHNOLOGY RESOURCES
PACING • 90 min pp. 618–623 **Chapter Opener**	SE **Start-up Activity,** p. 619 GENERAL	OSP **Parent Letter** ■ CD **Student Edition CD-ROM** CD **Guided Reading Audio CD** ■ TR **Chapter Starter Transparency*** VID **Brain Food Video Quiz**
Section 1 Forming New Substances • Describe how chemical reactions produce new substances that have different chemical and physical properties. • Identify four signs that indicate that a chemical reaction might be taking place. • Explain what happens to chemical bonds during a chemical reaction.	TE **Activity** Making a Chemical Reaction Happen, p. 621 ◆ BASIC SE **Quick Lab** Reaction Ready, p. 623 GENERAL CRF **Datasheet for Quick Lab*** SE **Model-Making Lab** Finding a Balance, p. 740 GENERAL CRF **Datasheet for LabBook***	OSP **Lesson Plans** (also in print) TR **Bellringer Transparency*** TR **P55 Reaction of Hydrogen and Chlorine*** CRF **SciLinks Activity*** GENERAL
PACING • 45 min pp. 624–629 **Section 2 Chemical Formulas and Equations** • Interpret and write simple chemical formulas. • Write and balance simple chemical equations. • Explain how a balanced equation shows the law of conservation of mass.	TE **Activity** Names of Compounds at Home, p. 625 ADVANCED TE **Connection Activity** Math, p. 627 GENERAL TE **Activity** Reactions in the Atmosphere, p. 627 ADVANCED SE **Connection to Language Arts** Diatomic Molecules, p. 628 GENERAL SE **Quick Lab** Conservation of Mass, p. 629 GENERAL CRF **Datasheet for Quick Lab***	OSP **Lesson Plans** (also in print) TR **Bellringer Transparency*** TR **P56 Writing Chemical Formulas and Equations*** TR **P57 Balancing a Chemical Equation***
PACING • 45 min pp. 630–633 **Section 3 Types of Chemical Reactions** • Describe four types of chemical reactions. • Classify a chemical equation as one of four types of chemical reactions.	TE **Demonstration** Single-Displacement Reaction, p. 631 GENERAL SE **Quick Lab** Identifying Reactions, p. 632 GENERAL SE **Skills Practice Lab** Putting Elements Together, p. 742 GENERAL LB **Inquiry Labs** Curses, Foiled Again!* BASIC LB **Labs You Can Eat** How to Fluff a Muffin* GENERAL SE **Science in Action** Math, Social Studies, and Language Arts, Activities, pp. 646–647 GENERAL	OSP **Lesson Plans** (also in print) TR **Bellringer Transparency*** TR **P58 Models of Reactions*** SE **Internet Activity,** p. 632 GENERAL
PACING • 90 min pp. 634–639 **Section 4 Energy and Rates of Chemical Reactions** • Compare exothermic and endothermic reactions. • Explain activation energy. • Interpret an energy diagram. • Describe five factors that affect the rate of a reaction.	SE **Quick Lab** Endo Alert, p. 635 GENERAL SE **Connection to Social Studies** The Strike-Anywhere Match, p. 636 GENERAL SE **Quick Lab** Which Is Quicker?, p. 637 GENERAL TE **Activity** Factors Affecting Rates, p. 637 BASIC SE **Connection to Biology** Enzymes and Inhibitors, p. 638 GENERAL SE **Skills Practice Lab** Speed Control, p. 640 GENERAL CRF **Datasheet for Chapter Lab*** SE **Skills Practice Lab** Cata-what? Catalyst!, p. 741 GENERAL CRF **Datasheet for LabBook*** LB **Whiz-Bang Demonstrations** Fire and Ice* GENERAL LB **Long-Term Projects & Research Ideas** Fruitful Chemistry* ADVANCED	OSP **Lesson Plans** (also in print) TR **Bellringer Transparency*** TR **LINK TO LIFE SCIENCE** L46 Photosynthesis* TR **P59 Energy Diagrams*** VID **Lab Videos for Physical Science**

PACING • 90 min

CHAPTER REVIEW, ASSESSMENT, AND STANDARDIZED TEST PREPARATION

CRF **Vocabulary Activity*** GENERAL
SE **Chapter Review,** pp. 642–643 GENERAL
CRF **Chapter Review*** ■ GENERAL
CRF **Chapter Tests A*** ■ GENERAL**, B*** ADVANCED**, C*** SPECIAL NEEDS
SE **Standardized Test Preparation,** pp. 644–645 GENERAL
CRF **Standardized Test Preparation*** GENERAL
CRF **Performance-Based Assessment*** GENERAL
OSP **Test Generator, Test Item Listing**

Online and Technology Resources

 Holt Online Learning

Visit **go.hrw.com** for access to Holt Online Learning, or enter the keyword **HS7 Home** for a variety of free online resources.

 **One-Stop Planner® CD-ROM**

This CD-ROM package includes:
• Lab Materials QuickList Software
• Holt Calendar Planner
• Customizable Lesson Plans
• Printable Worksheets

• ExamView® Test Generator
• Interactive Teacher's Edition
• Holt PuzzlePro®
• Holt PowerPoint® Resources

SKILLS DEVELOPMENT RESOURCES	SECTION REVIEW AND ASSESSMENT	CORRELATIONS
SE Pre-Reading Activity, p. 618 `GENERAL` **OSP** Science Puzzlers, Twisters & Teasers `GENERAL`		**National Science Education Standards** SAI 2
CRF Directed Reading A* ■ `BASIC`, B* `SPECIAL NEEDS` **WB** Workbook* Struggling Readers **CRF** Vocabulary and Section Summary* ■ `GENERAL` **SE** Reading Strategy Reading Organizer, p. 620 `GENERAL` **TE** Support for English Language Learners, p. 621	**SE** Reading Checks, pp. 621, 622 `GENERAL` **TE** Homework, p. 621 `GENERAL` **TE** Reteaching, p. 622 `BASIC` **TE** Quiz, p. 622 `GENERAL` **TE** Alternative Assessment, p. 622 `GENERAL` **SE** Section Review,* p. 623 ■ `GENERAL` **CRF** Section Quiz* ■ `GENERAL`	UCP 3; PS 1b, 3a, 3e; *LabBook:* PS 3e
CRF Directed Reading A* ■ `BASIC`, B* `SPECIAL NEEDS` **WB** Workbook* Struggling Readers **CRF** Vocabulary and Section Summary* ■ `GENERAL` **SE** Reading Strategy Discussion, p. 624 `GENERAL` **TE** Inclusion Strategies, p. 626 **TE** Support for English Language Learners, p. 626 **SE** Math Practice Counting Atoms, p. 627 `GENERAL` **MS** Math Skills for Science Balancing Chemical Equations* `GENERAL`	**SE** Reading Checks, pp. 625, 626, 628 `GENERAL` **TE** Homework, p. 625 `GENERAL` **TE** Reteaching, p. 628 `BASIC` **TE** Quiz, p. 628 `GENERAL` **TE** Alternative Assessment, p. 628 `GENERAL` **SE** Section Review,* p. 629 ■ `GENERAL` **CRF** Section Quiz* ■ `GENERAL`	UCP 3; SAI 1; PS 1b
CRF Directed Reading A* ■ `BASIC`, B* `SPECIAL NEEDS` **WB** Workbook* Struggling Readers **CRF** Vocabulary and Section Summary* ■ `GENERAL` **SE** Reading Strategy Mnemonics, p. 630 `GENERAL` **TE** Support for English Language Learners, p. 631 **CRF** Reinforcement Worksheet Fabulous Food Reactions* `BASIC`	**SE** Reading Checks, pp. 630, 631, 632 `GENERAL` **TE** Reteaching, p. 632 `BASIC` **TE** Quiz, p. 632 `GENERAL` **TE** Alternative Assessment, p. 632 `ADVANCED` **SE** Section Review,* p. 633 ■ `GENERAL` **CRF** Section Quiz* ■ `GENERAL`	UCP 3; PS 1b; *LabBook:*UCP 3; SAI 1, 2; PS 1b, 3e
CRF Directed Reading A* ■ `BASIC`, B* `SPECIAL NEEDS` **WB** Workbook* Struggling Readers **CRF** Vocabulary and Section Summary* ■ `GENERAL` **SE** Reading Strategy Paired Summarizing, p. 634 `GENERAL` **TE** Support for English Language Learners, p. 637 **TE** Inclusion Strategies, p. 638 **CRF** Reinforcement Worksheet Activation Energy* `BASIC` **CRF** Critical Thinking Shedding Light on Landfills* `ADVANCED`	**SE** Reading Checks, pp. 635, 636, 638 `GENERAL` **TE** Reteaching, p. 638 `BASIC` **TE** Quiz, p. 638 `GENERAL` **TE** Alternative Assessment, p. 638 `GENERAL` **SE** Section Review,* p. 639 ■ `GENERAL` **CRF** Section Quiz* ■ `GENERAL`	UCP 3; SAI 1; PS 1b, 3a, 3e; *Chapter Lab:* SAI 1, 2; *LabBook:* UCP 3; SAI 1; PS 3e

www.scilinks.org

Maintained by the **National Science Teachers Association.** See Chapter Enrichment pages that follow for a complete list of topics.

Check out *Current Science* articles and activities by visiting the HRW Web site at **go.hrw.com.** Just type in the keyword **HP5CS14T.**

 **Classroom Videos**

- **Lab Videos** demonstrate the chapter lab.
- **Brain Food Video Quizzes** help students review the chapter material.

Classroom CD-ROMs

- **Guided Reading Audio CD** (Also in Spanish)
- **Interactive Explorations**
- **Virtual Investigations**
- **Visual Concepts**
- **Science Tutor**

 **Holt Lab Generator CD-ROM**

Search for any lab by topic, standard, difficulty level, or time. Edit any lab to fit your needs, or create your own labs. Use the Lab Materials QuickList software to customize your lab materials list.

Visual Resources

CHAPTER STARTER TRANSPARENCY

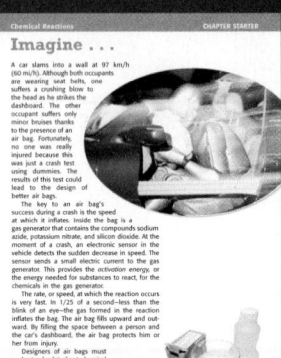

BELLRINGER TRANSPARENCIES

TEACHING TRANSPARENCIES

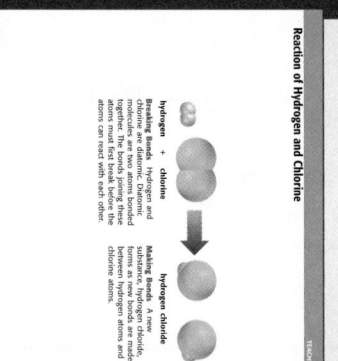

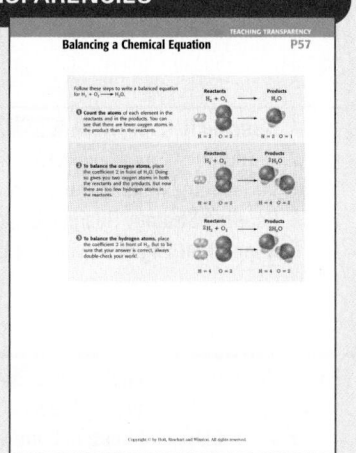

TEACHING TRANSPARENCIES

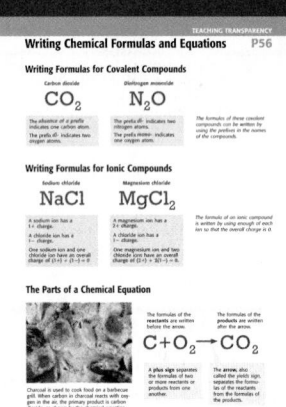

CONCEPT MAPPING TRANSPARENCY

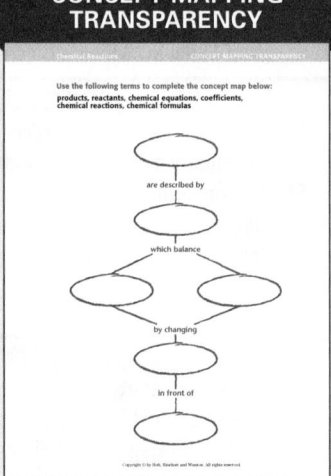

Planning Resources

LESSON PLANS

PARENT LETTER

TEST ITEM LISTING

One-Stop Planner® CD-ROM

This CD-ROM includes all of the resources shown here and the following time-saving tools:

- *Lab Materials QuickList Software*
- *Customizable lesson plans*
- *Holt Calendar Planner*
- *The powerful ExamView® Test Generator*

Meeting Individual Needs

DIRECTED READING A
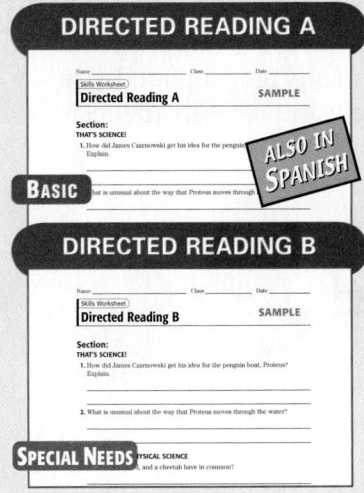
BASIC

DIRECTED READING B
SPECIAL NEEDS

VOCABULARY ACTIVITY
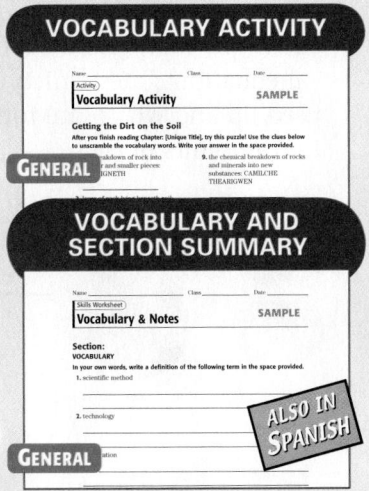
GENERAL

VOCABULARY AND SECTION SUMMARY
GENERAL

REINFORCEMENT
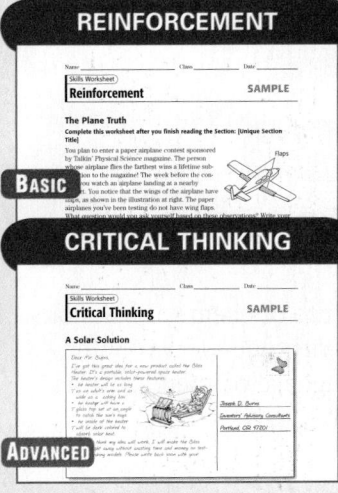
BASIC

CRITICAL THINKING
ADVANCED

SCILINKS ACTIVITY

GENERAL

SCIENCE PUZZLERS, TWISTERS & TEASERS
GENERAL

Labs and Activities

LONG-TERM PROJECTS & RESEARCH IDEAS
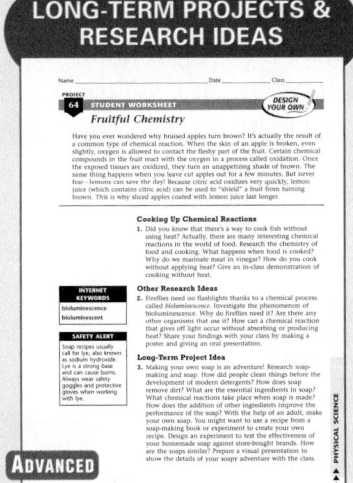
ADVANCED

WHIZ-BANG DEMONSTRATIONS
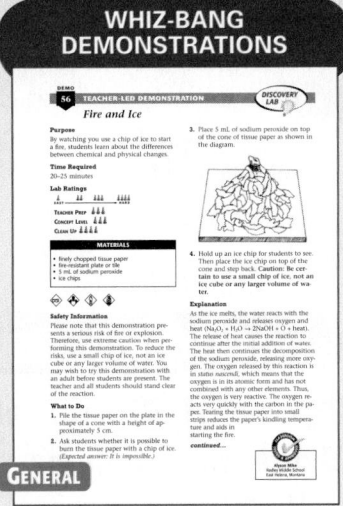
GENERAL

INQUIRY LABS
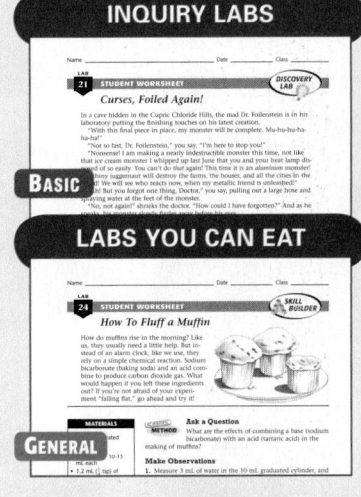
BASIC

LABS YOU CAN EAT
GENERAL

DATASHEETS FOR QUICK LABS

DATASHEETS FOR CHAPTER LABS

DATASHEETS FOR LABBOOK

Review and Assessments

SECTION QUIZ
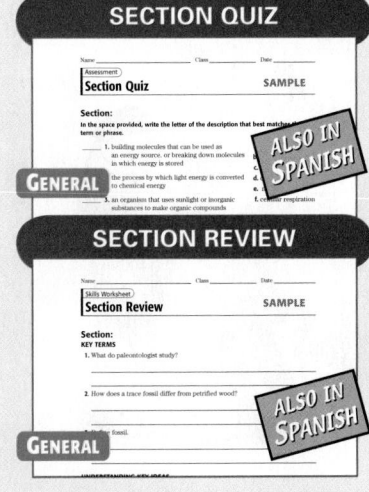
GENERAL

SECTION REVIEW
GENERAL

CHAPTER REVIEW
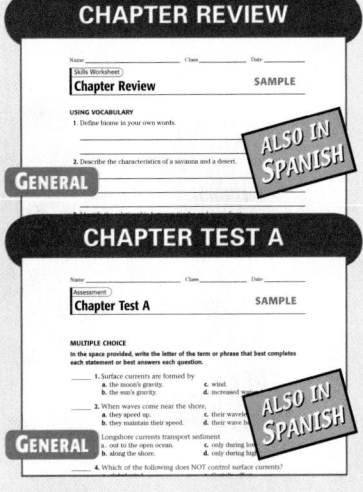
GENERAL

CHAPTER TEST A
GENERAL

CHAPTER TEST B
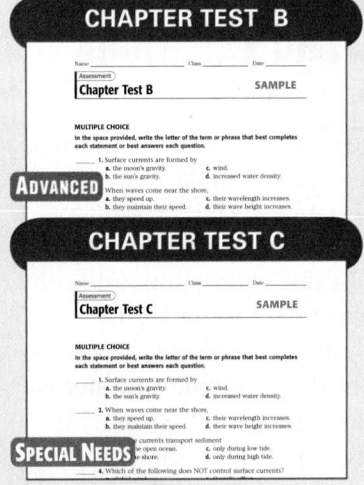
ADVANCED

CHAPTER TEST C
SPECIAL NEEDS

STANDARDIZED TEST PREPARATION
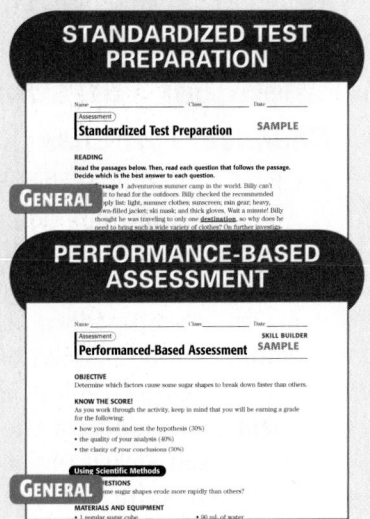
GENERAL

PERFORMANCE-BASED ASSESSMENT
GENERAL

This Chapter Enrichment provides relevant and interesting information to expand and enhance your presentation of the chapter material.

Section 1

Forming New Substances

Chemical Symbols

- To be able to discuss the nature of chemical reactions, scientists identify elements with one- or two-letter symbols. In this way, the language of chemical reactions can be understood universally.

Conserved Quantities

- In any chemical or physical change, the total amount of mass and energy is unchanged in the reaction. Both the law of conservation of mass and the law of conservation of energy apply to the chemical reactions discussed in this chapter.

Section 2

Chemical Formulas and Equations

Chemical Formulas

- Chemical formulas describe compounds and elements. A chemical formula describes one formula unit of a compound or element. If the substance is molecular, the formula unit represents one molecule. For example, the chemical formula for the ionic compound calcium chloride is $CaCl_2$, because each formula unit consists of one calcium ion and two chloride ions. The chemical formula for the covalent compound water is H_2O, because each molecule of water consists of two hydrogen atoms and one oxygen atom.

Chemical Equations

- Chemical formulas are used together to form chemical equations that describe a chemical reaction. A chemical equation states which elements or compounds are used up and which are formed, and it shows the relative amounts of each.

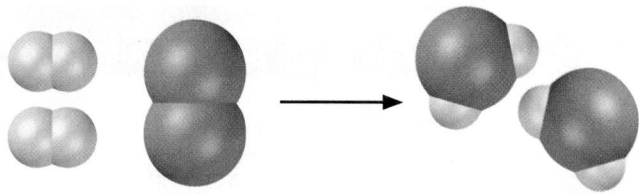

Is That a Fact!

- ◆ The reaction between hydrogen gas and oxygen gas to form water can be started with a small flame. However, water cannot be changed back into hydrogen and oxygen merely by cooling. The reverse chemical reaction can be accomplished only if some type of energy, such as electrical energy, is used to break the bonds between the hydrogen and oxygen atoms in the water molecules.

Section 3

Types of Chemical Reactions

Synthesis Reactions

- The formation of one product from two or more reactants is a synthesis reaction. For example, the formation of magnesium oxide from magnesium and oxygen (in early flashbulbs) and the formation of ammonia from nitrogen and hydrogen are synthesis reactions.

Decomposition Reactions

● A decomposition reaction is one in which a single compound produces two or more simpler substances. For example, the breakdown of water molecules into hydrogen and oxygen molecules is a decomposition reaction in which energy is used to break the bonds in the water molecules.

Single-Displacement Reactions

● Both metals and nonmetals undergo single-displacement reactions; for example, zinc, a metal, will react with hydrochloric acid to form zinc chloride and hydrogen gas. Chlorine, a nonmetal, will replace the bromine in sodium bromide to form sodium chloride and bromine.

Double-Displacement Reactions

● In a double-displacement reaction, two compounds exchange their ions. When a person takes milk of magnesia (magnesium hydroxide) to neutralize stomach acid, a double-displacement reaction occurs. The two products formed are magnesium chloride and water.

Is That a Fact!

◆ The reaction between baking soda, $NaHCO_3$, and tartaric acid, $H_2C_4H_4O_6$, in baking powder is a double-displacement reaction, followed by a decomposition reaction that produces carbon dioxide, CO_2. The bubbles of CO_2 make some doughs rise.

Section 4

Energy and Rates of Chemical Reactions

Chemical Kinetics

● For a chemical reaction to occur, reactant molecules must collide with enough energy and in the proper orientation to allow bonds to break and new bonds to form.

Endothermic Reactions

● Endothermic reactions are those that absorb energy. Photosynthesis in plants is an example of an endothermic reaction. Light energy from the sun drives the formation of glucose from carbon dioxide and water.

Exothermic Reactions

● Exothermic reactions are those in which energy is given off. For example, when hydrogen and oxygen react to form water, light and thermal energy are given off.

● In the body, exothermic reactions take place when food molecules are broken down in a series of reactions and absorbed by cells.

Catalysts

● *Catalysts* are substances that significantly increase the rate of a reaction. *Enzymes* are catalysts in living systems. These large protein molecules speed up many of the reactions in our body. For instance, the enzyme *amylase*, found in saliva, breaks down starch.

SciLinks is maintained by the National Science Teachers Association to provide you and your students with interesting, up-to-date links that will enrich your classroom presentation of the chapter.

Visit www.scilinks.org and enter the SciLinks code for more information about the topic listed.

Topic: Chemical Reactions
SciLinks code: HSM0274

Topic: Reaction Types
SciLinks code: HSM1272

Topic: Chemical Formulas
SciLinks code: HSM0271

Topic: Chemical Equations
SciLinks code: HSM0269

Topic: Exothermic and Endothermic Reactions
SciLinks code: HSM0555

Overview

Tell students that this chapter will help them learn about chemical reactions. The chapter describes what is involved in a chemical reaction, how chemical reactions are expressed, what the different kinds of chemical reaction are, and how energy and rates are involved in chemical reactions.

Assessing Prior Knowledge

Students should be familiar with the following topics:

• matter

• energy

• atoms

• elements

• chemical bonding

Identifying Misconceptions

The conservation of atoms in a chemical reaction will probably have to be reinforced repeatedly, as students may believe that chemical reactions change matter intrinsically. Once the conservation of atoms in a chemical reaction is established, many other concepts pertaining to reactions, such as formulas, equations, and types of reactions, should follow quite naturally. Students may have initial difficulty understanding that some reactions require energy input in order to go forward.

23
Chemical Reactions

The Big Idea Substances undergo chemical reactions, which form new substances whose properties differ from the properties of the original substances.

About the Photo

Dazzling fireworks and the Statue of Liberty are great examples of chemical reactions. Chemical reactions cause fireworks to soar, explode, and light up the sky. And the Statue of Liberty has its distinctive green color because of the reaction between the statue's copper and chemicals in the air.

PRE-READING ACTIVITY

 **Four-Corner Fold**

Before you read the chapter, create the FoldNote entitled "Four-Corner Fold" described in the **Study Skills** section of the Appendix. Label the flaps of the four-corner fold with "Chemical formulas," "Chemical equations," "Types of chemical reactions," and "Rates of chemical reactions." Write what you know about each topic under the appropriate flap. As you read the chapter, add other information that you learn.

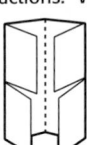

Standards Correlations

National Science Education Standards

The following codes indicate the National Science Education Standards that correlate to this chapter. The full text of the standards is at the front of the book.

Chapter Opener
SAI 2

Section 1 Forming New Substances
UCP 3; PS 1b, 3a, 3e; *LabBook:* PS 3e

Section 2 Chemical Formulas and Equations
UCP 3; SAI 1; PS 1b

Section 3 Types of Chemical Reactions
UCP 3; PS 1b; *LabBook:* UCP 3; SAI 1, 2; PS 1b, 3e

Section 4 Energy and Rates of Chemical Reactions
UCP 3; SAI 1; PS 1b, 3a, 3e; *LabBook:* UCP 3; SAI 1; PS 3e

Chapter Lab
SAI 1, 2

START-UP ACTIVITY
MATERIALS

FOR EACH STUDENT
• marshmallow models of hydrogen peroxide (3)

FOR EACH GROUP
• marshmallow model of water (1)
• marshmallow model of oxygen (1)

Safety Caution: Remind students to wear safety goggles while performing this activity. Students should not eat any of the marshmallows.

Answers

1. two
2. two; one
3. six; three

START-UP ACTIVITY

A Model Formula

Chemicals react in very precise ways. In this activity, you will model a chemical reaction and will predict how chemicals react.

Procedure

1. You will receive **several marshmallow models.** The models are marshmallows attached by **toothpicks.** Each of these models is a Model A.

2. Your teacher will show you an example of Model B and Model C. Take apart one or more Model As to make copies of Model B and Model C.

3. If you have marshmallows left over, use them to make more Model Bs and Model Cs. If you need more parts to complete a Model B or Model C, take apart another Model A.

4. Repeat step 3 until you have no parts left over.

Analysis

1. How many Model As did you use to make copies of Model B and Model C?

2. How many Model Bs did you make? How many Model Cs did you make?

3. Suppose you needed to make six Model Bs. How many Model As would you need? How many Model Cs could you make with the leftover marshmallows?

Chapter Review
PS 1b, 3a, 3e

Science in Action
SPSP 3, 5; ST 2

Imagine . . .

A car slams into a wall at 97 km/h (60 mi/h). Although both occupants are wearing seat belts, one suffers a crushing blow to the head as he strikes the dashboard. The other occupant suffers only minor bruises thanks to the presence of an air bag. Fortunately, no one was really injured because this was just a crash test using dummies. The results of this test could lead to the design of better air bags.

The key to an air bag's success during a crash is the speed at which it inflates. Inside the bag is a gas generator that contains the compounds sodium azide, potassium nitrate, and silicon dioxide. At the moment of a crash, an electronic sensor in the vehicle detects the sudden decrease in speed. The sensor sends a small electric current to the gas generator. This provides the activation energy, or the energy needed for substances to react, for the chemicals in the gas generator.

The rate, or speed, at which the reaction occurs is very fast. In 1/25 of a second—less than the blink of an eye—the gas formed in the reaction inflates the bag. The air bag fills upward and outward. By filling the space between a person and the car's dashboard, the air bag protects him or her from injury.

Designers of air bags must

Chapter Starter Transparency
Use this transparency to help students begin thinking about chemical reactions.

CHAPTER RESOURCES

Technology

Transparencies
• Chapter Starter Transparency

READING SKILLS

Student Edition on CD-ROM

Guided Reading Audio CD
• English or Spanish

Classroom Videos
• Brain Food Video Quiz

Workbooks

Science Puzzlers, Twisters & Teasers
• Chemical Reactions **GENERAL**

Focus

Overview

This section discusses the nature of chemical reactions. Students will learn some of the signs that a chemical reaction has taken place. They will also learn that bonds are broken and new bonds are formed during a chemical reaction.

 Bellringer

Ask students the following question: "What do baking bread, launching the space shuttle, and digesting food have in common?" (They all involve chemical reactions.)

Have them write their answer in their **science journal.**

Motivate

Discussion ———— GENERAL

Chemical Reactions at School

Ask students to think about the chemical reactions that occur in school every day. Have them consider the reactions in the meals cooking in the school cafeteria and the reactions in the batteries that provide energy to run equipment. List their responses on the board, and discuss the signs to look for in each chemical reaction. **LS Logical**

What You Will Learn

● Describe how chemical reactions produce new substances that have different chemical and physical properties.
● Identify four signs that indicate that a chemical reaction might be taking place.
● Explain what happens to chemical bonds during a chemical reaction.

Vocabulary
chemical reaction
precipitate

READING STRATEGY

Reading Organizer As you read this section, create an outline of the section. Use the headings from the section in your outline.

Forming New Substances

Each fall, a beautiful change takes place when leaves turn colors. You see bright oranges and yellows that had been hidden by green all summer. What causes this change?

To answer this question, you need to know what causes leaves to be green. Leaves are green because they contain a green substance, or *pigment*. This pigment is called *chlorophyll* (KLAWR uh FIL). During the spring and summer, the leaves have a large amount of chlorophyll in them. But in the fall, when temperatures drop and there are fewer hours of sunlight, chlorophyll breaks down to form new substances that have no color. The green chlorophyll is no longer present to hide the other pigments. You can now see the orange and yellow colors that were present all along.

Chemical Reactions

A chemical change takes place when chlorophyll breaks down into new substances. This change is an example of a chemical reaction. A **chemical reaction** is a process in which one or more substances change to make one or more new substances. The chemical and physical properties of the new substances differ from those of the original substances. Some results of chemical reactions are shown in **Figure 1.**

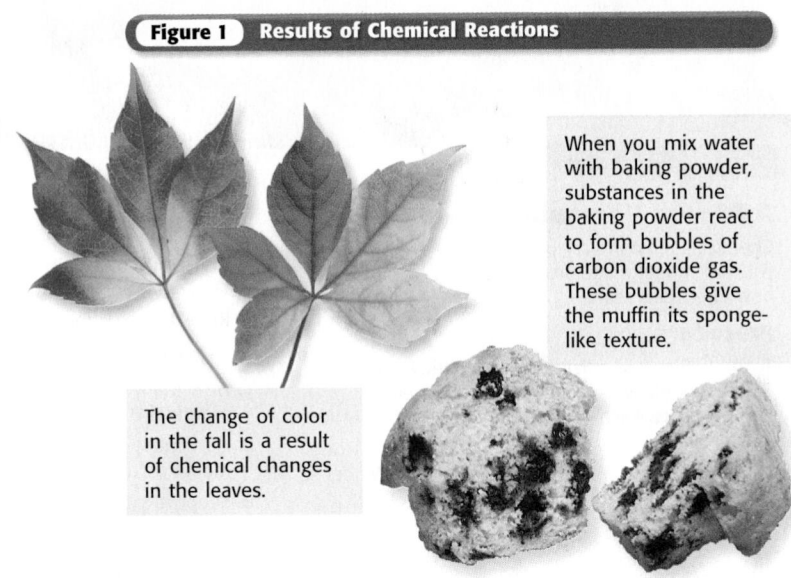

Figure 1 **Results of Chemical Reactions**

When you mix water with baking powder, substances in the baking powder react to form bubbles of carbon dioxide gas. These bubbles give the muffin its sponge-like texture.

The change of color in the fall is a result of chemical changes in the leaves.

CHAPTER RESOURCES

Chapter Resource File

 • **Lesson Plan**
 • **Directed Reading A** BASIC
 • **Directed Reading B** SPECIAL NEEDS

Technology

 Transparencies
 • Bellringer

Workbooks

 Interactive Textbook Struggling Readers

Is That a Fact!

Carbon dioxide has a number of well-known uses. When dissolved under pressure, it produces the effervescence in carbonated beverages. Because carbon dioxide gas does not combust and is denser than air, it is used in fire extinguishers to smother flames. Dry ice, or solid carbon dioxide, is valuable for its cooling effect. Carbon dioxide also changes directly from a solid to a gas, bypassing the liquid state.

Signs of Chemical Reactions

How can you tell when a chemical reaction is taking place? **Figure 2** shows some signs that tell you that a reaction may be taking place. In some chemical reactions, gas bubbles form. Other reactions form solid precipitates (pree SIP uh TAYTS). A **precipitate** is a solid substance that is formed in a solution. During other chemical reactions, energy is given off. This energy may be in the form of light, thermal energy, or electrical energy. Reactions often have more than one of these signs. And the more of these signs that you see, the more likely that a chemical reaction is taking place.

✓ **Reading Check** What is a precipitate? (*See the Appendix for answers to Reading Checks.*)

chemical reaction the process by which one or more substances change to produce one or more different substances

precipitate a solid that is produced as a result of a chemical reaction in solution

Figure 2 Some Signs of Chemical Reactions

Gas Formation
The chemical reaction in the beaker has formed a brown gas, nitrogen dioxide. This gas is formed when a strip of copper is placed into nitric acid.

Solid Formation
Here you see potassium chromate solution being added to a silver nitrate solution. The dark red solid is a precipitate of silver chromate.

Energy Change
Energy is released during some chemical reactions. The fire in this photo gives off light energy and thermal energy. During some other chemical reactions, energy is taken in.

Color Change
Don't spill chlorine bleach on your jeans! The bleach reacts with the blue dye on the fabric and causes the color of the material to change.

Teach

ACTIVITY ———— BASIC

Making a Chemical Reaction Happen Allow students the opportunity to carry out one or more of the chemical reactions described in this section. Using four index cards, write one sign of a chemical reaction on each card (gas formation, solid formation, color change, and energy change). Have students match the correct sign with each of the reactions observed. **LS** Kinesthetic — English Language Learners

Homework ———— GENERAL

Chemical Reactions at Home Ask students to list in their **science journal** the chemical reactions that they observe in their home. Students should include which of the signs mentioned in this section indicated that a chemical reaction was occurring. **LS** Intrapersonal

Answer to Reading Check

A precipitate is a solid substance that is formed in a solution.

SUPPORT FOR

English Language Learners

Signs of Chemical Reactions To check comprehension of signs of chemical reactions, review the photos on this page orally with students. Discuss the types of reactions shown (formations and changes). Elicit from students the difference between these types. Discuss what students see in the photos that indicates a reaction is taking place. Finally, ask them to write these indications next to the type of reaction in their science journals. **LS** Auditory/Visual

MISCONCEPTION ///ALERT

Signs of a Chemical Reaction Remind students that the signs described on this page are not present with every chemical reaction. Also, caution students that these signs can be very subtle. For example, gases can be formed in chemical reactions without forming visible bubbles. Also, an energy change in a reaction is not always accompanied by a release of thermal energy and light.

Physical Change or Chemical Change? Organize the class into two teams. Have students take turns asking the other team if a certain change is physical or chemical. Award points for correct answers, and continue until each student has had a chance to try to "stump" the other team. **LS** Interpersonal

Quiz ───── GENERAL

1. Name four possible signs that a chemical reaction has taken place. (gas formation, solid formation, energy change, and color change)

2. What happens to chemical bonds during a chemical reaction? (They break, and new ones are formed.)

Alternative Assessment ───── GENERAL

Using Models Allow students to make and break bonds using toothpicks and plastic-foam balls of two different sizes. Use the example given in **Figure 4** to guide students through the breaking of bonds between atoms of hydrogen (small balls) and chlorine (large balls) and the making of new bonds in hydrogen chloride. **LS** Kinesthetic

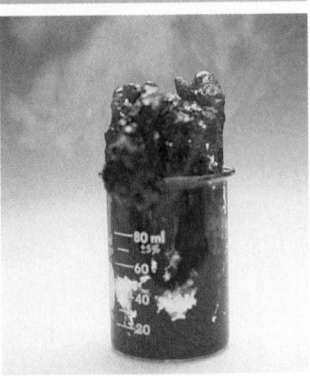

Figure 3 *The top photo shows the starting substances: table sugar and sulfuric acid, a clear liquid. The substances formed in this chemical reaction are very different from the starting substances.*

A Change of Properties

Even though the signs we look for to see if a reaction is taking place are good signals of chemical reactions, they do not guarantee that a reaction is happening. For example, gas can be given off when a liquid boils. But this example is a physical change, not a chemical reaction.

So, how can you be sure that a chemical reaction is occurring? The most important sign is the formation of new substances that have different properties. Look at **Figure 3.** The starting materials in this reaction are sugar and sulfuric acid. Several things tell you that a chemical reaction is taking place. Bubbles form, a gas is given off, and the beaker becomes very hot. But most important, new substances form. And the properties of these substances are very different from those of the starting substances.

Bonds: Holding Molecules Together

A *chemical bond* is a force that holds two atoms together in a molecule. For a chemical reaction to take place, the original bonds must break and new bonds must form.

Breaking and Making Bonds

How do new substances form in a chemical reaction? First, chemical bonds in the starting substances must break. Molecules are always moving. If the molecules bump into each other with enough energy, the chemical bonds in the molecules break. The atoms then rearrange, and new bonds form to make the new substances. **Figure 4** shows how bonds break and form in the reaction between hydrogen and chlorine.

✓ *Reading Check* What happens to the bonds of substances during a chemical reaction?

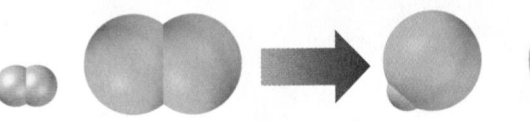

Figure 4   Reaction of Hydrogen and Chlorine

hydrogen + chlorine   hydrogen chloride

Breaking Bonds Hydrogen and chlorine are diatomic. Diatomic molecules are two atoms bonded together. The bonds joining these atoms must first break before the atoms can react with each other.

Making Bonds A new substance, hydrogen chloride, forms as new bonds are made between hydrogen atoms and chlorine atoms.

Answer to Reading Check

In a chemical reaction, the chemical bonds in the starting substances break, and then new bonds form to make new substances.

New Bonds, New Substances

What happens when hydrogen and chlorine are combined? A chlorine gas molecule is a diatomic (DIE uh TAHM ik) molecule. That is, a chlorine molecule is made of two atoms of chlorine. Chlorine gas has a greenish yellow color. Hydrogen gas is also a diatomic molecule. Hydrogen gas is a flammable, colorless gas. When chlorine gas and hydrogen gas react, the bond between the hydrogen atoms breaks. And the bond between the chlorine atoms also breaks. A new bond forms between each hydrogen and chlorine atom. A new substance, hydrogen chloride, is formed. Hydrogen chloride is a nonflammable, colorless gas. Its properties differ from the properties of both of the starting substances.

Let's look at another example. Sodium is a metal that reacts violently in water. Chlorine gas is poisonous. When chlorine gas and sodium react, the result is a familiar compound—table salt. Sodium chloride, or table salt, is a harmless substance that almost everyone uses. The salt's properties are very different from sodium's or chlorine's. Salt is a new substance.

Quick Lab

Reaction Ready

1. Place a **piece of chalk** in a **plastic cup**.
2. Add **5 mL of vinegar** to the cup. Record your observations.
3. What evidence of a chemical reaction do you see?
4. What type of new substance was formed?

Quick Lab

MATERIALS

FOR EACH PAIR OF STUDENTS
- chalk
- cup, clear plastic
- vinegar, 5 mL

Safety Caution: Remind students to wear safety goggles, gloves, and aprons.

Answers

3. fizzing, bubbles form, gas given off
4. a white, solid precipitate

Answers to Section Review

1. Sample answer: In one class of chemical reaction, two liquids are mixed, and a solid precipitate forms.
2. a
3. no
4. no; This is a physical change: the steam that is being formed is just another form of water.
5. Charcoal burning in a grill is a chemical change because new substances are formed in the process.
6. Formation of gas and light are clues that a chemical reaction is taking place.
7. Bonds in the starting substances are being broken.

SECTION Review

Summary

- A chemical reaction is a process by which substances change to produce new substances with new chemical and physical properties.
- Signs that indicate a chemical reaction has taken place are a color change, formation of a gas or a solid, and release of energy.
- During a reaction, bonds are broken, atoms are rearranged, and new bonds are formed.

Using Key Terms

1. Use the following terms in the same sentence: *chemical reaction* and *precipitate*.

Understanding Key Ideas

2. Most chemical reactions
   a. have starting substances that collide with each other.
   b. do not break bonds.
   c. do not rearrange atoms.
   d. cannot be seen.

3. If the chemical properties of a substance have not changed, has a chemical reaction occurred?

Critical Thinking

4. **Analyzing Processes** Steam is escaping from a teapot. Is this a chemical reaction? Explain.

5. **Applying Concepts** Explain why charcoal burning in a grill is a chemical change.

Interpreting Graphics

Use the photo below to answer the questions that follow.

6. What evidence of a chemical reaction is shown in the photo?

7. What is happening to the bonds of the starting substances?

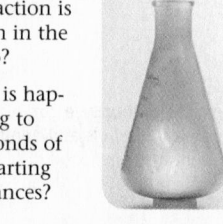

Developed and maintained by the National Science Teachers Association

For a variety of links related to this chapter, go to www.scilinks.org

Topic: Chemical Reactions
SciLinks code: HSM0274

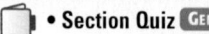

CHAPTER RESOURCES

Chapter Resource File

- Section Quiz GENERAL
- Section Review GENERAL
- Vocabulary and Section Summary GENERAL
- SciLinks Activity GENERAL
- Datasheet for Quick Lab

Technology

Transparencies
- P55 Reaction of Hydrogen and Chlorine

Focus

Overview

In this section, students will learn how to write chemical formulas and how to balance chemical equations. This section also explains how the law of conservation of mass is maintained in a balanced equation.

 Bellringer

Write the symbols for several common elements on the board. Have students list the symbols, and then have them try to remember the names of the matching elements. When they have finished, have them check their answers with the periodic table in their book.

Motivate

Discussion ——— GENERAL

Rearranging Atoms Revisit the teaching transparency "Reaction of Hydrogen and Chlorine" to review the nature of a chemical reaction. Help students trace where each atom in the chemical reaction ends up. Use this as a springboard into the idea of balanced chemical equations.
LS Visual

What You Will Learn

● Interpret and write simple chemical formulas.
● Write and balance simple chemical equations.
● Explain how a balanced equation shows the law of conservation of mass.

Vocabulary

chemical formula
chemical equation
reactant
product
law of conservation of mass

READING STRATEGY

Discussion Read this section silently. Write down questions that you have about this section. Discuss your questions in a small group.

chemical formula a combination of chemical symbols and numbers to represent a substance

Chemical Formulas and Equations

How many words can you make using the 26 letters of the alphabet? Many thousands? Now, think of how many sentences you can make with all of those words.

Letters are used to form words. In the same way, chemical symbols are put together to make chemical formulas that describe substances. Chemical formulas can be placed together to describe a chemical reaction, just like words can be put together to make a sentence.

Chemical Formulas

All substances are formed from about 100 elements. Each element has its own chemical symbol. A **chemical formula** is a shorthand way to use chemical symbols and numbers to represent a substance. A chemical formula shows how many atoms of each kind are present in a molecule.

As shown in **Figure 1,** the chemical formula for water is H_2O. This formula tells you that one water molecule is made of two atoms of hydrogen and one atom of oxygen. The small 2 in the formula is a subscript. A *subscript* is a number written below and to the right of a chemical symbol in a formula. Sometimes, a symbol, such as O for oxygen in water's formula, has no subscript. If there is no subscript, only one atom of that element is present. Look at **Figure 1** for more examples of chemical formulas.

Figure 1 Chemical Formulas of Different Substances

Water	Oxygen	Glucose
H_2O	O_2	$C_6H_{12}O_6$

Water molecules are made up of 3 atoms—2 atoms of hydrogen bonded to 1 atom of oxygen.

Oxygen is a diatomic molecule. Each molecule has 2 atoms of oxygen bonded together.

Glucose molecules have 6 atoms of carbon, 12 atoms of hydrogen, and 6 atoms of oxygen.

CHAPTER RESOURCES

Chapter Resource File

● **Lesson Plan**
● **Directed Reading A** BASIC
● **Directed Reading B** SPECIAL NEEDS

Technology

Transparencies
● Bellringer

Workbooks

Interactive Textbook Struggling Readers

Is That a Fact!

When hydrogen chloride gas is dissolved in water, it is known as *hydrochloric acid*. There is a small amount of concentrated hydrochloric acid in your stomach, where it is necessary for the digestion of food.

Carbon dioxide

CO$_2$

The *absence of a prefix* indicates one carbon atom.

The prefix *di-* indicates two oxygen atoms.

Dinitrogen monoxide

N$_2$O

The prefix *di-* indicates two nitrogen atoms.

The prefix *mono-* indicates one oxygen atom.

Figure 2 *The formulas of these covalent compounds can be written by using the prefixes in the names of the compounds.*

Writing Formulas for Covalent Compounds

If you know the name of the covalent compound, you can often write the chemical formula for that compound. Covalent compounds are usually composed of two nonmetals. The names of many covalent compounds use prefixes. Each prefix represents a number, as shown in **Table 1.** The prefixes tell you how many atoms of each element are in a formula. **Figure 2** shows you how to write a chemical formula from the name of a covalent compound.

Table 1	Prefixes Used in Chemical Names		
mono-	1	hexa-	6
di-	2	hepta-	7
tri-	3	octa-	8
tetra-	4	nona-	9
penta-	5	deca-	10

Writing Formulas for Ionic Compounds

If the name of a compound contains the name of a metal and the name of a nonmetal, the compound is ionic. To write the formula for an ionic compound, make sure the compound's charge is 0. In other words, the formula must have subscripts that cause the charges of the ions to cancel out. **Figure 3** shows you how to write a chemical formula from the name of an ionic compound.

Reading Check What kinds of elements make up an ionic compound? (*See the Appendix for answers to Reading Checks*.)

Sodium chloride

NaCl

A sodium ion has a 1+ charge.

A chloride ion has a 1− charge.

One sodium ion and one chloride ion have an overall **charge of (1+) + (1−) = 0.**

Magnesium chloride

MgCl$_2$

A magnesium ion has a 2+ charge.

A chloride ion has a 1− charge.

One magnesium ion and two chloride ions have an overall **charge of (2+) + 2(1−) = 0.**

Figure 3 *The formula of an ionic compound is written by using enough of each ion so that the overall charge is 0.*

Answer to Reading Check

Ionic compounds are made up of a metal and a nonmetal.

Teach

Homework ————— GENERAL

Formulas of Ionic and Covalent Compounds Write the chemical names given below on the board. Have students identify each compound as ionic or covalent. Then, have them use the table of prefixes on this page and a periodic table to write the formula for each compound.

• sulfur trioxide (covalent; SO$_3$)

• calcium fluoride (ionic; CaF$_2$)

• phosphorus pentachloride (covalent; PCl$_5$)

• dinitrogen trioxide (covalent; N$_2$O$_3$)

• lithium oxide (ionic; Li$_2$O)

LS Logical

 ————— ADVANCED

Names of Compounds at Home Have students write the names of compounds in the list of ingredients of products found around their homes. Encourage students to identify the compounds as ionic or covalent and to attempt to write the chemical formulas for each of them. Many of the compounds can be found in chemistry references.

LS Logical

Cultural Awareness GENERAL

Greek Roots The prefixes in the names of covalent compounds have their origins in the Greek language. Each prefix is a Greek numeric representation.

SUPPORT FOR

English Language Learners

Yield Discuss the meaning of the term *yield*. Explain that the yield arrow is similar in meaning to an equal sign in a mathematical equation, although not the same. Give examples of an equation and an expression using *yield* to illustrate.  Auditory/Logical

INCLUSION Strategies

- *Hearing Impaired*
- *Developmentally Delayed*
- *Learning Disabled*

Help students understand that combining the same atoms into different groupings creates different substances. Trace 30 quarters onto a piece of paper. Label each circle as an element. Include the following numbers of elements: 12 hydrogen, 6 carbon, 9 oxygen, 3 nitrogen. Make a copy for each student and have students cut out the circles. Ask students to rearrange their "atoms" to assemble each of the following substances (actual structures will be considered unimportant): oxygen (O_2), glucose ($C_6H_{12}O_6$), carbon dioxide (CO_2), vitamin C ($C_6H_8O_6$), nitroglycerin ($C_3H_5N_3O_9$), rubbing alcohol (C_3H_7OH), and water (H_2O).  Kinesthetic

Answer to Reading Check

Reactants are the starting substances in a chemical reaction, and products are the substances that are formed.

Figure 4 *Like chemical symbols, the symbols on this musical score are understood around the world!*

chemical equation a representation of a chemical reaction that uses symbols to show the relationship between the reactants and the products

reactant a substance or molecule that participates in a chemical reaction

product the substance that forms in a chemical reaction

Chemical Equations

Think about a piece of music, such as the one in **Figure 4.** Someone writing music must tell the musician what notes to play, how long to play each note, and how each note should be played. Words aren't used to describe the musical piece. Instead, musical symbols are used. The symbols can be understood by anyone who can read music.

Describing Reactions by Using Equations

In the same way that composers use musical symbols, chemists around the world use chemical symbols and chemical formulas. Instead of changing words and sentences into other languages to describe reactions, chemists use chemical equations. A **chemical equation** uses chemical symbols and formulas as a shortcut to describe a chemical reaction. A chemical equation is short and is understood by anyone who understands chemical formulas.

From Reactants to Products

When carbon burns, it reacts with oxygen to form carbon dioxide. **Figure 5** shows how a chemist would use an equation to describe this reaction. The starting materials in a chemical reaction are **reactants** (ree AK tuhnts). The substances formed from a reaction are **products.** In this example, carbon and oxygen are reactants. Carbon dioxide is the product.

✓ **Reading Check** What is the difference between reactants and products in a chemical reaction?

Figure 5   The Parts of a Chemical Equation

Charcoal is used to cook food on a barbecue grill. When carbon in charcoal reacts with oxygen in the air, the primary product is carbon dioxide, as shown by the chemical equation.

The formulas of the **reactants** are written before the arrow.

The formulas of the **products** are written after the arrow.

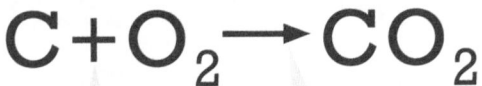

A **plus sign** separates the formulas of two or more reactants or products from one another.

The **arrow,** also called the *yields sign,* separates the formulas of the reactants from the formulas of the products.

SCIENCE HUMOR

Q: What does a doctor do with an injured chemist?

A: helium

Q: And what does a doctor do with a sick chemist?

A: curium

Q: And, what happens if the doctor can't cure her?

A: barium

MISCONCEPTION ALERT

Triatomic Molecules Some students may assume that triatomic molecules such as H_2O, CO_2, and N_2O consist of only two particles bonded together. For example, students may think that H_2O consists of a molecule of hydrogen, H_2, bonded to an atom of oxygen. Be sure to point out that in such molecules, there are three particles bonded together. In the case of H_2O, there are two hydrogen atoms bonded to one oxygen atom.

Figure 6 Examples of Similar Symbols and Formulas

CO$_2$

The chemical formula for the compound **carbon dioxide** is CO$_2$. Carbon dioxide is a colorless, odorless gas that you exhale.

CO

The chemical formula for the compound **carbon monoxide** is CO. Carbon monoxide is a colorless, odorless, and poisonous gas.

Co

The chemical symbol for the element **cobalt** is Co. Cobalt is a hard, bluish gray metal.

The Importance of Accuracy

The symbol or formula for each substance in the equation must be written correctly. For a compound, use the correct chemical formula. For an element, use the proper chemical symbol. An equation that has the wrong chemical symbol or formula will not correctly describe the reaction. In fact, even a simple mistake can make a huge difference. **Figure 6** shows how formulas and symbols can be mistaken.

The Reason Equations Must Be Balanced

Atoms are never lost or gained in a chemical reaction. They are just rearranged. Every atom in the reactants becomes part of the products. When writing a chemical equation, make sure the number of atoms of each element in the reactants equals the number of atoms of those elements in the products. This is called balancing the equation.

Balancing equations comes from the work of a French chemist, Antoine Lavoisier (lah vwah ZYAY). In the 1700s, Lavoisier found that the total mass of the reactants was always the same as the total mass of the products. Lavoisier's work led to the **law of conservation of mass.** This law states that mass is neither created nor destroyed in ordinary chemical and physical changes. This law means that a chemical equation must show the same numbers and kinds of atoms on both sides of the arrow.

Counting Atoms

Some chemical formulas contain parentheses. When counting atoms, multiply everything inside the parentheses by the subscript. For example, Ca(NO$_3$)$_2$ has one calcium atom, two (2 × 1) nitrogen atoms, and six (2 × 3) oxygen atoms. Find the number of atoms of each element in the formulas Mg(OH)$_2$ and Al$_2$(SO$_4$)$_3$.

law of conservation of mass
the law that states that mass cannot be created or destroyed in ordinary chemical and physical changes

CHAPTER RESOURCES

Technology

 Transparencies
• P56 Writing Chemical Formulas and Equations

Reteaching — BASIC

Writing Chemical Formulas
Remind students of the importance of writing chemical formulas correctly. As an example, write the formulas for water, H_2O, and hydrogen peroxide, H_2O_2, or for oxygen, O_2, and ozone, O_3, on the board. Discuss with students the properties of each substance and the dangers of mistaking one for the other. **English Language Learners**

LS Logical

Quiz — GENERAL

1. What is the difference between a reactant and a product? (reactant—a starting material in a chemical reaction; product—a substance formed in a chemical reaction)

2. What is the difference between the formula CO and the symbol Co? (CO is the compound carbon monoxide, and Co is the element cobalt.)

Alternative Assessment — GENERAL

Concept Mapping Write the following equation on the board:

$$C_6H_{12}O_6 + O_2 \rightarrow CO_2 + H_2O$$

Have students create a concept map that both shows all the components of this equation (the reactants and products) and balances the equation. **LS Logical**

Answer to Reading Check
The coefficient is 4.

CONNECTION TO Language Arts

WRITING SKILL **Diatomic Molecules** Seven of the chemical elements exist as diatomic molecules. Do research to find out which seven elements these are. Write a short report that describes each diatomic molecule. Be sure to include the formula for each molecule.

How to Balance an Equation

To balance an equation, you must use coefficients (KOH uh FISH uhnts). A *coefficient* is a number that is placed in front of a chemical symbol or formula. For example, 2CO represents two carbon monoxide molecules. The number *2* is the coefficient.

For an equation to be balanced, all atoms must be counted. So, you must multiply the subscript of each element in a formula by the formula's coefficient. For example, $2H_2O$ contains a total of four hydrogen atoms and two oxygen atoms. Only coefficients—not subscripts—are changed when balancing equations. Changing the subscripts in the formula of a compound would change the compound. **Figure 7** shows you how to use coefficients to balance an equation.

Reading Check If you see $4O_2$ in an equation, what is the coefficient?

Figure 7   Balancing a Chemical Equation

Follow these steps to write a balanced equation for $H_2 + O_2 \longrightarrow H_2O$.

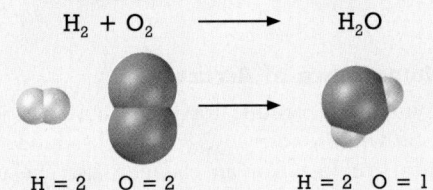

❶ **Count the atoms** of each element in the reactants and in the products. You can see that there are fewer oxygen atoms in the product than in the reactants.

❷ **To balance the oxygen atoms,** place the coefficient 2 in front of H_2O. Doing so gives you two oxygen atoms in both the reactants and the products. But now there are too few hydrogen atoms in the reactants.

❸ **To balance the hydrogen atoms,** place the coefficient 2 in front of H_2. But to be sure that your answer is correct, always double-check your work!

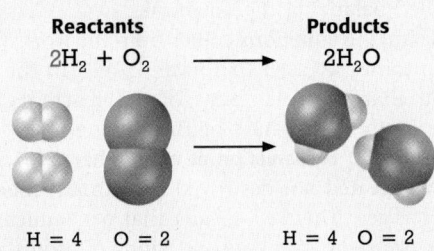

MATERIALS

FOR EACH STUDENT
• bag, large, strong, sealable plastic
• baking soda, 5 g (1 tsp)
• balance
• film canister, plastic, with lid
• vinegar, 5 mL (1 tsp)

Safety Caution: Remind students to use goggles, aprons, and gloves and NOT to squeeze the bag. The bag must be sealed completely.

Answer

7. The mass should be the same before and after the reaction. (Students may note an apparent loss of mass because the bag is buoyed up by the air that surrounds it. As the bag fills with CO_2, the overall density of the system decreases.)

Quick Lab

Conservation of Mass

1. Place **5 g of baking soda** into a **sealable plastic bag**.
2. Place **5 mL of vinegar** into a **plastic film canister**. Put the lid on the canister.
3. Place the canister into the bag. Squeeze the air out of the bag. Seal the bag tightly.
4. Use a **balance** to measure the mass of the bag and its contents. Record the mass.

5. Keeping the bag closed, open the canister in the bag. Mix the vinegar with the baking soda. Record your observations.
6. When the reaction has stopped, measure the mass of the bag and its contents. Record the mass.
7. Compare the mass of the materials before the reaction and the mass of the materials after the reaction. Explain your observations.

SECTION Review

Summary

- A chemical formula uses symbols and subscripts to describe the makeup of a compound.
- Chemical formulas can often be written from the names of covalent and ionic compounds.
- A chemical equation uses chemical formulas, chemical symbols, and coefficients to describe a reaction.
- Balancing an equation requires that the same numbers and kinds of atoms be on each side of the equation.
- A balanced equation illustrates the law of conservation of mass: mass is neither created nor destroyed during ordinary physical and chemical changes.

Using Key Terms

The statements below are false. For each statement, replace the underlined word to make a true statement.

1. A chemical <u>formula</u> describes a chemical reaction.

2. The substances formed from a chemical reaction are <u>reactants</u>.

Understanding Key Ideas

3. The correct chemical formula for carbon tetrachloride is
   a. CCl_3.   c. CCl.
   b. C_3Cl.   d. CCl_4.

4. Calcium oxide is used to make soil less acidic. Its formula is
   a. Ca_2O_2.   c. CaO_2.
   b. CaO.   d. Ca_2O.

5. Balance the following equations by adding the correct coefficients.
   a. $Na + Cl_2 \longrightarrow NaCl$
   b. $Mg + N_2 \longrightarrow Mg_3N_2$

6. How does a balanced chemical equation illustrate that mass is never lost or gained in a chemical reaction?

7. What is the difference between a subscript and a coefficient?

Math Skills

8. Calculate the number of atoms of each element represented in each of the following: $2Na_3PO_4$, $4Al_2(SO_4)_3$, and $6PCl_5$.

Critical Thinking

9. **Analyzing Methods** Describe how to write a formula for a covalent compound. Give an example of a covalent compound.

10. **Applying Concepts** Explain why the subscript in a formula of a chemical compound cannot be changed when balancing an equation.

For a variety of links related to this chapter, go to www.scilinks.org
Topic: Chemical Formulas; Chemical Equations
SciLinks code: HSM0271; HSM0269

CHAPTER RESOURCES

Chapter Resource File

- Section Quiz **GENERAL**
- Section Review **GENERAL**
- Vocabulary and Section Summary **GENERAL**
- Datasheet for Quick Lab

Technology

Transparencies
- P57 Balancing a Chemical Equation

Workbooks

Math Skills for Science **GENERAL**
- Balancing Chemical Equations

Focus

Overview

This section describes four types of chemical reactions. Students will learn how to determine the type of reaction that is represented by a chemical equation.

Bellringer

Have students answer the following questions in their **science journal:** "Are the products of a reaction always more complex than the reactants? Could products be simpler than the reactants? Explain."

Motivate

Discussion ———— GENERAL

Decomposition and Synthesis

Ask students to define the words *decompose* and *synthesize.* Challenge them to explain what happens during decomposition and synthesis reactions. **LS** Verbal/Logical

---

What You Will Learn

- Describe four types of chemical reactions.
- Classify a chemical equation as one of four types of chemical reactions.

Vocabulary

synthesis reaction
decomposition reaction
single-displacement reaction
double-displacement reaction

READING STRATEGY

Mnemonics As you read this section, create a mnemonic device to help you remember the four types of chemical reactions.

---

synthesis reaction a reaction in which two or more substances combine to form a new compound

---

Types of Chemical Reactions

There are thousands of known chemical reactions. Can you imagine having to memorize even 50 of them?

Remembering all of them would be impossible! But fortunately, there is help. In the same way that the elements are divided into groups based on their properties, reactions can be classified based on what occurs during the reaction.

Most reactions can be placed into one of four categories: synthesis (SIN thuh sis), decomposition, single-displacement, and double-displacement. Each type of reaction has a pattern that shows how reactants become products. One way to remember what happens in each type of reaction is to imagine people at a dance. As you learn about each type of reaction, study the models of students at a dance. The models will help you recognize each type of reaction.

Synthesis Reactions

A **synthesis reaction** is a reaction in which two or more substances combine to form one new compound. For example, a synthesis reaction takes place when sodium reacts with chlorine. This synthesis reaction produces sodium chloride, which you know as table salt. A synthesis reaction would be modeled by two people pairing up to form a dancing couple, as shown in **Figure 1.**

✓ *Reading Check* What is a synthesis reaction? (*See the Appendix for answers to Reading Checks.*)

$$2Na + Cl_2 \longrightarrow 2NaCl$$

Figure 1 *Sodium reacts with chlorine to form sodium chloride in this synthesis reaction.*

CHAPTER RESOURCES

Chapter Resource File

- **Lesson Plan**
- **Directed Reading A** BASIC
- **Directed Reading B** SPECIAL NEEDS

Technology

Transparencies
- Bellringer
- P58 Models of Reactions

Workbooks

Interactive Textbook Struggling Readers

Answer to Reading Check

A synthesis reaction is a reaction in which two or more substances combine to form one new compound.

$$H_2CO_3 \longrightarrow H_2O + CO_2$$

Figure 2 *In this decomposition reaction, carbonic acid, H_2CO_3, decomposes to form water and carbon dioxide.*

Decomposition Reactions

A **decomposition reaction** is a reaction in which a single compound breaks down to form two or more simpler substances. Decomposition is the reverse of synthesis. The dance model for a decomposition reaction would be a couple that finishes a dance and separates, as shown in **Figure 2.**

✓ *Reading Check* How is a decomposition reaction different from a synthesis reaction?

Single-Displacement Reactions

Sometimes, an element replaces another element that is a part of a compound. This type of reaction is called a **single-displacement reaction.** The products of single-displacement reactions are a new compound and a different element. The dance model for a single-displacement reaction would show a person cutting in on a couple who is dancing. A new couple is formed. And a different person is left alone, as shown in **Figure 3.**

decomposition reaction a reaction in which a single compound breaks down to form two or more simpler substances

single-displacement reaction a reaction in which one element or radical takes the place of another element or radical in a compound

Figure 3 *Zinc replaces the hydrogen in hydrochloric acid to form zinc chloride and hydrogen gas in this single-displacement reaction.*

$$Zn + 2HCl \longrightarrow ZnCl_2 + H_2$$

Teach

Demonstration —— GENERAL

Single-Displacement Reaction
Obtain silver nitrate from a high school chemistry lab to demonstrate the single-displacement reaction shown in **Figure 4** on the next page.

1. Write the following equation on the board:

   $Cu + 2AgNO_3 \rightarrow 2Ag + Cu(NO_3)_2$

2. Guide students through this equation by identifying the reactants and products:

   copper + silver nitrate → silver + copper(II) nitrate

3. Explain to students that you will demonstrate this reaction by dropping a copper penny into water that contains silver nitrate.

4. Ask students to share their observations about the penny. (It becomes coated with silver.)

5. Ask students to refer to the equation to determine which metal is more reactive. (Copper replaced the silver, so copper is more reactive than silver.)

LS Visual

Answer to Reading Check

In a decomposition reaction, a substance breaks down into simpler substances. In a synthesis reaction, two or more substances combine to form one new compound.

SUPPORT FOR

English Language Learners

Prefixes As students read the section, have them write the definitions of *decomposition* and *displacement*. If necessary, they may use a dictionary. Elicit from students what the meanings of the words have in common. (Both are negative) Discuss and write on the board other words that begin with the prefixes *de-* or *dis-*. Ask students what *de-* or *dis-* mean. (not) What other prefixes do they know that mean the same thing? (un-, anti-). **LS** Verbal

MISCONCEPTION
/////ALERT\\\\\

Limitations of Models The dancing models used in this section represent only general types of reactions. They do not show what happens in a particular reaction, nor do they show that reactants in a reaction undergo changes and form products that are different substances, with different properties, from those reactants.

Close

Reteaching ─────── BASIC

Role-Playing Organize the class into groups of four, and have them simulate each type of reaction in a manner similar to the "dancing partners" models (they would not necessarily need to dance, however!). **LS** Interpersonal

Quiz ──────────── GENERAL

1. Two reactants exchange ions to form two new compounds. What kind of reaction is this? (double-displacement)

2. One element takes the place of another element in a compound. What kind of reaction is this? (single-displacement)

3. The following is the reaction for the explosion of nitroglycerin:
$4C_3H_5(NO_3)_3 \rightarrow 12CO_2 + 10H_2O + 6N_2 + O_2$

   What kind of reaction is this? (decomposition)

Alternative Assessment ─────── ADVANCED

Other Models This section uses dance partners as an analogy to explain the different kinds of chemical reactions. Ask each student to come up with another analogy to describe chemical reactions. (For example, objects or food could be used.) **LS** Logical

Answer to Reading Check

In a single-displacement reaction, one element can replace another element if the replacing element is more reactive than the starting element.

Figure 4 **Reactivity of Elements**

$Cu + 2AgNO_3 \rightarrow 2Ag + Cu(NO_3)_2$
Copper is more reactive than silver.

$Ag + Cu(NO_3)_2 \rightarrow$ no reaction
Silver is less reactive than copper.

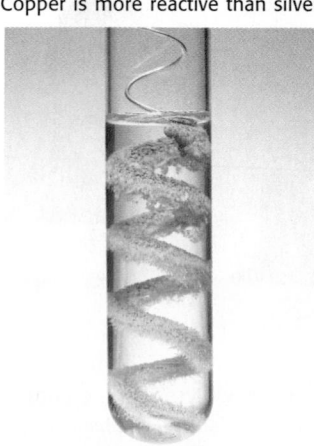 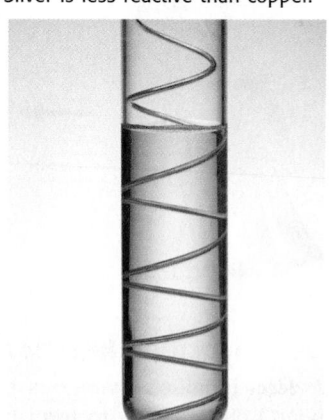

Reactivity of Elements

In a single-displacement reaction, a more reactive element can displace a less reactive element in a compound. For example, **Figure 4** shows that copper is more reactive than silver. Copper (Cu) can replace the silver (Ag) ion in the compound silver nitrate. But the opposite reaction does not occur, because silver is less reactive than copper.

The elements in Group 1 of the periodic table are the most reactive metals. Very few nonmetals are involved in single-displacement reactions. In fact, only Group 17 nonmetals participate in single-displacement reactions.

Reading Check Why can one element sometimes replace another element in a single-displacement reaction?

INTERNET ACTIVITY

For another activity related to this chapter, go to **go.hrw.com** and type in the keyword **HP5REAW**.

Quick Lab

Identifying Reactions

1. Study each of the following equations:

   $4Na + O_2 \rightarrow 2Na_2O$ $P_4 + 5O_2 \rightarrow 2P_2O_5$

   $2Ag_3N \rightarrow 6Ag + N_2$ $Zn + 2HCl \rightarrow ZnCl_2 + H_2$

2. Build models of each of these reactions using **colored clay.** Choose a different color of clay to represent each kind of atom.

3. Identify each type of reaction as a synthesis, decomposition, or single-displacement reaction.

MATERIALS

FOR EACH GROUP OR STUDENT
- clay, 3 colors

Answer

3. $4Na + O_2 \rightarrow 2Na_2O$: synthesis
   $2Ag_3N \rightarrow 6Ag + N_2$: decomposition
   $P_4 + 5O_2 \rightarrow 2P_2O_5$: synthesis
   $Zn + 2HCl \rightarrow ZnCl_2 + H_2$: single-displacement

Double-Displacement Reactions

A **double-displacement reaction** is a reaction in which ions from two compounds exchange places. One of the products of this type of reaction is often a gas or a precipitate. A dance model of a double-displacement reaction would be two couples dancing and then trading partners, as shown in **Figure 5.**

double-displacement reaction
a reaction in which a gas, a solid precipitate, or a molecular compound forms from the exchange of ions between two compounds

$$NaCl + AgF \longrightarrow NaF + AgCl$$

Figure 5 *A double-displacement reaction occurs when sodium chloride reacts with silver fluoride to form sodium fluoride and silver chloride (a precipitate).*

SECTION Review

Summary

- A synthesis reaction is a reaction in which two or more substances combine to form a compound.

- A decomposition reaction is a reaction in which a compound breaks down to form two or more simpler substances.

- A single-displacement reaction is a reaction in which an element takes the place of another element that is part of a compound.

- A double-displacement reaction is a reaction in which ions in two compounds exchange places.

Using Key Terms

1. In your own words, write a definition for each of the following terms: *synthesis reaction* and *decomposition reaction.*

Understanding Key Ideas

2. What type of reaction does the following equation represent?

   $$FeS + 2HCl \longrightarrow FeCl_2 + H_2S$$

   a. synthesis reaction
   b. double-displacement reaction
   c. single-displacement reaction
   d. decomposition reaction

3. Describe the difference between single- and double-displacement reactions.

Math Skills

4. Write the balanced equation in which potassium iodide, KI, reacts with chlorine to form potassium chloride, KCl, and iodine.

Critical Thinking

5. **Analyzing Processes** The first reaction below is a single-displacement reaction that could occur in a laboratory. Explain why the second single-displacement reaction could not occur.

   $$CuCl_2 + Fe \longrightarrow FeCl_2 + Cu$$
   $$CaS + Al \longrightarrow \text{no reaction}$$

6. **Making Inferences** When two white compounds are mixed in a solution, a yellow solid forms. What kind of reaction has taken place? Explain your answer.

Developed and maintained by the National Science Teachers Association

For a variety of links related to this chapter, go to www.scilinks.org

Topic: Reaction Types
SciLinks code: HSM1272

Focus

Overview

This section compares endothermic and exothermic reactions and examines the factors that affect reaction rates. Students will also learn how to interpret energy diagrams.

Bellringer

Pose the following to students at the beginning of class: "Now that you know a little about chemical reactions, think about the many chemical reactions that take place around you every day. Describe your favorite chemical reaction. How do you think energy is involved in the reaction?"

Motivate

Discussion ——— GENERAL

Exothermic/Endothermic Write the words *exothermic* and *endothermic* on the board. If *thermic* refers to heat, ask students to infer what the two words might mean. Next, display an ordinary houseplant and a match. Ask students to guess which object represents an exothermic reaction and which represents an endothermic reaction. Encourage students to discuss their reasoning.
LS Logical

What You Will Learn

- Compare exothermic and endothermic reactions.
- Explain activation energy.
- Interpret an energy diagram.
- Describe five factors that affect the rate of a reaction.

Vocabulary

exothermic reaction
endothermic reaction
law of conservation of energy
activation energy
inhibitor
catalyst

READING STRATEGY

Paired Summarizing Read this section silently. In pairs, take turns summarizing the material. Stop to discuss ideas that seem confusing.

Energy and Rates of Chemical Reactions

What is the difference between eating a meal and running a mile? You could say that a meal gives you energy, while running "uses up" energy.

Chemical reactions can be described in the same way. Some reactions release energy, and other reactions absorb energy.

Reactions and Energy

Chemical energy is part of all chemical reactions. Energy is needed to break chemical bonds in the reactants. As new bonds form in the products, energy is released. By comparing the chemical energy of the reactants with the chemical energy of the products, you can decide if energy is released or absorbed in the overall reaction.

Exothermic Reactions

A chemical reaction in which energy is released is called an **exothermic reaction.** *Exo* means "go out" or "exit." *Thermic* means "heat" or "energy." Exothermic reactions can give off energy in several forms, as shown in **Figure 1.** The energy released in an exothermic reaction is often written as a product in a chemical equation, as in this equation:

$$2Na + Cl_2 \longrightarrow 2NaCl + energy$$

Figure 1 Types of Energy Released in Exothermic Reactions

Light energy is released in the exothermic reaction that is taking place in these light sticks.

Electrical energy is released in the exothermic reaction that will take place in this battery.

Light and thermal energy are released in the exothermic reaction taking place in this campfire.

CHAPTER RESOURCES

Chapter Resource File

- Lesson Plan
- Directed Reading A BASIC
- Directed Reading B SPECIAL NEEDS

Technology

Transparencies
- Bellringer
- LINK TO LIFE SCIENCE L46 Photosynthesis

Workbooks

Interactive Textbook Struggling Readers

SCIENCE HUMOR

There once was a chemist named Rexo,

Who combined things in reactions quite "exo."

He took a swift fall,

And combusted it all,

From the tips of his toes to his necks-o!

Endothermic Reactions

A chemical reaction in which energy is taken in is called an **endothermic reaction.** *Endo* means "go in." The energy that is taken in during an endothermic reaction is often written as a reactant in a chemical equation. Energy as a reactant is shown in the following equation:

$$2H_2O + energy \rightarrow 2H_2 + O_2$$

An example of an endothermic process is photosynthesis. In photosynthesis, plants use light energy from the sun to produce glucose. Glucose is a simple sugar that is used for nutrition. The equation that describes photosynthesis is the following:

$$6CO_2 + 6H_2O + energy \rightarrow C_6H_{12}O_6 + 6O_2$$

Reading Check What is an endothermic reaction? (*See the Appendix for answers to Reading Checks.*)

The Law of Conservation of Energy

Neither mass nor energy can be created or destroyed in chemical reactions. The **law of conservation of energy** states that energy cannot be created or destroyed. However, energy can change forms. And energy can be transferred from one object to another in the same way that a baton is transferred from one runner to another runner, as shown in **Figure 2.**

The energy released in exothermic reactions was first stored in the chemical bonds in the reactants. And the energy taken in during endothermic reactions is stored in the products. If you could measure all the energy in a reaction, you would find that the total amount of energy (of all types) is the same before and after the reaction.

exothermic reaction a chemical reaction in which heat is released to the surroundings

endothermic reaction a chemical reaction that requires heat

law of conservation of energy the law that states that energy cannot be created or destroyed but can be changed from one form to another

Figure 2 *Energy can be transferred from one object to another object in the same way that a baton is transferred from one runner to another runner in a relay race.*

Endo Alert

1. Fill a **plastic cup** half full with **calcium chloride solution.**
2. Measure the temperature of the solution by using a **thermometer.**
3. Carefully add **1 tsp of baking soda.**
4. Record your observations.
5. When the reaction has stopped, record the temperature of the solution.
6. What evidence that an endothermic reaction took place did you observe?

MISCONCEPTION ALERT

Endothermic Reactions and Energy
Students may mistakenly think that endothermic reactions do not produce any energy. Explain that a certain amount of activation energy is required for any reaction to occur. However, in endothermic reactions, the activation energy required is greater than the energy produced in the reaction, so overall, energy is absorbed.

Teach

CONNECTION to Life Science — GENERAL

Photosynthesis One of the most important endothermic reactions is the one carried on continuously by plants and some aquatic organisms—*photosynthesis.* The photosynthetic capability of terrestrial plants is well known. In addition, in the uppermost layer of the ocean (the top 100 m or so), tiny geometrically shaped organisms called *phytoplankton* also make food using photosynthesis. Many fish and other sea animals depend on phytoplankton as their food source. Use the teaching transparency "Photosynthesis" to help students understand this important chemical reaction.

Answer to Reading Check

An endothermic reaction is a chemical reaction in which energy is taken in.

MATERIALS

FOR EACH STUDENT
• baking soda, 1 tsp
• calcium chloride solution, 5% (100 mL)
• cup, plastic
• thermometer

Safety Cautions: Remind students to review all safety cautions and icons before beginning this lab activity. Caution students to wear goggles and an apron when doing this activity.

Answer

6. The temperature decreased.

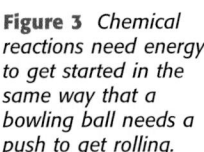

CONNECTION to Real World ——— GENERAL

MREs Some packaged meals used by the military, campers, hunters, and others are called *Meals Ready to Eat,* or MREs. MREs come in plastic containers and are fully cooked. The meals can be eaten cold but can also be heated by a flameless ration heater that uses an exothermic reaction. In about 12 min, the reaction in the ration heater releases enough energy to warm the MRE to 38°C.

CONNECTION to History ——— GENERAL

Matches Humans have been using fire since before recorded history. However, until the early 1800s, no fire had ever been started with a match. Matches that light from friction were invented in the 1820s by a British chemist named John Walker. Walker's matches were coated with phosphorus at one end. They caught fire when the phosphorus ignited because of the thermal energy produced by the friction of rubbing the match on a rough surface. Many matches today are safety matches. They light only if rubbed against the striking surface of their package, because the red phosphorus necessary for the reaction is on that surface, not in the match itself.

Figure 3 *Chemical reactions need energy to get started in the same way that a bowling ball needs a push to get rolling.*

activation energy the minimum amount of energy required to start a chemical reaction

CONNECTION TO Social Studies

WRITING SKILL **The Strike-Anywhere Match** Research the invention of the strike-anywhere match. Find out who invented it, who patented it, and when the match was introduced to the public. In your **science journal,** write a short report about what you learn from your research.

Rates of Reactions

A reaction takes place only if the particles of reactants collide. But there must be enough energy to break the bonds that hold particles together in a molecule. The speed at which new particles form is called the *rate of a reaction.*

Activation Energy

Before the bowling ball in **Figure 3** can roll down the alley, the bowler must first put in some energy to start the ball rolling. A chemical reaction must also get a boost of energy before the reaction can start. This boost of energy is called activation energy. **Activation energy** is the smallest amount of energy that molecules need to react.

Another example of activation energy is striking a match. Before a match can be used to light a campfire, the match has to be lit! A strike-anywhere match has all the reactants it needs to burn. The chemicals on a match react and burn. But, the chemicals will not light by themselves. You must strike the match against a surface. The heat produced by this friction provides the activation energy needed to start the reaction.

 **Reading Check** What is activation energy?

Sources of Activation Energy

Friction is one source of activation energy. In the match example, friction provides the energy needed to break the bonds in the reactants and allow new bonds to form. An electric spark in a car's engine is another source of activation energy. This spark begins the burning of gasoline. Light can also be a source of activation energy for a reaction. **Figure 4** shows how activation energy relates to exothermic reactions and endothermic reactions.

Is That a Fact!

Diesel engines have no spark plugs to provide activation energy to ignite the fuel in their cylinders. Although this may seem to be a flaw in the design of the engine, spark plugs are actually not necessary in diesel engines. Air in the cylinders of a diesel engine is compressed so much that its temperature is very high. When the fuel is squirted into the cylinder, the fuel ignites instantly because of the high temperature of the compressed air.

Answer to Reading Check
Activation energy is the energy that is needed to start a chemical reaction.

Figure 4 **Energy Diagrams**

Exothermic Reaction Once an exothermic reaction starts, it can continue. The energy given off as the product forms continues to supply the activation energy needed for the substances to react.

Endothermic Reaction An endothermic reaction continues to absorb energy. Energy must be used to provide the activation energy needed for the substances to react.

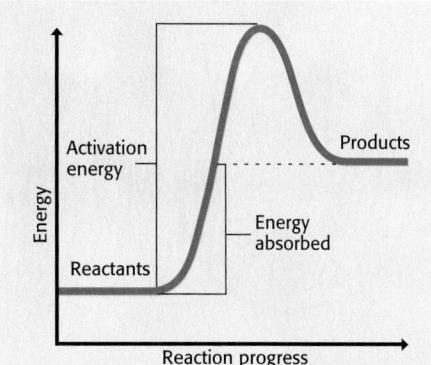

Factors Affecting Rates of Reactions

The rate of a reaction is a measure of how fast the reaction takes place. Recall that the rate of a reaction depends on how fast new particles form. There are four factors that affect the rate of a reaction. These factors are: temperature, concentration, surface area, and the presence of an inhibitor or catalyst.

Temperature

A higher temperature causes a faster rate of reaction, as shown in **Figure 5.** At high temperatures, particles of reactants move quickly. The rapid movement causes the particles to collide often and with a lot of energy. So, many particles have the activation energy to react. And many reactants can change into products in a short time.

Figure 5 *The light stick on the right glows brighter than the one on the left because the one on the right is warmer. The higher temperature causes the rate of the reaction to increase.*

Which Is Quicker?

1. Fill a **clear plastic cup** with **250 mL of warm water.** Fill a **second clear plastic cup** with **250 mL of cold water.**
2. Place **one-quarter of an effervescent tablet** in each of the two cups of water at the same time. Using a **stopwatch,** time each reaction.
3. Observe each reaction, and record your observations.
4. In which cup did the reaction occur at a faster rate?

SUPPORT FOR

English Language Learners

Energy Diagrams Students will need reinforcement of the vocabulary and the energy diagrams on this page. Before they read the graphs, review the definitions of *endothermic* and *exothermic*. Explain what each axis of the graph represents and the differences in the amount and location of the activation energy. As students read the graphs, ask questions to check comprehension of concepts. **LS** Visual/Auditory

ACTIVITY ———— **BASIC**

Factors Affecting Rates Have students make a concept map of the four factors that affect the rates of reactions. Their map should include an explanation of how each factor affects the rate. **LS** Visual
English Language Learners

MATERIALS

FOR EACH STUDENT
• cups, plastic, clear (2)
• effervescent tablet (one-quarter)
• stopwatch
• water, cold (250 mL)
• water, warm (250 mL)

Safety Caution: Remind students to review all safety cautions and icons before beginning this activity. Caution students to wear goggles and an apron when doing this activity. Students should not put the tablets in their mouth.

Teacher's Notes: The rate of a reaction usually doubles with each increase of 10°C. A difference in temperature of about 30°C should be sufficient to see a marked difference in the rate of gas production.

Answer

4. The reaction occurred at a faster rate in the warm water. The reaction produced gas bubbles at a faster rate in the warm water.

Concept Mapping Have students create a concept map that includes the terms *chemical reaction, reaction energy, reaction rate, endothermic reaction, exothermic reaction, temperature, surface area, catalyst,* and *inhibitor.* **LS** Visual

Quiz ———————— GENERAL

1. Why does grinding a solid into a powder increase reaction rate? (The powdered form exposes more particles of the reactant, allowing more collisions with another reactant.)

2. What is the difference between a reactant and a catalyst? (Reactants are changed into products during a reaction. A catalyst increases the speed of a reaction without being used up.)

Alternative Assessment ——— GENERAL

Instruction Manual Have students create an instruction manual entitled *How to Change Chemical Reaction Rates.* Encourage them to be creative in describing the factors that affect reaction rate as discussed in this section. **LS** Verbal

Answer to Reading Check

A high concentration of reactants allows the particles to run into each other more often, so the reaction proceeds at a faster rate.

Figure 6 **Concentration of Solutions**

▼ When the amount of copper sulfate crystals dissolved in water is **small,** the concentration of the copper sulfate solution is **low.**

▼ When the amount of copper sulfate crystals dissolved in water is **large,** the concentration of the copper sulfate solution is **high.**

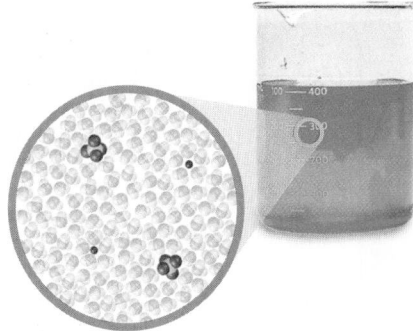
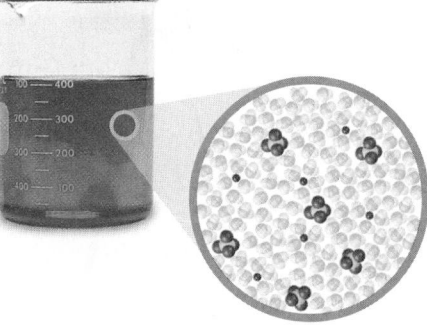

CONNECTION TO Biology

Enzymes and Inhibitors
Enzymes are proteins that speed up reactions in your body. Sometimes, chemicals called *inhibitors* stop the action of enzymes. Research how inhibitors are beneficial in reactions in the human body. Make a poster or a model that explains what you have learned, and present it to your class.

inhibitor a substance that slows down or stops a chemical reaction

catalyst a substance that changes the rate of a chemical reaction without being used up or changed very much

Concentration

In general, a high concentration of reactants causes a fast rate of a reaction. *Concentration* is a measure of the amount of one substance dissolved in another substance, as shown in **Figure 6.** When the concentration is high, there are many reactant particles in a given volume. So, there is a small distance between particles. The particles run into each other often. Thus, the particles react faster.

✔ **Reading Check** How does a high concentration of reactants increase the rate of a reaction?

Surface Area

Surface area is the amount of exposed surface of a substance. Increasing the surface area of solid reactants increases the rate of a reaction. Grinding a solid into a powder makes a larger surface area. Greater surface area exposes more particles of the reactant to other reactant particles. This exposure to other particles causes the particles of the reactants to collide with each other more often. So, the rate of the reaction is increased.

Inhibitors

An **inhibitor** is a substance that slows down or stops a chemical reaction. Slowing down or stopping a reaction may sometimes be useful. For example, preservatives are added to foods to slow down the growth of bacteria and fungi. The preservatives prevent bacteria and fungi from producing substances that can spoil food. Some antibiotics are examples of inhibitors. For example, penicillin prevents certain kinds of bacteria from making a cell wall. So, the bacteria die.

INCLUSION Strategies

• *Attention Deficit Disorder*
• *Behavior Control Issues*
• *Learning Disabled*

Clarify the meaning of the words *catalyst* and *inhibitor.* Blindfold one person. Tell the person to walk across the classroom and back within two minutes. After the student is blindfolded, clear a path from one side of the room to the other. Organize the rest of the students into two teams. One team is the catalyst and must help the blindfolded person get across the room safely. The other team is the inhibitor and must try to confuse the blindfolded person so he or she doesn't get across the room in time. Teams must not touch the blindfolded person or place anything in his or her path, and only two members of a team may speak at one time. Conclude the activity when the person makes it across the room or after 2 min, whichever comes first. **LS** Interpersonal

English Language Learners

Catalysts

Some chemical reactions would be too slow to be useful without a catalyst (KAT uh LIST). A **catalyst** is a substance that speeds up a reaction without being permanently changed. Because it is not changed, a catalyst is not a reactant. A catalyst lowers the activation energy of a reaction, which allows the reaction to happen more quickly. Catalysts called *enzymes* speed up most reactions in your body. Catalysts are even found in cars, as seen in **Figure 7.** The catalytic converter decreases air pollution. It does this by increasing the rate of reactions that involve the harmful products given off by cars.

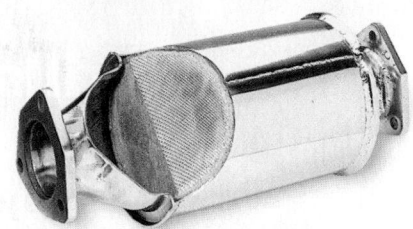

Figure 7 *This catalytic converter contains platinum and palladium. These two catalysts increase the rate of reactions that make the car's exhaust less harmful.*

Using Key Terms

The statements below are false. For each statement, replace the underlined term to make a true statement.

1. An <u>exothermic</u> reaction absorbs energy.

2. The rate of a reaction can be increased by adding <u>an inhibitor</u>.

Understanding Key Ideas

3. Which of the following will not increase the rate of a reaction?
   a. adding a catalyst
   b. increasing the temperature of the reaction
   c. decreasing the concentration of reactants
   d. grinding a solid into powder

4. How does the concentration of a solution affect the rate of reaction?

Critical Thinking

5. **Making Comparisons** Compare exothermic and endothermic reactions.

6. **Applying Concepts** Explain how chewing your food thoroughly can help your body digest food.

Interpreting Graphics

Use the diagram below to answer the questions that follow.

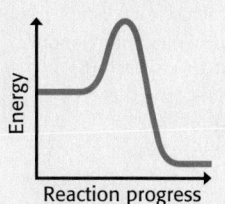

7. Does this energy diagram show an exothermic or an endothermic reaction? How can you tell?

8. A catalyst lowers the amount of activation energy needed to get a reaction started. What do you think the diagram would look like if a catalyst were added?

SCILINKS

Developed and maintained by the National Science Teachers Association

For a variety of links related to this chapter, go to www.scilinks.org

Topic: Exothermic and Endothermic Reactions
SciLinks code: HSM0555

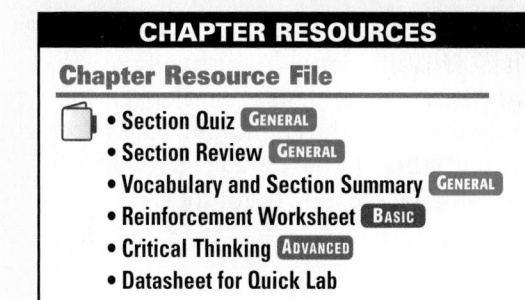

CHAPTER RESOURCES

Chapter Resource File

- Section Quiz GENERAL
- Section Review GENERAL
- Vocabulary and Section Summary GENERAL
- Reinforcement Worksheet BASIC
- Critical Thinking ADVANCED
- Datasheet for Quick Lab

Speed Control

Teacher's Notes

Time Required

One to two 45-minute class periods

Lab Ratings

EASY ———————————→ HARD

Teacher Prep 🧪🧪🧪
Student Set-Up 🧪🧪
Concept Level 🧪🧪
Clean Up 🧪🧪

MATERIALS

Materials listed are for groups of 2–3 students. For one of the acid solutions, use hydrochloric acid with a concentration between 0.5 M and 1.0 M. For the other acid solution, use 0.1 M hydrochloric acid. When making a solution of acid, you must always add the acid to the water. If aluminum strips are not available, substitute strips cut from aluminum cans or aluminum foil.

Safety Caution

Only hydrochloric acid of concentrations 1.0 M or less should be used. Students should not handle more-concentrated hydrochloric acid. In case of an acid spill, dilute the spill first with water. Then, wearing disposable plastic gloves, mop up the spill with wet cloths designated for spill cleanup.

Preparation Notes

The folded aluminum may actually react *faster* because folding may break open the oxide that coats the aluminum. Sandpaper the metal first, or have students sandpaper each strip before they begin the lab.

OBJECTIVES

Describe how the surface area of a solid affects the rate of a reaction.

Explain how concentration of reactants will speed up or slow down a reaction.

MATERIALS

- funnels (2)
- graduated cylinders, 10 mL (2)
- hydrochloric acid, concentrated
- hydrochloric acid, dilute
- strips of aluminum, about 5 cm x 1 cm each (6)
- scissors
- test-tube rack
- test tubes, 30 mL (6)

SAFETY

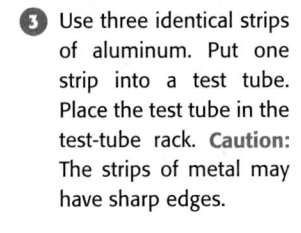

Speed Control

The reaction rate (how fast a chemical reaction happens) is an important factor to control. Sometimes, you want a reaction to take place rapidly, such as when you are removing tarnish from a metal surface. Other times, you want a reaction to happen very slowly, such as when you are depending on a battery as a source of electrical energy.

In this lab, you will discover how changing the surface area and concentration of the reactants affects reaction rate. In this lab, you can estimate the rate of reaction by observing how fast bubbles form.

Part A: Surface Area

Ask a Question

1 How does changing the surface area of a metal affect reaction rate?

Form a Hypothesis

2 Write a statement that answers the question above. Explain your reasoning.

Test the Hypothesis

3 Use three identical strips of aluminum. Put one strip into a test tube. Place the test tube in the test-tube rack. **Caution:** The strips of metal may have sharp edges.

CHAPTER RESOURCES

Chapter Resource File

 • Datasheet for LabBook
• Lab Notes and Answers

Technology

 Classroom Videos
• Lab Video

• Finding a Balance
• Cata-what? Catalyst!
• Putting Elements Together

4 Carefully fold a second strip in half and then in half again. Use a textbook or other large object to flatten the folded strip as much as possible. Place the strip in a second test tube in the test-tube rack.

5 Use scissors to cut a third strip of aluminum into the smallest possible pieces. Place all of the pieces into a third test tube, and place the test tube in the test-tube rack.

6 Use a funnel and a graduated cylinder to pour 10 mL of concentrated hydrochloric acid into each of the three test tubes. **Caution:** Hydrochloric acid is corrosive. If any acid should spill on you, immediately flush the area with water and notify your teacher.

7 Observe the rate of bubble formation in each test tube. Record your observations.

Analyze the Results

1 **Organizing Data** Which form of aluminum had the greatest surface area? the smallest surface area?

2 **Analyzing Data** The amount of aluminum and the amount of acid were the same in all three test tubes. Which form of the aluminum seemed to react the fastest? Which form reacted the slowest? Explain your answers.

3 **Analyzing Results** Do your results support the hypothesis you made? Explain.

Draw Conclusions

4 **Making Predictions** Would powdered aluminum react faster or slower than the forms of aluminum you used? Explain your answer.

Part B: Concentration

Ask a Question

1 How does changing the concentration of acid affect the reaction rate?

Form a Hypothesis

2 Write a statement that answers the question above. Explain your reasoning.

Test the Hypothesis

3 Place one of the three remaining aluminum strips in each of the three clean test tubes. (Note: Do not alter the strips.) Place the test tubes in the test-tube rack.

4 Using the second funnel and graduated cylinder, pour 10 mL of water into one of the test tubes. Pour 10 mL of dilute acid into the second test tube. Pour 10 mL of concentrated acid into the third test tube.

5 Observe the rate of bubble formation in the three test tubes. Record your observations.

Analyze the Results

1 **Explaining Events** In this set of test tubes, the strips of aluminum were the same, but the concentration of the acid was different. Was there a difference between the test tube that contained water and the test tubes that contained acid? Which test tube formed bubbles the fastest? Explain.

2 **Analyzing Results** Do your results support the hypothesis you made? Explain.

Draw Conclusions

3 **Applying Conclusions** Why should spilled hydrochloric acid be diluted with water before it is wiped up?

Disposal Information

For disposal, neutralize all hydrochloric acid with 0.1 M NaOH as required until the pH is between 6 and 8 and pour the solution down the drain. Aluminum strips that cannot be reused can be placed in the trash.

 Holt Lab Generator CD-ROM

Search for any lab by topic, standard, difficulty level, or time. Edit any lab to fit your needs, or create your own labs. Use the Lab Materials QuickList software to customize your lab materials list.

 **Tracy Jahn**
Berkshire Junior-Senior High School
Canaan, New York

Chapter Review

Assignment Guide

SECTION	QUESTIONS
1	11, 13
2	4–6, 14–17, 19–20
3	3, 7, 10, 21
4	1–2, 8–9, 12, 18, 22–23

ANSWERS

Using Key Terms

1. inhibitor
2. exothermic reaction
3. synthesis reaction
4. subscript

Understanding Key Ideas

5. c
6. d
7. d
8. c
9. a
10. **a.** synthesis
    b. single-displacement
    c. double-displacement
11. Chemical bonds are broken in a chemical reaction.
12. You can raise the temperature, increase the concentration of a reactant, increase the surface area of a reactant, and add a catalyst.
13. gas formation, solid formation, color change, and energy change

USING KEY TERMS

Complete each of the following sentences by choosing the correct term from the word bank.

subscript	exothermic reaction
inhibitor	synthesis reaction
product	reactant

1. Adding a(n) ___ will slow down a chemical reaction.

2. A chemical reaction that gives off heat is called a(n) ___.

3. A chemical reaction that forms one compound from two or more substances is called a(n) ___.

4. The 2 in the formula Ag_2S is a(n) ___.

UNDERSTANDING KEY IDEAS

Multiple Choice

5. Balancing a chemical equation so that the same number of atoms of each element is found in both the reactants and the products is an example of
    a. activation energy.
    b. the law of conservation of energy.
    c. the law of conservation of mass.
    d. a double-displacement reaction.

6. Which of the following is the correct chemical formula for dinitrogen tetroxide?
    a. N_4O_2
    b. NO_2
    c. N_2O_5
    d. N_2O_4

7. In which type of reaction do ions in two compounds switch places?
    a. a synthesis reaction
    b. a decomposition reaction
    c. a single-displacement reaction
    d. a double-displacement reaction

8. Which of the following actions is an example of the use of activation energy?
    a. plugging in an iron
    b. playing basketball
    c. holding a lit match to paper
    d. eating

9. Enzymes in your body act as catalysts. Thus, the role of enzymes is
    a. to increase the rate of chemical reactions.
    b. to decrease the rate of chemical reactions.
    c. to help you breathe.
    d. to inhibit chemical reactions.

Short Answer

10. Name the type of reaction that each of the following equations represents.
    a. $2Cu + O_2 \rightarrow 2CuO$
    b. $2Na + MgSO_4 \rightarrow Na_2SO_4 + Mg$
    c. $Ba(CN)_2 + H_2SO_4 \rightarrow BaSO_4 + 2HCN$

11. Describe what happens to chemical bonds during a chemical reaction.

12. Name four ways that you can change the rate of a chemical reaction.

13. Describe four clues that signal that a chemical reaction is taking place.

Math Skills

14 Write balanced equations for the following:

a. $Fe + O_2 \rightarrow Fe_2O_3$

b. $Al + CuSO_4 \rightarrow Al_2(SO_4)_3 + Cu$

c. $Mg(OH)_2 + HCl \rightarrow MgCl_2 + H_2O$

15 Calculate the number of atoms of each element shown in the formulas below:

a. $CaSO_4$

b. $4NaOCl$

c. $Fe(NO_3)_2$

d. $2Al_2(CO_3)_3$

CRITICAL THINKING

16 Concept Mapping Use the following terms to create a concept map: *products, chemical reaction, chemical equation, chemical formulas, reactants, coefficients,* and *subscripts.*

17 Evaluating Assumptions Your friend is very worried by rumors that he has heard about a substance called *dihydrogen monoxide* in the city's water system. What could you say to your friend to calm his fears? (Hint: Write the formula of the substance.)

18 Analyzing Ideas As long as proper safety precautions have been taken, why can explosives be transported long distances without exploding?

19 Applying Concepts You measured the mass of a steel pipe before leaving it outdoors. One month later, the pipe had rusted, and its mass had increased. Does this change violate the law of conservation of mass? Explain your answer.

20 Applying Concepts Acetic acid, a compound found in vinegar, reacts with baking soda to produce carbon dioxide, water, and sodium acetate. Without writing an equation, identify the reactants and the products of this reaction.

INTERPRETING GRAPHICS

Use the photo below to answer the questions that follow.

21 What evidence in the photo supports the claim that a chemical reaction is taking place?

22 Is this reaction an exothermic or endothermic reaction? Explain your answer.

23 Draw and label an energy diagram of both an exothermic and endothermic reaction. Identify the diagram that describes the reaction shown in the photo above.

Critical Thinking

16. 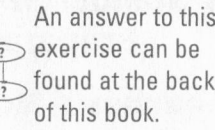 An answer to this exercise can be found at the back of this book.

17. The substance is H_2O, water. Water is non-toxic.

18. Sample answer: Explosives need to absorb energy to begin the reaction. As long as precautions are taken to prevent the activation energy from being absorbed by the explosives, they should be safe to transport.

19. Sample answer: no; The increased mass came from oxygen in the air, which was not part of the mass of the steel pipe when you first measured it.

20. The reactants are acetic acid and baking soda. The products are carbon dioxide, water, and sodium acetate.

Interpreting Graphics

21. Gas is produced, and light is given off.

22. exothermic; Energy is being given off.

23. Diagrams may vary, but both diagrams should show the energy of reactants and products with a "spike" between them. The diagram describing the photo should have the energy of the reactants higher than that of the products.

14. a. $4Fe + 3O_2 \rightarrow 2Fe_2O_3$
b. $2Al + 3CuSO_4 \rightarrow Al_2(SO_4)_3 + 3Cu$
c. $Mg(OH)_2 + 2HCl \rightarrow MgCl_2 + 2H_2O$

15. a. Ca: 1, S: 1, O: 4
b. Na: 4, O: 4, Cl: 4
c. Fe: 1, N: 2, O: 6
d. Al: 4, C: 6, O: 18

CHAPTER RESOURCES

Chapter Resource File

- Chapter Review **GENERAL**
- Chapter Test A **GENERAL**
- Chapter Test B **ADVANCED**
- Chapter Test C **SPECIAL NEEDS**
- Vocabulary Activity **GENERAL**

Workbooks

Study Guide
- Study Guide is also available in Spanish.

Teacher's Notes

To provide practice under more realistic conditions, give students 20 minutes to answer all of the questions in this Standardized Test Preparation.

Answer Key

Question	Answer
1	B
2	B
3	C
4	A
5	A
6	A
7	B
8	C
9	D
10	B
11	*
12	*

*See Test Doctor.

Multiple Choice

Use the picture below to answer question 1.

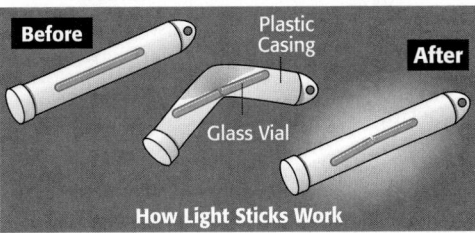

How Light Sticks Work

1. **The picture above shows a light stick. Light sticks begin to glow when the vial inside the stick is broken. Chemicals inside the vial mix with chemicals outside of the vial. Which of the following statements BEST supports the idea that a chemical reaction is occurring?**

   A. The vial is broken into smaller pieces.

   B. Energy is released in the form of light.

   C. Two different substances are combined.

   D. The substances are in a flexible container.

2. **Chemical reactions are used in many processes, such as cooking food, heating homes, and powering automobiles. In chemical reactions, energy is transferred from one molecule to another. How is this energy transferred?**

   A. by the gravitational attraction between molecules

   B. by the bumping of one molecule into another molecule

   C. by one molecule sending out electricity to another molecule

   D. by one molecule sending out heat waves to another molecule

3. **Some silverware is made with the element silver (Ag). Over time, this silverware will turn black if it is not cleaned with a special solution. Which of the following statements BEST explains why the element silver in the silverware turns black?**

   A. It absorbs energy when exposed to warm food.

   B. It breaks down into smaller and smaller particles.

   C. It reacts with substances in the air to form a new substance.

   D. It changes from one phase of matter into another phase of matter.

4. **Which of the following contains one oxygen atom?**

   A. H_2O

   B. CO_2

   C. $2N_2O$

   D. Co

5. **Which process causes substances to react to form one or more new substances?**

   A. chemical change

   B. physical change

   C. evaporation

   D. freezing

TEST DOCTOR

Question 1 A: The glass vial breaking into several smaller pieces represents a physical change. B: Correct. C: Different substances can be combined without resulting in a chemical reaction. D: The flexibility of the container is a physical property of the container and does not lend any support to the idea that a chemical reaction is occurring inside the container.

Question 2 A: Gravitational attraction does not play a role in energy transfer between molecules. B: Correct. C: Although electrical energy is often associated with chemical reactions, the energy transfer between molecules does not occur as described. D: Although heat is often associated with chemical reactions, neither molecule "sends out heat waves."

Question 3 A: While the silverware does absorb energy from warm food, this answer is incorrect because this energy transfer does not cause a chemical change. B: Silver tarnishes as it is exposed to the air, not because silverware is breaking down into smaller pieces. C: Correct. D: The silverware remains a solid even as it turns black.

Use the graph below to answer question 6.

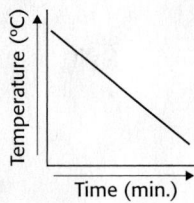

6. **The graph above shows the change in temperature over time in a chemical reaction. According to the graph, how would this reaction be described?**

   A. endothermic

   B. exothermic

   C. unbalanced

   D. combustion

7. **Which chemical equation correctly shows the formation of water from hydrogen and oxygen?**

   A. $H_2 + O_2 = H_2O$

   B. $2H_2 + O_2 = 2H_2O$

   C. $H_2 + 2O = H_2O$

   D. $H + O_2 = H_2O$

8. **A scientist carries out a reaction in a test tube. After the bubbling stops, she notices that the test tube is very warm. What might she conclude about the reaction?**

   A. The reaction happened very quickly.

   B. The reaction is endothermic.

   C. The reaction is exothermic.

   D. No reaction took place.

9. **A substance that is used to speed up a chemical reaction is called**

   A. a reactant.

   B. an inhibitor.

   C. a precipitate.

   D. a catalyst.

10. **During a laboratory experiment, Tran applied the law of conservation of energy. Which of the following did he assume to be true?**

    A. Energy is not changed.

    B. Energy is not created or destroyed.

    C. The total energy of the reactants is greater than the total energy of the products.

    D. The total energy of the reactants is less than the total mass of the products.

Open Response

11. **What are three ways by which the rate of a chemical reaction can be increased?**

12. **Compare synthesis and decomposition reactions, and give an example of each.**

Standardized Test Preparation

Question 8 A: There is no information given about the rate of this reaction. B: The overall reaction gives off energy, so it is not likely to be an endothermic reaction. C: Correct. D: There were two clues that indicated a chemical reaction—gas formation and an energy change.

Question 9 A: A reactant is needed in order for a reaction to occur; a reactant does not speed up a chemical reaction, but the amount of a reactant can affect the rate of the reaction. B: An inhibitor does not speed up a reaction; an inhibitor slows down a reaction. C: A precipitate is a solid product that is formed from a solution during a chemical reaction. D: Correct.

Question 10 A: Energy cannot be created or destroyed; however, it can be converted from one form of energy to another. B: Correct. C: This statement is the definition of an exothermic reaction. D: This statement is the definition of an endothermic reaction.

Question 11 Full-credit answers should include three of the following points. The rate of a chemical reaction can be increased by:

• increasing the temperature of the reactants

• increasing the surface area of the reactants

• increasing the concentration of the reactants

• adding a catalyst

Question 12 Full-credit answers should include the following points:

• In a synthesis reaction, two or more substances combine to form a new compound.

• In a decomposition reaction, a compound breaks down into two or more simpler substances.

• Examples may vary. The example of a synthesis reaction in the student book is when sodium reacts with chlorine to produce sodium chloride. The example of a decomposition reaction in the student book is carbonic acid breaking down into water and carbon dioxide.

Question 4 A: Correct. B: Carbon dioxide contains two oxygen atoms. C: This formula shows two molecules and therefore two oxygen atoms. D: This is the symbol for the element cobalt.

Question 5 A: Correct. B: Substances do not change their identities when they undergo physical changes. C: Substances do not change their identities during evaporation. D: Substances do not change their identities during freezing.

Question 6 A: Correct. B: In an endothermic reaction, energy is absorbed by the reaction, causing a drop in temperature. In an exothermic reaction, energy is released by the reaction, causing a rise in temperature. The graph shows an endothermic reaction. C: No equation is given for this chemical reaction, so it is not possible to tell whether the equation is unbalanced. D: Combustion would involve the release of energy, causing a rise in temperature.

Question 7 A: On the left side of this equation are 2 hydrogen atoms and 2 oxygen atoms, but on the right side are 2 hydrogen atoms and 1 oxygen atom. B: Correct. C: On the left side of the equation are 2 hydrogen and 2 oxygen atoms. The right side has 2 hydrogen atoms and 1 oxygen atom. D: The left side of the equation has 1 hydrogen atom and 2 oxygen atoms; the water molecule contains 2 hydrogen atoms and 1 oxygen atom.

Science, Technology, and Society

Background

Some students may be surprised to learn that in addition to being used in thermostats, mercury is also used in fluorescent bulbs. When an electric current is passed through mercury vapor, the vapor produces a low-heat, energy-efficient light.

Weird Science

Background

Students may be interested in the details of the chemical reaction that takes place in most light sticks. When the glass vial is broken, the hydrogen peroxide solution mixes with the phenyl oxalate ester and the fluorescent dye. The hydrogen peroxide oxidizes the phenyl oxalate ester. This reaction produces phenol and an unstable peroxyacid ester. The unstable peroxyacid ester then decomposes. This reaction produces additional phenol and a cyclic peroxy compound, which decomposes to carbon dioxide. This decomposition releases energy, which is absorbed by the fluorescent dye.

Science in Action

Science, Technology, and Society

Bringing Down the House!

Have you ever watched a building being demolished? It takes only minutes to demolish it, but a lot of time was spent planning the demolition. And it takes time to remove hazardous chemicals from the building. For example, asbestos, which is found in insulation, can cause lung cancer. Mercury found in thermostats can cause brain damage, birth defects, and death. It is important to remove these substances because most of the rubble is sent to a landfill. If hazardous chemicals are not removed, they could leak into the groundwater and enter the water supply.

Math ACTIVITY

A city produces 4 million tons of waste in 1 year. Of this waste, 82% is solid waste. If 38% of the solid waste comes from the construction and demolition of buildings, how many tons of waste does this represent?

Weird Science

Light Sticks

Have you ever seen light sticks at a concert? Your family may even keep them in the car for emergencies. But how do light sticks work? To activate the light stick, you have to bend it. Most light sticks are made of a plastic tube that contains a mixture of two chemicals. Also inside the tube is a thin glass vial, which contains hydrogen peroxide. As long as the glass vial is unbroken, the two chemicals are kept separate. But bending the ends of the tube breaks the glass vial. This action releases the hydrogen peroxide into the other chemicals and a chemical reaction occurs, which makes the light stick glow.

Social Studies ACTIVITY

Who invented light sticks? What was their original purpose? Research the answers to these questions. Make a poster that shows what you have learned.

Answer to Math Activity

4,000,000 tons $\times$ 0.82 $\times$ 0.38 = 1,200,000 tons

Answer to Social Studies Activity

Chemist Michael M. Rauhut, manager of exploratory research at American Cyanamid in Stamford, Connecticut, and his colleague Laszlo J. Bollyky developed the reaction now used in light sticks. The chemists who were working on the reaction were trying to develop an artificial chemiluminescence that would mimic the natural chemiluminescence of fireflies. The trademark name of Cyalume® was given to the light sticks that Rauhut and Bollyky invented.

Larry McKee

Arson Investigator Once a fire dies down, you might see an arson investigator like Lt. Larry McKee on the scene. "After the fire is out, I can investigate the fire scene to determine where the fire started and how it started," says McKee, who questions witnesses and firefighters about what they have seen. He knows that the color of the smoke can indicate certain chemicals. He also has help detecting chemicals from an accelerant-sniffing dog, Nikki. Nikki has been trained to detect about 11 different chemicals. If Nikki finds one of these chemicals, she begins to dig. McKee takes a sample of the suspicious material to the laboratory. He treats the sample so that any chemicals present will dissolve in a liquid. A sample of this liquid is placed into an instrument called a *gas chromatograph* and tested. The results of this test are printed out in a graph, from which the suspicious chemical is identified. Next, McKee begins to search for suspects. By combining detective work with scientific evidence, fire investigators can help find clues that can lead to the conviction of the arsonist.

Language Arts ACTiViTY

WRITING SKILL Write a one-page story about an arson investigator. Begin the story at the scene of a fire. Take the story through the different steps that you think an investigator would have to go through to solve the crime.

To learn more about these Science in Action topics, visit go.hrw.com and type in the keyword **HP5REAF**.

Check out Current Science® articles related to this chapter by visiting go.hrw.com. Just type in the keyword HP5CS14.

Answer to Language Arts Activity

Answers may vary but should reflect the information given in the passage about Larry McKee.

Chemical Compounds
Chapter Planning Guide

Compression guide:
To shorten instruction because of time limitations, omit Section 4.

OBJECTIVES	LABS, DEMONSTRATIONS, AND ACTIVITIES	TECHNOLOGY RESOURCES
PACING • 90 min pp. 648–653 **Chapter Opener**	SE **Start-up Activity,** p. 649 (GENERAL)	OSP **Parent Letter** ■ CD **Student Edition on CD-ROM** CD **Guided Reading Audio CD** ■ TR **Chapter Starter Transparency*** VID **Brain Food Video Quiz**
Section 1 Ionic and Covalent Compounds • Describe the properties of ionic and covalent compounds. • Classify compounds as ionic or covalent based on their properties.	TE **Demonstration** Observing Crystals, p. 651 ◆ (GENERAL) SE **Connection to Language Arts** Electrolyte Solutions, p. 652 (GENERAL) SE **Science in Action** Math, Social Studies, and Language Arts Activities, pp. 676–677 (GENERAL)	OSP **Lesson Plans** (also in print) TR **Bellringer Transparency*** SE **Internet Activity,** p. 651 (GENERAL)
PACING • 90 min pp. 654–659 **Section 2 Acids and Bases** • Describe four properties of acids. • Identify four uses of acids. • Describe four properties of bases. • Identify four uses of bases.	TE **Activity** Tasting a Weak Acid, p. 654 (GENERAL) TE **Demonstration** A Fruit Juice Indicator, p. 655 ◆ (GENERAL) SE **Connection to Biology** Acids Can Curl Your Hair!, p. 656 (GENERAL) TE **Activity** Comparing Acids and Bases, p. 656 (BASIC) TE **Demonstration** A Base From a Metal, p. 656 (GENERAL) TE **Demonstration** Making Soap, p. 657 (GENERAL) SE **School-to-Home Activity** Acids and Bases at Home, p. 658 (GENERAL) SE **Quick Lab** Blue to Red—Acid!, p. 658 (GENERAL) SE **Skills Practice Lab** Cabbage Patch Indicators, p. 670 (GENERAL) LB **Calculator-Based Labs** Cabbage Patch Indicators (ADVANCED) LB **Labs You Can Eat** Can You Say Seviche?* (GENERAL)	OSP **Lesson Plans** (also in print) TR **Bellringer Transparency*** CRF **SciLinks Activity*** (GENERAL) VID **Lab Videos for Physical Science**
PACING • 45 min pp. 660–663 **Section 3 Solutions of Acids and Bases** • Explain the difference between strong acids and bases and weak acids and bases. • Identify acids and bases by using the pH scale. • Describe the formation and uses of salts.	TE **Connection Activity** Math, p. 660 (GENERAL) SE **Quick Lab** pHast Relief!, p. 661 ◆ (GENERAL) CRF **Datasheet for Quick Lab*** SE **Connection to Biology** Blood and pH, p. 662 (GENERAL) SE **Skills Practice Lab** Making Salt, p. 744 (GENERAL) CRF **Datasheet for LabBook*** LB **EcoLabs & Field Activities** Greener Cleaners* (BASIC)	OSP **Lesson Plans** (also in print) TR **Bellringer Transparency*** TR P60 **pH Values of Common Materials***
PACING • 45 min pp. 664–669 **Section 4 Organic Compounds** • Explain why there are so many organic compounds. • Identify and describe saturated, unsaturated, and aromatic hydrocarbons. • Describe the characteristics of carbohydrates, lipids, proteins, and nucleic acids and their functions in the body.	TE **Connection Activity** Math, p. 665 (GENERAL) SE **Quick Lab** Food Facts, p. 667 (GENERAL) TE **Demonstration** Lipids and Water, p. 667 ◆ (GENERAL) SE **Connection to Social Studies** DNA "Fingerprinting" and Crime-Scene Investigation, p. 668 (GENERAL) TE **Activity** DNA, p. 669 ◆ (ADVANCED) LB **Long-Term Projects & Research Ideas** Tiny Plastic Factories* (ADVANCED)	OSP **Lesson Plans** (also in print) TR **Bellringer Transparency*** TR P61 **Structural Formulas*** TR *LINK TO LIFE SCIENCE* L4 **Phospholipid Molecule and Cell Membrane***

PACING • 90 min

CHAPTER REVIEW, ASSESSMENT, AND STANDARDIZED TEST PREPARATION

CRF **Vocabulary Activity*** (GENERAL)
SE **Chapter Review,** pp. 672–673 (GENERAL)
CRF **Chapter Review*** ■ (GENERAL)
CRF **Chapter Tests A*** ■ (GENERAL), **B*** (ADVANCED), **C*** (SPECIAL NEEDS)
SE **Standardized Test Preparation,** pp. 674–675 (GENERAL)
CRF **Standardized Test Preparation*** (GENERAL)
CRF **Performance-Based Assessment*** (GENERAL)
OSP **Test Generator, Test Item Listing**

Online and Technology Resources

Holt Online Learning

Visit **go.hrw.com** for access to Holt Online Learning, or enter the keyword **HS7 Home** for a variety of free online resources.

 **One-Stop Planner® CD-ROM**

This CD-ROM package includes:
• Lab Materials QuickList Software
• Holt Calendar Planner
• Customizable Lesson Plans
• Printable Worksheets
• ExamView® Test Generator
• Interactive Teacher's Edition
• Holt PuzzlePro®
• Holt PowerPoint® Resources

SKILLS DEVELOPMENT RESOURCES	SECTION REVIEW AND ASSESSMENT	CORRELATIONS
SE Pre-Reading Activity, p. 648 `GENERAL` **OSP** Science Puzzlers, Twisters & Teasers* `GENERAL`		**National Science Education Standards** UCP 1; SAI 1; PS 3a
CRF Directed Reading A* ■ `BASIC`, B* `SPECIAL NEEDS` **WB** Workbook* `Struggling Readers` **CRF** Vocabulary and Section Summary* ■ `GENERAL` **SE** Reading Strategy Reading Organizer, p. 650 `GENERAL` **TE** Reading Strategy Prediction Guide, p. 651 `GENERAL` **TE** Support for English Language Learners, p. 651	**SE** Reading Checks, pp. 651, 652 `GENERAL` **TE** Reteaching, p. 652 `BASIC` **TE** Quiz, p. 652 `GENERAL` **TE** Alternative Assessment, 652 `GENERAL` **SE** Section Review,* p. 653 `GENERAL` **CRF** Section Quiz* ■ `GENERAL`	UCP 1; SAI 2; PS 1a, 1b
CRF Directed Reading A* ■ `BASIC`, B* `SPECIAL NEEDS` **WB** Workbook* `Struggling Readers` **CRF** Vocabulary and Section Summary* ■ `GENERAL` **SE** Reading Strategy Reading Organizer, p. 654 `GENERAL` **TE** Inclusion Strategies, p. 657 **TE** Support for English Language Learners, p. 657 **MS** Math Skills for Science Creating Exponents* `GENERAL`	**SE** Reading Checks, pp. 654, 656, 659 `GENERAL` **TE** Homework, p. 657 `GENERAL` **TE** Reteaching, p. 658 `BASIC` **TE** Quiz, p. 658 `GENERAL` **TE** Alternative Assessment, p. 658 `GENERAL` **SE** Section Review,* p. 659 ■ `GENERAL` **CRF** Section Quiz* ■ `GENERAL`	UCP 1; SAI 1; SPSP 1, 4; PS 1a, 1b; *Chapter Lab:* SAI 1, 2; PS 1a, 1b
CRF Directed Reading A* ■ `BASIC`, B* `SPECIAL NEEDS` **WB** Workbook* `Struggling Readers` **CRF** Vocabulary and Section Summary* ■ `GENERAL` **SE** Reading Strategy Discussion, p. 660 `GENERAL` **TE** Support for English Language Learners, p. 661 **CRF** Reinforcement Worksheet A Simple Solution* `BASIC`	**SE** Reading Checks, pp. 660, 662 `GENERAL` **TE** Homework, p. 661 `GENERAL` **TE** Reteaching, p. 662 `BASIC` **TE** Quiz, p. 662 `GENERAL` **TE** Alternative Assessment, p. 662 `GENERAL` **SE** Section Review,* p. 663 `GENERAL` **CRF** Section Quiz* ■ `GENERAL`	UCP 1, 2, 4; SAI 1; ST 2; SPSP 1, 3; PS 1b; *LabBook:* UCP 3; SAI 1; PS 1b
CRF Directed Reading A* ■ `BASIC`, B* `SPECIAL NEEDS` **WB** Workbook* `Struggling Readers` **CRF** Vocabulary and Section Summary* ■ `GENERAL` **SE** Reading Strategy Paired Summarizing, p. 664 `GENERAL` **TE** Inclusion Strategies, p. 665 **TE** Support for English Language Learners, p. 666 **CRF** Critical Thinking Battle of the Breads* `ADVANCED`	**SE** Reading Checks, pp. 664, 667, 668 `GENERAL` **TE** Reteaching, p. 668 `BASIC` **TE** Quiz, p. 668 `GENERAL` **TE** Alternative Assessment, p. 668 `GENERAL` **SE** Section Review,* p. 669 `GENERAL` **CRF** Section Quiz* ■ `GENERAL`	UCP 1; SAI 1; ST 2; SPSP 1; PS 1a, 1b, 1c

SCI LINKS.
NSTA
www.scilinks.org
Maintained by the **National Science Teachers Association.** See Chapter Enrichment pages that follow for a complete list of topics.

Current Science®
Check out *Current Science* articles and activities by visiting the HRW Web site at **go.hrw.com.** Just type in the keyword **HP5CS15T.**

Classroom Videos
• **Lab Videos** demonstrate the chapter lab.
• **Brain Food Video Quizzes** help students review the chapter material.

Classroom CD-ROMs
• **Guided Reading Audio CD** (Also in Spanish)
• **Interactive Explorations**
• **Virtual Investigations**
• **Visual Concepts**
• **Science Tutor**

Holt Lab Generator CD-ROM
Search for any lab by topic, standard, difficulty level, or time. Edit any lab to fit your needs, or create your own labs. Use the Lab Materials QuickList software to customize your lab materials list.

Visual Resources

CHAPTER STARTER TRANSPARENCY

Strange but True!

BELLRINGER TRANSPARENCIES

Section: Ionic and Covalent Compounds

Take a rubber ball and stand in your group. Stand and face your partner. In Group 1, one student from each pair gives his or her ball to the other student. In Group 2, both students should hold both rubber balls, as in a tug of war. Which group represents a compound formed by ionic bonding and which represents a compound formed by covalent bonding?

Write a paragraph explaining the differences between the two types of bonds in your **science journal.**

Section: Acids and Bases

A lemon and a tomato are both fruits that contain citric acid, which gives them a tangy flavor. Make a list of other foods whose tanginess may be due to the presence of acids. What kinds of foods are non-acidic? Do you often eat these foods paired with an acidic food? Why or why not?

Record your thoughts in your **science journal.**

TEACHING TRANSPARENCIES

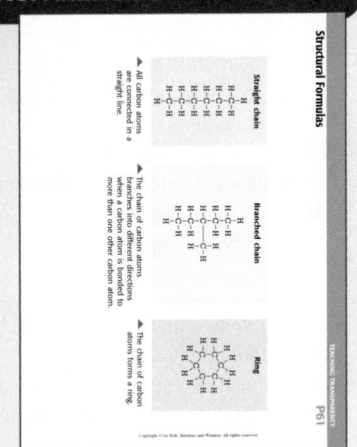

pH Values of Common Materials

Structural Formulas

TEACHING TRANSPARENCIES

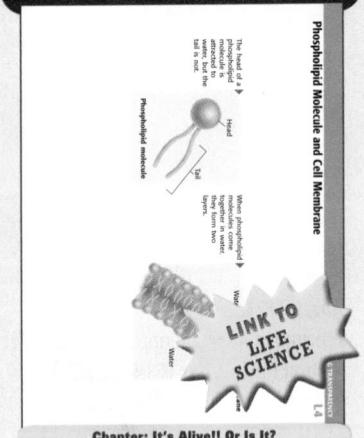

Phospholipid Molecule and Cell Membrane

LINK TO LIFE SCIENCE

Chapter: It's Alive!! Or Is It?

CONCEPT MAPPING TRANSPARENCY

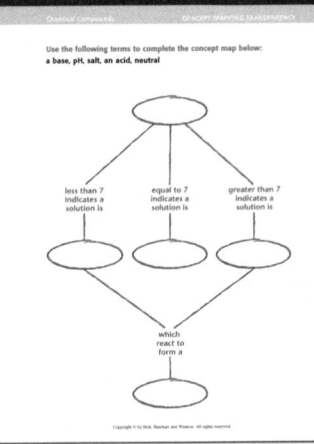

Use the following terms to complete the concept map below:
a base, pH, salt, an acid, neutral

Planning Resources

LESSON PLANS

Lesson Plan   SAMPLE

Section: Waves

Pacing

Regular Schedule: with lab(s):2 days   without lab(s):3 days
Block Schedule: with lab(s):1 1/2 days   without lab(s):1 day

Objectives

1. Relate the seven properties of life to a living organism.
2. Describe seven themes that can help you to organize what you learn about biology.
3. Identify the tiny structures that make up all living organisms.
4. Differentiate between reproduction and heredity and between metabolism and homeostasis.

National Science Education Standards Covered

LSInter1:Cells have particular structures that underlie their functions.
LSMat1:Most cell functions involve chemical reactions.
LSBeh1:Cells store and use information to guide their functions.
UCP1:Cell functions are regulated.
SI1: Cells can differentiate and form complete multicellular organisms.
PS1: Species evolve over time.
ESS1: The great diversity of organisms is the result of more than 3.5 billion years of evolution.
ESS2: Natural selection and its evolutionary consequences provide a scientific explanation for the fossil record of ancient life forms as well as for the striking molecular similarities observed among the diverse species of living organisms.
ST1: The millions of different species of plants, animals, and microorganisms that live on Earth today are related by descent from common ancestors.
ST2: The energy for life primarily comes from the sun.
SPS1P1: The complexity and organization of organisms accommodates the need for obtaining, transforming, transporting, releasing, and eliminating the matter and energy used to sustain the organism.
SPSP6: As matter and energy flows through different levels of organization of living systems—cells, organs, communities—and between living systems and the physical environment, chemical elements are recombined in different ways.
HNS1: Organisms have behavioral responses to internal changes and to external stimuli.

PARENT LETTER

Dear Parent,

Your son's or daughter's science class will soon begin exploring the chapter entitled "The World of Physical Science." In this chapter, students will learn about how the scientific method applies to the world of physical science and the role of physical science in the world. By the end of the chapter, students should demonstrate a clear understanding of the chapter's main ideas and be able to discuss the following topics:

1. physical science as the study of energy and matter (Section 1)
2. the role of physical science in the world around them (Section 1)
3. careers that rely on physical science (Section 1)
4. the steps used in the scientific method (Section 2)
5. examples of technology (Section 2)
6. how the scientific method is used to answer questions and solve problems (Section 2)
7. how our knowledge of science changes over time (Section 2)
8. how models represent real objects or systems (Section 3)
9. examples of different ways models are used in science (Section 3)
10. the importance of the International System of Units (Section 4)
11. the appropriate units to use for particular measurements (Section 4)
12. how area and density are derived quantities (Section 4)

Questions to Ask Along the Way

You can help your son or daughter learn about these topics by asking interesting questions such as the following:

• What are some surprising careers that our physical science?
• What is a characteristic of a good hypothesis?
• Where is it a good idea to use a model?
• Why do Americans measure things in terms of inches and yards and meters?

ALSO IN SPANISH

TEST ITEM LISTING

TEST ITEM LISTING
The World of Science   SAMPLE

MULTIPLE CHOICE

1. A limitation of models is that
   a. they are large enough to see.
   b. they do not act exactly like the things that they model.
   c. they are smaller than the things that they model.
   d. they model unfamiliar things.
   Answer: B   Difficulty: 1   Section: 3   Objective: 2

2. The length 10 m is equal to
   a. 100 cm.   c. 10,000 mm.
   b. 1,000 cm.   d. Both (a) and (c)
   Answer: D   Difficulty: 1   Section: 3   Objective: 2

3. To be valid, a hypothesis must be
   a. testable.   c. made into a law.
   b. supported by evidence.   d. Both (a) and (b)
   Answer: B   Difficulty: 1   Section: 3   Objective: 2

4. The statement "Sheila has a stain on her shirt" is an example of a(n)
   a. law.   c. observation.
   b. hypothesis.   d. prediction.
   Answer: B   Difficulty: 1   Section: 3   Objective: 2

5. A hypothesis is often developed out of
   a. observations.   c. laws.
   b. experiments.   d. Both (a) and (b)
   Answer: D   Difficulty: 1   Section: 3   Objective: 2

6. How many milliliters are in 3.5 kL?
   a. 3,500 mL.   c. 3,500, 000 mL.
   b. 0.0035 mL.   d. 35,000 mL.
   Answer: C   Difficulty: 1   Section: 3   Objective: 2

7. A map of Seattle is an example of a
   a. law.   c. model.
   b. theory.   d. unit.
   Answer: B   Difficulty: 1   Section: 3   Objective: 2

8. A lab has the safety icons shown below. These icons mean that you should wear
   a. safety goggles.   c. safety goggles and a lab apron.
   b. only a lab apron.   d. safety goggles, a lab apron, and gloves.
   Answer: B   Difficulty: 1   Section: 3   Objective: 2

9. The law of conservation of mass says the of mass before a chemical change is
   a. more than the total mass after the change.
   b. less than the total mass after the change.
   c. the same as the total mass after the change.
   d. not the same as the total mass after the change.
   Answer: C   Difficulty: 1   Section: 3   Objective: 2

10. In which of the following areas might you find a geochemist at work?
    a. studying the chemistry of rocks   c. studying fishes
    b. studying forestry   d. studying the atmosphere
    Answer: A   Difficulty: 1   Section: 3   Objective: 2

One-Stop Planner® CD-ROM

This CD-ROM includes all of the resources shown here and the following time-saving tools:

• **Lab Materials QuickList Software**
• **Customizable lesson plans**
• **Holt Calendar Planner**
• **The powerful ExamView® Test Generator**

Meeting Individual Needs

DIRECTED READING A
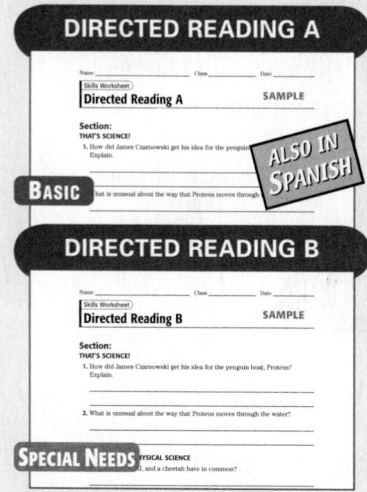
BASIC / ALSO IN SPANISH

DIRECTED READING B
SPECIAL NEEDS

VOCABULARY ACTIVITY
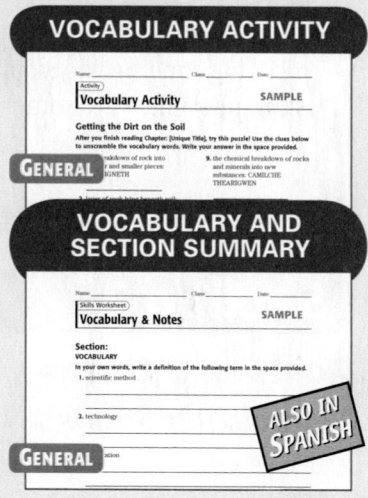
GENERAL

VOCABULARY AND SECTION SUMMARY
GENERAL / ALSO IN SPANISH

REINFORCEMENT
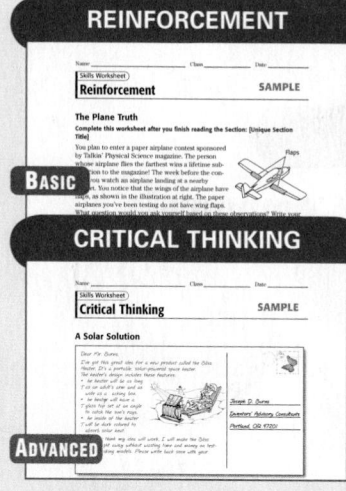
BASIC

CRITICAL THINKING
ADVANCED

SCILINKS ACTIVITY

GENERAL

SCIENCE PUZZLERS, TWISTERS & TEASERS
GENERAL

Labs and Activities

ECOLABS & FIELD ACTIVITIES
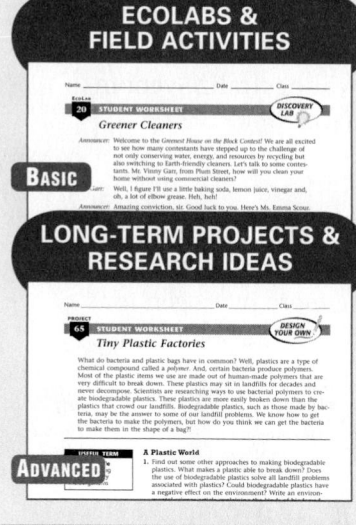
BASIC

LONG-TERM PROJECTS & RESEARCH IDEAS
ADVANCED

LABS YOU CAN EAT
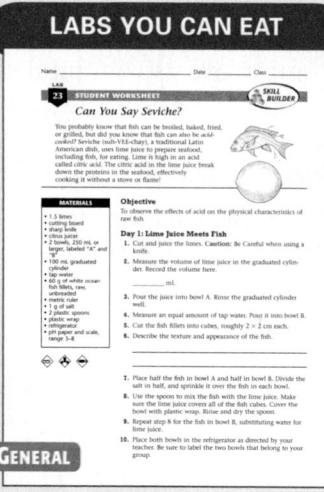
GENERAL

CALCULATOR-BASED LABS
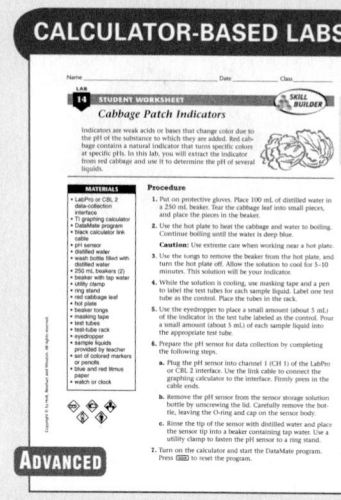
ADVANCED

DATASHEETS FOR QUICK LABS

DATASHEETS FOR CHAPTER LABS

DATASHEETS FOR LABBOOK

Review and Assessments

SECTION QUIZ
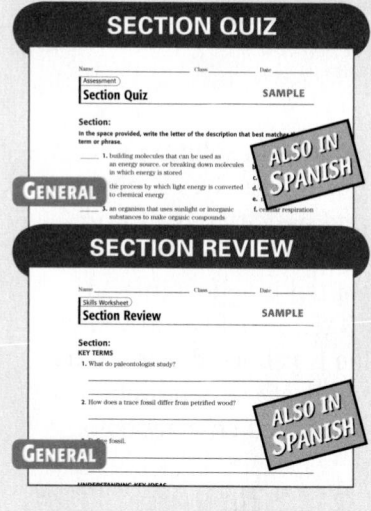
GENERAL / ALSO IN SPANISH

SECTION REVIEW
GENERAL / ALSO IN SPANISH

CHAPTER REVIEW
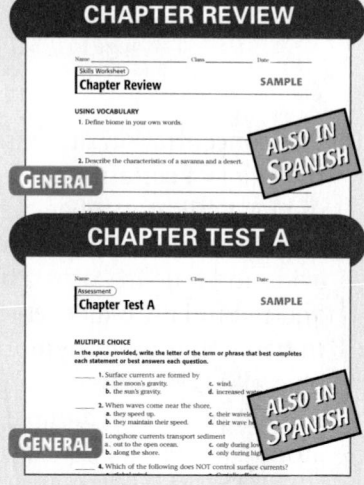
GENERAL / ALSO IN SPANISH

CHAPTER TEST A
GENERAL / ALSO IN SPANISH

CHAPTER TEST B
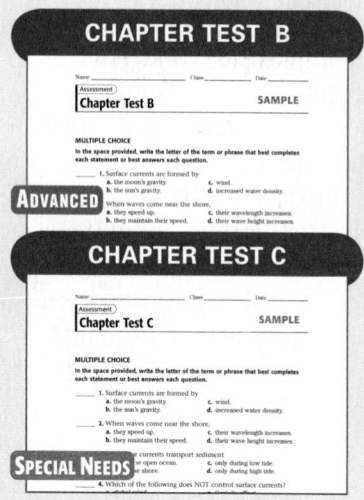
ADVANCED

CHAPTER TEST C
SPECIAL NEEDS

STANDARDIZED TEST PREPARATION
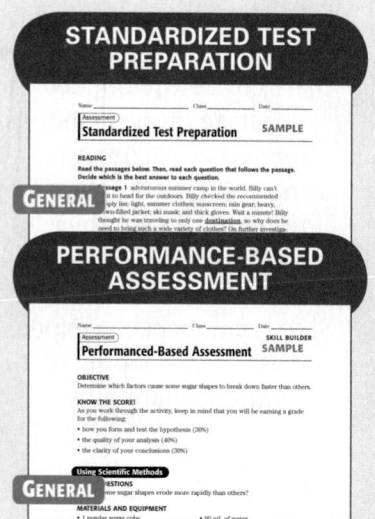
GENERAL

PERFORMANCE-BASED ASSESSMENT
GENERAL

This Chapter Enrichment provides relevant and interesting information to expand and enhance your presentation of the chapter material.

Section 1

Ionic and Covalent Compounds

Network Solids

- A crystal formed by covalent bonds between atoms is called a *network solid*. Each network solid could be thought of as one large molecule. Network solids are usually nonmetallic. Diamonds are examples of network solids. In a diamond, each carbon atom is covalently bonded to four other carbon atoms, forming a network solid. Silicon carbide also forms a network solid with covalent bonds between its atoms.

Is That a Fact!

- ◆ Water is one of the most common and important compounds on Earth. Each of a water molecule's hydrogen atoms shares its single electron with the molecule's oxygen atom, forming a covalent bond.

Diamonds

- Diamonds can be used in several ways, not just as jewelry. Diamonds are composed of carbon atoms that are covalently bonded in a complex network. This structure gives diamonds a unique combination of properties. Diamonds are very hard, have a high melting point, and do not conduct electric current. As a result of these properties, industry uses diamonds in tools that drill, cut, or grind. Furthermore, manufacturers can use diamonds in semiconductor devices. To counteract the expense of natural diamonds, scientists are developing methods to produce high-quality synthetic diamonds.

Is That a Fact!

- ◆ Not all ionic compounds are soluble in water. Silver chloride, zinc sulfide, copper(II) oxide, and magnesium phosphate are some ionic compounds that are not very water soluble.

Section 2

Acids and Bases

Neutralizing Stings

- Bee venom is acidic, while wasp venom is basic. You can reduce the pain of bee and wasp stings by neutralizing the venom. To neutralize a bee's acidic venom, apply a paste of sodium bicarbonate (baking soda and water) or a weak ammonia solution. To neutralize a wasp's venom, apply vinegar. Of course, stinging insects inject their venom beneath the skin's outermost layer, so a topical salve will neutralize venom only on or near the skin's surface.

Indicators

- The pH scale was introduced by S.P.L. Sørensen (1868–1939) to measure the concentration of hydrogen ions in solution. The more hydrogen ions there are in solution, the more acidic a solution is.

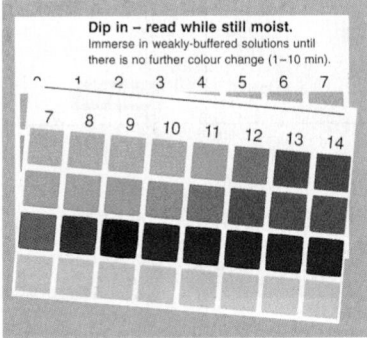

- The concentration of hydrogen ions in solution affects the color of certain natural dyes. These dyes can be used as indicators of acidity and basicity (alkalinity). Litmus, an indicator obtained from lichens, is red in acids and blue in bases. Phenol red is yellow in acids and red in bases; methyl red is red in acids and yellow in bases; and bromthymol blue is yellow in acids and blue in bases. However, most indicators do not change color at pH 7. For example, methyl red changes color around pH 5.

Section 3

Solutions of Acids and Bases

Salt Crystals

- The forces within a salt crystal hold the ions together in what is called a *crystal lattice*. Chemists define a crystal lattice as a repetitive, geometric packing arrangement. All of the ions in a crystal of table salt, NaCl, are part of one giant lattice. However, the smallest visible sodium chloride crystal still has more than a billion billion ions!

Is That a Fact!

- ◆ The mineral beryl is colorless. However, when beryl contains tiny amounts of the green salt chromium(III) oxide, the valuable green gemstone emerald is formed.

Section 4

Organic Compounds

Hodgkin and Vitamin B12

- In 1948, vitamin B12 was isolated as a red crystalline compound. Dorothy Hodgkin analyzed the vitamin's structure using X-ray crystallography. She won a Nobel Prize in 1964 for her work. Vitamin B12 is a complex, organic molecule containing 181 atoms.

Friedrich Wöhler

- In 1828, while attempting to prepare ammonium cyanate from cyanic acid and ammonia, Friedrich Wöhler (1800–1882) accidentally synthesized urea. This was the first artificially synthesized organic compound. Wöhler's work proved that a compound naturally produced by animals could be made in the laboratory from inorganic chemicals.

Marcelin Berthelot

- Marcelin Berthelot (1827–1907) further demonstrated that plants and animals are not the only sources of organic compounds. He synthesized many organic compounds from inorganic compounds and elements. In 1860, Berthelot synthesized acetylene from its elements, hydrogen and carbon. Berthelot also synthesized another commercially important organic compound, benzene.

Is That a Fact!

- ◆ Two compounds are considered structural isomers if they have the same molecular formula but different connections between atoms. Two compounds are stereoisomers if they have the same molecular formula and connections between atoms but different arrangements of atoms in three-dimensional space.

- ◆ An alkane containing 30 carbon atoms has 4,111,846,763 possible isomers.

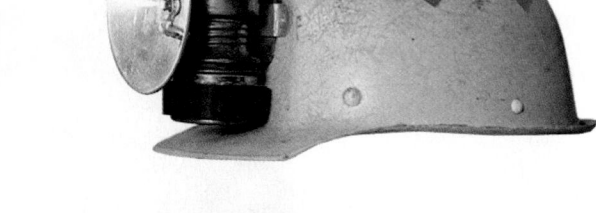

SciLinks is maintained by the National Science Teachers Association to provide you and your students with interesting, up-to-date links that will enrich your classroom presentation of the chapter.

Visit www.scilinks.org and enter the SciLinks code for more information about the topic listed.

Topic: Ionic Compounds
SciLinks code: HSM0817

Topic: Salts
SciLinks code: HSM1347

Topic: Covalent Compounds
SciLinks code: HSM0365

Topic: Aromatic Compounds
SciLinks code: HSM0095

Topic: Acids and Bases
SciLinks code: HSM0013

Topic: Organic Compounds
SciLinks code: HSM1078

Topic: pH Scale
SciLinks code: HSM1130

Overview

This chapter discusses chemical compounds. Students will learn about the properties of ionic and covalent compounds and acids and bases. The chapter discusses the pH scale and concludes with a discussion of organic compounds and their properties.

Assessing Prior Knowledge

Students should be familiar with the following topics:

- elements, compounds, and mixtures
- chemical bonding
- chemical reactions

Identifying Misconceptions

Students might assume that the properties of a chemical compound result from only the properties of the elements that compose the compound. Point out that the type of bond between atoms also determines the properties of a compound.

24

Chemical Compounds

The Big Idea

Chemical compounds are classified into groups based on their bonds and on their properties.

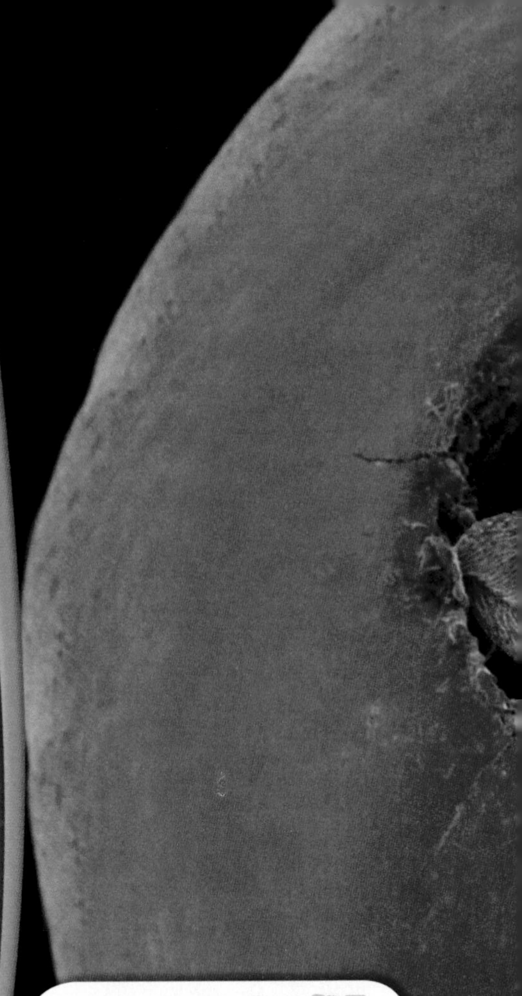

About the Photo

The bean weevil feeds on bean seeds, which are rich in chemical compounds such as proteins, carbohydrates, and lipids. The bean weevil begins life as a tiny grub that lives in the seed where it eats starch and protein. The adult then cuts holes in the seed coat and crawls out, as you can see in this photo.

PRE-READING ACTIVITY

FOLDNOTES Layered Book Before you read the chapter, create the FoldNote entitled "Layered Book" described in the **Study Skills** section of the Appendix. Label the tabs of the layered book with "Ionic and covalent compounds," "Acids and bases," "Solutions of acids and bases," and "Organic compounds." As you read the chapter, write information you learn about each category under the appropriate tab.

Standards Correlations

National Science Education Standards

The following codes indicate the National Science Education Standards that correlate to this chapter. The full text of the standards is at the front of the book.

Chapter Opener
UCP 1; SAI 1; PS 3a

Section 1 Ionic and Covalent Compounds
UCP 1; SAI 2; PS 1a, 1b

Section 2 Acids and Bases
UCP 1; SAI 1; SPSP 1, 4; PS 1a, 1b

Section 3 Solutions of Acids and Bases
UCP 1, 2, 4; SAI 1; ST 2; SPSP 1, 3; PS 1b; *LabBook:* UCP 3; SAI 1; PS 1b

Section 4 Organic Compounds
UCP 1; SAI 1; ST 2; SPSP 1; PS 1a, 1b, 1c

Chapter Lab
SAI 1, 2; PS 1a, 1b

Chapter Review
PS 1a, 1b, 1c

START-UP ACTIVITY

Sticking Together

In this activity, you will demonstrate the force that keeps particles together in some compounds.

Procedure

1. Rub **two balloons** with a **wool cloth.** Move the balloons near each other. Describe what you see.

2. Put one balloon against a wall. Record your observations.

Analysis

1. The balloons are charged by rubbing them with the wool cloth. Like charges repel each other. Opposite charges attract each other. Do the balloons have like or opposite charges? Explain.

2. If the balloon that was placed against the wall has a negative charge, what is the charge on the wall? Explain your answer.

3. The particles that make up compounds are attracted to each other in the same way that the balloon is attracted to the wall. What can you infer about the particles that make up such compounds?

Science in Action
SAI 1; ST 2; SPSP 5; HNS 1, 2; PS 1b

Chapter Starter Transparency
Use this transparency to help students begin thinking about the importance of chemical compounds.

Focus

Overview

In this section, students learn that chemical compounds can be classified by the bonds they contain: ionic bonds or covalent bonds. Students learn the distinguishing properties of each type of bond.

Bellringer

Give every student a foam ball. Organize the class into two groups, and organize each group into pairs. Tell partners to stand and face each other. In Group 1, have one student from each pair give his or her ball to the other student. In Group 2, tell both students to hold both foam balls, as in a tug of war. Explain that the students in Group 1 represent a compound formed by ionic bonding and that those in Group 2 represent a compound formed by covalent bonding. Ask students to write a paragraph in their **science journal** explaining the differences between the two types of bonds.

LS Kinesthetic English Language Learners

What You Will Learn

● Describe the properties of ionic and covalent compounds.
● Classify compounds as ionic or covalent based on their properties.

Vocabulary
chemical bond
ionic compound
covalent compound

READING STRATEGY

Reading Organizer As you read this section, create an outline of the section. Use the headings from the section in your outline.

chemical bond the combining of atoms to form molecules or compounds

ionic compound a compound made of oppositely charged ions

Ionic and Covalent Compounds

When ions or molecules combine, they form compounds. Because there are millions of compounds, it is helpful to organize them into groups. But how can scientists tell the difference between compounds?

One way to group compounds is by the kind of chemical bond they have. A **chemical bond** is the combining of atoms to form molecules or compounds. Bonding can occur between valence electrons of different atoms. *Valence electrons* are electrons in the outermost energy level of an atom. The behavior of valence electrons determines if an ionic compound or a covalent compound is formed.

Ionic Compounds and Their Properties

The properties of ionic compounds are a result of strong attractive forces called ionic bonds. An *ionic bond* is an attraction between oppositely charged ions. Compounds that contain ionic bonds are called **ionic compounds.** Ionic compounds can be formed by the reaction of a metal with a nonmetal. Metal atoms become positively charged ions when electrons are transferred from the metal atoms to the nonmetal atoms. This transfer of electrons also causes the nonmetal atom to become a negatively charged ion. Sodium chloride, commonly known as *table salt,* is an ionic compound.

Brittleness

Ionic compounds tend to be brittle solids at room temperature. So, they usually break apart when hit. This property is due to the arrangement of ions in a repeating three-dimensional pattern called a *crystal lattice,* shown in **Figure 1.** Each ion in a lattice is surrounded by ions of the opposite charge. And each ion is bonded to the ions around it. When an ionic compound is hit, the pattern of ions shifts. Ions that have the same charge line up and repel one another, which causes the crystal to break.

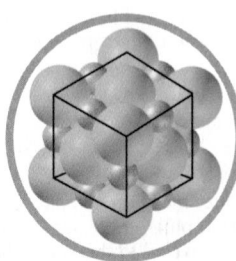

Figure 1 *The sodium ions, shown in purple, and the chloride ions, shown in green, are bonded in the crystal lattice structure of sodium chloride.*

CHAPTER RESOURCES

Chapter Resource File

• **Lesson Plan**
• **Directed Reading A** BASIC
• **Directed Reading B** SPECIAL NEEDS

Technology

Transparencies
• Bellringer

Workbooks

Interactive Textbook Struggling Readers

CONNECTION to Life Science ———— GENERAL

The body's nerve cells contain a large number of sodium, potassium, and chloride ions. The movement of these ions into and out of the cells causes a type of electric current to exist in the nerve cells. This electric current allows "messages" to move very quickly through the body's nervous system.

| Figure 2 | Melting Points of Some Ionic Compounds |

Potassium dichromate
Melting point: 398°C

Magnesium oxide
Melting point: 2,800°C

Nickel(II) oxide
Melting point: 1,984°C

High Melting Points

Because of the strong ionic bonds that hold ions together, ionic compounds have high melting points. These high melting points are the reason that most ionic compounds are solids at room temperature. For example, solid sodium chloride must be heated to 801°C before it will melt. The melting points of three other ionic compounds are given in **Figure 2.**

Solubility and Electrical Conductivity

Many ionic compounds are highly soluble. So, they dissolve easily in water. Water molecules attract each of the ions of an ionic compound and pull the ions away from one another. The solution that forms when an ionic compound dissolves in water can conduct an electric current, as shown in **Figure 3.** The solution can conduct an electric current because the ions are charged and are able to move freely past one another. However, an undissolved crystal of an ionic compound does not conduct an electric current.

✔ **Reading Check** Why do solutions of ionic compounds dissolved in water conduct an electric current? (*See the Appendix for answers to Reading Checks.*)

 **INTERNET ACTIVITY**

For another activity related to this chapter, go to **go.hrw.com** and type in the keyword **HP5CMPW.**

Figure 3 *The pure water does not conduct an electric current. However, the solution of salt water conducts an electric current, so the bulb lights up.*

Pure water

Salt water

Answer to Reading Check

Ionic solutions conduct an electric current because the ions in the solution are charged and are able to move past each other easily.

Chemical Bond Review On the board, create a table with the headings "Ionic" and "Covalent." Ask students to help you fill in the chart with descriptions of each type of bond and to give examples of compounds formed by each type of bond. LS Logical

Quiz — GENERAL

1. How are ionic compounds formed? (by the transfer of electrons from metal atoms to nonmetal atoms)

2. Give two examples of covalent compounds. (Answers will vary but may include sugar, water, and carbon dioxide.)

3. Potassium chloride is a crystalline solid that has a melting point of 770°C. Is this compound more likely to be ionic or covalent? (ionic)

Alternative Assessment — GENERAL

Writing **Bonding Story** Have students write a one- or two-page story that uses the concept of ionic and covalent bonds. For example, the story could be a mystery that can be solved only by determining which of the two types of bonds a certain compound has. LS Verbal

PORTFOLIO

covalent compound a chemical compound formed by the sharing of electrons

CONNECTION TO Language Arts

WRITING SKILL **Electrolyte Solutions** Ionic compounds that conduct electricity when they are dissolved in water are called *electrolytes*. Some electrolytes play important roles in the functioning of living cells. Electrolytes can be lost by the body during intense physical activity or illness and must be replenished for cells to work properly. Research two electrolytes that your body cells need and the function that they serve. Present your findings in a one-page research paper.

Figure 4 *Olive oil, which is used in salad dressings, is made of very large covalent molecules that do not mix with water.*

Covalent Compounds and Their Properties

Most compounds are covalent compounds. **Covalent compounds** are compounds that form when a group of atoms shares electrons. This sharing of electrons forms a covalent bond. A *covalent bond* is a weaker attractive force than an ionic bond is. The group of atoms that make up a covalent compound is called a molecule. A *molecule* is the smallest particle into which a covalently bonded compound can be divided and still be the same compound. Properties of covalent compounds are very different from the properties of ionic compounds.

Low Solubility

Many covalent compounds are not soluble in water, which means that they do not dissolve well in water. You may have noticed this if you have ever left off the top of a soda bottle. The carbon dioxide gas that gives the soda its fizz eventually escapes, and your soda pop goes "flat." The attraction between water molecules is much stronger than their attraction to the molecules of most other covalent compounds. So, water molecules stay together instead of mixing with the covalent compounds. If you have ever made salad dressing, you probably know that oil and water don't mix. Oils, such as the oil in the salad dressing in **Figure 4,** are made of covalent compounds.

✓ **Reading Check** Why won't most covalent compounds dissolve in water?

CONNECTION to History — ADVANCED

Bonding Theory Gilbert Newton Lewis (1875–1946) was an American chemist who developed the electron-pair bonding theory of atoms and molecules. He was the first chemist to describe covalent bonding. Lewis theorized that electrons in an atom usually form a tetrahedral arrangement of pairs around the nucleus. The octet rule is often associated with Lewis, although he never actually used the term "octet" for four pairs of electrons.

Answer to Reading Check

Most covalent compounds will not dissolve in water because the attraction of the water molecules to each other is much stronger than the attraction of the water molecules to the compound.

Low Melting Points

The forces of attraction between molecules of covalent compounds are much weaker than the bonds holding ionic solids together. Less heat is needed to separate the molecules of covalent compounds, so these compounds have much lower melting and boiling points than ionic compounds do.

Electrical Conductivity

Although most covalent compounds don't dissolve in water, some do. Most of the covalent compounds that dissolve in water form solutions that have uncharged molecules. Sugar is a covalent compound that dissolves in water and that does not form ions. So, a solution of sugar and water does not conduct an electric current, as shown in **Figure 5**. However, some covalent compounds do form ions when they dissolve in water. Many acids, for example, form ions in water. These solutions, like ionic solutions, conduct an electric current.

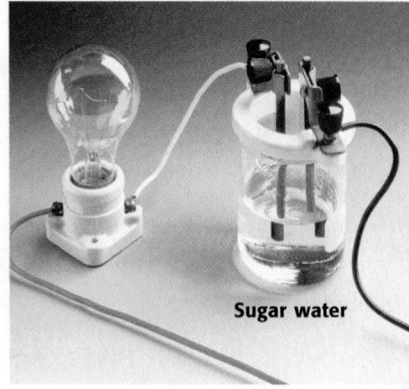

Figure 5 *This solution of sugar, a covalent compound, and water does not conduct an electric current because the molecules of sugar are not charged.*

SECTION Review

Summary

- Ionic compounds have ionic bonds between ions of opposite charges.

- Ionic compounds are usually brittle, have high melting points, dissolve in water, and often conduct an electric current.

- Covalent compounds have covalent bonds and consist of particles called molecules.

- Covalent compounds have low melting points, don't dissolve easily in water, and do not conduct an electric current.

Using Key Terms

1. Use each of the following terms in a separate sentence: *ionic compound, covalent compound,* and *chemical bond.*

Understanding Key Ideas

2. Which of the following describes an ionic compound?
   a. It has a low melting point.
   b. It consists of shared electrons.
   c. It conducts electric current in water solutions.
   d. It consists of two nonmetals.

3. List two properties of covalent compounds.

Math Skills

4. A compound contains 39.37% chromium, 38.10% oxygen, and potassium. What percentage of the compound is potassium?

Critical Thinking

5. **Making Inferences** Solid crystals of ionic compounds do not conduct an electric current. But when the crystals dissolve in water, the solution conducts an electric current. Explain.

6. **Applying Concepts** Some white solid crystals are dissolved in water. If the solution does not conduct an electric current, is the solid an ionic compound or a covalent compound? Explain.

For a variety of links related to this chapter, go to www.scilinks.org
Topic: Ionic Compounds; Covalent Compounds
SciLinks code: HSM0817; HSM0365

Answers to Section Review

1. Sample answer: Table salt is an ionic compound. Water is a covalent compound. The sodium ion and the chlorine ion in sodium chloride are held together by a chemical bond.

2. c

3. Sample answer: Two properties of covalent compounds are a low melting point and low solubility.

4. $100\% - 39.37\% - 38.10\% = 22.53\%$

5. A solution of ionic crystals in water can conduct an electric current because the ions are charged and are able to move freely past one another when in solution. But when ionic crystals are not in solution, their ions cannot move freely and therefore cannot conduct an electric current.

6. The solid is a covalent compound because covalent compounds do not conduct an electric current when dissolved in water.

CHAPTER RESOURCES

Chapter Resource File

- Section Quiz GENERAL
- Section Review GENERAL
- Vocabulary and Section Summary GENERAL

Focus

Overview

This section describes the properties and uses of acids and bases. Students will learn the properties of acids and bases and will learn about the uses of acids and bases.

 **Bellringer**

Show students a lemon and a tomato. Tell students that these fruits contain citric acid, which gives them a tangy flavor. Ask students to suggest other foods whose tanginess may be due to the presence of acids. (Sample answer: dill pickles, grapefruits, strawberries, or vinegar)

Motivate

ACTIVITY ——— GENERAL

Tasting a Weak Acid Have groups of students taste samples of carbonated water and compare the flavor of carbonated water with that of regular water. Have students report their findings. Explain that carbonated water contains carbonic acid, a weak acid that forms when carbon dioxide dissolves in water. The acid is responsible for the tangy flavor. Ask students if they can think of other foods that may be flavored with acids.

LS Kinesthetic

What You Will Learn

- Describe four properties of acids.
- Identify four uses of acids.
- Describe four properties of bases.
- Identify four uses of bases.

Vocabulary

acid
indicator
base

READING STRATEGY

Reading Organizer As you read this section, make a table comparing acids and bases.

acid any compound that increases the number of hydronium ions when dissolved in water

Acids and Bases

Would you like a nice, refreshing glass of acid? This is just what you get when you have a glass of lemonade.

Lemons contain a substance called an *acid*. One property of acids is a sour taste. In this section, you will learn about the properties of acids and bases.

Acids and Their Properties

A sour taste is not the only property of an acid. Have you noticed that when you squeeze lemon juice into tea, the color of the tea becomes lighter? This change happens because acids cause some substances to change color. An **acid** is any compound that increases the number of hydronium ions, H_3O^+, when dissolved in water. Hydronium ions form when a hydrogen ion, H^+, separates from the acid and bonds with a water molecule, H_2O, to form a hydronium ion, H_3O^+.

Reading Check How is a hydronium ion formed? (*See the Appendix for answers to Reading Checks.*)

Acids Have a Sour Flavor

Have you ever taken a bite of a lemon or lime? If so, like the boy in **Figure 1,** you know the sour taste of an acid. The taste of lemons, limes, and other citrus fruits is a result of citric acid. However, taste, touch, or smell should NEVER be used to identify an unknown chemical. Many acids are *corrosive,* which means that they destroy body tissue, clothing, and many other things. Most acids are also poisonous.

NEVER touch or taste a concentrated solution of a strong acid.

Figure 1 *Foods that have a sour taste usually contain acids.*

CHAPTER RESOURCES

Chapter Resource File

 • **Lesson Plan**
- **Directed Reading A** BASIC
- **Directed Reading B** SPECIAL NEEDS

Technology

 Transparencies
- Bellringer

Workbooks

 Interactive Textbook Struggling Readers

Answer to Reading Check

A hydronium ion forms when a hydrogen ion bonds to a water molecule in a water solution.

Figure 2 Detecting Acids with Indicators

The indicator, bromthymol blue, is pale blue in water.

When acid is added, the color changes to yellow because of the presence of the indicator.

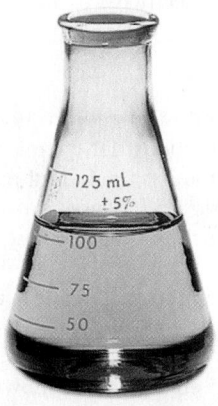 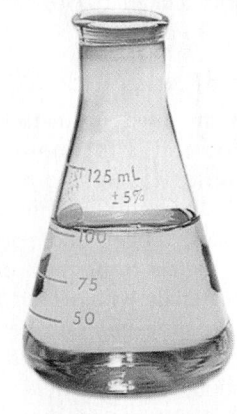

indicator a compound that can reversibly change color depending on conditions such as pH

Teach

Demonstration GENERAL

A Fruit Juice Indicator Place 1 mL of unsweetened purple grape juice and 9 mL of water into each of three test tubes. Instruct students to note the color of the diluted grape juice. Add a few drops of vinegar to the second test tube and a few drops of ammonia to the third test tube. Ask students to describe any color changes they observe. (In the second test tube, the color turns red. In the third test tube, the color turns blue.)

Finally, add ammonia to the second test tube and vinegar to the third test tube until the liquids change color again. Tell students that by the end of this section, they will be able to explain what they observed in this activity. **LS** Visual English Language Learners

Acids Change Colors in Indicators

A substance that changes color in the presence of an acid or base is an **indicator.** Look at **Figure 2.** The flask on the left contains water and an indicator called *bromthymol blue* (BROHM THIE MAWL BLOO). Acid has been added to the flask on the right. The color changes from pale blue to yellow because the indicator detects the presence of an acid.

Another indicator commonly used in the lab is litmus. Paper strips containing litmus are available in both blue and red. When an acid is added to blue litmus paper, the color of the litmus changes to red.

Acids React with Metals

Acids react with some metals to produce hydrogen gas. For example, hydrochloric acid reacts with zinc metal to produce hydrogen gas, as shown in **Figure 3.** The equation for the reaction is the following:

$$2HCl + Zn \longrightarrow H_2 + ZnCl_2$$

In this reaction, zinc displaces hydrogen in the compound, hydrochloric acid. This displacement happens because zinc is an active metal. But if the element silver were put into hydrochloric acid, nothing would happen. Silver is not an active metal, so no reaction would take place.

Figure 3 *Bubbles of hydrogen gas form when zinc metal reacts with hydrochloric acid.*

Cultural Awareness GENERAL

Food Preservation What do sauerkraut and ketchup have in common? Both are food items from different cultures that are flavored and preserved with vinegar. Have students research the use of acids to flavor and preserve foods from different cultures. Encourage students to present their findings to the class. **LS** Intrapersonal

Is That a Fact!

The proper way to use litmus paper is to dip a stirring rod into the solution to be tested and then touch the moist rod to the litmus paper. This procedure prevents the litmus from contaminating the solution and allows one piece of litmus paper to be used for three or four tests.

Comparing Acids and Bases
Have students make a chart that compares the properties of acids and bases. Encourage them to refer to their chart as they read through this section. **LS** Logical

Demonstration —— GENERAL

Safety Caution: Students should not look directly at the bright light produced by this reaction.

A Base from a Metal Explain to students that metal oxides react with water to form bases. Cut a piece of magnesium ribbon a few centimeters long. Hold the magnesium ribbon with a pair of tongs, and burn it over a plate or pie tin. Explain to students that the residue left from the reaction is magnesium oxide. Place the residue in a test tube, and add several drops of water. Ask students what will form in the test tube. (magnesium hydroxide, a base)

Ask them what color of litmus paper they would use to test the solution. (red)

Then ask them to predict what will happen to the litmus paper. (The litmus paper will turn blue.)

Ask a volunteer to use litmus paper to check the predictions.
LS Visual/Logical

CONNECTION TO Biology

Acids Can Curl Your Hair!
Permanents contain acids. Acids make hair curly by denaturing a certain amino acid in hair proteins. Research how acids are used in products that either curl or straighten hair. Then, make a poster that demonstrates this process. Present your poster to your classmates.
ACTiViTY

Acids Conduct Electric Current

When acids are dissolved in water, they break apart and form ions in the solution. The ions make it possible for the solution to conduct an electric current. A car battery is one example of how an acid can be used to produce an electric current. The sulfuric acid in the battery conducts electricity to help start the car's engine.

Uses of Acids

Acids are used in many areas of industry and in homes. Sulfuric acid is the most widely made industrial chemical in the world. It is used to make many products, including paper, paint, detergents, and fertilizers. Nitric acid is used to make fertilizers, rubber, and plastics. Hydrochloric acid is used to make metals from their ores by separating the metals from the materials with which they are combined. It is also used in swimming pools to help keep them free of algae. Hydrochloric acid is even found in your stomach, where it aids in digestion. Hydrofluoric acid is used to etch glass, as shown in **Figure 4.** Citric acid and ascorbic acid (Vitamin C) are found in orange juice. And carbonic acid and phosphoric acid help give a sharp taste to soft drinks.

Reading Check What are three uses of acids?

Figure 4 *The image of the swan was etched into the glass through the use of hydrofluoric acid.*

Is That a Fact!

Ammonia is a base even though it does not have hydroxide in its chemical formula. A solution of ammonia and water contains ammonium ions, NH_4^+, and hydroxide ions, OH^-.

Answer to Reading Check

Sulfuric acid is used in car batteries to conduct electric current. Hydrochloric acid is used as an algicide in swimming pools. Nitric acid is used to make fertilizers.

Figure 5 Examples of Bases

Soaps are made from sodium hydroxide, which is a base. Soaps remove dirt and oils from skin and feel slippery when you touch them.

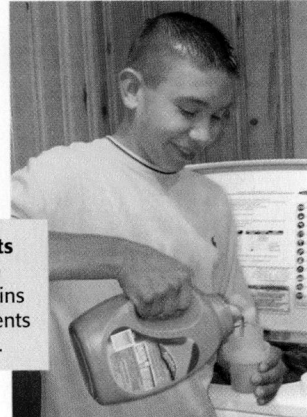

Bleach and detergents contain bases and are used for removing stains from clothing. Detergents feel slippery like soap.

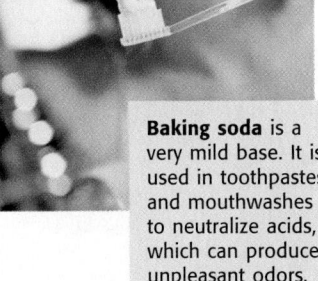

Baking soda is a very mild base. It is used in toothpastes and mouthwashes to neutralize acids, which can produce unpleasant odors.

Bases and Their Properties

A **base** is any compound that increases the number of hydroxide ions, OH⁻, when dissolved in water. For example, sodium hydroxide breaks apart to form sodium ions and hydroxide ions as shown below.

$$\text{NaOH} \longrightarrow \text{Na}^+ + \text{OH}^-$$

Hydroxide ions give bases their properties. **Figure 5** shows examples of bases that you are probably familiar with.

Bases Have a Bitter Flavor and a Slippery Feel

The properties of a base solution include a bitter taste and a slippery feel. If you have ever accidentally tasted soap, you know the bitter taste of a base. Soap will also have the slippery feel of a base. However, taste, touch or smell should NEVER be used to identify an unknown chemical. Like acids, many bases are corrosive. If your fingers feel slippery when you are using a base in an experiment, you may have gotten the base on your hands. You should immediately rinse your hands with large amounts of water and tell your teacher.

base any compound that increases the number of hydroxide ions when dissolved in water

NEVER touch or taste a concentrated solution of a strong base.

Homework ——— GENERAL

Writing **Soapmaking** Before soap was made commercially, people made their own soap. They combined an oil or fat with a strong base, such as lye (sodium hydroxide). Have students research some aspect of soapmaking and compile their findings into a short report. LS Verbal/Logical

Reteaching —— BASIC

Acids and Bases Review Have students make an outline of this section using the headings and subheadings. Under each heading and subheading, have students add at least two facts. Review the outlines as a class, and compile students' outlines to create a master outline that can be used as a study guide.
LS Logical

Quiz —— GENERAL

1. Classify each of the following compounds as acidic or basic: soap, vinegar, bleach, baking soda, ammonia, lemonade, and magnesium hydroxide.
(acidic: vinegar, lemonade; basic: soap, bleach, baking soda, ammonia, magnesium hydroxide)

2. When an acid is added to water, does the number of hydronium ions increase or decrease? (increase)

Alternative Assessment —— GENERAL

Writing **Acids and Bases Poster**
Have students create a poster-board display by using photographs from magazines. On one half of the poster board, students should compile photographs of acid compounds, and on the other half, students should compile photographs of basic compounds. Have students add information about each type of compound and display the posters for the class. **LS Visual** PORTFOLIO

SCHOOL to HOME

Acids and Bases at Home
Ask an adult to join in a contest with you. The object is to find products at home that contain an acid or a base. Each person will write the name of the product and the name of the acid or base that it contains. The person who finds the most products containing an acid or base is the winner. **ACTIVITY**

Figure 6 Detecting Bases with Indicators

The indicator, bromthymol blue, is pale blue in water.

When a base is added to the indicator, the indicator turns dark blue.

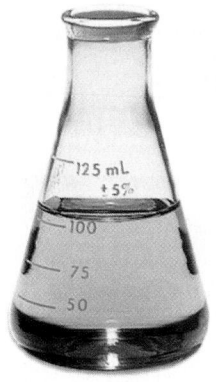

Bases Change Color in Indicators

Like acids, bases change the color of an indicator. Most indicators turn a different color in the presence of bases than they do in the presence of acids. For example, bases change the color of red litmus paper to blue. And the indicator, bromthymol blue, turns blue when a base is added to it, as shown in **Figure 6.**

Bases Conduct Electric Current

Solutions of bases conduct an electric current because bases increase the number of hydroxide ions, OH^-, in a solution. A hydroxide ion is actually a hydrogen atom and an oxygen atom bonded together. The extra electron gives the hydroxide ion a negative charge.

Blue to Red—Acid!

1. Pour about 5 mL of **test solution** into a **spot plate**. Test the solution using **red litmus paper** and **blue litmus paper** by dipping a **stirring rod** into it and then touching the rod to a piece of litmus paper.

2. Record any color changes. Clean the stirring rod.

3. Repeat the above steps with each solution. Use new pieces of litmus paper as needed.

4. Identify each solution as acidic or basic.

MATERIALS

FOR EACH GROUP
• litmus paper, red and blue
• spot plate
• stirring rod
• test solutions

Safety Caution: Students should wear safety goggles, gloves, and aprons. Remind students that they should not taste any of the solutions.

Have students test four acidic solutions and four basic solutions. Use common household solutions such as lemon juice, shampoo, baking soda, tap water, black coffee, milk, soft drinks, diluted household ammonia, milk of magnesia, and vinegar.

Answer
4. Answers may vary. Acids turn blue litmus paper red. Bases turn red litmus paper blue.

Uses of Bases

Like acids, bases have many uses. Sodium hydroxide is a base used to make soap and paper. It is also used in oven cleaners and in products that unclog drains. Calcium hydroxide, $Ca(OH)_2$, is used to make cement and plaster. Ammonia is found in many household cleaners and is used to make fertilizers. And magnesium hydroxide and aluminum hydroxide are used in antacids to treat heartburn. **Figure 7** shows some of the many products that contain bases. Carefully follow the safety instructions when using these products. Remember that bases can harm your skin.

✓ Reading Check What three ways can bases be used at home?

Figure 7 *Bases are common around the house. They are useful as cleaning agents, as cooking aids, and as medicines.*

SECTION Review

Summary

- An acid is a compound that increases the number of hydronium ions in solution.

- Acids taste sour, turn blue litmus paper red, react with metals to produce hydrogen gas, and may conduct an electric current when in solution.

- Acids are used for industrial purposes and in household products.

- A base is a compound that increases the number of hydroxide ions in solution.

- Bases taste bitter, feel slippery, and turn red litmus paper blue. Most solutions of bases conduct an electric current.

- Bases are used in cleaning products and acid neutralizers.

Using Key Terms

1. In your own words, write a definition for each of the following terms: *acid, base,* and *indicator*.

Understanding Key Ideas

2. A base is a substance that
   a. feels slippery.
   b. tastes sour.
   c. reacts with metals to produce hydrogen gas.
   d. turns blue litmus paper red.

3. Acids are important in
   a. making antacids.
   b. preparing detergents.
   c. keeping algae out of swimming pools.
   d. manufacturing cement.

4. What happens to red litmus paper when it touches a base?

Math Skills

5. A cake recipe calls for 472 mL of milk. You don't have a metric measuring cup at home, so you need to convert milliliters to cups. You know that 1 L equals 1.06 quarts and that there are 4 cups in 1 quart. How many cups of milk will you need to use?

Critical Thinking

6. **Making Comparisons** Compare the properties of acids and bases.

7. **Applying Concepts** Why would it be useful for a gardener or a vegetable farmer to use litmus paper to test soil samples?

8. **Analyzing Processes** Suppose that your teacher gives you a solution of an unknown chemical. The chemical is either an acid or a base. You know that touching or tasting acids and bases is not safe. What two tests could you perform on the chemical to determine whether it is an acid or a base? What results would help you decide if the chemical was an acid or a base?

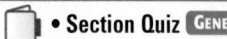

Developed and maintained by the National Science Teachers Association

For a variety of links related to this chapter, go to www.scilinks.org

Topic: Acids and Bases
SciLinks code: HSM0013

Answer to Reading Check

Bases can be used at home in the form of soap, oven cleaner, or antacid.

Answers to Section Review

1. Sample answer: An acid is a compound that increases the number of hydronium ions when dissolved in water. A base is a compound that increases the number of hydroxide ions when dissolved in water. An indicator is something that changes color in the presence of an acid or a base.

2. a

3. c

4. Red litmus paper turns blue when it touches a base.

5. 472 mL = 0.472 L $\times$ 1.06 qt $\times$ 4 cups = 2 cups

6. Sample answer: Acids have a sour flavor, change the color of indicators, react with metals, and conduct electric current. Bases have a bitter flavor, feel slippery, change the color of indicators, and conduct electric current.

7. Sample answer: A gardener or a farmer might use litmus paper to test soil samples to see if the soil is acidic or basic.

8. Sample answer: I would test the solution with red and blue litmus paper, and I would put zinc in the solution. If the solution is an acid, it should turn the blue litmus paper red and should react with the zinc. If the solution is a base, it should turn the red litmus paper blue and should not react with the zinc.

Focus

Overview

This section discusses the strength of acids and bases, the way that acids and bases neutralize each other, and the ways that acids and bases affect the environment. It also discusses the properties and uses of salts.

 Bellringer

Bring in product labels from vinegar products, citrus products, soaps, cleaning agents, and other household products that contain acids or bases. Ask students to work in pairs and to examine the labels to see if they can identify which ingredients are acids and which are bases.

Motivate

CONNECTION ACTIVITY
Math ——————— **GENERAL**

pH Scale Each one-point step on the pH scale represents a tenfold difference in acidity. Thus, a solution of pH 3 is 10 times as acidic as a solution of pH 4, and a solution of pH 9 is 10 times as basic as a solution of pH 8. Ask students: "How much more acidic than a solution of pH 6 is a solution of pH 2?" (6 − 2 = 4; 10^4 = 10,000 times as acidic)
LS Logical

What You Will Learn

● Explain the difference between strong acids and bases and weak acids and bases.
● Identify acids and bases by using the pH scale.
● Describe the formation and uses of salts.

Vocabulary

neutralization reaction
pH
salt

READING STRATEGY

Discussion Read this section silently. Write down questions that you have about this section. Discuss your questions in a small group.

Solutions of Acids and Bases

Suppose that at your friend's party, you ate several large pieces of pepperoni pizza followed by cake and ice cream. Now, you have a terrible case of indigestion.

If you have ever had an upset stomach, you may have felt very much like the boy in **Figure 1.** And you may have taken an antacid. But do you know how antacids work? An antacid is a weak base that neutralizes a strong acid in your stomach. In this section, you will learn about the strengths of acids and bases. You will also learn about reactions between acids and bases.

Strengths of Acids and Bases

Acids and bases can be strong or weak. The strength of an acid or a base is not the same as the concentration of an acid or a base. The concentration of an acid or a base is the amount of acid or base dissolved in water. But the strength of an acid or a base depends on the number of molecules that break apart when the acid or base is dissolved in water.

Strong Versus Weak Acids

As an acid dissolves in water, the acid's molecules break apart and produce hydrogen ions, H^+. If all of the molecules of an acid break apart, the acid is called a *strong acid*. Strong acids include sulfuric acid, nitric acid, and hydrochloric acid. If only a few molecules of an acid break apart, the acid is a weak acid. Weak acids include acetic (uh SEET ik) acid, citric acid, and carbonic acid.

✓ Reading Check What is the difference between a strong acid and a weak acid? (*See the Appendix for answers to Reading Checks.*)

Figure 1 *Antacids may help relieve your stomachache by reacting with the acid in your stomach.*

CHAPTER RESOURCES

Chapter Resource File

 • Lesson Plan
• Directed Reading A **BASIC**
• Directed Reading B **SPECIAL NEEDS**

Technology

 Transparencies
• Bellringer
• P60 pH Values of Common Materials

Workbooks

 Interactive Textbook Struggling Readers

Answer to Reading Check

In a strong acid, all of the molecules of the acid break apart when the acid is dissolved in water. In a weak acid, only a few of the acid molecules break apart when the acid is dissolved in water.

Strong Versus Weak Bases

When all molecules of a base break apart in water to produce hydroxide ions, OH⁻, the base is a strong base. Strong bases include sodium hydroxide, calcium hydroxide, and potassium hydroxide. When only a few molecules of a base break apart, the base is a weak base, such as ammonium hydroxide and aluminum hydroxide.

Acids, Bases, and Neutralization

When the base in an antacid meets stomach acid, a reaction occurs. The reaction between acids and bases is a **neutralization reaction** (NOO truhl i ZA shuhn ree AK shuhn). Acids and bases neutralize one another because the hydrogen ions (H^+), which are present in an acid, and the hydroxide ions (OH^-), which are present in a base, react to form water, H_2O, which is neutral. Other ions from the acid and base dissolve in the water. If the water evaporates, these ions join to form a compound called a *salt*.

The pH Scale

An *indicator*, such as litmus, can identify whether a solution contains an acid or base. To describe how acidic or basic a solution is, the pH scale is used. The **pH** of a solution is a measure of the hydronium ion concentration in the solution. A solution that has a pH of 7 is neutral, which means that the solution is neither acidic nor basic. Pure water has a pH of 7. Basic solutions have a pH greater than 7. Acidic solutions have a pH less than 7. **Figure 2** shows the pH values for many common materials.

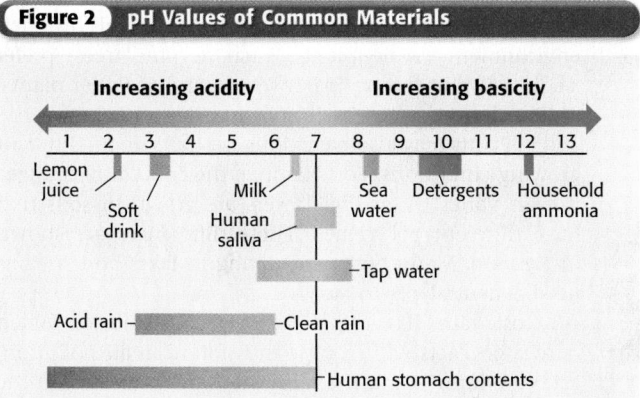

Figure 2 pH Values of Common Materials

Increasing acidity — Increasing basicity

1 2 3 4 5 6 7 8 9 10 11 12 13

Lemon juice
Soft drink
Milk
Human saliva
Sea water
Detergents
Household ammonia
Tap water
Acid rain — Clean rain
Human stomach contents

pHast Relief!

1. Pour **vinegar** into a **small plastic cup** until the cup is half full. Test the vinegar with **red and blue litmus paper.** Record your results.

2. Crush one **antacid tablet,** and mix it with the vinegar. Test the mixture with litmus paper. Record your results.

3. Compare the acidity of the solution before the antacid was added with the acidity of the solution after it was added.

neutralization reaction the reaction of an acid and a base to form a neutral solution of water and a salt

pH a value that is used to express the acidity or basicity (alkalinity) of a system

Homework ——— GENERAL

Dissolving Marble Have students research the effect of acid precipitation on statues, gravestones, and buildings. Tell students to make a small poster describing their findings and to display it to the class. **LS Visual**

Close

Reteaching — **BASIC**

Outlining the Section Have students use the heads, subheads, terms to learn, and any other words or phrases they need from this section to create an outline titled "Solutions of Acids and Bases." **LS** Logical

Quiz — GENERAL

1. Is the compound H_3PO_4 an acid or a base? How do you know? (It is an acid because it will form hydrogen ions if dissolved in water.)

2. Would you expect the pH of a sample of acid rain to be 4 or 9? Why? (4; because it is acidic)

3. What products would form when hydrochloric acid, HCl, and sodium hydroxide, NaOH, react? (The products would be water and the salt sodium chloride.)

Alternative Assessment — GENERAL

Concept Mapping Have students use the following terms to make a concept map that compares the properties of acids and bases: *acid, neutral, base, pH value greater than 7, pH value less than 7, salt, hydroxide ions, neutralize,* and *hydrogen ions.* **LS** Logical/ Visual

---

Figure 3 Using Indicators to Find pH

pH Indicator Scale

Dip in – read while still moist.
Immerse in weakly-buffered solutions until there is no further colour change (1–10 min).

1 2 3 4 5 6 7
7 8 9 10 11 12 13 14

pH 4   pH 10

CONNECTION TO Biology

WRITING SKILL **Blood and pH** Human blood has a pH between 7.38 and 7.42. If the blood pH is lower or higher, the body cannot function properly. Research what can cause the pH of blood to rise above or fall below normal ranges. Write a one-page paper that details your findings.

Figure 4 *To grow blue flowers, plant hydrangeas in soil that has a low pH. To grow pink flowers, use soil that has a high pH.*

Using Indicators to Determine pH

A combination of indicators can be used to find out how basic or how acidic a solution is. This can be done if the colors of the indicators are known at different pH values. **Figure 3** shows strips of pH paper, which contains several different indicators. These strips were dipped into two different solutions. The pH of each solution is found by comparing the colors on each strip with the colors on the indicator scale provided. This kind of indicator is often used to test the pH of water in pools and aquariums. Another way to find the pH of a solution is to use a pH meter. These meters can detect and measure hydronium ion concentration electronically.

✓ *Reading Check* How can indicators determine pH?

pH and the Environment

Living things depend on having a steady pH in their environment. Some plants, such as pine trees, prefer acidic soil that has a pH between 4 and 6. Other plants, such as lettuce, need basic soil that has a pH between 8 and 9. Plants may also have different traits under different growing conditions. For example, the color of hydrangea flowers varies when the flowers are grown in soils that have different pH values. These differences are shown in **Figure 4.** Many organisms living in lakes and streams need a neutral pH to survive.

Most rain has a pH between 5.5 and 6. When rainwater reacts with compounds found in air pollution, acids are formed and the rainwater's pH decreases. In the United States, most acid rain has a pH between 4 and 4.5, but some precipitation has a pH as low as 3.

Answer to Reading Check

Indicators turn different colors at different pH levels. The color on the pH strip can be compared with the colors on the indicator scale to determine the pH of the solution being tested.

Salts

When an acid neutralizes a base, a salt and water are produced. A **salt** is an ionic compound formed from the positive ion of a base and the negative ion of an acid. When you hear the word *salt,* you probably think of the table salt you use to season your food. But the sodium chloride found in your salt shaker is only one example of a large group of compounds called *salts.*

Uses of Salts

Salts have many uses in industry and in homes. You already know that sodium chloride is used to season foods. It is also used to make other compounds, including lye (sodium hydroxide) and baking soda. Sodium nitrate is a salt that is used to preserve food. And calcium sulfate is used to make wallboard, which is used in construction. Another use of salt is shown in **Figure 5.**

Figure 5 *Salts help keep roads free of ice by decreasing the freezing point of water.*

salt an ionic compound that forms when a metal atom replaces the hydrogen of an acid

---

SECTION Review

Summary

● Every molecule of a strong acid or base breaks apart to form ions. Few molecules of weak acids and bases break apart to form ions.

● An acid and a base can neutralize one another to make salt and water.

● pH is a measure of hydronium ion concentration in a solution.

● A salt is an ionic compound formed in a neutralization reaction. Salts have many industrial and household uses.

Using Key Terms

1. Use the following terms in the same sentence: *neutralization reaction* and *salt.*

Understanding Key Ideas

2. A neutralization reaction
   a. includes an acid and a base.
   b. produces a salt.
   c. forms water.
   d. All of the above

3. Explain the difference between a strong acid and a weak acid.

Math Skills

4. For each point lower on the pH scale, the hydrogen ions in solution increase tenfold. For example, a solution of pH 3 is not twice as acidic as a solution of pH 6 but is 1,000 times as acidic. How many times more acidic is a solution of pH 2 than a solution of pH 4?

Critical Thinking

5. **Analyzing Processes** Predict what will happen to the hydrogen ion concentration and the pH of water if hydrochloric acid is added to the water.

6. **Analyzing Relationships** Would fish be healthy in a lake that has a low pH? Explain.

7. **Applying Concepts** Soap is made from a strong base and oil. Would you expect the pH of soap to be 4 or 9? Explain.

 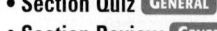

Developed and maintained by the National Science Teachers Association

For a variety of links related to this chapter, go to www.scilinks.org

Topic: pH scale; Salts
SciLinks code: HSM1130; HSM1347

Is That a Fact!

Explain to students that the indicator litmus is actually a pigment derived from lichens. Lichens are organisms formed from the union of fungal and algal cells that appear as colored scales on trees and rocks. Litmus paper is paper that has been impregnated with litmus.

CHAPTER RESOURCES

Chapter Resource File

- Section Quiz GENERAL
- Section Review GENERAL
- Vocabulary and Section Summary GENERAL
- Reinforcement Worksheet BASIC
- Datasheet for Quick Lab

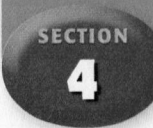
Focus

Overview

This section discusses organic compounds—covalent compounds that contain carbon. This section discusses how carbon forms bonds and introduces hydrocarbons and biochemicals.

 Bellringer

Ask students to list as many carbon-containing items as they can. Give them 3 minutes to complete their lists. Once the time is up, ask students to share some of their ideas. Point out that researchers have discovered millions of carbon compounds.

Motivate

Discussion ——— GENERAL

Amino Acids and Vegetarians Tell students that meat contains protein. Ask students how they think vegetarians can get all of the building blocks that they need to make proteins. (Sample answer: Vegetarians can get the building blocks of proteins from foods such as grains and legumes.) **LS** Verbal/Auditory

---

What You Will Learn

- Explain why there are so many organic compounds.
- Identify and describe saturated, unsaturated, and aromatic hydrocarbons.
- Describe the characteristics of carbohydrates, lipids, proteins, and nucleic acids and their functions in the body.

Vocabulary

organic compound	lipid
hydrocarbon	protein
carbohydrate	nucleic acid

READING STRATEGY

Paired Summarizing Read this section silently. In pairs, take turns summarizing the material. Stop to discuss ideas that seem confusing.

Organic Compounds

Can you believe that more than 90% of all compounds are members of a single group of compounds? It's true!

Most compounds are members of a group called organic compounds. **Organic compounds** are covalent compounds composed of carbon-based molecules. Fuel, rubbing alcohol, and sugar are organic compounds. Even cotton, paper, and plastic belong to this group. Why are there so many kinds of organic compounds? Learning about the carbon atom can help you understand why.

The Four Bonds of a Carbon Atom

All organic compounds contain carbon. Each carbon atom has four valence electrons. So, each carbon atom can make four bonds with four other atoms.

Carbon Backbones

The models in **Figure 1** are called *structural formulas*. They are used to show how atoms in a molecule are connected. Each line represents a pair of electrons that form a covalent bond. Many organic compounds are based on the types of carbon backbones shown in **Figure 1.** Some compounds have hundreds or thousands of carbon atoms as part of their backbone! Organic compounds may also contain hydrogen, oxygen, sulfur, nitrogen, and phosphorus.

☑ **Reading Check** What is the purpose of structural formulas? (*See the Appendix for answers to Reading Checks.*)

Figure 1 Three Models of Carbon Backbones

Straight chain	Branched chain	Ring
▲ All carbon atoms are connected in a straight line.	▲ The chain of carbon atoms branches into different directions when a carbon atom is bonded to more than one other carbon atom.	▲ The chain of carbon atoms forms a ring.

CHAPTER RESOURCES

Chapter Resource File

- Lesson Plan
- Directed Reading A BASIC
- Directed Reading B SPECIAL NEEDS

Technology

- Transparencies
  - Bellringer
  - P61 Structural Formulas

Workbooks

- Interactive Textbook Struggling Readers

Answer to Reading Check

Structural formulas show how atoms in a molecule are connected.

Figure 2 Three Types of Hydrocarbons

Alkane	Alkene	Alkyne
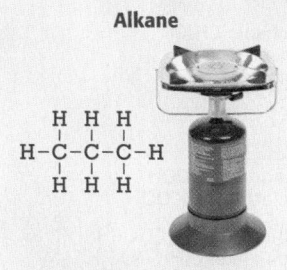	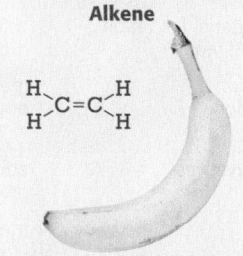	$H-C\equiv C-H$
The **propane** in this camping stove is a saturated hydrocarbon.	Fruits make **ethene**, which is a compound that helps ripen the fruit.	**Ethyne** is better known as acetylene. It is burned in this miner's lamp and in welding torches.

Hydrocarbons and Other Organic Compounds

Although many organic compounds contain several kinds of atoms, some contain only two. Organic compounds that contain only carbon and hydrogen are called **hydrocarbons.**

Saturated Hydrocarbons

The propane shown in **Figure 2** is a saturated hydrocarbon. A *saturated hydrocarbon,* or *alkane,* is a hydrocarbon in which each carbon atom in the molecule shares a single bond with each of four other atoms. A single bond is a covalent bond made up of one pair of shared electrons.

Unsaturated Hydrocarbons

An *unsaturated hydrocarbon,* such as ethene or ethyne shown in **Figure 2,** is a hydrocarbon in which at least one pair of carbon atoms shares a double bond or a triple bond. A double bond is a covalent bond made up of two pairs of shared electrons. A triple bond is a covalent bond made up of three pairs of shared electrons. Hydrocarbons that contain double or triple bonds are unsaturated because these bonds can be broken and more atoms can be added to the molecules.

Compounds that contain two carbon atoms connected by a double bond are called *alkenes.* Hydrocarbons that contain two carbon atoms connected by a triple bond are called *alkynes.*

Aromatic Hydrocarbons

Most aromatic (AR uh MAT ik) compounds are based on benzene. As shown in **Figure 3,** benzene has a ring of six carbons that have alternating double and single bonds. Aromatic hydrocarbons often have strong odors.

organic compound a covalently bonded compound that contains carbon

hydrocarbon an organic compound composed only of carbon and hydrogen

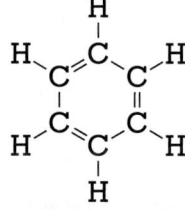

Figure 3 *Benzene is the starting material for manufacturing many products, including medicines.*

Table 1 Types and Uses of Organic Compounds

Type of compound	Uses	Examples
Alkyl halides	starting material for Teflon™ refrigerant (Freon™)	chloromethane, CH_3Cl bromoethane, C_2H_5Br
Alcohols	rubbing alcohol gasoline additive antifreeze	methanol, CH_3OH ethanol, C_2H_5OH
Organic acids	food preservatives flavorings	ethanoic acid, CH_3COOH propanoic acid, C_2H_5COOH
Esters	flavorings fragrances clothing (polyester)	methyl ethanoate, CH_3COOCH_3 ethyl propanoate, $C_2H_5COOC_2H_5$

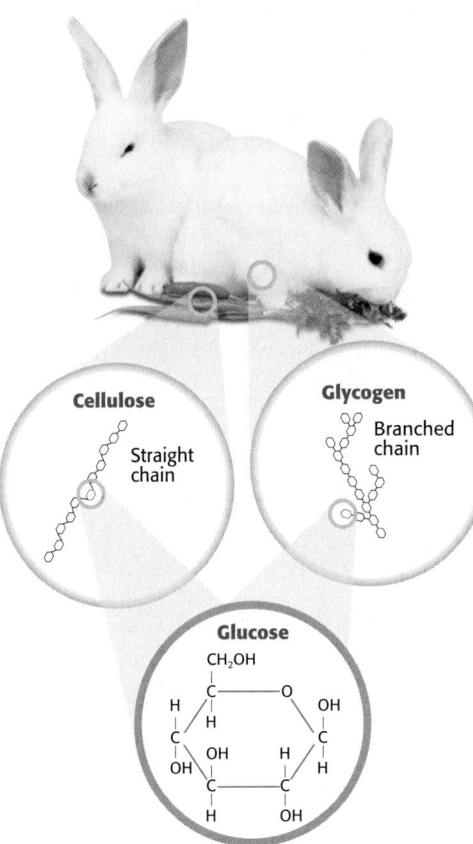

Figure 4 Glucose molecules, represented by hexagons, can bond to form complex carbohydrates, such as cellulose and glycogen.

Other Organic Compounds

There are many other kinds of organic compounds. Some have atoms of halogens, oxygen, sulfur, and phosphorus in their molecules. A few of these compounds and their uses are listed in **Table 1.**

Biochemicals: The Compounds of Life

Organic compounds that are made by living things are called *biochemicals*. Biochemicals are divided into four categories: carbohydrates, lipids, proteins, and nucleic acids (noo KLEE ik AS idz).

Carbohydrates

Carbohydrates are biochemicals that are composed of one or more simple sugar molecules bonded together. Carbohydrates are used as a source of energy. There are two kinds of carbohydrates: simple carbohydrates and complex carbohydrates.

Simple carbohydrates include simple sugars, such as glucose. **Figure 4** shows how glucose molecules can bond to form different complex carbohydrates. Complex carbohydrates may be made of hundreds or thousands of sugar molecules bonded together. *Cellulose* gives plant cell walls their rigid structure, and *glycogen* supplies energy to muscle cells.

Lipids

Lipids are biochemicals that do not dissolve in water. Fats, oils, and waxes are kinds of lipids. Lipids have many functions, including storing energy and making up cell membranes. Although too much fat in your diet can be unhealthy, some fat is important to good health. The foods in **Figure 5** are sources of lipids.

Lipids store excess energy in the body. Animals tend to store lipids as fats, while plants store lipids as oils. When an organism has used up most of its carbohydrates, it can obtain energy by breaking down lipids. Lipids are also used to store some vitamins.

Proteins

Most of the biochemicals found in living things are proteins. In fact, after water, proteins are the most common molecules in your cells. **Proteins** are biochemicals that are composed of "building blocks" called *amino acids*.

Amino acids are small molecules made up of carbon, hydrogen, oxygen, and nitrogen atoms. Some amino acids also include sulfur atoms. Amino acids bond to form proteins of many shapes and sizes. The shape of a protein determines the function of the protein. If even a single amino acid is missing or out of place, the protein may not function correctly or at all. Proteins have many functions. They regulate chemical activities, transport and store materials, and provide structural support.

Reading Check What are proteins made of?

Figure 5 *Vegetable oil, meat, cheese, nuts, eggs, and milk are sources of lipids in your diet.*

carbohydrate a class of energy-giving nutrients that includes sugars, starches, and fiber; composed of one or more simple sugars bonded together

lipid a type of biochemical that does not dissolve in water; fats and steroids are lipids

protein a molecule that is made up of amino acids and that is needed to build and repair body structures and to regulate processes in the body

Food Facts

1. Select **four empty food packages.**

2. Without reading the Nutrition Facts labels, rank the items from most carbohydrate content to least carbohydrate content.

3. Rank the items from most fat content to least fat content.

4. Read the Nutrition Facts labels, and compare your rankings with the real rankings.

5. Why do you think your rankings were right, or why were they wrong? Explain your answers.

Reteaching — BASIC

Concept Mapping Ask students to make a concept map using the terms in this section. Tell students that their concept map should focus on the characteristics of the four types of biochemicals and on their roles in the human body. **LS** Logical

Quiz — GENERAL

1. How many bonds does carbon form? (4)

2. Name four kinds of biochemicals. (proteins, nucleic acids, carbohydrates, and lipids)

Alternative Assessment — GENERAL

Building a Model Show students a drawing or a picture of a DNA molecule. Then, have students work in groups and use paper, string, clay, or other construction materials to make a model of a DNA molecule. Display the models around the class for everyone to enjoy. English Language Learners **LS** Interpersonal/Visual

Answer to Reading Check

Nucleic acids store genetic information and build proteins.

Figure 6 *Spider webs are made up of proteins that are shaped like long fibers.*

nucleic acid a molecule made up of subunits called *nucleotides*

Examples of Proteins

Proteins have many roles in your body and in living things. Enzymes (EN ZIEMZ) are proteins that are catalysts. *Catalysts* regulate chemical reactions in the body by increasing the rate at which the reactions occur. Some hormones are proteins. For example, insulin is a protein hormone that helps regulate your blood-sugar level. Another kind of protein, called *hemoglobin,* is found in red blood cells and delivers oxygen throughout the body. There are also large proteins that extend through cell membranes. These proteins help control the transport of materials into and out of cells. Some proteins, such as those in your hair, provide structural support. The structural proteins of silk fibers make the spider web shown in **Figure 6** strong and lightweight.

Nucleic Acids

The largest molecules made by living organisms are nucleic acids. **Nucleic acids** are biochemicals made up of *nucleotides* (NOO klee oh TIEDZ). Nucleotides are molecules made of carbon, hydrogen, oxygen, nitrogen, and phosphorus atoms. There are only five kinds of nucleotides. But nucleic acids may have millions of nucleotides bonded together. The only reason living things differ from each other is that each living thing has a different order of nucleotides.

Nucleic acids have several functions. One function of nucleic acids is to store genetic information. They also help build proteins and other nucleic acids. Nucleic acids are sometimes called *the blueprints of life,* because they contain all the information needed for a cell to make all of its proteins.

Reading Check What are two functions of nucleic acids?

CONNECTION TO Social Studies

DNA "Fingerprinting" and Crime-Scene Investigation The chemical structure of all human DNA is the same. The only difference between one person's DNA and another's is the order, or sequence, of the building blocks in the DNA. The number of ways these building blocks can be sequenced are countless.

DNA fingerprinting is new process. However, it has changed the way that criminal investigations are carried out. Research DNA fingerprinting. Find out when DNA fingerprinting was first used, who developed the process, and how DNA fingerprinting is used in crime-scene investigations. Present your findings in an oral presentation to your class. Include a model or a poster to help explain the process to your classmates.

Cultural Awareness — GENERAL

Lactose Intolerance Lactase is an enzyme that allows humans to break down lactose, the sugar in milk. Infants produce a lot of lactase, but most adults worldwide produce significantly less. As a result, many adults cannot digest lactose and therefore have trouble digesting milk. While only 10% of adult Americans of northern European ancestry are lactose intolerant, about 80% of African American adults and 60% of Hispanic adults are lactose intolerant. Scientists think that, over thousands of years, human populations that depended on cow's milk as a major food resource evolved the ability to continue producing lactase as adults. Have interested students research ways that people who are lactose intolerant can still eat foods that contain lactose. (Taking pills that contain lactase can help people digest lactose.) **LS** Verbal

DNA and RNA

There are two kinds of nucleic acids: DNA and RNA. A model of DNA (**d**eoxyribo**n**ucleic **a**cid) is shown in **Figure 7.** DNA is the genetic material of the cell. DNA molecules can store a huge amount of information because of their length. The DNA molecules in a single human cell have a length of about 2 m—which is more than 6 ft long! When a cell needs to make a certain protein, it copies a certain part of the DNA. The information copied from the DNA directs the order in which amino acids are bonded to make that protein. DNA also contains information used to build the second type of nucleic acid, RNA (**r**ibo**n**ucleic **a**cid). RNA is involved in the actual building of proteins.

Figure 7 *Two strands of DNA are twisted in a spiral shape. Four different nucleotides make up the rungs of the DNA ladder.*

SECTION Review

Summary

- Organic compounds contain carbon, which can form four bonds.
- Hydrocarbons are composed of only carbon and hydrogen.
- Hydrocarbons may be saturated, unsaturated, or aromatic hydrocarbons.
- Carbohydrates are made of simple sugars.
- Lipids store energy and make up cell membranes.
- Proteins are composed of amino acids.
- Nucleic acids store genetic information and help cells make proteins.

Using Key Terms

1. Use the following terms in the same sentence: *organic compound, hydrocarbon,* and *biochemical.*

2. In your own words, write a definition for each of the following terms: *carbohydrate, lipid, protein,* and *nucleic acid.*

Understanding Key Ideas

3. A saturated hydrocarbon has
   a. only single bonds.
   b. double bonds.
   c. triple bonds.
   d. double and triple bonds.

4. List two functions of proteins.

5. What is an aromatic hydrocarbon?

Critical Thinking

6. **Identifying Relationships** Hemoglobin is a protein that is in blood and that transports oxygen to the tissues of the body. Information stored in nucleic acids tells a cell how to make proteins. What might happen if there is a mistake in the information needed to make hemoglobin?

7. **Making Comparisons** Compare saturated hydrocarbons with unsaturated hydrocarbons.

Interpreting Graphics

Use the structural formula of this organic compound to answer the questions that follow.

$$\begin{array}{c} \text{H} \quad \text{H} \quad \text{H} \\ | \quad \; | \quad \; | \\ \text{H–C–C–C–H} \\ | \quad \; | \quad \; | \\ \text{H} \quad \text{H} \quad \text{H} \end{array}$$

8. What type of bonds are present in this molecule?

9. Can you determine the shape of the molecule from this structural formula? Explain your answer.

SCI LINKS. **NSTA**
Developed and maintained by the National Science Teachers Association

For a variety of links related to this chapter, go to www.scilinks.org

Topic: Aromatic Compounds; Organic Compounds

SciLinks code: HSM0095; HSM1078

ACTIVITY — ADVANCED

Writing **DNA** Suggest that interested students learn about how DNA stores the information that cells need to make proteins. Tell students to research the topic in the library and on the Internet and to compile their findings into a short report. **LS Verbal**

CHAPTER RESOURCES

Chapter Resource File

- Section Quiz **GENERAL**
- Section Review **GENERAL**
- Vocabulary and Section Summary **GENERAL**
- Critical Thinking **ADVANCED**
- Datasheet for Quick Lab

Cabbage Patch Indicators

Teacher's Notes

Time Required

One 45-minute class period

Lab Ratings

EASY ——————————→ HARD

Teacher Prep 🧪🧪
Student Set-Up 🧪🧪
Concept Level 🧪🧪
Clean Up 🧪🧪

MATERIALS

Materials listed are for groups of 2–3 students. Choose a wide variety of sample liquids, including bleach, ammonia, clear soda pop, lemon juice, milk, and baking soda (dissolved in water). Either red or blue litmus paper (or both) will work.

Safety Caution

Remind students to review all safety cautions and icons before beginning this lab activity. Caution students to use care when using the hot plate. Have students use tongs when handling the beaker with the hot water. Tell students that even diluted acids and bases can irritate the skin. Students should wash the affected area immediately if any sample liquid touches their skin.

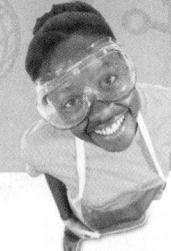

Skills Practice Lab

Skills Practice Lab

OBJECTIVES

Make a natural acid-base indicator solution.

Determine the pH of various common substances.

MATERIALS

- beaker, 250 mL
- beaker tongs
- eyedropper
- hot plate
- litmus paper
- pot holder
- red cabbage leaf
- sample liquids provided by teacher
- tape, masking
- test tubes
- test-tube rack
- water, distilled

SAFETY

Cabbage Patch Indicators

Indicators are weak acids or bases that change color due to the pH of the substance to which they are added. Red cabbage contains a natural indicator. It turns specific colors at specific pHs. In this lab you will extract the indicator from red cabbage. Then, you will use it to determine the pH of several liquids.

Procedure

1. Copy the table below. Be sure to include one line for each sample liquid.

Data Collection Table			
Liquid	Color with indicator	pH	Effect on litmus paper
Control			

DO NOT WRITE IN BOOK

Holt Lab Generator CD-ROM

Search for any lab by topic, standard, difficulty level, or time. Edit any lab to fit your needs, or create your own labs. Use the Lab Materials QuickList software to customize your lab materials list.

Dennis Hanson
Big Bear Middle School
Big Bear Lake, California

CLASSROOM TESTED & APPROVED

CHAPTER RESOURCES

Chapter Resource File

- **Datasheet for Chapter Lab**
- **Lab Notes and Answers**

Technology

Classroom Videos
- Lab Video

LabBook

- Making Salt

② Put on protective gloves. Place 100 mL of distilled water in the beaker. Tear the cabbage leaf into small pieces. Place the pieces in the beaker.

③ Use the hot plate to heat the cabbage and water to boiling. Continue boiling until the water is deep blue. **Caution:** Use extreme care when working near a hot plate.

④ Use tongs to remove the beaker from the hot plate. Turn the hot plate off. Allow the solution to cool on a pot holder for 5 to 10 minutes.

⑤ While the solution is cooling, use masking tape and a pen to label the test tubes for each sample liquid. Label one test tube as the control. Place the tubes in the rack.

⑥ Use the eyedropper to place a small amount (about 5 mL) of the indicator (cabbage juice) in the test tube labeled as the control.

⑦ Pour a small amount (about 5 mL) of each sample liquid into the appropriate test tube.

⑧ Using the eyedropper, place several drops of the indicator into each test tube. Swirl gently. Record the color of each liquid in the table.

⑨ Use the chart below to the find the pH of each sample. Record the pH values in the table.

⑩ Litmus paper has an indicator that turns red in an acid and blue in a base. Test each liquid with a strip of litmus paper. Record the results.

Analyze the Results

① **Analyzing Data** What purpose does the control serve? What is the pH of the control?

② **Examining Data** What colors in your samples indicate the presence of an acid? What colors indicate the presence of a base?

③ **Analyzing Results** Why is red cabbage juice considered a good indicator?

Draw Conclusions

④ **Interpreting Information** Which do you think would be more useful to help identify an unknown liquid—litmus paper or red cabbage juice? Why?

Applying Your Data

Unlike distilled water, rainwater has some carbon dioxide dissolved in it. Is rainwater acidic, basic, or neutral? To find out, place a small amount of the cabbage juice indicator (which is water-based) in a clean test tube. Use a straw to gently blow bubbles in the indicator. Continue blowing bubbles until you see a color change. What can you conclude about the pH of your "rainwater?" What is the purpose of blowing bubbles in the cabbage juice?

Analyze the Results

1. The control serves as a color comparison for test tubes containing the sample liquids. The control is reddish blue, which indicates that it is neutral, so the pH is about 7.

2. Reddish colors indicate acids. Bluish colors indicate bases.

3. Red cabbage juice is a good indicator because its color can indicate many pH values. It can be used to identify the relative strengths of acids and bases if their concentrations are the same.

Draw Conclusions

4. red cabbage juice; It would give you an approximate idea of the pH of the unknown liquid. The pH could then be used to help identify the substance. Litmus paper can indicate only whether the unknown liquid is acidic or basic.

Applying Your Data

Students should find that rainwater is slightly acidic. Blowing bubbles dissolves carbon dioxide in the cabbage juice.

pH 1 2 3 4 5 6 7 8 9 10 11 12 13 14

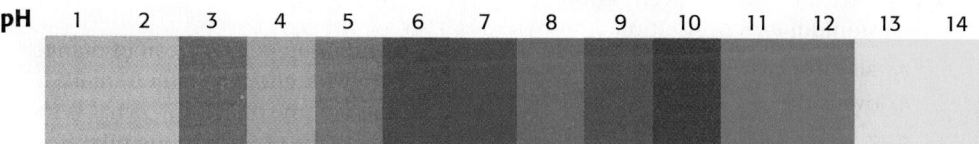

Disposal Information

Use the appropriate disposal technique for each sample liquid.

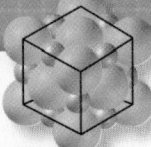

Assignment Guide

Section	Questions
1	1, 8, 16, 21
2	2, 3, 14–15, 18, 22
3	9, 11–12, 19–20
4	4–7, 10, 13, 17, 21, 23–26

ANSWERS

Using Key Terms

1. An ionic compound contains ionic bonds formed by atoms gaining or losing one or more electrons. A covalent compound contains covalent bonds formed by atoms sharing electrons.

2. An acid increases the number of hydronium ions when dissolved in water, and a base increases the number of hydroxide ions when dissolved in water.

3. pH is the measure of the hydronium ion concentration in a solution, and an indicator is a substance that changes color in the presence of an acid or a base.

4. A hydrocarbon is a compound composed only of hydrogen and carbon, and an organic compound is a carbon-based compound that may contain hydrogen, oxygen, sulfur, nitrogen, or phosphorus.

USING KEY TERMS

For each pair of terms, explain how the meanings of the terms differ.

1 *ionic compound* and *covalent compound*

2 *acid* and *base*

3 *pH* and *indicator*

4 *hydrocarbon* and *organic compound*

5 *carbohydrate* and *lipid*

6 *protein* and *nucleic acid*

UNDERSTANDING KEY IDEAS

Multiple Choice

7 Which of the following statements describes lipids?
   a. Lipids are used to store energy.
   b. Lipids do not dissolve in water.
   c. Lipids make up part of the cell membrane.
   d. All of the above

8 Ionic compounds
   a. have a low melting point.
   b. are often brittle.
   c. do not conduct electric current in water.
   d. do not dissolve easily in water.

9 An increase in the concentration of hydronium ions in solution
   a. raises the pH.
   b. lowers the pH.
   c. does not affect the pH.
   d. doubles the pH.

10 The compounds that store information for building proteins are
   a. lipids.
   b. hydrocarbons.
   c. nucleic acids.
   d. carbohydrates.

Short Answer

11 What type of compound would you use to neutralize a solution of potassium hydroxide?

12 Explain why the reaction of an acid with a base is called *neutralization*.

13 What characteristic of carbon atoms helps to explain the wide variety of organic compounds?

14 What kind of ions are produced when an acid is dissolved in water and when a base is dissolved in water?

Math Skills

15 Most of the vinegar used to make pickles is 5% acetic acid. So, in 100 mL of vinegar, 5 mL is acid diluted with 95 mL of water. If you bought a 473 mL bottle of 5% vinegar, how many milliliters of acetic acid would be in the bottle? How many milliliters of water were used to dilute the acetic acid?

16 If you dilute a 75 mL can of orange juice with enough water to make a total volume of 300 mL, what is the percentage of juice in the mixture?

5. A carbohydrate is composed of sugar molecules, and a lipid is a biochemical that does not dissolve in water.

6. A protein is composed of amino acids, and a nucleic acid is made of nucleotides.

Understanding Key Ideas

7. d
8. b
9. b
10. c
11. Potassium hydroxide is a base, so I would use an acid to neutralize it.

12. When an acid reacts with a base, the pH of the solution gets closer to pH 7, which indicates a neutral solution.

13. Each carbon atom has four valence electrons and can form four bonds. These bonds can be made to atoms of carbon or to atoms of other elements.

14. Acids produce hydronium ions in water, and bases produce hydroxide ions in water.

15. 473 mL × 5% = 473 mL × 0.05 = 23.65 mL acetic acid
    473 mL − 23.65 mL = 449.35 mL water

16. 75 mL ÷ 300 mL × 100% = 25% juice

CRITICAL THINKING

17. Concept Mapping Use the following terms to create a concept map: *acid, base, salt, neutral,* and *pH.*

18. Applying Concepts Fish give off the base, ammonia, NH_3, as waste. How does the release of ammonia affect the pH of the water in the aquarium? What can be done to correct the pH of the water?

19. Analyzing Methods Many insects, such as fire ants, inject formic acid, a weak acid, when they bite or sting. Describe the type of compound that should be used to treat the bite.

20. Making Comparisons Organic compounds are also covalent compounds. What properties would you expect organic compounds to have as a result?

21. Applying Concepts Farmers have been known to taste their soil to determine whether the soil has the correct acidity for their plants. How would taste help the farmer determine the acidity of the soil?

22. Analyzing Ideas A diet that includes a high level of lipids is unhealthy. Why is a diet containing no lipids also unhealthy?

INTERPRETING GRAPHICS

Use the structural formulas below to answer the questions that follow.

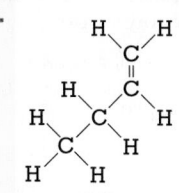

23. A saturated hydrocarbon is represented by which structural formula(s)?

24. An unsaturated hydrocarbon is represented by which structural formula(s)?

25. An aromatic hydrocarbon is represented by which structural formula(s)?

Critical Thinking

17. 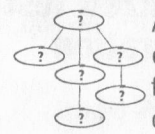 An answer to this exercise can be found at the end of this book.

18. The pH of the water will increase. An acid can be added to lower the pH and correct the problem.

19. A weak base should be used to treat the bite. It will neutralize the acid.

20. Organic compounds should have low melting points, should not dissolve well in water, and should not conduct an electric current in solution.

21. The taste of the soil can help a farmer determine if the soil is acidic or basic. If the soil tastes sour, it is acidic. If the soil tastes bitter, it is basic.

22. A diet containing no lipids is unhealthy because lipids are the major component of cell membranes and are important for storing energy and certain vitamins.

Interpreting Graphics

23. b and c

24. a and d

25. a

CHAPTER RESOURCES

Chapter Resource File

- Chapter Review **GENERAL**
- Chapter Test A **GENERAL**
- Chapter Test B **SPECIAL NEEDS**
- Chapter Test C **ADVANCED**
- Vocabulary Activity **GENERAL**

Workbooks

Study Guide
- Study Guide is also available in Spanish.

Teacher's Notes

To provide practice under more realistic conditions, give students 20 minutes to answer all of the questions in this Standardized Test Preparation.

Answer Key

Question	Answer
1	C
2	C
3	D
4	A
5	C
6	B
7	B
8	A
9	D
10	D
11	*
12	*

*See Test Doctor.

Multiple Choice

Use the chart below to answer question 1.

Properties of Some Compounds

Compound	Melting point	Solubility	Electrical conductivity in solution
A	801°C	high	yes
B	398°C	low	yes
C	20°C	low	no
D	1,200°C	high	yes

1. **Which of the compounds in the table above is most likely a covalent compound?**

    A. compound A

    B. compound B

    C. compound C

    D. compound D

2. **Akeem reads the following description of a substance: "clear liquid, boiling point of 78°C, flammable, soluble in water." Which of the properties listed is a chemical property?**

    A. clear liquid

    B. boiling point of 78°C

    C. flammable

    D. soluble in water

3. **A compound dissolved in water turns red litmus paper blue and changes the indicator bromthymol blue to dark blue. What kind of compound is it?**

    A. an acid

    B. water

    C. table salt

    D. a base

4. **What type of compound increases the number of hydronium ions when dissolved in water?**

    A. an acid

    B. a base

    C. an indicator

    D. hydrogen gas

5. **Which of the following is a kind of biochemical that does not dissolve in water and that is found in cell walls, fats, oils, and waxes?**

    A. glycogen

    B. carbohydrate

    C. lipid

    D. cellulose

6. **Jacques is going to perform a laboratory experiment with organic compounds. He can conclude that all the organic compounds he will study must contain a certain element. What is that element?**

    A. hydrogen

    B. carbon

    C. oxygen

    D. nitrogen

✚ TEST DOCTOR

Question 1 A, B, D: The high melting points and electrical conductivity in solution of these compounds indicate that they are most likely ionic compounds. C: Correct.

Question 2 A: Color (clear) and state (liquid), boiling point, and solubility in water are physical properties. Physical properties can be observed or measured without changing the matter's identity. C: Correct.

Question 3 A: An acid will not change the color of red litmus paper and will change the color of bromthymol blue to yellow. B: Water will not change the color of red litmus paper or change the color of bromthymol blue. C: Table salt will not change the color of red litmus paper or change the color of bromthymol blue. D: Correct.

Question 4 A: Correct. B: Bases increase the number of hydroxide ions when dissolved in water. C: An indicator changes color in the presence of an acid or a base. D: Hydrogen gas does not increase the number of hydronium ions when dissolved in water.

Question 5 A: Glycogen is a kind of carbohydrate that supplies energy to muscle cells. B: Carbohydrates are biochemicals that are

Use the figure below to answer question 7.

7. The figure above shows the structural formula of an organic compound. Which of the following statements is true about the compound?

A. The compound is a branched chain.

B. The compound is unsaturated.

C. The compound is a carbohydrate.

D. The compound is a weak base.

8. During a laboratory experiment, Juanita observes a model of two bonded atoms. She is told that the atoms are both nonmetals. Which of the following is a valid conclusion?

A. She is looking at a model of a covalent bond.

B. She is looking at a model of an acid.

C. She is looking at a model of an ionic bond.

D. She is looking at a model of a salt.

9. The ions in an ionic compound are arranged in a repeating, three-dimensional pattern. What is this pattern called?

A. ionic solution

B. chemical bond

C. valence electron

D. crystal lattice

10. What factor does the pH scale measure?

A. the degree of neutralization between acids and bases

B. the concentration of hydroxide ions in a solution

C. the number of salt molecules present in a solution

D. the concentration of hydronium ions in a solution

Open Response

11. Acids and bases are two kinds of chemical compounds. Compare at least four chemical and physical properties of acids and bases.

12. Alexa is writing a report about biochemicals. Describe the four categories of biochemicals that Alexa should include in her report. Give an example of each kind of biochemical.

Question 9 A: An ionic solution is a solution created when an ionic compound is dissolved in water. B: A chemical bond is an interaction that holds two atoms together. Chemical bonds hold ionic compounds together, but the term *chemical bond* is not the name of the pattern formed by the ions. C: Valence electrons are electrons that are found in the outermost shell of an atom. Valence electrons are the electrons involved in chemical bonding. D: Correct.

Question 10 A: Although pH can be used to determine the degree of neutralization, it does so by measuring the concentration of hydronium ions in a solution. B: The pOH scale is used to measure the concentration of hydroxide ions in a solution. C: The number of salt molecules in a solution can be measured best by the concentration of the solution. D: Correct.

Question 11 Full-credit answers should include four of these points:

• Acids have a sour flavor. Bases have a bitter flavor.

• When dissolved in water, acids increase the hydronium ion concentration, while bases increase the hydroxide ion concentration.

• Bases have a slippery feel; acids do not.

• Both acids and bases change the colors of indicators.

• Acids react with metals but bases do not.

• Both acids and bases conduct electric current.

Question 12 Full-credit answers should include these points:

• Carbohydrates are biochemicals composed of one or more bonded simple sugar molecules. Examples include glucose, cellulose, or glycogen.

• Lipids are biochemicals that do not dissolve in water, e.g., fats, oils, or waxes.

• Proteins are biochemicals that are composed of amino acids, e.g., enzymes, hormones, or hemoglobin.

• Nucleic acids are biochemicals made up of nucleotides, such as DNA or RNA.

composed of one or more simple sugar molecules bonded together. The properties listed do not describe carbohydrates. C: Correct. D: Cellulose is another kind of carbohydrate. Cellulose is found in cell walls, but it does not have the other properties listed.

Question 6 A: Many organic compounds contain hydrogen, but all organic compounds must contain carbon. B: Correct. C: Many organic compounds contain oxygen, but all organic compounds must contain carbon. D: Many organic compounds contain nitrogen, but all organic compounds must contain carbon.

Question 7 A: The bend in the chain of the structural formula may cause students to think that the compound is a branched chain. However, the backbone of this compound is still considered straight. B: Correct. C: Carbohydrates are much more complex than the compound shown. D: Bases usually contain a hydroxide ion (OH^-). The compound shown is an alkene, not a base.

Question 8 A: Correct. B: Using the information in the question, one cannot conclude that the model is an acid. C: A nonmetal and a metal can form an ionic bond. The question states that the atoms are nonmetals, so this answer is incorrect. D: Using the information in the passage, one cannot conclude that the model is a salt.

Science in Action

Science, Technology, and Society

Background

Getting tissue samples from archeological specimens isn't easy. Museum curators often won't give permission to study the DNA of a museum specimen because part of the specimen must be destroyed to study its genetic material. Even if DNA can be obtained, experiments can be difficult. Because there is so little DNA to work with, repeating experiments in order to verify results is not always possible.

Weird Science

Background

Silly Putty is a polymeric material with special properties that make it different from other polymers. The polymers in Silly Putty have covalent bonds within the molecules but hydrogen bonds between the molecules. The hydrogen bonds can be easily broken. When small amounts of stress are slowly applied to the putty, some of the hydrogen bonds break and the putty starts to "flow." When more stress is applied quickly, many hydrogen bonds break, causing the putty to tear or break off.

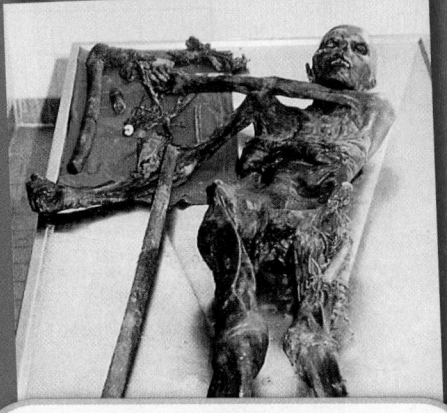

Science, Technology, and Society

Molecular Photocopying

To learn about our human ancestors, scientists can use DNA from mummies. Well-preserved DNA can be copied using a technique called polymerase chain reaction (PCR). PCR uses enzymes called *polymerases*, which make new strands of DNA using old strands as templates. Thus, PCR is called molecular photocopying. However, scientists have to be very careful when using this process. If just one of their own skin cells falls into the PCR mixture, it will contaminate the ancient DNA with their own DNA.

Social Studies ACTiViTY

WRITING SKILL DNA analysis of mummies is helping archeologists study human history. Write a research paper about what scientists have learned about human history through DNA analysis.

Weird Science

Silly Putty™

During World War II, the supply of natural rubber was very low. So, James Wright, at General Electric, tried to make a synthetic rubber. The putty he made could be molded, stretched, and bounced. But it did not work as a rubber substitute and was ignored. Then, Peter Hodgson, a consultant for a toy company, had a brilliant idea. He marketed the putty as a toy in 1949. It was an immediate success. Hodgson created the name Silly Putty™. Although Silly Putty™ was invented more than 50 years ago, it has not changed much. More than 300 million eggs of Silly Putty have been sold since 1950.

Math ACTiViTY

In 1949, Mr. Hodgson bought 9.5 kg of putty for $147. The putty was divided into balls, each having a mass of 14 g. What was his cost for one 14 g ball of putty?

Answer to Social Studies Activity
Answers may vary. Students' papers should outline what has been learned about human history through DNA analysis.

Answer to Math Activity
$147 ÷ 9,500 g = $0.01547/g
$0.01547/g × 14 g = $0.22 /14 g ball

Jeannie Eberhardt

Forensic Scientist Jeannie Eberhardt says that her job as a forensic scientist is not really as glamorous as it may seem on popular TV shows. "If they bring me a garbage bag from the crime scene, then my job is to dig through the trash and look for evidence," she laughs. Jeannie Eberhardt explains that her job is to "search for, collect, and analyze evidence from crime scenes." Eberhardt says that one of the most important qualities a forensic scientist can have is the ability to be unbiased. She says that she focuses on the evidence and not on any information she may have about the alleged crime or the suspect. Eberhardt advises students who think they might be interested in a career as a forensic scientist to talk to someone who works in the field. She also recommends that students develop a broad science background. And she advises students that most of these jobs require extensive background checks. "Your actions now could affect your ability to get a job later on," she points out.

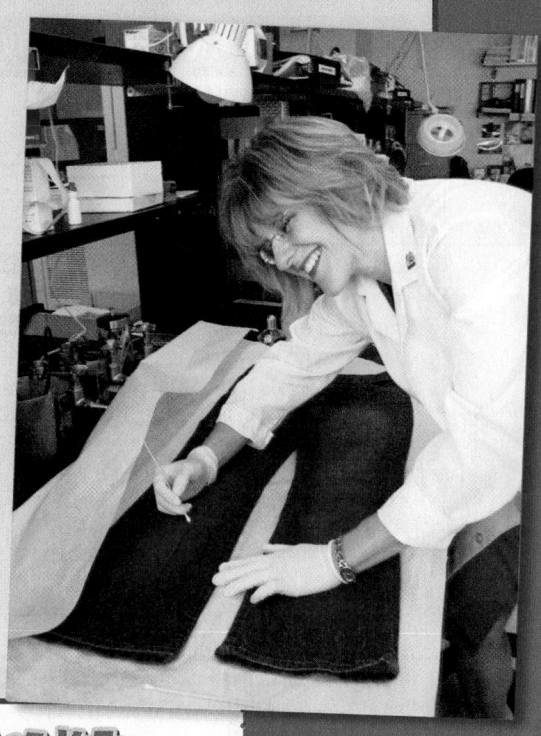

Language Arts ACTiViTY

WRITING SKILL Jeannie Eberhardt says that it is very important to be unbiased when analyzing a crime scene. Write a one-page essay explaining why it is necessary to focus on the evidence in a crime and not on personal feelings or news reports.

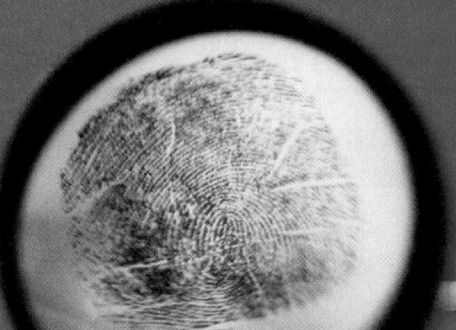

go hrw .com

To learn more about these Science in Action topics, visit go.hrw.com and type in the keyword **HP5CMPF**

Current Science

Check out Current Science® articles related to this chapter by visiting go.hrw.com. Just type in the keyword **HP5CS15**

Background

After Jeannie Eberhardt earned her master's degree in forensic science, she began working in a crime lab. "You have to be working and training for at least six months in a crime lab before you can do any work on real cases," she explained. For the first six months of her first job, Eberhardt went through an intensive on-the-job training program. She tested different materials and analyzed mock samples from an invented crime scene. Then she had to testify at a mock trial to defend her findings. In the trial, her co-workers and supervisors from the crime lab played the parts of the judge and the attorneys. They invited everyone who worked in the building to watch the trial and videotaped Eberhardt's testimony. After Eberhardt successfully analyzed the samples that she was given and showed that she could defend her work in court, she was finally allowed to work on real cases.

Answer to Language Arts Activity

Answers may vary. Students' essays should explain that focusing on evidence is important in determining who committed a crime. The essays may explain that personal feelings and news reports might interfere with a criminal investigation.

Atomic Energy
Chapter Planning Guide

Compression guide:
To shorten instruction
because of time limitations,
omit the Chapter Lab.

OBJECTIVES	LABS, DEMONSTRATIONS, AND ACTIVITIES	TECHNOLOGY RESOURCES
PACING • 90 min pp. 678–687 **Chapter Opener**	**SE Start-up Activity**, p. 679 (GENERAL)	**OSP Parent Letter** ■ **CD Student Edition CD-ROM** **CD Guided Reading Audio CD** ■ **TR Chapter Starter Transparency*** **VID Brain Food Video Quiz**
Section 1 Radioactivity • Describe how radioactivity was discovered. • Compare alpha, beta, and gamma decay. • Describe the penetrating power of the three kinds of nuclear radiation. • Calculate ages of objects using half-life. • Identify uses of radioactive materials.	**TE Demonstration** Blocking Radiation, p. 680 (GENERAL) **TE Activity** X rays and Gamma Rays, p. 682 (BASIC) **TE Connection Activity** Language Arts, p. 683 (ADVANCED) **TE Connection Activity** Math, p. 685 (GENERAL) **SE Science in Action** Math, Social Studies, and Language Arts Activities, pp. 700–701 (GENERAL)	**OSP Lesson Plans** (also in print) **TR Bellringer Transparency*** **TR P62 Alpha Decay of Radium-226; Beta Decay of Carbon-14*** **TR P63 The Penetrating Abilities of Nuclear Radiation*** **TR P64 Radioactive Decay and Half-Life*** **SE Internet Activity**, p. 686 (GENERAL) **CRF SciLinks Activity*** (GENERAL)
PACING • 90 min pp. 688–693 **Section 2 Energy from the Nucleus** • Describe nuclear fission. • Identify advantages and disadvantages of nuclear fission. • Describe nuclear fusion. • Identify advantages and disadvantages of nuclear fusion.	**TE Demonstration** Mousetrap Fission, p. 688 (GENERAL) **TE Connection Activity** History, p. 689 (GENERAL) **TE Connection Activity** Environmental Science, p. 690 (ADVANCED) **SE Quick Lab** Gone Fission, p. 691 (GENERAL) **CRF Datasheet for Quick Lab*** **SE Connection to Astronomy** Elements of the Stars, p. 692 (GENERAL) **SE Model-Making Lab** Domino Chain Reactions, p. 694 (GENERAL) **CRF Datasheet for Chapter Lab*** **LB Long-Term Projects & Research Ideas** Meltdown!* (ADVANCED)	**OSP Lesson Plans** (also in print) **TR Bellringer Transparency*** **TR P65 Fission of a Uranium-235 Nucleus; Fusion of Hydrogen-1 Nuclei*** **TR P66 How a Nuclear Power Plant Works*** **TR _LINK TO EARTH SCIENCE_ E87 Fusion of Hydrogen in the Sun*** **VID Lab Videos for Physical Science**

PACING • 90 min

CHAPTER REVIEW, ASSESSMENT, AND STANDARDIZED TEST PREPARATION

CRF Vocabulary Activity* (GENERAL)
SE Chapter Review, pp. 696–697 (GENERAL)
CRF Chapter Review* ■ (GENERAL)
CRF Chapter Tests A* ■ (GENERAL), **B*** (ADVANCED), **C*** (SPECIAL NEEDS)
SE Standardized Test Preparation, pp. 698–699 (GENERAL)
CRF Standardized Test Preparation* (GENERAL)
CRF Performance-Based Assessment* (GENERAL)
OSP Test Generator, Test Item Listing

Online and Technology Resources

 Holt Online Learning

Visit **go.hrw.com** for access to Holt Online Learning, or enter the keyword **HS7 Home** for a variety of free online resources.

 One-Stop Planner® CD-ROM

This CD-ROM package includes:
- Lab Materials QuickList Software
- Holt Calendar Planner
- Customizable Lesson Plans
- Printable Worksheets
- ExamView® Test Generator
- Interactive Teacher's Edition
- Holt PuzzlePro®
- Holt PowerPoint® Resources

SKILLS DEVELOPMENT RESOURCES	SECTION REVIEW AND ASSESSMENT	CORRELATIONS
SE Pre-Reading Activity, p. 678 GENERAL **OSP** Science Puzzlers, Twisters & Teasers GENERAL		**National Science Education Standards** UCP 1, 2, 3; SAI 1
CRF Directed Reading A* ■ BASIC , B* SPECIAL NEEDS **WB** Workbook* Struggling Readers **CRF** Vocabulary and Section Summary* ■ GENERAL **SE** Reading Strategy Reading Organizer, p. 680 GENERAL **TE** Reading Strategy Prediction Guide, p. 681 GENERAL **TE** Support for English Language Learners, p. 682 **SE** Connection to Environmental Science Radon in the Home, p. 684 GENERAL **TE** Reading Strategy Prediction Guide, p. 684 GENERAL **SE** Math Practice How Old Is It?, p. 685 GENERAL **TE** Inclusion Strategies, p. 685 **MS** Math Skills for Science Radioactive Decay and the Half-Life* GENERAL **CRF** Reinforcement Worksheet The Decay of a Nucleus* BASIC	**SE** Reading Checks, pp. 681, 683, 685, 686 GENERAL **TE** Homework, p. 681 GENERAL **TE** Reteaching, p. 686 BASIC **TE** Quiz, p. 686 GENERAL **TE** Alternative Assessment, p. 686 GENERAL **SE** Section Review,* p. 687 ■ GENERAL **CRF** Section Quiz* ■ GENERAL	UCP 1, 2, 3; SAI 2; ST 2; SPSP 1, 4, 5; HNS 1, 2, 3; PS 3a, 3e
CRF Directed Reading A* ■ BASIC , B* SPECIAL NEEDS **WB** Workbook* Struggling Readers **CRF** Vocabulary and Section Summary* ■ GENERAL **SE** Reading Strategy Reading Organizer, p. 688 GENERAL **TE** Support for English Language Learners, p. 689 **SE** Connection to Language Arts Storage Site, p. 691 GENERAL **TE** Inclusion Strategies, p. 691 **CRF** Reinforcement Worksheet Fission or Fusion?* BASIC **CRF** Critical Thinking The Blue Flame* ADVANCED	**SE** Reading Checks, pp. 688, 691, 692 GENERAL **TE** Reteaching, p. 692 BASIC **TE** Quiz, p. 692 GENERAL **TE** Alternative Assessment, p. 692 GENERAL **SE** Section Review,* p. 693 ■ GENERAL **CRF** Section Quiz* ■ GENERAL	UCP 2, 3; ST 1, 2; SPSP 3, 4, 5; PS 3a, 3e; *Chapter Lab:* UCP 2, 3; SAI 1; PS 3a, 3e

www.scilinks.org

Maintained by the **National Science Teachers Association**. See Chapter Enrichment pages that follow for a complete list of topics.

Check out *Current Science* articles and activities by visiting the HRW Web site at **go.hrw.com**. Just type in the keyword **HP5CS16T**.

Classroom Videos

• **Lab Videos** demonstrate the chapter lab.
• **Brain Food Video Quizzes** help students review the chapter material.

Classroom CD-ROMs

• **Guided Reading Audio CD** (Also in Spanish)
• **Interactive Explorations**
• **Virtual Investigations**
• **Visual Concepts**
• **Science Tutor**

Holt Lab Generator CD-ROM

Search for any lab by topic, standard, difficulty level, or time. Edit any lab to fit your needs, or create your own labs. Use the Lab Materials QuickList software to customize your lab materials list.

Visual Resources

CHAPTER STARTER TRANSPARENCY

BELLRINGER TRANSPARENCIES

Section: Radioactivity
In your **science journal** write a few sentences about the term *nuclear radiation*. Include what you know about nuclear radiation, any benefits, and any dangers you can think of. For example, when is radiation used to help people? When is radiation harmful?

Section: Energy from the Nucleus
Define each of the following terms in your own words in your **science journal**:
fission
fusion
Are the terms opposites, or are they similar? How is energy involved in each? Discuss your ideas with the group.

TEACHING TRANSPARENCIES

Alpha Decay of Radium-226 P62
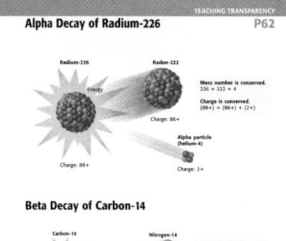

Beta Decay of Carbon-14
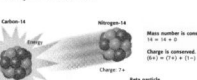

Radioactive Decay and Half-Life P64
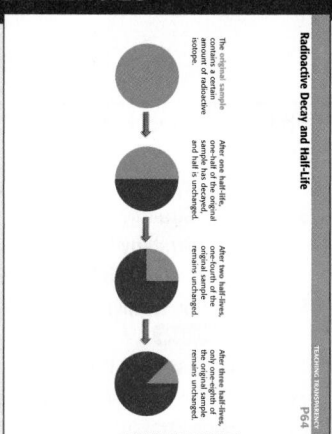

TEACHING TRANSPARENCIES

Fission of a Uranium-235 Nucleus P65
Fusion of Hydrogen-1 Nuclei
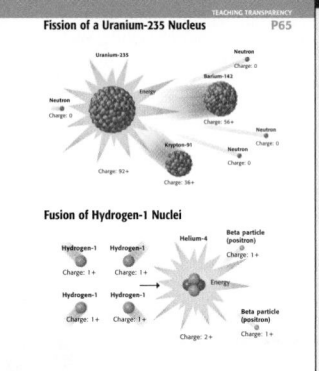

How a Nuclear Power Plant Works P66
The Penetrating Abilities of Nuclear Radiation P63
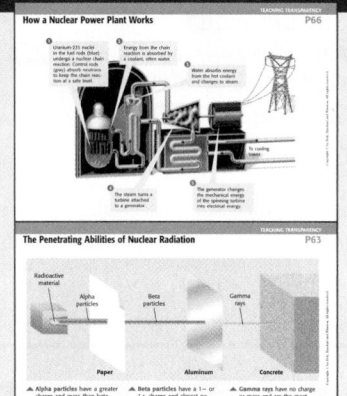

Fusion of Hydrogen in the Sun E87

Chapter: Formation of the Solar System

CONCEPT MAPPING TRANSPARENCY
Use the following terms to complete the concept map below: alpha particle, mass number, nuclei, nuclear fusion, atomic nucleus, nuclear fission, gamma ray, radioactive decay
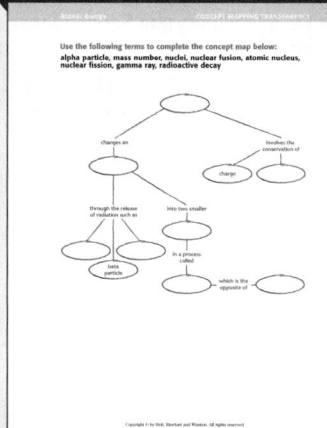

Planning Resources

LESSON PLANS
SAMPLE

PARENT LETTER
SAMPLE

ALSO IN SPANISH

TEST ITEM LISTING
The World of Science SAMPLE

One-Stop Planner® CD-ROM

This CD-ROM includes all of the resources shown here and the following time-saving tools:
- *Lab Materials QuickList Software*
- *Customizable lesson plans*
- *Holt Calendar Planner*
- *The powerful ExamView® Test Generator*

Meeting Individual Needs

DIRECTED READING A
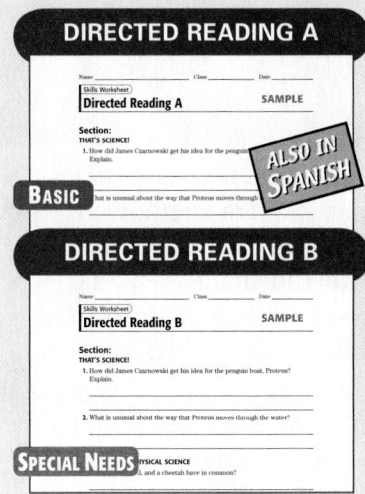
BASIC / ALSO IN SPANISH

DIRECTED READING B
SPECIAL NEEDS

VOCABULARY ACTIVITY
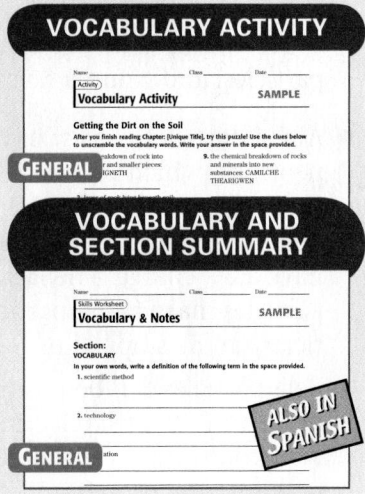
GENERAL

VOCABULARY AND SECTION SUMMARY
GENERAL / ALSO IN SPANISH

REINFORCEMENT
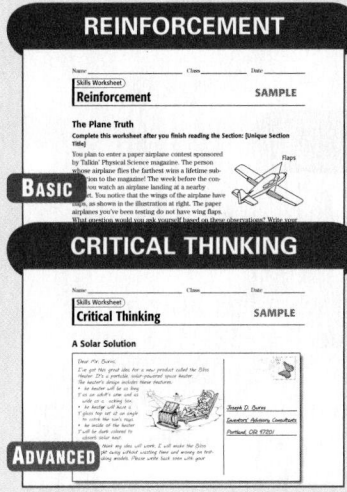
BASIC

CRITICAL THINKING
ADVANCED

SCILINKS ACTIVITY

GENERAL

SCIENCE PUZZLERS, TWISTERS & TEASERS
GENERAL

Labs and Activities

LONG-TERM PROJECTS & RESEARCH IDEAS
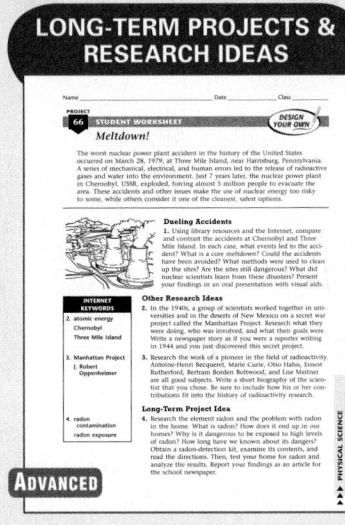
ADVANCED

DATASHEETS FOR QUICK LABS

DATASHEETS FOR CHAPTER LABS

DATASHEETS FOR LABBOOK

Review and Assessments

SECTION QUIZ
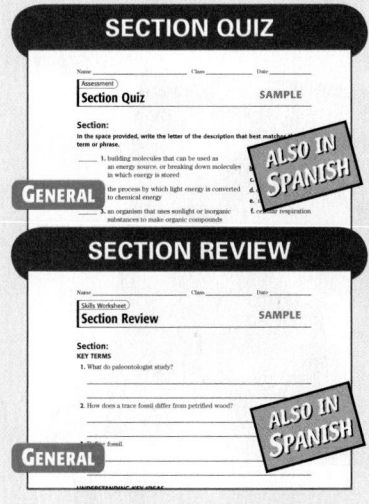
GENERAL / ALSO IN SPANISH

SECTION REVIEW
GENERAL / ALSO IN SPANISH

CHAPTER REVIEW
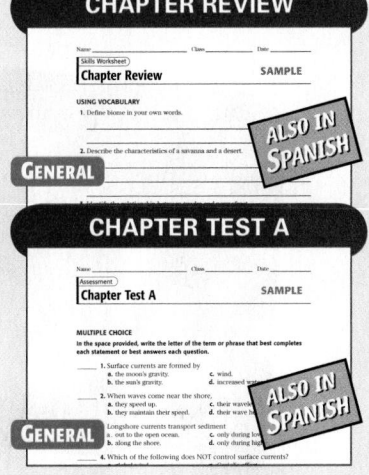
GENERAL / ALSO IN SPANISH

CHAPTER TEST A
GENERAL / ALSO IN SPANISH

CHAPTER TEST B
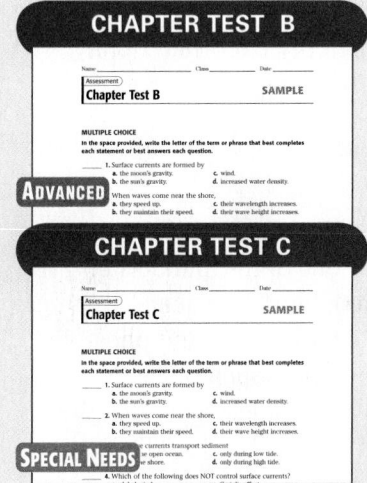
ADVANCED

CHAPTER TEST C
SPECIAL NEEDS

STANDARDIZED TEST PREPARATION
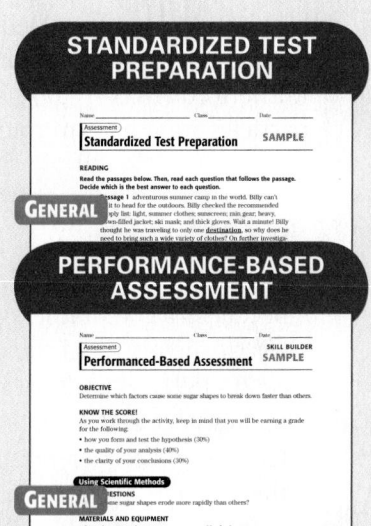
GENERAL

PERFORMANCE-BASED ASSESSMENT
GENERAL

This Chapter Enrichment provides relevant and interesting information to expand and enhance your presentation of the chapter material.

Section 1

Radioactivity

Before and After Radioactivity

- Radioactivity was discovered serendipitously by the French physicist Henri Becquerel (1852–1908) in 1896 while he was searching for evidence of X rays. X rays also had been discovered serendipitously by Wilhelm Conrad Roentgen (1845–1923) the previous year while he was studying cathode-ray tubes.

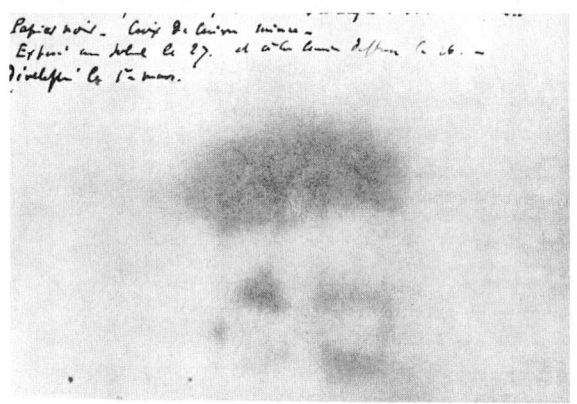

- Soon after Becquerel's discovery, Marie Curie (1867–1934) determined that the element thorium is radioactive. In 1898, Marie and her husband, Pierre (1859–1906), discovered polonium and radium, two new radioactive elements. Eventually, the Curies were able to quantify the amount of energy given off each hour by 1 g of radium—about 418 J.

- In 1899, André-Louis Debierne (1874–1949) discovered the radioactive element actinium. In 1908, Ernest Rutherford (1871–1937) helped discover that alpha particles were helium nuclei.

Is That a Fact!

- Antoine-César Becquerel (1788–1878), Henri Becquerel's grandfather, was one of the founders of electrochemistry. Alexandre-Edmond Becquerel (1820–1891), Henri's father, studied light and phosphorescence and invented the phosphoroscope. In fact, Henri Becquerel discovered radioactivity by using the minerals his father had collected and studied.

Alpha, Beta, Gamma

- Although there are many types of radiation, the three types discussed in this chapter are alpha particles, beta particles, and gamma rays.

- Alpha particles consist of two protons and two neutrons, which makes their mass much greater than that of beta particles. Alpha particles are identical to helium nuclei. Because they have no electrons, they have a 2+ charge. The large size and charge of alpha particles make alpha particles easy to block. Alpha particles can be stopped by a rubber glove or thick paper.

- Beta particles can be positively charged (positrons) or negatively charged (electrons). They can be stopped by wood only a few centimeters thick and by thin sheets of aluminum, iron, and lead.

- Gamma rays are high-energy photons that are similar to X rays in their effect. They have no mass or charge. All but the highest-energy gamma rays are stopped by thick concrete or thin sheets of lead.

Is That a Fact!

- It is fortunate that alpha particles are so easily stopped because they are potentially the most damaging if they enter the body.

Radioactive Decay

- The decay of naturally occurring isotopes is used to date fossils and rocks. The decay of artificially made isotopes has led to discoveries in nuclear energy, chemistry, and medicine.

- The decay of uranium-238 to lead-206 is a naturally occurring decay series. Uranium-238 decays through both alpha and beta decays accompanied by gamma decay to its end product, a stable isotope of lead.

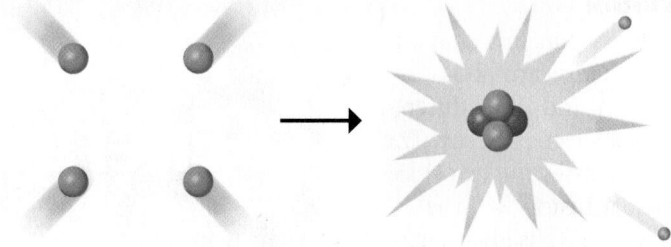

Is That a Fact!

◆ The alpha decay of radium-226 forms radon's most abundant isotope, radon-222, which undergoes alpha decay with a half-life of 3.8 days. The alpha particle and the radioactive polonium-198 made by the decay of radon-222 create a serious lung cancer risk.

Section 2

Energy from the Nucleus

Fission

● The German chemists Otto Hahn (1879–1968) and Fritz Strassmann (1902–1980) were the first to demonstrate the splitting of a nucleus through fission when they bombarded a sample of uranium with neutrons and detected nuclei much smaller than uranium.

● In 1939, this process was identified as nuclear fission by Austrian physicist Lise Meitner (1878–1968) and her nephew Otto Frisch.

● A large amount of energy can be generated from a continuous series of nuclear fissions called a *chain reaction*.

Is That a Fact!

◆ Controlled chain reactions occur in the reactors of nuclear power plants. Uncontrolled chain reactions occur during the detonation of atomic bombs.

Fusion

● Usually, two nuclei cannot collide because they are positively charged and repel each other. However, at very high temperature and pressure, nuclei can collide and fuse together to form a more massive nucleus.

● The fusion of hydrogen nuclei to produce helium nuclei is the principal source of the energy that is released as light by the sun and other stars.

● Nuclear fusion releases less energy per nuclear reaction than nuclear fission does because less matter is converted into energy. However, the energy released per gram of fuel is far greater in the fusion process because there are many more hydrogen atoms than uranium atoms in equal masses of the two fuels.

● Matter exists only in the plasma state at the extremely high temperatures required to make fusion occur. A chamber called a *tokamak* was conceived in the 1950s to magnetically confine the plasma used for fusion reactions. The confinement prevents the plasma from destroying the tokamak.

Is That a Fact!

◆ In 1991, a controlled nuclear fusion reaction at the Joint European Torus Laboratory in England generated 1.7 million watts. In 1993, the Tokamak Fusion Test Reactor at Princeton University generated a controlled fusion reaction of 6 million watts. But both events required more energy than they generated, so fusion as an energy source is not yet practical.

SCiLINKS®

NSTA
Developed and maintained by the
National Science Teachers Association

SciLinks is maintained by the National Science Teachers Association to provide you and your students with interesting, up-to-date links that will enrich your classroom presentation of the chapter.

Visit www.scilinks.org and enter the SciLinks code for more information about the topic listed.

Topic: Discovering Radioactivity
SciLinks code: HSM0412

Topic: Nuclear Fusion
SciLinks code: HSM1050

Topic: Radioactive Isotopes
SciLinks code: HSM1256

Topic: Nuclear Reactors
SciLinks code: HSM1054

Topic: Nuclear Fission
SciLinks code: HSM1048

Overview

Tell students that this chapter will help them learn about radioactivity and three different kinds of radioactive decay. The chapter discusses nuclear fission and nuclear fusion and the advantages and disadvantages of each.

Assessing Prior Knowledge

Students should be familiar with the following topics:
• atomic structure
• isotopes

Identifying Misconceptions

As students learn the material in this chapter, some of them may be confused by differences between nuclear changes and chemical changes with which students are more familiar. You may want to stress the differences between these concepts by explaining that nuclear changes involve changing the identity of the atoms themselves, while chemical changes involve changing the connections between atoms. Students might also have trouble understanding that because matter is converted into energy during nuclear changes, mass is not conserved in these changes.

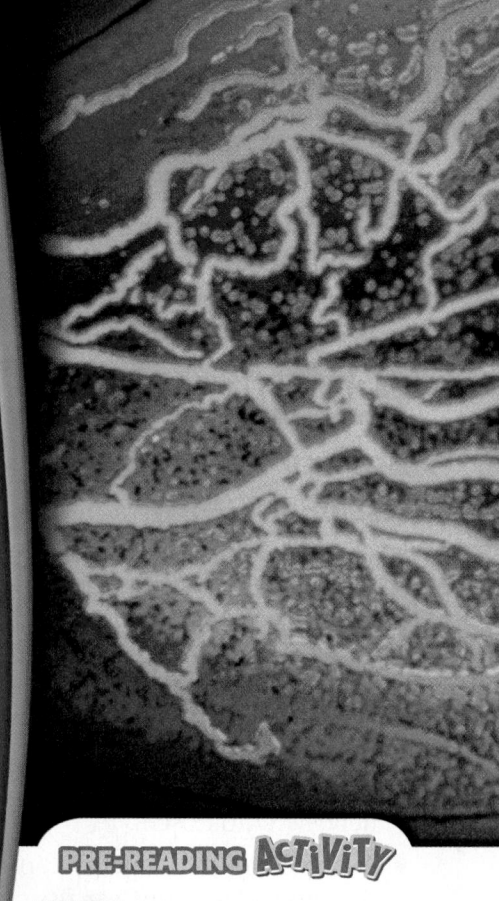

25
Atomic Energy

The Big Idea Radioactive decay, nuclear fission, and nuclear fusion are changes that release energy from the nuclei of atoms.

About the Photo
Look closely at the blood vessels that show up clearly in this image of a human hand. Doctors sometimes inject radioactive substances into a patient's body to help locate tumors and measure the activity of certain organs. Radioactive emissions from the substances are measured using a scanning device. Then, computers turn the data into an image.

PRE-READING ACTIVITY

Graphic Organizer

Spider Map Before you read the chapter, create the graphic organizer entitled "Spider Map" described in the **Study Skills** section of the Appendix. Label the circle "Radioactive Decay." Create a leg for each type of radioactive decay. As you read the chapter, fill in the map with details about each type of decay.

Standards Correlations

National Science Education Standards

The following codes indicate the National Science Education Standards that correlate to this chapter. The full text of the standards is at the front of the book.

Chapter Opener
UCP 1, 2, 3; SAI 1

Section 1 Radioactivity
UCP 1, 2, 3; SAI 2; ST 2; SPSP 1, 4, 5; HNS 1, 2, 3; PS 3a, 3e

Section 2 Energy from the Nucleus
UCP 2, 3; ST 1, 2; SPSP 3, 4, 5; PS 3a, 3e

Chapter Lab
UCP 2, 3; SAI 1; PS 3a, 3e

Chapter Review
UCP 3; SPSP 1, 3, 4; PS 3a, 3e

Science in Action
ST 2; SPSP 5; HNS 1, 3; PS 3a, 3e

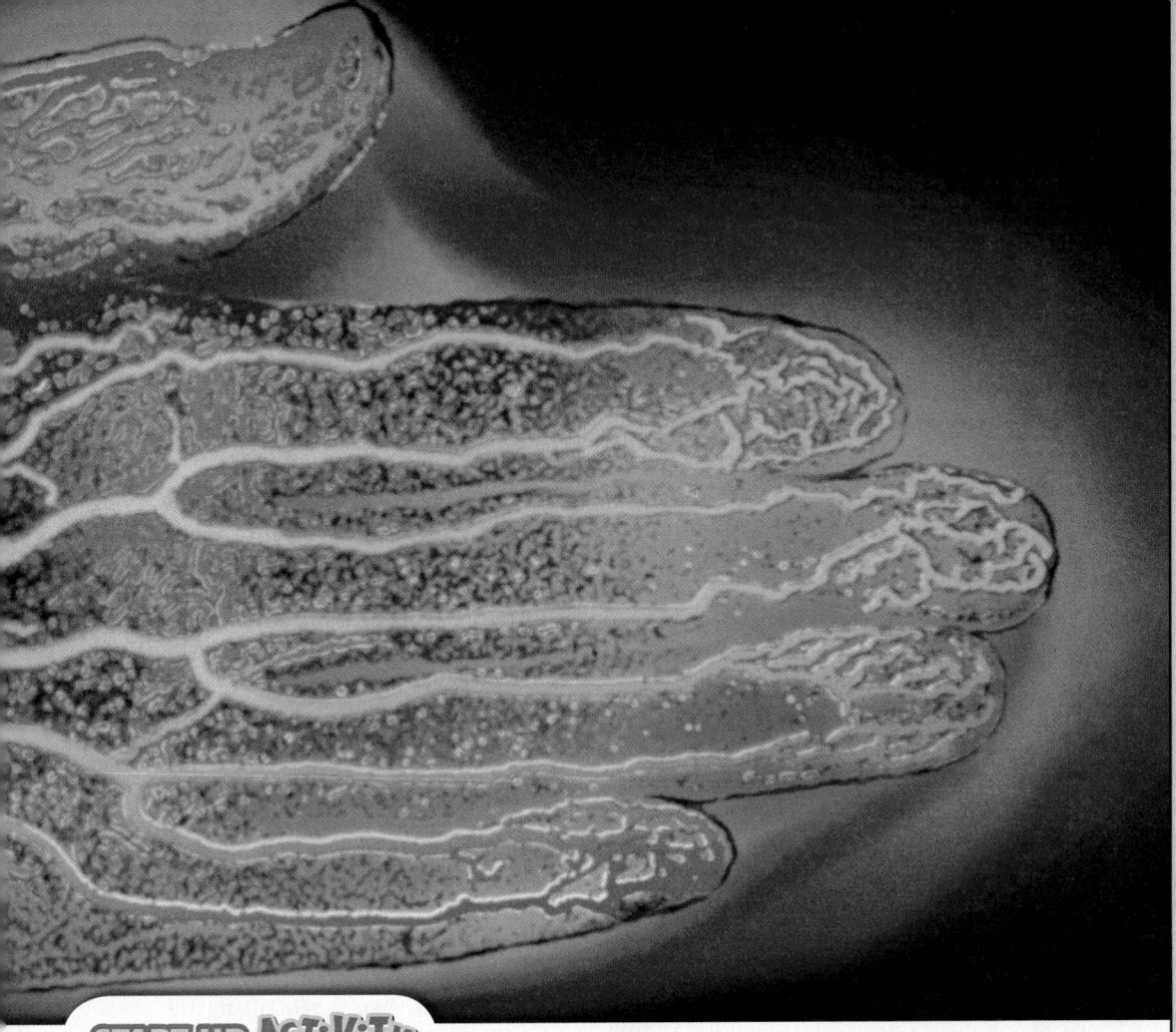

START-UP ACTIVITY
MATERIALS
FOR EACH GROUP
- box, with lid
- paper, graph
- pennies (100)

Safety Caution: Remind students to review all safety cautions and icons before beginning this lab activity.

Teacher's Notes: Because the process of radioactive decay modeled by this activity relies on the presence of a large number of nuclei, you might want students to enter their data into a class data table and graph the totals for the class.

Answers

1. Sample graph:

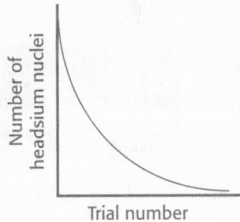

The number of headsium nuclei decreases over time. After each trial, the number of headsium nuclei is about half of the previous number.

2. The graphs have the same shape; however, the specific numbers of headsium nuclei at each trial are slightly different.

START-UP ACTIVITY
Watch Your Headsium!

In this activity, you will model the decay of unstable nuclei into stable nuclei.

Procedure

1. Place **100 pennies** with the heads' side up in a **box with a lid.** The pennies represent radioactive nuclei. Record 100 "headsium" nuclei as "Trial 0."

2. Close the box. Shake it up and down for 5 s.

3. Open the box. Remove the stable tails-up nuclei, or "tailsium" nuclei. Count the number of headsium nuclei remaining, and record it as "Trial 1."

4. Perform trials until you don't have any more pennies in the box or until you have finished five trials. Record your results.

Analysis

1. On a piece of **graph paper,** graph your data by plotting "Number of headsium nuclei" on the *y*-axis and "Trial number" on the *x*-axis. What trend do you see in the number of headsium nuclei?

2. Compare your graph with the graphs made by the other students in your class.

Would You Believe . . . ?

Replacing the battery in your camera can be a problem when you're traveling— especially 1.5 billion kilometers (932 million miles) from home! That's how far from Earth the *Cassini* spacecraft is as it studies Saturn. *Cassini's* camera and other equipment need an energy source that will work after a trip of nearly 7 years. Otherwise, the trip to study the atmosphere and moons of Saturn would be wasted. The answer? the radioactive element plutonium!

The nuclei (plural of nucleus) of plutonium atoms are radioactive, meaning they are unstable. They become stable by giving off radiation in the form of particles and energy. This process heats the materials surrounding the plutonium, and the thermal energy of the materials is converted into electrical energy by a

equipment. Because electrical energy can be produced using a sample of plutonium for 10 or more years, RTGs provide energy longer than any battery known, as described below.

In this chapter you will learn more about the energy given off by radioactive materials. In addition, you will learn about the energy associated with the splitting and joining of atomic nuclei. Read on to continue your own journey!

Chapter Starter Transparency
Use this transparency to help students begin thinking about the use of radioactive material to generate energy.

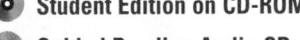

Chapter 25 • Atomic Energy **679**

Focus

Overview

In this section, students learn about alpha, beta, and gamma radiation and the penetrating ability of each. Students learn how to use an isotope's half-life to calculate the age of an object and learn other uses for radioactive materials.

Bellringer

On the board write the following statement, "In a few sentences, write what you know about the term *nuclear radiation.* Include any benefits and any dangers you can think of."

Motivate

Demonstration — GENERAL

Blocking Radiation Display three items for students:

• piece of paper

• sheet of aluminum

• concrete cinder block

Explain to students that they are going to learn about three types of radiation and that one type can be stopped by paper, one by aluminum, and the third only by concrete or lead. Ask students what different characteristics of the radiation or of the barrier might be important.

LS Visual/Logical

What You Will Learn

● Describe how radioactivity was discovered.

● Compare alpha, beta, and gamma decay.

● Describe the penetrating power of the three kinds of nuclear radiation.

● Calculate ages of objects using half-life.

● Identify uses of radioactive materials.

Vocabulary

radioactivity   isotope
mass number   half-life

READING STRATEGY

Reading Organizer As you read this section, create an outline of the section. Use the headings from the section in your outline.

Radioactivity

When scientists do experiments, they don't always find what they expect to find.

In 1896, a French scientist named Henri Becquerel found much more than he expected. He found a new area of science.

Discovering Radioactivity

Becquerel's hypothesis was that fluorescent minerals give off X rays. (*Fluorescent* materials glow when light shines on them.) To test his idea, he put a fluorescent mineral on top of a photographic plate wrapped in paper. After putting his setup in bright sunlight, he developed the plate and saw the strong image of the mineral he expected, as shown in **Figure 1.**

An Unexpected Result

Becquerel tried to do the experiment again, but the weather was cloudy. So, he put his materials in a drawer. He developed the plate anyway a few days later. He was shocked to see a strong image. Even without light, the mineral gave off energy. The energy passed through the paper and made an image on the plate. After more tests, Becquerel concluded that this energy comes from uranium, an element in the mineral.

Naming the Unexpected

This energy is called *nuclear radiation,* high-energy particles and rays that are emitted by the nuclei of some atoms. Marie Curie, a scientist working with Becquerel, named the process by which some nuclei give off nuclear radiation. She named the process **radioactivity,** which is also called *radioactive decay.*

Figure 1 *Sunlight could not pass through the paper. So, the image on the plate must have been made by energy given off by the mineral.*

CHAPTER RESOURCES

Chapter Resource File

 • Lesson Plan
• Directed Reading A BASIC
• Directed Reading B SPECIAL NEEDS

Technology

 Transparencies
• Bellringer
• P62 Alpha Decay of Radium-226; Beta Decay of Carbon-14

Workbooks

 Interactive Textbook Struggling Readers

WEIRD SCIENCE

A thorough scientist makes sure experimental results can be repeated. Becquerel tried to confirm his results, but cloudy weather stopped him. So, why did he develop the photographic plate anyway? One idea is that he was scheduled to speak about his research the next night and even a weak image would support his hypothesis. But when he saw a strong image, he realized that something special had happened.

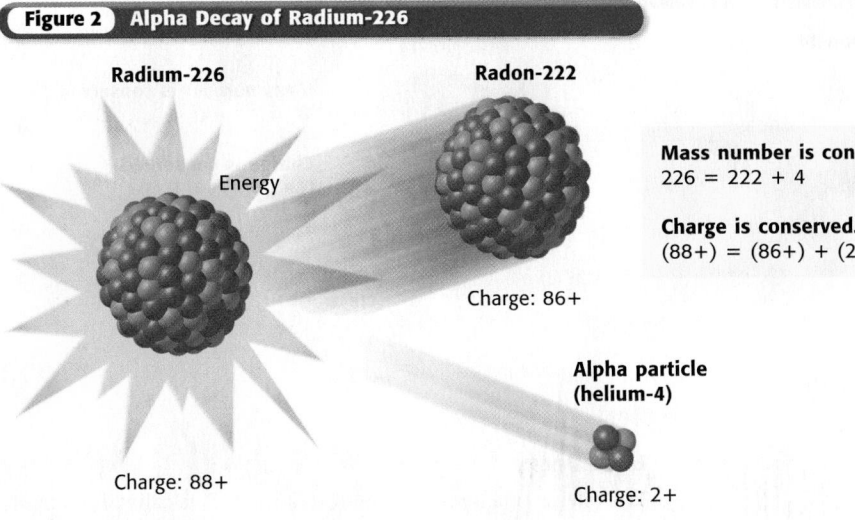

Figure 2 Alpha Decay of Radium-226

Radium-226

Radon-222

Energy

Mass number is conserved.
226 = 222 + 4

Charge is conserved.
(88+) = (86+) + (2+)

Charge: 86+

Charge: 88+

Alpha particle
(helium-4)

Charge: 2+

Kinds of Radioactive Decay

During *radioactive decay,* an unstable nucleus gives off particles and energy. Three kinds of radioactive decay are alpha decay, beta decay, and gamma decay.

Alpha Decay

The release of an alpha particle from a nucleus is called *alpha decay.* An *alpha particle* is made up of two protons and two neutrons. It has a mass number of 4 and a charge of 2+. The **mass number** is the sum of the numbers of protons and neutrons in the nucleus of an atom. An alpha particle is the same as the nucleus of a helium atom. Many large radioactive nuclei give off alpha particles and become nuclei of atoms of different elements. One example of a nucleus that gives off alpha particles is radium-226. (The number that follows the name of an element is the mass number of the atom.)

Conservation in Decay

Look at the model of alpha decay in **Figure 2.** This model shows two important things about radioactive decay. First, the mass number is conserved. The sum of the mass numbers of the starting materials is always equal to the sum of the mass numbers of the products. Second, charge is conserved. The sum of the charges of the starting materials is always equal to the sum of the charges of the products.

✓ Reading Check What two things are conserved in radioactive decay? (*See the Appendix for answers to Reading Checks.*)

radioactivity the process by which an unstable nucleus gives off nuclear radiation

mass number the sum of the numbers of protons and neutrons in the nucleus of an atom

SCIENCE HUMOR

Q: Why did the unstable nucleus use toothpaste?

A: It wanted to prevent decay.

Teach

READING STRATEGY ——GENERAL

Prediction Guide Before students read this section, have them write a few sentences explaining what radioactive decay is. Discuss their ideas with them as they begin the section. **LS** Logical

CONNECTION to Earth Science——GENERAL

Natural Radiation Humans are exposed daily to radiation from many sources. The better part of this radiation is from natural sources, including radioactive elements in the Earth and radiation from space and from the sun. There are even radioactive elements in the human body! Only 18% of the radiation a person receives in a year comes from artificial sources, such as medical X rays.

Answer to Reading Check
mass number and charge

Homework ——GENERAL

Models Ask students to make models or posters representing alpha particles, beta particles, and gamma rays. They must show the differences between the three types of radiation. Encourage students to be creative in their choice of materials and in their method of display. **LS** Visual/Logical

Figure 3 Beta Decay of Carbon-14

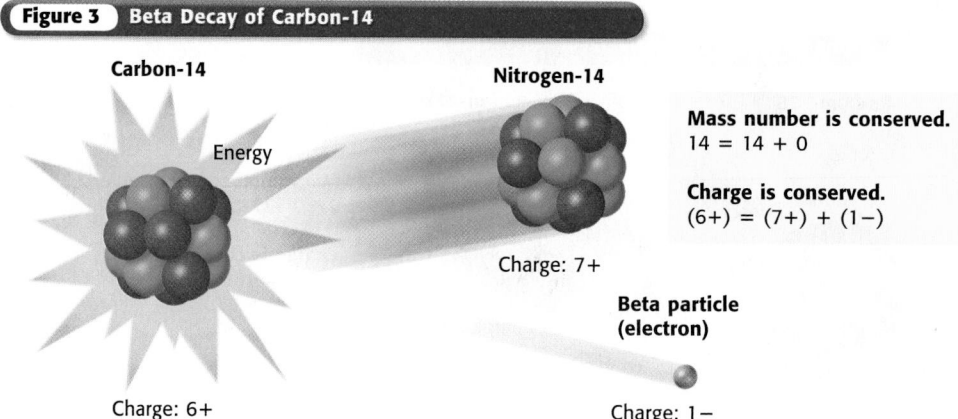

Carbon-14

Energy

Charge: 6+

Nitrogen-14

Charge: 7+

Mass number is conserved.
14 = 14 + 0

Charge is conserved.
(6+) = (7+) + (1−)

Beta particle (electron)

Charge: 1−

isotope an atom that has the same number of protons (or the same atomic number) as other atoms of the same element do but that has a different number of neutrons (and thus a different atomic mass)

Beta Decay

The release of a beta particle from a nucleus is called *beta decay*. A *beta particle* can be an electron or a positron. An electron has a charge of 1−. A positron has a charge of 1+. But electrons and positrons have a mass of almost 0. The mass number of a beta particle is 0 because it has no protons or neutrons.

Two Types of Beta Decay

A carbon-14 nucleus undergoes beta decay, as shown in the model in **Figure 3**. During this kind of decay, a neutron breaks into a proton and an electron. Notice that the nucleus becomes a nucleus of a different element. And both mass number and charge are conserved.

Not all isotopes of an element decay in the same way. **Isotopes** are atoms that have the same number of protons as other atoms of the same element do but that have different numbers of neutrons. A carbon-11 nucleus undergoes beta decay when a proton breaks into a positron and a neutron. But during any beta decay, the nucleus changes into a nucleus of a different element. And both mass number and charge are conserved.

Gamma Decay

Energy is also given off during alpha decay and beta decay. Some of this energy is in the form of light that has very high energy called *gamma rays*. The release of gamma rays from a nucleus is called *gamma decay*. This decay happens as the particles in the nucleus shift places. Gamma rays have no mass or charge. So, gamma decay alone does not cause one element to change into another element.

The Penetrating Power of Radiation

The three forms of nuclear radiation have different abilities to penetrate, or go through, matter. This difference is due to their mass and charge, as you can see in **Figure 4.**

Effects of Radiation on Matter

Atoms that are hit by nuclear radiation can give up electrons. Chemical bonds between atoms can break when hit by nuclear radiation. Both of these things can cause damage to living and nonliving matter.

Damage to Living Matter

When an organism absorbs radiation, its cells can be damaged. Radiation can cause burns like those caused by touching something that is hot. A single large exposure to radiation can lead to *radiation sickness*. Symptoms of this sickness include fatigue, loss of appetite, and hair loss. Destruction of blood cells and even death can result. Exposure to radiation can also increase the risk of cancer because of the damage done to cells. People who work near radioactive materials often wear a film badge. Radiation will make an image on the film to warn the person if the levels of radiation are too high.

✓ Reading Check Name three symptoms of radiation sickness.

Figure 4 The Penetrating Abilities of Nuclear Radiation

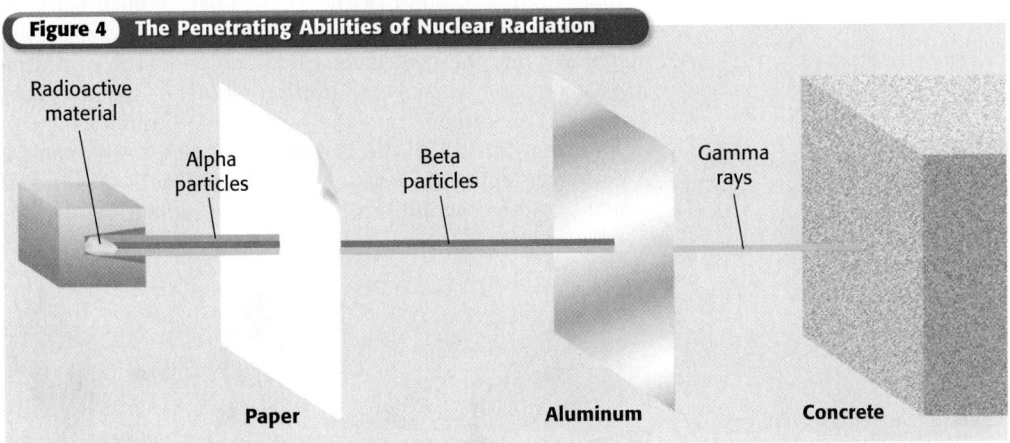

▲ **Alpha particles** have a greater charge and mass than beta particles and gamma rays do. Alpha particles travel about 7 cm through air and are stopped by paper or clothing.

▲ **Beta particles** have a 1− or 1+ charge and almost no mass. They are more penetrating than alpha particles. Beta particles travel about 1 m through air but are stopped by 3 mm of aluminum.

▲ **Gamma rays** have no charge or mass and are the most penetrating. They are blocked by very dense, thick materials, such as a few centimeters of lead or a few meters of concrete.

CONNECTION ACTIVITY
Language Arts — ADVANCED

Why Greek and Latin? Alpha particles, beta particles, and gamma rays are named for the first three letters of the Greek alphabet (α, β, and γ). Ask students to research why so many scientific phenomena are given Greek or Latin names. **LS Logical**

Answer to Reading Check
fatigue, loss of appetite, and hair loss

Is That a Fact!

Wilhelm Conrad Roentgen, Henri Becquerel, and the Curies all have units associated with radiation named after them.

• A *curie* (Ci) equals 3.7×10^{10} decays per second—approximately the activity of 1 g of radium.

• The SI unit is the *becquerel* (Bq), which equals one disintegration per second.

• The *roentgen* or *radiation unit* (rad) is used to express the dose of energy absorbed from radiation per kilogram of material.

BRAIN FOOD

Radiation in Food Natural radioactivity exists all around you—even in the food you eat. Potassium-40 and radium-226 are two radioactive isotopes found in food. Although these isotopes exist in extremely small amounts in foods, the variation between different foods is astounding; for example, 1 kg of fruit has an activity of 620 to 3,700 pCi of potassium-40. Brazil nuts have an activity of about 5,600 pCi of potassium-40 per kilogram!

READING STRATEGY — GENERAL

Prediction Guide Before students read the text under the Finding a Date by Decay head, ask them whether the following statements are true or false.

- Scientists measure the amount of uranium in human remains to determine how old they are. (false)

- We receive a steady supply of carbon-14 from the food we eat. (true)

- The rate of decay of carbon-14 does not change with changes in temperature and pressure. (true)

LS Logical

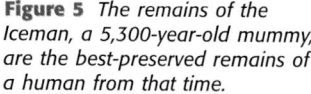

CONNECTION TO Environmental Science

WRITING SKILL **Radon in the Home** Radioactive radon-222 forms from the radioactive decay of uranium found in soil and rocks. Because radon is a gas, it can enter buildings through gaps in the walls and floors. Research the hazards of radon. Identify methods used to detect it and to prevent exposure to it. Present your findings by writing a pamphlet in the form of a public service announcement.

Damage to Nonliving Matter

Radiation can also damage nonliving matter. When metal atoms lose electrons, the metal is weakened. For example, radiation can cause the metal structures of buildings, such as nuclear power plants, to become unsafe. High levels of radiation from the sun can damage spacecraft.

Damage at Different Depths

Gamma rays go through matter easily. They can cause damage deep within matter. Beta particles cause damage closer to the surface. Alpha particles cause damage very near the surface. But alpha particles are larger and more massive than the particles of other kinds of radiation. So, if a source of alpha particles enters an organism, the particles can cause the most damage.

Finding a Date by Decay

Finding a date for someone can be tough—especially if the person is several thousand years old! Hikers in the Italian Alps found the remains of the Iceman, shown in **Figure 5,** in 1991. Scientists were able to estimate the time of death—about 5,300 years ago! How did the scientists do this? The decay of radioactive carbon was the key.

Carbon-14—It's in You!

Carbon atoms are found in all living things. A small percentage of these atoms is radioactive carbon-14 atoms. During an organism's life, the percentage of carbon-14 in the organism stays about the same. Any atoms that decay are replaced. Plants take in carbon from the atmosphere. Animals take in carbon from food. But when an organism dies, the carbon-14 is no longer replaced. Over time, the level of carbon-14 in the remains of the organism drops because of radioactive decay.

Figure 5 *The remains of the Iceman, a 5,300-year-old mummy, are the best-preserved remains of a human from that time.*

SCIENTISTS AT ODDS

Lung Cancer Most scientists think that the majority of lung cancer cases in the United States can be attributed to cigarette smoking. However, some scientists think that radon is responsible for some cases of lung cancer. Because some people are exposed to both cigarette smoke and radon, it may be impossible to determine exactly how many instances of lung cancer are caused by exposure to radon. Scientific estimates vary widely.

WEIRD SCIENCE

The Iceman was frozen in a glacier in the European Alps at an altitude of 3,200 m and was preserved for about 5,300 years in the ice. To protect the Iceman, the Institute for Anatomy in Innsbruck, Austria, keeps the Iceman in a cooler that simulates the temperature and environmental conditions of the glacier. A second cooler is ready as a backup if needed. If the Iceman warms up, he will begin to decompose.

Figure 6 Radioactive Decay and Half-Life

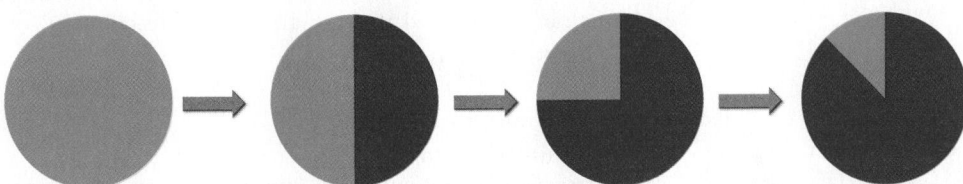

The **original sample** contains a certain amount of radioactive isotope.

After **one half-life**, one-half of the original sample has decayed, and half is unchanged.

After **two half-lives**, one-fourth of the original sample remains unchanged.

After **three half-lives**, only one-eighth of the original sample remains unchanged.

A Steady Rate of Decay

Scientists have found that every 5,730 years, half of the carbon-14 in a sample decays. The rate of decay is constant. The rate is not changed by other conditions, such as temperature or pressure. Each radioactive isotope has its own rate of decay, called half-life. A **half-life** is the amount of time it takes one-half of the nuclei of a radioactive isotope to decay. **Figure 6** is a model of this process. **Table 1** lists some isotopes that have a wide range of half-lives.

half-life the time needed for half of a sample of a radioactive substance to undergo radioactive decay

✓ *Reading Check* What is the half-life of carbon-14?

Determining Age

Scientists measured the number of decays in the Iceman's body each minute. They found that a little less than half of the carbon-14 in the body had changed. In other words, not quite one half-life of carbon-14 (5,730 years) had passed since the Iceman died.

Carbon-14 can be used to find the age of objects up to 50,000 years old. To find the age of older things, other elements must be used. For example, potassium-40 has a half-life of 1.3 billion years. It is used to find the age of dinosaur fossils.

How Old Is It?

One-fourth of the original carbon-14 of an antler is unchanged. As shown in **Figure 6**, two half-lives have passed. To determine the age of the antler, multiply the number of half-lives that have passed by the half-life of carbon-14. The antler's age is 2 times the half-life of carbon-14:

age = 2 × 5,730 years
age = 11,460 years

Determine the age of a wooden spear that contains one-eighth of its original amount of carbon-14.

Table 1 Examples of Half-Lives

Isotope	Half-life	Isotope	Half-life
Uranium-238	4.5 billion years	Polonium-210	138 days
Oxygen-21	3.4 s	Nitrogen-13	10 min
Hydrogen-3	12.3 years	Calcium-36	0.1 s

Really Short Lived The half-life of some isotopes is only a few seconds, or even a tiny fraction of a second. Some of these isotopes occur naturally as a result of the radioactive decay of other nuclei.

CHAPTER RESOURCES

Technology

Transparencies
• P64 Radioactive Decay and Half-Life

Workbooks

Math Skills for Science
• Radioactive Decay and the Half-Life GENERAL

CONNECTION ACTIVITY
Math ———— GENERAL

Half-Life Practice Tell students that the half-life of nitrogen-13 is 10 min. Then, present the following problems to students:

1. A 20 g nitrogen-13 sample is prepared for an experiment. If a scientist begins the experiment 20 min later, how many grams of nitrogen-13 remain? (5 g)

2. If only 2.5 g of nitrogen-13 remain at the end, how much time has passed from the time the sample was prepared? (One-eighth of the original sample remains, so three half-lives have passed. The total time since the sample was prepared is 30 min (3 × 10 min).

LS Logical

Answer to Math Practice
3 × 5,730 years = 17,190 years

INCLUSION Strategies

• *Developmentally Delayed*
• *Hearing Impaired*
• *Learning Disabled*

Modeling half-life will help students better understand it.

1. Place students into groups of three, and assign the roles of timer, puller, and recorder. Give 16 chips to each group.

2. Every 15 s, a timer says "Pull," and the puller takes half of the chips and places them in a pile. (There should be one pile for each pull.) The recorder records that a half-life has happened with each pull.

3. After 45 s, the timer calls, "Stop!"

4. Help students notice that the number of chips pulled got smaller but that the time between pulls didn't change.

LS Interpersonal Co-op Learning

Radiation Types Have students make a cartoon or comic book that creatively conveys facts about alpha particles, beta particles, and gamma rays. **LS** Visual

Quiz — GENERAL

1. Compare alpha, beta, and gamma radiation in terms of their size and mass. (Alpha particles are the largest and the most massive. They have a mass number of 4. Beta particles are much smaller and less massive. They have a mass number of 0. Gamma rays are a form of energy and therefore have no size or mass.)

2. Why is a half-life called a *half-life*? (One half-life represents the amount of time necessary for one-half of the original amount of an isotope to decay.)

Alternative Assessment — GENERAL

Decay Have students create a poster or other visual presentation to help explain the concepts of decay and half-life to the class. Suggest that students start with 16 or 32 carbon-14 nuclei. Encourage them to be creative with their poster or model. **LS** Visual
English Language Learners

Uses of Radioactivity

You have learned how radioactive isotopes are used to determine the age of objects. But radioactivity is used in many areas for many things. The smoke detectors in your home might even use a small amount of radioactive material! Some isotopes can be used as tracers. *Tracers* are radioactive elements whose paths can be followed through a process or reaction.

✓ **Reading Check** What is a tracer?

INTERNET ACTIVITY

For another activity related to this chapter, go to **go.hrw.com** and type in the keyword **HP5RADW.**

Radioactivity in Healthcare

Doctors use tracers to help diagnose medical problems. Radioactive tracers that have short half-lives are fed to or injected into a patient. Then, a detector is used to follow the tracer as it moves through the patient's body. The image in **Figure 7** shows an example of the results of a tracer study. Radioactive materials are also used to treat illnesses, including cancer. Radioactive materials can even help prevent illness. For example, many food and healthcare products are sterilized using radiation.

Radioactivity in Industry

Radioactive isotopes can also help detect defects in structures. For example, radiation is used to test the thickness of metal sheets as they are made. Another way radioactive isotopes are used to test structures is shown in **Figure 7.**

Some space probes have been powered by radioactive materials. The energy given off as nuclei decay is converted into electrical energy for the probe.

Figure 7 **Uses of Radioactivity in Healthcare and in Industry**

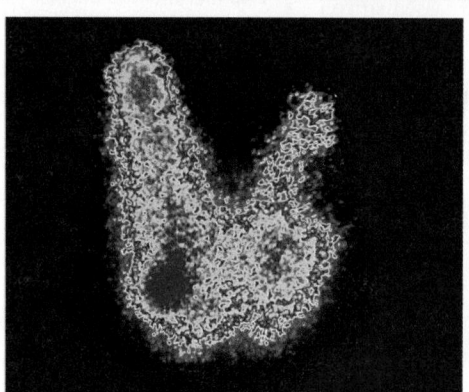

Radioactive iodine-131 was used to make this scan of a thyroid gland. The dark area shows the location of a tumor.

Tracers are used to find weak spots in materials and leaks in pipes. A Geiger counter is often used to detect the tracer.

Answer to Reading Check
A tracer is a radioactive element whose path can be followed through a process or reaction.

CONNECTION to Life Science — GENERAL

Tracers in Plants Scientists inject water composed of molecules that contain radioactive oxygen-15 or oxygen-19 atoms into a plant's root system. The plant uses these water molecules just as it uses water molecules that contain stable oxygen-16 atoms. A radiation counter detects the radioactive oxygen. Scientists can tell how much of the oxygen gas made by the plant through photosynthesis is made with the oxygen atoms from water molecules.

SECTION Review

Summary

- Henri Becquerel discovered radioactivity while trying to study X rays. Radioactivity is the process by which a nucleus gives off nuclear radiation.

- An alpha particle is composed of two protons and two neutrons. A beta particle can be an electron or a positron. Gamma rays are a form of light with very high energy.

- Gamma rays penetrate matter better than alpha or beta particles do. Beta particles penetrate matter better than alpha particles do.

- Nuclear radiation can damage living and nonliving matter.

- Half-life is the amount of time it takes for one-half of the nuclei of a radioactive isotope to decay. The age of some objects can be determined using half-lives.

- Uses of radioactive materials include detecting defects in materials, sterilizing products, diagnosing illness, and generating electrical energy.

Using Key Terms

1. Use the following terms in the same sentence: *mass number* and *isotope*.

Understanding Key Ideas

2. Which of the following statements correctly describes the changes that happen in radioactive decay?

   a. Alpha decay changes the atomic number and the mass number of a nucleus.

   b. Gamma decay changes the atomic number but not the mass number of a nucleus.

   c. Gamma decay changes the mass number but not the atomic number of a nucleus.

   d. Beta decay changes the mass number but not the atomic number of a nucleus.

3. Describe the experiment that led to the discovery of radioactivity.

4. Give two examples of how radioactivity is useful and two examples of how it is harmful.

Math Skills

5. A rock contains one-fourth of its original amount of potassium-40. The half-life of potassium-40 is 1.3 billion years. Calculate the rock's age.

6. How many half-lives have passed if a sample contains one-sixteenth of its original amount of radioactive material?

Critical Thinking

7. **Making Comparisons** Compare the penetrating power of the following nuclear radiation: alpha particles, beta particles, and gamma rays.

8. **Making Inferences** Why would uranium-238 not be useful in determining the age of a spear that is thought to be 5,000 years old? Explain your reasoning.

Interpreting Graphics

9. Look at the figure below. Which nucleus could not undergo alpha decay? Explain your answer.

Beryllium-10   **Hydrogen-3**

6 neutrons   2 neutrons
4 protons   1 proton

For a variety of links related to this chapter, go to www.scilinks.org

Topic: Discovering Radioactivity; Radioactive Isotopes

SciLinks code: HSM0412; HSM1256

CHAPTER RESOURCES

Chapter Resource File

- Section Quiz **GENERAL**
- Section Review **GENERAL**
- Vocabulary and Section Summary **GENERAL**
- Reinforcement Worksheet **BASIC**
- SciLinks Activity **GENERAL**

Answers to Section Review

1. Sample answer: The mass number of each isotope of an element is different.

2. a

3. Sample answer: A fluorescent mineral was placed on a photographic plate wrapped in paper. Because of cloudy weather, Becquerel left the materials in a drawer. After a few days, he developed the plate and saw a strong image of the mineral.

4. Sample answer: Radioactivity is useful in determining the age of objects and in diagnosing medical problems. Radioactivity is harmful because it can weaken structures and can damage cells in living things.

5. If one-fourth of the original amount of potassium-40 remains, two half-lives have passed. $2 \times 1,300,000,000$ years = $2,600,000,000$ years, or 2.6 billion years

6. four half-lives

7. Alpha particles are the least penetrating and are stopped by paper or clothing. Beta particles are more penetrating than alpha particles and are stopped by thin sheets of aluminum. Gamma rays are the most penetrating and are stopped by materials such as lead or concrete.

8. Sample answer: You do not expect to find uranium in a spear, because the spear is made of wood. In addition, the half-life of uranium is very long compared with the estimated age of the spear, so very little uranium would have decayed.

9. An alpha particle is made up of two protons and two neutrons. Hydrogen-3 could not undergo alpha decay because it is made up of only two neutrons and one proton, so it does not have enough protons to make an alpha particle.

Overview

In this section, students learn about nuclear fission and nuclear fusion. They also learn some of the pros and cons of each process as an alternative energy source.

 **Bellringer**

Write the words *fission* and *fusion* on the board. Ask students to write what they think each term means. Discuss some of their ideas with them.

Motivate

Demonstration — GENERAL

Mousetrap Fission Because of the preparation needed, you may want to make a videotape of this demonstration. Set up a closely spaced array of about 20 mechanical mousetraps. Place two table-tennis balls on top of each set mousetrap. Ask students to predict what would happen if you threw a ball into the array. Throw one ball into the array, causing a mousetrap to snap. Point out that this represents an uncontrolled chain reaction. How could a controlled reaction be simulated? (A controlled reaction could be modeled by catching enough balls so that only one ball from each trap sets off another trap.) **LS** Visual

---

SECTION
2

What You Will Learn

- Describe nuclear fission.
- Identify advantages and disadvantages of fission.
- Describe nuclear fusion.
- Identify advantages and disadvantages of fusion.

Vocabulary
nuclear fission
nuclear chain reaction
nuclear fusion

READING STRATEGY

Reading Organizer As you read this section, make a table comparing nuclear fission and nuclear fusion.

Energy from the Nucleus

From an early age, you were probably told not to play with fire. But fire itself is neither good nor bad. It simply has benefits and hazards.

Likewise, getting energy from the nucleus of an atom has benefits and hazards. In this section, you will learn about two ways to get energy from the nucleus—fission (FISH uhn) and fusion (FYOO zhuhn). Gaining an understanding of the advantages and disadvantages of fission and fusion is important for people who will make decisions about the use of this energy—people like you!

Nuclear Fission

The nuclei of some atoms decay by breaking into two smaller, more stable nuclei. **Nuclear fission** is the process by which a large nucleus splits into two small nuclei and releases energy.

The nuclei of some uranium atoms, as well as the nuclei of other large atoms, can undergo nuclear fission naturally. Large atoms can also be forced to undergo fission by hitting the atoms with neutrons, as shown by the model in **Figure 1**.

✔️ **Reading Check** What happens to a nucleus that undergoes nuclear fission? (*See the Appendix for answers to Reading Checks.*)

Figure 1 Fission of a Uranium-235 Nucleus

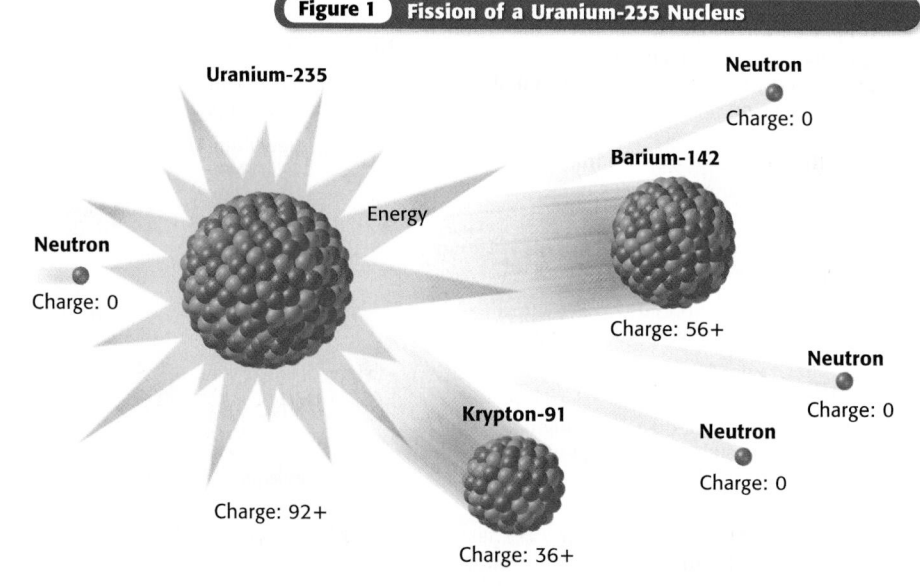

Uranium-235 — Charge: 92+
Neutron — Charge: 0
Energy
Neutron — Charge: 0
Barium-142 — Charge: 56+
Neutron — Charge: 0
Krypton-91 — Charge: 36+
Neutron — Charge: 0

CHAPTER RESOURCES

Chapter Resource File

- Lesson Plan
- Directed Reading A **BASIC**
- Directed Reading B **SPECIAL NEEDS**

Technology

- Transparencies
  - Bellringer
  - P65 Fission of a Uranium-235 Nucleus; Fusion of Hydrogen-1 Nuclei

Workbooks

- Interactive Textbook **Struggling Readers**

Answer to Reading Check

A nucleus that undergoes nuclear fission splits into two smaller, more stable nuclei.

Energy from Matter

Did you know that matter can be changed into energy? It's true! If you could find the total mass of the products in **Figure 1** and compare it with the total mass of the reactants, you would find something strange. The total mass of the products is slightly less than the total mass of the reactants. Why are the masses different? Some of the matter was converted into energy.

The amount of energy given off when a single uranium nucleus splits is very small. But this energy comes from a very small amount of matter. The amount of matter converted into energy is only about one-fifth the mass of a hydrogen atom. And hydrogen is the smallest atom that exists! Look at **Figure 2.** The nuclear fission of the uranium nuclei in one fuel pellet releases as much energy as the chemical change of burning about 1,000 kg of coal.

Nuclear Chain Reactions

Look at **Figure 1** again. Suppose that two or three of the neutrons produced split other uranium-235 nuclei. So, energy and more neutrons are given off. And then suppose that two or three of the neutrons that were given off split other nuclei and so on. This example is one type of **nuclear chain reaction,** a continuous series of nuclear fission reactions. A model of an uncontrolled chain reaction is shown in **Figure 3.**

Figure 2 *Each of these small fuel pellets can generate a large amount of energy through the process of nuclear fission.*

nuclear fission the splitting of the nucleus of a large atom into two or more fragments; releases additional neutrons and energy

nuclear chain reaction a continuous series of nuclear fission reactions

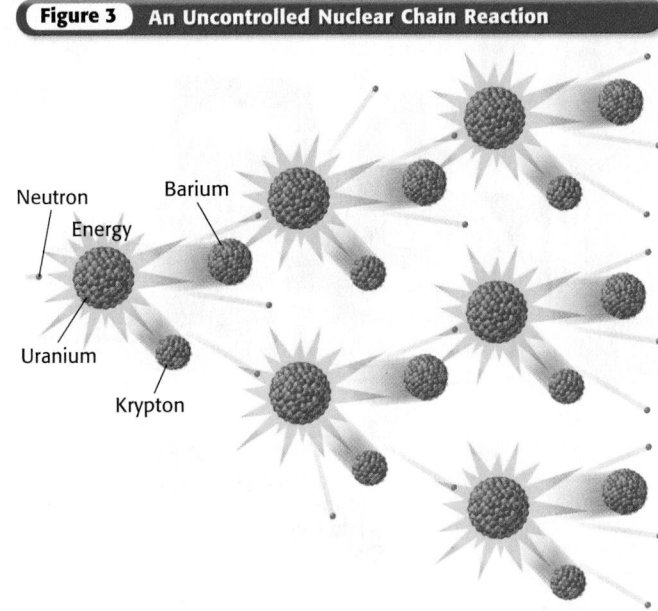

| Figure 3 | An Uncontrolled Nuclear Chain Reaction |

Neutron
Energy
Barium
Uranium
Krypton

Teach

CONNECTION ACTIVITY
History ——— GENERAL

Controlling Fission The first controlled nuclear chain reaction took place on December 2, 1942, at the University of Chicago. Nobel Prize-winning physicist Enrico Fermi, who had come to the United States from Italy in 1938, led the experiment. After his success in Chicago, Fermi was asked by the U.S. government to work on the Manhattan Project to develop the first atomic bomb. Have students research Fermi's work on controlling fission and on the Manhattan Project and write a report about their findings. **LS Logical**

Research ——— GENERAL

Scientists Ask students to research the work of Albert Einstein, Lise Meitner, the Curies, or Otto Hahn and to prepare a poster, model, story, skit, or concept map to present their findings to the class. **LS Logical/Verbal**

CONNECTION to
History ——— GENERAL

Atomic Bombs The first uncontrolled nuclear chain reaction occurred on July 16, 1945, when the world's first atomic bomb was detonated in the desert of New Mexico. This test was to see whether the atomic bombs designed by scientists on the top-secret Manhattan Project worked. The blast was equal to exploding 22,000 tons of TNT. Only a few weeks after this test, two atomic bombs were dropped on cities in Japan to end World War II.

SUPPORT FOR

English Language Learners
Fission and Fusion Students may need practice pronouncing and differentiating between these words. Model the pronunciation of each word and have students repeat. Ask them to read the fission and fusion paragraphs aloud to a partner. The listening partner should be able to discern whether the reader says fission or fusion. Provide each pair with a colored index card and a white index card. Tell students to show the white when they hear *fission* and the red when they hear *fusion.* **LS Auditory/Verbal**

BRAIN FOOD

Albert Einstein Although Albert Einstein is considered one of the greatest scientists of the 20th century, he did not begin to speak until the age of 3. In addition, most of his teachers considered him an academic failure because of his apparent lack of interest in classes.

Using the Figure—GENERAL

Reactor Types There are several types of nuclear reactors. The one shown in **Figure 4** is a pressurized water reactor. This reactor uses water under high pressure as a coolant. The pressure allows the water to become superheated without turning into steam. Another type of reactor uses water as a coolant but allows the water to boil and turn to steam. **LS** Visual

CONNECTION ACTIVITY
Environmental Science————ADVANCED

 Nuclear Plants? Many environmentalists and ecologists share concerns for the flora and fauna in areas around nuclear power plants. Have students research the issues raised by ecologists regarding nuclear power plants. Encourage them to be creative in their presentations. **LS** Logical/Verbal

Debate————GENERAL

Space Case Have students do research and hold a debate about the issue of using nuclear energy in spacecraft and satellites. Students on one side can defend the use of nuclear energy in space. The other side can point out the potential hazards associated with using nuclear energy in space. **LS** Verbal/Logical

Energy from a Chain Reaction

In an *uncontrolled chain reaction*, huge amounts of energy are given off very quickly. For example, the tremendous energy of an atomic bomb is the result of an uncontrolled chain reaction. On the other hand, nuclear power plants use *controlled chain reactions*. The energy released from the nuclei in the uranium fuel within the nuclear power plants is used to generate electrical energy. **Figure 4** shows how a nuclear power plant works.

Advantages and Disadvantages of Fission

Every form of energy has advantages and disadvantages. To make informed decisions about energy use, you need to know both sides. For example, burning wood to keep warm on a cold night could save your life. But a spark from the fire could start a forest fire. Nuclear fission has advantages and disadvantages that you should think about.

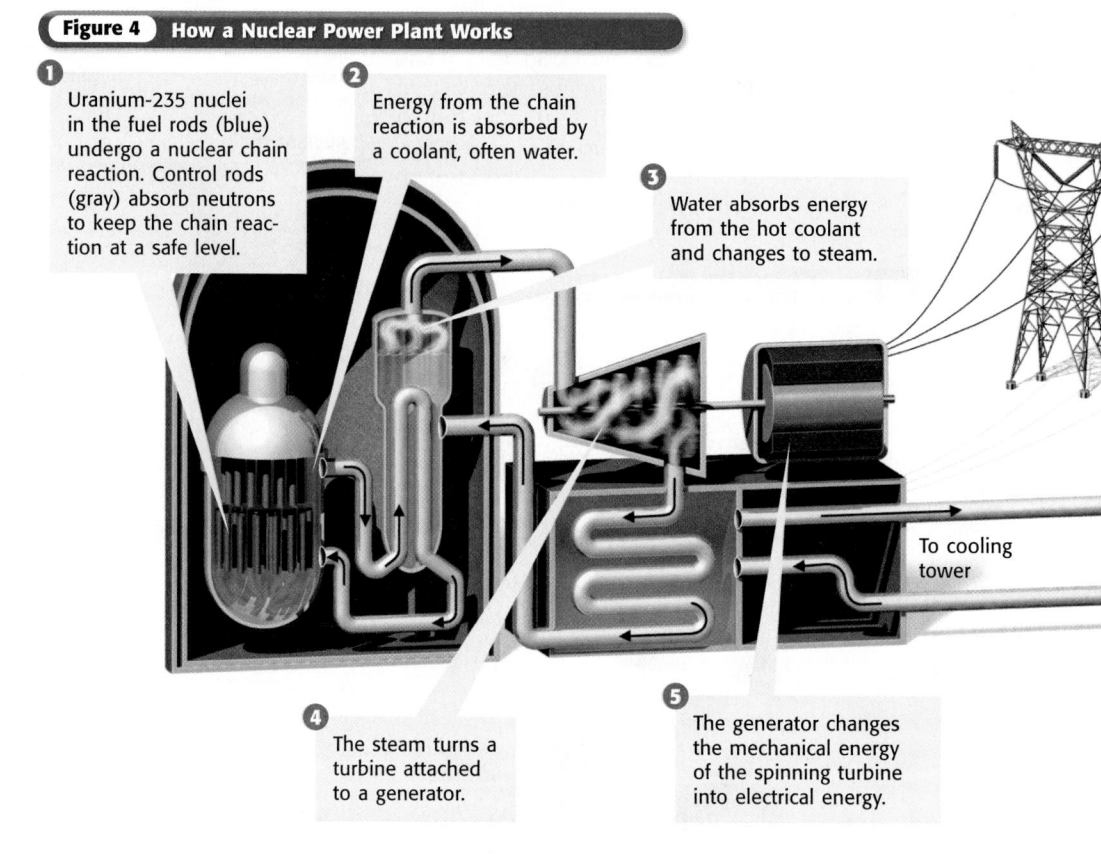

Figure 4 **How a Nuclear Power Plant Works**

❶ Uranium-235 nuclei in the fuel rods (blue) undergo a nuclear chain reaction. Control rods (gray) absorb neutrons to keep the chain reaction at a safe level.

❷ Energy from the chain reaction is absorbed by a coolant, often water.

❸ Water absorbs energy from the hot coolant and changes to steam.

To cooling tower

❹ The steam turns a turbine attached to a generator.

❺ The generator changes the mechanical energy of the spinning turbine into electrical energy.

CHAPTER RESOURCES

Technology

 **Transparencies**
• How a Nuclear Power Plant Works

SCIENCE HUMOR

Q: Why did the student bring a rod and reel to class?

A: The teacher said they would be studying fission.

Accidents

A concern that many people have about nuclear power is the risk of an accident. In Chernobyl, Ukraine, on April 26, 1986, an accident happened, as shown in **Figure 5.** An explosion put large amounts of radioactive uranium fuel and waste products into the atmosphere. The cloud of radioactive material spread over most of Europe and Asia. It reached as far as North America.

What Waste!

Another concern about nuclear power is nuclear waste. This waste includes used fuel rods, chemicals used to process uranium, and even shoe covers and overalls worn by workers. Controlled fission has been carried out for only about 50 years. But the waste will give off high levels of radiation for thousands of years. The rate of radioactive decay cannot be changed. So, the nuclear waste must be stored until it becomes less radioactive. Most of the used fuel rods are stored in huge pools of water. Some of the liquid wastes are stored in underground tanks. However, scientists continue to look for better ideas for long-term storage of nuclear waste.

Nuclear Versus Fossil Fuel

Nuclear power plants cost more to build than power plants that use fossil fuels. But nuclear power plants often cost less to run than plants that use fossil fuels because less fuel is needed. Also, nuclear power plants do not release gases, such as carbon dioxide, into the atmosphere. The use of fission allows our supply of fossil fuels to last longer. However, the supply of uranium is limited.

Reading Check What are two advantages of using nuclear fission to generate electrical energy?

Figure 5 *During a test at the Chernobyl nuclear power plant, the emergency protection system was turned off. The reactor overheated, which resulted in an explosion.*

CONNECTION TO Language Arts

WRITING SKILL **Storage Site** The government of the United States is required by law to build underground storage for nuclear waste. The waste must be stored for a very long time and cannot escape into the environment. In your **science journal,** write a one-page paper describing the characteristics of a good location for these underground storage sites.

Quick Lab

Gone Fission

1. Make two paper balls from a **sheet of paper.**
2. Stand in a group with your classmates. Make sure you are an arm's length from your other classmates.
3. Your teacher will gently toss a paper ball at the group. If you are touched by a ball, gently toss your paper balls at the group.
4. Explain how this activity is a model of a chain reaction. Be sure to explain what the students and the paper balls represent.

WEIRD SCIENCE

The first nuclear-powered submarine was the USS *Nautilus.* The *Nautilus* made its first sea run on January 17, 1955. Because a nuclear generator requires no oxygen, a nuclear-powered submarine can remain underwater for very long periods of time.

Is That a Fact!

The United States has the largest number of operational nuclear power plants in the world (more than 100). The country that comes closest to the United States is France, which has 56 reactors; however, France is only about one-seventeenth the area of the United States.

Reteaching ——— BASIC

Clay Models Have students model fission by breaking a piece of putty into smaller pieces and fusion by combining small pieces of putty to make one larger piece. **LS** Visual

Quiz ——— GENERAL

1. Define *nuclear fission.* (the splitting of the nucleus of a large atom into two or more fragments)

2. Define *nuclear fusion.* (the combination of the nuclei of small atoms to form a larger nucleus)

3. What is the main product of nuclear fusion in the sun? (helium nuclei)

Alternative Assessment ——— GENERAL

Concept Mapping Ask students to create concept maps to explain fission and fusion. Encourage students to label their diagrams carefully. Students should include where each type of reaction occurs. (fission: nuclear reactor, atomic bomb; fusion: stars, sun, hydrogen bomb) **LS** Visual

Answer to Reading Check

In nuclear fusion, two or more nuclei that have small masses combine to form a larger nucleus. During fusion, energy is released.

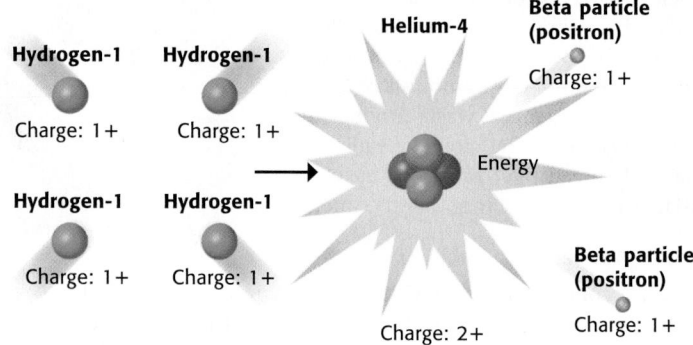

Figure 6 Nuclear Fusion of Hydrogen

Hydrogen-1 Charge: 1+
Hydrogen-1 Charge: 1+
Hydrogen-1 Charge: 1+
Hydrogen-1 Charge: 1+

Helium-4 Energy
Charge: 2+

Beta particle (positron) Charge: 1+
Beta particle (positron) Charge: 1+

---

nuclear fusion the combination of the nuclei of small atoms to form a larger nucleus; releases energy

CONNECTION TO Astronomy

Elements of the Stars
Hydrogen is not the only fuel that stars use for fusion. Research other elements that stars can use as fuels and the fusion reactions that make these elements. Make a poster showing what you learn.

ACTIVITY

Nuclear Fusion

Fusion is another nuclear reaction in which matter is converted into energy. In **nuclear fusion,** two or more nuclei that have small masses combine, or fuse, to form a larger nucleus.

Plasma Needed

In order for fusion to happen, the repulsion between positively charged nuclei must be overcome. Very high temperatures are needed—more than 100,000,000°C! At these high temperatures, matter is a plasma. *Plasma* is the state of matter in which electrons have been removed from atoms. So, plasma is made up of ions and electrons. One place that has such temperatures is the sun. In the sun's core, hydrogen nuclei fuse to form a helium nucleus, as shown in the model in **Figure 6.**

✔ **Reading Check** Describe the process of nuclear fusion.

Advantages and Disadvantages of Fusion

Energy for your home cannot yet be generated using nuclear fusion. First, very high temperatures are needed. Second, more energy is needed to make and hold the plasma than is generated by fusion. But scientists predict that fusion will provide electrical energy in the future—maybe in your lifetime!

Less Accident Prone

The concern about an accident such as the one at Chernobyl is much lower for fusion reactors. If a fusion reactor exploded, very little radioactive material would be released. Fusion products are not radioactive. And the hydrogen-3 used for fuel in experimental fusion reactors is much less radioactive than the uranium used in fission reactors.

Science Bloopers

Cold Fusion In 1989, two chemists at the University of Utah, B. Stanley Pons and Martin Fleischmann, claimed that they had produced nuclear fusion at room temperature. However, no one could duplicate their results. Most scientists have concluded that the reports were incorrect. Others still try to explain the results, which cannot be explained by current understanding.

Oceans of Fuel

Scientists studying fusion use hydrogen-2 and hydrogen-3 in their work. Hydrogen-1 is much more common than these isotopes. But there is enough of them in Earth's waters to provide fuel for millions of years. Also, a fusion reaction releases more energy per gram of fuel than a fission reaction does. So, fusion saves more resources than fission does, as shown in **Figure 7.**

Less Waste

The products of fusion reactions are not radioactive. So, fusion is a "cleaner" source of energy than fission is. There would be much less radioactive waste. But to have the benefits of fusion, scientists need money to pay for research.

Figure 7 *Fusing the hydrogen-2 in 3.8 L of water would release about the same amount of energy as burning 1,140 L of gasoline!*

SECTION Review

Summary

- In nuclear fission, a massive nucleus breaks into two nuclei.

- In nuclear fusion, two or more nuclei combine to form a larger nucleus.

- Nuclear fission is used in power plants to generate electrical energy. A limited fuel supply and radioactive waste products are disadvantages of fission.

- Nuclear fusion cannot yet be used as an energy source, but plentiful fuel and little waste are advantages of fusion.

Using Key Terms

Complete each of the following sentences by choosing the correct term from the word bank.

nuclear fission
nuclear fusion
nuclear chain reaction

1. During ___, small nuclei combine.

2. During ___, nuclei split one after another.

Understanding Key Ideas

3. Which of the following is an advantage nuclear fission has over fossil fuels?

a. unlimited supply of fuel

b. less radioactive waste

c. fewer building expenses

d. less released carbon dioxide

4. Which kind of nuclear reaction is currently used to generate electrical energy?

5. Which kind of nuclear reaction is the source of the sun's energy?

6. What particle is needed to begin a nuclear chain reaction?

7. In both fission and fusion, what is converted into energy?

Math Skills

8. Imagine that a uranium nucleus splits and releases three neutrons and that each neutron splits another nucleus. If the first split occurs in stage 1, how many nuclei will split during stage 4?

Critical Thinking

9. **Making Comparisons** Compare nuclear fission with nuclear fusion.

10. **Analyzing Processes** The floor of a room is covered in mousetraps that each hold two table-tennis balls. One ball is dropped onto a trap. The trap snaps shut, and the balls on it fly into the air and fall on other traps. What nuclear process is modeled here? Explain your answer.

Developed and maintained by the
National Science Teachers Association

For a variety of links related to this chapter, go to www.scilinks.org

Topic: Nuclear Fission; Nuclear Fusion
SciLinks code: HSM1048; HSM1050

CONNECTION to Earth Science —— GENERAL

Fusion Use the transparency "Fusion of Hydrogen in the Sun" to show students a fusion reaction of other hydrogen isotopes. Visual

CHAPTER RESOURCES

Chapter Resource File

- **Section Quiz** GENERAL
- **Section Review** GENERAL
- **Vocabulary and Section Summary** GENERAL
- **Reinforcement Worksheet** BASIC
- **Critical Thinking** ADVANCED
- **Datasheet for Quick Lab**

Technology

Transparencies
- *LINK TO EARTH SCIENCE* E87 Fusion of Hydrogen in the Sun

Domino Chain Reactions

Teacher's Notes

Time Required

One or two 45-minute class periods

Lab Ratings

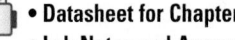

EASY ——————→ HARD

Teacher Prep 🧪

Student Set-Up 🧪🧪

Concept Level 🧪🧪🧪

Clean Up 🧪

Lab Notes

In this chapter, images of fission reactions show three neutrons produced when a uranium-235 nucleus splits. However, there are fissions that release only two neutrons. In this activity, each "fission" releases only two neutrons, each of which is represented by a domino.

Model-Making Lab

Domino Chain Reactions

Model-Making Lab

OBJECTIVES

Build models to represent controlled and uncontrolled nuclear chain reactions.

Compare models of controlled and uncontrolled nuclear chain reactions.

MATERIALS

• dominoes (15)
• stopwatch

Fission of uranium-235 is a process that relies on neutrons. When a uranium-235 nucleus splits into two smaller nuclei, it releases two or three neutrons that can cause neighboring nuclei to undergo fission. This fission can result in a nuclear chain reaction. In this lab, you will build two models of nuclear chain reactions, using dominoes.

Procedure

1 For the first model, set up the dominoes as shown below. When pushed over, each domino should hit two dominoes in the next row.

2 Measure the time it takes for all the dominoes to fall. To do this, start the stopwatch as you tip over the front domino. Stop the stopwatch when the last domino falls. Record this time.

3 If some of the dominoes do not fall, repeat steps 1 and 2. You may have to adjust the setup a few times.

4 For the second model, set up the dominoes as shown at left. The domino in the first row should hit both of the dominoes in the second row. Beginning with the second row, only one domino from each row should hit both of the dominoes in the next row.

5 Repeat step 2. Again, you may have to adjust the setup a few times to get all the dominoes to fall.

💿 **Holt Lab Generator CD-ROM**

Search for any lab by topic, standard, difficulty level, or time. Edit any lab to fit your needs, or create your own labs. Use the Lab Materials QuickList software to customize your lab materials list.

CHAPTER RESOURCES

Chapter Resource File

📁 • **Datasheet for Chapter Lab**
• **Lab Notes and Answers**

Technology

📹 **Classroom Videos**
• Lab Video

Larry Tackett
Andrew Jackson
Middle School
Cross Lanes, West Virginia

Analyze the Results

1 **Classifying** Which model represents an uncontrolled chain reaction? Which represents a controlled chain reaction? Explain your answers.

2 **Analyzing Results** Imagine that each domino releases a certain amount of energy as it falls. Compare the total amount of energy released in the two models.

3 **Analyzing Data** Compare the time needed to release the energy in the models. Which model took longer to release its energy?

Draw Conclusions

4 **Evaluating Models** In a nuclear power plant, a chain reaction is controlled by using a material that absorbs neutrons. Only enough neutrons to continue the chain reaction are allowed to continue splitting uranium-235 nuclei. Explain how your model of a controlled nuclear chain reaction modeled this process.

5 **Applying Conclusions** Why must uranium nuclei be close to each other in order for a nuclear chain reaction to happen? (Hint: What would happen in your model if the dominoes were too far apart?)

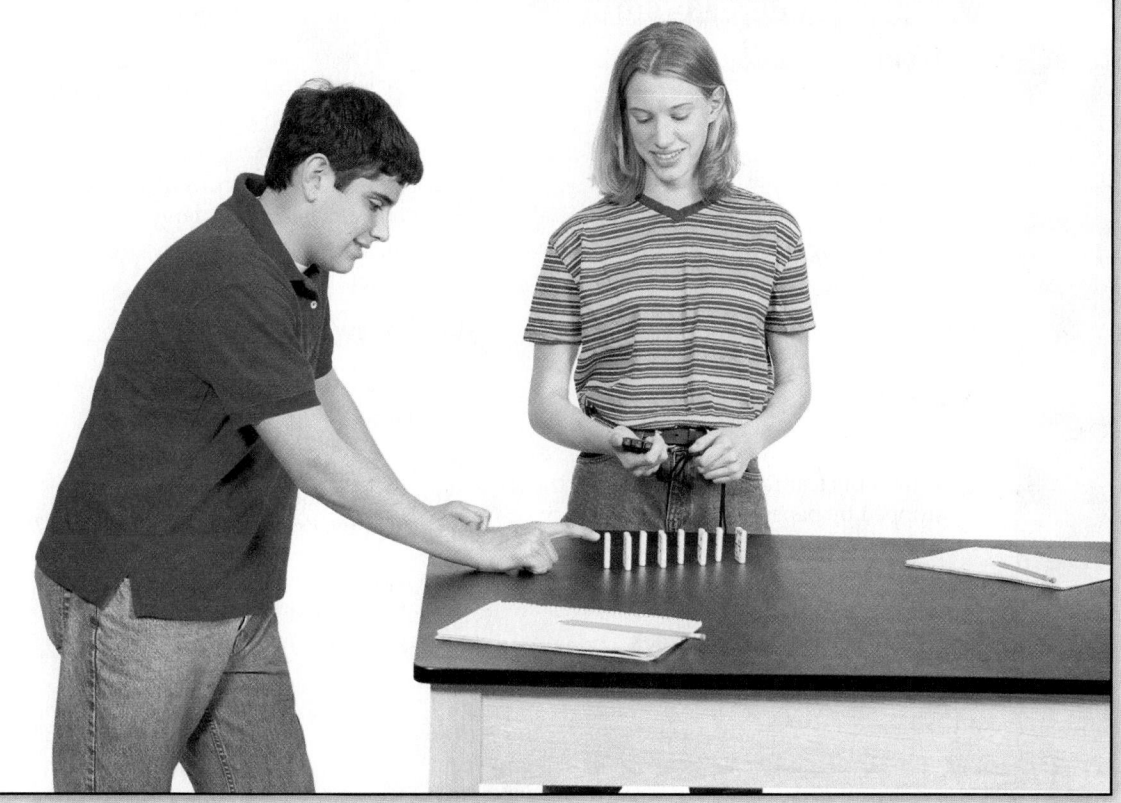

Analyze the Results

1. The first model represents an uncontrolled chain reaction. The second model represents a controlled chain reaction. The number of fission reactions doubles in each step of the first model and would quickly get out of control. Only one fission reaction occurs in each step of the second model, so the reaction happens at a steady, controlled rate.

2. The same amount of energy was released in each model because the same number of dominoes fell in each model.

3. The second model took longer to release its energy.

Draw Conclusions

4. In the second model, the dominoes were set up so that only one of each falling pair would knock down another pair of dominoes. So, only a few dominoes were used to continue the "reaction," just as only some neutrons may continue a chain reaction.

5. The nuclei must be close to each other so that a neutron produced in one fission has a greater chance of hitting another nucleus and causing it to split.

ANSWERS

Using Key Terms

1. Nuclear fission
2. half-life
3. Nuclear fusion
4. mass numbers

Understanding Key Ideas

5. d
6. b
7. a
8. c
9. d
10. c
11. Two dangers associated with nuclear fission are the potential for an accident that could release radioactive material and the potential of radioactive waste leaking into the environment.

USING KEY TERMS

The statements below are false. For each statement, replace the underlined term to make a true statement.

1 <u>Nuclear fusion</u> involves splitting a nucleus.

2 During one <u>beta decay</u>, half of a radioactive sample will decay.

3 <u>Radioactivity</u> involves the joining of nuclei.

4 Isotopes of an element have different <u>atomic numbers</u>.

UNDERSTANDING KEY IDEAS

Multiple Choice

5 Which of the following is a use of radioactive material?

a. detecting smoke
b. locating defects in materials
c. generating electrical energy
d. All of the above

6 Which particle both begins and is produced by a nuclear chain reaction?

a. positron   c. alpha particle
b. neutron   d. beta particle

7 Which nuclear radiation can be stopped by paper?

a. alpha particles   c. gamma rays
b. beta particles   d. None of the above

---

8 The half-life of a radioactive atom is 2 months. If you start with 1 g of the element, how much will remain after 6 months?

a. One-half of a gram will remain.
b. One-fourth of a gram will remain.
c. One-eighth of a gram will remain.
d. None of the sample will remain.

9 The waste products of nuclear fission

a. are harmless.
b. are safe after 20 years.
c. can be destroyed by burning them.
d. remain radioactive for thousands of years.

10 Which statement about nuclear fusion is false?

a. Nuclear fusion happens in the sun.
b. Nuclear fusion is the joining of the nuclei of atoms.
c. Nuclear fusion is currently used to generate electrical energy.
d. Nuclear fusion can use hydrogen as fuel.

Short Answer

11 What are two dangers associated with nuclear fission?

12 What are two of the problems that need to be solved in order to make nuclear fusion a usable energy source?

13 In fission, the products have less mass than the starting materials do. Explain why this happens.

---

12. Two problems that need to be solved to make nuclear fusion a practical energy source are finding a way to contain the plasma and finding a process that generates more electrical energy than is needed to heat and contain the plasma.

13. Some matter is converted into energy during fission, so the mass of the products is less than the mass of the starting materials.

Math Skills

14 A scientist used 10 g of phosphorus-32 in a test on plant growth but forgot to record the date. When measured some time later, only 2.5 g of phosphorus-32 remained. If phosphorus-32 has a half-life of 14 days, how many days ago did the experiment begin?

CRITICAL THINKING

15 **Concept Mapping** Use the following terms to create a concept map: *radioactive decay, alpha particle, beta particle, gamma ray,* and *nuclear radiation.*

16 **Expressing Opinions** Smoke detectors often use americium-243 to detect smoke particles in the air. Americium-243 undergoes alpha decay. Do you think that these smoke detectors are safe to have in your home if used properly? Explain. (Hint: Think about how penetrating alpha particles are.)

17 **Applying Concepts** How can radiation cause cancer?

18 **Analyzing Processes** Explain why nuclei of carbon, oxygen, and iron can be found in stars.

19 **Making Inferences** If you could block all radiation from sources outside your body, explain why you would still be exposed to some radiation.

INTERPRETING GRAPHICS

20 The image below was made in a manner similar to that of Becquerel's original experiment. What conclusions can be drawn from this image about the penetrating power of radiation?

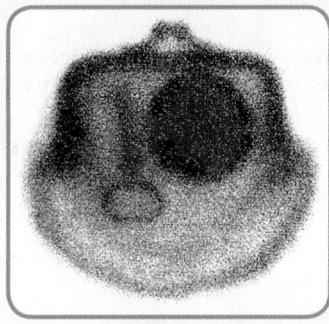

Use the graph below to answer the questions that follow.

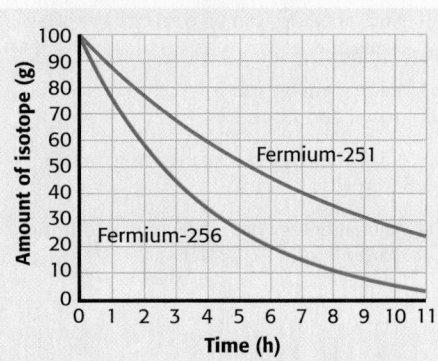

21 What is the half-life of fermium-256?

22 What is the half-life of fermium-251?

CHAPTER RESOURCES

Chapter Resource File

- Chapter Review `GENERAL`
- Chapter Test A `GENERAL`
- Chapter Test B `ADVANCED`
- Chapter Test C `SPECIAL NEEDS`
- Vocabulary Activity `GENERAL`

Workbooks

Study Guide
- Study Guide is also available in Spanish.

14. One-fourth of the original amount remains, so two half-lives have passed. Thus, the experiment began 28 days ago (2×14 days = 28 days).

Critical Thinking

15. An answer to this exercise can be found at the end of this book.

16. These smoke detectors should be safe to have in homes because alpha particles are not very penetrating and are stopped by about 7 cm of air.

17. Radiation can "knock" electrons out of atoms and break chemical bonds between atoms. If radiation breaks bonds in the DNA of a cell, the damage could cause the cell to divide uncontrollably. The cell is then cancerous.

18. Nuclear fusion in stars causes hydrogen nuclei to join together to form helium nuclei. If stars are hot enough, the hydrogen and helium nuclei could join together to form more massive nuclei, such as carbon and oxygen. These nuclei can continue to join together and form even more massive nuclei, such as iron.

19. The food you eat contains some radioactive nuclei, such as carbon-14 nuclei. Atoms of carbon-14 have the same chemical properties as atoms of nonradioactive carbon-12 and are used by your body to build molecules, such as proteins. Thus, there is always some radiation being released by nuclei of atoms that are part of your body.

Interpreting Graphics

20. Sample answer: Radiation penetrates cloth more easily than it penetrates metal. The darkness of the key and the round object (a compact) in the image demonstrate that these objects blocked more radiation than the cloth of the purse itself.

21. 2.6 h

22. 5.3 h

Teacher's Notes

To provide practice under more realistic conditions, give students 20 minutes to answer all of the questions in this Standardized Test Preparation.

Answer Key

Question	Answer
1	B
2	D
3	A
4	C
5	A
6	D
7	B
8	A
9	D
10	*
11	*

*See Test Doctor.

Multiple Choice

Use the image below to answer question 1.

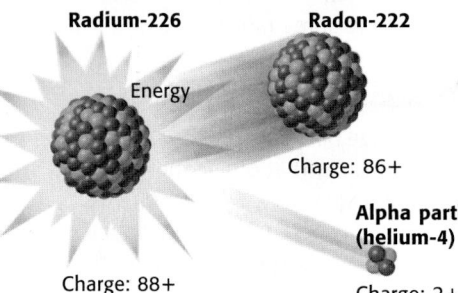

Radium-226   Radon-222

Energy

Charge: 86+

Alpha particle
(helium-4)

Charge: 88+   Charge: 2+

1. **The image above shows the decay of a radioactive nucleus. By which nuclear process is this nucleus decaying?**

   A. alpha decay

   B. beta decay

   C. nuclear fission

   D. nuclear fusion

2. **How is nuclear energy different from other forms of energy?**

   A. Nuclear energy can be converted to other forms of energy.

   B. Nuclear energy can travel through both matter and space.

   C. Nuclear energy can be used to generate electricity.

   D. Nuclear energy has been converted from matter.

3. **In a nuclear power plant, energy from nuclear fission reactions is absorbed by a coolant that travels through pipes that are submerged in large tanks of water. The thermal energy of the coolant is transferred to the water. Through what method is the thermal energy primarily transferred to the water?**

   A. conduction

   B. convection

   C. conversion

   D. radiation

4. **Who is credited with discovering radioactivity?**

   A. Marie Curie

   B. Pierre Curie

   C. Henri Becquerel

   D. Albert Einstein

5. **What type of radioactive decay causes a radium-226 nucleus to change to a radon-222 nucleus?**

   A. alpha decay

   B. beta decay of an electron

   C. beta decay of a positron

   D. gamma decay

TEST DOCTOR

Question 1 A: A helium nucleus is emitted during alpha decay. No helium nuclei are shown in the image. B: Correct. C: A nucleus splits into two smaller nuclei during nuclear fission. The image shows a nucleus changing into one different nucleus. D: Nuclei join together during nuclear fusion. The image does not show nuclei joining together.

Question 2 A: All forms of energy can be converted to other forms of energy. B: Light energy can travel through matter and space. C: Other forms of energy are used to generate electricity. D: Correct.

Question 3 A: Correct. B: Convection may happen in the coolant and in the water, but the thermal energy is not transferred from the coolant to the water by convection. C: Conversion is not a method of energy transfer. D: The coolant may radiate some thermal energy, but radiation is not the primary means of energy transfer from the coolant to the water.

Question 4 A and B: Marie and Pierre Curie were early researchers in the field of radioactivity, but they are not credited with discovering the process. C: Correct. D: Albert Einstein did not do much research with radioactivity.

6. Ernesto wants to build a shield that he can stand behind that will block gamma rays. Which material should he use?

   A. several sheets of paper

   B. doubled-up aluminum foil

   C. heavy leather pieces

   D. thick sheets of lead

7. Ellen has a 64-g sample of polonium-210. The half-life of polonium-210 is 138 days. How much of Ellen's sample will remain after 414 days?

   A. 2.0 g

   B. 8.0 g

   C. 32 g

   D. 58 g

Use the graph below to answer question 8.

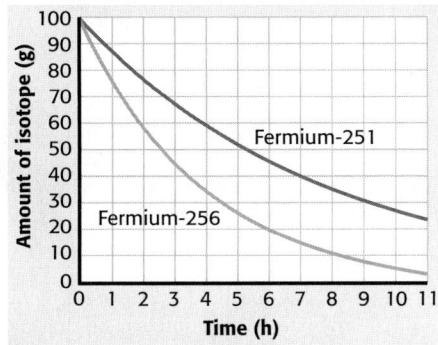

8. The graph above shows the decay rates of two isotopes of fermium. What is the approximate half-life of fermium-256?

   A. 2.5 h

   B. 5.3 h

   C. 5.5 h

   D. 11.0 h

9. A nuclear chain reaction is a continuous series of nuclear fission reactions. Chain reactions in nuclear power plants are controlled by inserting control rods in the nuclear reactor. How do control rods work?

   A. Control rods absorb excess uranium-235.

   B. Control rods absorb emitted barium-142.

   C. Control rods absorb excess energy.

   D. Control rods absorb emitted neutrons.

Open Response

10. Shoes made from plant material worn by prehistoric people were found in caves in Missouri and Kentucky. Scientists used carbon-14 dating to determine the age of the shoes. Explain how carbon-14 dating works.

11. Jacob and Asha are debating about the pros and cons of radioactivity. Jacob is arguing the disadvantages of radioactivity and Asha is defending the benefits of radioactivity. Describe two points that each student can make during the debate.

(vertical tab) **Standardized Test Preparation**

Question 9 A, B, and C: Nuclear fission of uranium-235 happens when the nucleus of a uranium-235 atom is struck with a neutron. Neutrons emitted by the fission reaction can then strike other uranium-235 atoms to cause more fission reactions. Control rods in nuclear reactors absorb some of the neutrons emitted by the fission reactions, thereby preventing the neutrons from causing additional fission reactions. D: Correct.

Question 10 Full-credit answers should include the following points:

- A half-life is the amount of time needed for one-half of the nuclei of a radioactive isotope to decay. The half-life of carbon-14 is 5,730 years.
- Scientists can measure the amount of carbon-14 in a shoe to determine how much of the carbon-14 has decayed and thus how many half-lives have passed.
- Scientists then multiply the number of half-lives that have passed by the half-life of carbon to determine the age of the shoes.

Question 11 Full-credit answers should include two reasons why radioactivity is bad and two reasons why radioactivity is beneficial.

Cons:

- Radioactivity can damage matter and living tissue.
- Radioactive material can be difficult to store and to dispose of.
- Uncontrolled nuclear chain reactions can be explosive.

Pros:

- Radioactivity can be used for finding the age of objects.
- Radioactivity can be used in medicine and industry.
- Nuclear power plants are less expensive to run and do not produce carbon dioxide.

Question 5 A: Correct. B: During beta decay of an electron, a neutron breaks into a proton and an electron, which increases the atomic number by 1. C: During beta decay of a positron, a proton is converted to a neutron and a positron, which decreases the atomic number by 1. D: No change in atomic number occurs during gamma decay.

Question 6 A, B, and C: Gamma rays can penetrate all of these materials. D: Correct. Gamma rays can be blocked by dense, thick materials, such as thick sheets of lead.

Question 7 A: 2.0 g of the sample will remain after five half-lives. Only three half-lives pass in 414 days. B: Correct. C: 32 g of the sample will remain after two half-lives. D: Students must divide 64 g by 2 three times. Students who select this answer may have mistakenly subtracted 2 from 64 g three times.

Question 8 A: Correct. B: This answer is the half-life of fermium-251. C: This answer is half of the total time shown on the graph. D: This answer is the time on the graph at which the amount of fermium-256 is closest to 0 g.

Science, Technology, and Society

Background

The FDA approved irradiation as a method to control mold in wheat flour in 1963. Since then, the process has been approved for many types of foods. The dose of ionizing radiation depends on the food and the organism being targeted. The doses are expressed in units of Grays (Gy). The energy added to food irradiated at 1 kGy is equal to the energy given off in 1 s by a 100 W light bulb. This energy raises the temperature of the food less than 1°C. The lowest doses (about 0.15 kGy) are used to prevent white potatoes from sprouting, while the highest doses (30 kGy) are used to sterilize dry spices and seasonings. The dose used to kill bacteria in meat is 4.50 kGy. Tests have shown that many foods can be irradiated without changing their properties. But some foods undergo significant changes. Irradiated alfalfa seeds do not sprout as well as untreated seeds, and meats with a high fat content develop bad odors. Because of these effects and the possibility of changes to the nutritional and chemical makeup of the foods, some experts have recommended that individual foods be extensively tested before they are approved for irradiation.

Science in Action

Science, Technology, and Society

Irradiated Food

One way to help keep food fresh for longer periods of time is to irradiate it. Exposing food to radiation can kill organisms such as mold or bacteria that cause food to spoil. In addition, irradiated potatoes and onions can be stored for a longer time without sprouting. Radiation can even be used to control pests such as beetles that could cause a lot of damage to stored grains.

Social Studies ACTIVITY

WRITING SKILL Food preservation is an important development of history. Write a one-page report that compares methods that you use to keep food from spoiling with methods used in the late 1800s.

Weird Science

Nuclear-Powered Bacteria

Deep under Earth's surface, there is no light. Temperatures are high, water is scarce, and oxygen is difficult to find. For many years, scientists thought that nothing could live under these extreme conditions. But in 1989, a team of scientists found bacteria living in rocks that are 500 m below Earth's surface. Since then, bacteria have been found living in rocks that are as deep as 3.5 km below Earth's surface! Scientists wondered what these bacteria use for food. These bacteria seem to get their food from an unusual source—the radioactive decay of uranium. The idea that radioactive decay can be a food source is new to science and is changing the way that scientists think about life.

Math ACTIVITY

How deep is 3.5 km? To help you imagine this depth, calculate how many Statues of Liberty could be stacked in a hole that is 3.5 km deep. The Statue of Liberty in New York is about 46 m tall.

Answer to Social Studies Activity
Modern preservation techniques include irradiation, refrigeration, freezing, and canning. Preservation methods used in the late 1800s include canning, salting, and drying.

Answer to Math Activity
3.5 km = 3,500 m
3,500 m ÷ 46 m = 76 Statues of Liberty

Marie and Pierre Curie

A Great Team You may have heard the saying "Two heads are better than one." For scientific discoveries, this saying is quite true. The husband and wife team Pierre and Marie Curie put their heads together and discovered the elements radium and polonium. Their work also helped them describe radioactivity.

Working side by side for long hours under poor conditions, Marie and Pierre Curie studied the mysterious rays given off by the element uranium. They processed huge amounts of an ore called *pitchblende* to collect the uranium from it. Strangely, the left-over material was more active than uranium. They spent several more months working with the material and discovered an element that was 300 times more active than uranium. Marie called it *polonium* in honor of Poland, which was the country in which she was born. For their research on radiation, the Curies were awarded the Nobel Prize in physics in 1903.

Language Arts ACTIVITY

WRITING SKILL Think of a time that you and a friend solved a problem together that neither of you could solve alone. Write a one-page story about how you each helped solve the problem.

go.hrw.com
To learn more about these Science in Action topics, visit go.hrw.com and type in the keyword **HP5RADF.**

Current Science
Check out Current Science® articles related to this chapter by visiting go.hrw.com. Just type in the keyword **HP5CS16.**

Answer to Language Arts Activity
Accept all reasonable responses.

Contents

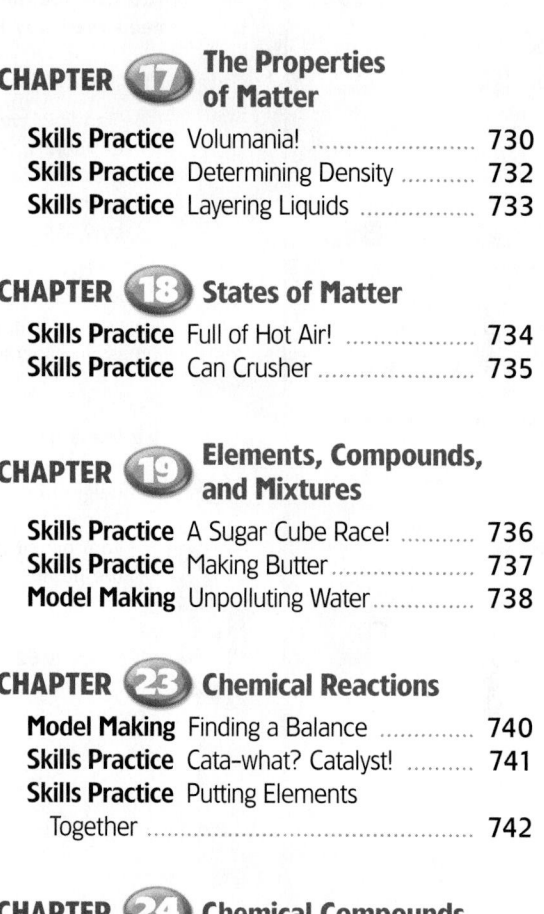

Skills Practice Lab

Stayin' Alive!

Teacher's Notes

Time Required

One 45-minute class period

Lab Ratings

EASY ———————→ HARD

Teacher Prep 🔬
Student Set-Up 🔬
Concept Level 🔬
Clean Up 🔬

MATERIALS

The materials listed on the student page are enough for each group of 5–6 students. You may wish to have your students use a calculator to complete this activity.

Skills Practice Lab

Stayin' Alive!

Every second of your life, your body's trillions of cells take in, use, and store energy. They repair themselves, reproduce, and get rid of waste. Together, these processes are called *metabolism*. Your cells use the food that you eat to provide the energy you need to stay alive.

Your Basal Metabolic Rate (BMR) is a measurement of the energy that your body needs to carry out all the basic life processes while you are at rest. These processes include breathing, keeping your heart beating, and keeping your body's temperature stable. Your BMR is influenced by your gender, your age, and many other things. Your BMR may be different from everyone else's, but it is normal for you. In this activity, you will find the amount of energy, measured in Calories, you need every day in order to stay alive.

MATERIALS

- bathroom scale
- tape measure

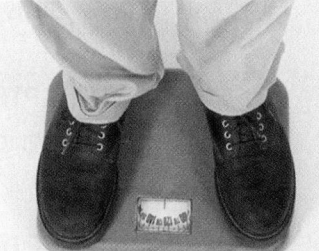

Procedure

1. Find your weight on a bathroom scale. If the scale measures in pounds, you must convert your weight in pounds to your mass in kilograms. To convert your weight in pounds (lb) to mass in kilograms (kg), multiply the number of pounds by 0.454.

   Example: If Carlos weighs 125 lb, his mass in kilograms is:

   $$125 \text{ lb} \times 0.454 = 56.75 \text{ kg}$$

2. Use a tape measure to find your height. If the tape measures in inches, convert your height in inches to height in centimeters. To convert your height in inches (in.) to your height in centimeters (cm), multiply the number of inches by 2.54.

   If Carlos is 62 in. tall, his height in centimeters is:

   $$62 \text{ in.} \times 2.54 = 157.48 \text{ cm}$$

Preparation Notes

Some students may consider their height and weight to be personal and won't want to weigh and measure themselves with the others in the class. Give these students the option of using the data of a fictional person, such as one of the following:

Jenny	80 lb	4 ft	age 11
Ben	65 lb	3 ft	age 12
Carlos	110 lb	5 ft 2 in.	age 11
Alexa	120 lb	4 ft 6 in.	age 12
Tasheika	90 lb	4 ft 6 in.	age 13

CHAPTER RESOURCES

Chapter Resource File

- Datasheet for LabBook
- Lab Notes and Answers

Kathy LaRoe
East Valley Middle School
East Helena, Montana

3 Now that you know your height and mass, use the appropriate formula below to get a close estimate of your BMR. Your answer will give you an estimate of the number of Calories your body needs each day just to stay alive.

Calculating Your BMR	
Females	**Males**
65 + (10 × your mass in kilograms)	66 + (13.5 × your mass in kilograms)
+ (1.8 × your height in centimeters)	+ (5 × your height in centimeters)
− (4.7 × your age in years)	− (6.8 × your age in years)

4 Your metabolism is also influenced by how active you are. Talking, walking, and playing games all take more energy than being at rest. To get an idea of how many Calories your body needs each day to stay healthy, select the lifestyle that best describes yours from the table at right. Then multiply your BMR by the activity factor.

Activity Factors	
Activity lifestyle	**Activity factor**
Moderately inactive (normal, everyday activities)	1.3
Moderately active (exercise 3 to 4 times a week)	1.4
Very active (exercise 4 to 6 times a week)	1.6
Extremely active (exercise 6 to 7 times a week)	1.8

Analyze the Results

1 In what way could you compare your whole body to a single cell? Explain.

2 Does an increase in activity increase your BMR? Does an increase in activity increase your need for Calories? Explain your answers.

Draw Conclusions

3 If you are moderately inactive, how many more Calories would you need if you began to exercise every day?

Applying Your Data

The best energy sources are those that supply the correct amount of Calories for your lifestyle and also provide the nutrients you need. Research in the library or on the Internet to find out which kinds of foods are the best energy sources for you. How does your list of best energy sources compare with your diet?

List everything you eat and drink in 1 day. Find out how many Calories are in each item, and find the total number of Calories you have consumed. How does this number of Calories compare with the number of Calories you need each day for all your activities?

Weepy Weeds

Teacher's Notes

Time Required

One or two 45-minute class periods

Lab Ratings

EASY ——————→ HARD

Teacher Prep 🧪🧪
Student Set-Up 🧪🧪
Concept Level 🧪🧪
Clean Up 🧪🧪

MATERIALS

The materials listed on the student page are enough for 1 student. The plant used in this lab can be any leafy plant, such as a bean plant or a coleus. The plant shown is a coleus with all but the top four leaves trimmed away.

Safety Caution

Remind students to review all safety cautions and icons before beginning this lab activity.

Lab Notes

If your lab period is short, you may want to eliminate the measurement of the height of water in the test tube at 40 min.

Although it is not essential to the activity, you may want to begin with an exact amount of water in each test tube. Students would then know that the difference can be due only to evaporation and transpiration.

Skills Practice Lab

Weepy Weeds

You are trying to find a way to drain an area that is flooded with water polluted with fertilizer. You know that a plant releases water through the stomata in its leaves. As water evaporates from the leaves, more water is pulled up from the roots through the stem and into the leaves. By this process, called *transpiration,* water and nutrients are pulled into the plant from the soil. About 90% of the water a plant takes up through its roots is released into the atmosphere as water vapor through transpiration. Your idea is to add plants to the flooded area that will transpire the water and take up the fertilizer in their roots.

How much water can a plant take up and release in a certain period of time? In this activity, you will observe transpiration and determine one stem's rate of transpiration.

MATERIALS

- clock
- coleus or other plant stem cutting
- glass-marking pen
- metric ruler
- paper, graph
- test tube (2)
- test-tube rack
- water

SAFETY

Procedure

1 Make a data table similar to the one below for recording your measurements.

	Height of Water in Test Tubes	
Time	Test tube with plant	Test tube without plant
Initial		
After 10 min		
After 20 min	*DO NOT WRITE IN BOOK*	
After 30 min		
After 40 min		
Overnight		

2 Fill each test tube approximately three-fourths full of water. Place both test tubes in a test-tube rack.

3 Place the plant stem so that it stands upright in one of the test tubes. Your test tubes should look like the ones in the photograph at right.

4 Use the glass-marking pen to mark the water level in each of the test tubes. Be sure you have the plant stem in place in its test tube before you mark the water level. Why is this necessary?

Holt Lab Generator CD-ROM

Search for any lab by topic, standard, difficulty level, or time. Edit any lab to fit your needs, or create your own labs. Use the Lab Materials QuickList software to customize your lab materials list.

CHAPTER RESOURCES

Chapter Resource File

- **Datasheet for LabBook**
- **Lab Notes and Answers**

David Sparks
Redwater Junior High School
Redwater, Texas

5 Measure the height of the water in each test tube. Be sure to hold the test tube level, and measure from the waterline to the bottom of the curve at the bottom of the test tube. Record these measurements on the row labeled "Initial."

6 Wait 10 min, and measure the height of the water in each test tube again. Record these measurements in your data table.

7 Repeat step 6 three more times. Record your measurements each time.

8 Wait 24 hours, and measure the height of the water in each test tube. Record these measurements in your data table.

9 Construct a graph similar to the one below. Plot the data from your data table. Draw a line for each test tube. Use a different color for each line, and make a key below your graph.

10 Calculate the rate of transpiration for your plant by using the following operations:

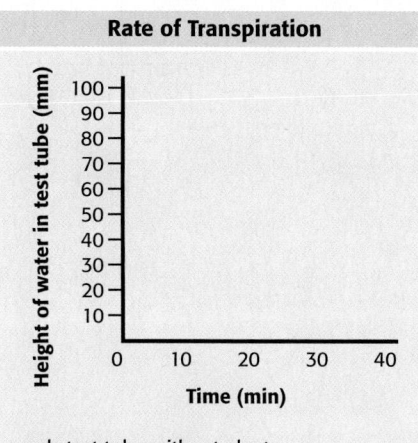

Rate of Transpiration

red—test tube without plant
blue—test tube with plant

Test tube with plant:
   Initial height
− Overnight height
   Difference in height of water **(A)**

Test tube without plant:
   Initial height
− Overnight height
   Difference in height of water **(B)**

Water height difference due to transpiration:
   Difference **A**
− Difference **B**
Water lost due to transpiration (in millimeters) in 24 hours

Analyze the Results

1 What was the purpose of the test tube that held only water?

2 What caused the water to go down in the test tube containing the plant stem? Did the same thing happen in the test tube with water only? Explain your answer.

3 What was the calculated rate of transpiration per day?

4 Using your graph, compare the rate of transpiration with the rate of evaporation alone.

5 Prepare a presentation of your experiment for your class. Use your data tables, graphs, and calculations as visual aids.

Applying Your Data

How many leaves did your plant sprigs have? Use this number to estimate what the rate of transpiration might be for a plant with 200 leaves. When you have your answer in millimeters of height in a test tube, pour this amount into a graduated cylinder to measure it in milliliters.

Procedure

4. Sample answer: It is necessary to mark the water level after the stem is placed in the test tube in order to account for the water that is displaced by the stem.

Analyze the Results

1. Sample answer: The test tube that held only water was a control; it would lose water only by evaporation.

2. Sample answer: Water in the test tube containing the plant stem was lost through evaporation and transpiration. Evaporation is the only means of water loss in the test tube without the plant stem.

3. Answers may vary according to several variables in the classroom, such as the amount of light and the temperature.

4. Answers may vary. Have students compare and contrast the lines on the graph and explain how the graph is easier to interpret than numbers in a data list.

Applying Your Data

Answers may vary.

Tracing Traits

Teacher's Notes

Time Required

Two 45-minute class periods, separated by several days so students have time to complete their surveys

Lab Ratings

EASY ————————→ HARD

Teacher Prep 🧪
Student Set-Up 🧪
Concept Level 🧪🧪
Clean Up 🧪

Lab Notes

Family histories will vary. Encourage students to include at least three generations in their histories.

Survey results will vary. Make sure that students actually surveyed each family member who was available. Responses will vary. You may check family members with shaded symbols against the survey results for accuracy.

Percentages will vary. A family member may receive a recessive allele from the father and a recessive allele from the mother. In such a case, this family member will exhibit the recessive form of the trait rather than the dominant form.

Because so many children are adopted or live in foster homes or group homes, please emphasize to your students that they may choose any family to study.

Inquiry Lab

Tracing Traits

Have you ever wondered about the traits you inherited from your parents? Do you have a trait that neither of your parents has? In this project, you will develop a family tree, or pedigree, similar to the one shown in the diagram below. You will trace an inherited trait through a family to determine how it has passed from generation to generation.

Procedure

1 The diagram at right shows a family history. On a separate piece of paper, draw a similar diagram of the family you have chosen. Include as many family members as possible, such as grandparents, parents, children, and grandchildren. Use circles to represent females and squares to represent males. You may include other information, such as the family member's name, birth date, or picture.

2 Draw a table similar to the one on the next page. Survey each of the family members shown in your family tree. Ask them if they have hair on the middle segment of their fingers. Write each person's name in the appropriate square. Explain to each person that it is normal to have either trait. The presence of hair on the middle segment is the dominant form of this trait.

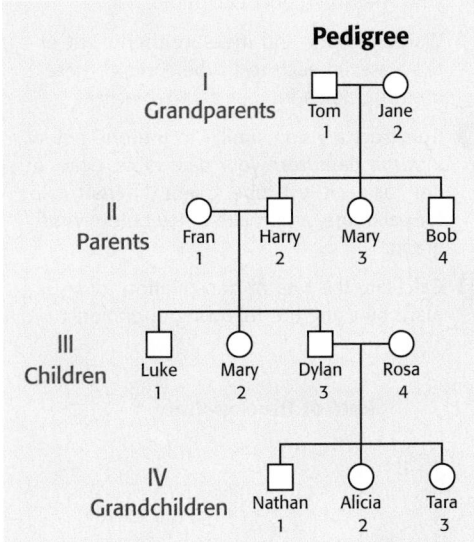

Pedigree

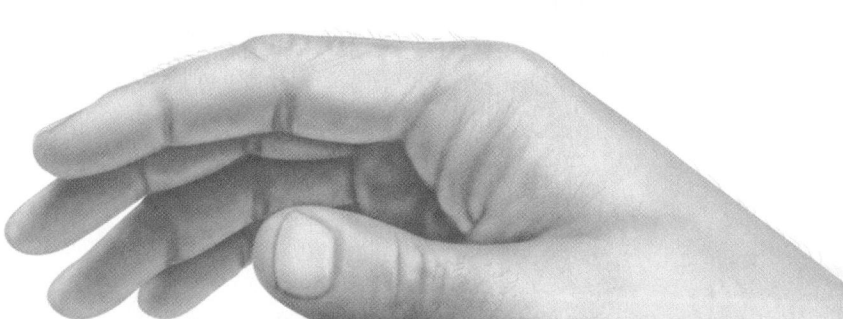

💿 Holt Lab Generator CD-ROM

Search for any lab by topic, standard, difficulty level, or time. Edit any lab to fit your needs, or create your own labs. Use the Lab Materials QuickList software to customize your lab materials list.

Kerry Johnson
Isbell Middle School
Santa Paula, California

CHAPTER RESOURCES

Chapter Resource File

📁 • Datasheet for LabBook
• Lab Notes and Answers

Dominant trait	Recessive trait	Family members with the dominant trait	Family members with the recessive trait
Hair present on the middle segment of fingers (*H*)	Hair absent on the middle segment of fingers (*h*)	DO NOT WRITE IN BOOK	

3 Trace this trait throughout the family tree you diagrammed in step 1. Shade or color the symbols of the family members who demonstrate the dominant form of this trait.

Analyze the Results

1 What percentage of the family members demonstrate the dominant form of the trait? Calculate this by counting the number of people who have the dominant trait and dividing this number by the total number of people you surveyed. Multiply your answer by 100. An example has been done at right.

Example: Calculating percentage

$$\frac{10 \text{ people with trait}}{20 \text{ people surveyed}} = \frac{1}{2}$$

$$\frac{1}{2} = 0.50 \times 100 = 50\%$$

2 What percentage of the family members demonstrate the recessive form of the trait? Why doesn't every family member have the dominant form of the trait?

3 Choose one of the family members who demonstrates the recessive form of the chosen trait. What is this person's genotype? What are the possible genotypes for the parents of this individual? Does this person have any brothers or sisters? Do they show the dominant or recessive trait?

Draw Conclusions

4 Draw a Punnett square like the one at right. Use this to determine the genotypes of the parents of the person you chose in step 3. Write this person's genotype in the bottom right-hand corner of your Punnett square. **Hint:** There may be more than one possible genotype for the parents. Don't forget to consider the genotypes of the person's brothers and sisters.

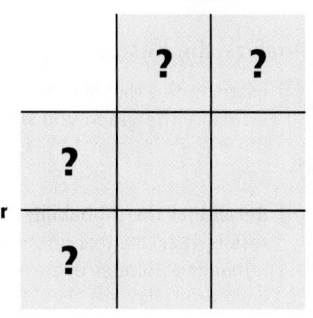

Father

Mother

Analyze the Results

1. Answers may vary.

2. Answers may vary.

3. The genotype of the recessive form of the characteristic must be *hh* (homozygous recessive). Each allele came from one of the individual's parents; Possible genotypes for the parents of the individual expressing the recessive form are *Hh* and *hh*; Does the student know whether either of the parents expresses the recessive form of the trait? Does the student know if the individual chosen has brothers or sisters? Are their genotypes known? If so, have the student decide if each of them has a dominant or recessive genotype. If a dominant genotype is found among the siblings and one of the parents is known to have the recessive form, ask the student what the genotype of the other parent must be (*Hh*).

Draw Conclusions

4. The Punnett square should show *hh* in the bottom right-hand corner. One of the parents must have the genotype *hh*. The other parent must have either *hh* or *Hh*. If any sibling has the dominant trait, the genotype of the other parent must be *Hh*.

Skills Practice Lab

The Half-life of Pennies

Teacher's Notes

Time Required

One 45-minute class period

Lab Rating

EASY → HARD

Teacher Prep 🜂
Student Set-Up 🜂
Concept Level 🜂🜂
Clean Up 🜂

Lab Notes

It is useful to use coin tosses to explain half-life because approximately half the coins will land heads and half will land tails. Therefore, about half the entire quantity of coins tossed will be eliminated with each successive toss.

Analyze the Results

1. The graphs should be very similar in shape. With each half-life and each shake, the number remaining will be reduced by half.

2. The remaining number of pennies is reduced by about half each time the pennies are shaken and tossed because there are only two faces on each coin. The rules of probability suggest that half will land heads and half will land tails, and therefore the amount will be reduced by about half with each shake.

Skills Practice Lab

The Half-life of Pennies

Carbon-14 is a special unstable element used in the absolute dating of material that was once alive, such as fossil bones. Every 5,730 years, half of the carbon-14 in a fossil specimen decays or breaks down into a more stable element. In the following experiment you will see how pennies can show the same kind of "decay."

MATERIALS

- container with a cover, large
- pennies (100)

Procedure

❶ Place 100 pennies in a large, covered container. Shake the container several times, and remove the cover. Carefully empty the container on a flat surface making sure the pennies don't roll away.

❷ Remove all the coins that have the "head" side of the coin turned upward. Record the number of pennies removed and the number of pennies remaining in a data table similar to the one at right.

❸ Repeat the process until no pennies are left in the container. Remember to remove only the coins showing "heads."

❹ Draw a graph similar to the one at right. Label the x-axis "Number of shakes," and label the y-axis "Pennies remaining." Using data from your data table, plot the number of coins remaining at each shake on your graph.

Analyze the Results

❶ Examine the Half-life of Carbon-14 graph at right. Compare the graph you have made for pennies with the one for carbon-14. Explain any similarities that you see.

❷ Recall that the probability of landing "heads" in a coin toss is 1/2. Use this information to explain why the remaining number of pennies is reduced by about half each time they are shaken and tossed.

Shake number	Number of coins remaining	Number of coins removed
1		
2	DO NOT WRITE IN BOOK	
3		

Half-life of Pennies

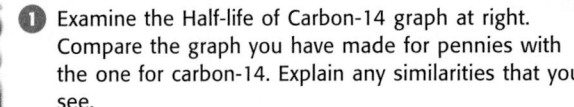

Half-life of Carbon-14

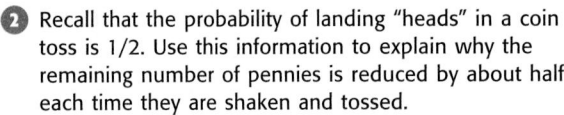

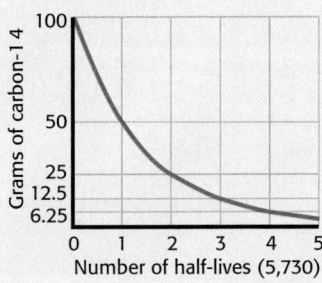

💿 **Holt Lab Generator CD-ROM**

Search for any lab by topic, standard, difficulty level, or time. Edit any lab to fit your needs, or create your own labs. Use the Lab Materials QuickList software to customize your lab materials list.

CHAPTER RESOURCES

Chapter Resource File

📁 • Datasheet for LabBook
• Lab Notes and Answers

CLASSROOM TESTED & APPROVED

Karma Houston-Hughes
Kyrene Middle School
Tempe, Arizona

Inquiry Lab

Orient Yourself!

You have been invited to attend an orienteering event with your neighbors. In orienteering events, participants use maps and compasses to find their way along a course. There are several control points that each participant must reach. The object is to reach each control point and then the finish line. Orienteering events are often timed competitions. In order to find the fastest route through the course, the participants must read the map and use their compass correctly. Being the fastest runner does not necessarily guarantee finishing first. You also must choose the most direct route to follow.

Your neighbors participate in several orienteering events each year. They always come home raving about how much fun they had. You would like to join them, but you will need to learn how to use your compass first.

MATERIALS

- compass, magnetic
- course map
- pencils (or markers), colored (2)
- ruler

Procedure

1 Together as a class, go outside to the orienteering course your teacher has made.

2 Hold your compass flat in your hand. Turn the compass until the N is pointing straight in front of you. (The needle in your compass will always point north.) Turn your body until the needle lines up with the N on your compass. You are now facing north.

3 Regardless of which direction you want to face, you should always align the end of the needle with the N on your compass. If you are facing south, the needle will be pointing directly toward your body. When the N is aligned with the needle, the S will be directly in front of you, and you will be facing south.

4 Use your compass to face east. Align the needle with the N. Where is the E? Turn to face that direction. You are facing east when the needle and the N are aligned and the E is directly in front of you.

5 In an orienteering competition, you will need to know how to determine which direction you are traveling. Now, face any direction you choose.

Preparation Notes

Find a suitable outdoor location for a simple orienteering course, and choose five control points for students to map. For example, you may wish to use several pieces of equipment in the playground, the flagpole, a tree, and a small hill. Be sure to mark each control point with either a specific color or a code word that students can collect or note on their maps when they reach each point.

Next, draw a map that includes the control points and the cardinal directions. Label a sixth spot as the starting point. Each group of students will need a copy of this map. Before groups begin exploring the orienteering course, have students perform steps 2–6 individually. An entire class period may be required for students to feel confident using a compass.

Analyze the Results

1. Answers may vary. Students should realize that the path shown on the map did not instruct them to follow the most direct route. They should propose a more direct route to follow. Their proposal should include the direction from one control point to the next.

Draw Conclusions

2. This route should be faster. Students should realize that in an orienteering event, participants generally need to determine the quickest route. Some students may also realize that the quickest route is not necessarily the most direct. For example, there may be obstacles in the way (such as hills or lakes) that could slow participants down. Orienteering maps include these landmarks.

6 Do not move, but rotate the compass to align the needle on your compass with the N. What direction are you facing? You are probably not facing directly north, south, east, or west. If you are facing between north and west, you are facing northwest. If you are facing between north and east, you are facing northeast.

7 Find a partner or partners to follow the course your teacher has made. Get a copy of the course map from your teacher. It will show several control points. You must stop at each one. You will need to follow this map to find your way through the course. Find and stand at the starting point.

8 Face the next control point on your map. Rotate your compass to align the needle on your compass with the N. What direction are you facing?

9 Use the ruler to draw a line on your map between the two control points. On your map, write the direction between the starting point and the next control point.

10 Walk toward the control point. Keep your eyes on the horizon, not on your compass. You might need to go around an obstacle, such as a fence or a building. Use the map to find the easiest way around.

11 Next to the control point symbol on your map, record the color or code word you find at the control point.

12 Repeat steps 8–11 for each control point. Follow the points in order as they are labeled. For example, determine the direction from control point 1 to control point 2. Be sure to include the direction between the final control point and the starting point.

Analyze the Results

1 The object of an orienteering competition is to arrive at the finish line first. The maps provided at these events do not instruct the participants to follow a specific path. In one form of orienteering, called *score orienteering,* competitors may find the control points in any order. Look at your map. If this course were used for a score-orienteering competition, would you change your route? Explain.

Draw Conclusions

2 If there is time, follow the map again. This time, use your own path to find the control points. Draw this path and the directions on your map in a different color. Do you believe this route was faster? Why?

Applying Your Data

Do some research to find out about orienteering events in your area. The Internet and local newspapers may be good sources for the information. Are there any events that you would like to attend?

CHAPTER RESOURCES

Chapter Resource File

- Datasheet for LabBook
- Lab Notes and Answers

David Jones
Andrew Jackson
Middle School
Cross Lanes, West Virginia

Topographic Tuber

Imagine that you live on top of a tall mountain and often look down on the lake below. Every summer, an island appears. You call it Sometimes Island because it goes away again during heavy fall rains. This summer, you begin to wonder if you could make a topographic map of Sometimes Island. You don't have fancy equipment to make the map, but you have an idea. What if you place a meterstick with the 0 m mark at the water level in the summer? Then, as the expected fall rains come, you could draw the island from above as the water rises. Would this idea really work?

Ask a Question

1 How do I make a topographic map?

Form a Hypothesis

2 Write a hypothesis that is a possible answer to the question above. Describe the method you would use.

Test the Hypothesis

3 Place a mark at the storage container's base. Label this mark "0 cm" with a transparency marker.

4 Measure and mark 1 cm increments up the side of the container until you reach the top of the container. Label these marks "1 cm," "2 cm," "3 cm," and so on.

5 The scale for your map will be 1 cm = 10 m. Draw a line 2 cm long in the bottom right-hand corner of the lid. Place hash marks at 0 cm, 1 cm, and 2 cm. Label these marks "0 m," "10 m," and "20 m."

6 Place the potato, flat side down, in the center of the container.

7 Place the lid on the container, and seal it.

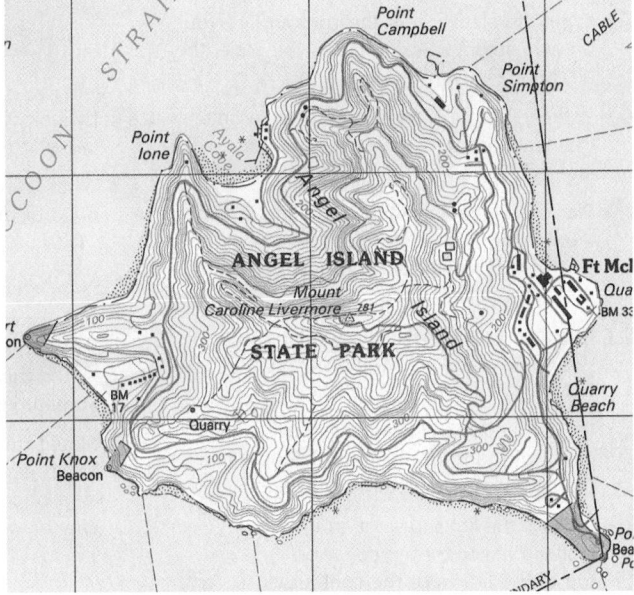

Lab Notes

Only islands that are at sea level begin at an elevation of 0 m. In order to calculate the elevation of an island that forms in a lake, you must also consider the elevation of the lake.

Topographic Tuber

Teacher's Notes

Time Required

One 45-minute class period

Lab Ratings

EASY ——————————————→ HARD

Teacher Prep 🧪🧪
Student Set-Up 🧪
Concept Level 🧪🧪🧪
Clean Up 🧪🧪

Preparation Notes

It may be easier for students to see the waterline if you add a few drops of food coloring to the water before they add it to the container. Before the activity, select several oddly shaped root vegetables from your local grocery store. Choose vegetables that have varied contour and shape. Sweet potatoes, for example, are available year-round and have many irregular shapes. If you cannot find naturally occurring root vegetables that have odd shapes, shape potatoes with a knife and peeler. You will then need to cut the potatoes in half lengthwise.

Analyze the Results

1. The contour interval of the topographic map is 10 m.
2. Steeper parts of the potato will have contour lines that are closer together.
3. Answers may vary. Elevation is indicated by numbers on the contour lines.

Draw Conclusions

4. Sample answer: no; Topographic maps do not necessarily start with a 0 m elevation contour line. It is possible to make a topographic map of Sometimes Island showing its contours, but it is impossible to know the island's elevation above sea level.
5. Sample answer: no; Flooding an island is not an effective way of mapping it.

8 Viewing the potato from above, use the transparency marker to trace the outline of the potato where it rests on the bottom of the container. The floor of the container corresponds to the summer water level in the lake.

9 Label this contour "0 m." (For this activity, assume that the water level in the lake during the summer is the same as sea level.)

10 Pour water into the container until it reaches the line labeled "1 cm."

11 Again, place the lid on the container, and seal it. Part of the potato will be sticking out above the water. Viewing the potato from above, trace the part of the potato that touches the top of the water.

12 Label the elevation of the contour line you drew in step 11. According to the scale, the elevation is 10 m.

13 Remove the lid. Carefully pour water into the container until it reaches the line labeled "2 cm."

14 Place the lid on the container, and seal it. Viewing the potato from above, trace the part of the potato that touches the top of the water at this level.

15 Use the scale to calculate the elevation of this line. Label the elevation on your drawing.

16 Repeat steps 13–15, adding 1 cm to the depth of the water each time. Stop when the potato is completely covered.

17 Remove the lid, and set it on a tabletop. Place tracing paper on top of the lid. Trace the contours from the lid onto the paper. Label the elevation of each contour line. Congratulations! You have just made a topographic map!

Analyze the Results

1 What is the contour interval of this topographic map?

2 By looking at the contour lines, how can you tell which parts of the potato are steeper?

3 What is the elevation of the highest point on your map?

Draw Conclusions

4 Do all topographic maps have a 0 m elevation contour line as a starting point? How would this affect a topographic map of Sometimes Island? Explain your answer.

5 Would this method of measuring elevation be an effective way to make a topographic map of an actual area on Earth's surface? Why or why not?

Applying Your Data

Place all of the potatoes on a table or desk at the front of the room. Your teacher will mix up the potatoes as you trade topographic maps with another group. By reading the topographic map you just received, can you pick out the matching potato?

Holt Lab Generator CD-ROM

Search for any lab by topic, standard, difficulty level, or time. Edit any lab to fit your needs, or create your own labs. Use the Lab Materials QuickList software to customize your lab materials list.

CHAPTER RESOURCES

Chapter Resource File

- Datasheet for LabBook
- Lab Notes and Answers

Michael E. Kral
West Hardin Middle School
Cecilia, Kentucky

Skills Practice Lab

Mysterious Minerals

Imagine sitting on a rocky hilltop, gazing at the ground below you. You can see dozens of different types of rocks. How can scientists possibly identify the countless variations? It's a mystery!

In this activity, you'll use your powers of observation and a few simple tests to determine the identities of rocks and minerals. Take a look at the Mineral Identification Key on the next page. That key will help you use clues to discover the identity of several minerals.

MATERIALS
- gloves, protective
- iron filings
- minerals, samples
- slides, microscope, glass
- streak plate

SAFETY

Procedure

1. On a separate sheet of paper, create a data chart like the one below.

2. Choose one mineral sample, and locate its column in your data chart.

3. Follow the Mineral Identification Key to find the identity of your sample. When you are finished, record the mineral's name and primary characteristics in the appropriate column in your data chart. **Caution:** Put on your safety goggles and gloves when scratching the glass slide.

4. Select another mineral sample, and repeat steps 2 and 3 until your data table is complete.

Analyze the Results

1. Were some minerals easier to identify than others? Explain.

2. A streak test is a better indicator of a mineral's true color than visual observation is. Why isn't a streak test used to help identify every mineral?

3. On a separate sheet of paper, summarize what you learned about the various characteristics of each mineral sample you identified.

Mineral Summary Chart						
Characteristics	1	2	3	4	5	6
Mineral name						
Luster						
Color						
Streak						
Hardness						
Cleavage						
Special properties						

DO NOT WRITE IN BOOK

Mysterious Minerals

Teacher's Notes

Time Required
One 45-minute class period

Lab Ratings

EASY ——————→ HARD

Teacher Prep
Student Set-Up
Concept Level
Clean Up

MATERIALS
The materials listed on the student page are sufficient for each student. Students may also work in groups of 3 to 4. You will need one streak plate per student or group. A class should be able to share 3 to 5 streak plates.

Safety Caution
Remind students to review all safety cautions and icons before beginning this lab activity. Students need to be careful with glass microscope slides. Broken slides are likely to have sharp edges. Caution students not to taste the mineral samples.

Preparation Notes

Explain to students that they are not determining the absolute hardness of the mineral samples. Instead, they are comparing the hardness of the samples with that of glass.

Your sample minerals should include pyrite, galena, hematite, magnetite, orthoclase (feldspar), quartz, muscovite, gypsum, hornblende (amphibole), garnet, biotite, and graphite.

Lab Notes

Each test in this lab tells the student more about the sample and narrows the possibilities. For example, the fact that a particular mineral sample does not have a streak eliminates hematite as a possibility but indicates that quartz is a possibility.

- It is possible for minerals that are softer than glass to leave a mark on glass. If the glass wipes clean and no scratch remains, then students will know that the mineral is softer than glass.

- Garnet is typically red, but it can also be pale green.

1. Students will find that some minerals required fewer steps to identify than others. For example, pyrite and galena are identified in two steps. Students may also find that they recognize some of the minerals and that the identification key is there merely to verify the identity.

2. For a mineral to leave a streak on the streak plate, the plate must be harder than the mineral. Therefore, extremely hard minerals do not leave a streak. Also, some minerals that are softer than a streak plate leave behind a colorless streak.

3. Answers will vary.

Applying Your Data

Scientists test minerals for their density, crystal form, reaction to acids, optical properties, fluorescence, and radioactivity. Students should create an identification key that is very similar to the one provided in the lab, but their key should include different characteristics.

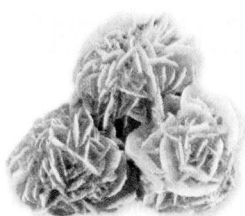

Mineral Identification Key

1. **a.** If your mineral has a metallic luster, **GO TO STEP 2.**
   b. If your mineral has a nonmetallic luster, **GO TO STEP 3.**

2. **a.** If your mineral is black, **GO TO STEP 4.**
   b. If your mineral is yellow, it is **PYRITE.**
   c. If your mineral is silver, it is **GALENA.**

3. **a.** If your mineral is light in color, **GO TO STEP 5.**
   b. If your mineral is dark in color, **GO TO STEP 6.**

4. **a.** If your mineral leaves a red-brown line on the streak plate, it is **HEMATITE.**
   b. If your mineral leaves a black line on the streak plate, it is **MAGNETITE.** Test your sample for its magnetic properties by holding it near some iron filings.

5. **a.** If your mineral scratches the glass microscope slide, **GO TO STEP 7.**
   b. If your mineral does not scratch the glass microscope slide, **GO TO STEP 8.**

6. **a.** If your mineral scratches the glass slide, **GO TO STEP 9.**
   b. If your mineral does not scratch the glass slide, **GO TO STEP 10.**

7. **a.** If your mineral shows signs of cleavage, it is **ORTHOCLASE FELDSPAR.**
   b. If your mineral does not show signs of cleavage, it is **QUARTZ.**

8. **a.** If your mineral shows signs of cleavage, it is **MUSCOVITE.** Examine this sample for twin sheets.
   b. If your mineral does not show signs of cleavage, it is **GYPSUM.**

9. **a.** If your mineral shows signs of cleavage, it is **HORNBLENDE.**
   b. If your mineral does not show signs of cleavage, it is **GARNET.**

10. **a.** If your mineral shows signs of cleavage, it is **BIOTITE.** Examine your sample for twin sheets.
    b. If your mineral does not show signs of cleavage, it is **GRAPHITE.**

Applying Your Data

Using your textbook and other reference books, research other methods of identifying different types of minerals. Based on your findings, create a new identification key. Give the key and a few sample minerals to a friend, and see if your friend can unravel the mystery!

Holt Lab Generator CD-ROM

Search for any lab by topic, standard, difficulty level, or time. Edit any lab to fit your needs, or create your own labs. Use the Lab Materials QuickList software to customize your lab materials list.

CHAPTER RESOURCES

Chapter Resource File

- **Datasheet for LabBook**
- **Lab Notes and Answers**

CLASSROOM TESTED & APPROVED

David Jones
Andrew Jackson
Middle School
Cross Lanes, West Virginia

Skills Practice Lab

Crystal Growth

Magma forms deep below the Earth's surface at depths of 25 km to 160 km and at extremely high temperatures. Some magma reaches the surface and cools quickly. Other magma gets trapped in cracks or magma chambers beneath the surface and cools very slowly. When magma cools slowly, large, well-developed crystals form. But when magma erupts onto the surface, it cools more quickly. There is not enough time for large crystals to grow. The size of the crystals found in igneous rocks gives geologists clues about where and how the rocks formed.

In this experiment, you will demonstrate how the rate of cooling affects the size of crystals in igneous rocks by cooling crystals of magnesium sulfate at two different rates.

Ask a Question

1 How does temperature affect the formation of crystals?

Form a Hypothesis

2 Suppose you have two solutions that are identical in every way except for temperature. How will the temperature of a solution affect the size of the crystals and the rate at which they form?

Test the Hypothesis

3 Put on your gloves, apron, and goggles.

4 Fill the beaker halfway with tap water. Place the beaker on the hot plate, and let it begin to warm. The temperature of the water should be between 40°C and 50°C. **Caution:** Make sure the hot plate is away from the edge of the lab table.

5 Examine two or three crystals of the magnesium sulfate with your magnifying lens. On a separate sheet of paper, describe the color, shape, luster, and other interesting features of the crystals.

6 On a separate sheet of paper, draw a sketch of the magnesium sulfate crystals.

MATERIALS

- aluminum foil
- basalt
- beaker, 400 mL
- gloves, heat-resistant
- granite
- hot plate
- laboratory scoop, pointed
- magnesium sulfate (MgSO₄) (Epsom salts)
- magnifying lens
- marker, dark
- pumice
- tape, masking
- test tube, medium-sized
- thermometer, Celsius
- tongs, test-tube
- watch (or clock)
- water, distilled
- water, tap, 200 mL

SAFETY

Skills Practice Lab

Crystal Growth

Teacher's Notes

Time Required

Two 45-minute class periods

Lab Ratings

EASY —————————————→ HARD

Teacher Prep 🧪🧪
Student Set-Up 🧪🧪🧪
Concept Level 🧪🧪
Clean Up 🧪🧪

MATERIALS

The materials listed are enough for a group of 4 to 5 students working cooperatively. Using a higher proportion of magnesium sulfate crystals to water will take significantly longer.

Safety Caution

Remind students to review all safety cautions and icons before beginning this lab activity.

Preparation Notes

Samples of igneous rocks may be obtained locally or through various science supply catalogs.

Lab Notes

Some volcanic rocks contain both large and small crystals because the magma cooled for a period of time before erupting. This period of time was long enough for some minerals to crystallize but too short for other minerals to form.

7. Use the pointed laboratory scoop to fill the test tube about halfway with the magnesium sulfate. Add an equal amount of distilled water.

8. Hold the test tube in one hand, and use one finger from your other hand to tap the test tube gently. Observe the solution mixing as you continue to tap the test tube.

9. Place the test tube in the beaker of hot water, and heat it for approximately 3 min. **Caution:** Be sure to direct the opening of the test tube away from you and other students.

10. While the test tube is heating, shape your aluminum foil into two small boatlike containers by doubling the foil and turning up each edge.

11. If all the magnesium sulfate is not dissolved after 3 min, tap the test tube again, and heat it for 3 min longer. **Caution:** Use the test-tube tongs to handle the hot test tube.

12. With a marker and a piece of masking tape, label one of your aluminum boats "Sample 1," and place it on the hot plate. Turn the hot plate off.

13. Label the other aluminum boat "Sample 2," and place it on the lab table.

14. Using the test-tube tongs, remove the test tube from the beaker of water, and evenly distribute the contents to each of your foil boats. Carefully pour the hot water in the beaker down the drain. Do not move or disturb either of your foil boats.

15. Copy the table below onto a separate sheet of paper. Using the magnifying lens, carefully observe the foil boats. Record the time it takes for the first crystals to appear.

Crystal-Formation Table				
Crystal formation	Time	Size and appearance of crystals		Sketch of crystals
Sample 1				
Sample 2		*DO NOT WRITE IN BOOK*		

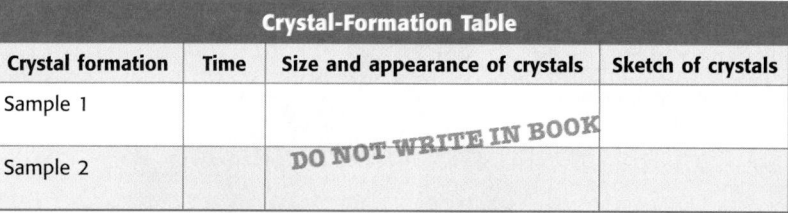

 Holt Lab Generator CD-ROM

Search for any lab by topic, standard, difficulty level, or time. Edit any lab to fit your needs, or create your own labs. Use the Lab Materials QuickList software to customize your lab materials list.

CHAPTER RESOURCES

Chapter Resource File

- Datasheet for LabBook
- Lab Notes and Answers

Gordon Zibelman
Drexel Hill Middle School
Drexel Hill, Pennsylvania

16 If crystals have not formed in the boats before class is over, carefully place the boats in a safe place. You may then record the time in days instead of in minutes.

17 When crystals have formed in both boats, use your magnifying lens to examine the crystals carefully.

Analyze the Results

1 Was your prediction correct? Explain.

2 Compare the size and shape of the crystals in Samples 1 and 2 with the size and shape of the crystals you examined in step 5. How long do you think the formation of the original crystals must have taken?

Draw Conclusions

3 Granite, basalt, and pumice are all igneous rocks. The most distinctive feature of each is the size of its crystals. Different igneous rocks form when magma cools at different rates. Examine a sample of each with your magnifying lens.

4 Copy the table below onto a separate sheet of paper, and sketch each rock sample.

5 Use what you have learned in this activity to explain how each rock sample formed and how long it took for the crystals to form. Record your answers in your table.

  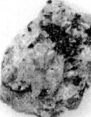

Igneous Rock Observations

	Granite	Basalt	Pumice
Sketch			
How did the rock sample form?	DO NOT WRITE IN BOOK		
Rate of cooling			

Communicating Your Data

Describe the size and shape of the crystals you would expect to find when a volcano erupts and sends material into the air and when magma oozes down the volcano's slope.

Analyze the Results

1. Answers may vary. A correct prediction would state that a cool solution will produce crystals more quickly than a warm solution. A correct prediction would also state that the crystals produced in a warm solution will be much larger than those produced in a cool solution.

2. Because the original crystals were small, students may conclude that they formed quickly.

Draw Conclusions

4. Accept all reasonable sketches.

5. See the chart at the bottom of this page.

Communicating Your Data

Volcanic rocks that form in the air as the result of a violent volcanic eruption would cool quickly and have small crystals. Volcanic rocks that form from lava oozing out of a volcano would cool more slowly and have larger crystals.

Igneous Rock Obsevations

	Granite	Basalt	Pumice
How did the rock sample form?	the slow cooling of magma beneath the Earth's surface	the quick cooling of lava on the Earth's surface	ejected magma from a volcano during a violent eruption
Rate of cooling	cools slowly; large crystals	cools quickly; small crystals	cools very quickly; very small or no crystals

Metamorphic Mash

Teacher's Notes

Time Required
One 45-minute class period

Lab Ratings

EASY ———————————————→ HARD

Teacher Prep 🧪
Student Set-Up 🧪🧪
Concept Level 🧪🧪
Clean Up 🧪🧪

MATERIALS
The materials listed on the student page are enough for 1 student.

Safety Caution
Remind students to review all safety cautions and icons before beginning this lab activity.

Procedure
3. The sequins should be lying in a random pattern. Any layering is the result of rolling the ball.
5. The sequins are all horizontal.

Analyze the Results
1. It represents the pressure that creates metamorphic rock.
2. Before the ball was flattened, the sequins were in a random pattern. Once the ball was flattened, they lined up perpendicular to the pressure.

Draw Conclusions
3. The sequins are aligned perpendicular to the force.
4. Because the grains line up at right angles to the pressure, they are perpendicular to the strongest stress.

Model-Making Lab

Metamorphic Mash

Metamorphism is a complex process that takes place deep within the Earth, where the temperature and pressure would turn a human into a crispy pancake. The effects of this extreme temperature and pressure are obvious in some metamorphic rocks. One of these effects is the reorganization of mineral grains within the rock. In this activity, you will investigate the process of metamorphism without being charred, flattened, or buried.

MATERIALS

- cardboard (or plywood), very stiff, small pieces
- clay, modeling
- knife, plastic
- sequins (or other small flat objects)

SAFETY

Procedure

1. Flatten the clay into a layer about 1 cm thick. Sprinkle the surface with sequins.

2. Roll the corners of the clay toward the middle to form a neat ball.

3. Carefully use the plastic knife to cut the ball in half. On a separate sheet of paper, describe the position and location of the sequins inside the ball.

4. Put the ball back together, and use the sheets of cardboard or plywood to flatten the ball until it is about 2 cm thick.

5. Using the plastic knife, slice open the slab of clay in several places. Describe the position and location of the sequins in the slab.

Analyze the Results

1. What physical process does flattening the ball represent?

2. Describe any changes in the position and location of the sequins that occurred as the clay ball was flattened into a slab.

Draw Conclusions

3. How are the sequins oriented in relation to the force you put on the ball to flatten it?

4. Do you think the orientation of the mineral grains in a foliated metamorphic rock tells you anything about the rock? Defend your answer.

Applying Your Data

Suppose you find a foliated metamorphic rock that has grains running in two distinct directions. Use what you have learned in this activity to offer a possible explanation for this observation.

Applying Your Data

Answers may vary. Sample answer: Two pressures acting on the rock at different times must have pushed on the rock in different directions.

CHAPTER RESOURCES

Chapter Resource File
- Datasheet for LabBook
- Lab Notes and Answers

💿 Holt Lab Generator CD-ROM

Search for any lab by topic, standard, difficulty level, or time. Edit any lab to fit your needs, or create your own labs. Use the Lab Materials QuickList software to customize your lab materials list.

CLASSROOM TESTED & APPROVED

Dwight Patton
Carrol T. Welch
Middle School
Horizon City, Texas

Inquiry Lab

Life in the Desert

Organisms that live in the desert have some unusual methods for conserving water. Conserving water is a special challenge for animals that live in the desert. In this activity you will invent a water-conserving "adaptation" for a desert animal, represented by a piece of sponge. You will protect your wet desert sponge so it will dry out as little as possible over a 24 h period.

MATERIALS

- balance
- sponge, dry, 8 cm × 8 cm × 2 cm (2 pieces)
- water
- other materials as needed

Ask a Question

1. How can an animal conserve water in the desert?

Form a Hypothesis

2. Plan a method for keeping your "desert animal" from drying out. Your "animal" must be in the open for at least 4 h during the 24 h period. Real desert animals expose themselves to the dry desert heat to search for food. Write your plan and predictions about the outcome of your experiment.

3. Design and draw data tables, if necessary. Have your teacher approve your plan before you begin.

Test the Hypothesis

4. Soak two pieces of sponge in water until they begin to drip. Place each piece on a balance, and record its mass.

5. Immediately protect one sponge according to your plan. Place both pieces in an area where they will not be disturbed. You should take your protected "animal" out for feeding for a total of at least 4 h.

6. At the end of 24 h, place each piece of sponge on the balance again, and record its mass.

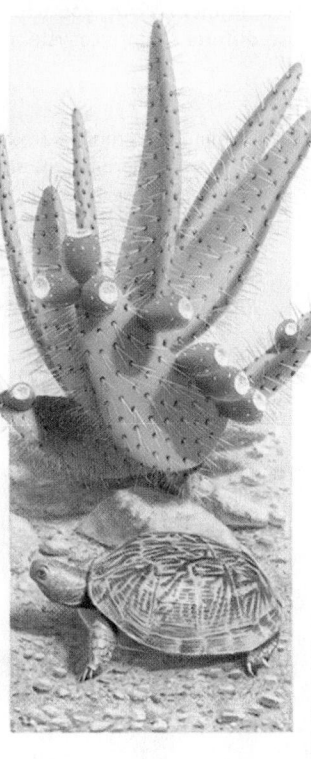

Analyze the Results

1. Describe the adaptation you used to help your "animal" survive. Was it effective? Explain.

2. What was the purpose of leaving one of the sponges unprotected? How did the water loss in each of your sponges compare?

Communicating Your Data

Conduct a class discussion about other adaptations and results. How can you relate these invented adaptations to adaptations for desert survival among real organisms?

Life in the Desert

Teacher's Notes

Time Required
One 45-minute class period

Lab Ratings

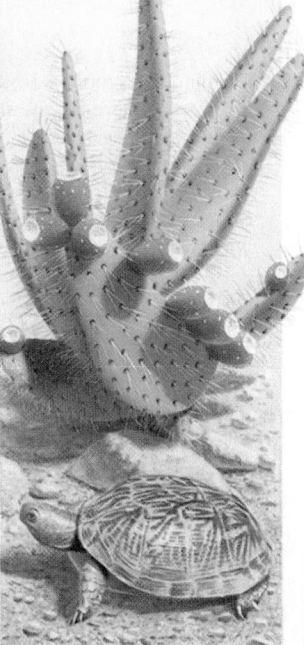

EASY ———————→ HARD

Teacher Prep 🜂
Student Set-Up 🜂🜂
Concept Level 🜂🜂
Clean Up 🜂

MATERIALS
The sponges used in this lab can be either natural sponges or the synthetic sponges available in grocery stores. Use 3 in. × 6 in. sponges, 1 per student, cut in half.

Analyze the Results

1. Students should describe the kind of covering or protection they provided for their "adapted" sponge. Effectiveness of the adaptation will be measured by the amount of water lost over 24 h. Students will want their sponges to dry out as little as possible.

2. The unprotected sponge represents the organism that has no adaptation for conserving water. The unprotected sponge should dry out far more than the protected sponge.

CHAPTER RESOURCES

Chapter Resource File

- Datasheet for LabBook
- Lab Notes and Answers

 Holt Lab Generator CD-ROM

Search for any lab by topic, standard, difficulty level, or time. Edit any lab to fit your needs, or create your own labs. Use the Lab Materials QuickList software to customize your lab materials list.

James Chin
Frank A. Day Middle School
Newtonville, Massachusetts

Discovering Mini-Ecosystems

Teacher's Notes

Time Required

One to two 45-minute class periods

Lab Ratings

EASY —————————→ HARD

Teacher Prep 🧪
Student Set-Up 🧪🧪
Concept Level 🧪🧪🧪
Clean Up 🧪

MATERIALS

Because this is mainly an observation activity, few materials are needed. If binoculars or magnifying lenses are available, however, they may be helpful.

Analyze the Results

1. Students may have many answers, but they should include answers such as different vegetation, organisms that live there, the soil type, density of vegetation, and amount of water present.

2. Students should recognize that the populations present in each area are adapted for life in that area.

3. Adaptations that students name will probably include camouflage, deep roots, and burrowing behavior.

Draw Conclusions

4. Answers may vary according to student observations.

Discovering Mini-Ecosystems

In your study of ecosystems, you learned that a biome is a very large ecosystem that includes a set of smaller, related ecosystems. For example, a coniferous forest biome may include a river ecosystem, a wetland ecosystem, and a lake ecosystem. Each of those ecosystems may include several other smaller, related ecosystems. Even cities have mini-ecosystems! You may find a mini-ecosystem on a patch of sidewalk, in a puddle of rainwater, under a leaky faucet, in a shady area, or under a rock. In this activity, you will design a method for comparing two different mini-ecosystems found near your school.

MATERIALS

- items to be determined by the students and approved by the teacher

SAFETY

Ask a Question

1. Examine the grounds around your school, and select two different areas you wish to investigate. Decide what you want to learn about your mini-ecosystems. For example, you may want to know what kind of living things each area contains. Be sure to get your teacher's approval before you begin.

Form a Hypothesis

2. For each mini-ecosystem, make data tables for recording your observations.

Test the Hypothesis

3. Observe your mini-ecosystem according to your plan at several different time points throughout the day. Record your observations.

4. Wait 24 h and observe your mini-ecosystem again at the same times that you observed it the day before. Record your observations.

5. Wait 1 week, and observe your mini-ecosystem again at the same times. Record your observations.

Analyze the Results

1. What factors determine the differences between your mini-ecosystems? Identify the factors that set each mini-ecosystem apart from its surrounding area.

2. How do the populations of your mini-ecosystems compare?

3. Identify some of the adaptations that the organisms living in your two mini-ecosystems have. Describe how the adaptations help the organisms survive in their environment.

Draw Conclusions

4. Write a report describing and comparing your mini-ecosystems with those of your classmates.

Lab Notes

Even if your school has no area where there is sand, dirt, grass, or trees, ask students to observe puddles, the underside of eaves, the area under drain spouts, and the ground under rocks. Students should observe the areas they have chosen at least twice a day.

CHAPTER RESOURCES

Chapter Resource File

- Datasheet for LabBook
- Lab Notes and Answers

CLASSROOM TESTED & APPROVED

Barry Bishop
San Rafael Junior High
Ferron, Utah

Model-Making Lab

Oh, the Pressure!

When scientists want to understand natural processes, such as mountain formation, they often make models to help them. Models are useful in studying how rocks react to the forces of plate tectonics. A model can demonstrate in a short amount of time geological processes that take millions of years. Do the following activity to find out how folding and faulting occur in the Earth's crust.

MATERIALS

- can, soup (or rolling pin)
- clay, modeling, 4 colors
- knife, plastic
- newspaper
- pencils, colored
- poster board, 5 cm × 5 cm squares (2)
- poster board, 5 cm × 15 cm strip

SAFETY

Ask a Question

1 How do synclines, anticlines, and faults form?

Form a Hypothesis

2 On a separate piece of paper, write a hypothesis that is a possible answer to the question above. Explain your reasoning.

Test the Hypothesis

3 Use modeling clay of one color to form a long cylinder, and place the cylinder in the center of the glossy side of the poster-board strip.

4 Mold the clay to the strip. Try to make the clay layer the same thickness all along the strip; you can use the soup can or rolling pin to even it out. Pinch the sides of the clay so that the clay is the same width and length as the strip. Your strip should be at least 15 cm long and 5 cm wide.

Oh, the Pressure!

Teacher's Notes

Time Required

One 45-minute class period

Lab Ratings

Teacher Prep 🧪🧪🧪
Student Set-Up 🧪🧪
Concept Level 🧪🧪🧪
Clean Up 🧪🧪🧪

MATERIALS

The materials listed on the student page are enough for a group of 3 to 4 students.

Safety Caution

Remind students to review all safety cautions and icons before beginning this lab activity.

Lab Notes

Homemade modeling dough may be substituted for modeling clay in this activity. In step 6, students may find it easier to trim each layer of clay with the plastic knife before stacking the layers together.

Preparation Notes

**Homemade Modeling Dough
(optional)** The night before the
activity, prepare enough modeling dough for each class, using
the recipe below. The recipe
provides enough dough for each
group. Combine the following
ingredients in a large saucepan
over low heat in the order that
they are listed:

• 2 cups cold water
• $\frac{1}{3}$ cup cooking oil
• 1 cup salt
• 4 tsp cream of tartar
• 2 cups flour
• food coloring

Constantly stir the mixture until
the modeling dough forms a
ball. Turn the modeling dough
out onto a floured surface. Use a
ruler to divide the dough into
fourths. When the dough cools
slightly, add 15–20 drops of food
coloring to each quarter. Fold
and knead to evenly distribute
the color throughout the dough.
Place the dough in an airtight
container, such as an 8 oz
yogurt container. If you freeze it,
the modeling dough will last for
months.

Just before the activity, cover all
workspaces with newspaper, and
secure the newspapers in place.
If the dough gets dry, rinse your
hands and continue to mold the
dough.

5. Flip the strip over on the newspaper your teacher has placed
across your desk. Carefully peel the strip from the modeling clay.

6. Repeat steps 3–5 with the other colors of modeling clay. Each
person should have a turn molding the clay. Each time you
flip the strip over, stack the new clay layer on top of the previous one. When you are finished, you should have a block of
clay made of four layers.

7. Lift the block of clay, and hold it parallel to and just above
the tabletop. Push gently on the block from opposite sides, as
shown below.

8. Use the colored pencils to draw the results of step 6. Use
the terms *syncline* and *anticline* to label your diagram. Draw
arrows to show the direction that each edge of the clay was
pushed.

9. Repeat steps 3–6 to form a second block of clay.

10. Cut the second block of clay in two at a 45° angle as seen
from the side of the block.

CHAPTER RESOURCES

Chapter Resource File

• **Datasheet for LabBook**
• **Lab Notes and Answers**

Daniel Bugenhagen
Yutan Jr.–Sr. High
Yutan, Nebraska

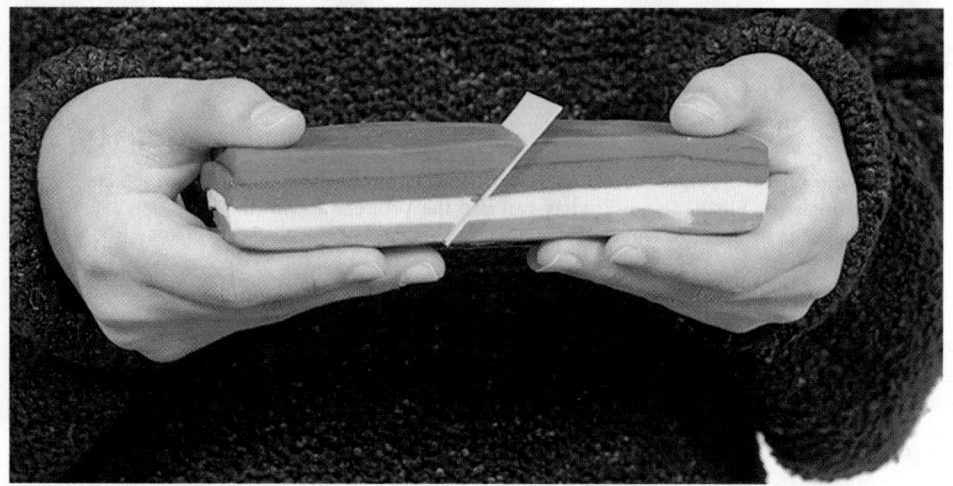

Lab Notes

Students should realize that stress is equivalent to pressure or force. Explain to them that rocks can undergo stress without deforming. When the stress becomes too great, the rocks become folded or faulted. This deformation is also called *strain*. Stress and the result of stress (strain) are two different concepts.

⑪ Press one poster-board square on the angled end of each of the block's two pieces. The poster board represents a fault. The two angled ends represent a hanging wall and a footwall. The model should resemble the one in the photograph above.

⑫ Keeping the angled edges together, lift the blocks, and hold them parallel to and just above the tabletop. Push gently on the two blocks until they move. Record your observations.

⑬ Now, hold the two pieces of the clay block in their original position, and slowly pull them apart, allowing the hanging wall to move downward. Record your observations.

Analyze the Results

① What happened to the first block of clay in step 7? What kind of force did you apply to the block of clay?

② What happened to the pieces of the second block of clay in step 12? What kind of force did you apply to them?

③ What happened to the pieces of the second block of clay in step 13? Describe the forces that acted on the block and the way the pieces of the block reacted.

Draw Conclusions

④ Summarize how the forces you applied to the blocks of clay relate to the way tectonic forces affect rock layers. Be sure to use the terms *fold, fault, anticline, syncline, hanging wall, footwall, tension,* and *compression* in your summary.

Analyze the Results

1. The first block got shorter and taller. The layers of clay became folded due to compression.

2. One of the pieces (the hanging wall) slid above the other piece (the footwall) due to compression.

3. One of the pieces (the footwall) moved up relative to the other piece (the hanging wall) as tension was released.

Draw Conclusions

4. The conclusion should be a complete summary of this activity, indicating the direction of pressure at each step. Any diagrams should be correctly labeled, and students should demonstrate a good understanding of the terms *fold, fault, anticline, syncline, hanging wall, footwall, tension,* and *compression.*

Earthquake Waves

Teacher's Notes

Time Required

One 45-minute class period

Lab Ratings

EASY —————→ HARD

Teacher Prep 🜊
Student Set-Up 🜊
Concept Level 🜊🜊🜊
Clean Up 🜊

MATERIALS

The materials listed on the student page are enough for 2 students.

Safety Caution

Remind students to review all safety cautions and icons before beginning this lab activity.

Preparation Notes

Be sure that students understand in step 6 how to calculate the distance from each city to the epicenter of the earthquake. These distances must be correct to accurately determine the epicenter of the earthquake on the map.

Emphasize to students that the circles on the map must intersect or come very close to intersecting in order to determine the epicenter of the earthquake. If the circles do not come close to intersecting, tell students that they must check their calculations.

Skills Practice Lab

Earthquake Waves

The energy from an earthquake travels as seismic waves in all directions through the Earth. Seismologists can use the properties of certain types of seismic waves to find the epicenter of an earthquake.

P waves travel more quickly than S waves and are always detected first. The average speed of P waves in the Earth's crust is 6.1 km/s. The average speed of S waves in the Earth's crust is 4.1 km/s. The difference in arrival time between P waves and S waves is called *lag time*.

In this activity, you will use the S-P-time method to determine the location of an earthquake's epicenter.

MATERIALS

- calculator (optional)
- compass
- ruler, metric

SAFETY

Procedure

1. The illustration below shows seismographic records made in three cities following an earthquake. These traces begin at the left and show the arrival of P waves at time zero. The second set of waves on each record represents the arrival of S waves.

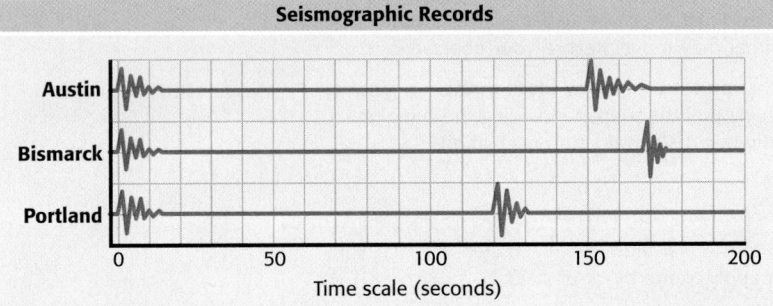

Seismographic Records

Austin
Bismarck
Portland

| 0 | 50 | 100 | 150 | 200 |

Time scale (seconds)

2. Copy the data table on the next page.

3. Use the time scale provided with the seismographic records to find the lag time between the P waves and the S waves for each city. Remember that the lag time is the time between the moment when the first P wave arrives and the moment when the first S wave arrives. Record this data in your table.

4. Use the following equation to calculate how long it takes each wave type to travel 100 km:

100 km ÷ *average speed of the wave = time*

Janel Guse
West Central Middle School
Hartford, South Dakota

5. To find lag time for earthquake waves at 100 km, subtract the time it takes P waves to travel 100 km from the time it takes S waves to travel 100 km. Record the lag time.

6. Use the following formula to find the distance from each city to the epicenter:

$$distance = \frac{measured\ lag\ time\ (s) \times 100\ km}{lag\ time\ for\ 100\ km\ (s)}$$

In your data table, record the distance from each city to the epicenter.

7. Trace the map below onto a separate sheet of paper.

8. Use the scale to adjust your compass so that the radius of a circle with Austin at the center is equal to the distance between Austin and the epicenter of the earthquake.

Epicenter Data Table		
City	Lag time (seconds)	Distance to the epicenter (km)
Austin, TX		
Bismarck, ND	DO NOT WRITE IN BOOK	
Portland, OR		

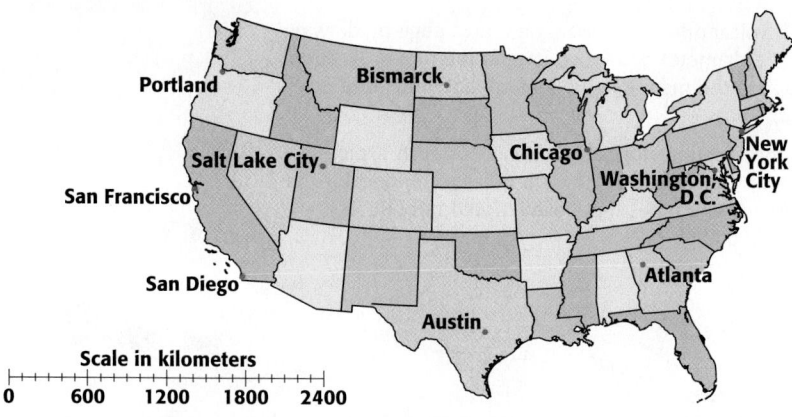

Scale in kilometers
0   600   1200   1800   2400

9. Put the point of your compass at Austin on your copy of the map, and draw a circle.

10. Repeat steps 8 and 9 for Bismarck and Portland. The epicenter of the earthquake is located near the point where the three circles meet.

Anayze the Results

1. Which city is closest to the epicenter?

Draw Conclusions

2. Why do seismologists need measurements from three different locations to find the epicenter of an earthquake?

Procedure

3. Austin: 150 s
   Bismarck: 168 s
   Portland: 120 s

6. Austin: 1,875 km; Bismarck: 2,100 km; Portland: 1,500 km

Analyze the Results

1. San Diego, California

Draw Conclusions

2. Sample answer: Seismologists require at least three intersecting circles to determine the epicenter of an earthquake. The first two circles intersect in two places. When a third circle is used, all three circles intersect in only one place near the epicenter.

Some Go "Pop," Some Do Not

Teacher's Notes

Time Required

One 45-minute class period

Lab Ratings

EASY ——————→ HARD

Teacher Prep 🧪🧪
Student Set-Up 🧪
Concept Level 🧪🧪🧪
Clean Up 🧪

MATERIALS

The materials listed on the student page are enough for 1 student. Students may wish to use tracing paper in step 1.

Preparation Notes

Students should be aware that volcanoes with a high water and silica content tend to erupt explosively. They should use this information to analyze the data in this activity. You may also wish to inform students that, in general, quietly erupting volcanoes are derived from basaltic magma, and explosively erupting volcanoes are derived from granitic magma. Remind students that oceanic crust is basaltic and low in silica, and continental crust is granitic and high in silica.

Students may need some practice finding locations by using latitude and longitude. If necessary, guide them through the steps needed to locate the first volcano on the chart.

Skills Practice Lab

Some Go "Pop," Some Do Not

Volcanic eruptions range from mild to violent. When volcanoes erupt, the materials left behind provide information to scientists studying the Earth's crust. Mild, or nonexplosive, eruptions produce thin, runny lava that is low in silica. During nonexplosive eruptions, lava simply flows down the side of the volcano. Explosive eruptions, on the other hand, do not produce much lava. Instead, the explosions hurl ash and debris into the air. The materials left behind are light in color and high in silica. These materials help geologists determine the composition of the crust underneath the volcanoes.

MATERIALS

- paper, graph (1 sheet)
- pencils (or markers), red, yellow, and orange
- ruler, metric

Procedure

1. Copy the map below onto graph paper. Take care to line the grid up properly.

2. Locate each volcano from the list on the next page by drawing a circle with a diameter of about 2 mm in the proper location on your copy of the map. Use the latitude and longitude grids to help you.

3. Review all the eruptions for each volcano. For each explosive eruption, color the circle red. For each quiet volcano, color the circle yellow. For volcanoes that have erupted in both ways, color the circle orange.

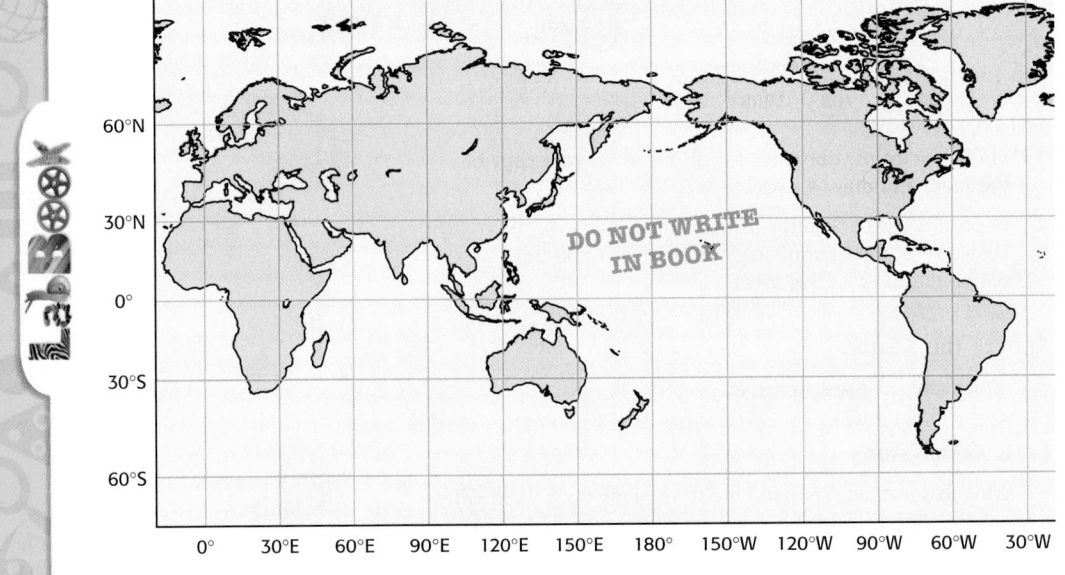

Lab Notes

In a very simple way, this lab models how the composition of magma can evolve. For example, basaltic (mafic) magma can evolve into granitic (felsic) magma through chemical differentiation processes. Scientists often use measurements of trace elements in the resulting rock to "fingerprint" the source of magma from which volcanic rocks formed.

 Holt Lab Generator CD-ROM

Search for any lab by topic, standard, difficulty level, or time. Edit any lab to fit your needs, or create your own labs. Use the Lab Materials QuickList software to customize your lab materials list.

C. John Graves
Monforton Middle School
Bozeman, Montana

Volcanic Activity Chart		
Volcano name	**Location**	**Description**
Mount St. Helens	46°N 122°W	An explosive eruption blew the top off the mountain. Light-colored ash covered thousands of square kilometers. Another eruption sent a lava flow down the southeast side of the mountain.
Kilauea	19°N 155°W	One small eruption sent a lava flow along 12 km of highway.
Rabaul caldera	4°S 152°E	Explosive eruptions have caused tsunamis and have left 1–2 m of ash on nearby buildings.
Popocatépetl	19°N 98°W	During one explosion, Mexico City closed the airport for 14 hours because huge columns of ash made it too difficult for pilots to see. Eruptions from this volcano have also caused damaging avalanches.
Soufriere Hills	16°N 62°W	Small eruptions have sent lava flows down the hills. Other explosive eruptions have sent large columns of ash into the air.
Long Valley caldera	37°N 119°W	Explosive eruptions have sent ash into the air.
Okmok	53°N 168°W	Recently, there have been slow lava flows from this volcano. Twenty-five hundred years ago, ash and debris exploded from the top of this volcano.
Pavlof	55°N 161°W	Eruption clouds have been sent 200 m above the summit. Eruptions have sent ash columns 10 km into the air. Occasionally, small eruptions have caused lava flows.
Fernandina	42°N 12°E	Eruptions have ejected large blocks of rock from this volcano.
Mount Pinatubo	15°N 120°E	Ash and debris from an explosive eruption destroyed homes, crops, and roads within 52,000 km^2 around the volcano.

Analyze the Results

1 According to your map, where are volcanoes that always have nonexplosive eruptions located?

2 Where are volcanoes that always erupt explosively located?

3 Where are volcanoes that erupt in both ways located?

4 If volcanoes get their magma from the crust below them, what can you say about the silica content of Earth's crust under the oceans?

5 What is the composition of the crust under the continents? How do we know?

Draw Conclusions

6 What is the source of materials for volcanoes that erupt in both ways? How do you know?

7 Do the locations of volcanoes that erupt in both ways make sense, based on your answers to questions 4 and 5? Explain.

Applying Your Data

Volcanoes are present on other planets. If a planet had only nonexplosive volcanoes on its surface, what would we be able to infer about the planet? If a planet had volcanoes that ranged from nonexplosive to explosive, what might that tell us about the planet?

Analyze the Results

1. Nonexplosive volcanoes are usually located on oceanic crust.

2. Explosive volcanoes are usually located on continental crust.

3. Volcanoes that erupt in both ways are usually located near boundaries between oceanic and continental crusts.

4. The crust under the oceans must be low in silica. Students may also know that the crust is likely to be made of basalt.

5. Continental crust is generally high in silica. Students may also know that the crust is likely to be made of granite.

Draw Conclusions

6. The volcanoes that erupt in both ways must be near the boundary between the oceanic crusts and the continental crusts. The crust must have both basalt and granite.

7. The volcanoes that erupt in both ways are located near the boundaries between continents and oceans. Students should understand that two different crusts must meet in these areas and that both granitic (felsic) and basaltic (mafic) magma is generated.

Applying Your Data

Answers should reflect the idea that the crust on planets with nonexplosive volcanoes must be low in silica compared to the crust on Earth. Students may also realize that planets that have only nonexplosive volcanoes must have basaltic crust. If a planet has all three types of volcanoes, it must have both basaltic and granitic crusts.

 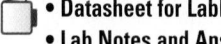

Skills Practice Lab

Volumania!

Teacher's Notes

Time Required

One 45-minute class period

Lab Ratings

EASY ———————————— HARD

Teacher Prep 🔺
Student Set-Up 🔺
Concept Level 🔺🔺
Clean Up 🔺

Part A: Finding the Volume of Small Objects

MATERIALS

The materials listed are for each group of 2–3 students. The objects used must be small enough to fit in the graduated cylinders but still be large enough to make a measurable change in the volume of the water. Rock or mineral samples, hardware (such as bolts or screws), and fishing weights work well.

Safety Caution

Caution students to tilt the graduated cylinder so objects can slide in gently to avoid breaking glass graduated cylinders. Remind students to read the volume when the meniscus is at eye level. Caution students to wear goggles during this lab.

Skills Practice Lab

Volumania!

You have learned how to measure the volume of a solid object that has square or rectangular sides. But there are lots of objects in the world that have irregular shapes. In this lab activity, you'll learn some ways to find the volume of objects that have irregular shapes.

Part A: Finding the Volume of Small Objects

Procedure

1. Fill a graduated cylinder half full with water. Read and record the volume of the water. Be sure to look at the surface of the water at eye level and to read the volume at the bottom of the meniscus, as shown below.

Read volume here

2. Carefully slide one of the objects into the tilted graduated cylinder, as shown below.

3. Read the new volume, and record it.

4. Subtract the old volume from the new volume. The resulting amount is equal to the volume of the solid object.

5. Use the same method to find the volume of the other objects. Record your results.

Analyze the Results

1. What changes do you have to make to the volumes you determine in order to express them correctly?

2. Do the heaviest objects always have the largest volumes? Why or why not?

Part A
- graduated cylinder
- water
- various small objects supplied by your teacher

Part B
- bottle, plastic (or similar container), 2L, bottom half
- funnel
- graduated cylinder
- pan, aluminum pie
- paper towels
- water

SAFETY

Analyze the Results

1. Sample answer: The units of milliliters should be changed to cubic centimeters because you are measuring the volume of a solid object.

2. Sample answer: no; Sometimes a heavier object will have a smaller volume than a lighter object because the matter is more tightly packed.

Part B: Finding the Volume of Your Hand

Procedure

1. Completely fill the container with water. Put the container in the center of the pie pan. Be sure not to spill any of the water into the pie pan.

2. Make a fist, and put your hand into the container up to your wrist.

3. Remove your hand, and let the excess water drip into the container, not the pie pan. Dry your hand with a paper towel.

4. Use the funnel to pour the overflow water into the graduated cylinder. Measure the volume. This measurement is the volume of your hand. Record the volume. (Remember to use the correct unit of volume for a solid object.)

5. Repeat this procedure with your other hand.

Analyze the Results

1. Was the volume the same for both of your hands? If not, were you surprised? What might account for a person's hands having different volumes?

2. Would it have made a difference if you had placed your open hand into the container instead of your fist? Explain your reasoning.

3. Compare the volume of your right hand with the volume of your classmates' right hands. Create a class graph of right-hand volumes. What is the average right-hand volume for your class?

Applying Your Data

Design an experiment to determine the volume of a person's body. In your plans, be sure to include the materials needed for the experiment and the procedures that must be followed. Include a sketch that shows how your materials and methods would be used in this experiment.

Using an encyclopedia, the Internet, or other reference materials, find out how the volumes of very large samples of matter—such as an entire planet—are determined.

Part B: Finding the Volume of Your Hand

MATERIALS

Plastic containers from whipped toppings and the like can also be used. Containers should be deep enough so students' fists can be submerged. Remind students that their container must be completely filled with water so that it overflows as their hand enters. The pie pan should be dry at the start. When students remove their hand from the container, they should allow the water cupped in their hand to drip back into the container and not into the pie pan. This water was not displaced and should not be measured.

Analyze the Results

1. Answers may vary. Often, the preferred hand will be slightly larger due to greater muscle development.

2. Sample answer: It would not make a difference; A hand's volume remains the same regardless of its shape.

3. Answers may vary by class. Check for correct graphing technique and interpretation.

Applying Your Data

Designs should center on finding the volume of the body through water displacement. The equipment designed should be large enough to perform the experiment and allow for overflow. Accept all reasonable answers and findings.

CHAPTER RESOURCES

Chapter Resource File

- **Datasheet for LabBook**
- **Lab Notes and Answers**

Holt Lab Generator CD-ROM

Search for any lab by topic, standard, difficulty level, or time. Edit any lab to fit your needs, or create your own labs. Use the Lab Materials QuickList software to customize your lab materials list.

Alyson Mike
Radley Middle School
East Helena, Montana

Determining Density

Teacher's Notes

Time Required

One 45-minute class period

Lab Ratings

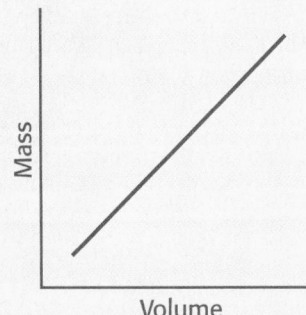

EASY ———————→ HARD

Teacher Prep ⚗
Student Set-Up ⚗
Concept Level ⚗⚗
Clean Up ⚗

Safety Caution

Caution students to tilt the graduated cylinder so marbles can slide in gently.

Analyze the Results

1. The mass and the volume of the marbles increases, but the marbles' density remains the same.
2. The graph is a straight line (see graph below).

Draw Conclusions

3. The density is the same for one marble as it is for several marbles.

Skills Practice Lab

Determining Density

The density of an object is its mass divided by its volume. But how does the density of a small amount of a substance relate to the density of a larger amount of the same substance? In this lab, you will calculate the density of one marble and of a group of marbles. Then, you will confirm the relationship between the mass and volume of a substance.

MATERIALS

- balance, metric
- graduated cylinder, 100 mL
- marbles, glass (8–10)
- paper, graph
- paper towels
- water

SAFETY

Procedure

1. Copy the table below. Include one row for each marble.

Mass of marble (g)	Total mass of marbles (g)	Total volume (mL)	Volume of marbles (mL) (total volume minus 50.0 mL)	Density of marbles (g/mL) (total mass divided by volume)
		DO NOT WRITE IN BOOK		

2. Fill the graduated cylinder with 50 mL of water. If you put in too much water, twist one of the paper towels, and use it to absorb excess water.

3. Measure the mass of a marble as accurately as you can (to at least .01 g). Record the mass in the table.

4. Carefully drop the marble in the tilted cylinder, and measure the total volume. Record the volume in the third column.

5. Measure and record the mass of another marble. Add the masses of the marbles together, and record this value in the second column of the table.

6. Carefully drop the second marble in the graduated cylinder. Complete the row of information in the table.

7. Repeat steps 5 and 6. Add one marble at a time. Stop when you run out of marbles, the water no longer completely covers the marbles, or the graduated cylinder is full.

Analyze the Results

1. Examine the data in your table. As the number of marbles increases, what happens to the total mass of the marbles? What happens to the volume of the marbles? What happens to the density of the marbles?

2. Graph the total mass of the marbles (y-axis) versus the volume of the marbles (x-axis). Is the graph a straight line?

Draw Conclusions

3. Does the density of a substance depend on the amount of substance present? Explain how your results support your answer.

Applying Your Data

Calculate the slope of the graph. How does the slope compare with the values in the column entitled "Density of marbles"? Explain.

CHAPTER RESOURCES

Chapter Resource File

- Datasheet for LabBook
- Lab Notes and Answers

Alyson Mike
Radley Middle School
East Helena, Montana

Applying Your Data

To find the slope of the graph, pick two points on the line. The slope is the difference between the y values of the points divided by the difference between the x values of the points. The slope of the graph should be equal to the density of the marbles because the graph shows mass versus volume, which means the slope is mass divided by volume—in other words, density.

Skills Practice Lab

Layering Liquids

You have learned that liquids form layers according to the densities of the liquids. In this lab, you'll discover whether it matters in which order you add the liquids.

Ask a Question

1 Does the order in which you add liquids of different densities to a container affect the order of the layers formed by those liquids?

Form a Hypothesis

2 Write a possible answer to the question above.

Test the Hypothesis

3 Using the graduated cylinders, add 10 mL of each liquid to the clear container. Remember to read the volume at the bottom of the meniscus, as shown below. Record the order in which you added the liquids.

4 Observe the liquids in the container. Sketch what you see. Be sure to label the layers and the colors.

5 Add 10 mL more of liquid C. Observe what happens, and record your observations.

6 Add 20 mL more of liquid A. Observe what happens, and record your observations.

Analyze the Results

1 Which of the liquids has the greatest density? Which has the least density? How can you tell?

2 Did the layers change position when you added more of liquid C? Explain your answer.

3 Did the layers change position when you added more of liquid A? Explain your answer.

MATERIALS

- beaker (or other small, clear container)
- funnel (3)
- graduated cylinder, 10 mL (3)
- liquid A
- liquid B
- liquid C

SAFETY

4 Find out in what order your classmates added the liquids to the container. Compare your results with those of a classmate who added the liquids in a different order. Were your results different? Explain why or why not.

Draw Conclusions

5 Based on your results, evaluate your hypothesis from step 2.

CHAPTER RESOURCES

Chapter Resource File

- • Datasheet for LabBook
- • Lab Notes and Answers

Disposal Information

Have students empty their containers into several disposable containers to keep the oil out of the drains. These can be capped, refrigerated, and thrown in the trash. It might be interesting to let these waste bottles stand overnight to see if the layers are visible the following day.

Holt Lab Generator CD-ROM

Search for any lab by topic, standard, difficulty level, or time. Edit any lab to fit your needs, or create your own labs. Use the Lab Materials QuickList software to customize your lab materials list.

CLASSROOM TESTED & APPROVED

Alyson Mike
Radley Middle School
East Helena, Montana

Skills Practice Lab

Layering Liquids

Teacher's Notes

Time Required
One 45-minute class period

Lab Ratings

EASY ————————→ HARD

Teacher Prep 🜂🜂🜂
Student Set-Up 🜂
Concept Level 🜂🜂
Clean Up 🜂🜂

Preparation Notes
Liquid A is red-colored water, liquid B is vegetable oil, and liquid C is dark corn syrup.

Analyze the Results

1. Liquid C has the greatest density; Liquid B has the least density; The liquids form layers with the least dense on top and the most dense on bottom.

2. The position of the layers did not change; Adding more of liquid C does not change its density, so its position stays the same.

3. The position of the layers did not change; Adding more of liquid A does not change its density, so its position stays the same.

4. All results should be identical; Liquid B is the top layer, liquid A is the middle layer, and liquid C is the bottom layer.

Draw Conclusions

5. Answers may vary, depending on the original prediction. The order in which the liquids are added does not affect the order of the layers formed.

Full of Hot Air!

Teacher's Notes

Time Required

One 45-minute class period

Lab Ratings

🧪	🧪🧪	🧪🧪🧪	🧪🧪🧪🧪
EASY			HARD

Teacher Prep 🧪🧪
Student Set-Up 🧪🧪
Concept Level 🧪🧪🧪
Clean Up 🧪🧪

Safety Caution

Keep all power cords away from the beakers and pans of hot water. Be careful—hot plates may stay hot for a long time. Students should wear heat-resistant gloves when handling the hot beaker.

Analyze the Results

1. Sample answer: When the balloon cooled, it contracted. When heated, it expanded. These observations confirm Charles's law.

2. Answers may vary, depending on the original hypothesis. Sample supported hypothesis: Increasing temperature increases the volume of a balloon, and decreasing temperature decreases the volume of a balloon.

Draw Conclusions

3. As the temperature increases, volume increases, and mass remains constant. Therefore, the density decreases. Conversely, density increases when temperature decreases.

Full of Hot Air!

Why do hot-air balloons float gracefully above Earth, but balloons you blow up fall to the ground? The answer has to do with the density of the air inside the balloon. *Density* is mass per unit volume, and volume is affected by changes in temperature. In this experiment, you will investigate the relationship between the temperature of a gas and its volume. Then, you will be able to determine how the temperature of a gas affects its density.

MATERIALS

- balloon
- beaker, 250 mL
- gloves, heat-resistant
- hot plate
- ice water
- pan, aluminum (2)
- ruler, metric
- water

SAFETY

Ask a Question

1. How does an increase or decrease in temperature affect the volume of a balloon?

Form a Hypothesis

2. Write a hypothesis that answers the question above.

Test the Hypothesis

3. Fill an aluminum pan with water about 4 cm to 5 cm deep. Put the pan on the hot plate, and turn the hot plate on.

4. Fill the other pan 4 cm to 5 cm deep with ice water.

5. Blow up a balloon inside the 500 mL beaker, as shown. The balloon should fill the beaker but should not extend outside the beaker. Tie the balloon at its opening.

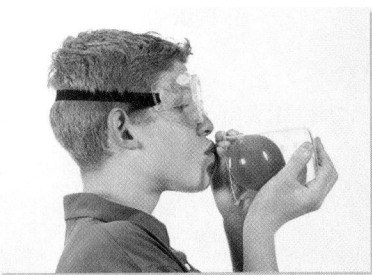

6. Place the beaker and balloon in the ice water. Observe what happens. Record your observations.

7. Remove the balloon and beaker from the ice water. Observe the balloon for several minutes. Record any changes.

8. Put on heat-resistant gloves. When the hot water begins to boil, put the beaker and balloon in the hot water. Observe the balloon for several minutes, and record your observations.

9. Turn off the hot plate. When the water has cooled, carefully pour it into a sink.

Analyze the Results

1. Summarize your observations of the balloon. Relate your observations to Charles's law.

2. Was your hypothesis from step 2 supported? If not, revise your hypothesis.

Draw Conclusions

3. Based on your observations, how is the density of a gas affected by an increase or decrease in temperature?

CHAPTER RESOURCES

Chapter Resource File

- Datasheet for LabBook
- Lab Notes and Answers

Sharon L. Woolf
Langston Hughes
Middle School
Reston, Virginia

Skills Practice Lab

Can Crusher

Condensation can occur when gas particles come near the surface of a liquid. The gas particles slow down because they are attracted to the liquid. This reduction in speed causes the gas particles to condense into a liquid. In this lab, you'll see that particles that have condensed into a liquid don't take up as much space and therefore don't exert as much pressure as they did in the gaseous state.

MATERIALS
- beaker, 1 L
- can, aluminum (2)
- gloves, heat-resistant
- hot plate
- tongs
- water

SAFETY

Procedure

1. Fill the beaker with room-temperature water.

2. Place just enough water in an aluminum can to slightly cover the bottom.

3. Put on heat-resistant gloves. Place the aluminum can on a hot plate turned to the highest temperature setting.

4. Heat the can until the water is boiling. Steam should be rising vigorously from the top of the can.

5. Using tongs, quickly pick up the can, and place the top 2 cm of the can upside down in the 1 L beaker filled with water.

6. Describe your observations.

Analyze the Results

1. The can was crushed because the atmospheric pressure outside the can became greater than the pressure inside the can. Explain what happened inside the can to cause the difference in pressure.

Draw Conclusions

2. Inside every popcorn kernel is a small amount of water. When you make popcorn, the water inside the kernels is heated until it becomes steam. Explain how the popping of the kernels is the opposite of what you saw in this lab. Be sure to address the effects of pressure in your explanation.

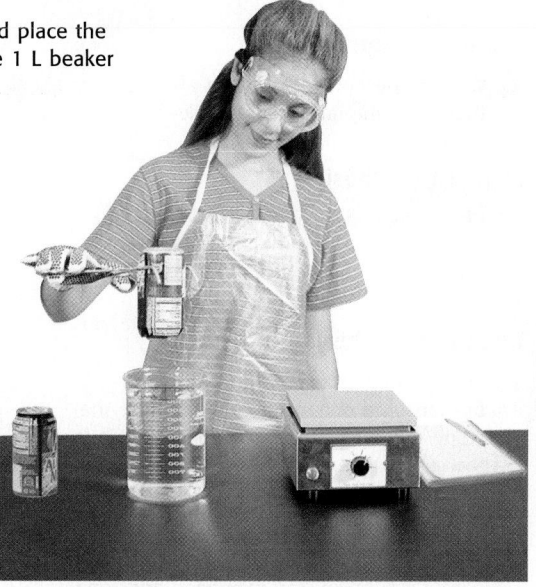

Applying Your Data

Try the experiment again, but use ice water instead of room-temperature water. Explain your results in terms of the effects of temperature.

CHAPTER RESOURCES

Chapter Resource File

- Datasheet for LabBook
- Lab Notes and Answers

Holt Lab Generator CD-ROM

Search for any lab by topic, standard, difficulty level, or time. Edit any lab to fit your needs, or create your own labs. Use the Lab Materials QuickList software to customize your lab materials list.

Applying Your Data

Sample answer: The can was crushed more quickly because the ice water made the steam condense more quickly. So, the pressure inside the can decreased further.

CLASSROOM TESTED & APPROVED

Lee Yassinski
Sun Valley Middle School
Sun Valley, California

Can Crusher

Teacher's Notes

Time Required
One 45-minute class period

Lab Ratings

EASY ———————————> HARD

Teacher Prep 🧪
Student Set-Up 🧪
Concept Level 🧪🧪
Clean Up 🧪

Safety Caution

Remind students to review all safety cautions and icons before beginning this lab activity. Caution students to keep all power cords away from beakers and pans of hot water to prevent spills. Heat-resistant gloves may not be necessary if tongs are properly used.

Analyze the Results

1. Sample answer: The steam inside the can cooled and condensed. The volume of water (condensed steam) is smaller than the volume of the steam, so the pressure inside the can was reduced.

Draw Conclusions

2. Sample answer: When the water inside the kernel becomes steam, the water expands about 100 times. The pressure inside the kernel increases. The pressure outside is unchanged, so the pressure inside forces the kernel to "explode."

LabBook

Skills Practice Lab

A Sugar Cube Race!

Teacher's Notes

Time Required

One 45-minute class period

Lab Ratings

EASY ——————→ HARD

Teacher Prep 🧪

Student Set-Up 🧪

Concept Level 🧪🧪

Clean Up 🧪

Preparation Notes

Remind students not to eat the sugar cube. Have hot water or hot plates and heat-resistant gloves ready for students who want to test temperature. Have paper towels on hand for students to wrap their cube in as they crush it.

Analyze the Results

1. Answers may vary, depending on the original prediction. Tested variables may include water temperature, surface area of cube, and stirring.

Skills Practice Lab

A Sugar Cube Race!

If you drop a sugar cube into a glass of water, how long will it take to dissolve? What can you do to speed up the rate at which it dissolves? Should you change something about the water, the sugar cube, or the process? In other words, what variable should you change? Before reading further, make a list of variables that could be changed in this situation. Record your list.

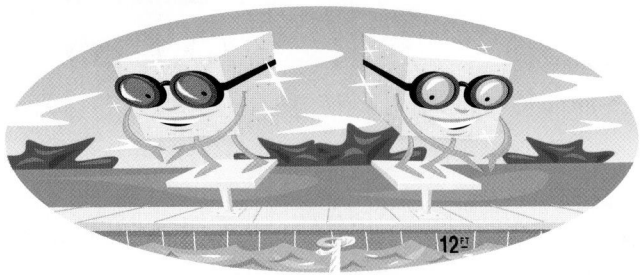

Ask a Question

1. Write a question you can test about factors that affect the rate sugar dissolves.

Form a Hypothesis

2. Choose one variable to test. Record your choice, and predict how changing your variable will affect the rate of dissolving.

Test the Hypothesis

3. Pour 150 mL of water into one of the beakers. Add one sugar cube, and use the stopwatch to measure how long it takes for the sugar cube to dissolve. You must not disturb the sugar cube in any way! Record this time.

4. Be sure to get your teacher's approval before you begin. You may need additional equipment.

5. Prepare your materials to test the variable you have picked. When you are ready, start your procedure for speeding up the rate at which the sugar cube dissolves. Use the stopwatch to measure the time. Record this time.

Analyze the Results

1. Compare your results with the prediction you made in step 2. Was your prediction correct? Why or why not?

Draw Conclusions

2. Why was it necessary to observe the sugar cube dissolving on its own before you tested the variable?

3. Do you think changing more than one variable would speed up the rate of dissolving even more? Explain your reasoning.

4. Discuss your results with a group that tested a different variable. Which variable had a greater effect on the rate of dissolving?

Draw Conclusions

2. Observing the sugar cube dissolving on its own provides a control so that you can measure the effect of the variable.

3. Changing two variables that each increase the dissolving rate should increase the rate of dissolving even more, but it would be difficult to determine which variable had the greater effect.

4. Accept all reasonable answers based on class data.

CHAPTER RESOURCES

Chapter Resource File

 • Datasheet for LabBook
• Lab Notes and Answers

Kenneth J. Horn
Fallston Middle School
Fallston, Maryland

Skills Practice Lab

Making Butter

A colloid is an interesting substance. It has properties of both solutions and suspensions. Colloidal particles are not heavy enough to settle out, so they remain evenly dispersed throughout the mixture. In this activity, you will make butter—a very familiar colloid—and observe the characteristics that classify butter as a colloid.

Procedure

1 Place a marble inside the container, and fill the container with heavy cream. Put the lid tightly on the container.

2 Take turns shaking the container vigorously and constantly for 10 min. Record the time when you begin shaking. Every minute, stop shaking the container, and hold it up to the light. Record your observations.

3 Continue shaking the container, taking turns if necessary. When you see, hear, or feel any changes inside the container, note the time and change.

4 After 10 min of shaking, you should have a lump of "butter" surrounded by liquid inside the container. Describe both the butter and the liquid in detail.

5 Let the container sit for about 10 min. Observe the butter and liquid again, and record your observations.

Analyze the Results

1 When you noticed the change inside the container, what did you think was happening at that point?

2 Based on your observations, explain why butter is classified as a colloid.

3 What kind of mixture is the liquid that is left behind? Explain.

MATERIALS

- clock or stopwatch
- container with lid, small, clear
- heavy cream
- marble

SAFETY

CHAPTER RESOURCES

Chapter Resource File

- Datasheet for LabBook
- Lab Notes and Answers

Holt Lab Generator CD-ROM

Search for any lab by topic, standard, difficulty level, or time. Edit any lab to fit your needs, or create your own labs. Use the Lab Materials QuickList software to customize your lab materials list.

CLASSROOM TESTED & APPROVED

Kenneth J. Horn
Fallston Middle School
Fallston, Maryland

Making Butter

Teacher's Notes

Time Required
One 45-minute class period

Lab Ratings

EASY ——————→ HARD

Teacher Prep 🧪🧪
Student Set-Up 🧪
Concept Level 🧪🧪
Clean Up 🧪🧪

MATERIALS

Materials listed are for each pair of students. If using glass containers, students should shake the container vigorously but not violently, because it might break. Be sure each lid fits tightly. A small or medium-sized ball bearing may be substituted for the marble. For best results, the cream should be room temperature, not cold.

Safety Caution

Caution students to wear safety goggles while performing this activity.

Analyze the Results

1. Answers may vary. Students should mention that the suspended materials were starting to settle out.

2. The butter appears to have characteristics of both a solution and a suspension.

3. The liquid left behind appears to be a suspension.

Unpolluting Water

Teacher's Notes

Time Required

One or two 45-minute class periods

Lab Ratings

△ △△ △△△ △△△△
EASY ————————→ HARD

Teacher Prep △△△
Student Set-Up △△△
Concept Level △△△
Clean Up △△

MATERIALS

Materials listed are for each group of 2–3 students. Use large filter paper for part D, or place filter paper in a funnel.

Special notes on materials:

1. Sand must be thoroughly washed to eliminate as much dust as possible. Put the sand in a bowl, and run water into it while stirring until the water runs clear. The finer the sand, the better the filtering action will be.

2. Use activated charcoal, available from pet-supply stores. This charcoal can be washed by quickly running water through the charcoal in a sieve or colander. Do not allow the charcoal to remain in water too long, or it will lose its absorbing power.

Safety Caution

Make sure all spills are cleaned up immediately.

Unpolluting Water

In many cities, the water supply comes from a river, lake, or reservoir. This water may include several mixtures, including suspensions (with suspended dirt, oil, or living organisms) and solutions (with dissolved chemicals). To make the water safe to drink, your city's water supplier must remove impurities. In this lab, you will model the procedures used in real water treatment plants.

Part A: Untreated Water

Procedure

1. Measure 100 mL of "polluted" water into a graduated cylinder. Be sure to shake the bottle of water before you pour so your sample will include all the impurities.

2. Pour the contents of the graduated cylinder into one of the beakers.

3. Copy the table below, and record your observations of the water in the "Before treatment" row.

Observations						
	Color	Clearness	Odor	Any layers?	Any solids?	Water volume
Before treatment						
After oil separation						
After sand filtration						
After charcoal						

DO NOT WRITE IN BOOK

Part B: Settling In

If a suspension is left standing, the suspended particles will settle to the top or bottom. You should see a layer of oil at the top.

Procedure

1. Separate the oil by carefully pouring the oil into another beaker. You can use a plastic spoon to get the last bit of oil from the water. Record your observations.

MATERIALS

- beaker, 250 mL (4)
- charcoal, activated, washed
- cup, plastic-foam, 8 oz (2)
- graduated cylinder
- nail, small
- paper, filter (2 pieces)
- rubber band
- ruler, metric
- sand, fine, washed
- scissors
- spoon, plastic (2)
- water, "polluted"

SAFETY

Preparation Notes

Make "polluted water" as follows: Put the following into a half-gallon milk jug:

1 cup cooking oil

¾ to 1 cup of dirt

1 or 2 drops of food coloring (yellow or red works best)

Fill the jug with water, put the cap on, and shake the jug well. It is important that students shake the mixture well before pouring their 100 mL sample. Students can estimate the water volume after Parts B–D using the approximate volume markings on the side of the beaker. Have students use a clean graduated cylinder in Part D to measure the volume of treated water.

Part C: Filtration

Cloudy water can be a sign of small particles still in suspension. These particles can usually be removed by filtering. Water treatment plants use sand and gravel as filters.

Procedure

1. Make a filter as follows:

   a. Use the nail to poke 5 to 10 small holes in the bottom of one of the cups.

   b. Cut a circle of filter paper to fit inside the bottom of the cup. (This filter will keep the sand in the cup.)

   c. Fill the cup to 2 cm below the rim with wet sand. Pack the sand tightly.

   d. Set the cup inside an empty beaker.

2. Pour the polluted water on top of the sand, and let the water filter through. Do not pour any of the settled mud onto the sand. (Dispose of the mud as instructed by your teacher.) In your table, record your observations of the water collected in the beaker.

Part D: Separating Solutions

Something that has been dissolved in a solvent cannot be separated using filters. Water treatment plants use activated charcoal to absorb many dissolved chemicals.

Procedure

1. Place activated charcoal about 3 cm deep in the unused cup. Pour the water collected from the sand filtration into the cup, and stir with a spoon for 1 min.

2. Place a piece of filter paper over the top of the cup, and fasten it in place with a rubber band. With the paper securely in place, pour the water through the filter paper and back into a clean beaker. Record your observations in your table.

Analyze the Results

1. Is your unpolluted water safe to drink? Why or why not?

2. When you treat a sample of water, do you get out exactly the same amount of water that you put in? Explain your answer.

3. Some groups may still have cloudy water when they finish. Explain a possible cause for this.

Analyze the Results

1. Students will have different opinions, depending on their results. Many will likely say that unpolluted water is safe to drink because it goes through so many filtering processes, but some may say it is unsafe because their samples still look cloudy after the experiment. (Note: Students should be discouraged from tasting the water. This activity does not include treatment with chlorine that takes place at most water treatment plants to kill bacteria.)

2. no; Some of the water is lost in the treatment processes.

3. Accept all reasonable answers. Sample answer: Dust from the charcoal and sand made the water cloudy. Bacteria in the water caused it to look cloudy.

Disposal Information

1. Solid charcoal should be dried and buried in a landfill that is approved for chemical disposal. You may want to consider drying and reusing the charcoal, although it will eventually lose its absorbing power.

2. Pour cooking oil into disposable containers, refrigerate (if possible) until the oil congeals, and put in the trash.

3. The sand can be reused if it is washed after this activity.

4. Spoon or pour the mud into disposable containers, and put them in the trash.

Model-Making Lab

Finding a Balance

Teacher's Notes

Time Required

One 45-minute class period

Lab Ratings

EASY ———————————→ HARD

Teacher Prep 🧪🧪
Student Set-Up 🧪
Concept Level 🧪🧪
Clean Up 🧪

MATERIALS

Create at least two envelopes per group. Label each envelope with an unbalanced chemical equation. In each envelope, place one paper arrow, some reactant molecules, and some product molecules. Include extra reactants and products so students do not just put the reactants on one side of the arrow and the products on the other. To create molecule models, draw squares onto a sheet of paper, and label them. Color the squares so that each element has a unique color. (Hint: Draw the molecule models on a sheet of paper, make enough photocopies for all your groups, color the squares, laminate the pages, and then cut out the squares.)

Sample equations:

$Na + Cl_2 \rightarrow NaCl$

$C_2H_4 + O_2 \rightarrow CO_2 + H_2O$

$Fe + O_2 \rightarrow FeO$

$Al + CuSO_4 \rightarrow Al_2(SO_4)_3 + Cu$

$Ba(CN)_2 + H_2SO_4 \rightarrow BaSO_4 + HCN$

Model-Making Lab

Finding a Balance

Usually, balancing a chemical equation involves just writing. But in this activity, you will use models to practice balancing chemical equations, as shown below. By following the rules, you will soon become an expert equation balancer!

MATERIALS

• envelopes, each labeled with an unbalanced equation

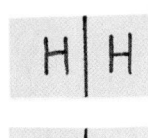

Example

$\_H_2 + \_O_2 \rightarrow \_H_2O$

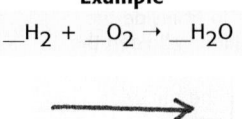

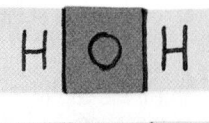

Balanced Equation

$2H_2 + O_2 \rightarrow 2H_2O$

Procedure

1. The rules are as follows:
   a. Reactant-molecule models may be placed only to the left of the arrow.
   b. Product-molecule models may be placed only to the right of the arrow.
   c. You may use only complete molecule models.
   d. At least one of each of the reactant and product molecules shown in the equation must be included in the model when you are finished.

2. Select one of the labeled envelopes. Copy the unbalanced equation written on the envelope.

3. Open the envelope, and pull out the molecule models and the arrow. Place the arrow in the center of your work area.

4. Put one model of each molecule that is a reactant on the left side of the arrow and one model of each product on the right side.

5. Add one reactant-molecule or product-molecule model at a time until the number of each of the different-colored squares on each side of the arrow is the same. Remember to follow the rules.

6. When the equation is balanced, count the number of each of the molecule models you used. Write these numbers as coefficients, as shown in the balanced equation above.

7. Select another envelope, and repeat the steps until you have balanced all of the equations.

Analyze the Results

1. The rules specify that you are allowed to use only complete molecule models. How are these rules similar to what occurs in a real chemical reaction?

2. In chemical reactions, energy is either released or absorbed. Devise a way to improve the model to show energy being released or absorbed.

CHAPTER RESOURCES

Chapter Resource File

 • Datasheet for LabBook
• Lab Notes and Answers

Laura Fleet
Alice B. Landrum
Middle School
Ponte Vedra Beach, Florida

Analyze the Results

1. Chemical reactions cannot involve partial molecules.

2. Answers may vary. Sample answer: Create a symbol for energy that can be used with the reaction models.

Skills Practice Lab

Cata-what? Catalyst!

Catalysts increase the rate of a chemical reaction without being changed during the reaction. In this experiment, hydrogen peroxide, H_2O_2, decomposes into oxygen, O_2, and water, H_2O. An enzyme present in liver cells acts as a catalyst for this reaction. You will investigate the relationship between the amount of the catalyst and the rate of the decomposition reaction.

Ask a Question

1 How does the amount of a catalyst affect reaction rate?

Form a Hypothesis

2 Write a statement that answers the question above. Explain your reasoning.

Test the Hypothesis

3 Put a small piece of masking tape near the top of each test tube, and label the tubes "1," "2," and "3."

4 Create a hot-water bath by filling the beaker half full with hot water.

5 Using the funnel and graduated cylinder, measure 5 mL of the hydrogen peroxide solution into each test tube. Place the test tubes in the hot-water bath for 5 min.

6 While the test tubes warm up, grind one liver cube with the mortar and pestle.

7 After 5 min, use the tweezers to place the cube of liver in test tube 1. Place the ground liver in test tube 2. Leave test tube 3 alone.

8 Observe the reaction rate (the amount of bubbling) in all three test tubes, and record your observations.

Analyze the Results

1 Does liver appear to be a catalyst? Explain your answer.

2 Which type of liver (whole or ground) produced a faster reaction? Why?

3 What is the purpose of test tube 3?

MATERIALS

- beaker, 600 mL
- funnel
- graduated cylinder, 10 mL
- hydrogen peroxide, 3% solution
- liver cubes, small (2)
- mortar and pestle
- tape, masking
- test tubes, 10 mL (3)
- tweezers
- water, hot

SAFETY

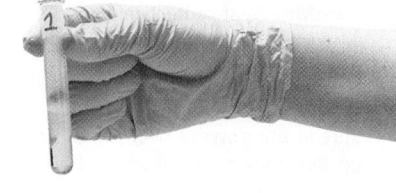

Draw Conclusions

4 How do your results support or disprove your hypothesis?

5 Why was a hot-water bath used? (Hint: Look in your book for a definition of *activation energy*.)

CHAPTER RESOURCES

Chapter Resource File

- Datasheet for LabBook
- Lab Notes and Answers

Disposal Information

Solutions may be washed down the sink if your school drains are connected to a sanitary sewer system with a treatment plant. Students should clean the lab area and wash their hands thoroughly.

Holt Lab Generator CD-ROM

Search for any lab by topic, standard, difficulty level, or time. Edit any lab to fit your needs, or create your own labs. Use the Lab Materials QuickList software to customize your lab materials list.

CLASSROOM TESTED & APPROVED

Rodney A. Sandefur
Naturita Middle School
Naturita, Colorado

Cata-what? Catalyst!

Teacher's Notes

Time Required

One 45-minute class period

Lab Ratings

🧪	🧪🧪	🧪🧪🧪	🧪🧪🧪🧪

EASY ————————————→ HARD

Teacher Prep 🧪🧪🧪
Student Set-Up 🧪
Concept Level 🧪🧪🧪
Clean Up 🧪🧪

MATERIALS

Materials listed are for each group of 2–3 students. Liver cubes should be about 1 cm³. Hot water can be obtained from the tap.

Safety Caution

Remind students to review all safety cautions and icons before beginning this lab activity. Use hydrogen peroxide solutions with concentrations of no more than 3%.

Analyze the Results

1. yes; The more vigorous bubbling in the test tubes with liver indicates a faster reaction rate.

2. ground liver; Grinding released more catalyst (enzyme) from the liver cells.

3. Test tube 3 is a control test tube. It is used to compare the rate of bubbling with liver to the rate without liver.

Draw Conclusions

4. Accept all reasonable answers.

5. The bath provides activation energy to start the reaction. The higher temperature also allows the reaction to happen faster.

Putting Elements Together

Teacher's Notes

Time Required

One to two 45-minute class periods

Lab Ratings

EASY ———————→ HARD

Teacher Prep 🧪🧪
Student Set-Up 🧪🧪
Concept Level 🧪🧪
Clean Up 🧪

Safety Caution

Remind students to review all safety cautions and icons before beginning this lab activity. Caution students to be careful around the open flame. All loose hair or clothing should be tied back. Students should wear protective gloves when working with the copper powder and use tongs properly when working near the flame. Caution students not to touch the hot evaporating dish with their bare hands.

Procedure Notes

Set up the ring stand so that the ring will be about 5 cm above the flame.

Skills Practice Lab

Putting Elements Together

A synthesis reaction is a reaction in which two or more substances combine to form a single compound. The resulting compound has different chemical and physical properties than the substances from which it is composed. In this activity, you will synthesize, or create, copper(II) oxide from the elements copper and oxygen.

MATERIALS

- balance, metric
- Bunsen burner (or portable burner)
- copper powder
- evaporating dish
- gauze, wire
- gloves, protective
- igniter
- paper, weighing
- ring stand and ring
- tongs

SAFETY

Procedure

1 Copy the table below.

Data Collection Table	
Object	**Mass (g)**
Evaporating dish	
Copper powder	DO NOT WRITE IN BOOK
Copper + evaporating dish after heating	
Copper(II) oxide	

2 Use the metric balance to measure the mass (to the nearest 0.1 g) of the empty evaporating dish. Record this mass in the table.

3 Place a piece of weighing paper on the metric balance, and measure approximately 10 g of copper powder. Record the mass (to the nearest 0.1 g) in the table. **Caution:** Wear protective gloves when working with copper powder.

4 Use the weighing paper to place the copper powder in the evaporating dish. Spread the powder over the bottom and up the sides as much as possible. Discard the weighing paper.

CHAPTER RESOURCES

Chapter Resource File

📁 • Datasheets for LabBook
• Lab Notes and Answers

5 Set up the ring stand and ring. Place the wire gauze on top of the ring. Carefully place the evaporating dish on the wire gauze.

6 Place the Bunsen burner under the ring and wire gauze. Use the igniter to light the Bunsen burner. **Caution:** Use extreme care when working near an open flame.

7 Heat the evaporating dish for 10 min.

8 Turn off the burner, and allow the evaporating dish to cool for 10 min. Use tongs to remove the evaporating dish and to place it on the balance to determine the mass. Record the mass in the table.

9 Determine the mass of the reaction product—copper(II) oxide—by subtracting the mass of the evaporating dish from the mass of the evaporating dish and copper powder after heating. Record this mass in the table.

Analyze the Results

1 What evidence of a chemical reaction did you observe after the copper was heated?

2 Explain why there was a change in mass.

3 How does the change in mass support the idea that this reaction is a synthesis reaction?

Draw Conclusions

4 Why was powdered copper used rather than a small piece of copper? (Hint: How does surface area affect the rate of the reaction?)

5 Why was the copper heated? (Hint: Look in your book for the discussion of activation energy.)

6 The copper bottoms of cooking pots can turn black when used. How is that similar to the results you obtained in this lab?

Applying Your Data

Rust, shown below, is iron(III) oxide—the product of a synthesis reaction between iron and oxygen. How does painting a car help prevent this type of reaction?

Disposal Information

Any leftover copper powder can be thrown in the trash. Students should wash their hands thoroughly after completing this lab. Dispose of the copper(II) oxide by letting it cool thoroughly, wrapping it in newspaper or paper towels, and then putting it in the trash.

○ **Holt Lab Generator CD-ROM**

Search for any lab by topic, standard, difficulty level, or time. Edit any lab to fit your needs, or create your own labs. Use the Lab Materials QuickList software to customize your lab materials list.

Paul Boyle
Perry Heights Middle School
Evansville, Indiana

CLASSROOM TESTED & APPROVED

Analyze the Results

1. The copper changed color, and the mass changed.

2. A change in mass occurred because the copper combined with oxygen from the air. The resulting copper(II) oxide has more mass than the original copper alone.

3. A synthesis reaction is one in which two or more substances join to form a new substance. The mass of the copper(II) oxide is greater than the mass of the copper alone, so a synthesis reaction, in which the copper combined with oxygen from the air, must have occurred, resulting in the change in mass.

Draw Conclusions

4. Powdered copper has a larger surface area than a piece of copper. More surface area increases the rate of the reaction because more copper is exposed to oxygen.

5. The copper was heated because the formation of copper(II) oxide requires a large activation energy.

6. The copper(II) oxide synthesized in this experiment is the same black powder that appears on copper pots.

Applying Your Data

Sample answer: Painting a car helps prevent rust from forming on it by creating a barrier between the iron of the car and the oxygen. If the iron and oxygen are not in contact, they cannot react to form rust.

Making Salt

Teacher's Notes

Time Required

One 45-minute class period, plus 10 minutes the following day

Lab Ratings

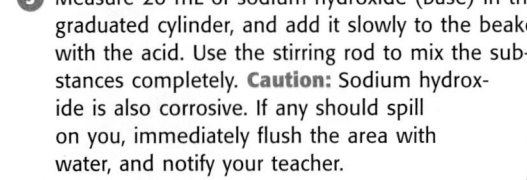

EASY ——————————→ HARD

Teacher Prep 🧪🧪
Student Set-Up 🧪🧪
Concept Level 🧪🧪
Clean Up 🧪🧪

Safety Caution

Review all proper safety precautions with your students. Students should wear safety goggles, protective gloves, and an apron. In case of an acid or a base spill, first dilute the spill with water. Then, while wearing disposable plastic gloves, mop up the spill with wet cloths designated for spill cleanup. A wet cloth mop can be rinsed out a few times and used until it falls apart. Work with another person nearby who can call for help in case of an emergency, and work near (no more than a few seconds away from) a safety shower and eyewash station known to be in operating condition.

Procedure Notes

You may wish to do this lab as a demonstration or class activity if time or materials are limited.

Making Salt

A neutralization reaction between an acid and a base produces water and a salt. In this lab, you will react an acid with a base and then let the water evaporate. You will then examine what is left for properties that tell you that it is indeed a salt.

Ask a Question

1 Write a question about reactions between acids and bases.

Form a Hypothesis

2 Write a hypothesis that may answer the question you asked in the step above.

Test the Hypothesis

3 Put on protective gloves. Carefully measure 25 mL of hydrochloric acid in a graduated cylinder, and then pour it into the beaker. Carefully rinse the graduated cylinder with distilled water to clean out any leftover acid. **Caution:** Hydrochloric acid is corrosive. If any should spill on you, immediately flush the area with water, and notify your teacher.

4 Add 3 drops of phenolphthalein indicator to the acid in the beaker. You will not see anything happen yet because this indicator won't show its color unless too much base is present.

5 Measure 20 mL of sodium hydroxide (base) in the graduated cylinder, and add it slowly to the beaker with the acid. Use the stirring rod to mix the substances completely. **Caution:** Sodium hydroxide is also corrosive. If any should spill on you, immediately flush the area with water, and notify your teacher.

6 Use an eyedropper to add more base, a few drops at a time, to the acid-base mixture in the beaker. Be sure to stir the mixture after each few drops. Continue adding drops of base until the mixture remains colored after stirring.

MATERIALS

- beaker, 100 mL
- eyedroppers (2)
- evaporating dish
- gloves, protective
- graduated cylinder, 100 mL
- hydrochloric acid
- magnifying lens
- phenolphthalein solution in a dropper bottle
- stirring rod, glass
- sodium hydroxide
- water, distilled

SAFETY

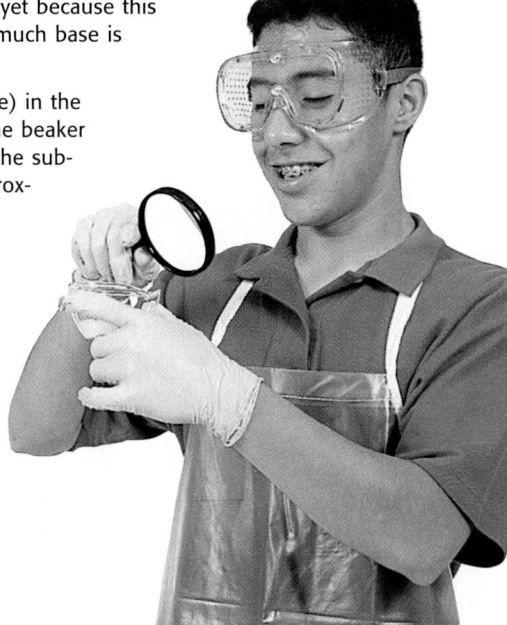

Safety Caution

Hydrochloric Acid Use only concentrations of hydrochloric acid below 1.0 M. Students should not handle concentrated solutions. Avoid contact with skin and eyes, and avoid breathing vapors. When making a solution, it is important always to add the acid to the water so that if something splashes out, it will most likely be water.

Safety Caution

Sodium Hydroxide Use only concentrations of sodium hydroxide below 1.0 M. Students should not handle concentrated solutions. Avoid contact with skin and eyes. You should wear goggles, a face shield, impermeable gloves, and a lab apron if you must prepare a solution of NaOH.

7 Use another eyedropper to add acid to the beaker, 1 drop at a time, until the color just disappears after stirring.

8 Pour the mixture carefully into an evaporating dish, and place the dish where your teacher tells you to allow the water to evaporate overnight.

9 The next day, examine your evaporating dish, and with a magnifying lens, study the crystals that were left. Identify the color, shape, and other properties of the crystals.

Analyze the Results

1 The following equation is for the reaction that occurred in this experiment:

$$HCl + NaOH \longrightarrow H_2O + NaCl$$

NaCl is ordinary table salt and forms very regular cubic crystals that are white. Did you find white cubic crystals?

2 The phenolphthalein indicator changes color in the presence of a base. Why did you add more acid in step 7 until the color disappeared?

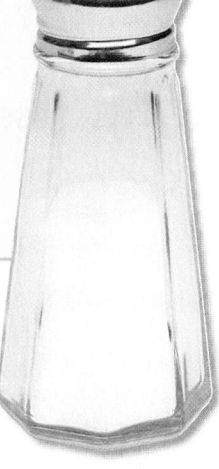

Applying Your Data

Another neutralization reaction occurs between hydrochloric acid and potassium hydroxide, KOH. The equation for this reaction is as follows:

$$HCl + KOH \longrightarrow H_2O + KCl$$

What are the products of this neutralization reaction? How do they compare with those you discovered in this experiment?

CHAPTER RESOURCES

Chapter Resource File

- Datasheet for LabBook
- Lab Notes and Answers

⊙ Holt Lab Generator CD-ROM

Search for any lab by topic, standard, difficulty level, or time. Edit any lab to fit your needs, or create your own labs. Use the Lab Materials QuickList software to customize your lab materials list.

CLASSROOM TESTED & APPROVED

Rodney A. Sandefur
Naturita Middle School
Naturita, Colorado

MATERIALS

The magnifying lens is not needed until day 2.

Safety Caution

Phenolphthalein Students should use only pre-mixed solutions (2 g in 100 mL 95% ethanol; add 100 mL water). Phenolphthalein solutions are flammable, and the vapors can explode when mixed with air. Ensure that there are no flames or sources of ignition, such as sparks, when you are using the phenolphthalein solution. Restrict the amount of phenolphthalein in the room to 100 mL.

Caution students not to taste the salt they create—it will have phenolphthalein in it.

Disposal Information

Hydrochloric Acid Titrate with 0.1 M NaOH as required until the pH is between 6 and 8, and then pour down the drain.

Sodium Hydroxide Titrate with 0.1 M HCl as required until the pH is between 5 and 9, and then pour down the drain.

Phenolphthalein Set out a container for any used indicator solutions that are left over at the end of the procedure. Titrate the mixture with 0.1 M HCl or 0.1 M NaOH as required until the pH is between 6 and 8, and then pour down the drain. Unused indicators should be tightly covered and returned to the storage shelf.

Analyze the Results

1. Students should observe white cubic crystals.

2. The phenolphthalein changing color in step 6 meant that too much base was present. Acid was added to bring the solution back to neutral.

Applying Your Data

The products are water and a salt, KCl (potassium chloride).

Contents

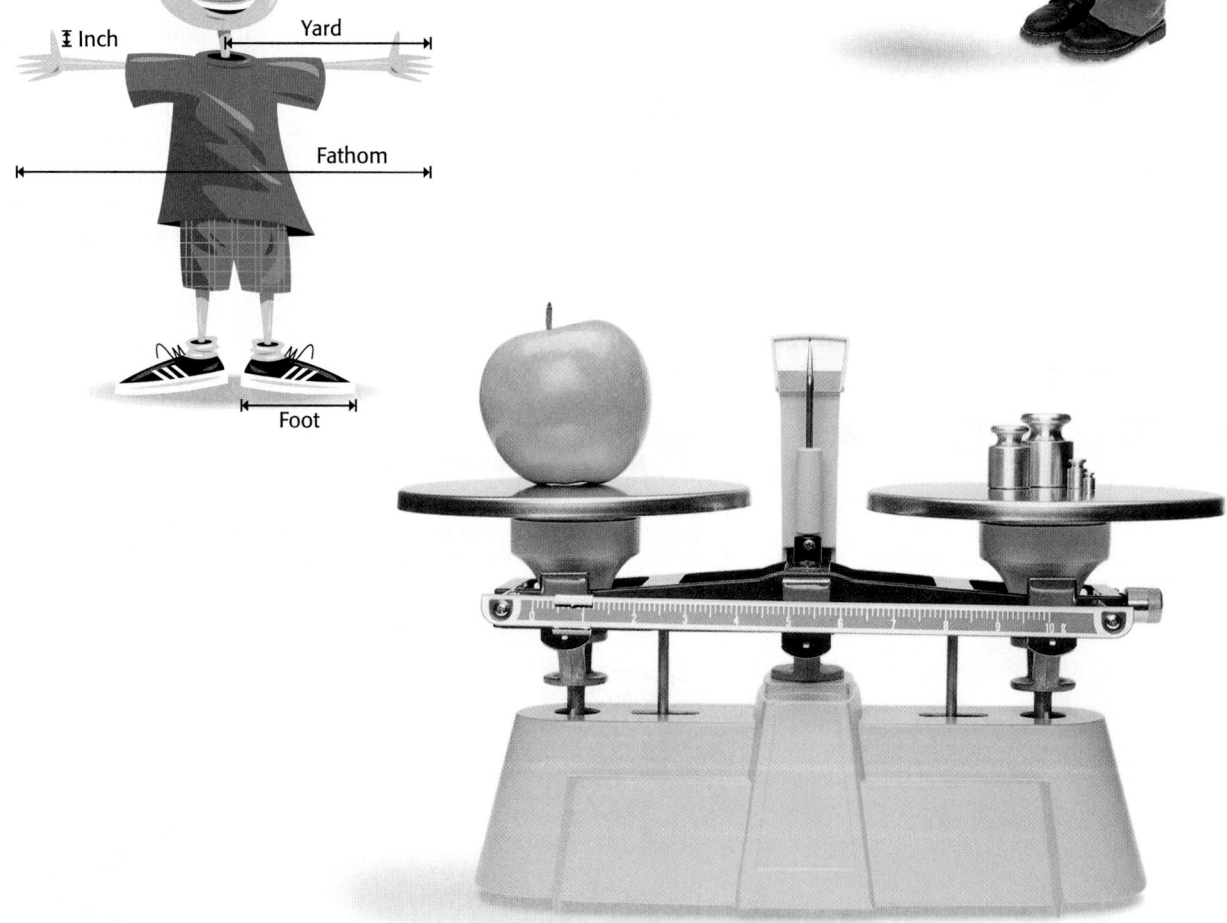

✓ *Reading Check* Answers

Chapter 1 Science in Our World

Section 1
Page 4: Science is the knowledge obtained by observing natural events and conditions in order to discover facts and formulate laws or principles that can be verified or tested.

Page 7: Society can influence technology development by identifying important problems that need technological solutions.

Page 9: A volcanologist studies volcanoes and their products, such as lava and gases.

Section 2
Page 10: a series of steps used by scientists to solve problems

Page 12: A hypothesis is testable if an experiment can be designed to test the hypothesis.

Page 14: only one

Page 16: because the scientist has learned something

Section 3
Page 19: a mathematical model

Page 20: to explain a broad range of observations, facts, and tested hypotheses, to predict what might happen, and to organize scientific thinking

Section 4
Page 22: stopwatch, graduated cylinder, meterstick, spring scale, balance, and thermometer

Page 25: the kilogram

Page 27: Safety symbols alert you to particular safety concerns or specific dangers in a lab.

Chapter 2 The Cell in Action

Section 1
Page 41: Red blood cells would burst in pure water because water particles move from outside, where particles were dense, to inside the cell, where particles were less dense. This movement of water would cause red blood cells to fill up and burst.

Page 43: Exocytosis is the process by which a cell moves large particles to the outside of the cell.

Section 2
Page 45: Cellular respiration is a chemical process by which cells produce energy from food. Breathing supplies oxygen for cellular respiration and removes the carbon dioxide produced by cellular respiration.

Page 47: One kind of fermentation produces CO_2, and the other kind produces lactic acid.

Section 3
Page 49: No, the number of chromosomes is not always related to the complexity of organisms.

Page 50: During cytokinesis in plant cells, a cell plate is formed. During cytokinesis in animal cells, a cell plate does not form.

Chapter 3 Plant Processes

Section 1
Page 62: Sample answer: Chlorophyll reflects more wavelengths of green light than wavelengths of other colors of light. So, most plants look green.

Page 65: Sample answer: Photosynthesis provides the oxygen that organisms need for cellular respiration. Photosynthetic organisms form the base of nearly all food chains on Earth.

Section 2
Page 67: Sample answer: Animals may eat fruits and discard the seeds away from the parent plant. Other fruits, such as burrs, get caught in an animal's fur. Some fruits are carried by the wind.

Page 68: plantlets, tubers, and runners

Section 3
Page 70: Sample answer: The shoot tips will probably bend toward the light.

Page 71: Sample answer: Plants respond to the change in the length of day.

Page 72: Sample answer: Evergreen trees always have some leaves on them. Deciduous trees lose all of their leaves around the same time each year.

Chapter 4 Heredity

Section 1
Page 86: the passing of traits from parents to offspring

Page 89: During his second set of experiments, Mendel allowed the first-generation plants, which resulted from his first set of experiments, to self-pollinate.

Page 90: A ratio is a relationship between two different numbers that is often expressed as a fraction.

Section 2
Page 92: A gene contains the instructions for an inherited trait. The different versions of a gene are called *alleles.*

Page 94: Probability is the mathematical chance that something will happen.

Page 96: In incomplete dominance, one trait is not completely dominant over another.

Section 3
Page 99: 23 chromosomes

Page 100: During meiosis, one parent cell makes four new cells.

Chapter 5   Genes and DNA

Section 1
Page 117:   Guanine and cytosine are always found in DNA in equal amounts, as are adenine and thymine.

Page 119:   every time a cell divides

Section 2
Page 120:   a string of nucleotides that give the cell information about how to make a specific trait

Page 123:   They transfer amino acids to the ribosome.

Page 124:   a physical or chemical agent that can cause a mutation in DNA

Page 125:   Sickle cell disease is caused by a mutation in a single nucleotide of DNA, which then causes a different amino acid to be assembled in a protein used in blood cells.

Page 126:   a near-identical copy of another organism, created with the original organism's genes

Chapter 6   The Evolution of Living Things

Section 1
Page 138:   if they mate with each other and produce more of the same type of organism

Page 140:   by their estimated ages and physical similarities

Page 142:   a four-legged land mammal

Page 144:   that they have common ancestry

Section 2
Page 147:   965 km (600 mi) west of Ecuador

Page 149:   that Earth had been formed by natural processes over a long period of time

Page 150:   Natural selection is the process by which organisms that are better adapted to their environment survive and reproduce more successfully than organisms that are less well adapted.

Section 3
Page 153:   because they often produce many offspring and have short generation times

Page 154:   Sample answer: A newly formed canyon, mountain range, or lake could divide the members of a population.

Chapter 7   The History of Life on Earth

Section 1
Page 167:   absolute dating

Page 169:   periods of sudden extinction of many species

Page 170:   the idea that the Earth's continents once formed a single landmass surrounded by ocean

Section 2
Page 172:   The early Earth was very different from today—there were violent events and a harsh atmosphere.

Page 175:   a mass extinction

Page 176:   "recent life"

Section 3
Page 179:   the hominid family

Page 180:   Africa

Page 183:   Paleontologists will review their ideas about the evolution of hominids.

Chapter 8   Maps as Models of the Earth

Section 1
Page 197:   A reference point is a fixed place on the Earth's surface from which direction and location can be described.

Page 198:   True north is the direction to the geographic North Pole.

Page 200:   lines of longitude

Section 2
Page 202:   Distortions are inaccuracies produced when information is transferred from a curved surface to a flat surface.

Page 205:   Azimuthal and conic projections are similar because they are both ways to represent the curved surface of the Earth on a flat map. Azimuthal projections show the surface of a globe transferred to a flat plane, whereas conic projections show the surface of a globe transferred to a cone.

Page 206:   Every map should have a title, a compass rose, a scale, the date, and a legend.

Page 208:   A GIS stores information in layers.

Section 3
Page 211:   An index contour is a darker contour line that is usually every fifth line. Index contours make it easier to read a map.

Chapter 9   Minerals of the Earth's Crust

Section 1
Page 225:   An element is a pure substance that cannot be broken down into simpler substances by ordinary chemical means. A compound is a substance made of two or more elements that have been chemically bonded.

Page 226:   Answers may vary. Silicate minerals contain a combination of silicon and oxygen; nonsilicate minerals do not contain a combination of silicon and oxygen.

Section 2
Page 229:   A mineral's streak is not affected by air or water, but a mineral's color may be affected by air or water.

Page 230:   Scratch the mineral with a series of 10 reference minerals. If the reference mineral scratches the unidentified mineral, the reference mineral is harder than the unidentified mineral.

Section 3

Page 235: Surface mining is used to remove mineral deposits that are at or near the Earth's surface. Subsurface mining is used to remove mineral deposits that are too deep to be removed by surface mining.

Page 237: Sample answer: Gemstones are nonmetallic minerals that are valued for their beauty and rarity rather than for their usefulness.

Chapter 10   Rocks: Mineral Mixtures

Section 1

Page 248: Types of rocks that have been used by humans to construct buildings include granite, limestone, marble, sandstone, and slate.

Page 252: Rock within the Earth is affected by temperature and pressure.

Page 253: The minerals that a rock contains determine a rock's composition.

Page 254: Fine-grained rocks are made of small grains, such as silt or clay particles. Medium-grained rocks are made of medium-sized grains, such as sand. Coarse-grained rocks are made of large grains, such as pebbles.

Section 2

Page 257: Felsic rocks are light-colored igneous rocks rich in aluminum, potassium, silicon, and sodium. Mafic rocks are dark-colored igneous rocks rich in calcium, iron, and magnesium.

Page 259: New sea floor forms when lava that flows from fissures on the ocean floor cools and hardens.

Section 3

Page 261: Halite forms when sodium and chlorine ions in shallow bodies of water become so concentrated that halite crystallizes from solution.

Page 263: Ripple marks are the marks left by wind and water waves on lakes, seas, rivers, and sand dunes.

Section 4

Page 265: Regional metamorphism occurs when pressure builds up in rock that is buried deep below other rock formations or when large pieces of the Earth's crust collide. The increased pressure can cause thousands of square miles of rock to become deformed and chemically changed.

Page 266: An index mineral is a metamorphic mineral that forms only at certain temperatures and pressures and therefore can be used by scientists to estimate the temperature, pressure, and depth at which a rock undergoes metamorphosis.

Page 269: Deformation causes metamorphic structures, such as folds.

Chapter 11   The Rock and Fossil Record

Section 1

Page 281: Catastrophists believed that all geologic change occurs rapidly.

Page 282: A global catastrophe can cause the extinction of species.

Section 2

Page 285: Geologists use the geologic column to interpret rock sequences and to identify layers in puzzling rock sequences.

Page 287: An unconformity is a surface that represents a missing part of the geologic column.

Page 288: A disconformity is found where part of a sequence of parallel rock layers is missing. A nonconformity is found where horizontal sedimentary rock layers lie on top of an eroded surface of igneous or metamorphic rock. Angular unconformities are found between horizontal sedimentary rock layers and rock layers that have been tilted or folded.

Section 3

Page 291: A half-life is the time it takes one-half of a radioactive sample to decay.

Page 292: strontium-87

Section 4

Page 294: An organism is caught in soft, sticky tree sap, which hardens and preserves the organism.

Page 296: A mold is a cavity in rock where a plant or an animal was buried. A cast is an object created when sediment fills a mold and becomes rock.

Page 298: To fill in missing information about changes in organisms in the fossil record, paleontologists look for similarities between fossilized organisms or between fossilized organisms and their closest living relatives.

Page 299: *Phacops* can be used to establish the age of rock layers because *Phacops* lived during a relatively short, well-defined time span and is found in rock layers throughout the world.

Section 5

Page 301: approximately 2 billion years

Page 302: The geological time scale is a scale that divides Earth's 4.6 billion–year history into distinct intervals of time.

Page 304: The Mesozoic era is known as the *Age of Reptiles* because reptiles, including the dinosaurs, were the dominant organisms on land.

Chapter 12   The Earth's Ecosystems

Section 1

Page 319: Sample answer: *Deciduous* comes from a Latin word that means "to fall off." In temperate deciduous forests, the trees lose their leaves in the fall.

Page 320: evergreen trees; squirrels, insects, finches, chickadees, jays, porcupines, elk, and moose

Page 322: During the dry season, grasses on the savanna dry out and turn yellow. But their deep roots survive for many months without water.

Page 323: Sample answer: Desert plants grow far apart. Some plants have shallow, widespread roots to take up water after a storm. Some desert plants have fleshy stems and leaves to store water. They also have waxy coatings to prevent water loss.

Page 324: Sample answer: Alpine tundra is tundra found at the top of tall mountains, above the tree line.

Section 2

Page 326: Sample answer: Plankton are tiny organisms that float near the surface of the water. They form the base of the ocean's feeding relationships.

Page 327: Sample answer: Fishes that live near the poles have adaptations for the near-freezing water. Animals in coral reefs need warm water to live. Some animals migrate to warmer waters to reproduce. Water temperature affects whether some animals can eat.

Page 329: Sample answer: Some animals get food from material that sinks to the bottom from the surface. Other animals get energy from chemicals released by thermal vents.

Page 330: Sample answer: When corals die, they leave behind their skeletons. Other corals grow on these remains. Over time, the layers build up to form a coral reef.

Section 3

Page 333: Sample answer: The littoral zone is the zone closest to shore in which light reaches the lake bottom. The open zone extends from the littoral zone and goes as deep as sunlight can reach. The deep-water zone lies beneath the open-water zone.

Page 334: A swamp is a wetland ecosystem in which trees and vines grow.

Page 335: Sample answer: Many fishes will die as the pond fills in because bacteria that decompose material in the pond use up the oxygen in the water.

Chapter 13 Earth's Systems and Cycles

Section 1

Page 346: The geosphere is the rocky part of Earth that extends from Earth's core to its surface. The atmosphere is the mixture of gases that surrounds Earth. The hydrosphere contains all of Earth's water. The biosphere contains all of Earth's life.

Page 349: When tectonic plates move, rock is deformed and broken. Some of the energy that is generated as rock is broken and deformed is released as vibrations that travel through the ground. This shaking is an earthquake.

Page 350: Large volcanic eruptions can lower the average global temperature. This occurs as a result of a decrease in the amount of sunlight that reaches Earth's surface. This decrease is caused by volcanic ash and sulfur gases in the Earth's atmosphere, which block and reflect sunlight.

Section 2

Page 353: Answers may vary. Sample answer: All weather is restricted to the troposphere. The ozone layer is located in the stratosphere. The mesosphere is the coldest layer in the atmosphere. In the thermosphere, oxygen and nitrogen absorb harmful X-ray and gamma-ray radiation from space.

Page 354: Energy comes to Earth from the sun as electromagnetic waves. These waves include ultraviolet wavelengths, visible light, and infrared wavelengths.

Page 356: Greenhouse gases in Earth's atmosphere absorb reradiated infrared energy from Earth's surface and retain the energy in the atmosphere as thermal energy. This thermal energy is conducted and convected through the atmosphere, warming the atmosphere.

Section 3

Page 359: Surface currents and deep currents form the pattern known as the ocean conveyor belt because they transport warm and cold water for thousands of miles throughout the global ocean.

Page 360: The ocean can keep temperatures in coastal areas cooler during the summer and warmer during the winter.

Page 362: Animals depend on a continuous supply of energy from the sun in order to obtain the food they need.

Page 363: Decomposition is a process that recycles the matter and energy stored in the bodies of animals and plants which have died. Generally, when an animal or plant dies, organisms called decomposers consume the dead plant and animal matter. These decomposers use some of the stored matter and energy and release what is left into the environment.

Section 4

Page 365: Water moves from the ocean, to the atmosphere, to the land, and back to the ocean.

Page 366: The carbon cycle is important to Earth's organisms because carbon is one of the most common molecules in organisms.

Chapter 14 Plate Tectonics

Section 1

Page 379: The crust is the thin, outermost layer of the Earth. It is 5 km to 100 km thick and is mainly made up of the elements oxygen, silicon, and aluminum. The mantle is the layer between the crust and core. It is 2,900 km thick, is denser than the crust, and contains most of the Earth's mass. The core is the Earth's innermost layer. The core has a radius of 3,430 km and is made mostly of iron.

Page 380: The five physical layers of the Earth are the lithosphere, asthenosphere, mesosphere, outer core, and inner core.

Page 383: Although continental lithosphere is less dense than oceanic lithosphere is, continental lithosphere has a greater mass because of its greater thickness and will displace more asthenosphere than oceanic lithosphere.

Page 384: Answers may vary. A seismic wave traveling through a solid will go faster than a seismic wave traveling through a liquid.

Section 2
Page 386: Similar fossils were found on landmasses that are very far apart. The best explanation for this phenomenon is that the landmasses were once joined.

Page 389: The molten rock at mid-ocean ridges contains tiny grains of magnetic minerals. The minerals align with the Earth's magnetic field before the rock cools and hardens. When the Earth's magnetic field reverses, the orientation of the mineral grains in the rocks will also change.

Section 3
Page 391: A transform boundary forms when two tectonic plates slide past each other horizontally.

Page 392: The circulation of thermal energy causes changes in density in the asthenosphere. As rock is heated, it expands, becomes less dense, and rises. As rock cools, it contracts, becomes denser, and sinks.

Section 4
Page 394: Compression can cause rocks to be pushed into mountain ranges as tectonic plates collide at convergent boundaries. Tension can pull rocks apart as tectonic plates separate at divergent boundaries.

Page 396: In a normal fault, the hanging wall moves down. In a reverse fault, the hanging wall moves up.

Page 398: Folded mountains form when rock layers are squeezed together and pushed upward.

Chapter 15   Earthquakes
Section 1
Page 413: During elastic rebound, rock releases energy. Some of this energy travels as seismic waves that cause earthquakes.

Page 415: Earthquake zones are usually located along tectonic plate boundaries.

Page 417: Surface waves travel more slowly than body waves but are more destructive.

Section 2
Page 419: Seismologists determine an earthquake's start time by comparing seismograms and noting differences in arrival times of P and S waves.

Page 420: Each time the magnitude increases by 1 unit, the amount of ground motion increases by 10 times.

Section 3
Page 423: With a decrease of one unit in earthquake magnitude, the number of earthquakes occurring annually increases by about 10 times.

Page 424: Retrofitting is the process of making older structures more earthquake resistant.

Page 426: You should crouch or lie face down under a table or desk.

Chapter 16   Volcanoes
Section 1
Page 439: Nonexplosive eruptions are common, and they feature relatively calm flows of lava. Explosive eruptions are less common and produce large, explosive clouds of ash and gases.

Page 440: Because silica-rich magma has a high viscosity, it tends to trap gases and plug volcanic vents. This causes pressure to build up and can result in an explosive eruption.

Page 442: Volcanic bombs are large blobs of magma that harden in the air. Lapilli are small pieces of magma that harden in the air. Volcanic blocks are pieces of solid rock erupted from a volcano. Ash forms when gases in stiff magma expand rapidly and the walls of the gas bubbles shatter into tiny glasslike slivers.

Section 2
Page 444: Eruptions release large quantities of ash and gases, which can block sunlight and cause global temperatures to drop.

Page 446: Calderas form when a magma chamber partially empties and the roof overlying the chamber collapses.

Section 3
Page 449: Volcanic activity is common at tectonic plate boundaries because magma tends to form at plate boundaries.

Page 451: When a tectonic plate subducts, it becomes hotter and releases water. The water lowers the melting point of the rock above the plate, causing magma to form.

Page 452: According to one theory, a rising body of magma, called a mantle plume, causes a chain of volcanoes to form on a moving tectonic plate. According to another theory, a chain of volcanoes forms along cracks in the Earth's crust.

Chapter 17   The Properties of Matter
Section 1
Page 467: liters (L) and milliliters (mL)

Page 468: You could measure the volume of an apple by submerging the apple in a container of water and measuring the volume of the water that the apple displaces.

Page 470: kilograms (kg), grams (g), and milligrams (mg)

Section 2

Page 472: Some physical properties are color, shape, odor, weight, volume, texture, state, and density.

Page 474: If the object's density is less than the water's density, the object will float.

Page 477: A physical change is a change that occurs to a substance or object that does not change the identity of the substance.

Section 3

Page 478: Reactivity describes the ability of two or more substances to combine and form one or more new substances.

Page 480: Chemical changes occur when one or more substances are changed into entirely new substances that have different properties. A chemical property of a substance determines whether a chemical change will occur.

Chapter 18 States of Matter

Section 1

Page 495: The particles in a crystalline solid are arranged in a repeating pattern of rows that forms an orderly, three-dimensional arrangement.

Page 496: Viscosity is a liquid's resistance to flow.

Section 2

Page 499: There are more particles of gas in the basketball than there are in the beach ball. More particles hit the inside surface of the basketball, which causes increased force.

Page 500 Charles's law states that the volume of a gas in a closed container changes as the temperature of the gas changes. If the temperature increases, the volume increases. If the temperature decreases, the volume decreases.

Section 3

Page 502: A change of state is the change of a substance from one physical form to another.

Page 504: Evaporation is the change of a substance from a liquid to a gas.

Page 506: As a substance changes state, its temperature remains constant until the change of state is complete.

Chapter 19 Elements, Compounds, and Mixtures

Section 1

Page 518: An element is a pure substance because it contains only one type of particle.

Page 520: Metals are shiny, conduct heat energy, and conduct electric current.

Section 2

Page 523: Three physical properties used to identify compounds are melting point, density, and color.

Page 524: Compounds can be broken down into elements or simpler compounds.

Section 3

Page 526: Substances in a mixture keep their identities because no chemical change takes place when a mixture is made.

Page 529: An alloy is a solid solution of metal or non-metal dissolved in another metal.

Page 531: As temperature increases, the solubility of a gas decreases.

Page 532: The particles of a suspension can be separated by passing the suspension through a filter.

Chapter 20 Introduction to Atoms

Section 1

Page 545: Dalton thought that elements are made of single atoms because elements always combine in specific proportions to form compounds.

Page 547: Rutherford could tell where the positively charged particles went because they hit a special coating that glowed where it was hit.

Page 548: Rutherford changed Thomson's model of the atom by proposing that the nucleus is a tiny, dense, positively charged area surrounded by electrons.

Section 2

Page 551: Protons and neutrons can be found in the nucleus.

Page 552: An atom becomes a positively charged ion when it loses an electron.

Page 554: Differences between isotopes are important when a certain isotope is radioactive.

Page 556: The four basic forces are the gravitational force, electromagnetic force, strong force, and weak force.

Chapter 21 The Periodic Table

Section 1

Page 568: Mendeleev had arranged elements based on increasing atomic mass.

Page 569: atomic number

Page 572: Most metals are solid at room temperature, ductile, malleable, and shiny. In addition, they are good conductors of electric current and thermal energy.

Page 574: Elements in a group often have similar chemical and physical properties.

Section 2

Page 577: It is easier for atoms of alkali metals to lose their outer electron than for atoms of transition metals to lose their outer electrons. Therefore, alkali metals are more reactive than transition metals.

Page 578: Yes, lanthanides and actinides are transition metals.

Page 579: silicon and germanium

Page 580: nitrogen and oxygen

Page 582: Atoms of noble gases have a full set of electrons in their outer level.

Chapter 22 Chemical Bonding

Section 1

Page 597: Most atoms form bonds only with their valence electrons.

Page 598: Atoms in Group 18 (the noble gases) rarely form chemical bonds.

Section 2

Page 599: Atoms are neutral because the number of protons in an atom always equals the number of electrons in the atom.

Page 601: Atoms in Group 17 give off the most energy when forming negative ions.

Section 3

Page 604: A covalent bond is a bond that forms when atoms share one or more pairs of electrons.

Page 606: There are two atoms in a diatomic molecule.

Page 608: Ductility is the ability to be drawn into wires.

Chapter 23 Chemical Reactions

Section 1

Page 621: A precipitate is a solid substance that is formed in a solution.

Page 622: In a chemical reaction, the chemical bonds in the starting substances break, and then new bonds form to make new substances.

Section 2

Page 625: Ionic compounds are made up of a metal and a nonmetal.

Page 626: Reactants are the starting substances in a chemical reaction, and products are the substances that are formed.

Page 628: 4

Section 3

Page 630: A synthesis reaction is a reaction in which two or more substances combine to form one new compound.

Page 631: In a decomposition reaction, a substance breaks down into simpler substances. In a synthesis reaction, two or more substances combine to form one new compound.

Page 632: In a single-displacement reaction, an element may replace another element if the replacing element is more reactive than the original element.

Section 4

Page 635: An endothermic reaction is a chemical reaction in which energy is taken in.

Page 636: Activation energy is the energy that is needed to start a chemical reaction.

Page 638: A high concentration of reactants allows the particles of the reactants to run into each other more often, so the reaction proceeds at a faster rate.

Chapter 24 Chemical Compounds

Section 1

Page 651: Ionic solutions conduct an electric current because the ions in the solution are charged and are able to move past each other easily.

Page 652: Most covalent compounds will not dissolve in water because the attraction of the water molecules to each other is much stronger than the attraction of the water molecules to the compound.

Section 2

Page 654: A hydronium ion forms when a hydrogen ion bonds to a water molecule in a water solution.

Page 656: Sulfuric acid is used in car batteries to conduct electric current. Hydrochloric acid is used as an algaecide in swimming pools. Nitric acid is used to make fertilizers.

Page 659: Bases can be used at home in the form of soap, oven cleaner, or antacid.

Section 3

Page 660: In a strong acid, all of the molecules of the acid break apart when the acid is dissolved in water. In a weak acid, only a few of the acid molecules break apart when the acid is dissolved in water.

Page 662: Indicators turn different colors at different pH levels. The color on the pH strip can be compared with the colors on the indicator scale to determine the pH of the solution being tested.

Section 4

Page 664: Structural formulas show how atoms in a molecule are connected.

Page 667: Proteins are made of building blocks called *amino acids.*

Page 668: Nucleic acids store genetic information and build proteins.

Chapter 25 Atomic Energy

Section 1

Page 681: mass number and charge

Page 683: fatigue, loss of appetite, and hair loss

Page 685: 5,730 years

Page 686: A tracer is a radioactive element whose path can be followed through a process or reaction.

Section 2

Page 688: A nucleus that undergoes nuclear fission splits into two smaller, more stable nuclei.

Page 691: Sample answer: Using nuclear fission to generate electrical energy can help our supply of fossil fuels last longer, can help protect the environment because gases such as carbon dioxide are not released during fission, and can save money because nuclear power plants often cost less to run than power plants that use fossil fuels.

Page 692: In nuclear fusion, two or more nuclei that have small masses combine to form a larger nucleus. During fusion, energy is released.

Study Skills

FoldNote Instructions

Have you ever tried to study for a test or quiz but didn't know where to start? Or have you read a chapter and found that you can remember only a few ideas? Well, FoldNotes are a fun and exciting way to help you learn and remember the ideas you encounter as you learn science!

FoldNotes are tools that you can use to organize concepts. By focusing on a few main concepts, FoldNotes help you learn and remember how the concepts fit together. They can help you see the "big picture." Below you will find instructions for building 10 different FoldNotes.

Pyramid

1. Place a sheet of paper in front of you. Fold the lower left-hand corner of the paper diagonally to the opposite edge of the paper.

2. Cut off the tab of paper created by the fold (at the top).

3. Open the paper so that it is a square. Fold the lower right-hand corner of the paper diagonally to the opposite corner to form a triangle.

4. Open the paper. The creases of the two folds will have created an X.

5. Using scissors, cut along one of the creases. Start from any corner, and stop at the center point to create two flaps. Use tape or glue to attach one of the flaps on top of the other flap.

Double Door

1. Fold a sheet of paper in half from the top to the bottom. Then, unfold the paper.

2. Fold the top and bottom edges of the paper to the crease.

Booklet

1. Fold a sheet of paper in half from left to right. Then, unfold the paper.

2. Fold the sheet of paper in half again from the top to the bottom. Then, unfold the paper.

3. Refold the sheet of paper in half from left to right.

4. Fold the top and bottom edges to the center crease.

5. Completely unfold the paper.

6. Refold the paper from top to bottom.

7. Using scissors, cut a slit along the center crease of the sheet from the folded edge to the creases made in step 4. Do not cut the entire sheet in half.

8. Fold the sheet of paper in half from left to right. While holding the bottom and top edges of the paper, push the bottom and top edges together so that the center collapses at the center slit. Fold the four flaps to form a four-page book.

Layered Book

1. Lay one sheet of paper on top of another sheet. Slide the top sheet up so that 2 cm of the bottom sheet is showing.

2. Hold the two sheets together, fold down the top of the two sheets so that you see four 2 cm tabs along the bottom.

3. Using a stapler, staple the top of the FoldNote.

Key-Term Fold

1. Fold a sheet of lined notebook paper in half from left to right.

2. Using scissors, cut along every third line from the right edge of the paper to the center fold to make tabs.

Four-Corner Fold

1. Fold a sheet of paper in half from left to right. Then, unfold the paper.

2. Fold each side of the paper to the crease in the center of the paper.

3. Fold the paper in half from the top to the bottom. Then, unfold the paper.

4. Using scissors, cut the top flap creases made in step 3 to form four flaps.

Three-Panel Flip Chart

1. Fold a piece of paper in half from the top to the bottom.

2. Fold the paper in thirds from side to side. Then, unfold the paper so that you can see the three sections.

3. From the top of the paper, cut along each of the vertical fold lines to the fold in the middle of the paper. You will now have three flaps.

Table Fold

1. Fold a piece of paper in half from the top to the bottom. Then, fold the paper in half again.

2. Fold the paper in thirds from side to side.

3. Unfold the paper completely. Carefully trace the fold lines by using a pen or pencil.

Two-Panel Flip Chart

1. Fold a piece of paper in half from the top to the bottom.

2. Fold the paper in half from side to side. Then, unfold the paper so that you can see the two sections.

3. From the top of the paper, cut along the vertical fold line to the fold in the middle of the paper. You will now have two flaps.

Tri-Fold

1. Fold a piece a paper in thirds from the top to the bottom.

2. Unfold the paper so that you can see the three sections. Then, turn the paper sideways so that the three sections form vertical columns.

3. Trace the fold lines by using a pen or pencil. Label the columns "Know," "Want," and "Learn."

Graphic Organizer Instructions

 Have you ever wished that you could "draw out" the many concepts you learn in your science class? Sometimes, being able to *see* how concepts are related really helps you remember what you've learned. Graphic Organizers do just that! They give you a way to draw or map out concepts.

All you need to make a Graphic Organizer is a piece of paper and a pencil. Below you will find instructions for four different Graphic Organizers designed to help you organize the concepts you'll learn in this book.

Spider Map

1. Draw a diagram like the one shown. In the circle, write the main topic.

2. From the circle, draw legs to represent different categories of the main topic. You can have as many categories as you want.

3. From the category legs, draw horizontal lines. As you read the chapter, write details about each category on the horizontal lines.

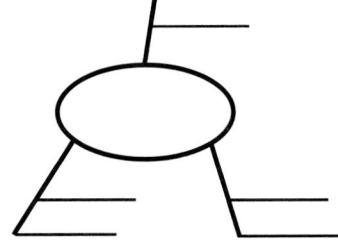

Comparison Table

1. Draw a chart like the one shown. Your chart can have as many columns and rows as you want.

2. In the top row, write the topics that you want to compare.

3. In the left column, write characteristics of the topics that you want to compare. As you read the chapter, fill in the characteristics for each topic in the appropriate boxes.

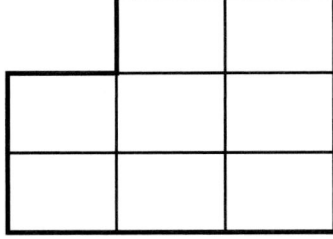

Chain-of-Events-Chart

1. Draw a box. In the box, write the first step of a process or the first event of a timeline.

2. Under the box, draw another box, and use an arrow to connect the two boxes. In the second box, write the next step of the process or the next event in the timeline.

3. Continue adding boxes until the process or timeline is finished.

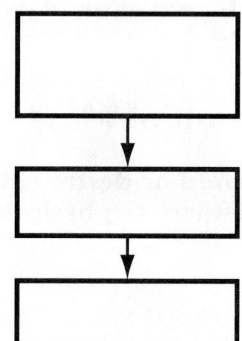

Concept Map

1. Draw a circle in the center of a piece of paper. Write the main idea of the chapter in the center of the circle.

2. From the circle, draw other circles. In those circles, write characteristics of the main idea. Draw arrows from the center circle to the circles that contain the characteristics.

3. From each circle that contains a characteristic, draw other circles. In those circles, write specific details about the characteristic. Draw arrows from each circle that contains a characteristic to the circles that contain specific details. You may draw as many circles as you want.

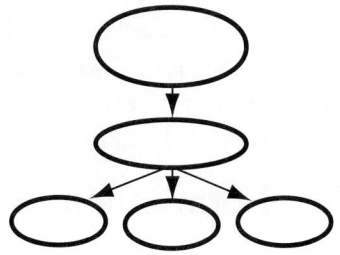

Physical Science Laws and Principles

Law of Conservation of Mass

Mass cannot be created or destroyed during ordinary chemical or physical changes.

The total mass in a closed system is always the same no matter how many physical changes or chemical reactions occur.

Law of Conservation of Energy

Energy can be neither created nor destroyed.

The total amount of energy in a closed system is always the same. Energy can be changed from one form to another, but all of the different forms of energy in a system always add up to the same total amount of energy no matter how many energy conversions occur.

Law of Universal Gravitation

All objects in the universe attract each other by a force called *gravity*. The size of the force depends on the masses of the objects and the distance between the objects.

The first part of the law explains why lifting a bowling ball is much harder than lifting a marble. Because the bowling ball has a much larger mass than the marble does, the amount of gravity between the Earth and the bowling ball is greater than the amount of gravity between the Earth and the marble.

The second part of the law explains why a satellite can remain in orbit around the Earth. The satellite is carefully placed at a distance great enough to prevent the Earth's gravity from immediately pulling the satellite down but small enough to prevent the satellite from completely escaping the Earth's gravity and wandering off into space.

Newton's Laws of Motion

Newton's first law of motion states that an object at rest remains at rest and an object in motion remains in motion at constant speed and in a straight line unless acted on by an unbalanced force.

The first part of the law explains why a football will remain on a tee until it is kicked off or until a gust of wind blows it off.

The second part of the law explains why a bike rider will continue moving forward after the bike comes to an abrupt stop. Gravity and the friction of the sidewalk will eventually stop the rider.

Newton's second law of motion states that the acceleration of an object depends on the mass of the object and the amount of force applied.

The first part of the law explains why the acceleration of a 4 kg bowling ball will be greater than the acceleration of a 6 kg bowling ball if the same force is applied to both balls.

The second part of the law explains why the acceleration of a bowling ball will be larger if a larger force is applied to the bowling ball.

The relationship of acceleration (a) to mass (m) and force (F) can be expressed mathematically by the following equation:

$$acceleration = \frac{force}{mass}, \text{ or } a = \frac{F}{m}$$

This equation is often rearranged to the form

$$force = mass \times acceleration, \text{ or } F = m \times a$$

Newton's third law of motion states that whenever one object exerts a force on a second object, the second object exerts an equal and opposite force on the first.

This law explains that a runner is able to move forward because of the equal and opposite force that the ground exerts on the runner's foot after each step.

Law of Reflection

The law of reflection states that the angle of incidence is equal to the angle of reflection. This law explains why light reflects off a surface at the same angle that the light strikes the surface.

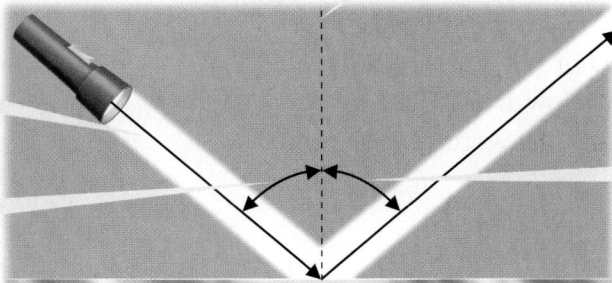

The beam of light traveling toward the mirror is called the *incident beam.*

A line perpendicular to the mirror's surface is called the *normal.*

The beam of light reflected off the mirror is called the *reflected beam.*

The angle between the incident beam and the normal is called the *angle of incidence.*

The angle between the reflected beam and the normal is called the *angle of reflection.*

Charles's Law

Charles's law states that for a fixed amount of gas at a constant pressure, the volume of the gas increases as the temperature of the gas increases. Likewise, the volume of the gas decreases as the temperature of the gas decreases.

If a basketball that was inflated indoors is left outside on a cold winter day, the air particles inside the ball will move more slowly. They will hit the sides of the basketball less often and with less force. The ball will get smaller as the volume of the air decreases.

Boyle's Law

Boyle's law states that for a fixed amount of gas at a constant temperature, the volume of a gas increases as the pressure of the gas decreases. Likewise, the volume of a gas decreases as its pressure increases.

If an inflated balloon is pulled down to the bottom of a swimming pool, the pressure of the water on the balloon increases. The pressure of the air particles inside the balloon must increase to match that of the water outside, so the volume of the air inside the balloon decreases.

Pascal's Principle

Pascal's principle states that a change in pressure at any point in an enclosed fluid will be transmitted equally to all parts of that fluid.

When a mechanic uses a hydraulic jack to raise an automobile off the ground, he or she increases the pressure on the fluid in the jack by pushing on the jack handle. The pressure is transmitted equally to all parts of the fluid-filled jacking system. As fluid presses the jack plate against the frame of the car, the car is lifed off the ground.

Archimedes' Principle

Archimedes' principle states that the buoyant force on an object in a fluid is equal to the weight of the volume of fluid that the object displaces.

A person floating in a swimming pool displaces 20 L of water. The weight of that volume of water is about 200 N. Therefore, the buoyant force on the person is 200 N.

Bernoulli's Principle

Bernoulli's principle states that as the speed of a moving fluid increases, the fluid's pressure decreases.

The lift on an airplane wing or on a Frisbee® can be explained in part by using Bernoulli's principle. Because of the shape of the Frisbee, the air moving over the top of the Frisbee must travel farther than the air below the Frisbee in the same amount of time. In other words, the air above the Frisbee is moving faster than the air below it. This faster-moving air above the Frisbee exerts less pressure than the slower-moving air below it does. The resulting increased pressure below exerts an upward force and pushes the Frisbee up.

Useful Equations

Average speed

$$\text{average speed} = \frac{\text{total distance}}{\text{total time}}$$

Example: A bicycle messenger traveled a distance of 136 km in 8 h. What was the messenger's average speed?

$$\frac{136 \text{ km}}{8 \text{ h}} = 17 \text{ km/h}$$

The messenger's average speed was **17 km/h.**

Average acceleration

$$\frac{\text{average}}{\text{acceleration}} = \frac{\text{final velocity} - \text{starting velocity}}{\text{time it takes to change velocity}}$$

Example: Calculate the average acceleration of an Olympic 100 m dash sprinter who reaches a velocity of 20 m/s south at the finish line. The race was in a straight line and lasted 10 s.

$$\frac{20 \text{ m/s} - 0 \text{ m/s}}{10 \text{s}} = 2 \text{ m/s/s}$$

The sprinter's average acceleration is **2 m/s/s south.**

Net force

Forces in the Same Direction
When forces are in the same direction, add the forces together to determine the net force.

Example: Calculate the net force on a stalled car that is being pushed by two people. One person is pushing with a force of 13 N northwest, and the other person is pushing with a force of 8 N in the same direction.

$$13 \text{ N} + 8 \text{ N} = 21 \text{ N}$$

The net force is **21 N northwest.**

Forces in Opposite Directions
When forces are in opposite directions, subtract the smaller force from the larger force to determine the net force. The net force will be in the direction of the larger force.

Example: Calculate the net force on a rope that is being pulled on each end. One person is pulling on one end of the rope with a force of 12 N south. Another person is pulling on the opposite end of the rope with a force of 7 N north.

$$12 \text{ N} - 7 \text{ N} = 5 \text{ N}$$

The net force is **5 N south.**

Appendix

Work

Work is done by exerting a force through a distance. Work has units of joules (J), which are equivalent to Newton-meters.

$$Work = F \times d$$

Example: Calculate the amount of work done by a man who lifts a 100 N toddler 1.5 m off the floor.

$Work = 100 \text{ N} \times 1.5 \text{ m} = 150 \text{ N•m} = 150 \text{ J}$

The man did **150 J** of work.

Power

Power is the rate at which work is done. Power is measured in watts (W), which are equivalent to joules per second.

$$P = \frac{Work}{t}$$

Example: Calculate the power of a weightlifter who raises a 300 N barbell 2.1 m off the floor in 1.25 s.

$Work = 300 \text{ N} \times 2.1 \text{ m} = 630 \text{ N•m} = 630 \text{ J}$

$$P = \frac{630 \text{ J}}{1.25 \text{ s}} = \frac{504 \text{ J}}{\text{s}} = 504 \text{ W}$$

The weightlifter has **504 W** of power.

Pressure

Pressure is the force exerted over a given area. The SI unit for pressure is the pascal (Pa).

$$pressure = \frac{force}{area}$$

Example: Calculate the pressure of the air in a soccer ball if the air exerts a force of 25,000 N over an area of 0.15 m^2.

$$pressure = \frac{25,000 \text{ N}}{0.15 \text{ m}^2} = \frac{167,000 \text{ N}}{\text{m}^2} = 167,000 \text{ Pa}$$

The pressure of the air inside the soccer ball is **167,000 Pa.**

Density

$$density = \frac{mass}{volume}$$

Example: Calculate the density of a sponge that has a mass of 10 g and a volume of 40 cm^3.

$$\frac{10 \text{ g}}{40 \text{ cm}^3} = \frac{0.25 \text{ g}}{\text{cm}^3}$$

The density of the sponge is $\frac{\textbf{0.25 g}}{\textbf{cm}^3}$.

Concentration

$$concentration = \frac{mass \text{ } of \text{ } solute}{volume \text{ } of \text{ } solvent}$$

Example: Calculate the concentration of a solution in which 10 g of sugar is dissolved in 125 mL of water.

$$\frac{10 \text{ g of sugar}}{125 \text{ mL of water}} = \frac{0.08 \text{ g}}{\text{mL}}$$

The concentration of this solution is $\frac{\textbf{0.08 g}}{\textbf{mL}}$.

Math Refresher

Science requires an understanding of many math concepts. The following pages will help you review some important math skills.

Averages

An **average,** or **mean,** simplifies a set of numbers into a single number that *approximates* the value of the set.

Example: Find the average of the following set of numbers: 5, 4, 7, and 8.

Step 1: Find the sum.
$$5 + 4 + 7 + 8 = 24$$

Step 2: Divide the sum by the number of numbers in your set. Because there are four numbers in this example, divide the sum by 4.
$$\frac{24}{4} = 6$$

The average, or mean, is **6.**

Ratios

A **ratio** is a comparison between numbers, and it is usually written as a fraction.

Example: Find the ratio of thermometers to students if you have 36 thermometers and 48 students in your class.

Step 1: Make the ratio.
$$\frac{36 \text{ thermometers}}{48 \text{ students}}$$

Step 2: Reduce the fraction to its simplest form.
$$\frac{36}{48} = \frac{36 \div 12}{48 \div 12} = \frac{3}{4}$$

The ratio of thermometers to students is **3 to 4,** or $\frac{3}{4}$. The ratio may also be written in the form 3:4.

Proportions

A **proportion** is an equation that states that two ratios are equal.
$$\frac{3}{1} = \frac{12}{4}$$

To solve a proportion, first multiply across the equal sign. This is called *cross-multiplication.* If you know three of the quantities in a proportion, you can use cross-multiplication to find the fourth.

Example: Imagine that you are making a scale model of the solar system for your science project. The diameter of Jupiter is 11.2 times the diameter of the Earth. If you are using a plastic-foam ball that has a diameter of 2 cm to represent the Earth, what must the diameter of the ball representing Jupiter be?
$$\frac{11.2}{1} = \frac{x}{2 \text{ cm}}$$

Step 1: Cross-multiply.
$$\frac{11.2}{1} \diagdown\!\!\!\!\diagup \frac{x}{2}$$
$$11.2 \times 2 = x \times 1$$

Step 2: Multiply.
$$22.4 = x \times 1$$

Step 3: Isolate the variable by dividing both sides by 1.
$$x = \frac{22.4}{1}$$
$$x = 22.4 \text{ cm}$$

You will need to use a ball that has a diameter of **22.4** cm to represent Jupiter.

Percentages

A **percentage** is a ratio of a given number to 100.

> **Example:** What is 85% of 40?

Step 1: Rewrite the percentage by moving the decimal point two places to the left.

$$0.85$$

Step 2: Multiply the decimal by the number that you are calculating the percentage of.

$$0.85 \times 40 = 34$$

85% of 40 is **34.**

Decimals

To **add** or **subtract decimals,** line up the digits vertically so that the decimal points line up. Then, add or subtract the columns from right to left. Carry or borrow numbers as necessary.

> **Example:** Add the following numbers: 3.1415 and 2.96.

Step 1: Line up the digits vertically so that the decimal points line up.

$$\begin{array}{r} 3.1415 \\ + 2.96 \\ \hline \end{array}$$

Step 2: Add the columns from right to left, and carry when necessary.

$$\begin{array}{r} ^{1\ 1} \\ 3.1415 \\ + 2.96 \\ \hline 6.1015 \end{array}$$

The sum is **6.1015.**

Fractions

Numbers tell you how many; **fractions** tell you *how much of a whole.*

> **Example:** Your class has 24 plants. Your teacher instructs you to put 5 plants in a shady spot. What fraction of the plants in your class will you put in a shady spot?

Step 1: In the denominator, write the total number of parts in the whole.

$$\frac{?}{24}$$

Step 2: In the numerator, write the number of parts of the whole that are being considered.

$$\frac{5}{24}$$

So, $\frac{5}{24}$ of the plants will be in the shade.

Reducing Fractions

It is usually best to express a fraction in its simplest form. Expressing a fraction in its simplest form is called *reducing* a fraction.

> **Example:** Reduce the fraction $\frac{30}{45}$ to its simplest form.

Step 1: Find the largest whole number that will divide evenly into both the numerator and denominator. This number is called the *greatest common factor* (GCF).

Factors of the numerator 30:
1, 2, 3, 5, 6, 10, **15,** 30

Factors of the denominator 45:
1, 3, 5, 9, **15,** 45

Step 2: Divide both the numerator and the denominator by the GCF, which in this case is 15.

$$\frac{30}{45} = \frac{30 \div 15}{45 \div 15} = \frac{2}{3}$$

Thus, $\frac{30}{45}$ reduced to its simplest form is $\frac{2}{3}$.

Adding and Subtracting Fractions

To **add** or **subtract fractions** that have the **same denominator,** simply add or subtract the numerators.

Examples:

$$\frac{3}{5} + \frac{1}{5} = ? \text{ and } \frac{3}{4} - \frac{1}{4} = ?$$

Step 1: Add or subtract the numerators.

$$\frac{3}{5} + \frac{1}{5} = \frac{4}{} \text{ and } \frac{3}{4} - \frac{1}{4} = \frac{2}{}$$

Step 2: Write the sum or difference over the denominator.

$$\frac{3}{5} + \frac{1}{5} = \frac{4}{5} \text{ and } \frac{3}{4} - \frac{1}{4} = \frac{2}{4}$$

Step 3: If necessary, reduce the fraction to its simplest form.

$\frac{4}{5}$ cannot be reduced, and $\frac{2}{4} = \frac{1}{2}$.

To **add** or **subtract fractions** that have **different denominators,** first find the least common denominator (LCD).

Examples:

$$\frac{1}{2} + \frac{1}{6} = ? \text{ and } \frac{3}{4} - \frac{2}{3} = ?$$

Step 1: Write the equivalent fractions that have a common denominator.

$$\frac{3}{6} + \frac{1}{6} = ? \text{ and } \frac{9}{12} - \frac{8}{12} = ?$$

Step 2: Add or subtract the fractions.

$$\frac{3}{6} + \frac{1}{6} = \frac{4}{6} \text{ and } \frac{9}{12} - \frac{8}{12} = \frac{1}{12}$$

Step 3: If necessary, reduce the fraction to its simplest form.

The fraction $\frac{4}{6} = \frac{2}{3}$, and $\frac{1}{12}$ cannot be reduced.

Multiplying Fractions

To **multiply fractions,** multiply the numerators and the denominators together, and then reduce the fraction to its simplest form.

Example:

$$\frac{5}{9} \times \frac{7}{10} = ?$$

Step 1: Multiply the numerators and denominators.

$$\frac{5}{9} \times \frac{7}{10} = \frac{5 \times 7}{9 \times 10} = \frac{35}{90}$$

Step 2: Reduce the fraction.

$$\frac{35}{90} = \frac{35 \div 5}{90 \div 5} = \frac{7}{18}$$

Dividing Fractions

To **divide fractions,** first rewrite the divisor (the number you divide by) upside down. This number is called the *reciprocal* of the divisor. Then multiply and reduce if necessary.

Example:

$$\frac{5}{8} \div \frac{3}{2} = ?$$

Step 1: Rewrite the divisor as its reciprocal.

$$\frac{3}{2} \rightarrow \frac{2}{3}$$

Step 2: Multiply the fractions.

$$\frac{5}{8} \times \frac{2}{3} = \frac{5 \times 2}{8 \times 3} = \frac{10}{24}$$

Step 3: Reduce the fraction.

$$\frac{10}{24} = \frac{10 \div 2}{24 \div 2} = \frac{5}{12}$$

Scientific Notation

Scientific notation is a short way of representing very large and very small numbers without writing all of the place-holding zeros.

> **Example:** Write 653,000,000 in scientific notation.

Step 1: Write the number without the place-holding zeros.

653

Step 2: Place the decimal point after the first digit.

6.53

Step 3: Find the exponent by counting the number of places that you moved the decimal point.

6.53000000

The decimal point was moved eight places to the left. Therefore, the exponent of 10 is positive 8. If you had moved the decimal point to the right, the exponent would be negative.

Step 4: Write the number in scientific notation.

6.53 × 10⁸

Area

Area is the number of square units needed to cover the surface of an object.

Formulas:

area of a square = side × side
area of a rectangle = length × width
area of a triangle = $\frac{1}{2}$ × base × height

Examples: Find the areas.

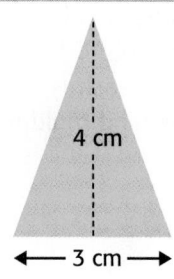

Triangle

area = $\frac{1}{2}$ × base × height

area = $\frac{1}{2}$ × 3 cm × 4 cm

area = **6 cm²**

4 cm

3 cm

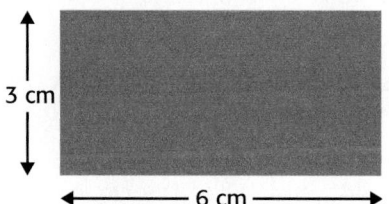

3 cm

6 cm

Rectangle

area = length × width
area = 6 cm × 3 cm
area = **18 cm²**

Square

area = side × side
area = 3 cm × 3 cm
area = **9 cm²**

3 cm

3 cm

Volume

Volume is the amount of space that something occupies.

Formulas:

volume of a cube =
side × side × side

volume of a prism =
area of base × height

Examples:

Find the volume of the solids.

Cube

volume = side × side × side
volume = 4 cm × 4 cm × 4 cm
volume = **64 cm³**

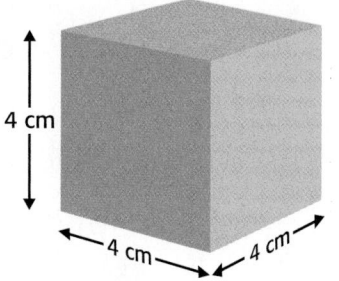

4 cm

4 cm   4 cm

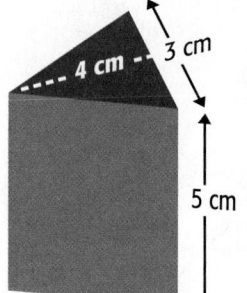

4 cm   3 cm

5 cm

Prism

volume = area of base × height
volume = (area of triangle) × height
volume = ($\frac{1}{2}$ × 3 cm × 4 cm) × 5 cm
volume = 6 cm² × 5 cm
volume = **30 cm³**

Making Charts and Graphs

Pie Charts

A pie chart shows how each group of data relates to all of the data. Each part of the circle forming the chart represents a category of the data. The entire circle represents all of the data. For example, a biologist studying a hardwood forest in Wisconsin found that there were five different types of trees. The data table at right summarizes the biologist's findings.

Wisconsin Hardwood Trees	
Type of tree	**Number found**
Oak	600
Maple	750
Beech	300
Birch	1,200
Hickory	150
Total	3,000

How to Make a Pie Chart

1 To make a pie chart of these data, first find the percentage of each type of tree. Divide the number of trees of each type by the total number of trees, and multiply by 100.

$$\frac{600 \text{ oak}}{3,000 \text{ trees}} \times 100 = 20\%$$

$$\frac{750 \text{ maple}}{3,000 \text{ trees}} \times 100 = 25\%$$

$$\frac{300 \text{ beech}}{3,000 \text{ trees}} \times 100 = 10\%$$

$$\frac{1,200 \text{ birch}}{3,000 \text{ trees}} \times 100 = 40\%$$

$$\frac{150 \text{ hickory}}{3,000 \text{ trees}} \times 100 = 5\%$$

2 Now, determine the size of the wedges that make up the pie chart. Multiply each percentage by 360°. Remember that a circle contains 360°.

$20\% \times 360° = 72°$ $25\% \times 360° = 90°$

$10\% \times 360° = 36°$ $40\% \times 360° = 144°$

$5\% \times 360° = 18°$

3 Check that the sum of the percentages is 100 and the sum of the degrees is 360.

$20\% + 25\% + 10\% + 40\% + 5\% = 100\%$

$72° + 90° + 36° + 144° + 18° = 360°$

4 Use a compass to draw a circle and mark the center of the circle.

5 Then, use a protractor to draw angles of 72°, 90°, 36°, 144°, and 18° in the circle.

6 Finally, label each part of the chart, and choose an appropriate title.

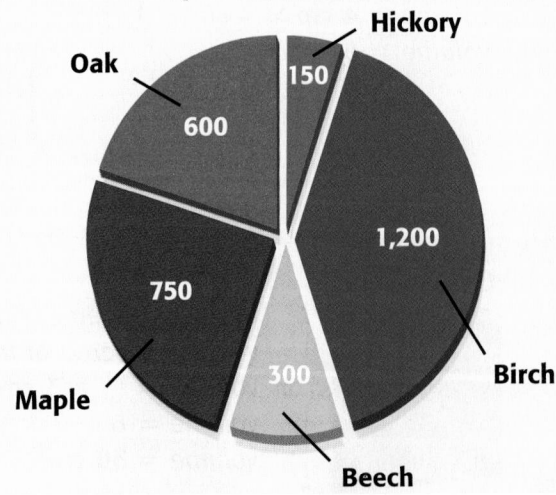

A Community of Wisconsin Hardwood Trees

Line Graphs

Line graphs are most often used to demonstrate continuous change. For example, Mr. Smith's students analyzed the population records for their hometown, Appleton, between 1900 and 2000. Examine the data at right.

Because the year and the population change, they are the *variables*. The population is determined by, or dependent on, the year. Therefore, the population is called the **dependent variable,** and the year is called the **independent variable.** Each set of data is called a **data pair.** To prepare a line graph, you must first organize data pairs into a table like the one at right.

Population of Appleton, 1900–2000	
Year	Population
1900	1,800
1920	2,500
1940	3,200
1960	3,900
1980	4,600
2000	5,300

How to Make a Line Graph

1 Place the independent variable along the horizontal (*x*) axis. Place the dependent variable along the vertical (*y*) axis.

2 Label the *x*-axis "Year" and the *y*-axis "Population." Look at your largest and smallest values for the population. For the *y*-axis, determine a scale that will provide enough space to show these values. You must use the same scale for the entire length of the axis. Next, find an appropriate scale for the *x*-axis.

3 Choose reasonable starting points for each axis.

4 Plot the data pairs as accurately as possible.

5 Choose a title that accurately represents the data.

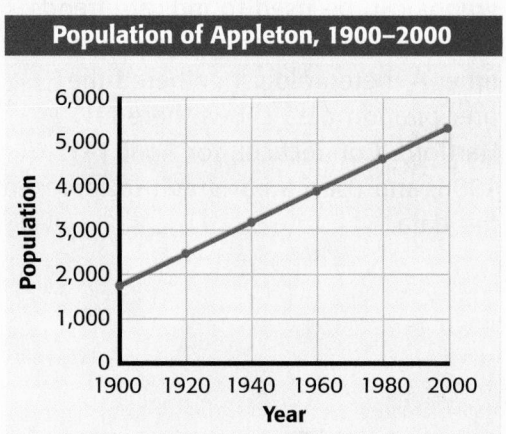

Population of Appleton, 1900–2000

How to Determine Slope

Slope is the ratio of the change in the *y*-value to the change in the *x*-value, or "rise over run."

1 Choose two points on the line graph. For example, the population of Appleton in 2000 was 5,300 people. Therefore, you can define point *a* as (2000, 5,300). In 1900, the population was 1,800 people. You can define point *b* as (1900, 1,800).

2 Find the change in the *y*-value.
(*y* at point *a*) − (*y* at point *b*) =
5,300 people − 1,800 people =
3,500 people

3 Find the change in the *x*-value.
(*x* at point *a*) − (*x* at point *b*) =
2000 − 1900 = 100 years

4 Calculate the slope of the graph by dividing the change in *y* by the change in *x*.

$$slope = \frac{change\ in\ y}{change\ in\ x}$$

$$slope = \frac{3,500\ people}{100\ years}$$

$$slope = 35\ people\ per\ year$$

In this example, the population in Appleton increased by a fixed amount each year. The graph of these data is a straight line. Therefore, the relationship is **linear.** When the graph of a set of data is not a straight line, the relationship is **nonlinear.**

Using Algebra to Determine Slope

The equation in step 4 may also be arranged to be

$$y = kx$$

where y represents the change in the y-value, k represents the slope, and x represents the change in the x-value.

$$slope = \frac{change\ in\ y}{change\ in\ x}$$

$$k = \frac{y}{x}$$

$$k \times x = \frac{y \times x}{x}$$

$$kx = y$$

Bar Graphs

Bar graphs are used to demonstrate change that is not continuous. These graphs can be used to indicate trends when the data cover a long period of time. A meteorologist gathered the precipitation data shown here for Hartford, Connecticut, for April 1–15, 1996, and used a bar graph to represent the data.

Precipitation in Hartford, Connecticut April 1–15, 1996			
Date	Precipitation (cm)	Date	Precipitation (cm)
April 1	0.5	April 9	0.25
April 2	1.25	April 10	0.0
April 3	0.0	April 11	1.0
April 4	0.0	April 12	0.0
April 5	0.0	April 13	0.25
April 6	0.0	April 14	0.0
April 7	0.0	April 15	6.50
April 8	1.75		

How to Make a Bar Graph

1 Use an appropriate scale and a reasonable starting point for each axis.

2 Label the axes, and plot the data.

3 Choose a title that accurately represents the data.

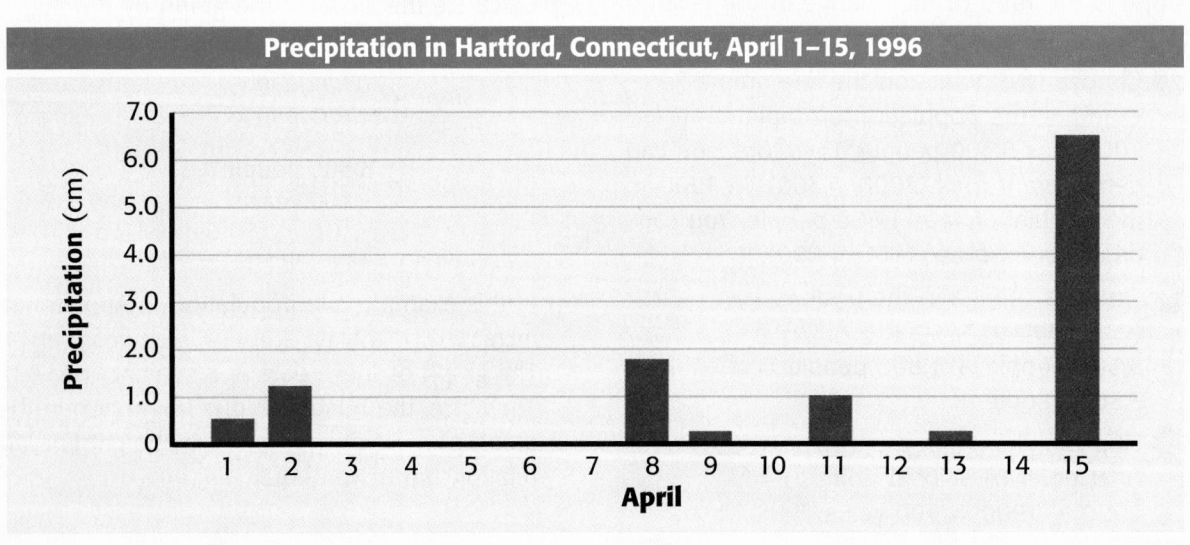

Measuring Skills

Using a Graduated Cylinder

When using a graduated cylinder to measure volume, keep the following procedures in mind:

1. Place the cylinder on a flat, level surface before measuring liquid.

2. Move your head so that your eye is level with the surface of the liquid.

3. Read the mark closest to the liquid level. On glass graduated cylinders, read the mark closest to the center of the curve in the liquid's surface.

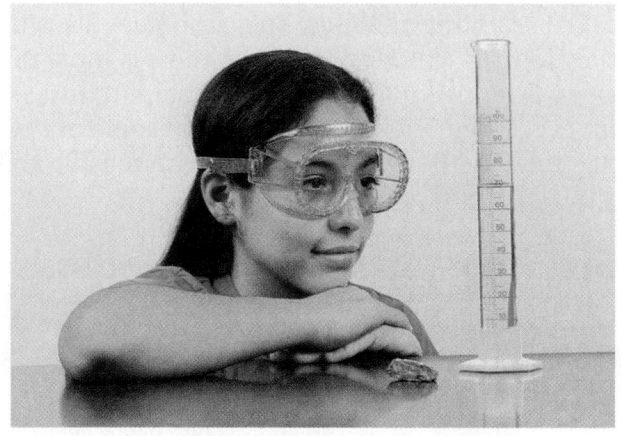

Using a Meterstick or Metric Ruler

When using a meterstick or metric ruler to measure length, keep the following procedures in mind:

1. Place the ruler firmly against the object that you are measuring.

2. Align one edge of the object exactly with the 0 end of the ruler.

3. Look at the other edge of the object to see which of the marks on the ruler is closest to that edge. (Note: Each small slash between the centimeters represents a millimeter, which is one-tenth of a centimeter.)

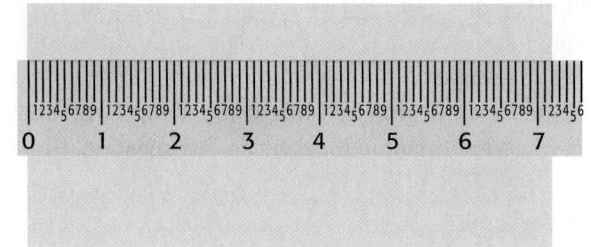

Using a Triple-Beam Balance

When using a triple-beam balance to measure mass, keep the following procedures in mind:

1. Make sure the balance is on a level surface.

2. Place all of the countermasses at 0. Adjust the balancing knob until the pointer rests at 0.

3. Place the object you wish to measure on the pan. **Caution:** Do not place hot objects or chemicals directly on the balance pan.

4. Move the largest countermass along the beam to the right until it is at the last notch that does not tip the balance. Follow the same procedure with the next-largest countermass. Then, move the smallest countermass until the pointer rests at 0.

5. Add the readings from the three beams together to determine the mass of the object.

6. When determining the mass of crystals or powders, first find the mass of a piece of filter paper. Then, add the crystals or powder to the paper, and remeasure. The actual mass of the crystals or powder is the total mass minus the mass of the paper. When finding the mass of liquids, first find the mass of the empty container. Then, find the combined mass of the liquid and container. The mass of the liquid is the total mass minus the mass of the container.

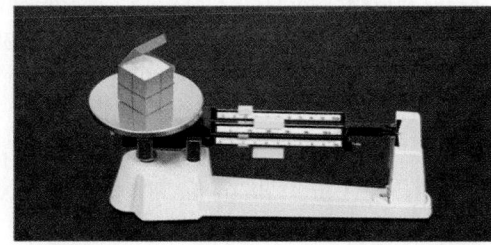

Scientific Methods

The ways in which scientists answer questions and solve problems are called **scientific methods.** The same steps are often used by scientists as they look for answers. However, there is more than one way to use these steps. Scientists may use all of the steps or just some of the steps during an investigation. They may even repeat some of the steps. The goal of using scientific methods is to come up with reliable answers and solutions.

Six Steps of Scientific Methods

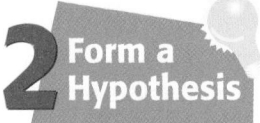
1 Ask a Question

Good questions come from careful **observations.** You make observations by using your senses to gather information. Sometimes, you may use instruments, such as microscopes and telescopes, to extend the range of your senses. As you observe the natural world, you will discover that you have many more questions than answers. These questions drive investigations.

Questions beginning with *what, why, how,* and *when* are important in focusing an investigation. Here is an example of a question that could lead to an investigation.

> **Question:** How does acid rain affect plant growth?

2 Form a Hypothesis

After you ask a question, you need to form a **hypothesis.** A hypothesis is a clear statement of what you expect the answer to your question to be. Your hypothesis will represent your best "educated guess" based on what you have observed and what you already know. A good hypothesis is testable. Otherwise, the investigation can go no further. Here is a hypothesis based on the question, "How does acid rain affect plant growth?"

> **Hypothesis:** Acid rain slows plant growth.

The hypothesis can lead to predictions. A prediction is what you think the outcome of your experiment or data collection will be. Predictions are usually stated in an if-then format. Here is a sample prediction for the hypothesis that acid rain slows plant growth.

> **Prediction:** If a plant is watered with only acid rain (which has a pH of 4), then the plant will grow at half its normal rate.

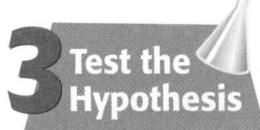
3 Test the Hypothesis

After you have formed a hypothesis and made a prediction, your hypothesis should be tested. One way to test a hypothesis is with a controlled experiment. A **controlled experiment** tests only one factor at a time. In an experiment to test the effect of acid rain on plant growth, the **control group** would be watered with normal rain water. The **experimental group** would be watered with acid rain. All of the plants should receive the same amount of sunlight and water each day. The air temperature should be the same for all groups. However, the acidity of the water will be a variable. In fact, any factor that is different from one group to another is a **variable.** If your hypothesis is correct, then the acidity of the water and plant growth are *dependant variables.* The amount a plant grows is dependent on the acidity of the water. However, the amount of water each plant receives and the amount of sunlight each plant receives are *independent variables.* Either of these factors could change without affecting the other factor.

Sometimes, the nature of an investigation makes a controlled experiment impossible. For example, the Earth's core is surrounded by thousands of meters of rock. Under such circumstances, a hypothesis may be tested by making detailed observations.

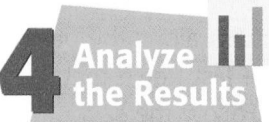
4 Analyze the Results

After you have completed your experiments, made your observations, and collected your data, you must analyze all the information you have gathered. Tables and graphs are often used in this step to organize the data.

5 Draw Conclusions

After analyzing your data, you can determine if your results support your hypothesis. If your hypothesis is supported, you (or others) might want to repeat the observations or experiments to verify your results. If your hypothesis is not supported by the data, you may have to check your procedure for errors. You may even have to reject your hypothesis and make a new one. If you cannot draw a conclusion from your results, you may have to try the investigation again or carry out further observations or experiments.

6 Communicate Results

After any scientific investigation, you should report your results. By preparing a written or oral report, you let others know what you have learned. They may repeat your investigation to see if they get the same results. Your report may even lead to another question and then to another investigation.

Scientific Methods in Action

Scientific methods contain loops in which several steps may be repeated over and over again. In some cases, certain steps are unnecessary. Thus, there is not a "straight line" of steps. For example, sometimes scientists find that testing one hypothesis raises new questions and new hypotheses to be tested. And sometimes, testing the hypothesis leads directly to a conclusion. Furthermore, the steps in scientific methods are not always used in the same order. Follow the steps in the diagram, and see how many different directions scientific methods can take you.

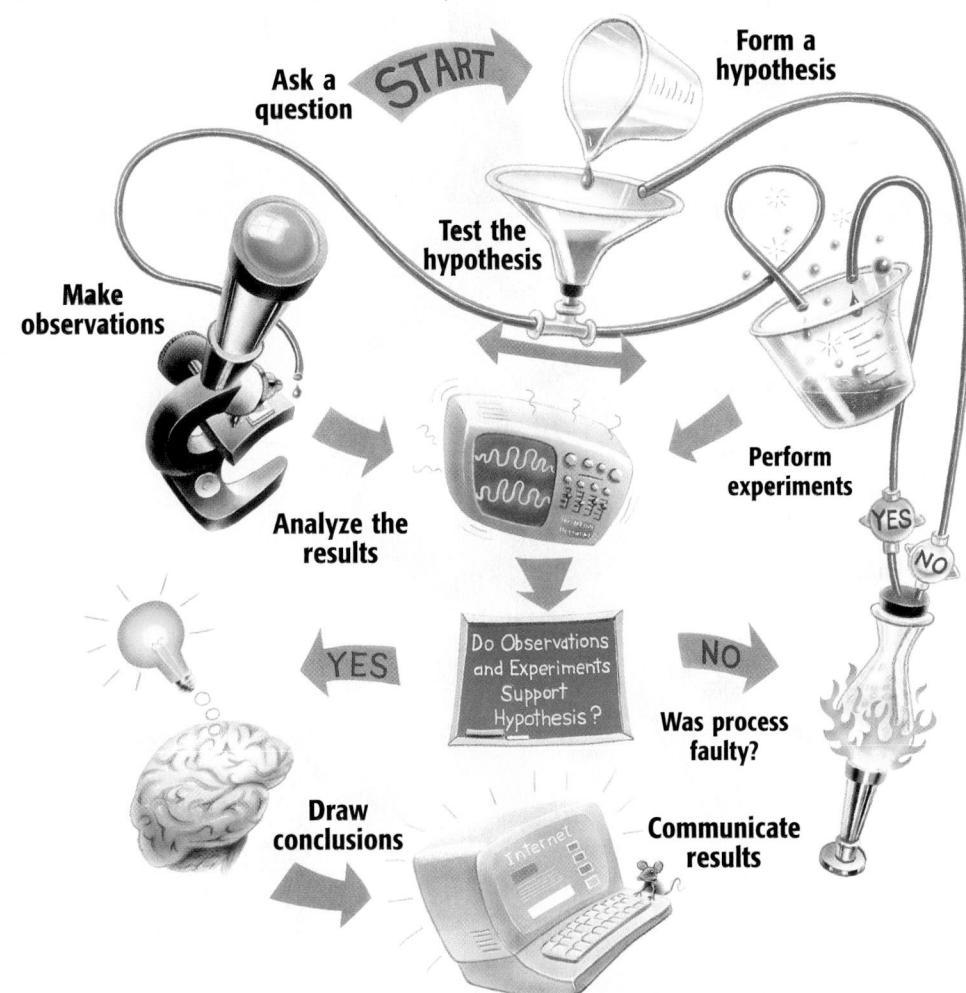

Using the Microscope

Parts of the Compound Light Microscope

- The **ocular lens** magnifies the image 10×.
- The **low-power objective** magnifies the image 10×.
- The **high-power objective** magnifies the image either 40× or 43×.
- The **revolving nosepiece** holds the objectives and can be turned to change from one magnification to the other.
- The **body tube** maintains the correct distance between the ocular lens and objectives.
- The **coarse-adjustment knob** moves the body tube up and down to allow focusing of the image.

- The **fine-adjustment knob** moves the body tube slightly to bring the image into sharper focus. It is usually located in the center of the coarse-adjustment knob.
- The **stage** supports a slide.
- **Stage clips** hold the slide in place for viewing.
- The **diaphragm** controls the amount of light coming through the stage.
- The light source provides a **light** for viewing the slide.
- The **arm** supports the body tube.
- The **base** supports the microscope.

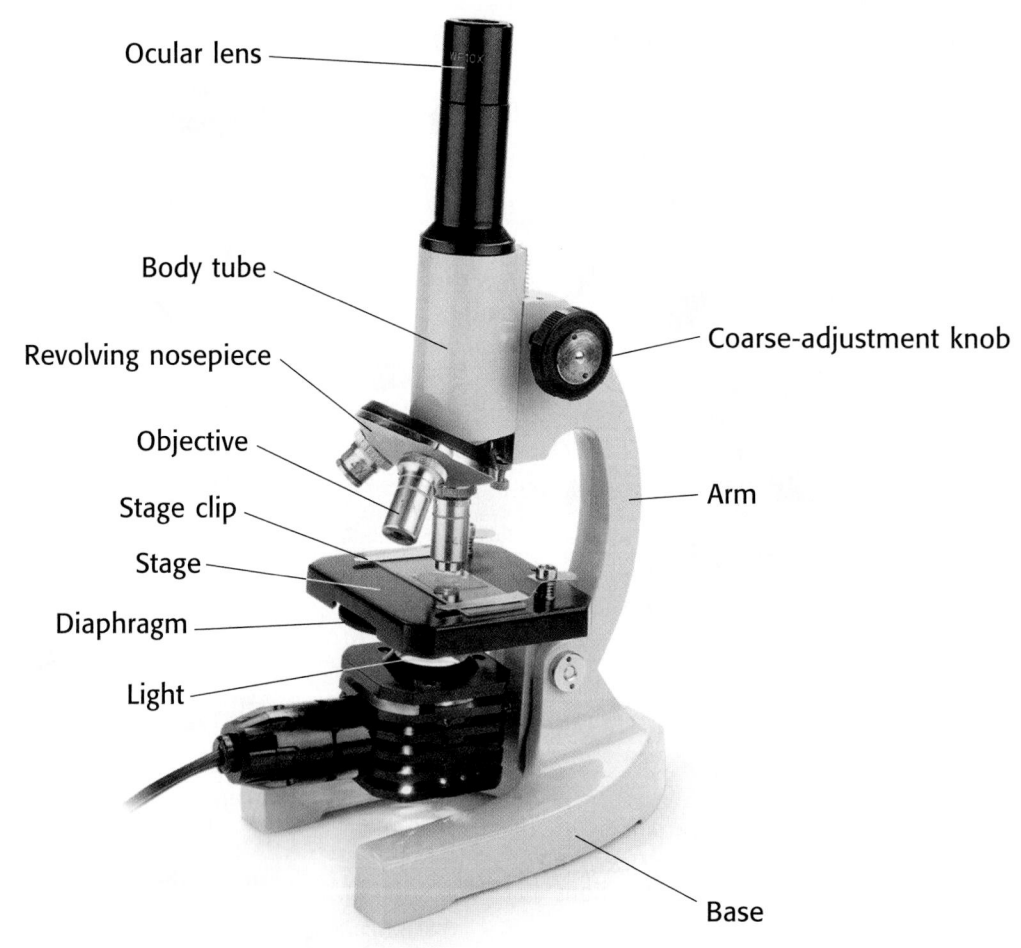

Ocular lens

Body tube

Revolving nosepiece

Objective

Stage clip

Stage

Diaphragm

Light

Coarse-adjustment knob

Arm

Base

Appendix

Proper Use of the Compound Light Microscope

1. Use both hands to carry the microscope to your lab table. Place one hand beneath the base, and use the other hand to hold the arm of the microscope. Hold the microscope close to your body while carrying it to your lab table.

2. Place the microscope on the lab table at least 5 cm from the edge of the table.

3. Check to see what type of light source is used by your microscope. If the microscope has a lamp, plug it in and make sure that the cord is out of the way. If the microscope has a mirror, adjust the mirror to reflect light through the hole in the stage. **Caution:** If your microscope has a mirror, do not use direct sunlight as a light source. Direct sunlight can damage your eyes.

4. Always begin work with the low-power objective in line with the body tube. Adjust the revolving nosepiece.

5. Place a prepared slide over the hole in the stage. Secure the slide with the stage clips.

6. Look through the ocular lens. Move the diaphragm to adjust the amount of light coming through the stage.

7. Look at the stage from eye level. Slowly turn the coarse adjustment to lower the objective until the objective almost touches the slide. Do not allow the objective to touch the slide.

8. Look through the ocular lens. Turn the coarse adjustment to raise the low-power objective until the image is in focus. Always focus by raising the objective away from the slide. Never focus the objective downward. Use the fine adjustment to sharpen the focus. Keep both eyes open while viewing a slide.

9. Make sure that the image is exactly in the center of your field of vision. Then, switch to the high-power objective. Focus the image by using only the fine adjustment. Never use the coarse adjustment at high power.

10. When you are finished using the microscope, remove the slide. Clean the ocular lens and objectives with lens paper. Return the microscope to its storage area. Remember to use both hands when carrying the microscope.

Making a Wet Mount

1. Use lens paper to clean a glass slide and a coverslip.

2. Place the specimen that you wish to observe in the center of the slide.

3. Using a medicine dropper, place one drop of water on the specimen.

4. Hold the coverslip at the edge of the water and at a 45° angle to the slide. Make sure that the water runs along the edge of the coverslip.

5. Lower the coverslip slowly to avoid trapping air bubbles.

6. Water might evaporate from the slide as you work. Add more water to keep the specimen fresh. Place the tip of the medicine dropper next to the edge of the coverslip. Add a drop of water. (You can also use this method to add stain or solutions to a wet mount.) Remove excess water from the slide by using the corner of a paper towel as a blotter. Do not lift the coverslip to add or remove water.

SI Measurement

The International System of Units, or SI, is the standard system of measurement used by many scientists. Using the same standards of measurement makes it easier for scientists to communicate with one another.

SI works by combining prefixes and base units. Each base unit can be used with different prefixes to define smaller and larger quantities. The table below lists common SI prefixes.

SI Prefixes

Prefix	Symbol	Factor	Example
kilo-	k	1,000	kilogram, 1 kg = 1,000 g
hecto-	h	100	hectoliter, 1 hL = 100 L
deka-	da	10	dekameter, 1 dam = 10 m
		1	meter, liter, gram
deci-	d	0.1	decigram, 1 dg = 0.1 g
centi-	c	0.01	centimeter, 1 cm = 0.01 m
milli-	m	0.001	milliliter, 1 mL = 0.001 L
micro-	μ	0.000 001	micrometer, 1 μm = 0.000 001 m

SI Conversion Table

SI units	From SI to English	From English to SI
Length		
kilometer (km) = 1,000 m	1 km = 0.621 mi	1 mi = 1.609 km
meter (m) = 100 cm	1 m = 3.281 ft	1 ft = 0.305 m
centimeter (cm) = 0.01 m	1 cm = 0.394 in.	1 in. = 2.540 cm
millimeter (mm) = 0.001 m	1 mm = 0.039 in.	
micrometer (μm) = 0.000 001 m		
nanometer (nm) = 0.000 000 001 m		
Area		
square kilometer (km^2) = 100 hectares	1 km^2 = 0.386 mi^2	1 mi^2 = 2.590 km^2
hectare (ha) = 10,000 m^2	1 ha = 2.471 acres	1 acre = 0.405 ha
square meter (m^2) = 10,000 cm^2	1 m^2 = 10.764 ft^2	1 ft^2 = 0.093 m^2
square centimeter (cm^2) = 100 mm^2	1 cm^2 = 0.155 in.^{2}	1 in.^{2} = 6.452 cm^2
Volume		
liter (L) = 1,000 mL = 1 dm^3	1 L = 1.057 fl qt	1 fl qt = 0.946 L
milliliter (mL) = 0.001 L = 1 cm^3	1 mL = 0.034 fl oz	1 fl oz = 29.574 mL
microliter (μL) = 0.000 001 L		
Mass		*Equivalent weight at Earth's surface
kilogram (kg) = 1,000 g	1 kg = 2.205 lb*	1 lb* = 0.454 kg
gram (g) = 1,000 mg	1 g = 0.035 oz*	1 oz* = 28.350 g
milligram (mg) = 0.001 g		
microgram (μg) = 0.000 001 g		

Temperature Scales

Temperature can be expressed by using three different scales: Fahrenheit, Celsius, and Kelvin. The SI unit for temperature is the kelvin (K).

Although 0 K is much colder than 0°C, a change of 1 K is equal to a change of 1°C.

Three Temperature Scales			
	Fahrenheit	Celsius	Kelvin
Water boils	212°	100°	373
Body temperature	98.6°	37°	310
Room temperature	68°	20°	293
Water freezes	32°	0°	273

Temperature Conversions Table		
To convert	**Use this equation:**	**Example**
Celsius to Fahrenheit °C → °F	$°F = \left(\dfrac{9}{5} \times °C\right) + 32$	Convert 45°C to °F. $°F = \left(\dfrac{9}{5} \times 45°C\right) + 32 = 113°F$
Fahrenheit to Celsius °F → °C	$°C = \dfrac{5}{9} \times (°F - 32)$	Convert 68°F to °C. $°C = \dfrac{5}{9} \times (68°F - 32) = 20°C$
Celsius to Kelvin °C → K	$K = °C + 273$	Convert 45°C to K. $K = 45°C + 273 = 318\ K$
Kelvin to Celsius K → °C	$°C = K - 273$	Convert 32 K to °C. $°C = 32K - 273 = -241°C$

Properties of Common Minerals

	Mineral	Color	Luster	Streak	Hardness
Silicate Minerals	Beryl	deep green, pink, white, bluish green, or yellow	vitreous	white	7.5–8
	Chlorite	green	vitreous to pearly	pale green	2–2.5
	Garnet	green, red, brown, black	vitreous	white	6.5–7.5
	Hornblende	dark green, brown, or black	vitreous	none	5–6
	Muscovite	colorless, silvery white, or brown	vitreous or pearly	white	2–2.5
	Olivine	olive green, yellow	vitreous	white or none	6.5–7
	Orthoclase	colorless, white, pink, or other colors	vitreous	white or none	6
	Plagioclase	colorless, white, yellow, pink, green	vitreous	white	6
	Quartz	colorless or white; any color when not pure	vitreous or waxy	white or none	7
Nonsilicate Minerals	**Native Elements**				
	Copper	copper-red	metallic	copper-red	2.5–3
	Diamond	pale yellow or colorless	adamantine	none	10
	Graphite	black to gray	submetallic	black	1–2
	Carbonates				
	Aragonite	colorless, white, or pale yellow	vitreous	white	3.5–4
	Calcite	colorless or white to tan	vitreous	white	3
	Halides				
	Fluorite	light green, yellow, purple, bluish green, or other colors	vitreous	none	4
	Halite	white	vitreous	white	2.0–2.5
	Oxides				
	Hematite	reddish brown to black	metallic to earthy	dark red to red-brown	5.6–6.5
	Magnetite	iron-black	metallic	black	5.5–6.5
	Sulfates				
	Anhydrite	colorless, bluish, or violet	vitreous to pearly	white	3–3.5
	Gypsum	white, pink, gray, or colorless	vitreous, pearly, or silky	white	2.0
	Sulfides				
	Galena	lead-gray	metallic	lead-gray to black	2.5–2.8
	Pyrite	brassy yellow	metallic	greenish, brownish, or black	6–6.5

Appendix

Density (g/cm³)	Cleavage, Fracture, Special Properties	Common Uses
2.6–2.8	1 cleavage direction; irregular fracture; some varieties fluoresce in ultraviolet light	gemstones, ore of the metal beryllium
2.6–3.3	1 cleavage direction; irregular fracture	
4.2	no cleavage; conchoidal to splintery fracture	gemstones, abrasives
3.0–3.4	2 cleavage directions; hackly to splintery fracture	
2.7–3	1 cleavage direction; irregular fracture	electrical insulation, wallpaper, fireproofing material, lubricant
3.2–3.3	no cleavage; conchoidal fracture	gemstones, casting
2.6	2 cleavage directions; irregular fracture	porcelain
2.6–2.7	2 cleavage directions; irregular fracture	ceramics
2.6	no cleavage; conchoidal fracture	gemstones, concrete, glass, porcelain, sandpaper, lenses
8.9	no cleavage; hackly fracture	wiring, brass, bronze, coins
3.5	4 cleavage directions; irregular to conchoidal fracture	gemstones, drilling
2.3	1 cleavage direction; irregular fracture	pencils, paints, lubricants, batteries
2.95	2 cleavage directions; irregular fracture; reacts with hydrochloric acid	no important industrial uses
2.7	3 cleavage directions; irregular fracture; reacts with weak acid; double refraction	cements, soil conditioner, whitewash, construction materials
3.0–3.3	4 cleavage directions; irregular fracture; some varieties fluoresce	hydrofluoric acid, steel, glass, fiberglass, pottery, enamel
2.1–2.2	3 cleavage directions; splintery to conchoidal fracture; salty taste	tanning hides, salting icy roads, food preservation
5.2–5.3	no cleavage; splintery fracture; magnetic when heated	iron ore for steel, pigments
5.2	no cleavage; splintery fracture; magnetic	iron ore
3.0	3 cleavage directions; conchoidal to splintery fracture	soil conditioner, sulfuric acid
2.3	3 cleavage directions; conchoidal to splintery fracture	plaster of Paris, wallboard, soil conditioner
7.4–7.6	3 cleavage directions; irregular fracture	batteries, paints
5	no cleavage; conchoidal to splintery fracture	sulfuric acid

Sky Maps

Spring

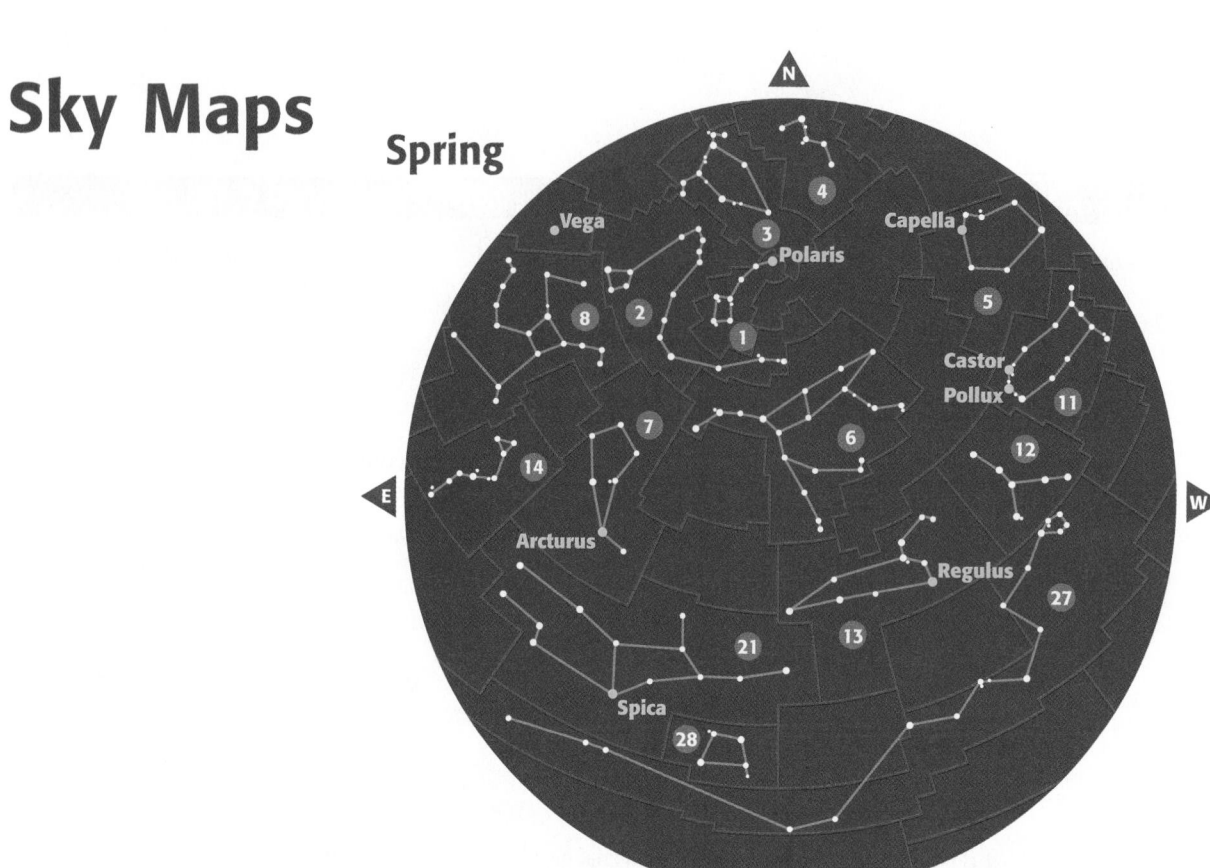

Summer

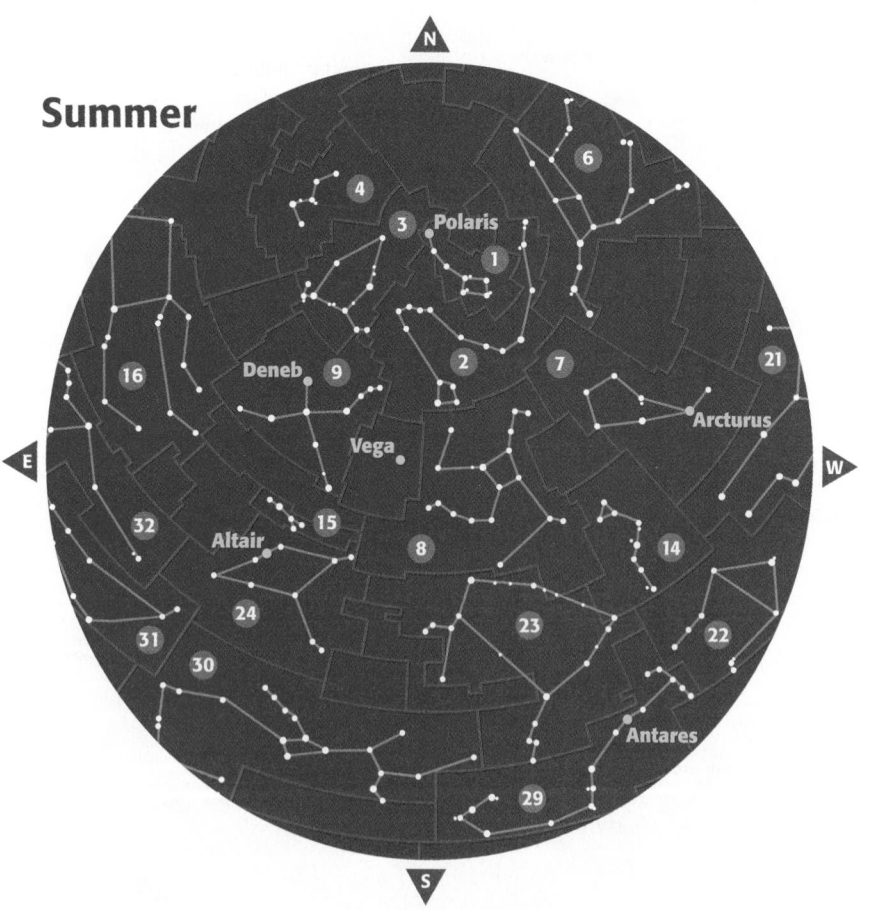

Constellations

1. Ursa Minor
2. Draco
3. Cepheus
4. Cassiopeia
5. Auriga
6. Ursa Major
7. Bootes
8. Hercules
9. Cygnus
10. Perseus
11. Gemini
12. Cancer
13. Leo
14. Serpens
15. Sagitta
16. Pegasus
17. Pisces

Autumn

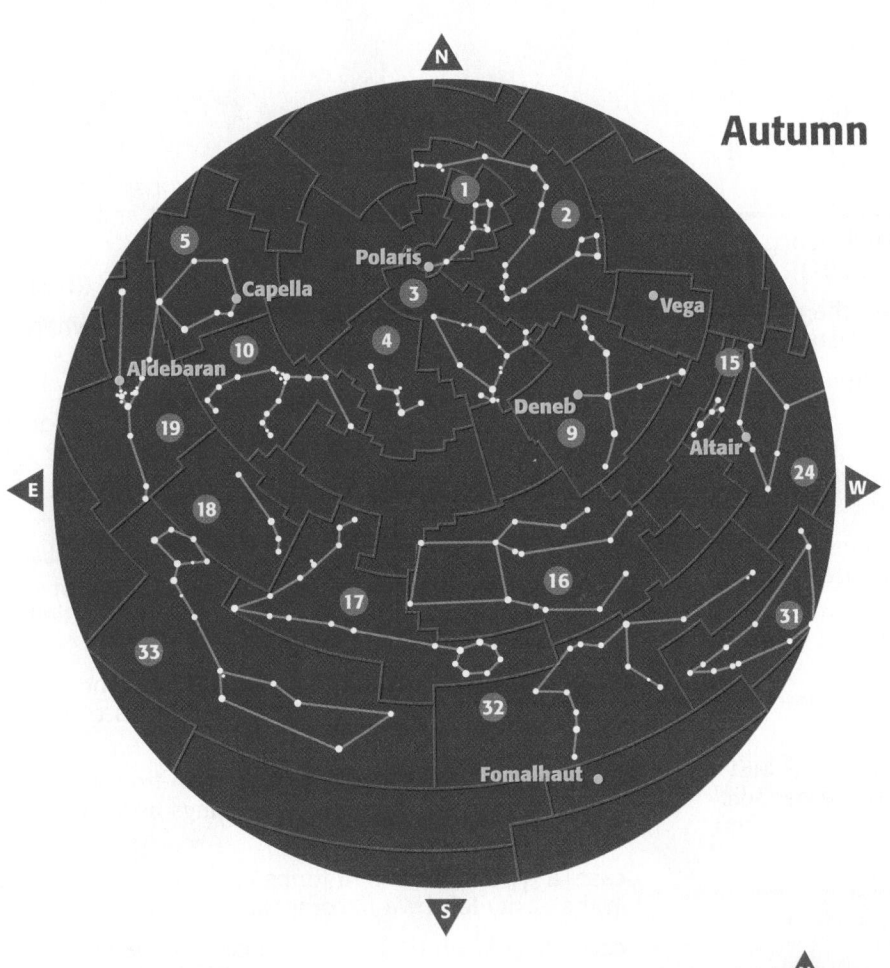

Constellations

18 Aries
19 Taurus
20 Orion
21 Virgo
22 Libra
23 Ophiuchus
24 Aquila
25 Lepus
26 Canis Major
27 Hydra
28 Corvus
29 Scorpius
30 Sagittarius
31 Capricornus
32 Aquarius
33 Cetus
34 Columba

Winter

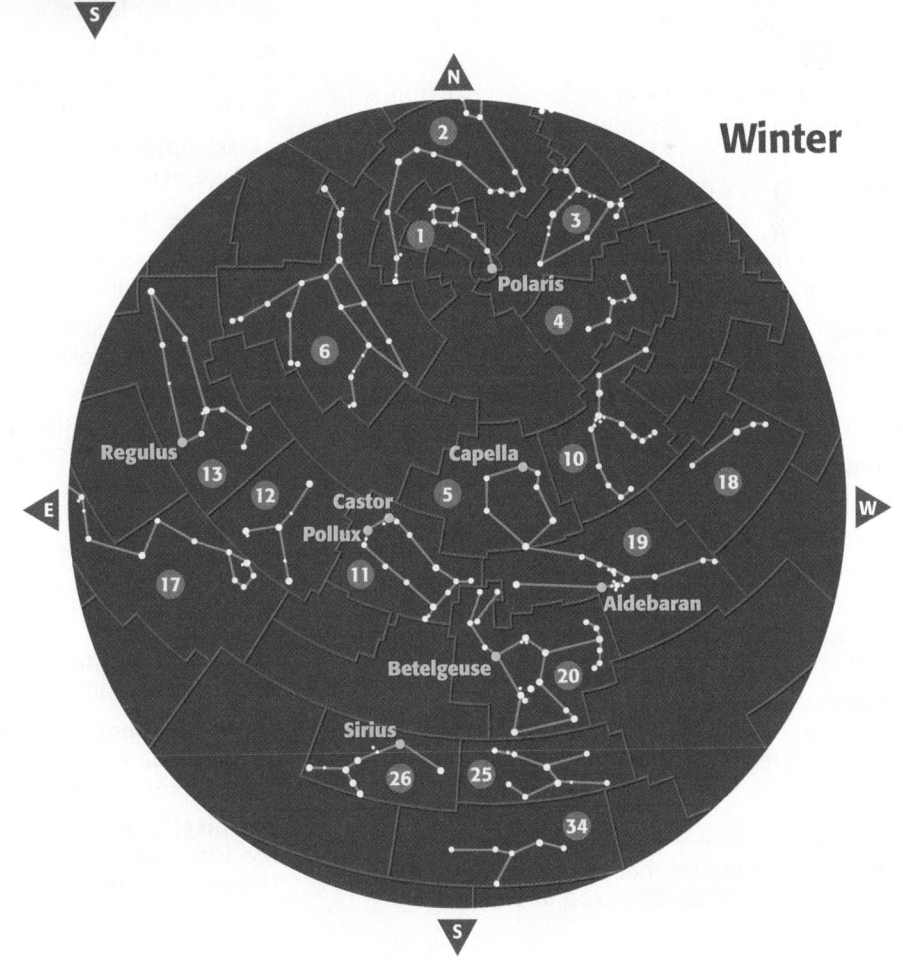

Glossary

Glossary

A

absolute dating any method of measuring the age of an event or object in years (167, 291)

acid any compound that increases the number of hydronium ions when dissolved in water (654)

activation energy the minimum amount of energy required to start a chemical reaction (636)

active transport the movement of substances across the cell membrane that requires the cell to use energy (42)

adaptation a characteristic that improves an individual's ability to survive and reproduce in a particular environment (139)

alkali metal (AL kuh LIE MET uhl) one of the elements of Group 1 of the periodic table (lithium, sodium, potassium, rubidium, cesium, and francium) (577)

alkaline-earth metal (AL kuh LIEN UHRTH MET uhl) one of the elements of Group 2 of the periodic table (beryllium, magnesium, calcium, strontium, barium, and radium) (577)

allele (uh LEEL) one of the alternative forms of a gene that governs a characteristic, such as hair color (92)

aquifer a body of rock or sediment that stores groundwater and allows the flow of groundwater (361)

area a measure of the size of a surface or a region (24)

asthenosphere the soft layer of the mantle on which the tectonic plates move (381)

atmosphere a mixture of gases that surrounds a planet or moon (347)

atom the smallest unit of an element that maintains the properties of that element (545)

atomic mass the mass of an atom expressed in atomic mass units (555)

atomic mass unit a unit of mass that describes the mass of an atom or molecule (551)

atomic number the number of protons in the nucleus of an atom; the atomic number is the same for all atoms of an element (553)

azimuthal projection (az uh MYOOTH uhl proh JEK shuhn) a map projection that is made by moving the surface features of the globe onto a plane (205)

B

base any compound that increases the number of hydroxide ions when dissolved in water (657)

biome a large region characterized by a specific type of climate and certain types of plant and animal communities (318)

biosphere the part of Earth where life exists (347)

boiling the conversion of a liquid to a vapor when the vapor pressure of the liquid equals the atmospheric pressure (504)

Boyle's law the law that states that the volume of a gas is inversely proportional to the pressure of a gas when temperature is constant (500)

C

caldera a large, semicircular depression that forms when the magma chamber below a volcano partially empties and causes the ground above to sink (446)

carbohydrate a class of energy-giving nutrients that includes sugars, starches, and fiber; contains carbon, hydrogen, and oxygen (667)

carbon cycle the movement of carbon from the nonliving environment into living things and back (367)

cast a type of fossil that forms when sediments fill in the cavity left by a decomposed organism (296)

catalyst (KAT uh LIST) a substance that changes the rate of a chemical reaction without being used up or changed very much (638)

catastrophism a principle that states that geologic change occurs suddenly (281)

cell cycle the life cycle of a cell (48)

cellular respiration the process by which cells use oxygen to produce energy from food (45, 63)

Cenozoic era (SEN uh ZOH ik ER uh) the most recent geologic era, beginning 65 million years ago; also called the *Age of Mammals* (177)

change of state the change of a substance from one physical state to another (502)

Charles's law the law that states that the volume of a gas is directly proportional to the temperature of a gas when pressure is constant (500)

chemical bond an interaction that holds atoms or ions together (597, 650)

chemical bonding the combining of atoms to form molecules or ionic compounds (597)

chemical change a change that occurs when one or more substances change into entirely new substances with different properties (481)

chemical equation a representation of a chemical reaction that uses symbols to show the relationship between the reactants and the products (626)

chemical formula a combination of chemical symbols and numbers to represent a substance (624)

chemical property a property of matter that describes a substance's ability to participate in chemical reactions (478)

chemical reaction the process by which one or more substances change to produce one or more different substances (620)

chlorophyll (KLAWR uh FIL) a green pigment that captures light energy for photosynthesis (63)

chromosome in a eukaryotic cell, one of the structures in the nucleus that are made up of DNA and protein; in a prokaryotic cell, the main ring of DNA (48)

cleavage the splitting of a mineral along smooth, flat surfaces (229)

colloid (KAHL OYD) a mixture consisting of tiny particles that are intermediate in size between those in solutions and those in suspensions and that are suspended in a liquid, solid, or gas (532)

composition the chemical makeup of a rock; describes either the minerals or other materials in the rock (253)

compound a substance made up of atoms of two or more different elements joined by chemical bonds (225, 523)

compression stress that occurs when forces act to squeeze an object (395)

concentration the amount of a particular substance in a given quantity of a mixture, solution, or ore (530)

condensation the change of state from a gas to a liquid (505)

conduction the transfer of energy as heat through a material (355)

conic projection a map projection that is made by moving the surface features of the globe onto a cone (204)

continental drift the hypothesis that states that the continents once formed a single landmass, broke up, and drifted to their present locations (387)

contour interval the difference in elevation between one contour line and the next (211)

contour line a line that connects points of equal elevation (210)

controlled experiment an experiment that tests only one factor at a time by using a comparison of a control group with an experimental group (14)

convection the transfer of thermal energy by the circulation or movement of a liquid or gas (355)

convergent boundary the boundary formed by the collision of two lithospheric plates (391)

core the central part of the Earth below the mantle (347, 379)

covalent bond (koh VAY luhnt BAHND) a bond formed when atoms share one or more pairs of electrons (604)

covalent compound a chemical compound that is formed by the sharing of electrons (652)

crater a funnel-shaped pit near the top of the central vent of a volcano (446)

crust the thin and solid outermost layer of the Earth above the mantle (347, 379)

crystal a solid whose atoms, ions, or molecules are arranged in a definite pattern (225)

crystal lattice (KRIS tuhl LAT is) the regular pattern in which a crystal is arranged (603)

cylindrical projection (suh LIN dri kuhl proh JEK shuhn) a map projection that is made by moving the surface features of the globe onto a cylinder (203)

cytokinesis the division of the cytoplasm of a cell (50)

D

decomposition reaction a reaction in which a single compound breaks down to form two or more simpler substances (631)

deep current a streamlike movement of ocean water far below the surface (359)

deep-water zone the zone of a lake or pond below the open-water zone, where no light reaches (333)

deformation the bending, tilting, and breaking of the Earth's crust; the change in the shape of rock in response to stress (413)

density the ratio of the mass of a substance to the volume of the substance (26, 230, 473)

deoxyribonucleic acid (DNA), a molecule that is present in all living cells and that contains the information that determines the traits that a living thing inherits and needs to live (116)

deposition the process in which material is laid down (249)

desert an area that has little or no plant life, long periods without rain, and extreme temperatures; usually found in hot climates (323)

diamond is the hardest material known. It is used as a jewel and on cutting tools, such as saws, drills, and files (579)

diffusion (di FYOO zhuhn) the movement of particles from regions of higher density to regions of lower density (40)

divergent boundary the boundary between two tectonic plates that are moving away from each other (391)

dominant trait the trait observed in the first generation when parents that have different traits are bred (89)

dormant describes the inactive state of a seed or other plant part when conditions are unfavorable to growth (68)

double-displacement reaction a reaction in which a gas, a solid precipitate, or a molecular compound forms from the exchange of ions between two compounds (633)

E

elastic rebound the sudden return of elastically deformed rock to its undeformed shape (413)

electron a subatomic particle that has a negative charge (546)

electron cloud a region around the nucleus of an atom where electrons are likely to be found (548)

element a substance that cannot be separated or broken down into simpler substances by chemical means (225, 519)

elevation the height of an object above sea level (210)

endocytosis (EN doh sie TOH sis) the process by which a cell membrane surrounds a particle and encloses the particle in a vesicle to bring the particle into the cell (42)

endothermic reaction a chemical reaction that requires heat (635)

eon (EE AHN) the largest division of geologic time (303)

epicenter the point on Earth's surface directly above an earthquake's starting point, or focus (418)

epoch (EP uhk) a subdivision of a geologic period (303)

equator the imaginary circle halfway between the poles that divides the Earth into the Northern and Southern Hemispheres (199)

era a unit of geologic time that includes two or more periods (303)

erosion the process by which wind, water, ice, or gravity transports soil and sediment from one location to another (249, 350)

estuary (ES tyoo er ee) an area where fresh water from rivers mixes with salt water from the ocean (330)

evaporation (ee vap uh RAY shuhn) the change of a substance from a liquid to a gas (504)

evolution the process in which inherited characteristics within a population change over generations such that new species sometimes arise (139)

exocytosis (EK soh sie TOH sis) the process in which a cell releases a particle by enclosing the particle in a vesicle that then moves to the cell surface and fuses with the cell membrane (43)

exothermic reaction a chemical reaction in which heat is released to the surroundings (635)

extinct describes a species that has died out completely (169)

extinction the death of every member of a species (303)

extrusive igneous rock rock that forms as a result of volcanic activity at or near the Earth's surface (259)

F

fault a break in a body of rock along which one block slides relative to another (396)

fermentation the breakdown of food without the use of oxygen (45)

focus the point along a fault at which the first motion of an earthquake occurs (418)

folding the bending of rock layers due to stress (395)

foliated describes the texture of metamorphic rock in which the mineral grains are arranged in planes or bands (267)

fossil the trace or remains of an organism that lived long ago, most commonly preserved in sedimentary rock (140, 166, 295)

fossil record a historical sequence of life indicated by fossils found in layers of the Earth's crust (140)

fracture the manner in which a mineral breaks along either curved or irregular surfaces (229)

G

gap hypothesis a hypothesis that is based on the idea that a major earthquake is more likely to occur along the part of an active fault where no earthquakes have occurred for a certain period of time (423)

gas a form of matter that does not have a definite volume or shape (496)

gene one set of instructions for an inherited trait (92)

generation time the period between the birth of one generation and the birth of the next generation (153)

genotype the entire genetic makeup of an organism; also the combination of genes for one or more specific traits (93)

geologic column an arrangement of rock layers in which the oldest rocks are at the bottom (285)

geologic time scale the standard method used to divide the Earth's long natural history into manageable parts (169, 303)

geosphere the mostly solid, rocky part of the Earth; extends from the center of the core to the surface of the crust (347)

group a vertical column of elements in the periodic table; elements in a group share chemical properties (574)

H

half-life the time needed for half of a sample of a radioactive substance to undergo radioactive decay (291, 685)

halogen (HAL oh juhn) one of the elements of Group 17 of the periodic table (fluorine, chlorine, bromine, iodine, and statine); halogens combine with most metals to form salts (581)

hardness a measure of the ability of a mineral to resist scratching (230)

heredity the passing of genetic traits from parent to offspring (86)

hominid a type of primate characterized by bipedalism, relatively long lower limbs, and lack of a tail; examples include humans and their ancestors (179)

Homo sapiens (HOH moh SAY pee UHNZ) the species of hominids that includes modern humans and their closest ancestors and that first appeared about 100,000 to 150,000 years ago (182)

homologous chromosomes (hoh MAHL uh guhs KROH muh SOHMZ) chromosomes that have the same sequence of genes and the same structure (49, 98)

hot spot a volcanically active area of Earth's surface far from a tectonic plate boundary (452)

hydrocarbon an organic compound composed only of carbon and hydrogen (665)

hydrosphere (347)

hypothesis (hie PAHTH uh sis) an explanation that is based on prior scientific research or observations and that can be tested (12)

I

index contour on a map, a darker, heavier contour line that is usually every fifth line and that indicates a change in elevation (211)

index fossil a fossil that is found in the rock layers of only one geologic age and that is used to establish the age of the rock layers (298)

indicator a compound that can reversibly change color depending on conditions such as pH (655)

inertia (in UHR shuh) the tendency of an object to resist being moved or, if the object is moving, to resist a change in speed or direction until an outside force acts on the object (470)

inhibitor a substance that slows down or stops a chemical reaction (638)

intrusive igneous rock rock formed from the cooling and solidification of magma beneath the Earth's surface (258)

ion a charged particle that forms when an atom or group of atoms gains or loses one or more electrons (600)

ionic bond (ie AHN ik BAHND) a bond that forms when electrons are transferred from one atom to another, which results in a positive ion and a negative ion (600)

ionic compound a compound made of oppositely charged ions (650)

isotope (IE suh TOHP) an atom that has the same number of protons (or the same atomic number) as other atoms of the same element do but that has a different number of neutrons (and thus a different atomic mass) (291, 553, 682)

L

latitude the distance north or south from the equator; expressed in degrees (199)

lava plateau a wide, flat landform that results from repeated nonexplosive eruptions of lava that spread over a large area (447)

law a summary of many experimental results and observations; a law tells how things work (20)

law of conservation of energy the law that states that energy cannot be created or destroyed but can be changed from one form to another (635)

law of conservation of mass the law that states that mass cannot be created or destroyed in ordinary chemical and physical changes (627)

lipid a type of biochemical that does not dissolve in water; fats and steroids are lipids (667)

liquid the state of matter that has a definite volume but not a definite shape (496)

lithosphere the solid, outer layer of the Earth that consists of the crust and the rigid upper part of the mantle (381)

littoral zone (LIT uh ruhl ZOHN) the shallow zone of a lake or pond where light reaches the bottom and nurtures plants (333)

longitude the distance east and west from the prime meridian; expressed in degrees (200)

luster the way in which a mineral reflects light (228)

M

magma chamber the body of molten rock that feeds a volcano (440)

magnetic declination the difference between the magnetic north and the true north (198)

mantle the layer of rock between the Earth's crust and core (347, 379)

map a representation of the features of a physical body such as Earth (196)

marsh a treeless wetland ecosystem where plants such as grasses grow (334)

mass a measure of the amount of matter in an object (25, 469)

mass number the sum of the numbers of protons and neutrons in the nucleus of an atom (554, 681)

matter anything that has mass and takes up space (466)

meiosis (mie OH sis) a process in cell division during which the number of chromosomes decreases to half the original number by two divisions of the nucleus, which results in the production of sex cells (gametes or spores) (98)

melting the change of state in which a solid becomes a liquid by adding heat (503)

meniscus (muh NIS kuhs) the curve at a liquid's surface by which one measures the volume of the liquid (467)

mesosphere the strong, lower part of the mantle between the asthenosphere and the outer core (193); *also* the layer of the atmosphere between the stratosphere and the thermosphere and in which temperature decreases as altitude increases (381)

Mesozoic era (MES oh ZOH ik ER uh) the geologic era that lasted from 248 million to 65 million years ago; also called the *Age of Reptiles* (175)

metal an element that is shiny and that conducts heat and electricity well (520, 521)

metallic bond a bond formed by the attraction between positively charged metal ions and the electrons around them (607)

metalloid elements that have properties of both metals and nonmetals (520, 521)

meter the basic unit of length in the SI (symbol, m) (24)

mineral a class of nutrients that are chemical elements that are needed for certain body processes (225)

mitosis in eukaryotic cells, a process of cell division that forms two new nuclei, each of which has the same number of chromosomes (49)

mixture a combination of two or more substances that are not chemically combined (526)

model a pattern, plan, representation, or description designed to show the structure or workings of an object, system, or concept (18)

mold a mark or cavity made in a sedimentary surface by a shell or other body (296)

molecule (MAHL i KYOOL) the smallest unit of a substance that keeps all of the physical and chemical properties of that substance (605)

mutation a change in the nucleotide-base sequence of a gene or DNA molecule (124)

N

natural selection the process by which individuals that are better adapted to their environment survive and reproduce more successfully than less well adapted individuals do; a theory to explain the mechanism of evolution (150)

neutralization reaction (NOO truhl i ZA shuhn ree AK shuhn) the reaction of an acid and a base to form a neutral solution of water and a salt (661)

neutron a subatomic particle that has no charge and that is found in the nucleus of an atom (551)

nitrogen cycle the process in whichh nitrogen circulates among the air, soil, water, plants, and animals in an ecosystem (367)

noble gas one of the elements of Group 18 of the periodic table (helium, neon, argon, krypton, xenon, and radon); noble gases are unreactive (582)

nonfoliated describes the texture of metamorphic rock in which the mineral grains are not arranged in planes or bands (268)

nonmetal an element that conducts heat and electricity poorly (520, 521)

nonsilicate mineral a mineral that does not contain compounds of silicon and oxygen (226)

nuclear fission (NOO klee uhr FISH uhn) the splitting of the nucleus of a large atom into two or more fragments; releases additional neutrons and energy (689)

nuclear fusion (NOO klee uhr FYOO zhuhn) the combination of the nuclei of small atoms to form a larger nucleus; releases energy (692)

nucleic acid (noo KLEE ik AS id) a molecule made up of subunits called *nucleotides* (668)

nucleotide in a nucleic-acid chain, a subunit that consists of a sugar, a phosphate, and a nitrogenous base (116)

nucleus (NOO klee uhs) in physical science, an atom's central region, which is made up of protons and neutrons (548)

O

open-water zone the zone of a pond or lake that extends from the littoral zone and that is only as deep as light can reach (333)

ore a natural material whose concentration of economically valuable minerals is high enough for the material to be mined profitably (234)

organic compound a covalently bonded compound that contains carbon (665)

osmosis (ahs MOH sis) the diffusion of water through a semipermeable membrane (41)

P

paleontology the scientific study of fossils (283)

Paleozoic era (PAY lee OH ZOH ik ER uh) the geologic era that followed Precambrian time and that lasted from 543 million to 248 million years ago (174)

passive transport the movement of substances across a cell membrane without the use of energy by the cell (42)

pedigree a diagram that shows the occurrence of a genetic trait in several generations of a family (104)

period a unit of geologic time into which eras are divided (303)

period in chemistry, a horizontal row of elements in the periodic table (574)

periodic describes something that occurs or repeats at regular intervals (569)

periodic law the law that states that the repeating chemical and physical properties of elements change periodically with the atomic numbers of the elements (569)

pH a value that is used to express the acidity or basicity (alkalinity) of a system (661)

phenotype (FEE noh TIEP) an organism's appearance or other detectable characteristic (92)

photosynthesis (FOHT oh SIN thuh sis) the process by which plants, algae, and some bacteria use sunlight, carbon dioxide, and water to make food (44, 63)

physical change a change of matter from one form to another without a change in chemical properties (476)

physical property a characteristic of a substance that does not involve a chemical change, such as density, color, or hardness (473)

plankton the mass of mostly microscopic organisms that float or drift freely in freshwater and marine environments (326)

plate tectonics the theory that explains how large pieces of the Earth's outermost layer, called *tectonic plates*, move and change shape (170, 391)

Precambrian time (pree KAM bree uhn TIEM) the period in the geologic time scale from the formation of the Earth to the beginning of the Paleozoic era, from about 4.6 billion to 543 million years ago (172)

precipitate (pree SIP uh TAYT) a solid that is produced as a result of a chemical reaction in solution (621)

pressure the amount of force exerted per unit area of a surface (499)

primate a type of mammal characterized by opposable thumbs and binocular vision (178)

prime meridian the meridian, or line of longitude, that is designated as 0° longitude (200)

probability the likelihood that a possible future event will occur in any given instance of the event (94)

product a substance that forms in a chemical reaction (626)

protein a molecule that is made up of amino acids and that is needed to build and repair body structures and to regulate processes in the body (667)

proton a subatomic particle that has a positive charge and that is found in the nucleus of an atom (551)

pure substance a sample of matter, either a single element or a single compound, that has definite chemical and physical properties (519)

P wave a seismic wave that causes particles of rock to move in a back-and-forth direction (416)

R

radiation the transfer of energy as electromagnetic waves (355)

radioactive decay the process in which a radioactive isotope tends to break down into a stable isotope of the same element or another element (291)

radioactivity the process by which an unstable nucleus gives off nuclear radiation (681)

radiometric dating a method of determining the age of an object by estimating the relative percentages of a radioactive (parent) isotope and a stable (daughter) isotope (291)

reactant (ree AK tuhnt) a substance or molecule that participates in a chemical reaction (626)

recessive trait a trait that is apparent only when two recessive alleles for the same characteristic are inherited (89)

reclamation the process of returning land to its original condition after mining is completed (235)

relative dating any method of determining whether an event or object is older or younger than other events or objects (167, 285)

relief the variations in elevation of a land surface (211)

remote sensing the process of gathering and analyzing information about an object without physically being in touch with the object (207)

ribosome a cell organelle composed of RNA and protein; the site of protein synthesis (123)

rift zone an area of deep cracks that forms between two tectonic plates that are pulling away from each other (450)

ribonucleic acid (RNA), a molecule that is present in all living cells and that plays a role in protein production (122)

rock a naturally occurring solid mixture of one or more minerals or organic matter (249)

rock cycle the series of processes in which a rock forms, changes from one type to another, is destroyed, and forms again by geological processes (249, 365)

S

salt an ionic compound that forms when a metal atom replaces the hydrogen of an acid (663)

savanna a grassland that often has scattered trees and that is found in tropical and subtropical areas where seasonal rains, fires, and drought happen (322)

science the knowledge obtained by observing natural events and conditions in order to discover facts and formulate laws or principles that can be verified or tested (4)

scientific methods a series of steps followed to solve problems (10)

sea-floor spreading the process by which new oceanic lithosphere forms as magma rises toward the surface and solidifies (388)

seismic gap an area along a fault where relatively few earthquakes have occurred recently but where strong earthquakes have occurred in the past (423)

seismic wave a wave of energy that travels through the Earth and away from an earthquake in all directions (416)

seismogram a tracing of earthquake motion that is created by a seismograph (418)

seismograph an instrument that records vibrations in the ground and determines the location and strength of an earthquake (418)

seismology (siez MAHL uh jee) the study of earthquakes (413)

selective breeding the human practice of breeding animals or plants that have certain desired traits (148)

sex chromosome one of the pair of chromosomes that determine the sex of an individual (103)

silicate mineral a mineral that contains a combination of silicon, oxygen, and one or more metals (226)

single-displacement reaction a reaction in which one element takes the place of another element in a compound (631)

solid the state of matter in which the volume and shape of a substance are fixed (495)

solubility the ability of one substance to dissolve in another at a given temperature and pressure (530)

solute in a solution, the substance that dissolves in the solvent (528)

solution a homogeneous mixture of two or more substances uniformly dispersed throughout a single phase (528)

solvent in a solution, the substance in which the solute dissolves (528)

soot is formed from burning oil, coal, and wood and is used as a pigment in paints and crayons (579)

speciation (SPEE shee AY shuhn) the formation of new species as a result of evolution (154)

species a group of organisms that are closely related and can mate to produce fertile offspring (139)

states of matter the physical forms of matter, which include solid, liquid, and gas (495)

stoma one of many openings in a leaf or a stem of a plant that enable gas exchange to occur (plural, *stomata*) (64)

strata layers of rock (singular, *stratum*) (261)

stratification the process in which sedimentary rocks are arranged in layers (263)

streak the color of the powder of a mineral (229)

sublimation (SUHB luh MAY shuhn) the process in which a solid changes directly into a gas (506)

subsidence (suhb SIED'ns) the sinking of regions of the Earth's crust to lower elevations (400)

superposition a principle that states that younger rocks lie above older rocks if the layers have not been disturbed (285)

surface current a horizontal movement of ocean water that is caused by wind and that occurs at or near the ocean's surface (359)

surface tension the force that acts on the surface of a liquid and that tends to minimize the area of the surface (496)

suspension a mixture in which particles of a material are more or less evenly dispersed throughout a liquid or gas (532)

swamp a wetland ecosystem in which shrubs and trees grow (334)

S wave a seismic wave that causes particles of rock to move in a side-by-side direction (416)

synthesis reaction (SIN thuh sis ree AK shuhn) a reaction in which two or more substances combine to form a new compound (630)

T

tectonic plate a block of lithosphere that consists of the crust and the rigid, outermost part of the mantle (382)

temperature a measure of how hot (or cold) something is; specifically, a measure of the average kinetic energy of the particles in an object (26, 498)

tension stress that occurs when forces act to stretch an object (395)

texture the quality of a rock that is based on the sizes, shapes, and positions of the rock's grains (254)

theory an explanation that ties together many hypotheses and observations (20)

topographic map (TAHP uh GRAF ik MAP) a map that shows the surface features of Earth (210)

trace fossil a fossilized mark that is formed in soft sediment by the movement of an animal (296)

trait a genetically determined characteristic (148)

transform boundary the boundary between tectonic plates that are sliding past each other horizontally (391)

transpiration the process by which plants release water vapor into the air through stomata; *also* the release of water vapor into the air by other organisms (64)

tropism (TROH PIZ uhm) growth of all or part of an organism in response to an external stimulus, such as light (70)

true north the direction to the geographic North Pole (198)

tundra a treeless plain found in the Arctic, in the Antarctic, or on the tops of mountains that is characterized by very low winter temperatures and short, cool summers (324)

U

unconformity a break in the geologic record created when rock layers are eroded or when sediment is not deposited for a long period of time (287)

uniformitarianism a principle that states that geologic processes that occurred in the past can be explained by current geologic processes (281)

uplift the rising of regions of the Earth's crust to higher elevations (400)

V

valence electron (VAY luhns ee LEK TRAHN) an electron that is found in the outermost shell of an atom and that determines the atom's chemical properties (597)

variable a factor that changes in an experiment in order to test a hypothesis (14)

vent an opening at the surface of the Earth through which volcanic material passes (440)

viscosity the resistance of a gas or liquid to flow (496)

volcano a vent or fissure in the Earth's surface through which magma and gases are expelled (438)

volume a measure of the size of a body or region in three-dimensional space (25, 466, 499)

W

water cycle the continuous movement of water from the ocean to the atmosphere to the land and back to the ocean (365)

weight a measure of the gravitational force exerted on an object; its value can change with the location of the object in the universe (469)

wetland an area of land that is periodically underwater or whose soil contains a great deal of moisture (334)

Spanish Glossary

A

absolute dating/datación absoluta cualquier método que sirve para determinar la edad de un suceso u objeto en años (167, 291)

acid/ácido cualquier compuesto que aumenta el número de iones de hidrógeno cuando se disuelve en agua (654)

activation energy/energía de activación la cantidad mínima de energía que se requiere para iniciar una reacción química (636)

active transport/transporte activo el movimiento de substancias a través de la membrana celular que requiere que la célula gaste energía (42)

adaptation/adaptación una característica que mejora la capacidad de un individuo para sobrevivir y reproducirse en un determinado ambiente (139)

alkali metal/metal alcalino uno de los elementos del Grupo 1 de la tabla periódica (litio, sodio, potasio, rubidio, cesio y francio) (577)

alkaline-earth metal/metal alcalinotérreo uno de los elementos del Grupo 2 de la tabla periódica (berilio, magnesio, calcio, estroncio, bario y radio) (577)

allele/alelo una de las formas alternativas de un gene que rige un carácter, como por ejemplo, el color del cabello (92)

aquifer/acuífero un cuerpo rocoso o sedimento que almacena agua subterránea y permite que fluya (361)

area/área una medida del tamaño de una superficie o región (24)

asthenosphere/astenosfera la capa blanda del manto sobre la que se mueven las placas tectónicas (381)

atmosphere/atmósfera una mezcla de gases que rodea un planeta o una luna (347)

atom/átomo la unidad más pequeña de un elemento que conserva las propiedades de ese elemento (545)

atomic mass/masa atómica la masa de un átomo, expresada en unidades de masa atómica (555)

atomic mass unit/unidad de masa atómica una unidad de masa que describe la masa de un átomo o una molécula (551)

atomic number/número atómico el número de protones en el núcleo de un átomo; el número atómico es el mismo para todos los átomos de un elemento (553)

azimuthal projection/proyección azimutal una proyección cartográfica que se hace al transferir las características de la superficie del globo a un plano (205)

B

base/base cualquier compuesto que aumenta el número de iones de hidróxido cuando se disuelve en agua (657)

biome/bioma una región extensa caracterizada por un tipo de clima específico y ciertos tipos de comunidades de plantas y animales (318)

biosphere/biosfera la parte de la Tierra donde existe la vida (347)

boiling/ebullición la conversión de un líquido en vapor cuando la presión de vapor del líquido es igual a la presión atmosférica (504)

Boyle's law/ley de Boyle la ley que establece que el volumen de un gas es inversamente proporcional a su presión cuando la temperatura es constante (500)

C

caldera/caldera una depresión grande y semicircular que se forma cuando se vacía parcialmente la cámara de magma que hay debajo de un volcán, lo cual hace que el suelo se hunda (446)

carbohydrate/carbohidrato una clase de nutrientes que proporcionan energía; incluye los azúcares, los almidones y las fibras; contiene carbono, hidrógeno y oxígeno (667)

carbon cycle/ciclo del carbono el movimiento del carbono del ambiente sin vida a los seres vivos y de los seres vivos al ambiente (367)

cast/molde un tipo de fósil que se forma cuando un organismo descompuesto deja una cavidad que es llenada por sedimentos (296)

catalyst/catalizador una substancia que cambia la tasa de una reacción química sin consumirse ni cambiar demasiado (638)

catastrophism/catastrofismo un principio que establece que los cambios geológicos ocurren súbitamente (281)

cell cycle/ciclo celular el ciclo de vida de una célula (48)

cellular respiration/respiración celular el proceso por medio del cual las células utilizan oxígeno para producir energía a partir de los alimentos (45, 63)

Cenozoic era/era Cenozoica la era geológica más reciente, que comenzó hace 65 millones de años; también llamada *Edad de los Mamíferos* (177)

change of state/cambio de estado el cambio de una substancia de un estado físico a otro (502)

Charles's law/ley de Charles la ley que establece que el volumen de un gas es directamente proporcional a su temperatura cuando la presión es constante (500)

chemical bond/enlace químico una interacción que mantiene unidos los átomos o los iones (597, 650)

chemical bonding/formación de un enlace químico la combinación de átomos para formar moléculas o compuestos iónicos (597)

chemical change/cambio químico un cambio que ocurre cuando una o más substancias se transforman en substancias totalmente nuevas con propiedades diferentes (481)

chemical equation/ecuación química una representación de una reacción química que usa símbolos para mostrar la relación entre los reactivos y los productos (626)

chemical formula/fórmula química una combinación de símbolos químicos y números que se usan para representar una substancia (624)

chemical property/propiedad química una propiedad de la materia que describe la capacidad de una substancia de participar en reacciones químicas (478)

chemical reaction/reacción química el proceso por medio del cual una o más substancia cambian para producir una o más substancias distintas (620)

chlorophyll/clorofila un pigmento verde que capta la energía luminosa para la fotosíntesis (63)

chromosome/cromosoma en una célula eucariótica, una de las estructuras del núcleo que está hecha de ADN y proteína; en una célula procariótica, el anillo principal de ADN (48)

cleavage/exfoliación el agrietamiento de un mineral en sus superficies lisas y planas (229)

colloid/coloide una mezcla formada por partículas diminutas que son de tamaño intermedio entre las partículas de las soluciones y las de las suspensiones y que se encuentran suspendidas en un líquido, sólido o gas (532)

composition/composición la constitución química de una roca; describe los minerales u otros materiales presentes en ella (253)

compound/compuesto una substancia formada por átomos de dos o más elementos diferentes unidos por enlaces químicos (225, 523)

compression/compresión estrés que se produce cuando distintas fuerzas actúan para estrechar un objeto (395)

concentration/concentración la cantidad de una cierta substancia en una cantidad determinada de mezcla, solución o mena (530)

condensation/condensación el cambio de estado de gas a líquido (505)

conduction/conducción la transferencia de energía en forma de calor a través de un material (355)

conic projection/proyección cónica una proyección cartográfica que se hace al transferir las características de la superficie del globo a un cono (204)

continental drift/deriva continental la hipótesis que establece que alguna vez los continentes formaron una sola masa de tierra, se dividieron y se fueron a la deriva hasta terminar en sus ubicaciones actuales (387)

contour interval/distancia entre las curvas de nivel la diferencia en elevación entre una curva de nivel y la siguiente (211)

contour line/curva de nivel una línea que une puntos que tienen la misma elevación (210)

controlled experiment/experimento controlado un experimento que prueba sólo un factor a la vez, comparando un grupo de control con un grupo experimental (14)

convection/convección la transferencia de energía térmica mediante la circulación o el movimiento de un líquido o gas (355)

convergent boundary/límite convergente el límite que se forma debido al choque de dos placas de la litosfera (391)

core/núcleo la parte central de la Tierra, debajo del manto (347, 379)

covalent bond/enlace covalente un enlace formado cuando los átomos comparten uno más pares de electrones (604)

covalent compound/compuesto covalente un compuesto químico que se forma al compartir electrones (652)

crater/cráter una depresión con forma de embudo que se encuentra cerca de la parte superior de la chimenea central de un volcán (446)

crust/corteza la capa externa, delgada y sólida de la Tierra, que se encuentra sobre el manto (347, 379)

crystal/cristal un sólido cuyos átomos, iones o moléculas están ordenados en un patrón definido (225)

crystal lattice/red cristalina el patrón regular en el que un cristal está ordenado (603)

cylindrical projection/proyección cilíndrica una proyección cartográfica que se hace al transferir las características de la superficie del globo a un cilindro (203)

cytokinesis/citoquinesis la división del citoplasma de una célula (50)

D

decomposition reaction/reacción de descomposición una reacción en la que un solo compuesto se descompone para formar dos o más substancias más simples (631)

deep current/corriente profunda un movimiento del agua del océano que es similar a una corriente y ocurre debajo de la superficie (359)

deep-water zone/zona de aguas profundas la zona de un lago o laguna debajo de la zona de aguas abiertas, a donde no llega la luz (333)

deformation/deformación el proceso de doblar, inclinar y romper la corteza de la Tierra; el cambio en la forma de una roca en respuesta a la tensión (413)

density/densidad la relación entre la masa de una substancia y su volumen (26, 230, 473)

deoxyribonucleic acid DNA/ADN ácido desoxirribonucleico una molécula que está presente en todas las células vivas y que contiene la información que determina los caracteres que un ser vivo hereda y necesita para vivir (116)

deposition/deposición el proceso por medio del cual un material se deposita (249)

desert/desierto una región con poca vegetación o sin vegetación, largos períodos sin lluvia y temperaturas extremas; generalmente se ubica en climas calientes (323)

diamond/diamante una forma sólida, cristalina e incolora del carbono (579)

diffusion/difusión el movimiento de partículas de regiones de mayor densidad a regiones de menor densidad (40)

divergent boundary/límite divergente el límite entre dos placas tectónicas que se están separando una de la otra (391)

dominant trait/carácter dominante el carácter que se observa en la primera generación cuando se cruzan progenitores que tienen caracteres diferentes (89)

dormant/aletargado término que describe el estado inactivo de una semilla u otra parte de las plantas cuando las condiciones son desfavorables para el crecimiento (68)

double-displacement reaction/reacción de doble desplazamiento una reacción en la que se forma un gas, un precipitado sólido o un compuesto molecular a partir del intercambio de iones entre dos compuestos (633)

E

elastic rebound/rebote elástico ocurre cuando una roca deformada elásticamente vuelve súbitamente a su forma no deformada (413)

electron/electrón una partícula subatómica que tiene carga negativa (546)

electron cloud/nube de electrones una región que rodea al núcleo de un átomo en la cual es probable encontrar a los electrones (548)

element/elemento una substancia que no se puede separar o descomponer en substancias más simples por medio de métodos químicos (225, 519)

elevation/elevación la altura de un objeto sobre el nivel del mar (210)

endocytosis/endocitosis el proceso por medio del cual la membrana celular rodea una partícula y la encierra en una vesícula para llevarla al interior de la célula (42)

endothermic reaction/reacción endotérmica una reacción química que necesita calor (635)

eon/eón la mayor división del tiempo geológico (303)

epicenter/epicentro el punto de la superficie de la Tierra que queda justo arriba del punto de inicio, o foco, de un terremoto (418)

epoch/época una subdivisión de un período geológico (303)

equator/ecuador el círculo imaginario que se encuentra a la mitad entre los polos y divide a la Tierra en los hemisferios norte y sur (199)

era/era una unidad de tiempo geológico que incluye dos o más períodos (303)

erosion/erosión el proceso por medio del cual el viento, el agua, el hielo o la gravedad transporta tierra y sedimentos de un lugar a otro (249, 350)

estuary/estuario un área donde el agua dulce de los ríos se mezcla con el agua salada del océano (330)

evaporation/evaporación el cambio de una substancia de líquido a gas (504)

evolution/evolución el proceso por medio del cual las características heredadas dentro de una población cambian con el transcurso de las generaciones de manera tal que a veces surgen nuevas especies (139)

exocytosis/exocitosis el proceso por medio del cual una célula libera una partícula encerrándola en una vesícula que luego se traslada a la superficie de la célula y se fusiona con la membrana celular (43)

exothermic reaction/reacción exotérmica una reacción química en la que se libera calor a los alrededores (635)

extinct/extinto término que describe a una especie que ha desaparecido por completo (169)

extinction/extinción la muerte de todos los miembros de una especie (303)

extrusive igneous rock/roca ígnea extrusiva una roca que se forma como resultado de la actividad volcánica en la superficie de la Tierra o cerca de ella (259)

F

fault/falla una grieta en un cuerpo rocoso a lo largo de la cual un bloque se desliza respecto a otro (396)

fermentation/fermentación la descomposición de los alimentos sin utilizar oxígeno (45)

focus/foco el punto a lo largo de una falla donde ocurre el primer movimiento de un terremoto (418)

folding/plegamiento fenómeno que ocurre cuando las capas de roca se doblan debido a la compresión (395)

foliated/foliada término que describe la textura de una roca metamórfica en la que los granos de mineral están ordenados en planos o bandas (267)

fossil/fósil los indicios o los restos de un organismo que vivió hace mucho tiempo, comúnmente preservados en las rocas sedimentarias (140, 166, 295)

fossil record/registro fósil una secuencia histórica de la vida indicada por fósiles que se han encontrado en las capas de la corteza terrestre (140)

fracture/fractura la forma en la que se rompe un mineral a lo largo de superficies curvas o irregulares (229)

G

gap hypothesis/hipótesis del intervalo una hipótesis que se basa en la idea de que es más probable que ocurra un terremoto importante a lo largo de la parte de una falla activa donde no se han producido terremotos durante un determinado período de tiempo (423)

gas/gas un estado de la materia que no tiene volumen ni forma definidos (496)

gene/gene un conjunto de instrucciones para un carácter heredado (92)

generation time/tiempo de generación el período entre el nacimiento de una generación y el nacimiento de la siguiente generación (153)

genotype/genotipo la constitución genética completa de un organismo; *también* la combinación genes para uno o más caracteres específicos (93)

geologic column/columna geológica un arreglo de las capas de roca en el que las rocas más antiguas están al fondo (285)

geologic time scale/escala de tiempo geológico el método estándar que se usa para dividir la larga historia natural de la Tierra en partes razonables (169, 303)

geosphere/geosfera la capa de la Tierra que es principalmente sólida y rocosa; se extiende desde el centro del núcleo hasta la superficie de la corteza terrestre (347)

group/grupo una columna vertical de elementos de la tabla periódica; los elementos de un grupo comparten propiedades químicas (574)

H

half-life/vida media el tiempo que tarda la mitad de la muestra de una substancia radiactiva en desintegrarse por desintegración radiactiva (291, 685)

halogen/halógeno uno de los elementos del Grupo 17 de la tabla periódica (flúor, cloro, bromo, yodo y ástato); los halógenos se combinan con la mayoría de los metales para formar sales (581)

hardness/dureza una medida de la capacidad de un mineral de resistir ser rayado (230)

heredity/herencia la transmisión de caracteres genéticos de padres a hijos (86)

hominid/homínido un tipo de primate caracterizado por ser bípedo, tener extremidades inferiores relativamente largas y no tener cola; incluye a los seres humanos y sus ancestros (179)

Homo sapiens/Homo sapiens la especie de homínidos que incluye a los seres humanos modernos y a sus ancestros más cercanos; apareció hace entre 100,000 y 150,000 años (182)

homologous chromosomes/cromosomas homólogos cromosomas con la misma secuencia de genes y la misma estructura (49, 98)

hot spot/mancha caliente un área volcánicamente activa de la superficie de la Tierra que se encuentra lejos de un límite entre placas tectónicas (452)

hydrocarbon/hidrocarburo un compuesto orgánico compuesto únicamente por carbono e hidrogeno (665)

hydrosphere/hidrosfera la porción de la Tierra que es agua (347)

hypothesis/hipótesis una explicación que se basa en observaciones o investigaciones científicas previas y que se puede probar (12)

I

index contour/índice de las curvas de nivel en un mapa, la curva de nivel que es más gruesa y oscura, la cual normalmente se encuentra cada quinta línea e indica un cambio en la elevación (211)

index fossil/fósil guía un fósil que se encuentra en las capas de roca de una sola era geológica y que se usa para establecer la edad de las capas de roca (298)

indicator/indicador un compuesto que puede cambiar de color de forma reversible dependiendo de condiciones tales como el pH (655)

inertia/inercia la tendencia de un objeto a no moverse o, si el objeto se está moviendo, la tendencia a resistir un cambio en su rapidez o dirección hasta que una fuerza externa actúe en el objeto (470)

inhibitor/inhibidor una substancia que desacelera o detiene una reacción química (638)

intrusive igneous rock/roca ígnea intrusiva una roca formada a partir del enfriamiento y solidificación del magma debajo de la superficie terrestre (258)

ion/ion una partícula cargada que se forma cuando un átomo o grupo de átomos gana o pierde uno o más electrones (600)

ionic bond/enlace iónico un enlace que se forma cuando los electrones se transfieren de un átomo a otro, y que produce un ion positivo y uno negativo (600)

ionic compound/compuesto iónico un compuesto formado por iones con cargas opuestas (650)

isotope/isótopo un átomo que tiene el mismo número de protones (o el mismo número atómico) que otros átomos del mismo elemento, pero que tiene un número diferente de neutrones (y, por lo tanto, otra masa atómica) (291, 553, 682)

L

latitude/latitud la distancia hacia el norte o hacia el sur del ecuador; se expresa en grados (199)

lava plateau/meseta de lava un accidente geográfico amplio y plano que se forma debido a repetidas erupciones no explosivas de lava que se expanden por un área extensa (447)

law/ley un resumen de muchos resultados y observaciones experimentales; una ley dice cómo funcionan las cosas (20)

law of conservation of energy/ley de la conservación de la energía la ley que establece que la energía ni se crea ni se destruye, sólo se transforma de una forma a otra (635)

law of conservation of mass/ley de la conservación de la masa la ley que establece que la masa no se crea ni se destruye por cambios químicos o físicos comunes (627)

lipid/lípido un tipo de substancia bioquímica que no se disuelve en agua; las grasas y los esteroides son lípidos (667)

liquid/líquido el estado de la materia que tiene un volumen definido, pero no una forma definida (496)

lithosphere/litosfera la capa externa y sólida de la Tierra que está formada por la corteza y la parte superior y rígida del manto (381)

littoral zone/zona litoral la zona poco profunda de un lago o una laguna donde la luz llega al fondo y nutre a las plantas (333)

longitude/longitud la distancia hacia el este y hacia el oeste del primer meridiano; se expresa en grados (200)

luster/brillo la forma en que un mineral refleja la luz (228)

M

magma chamber/cámara de magma la masa de roca fundida que alimenta un volcán (440)

magnetic declination/declinación magnética la diferencia entre el norte magnético y el norte verdadero (198)

mantle/manto la capa de roca que se encuentra entre la corteza terrestre y el núcleo (347, 379)

map/mapa una representación de las características de un cuerpo físico, tal como la Tierra (196)

marsh/pantano un ecosistema pantanoso sin árboles, donde crecen plantas tales como el pasto (334)

mass/masa una medida de la cantidad de materia que tiene un objeto (25, 469)

mass number/número de masa la suma de los números de protones y neutrones que hay en el núcleo de un átomo (554, 681)

matter/materia cualquier cosa que tiene masa y ocupa un lugar en el espacio (466)

meiosis/meiosis un proceso de división celular durante el cual el número de cromosomas disminuye a la mitad del número original por medio de dos divisiones del núcleo, lo cual resulta en la producción de células sexuales (gametos o esporas) (98)

melting/fusión el cambio de estado en el que un sólido se convierte en líquido al añadirse calor (503)

meniscus/menisco la curva que se forma en la superficie de un líquido, la cual sirve para medir el volumen de un líquido (467)

mesosphere/mesosfera la parte fuerte e inferior del manto que se encuentra entre la astenosfera y el núcleo externo (193); *también*, la capa de la atmósfera que se encuentra entre la estratosfera y la termosfera, en la cual la temperatura disminuye al aumentar la altitud (381)

Mesozoic era/era Mesozoica la era geológica que comenzó hace 248 millones de años y terminó hace 65 millones de años; también llamada *Edad de los Reptiles* (175)

metal/metal un elemento que es brillante y conduce bien el calor y la electricidad (520, 521)

metallic bond/enlace metálico un enlace formado por la atracción entre iones metálicos cargados positivamente y los electrones que los rodean (607)

metalloid/metaloides elementos que tienen propiedades tanto de metales como de no metales (520, 521)

meter/metro la unidad fundamental de longitud en el sistema internacional de unidades (símbolo: m) (24)

mineral/mineral un sólido natural e inorgánico que tiene una estructura química definida (225)

mitosis/mitosis en las células eucarióticas, un proceso de división celular que forma dos núcleos nuevos, cada uno de los cuales posee el mismo número de cromosomas (49)

mixture/mezcla una combinación de dos o más substancias que no están combinadas químicamente (526)

model/modelo un diseño, plan, representación o descripción cuyo objetivo es mostrar la estructura o funcionamiento de un objeto, sistema o concepto (18)

mold/molde una marca o cavidad hecha en una superficie sedimentaria por una concha u otro cuerpo (296)

molecule/molécula la unidad más pequeña de una substancia que conserva todas las propiedades físicas y químicas de esa substancia (605)

mutation/mutación un cambio en la secuencia de la base de nucleótidos de un gene o de una molécula de ADN (124)

N

natural selection/selección natural el proceso por medio del cual los individuos que están mejor adaptados a su ambiente sobreviven y se reproducen con más éxito que los individuos menos adaptados; una teoría que explica el mecanismo de la evolución (150)

neutralization reaction/reacción de neutralización la reacción de un ácido y una base que forma una solución neutra de agua y una sal (661)

neutron/neutrón una partícula subatómica que no tiene carga y que se encuentra en el núcleo de un átomo (551)

nitrogen cycle/ciclo del nitrógeno el proceso por medio del cual el nitrógeno circula en el aire, el suelo, el agua, las plantas y los animales de un ecosistema (367)

noble gas/gas noble uno de los elementos del Grupo 18 de la tabla periódica (helio, neón, argón, criptón, xenón y radón); los gases nobles son no reactivos (582)

nonfoliated/no foliada término que describe la textura de una roca metamórfica en la que los granos de mineral no están ordenados en planos ni bandas (268)

nonmetal/no metal un elemento que es mal conductor del calor y la electricidad (520, 521)

nonsilicate mineral/mineral no-silicato un mineral que no contiene compuestos de sílice y oxígeno (226)

nuclear fission/fisión nuclear la partición del núcleo de un átomo grande en dos o más fragmentos; libera neutrones y energía adicionales (689)

nuclear fusion/fusión nuclear combinación de los núcleos de átomos pequeños para formar un núcleo más grande; libera energía (692)

nucleic acid/ácido nucleico una molécula formada por subunidades llamadas *nucleótidos* (668)

nucleotide/nucleótido en una cadena de ácidos nucleicos, una subunidad formada por un azúcar, un fosfato y una base nitrogenada (116)

nucleus/núcleo en ciencias físicas, la región central de un átomo, la cual está constituida por protones y neutrones (548)

O

open-water zone/zona de aguas superiores la zona de un lago o una laguna que se extiende desde la zona litoral y cuya profundidad sólo alcanza hasta donde penetra la luz (333)

ore/mena un material natural cuya concentración de minerales con valor económico es suficientemente alta como para que el material pueda ser explotado de manera rentable (234)

organic compound/compuesto orgánico un compuesto enlazado de manera covalente que contiene carbono (665)

osmosis/ósmosis la difusión del agua a través de una membrana semipermeable (41)

P

paleontology/paleontología el estudio científico de los fósiles (283)

Paleozoic era/era Paleozoica la era geológica que vino después del período Precámbrico; comenzó hace 543 millones de años y terminó hace 248 millones de años (174)

passive transport/transporte pasivo el movimiento de substancias a través de una membrana celular sin que la célula tenga que usar energía (42)

pedigree/pedigrí un diagrama que muestra la incidencia de un carácter genético en varias generaciones de una familia (104)

period/período una unidad de tiempo geológico en la que se dividen las eras (303)

period in chemistry/período en química una hilera horizontal de elementos en la tabla periódica (574)

periodic/periódico término que describe algo que ocurre o que se repite a intervalos regulares (569)

periodic law/ley periódica la ley que establece que las propiedades químicas y físicas repetitivas de un elemento cambian periódicamente en función del número atómico de los elementos (569)

pH/pH un valor que expresa la acidez o la basicidad (alcalinidad) de un sistema (661)

phenotype/fenotipo la apariencia de un organismo u otra característica perceptible (92)

photosynthesis/fotosíntesis el proceso por medio del cual las plantas, las algas y algunas bacterias utilizan la luz solar, el dióxido de carbono y el agua para producir alimento (44, 63)

physical change/cambio físico un cambio de materia de una forma a otra sin que ocurra un cambio en sus propiedades químicas (476)

physical property/propiedad física una característica de una substancia que no implica un cambio químico, tal como la densidad, el color o la dureza (473)

plankton/plancton la masa de organismos en su mayoría microscópicos que flotan o se encuentran a la deriva en ambientes de agua dulce o marina (326)

plate tectonics/tectónica de placas la teoría que explica cómo se mueven y cambian de forma las placas tectónicas, que son grandes porciones de la capa más externa de la Tierra (170, 391)

Precambrian time/tiempo Precámbrico el período en la escala de tiempo geológico que abarca desde la formación de la Tierra hasta el comienzo de la era Paleozoica; comenzó hace aproximadamente 4.6 mil millones de años y terminó hace 543 millones de años (172)

precipitate/precipitado un sólido que se produce como resultado de una reacción química en una solución (621)

pressure/presión la cantidad de fuerza ejercida en una superficie por unidad de área (499)

primate/primate un tipo de mamífero caracterizado por tener pulgares oponibles y visión binocular (178)

prime meridian/meridiano de Greenwich el meridiano, o línea de longitud, que se designa como longitud 0° (200)

probability/probabilidad la probabilidad de que ocurra un posible suceso futuro en cualquier caso dado del suceso (94)

product/producto una substancia que se forma en una reacción química (626)

protein/proteína una molécula formada por aminoácidos que es necesaria para construir y reparar estructuras corporales y para regular procesos del cuerpo (667)

proton/protón una partícula subatómica que tiene una carga positiva y que se encuentra en el núcleo de un átomo (551)

pure substance/substancia pura una muestra de materia, ya sea un solo elemento o un solo compuesto, que tiene propiedades químicas y físicas definidas (519)

P wave/onda P una onda sísmica que hace que las partículas de roca se muevan en una dirección de atrás hacia delante (416)

R

radiation/radiación la transferencia de energía en forma de ondas electromagnéticas (355)

radioactive decay/desintegración radiactiva el proceso por medio del cual un isótopo radiactivo tiende a desintegrarse y formar un isótopo estable del mismo elemento o de otro elemento (291)

radioactivity/radiactividad el proceso por medio del cual un núcleo inestable emite radiación nuclear (681)

radiometric dating/datación radiométrica un método para determinar la edad de un objeto estimando los porcentajes relativos de un isótopo radiactivo (precursor) y un isótopo estable (hijo) (291)

reactant/reactivo una substancia o molécula que participa en una reacción química (626)

recessive trait/carácter recesivo un carácter que se hace aparente sólo cuando se heredan dos alelos recesivos de la misma característica (89)

reclamation/restauración el proceso de hacer que la tierra vuelva a su condición original después de que se terminan las actividades de explotación minera (235)

relative dating/datación relativa cualquier método que se utiliza para determinar si un acontecimiento u objeto es más viejo o más joven que otros acontecimientos u objetos (167, 285)

relief/relieve las variaciones en elevación de una superficie de terreno (211)

remote sensing/teledetección el proceso de recopilar y analizar información acerca de un objeto sin estar en contacto físico con el objeto (207)

ribosome/ribosoma un organelo celular compuesto de ARN y proteína; el sitio donde ocurre la síntesis de proteínas (123)

rift zone/zona de rift un área de grietas profundas que se forma entre dos placas tectónicas que se están alejando una de la otra (450)

ribonucleic acid RNA/ARN ácido ribonucleico una molécula que está presente en todas las células vivas y que juega un papel en la producción de proteínas (122)

rock/roca una mezcla sólida de uno o más minerales o de materia orgánica que se produce de forma natural (249)

rock cycle/ciclo de las rocas la serie de procesos por medio de los cuales una roca se forma, cambia de un tipo a otro, se destruye y se forma nuevamente por procesos geológicos (249, 365)

S

salt/sal un compuesto iónico que se forma cuando un átomo de un metal reemplaza el hidrógeno de un ácido (663)

savanna/sabana una región de pastizales que, a menudo, tiene árboles dispersos; se encuentra en áreas tropicales y subtropicales donde se producen lluvias, incendios y sequías estacionales (322)

science/ciencia el conocimiento que se obtiene por medio de la observación natural de acontecimientos y condiciones con el fin de descubrir hechos y formular leyes o principios que puedan ser verificados o probados (4)

scientific methods/métodos científicos una serie de pasos que se siguen para solucionar problemas (10)

sea-floor spreading/expansión del suelo marino el proceso por medio del cual se forma nueva litosfera oceánica a medida que el magma se eleva hacia la superficie y se solidifica (388)

seismic gap/brecha sísmica un área a lo largo de una falla donde han ocurrido relativamente pocos terremotos recientemente, pero donde se han producido terremotos fuertes en el pasado (423)

seismic wave/onda sísmica una onda de energía que viaja a través de la Tierra y se aleja de un terremoto en todas direcciones (416)

seismogram/sismograma una gráfica del movimiento de un terremoto elaborada por un sismógrafo (418)

seismograph/sismógrafo un instrumento que registra las vibraciones en el suelo y determina la ubicación y la fuerza de un terremoto (418)

seismology/sismología el estudio de los terremotos (413)

selective breeding/reproducción selectiva la práctica humana de cruzar animales o plantas que tienen ciertas caracteres deseadas (148)

sex chromosome/cromosoma sexual uno de los dos cromosomas que determinan el sexo de un individuo (103)

silicate mineral/mineral silicato un mineral que contiene una combinación de sílice, oxígeno y uno o más metales (226)

single-displacement reaction/reacción de sustitución simple una reacción en la que un elemento toma el lugar de otro elemento en un compuesto (631)

solid/sólido el estado de la materia en el cual el volumen y la forma de una sustancia están fijos (495)

solubility/solubilidad la capacidad de una substancia de disolverse en otra a una temperatura y una presión dadas (530)

solute/soluto en una solución, la sustancia que se disuelve en el solvente (528)

solution/solución una mezcla homogénea de dos o más sustancias dispersas de manera uniforme en una sola fase (528)

solvent/solvente en una solución, la sustancia en la que se disuelve el soluto (528)

speciation/especiación la formación de especies nuevas como resultado de la evolución (154)

species/especie un grupo de organismos que tienen un parentesco cercano y que pueden aparearse para producir descendencia fértil (139)

states of matter/estados de la material las formas físicas de la materia, que son sólida, líquida y gaseosa (495)

stoma/estoma una de las muchas aberturas de una hoja o de un tallo de una planta, la cual permite que se lleve a cabo el intercambio de gases (64)

strata/estratos capas de roca (261)

stratification/estratificación el proceso por medio del cual las rocas sedimentarias se acomodan en capas (263)

streak/veta el color del polvo de un mineral (229)

sublimation/sublimación el proceso por medio del cual un sólido se transforma directamente en un gas (506)

subsidence/hundimiento del terreno el hundimiento de regiones de la corteza terrestre a elevaciones más bajas (400)

superposition/superposición un principio que establece que las rocas más jóvenes se encontrarán sobre las rocas más viejas si las capas no han sido alteradas (285)

surface current/corriente superficial un movimiento horizontal del agua del océano que es producido por el viento y que ocurre en la superficie del océano o cerca de ella (359)

surface tension/tensión superficial la fuerza que actúa en la superficie de un líquido y que tiende a minimizar el área de la superficie (496)

suspension/suspensión una mezcla en la que las partículas de un material se encuentran dispersas de manera más o menos uniforme a través de un líquido o de un gas (532)

swamp/ciénaga un ecosistema de pantano en el que crecen arbustos y árboles (334)

S wave/onda S una onda sísmica que hace que las partículas de roca se muevan en una dirección de lado a lado (416)

synthesis reaction/reacción de síntesis una reacción en la que dos o más sustancias se combinan para formar un compuesto nuevo (630)

T

tectonic plate/placa tectónica un bloque de litosfera formado por la corteza y la parte rígida y más externa del manto (382)

temperature/temperatura una medida de qué tan caliente (o frío) está algo; específicamente, una medida de la energía cinética promedio de las partículas de un objeto (26, 498)

tension/tensión estrés que se produce cuando distintas fuerzas actúan para estirar un objeto (395)

texture/textura la cualidad de una roca que se basa en el tamaño, la forma y la posición de los granos que la forman (254)

theory/teoría una explicación que relaciona muchas hipótesis y observaciones (20)

topographic map/mapa topográfico un mapa que muestra las características superficiales de la Tierra (210)

trace fossil/fósil traza una marca fosilizada que se forma en un sedimento blando debido al movimiento de un animal (296)

trait/carácter una característica determinada genéticamente (148)

transform boundary/límite de transformación el límite entre placas tectónicas que se están deslizando horizontalmente una sobre otra (391)

transpiration/transpiración el proceso por medio del cual las plantas liberan vapor de agua al aire por medio de los estomas; *también*, la liberación de vapor de agua al aire por otros organismos (64)

tropism/tropismo el crecimiento de un organismo o de una parte de él en respuesta a un estímulo externo, como por ejemplo, la luz (70)

true north/norte verdadero la dirección al Polo Norte geográfico (198)

tundra/tundra una llanura sin árboles situada en la región ártica o antártica o en la cumbre de las montañas; se caracteriza por temperaturas muy bajas en el invierno y veranos cortos y frescos (324)

U

unconformity/disconformidad una ruptura en el registro geológico, creada cuando las capas de roca se erosionan o cuando el sedimento no se deposita durante un largo período de tiempo (287)

uniformitarianism/uniformitarianismo un principio que establece que es posible explicar los procesos geológicos que ocurrieron en el pasado en función de los procesos geológicos actuales (281)

uplift/levantamiento la elevación de regiones de la corteza terrestre a elevaciones más altas (400)

V

valence electron/electrón de valencia un electrón que se encuentra en el orbital más externo de un átomo y que determina las propiedades químicas del átomo (597)

variable/variable un factor que se modifica en un experimento con el fin de probar una hipótesis (14)

vent/chimenea una abertura en la superficie de la Tierra a través de la cual pasa material volcánico (440)

viscosity/viscosidad la resistencia de un gas o un líquido a fluir (496)

volcano/volcán una chimenea o fisura en la superficie de la Tierra a través de la cual se expulsan magma y gases (438)

volume/volumen una medida del tamaño de un cuerpo o región en un espacio de tres dimensiones (25, 466, 499)

W

water cycle/ciclo del agua el movimiento continuo del agua: del océano a la atmósfera, de la atmósfera a la tierra y de la tierra al océano (365)

weight/peso una medida de la fuerza gravitacional ejercida sobre un objeto; su valor puede cambiar en función de la ubicación del objeto en el universo (469)

wetland/pantano un área de tierra que está periódicamente bajo el agua o cuyo suelo contiene una gran cantidad de humedad (334)

Spanish Glossary

Index

Index

Index

Index

organic compounds, 593, 664–669
  biochemicals, 666–669
  hydrocarbons, **665,** 665–666
  types and uses of, **666**
organic sedimentary rock, 262, **262**
organisms
  comparing, 144, **144**
  differences among, **138,**
    138–139
  examining, 142–143
  history of changing, 298
  multicellular, 173
orienteering, lab on, 711–712
orthoclase, 778–779
osmosis, 41
  cell and, 41, **41**
outer core, 347, **381**
ovary, 66
ovules, 66
oxides, **227,** 778–779
oxygen, 65, 173, 226, 580
  in atmosphere, 352, **352,** 353
  chemical formula for, **624**
  reactivity with, **478**
oxygen production, lab on rate of,
    74–75
ozone, 173, 352, 353
ozone shield, 357

P

pahoehoe, 441, **441**
Pakicetus, **142**
paleobotanists, 283
paleontologists, 166, 168, 283,
    294
  amateur, 313
  invertebrate, 283
  vertebrate, 283
paleontology, 283
Paleozoic era, 168, 174, **174,** 304,
    304
pampas, 322
Pangaea, 170
  breakup of, 387, **387**
paper bags, 490
parallels, 199
parent isotope, 291
Paricutín, 445
particles of matter, 494, **494,** 518,
    518
  charged, 600
  colloidal, 737
  in solutions, 529, **529**
passive transport, 42, **42**
past
  ownership of, 190
  using fossils to interpret, **297,**
    297–298
Pauling, Linus, 117
Peary, Robert E., 35, 221
peas, self-pollinating, 87, **87**
pedigree, 104, **104**
  lab on, 708–709
pegmatites, **233,** 245

Pele's hair, 460
People in Science. *See also*
    Careers
  Curie, Marie and Pierre, 701, **701**
  Goldsworthy, Andy, 515, **516**
  Henson, Matthew, 35, **35,** 221,
    221
  Hill, Emerald, 245, **245**
  Leakey family, **191**
  May, Lizzie, 313
  Pierotti, Raymond, 163, **163**
  Pyrtle, Ashanti Johnson, 375,
    375
  Seaborg, Glenn T., 591
  Villa-Komaroff, Lydia, 135, **135**
  Wegener, Alfred, 409, **409**
percentages, 573, 765
percolation, 365
period, 303, 574
periodic law, 569
periodic table of elements,
    584–585
  alkali metals in, 576, **576**
  alkaline-earth metals in, 577,
    577
  boron group, 579
  carbon group, 579
  classes of elements in, 572–573
  decoding, 574
  halogens, 581, **581**
  hydrogen, 582, **582**
  lab with, **570–571**
  nitrogen group, 580
  noble gases, 582, **582**
  oxygen group, 580
  Seaborg's revision of, 591, **591**
  transition metals in, 577–578,
    578
  valence electrons and, 598, **598**
periods, 574
permafrost, 324
permineralization, 295
petrifaction, 295
petrologist, 277, **277**
pH, 661, 670–671
  blood and, 662
  environment and, 662, **662**
  using indicators to determine,
    662, **662**
phacops, 299, **299**
Phanerozoic eon, **302,** 303
phenotype, 92, **92**
phosphates, lab on, 336–337
phosphoric acid, 656
phosphorus, 580
photosynthesis, 44, **46, 62,** 62–65,
    63, **63,** 173, 366, **366,** 525
  connection between respiration
    and, **46,** 47
  importance of, 65, **65**
phototropism, 70, 71
pH scale, 661, **661**
phyllite, 267, **267**
physical changes, 476
  chemical changes versus, 482,
    482

  examples of, 476, **476**
  lab in identifying, 484–485
  matter and, 477, **477**
physical models, 18, **18**
physical properties, 472–477
  chemical properties versus, 479,
    479
  of compounds, 523
  defined, 472
  of elements, 574
  examples of, **473**
physicists, experimental, 565, **565**
pie charts, 768
Pierotti, Raymond, 163, **163**
pigments, 44, 620
pillow lava, 441, **441**
pitchblende, 701
plagioclase, 778–779
plankton, 326, **326,** 330
plantlets, 68, **69**
plants
  cells of, **44**
  characteristics of, 88, **88**
  endangered species, 213
  first-generation, 89, **89,** 92
  long-day, 72
  medicinal, 162
  responses to environment,
    70–73
  safety with, xxxiii
  self-pollinating, 87, **87**
  short-day, 72, **72**
  true-breeding, 87
plant tropisms, 70–71
plasma, 514, **514,** 692
plastic bags, 490
plastic deformation, 413
plate boundaries, mountain
    building at, 348
plate motion, using satellites in
    tracking, 408
plate tectonics, 170, 348, **348,** 391.
    See also tectonic plates
  mountain building and,
    398–399
  theory of, 390–393
plum-pudding model, 546, **546**
Pluto, 82
plutons, **233,** 258
polar ice, 331
polar tundra, 324, **324**
polio, vaccine for, 6
pollen, 66
pollination, 66, **66**
polonium, 701
polymerase chain reaction (PCR),
    676
polymerases, 676
Pompeii, 448
pond, lake ecosystems and, 333,
    333
population, 138, 149
  changes in, 152–153
positive ions, forming, 601, **601**
potassium, 226
potassium-40, 292

Index

Index

Acknowledgments

continued from page ii

John Brockhaus, Ph.D.
Director of Geospatial Science Information Program
Department of Geography and Environmental Engineering
United States Military Academy
West Point, New York

Barbara Christopher
Science Writer and Editor
Austin, Texas

Joe W. Crim, Ph.D.
Professor and Head of Cellular Biology
Department of Cellular Biology
University of Georgia
Athens, Georgia

Roger J. Cuffey, Ph.D.
Professor of Paleontology
Department of Geosciences
Pennsylvania State University
University Park, Pennsylvania

Scott Darveau, Ph.D.
Assistant Professor of Chemistry
Chemistry Department
University of Nebraska at Kearney
Kearney, Nebraska

Jim Denbow, Ph.D.
Associate Professor of Archaeology
Department of Anthropology and Archaeology
University of Texas at Austin
Austin, Texas

Cassandra Eagle, Ph.D.
Professor of Organic Chemistry
Chemistry Department
Appalachian State University
Boone, North Carolina

Turgay Ertekin, Ph.D.
Professor and Chairman of Petroleum and Natural Gas Engineering
Energy and Geo-Environmental Engineering
Pennsylvania State University
University Park, Pennsylvania

David Haig, Ph.D.
Professor of Biology
Department of Organismic and Evolutionary Biology
Harvard University
Cambridge, Massachusetts

P. Shiv Halasyamani, Ph.D.
Associate Professor of Chemistry
Department of Chemistry
University of Houston
Houston, Texas

David Hershey, Ph.D.
Education Consultant
Hyattsville, Maryland

Richard N. Hey, Ph.D.
Professor of Geophysics
Department of Geophysics & Planetology
University of Hawaii at Manoa
Honolulu, Hawaii

Ken Hon, Ph.D.
Associate Professor of Volcanology
Geology Department
University of Hawaii at Hilo
Hilo, Hawaii

Susan Hough, Ph.D.
United States Geological Survey (USGS)
Pasadena, California

Steven A. Jennings, Ph.D.
Associate Professor
Department of Geography and Environmental Studies
University of Colorado
Colorado Springs, Colorado

Mark N. Kobrak, Ph.D.
Assistant Professor of Chemistry
Chemistry Department
Brooklyn College of the City University of New York
Brooklyn, New York

Daniela Kohen, Ph.D.
Assistant Professor of Chemistry
Chemistry Department
Carleton College
Northfield, Minnesota

Joel S. Leventhal, Ph.D.
Emeritus Scientist, Geochemistry
U.S. Geological Survey
Lakewood, Colorado

Richard F. Niedziela, Ph.D.
Assistant Professor of Chemistry
Department of Chemistry
DePaul University
Chicago, Illinois

Eva Oberdoerster, Ph.D.
Lecturer
Department of Biology
Southern Methodist University
Dallas, Texas

Kenneth K. Peace
Manager of Transportation
WestArch Coal, Inc.
St. Louis, Missouri

Enrique Peacock-López, Ph.D.
Professor of Chemistry
Department of Chemistry
Williams College
Williamstown, Massachusetts

Kate Queeney, Ph.D.
Assistant Professor of Chemistry
Chemistry Department
Smith College
Northampton, Massachusetts

Michael H. Renfroe, Ph.D.
Professor of Biology
Department of Biology
James Madison University
Harrisonburg, Virginia

Kenneth H. Rubin, Ph.D.
Associate Professor
Department of Geology & Geophysics
University of Hawaii at Manoa
Honolulu, Hawaii

Laurie Santos, Ph.D.
Assistant Professor
Department of Psychology
Yale University
New Haven, Connecticut

Patrick K. Schoff, Ph.D.
Research Associate
Natural Resources Research Institute
University of Minnesota at Duluth
Duluth, Minnesota

Fred Seaman, Ph.D.
Retired Research Associate
College of Pharmacy
The University of Texas at Austin
Austin, Texas

Daniel Z. Sui, Ph.D.
Professor
Department of Geography
Texas A&M University
College Station, Texas

Colin D. Sumrall, Ph.D.
Lecturer of Paleontology
Earth and Planetary Sciences
The University of Tennessee
Knoxville, Tennessee

Richard S. Treptow, Ph.D.
Professor of Chemistry
Department of Chemistry and Physics
Chicago State University
Chicago, Illinois

Peter W. Weigand, Ph.D.
Professor Emeritus
Department of Geological Sciences
California State University
Northridge, California

Dale Wheeler
Associate Professor of Chemistry
A. R. Smith Department of Chemistry
Appalachian State University
Boone, North Carolina

Teacher Reviewers

Diedre S. Adams
Physical Science Instructor
West Vigo Middle School
West Terre Haute, Indiana

Barbara Gavin Akre
Teacher of Biology, Anatomy-Physiology, and Life Science
Duluth Independent School District
Duluth, Minnesota

Laura Buchanan
Science Teacher and Department Chair
Corkran Middle School
Glen Burnie, Maryland

Sarah Carver
Science Teacher
Jackson Creek Middle School
Bloomington, Indiana

Robin K. Clanton
Science Department Head
Berrien Middle School
Nashville, Georgia

Hilary Cochran
Science Teacher
Indian Crest Junior High
School
Souderton, Pennsylvania

Karen Dietrich, S.S.J., Ph.D.
*Principal and Biology
Instructor*
Mount Saint Joseph
Academy
Flourtown, Pennsylvania

Randy Dye, M.S.
Science Department Head
Wood Middle School
Fort Leonard Wood,
Missouri

Trisha Elliott
*Science and Mathematics
Teacher*
Chain of Lakes Middle
School
Orlando, Florida

Liza M. Guasp
Science Teacher
Celebration K–8 School
Celebration, Florida

Meredith Hanson
Science Teacher
Westside Middle School
Rocky Face, Georgia

Denise Hulette
Science Teacher
Conway Middle School
Orlando, Florida

James Kerr
*Oklahoma Teacher of the Year
2002–2003*
Union Public Schools
Tulsa, Oklahoma

Laura Kitselman
*Science Teacher and
Coordinator*
Loudoun Country Day
School
Leesburg, Virginia

Debra S. Kogelman, MAed.
Science Teacher
University of Chicago
Laboratory Schools
Chicago, Illinois

Tiffany Kracht
Science Teacher
Chain of Lakes Middle
School
Orlando, Florida

Deborah L. Kronsteiner
Science Teacher
Spring Grove Area Middle
School
Spring Grove, Pennsylvania

Jennifer L. Lamkie
Science Teacher
Thomas Jefferson Middle
School
Edison, New Jersey

Bill Martin
Science Teacher
Southeast Middle School
Kernersville, North
Carolina

Maureen Martin
Green Team Science Teacher
Jackson Creek Middle
School
Bloomington, Indiana

Thomas Lee Reed
Science Teacher
Rising Starr Middle School
Fayetteville, Georgia

Shannon Ripple
Science Teacher
Canyon Vista Middle
School
Round Rock, Texas

Susan H. Robinson
Science Teacher
Oglethorpe County Middle
School
Lexington, Georgia

Cary B. Rosillo
Science Teacher
Independence Middle
School
Jupiter, Florida

Elizabeth J. Rustad
Science Department Chair
Coronado Elementary
Gilbert, Arizona

Helen P. Schiller
Instructional Coach
The School District of
Greenville County
Greenville, South Carolina

Mark Schnably
Science Instructor
Thomas Jefferson Middle
School
Winston-Salem, North
Carolina

Stephanie Snowden
Science Teacher
Canyon Vista Middle
School
Austin, Texas

Marci L. Stadiem
Science Department Chair
Cascade Middle School
Seattle, Washington

Martha Tedrow
Science Teacher
Thomas Jefferson Middle
School
Winston-Salem, North
Carolina

Sherrye Valenti
Curriculum Leader
Science Department
Wildwood Middle School
Wildwood, Missouri

ZoEllen Warren
Science Teacher
Oakville Middle School
Archer, Florida

Angie Williams
Teacher
Riversprings Middle School
Crawfordville, Florida

Lab Testing

Barry Bishop
Science Teacher
San Rafael Junior High
School
Ferron, Utah

Paul Boyle
Science Teacher
Perry Heights Middle School
Evansville, Indiana

Daniel Bugenhagen
Science Teacher
Yutan Junior-Senior High
School
Yutan, Nebraska

James Chin
Science Teacher
Frank A. Day Middle School
Newtonville, Maryland

Rebecca Ferguson
Science Teacher
North Ridge Middle School
North Richland Hills, Texas

Laura Fleet
Science Teacher
Alice B. Landrum Middle
School
Ponte Vedra Beach, Florida

Susan Gorman
Science Teacher
North Ridge Middle School
North Ridge, Texas

C. John Graves
Science Teacher
Monforton Middle School
Bozeman, Montana

Janel Guse
Science Teacher
West Central Middle School
Hartford, South Dakota

Dennis Hanson
Science Teacher
Big Bear Middle School
Big Bear Lake, California

Norman Holcomb
Science Teacher
Marion Elementary School
Maria Stein, Ohio

Kenneth J. Horn
Science Teacher
Fallston Middle School
Fallston, Maryland

Karma Houston-Hughes
Science Mentor
Kyrene Middle School
Tempe, Arizona

Tracy Jahn
Science Teacher
Berkshire Junior-Senior
High School
Canaan, New York

Kerry Johnson
Science Teacher
Isbell Middle School
Santa Paula, California

David Jones
Science Teacher
Andrew Jackson Middle
School
Cross Lanes, West Virginia

Michael E. Krai
Science Teacher
West Hardin Middle School
Cecilia, Kentucky

Kathy LaRoe
Science Teacher
East Valley Middle School
East Helena, Montana

Maurine Marchani
Science Teacher
Raymond Park Middle School
Indianapolis, Indiana

Jason P. Marsh
Biology Teacher
Montevideo High School
and Montevideo Country
School
Montevideo, Minnesota

Kevin McCurdy
Science Teacher
Elmwood Junior High School
Rogers, Arkansas

Alyson Mike
Science Teacher
Radley Middle School
East Helena, Montana

Dwight Patton
Science Teacher
Carrol T. Welch Middle
    School
Horizon City, Texas

Joseph Price
Science Teacher
H.M. Browne Junior High
    School
Washington, D.C.

Terry Rakes
Science Teacher
Elmwood Junior High School
Rogers, Arkansas

Debra Sampson
Science Teacher
Booker T. Washington
    Middle School
Elgin, Texas

Rodney A. Sandefur
Science Teacher
Naturita Middle School
Naturita, Colorado

Helen Schiller
Science Teacher
Northwood Middle School
Taylors, South Carolina

David Sparks
Science Teacher
Redwater Junior High School
Redwater, Texas

Larry Tackett
Science Teacher
Andrew Jackson Middle
    School
Cross Lanes, West Virginia

Sharon L. Woolf
Science Teacher
Langston Hughes Middle
    School
Reston, Virginia

Lee Yassinski
Science Teacher
Sun Valley Middle School
Sun Valley, California

Gordon Zibelman
Science Teacher
Drexel Hill Middle School
Drexel Hill, Pennsylvania

Answer Checking

Hatim Belyamani
Austin, Texas

John A. Benner
Austin, Texas

Catherine Podeszwa
Duluth, Minnesota

Credits

Chapter Eighteen 492-493 (all), Teresa Nouri Rishel/Dale Chihuly Studio; 495 (bl), Digital Image copyright © 2005 PhotoDisc; 495 (br), Susumu Nishinaga/Science Photo Library/Photo Researchers, Inc.; 496 (tr), Victoria Smith/HRW; 496 (bl), © Dr Jeremy Burgess/Photo Researchers, Inc.; 497 (tr), Scott Van Osdol/HRW; 498 (br), AP Photo/Beth Keiser; 499 (bl), Corbis Images; 499 (br), Victoria Smith/HRW; 503 (bc), Scott Van Osdol/HRW; 503 (tr), Richard Megna/Fundamental Photographs; 505 (bl), Ed Reschke/Peter Arnold, Inc.; 506 (tl), Omni Photo Communications, Inc./Index Stock Imagery, Inc.; 508 (br), Victoria Smith/HRW; 509 (br), Sam Dudgeon/HRW; 510 (bc), Sam Dudgeon/HRW; 511 (bl), Charles D. Winters/Photo Researchers, Inc.; 514 (tr), CORBIS Images/HRW; 514 (tl), Scoones/SIPA Press; 515 (cr), Susanna Frohman/San Jose Mercury News/NewsCom; 515 (bl), Andrew Goldsworthy

Chapter Nineteen 516-517 (all), Scott Van Osdol/HRW; 518 (br), Jonathan Blair/Woodfin Camp & Associates, Inc.; 518 (bl), Victoria Smith/HRW; 519 (br), Russ Lappa/Photo Researchers, Inc.; 519 (bl, bc), Charles D. Winters/Photo Researchers, Inc.; 520 (tl), © Zack Burris/Zack Burris, Inc.; 520 (tcl), Yann Arthus-Bertrand/CORBIS; 520 (tcr, tr), Walter Chandoha; 521 (lead), Victoria Smith/HRW; 521 (copper, tin, sulfur), Sam Dudgeon/HRW; 521 (neon), Runk/Shoenberger/Grant Heilman Photography Inc.; 521 (silicon), Joyce Photographics/Photo Researchers, Inc.; 521 (boron), Russ Lappa/Photo Researchers, Inc.; 521 (antimony), Charles D. Winters/Photo Researchers, Inc.; 521 (iodine), Larry Stepanowicz; 522 (bl), Runk/Schoenberger/Grant Heilman Photography; 523 (bl), Runk/Shoenberger/Grant Heilman Photography; 523 (bc), Richard Megna/Fundamental Photographs; 523 (br), Sam Dudgeon/HRW; 524 (tl), Richard Megna/Fundamental Photographs; 525 (tr), John Kaprielian/Photo Researchers, Inc.; 526 (br), Sam Dudgeon/HRW; 527 (tl), Charles D. Winters; 527 (cl), Sam Dudgeon/HRW; 527 (bc), Charles D. Winters/Photo Researchers, Inc.; 527 (bl), Klaus Guldbrandsen/Science Photo Library/Photo Researchers, Inc.; 527 (tr, cr, br), John Langford/HRW; 528 (tl), Sam Dudgeon/HRW; 529 (bl), Richard Haynes/HRW; 530 (tr), Sam Dudgeon/HRW; 531 (all), John Langford/HRW; 532 (bl), HRW; 532 (br), Lance Schriner/HRW; 533 (tr), Sam Dudgeon/HRW; 534 (bl), © Stuart Westmoreland/Getty Images; 535 (b), Sam Dudgeon/HRW; 536 (tr), Sam Dudgeon/HRW; 536 (tl), Walter Chandoha; 537 (tr), Sam Dudgeon/HRW; 540 (tl), Peter Van Steen/HRW; 541 (tr), Courtesy of Aundra Nix; 541 (cr), Astrid & Hans-Frieder Michler/SPL/Photo Researchers, Inc.

Chapter Twenty 542-543 (all), P. Loiez Cern/Science Photo Library/Photo Researchers, Inc.; 544 (bl), Victoria Smith/HRW; 544 (bc), Courtesy JEOL; 545 (b), Corbis-Bettmann; 548 (br), John Zoiner; 548 (bc), Mavournea Hay/HRW; 550 (b), Sam Dudgeon/HRW; 555 (tr), Corbis Images; 557 (b), Sam Dudgeon/HRW; 558 (br), Victoria Smith/HRW; 559 (br), Sam Dudgeon/HRW; 560 (bl), Corbis-Bettmann; 561 (bl), Fermilab; 564 (tr), NASA; 564 (tl), Giraudon/Art Resource, NY; 565 (br), Fermi National Accelerator Laboratory/CORBIS; 565 (tr), Stephen Maclone

Chapter Twenty One 566-567 (all), Gerard Perrone/Courtesy of Eric Ehlenberger; 569 (tr), Sam Dudgeon/HRW; 572 (all), Sam Dudgeon/HRW; 573 (tr), Sam Dudgeon/HRW; 573 (tc), Richard Megna/Fundamental Photographs; 573 (bl), Russ Lappa/Photo Researchers, Inc.; 573 (bc), Lester V. Bergman/Corbis-Bettmann; 573 (tl), Sally Anderson-Bruce/HRW; 574 (bc, br), Richard Megna/Fundamental Photographs; 574 (bl), Tom Pantages Photography; 575 (br), HRW; 575 (tr), Sam Dudgeon/HRW; 576 (bl), Charles D. Winters/Photo Researchers, Inc.; 576 (bc, br), Richard Megna/Fundamental Photographs; 577 (tr), Sam Dudgeon/HRW; 578 (tl, cl), Sam Dudgeon/HRW; 578 (tr), ©1990 P. Petersen/Custom Medical Stock Photo; 578 (tc, bl), Victoria Smith/HRW; 579 (cr), Phillip Hayson/Photo Researchers, Inc.; 579 (br), Sam Dudgeon/HRW; 580 (tl), Sam Dudgeon/HRW; 580 (b), CORBIS Images/HRW; 581 (tl, tc), Richard Megna/Fundamental Photographs; 581 (tr), Charlie Winters/HRW; 582 (bl), NASA; 582 (tl), © Jeff Greenberg/Visuals Unlimited; 583 (tr), Sam Dudgeon/HRW; 584 (b), Sam Dudgeon/HRW; 585 (br), John Langford/HRW; 586 (tl), Sam Dudgeon/HRW; 590 (tr), CORBIS Images/HRW; 591 (cr), © Lawrence Berkeley National Laboratory/Photo Researchers, Inc.; 591 (cl), © Bettmann/CORBIS

Unit Six 592 (c), Argonne National Laboratory/Corbis-Bettmann; 592 (b), Wally McNamee/Corbis; 593 (tr), Sygma; 593 (bl), Reuters/Nasa/Hulton Archive/Getty Images; 593 (c), Archive France/Hulton Archive/Getty Images; 593 (br), General Motors Corporation. Used with permission, GM Media Archives.

Chapter Twenty Two 594-595 (all), © Doug Struthers/Getty Images; 596 (bl), © Charles Gupton/CORBIS; 600 (br), © Konrad Wothe/Minden Pictures; 603 (cl), Paul Silverman/Fundamental Photographs; 606 (tr), Sam Dudgeon/HRW; 607 (tc), Sam Dudgeon/HRW; 607 (bl), © Jonathan Blair/CORBIS; 608 (tr), Victoria Smith/HRW; 609 (tr), John Langford/HRW; 611 (b), Sam Dudgeon/HRW; 612 (br), Victoria Smith/HRW; 613 (cr, br), Sam Dudgeon/HRW; 613 (tc), © Konrad Wothe/Minden Pictures; 616 (tr), Peter Oxford/Nature Picture Library; 616 (tl), Diaphor Agency/Index Stock Imagery, Inc.; 617 (cr), Steve Fischbach/HRW; 617 (bl), W. & D. McIntyre/Photo Researchers, Inc.

Chapter Twenty Three 618-619 (all), Corbis Images; 620 (bl), Rob Matheson/The Stock Market; 620 (br), Sam Dudgeon/HRW; 621 (cl, cr), Richard Megna/Fundamental Photographs, New York; 621 (br), Scott Van Osdol/HRW; 621 (bl), J.T. Wright/Bruce Coleman Inc./Picture Quest; 622 (all), Charlie Winters; 623 (br), Charlie Winters/HRW; 626 (tl), John Langford/HRW; 626 (bl), Richard Haynes/HRW; 627 (tr), Charles D. Winters/Photo Researchers, Inc.; 627 (tc), John Langford/HRW; 627 (tl), © Ingram Publishing; 632 (tl), Peticolas/Megna/Fundamental Photographs; 632 (tr), Richard Megna/Fundamental Photographs; 634 (bl), Victoria Smith/HRW; 634 (bc), Peter Van Steen/HRW; 634 (br), © Tom Stewart/The Stock Market; 635 (br), © David Stoecklein/CORBIS; 636 (t), Michael Newman/PhotoEdit; 637 (cr), Richard Megna/Fundamental Photographs; 638 (t), Sam Dudgeon/HRW; 639 (tr), Dorling Kindersley Limited courtesy of the Science Museum, London/CORBIS; 639 (bl), Victoria Smith/HRW; 640 (b), Victoria Smith/HRW; 642 (tr), Richard Megna/Fundamental Photographs; 643 (cr), Richard Megna/Fundamental Photographs; 643 (br), Rob Matheson/The Stock Market; 646 (tr), Tony Freeman/PhotoEdit; 646 (tl), Henry Bargas/Amarillo Globe-News/AP/Wide World Photos; 647 (all), Bob Parker/Austin Fire Investigation

Chapter Twenty Four 648-649 (all), © Dr. Dennis Kunkel/Visuals Unlimited; 650 (bl), © Andrew Syred/Microscopix Photolibrary; 651 (all), Richard Megna/Fundamental Photographs; 652 (b), Victoria Smith/HRW; 653 (tr), Richard Megna/Fundamental Photographs; 654 (br), Sam Dudgeon/HRW; 655 (br), Charles D. Winters/Timeframe Photography, Inc.; 655 (tl, tr), Peter Van Steen/HRW; 656 (br), Tom Tracy/The Stock Shop/Medichrome; 657 (tc), Victoria Smith/HRW; 657 (tr), © Peter Cade/Getty Images; 657 (tl), © Bob Thomason/Getty Images; 658 (all), Peter Van Steen/HRW; 659 (tr), Peter Van Steen/HRW; 662 (bl), Digital Image copyright © 2005 PhotoDisc; 662 (tl), Victoria Smith/HRW; 662 (tc, tr), Scott Van Osdol/HRW; 663 (tr), Miro Vinton/Stock Boston/PictureQuest; 665 (tl), Sam Dudgeon/HRW; 665 (tc), John Langford/HRW; 665 (tr), Charles D. Winters/Timeframe Photography, Inc.; 666 (tc), Digital Image copyright © 2005 PhotoDisc; 667 (bl), Sam Dudgeon/HRW; 668 (tl), Hans Reinhard/Bruce Coleman, Inc.; 669 (tr), CORBIS Images/HRW; 670 (b), Sam Dudgeon/HRW; 672 (tr), Peter Van Steen/HRW; 673 (all), Digital Image copyright © 2005 PhotoDisc; 676 (tr), Dan Loh/AP/Wide World Photos; 676 (tl), Sygma; 677 (tr), Nicole Guglielmo; 677 (bl), Corbis Images

Chapter Twenty Five 678-679 (all), GJLP/CNRI/PhotoTake; 680 (br), Henri Becquerel/The Granger Collection; 680 (bl), Roberto De Gugliemo/Science Photo Library/Photo Researchers, Inc.; 681 (tr), Digital Image copyright © 2005 PhotoDisc; 684 (br), Sygma; 686 (br), Tim Wright/CORBIS; 686 (bl), Custom Medical Stock Photo; 687 (tr), Roberto De Gugliemo/Science Photo Library/Photo Researchers, Inc.; 689 (tr), Emory Kristof/National Geographic Society Image Collection; 691 (tr), © Shone/Gamma; 693 (tc), Sam Dudgeon/HRW; 693 (tr), John Langford/HRW; 694 (all), Sam Dudgeon/HRW; 695 (b), Sam Dudgeon/HRW; 696 (tl), Tim Wright/CORBIS; 697 (bl), John Langford/HRW; 697 (cr), Science Photo Library/Photo Researchers, Inc.; 700 (tl), Courtesy USDA; 700 (tr), SABA Press Photos, Inc.; 701 (cr), © Underwood & Underwood/CORBIS; 701 (bl), © The Nobel Foundation

STAFF CREDITS

The people who contributed to *Holt Science & Technology* are listed below. They represent editorial, design, production, eMedia, permissions, and marketing.

Chris Allison, Melanie Baccus, Wesley M. Bain, Juan Baquera, Angela Beckmann, Ed Blake, Sara Buller, Marc Burgamy, Rebecca Calhoun, Kimberly Cammerata, Soojinn Choi, Eddie Dawson, Julie Dervin, Michelle Dike, Lydia Doty, Jen Driscoll, Leigh Ann Garcia, Catherine Gnader, Diana Goetting, Tim Hovde, Wilonda leans, Jevara Jackson, Simon Key, Jane A. Kirschman, Cathy Kuhles, Laura Likon, Denise Mahoney, Michael Mazza, Kristen McCardel, Richard Metzger, Micah Newman, Janice Noske, Joeleen Ornt, Cathy Paré, Jenny Patton, Laura Prescott, Bill Rader, Peter D. Reid, Curtis Riker, Michael Rinella, Jeff Robinson, Audrey Rozsypal, Beth Sample, Margaret Sanchez, Kay Selke, Elizabeth Simmons, Chris Smith, Dawn Marie Spinozza, Sherry Sprague, Jeff Streber, JoAnn Stringer, Roshan Strong, Jeannie Taylor , Bob Tucek, Tam Voynick, Clay Walton, Kira J. Watkins, Ken Whiteside, Holly Whittaker, David Wisnieski, Monica Yudron, Patty Zepeda

TEACHER'S EDITION CREDITS

1E (cl), Craig Line/AP/Wide World Photos; 1E (bl), © Chip Simons Photography; 1E (br), John Mitchell/Photo Researchers, Inc.; 1F (r), Sam Dudgeon/HRW; 1F (r), Art by Christopher Sloan/Photograph by Mark Thiessen both National Geographic Image Collection/National Geographic Image Collection; 37E (t), Photo Researchers, Inc.; 37F (tl), L. Willatt, East Anglian Regional Genetics Service/SPL/Photo Researchers, Inc.; 37F (r), Ed Reschke/Peter Arnold, Inc.; 59E (r), George Bernard/Earth Scenes; 59F (bl), Visuals Unlimited/E. Webber; 59F (cl), Visuals Unlimited/Bill Beatty; 59F (cr), Visuals Unlimited/Bill Beatty; 59F (r), © Cathlyn Melloan/Getty Images/Stone; 83E (l), Ned M. Seidler/National Geographic Society Image Collection; 133E (l), Hulton Archive/Getty Images; 133F (l), Visuals Unlimited/Science Visuals Unlimited/Keith Wood; 133F (r), Volker Steger/Peter Arnold; 135E (l), Courtesy of Betsy Webb, Pratt Museum, Homer, Alaska; 163F (r), Neanderthal Museum; 193E (t), Sam Dudgeon/HRW; 193E (b), HO/NewsCom; 193F (tl), Spaceimaging.com/Getty Images/NewsCom; 193F (bl), Strategic Planning Office, City of Seattle; 193F (r), USGS; 221E (bl), Mark A. Schneider/Photo Researchers, Inc.; 221E (br), Mark A. Schneider/Photo Researchers, Inc.; 221F (tr), Breck P. Kent; 221F (bl), Stewart Cohen/Index Stock Photography, Inc.; 221F (tl), © SuperStock; 245E (r), J.D. Griggs/USGS; 245E (aragonite), Breck P. Kent; 245E (limestone), Breck P. Kent; 245E (calcite), Mark Schneider/Visuals Unlimited; 245E (siltstone), Sam Dudgeon/HRW; 245E (sandstone), Dorling Kindersley; 245E (conglomerate), Breck P. Kent; 245F (tl), CORBIS Images/HRW; 245F (mica), Tom Pantages; 245F (chlorite), Sam Dudgeon/HRW; 245F (mica), Tom Pantages; 277E (br), Tom Till/DRK Photo; 277F (t), © Louie Psihoyos/psihoyos.com; 277F (br), Ken Lucas/Visuals Unlimited; 315E (tl), Stuart Westmorland/Getty Images/Stone; 315F (bl), Jeff Hunter/Image Bank/Getty Images; 315F (r), © Dwight R. Kuhn; 343E (l), Steve Satushek/Brand X Pictures/gettyimages; 343F (l), CORBIS; 343 (r), Provided by the SeaWiFS Project, NASA/Goddard Space Flight Center and ORBIMAGE/NASA/Seawifs; 409E (b), Michael S. Yamashita/CORBIS; 409F (tr), Paul Chesley/Getty Images/Stone; 435E (bl), © National Geographic Image Collection/Robert W. Madden; 435E (tl), E. R. Degginger/Color-Pic, Inc.; 435F (l), Alberto Garcia/SABA/CORBIS; 435F (r), Roger Ressmeyer/CORBIS; 435F (br), Victoria Smith/HRW; 463E (cl), Sam Dudgeon/HRW; 463F (cr), © Rob Boudreau/Getty Images/Stone; 463F (tl), John Langford/HRW; 463F (tc), Lance Schriner/HRW; 463F (bl), © Royalty Free/CORBIS; 491E (br), Richard Megna/Fundamental Photographs, New York; 491E (cl), © Dr. Jeremy Burgess/Photo Researchers, Inc.; 491F (bl), Ed Reschke/Peter Arnold, Inc.; 491F (tr), Omni Photo Communications, Inc./Index Stock Imagery, Inc.; 515E (cl), Joyce Photographics/Photo Researchers, Inc.; 515E (bl), Sam Dudgeon/HRW ; 515E (cl), Runk/Shoenberger/Grant Heilman Photography; 515E (c), Richard Megna/Fundamental Photographs 515E (cr), Sam Dudgeon/HRW; 515F (tl), Sam Dudgeon; 515F (bl), Sam Dudgeon; 515F (cr), Lance Schriner/HRW; 541E (bl), Victoria Smith/HRW; 541E (tr), Corbis-Bettmann; 541F (cr), © Royalty-Free/CORBIS; 541F (tl), Sam Dudgeon/HRW; 565E (tl), Sam Dudgeon/HRW; 565E (bl), Richard Megna/Fundamental Photographs, New York; 565F (tl), © Jeff Greenberg/Visuals Unlimited; 565F (cr), NASA; 593E (cl), © Charles Gupton/CORBIS; 593E (br), Paul Silverman/Fundamental Photographs, New York; 593F (tr), © Jonathan Blair/CORBIS; 593F (cl), Sam Dudgeon/HRW; 617E (cl), © David Stoecklein/CORBIS; 617F (cr), © Tom Stewart/The Stock Market; 647E (cl), Richard Megna/Fundamental Photographs, New York; 647F (cr) Victoria Smith/HRW; 647F (tl), Miro Vinton/Stock Boston/PictureQuest; 647F (cr), Charles D. Winters; 677E (cl), Henri Becquerel/The Granger Collection; 677E (br), Roberto De Gugliemo/Science Photo Library/Photo Researchers, Inc.; 677F (cl), © Shone/Gamma

Answers to Concept Mapping Questions

The following pages contain sample answers to all of the concept mapping questions that appear in the Chapter Reviews. Because there is more than one way to do a concept map, your students' answers may vary.

CHAPTER 1   Science in Our World

19.

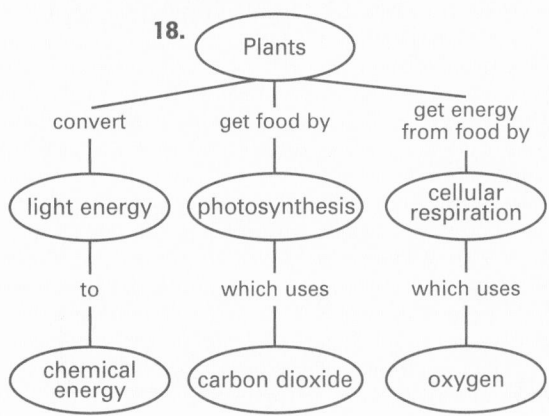

Questions —based on→ observations
observations —are used to develop a→ hypothesis
hypothesis —which leads to the formation of→ predictions
predictions —which can be used to set up→ controlled experiments
controlled experiments —in which the factor that is changed is known as the→ variable

CHAPTER 3   Plant Processes

18.

Plants
- convert → light energy → to → chemical energy
- get food by → photosynthesis → which uses → carbon dioxide
- get energy from food by → cellular respiration → which uses → oxygen

CHAPTER 5   Genes and DNA

16.

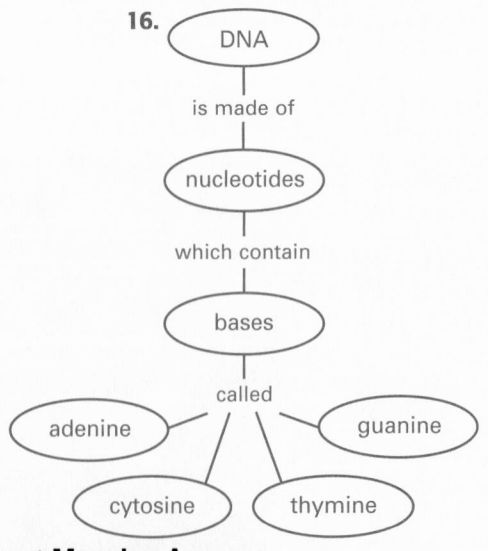

DNA —is made of→ nucleotides —which contain→ bases —called→ adenine, guanine, cytosine, thymine

CHAPTER 2   The Cell in Action

15.

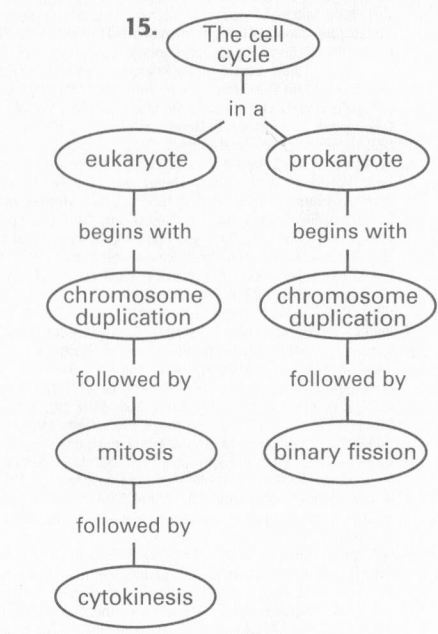

The cell cycle —in a→
- eukaryote —begins with→ chromosome duplication —followed by→ mitosis —followed by→ cytokinesis
- prokaryote —begins with→ chromosome duplication —followed by→ binary fission

CHAPTER 4   Heredity

16.

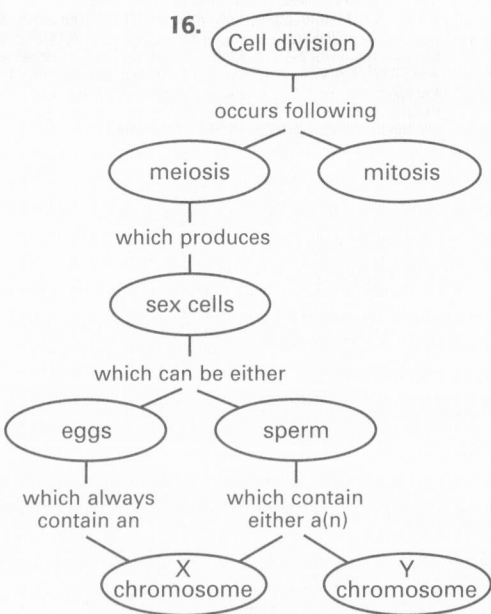

Cell division —occurs following→ meiosis, mitosis
meiosis —which produces→ sex cells —which can be either→ eggs, sperm
eggs —which always contain an→ X chromosome
sperm —which contain either a(n)→ X chromosome, Y chromosome

CHAPTER 6 — The Evolution of Living Things

17.

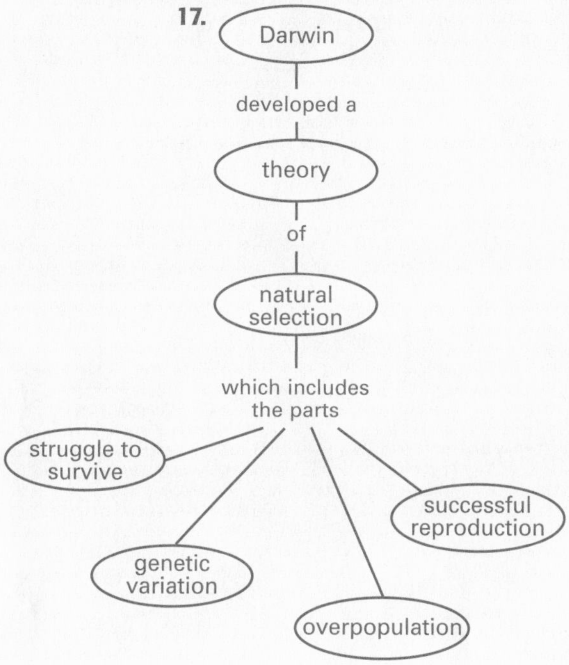

Darwin
— developed a —
theory
— of —
natural selection
— which includes the parts —
- struggle to survive
- genetic variation
- overpopulation
- successful reproduction

CHAPTER 7 — The History of Life on Earth

19.

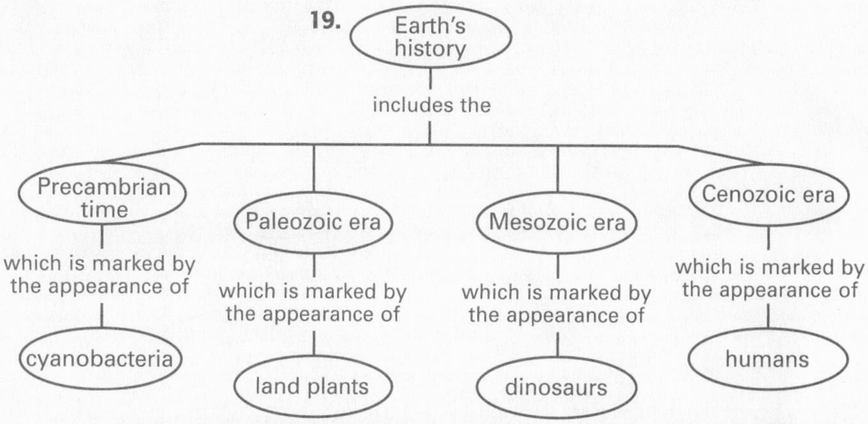

Earth's history
— includes the —
- Precambrian time — which is marked by the appearance of — cyanobacteria
- Paleozoic era — which is marked by the appearance of — land plants
- Mesozoic era — which is marked by the appearance of — dinosaurs
- Cenozoic era — which is marked by the appearance of — humans

CHAPTER 8 — Maps as Models of the Earth

20.

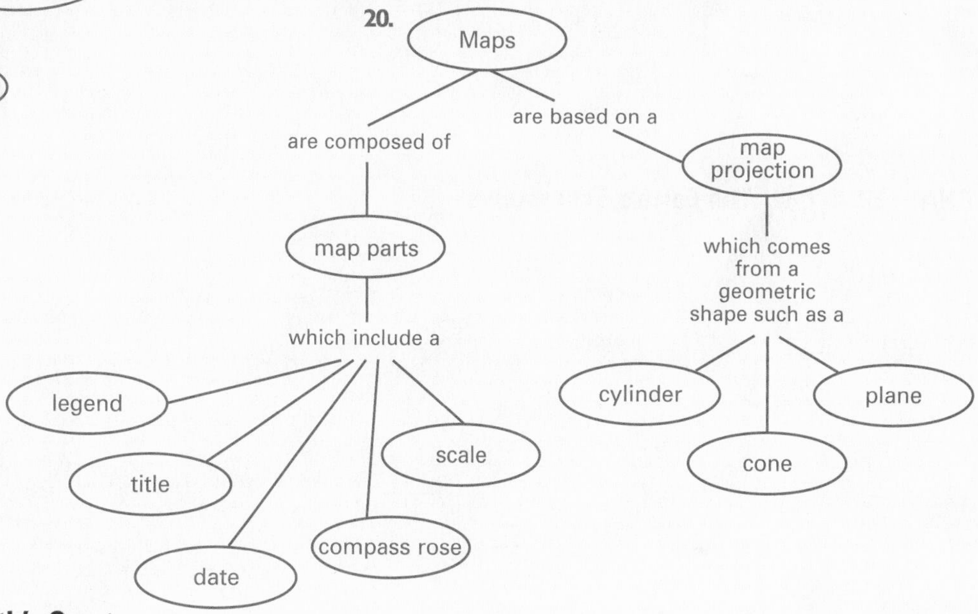

Maps
— are composed of —
map parts
— which include a —
- legend
- title
- date
- compass rose
- scale

— are based on a —
map projection
— which comes from a geometric shape such as a —
- cylinder
- cone
- plane

CHAPTER 9 — Minerals of the Earth's Crust

15.

Minerals
— are classified as —
- silicate minerals
  — which include —
  - quartz
- nonsilicate minerals
  — which are further classified as —
  - carbonates — which include — calcite
  - sulfates — which include — gypsum

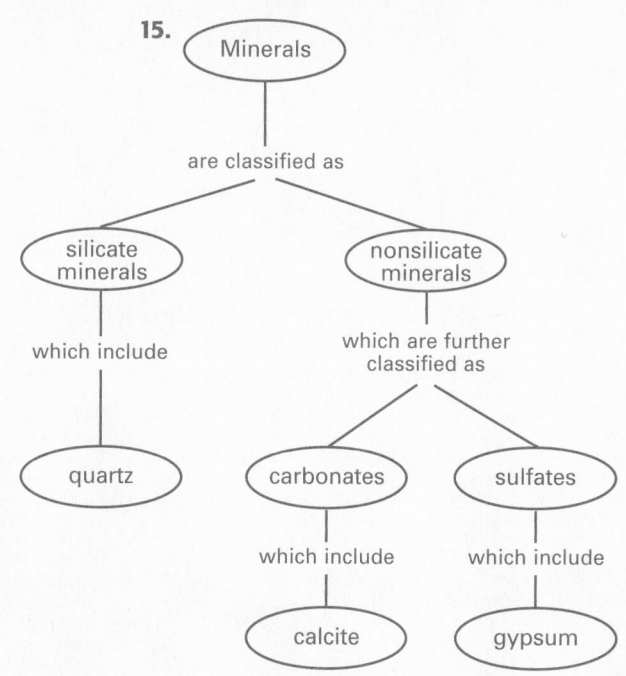

CHAPTER 10 Rocks: Mineral Mixtures

17.

Rocks
— can be —
metamorphic · sedimentary · igneous

metamorphic — which can be — foliated, nonfoliated

sedimentary — which can be — chemical, clastic, organic

igneous — which can be — extrusive, intrusive

CHAPTER 11 The Rock and Fossil Record

18.

The age
— of rock formations can be determined by —
relative dating · absolute dating

relative dating — which is based on — superposition, the geologic column

absolute dating — which includes — radiometric dating
— which measures the — radioactive decay
— of — isotopes
— with a known — half-life

CHAPTER 12 The Earth's Ecosystems

16.

Biomes
— are characterized by — abiotic factors, plants and animals

Biomes — include — desert, tropical rain forest, tundra

tropical rain forest — in which most animals live in the — canopy

tundra — which has a frozen soil layer called — permafrost

CHAPTER 13 Earth Systems and Cycles

22.

geosphere
— is divided into —
compositional layers · physical layers

compositional layers — which include — core, crust, mantle

physical layers — which include — lithosphere, asthenosphere, mesosphere, outer core, inner core

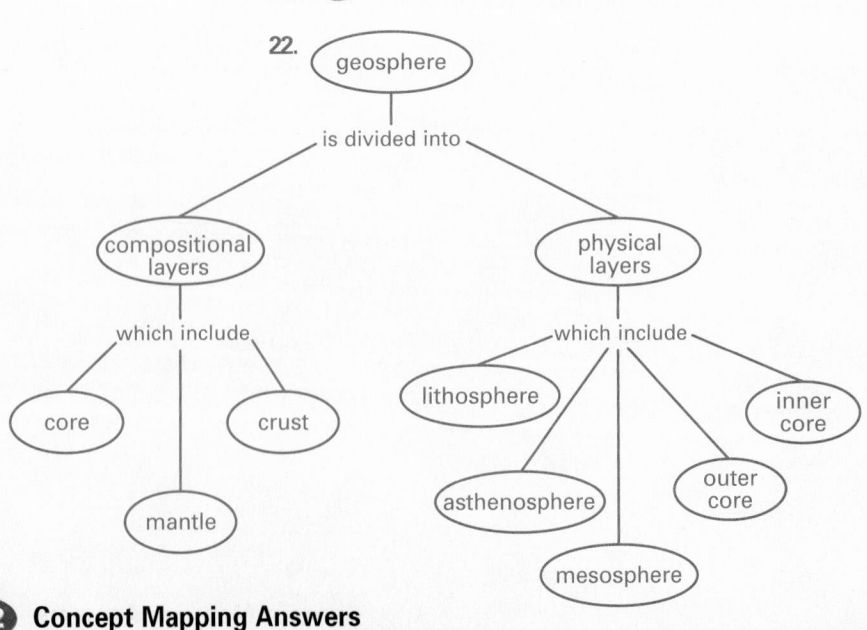

CHAPTER 14 Plate Tectonics

17.

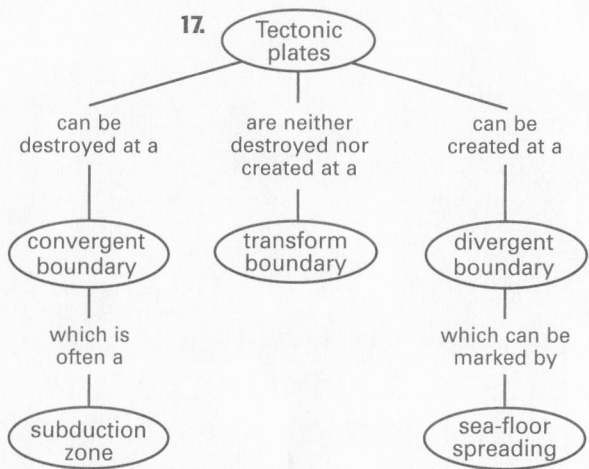

Tectonic plates

- can be destroyed at a → convergent boundary → which is often a → subduction zone
- are neither destroyed nor created at a → transform boundary
- can be created at a → divergent boundary → which can be marked by → sea-floor spreading

CHAPTER 15 Earthquakes

16.

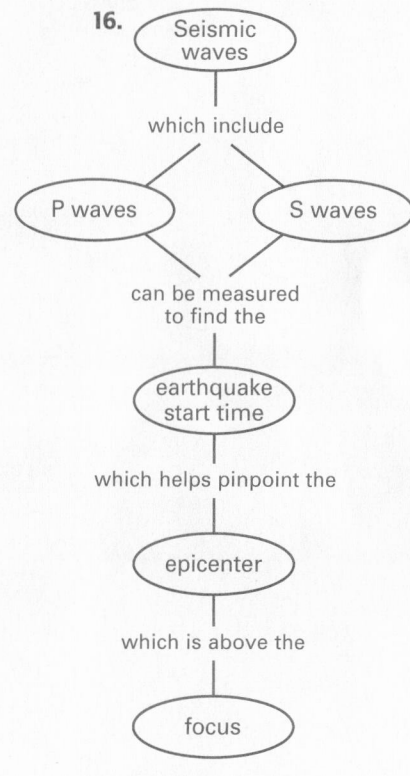

Seismic waves → which include → P waves, S waves → can be measured to find the → earthquake start time → which helps pinpoint the → epicenter → which is above the → focus

CHAPTER 16 Volcanoes

17.

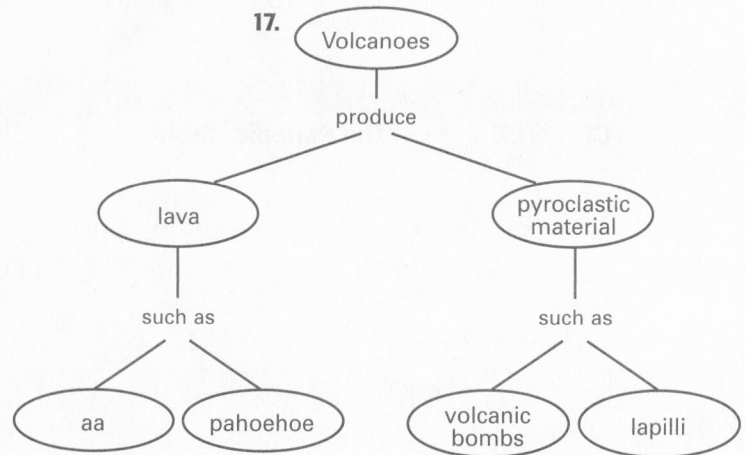

Volcanoes → produce → lava, pyroclastic material

- lava → such as → aa, pahoehoe
- pyroclastic material → such as → volcanic bombs, lapilli

CHAPTER 17 The Properties of Matter

17.

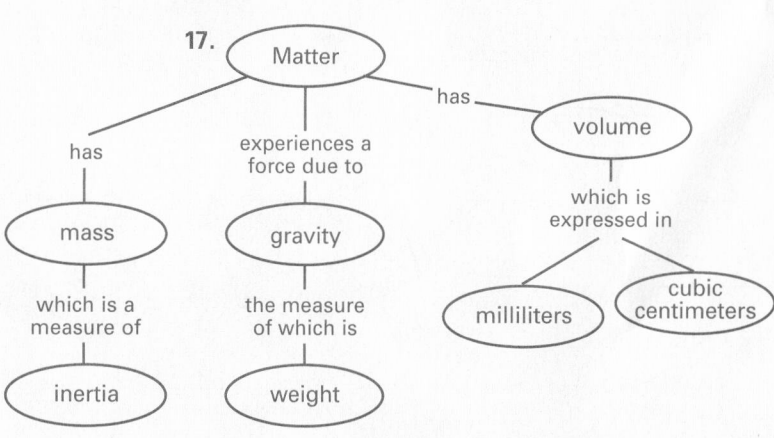

Matter

- has → mass → which is a measure of → inertia
- experiences a force due to → gravity → the measure of which is → weight
- has → volume → which is expressed in → milliliters, cubic centimeters

CHAPTER 18 States of Matter

16.

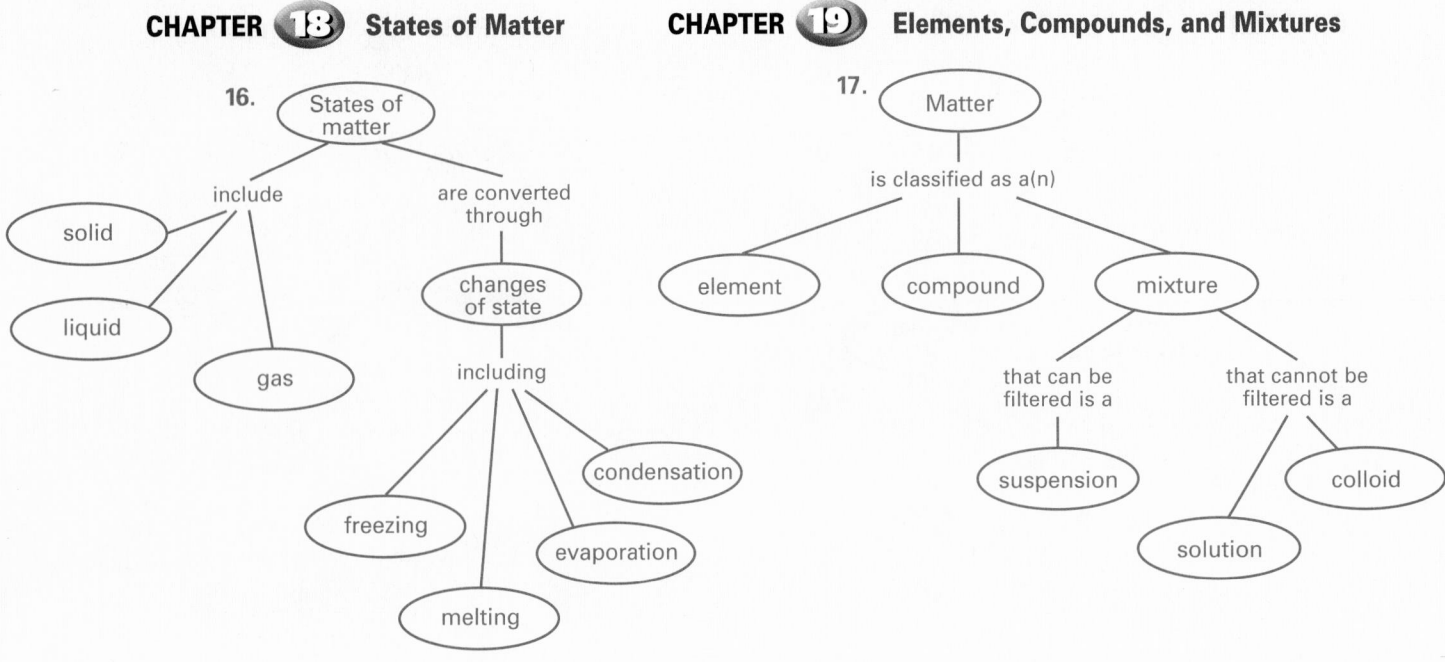

States of matter
- include
  - solid
  - liquid
  - gas
- are converted through
  - changes of state
    - including
      - freezing
      - melting
      - evaporation
      - condensation

CHAPTER 19 Elements, Compounds, and Mixtures

17.

Matter
- is classified as a(n)
  - element
  - compound
  - mixture
    - that can be filtered is a
      - suspension
    - that cannot be filtered is a
      - solution
      - colloid

CHAPTER 20 Introduction to Atoms

15.

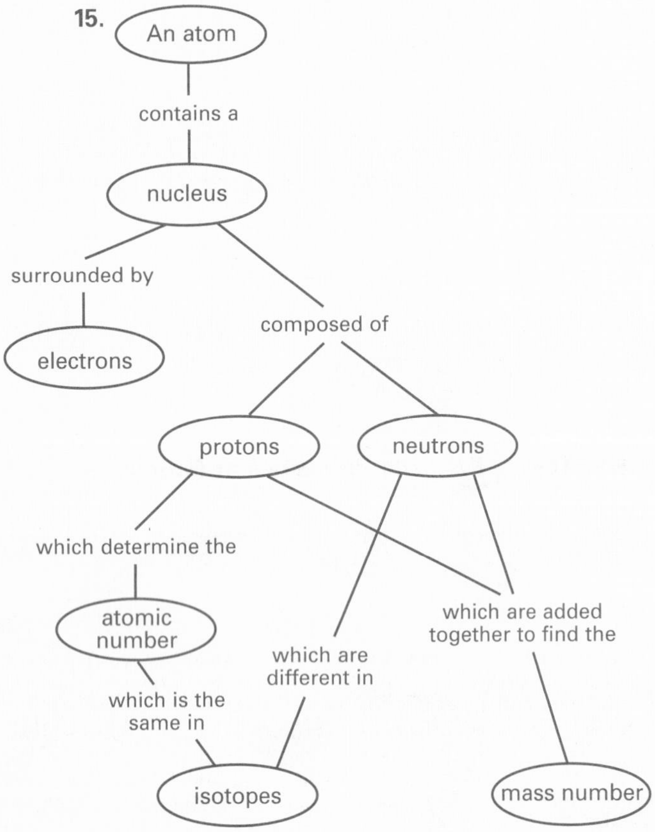

An atom
- contains a
  - nucleus
    - surrounded by
      - electrons
    - composed of
      - protons
        - which determine the
          - atomic number
            - which is the same in
              - isotopes
      - neutrons
        - which are different in
          - isotopes
        - which are added together to find the
          - mass number

CHAPTER 21 The Periodic Table

15.

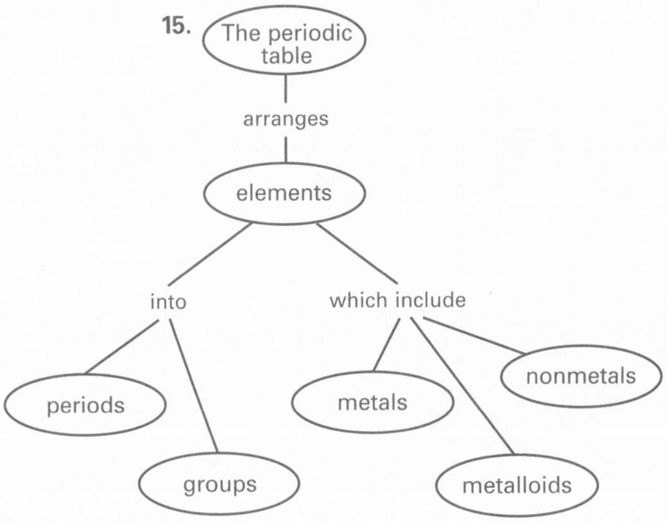

The periodic table
- arranges
  - elements
    - into
      - periods
      - groups
    - which include
      - metals
      - metalloids
      - nonmetals

CHAPTER 22 Chemical Bonding

16.

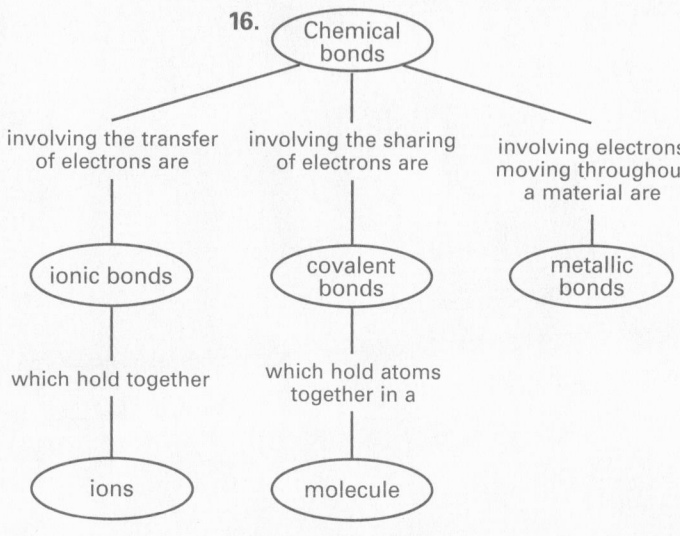

CHAPTER 23 Chemical Reactions

16.

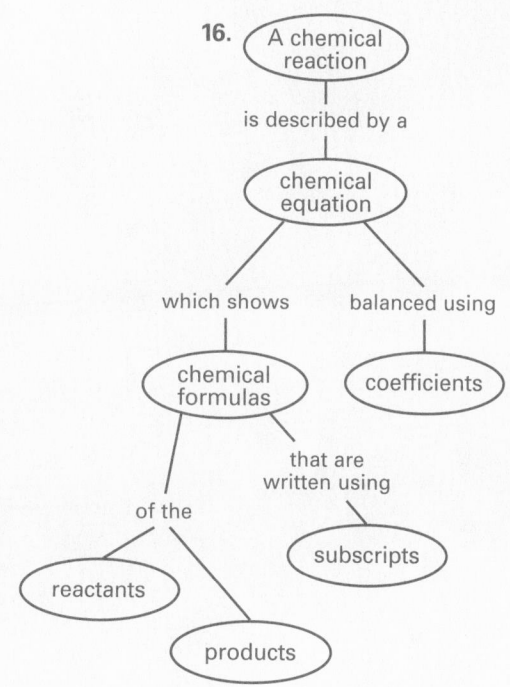

CHAPTER 24 Chemical Compounds

15.

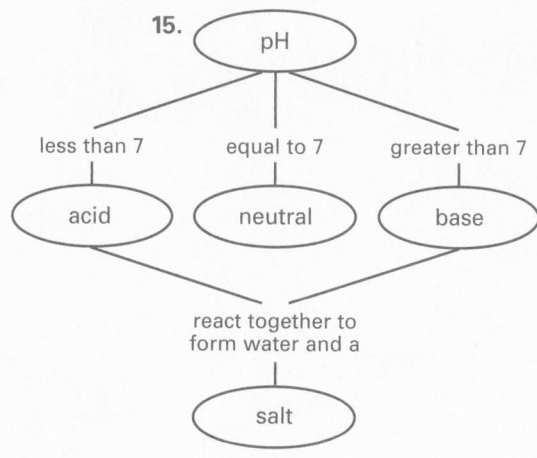

CHAPTER 25 Atomic Energy

15.

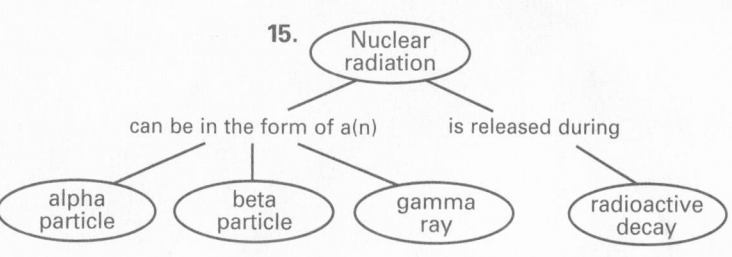